Process Tables and Technical Budgets

Space Mission Engineering	Source	Page
Space Mission Engineering Process	Table 3-1	46
Process for Identifying Alternative Mission Architectures	Table 4-2	63
Defining Mission Concepts	Table 4-7, 4-9	67, 76
Concept Exploration Process	Fig. 4-5	75
Baseline Mission Selection and Evaluating Alternatives	Table 5-11	98
Principal Areas for Key System Trades	Table 5-2	87
Requirements Definition Process	Table 6-1	106
Mission Geometry Evaluation Process	Tables 8-1, 8-2, D-1	149, 150, 973–978
Coverage Formulas	Tables 8-11, 8-12, App. C	184, 186, 963–972
Orbits		
Single Satellite Orbit Selection Process	Table 10-1	236
Constellation Design Process	Table 10-24	270
Keplerian Orbit Formulas	Table 9-4, App. C	205, 963–972
Interplanetary Orbit Design Process	Table 10-30	279
Hohmann Transfer Summary Procedure	Table 10-32	282
Mission Design Considerations for Orbital Debris	Table 7-3	140
Error Budget Development	Table 6-5	115
Cost Estimation Process	Table 11-3	294
Principal Elements of Mission Timeline	Table 4-8	74
Spacecraft Design Elements	**Source**	**Page**
Budgets		
Delta V Budget	Table 10-7	252
Link Budget	Table 16-12	479
Observational Payload Budget	Table 16-1	455
Mapping and Pointing Error Budgets	Table 8-15	192
Mass Budget	Table 14-18	422
Power Budget	Table 14-20	424
Propellant Budget	Table 14-19	423
Design Drivers	Tables 4-16, 14-2	80, 398
Manufacturing, Integration, and Test Process	Table 23-1	712
Subsystems Design Process	**Source**	**Page**
Attitude Determination and Control System	Table 19-1	567
Tracking, Telemetry, and Command System	Table 21-1	628
Computer System	Table 20-1	602
Software Sizing Process	Table 20-8	613
Guidance and Navigation	Table 19-17	592
Mechanisms	Table 22-5	681
Payloads	Table 15-6	446
Communications Payloads	Tables 16-1, 16-4, 16-14	455–481
Observation Payloads	Table 17-6	509
Optical Sensor Design Calculations	Table 17-9	518–520
Power System	Table 21-10	642
Propulsion System	Table 18-1	528
Structures	Table 22-1	663
Thermal System	Fig. 22-18	691
Launch and Operations	**Source**	**Page**
Launch Cost Estimation Process	Table 10-10	257
Launch Vehicle Selection Process	Fig. 26-4	830
Launch Operations Timeline	Figs. 27-2, 27-8	864, 874
Mission Operations		
Process Flow	Fig. 29-2	910
Planning and Scheduling Process	Fig. 29-5	925
Development Process	Table 29-4	914
Realtime Flight Operations Process	Fig. 29-6	927
Data Processing and Management Process	Fig. 29-8	930
Anomalies Detection Process	Fig. 29-7	929

Symbol	Measurement
A	ampere
AU	astronomical unit
C	coulomb
C	celsius
dB	decibel
deg	degree (angular)
eV	electron volt
Hz	hertz
g	gram
J	joule
K	kelvin
kg	kilogram
km	kilometer
m	meter
N	newton
Ω	ohm
rad	radian
s	second
sec	second
sr	steradian
Pa	pascal
T	tesla
V	volt
W	watt
yr	year

The Greek Alphabet		
Alpha	Α	α
Beta	Β	β
Gamma	Γ	γ
Delta	Δ	δ
Epsilon	Ε	ε
Zeta	Ζ	ζ
Eta	Η	η
Theta	Θ	θ
Opta	Ι	ι
Kappa	Κ	κ
Lambda	Λ	λ
Mu	Μ	μ
Nu	Ν	ν
Xi	Ξ	ξ
Omicron	Ο	ο
Pi	Π	π
Rho	Ρ	ρ
Sigma	Σ	σ
Tau	Τ	τ
Upsilon	Υ	υ
Phi	Φ	ϕ
Chi	Χ	χ
Psi	Ψ	ψ
Omega	Ω	ω

THE SPACE TECHNOLOGY LIBRARY

Published jointly by Microcosm Press and Springer

An Introduction to Mission Design for Geostationary Satellites, J. J. Pocha
Space Politics and Policy, E. Sadeh
Space Mission Analysis and Design, 1st ed., James R. Wertz and Wiley J. Larson
Space Mission Analysis and Design, 2nd ed., Wiley J. Larson and James R. Wertz
Space Mission Analysis and Design Workbook, Wiley J. Larson and James R. Wertz
Space Mission Analysis and Design, 3rd ed., James R. Wertz and Wiley J. Larson
Handbook of Geostationary Orbits, E. M. Soop
Spacecraft Structures and Mechanisms, From Concept to Launch, Thomas P. Sarafin
Spaceflight Life Support and Biospherics, Peter Eckart
Reducing Space Mission Cost, James R. Wertz and Wiley J. Larson
The Logic of Microspace, Rick Fleeter
Space Marketing: A European Perspective, Walter A. R. Peeters
Fundamentals of Astrodynamics and Applications, 3rd ed., David A. Vallado
Orbit and Constellation Design and Management, James R. Wertz
Influence of Psychological Factors on Product Development, Eginaldo Shizuo Kamata
Essential Spaceflight Dynamics and Magnetospherics, Boris Rauschenbakh, Michael Ovchinnikov, and Susan McKenna-Lawlor
Space Psychology and Psychiatry, 2nd ed., Nick Kanas and Dietrich Manzey
Fundamentals of Space Medicine, Gilles Clément
Fundamentals of Space Biology, Gilles Clément and Klaus Slenzka
Microgravity Two-Phase Flow and Heat Transfer, Kamiel Gabriel

Space Mission Engineering: The New SMAD

Edited By

James R. Wertz
Microcosm
University of Southern California

David F. Everett
NASA Goddard Space Flight Center

Jeffery J. Puschell
Raytheon

Space Technology Library

Published by

Microcosm Press

Torrance, CA

Library of Congress Cataloging-in Publication Data

A C.I.P. Catalogue record for this book is available from the Library of Congress.

ISBN 978-1-881-883-15-9 (pb) (acid-free paper)
ISBN 978-1-881-883-16-6 (hb) (acid-free paper)

Cover photo of Earth from Space: View of Africa and the Indian Ocean taken in Dec. 1972, by Apollo 17, the last of the Apollo missions to explore the Moon. Photo courtesy of NASA.

Cover design by Chris Maruyama

Published by
Microcosm Press
3111 Lomita Blvd.,
Torrance, CA 90505 USA

Sold and distributed worldwide by
Microcosm Astronautics Books
3111 Lomita Blvd.,
Torrance, CA 90505 USA

Printed on acid-free paper

Third Printing, 2018

Printed in the United States of America

Table of Contents

Part II—Spacecraft and Payload Design

Part III—Launch and Operations

Appendices

Authors

Henry Apgar. President, MCR Technologies, LLC, El Segundo, California. MBA, Northeastern University; BS (Electrical Engineering), Rutgers University. Chapter 11—*Cost Estimating*.

Matthew Ashmore. Senior Mechanisms Engineer. ATK Space Systems and Services, Beltsville, Maryland. BS (Aerospace Engineering), University of Maryland. Chapter 22.1.5—*Mechanisms and Deployables*.

Karl D. Bilimoria. Aerospace Engineer, NASA Ames Research Center, Moffett Field, California. PhD (Aerospace Engineering), Virginia Tech; MS (Aerospace Engineering), Virginia Tech; BS (Aeronautical Engineering), Indian Institute of Technology–Kanpur. Section 19.2—*Spacecraft Trajectory Navigation and Control Systems*.

Robert S. Bokulic. Principal Professional Staff, Johns Hopkins University / Applied Physics Laboratory (JHU/APL), Laurel, Maryland. MS (Electrical Engineering), Johns Hopkins University; BS (Electrical Engineering), Virginia Polytechnic Institute and State University. Section 21.1—*Telemetry, Tracking, and Command (TT&C)*.

Constantine Cassapakis. CEO ex Officio, L'Garde Inc., Tustin, California. PhD (Experimental Particle Physics), The University of New Mexico/Los Alamos Science Lab; MS (Physics), The University of New Mexico; MA (Mathematics), Eastern New Mexico University; BS (Physics and Mathematics), Eastern New Mexico University. Section 25.2—*Inflatable Structures*.

Becky Christofferson. Systems Engineer, Microcosm Inc., Hawthorne, California. BS, Aerospace Engineering, University of Southern California. Appendix I—*Earth Satellite Parameters*.

John T. Collins. Senior System Engineer, Microcosm, Inc., Hawthorne, California. BS (Astronomy), University of Illinois; BS (Aerospace Engineering) University of Illinois. Section 11.4—*Example Space Missions Estimates*.

Christopher C. DeBoy. Group Supervisor, RF Engineering, Space Department, Johns Hopkins University/Applied Physics Laboratory (JHU/APL), Laurel, Maryland. MS (Electrical Engineering), Johns Hopkins University; BS (Electrical Engineering), Virginia Polytechnic Institute and State University. Section 21.1—*Telemetry, Tracking, and Command (TT&C)*.

Scott W. Enger. Electrical Engineer, Senior Staff, Lockheed Martin, Littleton, Colorado. BS (Electrical Engineering, Colorado State University. Section 21.2— *Power*.

Jaime Esper. Senior Aerospace Engineer, NASA Goddard Space Flight Center, Greenbelt, Maryland. MS (Mechanical [Aerospace] Engineering), The George Washington University; MS (Astronomy), University of Florida; BS (Physics), University of Florida. Section 23.6—*Alternative Approaches to Space Manufacturing*.

John S. Eterno. Program Director for Systems Engineering, Space Science Department, Space Science and Engineering Division, Southwest Research Institute, San Antonio, TX. PhD (Aeronautics and Astronautics), Massachusetts Institute of Technology; MS (Aeronautics and Astronautics), Massachusetts Institute of Technology; BS (Fluid, Thermal, and Aerospace Sciences), Case Western Reserve University. Section 19.1—*Spacecraft Attitude Determination and Control Systems*.

David F. Everett. Senior Systems Engineer, NASA Goddard Space Flight Center, Greenbelt, Maryland. MS (Electrical Engineering), University of Maryland; BS (Electrical Engineering), Virginia Polytechnic Institute and State University. Chapter 14—*Overview of Spacecraft Design;* Appendix A—*Mass and Power Distribution for Spacecraft*.

Stuart Eves. Principal Engineer, Surrey Satellite Technology Limited, Guildford, Surrey, United Kingdom. PhD (Constellation Design), Cranfield University; MSc (Astrophysics), London University; BSc (Physics with Astrophysics), London University. Section 23.1—*LEO Communications Constellation*; Section 23.2—*LEO Monolithic vs. Distributed Architectures*.

Rick Fleeter. Associate Professor, Brown University, Providence, RI; Visiting Professor, University of Rome. PhD (Thermodynamics), Brown University; MSc (Astronautics), Stanford University; AB (Engineering and Economics), Brown University. Section 25.3 —*SmallSats*.

Donald W. Gates, Jr. Senior Systems Engineer, Boeing, Lanham, Maryland. BS (Information Systems Management), University of Maryland. Chapter 27—*Launch Operations*.

Paul Graven. Director of Technology Programs, Microcosm, Inc., Hawthorne, California. M.P.P. (Science & Technology Policy and National Security Policy), Harvard University, JFK School of Government; MS (Aeronautics & Astronautics), Stanford University; BS (Engineering & Applied Science and Economics), California Institute of Technology. Section 20.4—*Modular Approaches*.

Mike Gruntman. Professor of Astronautics and Professor of Aerospace Engineering, Viterbi School of Engineering, University of Southern California, Los Angeles, California. PhD (Physics), Space Research Institute (IKI), USSR Academy of Sciences; MS (Physics), Moscow Physical-Technical Institute. Section 1.2—*The History of Spaceflight*.

L. Jane Hansen. President, HRP Systems, Inc., Rolling Hills Estate, California. MBA, Pepperdine University; BS (Applied Mathematics), California Polytechnic State University at San Luis Obispo. Chapter 20— *Spacecraft Subsystems III—On-Board Processing*.

William A. Hargus, Jr. Micro Propulsion Program Manager, Air Force Research Lab, Spacecraft Propulsion, Edwards AFB, California. PhD (Mechanical), Stanford University; MS (Aerospace), Pennsylvania State University; BS (Aerospace), University of Texas; Associate Fellow of the American Institute of Astronautics and Aeronautics; Associate Editor of the JANNAF Journal of Propulsion and Energetics. Section 18.6—*Electric Propulsion*.

Brian Harvey. Spaceflight Writer, Dublin, Ireland. M.A. (Economic and Social History), University College, Dublin; BA (History and Political Science), Dublin University (Trinity College). Section 25.5—*Differences Between International Approaches to Space*.

Herbert Hecht. Chief Engineeer, SoHaR Inc., Culver City, California. PhD (Engineering), University of California Los Angeles; MS (Electrical Engineering), Polytechnic Institute of Brooklyn; BS (Electrical Engineering, City University, New York. Section 24.1—*Reliability*.

Myron J. Hecht. Senior Project Leader, The Aerospace Corporation, El Segundo, California. J.D., University of California Los Angeles; MBA, University of California Los Angeles; MS (Nuclear Engineering), University of California Los Angeles; BS (Chemistry), University of California Los Angeles. Section 24.1—*Reliability*.

Robert Hoyt. President, CEO, and Chief Scientist, Tethers Unlimited, Inc., Bothell, Washington. PhD (Aero/Astro), University of Washington; B.A (Physics), Williams College. Section 25.1—*Space Tethers*.

Scott Hull. Orbital Debris Engineer, NASA Goddard Space Flight Center, Greenbelt, Maryland. BS, (Materials Engineering), Drexel University. Chapter 30—*End of Mission Considerations*.

Michael S. Hurley, Jr. Spacecraft Development Secction Head, Naval Research Lab, Washington, DC. M.B.A, George Mason University; ME (Mechanical Engineering), Virginia Tech; BS (Engineering), Virgina Tech. Section 13.4—*Cost vs. Reliability—Focusing on the Mission Objectives*.

John M. Jurist. Adjunct Professor of Space Studies, University of North Dakota, Grand Forks; PhD (Biophysics), University of California, Los Angeles Medical School; MS (Biophysics and Nuclear Medicine), University of California, Los Angeles Medical School; AB (Physics), University of California, Los Angeles. Section 1.4—*Spaceflight Economics*; Section 12.1—*Sources of Space Financing*; Section 12.2—*GAAP Amortization and Return on Investment*.

Christopher Lashley. Mechanisms Group Manager, ATK Spacecraft Systems and Services, Beltsville, Maryland. MS University of Maryland; BS University of Maryland. Chapter 22.1.5 — *Mechanisms and Deployables*.

David E. Lee. Program Manager and Lead, Integrated Concept Development Facility, Northrop Grumman Aerospace Systems, Redondo Beach, California. PhD (Mechanical Engineering), University of California, Los Angeles; MS (Manufacturing Engineering), University of California, Los Angeles; BA (Mathematics), University of California, Los Angeles. Section 23.3—*Spacecraft Integration and Test*.

Ivett A. Leyva. Lead, Combustion Devices Group, Aerophysics Branch, Air Force Research Laboratory, Edwards Air Force Base, California. PhD (Aeronautics), Caltech; MS (Aeronautics), Caltech; BS (Engineering and Applied Science), Caltech. Chapter 18—*Spacecraft Subsystems I—Propulsion*.

David Livingston. Host of The Space Show and Executive Director of One Giant Leap Foundation, Inc., Tiburon, California. DBA, Golden Gate University; MBA, (International Business Management), Golden Gate University; BA (Political Science), University of Arizona; Adjunct Professor of Space Policy, Odegard School of Aerospace Sciences, University of North Dakota. Section 1.4—*Spaceflight Economics*; Section 12.1—*Sources of Space Financing*; Section 12.2—*GAAP Amortization and Return on Investment*.

Ron Madler. Professor and Dean of Engineering, Embry-Riddle Aeronautical University, Prescott, Arizona. PhD, MS, BS (Aerospace Engineering Science), University of Colorado. Section 7.5— *Orbital Debris*.

Benjamin Malphrus. Chair, Department of Earth and Space Sciences, Morehead State University Space Science Center, Morehead, KY; EdD (Physics and Astronomy), West Virginia University; MAT (Physics), University of South Carolina-Columbia; BA (Art), University of South Carolina-Columbia. Section 25.4—*CubeSats*.

Joseph K. McDermott. Senior Manager, Electrical Power Systems, Lockheed Martin Space Systems Company, Denver, Colorado. ME (Engineering Management), University of Colorado; BS (Chemistry), Loras College. Section 21.2—*Power*.

Wade Molnau. Senior Engineering Manager, General Dynamics Advanced Information Systems, Bloomington, Minnesota. PhD, MS, BS (Industrial Engineering), Arizona State University. Section 23.5—*Multi-Spacecraft Manufacturing*.

Ron Noomen. Assistant Professor, Aerospace Engineering, Delft University of Technology, Delft, The Netherlands. MSc (Aerospace Engineering), Delft University of Technology. Section 10.7—*Design of Interplanetary Orbits*.

John E. Oberright. Senior Systems Engineer, Goddard Space Flight Center, Greenbelt, Maryland. BME (Mechanical Engineering), Catholic University of America. Section 22.2—*Spacecraft Thermal Control*.

Jean Olivieri. Senior Director of Structures Production, SpaceX, Hawthorne, CA. MSE, Arizona State University; BSE, University of Arizona; PMP, George Washington University. Section 23.5—*Multi-Spacecraft Manufacturing*.

David Parsley. SBIRS Deputy Director/Program Manager HEO Payloads, Northrop-Grumman Electronic Systems, Azusa, California. MS, BS (Electrical Engineering), University of Utah. Section 23.4—*System Mission Verification and Validation*.

Ed Pentaleri. Principal Systems Engineer, Space Systems/Loral, Palo Alto, California. MS (Physics), San Jose State University; BS (Mechanical and Nuclear Engineering), University of California, Berkeley. Chapter 16—*Communications Payloads*.

Kent M. Price. Principal Engineer, Space Systems/Loral, Palo Alto, California. MS (Physics), University of Sydney, Australia; BS (Physics), Yale University. Chapter 16—*Communications Payloads*.

Michael Pryzby. Sr. Systems Engineer/Program Manager, ATK Aerospace, Springfield, Virginia. MSE (Systems Engineering), Johns Hopkins University; BS (Mechanical Engineering), Virginia Polytechnic Institute and State University. Section 22.1—*Spacecraft Structures and Mechanisms*.

Bill Purdy. Mechanical Engineer, Purdy Engineering, Poolesville, Maryland. BSME University of Maryland. Chapter 13.4—*Cost vs. Reliability—Focusing on Mission Objectives*.

Lloyd Purves. Senior Systems Engineer, NASA Goddard Space Flight Center, Greenbelt, Maryland. BS (Electrical Engineering), Union College; Graduate courses (Aerospace Engineering), University of Maryland. Section 6.5—*System Engineering Tools*.

Jeffery J. Puschell. Principal Engineering Fellow, Raytheon Space and Airborne Systems, El Segundo, California. PhD (Astrophysics), University of Minnesota; AB with honors (Physics), The University of Chicago. Chapter 6—*Formal Requirements Definition;* Chapter 15 —*Overview of Payload Design*; Chapter 17—*Observation Payloads*.

James Rendleman. Consultant/Attorney, Rendleman & Associates, Colorado Springs, Colorado. BS (Chemistry), University of Chapel Hill; MBA, MPA, Golden Gate University; JD, Whittier Law School; LLM, University of San Diego School of Law. Chapter 12.3 —*Space Law and Policy Considerations*.

Markus Rufer. Executive Vice President, COO, Scorpius Space Launch Company, Hawthorne, California. MS (Mechanical Engineering), Federal Technology Institute; MBA, Alameda University. Section 23.7—*Intangible Factors in Manufacturing*.

Nicola Sarzi-Amade. Vice President, Scorpius Space Launch Company, Hawthorne, California. Systems Engineer, Microcosm, Inc., Hawthorne, California. PhD (Astronautical Engineering), University of Southern California; MS (Aerospace Engineering), University of California, Irvine; Laurea (Aerospace Engineering), Politecnico di Milano. Section 7.3—*Radiation Belts*; Appendices; Inside Front Cover.

Jeremiah P. Schneider. Electrical Engineer, Lockheed Martin Space Systems Company, Littleton, Colorado. MS (Systems Engineering), University of Denver; BS (Electrical Engineering), University of Colorado at Denver. Section 21.2—*Power*.

Rabindra (Rob) Singh. Executive Director, Communications Systems Space Systems Loral, Palo Alto, California. MASc (Electrical Engineering), University of Waterloo, Canada; BASc (Systems Design Engineering), University of Waterloo, Canada. Chapter 16—*Communications Payloads*.

Frederick A. Slane. Executive Director, Space Infrastructure Foundation, Colorado Springs, Colorado. MBA (International Business), University of Colorado; MS (Physics), University of New Mexico; BS (Aeronautics Engineering), Air Force Institute of Technology; BA (Physics/Mathematics), Willamette University. Section 6.6—*The Role of Standards in Space System Development*.

Geoffrey Smit. Senior Engineering Specialist, The Aerospace Corporation, El Segundo, CA. PhD (Mechanical Engineering/Aerospace Sciences), Northwester University; MBA, University of Chicago; BS, (Mechanical Engineering), University of Witwatersrand, Johannesburg, ZA; Appendix G—*Statistical Error Analysis.*

Milton "Skip" Smith.. Attorney, Sherman & Howard L.L.C. Colorado Springs, Colorado. PhD, McGill University Institute of Air & Space Law; MS, McGill University Institute of Air & Space Law; JD, George Washington University Law School; BS, United States Air Force Academy. *Section 12.3—Space Law and Policy Considerations.*

Trevor C. Sorensen. Professor/Project Manager, Hawaii Space Flight Laboratory, University of Hawaii, Honolulu, Hawaii. D.E. (Aerospace Engineering), University of Kansas; MS (Aerospace Engineering), University of Kansas; BS (Aerospace Engineering), University of Kansas. Chapter 29—*Mission Operations*.

David B. Spencer. Associate Professor of Aerospace Engineering, The Pennsylvania State University, University Park, Pennsylvania. PhD (Aerospace Engineering Sciences), University of Colorado; MBA, Pennsylvania State University; MS (Aeronautics and Astronautics), Purdue University; BS (Mechanical Engineering), University of Kentucky. Section 7.5—*Orbital Debris.*

Scott R. Starin. Senior Aerospace Engineer, Goddard Space Flight Center, Greenbelt, Maryland. MS (Aerospace Engineering), Ohio State University; BS (Physics), North Carolina State University; BS (Human Relations to Technology), North Carolina State University; BS (Aerospace Engineering), North Carolina State University. Section 19.1—*Spacecraft Attitude Determination and Control Systems.*

Craig L. Stevens. Aerospace Engineer, NASA Goddard Space Flight Center, Greenbelt, Maryland. BS, MS Virginia Polytechnic Institute and State University. Section 22.1.3—*Structural Analysis and Sizing.*

W. Kent Tobiska. President and Chief Scientist, Space Environment Technologies, Pacific Palisades, California; Director of Utah State University Space Weather Center, Logan, Utah. PhD (Aerospace Engineering with Solar and Atmospheric Physics), University of Colorado; MS (Aerospace Engineering), University of Colorado. Section 7.1—*Summary of Space Environment and Weather*; Section 7.2—*The Earth's Magnetic Field*; Section 7.3—*Radiation Belts.*

Robert J. Twiggs. Professor of Astronautics, Morehead State University, Morehead, Kentucky. MS (Electrical Engineering), Stanford University; BS (Electrical Engineering), University of Idaho. Section 25.4—*CubeSats.*

Richard E. Van Allen. Vice President and Director, Space Systems Division, Microcosm, Inc., Hawthorne, California. PhD (Aerospace Engineering), Purdue University; MS (Aerospace Engineering), Purdue University; BS (Aeronautical and Astronautical Engineering), Purdue University. Section 18.7—*Alternative Propulsion Systems for In-Space Use.*

Jeff Volosin. Deputy Division Chief, Exploration and Space Communication, NASA/GSFC, Greenbelt, Maryland. Adjunct Professor (Astronautical Engineering), Capitol College; BS (Space Science), Florida Institute of Technology. Chapter 28—*Ground System Design.*

David B. Watson. Sr. Manager, Mechanical Engineer, ATK Space Systems, Beltsville, Maryland. MS, Univsersity of Missouri; BSAOE, Virginia Tech. Chapter 22.1.2—*Design Concepts.*

James R. Wertz. President, Microcosm, Inc., Hawthorne, California. PhD (Relativity and Cosmology), University of Texas, Austin; MS (Administration of Science and Technology), George Washington University; SB (Physics), Massachusetts Institute of Technology. Chapter 1—*Introduction*; Chapter 2—*Space Mission Communities*; Chapter 3—*Space Mission Engineering*; Chapter 4—*Mission Concept Definition and Exploration*; Chapter 5—*Mission Analysis and Mission Utility*; Chapter 8—*Space Mission Geometry—What the Spacecraft Sees*; Chapter 9—*Orbits and Astrodynamics*; Chapter 10—*Orbit and Constellation Design—Selecting the Right Orbit*; Chapter 13—*Reducing Space Mission Cost and Schedule*; Appendix E,—*Time and Date Systems.*

Julie Wertz. Systems Engineer, Jet Propulsion Laboratory, Pasadena, California. PhD (Astronautical Engineering), Massachusetts Institute of Technology; MS (Astronautical Engineering), Massachusetts Institute of Technology; BS (Aeronautical and Astronautical Engineering), Massachusetts Institute of Technology. Section 24.2—*Space System Risk Analysis.*

James S. Wood. Launch Services Program Chief Engineer, Kennedy Space Center, Kennedy Space Center, Florida. BS, Pittsburg State University, Pittsburg. Chapter 26—*Launch Vehicles.*

Marcus Young. Program Manager, Advanced Propulsion Concepts, Air Force Research Laboratory, Edwards Air Force Base, California. PhD (Aerospace Engineering), University of Southern California; MS (Aerospace Engineering), University of Southern California; BS (Aerospace Engineering), University of Southern California. Section 18.7—*Alternative Propulsion Systems for In-Space Use.*

Charles M. Zakrzwski. Systems Engineer, NASA Goddard Space Flight Center, Greenbelt, Maryland. MS (Aeronautical and Astronautical Engineering), Ohio State University; BS (Aerospace Engineering), Pennsylvania State University. Section 18.5—*System Design Elements (Propulsion)*

Advisory Committee

Stuart Eves, *Surrey Satellite Tech Ltd.*
Michael Gruntman, *University of Southern California*
Jane Hansen, *HRP Systems, Inc.*
John E. Kessee, *MIT*
Jin Kang, *United States Naval Academy*
James Longuski, *Purdue University*
Ronald A. Madler, *Embry-Riddle University*
Landis Markley, *NASA Goddard Space Flight Center*
John Martin, *NASA Goddard Space Flight Center*
John C. Mather, *NASA Goddard Space Flight Center*
Carlos Niederstrasser, *Orbital Sciences Corp.*
Ron Noomen, *Delft University of Technology*
Lloyd R. Purves, *NASA Goddard Space Flight Center*
Steven Raque, *West Virginia University*
Aaron Q. Rogers, *Johns Hopkins University; Applied Physics Lab*
Frederick A. Slane, *Space Infrastructure Foundation*
Michael Swartwout, *St. Louis University*
Richard Van Allen, *Microcosm, Inc.*

Reviewers

Viqar Abbasi, *Canadian Space Agency*
Ossama Abdelkhali, *Michigan Tech University*
Stephen P. Airey, *ESA*
Thomas Bauer, *Microcosm, Inc.*
Grant Bonin, *UTIAS Flight Laboratory*
Mario Ciaramicoli, *ISU*
Amanda C. Cordova, *The Boeing Company*
Bernd Dachwald, *Aachen University*
Bruce Davis, *University of Colorado Boulder*
Simon Dawson, *SSI*
Cornelius J. Dennehy, *NASA Goddard Space Flight Center*
Jorge Diaz del Rio, *ESA-ESAC*
Michel Doyon, *Canadian Space Agency*
Don Edberg, *Cal State Polytechnic*
David Geller, *Utah State University*
Doug Griffin, *STFC,RAL,SSTD*
Marcus Hallmann, *DLR-Germany*
Chan Ham, *Southern Polytechnic State University*
Terry Hart, *Lehigh University*
Jeffrey Hoffman, *MIT*
Greg Holt, *NASA Johnson Space Center*
Alexander Jablonski, *Canadian Space Agency*
Julie Jackson, *Microcosm, Inc.*
Tom E. Jones, *NASA Goddard Space Flight Center*
Jin Kang, *United States Naval Academy*
Stephen Kemble, *EADS-Astrium*
James Keravala, *Shackleton Energy Company*
Andrew Ketsdever, *UCCS*
Charles Kilmer, *The Boeing Company*
Robert Klungle, *Aerospace Corporation*
Pam Lindbloom-Esquinca, *Microcosm Astronautics Books*
Ronald A. Madler, *Embry-Riddle University*
Craig A. McLaughlin, *University of Kansas*
Carlos Niederstrasser, *Orbital Sciences Corp.*
Darius Nikanpour, *Canadian Space Agency*
James O'Donnell, Jr., *NASA Goddard Space Flight Center*
Hayrani Oz, *Ohio State University*
David W. Peters, *NASA Goddard Space Flight Center*
Steven Raque, *West Virginia University*
Terry Rector, *Com Dev-USA*
Aaron Q. Rogers, *Johns Hopkins University; Applied Physics Lab*
Michael Safyan, *ISU*
Nicola Sarzi-Amade, *Microcosm, Inc.*
Ryan Sellers, *Cal State Polytechnic*
Anthony Shao, *Microcosm, Inc.*
Wayne Shiroma, *University of Hawaii*
Daniel Showalter, *Canadian Space Agency*
William Sluder, *NASA Goddard Space Flight Center*
David Spencer, *Penn State University*
Amanada Stiles, *X PRIZE*
Mike Swartwout, *St. Louis University*
James Volp, *ISU*
Nestor Voronka, *Tethers Unlimited*
Erika B. Wagner, *X PRIZE Lab@MIT*

Preface

This book is intended as a replacement for *Space Mission Analysis and Design*, known as SMAD to a great many engineers and students. SMAD was first published in 1991 and served as a practical and widely used reference and text for more than 20 years with over 65,000 copies in print. Nonetheless, the worlds of space exploration, space usage, and how books are used and published have all changed in the intervening period, and it is time for a new, unique, and hopefully more useable and useful reference and text in *Space Mission Engineering (SME)*—i.e., defining the parameters and trading on requirements so as to meet the broad, often poorly defined, objectives of a space mission at minimum cost and risk. This is a definition that was introduced in the first edition of SMAD to try and distinguish mission engineering from the more formal process of space systems engineering which had, in many cases, become simply a process of keeping track of all of the requirements and constraints and determining how each was to be met and verified. Certainly both processes are needed, but our emphasis here is on how to go about starting with a blank sheet of paper and **creating** a space mission to meet the needs of the end user as economically and quickly as possible.

It is clear that the technology exists today, or can be created, to do essentially anything we choose to do in space. The major challenges facing us are that space has become dramatically expensive and far too slow to achieve the objectives set for it, and, as a result, is far less useful to the end user than it should be. President Kennedy's call for landing a man on the Moon was followed 8 1/2 years later by the Apollo 11 mission, including developing from scratch the Saturn V launch vehicle—the largest, most reliable, and lowest cost per pound launcher ever built. Today the Saturn V no longer exists and we most likely couldn't finish doing the system design and verification needed for a Moon mission in 8.5 years, even if we could afford to go there.

Fortunately, the space business is beginning to change again, at least in some areas. SmallSats and CubeSats, with dramatically lower cost and shorter schedules, are starting to be taken seriously. Dr. Pedro Rustan [2004], at the time the Head of Advanced Science and Technology for the National Reconnaissance Office, pointed out in 2004 that the goal for space mission engineering should not be just creating low-cost, responsive small satellites, but using the same or comparable techniques to dramatically reduce the cost and schedule for all space systems, including those that are inherently very large and complex.

As a consequence of the need to change the way we do business in space, SME has two complimentary objectives: (a) to explain how and why space missions are built the way they are and (b) to explain how it can be done "faster, better, cheaper." The difficulty of doing this is best captured by the experience of Dan Goldin, the Director of NASA from 1992 to 2001, who introduced this mantra to try to convince the space community that change was critical. After all, almost every other aspect of modern technology has become faster, better, and cheaper in its implementation—including computers, communications, television, automobiles, and aircraft. But culture is very hard to change. Today, if you say "faster, better, cheaper" in a meeting of aerospace engineers, you will almost certainly hear several people respond with "faster, better, cheaper—pick any two." This suggests, of course, that in the view of many space engineers faster, better, and cheaper isn't possible—that space technology is, in effect, as good as it is ever going to get and improvements in one area will mean doing more poorly in some other area. This is the real challenge for SME—to show both where we are today (and how to build space missions according to today's rules) and show clearly that the goals of Dan Goldin, Pete Rustan, and many others can indeed be met as technology advances. It is also our goal to explain how this can be accomplished in as specific and practical terms as possible. Our objective for SME is to satisfy both needs. We would much appreciate feedback from readers about whether we have been successful or how we could do it better. (Send E-mails to bookproject@smad.com or to any of the editors listed below.)

One of the major changes for this volume is that it is both a physical book and a website, www.sme-smad.com. (The password is ASTRODATA and isn't case sensitive.) The website is not intended as a stand-alone site, but as an extension of this volume. It contains articles which go into more detail on many topics, downloadable Excel models for most of the mathematical tables and plots, data tables that can be updated from time-to-time, and a complete listing of all of the references with an annotated bibliography. Nearly all of the references and bibliography have a direct link to where the material can be downloaded for free or, for copyright material, where it can be purchased and downloaded, or where books can be purchased and shipped with next day delivery. Nearly all the sample plots and tables can be customized to your particular space mission. Our goal here is to make the book fit your mission as much as possible and let you find additional details and more in-depth assessments of specific topics within a day or less. We hope it works well and would appreciate your suggestions on how to make it work better.

It is very difficult to express our full appreciation for over 120 authors, reviewers, and advisory committee members, all of whom worked dramatically hard with no contract, no compensation, and no reward other than seeing the work done and a copy of the book when it was complete. These are among the most experienced and busy individuals in the community, giving up free time to provide this material for you, the reader. Without them, it would not have been possible. We are truly indebted to them for putting in many more hours than most of them had anticipated. Among the reviewers, we would like to especially thank Steve Raque, Mike Swartwout, Jin Kang, Tom Bauer, and Markus Rufer, who reviewed many chapters and made major contributions to the success of the volume. A special thank you goes to Goddard Space Flight Center for supplying many authors and reviewers, and considerable technical data as well.

The work of creating the camera-ready copy fell to the Microcosm Publications Department, under the direction of Chris Maruyama and Donna Klungle. Jenny Greer and Julie Jackson did much of the 2-column formatting. Nearly all of the art work, including the color version of all of the figures and tables for the educator package, was created by Chris Maruyama. Most of the background work, references, bibliography, web references, and Excel models have been created under the direction of Nicola Sarzi-Amade by Nicola, Anthony Shao, Becky Christofferson, and Kyungmo Koo.

As anyone who has undertaken projects of this sort knows, one of the largest contributions comes from the families of the three editors. We greatly appreciate their forbearance and patience with a project that took longer than we hoped and far more evening and weekend hours than any of us would have guessed or wished.

Ultimately, if this book belongs to anyone, it is Pam Lindbloom-Esquinca, the manager of the Microcosm bookstore, and the force behind creating this volume. It was Pam that told us very forcefully to go out and do it, put up several years of bookstore profits to create the camera-ready copy, pushed and cajoled all of the authors, reviewers, and editors, and dove in to help with editing, references, and anything else that needed to be done. The book would not have occurred without you, Pam. You have made a significant contribution to astronautics that is greatly appreciated.

If you have ideas or suggestions on how we can make the book or the associated website better or more useful, please let us know. In many ways, this book is a new experiment and your feedback is both welcome and appreciated.

July, 2011

James R. Wertz
Microcosm, Inc./USC
Torrance, CA
jwertz@smad.com

David F. Everett
NASA GSFC
Greenbelt, MD
David.F.Everett@nasa.gov

Jeffery J. Puschell
Raytheon
El Segundo, CA
jpuschell@raytheon.com

Dedication

Microcosm Press and Microcosm Astronautics Books would like to expressly thank the editors for their vision, the authors for their views, the reviewers and researchers for their help and all for their hard work.

We would like to thank NASA, the US Air Force, US Army, US Navy, European Space Agency, Canadian Space Agency and all the universities, industry and commercial companies that support space programs, for their inspiration.

We would also like to thank the professors that will use this text to teach the next generation for giving us purpose. We would like to thank the small companies that keep on living the dream and the large companies that keep the dream alive, all of whom have been great supporters.

In the end, this book is for us all. We are a small community, in the grand scheme of things, and we take pride in the accomplishments of ourselves and each other. The willingness to share these accomplishments and the knowledge we learn from them is one of our greatest attributes.

So this book is dedicated to us all. May we all live long and prosper!!

Pam Esquinca
Chris Maruyama

1 Introduction

James R. Wertz, ***Microcosm, Inc./USC***

The goal of this book is to lay out the entire process of analyzing and designing space missions—from an initial vague concept or mission objective to designing, building, launching, operating, and eventually deorbiting one or more spacecraft. In the words of former NASA Administrator Dan Goldin, our objective is to do this "faster, better, cheaper" than it has been done before. Although many throughout the space community will argue that this is effectively impossible ("faster, better, cheaper—pick any two" is a common rejoinder), experience has shown that it is possible and that progress is real. Perhaps most important, we **must** find ways to do the job faster, better, and cheaper if we are to accomplish the missions that we want to accomplish within the budgets that are available and enable some of the remarkable benefits that space can bring about. To do this, we need to understand both how and why things are done as they are today, so that we can make the process better tomorrow.

In a sense, this book is intended as a microcosm of the faster, better, cheaper mission engineering process. Our goal with *Space Mission Engineering* is to greatly improve and shorten the preliminary mission design process by making it easier and faster to apply equations and examples and find reference data in time to be of use in a current project. For example, most of the analytic models, numerical tables, and plots throughout the book are immediately available to you on the book website and can be changed to show your specific problem of interest. Some extended discussions of relevant material that is a bit too long for the printed text is also there. Most of the references cited throughout the book are immediately available on the web and nearly all of the remainder are available within a day or so, although, of course, copyright material must be purchased from the owner or an appropriate reseller. We also have a bibliography for each chapter on the website, both so that you can have immediate access to that information, and also so that it can be updated from time-to-time as new books and professional papers appear. Details of what's on the website, how to use it, and other sources of mission engineering information, are described in Sec. 1.6. Note that the website is an adjunct to the book, and not a substitute.

Looking at the organization of the book, Chaps. 1 and 2 provide the philosophical basis and broad context for determining what space mission engineering is all about. Chaps. 3–6 then provide the basic engineering details of defining a space mission, undergoing system trades to find the best available solution (or at least an acceptable one), quantifying the cost and utility of the mission, and undertaking the formal requirements definition process. Chaps. 7–10 look specifically at the space environment, orbit and mission geometry, and orbit and constellation design. Chapters 11–13 then look at financial and legal issues and the fundamental problem of reducing cost and schedule. Part II (Chaps. 14–25) goes through the process of spacecraft and payload design. Part III (Chaps. 26–31) covers launch, operations, and end-of-life. Finally, the appendices and end-pages summarize the numerical data and basic formulas that you will need for preliminary mission design.

1.1 What is Space Mission Engineering?

***Space Mission Engineering* is the definition of mission parameters and refinement of requirements so as to meet the broad and often poorly defined objectives of a space mission in a timely manner at minimum cost and risk. The goal of this book is to give you the processes and tools to do that.**

Table 1-0, Fig. 1-0, Eq. 1-0

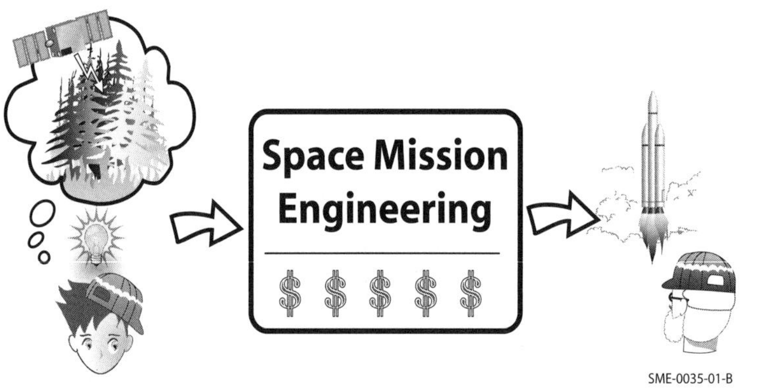

Fig. 1-1. Space Mission Engineering is the Process of Going From Broad Mission Objectives or a Vague Concept to an Operational Mission. Unfortunately many modern space programs perform well, but cost too much and take too long, which is a fundamental problem that is addressed throughout this book.

A good example of the space mission engineering process is the Apollo program that resulted in landing the first humans on the Moon and is one of the major technological achievements of modern times. But how well did it work from an engineering perspective? In its fundamental goal of putting people on the Moon and returning them safely to Earth it was completely successful. In a task that was very high risk, Apollo landed people on the Moon, gave them the time and tools to explore their immediate environment, and returned all of them safely to Earth.* However, our space mission engineering goal is to do this at minimum cost and risk—and we don't really know whether we achieved that. Realistically, we'll settle for reasonable cost and risk.

Like the Apollo program, most modern space missions perform well, and therefore, the space mission engineering job is well done in many ways. However, in another respect, the job is done very badly in that most large space programs today cost too much and take too long (Fig. 1-1). To be more specific, the United States launches approximately 20 space missions per year (including both manned and unmanned, Earth orbiting and interplanetary). The combined US space budget for NASA, DoD, the Intelligence Community, and a few other agencies is on the order of $60 billion/year. (See Sec. 1.5.) This implies that in recent years,

Space systems launched by the United States have cost an average of $3 billion/launch. The average time from concept to launch is not well known, but is certainly approaching a decade if not more.

In my view, that is too much and too long, and fixing it is going to require major changes in how space business is done. Certainly some people within the space community will argue that the cost and time are necessary and appropriate and we will return to this question in Chap. 13. However, irrespective of whether you believe we are doing the job well or badly or, perhaps some combination of both, the goal of this book is to allow you to do it **better**—to create new missions, defined by you, the reader, that are safer, better, more reliable, with greater performance, done more quickly and at lower cost than has been the case in the last decade. In other words, we want space missions to evolve, just as other products in the marketplace evolve.

A part of this evolution includes updating the space mission engineering process from when it was presented 20 years ago in the first edition of *Space Mission Analysis and Design*, known as SMAD [Wertz and Larson, 1991]. The process presented here differs from that in SMAD by adding a timeliness requirement and identifying the people and groups involved, often called the *stakeholders*. There are specific reasons for these changes as discussed in Sec. 3.2.

There is another respect in which the Apollo program was a good example of space mission engineering. Initially, the objectives were broad and had very little definition. President Kennedy, in his proclamation in support of Apollo, did not specify how many people would go on each mission, or how long they would stay, or how much Lunar material they would bring back. The Apollo program itself defined the more detailed objectives, largely by determining what was reasonably feasible within the constraints of the technology. The successive Apollo missions continued to evolve and each landing became more complex and more successful in terms of the areas explored and the material returned. As presented in some detail by Johnson [2002], Apollo was one of the first major examples of systems management and systems engineering at a massive level. Apollo took a vague, poorly defined objective (as it should be) and, using 100's of thousands of people, built the largest, most reliable, and lowest cost per kg rocket ever built, and used that rocket to have 2 people step onto the surface of the Moon only 8.5 years after Kennedy expressed his initial vision. As Johnson calls it, the "Secret of

*Astronauts Gus Grissom, Ed White, and Roger Chaffee were killed in a fire inside the Apollo 1 Command Module during a ground test prior to any of the operational or test flights.

Apollo" was the organizational and engineering process that was able to achieve that.*

In another respect, Apollo wasn't a good example of space mission engineering. It may or may not have been minimum cost and risk, but it certainly wasn't cheap. (Apollo cost well over $150 billion in today's dollars.) What we would like to do today is to do missions much more substantive than Apollo, and for a lot less money. As we will see in Sec. 1.5 and Chap. 2, there is an enormous potential in space and we have only begun to scratch the surface of what can be accomplished for science, for commerce, for the military, for protecting the environment here on Earth, and for starting to use the resources of space for the benefit of mankind. We would like to change that and have missions become faster, cheaper, more useful, and in far greater numbers. All of this requires thinking seriously about both performance **and** cost and finding new ways to do business in space.

What happened? How did we go from having a competent, robust, very active space program to one that is still very competent but is also, for the number of missions launched, dramatically expensive and very slow to respond? At least a portion of the answer probably lies in the *Space Spiral* shown in Fig. 1-2. The ever-increasing cost of space missions leads to longer schedules and fewer missions. This leads to a demand for higher reliability, which, in turn, leads to higher cost, longer schedules, and fewer missions.

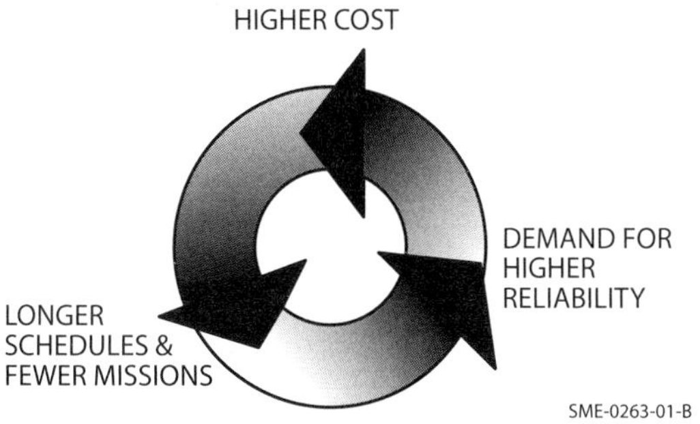

Fig. 1-2. The Space Spiral is a Significant Contributor to Increasing Costs and Longer Schedules.

Chapter 13 provides a detailed assessment of how to solve this problem. A part of the solution is to find ways to reverse the Space Spiral by having a mix of smaller, lower-cost missions and larger, more expensive ones, such that there is less demand for absolute guarantees of success, which are unachievable in the real world. An analogy is a military commander whose troops are on one side of a large canyon and he expects them to be attacked the next day by an enemy force that will move across a bridge over the canyon. The commander sends 3 airplanes to knock out the bridge, when the job could be done by a single plane. It is not that the commander believes that his planes are poorly built or that his pilots are incompetent, it's just that in the real world things go wrong and if you really want that bridge to not be there in the morning, you provide multiple ways of getting the job done. Similarly, in spaceflight, we will achieve a higher level of mission reliability by having multiple, diverse assets available instead of trying to make a single, dramatically expensive asset work perfectly.†

The broad timeline over which space missions are created is described in Sec. 3.4.2. The first phase is Concept Exploration, which is the initial study phase that results in a broad definition of the space mission and an initial estimate of cost, schedule, and performance. While much of this is a vague and "fuzzy" process, it's a critical part of space mission engineering because most of the cost, risk, schedule, and utility of the mission are determined by the end of concept exploration. Therefore, it's important to do this job carefully, thinking about what can be done to reduce the cost and complexity of the mission or increase the utility to the end users and those who will ultimately be asked to pay for the mission. By far the majority of mission concepts die during or at the end of concept exploration. This may be because there is insufficient performance or utility to the end user or because the technology doesn't yet exist to proceed, but it is most often simply because space missions are very expensive and no one is willing to pay to proceed to subsequent, ever more expensive, steps.

Even large, well-defined, active space programs can run into budget overruns and extended schedule delays. The reasons for this, and possible solutions, are described in Secs. 1.3 and 1.4 and in more detail in 13.6. As a result, missions on which hundreds of millions or billions of dollars have been spent are, nonetheless, cancelled from time to time or, when not cancelled, cause major delays in other important programs due to "soaking up" the available resources. This again emphasizes the need for good mission engineering throughout the mission lifecycle. We need to continuously look for ways to constrain cost and schedule growth and to sell the program and keep it sold, if it is still worth doing.

While there are problems with today's space missions, there is also dramatic potential, as described in Sec. 1.5 and Chap. 2. While some missions, such as navigation, communications, and direct broadcast are well-established and routine activities, other missions, such as utilization of space resources, space manufacturing, and

* Many people would argue that the US has lost some key element of the skill or will that was needed to allow Americans to walk on the Moon over 40 years ago and, consequently, the next people to walk on the Moon, and explore it in more depth, will likely be Chinese.

†Both aircraft and ground vehicles are much more reliable than space systems. Launch vehicles are about 90% reliable. We would never use airplanes or automobiles that had a 10% chance of a catastrophic failure that would destroy both the vehicle and its cargo when first used. We can either spend ever more money searching for perfection or find ways to accomplish our space mission objectives in the presence of occasional system failures.

the exploration of space itself, have just begun. These are truly exciting activities for a new generation of space mission engineers who can see further and do more. It's an exciting adventure.

1.2 The History of Spaceflight

Mike Gruntman,
University of Southern California

1.2.1 Humble Beginnings

The heavens had been attracting the imagination of humans for millennia. Some even argue that ancient texts, including the Old Testament, described spaceships in the sky. Reaching the cosmos requires powerful rockets. So, the first steps of the humans toward spaceflight were in rocketry. For centuries an essentially international endeavor of the pursuit of spaceflight attracted people from various lands who advanced the enabling science and technology.

Ancient Greeks observed the principle of jet propulsion more than 2,000 years ago. One thousand years later the first primitive rockets appeared in China and perhaps in India, later rediscovered in many other lands. A combination of charcoal, sulfur, and saltpeter—black powder—propelled the missiles. Natural abundance of saltpeter in China and India facilitated the emergence of the first war rockets in these countries.

Rockets had established a foothold in Europe some time in the 13th century. The word 'rocket' likely originated from the 'rocchetta,' a diminutive of the Italian word 'rocca' for distaff, a staff for holding the bunch of flux or wool from which the thread is drawn by spinning.

The early 19th century witnessed a major step in perfecting the rocket. A British inventor, William Congreve, turned ineffective and erratic missiles into a modern weapon system with standardized and interchangeable parts. These British war rockets, known as the Congreves (See Fig. 1-3), debuted during the Napoleonic wars. Then brought across the Atlantic Ocean, the Congreves bombarded Fort McHenry near Baltimore in 1813. Francis Scott Key immortalized the deadly missiles in his famous line "...And the rockets' red glare..." in the American National Anthem.

War rocketry rapidly proliferated throughout Europe and reached North and South Americas and Asia. The young Chilean republic was among the first to employ the domestically-made rockets—in 1819—in the fight against its former colonial ruler, Spain. Many European countries—particularly Austria, France, and Russia—established large-scale manufacturing of war rockets. The Russian army even built in 1834 an iron-clad submarine with a crew of 10 men which fired missiles from a submerged position.

The Mexican War, 1846–1848, advanced rocketry beyond an occasional experimentation in the United States. In a short period of a few months, the Army and the Navy completed the purchase, evaluation, prototyping, and testing of a new type of spin-stabilized war rockets. (These rockets became known as the Hales, after their inventor William Hale.) The US Army formed the first missile unit, the Rocket and Mountain Howitzer battery. The mass-produced new missiles quickly reached the rocket battery deployed in Mexico with the American expeditionary force. Thus the two military services succeeded in 1840s in a joint procurement and fielding of a new technologically advanced weapon system in less than one year.

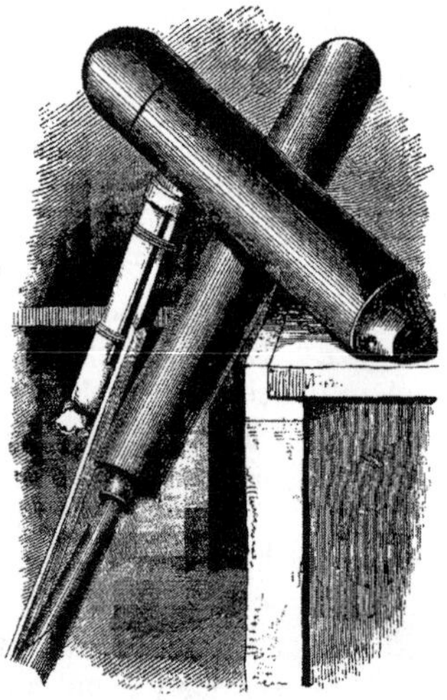

Fig. 1-3. Nineteenth Century Rockets: *Hale* (front), *Congreve* (with the centrally mounted guiding stick), and *skyrocket* (back). [Scoffern, 1859; Gruntman, 2004]

By the end of the 19th century, war rocketry had lost the competition to artillery with the introduction of rifled barrels, breech loading, and the Bessemer steel process. At this time the writers stepped in and replaced the men of sword as keepers of the interest in rocketry and spaceflight.

Nobody captured public imagination in space adventures more than the French writer Jules Verne (See Fig. 1-4). His novels "put on fire" and motivated many young men who would decades later transform a dream of spaceflight into a reality. Jules Verne's classic novel *From the Earth to the Moon* (first published in 1865) became a seminal work on spaceflight.

Early science fiction writers sent main characters on space voyages to satisfy their curiosity, as a bet, or to escape debts. Then, an American author, Edward Everett Hale, published a novel *The Brick Moon* in 1870. The story described a launch of an artificial satellite into orbit along a meridian to help sailors at sea in determining their longitude, in the same way as the Moon aids in determining latitude. It was the first description of an application satellite.

1.2.2 Great Pioneers

The late 19th century brought the realization that until the rocket was perfected there would be no trips through outer space, no landing on the Moon, and no visits to

Fig. 1-4. Jules Verne, *From the Earth to the Moon*—The future express. "Yes, gentleman," continued the orator," in spite of the opinion of certain narrow-minded people, who would shut up the human race upon this globe…we shall one day travel to the Moon, the planets, and the stars…" [Horne, 1911; Gruntman, 2004]

other planets to meet possible inhabitants. A long period followed when isolated visionaries and thinkers, including amateurs, began practical work and sketched out the sinews of the spaceflight concept. Many "intellectuals" of the day and assorted "competent authorities" dismissed the idea of space travel as ridiculous.

A number of outstanding individuals at the end of the 19th century and the beginning of the 20th century laid the foundations of practical rocketry and spaceflight. Four visionaries in 4 countries working under very different conditions became the great pioneers of the space age: the Russian Konstantin E. Tsiolkovsky; the French Robert Esnault-Pelterie; the American Robert H. Goddard; and the German Hermann Oberth. They contributed in unique ways to advancing the concept of spaceflight.

The writings of Konstantin E. Tsiolkovsky (1857–1935) combined development of scientific and technological ideas with the vision of space applications. While he never built rockets, Tsiolkovsky inspired a generation of Soviet rocket enthusiasts, including Sergei P. Korolev and Valentin P. Glushko, who achieved the first satellite.

An engineering graduate of the Sorbonne University, Robert Esnault-Pelterie, 1881–1957, first gained fame as an aviation pioneer who had introduced among other things an enclosed fuselage, aileron, joystick for plane control, four-bladed propeller, and safety belt. His prestige brought the much-needed credibility to the emerging space effort. It was Esnault-Pelterie who first published a spaceflight-related article in a mainstream archival physics journal in 1913; he also introduced the word "astronautics" in the language of science.

With a Ph.D. degree in what we would call today solid-state physics, Robert H. Goddard, 1882–1945, actually demonstrated the first liquid-propellant rocket engine in 1926. Goddard achieved numerous other firsts in rocketry. One of his rockets reached a 9,000 ft (2,700 m) altitude in 1937. Many results of Goddard's work remained largely unknown to contemporary scientists and engineers because of self-imposed secrecy, caused in part by ridicule by the ignorant and arrogant mainstream media.

Hermann Oberth, 1894–1989, published a detailed design of a sophisticated rocket in his book *The Rocket into Interplanetary Space* [Oberth, 1923]. He introduced numerous ideas including staging, film cooling of engine walls, and pressurization of propellant tanks. Oberth played an important role in early practical development of rocketry in Germany and provided inspiration for a generation of European space enthusiasts.

1.2.3 Building the Foundation

Powerful rockets belonged to a category of inherently complex advanced technologies where a lonely creative and gifted inventor could not succeed. Only concerted efforts of numerous well-organized professional scientists and engineers supported by significant resources could lead to practical systems. The totalitarian states were first to marshal the necessary resources and organize a large-scale development of ballistic missiles. In the Soviet Union, the military-sponsored *Jet Propulsion Scientific Research Institute* (RNII) employed 400 engineers and technicians in a sprawling complex in Moscow in the early 1930s. Later in the decade the Soviet program suffered from political purges and resumed its growth after 1944.

The German Army stepped up its rocket effort in 1932 by establishing a dedicated group that included Wernher von Braun. The German program grew immensely and by 1942 produced the first truly modern ballistic missile the A-4, better known as the V-2. The fueled A-4 weighed more than 12.5 metric tons and delivered a 1,000 kg warhead to distances up to 300 km. The German accomplishments also included mass production of the missiles. In a short period, under tremendous difficulties of wartime, the industry built 5,800 A-4's, with 2,000 fired operationally against England and liberated parts of Europe. The rocket manufacturing widely used slave labor from concentration camps, accompanied by atrocities especially during the construction of the underground facilities.

In the United States during WWII, rocketry concentrated on jet assisted take off (JATO) of the airplanes and on barrage solid-propellant missiles. The first American private rocket enterprises Reaction Motors and Aerojet Engineering Corp. were formed in December 1941 and in March 1942, respectively. After the war, several centers of rocketry emerged in the industry and government under sponsorship of the Army, Navy, and Air Force.

The US Army brought a number of captured German V-2 missiles to the United States. Military personnel and industrial contractors launched more than 60 V-2's from the White Sands Missile Range in New Mexico by 1951. Many missiles carried science payloads studying the upper atmosphere, ionosphere, solar radiation, and cosmic rays. These first rocket experiments gave birth to a vibrant experimental space science. Subsequently, many government and university scientists became energetic advocates of space exploration.

The US Army followed its century-long tradition of the arsenal system with significant in-house engineering capabilities. By the early 1950s, it had concentrated the development of ballistic missiles and emerging space activities at the Redstone Arsenal in Huntsville, AL. The California Institute of Technology (Caltech) managed another important Army rocket center, the Jet Propulsion Laboratory (JPL), in Pasadena, CA. The JPL grew out of pioneering research and development programs from the group of Theodore von Kármán at Caltech.

The Redstone Arsenal became the home to more than 100 "imported" German rocketeers, headed by Wernher von Braun. The Germans had come to work in the United States under contracts through *Operation Paperclip*. While von Braun's rocketeers got the most publicity, the Paperclip program brought to the United States in total more than 600 German specialists in various areas of science and technology. In contrast to the compact von Braun group, the other scientists and engineers were dispersed among various American industrial and research organizations.

The Army, the Air Force, and the Navy were carrying out essentially independent development programs in guided missiles, with some overlap, occasional cooperation, and determined rivalry. In 1956, Secretary of Defense Charles E. Wilson attempted to resolve the problem of duplication by defining the "roles and missions" of the services. Consequently, the Air Force asserted control over intercontinental warfare, with the Army's role reduced to shorter range missiles.

The fateful roles-and-missions decision did not stop a most active leader of the Army's missile program, General John B. Medaris, and von Braun from finding ways to advance their visionary space agenda. In addition to such Army achievements as the development of the operationally-deployed ballistic missiles Redstone and Jupiter in 1950s, they would succeed in launching the first American artificial satellite, Explorer I, to space. Only by the end of 1950s, the Army had finally lost its programs in long-range ballistic missiles and space when the newly formed civilian space agency, the National Aeronautics and Space Administration (NASA), took over and absorbed the JPL and von Braun's team at Redstone.

In contrast to the Army, the Navy and especially the new service Air Force (formed in 1947) relied primarily on the contractors from the aircraft industry in their ballistic missile programs. In late 1940s and early 1950s, the Naval Research Laboratory (NRL) with Glenn L. Martin Co. developed the Viking sounding rocket as a replacement of the dwindling supply of the captured V-2's. This program laid the foundation for Martin's future contributions to ballistic missiles that would include the Titan family of Intercontinental Ballistic Missiles, (ICBM) and space launchers.

In 1946, the Air Force initiated development of a new test missile, the MX-774. The Convair (Consolidated Vultee Aircraft Corp.) team led by Karel J. (Charlie) Bossart introduced many innovations in the MX-774 missiles that reached an altitude of 30 miles. Based on this early experience, Convair later developed the first American ICBM, the Atlas. The Atlas program, including missile deployment became a truly national effort that dwarfed the Manhattan Project of World War II.

Other major ballistic missile programs initiated in 1950s included ICBMs Titan and Minuteman and Intermediate Range Ballistic Missile (IRBM) Thor. The Glenn L. Martin Company, Boeing Company, and Douglas Aircraft Company led the development, as prime contractors, of these missiles, respectively. Aerojet and the Rocketdyne Division of North American Aviation emerged as leading developers of liquid-propellant rocket engines. The Navy selected the Lockheed Aircraft Corporation as the prime contractor for its submarine-launched solid-propellant IRBM Polaris.

The Soviet government made rocket development a top national priority in 1946. The rocketeers first reproduced the German V-2 and then proceeded with building larger and more capable ballistic missiles. Soviet rocket pioneers from the early 1930s Korolev and Glushko emerged as the chief designer of ballistic missile systems and the main developer of the enabling liquid-propellant engines.

Both the Soviet Union and United States pursued development of the ICBMs, R-7, and Atlas. These large ballistic missiles called for new testing sites —the existing American White Sands and the Soviet Kapustin Yar did not meet the requirements of safety and security. Consequently, the United States established a new missile test range at Cape Canaveral in Florida in 1949 and later another site at the Vandenberg Air Force Base in California in 1958. Cape Canaveral would subsequently support space launches into low-inclination orbit while Vandenberg would send satellites into polar orbit, especially important for reconnaissance payloads. The Soviet Union initiated the construction of a new missile test site at Tyuratam (now commonly known as Baikonur) in Kazakhstan in 1955 and another site later in Plesetsk.

1.2.4 The Breakthrough to Space

In the 1950s, spaceflight advocates scattered among various parts of the US government, industry, and academia pressed for the American satellite. The national security policies would shape the path to space.

Rapidly progressing development of long-range ballistic missiles and nuclear weapons threatened devastating consequences should the Cold War turn into a full-scale military conflict. New technologies allowed no time for preparation for hostilities and mobilization and made an intelligence failure such as Pearl Harbor absolutely unacceptable. Therefore, monitoring military developments of the adversary, with accurate knowledge of its offensive potential and deployment of forces, became a key to national survival and (avoiding a fatal miscalculation,) reduced the risk of war.

Obtaining accurate information about closed societies of the communist world presented a major challenge. The perceived "bomber gap" and later the "missile gap" clearly demonstrated the importance of such information for the national policies. Consequently, President Dwight D. Eisenhower authorized development of overhead reconnaissance programs to be conducted in peacetime. The U-2 aircraft first overflew the Soviet Union in 1956, resolving the uncertainties of the bomber gap. Reconnaissance from space became a top priority for President Eisenhower who considered rare and sporadic U-2 overflights only a temporary measure because of improving Soviet air defenses. In 1956, the Air Force selected Lockheed's Missile Systems Division to build reconnaissance satellites.

The international legality and acceptability of overflights of other countries by Earth-circling satellites—*freedom of space*—was uncertain in the 1950s. The Eisenhower administration considered testing the principle of freedom of space by launching a purely scientific satellite critically important for establishing a precedent enabling future space reconnaissance.

This was the time when scientists in many countries were preparing for the International Geophysical Year (IGY) to be conducted from July 1957–December 1958. They planned comprehensive world-wide measurements of the upper atmosphere, ionosphere, geomagnetic field, cosmic rays, and auroras. Space advocates emphasized that artificial satellites could greatly advance such studies. Consequently, both the United States and the Soviet Union announced their plans of placing into orbit artificial satellites for scientific purposes during the IGY. Both countries succeeded.

President Eisenhower insisted on clear decoupling of American scientific satellites from military applications in order to first assert freedom of space. This national security imperative determined the publicly visible path to the satellite. In 1955, the US government selected the NRL proposal to develop a new space launch vehicle and a scientific satellite, both known as the Vanguard. The choice of the new system was made over a more mature technology of the Project Orbiter advocated by Army's Medaris and von Braun. The Army proposed to use the Jupiter C, an augmented Redstone ballistic missile. In fact, a test launch of the Jupiter C on September 20, 1956, could have put a simple satellite into orbit had the Army been permitted to use a solid-propellant missile — as it would later do launching the Explorer I—instead of an inactive fourth stage.

John P. Hagen led the Vanguard program with Glenn L. Martin Co. as the prime contractor of the launch vehicle and with NRL providing technical direction. The Vanguard program also built scientific satellites and established a process of calling for proposals and selecting space science experiments. In addition, it deployed a network of the Minitrack ground stations to detect and communicate with the satellites which laid the foundation for the future NASA Spaceflight Tracking and Data Network (STDN). Many optical stations around the world would also observe the satellites by the specially designed Baker-Nunn telescope tracking cameras.

The Soviet Union focused its resources on demonstrating the first ICBM. After the R-7 had successfully flown for the full range, Korolev launched the world's first artificial satellite, Sputnik, into orbit on October 4, 1957. Ironically, this Soviet success had finally resolved the lingering issue of the space overflight rights that so concerned President Eisenhower: no country protested the overflight by the Soviet satellite, thus establishing the principle of freedom of space (see Fig. 1-5).

The second, much larger Soviet satellite with the dog Laika aboard, successfully reached orbit on November 3, 1957. The Vanguard program had been steadily progressing but was not ready for launch yet. On November 8, the Secretary of Defense gave the permission to the eager Army team led by Medaris and von Braun to also attempt launching satellites. On January 31, 1958, the Army's modified Jupiter C missile successfully placed the first American satellite Explorer I into orbit.

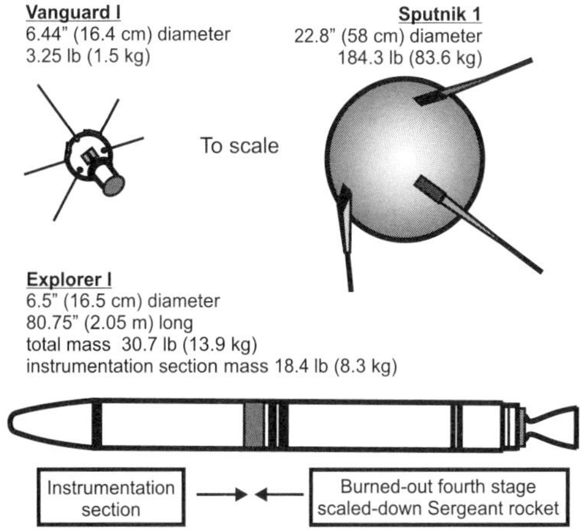

Fig. 1-5. Comparative Sizes and Masses of the Earth Satellites Sputnik 1, Explorer I, and Vanguard I [Gruntman, 2004].

Subsequently the Vanguard launch vehicle deployed the Vanguard I satellite into orbit on March 17, 1958. Popular sentiments in the United States have sometimes blamed the Vanguard program for losing the competition to the Soviet Union. It is grossly unfair. The Vanguard program demonstrated a record fast development of a new space launcher, with only 30 months from the vehicle authorization in August 1955 to the first successful launch in March 1958. The Vanguard spacecraft remains today the oldest man-made object in orbit, and it will reenter the atmosphere in a couple hundred years. We have time to find funding to bring the satellite back to the planet Earth for a place of honor in a museum.

There was no technological gap between the Soviet Union and the United States in the beginning of the space age. Being the first in launching the satellite was a matter of focus and national commitment. Fourteen months after the launch of Sputnik, the United States had placed spacecraft into orbit by 3 entirely different launchers developed by 3 different teams of government agencies and industrial contractors. (The Air Force's Atlas deployed the first communications satellite SCORE in December 1958.)

The last years of the Eisenhower administration shaped the structure of the American space program. The president established a new Advanced Research Projects Agency (ARPA, the predecessor of DARPA), to fund and direct the growing national space effort. The security-conscious president resisted expansion of the government programs but always supported advancement of spaceflight in the interests of national security.

Bending to powerful political forces Eisenhower reluctantly agreed to establish a new government agency responsible for a civilian effort in space. The president signed the National Aeronautics and Space Act into law which formed NASA on October 1, 1958. Within a short period of time, NASA subsumed the National Advisory Committee for Aeronautics (NACA), Army's Jet Propulsion Laboratory and major elements of the ballistic missile program in Huntsville, and NRL's Vanguard group.

NASA vigorously embarked on scientific exploration of space, launching increasingly capable spacecraft to study the space environment and the Sun and creating space astronomy. The missions to flyby the Moon and, later, nearby planets followed. These first space missions began a new era of discovery that laid the foundation for the flourishing American space science and planetary exploration of today. At the same time, NASA embarked on preparation for human spaceflight.

Rocketry Industry "Namescape"

Mergers and acquisition have significantly changed the "namescape" of rocket industry. Titan's prime contractor, the Martin Company, merged with Marietta in 1961, forming Martin Marietta. Convair became Space System Division of General Dynamics in 1954, known as General Dynamics—Astronautics. Martin Marietta acquired General Dynamics' Space System Division in 1995 and then merged in the same year with Lockheed, forming The Lockheed Martin Corporation. Thus both, the Atlas and the Titan families of space launchers ended up under the same corporate roof. Another important component of Lockheed Martin's rocket assets is the submarine-launched solid-propellant Tridents. Boeing added to its Minuteman missiles the Delta family of space launchers after acquiring McDonnell-Douglas in 1997.

Gruntman [2004], p. 253

At the same time the military space program focused on communications, early warning, command and control, and support of military operations. The Air Force led this effort with the Navy engaged in selected important programs, such as space based navigation. The Army preserved the responsibility for major elements of missile defense.

Another national security program dealt with space reconnaissance and was directed jointly by the intelligence community and the military. In 1960, President Eisenhower established a special office in the Department of Defense (DoD), staffed by military officers and government civilians, to direct space reconnaissance, separated from military procurement and hidden by an extra protective layer of secrecy. This organization would become the National Reconnaissance Office (NRO) overseen by the Air Force and the CIA. The image intelligence satellite Corona achieved the first successful overflight of the Soviet Union in August 1960, returning images that effectively resolved the uncertainties of the perceived missile gap.

President Eisenhower handed over to his successor in the White House a structure of the national space program that has essentially survived in its main features until the present day. NASA leads the civilian space effort. National security space consists of two main components. The services are responsible for military space while the intelligence community and military directs gathering and processing of the intelligence information from space. While these 3 programs are sometimes viewed as separate, they all had originated from the early military space effort and they all have been interacting to varying degrees during the years.

1.2.5 Spacefaring Civilization

The heating up competition in space with the Soviet Union erupted into the public focus when the first man, Soviet cosmonaut Yuri Gagarin, orbited the Earth on April 12, 1961. President Kennedy responded by challenging the nation to land "a man on the Moon and returning him safely [back] to the Earth." The resulting Apollo program culminated with astronauts Neil Armstrong and Edwin (Buzz) Aldrin taking man's first steps on the Moon in July 1969.

The late 1950s and early 1960s witnessed emerging commercial applications in space. The first transatlantic telephone cable had connected Europe and North America in 1956 to meet the increasing demand in communications. Space offered a cost-competitive alternative, and industrial companies showed much interest and enthusiasm for it, especially AT&T, RCA, General Electric, and Hughes Aircraft. The DoD supported the development of space communications on the government side. It was not clear at the time whether satellites in low, medium, or geostationary orbits would offer the best solution. While geostationary satellites provided excellent coverage, the technical challenges of building and deploying such satellites and their control had not yet been met.

Initially, the industry invested significant resources in the development of space communications. The situation drastically changed when President Kennedy signed the Communications Satellite Act in 1962. Now government, including NASA, became a major player in

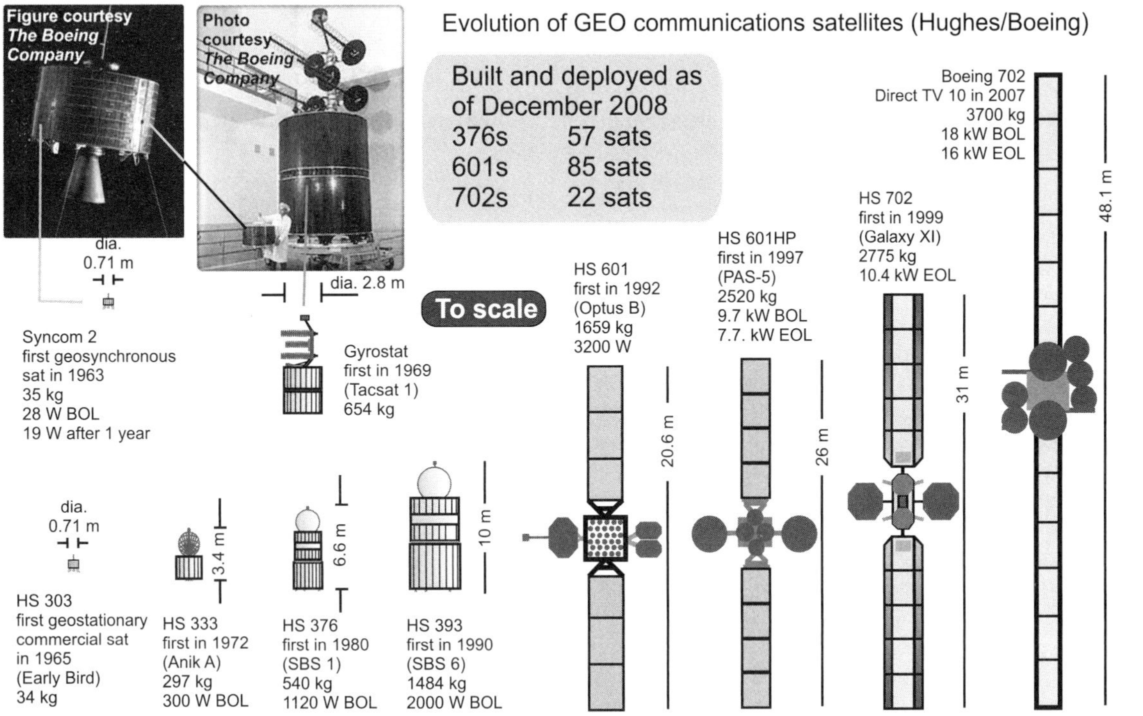

Fig. 1-6. Spectacular Growth of Communication Satellite Capabilities. Example of satellites developed by Hughes/Boeing [Gruntman, 2008].

commercial space communications, with the authority to regulate and to a significant extent dictate the development. Consequently, the Communications Satellite (Comsat) Corporation was formed in 1963 to manage procurement of satellites for the international communications consortium Intelsat.

The Hughes Aircraft Company demonstrated a practical geostationary communication satellite with launches of 3 test spin-stabilized Syncom satellites in 1963–1964. As the technology progressed, several companies introduced 3-axis stabilized geostationary satellites. Since the beginning of the space age, satellite communications have been dominating commercial space, with most of the activities today concentrated in the direct-to-home TV broadcasting and fixed satellite services. Figure 1-6 demonstrates the astounding increase in capabilities of geostationary communication satellites with the example of one family of satellites built by Hughes, now part of the Boeing Company.

Military and reconnaissance satellites provided critically important capabilities essential for national survival. NASA missions, especially manned missions, were highly visible and reflected on the nation's international prestige, so important in the Cold War battles. As a result, National Security Space (NSS) and NASA missions had one feature in common: failure was not an option, which inevitably led to a culture of building highly-reliable systems. Space missions were thus performance driven, with cost being of secondary importance. The consequent high-cost of the space undertaking led, in turn, to increased government oversight which drove the schedules and costs further up. The government-regulated commercial space, dominated by the same industrial contractors, could not develop a different culture.

After landing twelve astronauts on the Moon, NASA brought to us spectacular achievements in space science and in exploration of the Solar system. Numerous space missions advanced our understanding of the Sun's activity and the near-Earth environment. NASA spacecraft visited all planets of the Solar system with the exception of Pluto*—the New Horizons mission is presently enroute to the latter.

The Soviet Union established a permanent space station, Mir, in low-Earth orbit. The American human space flight concentrated on the development of the Space Shuttle and the International Space Station (ISS). The Space Shuttle carried astronauts to low-Earth orbit from 1981 to 2011. The ISS, with a mass of about 400 metric tons, has the opportunity to demonstrate what humans can do in space.

Today, space affects government, business, and culture. Many countries project military power, commercial interests, and national image though space missions. It is a truly high-technology frontier, expensive and government-controlled or government-regulated. Space has become an integral part of everyday lives of people. We are accustomed to weather forecasts based on space-based sensors. Satellites deliver TV broadcasts to individual homes. The Global Positioning System (GPS)

* Pluto is now officially a dwarf planet. See App. B.

reaches hundreds of millions of users worldwide, guiding drivers on the road, aircraft in the air, and hikers in the mountains.

After the end of the Cold War, the transformation of space from a primarily strategic asset into increasingly integrated tactical applications, supporting the warfighter, accelerated. NSS provides critically important capabilities in command and control, communications, reconnaissance, monitoring of international treaties, and guiding precision munitions to targets. Missile defense heavily relies on space sensors and communications for early warning and intercept guidance. NSS spends annually twice as much as NASA.

The space enterprise has become a true international endeavor. Seven countries joined the Soviet Union and United States in the elite club of nations that launched their own satellites on their own space launchers: France (1965), Japan (1970), People's Republic of China (1970), United Kingdom (1971), India (1980), Israel (1988), and Iran (2009). The European countries have combined their efforts and launch their satellites today through the European Space Agency (ESA). Canada also conducts an active space program. Brazil has an active space program and it is only a question of time until it successfully launches its satellite. South Korea also pursues development of space launch capabilities, with Russia initially providing important parts of launch technology. The secretive North Korea tries to launch a satellite. In addition, numerous other countries bought and operate various satellite systems.

Very few countries presently match the American commitment to space exploration and space applications. "Only France (and the old Soviet Union in the past) approaches the US space expenditures in terms of the fraction of the gross domestic product (GDP). Most other industrialized countries (Europe and Japan) spend in space, as fraction of GDP, 4 to 6 times less than the United States." [Gruntman, 2004, p. 462] People's Republic of China and India are expanding their space programs. The highly space-capable Russia is also increasing its space activities after the decline of the 1990s.

For many years, the United States has led the world in space. The health and the future of the American space enterprise depend on the national commitment—there is no limit to what we can do. President Kennedy observed that "for while we cannot guarantee that we shall one day be first [in space], we can guarantee that any failure to make this effort [in space] will make us last..." Gruntman [2004, p.383].

1.3 Spaceflight Technology

Space is exceptionally expensive and nearly all spaceflight hardware is uniquely built for use in space or launch systems. This section addresses the question of why this is the case and how space technology differs from non-space technology. There are several key ideas that are involved:

1. Getting to space is really hard
2. Rockets are a lousy way to get anywhere, but better than any alternative we have available
3. Space parts are nearly all unique

This section addresses each of these and introduces the idea of *Technology Readiness Levels* (TRLs) that are often used to help manage the space development and acquisition process, but may, in some respects, contribute to the problem as well as the solution.

1.3.1 Getting to Space is Really Hard

The easiest place to get to in space, and the closest, is low Earth orbit (LEO), which is the space between the top of the atmosphere at roughly 100 km and the beginning of the Van Allen radiation belts at about 1,000 km. To get there, and stay there rather than fall back to Earth, we need to go up about 200 km, turn left, and accelerate to 7.8 km/s. Taking into account the losses along the way caused primarily by gravity and atmospheric drag, we realistically need to provide a change in velocity, called *delta V,** of over 9 km/s. This is an extremely high velocity relative to any moving objects we have experience with. Commercial jet aircraft travel at about Mach 0.8 (= 610 mph = 0.34 km/s). The muzzle velocity of a modern rifle with a high speed cartridge is quite a bit higher at around 4,000 fps (= 1.22 km/s), but still far short of the velocity we need of 9 km/s.

Modern launch vehicles have multiple stages, such that the first stage is dropped off after its fuel is used to reduce the mass that is being accelerated, then the second stage is dropped off when it's done, and so on. Consider this in the context of our high-speed rifle bullet at 4,000 fps. To increase the final speed, we'll make our first bullet large enough to hold another gun inside the first bullet, such that after you fire the first bullet, a gun pops out of that bullet and fires again, so that the second bullet is now going at 8,000 fps. This is basically what staging does for us. However, our rifle is so inefficient relative to launch vehicles that we would have to add 6 larger rifles, for a total of 8 consecutive rifles each contained in a bullet fired from a larger rifle in order to get to the velocity we need. That very first rifle is going to have to be pretty big. (See Fig. 1-7.)

Another way to get a feel for the high velocities involved is to consider someone in a vacuum falling freely toward the Earth at 1 g (9.8 m/s^2). It would take 13 min of continuous falling to reach orbital velocity, without any drag, gravity losses, or whatever.

*ΔV, using the Greek Δ (delta) is the standard math symbol for a change in V, the velocity. Given the propensity of modern word processors and E-mail programs to mess up Greek letters, many people have found it easier to simply write out the Greek, so a change in velocity in astronautics is often written delta V. In this book we will usually write "delta V" in the text and ΔV in equations.

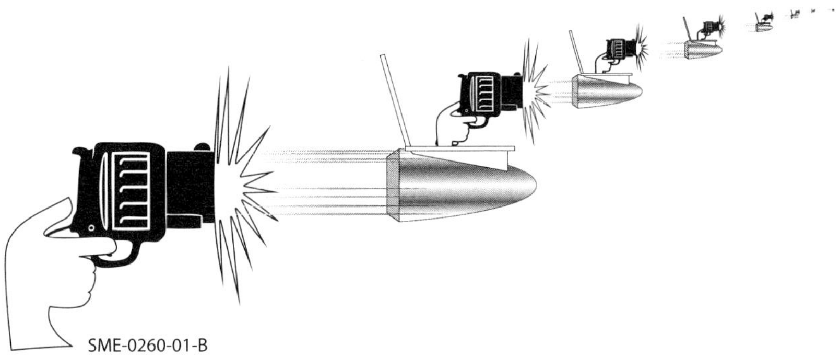

Fig. 1-7. Rocket Stages are Similar to Firing a Rifle with a Bullet that Contains a Rifle with Another Bullet, and So On, for Lots of Times. To get to the lowest energy orbit with a muzzle velocity of only 4,000 fps will require 8 successively larger riles. The first rifle will need to be very large.

Of course, going to higher orbits, the Moon, or planets is even harder, but at least we have more time for things to occur. Once we have gotten to orbital velocity and above the atmosphere, we can spend more-or-less as long as is needed to build up higher velocities to go elsewhere. Nonetheless, it's still a dramatically challenging problem such that virtually all missions are designed around the idea of minimizing the total delta V required to conduct the mission.

As we'll see in Sec. 1.3.2, we build up our velocity of 7.8 km/s (or higher), by throwing burned fuel out the back end of the rocket at 3 to 4 km/s. We can get to orbit by this process, but just marginally. If anything goes wrong there is likely to be a very large explosion and a very expensive payload will become debris in the ocean. If the orbital velocity were less, the problem would be much easier. If we lived on the Moon with a low Lunar orbital velocity of 1.7 km/s, space travel would be easy and we would all have rocketmobiles for heading to the store. If we lived on Jupiter (a bit challenging, since there really isn't a solid surface to live on) with a low Jovian orbital velocity of 42 km/s, there wouldn't be a space program and we would be tied to the (nonexistent) surface of the planet until we could invent something really new that we haven't thought of yet. Here on Earth, we can have a space program, but getting there is really hard.

1.3.2 Rockets are a Lousy Way to Get Anywhere

Not only is getting to orbit very hard, but rockets are a really bad way to do the job, although they're better than anything else we have at the moment. To understand the nature of the problem think of a rocket out in space near the Earth, rather like an ice skater on a frozen lake. To go north on the lake, we throw something, say a frozen turkey, as hard as we can to the south and, in reaction, we head northward. Similarly, in the rocket, to go to Jupiter we throw a lot of propellant out in the direction opposite the way we want to go. The problem for both the skater and rocket is that we're not pushing against anything around us like the Earth or even the air, so the center of mass of the system doesn't go anywhere. To get a kilometer north of where we started, the turkey which is likely lighter than the skater is going to have to be several kilometers south of where we started. (We're assuming the ice is very hard and perfectly smooth such that we can't push against it as skaters normally would.) Similarly, if we are going to get our rocket to Jupiter, there's going to have to be an awful lot of propellant a long ways in the direction opposite of where Jupiter is. In fact, the rocket and the propellant are both in orbit around the Sun and the velocity will change as we get closer to or further from the Sun, but the rules of astrodynamics unfortunately don't change the basic problem of the rocket being inefficient.

There is another way in which our rocket is inefficient. Let's suppose our rocket has a mass of 100 kg without the propellant and has 100 kg of propellant on board for a total mass of 200 kg. We then throw out the propellant as one lump at 3 km/s. (That would be pretty hard, but, again, this is just an example.) Now the relative velocity between them is 3 km/s, the propellant is moving at 1.5 km/s relative to the initial center of mass, and the rocket is going at 1.5 km/s in the opposite direction, again relative to the initial center of mass. If I wanted to get the rocket to 3 km/s, it would appear that I would have to add another 100 kg of propellant to the rocket, but unfortunately it's harder than that. If we start with 300 kg (100 kg for the rocket and 200 kg for the propellant), and throw 100 kg out at 3 km/s, now, relative to the initial center of mass, the propellant mass is moving at 2 km/sec and the rocket (with its 100 kg of extra propellant) is moving at only 1 km/s in the opposite direction. If I then throw the second glob of propellant out at 3 km/s, this will give the rocket an additional 1.5 km/s, such that the final velocity of the rocket is only 2.5 km/s, even though we have doubled the amount of propellant. The basic problem is that as we add propellant, we have to accelerate not only the rocket, but all of the rest of the propellant that we've put in it. As the percentage of propellant becomes higher and higher, we are using up most of the energy simply accelerating the propellant that we are bringing along and the rocket becomes less and less efficient. (Real launch vehicles are typically around 90% propellant.)

The end result of all this is that a launch vehicle is quite a few tons of the highest explosive you can find and

Alternatives to Rockets

Rockets aren't the only way to get to space, but they're the best we have so far. Two alternatives are described here. Once we're in space, there are a few more options such as the space tether (Sec. 25.1) or solar sails (Sec. 18.7)

Gun Launch

If we could build an air gun or something similar that would have a muzzle velocity high enough to get to orbital velocity, then all we would have to accelerate is the spacecraft itself and we could avoid all of the problems of staging and having to accelerate mostly propellant. What's more, the gun itself could stay on the ground and be used multiple times. But can we build such a gun? The answer is yes, but there are a few problems with it.

First, the acceleration has to be pretty high. At a constant acceleration of only 1,000 g's, the gun barrel would have to be over 4 km long, so we probably need a few thousand g's of acceleration. Since people can only withstand 6 or 7 g's, or a bit more, the gun launch will be limited to electronics and similar stuff. But some electronics can withstand that level of loads, so it still may be possible. Second, at the end of the gun, where the capsule is going at over 8 km/s, it's still deep in the atmosphere where drag is very high (As discussed in Sec. 9.4, drag is proportional to the atmospheric density and to V^2), so that's a real problem for both heating and slowing down.

Unfortunately, the largest problem is that we still need some sort of upper stage. As we'll see in Sec. 9.1, orbits are elliptical, which means that after 1 orbit the capsule comes back through the point where it was last accelerated. Since that's at least 90 min later, the gun itself will have moved quite a ways eastward due to the Earth's rotation, but we will still be down essentially at the Earth's surface. To avoid this, we need a small upper stage that can more-or-less circularize the orbit when we get to space. But this means that we need a tank strong enough to hold propellant that weighs several thousand times what it weighs just sitting around. Also, we need a propellant that won't explode when subjected to loads of that magnitude, and that may be even harder to find.

Gun launch to orbit isn't impossible, but it is very challenging, and not yet a practical solution. However, gun launch or, perhaps better, electromagnetic rail launch (similar to many modern carnival rides), may be an excellent solution for getting to orbit from the surface of the Moon where the orbital velocity is only 1.7 km/s and there is no atmosphere to get in the way.

The Space Elevator

The *Space Elevator* is a cable extending 36,000 km from geosynchronous orbit (GEO) to the surface of the Earth. To hold up the cable there must be another large cable or counterweight extending upward from GEO such that the center of mass of the system is in GEO and orbiting with a velocity equal to the rotation rate of the Earth on its axis. People or machinery then climb the cable (i.e., ride up an "elevator") from the Earth's surface to GEO, step off, and they are at orbital velocity in GEO.

As with the gun launch, there are a few practical considerations that make the space elevator challenging to build. Most people have concentrated on is the difficulty of creating a cable strong enough to support its own mass over a length of 36,000 km. This is generally addressed by considering very strong materials, such as carbon nanotubes, and using a cable that is tapered with the thickest part in GEO and coming down to a very small strand at the Earth's surface. Even with this approach, it is probably not buildable with today's technology because strong enough materials aren't readily available or usable.

A second problem to consider is what happens to all of the spacecraft in LEO that might run into the cable at 7.5 km/s. As discussed in Sec. 7.5, the kinetic energy associated with the collision is proportional to the square of the velocity. Thus a 1 kg, 10 cm diameter CubeSat (about the smallest satellite or fragment that is visible in LEO) would have the equivalent kinetic energy of hitting the cable with a bowling ball at 2,000 mph. That would likely not be good for either the cable or the satellite.

While rockets are a very poor means of transportation to and in space, they will be what we have to work with for quite a while.

somebody with a match. (Jet fuel and nearly 100% pure oxygen is one of the less explosive mixtures that is often used.) There are, of course, alternatives to rockets, but none of them seem too promising. Two of the more interesting approaches, the gun launch and the space elevator, are described in the boxed example. We can also find ways to supplement the system in some fashion. For example, some launch systems, like Pegasus, are air launched, where the launch vehicle is given an initial altitude and velocity before heading to space. The problem is that getting a start at, say, 10 km altitude and Mach 2 or less, doesn't really help very much when I need to get to 200 km and Mach 27. In addition, there's a limit to how heavy a rocket a modern aircraft can carry. The value of an air launch is largely to get away from the launch ranges and allow launch to occur out over the ocean where there are far fewer rules, restrictions, and obstacles.

1.3.3 Space Parts are All Unique

Nearly all of the parts used in space systems are built uniquely for that purpose. This seems a bit strange in that rockets and spacecraft are just another approach to transportation, observations, and communications and should therefore, use much of same hardware used for similar functions on Earth. While many people interested in cost reduction are striving to make this happen (see Chap. 13), there are some practical considerations that make it difficult.

The first problem is that many of the parts used in spacecraft don't have any applications on Earth or create problems in space that would never be an issue for Earth equipment. Unfortunately, the spacecraft doesn't have any platform to sit on, such that even very small forces can cause it to move or rotate. Even the pressure of sunlight can cause a spacecraft to rotate or tumble. It's a bit difficult to envision a typical piece of Earth equipment that would flip over just from light pressure when exposed to sunlight. This implies that the attitude control equipment on a spacecraft is typically far more sensitive than would be of much use in most ground-based equipment. In addition, even trivial moving parts, such as a filter wheel or the moving mirror in a single lens reflex camera, will cause the spacecraft to recoil in the opposite direction. This tends to affect the mechanical parts on a spacecraft.

The second problem has to do with the space environment, which is very well understood, but inherently different than the environment on Earth. Unfortunately, there are two features of the space environment that have a major impact on electronics. First is the higher radiation level that has a particularly strong effect on computers and microelectronics. An even larger problem is the thermal environment. Nearly all electronics on Earth rely on natural convection or forced air to provide cooling and, unfortunately, neither of these work in the 0-g, vacuum environment in space. This means that most pieces of desktop or laboratory electronics will likely work for a only short time in space and then burn out or be stopped by the radiation.

Perhaps the biggest difficulty with using most commercial or industrial parts in space is simply the high cost of transportation. It's typically on the order of $10,000 to $20,000 per kg to LEO, 5 times that to GEO, and even more to Lunar or planetary orbits. This means that the "excess" mass associated with making products robust on Earth is too expensive for space use. Typically, we build a box for an electronics gizmo by taking a piece of sheet metal, folding it a few times, and welding it. For space applications we take a block of aluminum the size of the box and machine away everything that isn't the box. This eliminates the mass of the folded sheet metal and the welds.

These issues are exacerbated by the need to know the detailed history of each part to be **sure** that it will work successfully. When I was working on the TDRS communications satellite program, a metal foundry in West Virginia announced that the quenching (water spray) on their aluminum milling machine hadn't been working correctly for several months and it was possible that there could be soft spots in some of the aluminum milled at that facility. The TDRS builder, TRW, was able to go back, locate, and test every single piece of equipment on TDRS that had any aluminum that had been milled at that plant. No problems were found. Nonetheless, imagine the difficulty and the cost if every piece of aluminum, plastic, or electronics in your car came with a complete history of where all of the material in that component had been mined, milled, manufactured, and integrated into the final product. That requirement in itself would eliminate nearly all commercial and industrial equipment from consideration.

Fortunately, the "rules" by which spacecraft are built are changing somewhat and there is more potential for change in the future. Nonetheless, it remains exceptionally challenging to introduce new technology into the space arena as described in the next subsection.

1.3.4 Technology Readiness Levels

The *Technology Readiness Level* (TRL) is a numerical scale used to express the degree to which any particular technology is ready for application in operational space missions. As shown in Fig. 1-8, TRLs range from 1, in which only the basic principles have been observed,

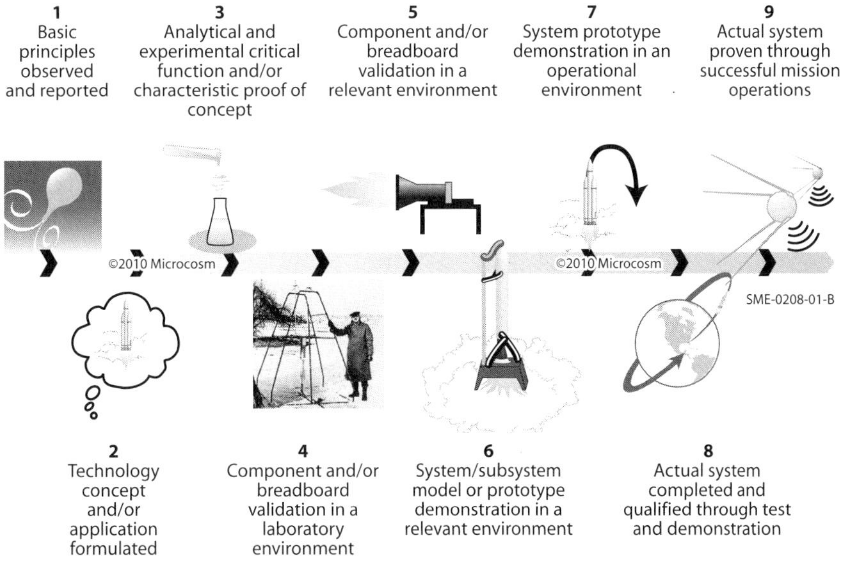

Fig. 1-8. Technology Readiness Levels (TRLs) as Used By NASA. Slightly different definitions are used by DoD as shown in Table 1-1 for hardware and in Table 1-2 for software.

to 9 for a fully mature technology that has been used successfully in mission operations. While different organizations have somewhat different formal definitions, the basic levels and ideas are now reasonably consistent. The verbal descriptions of what is required at each level for DoD are given in Table 1-1 for hardware and in Table 1-2 for software. The use of TRLs in cost modeling is discussed in Sec. 11.3.5

Table 1-1. Technology Readiness Levels (TRLs) for DoD Hardware Development. [DoD, 2009]

TRL	Definition	Description	Supporting Information
1	Basic principles observed and reported.	Lowest level of technology readiness. Scientific research begins to be translated into applied research and development (R&D). Examples might include paper studies of a technology's basic properties.	Published research that identifies the principles that underlie this technology. References to who, where, when.
2	Technology concept and/or application formulated.	Invention begins. Once basic principles are observed, practical applications can be invented. Applications are speculative, and there may be no proof or detailed analysis to support the assumptions. Examples are limited to analytic studies.	Publications or other references that outline the application being considered and that provide analysis to support the concept.
3	Analytical and experimental critical function and/or characteristic proof of concept.	Active R&D is initiated. This includes analytical studies and laboratory studies to physically validate the analytical predictions of separate elements of the technology. Examples include components that are not yet integrated or representative.	Results of laboratory tests performed to measure parameters of interest and comparison to analytical predictions for critical subsystems. References to who, where, and when these tests and comparisons were performed.
4	Component and/or breadboard validation in a laboratory environment.	Basic technological components are integrated to establish that they will work together. This is relatively "low fidelity" compared with the eventual system. Examples include integration of "ad hoc" hardware in the laboratory.	System concepts that have been considered and result from testing laboratory-scale breadboards. References to who did this work and when. Provide an estimate of how breadboard hardware and test results differ from the expected system goals.
5	Component and/or breadboard validation in a relevant environment.	Fidelity of breadboard technology increases significantly. The basic technological components are integrated with reasonably realistic supporting elements so they can be tested in a simulated environment. Examples include "high-fidelity" laboratory integration of components.	Results from testing a laboratory breadboard system are integrated with other supporting elements in a simulated operational environment. How does the "relevant environment" differ from the expected operational environment? How do the test results compare with expectations? What problems, if any, were encountered? Was the breadboard system refined to more nearly match the expected system goals?
6	System/subsystem model or prototype demonstration in a relevant environment.	Representative model or prototype system, which is well beyond that of TRL 5, is tested in a relevant environment. Represents a major step up in a technology's demonstrated readiness. Examples include testing a prototype in a high-fidelity laboratory environment or in a simulated operational environment.	Results from laboratory testing of a prototype system that is near the desired configuration in terms of performance, weight, and volume. How did the test environment differ from the operational environment? Who performed the tests? How did the test compare with expectations? What problems, if any, were encountered? What are/were the plans, options, or actions to resolve problems before moving to the next level?
7	System prototype demonstration in an operational environment.	Prototype near or at planned operational system. Represents a major step up from TRL 6 by requiring demonstration of an actual system prototype in an operational environment (e.g., in an aircraft, in a vehicle, or in space).	Results from testing a prototype system in an operational environment. Who performed the tests? How did the test compare with expectations? What problems, if any, were encountered? What are/were the plans, options, or actions to resolve problems before moving to the next level?
8	Actual system completed and qualified through test and demonstration.	Technology has been proven to work in its final form and under expected conditions. In almost all cases, this TRL represents the end of true system development. Examples include developmental test and evaluation (DT&E) of the system in its intended weapon system to determine if it meets design specifications.	Results of testing the system in its final configuration under the expected range of environmental conditions in which it will be expected to operate. Assessment of whether it will meet its operational requirements. What problems, if any, were encountered? What are/were the plans, options, or actions to resolve problems before finalizing the design?
9	Actual system proven through successful mission operations.	Actual application of the technology in its final form and under mission conditions, such as those encountered in operational test and evaluation (OT&E). Examples include using the system under operational mission conditions.	OT&E reports.

Table 1-2. Technology Readiness Levels (TRLs) for DoD Software Development. [DoD, 2009]

TRL	Definition	Description	Supporting Information
1	Basic principles observed and reported.	Lowest level of software technology readiness. A new software domain is being investigated by the basic research community. This level extends to the development of basic use, basic properties of software architecture, mathematical formulations, and general algorithms.	Basic research activities, research articles, peer-reviewed white papers, point papers, and early lab model of basic concept may be useful for substantiating the TRL.
2	Technology concept and/or application formulated.	Once basic principles are observed, practical applications can be invented. Applications are speculative, and there may be no proof or detailed analysis to support the assumptions. Examples are limited to analytic studies using synthetic data.	Applied research activities, analytic studies, small code units, and papers comparing competing technologies.
3	Analytical and experimental critical function and/or characteristic proof of concept.	Active R&D is initiated. The level at which scientific feasibility is demonstrated through analytical and laboratory studies. This level extends to the development of limited functionality environments to validate critical properties and analytical predictions using non-integrated software components and partially representative data.	Algorithms run on a surrogate processor in a laboratory environment, instrumented components operating in a laboratory environment, laboratory results showing validation of critical properties.
4	Module and/or subsystem validation in a laboratory environment (i.e.,software prototype development environment).	Basic software components are integrated to establish that they will work together. They are relatively primitive with regard to efficiency and robustness compared with the eventual system. Architecture development initiated to include interoperability, reliability, maintainability, extensibility, scalability, and security issues. Emulation with current/legacy elements as appropriate. Prototypes developed to demonstrate different aspects of eventual system.	Advanced technology development, stand-alone prototype solving a synthetic full-scale problem, or stand alone prototype processing fully representative data sets.
5	Module and/or subsystem validation in a relevant environment.	Level at which software technology is ready to start integration with existing systems. The prototype implementations conform to target environment/interfaces. Experiments with realistic problems. Simulated interfaces to existing systems. System software architecture established. Algorithms run on a processor with characteristics expected in the operational environment.	System architecture diagram around technology element with critical performance requirements defined. Processor selection analysis, Simulation/Stimulation (Sim/Stim) Laboratory buildup plan. Software placed under configuration management. Commercial-off-the-shelf/ government-off-the-shelf (COTS/GOTS) components in the system software architecture are identified.
6	Module and/or subsystem validation in a relevant end-to-end environment.	Level at which the engineering feasibility of a software technology is demonstrated. This level extends to laboratory prototype implementations on full scale realistic problems in which the software technology is partially integrated with existing hardware/software systems.	Results from laboratory testing of a prototype package that is near the desired configuration in terms of performance, including physical, logical, data, and security interfaces. Comparisons between tested environment and operational environment analytically understood. Analysis and test measurements quantifying contribution to system-wide requirements such as throughput, scalability, and reliability. Analysis of human-computer (user environment) begun.
7	System prototype demonstration in an operational, high-fidelity environment.	Level at which the program feasibility of a software technology is demonstrated. This level extends to operational environment prototype implementations, where critical technical risk functionality is available for demonstration and a test in which the software technology is well integrated with operational hardware/software systems.	Critical technological properties are measured against requirements in an operational environment.
8	Actual system completed and mission qualified through test and demonstration in an operational environment.	Level at which a software technology is fully integrated with operational hardware and software systems. Software development documentation is complete. All functionality tested in simulated and operational scenarios.	Published documentation and product technology refresh build schedule. Software resource reserve measured and tracked.
9	Actual system proven through successful mission-proven operational capabilities.	Level at which a software technology is readily repeatable and reusable. The software based on the technology is fully integrated with operational hardware/ software systems. All software documentation verified. Successful operational experience. Sustaining software engineering support in place. Actual system.	Production configuration management reports. Technology integrated into a reuse "wizard."

The idea of TRLs was first introduced at NASA by Sadin, et al. [1989] and has since been expanded somewhat by Mankins [1995], also at NASA headquarters. The basic goal of the TRL is to evaluate and ultimately minimize risk on very expensive space programs by requiring that technology is mature before it is applied to a program where immature technology could cause program delays, cost overruns, or on-orbit failures.

When you try to apply the idea of TRLs, several problems arise. Does the TRL apply to the technology broadly or the specific implementation being proposed for a given mission? If 20 m solar arrays were used on a previous mission, what TRL is applicable to 30 m solar arrays for a new mission? Here it would seem unreasonable to go back and require that the longer array be regarded as an entirely new technology. On the other hand, if we have 3 m diameter space-qualified telescope mirror, it might be reasonable to regard a 4.5 m mirror as new technology that has to go through a development and test program before being acceptable for space application, because the difficulty of building precision optics is a very strong function of their size. Similarly, the TRL of a systems is usually regarded as the lowest TRL of any of its components. Yet there is clearly a fundamental difference between a spacecraft that is simply using a new sensor that has never flown in space and one that is using 100 W more power than any previous spacecraft.

While TRLs are a useful guideline, arbitrarily applying rules is rarely a good approach. What we really want to determine about any spacecraft component or spacecraft technology are the following:

- Can it be built in a timely manner at a cost consistent with the needs of the program?
- Will it survive launch and work in the space environment that we want to use it in?
- If it has a limited lifetime, will it last sufficiently long to be useful in the system we want to fly it on?

Ultimately, there is no substitute for thinking carefully about the fundamental question, Will it work in space. This is a main topic in Chap. 7.

1.4 Spaceflight Economics

John M. Jurist, *University of North Dakota*
David M. Livingston, *The Space Show*

Historically, getting into space, doing things in the space environment, and returning information or materials back to Earth has often been viewed as outrageously expensive. This section examines some of the factors that contribute to the high costs of space access and utilization. Potential approaches to reducing costs are also discussed.

1.4.1 Space Budgets

According to the Space Foundation [2010], the total global space-related spending in 2008 was about $257.2 billion dollars. Their report showed that global space spending appeared to be rising at a decelerating rate from 2005 to 2008 as illustrated in Fig. 1-9. The world spending on space activities was devoted mostly to commercial satellite services and commercial infrastructure according to their report. Spending on commercial transport services, about $40 million, was so small as to disappear in a graphical representation of the major spending categories (Fig. 1-10).

Commercial space infrastructure spending in 2008 totaled $81.97 billion plus $950 million for insurance and $180 million for independent research and development (R&D) as shown in Fig. 1-11.

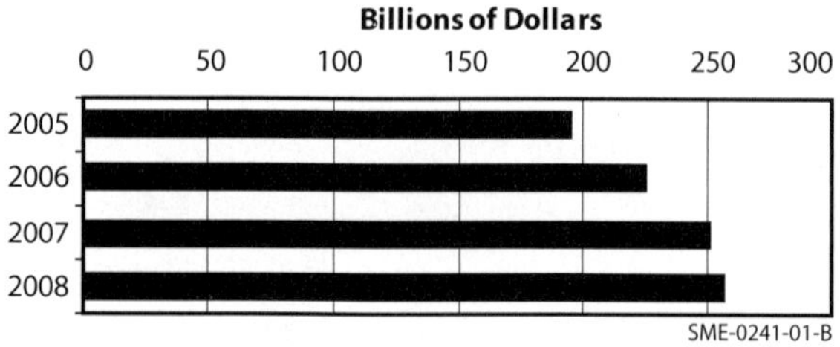

Fig. 1-9. US Aerospace Industry Cost Trends. [Modified from Space Foundation, 2009, Table 1b.]

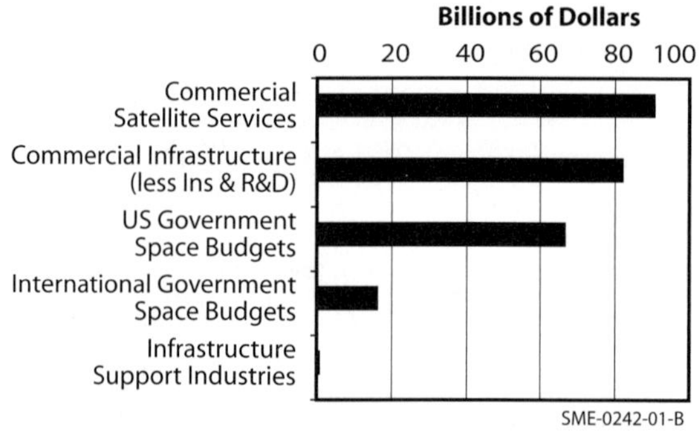

Fig. 1-10. 2008 Global Space Spending By Major Category. Space commercial transportation services at $40 million are invisible on this scale. [Modified from Space Foundation, 2009, Fig. 1c.]

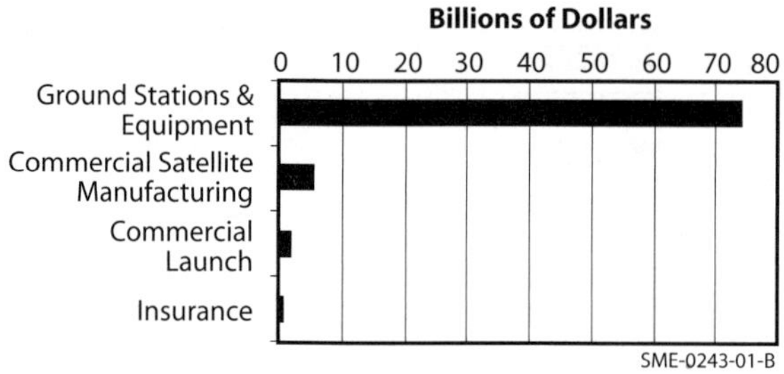

Fig. 1-11. 2008 Commercial Space Infrastructure Spending By Major Category. Independent R&D is invisible at $180 million on this scale. [Modified from Space Foundation, 2009, Fig. 1d.]

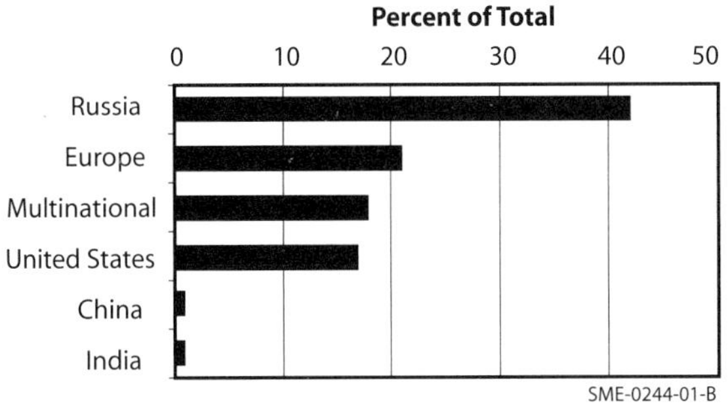

Fig. 1-12. 2008 Commercial Orbital Launch Market in 2004–2008 Based on Number of Commercial Payloads Launched. The US market share was 100% up until the first commercial Ariane launch in 1984. [Modified from Space Foundation, 2009, Fig. 1e.]

Commercial payloads launched in 2008 were dominated by the Russians and the Europeans. Together, they accounted for 63% of the total number of payloads. The United States (US) accounted for 17% as illustrated in Fig. 1-12.

The 2008 US space budget is shown by agency for 2008 in Fig. 1-13. Department of Energy (DOE) and the Federal Aviation Administration (FAA) space spending are invisible on the graph at $30 million and $10 million.

Putting the spending described above into better perspective may result from considering some historical examples of major space projects:

- Apollo Program
- Hubble Space Telescope (HST)
- International Space Station (ISS)

The NASA history website [2004] summarizes the cost of the Apollo program:

"It had been an enormous undertaking, costing $25.4 billion... with only the building of the Panama Canal rivaling the Apollo program's size as the largest non-military technological endeavor ever undertaken by the United States and only the Manhattan Project to build the atomic bomb in World War II being comparable in a wartime setting."

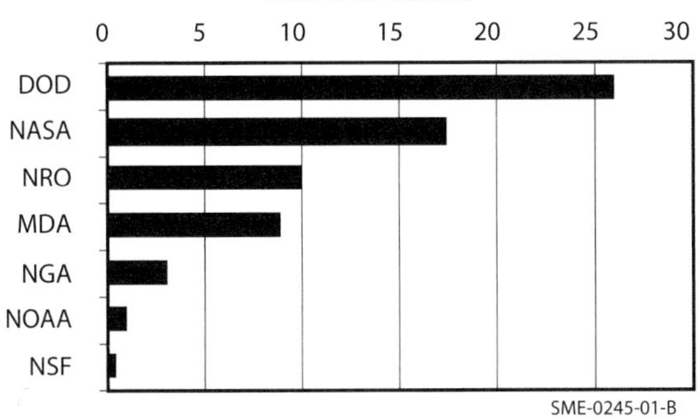

Fig. 1-13. 2008 US Governmental Space Budgets By Agency. [Modified from Space Foundation, 2009, Fig. 1m.]

Unfortunately, this reference does not specify whether this figure includes the predecessor Mercury and Gemini programs, but most authors assume that it was for Apollo only. Also, the money was spent over a number of years, so the annual spending amounts would be needed to accurately adjust the cost to current dollars. The Consumer Price Index (CPI) as an approximate inflation compensation tool is shown in Fig. 12-4. Using the data underlying that discussion, the CPI ranged from 29.9 to 36.7 during the period 1961 to 1969, and was 214.5 in 2009. Significant inflation occurred during the lifespan of the Apollo program and is attributed in part to the war in Vietnam. Thus, correcting the $25.4 billion for inflation requires multipliers ranging from 5.84 to 7.17 and results in values of between $148.5 billion and $182.2 billion in 2009 dollars.

The Hubble Space Telescope (HST) was launched on April 24, 1990 aboard Space Shuttle Discovery (STS-31) and deployed the following day. Its cost was $1.5 billion at launch [Greene, 2010]. This does not include the costs associated with the 5 Shuttle missions dedicated to repair and servicing of HST that were launched in December 1993, February 1997, December 1999, February 2002, and May 2009.

Obtaining reliable cost information for the International Space Station (ISS) is essentially impossible. One Wapedia [2010] article states that:

"The cost of the station has been estimated by ESA as €100 billion over 30 years, and, although estimates range from $35 billion to $160 billion, the ISS is believed to be the most expensive object ever constructed."

In addition to the difficulties in defining reliable cost data for large government-funded multi-year space projects, project managers must satisfy different constituencies with different agendas. The US Congress, for example, may require specific design decisions based on providing or maintaining employment in their members' districts rather than on best available engineering advice. One might speculate that an emphasis on political considerations in addition to management and technical issues influencing the process of decision-making drives up total project costs inordinately. The influence of tightly focused investigator-led missions or of artificially imposed deadlines on total project cost efficiency is unclear, as is the present emphasis on "commercial space development."

1.4.2 Diversity of Opinions

At the current stage of space technology, differing technical approaches to holding costs down are being proffered. For example, it is unclear whether Reusable Launch Vehicles (RLVs) in which vehicle costs can be amortized over many flights would be more or less expensive over their complete life cycle than simple expendable launch vehicles (ELVs). Recent advances in material properties allow parts counts of ELVs to be reduced—thereby potentially reducing their costs [Jurist et al., 2009].

A currently fashionable tenet is that increasing launch rates will drive down launch costs and that RLVs are the way to accomplish that task. Another tenet considers development of RLVs to be considerably more expensive than ELVs with comparable performance.

These tenets are hotly debated in some quarters. There are additional opinions as well:

Clayton Mowry, the president and chairman of Arianespace US, when asked about high launch costs and the high cost of space access recently commented that: "There is no elasticity of demand for satellite launches in the markets we see today" [Mowry, 2010a]. This remark about elasticity was an extension of what he said in a recent Space Show interview [Mowry, 2010b]:

"It's [total program cost] driven by spacecraft and applications in space. What you are able to do when you are up there. To focus on the launch price is a bit misguided. The launch price is generally less than 10% of the overall cost. People will say the satellite will cost $200 million or $300 million and the launch price is $100 million. Therefore [it] is 25% of the cost, or 30% of the cost, or maybe even half the cost with a smaller spacecraft. Maybe the launch costs more than the satellite itself. That is a gross simplification of what takes place with a launching system. When we look at communication satellites, you've got not only the spacecraft itself, the launch price, insurance which is a significant amount of money, the operations, ground systems to fly the satellite, the people it takes to keep something in orbit for 15 years flying properly, and all the overhead that's associated with that. When you do those numbers and you look at the launch price, it ends up being somewhat less than 10% of the overall cost structure. If you took away that piece with 8% or 9% of the overall cost structure and you did not have it, would it mean they would be building and launching more satellites in that class? The answer is simply no. The demand for those spacecraft is driven by the applications. ...The launch price is a small portion of that."

Charles Precourt [2010a,b] had a different take on the problem when asked about the factors contributing to high launch costs:

"Fundamentally it does not come down to only the design; a design will cost more if the acquisition strategy of the procuring agency is not efficient. The question is: Can you gain significant efficiencies within government systems acquisition management practices by placing more burden on the contractors to design and manufacture directly from the agency's higher level requirements?"

"This would be in contrast to the manufacturers waiting for blueprints from the agency which detail lower levels of system requirements, which is the current practice in several areas of Constellation. The result of shifting this detailed design burden to the contractors is delivery acceleration of produced materials, hardware, and systems. Slips in delivery schedule are the key driver of cost, not the design itself."

"Carrying a workforce is also costly, so minimizing the time between milestones, lowers total costs. If the time required for the agency to develop blueprint level requirements exceeds what a contractor could create, then the program timeline is stretched out with no payoff. Time to design means money. So again, it's not about the design itself, it's about how you acquire it."

A lesson to be gained from these quotations is that total project or mission cost is a multifactorial problem with relative weightings that are different with commercial and government projects. A multibillion dollar commercial satellite must be reliable over its design lifetime. The associated insurance for the commercial project is a significant cost that may not be directly identified in a government project. The cost of debris mitigation of a commercial satellite is incurred up front even though the mitigation takes place at the end of the satellite lifetime, and the satellite operating corporation assumes some liability even after the satellite's primary mission has ended. Range costs and insurance may not be directly identified in a government space project, and the spacecraft operations and monitoring over its mission lifetime may be performed by university grantees and funded through research and training grants.

1.4.3 Overview of Economics of Aerospace Systems

Getting into space, doing things in the space environment, and returning things back to Earth are all expensive. Returning information back to Earth is cheap. Two primary metrics are generally used to specify launch and payload costs: Cost per unit mass delivered to space or total cost for a payload delivered to space. The former is more appropriately applied for delivery of commodities or multiple payloads and the latter for dedicated launches of specific payloads.

Some of the relevant factors are discussed below. Space programs tend to be over budget and completed late. These problems appear to be partly rooted in starting out with ill-defined projects that require research, development, and testing as part of the early and mid-portions of the program. The space industry and its companies are unique. As such, space companies do not really compare easily to terrestrial businesses, even to those with similar risks.

Other factors relate to the specific type of space business, but most cannot be started in a garage or a tiny warehouse and then ramped up from a small part time business. Component manufacturing for a lot of space businesses cannot benefit from assembly line production or from huge global or regional markets. One exception to the market comparison is the communication satellite but even with a global market, the satellites and launch vehicles are not mass produced, they require exceptionally careful fabrication in pristine environments (clean room manufacturing with positive atmospheric pressure, filtered air, special overalls and hair covers). Additionally, reliability and performance standards that are not commonly found in most terrestrial businesses are a must, given the expenses involved.

Comparisons of Various Industries

SPACE INDUSTRY:
- High technical risks—complex systems
- Routine requirements for clean room assembly and testing
- Hostile operating environment
- Labor intensive production
- High entry barriers—expensive R&D and tooling
- Complex and costly integration technology and methodology
- Launchers are finicky—need lots of attention
- Narrow market—few customers
- Few suppliers—limited competition
- Long lead times
- Transportation infrastructure critical
- Extensive testing during and following manufacture and during prelaunch phase
- Heavy regulatory burdens
- Not location centric

MINING:
- Hostile operating environment for men and machines
- Dirty, potentially hostile environment
- Labor intensive
- High entry barriers—expensive essentially hand made equipment
- Equipment needs lots of maintenance
- Limited markets—broader than for space industry
- Limited numbers of mines—geography limits competition
- Long lead times for mines to become productive
- Transportation infrastructure critical
- Heavy regulatory burdens
- Location centric

BIG PHARMA:
- High technical risks—complex equipment and methodologies
- High entry barriers
- Wide markets
- Long lead times
- Transportation infrastructure moderately critical
- Heavy regulatory burdens
- Not location centric

BIOTECH (STARTUPS):
- High technical risks
- Labor intensive
- Low entry barriers—usually evolve from academic laboratories
- Narrow markets—goal is acquisition by Big Pharma
- Long lead times

BIOTECH (STARTUPS) Continued:
- Transportation infrastructure not critical
- Regulatory burdens low until human trials begin
- Usually location centric

AMBULATORY SURGICAL CENTERS:
- Low technical risks
- Labor intensive
- Moderate entry barriers—no more than several million dollars
- Broad markets with favorable demographic trends
- Short lead times—roughly 1 yr from funding to operations with 1–2 months float on receivables
- Transportation infrastructure not critical
- Heavy regulatory burdens
- Extremely high returns on initial investment
- Location centric

EARLY MICROCOMPUTER INDUSTRY (HARDWARE):
- Variable technical risk—ICs developed for other purposes
- Low entry barriers
- Wide market
- Highly competitive market over time
- Variable lead times
- Transportation infrastructure not critical
- Low regulatory burden
- High returns on initial investment
- Not location centric

EARLY MICROCOMPUTER INDUSTRY (SOFTWARE):
- Low technical risk
- Low entry barriers
- Potentially broad market
- Variable competition increasing over time
- Transportation infrastructure not critical
- Low regulatory burden
- Very high returns on initial investment
- Not location centric

SANDWICH SHOP:
- No technical risk
- Low to moderate entry barriers
- Potentially broad market
- Variable competition increasing over time
- Transportation infrastructure not critical
- Low to moderate regulatory burden
- Variable return on investment
- Location centric

The frequent argument that the space industry needs to follow the microcomputer industry model is, in our opinion, invalid. Early microcomputer hardware was frequently designed and produced by a few people working in their spare time. Early software was often developed by one or a few people also keeping their day jobs with the only entry barrier being access to a microcomputer. The high technical, financial, and regulatory risks associated with the space industry are responsible for the cliché "that the way to make a small fortune in space is to start out with a large one."

Perhaps the only other sector with many similarities to space business is mining. Direct comparisons between various economic sectors and industries are difficult and subject to debate. Some simple comparisons between the space industry and various other industries, including small entrepreneurial efforts are made in the boxed section above.

Rational commercial endeavors seek to create high returns for investors. Corporate officers are legally required to protect the financial interests of their shareholders, a responsibility known as the *fiduciary relationship*. Deviation from the capitalistic goal of seeking high returns is more common in closely held corporations* and those largely funded by one or a few people with special interests (angel investors—defined in Sec. 12.1.4) and less likely in those funded by venture capitalists (also defined in Sec. 12.1.4) or in publicly held corporations.

Although one might argue that return to the public treasury by government investment is or should be the dominant motivation for expenditure of taxpayer money, other factors are also important. Those factors may include expenditures for national security, creation of new markets to encourage long-term economic growth, and support of existing markets to provide employment stability. The end result is that programs funded by government investment must satisfy multiple constituencies—including Congress. Private corporate managment must satisfy the corporate board of directors and indirectly the shareholders who elect the board.

1.4.4 General Accepted Accounting Practices (GAAP) and Government Accounting

Whenever government funding is involved, corporate vendors must adhere to a variant of General Accepted Accounting Practices. GAAP is also a necessity for compliance with US securities laws. Often, this requires keeping and reconciling multiple sets of financial records. GAAP is discussed in more detail in Sec. 12.2.1.

1.4.5 Why is Space Expensive?

Because design, development, fabrication, testing, and operation of both launch vehicles and payloads are so labor-intensive, labor costs are a dominant factor in space mission design and implementation.

Based on data accumulated by NASA, the total cost of an engineering man-year in 2007 was estimated at $252,000 in the United States (then-year dollars) [Koelle, 2010]. This figure appears to be increased considerably when compared to $208,700 in 2000 and $156,200 in 1990, but inflation during the same period largely parallels the increase. From 1960 to the late 1970s engineering costs outpaced inflation as represented by the Consumer Price Index. Figure 1-14 shows US aerospace industry cost trends as derived from Koelle's data in then-year dollars and in 2007 dollars in order to account for general inflation.

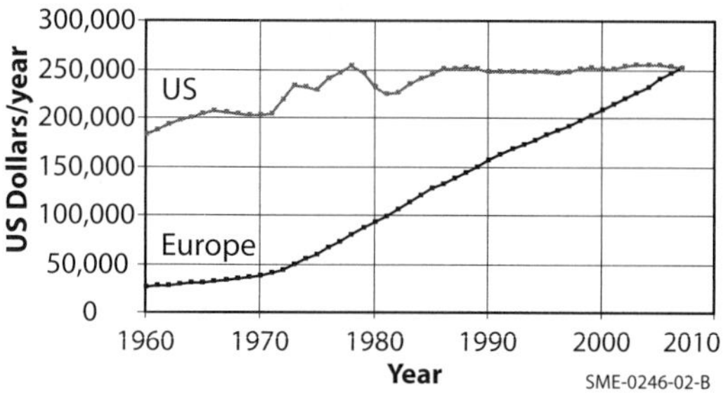

Fig. 1-14. US Aerospace Labor Cost Trend in Then-Year Dollars. Modified from Koelle [2007], Table 1-II.

Koelle also developed relative productivity factors per working hour and effective working hours per year for the United States versus other countries. The productivity models incorporated relative education and standard work week, among other variables.

In order to attain the requisite reliability, launch vehicles, satellites and other payloads are essentially hand built with great attention to post-production testing and maintenance of quality control. Use of clean room technology for fabrication and assembly drives costs up markedly compared to more traditional manufacturing. Transportation of completed hardware to its launch destination also adds to costs because of the attention paid to prevention of shipping damage. Arrival at the destination then necessitates further testing.

In addition to his work described previously, Koelle developed a series of parametric equations for estimating standard aerospace industry costs associated with development of rockets, missiles, and space transportation systems. Koelle's models use linear regression equations relating the logarithm of cost to the logarithm of the mass of the system or subsystem. Individual constants have been derived from historical data for various types of rocket motors, airframes, and other systems. The historical data include suborbital rockets and liquid-fueled missiles. Additional multiplicative factors relate to the experience of the development team, the technical complexity of the development, development time compression requirements, and management structure.

Finally, Koelle developed a similar set of models to estimate the cost of a first production unit (Theoretical First Unit or TFU). This is significant because production costs tend to decline with increased production numbers—the so-called learning curve discussed in Sec. 12.2.3.

Compared to, for example, automobile manufacturing, production runs for launch vehicles and satellites are very small. This precludes taking full advantage of mass production techniques and of progressively working down the learning curve that reduces production costs with increases in production run.

One aspect of maintaining high quality in the manufacture, processing, and assembly of satellites and rocket components, and payload integration is the frequent use of clean room environments. This drives up overall project and mission costs. Attaining the required

* A closely-held corporation is one in which there are few shareholders and which may not meet the standards required for a publicly-held corporation. Different states have different requirements on the maximum number of allowed shareholders before a corporation must be registered as a public corporation. Closely held corporations tend to be smaller in terms of capitalization and are frequently run more informally than public corporations.

high reliability also requires considerable post-production testing and quality assurance both at the subsystem and fully integrated systems level. Long drawn out programs and technical advances frequently result in shortened life cycles for a specific program because of the temptation to initiate development of advanced models (new and improved versions). Low launch rates, and especially launch uncertainties tied to vehicle problems, range and safety considerations, orbital dynamics, and weather drive up costs. This contributes to the so-called "standing army" problem.

Given the fact that on-site repair and refurbishment of a space asset such as a satellite is impossible at worst (as in a planetary probe, for example) and extremely expensive at best (as in repairing the Hubble Space Telescope), reliability is very important. That reliability comes from extensive design and testing at all phases of product development, manufacturing, and delivery to the end user.

Launch vehicles are very complex and have multiple failure modes—many of which can result in loss of mission and loss of vehicle. The potential loss of very expensive satellites and space vehicles drives the need for very high reliability of launch vehicles and high insurance costs to cover associated risks. The reliability problem drives design toward redundancy and fault tolerance.

For example, as stated previously, launch vehicle cost accounts for perhaps 10% of the total mission cost of a satellite or space vehicle placed into space. The remainder comes from amortization of research and development of the launch vehicle, payload integration into the vehicle, pre-launch testing and verification of the vehicle systems, payload insurance against loss, range fees for tracking and range safety, as well as operation and control of the satellite or vehicle. This may result, for example, in a 95% probability of successful payload placement. By cutting the launch vehicle cost in half and reducing launch reliability to 90%, the risk of mission loss is doubled while 5% of the total cost of payload placement and operation is saved.

The high cost of space launch motivates manifesting multiple payloads whenever possible. Launch service personnel must then consider payload integration to assure that multiple payloads do not interfere with one another. This adds another dimension to the cost problem. Payload integration costs are also incurred when assuring that a given payload is compatible with the internal environment of the launch vehicle and assuring that the interaction of the payload or payloads with the vehicle dynamics are within tolerable limits for the specified vehicle. These are labor intensive activities.

Technical advances lead to potential improvements of a given launch vehicle and spacecraft. At some point, incorporation of these advances into production become desirable for various, and often noneconomic, reasons. With low production rates, research and development (R&D) costs cannot be amortized over a large production run and unit costs are high as a result. Keeping vehicle production lines open and waiting for additional demand reduces programmatic costs at the expense of increasing overhead. This tradeoff results in decision-making determined by reimbursement mechanisms associated with the procurement contract.

It is a truism that delays drive up costs. These delays result in increased labor costs, additional management oversight, increased finance costs (interest on loaned capital), and opportunity costs.

1.4.6 How Might Costs Be Minimized?

Extrapolation of that which is not forbidden by science and technology to what may be possible involves a risk that does not exist with already proven technology. That risk usually results in cost overruns and is not limited to space technology, but can occur in non space-related activities. One way to hold down R&D costs is to make use of already-developed technology to the maximum possible extent. This tends to drive evolutionary progress at the expense of revolutionary progress.

Given that a launch system consists of a collection of parts, most of which have non-zero probabilities of failure during a launch, reducing the parts count of a system may improve reliability. In addition, designing for fault tolerance with redundancy or other modalities may improve overall reliability and modestly reduce total launch costs. Design processes should ideally seek the "sweet spot" in the tradeoff of reliability and component cost.

A very important consideration in creating a large scale business with large capital investment is to clearly identify the products or services to be supplied rather than adhering to the "build it and they will come" philosophy of hoping for demand to eventually manifest itself.

As an example of minimizing cost, we will consider range costs which are a large component of the total flyaway costs of launching into orbit. Comprehensive analysis of orbital launch economics shows that cost-effective launch operations are inhibited by high (and perhaps unwarranted) range fees imposed on a launch company for use of a federal range. The adverse economic impact of range fees are only a symptom of the underlying disease. The fundamental problem is badly outdated federal launch and operational systems and an infrastructure that will not support high flight rates and commercial operations. The federal range launch infrastructure was historically developed for missile launches [Muncy, 2005]. This governmental infrastructure is now maintained, operated, and updated by numerous government contracts. For example, the US Air Force has a contract for operations, a certain company has the contract to repair broken equipment, another company handles R&D needs, and still another company handles the procurement of new or replacement equipment. There is no single entity with the authority to make rational economic decisions related to the launch infrastructure. The systems are outdated and they are not user friendly. It is challenging if not impractical for a federal range to cycle more than one launch daily. Therefore, the existing federal range launch infrastructure cannot support the commercial launch needs anticipated by private launch companies with their commercially designed rockets and their projected markets.

Discounting range fees does not solve the underlying problem although such discounting may allow a more cost effective economic profile for a commercial operation. However, discounting does nothing to modernize the obsolete infrastructure, systems, and management of federal ranges.

If the goal is to have frequent multiple launches, it is essential to run the spaceports or ranges as rational economic entities. It may be possible to privatize and streamline federal range operations, but there is not much interest among the range operating entities or the US Congress to do this. Unless this changes, the federal range will still be operated uneconomically and require taxpayer subsidy.

Pressure to overhaul the federal ranges and launch infrastructure might increase as private spaceports receive licenses for vertical launches. A good example of potential pressure can be seen by examining the developing private Spaceport America in New Mexico. This range plans to offer private rocket companies state of art launch and range services designed to be commercial from the ground up. As it offers launch services, what will happen to the Florida Spaceport which is stuck in the federal range environment? If Florida wants to compete for private launch business, it will have to modernize. Simply put, without comprehensive modernization, the existing Florida launch infrastructure will not easily support competitive commercial launch services. While the Mid-Atlantic Regional Spaceport (MARS), the commercial component of the federal Wallops Island Launch Facility, and Kodiak Island may be able to launch private rockets with lower range costs, their infrastructure is still not suitable for anticipated commercial operations.

Regulatory relief may be as important as range cost relief. Some launch companies have opted to avoid the national ranges entirely by choosing air launch or sea launch. Two NewSpace CEOs have privately indicated that they would not use the national ranges even if they were free because of the regulatory burden.

1.4.7 Other Launch Cost Issues

Major trends in the space industry in the US appear to be:

- Decreasing cost of basic electronics
- Increased capability of software due to more capable, faster processors
- Increasing performance capability of electronic packages of a specific size
- Increasing capability of mission-related software,
- Increasing reliability of basic components
- Increased use of advanced composite technology to reduce structural masses
- Increased use of computer technology for decreasing staffing requirements for launch day operations
- Motivation to use commercial launch providers whenever possible for government projects as well as for commercial projects
- Increasing political pressure to separate NASA from launch services
- Establishment of private spaceports to compete with federal ranges
- Severe budgetary pressure on federal discretionary spending

The trends outlined above result in decreased size and mass of payloads designed to provide specified capabilities. Because of this resultant trend, launch cost per unit mass of payload becomes less important at some point than total launch cost for dedicated missions as the last stage becomes the most massive part of the orbited mass. Additional study of the minimum feasible size of an orbital launch system is indicated to better define where this break point may exist. Decreased mass of specific payload packages and the availability of excess payload mass in existing specific launch vehicle configurations drive a tendency to manifest multiple payloads on a given launcher. That results in entities providing payload brokering to multiple space programs. An example of such an entity is Detachment 12 at Kirtland Air Force Base, New Mexico. Current technological, economic, and regulatory realities forbid payload delivery to LEO for true costs of less than about \$2,000/kg [Jurist et al., 2005].

Mowry [2010b] has said that one of the successful strategies employed by Arianespace is to make multiple rockets at one time, all identical. The only alterations needed per rocket deal with specific payload interfacing. Not only does this strategy allow for greater probability of launch success, it maximizes the potential for some cost reductions. This is related to the learning curve discussed in Sec. 12.2.3. The SpaceX Falcon 1 is being replaced by the Falcon 1e, which has yet to fly. The Falcon 9 has flown 2 successful orbital launches at the time of this writing. As of September 2010, their offered prices to LEO are \$10,792/kg and \$5,358/kg for the Falcons 1e and 9, respectively, exclusive of insurance [SpaceX, 2010a, 2010b].

Creating fleets of reusable launch vehicles (RLVs) is unlikely to solve the launch cost problem unless they are large and have lifetimes of many frequent flights. Of course, this presupposes sufficient demand for space launch. Present technology may permit orbital RLVs, but economic factors currently forbid them. The shuttle Space Transportation System (STS) is only partly reusable and is generally considered to be an economic failure. Nobody has currently demonstrated or convincingly documented the ability to:

- Design, fabricate, and economically fly orbital RLVs
- Finance and then amortize the necessary R&D
- Define a clear, solid business plan to implement the program required to do so

- Demonstrate the market that would support the costs of creating such vehicles
- Develop a viable strategy to go from our present flight rate of expendables to the high flight rates of RLVs projected for the mature industry which would permit achieving low cost flights to LEO

Two of the many major obstacles to attaining this goal are the nontechnical factors of range costs as discussed previously and insurance (discussed in Sec. 12.2.4).

Advances in electronic miniaturization and performance have led to improved capability of unmanned space vehicles. Humans in space, on the other hand, are massive and not subject to miniaturization. They require massive life support systems and large quantities of consumable supplies. There are many unresolved issues related to long-term human space flight, such as the effects of microgravity, health effects of prolonged low level and episodic high level radiation exposures, and degradation of life support systems. The trends toward miniaturized electronic systems therefore drive decision-making processes toward unmanned systems at the expense of human-tended missions and have the paradoxical effect of driving up the costs of human space flight. Further consideration of this issue is beyond the scope of this text.

1.5 The Wide Range of Space Mission Applications

The goal of space mission engineering should be to satisfy the needs of the customer or end user as effectively, as quickly, and at as low a cost as possible. But who is that customer or end user and what is it that they want? The answer differs greatly, depending largely on 3 key issues:

1. The aspect of space that you're exploiting
2. Where you're coming from, i.e., the space community you're in, and
3. What you perceive as the role of space

In Chap. 2, we'll explore the various space communities and what they perceive as the role of space. Here we'll summarize the varying characteristics of space that are exploited in different space missions and look at the very wide range of mission applications that these imply. If our mission doesn't rely on some fundamental and unique characteristic of space, it will likely cost more to do in space than on Earth. For example, there is little reason to manufacture and distribute low-cost consumer goods or manage a restaurant chain in Cleveland from space.

What fundamental characteristics of space make space missions worthwhile? Table 1-3 lists the primary characteristics of space that distinguish it from Earth-based activities. Exploring and utilizing space serves various objectives, from extremely practical telecommunications and weather, to major scientific observatories hoping to understand the Universe better, to advance military applications and exploring and exploiting the Moon and the planets. Space missions are very diverse partly because they use many different characteristics of space. For example, materials processing uses the micro-gravity and high vacuum of space, without regard to the spacecraft's position over the Earth. Conversely, communications or observation satellites emphasize Earth coverage as the most fundamental space characteristic used to achieve their mission.

Table 1-3 reveals a second important feature—the varying levels at which different characteristics are currently being used in space. For example, many missions use the global perspective of space—for telecommunications, weather, navigation, and other aspects of Earth monitoring. Space-based telecommunications will likely continue to grow, but is already a major and mature industry.

Satellite communications by telephone and television have become a part of everyday life and have helped to bring about a communications revolution that has contributed significantly to our shrinking world. Equally dramatic changes are likely in the future as new applications for space-based communications and navigation continue to emerge and every cell phone, car, and notebook computer will know where it is on the Earth to within a few meters.

In contrast to telecommunications, materials processing and precision manufacturing in the gravity-free environment of space is only in its infancy. Major strides appear possible in pharmaceutical and semiconductor devices that may bring about an entirely new industrial segment. Exploiting space's almost limitless resources is even further removed. Unlimited continuous power and huge, accessible supplies of physical materials may, in the long run, maintain an industrialized society without destroying the Earth's fragile environment. These objectives will require greater vision, and lower launch costs, than is required for the more fully developed areas of communications, resource mapping, and monitoring.

We see from Table 1-3 that we have either not used or only begun to use most of the major characteristics of space, so changes in future space exploration should be far larger than what has occurred to date. To take practical advantage of these characteristics, we must greatly reduce the costs of exploring and exploiting space. Finding ways to lower these costs is a principal objective of this book. (See Chap. 13 and Wertz and Larson [1996].)

Based on Table 1-3, we would expect to find a wide range of space mission applications and this is indeed the case as shown in Fig. 1-15. Note that some missions fall into multiple categories. For example, GPS is a navigation system used by a large number of people worldwide, but is funded, built, and run by US Air Force as a military mission. Similarly, the Apollo program could reasonably fall under exploration or science and, in many respects, there is a great deal of overlap between those two catego-

Table 1-3. Characteristics of Space Exploited by Various Space Missions. Note the wide variety and that many are only beginning to be used. (Spacecraft acronyms are defined in the index.)

Characteristic	Relevant Missions	Degree of Utilization	Sample Missions
Global Perspective	Communications Direct Broadcast Navigation Weather Surveillance	Some are mature industries; major new advances will come with increased onboard processing	IntelSat GeoEye NOAA weather satellites Direct TV FireSat II, SCS
Above the Atmosphere	Scientific observations at all wavelengths	Well developed; space observatories will continue to dramatically change our view of the universe	Hubble Space Telescope Spitzer Chandra X-Ray Observatory
Gravity-free Environment	Materials processing in space	Largely dormant because of high cost; may be many future applications	ISS Wake Shield Facility Space Manufacturing
Abundant Resources	Space industrialization Asteroid mining Solar power satellites	Essentially none	Space colonies Solar power satellites Asteroid mining
Exploration of Space Itself	Exploration of Moon and planets, scientific probes, asteroid and comet missions	Initial flybys and some planet orbitting missions have been done; Some landings done or planned; limited human exploration	Manned Lunar or Martian bases Apollo Mars rovers Space tourism

ries. One category that has been omitted is weapons of mass destruction in space, which are banned by international treaty. (See Sec. 12.3.) This is important in that space is often referred to as the "ultimate high ground." The implication of this is that unilateral control of space represents a very strong position from which to militarily control the Earth below. Fortunately, the major space-faring nations at the start of the space age, the United States and the Soviet Union, have chosen to peacefully co-exist in space.

Certainly the most striking feature of Fig. 1-15 is the exceptional variety of mission applications. This is both a challenge and an opportunity for space mission engineering. Most people work in only one, or at most a few, of these many application areas. Our view of "the space program" and how spacecraft are designed, built, and flown is constrained by this limited exposure. It is likely that large weather satellites in GEO, student CubeSats, and spacecraft built for space tourism will have relatively little in common. This makes it hard to generalize about how these missions are or should be built. But it is also an opportunity to bring concepts, hardware, software, and processes developed in one arena into other areas to give us a wider range of tools, equipment, and processes to solve the problems of the end user. Can we, for example, use rapidly advancing CubeSat technology to dramatically lower the cost of other, larger application and surveillance satellites? We will return to this theme in Chap. 2 where we look at the very diverse set of space communities that largely act independently of each other. Ultimately, the main characteristic that nearly all of the application areas and space communities have in common is a desire to achieve their objectives in a timely manner at minimum cost and risk—i.e., to do a good job of space mission engineering.

1.6 Sources of More Information

Text and reference books such as this one often have extensive references and bibliographies. However, the books and papers cited are frequently hard to find and, of course, the lists aren't updated after the book is published. Our goal with Space Mission Engineering is to dramatically change this, such that much of the information cited is immediately available on the web and nearly all of the remainder is available within a day or two, so that you can use the full resources of this book for a project or proposal that is due next week. Here's how we're doing that.

This book has an associated website, www.smesmad.com. The password for the website (not case sensitive) is ASTRODATA. As discussed below, the website has 6 main types of data:

- ***Reference Material***—all of the references and bibliographic material from throughout the book with direct links to where you can obtain it.
- ***Information Tables***—most of the information tables in the book that can be updated are on the web and are updated from time-to-time as the information changes.
- ***Numerical Tables and Graphs***—Most of the graphs and numerical tables in the book are adjustable for your particular project of interest. The Excel models that created them are on the website for you to download.
- ***Extended Discussion***—Some relevant material that is beyond the scope of the printed text is included on the website.
- ***Standards***—Astronautics standards are regularly updated so references to them are on the website.

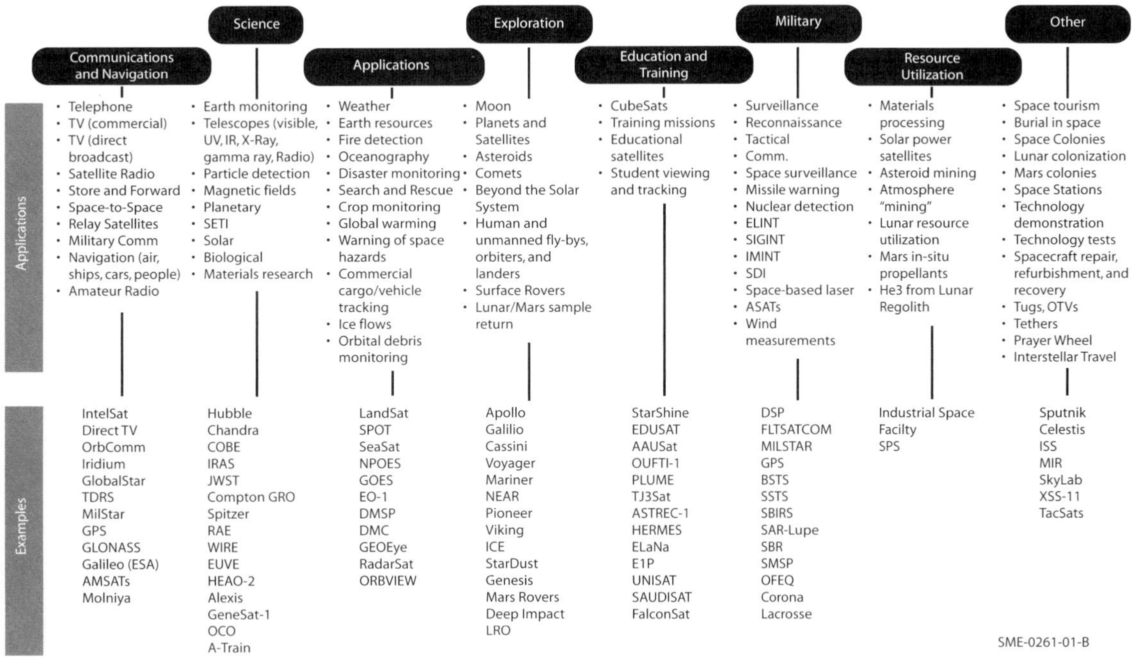

Fig. 1-15. The Wide Range of Space Mission Applications. Note that some missions fall into multiple categories. See the index for definition of mission acronyms

- ***Errata***—Sadly, virtually all technical and reference texts are in need of fixing typographical (or mental) errors that inevitably occur. These are also on the website.

Wherever there is material available on the website, it is marked in the text by a "computer button," such as:

REFERENCE MATERIAL

Each chapter in the book has the usual list of references, primarily to professional papers and other books. This list is reproduced on the website with a web reference to where you can obtain each reference. Some of the papers and a small number of books are available for free and can be downloaded immediately. Most professional papers are copyright, typically by one of the professional societies discussed below. In this case, the link from the book website will take you to where that specific paper can be purchased from the society that published it. In most cases, you can get additional information and an abstract or one page of text for no cost and can purchase the full paper, typically for $15 to $30. It can then be downloaded immediately. Books can, of course, be purchased from nearly any online bookseller. In most cases, the link from the book website will take you to the description of that volume on the Microcosm Astronautics Books website, or to a more recent edition of the same book, if one has been published. From there, the book can be purchased and shipped via next day air or normal delivery. The Microcosm bookstore is the publisher of this volume and maintains the book website. It tries to keep all of the book references in stock and available, many with a reduction from the list price.

References are, of course, fixed at the time that the chapter is written. Therefore, the website for each chapter also includes an annotated bibliography of books and some survey papers that are relevant to the chapter, with a 2–3 sentence description of each and a web link to where it can be purchased or downloaded at no cost. The bibliography is only on the website so that it can be continuously updated as new volumes become available. In addition, the bookstore manager is knowledgeable about what is available in astronautics books and can provide suggestions and recommendations. The current contact information is www.astrobooks.com, bookstore@smad.com, 1-888-ASTROBK, or 310-219-2700 extension 105. If this information changes, it will be on the website. Finally, Microcosm attempts to have available on site one copy of each of the items referenced in the bibliography. If you're in southern California, feel free to come by and look at the reference material during normal business hours. We're about 2 miles from LAX at 4940 W. 147th St., Hawthorne, CA 90250. The goal here is to provide as nearly as possible "instant access" to high quality, referenced and reviewed technical information in astronautics, without violating the copyright rights of those who own the material. If you have any suggestions on how we might do this better, please get in touch with us.

INFORMATION TABLES

Much of the material in tables throughout the book—such as hardware manufacturers, lists of missions, or professional societies—changes with time. For this reason, many of the tables in the book are also included on the website with either more or updated information. For example, Table 2-2 is a list of representative interplanetary missions. The author has created a more extensive list, along with website references for each mission. Thus this table is on the website with more missions, more information about each mission, and web references for all of them. To find any of the tables on the website, use the search box on the left side of the website labeled "Table" and enter the Table number. For the list of interplanetary missions, enter 2-2, or 2.2.

NUMERICAL TABLES AND GRAPHS

Like most texts, this volume has many numerical tables and plots of representative values, such as the Earth satellite table in the inside rear cover or the orbit decay plot in Fig. 9-18. In both cases, these are made more useful by being downloadable to your computer and modified for your particular mission. The originals of these tables and plots are done in Excel. The Excel model itself (often with some modifications to make it more widely applicable) is then put on the website. For example, the table of satellite orbits on the inside rear cover is on the website. You can adjust the range of altitudes or other parameters and can also change the central body from the Earth to any other planet. You can even create your own planet if you'd like. It also allows you to plot a number of the variables so that you seen how different parameters vary with altitude. Similarly, Fig. 9-18 allows you to plot the decay of both apogee and perigee over time for essentially any circular or elliptical low-Earth orbit. As with the informational tables, use the search boxes on the left side of the website labeled "Table," or "Figure" and enter the table or figure number, such as H-1 for the satellite parameters on the inside rear cover or 9-18 or 9.18 for the orbit decay plot.

A word of caution—we have tried to make the Excel models very easy to use by clearly distinguishing the user inputs, but we have not prevented you from changing formulas or entering values that would not be meaningful. You can download the Excel model to your computer and change it as you choose at your own risk. If you choose to have gravity fall off as $1/r^3$, you can do so, with perhaps interesting, but likely not very realistic, results. We recommend that after a few experiments of this sort, you download the model again and start over.

EXTENDED DISCUSSION

In some cases, there is an occasional need for a more extended discussion than would be needed by most readers of the book. If this discussion is well covered in one of the outside references, we will simply reference the other books or papers. However, in some cases, alternative sources either don't exist or are inconvenient to find. In these cases, a more extended discussion is included on the web and referred to in this volume with the GET MORE button. For example, vector and matrix arithmetic is well known and covered in many standard texts and college courses. Therefore, we haven't included it here. However, for those that would like a good summary, with consistent notation, we have reprinted the material from an appendix to an older astronautics reference (with permission) on the website and referenced it in App. F.

STANDARDS

Many areas in astronautics have standards similar to those throughout engineering and manufacturing that are developed, maintained, and published by the professional societies in order to reduce both errors and costs. These standards are updated and expanded on a regular basis as the industry evolves. Therefore, we have put the source of the standards on the website and used the GET STND button to show you where there are applicable standards. Typically these can be downloaded at no cost.

ERRATA

While none of us would like to admit that errata are ever necessary, in the rare event that they are required, errata for each chapter are included at the end of that chapter on the website.

The major astronautics professional societies worldwide, listed in Table 1-4, publish a large fraction of the professional data used by the astronautics industry. This is primarily in professional journals, listed in Table 1-5, published by the societies or as a part of conferences. Many individual conferences are arranged on specific topics. However, most of the major conferences, listed in Table 1-6, occur annually or biannually. In addition, several of the societies publish books that are either conference proceedings or individual volumes on specific topics. The individual books can typically be purchased through the normal book retail outlets on the web (such as Amazon, Barnes and Nobel, or Microcosm Astronautics Books), but very few are available in physical bookstores, other than Microcosm Books, because of the relatively low volume. A great deal of both popular and technical material also exists in various sites on the web, although much of the web-based material is not refereed or well-edited, and may be less reliable.

There are also a large number of websites associated with space data and space news. These change rapidly, however, and are listed only in Table 1web-1 on the website. Note that most of the websites associated with space are concerned with news, events, and specific space missions and rarely contain validated technical information. If you have additional suggestions on how to provide better information to the Space Mission Engineering readers, please let us know at bookstore@smad.com or bookproject@smad.com.

Table 1-4. Major Astronautics Professional Societies. Most of the larger professional societies cover fields other than astronautics as well.

Society	Comments	Website
AIAA = American Institute of Aeronautics and Astronautics	The largest American professional society with a major focus on astronautics. Holds national and regional conferences. Publishes both refereed journals and many books. AIAA technical committees create many of the standards used in the space industry. (See Sec. 6.6.)	www.aiaa.org
AAS = American Astronautical Society	The largest of the American societies devoted exclusively to astronautics and space exploration. (Note that another AAS = American Astronomical Society, is the largest astronomical organization is the US.)	astronautical.org
BIS = British Interplanetary Society	One of the oldest professional societies in astronautics. Publishes papers on topics, such as interstellar travel, that are more far-reaching than many of the other professional journals.	www.bis-spaceflight.com
IAF = International Astronautical Federation	The IAF is the principal worldwide organization for astronautics with an annual conference held at various locations throughout the World. The IAF is a collection of organizations, i.e., organizations not people are IAF members. Associated with the IAF, are the ***IAA*** = International Academy of Astronautics, which is a worldwide association of astronautics professionals, and the ***IISL*** = International Institute of Space Law, which focuses on legal and treaty issues in the exploration of space.	www.iafastro.com
IEEE = Institute of Electrical and Electronics Engineers	The world's largest professional technical society. Focused on electrical engineering, but does a great deal of work in astronautics, including publication of many relevant papers.	www.ieee.org
INCOSE = International Council on Systems Engineering	A relatively recent organization, founded in 1990, but with a strong interest in space systems engineering. Intended to be a focal point for the dissemination of systems engineering knowledge.	www.incose.org
SEDS = Students for the Exploration and Development of Space	An independent student-based organization (both graduate and undergraduate) with chapters at various universities around the World. Loosely affiliated with some of the professional space organizations. Runs both conferences and various local activities.	seds.org
NSS = National Space Society	Independent educational organizations formed from the merger in 1987 of the National Space Institute and the L5 Society. Dedicated to the creation of a spacefaring civilization.	www.nss.org

Table 1-5. Major Professional Journals in Astronautics. Most are published by one of the professional societies. Technical journals are those that provide refereed professional articles, typically for specialists in a particular area. Popular journals are monthly magazines with broader appeal and relevant to a broad segment of the astronautics community. Many of the larger aerospace organizations also publish semi-technical journals on work being done within the organization.

	Comments	Abbreviation	Content
AIAA	*Journal of Spacecraft and Rockets*	JSR	Technical
	Journal of Guidance, Control, and Dynamics	JGCD	Technical
	Journal of Aerospace Computing, Information, and Communication	—	Technical
	Journal of Propulsion and Power	JPP	Technical
	Aerospace America	AA	Popular
AAS	*Journal of the Astronautical Sciences* (quarterly)	JAS	Technical
	Space Times (bi-monthly)	ST	Popular
BIS	*Journal of the British Interplanetary Society*	JBIS	Technical
	Spaceflight (includes a running chronology of space missions)	—	Popular
	Aviation Week and Space Technology (weekly)	Av Week	News
	Space News (weekly)	SN	News

Get Info

Table 1-6. Representative Regularly-Held Conferences in Astronautics. Conferences are typically organized and run by, or on behalf of, one or more of the professional societies. For more information see the website of the sponsoring professional society.

Sponsor	Conference	Location	Date
AIAA	Aerospace Sciences Meeting	Florida	Jan
AIAA, FAA	Commercial Space Transportation Conference	Varied (US)	Feb
AIAA, ASME, ASCE, AHS, ASC	Structures, Structural Dynamics and Materials Conference	Colorado	April
AIAA	Atmospheric Space Environments Conference	Hawaii	June
AIAA, ASME, SAE, ASEE	Joint Propulsion Conference	San Diego	July
AIAA	Guidance, Navigation, and Control Conference	Varied (US)	Aug
AIAA	Modeling and Simulation Technologies Conference	Varied (US)	Aug
AIAA	Space 20(year) (largest of the AIAA conferences)	Varied (US)	Sept
AIAA	AIAA Aerospace Sciences Meeting	Varied (US)	Jan
AAS	Guidance and Control Conference	Colorado	Feb
AAS, AIAA	Space Flight Mechanics Conference	Varied (US)	Feb
AAS	Goddard Memorial Symposium	NASA GSFC	Mar
AAS, AIAA	Astrodynamics Specialist Conference	Varied (US)	July
AIAA (LA & Orange County Sections)	Reinventing Space (= Responsive Space Conference prior to 2011)	Los Angeles	Apr/May
IAF, IISL	International Astronautical Congress (IAC)	Varied (Worldwide)	Oct
Utah State University, AIAA	SmallSat Conference	Logan, UT	Aug
IEEE, AESS, AIAA, PHM Society	IEEE Aerospace Conference	Big Sky, MT	Mar

References

Get Ref

For annotated bibliography of introduction, see the book website.

Department of Defense. 2009. *Technology Readiness Assessment (TRA) Deskbook*. Jul.

Greene, Nick. 2010. "Hubble Space Telescope." *Space/Astronomy*.

Gruntman, Mike. 2004. *Blazing the Trail: The Early History of Spacecraft and Rocketry*. Reston, VA: AIAA.

Gruntman, Mike. 2008. "Space Systems Fundamentals." course notes.

Horne, Charles F. 1911. *Works of Jules Verne*. vol. 3. New York: Parke and Co.

Johnson, Stephen B. 2002. *The Secret of Apollo: Systems Management in American and European Space Programs*. Baltimore, MD: Johns Hopkins University Press.

Jurist, J.M., D.C. Hook, and D.M. Livingston. 2009. "Small Unit Space Transport and Insertion (SUSTAIN): How to Do It and Use It as a Driver for Low-Cost Responsive Orbital Launch." 7th Responsive Space Conf. AIAA-RS7-2009-1002. Apr. 27–30.

Jurist, J.M., S. Dinkin, and D.M. Livingston. 2005. "When Physics, Economics, and Reality Collide: the Challenge of Cheap Orbital Access." AIAA, Space 2005 Conference. AIAA-2005-6620. Long Beach, CA. Aug. 30–Sept. 1.

Koelle, Dietrich E. 2007. *Handbook of Cost Engineering for Space Transportation Systems (Rev 2) with Transcost 7.2*. Ottobrunn, Germany: TransCostSystems.

Koelle, Dietrich E. 2010. *Handbook of Cost Engineering for Space Transportation Systems (Rev. 3) with Transcost 8.0*. Ottobrunn, Germany: TransCostSystems.

Mankins, John C. 1995. "Technology Readiness Levels, A White Paper." Advanced Concepts Office, Office of Space Access and Technology, NASA. Apr. 6.

Mowry, Clayton. 2010a. E-mail to D. Livingston. Sep. 6.

Mowry, Clayton. 2010b. Interview on *The Space Show*. Aug. 3.

Muncy, J. 2005. Interview on *The Space Show*. May 16.

NASA History Program Office. 2004. "Project Apollo: A Retrospective Analysis." Oct. 22.

Oberth, Hermann. 1923. *Die Rakete zu den Planeternäumen*. R. Oldenbourg, Munich and Berlin.

Precourt, C. 2010a. *The Space Show* Interview. Aug. 13.

Precourt, C. 2010b. E-mail to D. Livingston. Sep. 13.

Sadin, S.T., F.P. Povinelli, and R. Rosen. 1989. "NASA Technology Push Towards Future Space Mission Systems." Space and Humanity Conference, Bangalore, India. S39th IAF Congress. *Acta Astronautica*, vol. 20, pp 73–77.

Scoffern, John. 1859. *Projectile Weapons of War and Explosive Compounds*. London, UK: Longman, Brown, and Co. Reprinted in 2009 by General Books LLC.

Space Foundation. 2009. *The Space Report 2009*.

Space Foundation. 2010. *The Space Report 2010*.

SpaceX. 2010a. "Falcon 1 Overview." Website

SpaceX. 2010b. "Falcon 9 Overview." Website.

Wapedia. 2010. "International Space Station." Website.

Wertz, J.R., W.J. Larson. 1991. *Space Mission Analysis and Design. 1st ed.* Dordrecht, The Netherlands: Kluwer Academic Publishers and Microcosm Press

Wertz, J.R. and W.J. Larson. 1996. *Reducing Space Mission Cost*. El Segundo, CA: Microcosm Press and Springer.

2 Space Mission Communities

James R. Wertz, *Microcosm, Inc./USC*

We often think of the space enterprise as a monolithic whole with different groups working on different types of spacecraft. In fact, looking at this more closely, we see that the space enterprise really consists of a number of very different communities, each with very different budgets, timescales, and fundamental objectives. Each community tends to regard themselves as the "real" space program and, therefore, to ignore the others.

While the differences are real and substantial, the different communities are more related than is often seen to be the case. Failures and successes in one community tend to affect all the rest. The Iridium bankruptcy had a major impact on all space activity by making it much harder to raise capital, reducing the number of launch options available (and thereby increasing the cost), and increasing the apparent risk of space activities. Significantly reducing launch cost will have a major impact on all of the space activity, in part by reducing cost, but also by changing the way spacecraft are built. Anything that dramatically increases the use of space will impact all areas by driving down cost. CubeSats, intended for the low-cost education and science community are being adapted by others to drive down the cost of a variety of programs. Any major advance in large space telescopes could be used for Earth observation, for planetary monitoring, or military surveillance.

The importance of this for space mission engineering is that it affects how we design and build space missions. We can't realistically expect to find the same technology or same processes used for a million dollar smallsat as for a multi-billion dollar interplanetary mission or military surveillance spacecraft. On the other hand, major breakthroughs in cost and performance can come about by applying technologies or processes from one community to the problems found in another.

Perhaps the most critical issue for space mission engineering is to clearly recognize the basic goals and objectives of the community for which the space mission is being designed as well as a broad sense of the budgets and timescales that are involved. While we are always trying to build a space mission to achieve the basic objectives at minimum cost and risk, what this means in practical terms changes dramatically based on the space mission community in which we are working.

2.1 Multiple Space Communities

Table 2-1 lists the primary space communities and their basic objectives and typical cost. Notice the dramatically wide range of mission cost, going from approximately $20,000 at the low end to nearly $200 billion for the Apollo program. Although it can't be measured quantitatively, the basic goals and objectives of the people who work in these communities are equally diverse, and, therefore, so are the perceptions, methods, and processes that they use.

2.1.1 Human Spaceflight*

For many people, human spaceflight **is** the space program. Launches make the evening news and disasters become known worldwide. Astronauts give a visible face and a human side to what is otherwise viewed as an almost entirely technological enterprise. It is also the most expensive of the space activities. The Apollo program (Fig. 2-1) cost approximately $200 billion in 2010 dollars, but is widely regarded as one of the most significant events of the 20th century. The International Space Station, ISS (Fig. 2-2), cost about half what Apollo cost, but has not captured the imagination of the World in the same sense that landing on the Moon did.

The reasons for having a human spaceflight program, and, therefore, the purpose and objectives of such a program vary significantly among proponents, but fall broadly into 3 categories. First, there are many tasks that

* For the first 40 years of space exploration, the general distinction was made between *manned* spaceflight and *unmanned* spaceflight, depending on whether people were on board the spacecraft, and using "man" in its broad meaning of humankind. In order to be more politically correct, *manned spaceflight* has become *human spaceflight*, but *unmanned spaceflight* is a bit more challenging. *Robotic spacecraft* has become the most widely used term, but conveys the incorrect impression that all spacecraft without people are somehow robots, which certainly isn't the case with any reasonable definition of robot. On the other hand, "inhuman spaceflight" doesn't seem to convey the right impression and "unhuman spaceflight" isn't much better. Throughout this volume we will try to avoid the terminology altogether, but, when that's not possible, we will typically use "human spaceflight" and "unmanned spacecraft" in order to be half politically correct.

Table 2-1. The Principal Space Communities. See text for discussion. NRE (Non-Recurring Engineering) is the development cost.

Community	Basic Objective	Example Missions	Typical Mission Cost
Human Spaceflight	Explore and exploit human capabilities	Apollo, ISS, MIR	$2 billion–$200 billion
Interplanetary	Explore beyond Earth	Galileo, Cassini, Mars Rovers	$1 billion–$5 billion
Military and Intelligence	Give sponsor a military advantage over their adversary	GPS, ComSats, Surveillance Satellites	$1 billion–$10 billion
Commercial	Make money	IntelSat, ComSats, GeoEye, GlobalStar, Iridium	$100 million–$1 billion
Science and Applications	Gain/apply scientific knowledge (Earth, astronomy, space itself)	Weather Sats, Hubble, Chandra, JWST	$100 million–$10 billion
Education	Teach, train, inspire	StarShine, CubeSats, Spheres	$100 thousand–$500 thousand
Launch	Put payloads or people into space	Shuttle, RLVs, Ariane, Atlas, Cosmos, Delta, Pegasus	**NRE:** $100 M–$50 B **Recurring:** $10 M–$1 B
Smallsat	Demonstrate utility of small, low-cost missions	CanX-2, AmSats, Explorers, SurreySats, DMC, Alexis	$20,000–$20 million
Alt Space (Alternative Space)	Advance civilization's expansion into space	Apollo, Lunar Colonies, Human Mars Mission	$200 billion and up (possibly with commensurate income)

Fig. 2-1. The Apollo Program. Top: Buzz Aldrin's footprint in the Lunar soil on Apollo 11. Bottom: The Lunar Module and Lunar Rover on Apollo 17. On this mission, Harrison Schmitt and Eugene Cernan, the last man on the Moon in the Apollo program, explored the Taurus-Littrow valley in the Montes Taurus mountains. (Photo courtesy of NASA)*

people can do much better and more efficiently than machinery. Simple tasks, such as running a communications relay mission are most easily and economically done by simple machinery. But more complex tasks, such as exploring the surface of the Moon or evaluating and fixing problems that occur, can best be done by having people in space.

Second is the political element. The Soviet Union became a super power, on a par with or superior to the United States, by launching the first satellite and first person into space. The Race to the Moon was a political challenge for superiority here on Earth and the Apollo 11 landing reestablished the superiority of the United States for much of the World.

Finally, for many people the purpose of human spaceflight is to make space exploration a human activity, i.e., to have **people** explore, learn, walk on the Moon, discover new places, and find new things, just as explorers and discoverers have done for centuries. It is in this sense that astronauts are representatives of mankind, turning over a rock on the Moon to find what is under it, and ultimately, turning over many rocks on many moons and planets throughout the Solar System. This view is carried further by the Alt Space community discussed in Sec. 2.1.9.

The human space program is dramatically expensive because spacecraft carrying people are inherently large and heavy and the cost per pound to space is very high, and also because all of the human spacecraft and their equipment must be *man-rated or human-rated,* i.e., tested and certified to be safe to be operated by or near people. This typically means double or triple redundancy in any components where a failure is possible, plus eliminating any sharp edges or possible source of combustion, explosions, or toxic substances. Even if the

Get More * See the book website for color versions of each of the photos in this chapter. In addition, the Educator Package contains high resolution, color versions of each of these photos and several additional photos representing each of the various space communities.

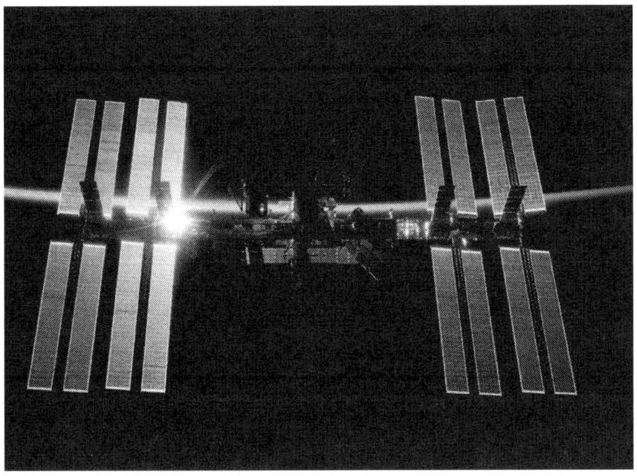

Fig. 2-2. The International Space Station (ISS). Seen here at sunrise. ISS is 110 m long, 50 m wide, and 20 m high and is normally at an altitude of about 350 km. (Photo courtesy of NASA)

equipment is similar or identical to non-human-rated equipment, it will be more expensive because of the higher level of testing, analysis, and certification required.

Because of the high cost of launch and in-space activity for human spaceflight, only a small number of countries are involved in human missions. As of 2010, the only countries doing human space launch are the US, Russia, and China, although Europe and India may do so within a few years. In addition, many countries have astronauts that have flown, primarily on the American or Russian human space missions. In addition, a limited number of *space tourists* have flown on both American and Russian space missions.

This volume does not cover mission engineering for human spaceflight, although of course many aspects are the same for both human and unmanned missions. Orbit properties, the space environment, and the torque available from reaction wheels are the same, irrespective of the payload. There are many good books on human spaceflight in the website bibliography, including excellent ones by Eckart [1996, 2006], Larson and Pranke [1999], Churchill [1997], Clement [2005], Clement et al. [2006], Harrison [2001], and Kanas and Manzey [2003]. Johnson [2002] provides a particularly well-done discussion of the development of systems engineering and systems management that allowed the Apollo program to be successful.

2.1.2 Interplanetary

Interplanetary spaceflight involves sending spacecraft to other planets. A number of well-known interplanetary missions are shown in Table 2-2. The fundamental purpose of interplanetary spacecraft is scientific exploration of all of the elements of the Solar System, both for the purpose of learning more about the solar system and also for learning about the history and possible evolution of the Earth, both past and future. Two central questions are whether there is any potential for life anywhere else in the Solar System, either now or in the past, and how the Solar System formed and evolved. One of the major results of the interplanetary program is that the planets and their satellites are much more individually unique and complex than nearly anyone had anticipated. This, in turn, leads to the objective of both more exploration and more "fine-grained" exploration of the Solar System. The Mars Rovers, Spirit and Opportunity have captured the interest of the public both for their many views of the Martian surface (Fig. 2-3) and their ability to survive for an extended stay in a harsh and dusty environment. They are "the little rovers that could."

Interplanetary programs are typically expensive, ranging from several billion dollars for the large planet observatories such as Galileo or Cassini to a few hundred million for Explorer and Discovery programs. The high cost is driven by several factors—the need to survive for an extended period en route in a high radiation environment and the need to act largely autonomously or with commands stored in advance, due to the long travel time for signals to reach the spacecraft.* The one-way travel time for signals to reach Jupiter ranges from 35 min to over 50 min when Jupiter and the Earth are on opposite sides of the Sun. In addition, they need a substantial propulsion system to either orbit or land on a planet or satellite, precision pointing for very high resolution observations, and larger than typical antennas and solar arrays to provide communications and power back to Earth.

This volume focuses primarily on Earth-orbiting spacecraft, but does include a section on interplanetary orbit design (Sec. 10.7). In addition, most of the web Excel models allow the central body to be any of the Solar System objects, such that you can quickly find all of the relevant orbit and viewing parameters for a Sun synchronous orbit about Mars or Titan. There are quite a few volumes in the website bibliography dealing with the results of specific interplanetary missions and a much smaller number dealing specifically with interplanetary mission design, including Brown [1998], Kemble [2006], and Young [2007].

While interplanetary travel is challenging, practical *interstellar travel*, i.e., going to the stars, is dramatically more challenging. Proxima Centauri, a very small companion to Alpha Centauri, is the nearest star to the Sun at 4.24 light years away. This is 7,000 times further than Pluto. The physics of interstellar travel, including relativistic effects, is summarized by Wertz [2009] Sec. 12.8. Approaches to getting there are discussed by Mallove and Matloff [1989] and in the old, but **very** extensive bibliography (thousands of references) by Forward,

* The NASA *Discovery program* is for missions costing less than $425 million (in FY10$). Over the years, the name "Explorer" has been given to a great many missions. However, generally an "*Explorer mission*" is one operating on a constrained budget, such as *University-Class Explorer* (UNEX)—less than $15 million, *Small Explorer* (SMEX)—less than $120 million, and *Medium-Class Explorer* (MIDEX) —less than $180 million.

Get Info

Table 2-2. Representative Interplanetary Missions. See the associated website table for additional missions, additional details on these missions, and web references for all of them.

Mission Name	Mission Objective	Launch Date, Vehicle	Comments
Pioneer 10	Explore Jupiter; safely cross asteroid belt	3/3/72, Atlas/Centaur/ TE-364	First to observe Jupiter. First to travel through asteroid belt. Last signal detected on 1/23/03.
Pioneer 11	Explore Jupiter and Saturn (including ring system)	4/6/73, Atlas/ Centaur/ TE-364	First to observe Saturn + ring system up close.
Mariner 10	Observe Mercury and Venus	11/3/73, Atlas/Centaur	First craft to Mercury. First to use gravity assist. First to visit 2 planets.
Viking 1	Mars surface sample analysis; look for life	8/20/75, Titan-IIIE/Centaur	Orbiter+lander. No sign of life detected. First successful Martian Lander.
Voyager 2	Jupiter and outer planet close flyby's	8/20/77, Titan/Centaur	—
Voyager 1	Close Jupiter and outer planet flyby's	9/5/77, Titan-IIIE/Centaur	Most distant man-made object in space. Passed termination shock of heliosphere in 12/04.
Pioneer Venus	Venus orbiter	5/20/78, Atlas/Centaur	—
International Cometary Explorer (ICE)	Study Solar radiation and plasma	8/12/78, Delta	Also known as ISEE-3. First in halo orbit. After primary mission (1981), intercepted comet Giacobini-Zinner.
Vega 1	Study Venus and Halley's Comet	12/15/84, Proton-8K82K	Balloon and lander for Venus. Soviet/French mission.
Sakigake	Observe Halley's Comet; technology testbed	1/7/85, M-3SII-1	First Japanese interplanetary probe. Also named MS-T5.
Giotto	Study Halley's Comet	7/2/85, Ariane 1	ESA's first deep space mission. Passed Halley's Comet at 600 km then flew by comet Grigg-Skjellerup.
Galileo	Detailed exploration of Jupiter system	10/18/89, Shuttle/IUS	Discovered additional moons, Io volcanoes, Jupiter rings. First use of Earth swingby.
Ulysses	Observation of Solar polar regions	10/6/90, Shuttle/IUS/ PAM-S	ESA/NASA mission. Maximum Solar latitude 80.2 deg. Highest escape energy ever used.
Clementine	Study topography and geology of the Moon	1/25/94, Titan IIG	Extension to flyby of asteroid 1620 Geographos failed.
Near Earth Asteroid Rendezvous (NEAR)	Orbit 433 Eros	2/17/96, Delta II-7925	First mission to orbit and land on asteroid. NASA Discovery mission.
Mars Pathfinder (MPF)	Mars orbiter and lander	12/2/96, Delta II-7925	"Faster, better, cheaper" design. Sojourner rover (for 30 SOLs).
Cassini/Huygens	Explore Saturnian system	10/15/97, Titan-IVB/Centaur	Cassini main vehicle. Huygens probe descended in atmosphere.
Lunar Prospector	Mapping Lunar resources	1/7/98, Athena II	NASA Discovery mission.
Stardust	Capture and return dust from comet P/Wild 2.	2/7/99, Delta II	First return of particles from beyond Moon's orbit. NASA Discovery mission.
Genesis	Observe Solar wind and return particles to Earth	8/8/01, Delta II-7326	NASA Discovery mission. Drogue parachutes failed during landing at Earth.
Mars Exploration Rovers (MER)	Study past water activity on Mars	6/10/03, Delta II-7925 (A); 7/3/03, Delta II-7925Heavy (B)	Mars Rovers "Spirit" and "Opportunity," designed for 90 SOLs but still active after 7 years.
SMART 1	Test solar-electric propulsion; Lunar science	9/27/03, Ariane 5	First European satellite to travel around Moon. Lunar impact on 9/3/06. Piggyback launch.
MESSENGER	Observe physical phenomena at Mercury	8/3/04, Delta II-7925Heavy	First Mercury observations since Mariner 10 (1974–1975).
Deep Impact	Study comet Tempel 1	1/12/05, Delta II-2925	Discovery mission. Impactor + flyby.
New Horizons	First mission to Pluto	1/19/06, Atlas V-551	—
Lunar Reconnaissance Orbiter (LRO)	Identify landing sites and resources	6/18/09, Atlas V-401	Accompanied by LCROSS, to observe impact of Centaur upper stage.

Fig. 2-3. Panorama of Mars as Seen By the Mars Rover Spirit. (Photo courtesy of NASA)

listed in the website bibliography for Chap. 10. Because interstellar travel isn't practical in the near term,* it is often included as part of the Alt Space community described in Sec. 2.1.9.

2.1.3 Military and Intelligence

The *military and intelligence space program* is intended to collect data with military utility wherever and whenever it can. (The Outer Space Treaty of 1967 bans weapons of mass destruction in space and requires that the Moon and other celestial bodies be used only for "*peaceful purposes*," defined by the U.S. as "non-aggressive," meaning that defensive measures are permitted. See Sec. 12.3.) Military and intelligence space activity can be broadly divided into categories based on specific objectives, such as:

- *Reconnaissance and Surveillance*, obtaining high-resolution imagery of the ground or air space, typically in the visible or infrared (often called *IMINT*)
- *Signals Intelligence*, intercepting communications (often called *SIGINT*)
- Detection of nuclear explosions
- Military communications
- *Guidance and Navigation*, implemented largely with GPS (Fig. 2-4 and Sec. 19.2.2.3), which is built, launched, and operated by the Air Force
- *Space Situational Awareness (SSA)*, which is obtaining knowledge about what an adversary may be doing in space, or, potentially, about space debris or other space hazards

* As shown in Table 2-2, Voyager I is often regarded as the first interstellar probe because it left the solar system and is exploring interstellar space. However, it isn't headed for any nearby star and will simply continue to drift, sending back data on the interstellar medium.

The military space program is largely pragmatic, i.e., it will use the lowest cost, most effective means to obtain the needed data, irrespective of whether it uses spacecraft, aircraft, high altitude balloons, or terrestrial resources. Similarly, it will at least evaluate the use of space resources in new ways that have the potential of providing military utility. For example, the National Security Space Office (NSSO) has studied using satellite solar power to provide power to remote military outposts in order to reduce the cost and risk of bringing fuel to remote locations. (Typically fuel is one of the biggest items in the military logistics supply chain.)

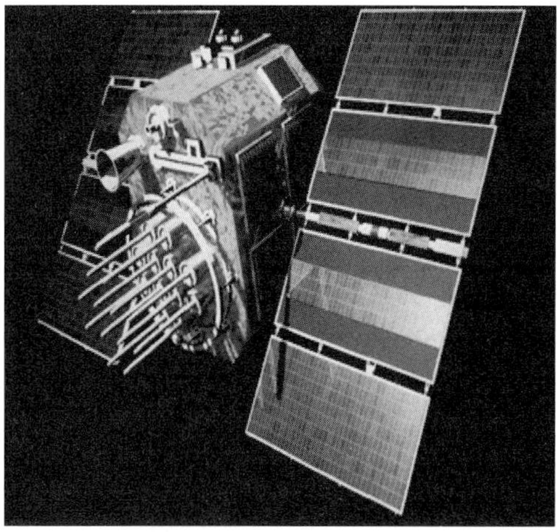

Fig. 2-4. Drawing of GPS Satellite. The GPS constellation, at an altitude of approximately 20,000 km (half-GEO), is run by the Air Force to provide precision navigation services for the military and also for a great many civilian applications.

Because of the wide variety of military and intelligence applications, there is also a wide range of costs. Traditionally, military *"programs of record,"* i.e., long-term programs approved by both DoD and Congress, are large and very expensive spacecraft with a long operational life and, unfortunately, an equally long development cycle. In an attempt to reduce both cost and schedule and meet urgent needs of military commanders, the Operationally Responsive Space Office (ORSO) was created in 2008. In 2009, the National Reconnaissance Office, often regarded as building the best and most expensive observations satellites in the world, began buying extremely low-cost CubeSats, which are 10 cm cubes with equally small, low-cost components. (See Sec. 2.1.8 and Sec. 25.4.) While large, expensive programs will certainly continue, augmenting these larger spacecraft with much smaller, lower-cost and more quickly replaceable satellites is at least a possibility for the future, in part because of continuing pressure on the defense budget to do more with less and reduce the fragility of current systems. (See Wertz [2010], for a discussion of the arguments for low-cost, much smaller military options.) This potential transition is hampered by the lack of an appropriate small, low-cost launch vehicle.

There is also a broader view of military space reflected in the title of the book *Mastering the Ultimate High Ground* [Lambeth, 2003]. From a military perspective, space is the ultimate high ground, such that whoever controls space, controls the Earth. This, in turn, implies the need to defend space assets and be fully aware of what is going on in space, i.e., the space situational awareness mission. Other authors that discuss military space include Chun and Taylor [2006], Klein [2006], Parkinson and Spilker Jr. [1996], and Richelson [2001].

Fig. 2-5. IntelSat 603. This satellite was launched in 1990 on an unmanned Soviet launcher, but a launch failure left it in a useless low-Earth orbit. In 1992 it was captured (by hand), repaired, and sent successfully on its way to GEO by the crew of STS-49. (Photo courtesy of NASA)

2.1.4 Commercial

Of all of the space communities, the *commercial community* is one of the largest and has the most straightforward objective—to make money. Historically, this has been done primarily with geosynchronous communications satellites, such as IntelSat, shown in Fig. 2-5, and direct broadcast television and radio. The GEO commsat community is now a mature industry with approximately 300 satellites on orbit, substantial competition for building new ones, and an active market in used GEO satellites. (As discussed in Sec. 1.2, the use of GEO for communications was first described by science fiction writer Arthur C. Clarke in 1945.)

So far as the communications portion of the industry is concerned, the basic objective is not to minimize cost or maximize performance, but to minimize the cost per unit of performance (for example, the cost per phone call). There is ample capital available in the communications market to support systems of essentially any size, so long as the cost per call is minimized so that the operator can compete successfully for communications business.

Other elements of the commercial space industry are less mature. There have been only a small number of commercial observations satellites, such as GeoEye-1, shown in Fig. 2-6. Space tourism is underway as a commercial activity, as is one of the more unusual space businesses, burial in space [Chafer and Price, 2002]. In this case, a small vial of cremation ashes is launched into low Earth orbit where it will typically decay and burn up in the atmosphere after a short period.

Fig. 2-6. Graphic Rendition of GeoEye-1 Launched into a Sun Synchronous Orbit in 2008. The satellite provides 0.5 m resolution imagery to Google-Earth and slightly better imagery to the government. (Photo courtesy of GeoEye)

The success or lack of success of commercial space activities has a very strong effect on non-commercial space activities. The bankruptcy of the Iridium low-Earth orbit communications constellation in 1999 had a very chilling effect on other aspects of space. There were many similar constellations being planned, had Iridium proven to be financially successful, including the Teledesic "internet in the sky" constellation with potentially as many as 840 satellites. The Iridium bankruptcy made it difficult to obtain financing for commercial space ven-

Table 2-3. The NASA Great Observatories. (See the associated website for references to individual spacecraft and their results.)

Name	Name Before Launch	Spectral Region	Year Launched	End-of-Life	Comments	Follow-On Mission
Hubble Space Telescope, HST	Large Space Telescope, LST	Visible, UV, and Near-IR	1990	—	Launched and serviced by Space Shuttle.	James Webb Space Telescope, JWST (IR and visible)
Compton Gamma Ray Observatory, CGRO	Gamma Ray Observatory, GRO	Gamma Ray	1991	2000	Shuttle-launched	Fermi Gamma-Ray Space Telescope, formerly Gamma-Ray Large Area Space Telescope, GLAST
Chandra X-Ray Observatory, CXO	Advanced X-Ray Astrophysics Facility, AXAF	X-Ray	1999	—	Shuttle-launched; extended delays due to cost of HST	Constellation-X provides greater sensitivity, but lower resolution
Spitzer Space Telescope, SST	Space Infrared Telescope Facility, SIRTF	Infrared	2003	—	Launched on Delta II	JWST observations will replace SST in the near infrared

tures and prevented the significant launch cost reductions that would probably have come about with a major spurt in the number of LEO satellites. GlobalStar and ORBComm LEO communications constellations have been launched, but have contained much smaller numbers of satellites with less ambitious goals than Iridium.

The fundamental impediment to substantial growth in commercial space is the high cost of launch, which in turn, drives up the cost of spacecraft, as discussed in Chap. 13. For example, there are a number of manufacturing processes that can occur in space, that simply can't occur on the Earth's surface. (See Sec. 7.4.) This has led to a long-term interest in space manufacturing, with some experiments done on the Space Station and free-flying payloads. Unfortunately, the high cost has thus far made any significant space manufacturing activity uneconomical. Similarly, solar power satellites have been considered for an extended period as a means of providing clean energy in nearly unlimited amounts to the Earth's surface [Glaser et al., 1998]. But this won't occur in any reasonable quantity until there is a reduction in the cost of launch by a factor of 5 to 10.

Commercial space activity is discussed by Haskell and Rycroft [1998], Peeters [2000], in a series of telecommunications books by Elbert [1990, 1992, 2003, 2008], and in a number of volumes listed in the web bibliography on communications satellites.

2.1.5 Science and Applications

Science and Applications Satellites monitor the Earth and space for both scientific studies and Earth applications such as weather prediction and monitoring global conditions on both land and oceans. Weather forecasting is now largely done with analytic models based on satellite data. The first photos of the aftermath of Hurricane Katrina were made by a small satellite from the Disaster Monitoring Constellation built by SSTL. Much of the scientific data about the Earth as a whole and the universe at large comes from scientific satellites. The science and applications community tends to break down further, either by what they are studying (such as weather, Earth resources, Mars, or asteroids) or by the wavelength they are working at (such as visible, IR, UV, or X-Ray). The NASA Great Observatories program, shown in Table 2-3, is intended to take advantage of the fact that satellites outside of the Earth's atmosphere can see the Universe without the distortions caused by the atmosphere and in wavelengths not visible from the Earth's surface. The most well-known of these is the Hubble Space Telescope that has both created enormous amounts of scientific data and sparked the human imagination with images of remarkable clarity of things and places we only thought we understood (Fig. 2-7).

Fig. 2-7. Hubble Space Telescope after Release by the Final Shuttle Servicing Mission in 2009. (Photo courtesy of NASA)

In the future, both science and applications missions are likely to bifurcate in two distinct directions. Some of the science missions will continue to use very large, very expensive instruments and spacecraft as they continue to push the state of the art in terms of both size and sensitivity. However, continued budget pressure will likely stretch out the time and reduce the frequency of very large science observatories, at least until there is a continued human presence on the Moon or in orbit that can provide servicing for them. In the second branch, many observations and measurements will be taken over by much lower cost, smaller satellite missions that come about by the continued microminiaturization of electronics components and the development of radiation hardened, low-cost components.

The basic objectives of the science and applications community will not change—to provide continued, improved monitoring of the Earth and space and to stretch the boundaries of our knowledge of the Earth and its place in the universe. This includes, particularly, the search for life elsewhere in the universe and solutions to fundamental problems on Earth ranging from weather to environmental monitoring to earthquake prediction to disaster monitoring.

There are many volumes in the website bibliography on the results of both science and applications missions, including the COBE mission which resulted in the first Nobel Prize for NASA scientists Mather and Boslough [1996]. Among the volumes describing observing techniques and analysis are those by Elachi and van Zyl [2006], Conway [1997], Cruise et al. [2006], Lacomme et al. [2001], Lillesand et al. [2008], Olsen [2007], and Schowengerdt [2007].

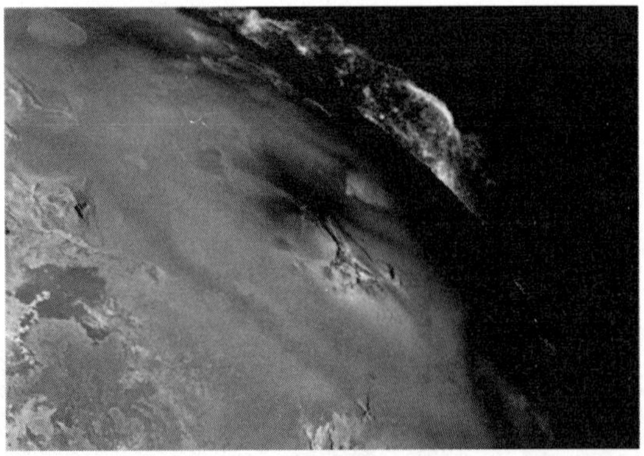

Fig. 2-8. Jupiter's Moon Io Photographed by the Chandra X-Ray Observatory. (Photo courtesy of NASA)

2.1.6 Education

The goal of the *space educational community* is to provide the best possible educational environment at all levels—from primary and secondary education to the undergraduate and graduate level. Clearly a part of this can be done by looking at data and results from a wide variety of missions such as the Apollo program or the Mars Rovers. But the real issue for educators is to launch satellites built, and, if possible, operated by students so that they can get real, first-hand experience of the problems and issues involved. A literally shining example of this approach is the StarShine satellite developed by Gil Moore (Fig. 2-9). StarShine consisted of a 48-cm hollow aluminum sphere covered with 878 front surface mirrors that were polished by 25,000 children in 660 schools in 18 countries. StarShine 1 was launched from the Space Shuttle during a trip to the ISS in 1999 (2 others have been launched since then) and was visible to the naked eye before sunrise and after sunset. Young students tracked the satellite and older students determined its orbit, decay rate, and the atmospheric density during the 8-month flight.

Fig. 2-9. Gil Moore holding a Mock-up of the StarShine Satellite. Right: sunshine reflecting off **one** of the mirrors. (Photo courtesy of Gil Moore)

Although there have been some successes, the most fundamental problem with all student satellites is finding a launch. NASA had determined that launching student satellites was not a part of its fundamental charter and most educational institutions couldn't afford to buy even a secondary launch opportunity for student payloads. Thus, it was nearly impossible to launch a student satellite while the student was still a student, or even while they were still in aerospace at all.

Much of this difficulty changed in 1999, with the invention of CubeSats by Bob Twiggs at Stanford University and Jordi Puig-Suari at California State Polytechnic University. (See Sec. 25.4 for a detailed discussion of CubeSats.) The purpose of the CubeSat was to find a way to drive down launch costs for student built satellites. This was done by building a standard launch container (named the Poly PicoSat Orbital Deployer, or P-POD, by the Cal Poly students) capable of holding and launching three 10 × 10 × 10 cm CubeSats. While CubeSats have greatly increased the potential for educational satellites, getting a ride to orbit remains a major problem, although it looks like solutions may occur within a few years. There are no books currently available exclusively on education satellites, largely because there have been very few education satellites in the past.

Fig. 2-10. An Early CubeSat 10 × 10 × 10 cm Satellite. (Photo courtesy of Pumpkin, Inc.)

2.1.7 Launch

There is a standing joke within the launch community that the fundamental purpose of spacecraft is to serve as ballast for testing and flying launch vehicles. Because of the cost and difficulty of launching to orbit, the launch community is largely a group apart from the spacecraft community, for which launch is simply a service to be provided. Launch vehicles and launch vehicle selection are discussed in detail in Chap. 26 and all of the modern launch vehicles available throughout the world are described by Isakowitz, et al. [2004].

Historically, launch vehicles have been about 90% reliable since not long after the opening of the space program. The most reliable, and lowest cost per pound to orbit, was the Saturn V (Fig. 2-11), developed for the Apollo program. Because there were only a small number of launches, the potential long-term reliability is not known and the low cost is due in part to being able to launch a small city to orbit (120,000 kg to LEO). One of the other vehicles with an excellent reliability record has been the Delta II, shown in Fig. 2-12, which had only 2 failures in its first 110 launches. The Russian (and former Soviet) Soyuz launcher had only 21 failures out of 704 launches (97% reliability) over more than 40 years, and most of those failures occurred during early development and testing.

Fig. 2-11. Saturn V Launch of Apollo 15 in 1971. The Saturn V was 110 m high, 10 m in diameter, and weighed 3,000,000 kg at liftoff. (Photo courtesy of NASA)

While launch is not the most expensive element of most large space missions, it tends to drive mission cost. It's not economically worthwhile to build a satellite for a few million dollars and launch it for $100 million. Therefore, much (but certainly not all) of the high cost of satellites can be attributed to the fact that it costs $10,000 to $20,000 per kg to get to low-Earth orbit and $80,000 to $150,000 per kg to get to the surface of the Moon.

It is clearly important to drive down launch costs in the future in order to create a robust space program that can be sustained over the long term. Unfortunately, it is not clear how to do this. With the exception of the Space Shuttle Orbiter and the Solid Rocket Boosters (SRBs) on the side of the Shuttle, all traditional launch vehicles have been *expendable*, i.e., used only once with the spent stages lost in the ocean or burned up on reentry. Although I do not agree with this conclusion, it is the consensus of the American launch community that the solution to the cost problem is to create a fully or partially *reusable launch vehicle*, in which portions of the launch vehicle are brought back to Earth, refurbished, and flown again. In the simplest terms, this argument is often expressed as "think how expensive air travel would be if you threw away a 747 every time you used it." (For the counter argument see, for example, Wertz [2000] or [2004].) Irrespective of what solutions might ultimately be successful, it is critical to the worldwide space program to significantly reduce the cost of launch for payloads of all sizes, from CubeSats and smallsats to large communications and reconnaissance satellites, to payloads going to the Moon or Mars. This problem has been discussed by a number of authors, including London [1994], Wertz [2000, 2004], and Hujsak [1994]. The standard reference for rocket propulsion is Sutton [2010]. An excellent cost model specifically for space transportation systems is provided by Koelle [2010].

Fig. 2-12. Delta II Launch of the Mars Rover Spirit in 2003. (Photo courtesy of NASA)

2.1.8 Smallsat

Smallsats are broadly defined as satellites weighing less than about 1000 lbs or 500 kg. However, with the advent of CubeSats and very small satellites, a variety of terms have come into use and it has become clear that there is a need for more well-defined terminology. The terminology now most widely adopted for small satellites is the following:

MiniSat	100 to 500 kg
MicroSat	10 to 100 kg
NanoSat	1 to 10 kg
PicoSat	0.1 to 1 kg

A *1U CubeSat* fits within a 10 cm × 10 cm × 10 cm cube and weighs at most 1 kg. Therefore, it's a large PicoSat. A common alternative configuration is a *3U CubeSat*, consisting of three 1U CubeSats in a line (i.e., 10 cm × 10 cm × 30 cm), which would be a NanoSat configuration.* (See Sec. 25.4 for a detailed discussion.)

Smallsats have been flown since the beginning of the space program, largely because of limitations on the size and mass capability of launch systems. Historically, about 20% of all satellites launched are less than 400 kg. Generally, smallsats are simpler than larger satellites, typically have only a single payload, and have a much more limited capability. (One of the principal reasons for building bigger, more expensive satellites is to obtain higher levels of performance.) However, in recent years the microminiaturization that has created iPhones, Blackberrys, and music players with nearly unlimited memory, has also allowed a dramatic increase in the capability of smallsats while maintaining very low cost. In addition, small satellites are ordinarily built in 1 to 3 years (largely because there isn't enough money to have a program last longer). This, and a higher tolerance for risk, allows small satellites to take advantage of new technology much faster than traditional satellite programs. Thus a 15 year old large satellite, built 20 years ago with technology from 25 to 30 years ago with largely analog electronics and mechanical systems, may or may not be more capable than a very small, low-cost satellite built a few years ago using the very latest computer technology and almost entirely software driven subsystems.

Like the satellites themselves, the basic objectives of the smallsat community are typically much less complex than those of traditional satellite systems. Ordinarily, traditional satellite programs will be requirements-driven with a very extensive list of potentially contradictory requirements and constraints from different potential users and multiple payloads that may or may not work well together. Smallsats, on the other hand will tend to have a single payload, many fewer requirements, and be much more oriented to providing whatever capability can be accomplished at modest cost. An example is the Alexis spacecraft, shown in Fig. 2-13. When the Chandra X-Ray telescope was being designed and built, there were extensive delays, due in part to cost overruns on Hubble. (Chandra was initially designed in the early 1970's and finally launched in 1999.) The community identified a need for continuing X-Ray observations and wanted whatever could be done quickly and at very low cost, rather than meet an extensive set of requirements. Alexis was built for approximately $17 million vs. approximately $2.75 billion for Chandra.

For many years, the world leader in low-cost small satellites has been Surrey Satellite Technology Limited, SSTL, started by Sir Martin Sweeting as an outgrowth of

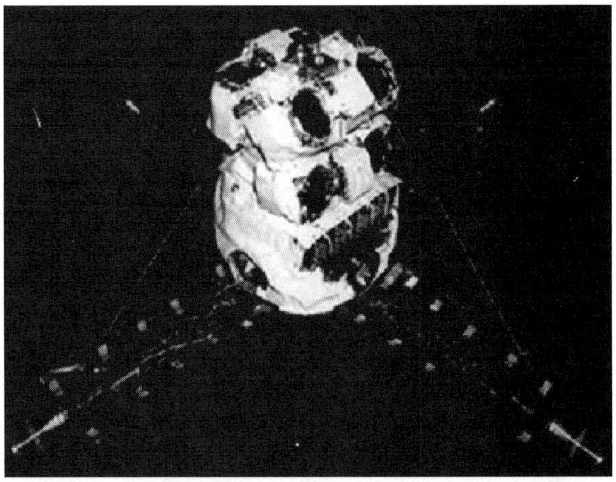

Fig. 2-13. The Alexis Small X-ray Satellite was Launched in 1993. The satellite lasted 12 years on orbit in spite of a launch failure that broke off one of the solar arrays. (Photo courtesy of Comtech AeroAstro)

the space activity at the University of Surrey. SSTL started with small, low-cost communications satellites, and has since created a set of low-cost observation satellites, such as those that are a part of the Disaster Monitoring Constellation, DMC (Fig. 2-14). "Surrey Sats" often become the first satellite in a space program being started by one of the smaller space-faring nations.

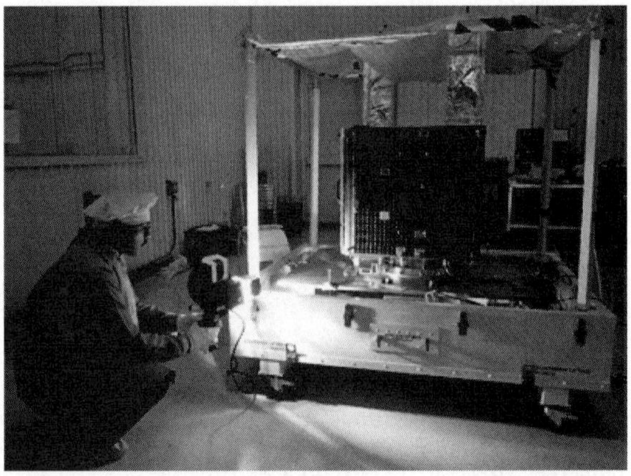

Fig. 2-14. Testing one of the SSTL Small Satellites that Make Up the Disaster Monitoring Constellation (DMC). NigeriaSat, a part of the DMC, took the first photos published in *Aviation Week and Space Technology* of the aftermath of Hurricane Katrina. (Photo courtesy of Surrey Satellite Technology)

For many smallsat programs, the basic objective is to find a reasonable compromise between what we would like and what we can afford, what is often called *trading on requirements*. This is one of several key characteristics that allow smallsats to be much more economical than their larger counterparts (See Chap. 13 and also Wertz and Larson [1996] and Wertz and Dawson [1996]). Smallsats typically are simpler, are built with much smaller teams, and in a shorter time than tra-

* For small satellites, this distinction by mass may or may not be useful. (There really is not much difference between a 1U and a 3U CubeSat.) For an alternative definition, see Swartout [2009].

ditional satellites, all of which contribute further to low cost. Intuition suggests that there is an irreducible "overhead" associated with building satellites, such that smaller satellites will become less efficient in terms of cost, but this does not appear to be the case. Figure 2-15 shows a verification plot for Version 7.4 of the *Small Satellite Cost Model* (SSCM), created by the Aerospace Corp. specifically for modeling the cost of small satellites, which always seem to be overestimated by the traditional large satellite cost models [Wertz and Larson, 1996]. The plot is actual vs. estimated cost only for the programs that make up the model, so by definition, the data will fit the model very well. What is interesting is the lower left hand corner of the plot in which the estimates from the model are all higher than the actual cost. At the very low cost end, even the SSCM overestimates satellite cost. The message here is that, in practice, there is something about very low-cost systems that makes them even lower cost than we would expect. It may be that it is the simpler design, the shorter schedule, or the smaller number of people, but the effect appears to be real from at least this limited set of data. Interestingly, SSCM Version 7.4 was created before the invention of CubeSats and the CubeSat cost estimates would seem to continue this trend, although no statistical analysis has been done to verify this.

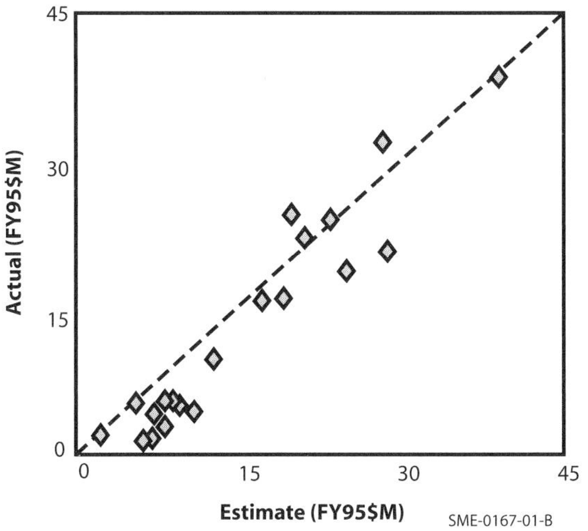

Fig. 2-15. Cost Estimates vs. Actual Cost for the Programs in the Aerospace Corporation Small Satellite Cost Model Database [Bearden, Boudreault, and Wertz,1996].

The future of smallsats and the smallsat community is uncertain. Smallsats will continue to be developed and flown and will be a significant fraction of the total satellite population. They will also become much more competent as both CubeSat technology and other elements of microminiaturization continue. What is less certain is whether they will continue to be used primarily for education and experimental purposes or whether they will play a much larger role in military, science, and applications programs. Smallsats themselves appear to be fully capable of taking on a much larger role and leading the way in driving down space system cost. However, for Smallsats to take on a true operational role, small, low-cost, launch-on-demand must become real.

There are a number of excellent books on Smallsats listed in the website bibliography. Ford [2010] provides effectively a handbook on how to build a communications satellite in your garage. Other standard and useful references are Sarsfield [1998], Fleeter [2000], and Wertz and Larson [1996], which includes a list of 90 representative smallsat programs over a 15-year period and detailed case studies of 10 of them.

2.1.9 Alt Space (Alternative Space)

The Alt Space (Alternative Space) community, or Spacers, is the community that has a long-term objective of fully utilizing space—i.e., colonizing and living on the Moon and planets, mining the solar system resources, and traveling to the stars.* They regard the current space program as simply the first step in a broad, long-term program of development and settlement in space. Many of the engineers, scientists, and program managers in the more traditional space program regard the Alt Space community as unrealistic dreamers that don't fully realize the cost or technical challenges associated with space exploration. On the other hand, the Alt Space community regards many of the more traditional communities as having too narrow a perspective to see the long-term potential and as being unwilling to develop the means to get there.

At the time of the Apollo 11 landing on the Moon, Wernher von Braun, the head of Marshall Space Flight Center that developed the Saturn V launch vehicle, described it as the most important event in history since fish came out of the sea onto the land [Mailer, 1970]. On the other hand, historian Gerard DeGroot [2006] described the Apollo program as "an expensive distraction of little scientific or cultural worth." These differing views of the significance of Apollo don't represent so much differing assessments of the Apollo mission, as they do differing views of the future. In the view of von Braun, people will, in the long term, leave Earth, settle the planets and moons of the Solar System, and create

* The *New-Space community* is a subset of the Alt Space community that is interested in the private spaceflight industry. To date, this has primarily involved the development of a form of space tourism involving suborbital flights using a rocket or rocket/plane combination to launch human passengers to an altitude of 100 km, often thought of as the "edge of space." This may serve to popularize space tourism, but in terms of energy required, and therefore the cost and complexity of accomplishing the mission, this is a far less difficult task than launching tourists into orbit, as has been done several times with visitors to the Space Station. The long-term NewSpace goals remain the same as the Alt Space community—to enable large numbers of people to go to orbit and visit the Moon and planets.

new civilizations away from Earth. In the view of DeGroot, people will always remain tied to the Earth and space will be used for the purpose of bringing back knowledge and possibly some materials for use on Earth, but not as a future home for mankind.

Fig. 2-16. Drawing of a Potential Human Mission to Mars. (Graphic courtesy of NASA)

A second objective of the Alt Space community is to overcome the limitations of life on Earth. The perception within this community is that the Earth is limited in its capacity to support continued human growth and development. In this view, there are serious threats to the continuation of modern civilization including ever more scarce resources, pollution, natural disasters, climate change, and nuclear or biological warfare. If civilization is to continue in spite of a major disaster or long-term slow degradation, then we need to develop a "home-away-from-home," much as the Europeans did in moving to North and South America. Therefore, they see space colonization and settlement as a means of potentially overcoming the physical limitations of sharing a planet that is rapidly becoming too small.

Although there may be great interest in the results of specific space missions, the Alt Space community as a whole is typically not as interested in the specific technical or scientific return from a particular mission as they are in whether it can further the long-term objective of space settlement. Some of the missions that would be seen as most furthering this objective are listed in Table 2-4. It is also important to note that there are probably far more people in the Alt Space community than in traditional space program development and they are vocal supporters of space exploration. While some space programs are privately funded, most space activity ultimately depends on spending public money for programs that are increasingly expensive. Therefore, the traditional programs in science, applications, and even military need the support and encouragement of the Alt Space community, just as the Alt Space community needs the technology developments that can only come about through real engineering, development, testing, and flying.

All of the missions listed in Table 2-4 are technically feasible, although the perception of the level of difficulty varies dramatically, depending on the point of view of those doing the evaluating. Similarly, the degree to which they will come about and in what time frame depends strongly on both the cost and perceived cost of the missions. A clear problem here is that using existing cost models for either human or unmanned spaceflight would indicate that any of these missions are in the 100's of billions of dollars or higher, and possibly much higher. However, current cost models were empirically developed based on entirely different missions with different rules, processes, requirements, and projected results.These traditional cost model estimates may be sufficiently far off so as to be effectively useless and may damage the prospects for advanced missions by giving the potentially false impression that the missions are too expensive to be economically justified. (See, for example, Wertz [1999] for a discussion of creating a 1,000-person Lunar colony for somewhat less than the cost of the ISS.) In the 1970's Gerard O'Neill had done extensive cost modeling for Space Settlements [O'Neill, 1974, 1975; O'Neill, et al., 1979], but the idea was largely killed when space cost modeling "experts" testified before Congress that his estimates were low by orders of magnitude, even though the professional cost models were based on data almost entirely unrelated to the Space Settlement process.

Fig. 2-17. O'Neill Space Colony. These space colonies were designed for the Earth/Moon L4 or L5 Lagrange points. (See Sec. 10.5.) (Graphic courtesy of NASA)

Because of its popular appeal, there are a great many books on the long-term exploration and settlement of space listed on the website bibliography. By far, the most technically detailed are the series of conference proceedings (9 volumes) on Space Settlements published by the Space Studies Institute founded by O'Neill. There are

Table 2-4. Representative Alt Space Missions. These are future missions that advance the prospects for the long term settlement and utilization of space. The fundamental requirement for nearly all of these missions is much lower cost launch to orbit.

Mission	Objective or Result
Satellite Solar Power	Reduce the reliance on fossil or nuclear fuels; "greener" energy.
He^3 Mining from the Lunar Regolith	Provide fuel for clean nuclear power that does not create long-term, toxic radioactive waste.
Space Tourism	Drives the economic engine of space development by significantly increasing the amount of money available for space.
Search for Extraterrestrial Life	If extraterrestrial life is found it could dramatically impact our perception of our place in the Universe and the motivation for space development, exploration, and settlement.
Human Mission to Mars	Advances popular interest in space exploration and settlement, particularly if any evidence of past life on Mars is found (Fig. 2-16).
Space Manufacturing	Provides processes and results not possible in a 1-g environment and serves as an economic driver for space development. (Pure chemicals, large crystals, ultrasound ball bearings, "foam steel").
Asteroid Mining	Provides iron and other resources that can be used without further damaging Earth's environment.
Lunar Colonization and Settlement	Provides for science, exploration, and development away from Earth and drives the economics of space exploration.
Space Settlements	This is settlement in colonies in space itself (typically at the Earth/Moon Lagrange Point), not on the Moon or planets; originally conceptualized by Gerard O'Neill; provides benefits similar to Lunar colonization and settlement, but with a 1-g or nearly 1-g environment (Fig. 2-17).
Settlement of Mars, Other Planets, and Moons	This is a long-term goal of Alt Space, but not necessarily regarded as realistic in the near-term.
Interstellar Travel	The ultimate goal of the Alt Space community. Not realistic in the near term.

also many books on the broad, long-term justification for space exploration, including, for example, those by Berinstein [2002], Burrows [2006], Hardersen [1997], Harrison [2001], White [1998], Zimmerman [2010], and Zubrin[1999].

2.2 Differences and Similarities Between Communities

As described in Chap. 1, the basic goal of space mission engineering is to design a space mission to meet a set of broad, often poorly defined objectives at minimum cost and risk. The purpose of introducing and discussing the various space communities is to allow the reader to do that job better—either by coming up with new and innovative solutions or designing a mission with better performance, lower cost, reduced risk or some combination of these. This comes about in 3 distinct ways:

1. By having a better understanding of the basic objectives of the particular community (or communities) that represents the customer or end user of your mission.
2. By creating opportunities for multiple communities to work together for a common goal or to benefit the broader space enterprise.
3. To potentially apply technologies, processes, and methods developed in one space community to the benefit of other space communities.

All of these are potentially applicable to almost any space mission.

First, we need to recognize and work with the basic goals and objectives of the community we are in and, similarly, to recognize the differing goals and objectives of other communities. Nearly all of the authors of this volume spend most of their career within one of these communities. Yet it is important that the process and procedures that they and others describe be applicable across a broad range of communities or that the differences be clearly explained and identified.

Second, we want to create the opportunity for different communities to work together on a common problem or issue. For example, the science and military communities have relatively very little in common and frequently look only inward, within their own group or organization, for processes and technology. But they have a common interest in developing large space optics with high resolution and working at multiple wavelengths. Development funds are extremely scarce for inherently expensive large space systems. In the past, having two groups work together was often the "kiss of death" because both groups would bring firm requirements that were either incompatible or would drive up the cost to the point where the solution was unaffordable. If we can recognize the objectives of the other community and try to search out the overlap, rather than the differences, there is room for real progress at much lower cost.

A very large aperture telescope in GEO has been a long-term goal of the military and intelligence community for decades, such that it can provide continuous optical surveillance of a battlefield or other region of interest. The science community would like a very large aperture telescope for looking at the universe. Both tend to work within their respective communities to develop a set of agreed-to requirements that are then chiseled in stone and can become forever immutable. (There is also a certain amount of "not invented here" and intellectual ownership of the solution that are often involved within each community when looking at solutions invented by a different community.) The Smallsat community, however, has learned the importance of, and processes for, trading on requirements so as to meet broad objectives at minimum cost and risk. If the differences can be set aside, such that the communities and organizations can work together, it may be possible to make a major breakthrough to the benefit of both military and civilian space. If the military and intelligence community can contribute a significant share of the funding, and the science community can contribute its knowledge of large space telescopes (and, importantly, of the potential problems and failure modes), a major new development could be possible. In addition, building 2 or 3 such telescopes can significantly drive down the recurring cost for each and potentially allow the creation of a small production line that both further reduces cost and allows us to maintain the skill base that created the system.

Our third approach is to apply the technologies, processes, and approaches from one community to the space missions of another. For example, battery technology is always a problem for LEO space missions because of the large number of charge/discharge cycles and the long duration of many of these space missions. Battery technology in the commercial electronics arena is advancing very rapidly due to the increasing need for longer life in nearly all cordless consumer electronics. In the far distant past, phones were used mostly for making phone calls. Today they are used for multiple applications and may be in nearly continuous use throughout the day and, therefore, in need of smaller, lighter weight, more efficient, and longer-lasting batteries. These batteries are now being used on CubeSats and Smallsats, where there is much less prohibition against using commercial electronics. As these batteries show their performance characteristics (and, potentially, failure modes) on orbit, they can become more widely adopted across the space enterprise.

Finally, it is important to note that any one person or organization can reasonably be a member of multiple space communities. It is possible to be a member of the military space community working on small science satellites and a strong supporter of Alt Space objectives. (After all, your "day job" may not reflect what you believe about the long-term future of mankind.) There are substantial advantages to this being the case. That person or organization that crosses boundaries can serve both to bring the various communities closer together and to recognize the potential of using the technologies, processes, and methods from one area to benefit another.

2.3 Changing Missions

None of the space mission communities is a static entity. In Sec. 2.1, we describe the likely future evolution of these communities and the principal drivers that will bring that about. Here we will summarize the changing missions across the whole space enterprise and how this is likely to affect individual communities.

In the near term, the most obvious change is the rapid and continuing advance of microelectronics. At the same time, a number of organizations are working on methods for radiation hardening electronics produced by ordinary production processes. As we have discussed, battery technology is also advancing very rapidly because of the push of consumer electronics. The net effect of all of these changes is to make Smallsat evolution extremely rapid in terms of increased capability in an ever smaller package. This at least suggests a significant change in nearly all missions. If capabilities are advancing rapidly and being tested on orbit in Smallsats, then it becomes difficult to justify creating spacecraft that last 15 years using technology that will become obsolete in a few years and may even be so by the time the system is launched. Thus, in at least some areas, there may be a change from long-term missions to much shorter ones in order to take advantage of advancing technology.

Related to the ever smaller electronics is the ever more powerful on-board processor and the push for increasing amounts of information and data, available instantly. The mythical FireSat mission was developed some 20 years ago for the *Space Mission Analysis and Design* book [Wertz and Larson, 1991]. In FireSat, IR images of forested regions were sent to the ground for analysis, fires were identified, and maps or other data were then sent to the firefighter in the field. Today it may make more sense to have a fire detection algorithm on board the spacecraft, complete with a filter to eliminate large barbecues and 4th of July celebrations, and then simply send the coordinates and technical details of the fire to the firefighter in the field, so that they are displayed in his or her truck on a detailed map of the region provided by any of the GPS navigation map providers. In a sense, this isn't a change in mission objectives, only a change in methods of implementation. But, in a broader sense, it is a change in objectives to focus more on information and less on data.

As we have discussed, the most substantial change in space missions will come about if there is a reduction in launch cost for any reason by a factor of 2 to 10. This changes the list of possible missions that are economically feasible and, depending on the result, may bring about a major increase in the number of missions flown which will further reduce costs. This change would affect the entire space enterprise and even begin to open the possibility for more expanded space exploration in some of the Alt Space missions described in Sec. 2.1.9.

References

For annotated bibliography of space mission communities, see the book website.

Bearden, David, R. Boudreault, and J. R. Wertz. 1996. *Reducing Space Mission Cost*. El Segundo, CA: Microcosm Press.

Berinstein, Paula. 2002. *Making Space Happen: Private Space Ventures and the Visionaries Behind Them.* Medford, NJ: Plexus.

Brown, Charles D. 1998. *Spacecraft Mission Design. 2nd ed.* with software disk. Reston, VA: AIAA.

Burrows, William E. 2006. *The Survival Imperative: Using Space to Protect Earth.* New York: Forge.

Chafer, Charles M., and Cynthia S. Price. 2002. "Burial." *Macmillan Reference USA Science Library: Space Sciences.* Macmillan Reference USA.

Chun, Clayton K. S. and Chris Taylor. 2006. *Defending Space: US Anti-Satellite Warfare and Space Weaponry*. New York: Osprey Publishing, Ltd.

Churchill, Susanne E. 1997. *Fundamentals of Space Life Sciences.* Malabar, FL: Krieger Publishing.

Clement, Gilles. 2005. *Fundamentals of Space Medicine.* El Segundo, CA: Microcosm Press and Springer.

Clement, Gilles and Klaus Slenzka. 2006. *Fundamentals of Space Biology: Research on Cells, Animals, and Plants in Space.* El Segundo, CA: Microcosm Press and Springer.

Conway, Eric D. 1997. *An Introduction to Satellite Image Interpretation.* Baltimore, MD: Johns Hopkins University Press.

Cruise, A. M., J. A. Bowles, T. J. Patrick, and C. V. Goodall. 2006. *Principles of Space Instrument Design.* Cambridge, UK: Cambridge University Press.

DeGroot, Gerard J. 2006. *Dark Side of the Moon*. New York: New York University Press.

Eckart, Peter. 1996. *Spaceflight Life Support and Biospherics.* Torrance, CA: Microcosm Press and Springer.

Eckart, Peter. 2006. *The Lunar Base Handbook. 2nd ed.* Boston, MA: The McGraw-Hill Companies.

Elachi, Charles and Jakob van Zyl. 2006. *Introduction to the Physics and Techniques of Remote Sensing.* Hoboken, NJ: John Wiley and Sons

Elbert, B. R. 1990. *International Telecommunication Management.* Norwood, MA: Artech House.

Elbert, B. R. 1992. *Networking Strategies for Information Technology.* Norwood, MA: Artech House.

Elbert, B. R. 2003. *The Satellite Communication Applications Handbook.* Norwood, MA: Artech House.

Elbert, B. R. 2008. *Introduction to Satellite Communication. 3rd ed.* Norwood, MA: Artech House.

Fleeter, Rick. 2000. *The Logic of Microspace*. El Segundo, CA: Microcosm Press and Springer.

Ford, Steve. 2010. *The Radio Amateur's Satellite Handbook*. Newington, CT: American Radio Relay League.

Glaser, P. E., F. P. Davidson, and K. I. Csigi. 1998. *Solar Power Satellites: A Space Energy System for Earth.* Chichester, UK: John Wiley and Sons.

Hardersen, Paul S. 1997. *The Case for Space: Who Benefits from Explorations of the Last Frontier?* Shrewsbury, MA: ATL Press.

Harrison, Albert A. 2001. *Spacefaring: The Human Dimension.* Berkeley, CA: University of California Press.

Haskell, G. and M. J. Rycroft. 1998. *New Space Markets.* Dordrecht, The Netherlands: Kluwer Academic Publishers.

Hujsak, Edward. 1994. *The Future of U.S. Rocketry.* La Jolla, CA: Mina-Helwig.

Isakowitz, Steven J., Joshua B. Hopkins, and Joseph P. Hopkins Jr. 2004. *International Reference Guide to Space Launch Systems.* Reston, VA: AIAA.

Johnson, S. B. 2002. *The Secret of Apollo: Systems Management in American and European Space Programs.* Baltimore, MD: Johns Hopkins University Press.

Kanas, Nick and Dietrich Manzey. 2003. *Space Psychology and Psychiatry.* El Segundo, CA: Microcosm Press and Springer.

Kemble, Stephen. 2006. *Interplanetary Mission Analysis and Design.* Chichester, UK: Praxis and Springer.

Klein, John J. 2006. *Space Warfare: Strategy, Principles, and Policy*. New York: Routledge.

Koelle, Dietrich E. 2010. *Handbook of Cost Engineering for Space Transportation Systems (Rev. 3) with Transcost 8.0.* Ottobrunn, Germany: TransCostSystems.

Lacomme, P., J. P. Hardange, J. C. Marchais and E. Normant. 2001. *Air and Spaceborne Radar Systems.* Norwich, NY: William Andrew.

Lambeth, Benjamin S. 2003. *Mastering the Ultimate High Ground: Next Steps in the Military Uses of Space*. Santa Monica, CA: RAND.

Larson, Wiley J. and Linda K. Pranke. 1999. *Human Spaceflight: Mission Analysis and Design.* New York: The McGraw-Hill Companies.

Lillesand, Thomas M., Ralph W. Kiefer, and Jonathan W. Chipman. 2008. *Remote Sensing and Image Interpretation. 6th ed.* Hoboken, NJ: John Wiley and Sons.

London, John R. 1994. *LEO on the Cheap: Methods for Achieving Drastic Reductions in Space Launch Costs*. Maxwell AFB, AL: Air University Press.

Mailer, Norman. 1970. *Of a Fire on the Moon.* Boston, MA: Little, Brown and Co.

Mallove, Eugene F. and Gregory L. Matloff. 1989. *The Starflight Handbook: a Pioneer's Guide to Interstellar Travel.* Hoboken, NJ: John Wiley and Sons.

Mather, John C. and John Boslough. 1996. *The Very First Light: the True inside Story of the Scientific Journey Back to the Dawn of the Universe.* New York: Basic Books.

Olsen, R. C. 2007. *Remote Sensing from Air and Space.* Bellingham, WA: SPIE.

O'Neill, Gerard K. 1974. "The Colonization of Space." *Physics Today,* vol. 27, no. 9. Sept. pp. 32–40.

O'Neill, G. K. 1975. "Space Colonies and Energy Supply to the Earth." *Science,* vol. 190. Dec. 5. pp. 943–947.

O'Neill, G. K., J. Billingham, W. Gilbreath, and B. O'Leary. 1979. "Space Resource and Space Settlements." NASA SP-428. Washington, DC.

Parkinson, Bradford W. and James J. Spilker Jr. 1996. *The Global Positioning System: Theory and Applications.* Washington, DC: AIAA

Peeters, Walter A. R. 2000. *Space Marketing: A European Perspective*. Dordrecht, The Netherlands: Kluwer Academic Publishers and Microcosm Press.

Richelson, Jeffrey T. 2001. *America's Space Sentinels: DSP Satellites and National Security*. Lawrence, KS: University Press of Kansas.

Sarsfield, L. P. 1998. *The Cosmos on a Shoestring*. Santa Monica, CA: RAND.

Schowengerdt, Robert A. 2007. *Remote Sensing, Models, and Methods for Image Processing. 3rd ed.* Burlington, MA: Academic Press.

Sutton, George P. and Oscar Biblarz. 2010. *Rocket Propulsion Elements. 8th ed.* Hoboken, NJ: John Wiley and Sons.

Swartwout, M. A. 2009. "The First One Hundred University-Class Spacecraft, 1981–2008." *IEEE Aerospace and Electronic Systems Magazine,* vol 24, no 3.

Wertz, J. R. 1999. "Architecture for Developing an Economically Viable International, Large-Scale Lunar Colony." IAF Specialists Symposium on Novel Concepts for Smaller, Faster, Better Space Missions. Redondo Beach, CA. Apr. 19–21.

Wertz, J. R. 2000. "Economic Model of Reusable vs. Expendable Launch Vehicles." IAF Congress. Rio de Janeiro. Oct. 2–6.

Wertz, J. R. 2004. "Reusability: The Death Knell of Low-Cost, Responsive Access to Space?" *Space News.* Mar. 22. p. 11.

Wertz, J. R. 2009. *Orbit & Constellation Design and Management.* Hawthorne, CA: Microcosm Press and Springer.

Wertz, J. R. and Simon Dawson. 1996. "What's the Price of Low Cost?" 10th Annual AIAA/USU Conference on Small Satellites. Logan, UT. Sept.

Wertz, J. R. and Wiley J. Larson. 1996. *Reducing Space Mission Cost.* El Segundo, CA: Microcosm Press and Springer.

Wertz, J. R. and Wiley J. Larson. 1991. *Space Mission Analysis and Design. 1st ed.* Dordrecht, The Netherlands: Kluwer Academic Publishers and Microcosm Press.

Wertz, J. R., R. E. Van Allen, and T. Barcley. 2010. "NanoEye—Military Relevant Surveillance for Less Than $5 Million Total Recurring Mission Cost." 8th Responsive Space Conference. Los Angeles, CA. Mar. 8–11.

White, Frank. 1998. *The Overview Effect: Space Exploration and Human Evolution.* Reston, VA: AIAA.

Young, Anthony. 2007. *Lunar and Planetary Rovers: the Wheels of Apollo and the Quest for Mars.* Berlin, Germany: Springer.

Zimmerman, Robert. 2010. *The Universe in a Mirror: the Saga of the Hubble Telescope and the Visionaries Who Built It.* Princeton, NJ: Princeton University Press.

Zubrin, Robert. 1999. *Entering Space: Creating a Spacefaring Civilization.* New York: Putnam.

3 Space Mission Engineering

James R. Wertz, *Microcosm, Inc./USC*

As discussed in Chap. 1,

> ***Space Mission Engineering* is the refinement of requirements and definition of mission parameters to meet the broad objectives of a space mission in a timely manner at minimum cost and risk.**

It begins with one or more broad objectives and constraints and then proceeds to define a space system that will meet them within an appropriate timeframe at the lowest possible cost and risk. Broad objectives and constraints are the key to this process. Procurement plans for space systems too often substitute detailed numerical requirements for broad mission objectives. To get the most performance for the money spent, we must require of the system only what it can reasonably achieve. Thus, while our overall objectives to communicate, navigate, or observe will generally remain the same, we will achieve these objectives differently as technology and our understanding of the process and problem evolve. This chapter summarizes, and the book as a whole details, this process of defining and refining both what is to be done and what mission concept will do it at the lowest cost and risk.

We have introduced the term "mission engineering" to distinguish it from *systems engineering*, which is concerned primarily with the formal requirements definition process and how to validate that all of the requirements will, in fact, be met. *Mission engineering* is a broader process and is concerned with whether the needs of the end user are satisfied. As we discussed in Sec. 2.1.4, a historical example of this distinction is the Iridium communications constellation. From a technical perspective, Iridium worked very well. The launch process had no failures and all of the satellites worked well on orbit. The only real problem was that the system lost money and Iridium itself declared bankruptcy in 1999. The backers of Iridium lost $5.5B. In my view, this is a mission failure. It didn't meet the fundamental objective of a commercial system—to make money for the people and organizations that paid for it. In a sense it is similar to a scientific satellite that works perfectly but fails to return data to the scientist, or a military satellite that is technically perfect, but is launched after the war is over. They haven't met the very fundamental objectives of the people that created them—to make money, to advance our knowledge of the Universe, or to save lives or otherwise impact the outcome of a war or battle. These are the things that a space mission must do to be useful, irrespective of whether it meets all of the technical requirements placed on it. It is the goal of space mission engineering to see that this "usefulness" criteria is met, as rapidly and at as low a cost as possible.

There are now a number of references available on the mission design process and the definition of mission objectives. Johnson [2002] does an excellent job of describing this process for Apollo—the largest space program ever undertaken. Maier and Rechtin [2009], Chesley, et al. [2008], and Larson, et al. [2009] describe the process of building large, formal space systems, largely for DoD. Shishko [2010] provides an overview from the NASA perspective. Ford [2010], Fleeter [2000], and Wertz and Larson [1996] discuss this process from the perspective of very low-cost missions, smallsats, and methods for dramatically reducing mission cost, respectively. Sandau [2006] and Sarsfield [1998] look specifically at low-cost Earth observation and science missions. Boden, Larson, and Squib [2006] discuss the mission engineering process specifically for mission operations. Finally, Kay [1995] examines the fundamental difficulty of doing technical trades within a democratic political environment. Chap. 13 describes the mission engineering process specifically oriented toward reducing mission cost.

3.1 The Space Mission Engineering Process

Table 3-1 summarizes our approach to the space mission engineering process. As discussed in Chap. 2, space missions range widely from communications, to planetary exploration, to proposals for space manufacturing, to burial in space. No single process can fully cover all contingencies, but the method in Table 3-1

Table 3-1. The Space Mission Engineering Process. This table is relevant for a *need-based mission*, i.e., one that is intended to fulfill a specific (though possibly not well-defined) set of mission needs, and is the most common type of space mission. The alternative is a *capability-driven system*, discussed in Sec. 3.1.2.

Typical Flow	Step	Where Discussed
	Define Objectives and Constraints	
	1. Define the Broad (Qualitative) Objectives and Constraints	Sec. 3.3
	2. Define the Principal Players	Sec. 3.4
	3. Define the Program Timescale	Sec. 3.4
	4. Estimate the Quantitative Needs, Requirements, and Constraints	Sec. 3.5
	Define Alternative Mission Concepts or Designs	
	5. Define Alternative Mission Architectures	Sec. 4.1
	6. Define Alternative Mission Concepts	Secs. 4.2, 4.3
	7. Define the Likely System Drivers and Key Requirements	Sec. 4.4
	Evaluate the Alternative Mission Concepts	
	8. Conduct Performance Assessments and System Trades	Sec. 5.3
	9. Evaluate Mission Utility	Sec. 5.4
	10. Define the Baseline Mission Concept and Architecture	Sec. 5.5
	11. Revise the Quantitative Requirements and Constraints	Sec. 5.5
	12. Iterate and Explore Other Alternatives	Sec. 5.5
	Define and Allocate System Requirements	
	13. Define System Requirements	Sec. 6.1
	14. Allocate the Requirements to System Elements	Sec. 6.2

summarizes a practical approach evolved over the first 50 years of space exploration.

The process we have defined here is based broadly on the space mission analysis and design process defined more than 20 years ago by Wertz and Larson [1991, 1999]. However, it has evolved in significant ways by asking us to identify the principal players in the space mission and their goals and objectives and the intended program timescale. A few other changes have been made as well to clarify how to go about getting to the mission concept that we want to achieve. In the end, it isn't so much the specific steps that matter, so much as having a process that we have carefully thought through to get us to a design concept that achieves our goal of meeting the end-users' objectives in a timely manner at minimum cost and risk.

Space is expensive. Cost is a fundamental limitation to nearly all space missions and is becoming more so. Consequently, Table 3-1 and subsequent ones reflect the assessment of each author on how things traditionally have been done **and** how they should be done differently, both to lower cost and to achieve the greatest return from the space investment.

Space mission engineering is an inherently iterative process, gradually refining both the requirements and methods of achieving them. Thus, we must repeat the broad process defined in Table 3-1 many times for each mission. The first several iterations may take only a day, but more detailed assessments will take far longer.

Successive iterations through Table 3-1 will usually lead to a more detailed, better-defined mission concept. In defining and refining the approach, there is strong pressure to proceed to ever greater detail, and never revise a decision once it has been made. But we must still return regularly to the broad mission objectives and search for ways to achieve them at a lower cost. Methods may change as a result of evolving technology, a new understanding of the problem, or simply fresh ideas and approaches as more individuals become involved.

Finally, we must document the results of this iterative process. If we wish to go back and reexamine decisions as new data becomes available, we must clearly understand and convey to others the reasons for each decision. We need this documentation for decisions based on detailed technical analyses, and, equally important, for those based on simplicity, ease of assessment, or political considerations.

3.1.1 The Need-Driven Process

Table 3-1 illustrates the process for a *need-based mission*, i.e., one in which we are trying to fulfill a specific set of mission objectives, such as identify and monitor forest fires, provide better communications to the warfighter, explore the Universe in the infrared region of the spectrum, or make money by providing direct broadcast of worldwide sporting events. (The alternative type of capability-based mission is discussed in Sec. 3.1.2.) To illustrate the broad process of Table 3-1, we will go through each of the top-level steps and indicate the type of information that needs to be developed:

In **Step 1**, we define what the mission needs to achieve. What are our qualitative goals, and why? This information should come largely from a mission statement of what the mission is attempting to achieve. (See Sec. 3.2.) We need to return to these broad goals over and over to verify whether we are achieving what we set out to do and whether we could do it better or at lower cost.

Step 2 identifies the principal players (often called *stakeholders*) and the space community that they are a part of. Is this a military mission intended to provide information to the warfighter in battle and funded by Congress? Is it the sports broadcasting mission intended to make money for the organizations or people that funded it? Notice that the end user and the people that have put up the money are typically not the same group and, in the end, it would be best to have both groups satisfied with the end results.

Step 3 defines the timeline over which the program needs to be executed to be useful. There is very little utility to the warfighter if the space system works exceptionally well, but isn't launched until after the war is over. If our sports broadcasting network has lined up 2 million customers and then there is a 3-year delay in the program, it is likely that most of those customers will have found other solutions and won't be there when the space system is finally launched.

Step 4 is significantly different from those above. It **quantifies** how well we wish to achieve the broad objectives, given our needs, applicable technology, who the users are, and cost and schedule constraints. These quantitative requirements should be subject to trade as we go along. A major error in many space-system procurements is to set requirements in concrete at a relatively early stage. For example, our sports broadcasting network might have set an initial goal of being able to broadcast 100 different sports channels, because of the marketing appeal that this would have. But it may turn out that this would require a larger spacecraft, or worse, a larger launch vehicle, than anyone currently has, and, therefore, may take far more time and money than anyone had initially planned for. It may be a much better choice to have 70 sports channels at low cost in the near future, than 100 sports channels at many times the cost and much further out in time. Space mission engineering provides the quantitative data needed to support such decisions.

Step 5 defines alternate combinations of mission elements or the *space mission architecture* to meet the mission objectives and requirements. We do this by looking at the individual mission elements, defined in Sec. 4.1, such as the payload that will do the work or the orbit that the spacecraft is in, and consider the principal alternatives for each of them that would best meet mission objectives.

In addition to identifying all of the pieces, we need to understand how they all work together to meet the needs of the end user. **Step 6** begins this process by developing alternative mission concepts. A *mission concept* or *concept of operations* is a broad statement of how the mission will work in practice. How do the various sporting events get broadcast and delivered to the satellite so they can be sent down to the sports fan sitting in her living room? Typically, the most effective mission concepts are ones that are totally transparent to the end user. Neither the warfighter getting shot at nor the sports fan in front of her TV knows or cares very much about space systems and typically don't want to. There is a longstanding joke in the space community that the warfighter on the ground will say that they don't need any space systems. All they need is their rifle, their communications gear, and their GPS. This is a good result. Neither the warfighter on the ground nor the driver in their car trying to figure out which way to turn needs to know anything at all about that remarkable array of atomic clocks and software at half-geosynchronous altitude, called the Global Positioning System, that can tell you where you are anywhere on the surface of the Earth to within a few meters. This indicates a truly successful mission concept that has been well executed.

In any real system, many things influence overall cost, performance, or the design of detailed components. However, these are influenced mainly by a relatively small number of key parameters or components, called *drivers*. Thus, there may be *cost*, *performance*, or *system drivers* which affect the design of the overall space system. In **Step 7**, we identify the principal cost and performance drivers for each alternative mission concept. Similarly, there are *critical requirements* that are those that have the greatest impact on cost, risk, and schedule. For most space missions, system drivers include the number of satellites, altitude, power, and instrument size and weight; critical requirements usually include lifetime, availability, coverage, and resolution or signal strength. (Section 4.4 gives a more detailed list of the most common system drivers and critical requirements.) By explicitly identifying the system drivers and the critical requirements, we can concentrate our effort on parameters having the most impact on the design and therefore on the cost and performance of the space mission. This improves our chances of getting the best possible design within the available budget. As discussed in Sec. 4.4, the system drivers and critical requirements are likely to be different for different mission concepts. What is hard in one approach to achieving our objectives may be simple in another approach and vice versa.

Step 8, conducting *performance assessments* and *system trades*, is typically the most involved step in mission design because it defines in detail what the system is and does. Here we determine the power, weight, and pointing budgets* and decide what to process on the ground or in space. Characterizing the mission and trading among alternatives is often the most costly step because it requires the expertise of many people. Developing detail is always comforting in managing any design process but, as noted earlier, we must take care not to overdo details while characterizing the mission. Achieving the mission objectives and meeting the needs of the end user must remain our primary focus.

---

* A *budget* is a numerical list of the components of any overall system parameter. Thus, the total spacecraft *mass budget* would consist of the masses assigned to the payload instruments, the various subsystems, the propellant required, and typically some margin for growth.

The above issues form the basis of *mission utility analysis*, **Step 9**, in which we quantify how well we are meeting both the broad objectives and the needs of the end user as a function of either cost or key system-design choices. We would like to provide the decision maker a single chart of how well the needs of the end user are satisfied vs. cost. More typically, we must settle for something less ideal, such as the number of hours per day that our hypothetical sports fan is expected to watch our network. Only the user or developer of the system can ultimately determine the goodness of these critical performance measures, called *Measures of Effectiveness* (MoEs) or *Figures of Merit* (FoMs). Consequently, mission definition must be, to some degree, a joint process between those who understand the mission engineering process and those who eventually must use the system or justify its cost.

Having evaluated alternative designs and done a preliminary assessment of mission utility, we select one or more baseline system designs in **Step 10**. A *baseline design* is a single consistent definition of the system that meets most or all of the mission objectives. A *consistent system definition* is a single set of values for all of the system parameters which are consistent with each other—e.g., number of channels and coverage area which correspond to the assigned altitude, antenna size, power, and resulting spacecraft weight. In actually designing a space system, many parameters are being defined and changed simultaneously. The baseline provides a temporary milestone against which to measure progress. It also allows us to limit the number of options which must be evaluated. Rather than looking at all possible combinations of altitude, antenna size, power, and spacecraft mass (a nearly impossible task), it is much more feasible to look at the impact of varying each of these individually relative to one or two baseline designs. As the system design matures, the baseline becomes more firm, and eventually becomes the system design. However, we should always remember that the baseline is only a starting point for the iterative trade process and should **not** be regarded as an ironclad definition of mission parameters.

Having determined the critical requirements and their impact on the mission design and mission utility, **Step 11** is to revise the system requirements and constraints consistent with what we have learned. We need to find the requirements that reflect what we want to achieve (our mission objectives) and what can be achieved with the tools, techniques, and hardware available to us. As a final step in concept exploration, **Step 12** is to go back and explore other alternatives and iterate on the design. As we will see in Sec. 3.1.3, the result we are looking for is a balance between what we would like to have and what we can achieve in a timely manner within a budget and level of risk we are willing to accept. When we start out, we don't know what this will be. This is the reason for exploring alternatives and looking for options. Is there another approach that achieves our objectives better or at lower cost? Or if we change the focus of our objectives a bit, can we get there at lower cost and less risk? For our sports network, should we consider two satellites of 50 or 35 channels each? Or should we change our objectives a bit to carry not only live sporting events, but also sports highlight shows and a sports-oriented shopping channel?

The first 12 steps are what are called *concept exploration*—looking at alternative requirements, constrains, and system options. Because builders of a space system typically work from specific requirements, we must translate the now better-defined objectives, constraints, and requirements into well-defined system requirements in **Step 13**. This is where the more traditional process of systems engineering begins. Finally, in **Step 14**, we *flow down* or allocate these numerical requirements to the components of the overall space mission in the same way that a budget allocates weight and power to the spacecraft's components. This will turn into a detailed list of requirements and, ultimately, into a space mission on orbit. The degree to which this meets our new set of mission objectives is a measure of how well we have done the mission engineering. Like GPS, we would typically like the end user to not know or care about space mission engineering or space at all. Success isn't measured by how well we have followed the steps outlined either here or in Chap. 1, but in whether the end user and the customer that put up all of the money to get there are fully satisfied by the result.

3.1.2 The Capability-Driven Process

Most missions follow the process outlined in the preceding section, i.e., a mission need is defined and then we start out to design a space mission that can meet that need at minimum cost and risk. However, most major breakthroughs in doing things better, faster, or cheaper come not from defining needs and how to fill them, but rather by identifying a new capability, or perhaps a new way to use an existing capability, and then finding a space mission that could use that capability. Some of the obvious potential breakthroughs could include, for example, a major reduction in launch cost or more computer capability or a new propulsion system that could provide far higher delta V. Indeed, much of space research is spent trying to find these breakthroughs, what are often called *game-changing technologies* or *disruptive technologies.*

An example of this type of game-changing technology is nuclear electric propulsion, proposed as a potential NASA program which has since been cancelled as being too expensive. This would have used nuclear power, essentially similar to that which has been safely used in submarines for decades, in space to provide 50 kW to 100 kW of power for large spacecraft for both electric propulsion and to provide high power for other mission aspects. This would most likely make no difference to some space missions, such as smallsats. However, there are many missions for which it could make a dramatic difference. Some examples of the things that might be enabled include:

- Synthetic aperture radar missions with continuous imaging that can see through clouds and at night to provide continuous surveillance, possibly from GEO.
- High delta V missions that could put spacecraft in orbit around planets and asteroids with high data rate, high-resolution images coming back from distant parts of the solar system.
- Reducing the round trip time to Mars from roughly 2.7 years to about 5 months due to cutting out one synodic period and, therefore, enabling near-term human missions to Mars.
- Allowing very high power transmissions from GEO such that our sports network defined in the previous section becomes a thousand channels of high-definition sports programs (which may or may not be a good thing, depending, perhaps, on whether your goal is to get a sports fanatic to get off the couch and mow the lawn).

While most breakthroughs in technology or ways of applying existing technology won't have effects that are this large, they may still have a major impact on what missions are possible and what level of mission performance can be achieved at what cost. This in turn, fundamentally changes how we go about defining a space mission. The major change is that we start out differently and ask ourselves, what would this new process or technology enable? If we had nearly unlimited power, or far more computing, or the ability to repair spacecraft at low cost, what would this let us do that we can't do today, either because it is impractical or far too expensive?

Step 2 in the capabilities-based process is the same as before, only asked for a different reason. Now we are looking for the principal players in order to explain the new technology to them and how it can enable missions that weren't previously possible or weren't economical to undertake. This is where things often get difficult. Previously, we had a customer or end user that wanted an answer and we went about finding the best possible answer. Now we have an answer and are looking for someone who wants to ask the question for which we have the answer and, more importantly, pay for the answer that we've found. This means we are likely to be looking for someone willing to pay for what may be a very expensive space mission and, therefore, we will probably need to be very convincing. For this reason, capability-driven missions are often very difficult to make happen. Nonetheless, they are also the real source of major breakthroughs.

Most of the remainder of the mission engineering process proceeds as defined in Table 3-1, with the caveat that we continually go back and review both the needs of the end user and the capabilities that are available. As with the need-driven process, the purpose is not to make the most use possible of whatever new capability or process we have found, as it is to use the new capability to allow us to meet a set of mission objectives and end-user needs better, more quickly, or at lower cost and risk.

3.1.3 Finding the Right Balance

A key issue in mission engineering is iterating the design a number of times to try to get to a system that does the job well. We want to convince ourselves that we have looked at the reasonable alternatives and found the solution that best meets the needs of the customer and the end user.

If we start with objectives, we must look at what capabilities are available and cost effective. If we start with a capability, we must look closely at the mission needs that it can fulfill and who the players are who could make use of that capability at the likely price. Ultimately, every practical mission must balance needs and capability. We are trying to meet our mission objectives by balancing needs and capabilities.

Going through the space mission engineering process, there are 3 possible adverse outcomes:

- We simply can't do what is needed (e.g., we don't have a launch vehicle with sufficient volume to launch our payload)
- We can do something but it doesn't have sufficient utility to the customer (e.g., the payload that we can build doesn't have enough resolution to be helpful to the problem we're trying to solve)
- We can do it and it's useful, but it isn't worth the cost or risk or can't be done in time (by the time we get it built, the comet we're trying to explore will have swung past the Sun and be on its way back to the Oort Cloud)

In order to proceed, the mission must be achievable and useful, but must also be worth the cost to whoever is putting up the money to do it.

If the space mission engineering process is successful, we will have defined a space mission that is sufficiently low-cost, low-risk, and near-term, with sufficient performance that the customer is willing and anxious to proceed to build the system. If we have done it correctly, we will be able to accomplish the mission within the time and cost that we have estimated (or at least reasonably close) and will be able to meet the ultimate objectives of the customer. We don't need more Iridiums. It is not sufficient that the system work—it has to work well enough to meet, or preferably exceed, the expectations of the customer and the end user, including cost and timeliness.

At its best, space mission engineering is a lot like determining what car to buy for an individual. We have some characteristics that we need, such as safety, reliability, and enough space for the people we expect to be riding in it. We also have a limited budget and need something that falls within, or reasonably close, to that budget. There are many different cars available in the marketplace, new ones with new features and capabilities are coming out all the time, and we can add features to almost any car we buy. We're looking for the right balance between what we want and what we can reasonably afford, so that we're happy with the new car (or space mission) that we buy for many years to come.

3.2 FireSat II and the Supplemental Communications System (SCS)

In 1990, the concept of a hypothetical space mission called FireSat was introduced to illustrate the process of space mission design [Wertz and Larson, 1991]. Since then, FireSat has become a standard example mission throughout the astronautics community, but has never been funded and built, although space assets have certainly been used to photograph and monitor forest fires. This is probably related, at least in part, to the fact that the estimated cost of FireSat was \$704M (inflated to FY10\$) as a traditional pair of spacecraft and \$85M as two smallsats. It simply wasn't worth that much money in order to achieve a relatively modest level of mission utility. Chapter 1 discusses how this is the case for many missions—they cost too much and take too long for what they are able to achieve. However, in the 20 years since FireSat was first proposed, substantial advances have been made in the capability of small satellites and an entirely new vocabulary has been created with minisats, microsats, nanosats, and picosats. (See Sec. 2.1.8.)

FIRESAT II
MISSION STATEMENT

Because forest fires pose an ever-increasing threat to lives and property, have a significant impact on recreation and commerce, and also have an even higher public visibility (largely because of the ability to transmit television images from nearly anywhere in real time), the United States needs a more effective system to identify and monitor them. In addition, it would be desirable (but not required) to monitor forest fires for other nations; collect statistical data on fire outbreaks, spread, speed, and duration; and provide other forest management data. This must be done at low cost to make the system affordable to the Forest Service and not give the perception of wasting money that could be better spent on fire-fighting equipment or personnel.

Ultimately, the Forest Service's fire-monitoring office, fire management officers in the field, and individual firefighters and rangers fighting the fire will use the data. Data flow and formats must meet the needs of all of the groups without specialized training and must allow them to respond promptly and efficiently to changing conditions.

Fig. 3-1. Mission Statement for the Hypothetical FireSat II Mission. FireSat II is used as one of two primary examples throughout this book.

Can these very small satellites, or other advances, such as improved on-board computing, finally make FireSat a practical system? To find out, we will introduce a new hypothetical mission, called *FireSat II,* for this volume. FireSat II will have broadly the same objectives as the original FireSat mission, i.e., to detect and monitor forest fires in the United States and Canada, but with an additional objective of being very low cost. This reflects the idea that the original FireSat concept was a buildable spacecraft, but not a practical one that achieved what the end user needed at an acceptable cost and risk. We will use FireSat II as one of two example missions throughout the book and will look specifically at ways to implement the mission at very low cost in Chap. 13.

SUPPLEMENTAL COMMUNICATIONS SYSTEM (SCS)
MISSION STATEMENT

There is ever-increasing need for high-quality, real-time global communications to meet military needs to save lives, bring to bear the necessary resources, and avoid collateral damage. Large military communications systems currently exist, but these are often overloaded in a time of conflict and may not be available to an individual or small unit in a remote location. A secondary mission of equal importance is to aid in natural disaster relief, particularly in remote areas with severe damage where traditional communications systems may be destroyed, unavailable, or overloaded.

The end user for SCS is an individual or small group in a remote location with very limited resources. The user needs two-way, real-time communications with either a command post broadly in the same vicinity, or with planners and rescuers in CONUS or other locations scattered around the world. The communications content can range from brief text messages, to voice communications, to photos taken, for example, from a cell phone.

Fig. 3-2. Mission Statement for SCS. SCS will also be used as a principal example throughout the book.

As a second example, we will use a small constellation, the *Supplemental Communications System* (SCS), that is intended to provide better communications to military or disaster relief personnel that are in remote areas where communications are either disrupted or didn't exist in the first place. While we will use many examples from real space missions for specific topics, we will use these two hypothetical missions throughout the book to follow the whole space mission engineering process. Our goal is to start with a "blank sheet of paper" (or, in this case, with a small text box in Fig. 3-1 for FireSat II and Fig. 3-2 for SCS), and define a space mission that meets this set of broad, not too well defined, mission objectives in a timely manner at minimum cost and risk.

The *mission statements* shown in the two figures define what is needed to be useful. They don't describe the orbit, or the required bandwidth, or the resolution that must be achieved, or the size of the spacecraft, or the cost, or timeframe. All of these are to be determined by the space mission engineering process. In a sense the process is simple. We do what is in the figure quickly, cheaply, and at low risk.

We want to stress that the parameters developed throughout the book are by no means the only possible set for FireSat II or SCS, nor are they necessarily the best. To show how solutions may vary, we will present alternatives along the way. Our example system simply illustrates the iterative process of space mission engineering. Different assumptions, requirements, or proposed solutions may lead to dramatically different results.

For both missions, we know that the system is technically feasible because they can be accomplished by existing, but relatively expensive, systems. What we don't know is whether they can be done sufficiently near term and at low enough cost and risk to be of interest to our potential customer. Therefore, our goal should not be a stringent set of requirements, but rather a strong system solution that can do the job economically and quickly such that the customer can gain benefit from the mission. Cost and timeline will be two key characteristics that determine whether our missions succeed or fail.

3.3 Mission Objectives and Constraints (Step 1)

The first step in the space mission engineering process is to define the *mission objectives*: the broad goals that the system must achieve to be productive. Figure 3-3 shows sample objectives for the FireSat II mission and Fig. 3-4 for SCS. We draw these qualitative mission objectives largely from the mission statements in Figs. 3-1 and 3-2. In contrast, the *mission requirements* and *constraints,* discussed in Sec. 3.5, are quantitative expressions of how well we achieve our objectives—balancing what we want against what the budget will allow. Thus, whereas we are likely to modify objectives only slightly or not at all during concept exploration, we will trade on requirements and revise our constraints many times throughout the process. For FireSat II to be FireSat II, it must detect, identify, monitor, and report forest fires. That is what the mission is about. How accurately or how often it does that depends on what is achievable at what cost. As we trade and design elements of the system during concept exploration, we must ensure that the system meets its fundamental objective.

Ordinarily, space missions have multiple objectives. Some are *secondary objectives* that can be met by the defined set of equipment, and some are additional objectives which may demand more equipment. Nearly all space missions have a *hidden agenda* that consists of secondary, often nontechnical, objectives. Frequently political, social, or cultural, they are equally real and equally important to satisfy. For example, a secondary objective for FireSat II could be to show the public a visible response to frequent forest fires. Third World nations produce satellites in part to show that their developing technology makes them important players in international politics. Of course, this political objective for space programs has been important for many years in the United States, the former Soviet Union, and now China as it seeks to establish itself as a major world power. If we are to meet all of a space mission's objectives, we must identify secondary and nontechnical objectives as well as primary ones. As discussed in Sec. 3.2, we have added the words "and at low cost" to the end of the primary mission objective to emphasize the imprecise, but nonetheless very real, need for a reduced-cost solution if FireSat II is to be funded.

FIRESAT II
MISSION OBJECTIVES

***Primary Objective*:**

- To detect, identify, monitor, and report forest fires throughout the United States, including Alaska and Hawaii, in near real time and at low cost.

***Secondary Objectives*:**

- To demonstrate to the public that positive action is underway to contain forest fires.
- To collect statistical data on the outbreak and growth of forest fires.
- To monitor forest fires for other countries.
- To collect other forest management data.

Fig. 3-3. FireSat II Mission Objectives. Unlike *requirements*, which specify numerical levels of performance, the *mission objectives* are broad statements of what the system must do to be useful.

SCS
MISSION OBJECTIVES

***Primary Objectives*:**

- To provide supplementary, continuous real-time communications at low cost to troops, including individual soldiers, in remote locations (at mid and low latitudes) using cell phone-size equipment, if possible, equipment that they already have.
- To provide the same or similar levels of communications to disaster relief workers in a remote location.

***Secondary Objectives*:**

- To support comparable communications worldwide, depending on the cost.
- To give the individual remote soldier or disaster relief worker the sense that they are a part of a team that will provide them the support they need.
- To provide similar support to allies and relief workers from other countries.
- To automatically and autonomously collect GPS or comparable data to monitor and track the location of system users in real time.

Fig. 3-4. SCS Mission Objectives. SCS has two primary objectives corresponding to the two missions defined for it in Fig. 3-2.

Multiple objectives also occur when we use a single satellite to meet different demands, as in the case of SCS. In the case of FireSat II, we might use its temperature-sensing instruments to monitor global changes in ocean temperatures as well. In this case, the secondary objectives could become as important as the primary ones. A second example would be adding a communications payload to FireSat II to permit better communications among the distributed groups who fight forest fires, or add a GPS receiver to the SCS unit to allow autonomous monitoring of the location of individuals or small groups on the ground to allow rescue or support of people who can no longer communicate. Although the primary objective usually will be quite stable, secondary objectives may shift to meet the users' needs and the redefined potential of the space mission concept.

Table 3-2. The Principal Players, Their Objectives, and What Might Change Those Objectives for Representative Systems. See text for discussion.

Mission	FireSat II	SCS	Safari Airplane
Primary Customer / Objective	US Forest Service / Detect and monitor forest fires in US and Canada using as little financial resources as possible	Both DoD and Disaster Relief Agency / Supplemental, continuous, real-time communications	African safari operator / Improve profits by moving people quickly between sites
Secondary Customer / Objective	Congress / Demonstrate to the public that action is being taken and government funds spent wisely	Congress / Satisfy military needs and, at the same time, respond to public perception of slow disaster relief support	National Bank of Kenya / Make money on a commercial loan; support increased safari business
Operator / Objective	FireSat II Mission Operations Office / Provide forest fire data to the end user in real time; archive data; monitor and maintain the health and safety of FireSat II	SCS Spacecraft Operations Office / Monitor and maintain the continuously operating communications link; monitor and maintain the health and safety of the satellites	2 pilots hired by the safari company / Provide rapid, safe interlocation transportation
End User / Objective	Forest fire field management or firefighter in truck / Track current location of fire relative to themselves	Individual soldier or relief worker in the field / Explain situation and get the right help where it's needed as quickly as possible	People on safari / Don't care about airplane—just want to see as much as they can in 10 days
What Might Change System Objectives	Change in administration; change in projected system cost (up or down); major fire that didn't have sufficient monitoring resources	Splitting procurement to buy 2 systems; major disaster where communications weren't available in a timely manner	Safari company sold to either much bigger or much smaller company; a new, very remote site for wildlife viewing is opened

As in the case of most top-level trades, we strongly recommend against numerical formulas that try to "score" how well a mission meets its objectives. We can compute probabilities for achieving some technical objectives, but trying to numerically combine the coverage characteristics of different constellations with the political or psychological impact of putting a system in place is too simplistic for effective decision-making. Instead, we must identify objectives separately so we can judge how to balance alternative objectives and mission concepts.

Good mission objectives incorporate user needs and, at least indirectly, the characteristics of space that we are exploiting to achieve them. (See Table 1-3 in Sec. 1.5 for a list of these characteristics.) As stated earlier, space is expensive. If our end objective does not use one of the fundamental space characteristics, it will likely cost more to do in space than on Earth. There is little reason to manufacture and distribute low-cost consumer goods or manage a restaurant chain from space.

3.4 Principal Players and Program Timescales (Steps 2 and 3)

3.4.1 Identifying the Principal Players

In a sense, we could design and build a passenger airplane by just looking at the specifications provided by the airline that wants to buy it and responding to all of those specifications. But we would do a much better job if we also looked at the needs and interests of both pilots and airplane passengers. What set of features meets the needs of the pilot to ensure safe and efficient operations? What do passengers want in choosing an airline? Can we help our hypothetical start-up airline by providing them information on what pilots complain about the most in small airplanes, what passengers normally ask about, or the trends in the growth of the width of passenger rear ends over the last few decades? This help would be even more important if, for example, our customer wasn't an airline, but an African safari company that was an expert in African wildlife, but had never bought an airplane before and doesn't have a group of pilots on its staff. Similarly, it might be helpful to understand what banks that finance the purchase of aircraft normally require to make the purchase go smoothly. We could do a better job for our customer by telling them that we work with banks that finance aircraft on a regular basis and what our experience has typically been.

This analogy works well in the space mission engineering arena. As we have said several times, our goal is to start with a set of broad, often poorly defined mission objectives and to meet those objectives in a timely manner at minimum cost and risk. This means understanding the real needs of our customer and his customers, both those who are supplying the money to build the mission and the operators and end users that will ultimately use it. Typically, there are four distinct groups, each with their own goals and objectives, as defined in Table 3-2. The *end user* is the set of people that will actually use the data, and typically don't care very much about space. Most GPS users don't really care about what frequency it uses or the algorithms used to compute the position. (Most users also don't care that GPS measures time really, really well or that this is an important part of the process.) For FireSat II, the end user is either the fire management boss in the field or the firefighter with a shovel in their truck. For SCS, it's the field commander, the soldier that needs help, or the rescue worker in a remote mountainous area. For each of these end users, they have far more important things to think about than space systems. They really don't care very much about us or about this really neat space system we're designing for them, so long as it works. If it doesn't work they are likely to think about us a great deal in ways that we would probably prefer to not be thought about.

While the end user doesn't care about us or the space system, we very much care about them. Someone is going to be asked to spend lots of money satisfying at least one aspect of their needs and that means that we really want to understand those needs very well. The best mission engineering will be done by a combination of people that understand space missions very well and people that understand the end user very well. If we're going to do the very best possible job of creating a strong design for FireSat II, we need an ex-forest ranger or a former forest fire field commander on our team. They can't design the system because space mission engineering isn't their forte, but they can be sure that what we're designing and ultimately implementing will genuinely meet the needs of the end user.

In addition to the end user, there is the *operator* that will actually fly the spacecraft, i.e., the pilot in our airplane analogy. These are the people that care the most about the satellite, even more than the people that buy it, because they have to live with it day-to-day, potentially for many years. They are interested in the practical aspects of space systems. How do you command it? How do you get the data down; and how do you process it, analyze it, archive it, and get it to the end user? The operator is also interested in monitoring the health and safety of the spacecraft itself. How much fuel is left? What's the temperature of the payload? Will a spacecraft maneuver inadvertently get direct sunlight on a surface that is intended to always be in the shade? Often the most asked question by spacecraft operators is: How could an intelligent engineer have been so dumb as to design the spacecraft this way? This suggests that it might be a good idea to have a spacecraft operator on the initial design team and even pay attention to what they're saying from time-to-time.

As implied above, the end user and the operator are rarely the same as the customer for a space system. The *primary customer* or *sponsor* is the person or group, or possibly collection of groups, that actually buy the space system. Certainly, their goal is also to satisfy the needs of the end user, but they may have ancillary goals along the way as well. Our African safari team has a clear objective of making money and we want to understand this as well. If we sell them a magnificent airplane that costs so much that they can't afford to run safaris or if they have to charge a price that is too high to get any customers, then we haven't done a good job. For FireSat II, let's assume that our customer is the US Forest Service. While they're not interested in making a profit, if we sell them a FireSat II system that doesn't work well, costs so much that they can't afford other critical equipment, or takes so long that all of northern California burns down before the system was in place, then again, we haven't done a good job, irrespective of whether we have met all of the specifications that were put in place. This will likely be made very clear to the provider of FireSat II in future discussions with the Forest Service and with Congress.

The idea of explaining the results to Congress leads to the concept of a *secondary customer*, i.e., not the people or group that signs the contract, but the people or groups that they must satisfy and who may have put up the money for the project—and likely more money than they would have preferred to spend. For US Government programs such as FireSat II and SCS, this would be the US Congress. Once again, there may be additional issues in dealing with Congress or any financial backer. It is likely that Congress regards its role in FireSat II as different than that of the Forest Service. Both would probably regard themselves as the ultimate decision-maker. It is in our best interest to recognize the role that Congress plays and to be sure that the system we build meets those needs and objectives as well. Most formal proposals to the Government for large space systems include a several page executive summary that includes a map of the United States showing all of the states in which some part of this space system is going to be built. That is because FireSat II, SCS, and many space programs, both military and civilian, are ultimately funded by the people of the United States, and the American people would like to have the jobs that these programs create spread throughout the United States. It will be very hard to get Congressional funding for any **large** space program that is built exclusively in either California or Iowa.

Another complication arises when there are multiple customers or multiple stakeholders in any one space venture. The International Space Station (ISS) includes both funding and hardware from many countries. It is probable that the goals and interests of, for example, the United States, Canada, and Russia in the ISS are not all identical. It would be surprising if they were. As discussed in Sec. 3.3 above, most space programs have both technical and non-technical (potentially political), objectives. In order for the project to be funded to meet the needs of the end user, it also has to satisfy the needs and objectives of the multiple customers involved, including the non-technical objectives. It is unlikely that this will happen by chance. In order for the competent space mission engineer to ensure that these diverse goals and objectives are met, he or she must understand these goals and objectives; and therefore, must also understand who the principal players are, the community they come from, and their principal objectives. Suppose, for example, we are considering a major expansion of the ISS, but that expansion does not make any use of the robot arm created by Canada for the ISS and a major source of Canadian pride. It is almost certain that we wouldn't get any political support or any funding from Canada, and could well get substantial opposition to our plan, and possibly to other joint Canadian-US space programs as well.

Table 3-3. Representative Space Mission Timeline. The names used here are generic, but fairly widely used. Each of the large space organizations have their own set of mission phases, typically defined by formal Milestone reviews that are required for "graduation" to the next phase.

Phase	End Defined By	Typical Duration (small program)	Typical Duration (major program)
CONCEPT EXPLORATION	Start of technology funding; preliminary requirements release	1–6 months	2–10 years
	DETAILED DEVELOPMENT		
Risk Reduction/Technology Development	Start of program funding	0–12 months	1–10 years
Detailed Design and Development	Formal requirements release	2–12 months	0.5–4 years
	PRODUCTION AND DEPLOYMENT		
Production	Ship to Launch Site	6–24 months	2–5 years
Launch	Lift-Off and Arrival in Low-Earth Orbit	1 month	3 – 12 months
On-Orbit Check-Out /Transfer to Operational Orbit	Start of operations	0–10 days	1–3 months in Earth orbit***
	OPERATIONS AND SUPPORT		
Operations	Spacecraft dies or decision to be put to sleep	1 month–5 years*	5–15 years*
Disposal	Re-entry or turn-off**	0–5 years	up to 25 years

* Upper limit shown is typical design life. In practice, on-orbit spacecraft rarely wear out and can live for many years after the formal end of their design life if they have enough propellant or other consumables on board.
** Data analysis may continue for an extended period. *** Up to 10 years for Interplanetary

The potential principal players in FireSat II, SCS, and our safari airplane system are identified in Table 3-2 above, along with the principal objectives that they will be trying to meet and potential changes in those objectives. Note that it is entirely possible for these principal players to change from time-to-time, either because a new administration comes into power or because some players drop out or others join in order to find sufficient resources or support to make the program occur. A famous example is the GPS program which did not originally have sufficient political support to be funded in Congress. The Nuclear Detection System (NDS) was added as a secondary payload to each of the GPS satellites in order to gain sufficient support to be fundable in Congress. It would be of no use to the many users of GPS if we had designed a remarkably capable system, but weren't able to make it achieve enough Congressional support to be funded.

3.4.2 Defining the Space Mission Timeline

Much the same logic applies to the program timeline as it does to the principal players. If the timeline we create and the space system that we build on that timeline don't support the needs of the users, we have done a bad job of space mission engineering. We can always argue (and often do) that this wonderful space system will be of great use in future forest fires or future wars or disasters, but that is of very little comfort to those who were killed or who lost their homes or loved ones while we were spending time arguing over specifications or how many reaction wheels are needed. In order to be useful, results must also be timely, although of course, the meaning of timeliness can change with the circumstances.

At a top level, the space mission life cycle goes through four broad phases:

- *Concept Exploration*, the initial study phase, which results in a broad definition of the space mission and its components, cost, and schedule.
- *Detailed Development*, the formal design phase, which results in a detailed definition of the system components and, in major programs, technology development and validation of test hardware and software.
- *Production and Deployment*, the construction of the ground and flight hardware and software and launch of the first satellite or constellation.
- *Operations and Support*, the day-to-day operation of the space system, its maintenance and support, and finally its deorbit at the end of the mission.

These four phases are broken down into a finer level of detail in Table 3-3 along with a definition of what typically defines the end of one phase and the beginning of the next and the typical duration for both small programs and major programs.

Essentially all programs go through the eight phases defined in Table 3-3, but the amount of time spent varies dramatically. For a small program, the time frames are measured in weeks or months and the overall mission will typically take from 1 to 3 years from a broad mission statement to launch. The design life for these small missions will typically be 1 to 5 years, although many of them have lived much longer because well-designed, simple spacecraft have little wear-out once they are on orbit.

Major programs operate on a very different time scale. Here each phase can last for years and the program can go for decades from concept inception to launch. For example, The Chandra X-ray telescope,* one of the Great Observatory missions (see Table 2-3), was initially proposed to NASA in 1976 by scientists at the Smithsonian

Astrophysical Observatory. It was finally launched in 1999 and is still operational as of 2010. Largely because of the high cost, major programs will typically have an on-orbit design life of 10 to 15 years in order to get as much utility as possible.

In most cases, the timeline for both small and large programs is dominated not by technology or the difficulty of achieving the results, but rather by financing and the ability to raise the money for the program. Chandra was delayed in large part due to the high cost of the Hubble Space Telescope. There simply wasn't enough room in the NASA budget for two major programs proceeding simultaneously at full speed. Small programs, by definition, are much less expensive than larger ones, but are typically financed by organizations or governments that have much smaller overall budgets and, therefore, are still major expenses for the group that is funding them. An extended timeline also opens the potential for political problems. Each new administration will review ongoing, expensive programs and may not be strongly supportive of programs begun under a previous administration and unlikely to generate results before the next administration.

Typically, the major space organizations, such as NASA, the Air Force, or ESA, have their own, very formal process and sequence for major programs. The NASA project life cycle is shown in Fig. 3-5 and the systems engineering to be done in each phase is shown in Fig. 3-6. The upper row of triangles in Fig. 3-5 represents the key decision points which are basically the hurdles to be overcome in order to proceed to the next step, with the potential for both schedule delays and funding adjustments (typically upward) at each. This by no means represents all of the formal reviews for a major program. The triangle labeled PDR is the Preliminary Design Review for the program as a whole, with a specific set of criteria to be met before getting through Key Decision Point C. (These are the things listed under the box called "virtual prototyping" in Fig. 3-6.) However, in addition to the PDR for the system as a whole, there is likely to be a PDR for each of the subsystems of the spacecraft and the ground segment and there may be a similar set for the launch segment. Most of the major space organizations have a process fundamentally similar to the NASA process outlined in Fig. 3-5. (See, for example, DAU [2010] or ESA BSSC [1991].)

Recall that our original goal in this process was to satisfy the needs of the customers, operator, end user, and ultimately the American people at low cost and in a timely manner. Today, American space programs take a minimum of 1 year to put in place and, quite often, many years. In the current paradigm, there are very few things faster than a spacecraft in orbit and very few things slower than the process of getting it there.

There are a number of alternatives that can dramatically speed up the space mission implementation process in the future.* The most straightforward of these is to build both spacecraft and launch vehicles to inventory and launch them from inventory within a few hours or days of an identified need. ICBMs are rockets that can be launched within minutes, although the cost of the system is very high. We would like to do the same thing for spacecraft at a much lower cost. The former Soviet Union, and now Russia, have had launch-on-demand from inventory for both spacecraft and launch vehicles for many years. (See Sec. 25.5.) For example, on Friday, April 2, 1982, war broke out between Argentina and the United Kingdom over the Falklands Islands in the South Atlantic east of Argentina, a region of the world where there was very limited satellite coverage. The war ended on June 14, 1982, when Argentina surrendered. During this 73-day period, the Soviets launched 29 payloads into orbit, most in direct response to the war.

The technology for launch-on-demand (i.e., within a day) has been available for many years, but requires that the cost come down to the point where it is economically appropriate to keep assets in inventory. The idea of low-cost, rapid missions led to the creation of the Responsive Space Conference in 2003 by the LA Section of the AIAA [Wertz and Kulpa, 2003], which has been held annually since that time. The technical papers from all of the Responsive Space Conferences are available online at no cost [Responsive Space Conference, 2010]. The push for responsive space has led to the creation by the Air Force of the Operationally Responsive Space Office (ORSO) in 2006 with the objective of providing a rapid response to urgent needs of Air Force commanders [Wertz, Van Allen, and Shelner, 2006; Doyne et al., 2007]. The ORSO has created the idea of a "6-day spacecraft" that could be assembled and tested in 6 days from components and subsystems that are stored at a single location.

Irrespective of whether we choose to build a spacecraft rapidly, or build it more slowly to inventory and then launch when needed, the basic idea remains the same—to satisfy the needs of the user community within a few hours or days of the need being identified. More traditional missions will continue to take a very long time to implement, as is appropriate for major developments in new technology. What we are trying to achieve in Responsive Space is an excellent product, at a low cost, in a timely manner.

3.5 Preliminary Estimate of Mission Needs, Requirements, and Constraints (Step 4)

Having defined the broad objectives that the space mission is to achieve, and who is trying to achieve them on what schedule, we wish to transform these objectives into preliminary sets of numerical requirements and

* Chandra went through the first 22 years of concept exploration as the Advanced X-Ray Astrophysics Facility (AXAF) and received its current name in 1998, a year before launch on board the Space Shuttle Columbia.

* For a detailed list of alternatives, see Chap. 13 or Wertz et al. [2011].

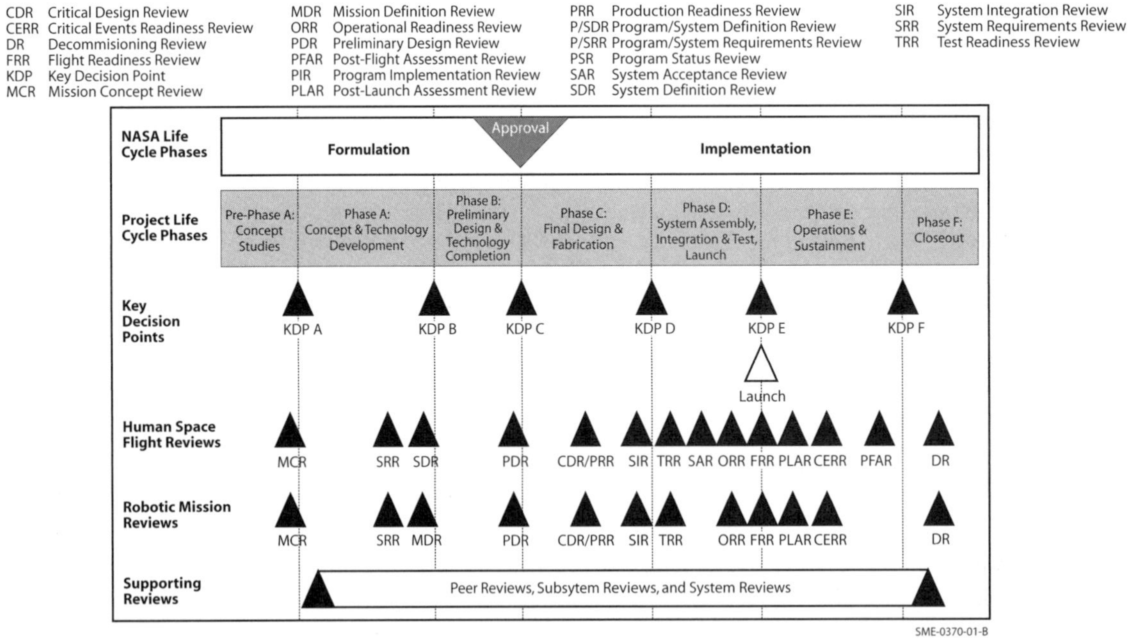

Fig. 3-5. NASA Project Life Cycle. Each of the triangles represents a major milestone. Courtesy of NASA [2007].

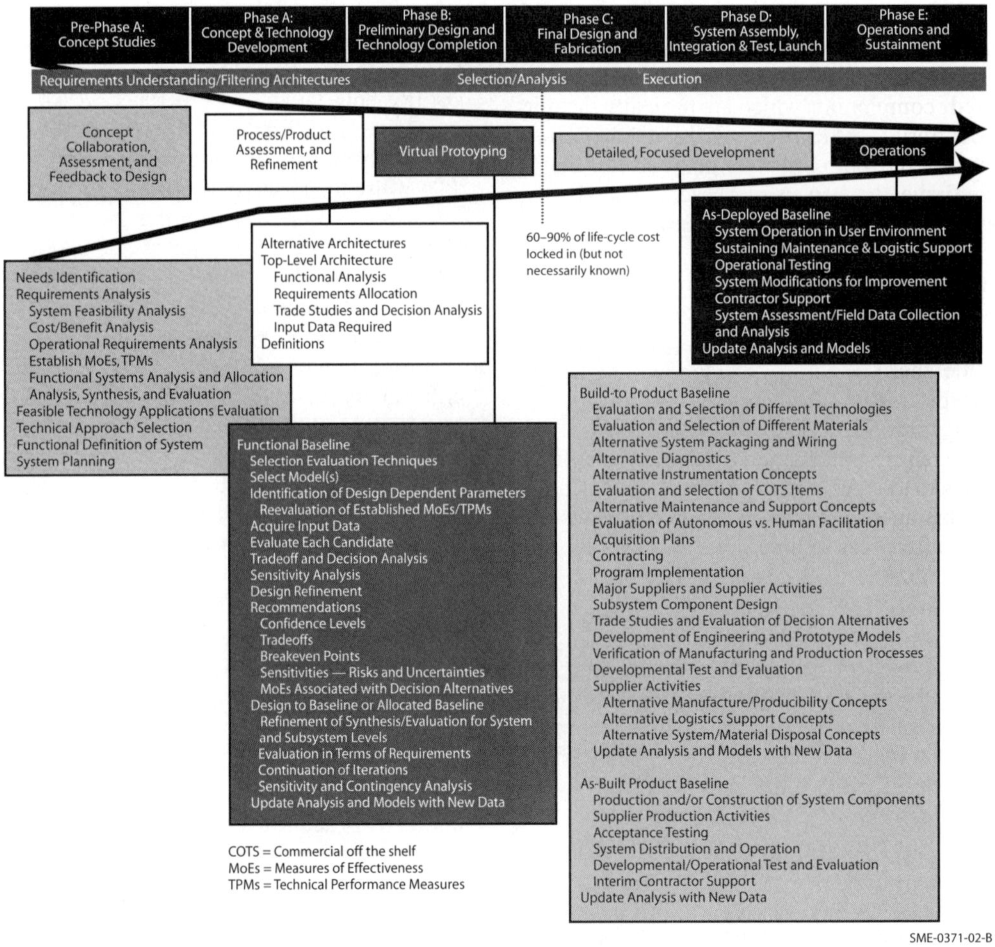

Fig. 3-6. System Engineering Activities in Each Phase of a Major NASA Mission. Courtesy of NASA [2007].

constraints on the space mission's development, performance, and operation. These requirements and constraints will largely establish the operational concepts that will meet our objectives. Thus, we must develop requirements which truly reflect the mission objectives and be willing to change them as we more clearly define the space system.

To transform mission objectives into requirements,* we must look at three broad areas:

- *Functional Requirements*, which define how well the system must perform to meet its objectives.
- *Operational Requirements,* which determine how the system operates and how users interact with it to meet their specific needs.
- *Constraints,* which limit cost, schedule, and implementation techniques available to the system designer.

The needs, requirements, and constraints for any specific mission will depend upon the mission itself and how we implement it. For example, the mission may be a commercial venture, a government scientific program, or a crash emergency program responding to a dire need. Still, most space missions develop their initial requirements in areas similar to those shown in Table 3-4.

Establishing top-level mission requirements is extremely difficult, depending on mission needs and on the perceived complexity or cost of meeting them. Therefore, contrary to frequent practice, we should iterate the numerical requirements many times in the design process. The first estimate of mission requirements typically comes from the goals and objectives combined with some view of what is feasible. Often, we can reiterate or slightly modify requirements and specifications from previous missions, thus carrying over information known from those missions. Of course, we must be prepared to trade these requirements as we develop the mission concept, thereby avoiding the problem of keeping old and inappropriate requirements.

The next step in setting up preliminary mission requirements is to look for the "hidden agenda" discussed in Sec. 3.3. This agenda contains the implicit goals and constraints of all of the principal players identified in Sec. 3.4. For example, the FireSat II mission may need to be perceived as responding quickly to a public demand for action and SCS may need to be built entirely in the US to be acceptable to Congress. Thus, an extended R&D program to develop the most appropriate FireSat II satellite may not be acceptable and using a communications payload from Europe on SCS would not let the program go forward without a fight, even though the European payload might be better, lower cost, or both.

As discussed further in Sec. 12.3, we must recognize that developing a space mission depends on political, legal, and economic constraints, as well as technology. Thus, the most appropriate solution must meet mission technical requirements **and** the political and economic goals of everyone involved. For example, satellite systems for a small nation may use components built in that nation or develop some new components locally, even though they would cost less if bought in other countries. In this case, we would spend more money to meet a political constraint: using the space mission to develop and promote national engineering resources. The technical community often sets aside nontechnical considerations and regards them as less important or less real than technical constraints. But a successful mission design must include **all** requirements and constraints placed on the system, even if they are not necessarily written in a specifications document.

Finally, we reiterate that preliminary mission requirements should be subject to later trades. Mission designers often simply try to meet the procuring group's requirements and constraints, because not meeting them appears to put them at a strong competitive disadvantage. Consequently, designers may not modify the initial requirements, even if changes could make the system cost less or perform better for a given cost. Chapter 13 provides the details of this process of *trading on requirements* to maximize performance vs. cost.

As an example, we consider the requirement for mission design life.† This exemplifies the difficulty of establishing requirements. The length of the mission is often indefinite, as is the case with both FireSat II and SCS. We want to identify and monitor forest fires and provide communications for natural disasters continuously at a reasonable cost per year. In practice, however, we must develop a system that meets this need and then deploy it with an established design life and, perhaps, a replenishment philosophy. The design life of the individual FireSat II or SCS spacecraft will strongly affect cost and will determine the level of redundancy, propellant budgets, and other key system parameters. In principle, we would like to obtain a graph of spacecraft cost vs. design life as shown in Fig 3-7. We could then easily compute the total expected cost per year for different design lives, as shown by the heavy dark line, and the design life that results in the minimum spacecraft cost per

* The alternative to starting with the question of what the system must do to meet the mission needs is the Capabilities-Driven Process, defined in Sec. 3.1.2. In this case, we would start our requirements definition by writing down what the system can do and asking whether that has utility. For example, our primary requirement might be to achieve 1 m resolution on the Earth, simply because a new breakthrough allows this to be done at very, very low cost. We then ask what the missions are that this new capability would support and what are the secondary functional requirements, operational requirements, and constraints that would support the mission or missions using this new capability.

† The *design life* is the intended minimum operational lifetime on orbit. Most spacecraft will last much longer. The design life is used for things such as propellant budgets, redundancy requirements, solar array sizing (because of degradation due to radiation), and any component with a predicable wear-out.

Table 3-4. Representative Initial Requirements. These should be adjusted over time to balance what is desired with what is affordable.

Requirement	Where Discussed	Factors which Normally Impact the Requirement	FireSat II Example	SCS Example
Functional Requirements				
Performance	Chaps. 15, 16, 17	User needs, payload aperture, orbit	Work through light clouds 50 m resolution 1 km geolocation accuracy	300 simultaneous users Continuous link to CONUS 65 kbps bandwidth per user
Coverage	Secs.10.2, 10.6	Orbit altitude and inclination, swath width, number of satellites, scheduling process	Coverage of specified forest areas within the US at least twice daily	Primary: ± 50 deg lat. band Polar: All areas outside of ±40 deg latitude band
Interpretation	Sec. 5.4	Cloud cover, image quality, manual or automated interpretation	Identify an emerging forest fire within 8 hours; with less than 10% false positives	Not applicable
Timeliness	Sec. 10.6	Interpretation, communications, processing, operations	Interpreted data to end user within 5 min	Less than 150 ms total lag
Secondary Missions	Secs. 3.1, 3.3	As above	Monitor changes in mean forest temp. to ±2 C	Automatic geolocation data
Operational Requirements				
Commanding	Sec. 21.1	Who will do commanding, tasking from the field, need for real-time schedule changes	Commandable within 3 min of events; download units of stored coverage areas	Entire system commanded by primary or back-up ground stations in CONUS
Mission Design Life	Secs. 3.4, 3.5, 14.2	Duration of need, level of redundancy, altitude	8 years	10 years
System Availability	Sec. 24.1	Level of redundancy, where processing and interpretation occur	95% excluding weather, 24 hour maximum downtime	99% availability, irrespective of weather
Survivability	Chap. 7	Orbit, hardening	Natural environment only; not in radiation belts	10 year survival in the Van Allen belts
Data Distribution	Chaps. 16, 29; Sec. 21.1	User needs, communications architecture; ancillary communications channels	Up to 500 fire-monitoring offices + 2,000 rangers worldwide (max. of 100 simultaneous users)	Can send to any user worldwide on the system and to any user with comm. connectivity via operations
Data Content, Form, and Format	Chaps. 4, 14, 20	User equipment, available bandwidth, level and place of processing	Location and extent in lat/long for local plotting, avg. temp. for each 40 m^2	Voice, text, images
User Equipment	Chap. 16	Mass, size, and power; existing equipment or new, user interface	10 × 20 cm display with zoom and touch controls; built-in GPS quality map	Hand-held communications transceiver less than 500 g or add-on to cell phone
Constraints				
Cost	Chaps. 11, 12, 13	Manned flight, number of space-craft, size and complexity, orbit	Non-recurring < $10M Recurring < $3M/year	Non-recurring < $30M Recurring < $10M/year
Schedule	Sec. 3.4	Financing, technical readiness	Operational within 3 years	Operational within 4 years
Risk	Sec. 24.2	Primary and secondary customers, schedule, cost	Probability of success > 90%	Probability of success > 95%
Regulations	Sec. 12.3	Law and policy	Orbital debris, civil program regulations	DoD and civil program regulations
Political	Sec. 12.3	Sponsor, whether international program, debris removal	Responsive to public demand for action	Public demand for better disaster response
Environment	Chap. 7	Orbit, lifetime	Natural	Natural, jamming, weather
Interfaces	Chaps. 28, 29	Level of user and operator infrastructure	Interoperable through NOAA ground stations	Simple to use
Development Constraints	Chap. 3	Primary and secondary customers, schedule, cost	None	Must use all American components

year. For the case of Fig. 3-7, we would choose a design life of 6 years. We could also assess technological obsolescence, or the point at which we wish to replace the spacecraft because of better or cheaper technology.

In practice, figures such as 3-7 are almost never created or, at best, are done qualitatively. The mission design life is normally assigned rather arbitrarily with a general perception of cost per year. Thus, there may be a push to produce spacecraft lasting 5 or 10 years because people believe that these will be more economical than ones lasting only a few years. No matter how we choose the design life requirement, we would like to go through the process described above for decisions about mission lifetime. If at all possible, it would be desirable to create a graph similar to Fig. 3-7 based on even crude estimates of spacecraft cost. Doing so provides a much stronger basis for establishing mission requirements and, e.g., determining whether we should push harder for a longer spacecraft lifetime or back off on this requirement to reduce spacecraft cost.

Having made a preliminary estimate of mission requirements and constraints, we proceed in Chap. 4 to define and characterize one or more baseline mission concepts. The issue of refining requirements, revising our baseline, and assessing how well objectives can be met is discussed in Chap. 5. However, we always want to return to our basic goals:

- Meeting the mission objectives in a timely manner at minimum cost and risk, and
- Making all of the principal players delighted with the resulting space system by doing a better job, quicker, and at lower cost than they had expected

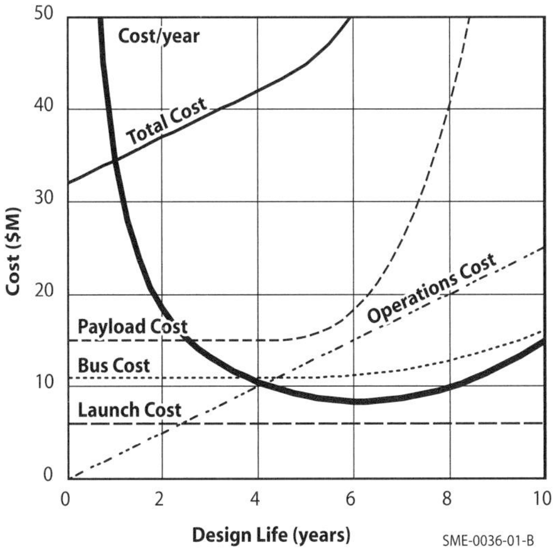

Fig. 3-7. Hypothetical Curve of Cost vs. Spacecraft Design Life. The cost per year is the total cost divided by the design life. In principle, we should use such curves to set the Spacecraft Design Life requirement. In practice, they rarely exist.

References

For annotated bibliography of space mission engineering, see the book website.

Boden, D. G., Gael Squibb, and Wiley G. Larson. 2006. *Cost Effective Space Mission Operations. 2nd ed.* Boston, MA: The McGraw-Hill Companies.

Chesley, J., W. J. Larson, M. McQuade, and R. J. Menrad. 2008. *Applied Project Management for Space Systems*. New York: The McGraw-Hill Companies.

Defense Acquisition University. 2010. "Integrated Defense Acquisition, Technology, and Logistics Life Cycle Management System."

Doyne, T., P. Wegner, C. Olmedo, G. Moretti, M. Hurley, M. Johnson, T. Duffey, and C.Huffine. 2007. "ORS and TacSat Activities Including the Emerging ORS Enterprise." 5th Responsive Space Conference. RS5-2007-4001. Los Angeles, CA. Apr. 23–26.

ESSC. 1991. ESA Board for Software Standardisation and Control. *ESA Software Engineering Standards*.

Fleeter, Rick. 2000. *The Logic of Microspace*. Torrance, CA: Microcosm Press and Springer.

Ford, Steve. 2010. *The ARRL Satellite Handbook*. Newington, CT: American Radio Relay League.

Johnson, S. B. 2002. *The Secret of Apollo: Systems Management in American and European Space Programs*. Baltimore, MD: The Johns Hopkins University Press.

Kay, W. D. 1995. *Can Democracies Fly in Space?: the Challenge of Revitalizing the U.S. Space Program.* Westport, CT: Praeger.

Larson, W. J., D. Kirkpatrick, J. J. Sellers, L. D. Thomas, D. Verma. 2009. *Applied Space Systems Engineering*. New York: The McGraw-Hill Companies.

Maier, M. W. and E. Rechtin. 2009. *The Art of Systems Architecting. 3rd ed.* New York: CRC Press.

NASA. 2007. *Systems Engineering Handbook*. Hanover, MD: NASA.

Responsive Space. 2010. Website.

Sandau, T. 2006. *International Study on Cost-Effective Earth Observation Missions*. Leiden, The Netherlands: Taylor & Francis.

Sarsfield, L. P. 1998. *The Cosmos on a Shoestring: Small Spacecraft for Space and Earth Science.* Santa Monica, CA: RAND.

Shishko, Robert. 2010. *NASA Systems Engineering Handbook*. Memphis, TN: General Books.

Wertz, James R. and Wiley J. Larson. 1991 *Space Mission Analysis and Design. 1st ed.* Dordrecht, The Netherlands: Kluwer Academic Publishers and Microcosm Press.

Wertz, J. R. and W. J. Larson. 1996. *Reducing Space Mission Cost.* Torrance, CA and Dordrecht, The Netherlands: Microcosm Press and Kluwer Academic Publishers.

Wertz, J. R. and W. J. Larson. 1999. *Space Mission Analysis and Design. 3rd ed.* Hawthorne, CA and New York: Microcosm Press and Springer.

Wertz, J. R. and J. Kulpa. 2003. "Responsive Launch with the Scorpius Family of Low-Cost Expendable Launch Vehicles." 1st Responsive Space Conference. RSI-2003-5001 Redondo Beach, CA. Apr. 1–3

Wertz, J. R., R. Van Allen, and C. J. Shelner. 2006. "Aggressive Surveillance as a Key Application Area for Responsive Space." 4th Responsive Space Conference. RS4-2006-1004 Los Angeles, CA. Apr. 24–27.

Wertz, J. R., et al. 2011. "Methods for Achieving Dramatic Reductions in Space Mission Cost." Reinventing Space Conference. AIAA-RS-2011-500. Los Angeles, CA. May 2–5.

4 Mission Concept Definition and Exploration

James R. Wertz, ***Microcosm, Inc./USC***

In Chap. 3, we defined the broad mission objectives, the principal players in the development of the mission, the program timescale that we have to develop it on, and a preliminary list of requirements and constraints. In this chapter, we begin the process of defining alternative mission concepts that will achieve these objectives. Of course, our goal is to look at a number of these concepts to find out how we can meet our mission objectives in a timely manner at minimum cost and risk, such that the various players in the process will be delighted and amazed at the end product we have produced. Sadly, in modern space missions, that does not happen as often as we would like, and it is up to the new generation of space mission engineers to change that.

Most of the references in the introduction to Chap. 3 also discuss the process of concept definition and exploration. In addition, Fortescue, et al. [2003], Griffin and French [2004], and Pisacane and Moore [2005] provide a broad discussion for general missions. Elbert [2003, 2008], Gordon and Morgan [1993], and Maral and Bousquet [2010] provide excellent discussions for geosynchronous communications missions. Kemble [2006] discusses concept exploration for interplanetary missions. Chapter 13 discusses the major differences for low-cost missions.

In common use, "mission architecture," "mission concept," and "concept of operations" are frequently interchangeable and, at best, vaguely defined. Throughout this chapter, we wish to clearly distinguish between them. The *mission architecture*, introduced in Sec. 4.1, consists of the definition of each of the eight major components of the mission, i.e., the elements that make up the mission. The *mission concept*, discussed in Sec. 4.2, is a broad statement of how the mission will work in practice—how all the pieces fit together to meet the needs of all of the players involved. This should not be confused with *mission operations*, which provides the details of how people operate and control the mission.

Another way to think about the overall architecture is by an analogy with a swift water rescue team being set up by the local fire department. In this case, the Mission Architecture is all of the equipment and people that we need to make it happen—the boat, the fire truck that can carry the boat, the roads we can use, the radio equipment to keep in touch with home base, and the boat launching locations that we will use to get into the water. The Mission Concept is broadly how we will use these resources to rescue people. We'll use the truck to get as close to the people needing help as possible. We'll launch the boat, but stay in close contact on the radio and be searching for other options if the boat can't get to where it needs to be. We'll get the people that need help into the boat and assess whether we need the helicopter to get them to a hospital. Finally, the Mission Operations is the detailed process of getting the boat through the swift water, to the people that need help, and getting them the help they need. The Concept Definition and Exploration Process is the planning and thinking very carefully about all of this in advance (and the simulations and dry runs) to make sure that when the call for help arrives, we're genuinely ready to go. Similarly with FireSat II—when forest fires occur, we want to provide the right data to the right people in time to help them do whatever needs to be done.

4.1 Defining Alternative Mission Architectures (Step 5)—Choosing the Pieces

All space missions consist of a set of 8 *elements* or *components* as shown in Fig. 4-1. The collection of these elements form a *space mission architecture*. The elements themselves are defined in Table 4-1 and discussed below.

The *subject* of the mission is the thing that is sensed by or interacts with the space payload. There are two broad types of subjects. *Passive subjects* are ones that the mission designer can't control, such as the fire for FireSat II; moisture content, atmospheric temperature, or pressure for weather missions; types of vegetation, water, or geological formations for Earth-sensing missions; or a rocket or intercontinental ballistic missile for space defense missions. Although mission designers can't control the subject itself, they can control how to sense the subject. For FireSat II, it is likely that we would sense the heat from the fire. But we could also sense the light, the smoke, the increased CO_2 level, the reduction in oxygen, or some combination of all of those. (Home fire detection systems often use both smoke detection and CO_2 detection, for example.)

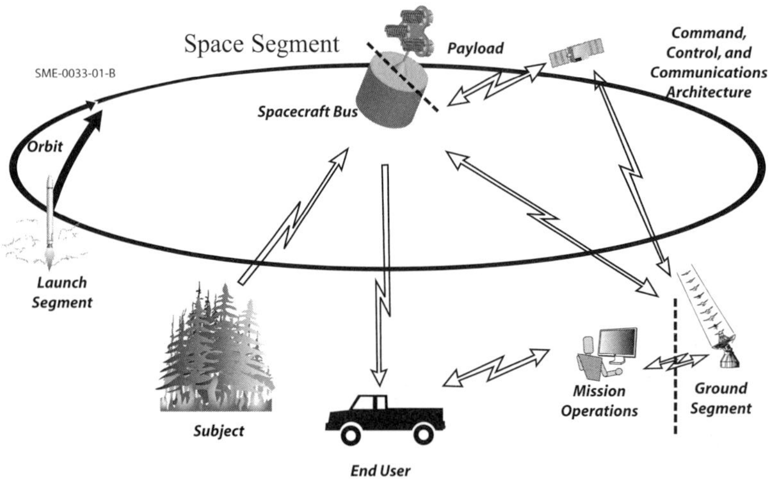

Fig. 4-1. Space Mission Architecture. All space missions include these basic elements to some degree. See Table 4-1 for definitions and the text for discussion. Requirements for the system flow from the operator, end user, and developer and are normally allocated to the various mission elements.

Table 4-1. The Space Mission Architecture Consists of Eight Elements or Components Plus the Mission Concept and End User. All of these must work together to meet the mission objectives and needs of the end user at a reasonable cost, risk, and schedule.

Segment	Description	Where Discussed
1. Subject	What the spacecraft observes (***passive subject***) or interacts with (***active*** or ***controllable subject***).	Sec. 15.2
Space Segment or Spacecraft Consisting of:		
2. Payload	Spacecraft hardware and software that observe or interact with the subject.	Chaps. 15, 16, 17
3. Spacecraft Bus	The other spacecraft subsystems needed to support the payload.	Chap. 14
4. Ground Segment	The communications equipment and facilities that communicate with and control the spacecraft.	Chap. 28
5. Mission Operations	The people and software that run the space mission on a day-to-day basis.	Chaps. 29, 30
6. Command, Control, and Communications Architecture	How all of the parts of the space mission communicate with each other.	Secs. 16.1, 21.1
7. Orbit	The path of the spacecraft during its operational mission. If there is more than one spacecraft in coordinated orbits, it's a ***constellation***.	Chaps. 9, 10
8. Launch Segment	How the spacecraft gets into orbit; may include ***upper stages*** or ***integral propulsion***.	Chaps. 26, 27
Mission Concept	The ***end users*** are the people or equipment that actually make use of the data generated or transmitted by the spacecraft. The ***mission concept*** is the definition of how the mission elements work together to meet the needs of the end user.	Secs. 1.1, 3.4, 4.3

In contrast to the passive subjects, *active* or *controllable subjects* are ones for which the design and basic parameters can be controlled by mission designers. These include GPS receivers, direct broadcast television dishes, and the user equipment for SCS. Here the mission designer has the opportunity to trade between putting more capability at the user end or more capability on the spacecraft. Since there are normally lots of users and few spacecraft, it would seem to make sense to put as much capability as possible on board the spacecraft and allow the user equipment to be simple and low cost. But memory and logic are remarkably cheap these days, so, for example, all of the map data on which your GPS coordinates are displayed are in the receiver that is with the end user, not sent down on the message from the GPS satellite.

The *payload* consists of the hardware and software that sense or interact with the subject. Typically, we trade off and combine several sensors and experiments to form the payload, which largely determines the mission's cost, complexity, and effectiveness. In most cases, multiple payloads significantly increase cost.

The *spacecraft bus* consists of a set of subsystems, defined in Chap. 14, that support the payload by providing orbit and attitude maintenance, power, command, telemetry and data handling, structure and rigidity, and temperature control. The payload and spacecraft bus together are called the *spacecraft*, *space segment*, or *launch vehicle payload.*

The *launch system* includes the launch facility, launch vehicle, and any upper stage required to place the spacecraft in orbit, as well as interfaces, payload fairing, and associated ground support equipment and facilities. The selected launch system constrains the size, shape, and mass of the spacecraft.

The *orbit* is the spacecraft's path or trajectory in space. Typically, there is a separate initial parking orbit, transfer orbit, and final mission orbit. There may also be an end-of-life or disposal orbit. The mission orbit significantly influences every element of the mission and provides many options for trades in mission architecture.

The *command, control, and communications (C3) architecture* is the arrangement of components that satisfy the mission's communication, command, and control requirements. It depends strongly on the amount of data and timing requirements for the data to be transferred, as well as the number, location, availability, and communicating ability of the space and ground assets.

The *ground system* consists of the facilities and communications equipment associated with both fixed and mobile ground stations around the world, connected by various data links. They allow us to command and track the spacecraft, receive and process telemetry and mission data, and distribute the information to the operators and end users.

Mission operations consist of the people, computers, and software that execute the mission operations concept and attendant policies, procedures, and data flows.

Finally, the *mission concept* is how all of these elements work together to satisfy the needs of the key players in the system. For FireSat II, how do firefighters in the truck get the information that they need to do their job? Most likely a simple image from space isn't going to do them much good. What they need is the interpreted results—what's a forest fire? Where is the fire and which way is it going? We need to put that information on a map and deliver it to firefighters in their truck in near-real-time in order to be useful. For SCS, our basic goal is to let disaster relief workers in a remote location communicate with the people that can provide the help and guidance they need to reduce suffering and save lives and property. These are the things that our mission concept needs to tell us.

Our goal is to arrive at a set of candidate architectures for further evaluation large enough to encompass all approaches offering significant advantages, but small enough to make the more detailed definition and evaluation manageable. Table 4-2 summarizes the mechanism for doing this.

Step A. Identify mission elements subject to trade. We begin by examining our basic mission concept and each of the eight mission elements in light of the preliminary requirements and constraints from Sec. 3.5 to determine which have more than one option. Usually this step greatly reduces the number of tradeable elements.

Table 4-2. Process Summary for Identifying Alternative Mission Architectures. This highly creative endeavor can have a significant impact on mission cost and complexity.

Step	Where Discussed
A. ***Identify the mission elements subject to trade.***	Table 4-3
B. ***Identify the main options for each tradeable element.***	Table 4-4
C. ***Look for options that work well together or don't work well together.***	Table 4-5
D. ***Look for other alternatives that could substantially influence how we do the mission.***	Table 4-15, Chap. 13

Table 4-3 summarizes this process for FireSat II and SCS. Both missions have multiple options that will affect not only cost, but also performance, flexibility, and long-term mission utility. Thus, we should carry through several different options so the decision-making audience can understand the main alternatives.

Table 4-3 lists one of the options as "cost only," meaning that the trade depends mainly on cost and only secondarily on how or how well the mission is accomplished. An example would be the launch system, for which the main concern normally is what launch vehicle will get the spacecraft into orbit at the lowest cost. Still, these trades may be important in selecting the mission concept. For example, a major increase in the launch cost may outweigh being able to use a smaller number of satellites in a higher orbit.

Step B. Identify the main options for each tradeable element. Although in theory we have almost an unlimited number of options, we normally draw them from a limited set such as those listed in Table 4-4. Thus, we first choose options that apply to our mission and then look for special circumstances which may lead us to consider alternatives not listed in the table.

Step C. Look for options that work well together or don't work well together. We don't want to carry all possible options forward, because we simply won't have the resources to examine them in detail. We need to find an intelligent way to limit our choices somewhat. The first step in reducing the number of options is to identify the system drivers, as discussed in Sec. 4.4. The *system drivers* are parameters or characteristics that largely determine the system's cost and performance. We look at these options first because they normally dominate the design process and mandate our choices for other elements, thus greatly reducing our options.

Table 4-5 shows two major options for both FireSat II and SCS. Here the major options or system drivers are shown in bold. For FireSat II, there are two major drivers—whether the orbit is LEO or GEO and how to determine what a forest fire is. These are trades that we will have to carry with us for a long time and determine how they impact the overall cost, performance, risk, and schedule. These will determine many of our choices in

Table 4-3. Selecting FireSat II and SCS Elements that can be Traded. Not all options are compatible with each other and there may be options we haven't thought of yet. See text for discussion.

	FireSat II		SCS	
Element of Mission Architecture	**Can Be Traded**	**Reason**	**Can Be Traded**	**Reason**
Mission Concept	Yes	Want to remain open to alternative approaches	No	Mission objective is to be a communications system
Subject	No	Passive subject is well defined (could detect something besides heat, but unlikely)	Yes	Active subject—can consider how much we want the receiver to do
Payload	Yes	Can select complexity and wavelength	Yes	Power and frequency are the key issues
Spacecraft Bus	Yes	Multiple options based on scan mechanism and power	Yes	Multiple options based largely on launch capacity
Launch System	Cost only	Choose minimum cost for selected orbit	Yes	Find low-cost launch and use that to drive the spacecraft
Orbit	Yes	Options are low, medium, or high altitude with varying number of satellites	Yes	Classic orbit is elliptical, but high altitude equatorial, circular orbit may be better
Ground System	Yes	Could share NOAA control facility, use dedicated FireSat II facility, or direct downlink to users	Yes	Could have dedicated system or use commercial service-provided system
Communications Architecture	Yes	Depends on where image interpretation is done	No	Largely defined by mission concept
Mission Operations	Yes	Can adjust level of automation	Not much	Mostly automated operations, may have some level of control

other areas. If the spacecraft is in LEO, it can be a small spacecraft, possibly with solar arrays simply mounted on the spacecraft body, and it will be launched by a small launch vehicle. On the other hand, if FireSat II is in GEO, it will have to be a large spacecraft with ample power, 1- or 2-axis solar arrays, and a medium to large launch vehicle. As discussed in Sec. 4.3, our other major trade is, how do we determine what a forest fire is? Is it a manual process, or one that is automated on board? How do we distinguish a forest fire from a really large barbeque?

Similarly, we have two major system drivers for SCS. Again the orbit is key because it determines how large the Earth appears and how far away it is. In a Molniya orbit (Sec. 9.5.4) both the angular size and distance vary greatly over the orbit, which makes our spacecraft and payload design more complicated. Here our other major trade element is the subject. Will it be possible to work with an ordinary cell phone, possibly with some wire antenna attached? Will we have to equip our soldiers and disaster workers with a special phone in advance? What are the conditions under which we can communicate and how much data can we send?

The next step in reducing options is to look for trades that are at least somewhat independent of the overall concept definition or which will be determined by the selection of other elements. For example, the spacecraft bus ordinarily has many options. However, once we have defined the orbit and payload, we can select the spacecraft bus that meets the mission requirements at the lowest cost. Although bus options may not be a recognized part of the trade process, they may play a key role in selecting workable mission concepts because of cost, risk, or schedule.

The third technique for reducing options is to examine the combinations we have available and retain only sensible combinations. For example, nearly any launch vehicle above a minimum size will work for a given orbit and spacecraft. Because cost is the main launch-vehicle trade, we should retain in the option list only the lowest-cost launch vehicle that will fulfill the mission. This does not mean that we will ultimately launch the spacecraft on that vehicle. Instead, we should design the spacecraft to be compatible with as many launch vehicles as possible and then select the vehicle based on cost (which may well have changed) when we are deciding about initial deployment.

Step D. Look for other alternatives that could substantially influence how we do the mission. Finally, we want to look for alternative ways to do the mission. We'll return to this in Chap. 13 as we look at ways to reduce mission cost, but we want to be aware from the very beginning that looking for major alternatives is the principal way to reduce cost, improve performance, and have a customer and end user that are delighted with what we have accomplished. For example, can data from FireSat II be combined with data from another source to provide better, more frequent monitoring than would be possible with a satellite system alone? Can we use FireSat II to track volcanic activity so as to spread the cost over a larger number of users? The key point is that alternatives nearly always exist. We must look carefully for them and be willing to revise normal requirements and constraints to meet our fundamental mission objectives. This is the step where real creativity is important.

Table 4-4. Common Alternatives for Mission Elements. This table provides a broad checklist for identifying the main alternatives for elements of the mission architecture.

Mission Element [Where Discussed]	Option Area	Most Common Options	FireSat II Options	SCS Options
Mission Concept [Sec. 4.2]	Data delivery	Direct downlink to user, automated ground processing, man-in-the-loop processing and transmission	Direct downlink or through mission control	Choice of sending voice, text, images, or video
	Tasking	Ground commanding, autonomous tasking, simple operations (no tasking required)	Simple operation or ground commands	Simple operation or ground commands
Controllable Subject [Sec. 15.2]	Selection	Standard ground stations, private TV receivers, ship or aircraft transceivers, special purpose equipment	N/A [See Sec. 9.3]	Through modified cell phone or special equipment
	Performance	EIRP, G/T (See Sec. 13.3 for definitions)		Make do with whatever system can provide
	Steering	Fixed or tracking		Limited or no pointing
Passive Subject [Sec. 15.2]	What is to be sensed	Subject itself, thermal environment, emitted radiation, contrast with surroundings	Heat or visible light; chemical composition; particles	N/A
Payload [Chaps.15, 16, 17] (some items may not apply, depending on mission type)	Frequency	Communications: normal bands Observations: IR, visible, microwave Radar: L, C, S bands, UHF Single or multiple frequency bands, single or multiple instruments	IR, visible Single or multiple bands	Selection of communications band and output power
	Size vs. sensitivity	Small aperture with high power (or sensitivity) or vice versa	Aperture	Aperture and power
Spacecraft Bus [Chap. 14]	Propulsion	Whether needed; cold gas, monopropellant, bipropellant	Monopropellant, bipropellant	Monopropellant, bipropellant
	Orbit control	Whether needed, onboard vs. ground	Needed, onboard or ground	Needed, onboard or ground
	Navigation	Onboard (GPS or other) vs. ground-based	Probably onboard	On-board or ground
	Attitude determination and control	None, spinning, 3-axis; articulated payload vs. spacecraft pointing; actuators and sensors	3-axis, articulated payload or Earth-fixed	3-axis, Earth fixed
	Power	Solar vs. nuclear or other; body-mounted vs. 1- or 2-axis pointed arrays	Body mounted solar array	Solar array, body mounted or 1-axis
Launch System [Chap. 27]	Launch vehicle	SSLV Atlas, Delta, STS, Titan, Pegasus, Ariane, other foreign	Small launch vehicle, probably has to be US	Small or medium launch vehicle, probably has to be US
	Upper stage	Pam-D, IUS, TOS, Centaur, integral propulsion, other foreign	Not needed	Small upper stage or integral propulsion
	Launch site	Kennedy, Vandenberg, Wallops, Kwajalein, Kourou, other foreign	KSC, Wallops, or Kwajalein	KSC, Wallops, or Kwajalein
Orbit [Chaps. 9, 10]	Special orbits	None, geosynchronous, Sun-synchronous, frozen, Molniya, repeating ground track	Single GEO satellite, low-Earth constellation	Molniya; MEO circular, equatorial or polar
	Altitude	Low-Earth orbit, mid-altitude,geosynchronous	LEO	Mid-altitude or elliptical
	Inclination	0°, 28.5°, 57°, 63.4°, 90°, 98°	55 deg	0 deg or 90 deg
	Constellation configuration	Number of satellites; Walker pattern, other patterns; number of orbit planes	2 to 6 satellites	3 or 4 satellites, could grow
Ground System [Chap. 28]	Existing or dedicated	AFSCN, NASA control center, USN or other shared system, dedicated system	Shared NOAA system, dedicated system	Shared military system, USN, or internet node
Communications Architecture [Chap. 17]	Timeliness	Store and dump, real-time link	Either option	Real time
	Control and data dissemination	Single or multiple ground stations, direct to user, user commanding, commercial links	1 ground station; commercial or direct data transfer	Direct user-to-user
	Relay mechanism	TDRSS, satellite-to-satellite crosslinks, commercial communications relay	TDRS or commercial	Crosslinks or transfer via ground
Mission Operations [Chap. 29]	Automation level	Fully automated ground stations, part-time operations, full-time (24-hr) operations	Any of the options listed	Nearly fully automated
	Autonomy level	Full ground command and control, partial autonomy, full autonomy (not yet readily available)	Any, need some ground control	Any

Table 4-5. Two of the Principal Options for both FireSat II and SCS. While, in principle, we could evaluate all possible combinations, we try to find options that work together to meet mission objectives. The key design choices that determine most of the other elements are in bold.

Element	FireSat II		SCS	
	Option A	Option B	Option A	Option B
Mission Concept	**Automated fire detection on board the spacecraft with direct downlink**	**Manual fire detection at the ground station with results relayed via FireSat II**	Continuous voice, image, text, and slow video between remote user and local or CONUS command	Continuous voice, image, text, and slow video between remote user and local or CONUS command
Subject	Heat from forest fire	Heat from forest fire	**Phone built just for SCS users**	**Existing hand-held cell phone or equivalent**
Payload	Small-aperture IR	Large-aperture IR	Mid-sized comm., must accommodate variable range and angular size of Earth	Mid-size comm., fixed antenna, fixed power
Spacecraft Bus	Small, 3-axis, Earth-pointing	Mid-large size, 3-axis, Earth-pointing	Mid-size, 3-axis	Mid-size, 3-axis, Earth-pointing
Launch System	Small launch vehicle	Large launch vehicle	Mid-sized launch vehicle	Mid-sized launch vehicle
Orbit	**LEO, 2 satellites, 55 deg**	**Geosynchronous, 1 satellite centered over west coast of U.S.**	**3 or 4 satellites in Molniya orbits**	**3 or 4 satellites in mid-altitude, circular equatorial orbits**
Ground System	Single, dedicated ground station	Single, dedicated ground station	Multiple shared to ground station network	Single, dedicated ground station in CONUS
Communications Architecture	TDRS data downlink; commercial links to users	Direct to station; results relayed to users via FireSat II	Direct link to local command center; Use ground stations as relays for data return to CONUS	Direct link to local command center; Fixed crosslinks between all satellites gives redundant link to CONUS
Mission Operations	Continuous during fire season, partial otherwise	Continuous during fire season, partial otherwise	Continuous, nearly fully automated	Continuous, nearly fully automated

4.2 Defining Alternative Mission Concepts (Step 6)—How the Pieces Work Together

The broad *mission concept* is the most fundamental statement of how the mission will work—that is, how it gets its data or carries out the mission to satisfy the end users' needs. The mission concept as we are using it here consists of the four principal elements in Table 4-6. Notice that most of these elements are associated with data or information. Except for manufacturing in space and a small number of other space payloads, most space missions are concerned fundamentally with the generation or flow of information. Thus, FireSat II's mission is to generate and communicate to an end user information about forest fires. SCS and other communications satellites move data and information from one place to another. Weather, surveillance, and navigation satellites are all concerned with generating and communicating information. Thus, data flow is central to most space missions. How will FireSat II determine where a fire is and how big it is? How will the system communicate that information to the firefighter in a truck or plane? Once we answer these broad questions, we begin to understand FireSat II's abilities and limits.

As Table 4-7 shows, defining the mission concept consists of defining the various options that are available and then selecting the most appropriate. Section 4.3 describes how we define options and take a first cut at the broad choices available to us. The process of selecting among them, described in Sec. 5.4, is called *system trades*. Here we are interested in what these trades are and what some of the broader alternatives are to generate and transmit data. The process of defining how to transmit the data between the spacecraft and various users and controllers on the ground is called the *communications architecture* and is discussed in Chap. 16.

The program timeline differs from other elements of the mission concept in Table 4-7. It represents the overall schedule for developing, planning, and carrying out the mission. This defines whether it is a one-time only scientific experiment or a long-term operational activity that will require us to replace and update satellites. In either case, we must decide whether the need for the mission is immediate or long term. Should we give high priority to near-term schedules or allow more extensive planning and technology development for the mission? Of course, much of this has to do with the funding for the mission: whether money is available immediately or will be available only over time as we begin to demonstrate the mission's usefulness.

4.2.1 Data Delivery

Space missions involve two distinct types of data—mission data and housekeeping data. *Mission data* is generated, transmitted, or received by the mission payload. This is the basic information that is central to what the mission is all about. For FireSat II, this data starts out as infrared images on a focal plane and ends up as the latitude, longitude, and basic characteristics of a forest fire transmitted to a firefighter on the ground. The mission

Table 4-6. Elements of the Mission Concept. See Table 4-7 for a list of key trades and where discussed. Note that we discuss communications architecture in Chap. 16.

Element	Definition	FireSat II Example	SCS Example
Data Delivery	How mission and housekeeping data are generated or collected, distributed, and used	How is imagery collected? How are forest fires identified? How are the results transmitted to the firefighter in the field?	How do we get data to and from relief worker to the command post, either local or in CONUS?
Tasking, Scheduling, and Control	How the system decides what to do in the long term and short term	What sensors are active and when is data being transmitted and processed? Which forested areas are receiving attention this month?	Who controls SCS and sets its priorities?
Communications Architecture	How the various components of the system talk to each other	What communications network is used to transmit forest fire data to the users in the field?	How do the satellites talk to each other and to the ground?
Program Timeline	The overall schedule for planning, building, deployment, operations, replacement, and end-of-life	When will the first FireSat II become operational? What is the schedule for satellite replenishment?	When will the first SCS constellation become operational? What is the schedule for constellation augmentation and replenishment?

Table 4-7. Process for Defining the Mission Concept. See Table 4-6 for definitions and examples.

Step	Key Trades	Where Discussed
A. Define data delivery process for Mission and housekeeping data	Space vs. ground processing Level of autonomy Central vs. distributed processing	Sec. 4.2.1
B. Define tasking, scheduling, and control for Mission and housekeeping data for long term and short term	Level of autonomy Central vs. distributed control	Sec. 4.2.2
C. Define communications architecture for Mission and housekeeping data	Data rates bandwidth Timeliness of communications	Chap. 16
D. Define preliminary program timeline for Concept development Production and deployment Operations and end-of-life	Replenishment and end-of-life options Deployment strategy for multiple satellites Level of timeline flexibility	Sec. 4.2.3
E. Iterate and document	N/A	N/A

data has potentially very high data rates associated with it. However, the need for this data may be sporadic. Thus, FireSat II may generate huge quantities of raw data during periods of time that it is passing over the forests, but there is little need for this same level of data when it is over the poles or the oceans. For SCS the mission data is the communications content (voice, images, text, or data) between the soldier or relief worker and the local or CONUS command post. While the communications channel is intended to be continuously available, the usage will change greatly depending on the circumstances at the time.

Ultimately, the processed mission data may go directly to the end users or through ground stations and communication networks associated with mission operations. This will, of course, have a fundamental effect on how the mission works. In the first case, FireSat II would process its imagery and send the forest fire information as it is being observed to the firefighters in the field. In the second case, data would go instead to an operations center, where a computer system or human operators would evaluate it, compare it with previous data, and determine the location and characteristics of a forest fire. Then, the operations center would transmit this information to the firefighters in the field. The result is about the same in both cases, but the system's abilities, limits, characteristics, and costs may be very different. For SCS we are simply interested in moving data from place to place. Here, the ground station has relatively little to do with the data, unless it is serving as a relay from one place to another.

In contrast to the mission data, *housekeeping data* is the information used to support the mission itself—the spacecraft orbit and attitude, the battery temperature and state of charge, and the status and condition of all the spacecraft subsystems. Although FireSat II and SCS are very different missions, the housekeeping data is about the same for both of them, although there may be differences in the details, such as the accuracy required for various elements. Unlike the mission data, which is typically sporadic and may have huge data rates, the housekeeping data is usually continuous and at a low data rate. Continuously monitoring system performance does not require much information transfer by modern standards. In addition, rather than going to the end user, housekeeping data goes to the system monitoring and control activity within mission operations. Although housekeeping and mission data are distinct, we often need housekeeping data to

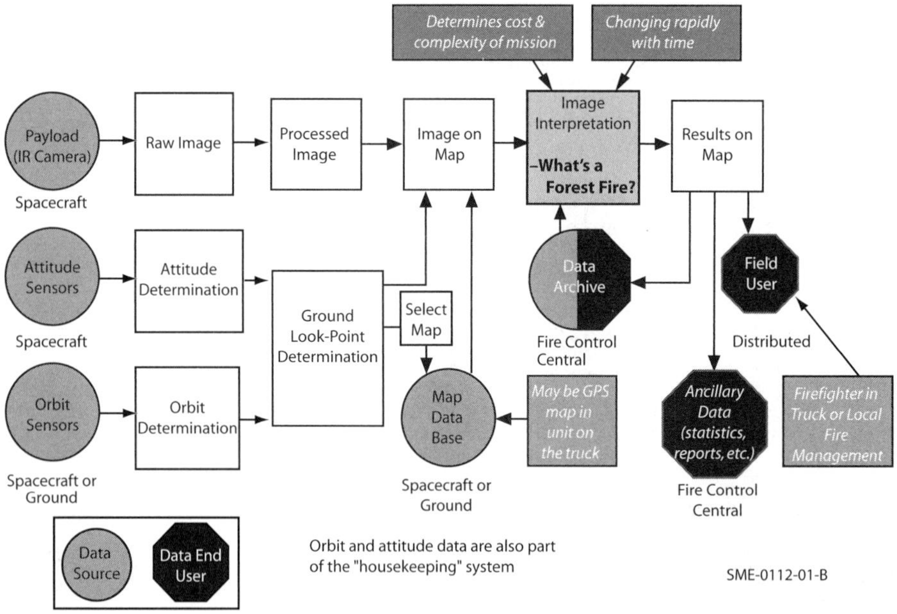

Fig. 4-2. FireSat II Data-Flow Diagram. The purpose of the data flow analysis is to view the space mission from a data-oriented perspective. We want to know where the data comes from, what processing must be done, and where the results are used. Our principal mission objective is to provide the necessary data to the end user in a timely manner at minimum cost and risk.

make the mission data useful. For example, we must know the spacecraft's orbit and attitude to determine the ground lookpoint of the payload sensors and thereby locate the fire. For SCS, we need to know which of the spacecraft can see which end users at any given time.

For both mission and housekeeping data, the data delivery system should be an information management-oriented process. We want to take a large amount of raw data, frequently from a variety of sensors or receivers, and either move that data to another user or efficiently transform it into the information the users need and provide it to them in a timely manner. For FireSat II, we do not know at first whether sending data directly to the field or sending it first to a mission operations center for interpretation and analysis is the best approach. But we do know our choice will dramatically affect how well the mission works and whether or not it is an efficient and effective system.

The principal trades associated with data delivery are:

- **Space vs. Ground**—how much of the data processing occurs on board the spacecraft vs. how much is done at mission operations or by the end user?
- **Central vs. Distributed Processing**—is one computer talking to another computer, or does one large central computer on the spacecraft or on the ground process everything?
- **Level of Autonomy***—how much do people need to intervene in order to provide intelligent analysis and minimize costs?

These trades are both strongly interrelated and are changing dramatically as the amount of processing available at low cost continues to increase. For example, autonomy is important by itself, but is also a key element of the space vs. ground trade. If human intervention is required (i.e., it can't be done autonomously), then the process must be done on the ground—or it must be a very large spacecraft. We will discuss each of these trades below after we have looked at the data delivery process as a whole. Autonomy is discussed in Sec. 4.2.2, because it is also critical to tasking and control.

The best way to start looking at the data-delivery problem is a *data-flow analysis*. This defines where the data originates and what has to happen to it before it gets to where it needs to go. To examine the data flow we use a *data-flow diagram* as shown in Fig. 4-2 for the FireSat II mission. A data-flow diagram lets us outline the tasks that we need to do, even though we don't understand yet how we will do most of them. For FireSat II we know that we need some type of information collection, probably a camera or imager or some other mechanism for detecting forest fires. As shown across the top row of Fig. 4-2 this imaging information must be digitized, probably filtered in some fashion, and its geographic coordinates determined. We must then interpret the image to identify whether a fire exists, put the results on the map, and distribute the map to the end user, i.e., the fire management team in the field or the individual firefighter in a truck out in the forest.

* The language here can be confusing. An *autonomous operation* runs without human intervention. An *autonomous spacecraft* runs without intervention from outside the spacecraft.

Even this very top-level flow suggests one of the major trades—where's the map? It could be at the mission operations center, it could be on the spacecraft, or it could be in the receiver in the truck, as is the case with GPS receivers. If the user's fire-monitoring receiver includes a GPS receiver and the associated maps, then all FireSat II would need to send down would be lat/long coordinates and perhaps some fire data, such as intensity or temperature. This could significantly decrease the bandwidth required to transmit data to the user and, therefore, lead to a lower cost, simpler FireSat II. (Recall from Sec. 3.2 that we created FireSat II to see if more modern technology could lead to a lower cost FireSat II that was more likely to be built than the original FireSat.) We don't know yet what the right answer is, but we want to watch as we go along for alternative ways to do things better, quicker, or at lower cost or risk.

To put the image on a map or determine its geographic coordinates, we need to determine the spacecraft's orbit and attitude. The attitude will almost certainly be determined on board. The orbit may be determined either on board or by observations from the ground. In either case, the orbit and attitude information are combined to determine where on the ground the sensor is looking.

Even though we are not certain yet how the data will be used, we can be fairly sure that our end data from FireSat II will have several applications other than immediate use by the firefighters. We will want to archive it in some central location for record keeping and improving our capacity to analyze and interpret future data. Finally, we will sort out a large amount of ancillary data, such as statistics, reports, and forest-management information, and use it over an extended period. The need for this data does not have the real-time demand of the fire data itself.

The importance of the data-flow diagram is that it lets us see what has to happen in order to make our mission work. For FireSat II, we need to combine the mission sensor with orbit and attitude information in order to make our system work in real time. However, the most difficult step is probably the one labeled "Image Interpretation—**What's a Forest Fire?**" Can an automated system quickly detect forest fires and send information directly to the user, or do we need extensive interpretation and analysis by trained experts in mission operations? What type of experiments or information must we have to determine which of these is best? Even after we have selected an approach, we should revisit it regularly to see that it still makes sense. If we decide that FireSat II's real-time requirements demand data processing in a computer on board the spacecraft, we may dramatically drive up the cost because on-board processing and software is expensive. Our mission analysis may result in an automated FireSat II that costs several times the annual budget of the Forest Service. If so, we need to reconsider whether it would be more economical to have an analyst on the ground interpret the data and then simply phone the results to an appropriate fire station. On the other hand, onboard processing has become dramatically cheaper and getting the data to a mission operations center in Philadelphia may be both complex and expensive if the fire is in California. The data-flow diagram is valuable in helping to identify and track these central issues.

SCS is a very different mission than FireSat II and this is reflected in the SCS data flow diagram in Fig. 4-3. Here, our goal is not to create data, but to get it back and forth continuously and reliably between a command post that can have good communications equipment, and an end user in the middle of a jungle, desert, or remote island hit by a tsunami, who almost certainly doesn't have good equipment and may have very little more than their cell phone. Here, it is likely that whatever equipment the end user has and the communications link that can be set up between them and the satellite will determine how well the job can be done. From our perspective of providing communications, the rest of the problem is relatively easy and we can concentrate most of our effort on what makes the problem the most workable with the equipment that the end user has or can get.

We will now look at two of the three principal trades associated with data delivery: space vs. ground processing and central vs. distributed processing. Section 4.2.2 discusses the level of autonomy.

Space vs. Ground Processing Trades. In most earlier space missions, ground stations processed nearly all of the data because spaceborne processors couldn't do much. Chapter 20 describes several reasons on-board processing lags ground processing. But many on-board processors are now available with greatly increased capacity, and in many cases, on-broad processing can be as capable as ground processing. Consequently, a major trade for future missions is how much to process data on board the spacecraft vs. on the ground, either at a mission-operations facility or with the end user.

Section 5.2 describes how we undertake these and other system trades and compare the results. The main issues in the space vs. ground trade are as follows:

Autonomy—How independent do we want the system to be of analysis and control by a mission operator? If evaluation by people is critical, we will likely do much of the data processing on the ground. If autonomous processing is appropriate, it can be done on board the spacecraft, at a central ground facility, or among the end users, as is the case with a GPS receiver. The level of autonomy is both a key trade in its own right and an element of the space vs. ground trade.

Data Latency—How late can the data get to the end user? If we are allowed only fractions of a second, we must go to automated processes, probably on board the spacecraft. For FireSat II, although we need the data in "near real time," the delays associated with sending the data to the ground for processing are not critical.

Communications Bandwidth—How much data needs to be transmitted? If we have large amounts of data from a sensor, we should process and compress it as near the source as possible. Bringing down all of the FireSat II imaging data and then deciding what to process further on the ground will cause an enormous communications problem and will probably drive up the FireSat II mission's cost needlessly. For SCS our problem is likely to be how large a data bandwidth can we achieve with the limited equipment available to the end user.

Single vs. Multiple Users—If there are a large number of end users, as would be the case for FireSat II, we may be able to save considerable money by doing a high level of processing on board the spacecraft and sending the results directly down to the individual users. However, processing in the end-user equipment is becoming very low cost. It may be more economical to simply let the user equipment do a good part of the work, such as plotting the forest data on a map.

Location of End User—Is the "end user" for any particular data element on the ground or in space? In a space-to-space relay or a system for providing automatic orbit maintenance, the end application is in space. In this case, sending data to the ground for processing and then returning the results to the space system is likely to be complex and costly. On the ground, the complexity of the system is strongly affected by whether there is one end user at the mission operations center or multiple, scattered users, as in the case of FireSat II and SCS.

Upgradability—In older space missions one of the reasons for doing processing on the ground was to be able to make changes and upgrades from time-to-time. However, software is the one piece of the spacecraft that we can get at and upgrade after launch. It may be cheaper and easier to upgrade software on board the spacecraft than to try to find and change the software in many ground units for either FireSat II or SCS.

Even if we choose to process data mostly in space, the basic system design should allow us to obtain or recreate selected raw data for analysis on the ground. A fully automated FireSat II should have some means to record or broadcast the raw imaging data, so mission planners and analysts can evaluate how well the system is working, fix problems, and plan alternative and better techniques for later missions.

In the past, space software has been much more expensive than ground software. Therefore, in many cases processing on the ground was generally lower cost than processing on board the spacecraft. However, this is changing rapidly and, therefore, software cost should not be a major trade element in the space vs. ground processing trade. Today, the cost of software is a function of what is done and how reliable we need to make it, rather than where it is done.

The space vs. ground processing trade will be a key issue for many future missions. For short-lived, non-time-critical missions, such as a student payload to measure material properties in 0-g, it will probably be more economical to work on the ground with little automation. For long-lived missions, or time-critical applications, we will have to automate the processing and then do space vs. ground trades to minimize the operations and end-user costs. In any case, we wish to use the data flow analysis to evaluate where the data is coming from and where it will be used. If possible, we would like to minimize the communication requirements and *associate* data (e.g., attach time or position tags) as early as possible after the relevant data has been created.

For FireSat II the payload sensor generates an enormous amount of data, most of which will not be useful. One way to effectively deal with large amounts of raw data on board the spacecraft is to *compress* the data (i.e., reduce the amount of data to be stored or transmitted) prior to transmitting it to the ground. The data is then recreated on the ground using *decompression* algorithms. There are a variety of methods for compressing data, both lossless and lossy. *Lossless data compression* implies that no information is lost due to compression while *lossy compression* has some "acceptable" level of loss. Lossless compression can achieve about a 5 to 1 ratio whereas lossy compression can achieve up to 80 to 1 reduction in data. Many of the methods of data compres-

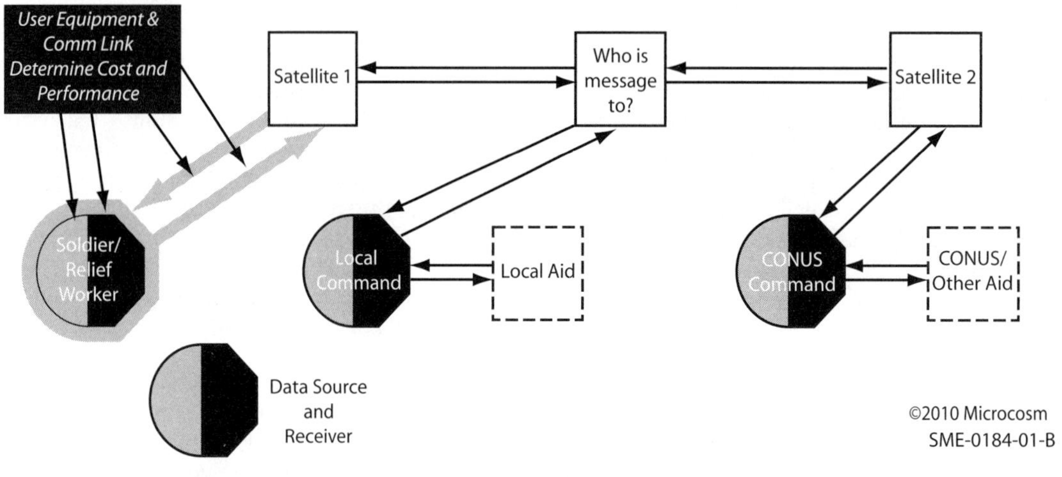

Fig. 4-3. SCS Data-Flow Diagram. For SCS, the problem is establishing reliable two-way communications and our principal problem area is communicating with the end user in the field.

sion store data only when the value changes. Other approaches are based on quantization where a range of values is compressed using mathematical algorithms or fractal mathematics. By using these methods, we can compress the data to a smaller data set that is transmitted to the ground and the image is recreated based on the decompression algorithm. With the use of fractals, we can even interpolate a higher resolution solution than we started with by running the fractal for an extended period of time [Lu, 1997]. We select a method for data compression based on its strengths and weaknesses, the critical nature of the data, and the need to recreate it exactly [Sayood, 2005].

When we transmit housekeeping data we will generally use lossless compression for several reasons. First, raw housekeeping data is not typically voluminous. Second, it is important that none of the data is lost due to compression. However, when we transmit an image we might easily use lossy compression. We could either preview the image using lossy compression or we could say that the recovered image is "good enough." Alternatively, given the advances in on-board storage, we may choose to take very high-resolution imagery and send it to the ground in a low-resolution version. Either the operator or end user could select those images for which they wanted more detail, transmit that request to the spacecraft, and get high-resolution imagery only of those data frames where it was needed. For FireSat II, if the forest fire identification is done on board, we might choose to send to the ground only high-resolution imagery of the area within, say, 0.5 km of an identified fire.

This process is indicative of a broader trade across the space community. On one hand, there is an ever-increasing demand for more bandwidth. Thousands of years ago, when dinosaurs roamed the plains of North America, cell phones were used only for phone calls. Now they are used for sending full-color images. We may anticipate that they will soon be used for 3-D, high-resolution, video. On the other hand, while our firefighter in the field may want to see a high-resolution picture so that they can interpret for themselves what actions are most appropriate, it is unlikely that they really want a continuous 3-D movie of the fire. They're pretty busy doing other things. Somehow we need to determine what the right amount of information is and how to get it to the end user.

Although the problem is very different, much the same analysis applies to SCS. Here we are not creating data, only transmitting it. What we need to transmit is the amount of data that the end user and the command post want to send, which may vary greatly, depending on the circumstances.

Central vs. Distributed Processing Trade. This is a relatively new issue, because most older spacecraft did not have sufficient processing capability to make this a meaningful trade. However, as discussed above, the situation has changed. The common question now is, "how many computers should the spacecraft have?" Typically, weight and parts-count-conscious engineers would like to avoid distributed processing. However, centralized processing can make integration and test extremely difficult. Because integration and test of both software and hardware may drive cost and schedule, we must seriously consider them as part of the processing trade.

Our principal recommendations in evaluating central vs. distributed processing are:

- Group like-functions together
- Group functions where timing is critical in a single computer
- Look for potentially incompatible functions before assigning multiple functions to one computer
- Maintain the interface between groups and areas of responsibility outside of the computer
- Give serious consideration to integration and test before grouping multiple functions in a single computer

Grouping like-functions has substantial advantages. For example, attitude determination and attitude control may well reside in the same computer. They use much of the same data, share common algorithms, and may have time-critical elements. Similarly, orbit determination and control could reasonably reside in a single navigation computer, together with attitude determination and control. These hardware and software elements are likely to be the responsibility of a single group and will tend to undergo common integration and testing.

In contrast, adding payload processing to the computer doing the orbit and attitude activities could create major problems. We can't fully integrate software and hardware until after we have integrated the payload and spacecraft bus. In addition, two different groups usually handle the payload and spacecraft bus activities. The design and manufacture of hardware and software may well occur in different locations following different approaches. Putting these functions together in a single computer greatly increases cost and risk during the integration and test process, at a time when schedule delays are extremely expensive.

Another problem which can arise from time-to-time is incompatible functions, that is, activities which do not work well together. One example would be sporadic, computationally-intensive functions which demand resources at the same time. Another example occurs when the initial processing of either spacecraft bus or payload sensors may well be an interrupt-driven activity in which the computer is spending most of its time servicing interrupts to bring in observation data. This could make it difficult for the same computer to handle computationally-intensive processing associated with higher-level activities. This can be accommodated either by having the functions handled in separate computers or using a separate I/O processor to queue data from the process with a large number of interrupts.

Finally, we must consider the groups who oversee different activities. Integration and test of any computer and its associated software will be much more difficult if two distinct groups develop software for the same computer. In this case, significant delays and risks can occur. This does not necessarily mean, however, that elements controlled by different groups cannot be accommodated in the same computer. One approach might be to have two engineering groups be responsible for development of specifications and ultimately for testing. The detailed specifications are then handed over to a single programming group, which then implements them in a single computer. This allows a single group to be responsible for control of computer resources. Thus, for example, the orbit control and attitude control functions may be specified and tested by different analysis groups. However, it may be reasonable to implement both functions in a single computer by a single group of programmers.

4.2.2 Tasking, Scheduling, and Control

Tasking, scheduling, and control is the other end of the data-delivery problem. If the purpose of our mission is to provide data or information, how do we decide what information to supply, whom to send it to, and where to obtain it? Many of the issues are the same as in data delivery but with several key differences. Usually, tasking and control involve very low data rates and substantial decision-making. Thus, we should emphasize how planning and control decisions are made rather than data management.

Tasking and scheduling typically occur in two distinct time frames. *Short-term tasking* addresses what the spacecraft should be doing at this moment. Should SCS be recharging its batteries, sending data to a ground station, turning to look at a disaster relief area, or simply looking at the World below waiting for someone to start sending data? In contrast, *long-term planning* establishes general tasks the system should do. For example, in some way the FireSat II system must decide whether to concentrate its resources on northwestern Pacific forests for several weeks before beginning to look systematically at forests in Brazil. During concept exploration, we don't need to know precisely how these decisions are made. We simply want to identify them and know broadly how they will occur.

On the data distribution side, direct downlink of data works well. We can process data on board, send it simultaneously to various users on the ground, and provide a low-cost, effective system. On the other hand, direct distributed control raises serious problems of tasking, resource allocation, and responsibility. The military community wants distributed control so a battlefield commander can control resources to meet mission objectives. For FireSat II and SCS, this would translate into the local commanders deciding how much resource to apply in a particular area. The two problems here are the limited availability of resources in space and broad geographic coverage. For example, both FireSat II and SCS may have limited power or data rates. In either case, if one regional office controls the system for a time, they may use most or all of that resource, such that other users would have very little left. Also, both systems could be in a position to cover different areas of interest at the same time. Distributed control can create conflicts that are in need of a process for resolution.

For most space systems, some level of centralized control is probably necessary to determine how to allocate space resources among various tasks. Within this broad resource allocation, however, we may have room for distributed decisions on what data to collect and make available, as well as how to process it. For example, the remote fire station may be interested in information from a particular spectral band that could provide clues on the characteristics of a particular fire. If this is an appropriate option, the system must determine how to feed that request back to the satellite. We could use a direct command, or, more likely, send a request for specific data to mission operations, which then carries out the request.

Note that this problem with local control arises largely from the fact that space resources are inherently expensive, so we are trying to optimize the use of the resource. It is rather like asking who should be allowed to use the government's car. That's a reasonable question if each car costs a significant fraction of the budget of a government organization. If cars become more economical, it's reasonable to have a car assigned to a particular person, although others may use it from time to time. If spacecraft become less expensive then we could reasonably assign different space resources to individual military commanders who can then depend on them being available to meet their mission needs. In this model, distributed control by individual commanders may be a good choice.

Spacecraft Autonomy. Usually, high levels of autonomy and independent operations occur in the cheapest and most expensive systems. The less costly systems have minimal tasking and control simply because they cannot afford the operations cost of deciding what needs to be done. Most often, they continuously carry on one of a few activities, such as receiving and relaying radio messages or continuously transmitting an image of what is directly under the spacecraft. What is done is determined automatically on board to save money. In contrast, the most expensive systems have autonomy for technical reasons, such as the need for a very rapid response (missile detection systems), or a problem of very long communications delays (interplanetary missions). Typically, autonomy of this type is extremely expensive because the system must make complex, reliable decisions and respond appropriately to changes.

Autonomy can also be a critical issue for long missions and for constellations, in which cost and reliability are key considerations. For example, long-duration orbit maneuvers may use electric propulsion, which is highly efficient, but slow. (See Chap. 18 for details.) Thruster firings are ordinarily controlled and monitored from the ground, but electric propulsion maneuvers may take several months. Because monitoring and controlling long thruster burns would cost too much, electric propulsion requires some level of autonomy.

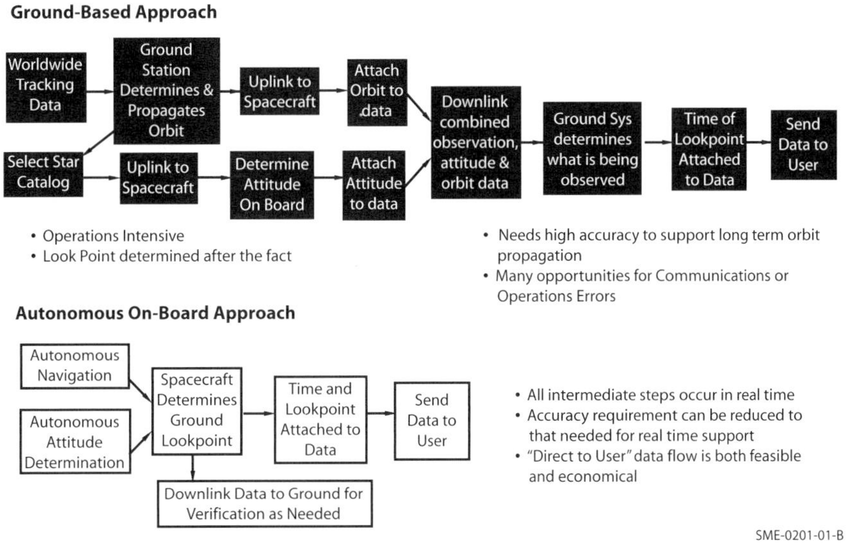

Fig. 4-4. Comparison of Traditional vs. Autonomous Approach to Satellite Navigation. In some circumstances, use of autonomous operations may significantly reduce mission complexity and thereby increase reliability and reduce cost.

As shown in Fig. 4-4, autonomy can add to mission reliability simply by reducing the complexity of mission operations. We may need to automate large constellations for higher reliability and lower mission operations costs. Maintaining the relative positions between the satellites in a constellation is routine but requires many computations. Thus, it is at least possible that on-board automation—with monitoring and operator override if necessary—will give us the best results.

With the increased level of on-board processing available, it is clearly possible to create fully autonomous satellites. The question is, should we do so or should we continue to control satellites predominantly from the ground?

Three main functions are associated with spacecraft control: controlling the payload, controlling the attitude of the spacecraft and its appendages, and controlling the spacecraft orbit. Many space payloads and bus systems do not require real-time control except for changing mode or handling anomalies. Thus, both the FireSat II and SCS payloads will probably fly rather autonomously until a command changes a mode or an anomaly forces the payload to make a change or generate a warning. Autonomous, or at least semi-autonomous, payloads are reasonable for many satellites. There are, of course, exceptions such as Hubble Space Telescope, which is an ongoing series of experiments being run by different principal investigators from around the world. In this case, operators control the payload, although we would still use some automatic operations to save money or to make the operator's job easier.

Controlling the attitude of the spacecraft and its appendages is done autonomously on board for nearly all satellites. Controlling the attitude from the ground is too expensive and too risky. The attitude control system on board most spacecraft provides various attitude control modes and can work over extended periods with little or no intervention from the ground.

Ground control has remained strongest in orbit maintenance and control, in which virtually all thruster firings intended to change the orbit are set up and enabled by ground command. This ground control will probably continue whenever large rocket engines produce orbit maneuvers such as when a kick stage moves the satellite from a parking orbit into a geosynchronous transfer orbit. Once in their operational orbit, however, many satellites either leave the orbit entirely uncontrolled or simply maintain the orbit at a given altitude or within a given window. In this case, low-thrust propulsion is both feasible and desirable because it is much less disturbing to the normal spacecraft environment. Low-thrust orbit maneuvers have been used on geosynchronous spacecraft for a long time so normal satellite operations can continue during the course of these stationkeeping maneuvers.

With low-thrust propulsion and current technology, such as GPS, for autonomous navigation, autonomous orbit control is cheap, easy, and inherently less risky than autonomous attitude control. If the attitude control system stops working for even a short time, the spacecraft can have serious problems, including loss of power, loss of control, and pointing of sensitive payloads toward the Sun. In contrast, if we lose low-thrust orbit control for a while, nothing disastrous happens to the spacecraft. The spacecraft proceeds in its orbit drifting slowly out of its assigned position. This is easily detected and corrected by the ground, assuming that the orbit control system didn't fail completely. (For a more extended discussion of autonomous orbit control, see Wertz and Gurevich [2001a, 2001b], and Plam et al. [2008].)

Current satellite technology allows us to have fully autonomous, low-cost satellites. Autonomy can reduce cost and risk while enabling mission operations people to

Table 4-8. Principal Elements of the Mission Timeline. Key milestones in the mission or project timeline can have a significant effect on how the space system is designed and operated.

Element	Typically Driven By	Where Discussed
Planning and Development	Funding constraints System need date	Sec. 3.5 Sec. 3.4
Production	Funding constraints Technology development System need date	Sec. 3.5, Chap. 14 Sec. 1.3 Sec. 3.4
Initial Launch	Spacecraft completion Launch availability System need date	Chap. 14 Chaps. 26, 27 Sec. 3.4
Constellation Build-up (if applicable)	Production schedule Launch availability Satellite lifetime	Sec. 23.5 Chaps. 26, 27 Sec. 3.4, Chap. 30
Normal Mission Operations	Planned operational life Satellite lifetime (planned or failure constrained)	Chap. 29 Sec. 3.4, Chap. 30
Replenishment	Production schedule Failure of on-orbit satellites Launch availability Satellite lifetime (planned or failure constrained)	Sec. 23.5 Chaps. 23, 24 Chaps. 26, 27 Sec. 3.4, Chap. 30
End-of-Mission Disposal	Legal and political constraints Danger to other spacecraft	Chap. 30 Sec. 7.5

do what they do best—solve problems, handle anomalies, and make long-term decisions. I believe that fully autonomous satellites, including autonomous orbit maintenance, will come about over the next decade as lower costs and risks, validated by on-orbit experiments, begin to outweigh the value of tradition.

4.2.3 Mission Timeline

The *mission timeline* is the overall schedule from concept definition through production, operations, and ultimately replenishment, and end-of-mission. It covers individual satellites and the whole system. Table 4-8 shows the mission timeline's main parts and where they are discussed. Notice that two distinct, potentially conflicting, demands can drive planning and production. One is the demand for a particular schedule or time by which the system must be operational. Thus, a mission to Halley's Comet depends on launching a satellite in time to rendezvous with the comet. On the other hand, funding constraints frequently slow the mission and cause schedule gaps that add both cost and further delays. Of course, funding constraints can affect much more than timelines. They can determine whether we will do a mission, as well as its scope.

If the mission involves a constellation of satellites, a key timeline driver is the need to have the full constellation up for most of the satellite's lifetime. If a single satellite will last 5 years and we need a constellation of 50, we'll never get a full constellation with a launch rate of 5 per year. If having the full constellation is important, we must deploy the initial constellation within 20–25% of an individual satellite's lifetime. This schedule allows some margin for almost inevitable delays as difficulties arise during the mission. If the constellation must remain complete, we need to plan for regular replenishment of satellites. We can replenish on a predefined timeline, as satellites wear out or become technically obsolete, or we can respond to on-orbit failures, collisions, or other catastrophic events that "kill" a particular satellite.

Two areas of the mission timeline typically do not receive adequate attention during concept exploration: performance with less than a full set of satellites while building up the constellation, and end-of-life disposal. In a constellation of satellites we would like to increase performance levels as we add satellites. If FireSat II or SCS are constellations, we want to achieve some level of utility with the first satellite launch and more with each added launch until all satellites are in place. As described further in Sec. 10.6, designers of constellations often concentrate only on the full constellation's performance. However, the period of time before the constellation is fully in place can frequently be long and may well be a critical phase, since a large fraction of the funding has been spent, but full capability has not been achieved. Thus, it is particularly important for constellation design to take into account the problem of performance with less than a full set of satellites. In addition, we want graceful degradation, so a satellite failure will still allow strong performance until we replace the failed satellite. These issues are important during concept exploration because they may significantly affect the design of the constellation and the entire system.

There is now growing concern with disposal of satellites after their useful life in orbit. We have already recognized this need for geosynchronous satellites because the geosynchronous ring is rapidly filling. But it

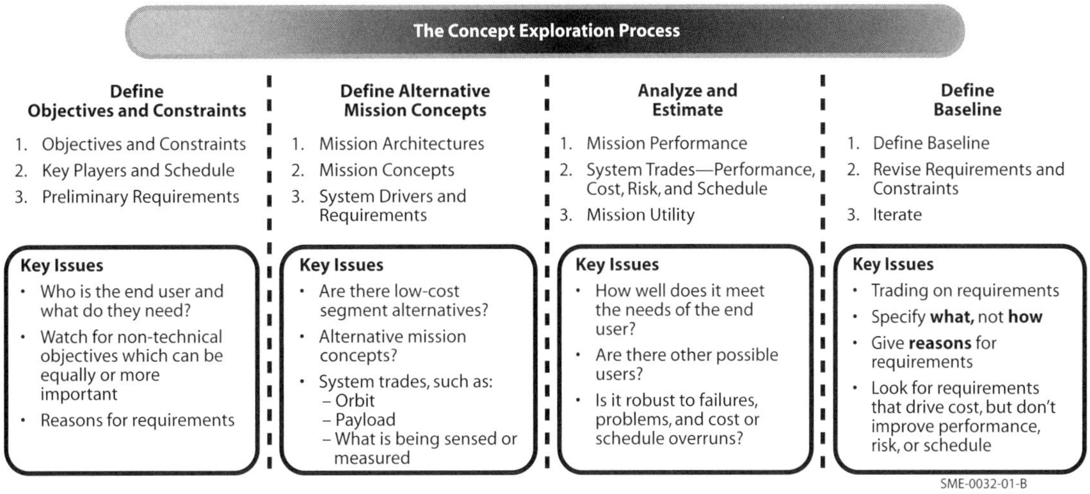

Fig. 4-5. Concept Exploration is the Early Part of the Overall Space Mission Engineering Process shown in Table 3-1. See text for discussion.

is also very important for low-Earth orbit constellations in which debris and spent satellites left in the pattern can threaten the remaining constellation, as occured with the collision between Iridium 33 and Cosmos 2251 in February, 2009. Again, we must address this issue early in concept definition.

4.3 Introduction to Concept Exploration

Concept exploration is the early part of the overall space mission engineering process in which we look at different ways to meet the needs of both the customer and end user. As summarized in Fig. 4-5, this process can be broadly divided into four parts:

- **Defining the objectives and key players** (Chap. 3). Here the key issues are who the key players are, what do they need to accomplish, and what are the reasons for the various requirements that we will create along the way?
- **Defining the alternative mission concepts** (Chap. 4). Here we ask what elements we will bring together to do the mission (the *mission architecture*) and how they will work together to meet the user's needs (the *mission concept*). The key questions here are looking at alternative mission concepts, finding the system drivers and critical requirements, and trying to find low-cost solutions that could do the job better at lower cost.
- **Analyzing the mission and estimating how well it works** (Secs. 5.1 to 5.4). This gets to the heart of the matter by asking in a quantitative way how well we can do what we set out to do. How many lives and how much property can be saved by building FireSat II or how much better can we be at responding to disasters by building SCS?
- **Defining the baseline approach and evaluating alternatives** (Secs. 5.5 and 5.6). Here we want to go back and re-examine the requirements and constraints to see if these are really the way to best meet our overall mission objectives. We also want to look for requirements that drive cost, but don't improve performance or reduce risk or schedule.

Throughout concept exploration a key step is to document the reasons for various choices. The purpose here is to allow ourselves or others to re-examine these choices at a later date. Space mission engineering and concept exploration are highly iterative. We go back many times to look at alternatives and try to find better ways of achieving our objectives. If we don't document the reasons for choices then we have to either assume that they were written on stone tablets and are defined to be correct or redo the analysis on which they were based, neither of which is a good solution.

You may sense a trend in this discussion that we are looking for alternatives, for new ways of doing things better, faster, cheaper, or all three. That's what concept exploration is all about. We may find that our first approach turns out to be the very best way to do the mission. Or we may find alternative approaches or new technologies that can provide a better approach. Airplanes and automobiles are continuously evolving—much of it based on the continuing advances in performance and reduction in mass and cost of electronics. Large numbers of electronic systems started primarily in expensive cars to allow them to do things with more precision and, in many cases, simply wow the buyer or passenger. Now electronic systems can make the car perform better and safer and be lighter and lower cost. Can we use these same electronic systems or approaches to allow a 100 kg spacecraft to do what a 1,000 kg spacecraft used to do? That, of course, depends on what we're asking the spacecraft to do. But most systems built today, from cameras to telephones to automobiles and airplanes are smaller, lower cost, and more competent than they were decades ago. Advances in microelectronics led to a whole new approach in aviation. Maybe we don't need to have the pilot actually on the airplane. What if we could have the pilot in an office somewhere flying an airplane via remote control? Unmanned aerial vehicles, UAVs, are now commonplace and likely to become much more so as a new idea in aviation gains acceptance.

It isn't just more use of microelectronics, but all aspects of the space mission, that we want to look at and challenge. What can SCS do to make it easier for the soldier in a remote location or a disaster relief worker to get their job done safer and more quickly? Can FireSat II detect forest fires by looking at something other than the heat from the fire? Can it look at the light or smoke or increase in CO_2? Is there a better way to communicate the information to the people who need it? Can we combine the space asset with other assets to do the job better, faster, and cheaper? All of these are a part of concept exploration.

Once we have established alternative mission concepts, architectures, and system drivers, we must further define the mission concepts in enough detail to allow a meaningful comparison of the alternatives. For concept exploration, the steps in this process correspond to the space mission elements. Figure 4-5 above illustrates the sequence of activities. The definition of objectives and constraints was discussed in Chap. 3. Each of the steps in defining alternative mission concepts is described below and summarized in Table 4-9. **Our goal is to develop just enough detail to allow quantitative comparisons between the alternatives.**

A. Define the Preliminary Mission Concept (Chap. 4)

As described in Sec. 4.2, the key elements are data delivery, tasking, scheduling, and control, communications architecture, and mission timeline. We begin with a broad concept and refine this concept as we define the various mission elements in the steps below.

B. Define the Subject Characteristics (Sec. 15.2)

We can divide space missions into two broad categories. Missions with *active* or *controllable subjects* service other system elements, typically run by the operators or users, such as Comsat ground stations or GPS navigation receivers. Missions with *passive* subjects sense elements that are not a part of the mission system, such as the galaxies observed by a space telescope. Our first step in defining the system elements is to determine the subject's key characteristics. If a mission interacts with user equipment, we must define the subject characteristics either from known information for well-established services or by a trade study involving the rest of the system. The parameters for specifying passive subjects are largely the same as those for specifying user elements, except that we don't have a "receiver" to characterize, and the effective isotropic radiated power (EIRP) specification for the transmitter is replaced by the definition of the object's emission intensity as a function of the wavelength. Table 4-10 summarizes the characteristics of both types of elements.

Table 4-9. Summary of the Process for Defining Alternative Mission Concepts. See text for details.

	Step	Where Discussed
A	Define the preliminary mission concept	Chap. 4
B	Define the subject characteristics	Sec. 15.2
C	Determine the orbit or constellation characteristics	Chap. 10
D	Determine payload size and performance	Chaps. 15, 16, 17
E	Select the mission operations approach	
	• Communications architecture	Sec. 16.2
	• Ground system	Chap. 28
	• Operations	Chap. 29
F	Design the spacecraft bus to meet payload, orbit, and communications requirements	Chaps. 14, 18–23
G	Select a launch and orbit transfer system	Chap. 26
H	Determine deployment, logistics, and end-of-life strategies	Chaps. 23, 27, 30
I	Provide costing support	Chap. 11
J	Look for major alternatives	Chaps. 13, 25
K	Document and Iterate	Sec. 6.4

C. Determine the Orbit and Constellation Characteristics (Chap. 10)

The mission orbit influences every part of space mission development and operation. Combined with the number of spacecraft, it determines all aspects of space-to-ground and ground-to-space sensor and communication coverage. For the most part, the orbit determines sensor resolution, transmitter power, and data rate. The orbit determines the spacecraft environment and, for military spacecraft, strongly influences survivability. Finally, the orbit determines the size and cost of the launch and delivery system. Chapter 10 gives detailed directions for orbit design. As Table 4-11 shows, the design should include parameters for the mission and transfer orbits, propellant requirements, and constella-

Table 4-10. Characteristics of Space Mission Subjects. See Chap. 16 for definitions of communications parameters.

Controllable Subjects	Passive Subjects
1. Quantity	*1.* Quantity and Distribution
2. Location or range	*2.* Location or range
3. Transmitter EIRP	*3.* Emission intensity (W/sr) as a function of frequency or spectral band
4. Receiver G/T	*4.* Needed resolution
5. Frequency and bandwidth	*5.* Needed temporal coverage (duty cycle)
6. Duty cycle	
7. Processing capability	

Table 4-11. Summary of Orbit and Constellation Characteristics for Earth Orbit. See Chaps. 9 and 10 for discussion. See Sec. 10.7 for interplanetary orbits.

1	Altitude	These are the most important
2	Inclination	
3	Eccentricity	
4	Argument of perigee for noncircular orbits	
5	ΔV budget for orbit transfer	
6	ΔV budget for orbit maintenance	
7	Whether orbit will be controlled or uncontrolled	
8	Number and relative orientation of orbit planes (constellations)	
9	Number and spacing of spacecraft per orbit plane (constellations)	
10	Collision avoidance and debris mitigation strategy	

tion characteristics. As space becomes more crowded, a key, but often overlooked, element is designing constellations for collision avoidance and debris mitigation. The problem is discussed in detail in Sec. 7.5 and possible solutions are discussed in Sec. 13.1.1 (See Fig. 13-2).

D. Determine the Payload Size and Performance (Chaps. 15, 16, and 17)

We next use the subject characteristics from Step B and orbit characteristics from Step C to create a mission payload concept. We can divide most mission payloads into six broad categories: observation or sensing, communications, navigation, in situ sampling and observations, sample return, and crew life support and transportation. More than 90% of current space-system payloads observe, sense, or communicate. Even navigation payloads are basically communications payloads with ancillary data processing and stable time-base equipment to provide the navigation signal. Detailed directions for sizing and definition appear in Chap. 16 for communications payloads and in Chap. 17 for observation payloads. Table 4-12 summarizes the key parameters we need to specify.

Table 4-12. Summary of Typical Payload Characteristics. For multiple payloads, we must determine parameters for each payload.

1. Physical Parameters
- 1.1 Envelope dimensions
- 1.2 Mass properties
- 1.3 Moving parts

2. Viewing and Pointing
- 2.1 Aperture size and shape
- 2.2 Size and orientation of clear field of view required
- 2.3 Primary pointing direction*
- 2.4 Pointing direction range and accuracy required
- 2.5 Tracking or scanning rate
- 2.6 Pointing or tracking duration

3. Electrical Power
- 3.1 Voltage
- 3.2 Average and peak power
- 3.3 Standby, operating

4. Operations
- 4.1 Operating modes
- 4.2 Duty cycle
- 4.3 Need for eclipse operations

5. Telemetry and Commands
- 5.1 Number of command and telemetry channels
- 5.2 Command memory size and time resolution
- 5.3 Data rates or quantity of data

6. Thermal Control
- 6.1 Temperature limits (operating/non-operating)
- 6.2 Heat rejection to space (average and peak, duty cycle)

*e.g., Sun, stars, nadir, ground target, another spacecraft

System-level payload trades typically involve the user element, selecting a mission orbit, and allocating pointing and tracking functions between the payload and spacecraft elements. User element trades involve balancing the performance of the payload and user equipment to get the lowest overall system cost for a given orbit and constellation design. As an example, if a single geosynchronous spacecraft must service thousands of ground stations, such as direct broadcast TV, we would minimize the system cost by selecting a large, powerful spacecraft that can broadcast to simple and inexpensive ground terminals. A system designed for high bandwidth communication between half a dozen ground stations uses more complex and capable ground systems and saves cost with a simpler spacecraft.

Payload vs. orbit trades typically try to balance the resolution advantages of low altitude against the fewer spacecraft needed for the same coverage at higher altitudes. At a higher altitude, we need a sensor with a larger aperture and better sensitivity to obtain the same resolution; the more capable sensor both costs more and needs a larger spacecraft and launch system.

Payload vs. spacecraft trades usually try to meet pointing and tracking requirements at the lowest cost. At one extreme, the payload does all the pointing independently of the spacecraft attitude; an example is the use of gimballed scan platforms on the Mariner MK-II spacecraft. At the opposite extreme, Space Telescope and Chandra X-Ray Observatory point the entire spacecraft with the required level of accuracy. An intermediate approach is to point the entire spacecraft to a lower level of accuracy, allowing the payload to do fine pointing over a limited field of regard.

E. Select the Mission Operations Approach: Communications Architecture, Ground System, and Operations (Sec. 16.2, Chaps. 28 and 29)

We next select and size the elements needed to support communications and control of the spacecraft and payload. Table 4-13 gives the key parameters. Typically a *mission operations control center* commands and controls the spacecraft and delivers data to the user. With rare exceptions, we would choose an existing control center, based on the user's needs, downlink data rates, and, in some cases, security considerations. Both NASA and the Air Force have existing systems. Some institutions, such as Intelsat, use custom systems. Most commercial operators employ system-specific control centers. If needed, we can interconnect most systems with different options for relaying communications.

Table 4-13. Summary of Mission Operations Characteristics.

1. Communications Architecture	
1.1	Number and distribution of ground stations
1.2	Downlink and uplink path design
1.3	Crosslink characteristics, if used
1.4	Relay satellites used
1.5	Communications link budget
1.6	Space-to-ground data rates
2. Ground System	
2.1	Use of existing or dedicated facilities
2.2	Use of facilities
2.3	Required transmit and receive characteristics
2.4	Required data handling
3. Operations	
3.1	Level of automation
3.2	Software to be created
3.3	Full-time or part-time staffing
3.4	Number of personnel
3.5	Amount of commanding required
3.6	Getting the data to the end user
3.7	Timeliness of data distribution

The *communications architecture* transfers the required mission data (payload and housekeeping data) from the spacecraft down to the mission operations control center. In addition, we must send commands back to the spacecraft, and meet other requirements such as encryption. Thus, we select the communications relay elements along with the mission control system after most payload and orbit trades are complete. Typical options are SGLS for Air Force missions or TDRSS, DSN, or STDN with the NASA mission control centers. Custom systems are required for some applications and are commonly used for commercial missions in geosynchronous orbit. Chapter 16 describes communications architectures, and Chap. 29 treats operations.

F. Design the Spacecraft Bus to Meet Payload, Orbit, and Communications Requirements (Chaps. 14, 18 to 23)

The spacecraft and its subsystems support the payload in the mission orbit—point it and supply power, commands, data handling, and thermal control. They must be compatible with the communications architecture and mission-operations concept. These elements, along with the launch system, drive the spacecraft design. We usually choose the launch system that costs the least to place the minimum required weight in the mission or transfer orbit. Once we make this selection, the spacecraft's stowed configuration is constrained by the shroud volume of the selected vehicle or vehicles. Table 4-14 summarizes the items we need to specify while defining the spacecraft. Chapter 14 covers how we synthesize spacecraft concepts and their definition and sizing.

A key spacecraft vs. launch system trade is the use of integral propulsion. Many commercial spacecraft ride the launch system to transfer orbit and then insert themselves into the mission orbit using integral propulsion or an internal stage. Some spacecraft depend on a launch system with an upper stage for insertion directly into the mission orbit. They do not carry large integral propulsion subsystems.

Table 4-14. Summary of Spacecraft Characteristics. See Chapter 14 for discussion.

1. General arrangement including payload fields of view (deployed and stowed)	
2. Functional block diagram	
3. Mass properties, by mission phase (mass and moments of inertia)	
4. Summary of subsystem characteristics	
4.1	***Power:*** conversion approach; array and battery size; orbit average and peak payload power; orbit average and peak overall spacecraft power
4.2	***Attitude control:*** attitude determination and control components; operating modes; ranges and accuracy
4.3	***Navigation and orbit control:*** accessing requirements; use of GPS; on-board vs. ground
4.4	***Telemetry and command*:** command/telemetry format; command and time resolution; telemetry storage capacity; number of channels by type
4.5	***Computer*:** speed and memory; data architecture
4.6	***Propulsion*:** amount and type of propellant; thruster or motor sizes
4.7	***Communications*:** link margins for all links; command uplink data rate; telemetry downlink data rates
4.8	***Primary structure and deployables***
4.9	***Unique thermal requirements***
4.10	***Timing*:** resolution and accuracy
5. System parameters	
5.1	Lifetime and reliability
5.2	Level of autonomy
5.3	End of life and system disposal

Another trade between the spacecraft and launch system involves guidance of the upper stage. Often, the spacecraft control system can guide the upper stage, which may allow deletion of equipment from that stage, thereby increasing performance and lowering cost. This trade is particularly important when using 3-axis-stabilized stages.

G. Select a Launch and Orbit Transfer System (Chap. 26)

The launch system and its upper stage need to deliver the spacecraft to the mission orbit or to a transfer orbit from which the spacecraft can reach the mission orbit on its own. The chosen launch system usually determines the launch site. The launch site organization provides prelaunch processing, checkout, and installation to the launch vehicle, often on the launch pad as described in Chap. 27.

Launch vehicles and upper stages may be combined in many ways to match almost any combination of payload and mission orbit. Chapter 26 details the characteristics and selection of launch systems. Selecting a launch system typically involves the trades with the spacecraft discussed above. In addition, we must decide between a single spacecraft launch and manifesting two or more spacecraft in a shared launch. In general, multiple manifesting costs less, but constrains the schedule. Finally, we should bring some launch system parameters to the system level design process: type of vehicle, cost per launch, and flow times for processing and prelaunch activities at the launch site.

H. Determine Logistics, Deployment, Replenishment, and Spacecraft Disposal Strategies (Chaps. 23, 27, and 30)

Logistics is the process of planning to supply and maintain the space mission over time. Whereas only military missions typically demand formal plans, the process described in Chap. 23 can strongly affect costs for any multi-year mission requiring extended support. Historically, most life-cycle costs have been locked in by the end of concept exploration, so we must evaluate operations, support, and replenishment during this phase.

Planners often overlook the sequence for building up and maintaining satellite constellations. To deploy a constellation effectively, we must create performance plateaus which allow us to deploy in stages and to degrade the system gracefully if individual satellites fail. These performance plateaus develop from the constellation design, as described in Sec. 10.6.

Section 7.5 describes the ever-increasing problem associated with *orbital debris,* consisting of defunct satellites and associated parts. Because of this problem, all new satellite designs should plan for de-orbiting or otherwise disposing of satellites at the end of their useful life, as discussed in Chap. 30. In particular, satellites must be removed from areas such as the geostationary ring, where they would seriously threaten other spacecraft, and from any low-Earth orbit constellation.

I. Provide Costing Support for the Concept-Definition Activity (Chap. 11)

Developing costs for system elements is vital to two objectives: finding the best individual mission architecture and comparing mission architectures at the system level. Chapter 11 describes parametric, analogous, and bottoms-up methods for costing. Typically, for concept exploration, we use only the first two because we lack a detailed definition of the design. At this level, we simply want relative comparisons rather than absolute estimates, so we can accept the greater uncertainty in these methods.

J. Look for Major Alternatives (Chaps. 13 and 25)

As discussed previously in Step D, a key characteristic of reducing mission cost is to look for major alternatives for one of the principal mission elements. Iridium, for example, was the first communications satellite system to choose a low Earth orbit, where all previous communications satellites had been in GEO or in a Molniya highly elliptical orbit. The GPS constellation changed the nature of navigation by having the computational work done, along with the maps, in the GPS receiver that the user has. Table 4-15 gives a few examples of potential alternatives for the mission elements. It is in this step that the creativity of the mission designer is the most important and where innovative solutions to improving performance or reducing cost, risk, or schedule are created.

Table 4-15. Representative Examples of Major Alternatives for the Mission Elements. See Chap. 13 for a detailed discussion.

	Mission Element	Representative Alternatives
A	***Mission Concept***	Combine with ground information or another space mission, use suborbital flight, use data from an existing mission, process data on board and send only the results.
B	***Controllable Subject***	Use existing equipment not intended for this mission (cell phone or GPS receiver).
C	***Passive Subject***	Look for alternative features to sense or observe. Use secondary features or data from another system.
D	***Payload***	Visible, IR, multi-spectral. Use existing equipment built for other purposes.
E	***Spacecraft Bus***	Use small spacecraft or CubeSat components. Use a fractionated spacecraft.
F	***Launch Vehicle***	Use integral propulsion or low thrust to fly the spacecraft to its final orbit.
G	***Orbit***	Use very low altitude LEO, medium altitude, or Molniya.
H	***Ground System***	Use commercial ground station or AMSAT for science missions.
I	***Communications Architecture***	Use commercial network. Use Internet for both data delivery and commanding.
J	***Mission Operations***	PC-based. Omit standard ground operations.

K. Document and Iterate.

As always we need to document our conclusions (and the reasons for them) and then go back and look again.

4.4 Defining System Drivers and Critical Requirements (Step 7)

System drivers are the principal mission parameters or characteristics which influence performance, cost, risk, or schedule **and** which the user or designer can control. For example, the temperature at which a forest fire burns may heavily influence how easily it can be detected; however, this is beyond our control and, therefore, is not a system driver. Correctly identifying the system drivers is a critical step in mission analysis and design. Misidentifying system drivers is one of the most common causes of mission analysis error. For example, we may focus a great deal of time and effort on getting the most coverage for an orbit when the system's ultimate performance depends mainly on data rates or cloud cover.

Table 4-16 lists the most common system drivers for space missions, along with what limits them, what they limit, and where they are discussed. The table helps us ensure that we do not overlook system drivers. In identifying these drivers we must clearly determine whether we are looking for drivers of *performance*, *cost*, *risk*, or *schedule*. These may be the same or different. To identify system drivers, we:

1. **Identify the Area of Interest.** Explicitly identify the area of interest, typically performance, cost, risk, or schedule.
2. **Identify Parameters Which Measure the Area of Interest.** Define numerical parameters which measure the identified area of interest. (See Sec. 5.3 on measures of effectiveness and performance parameters for more details on how to do this.) The important point is to find parameters that genuinely measure the goal rather than ones which are simply easy to compute.
3. **Develop First-Order Algorithms.** Develop a formula or algorithm to express the first-order estimate for the value of the parameter identified above. This could include either system algorithms as defined in Sec. 5.3.2 (Table 5-5), or unique algorithms for the identified parameter. (See Table 4-17 for the FireSat II example.)
4. **Examine the Factors.** Examine each of the factors in the expression identified in Step 3. Those which can be adjusted and which have the strongest effect on results are the system drivers.
5. **Look for Possible "Hidden Drivers."** Examine each of the first-order algorithms for implicit variables or for factors affecting more than one characteristic. For example, altitude will influence the ground resolution of a given instrument, the area covered by the field of view, and the spacecraft's velocity relative to the Earth. Therefore, it will more strongly influence effective area search rates than a single formula may show.

The way we have defined our particular problem, or which parameters are available to us, may affect our list of system drivers. Thus, defining system drivers depends in part on the physical and technical nature of the problem and in part on the constraints imposed on the mission design and the solution we have chosen. Usually, we

Table 4-16. Common System Drivers. System drivers can frequently be identified by examining the parameters in this list.

Driver	What Limits Driver	What Driver Limits	Where Discussed
Size	Shroud size, available weight, aerodynamic drag	Payload size (frequently antenna diameter or aperture)	Chaps. 14, 15
On-orbit Weight	Altitude, inclination, launch vehicle	Payload weight, largely determines design and manufacturing cost, propellant load	Chaps. 14, 15
Power	Size, weight (control is secondary problem)	Payload & bus design, system sensitivity, on-orbit life, data rates	Secs. 14.5, 21.2
Propellant	Available mass	Delta V, flexibility, on-orbit responsiveness	Secs. 14.5, 18.1
Data Rate	Storage, power, antenna sizes, limits of existing systems	Information sent to user, can push demand for on-board processing	Secs. 16.3, 21.1
Communications	Coverage, availability of ground stations or relay satellites	Timeliness, ability to command	Sec. 21.1, Chap. 16
Pointing	Cost, weight	Resolution, geolocation, overall system accuracy; pushes spacecraft cost	Secs. 14.5, 19.1
Number of Spacecraft	Cost	Coverage frequency and overlap	Sec. 10.6
Altitude	Launch vehicle, performance demands, weight, radiation environment	Performance, survivability, coverage (instantaneous and rate), communications, resolution	Chap. 10
Coverage (geometry and timing)	Orbit, scheduling, payload field of view and observation time	Data frequency and continuity, maneuver requirements	Sec. 10.2
Scheduling	Timeline and operations, decision making, communications	Coverage, responsiveness, mission utility	Secs. 3.4, 4.2, Chap. 29
Operations	Cost, crew size, communications	Frequently principal cost driver, principal error source, pushes demand for autonomy; can also save "lost" missions	Chap. 29

Table 4-17. Identification of Performance Drivers for FireSat II. First-order algorithms are given to allow us to estimate the performance drivers. Definition of performance drivers may change as we create more detailed definitions of the system and system algorithms. Comparison of columns two and three shows that the performance drivers may depend on the mission concept used.

Key Parameters	First Order Algorithm (Low-Earth Orbit)	First Order Algorithm (Geosynchronous)	Performance Drivers
Observation Frequency	(Number of spacecraft)/12 hr	Scan frequency	Number of spacecraft for low orbit
Time Late	Onboard storage delay + processing time	Communications + processing time	Storage delay (if applicable)
Resolution	Distance × [(wavelength/ aperture) + control error]	Distance × [(wavelength/ aperture) + control error]	Altitude, aperture, control accuracy
Observation Gap	Cloud cover interval or coverage gap	Cloud cover interval or coverage gap	None (weather dominated)

want to make these constraints explicit, so we will know which variables are available for adjustment and which are assumed to be given. Table 4-17 shows the major performance drivers for FireSat II.

System drivers are the defining mission parameters that most strongly affect performance, cost, risk, and schedule. Similarly, *Critical requirements* (also called *driving requirements* or *key requirements*) are the mission requirements that dominate the space mission's overall design and, therefore, most strongly affect performance, cost, risk, or schedule. For a human mission to Mars, the critical requirements will be clear: get to Mars all of the required mass to explore the planet and return, and maintain crew safety for a long mission in widely varying environments. For less ambitious space missions, we cannot establish the critical requirements so easily. Because we want to achieve the best performance at minimum cost, we need to identify these key requirements as early as possible so they can be a part of the trade process. The goal of mission engineering is to adjust both the critical requirements (e.g., coverage and resolution) and the system drivers (e.g., altitude and aperture) to satisfy the mission objectives at minimum cost and risk.

Table 4-18 lists the most common critical requirements, the areas they typically affect, and where they are discussed. There is no single mechanism to find the critical requirements for any particular mission. Like the system drivers discussed above, they may be a function of the mission concept selected. Consequently, once we establish the alternative mission concepts, we usually can determine the critical requirements by inspection. Often, concept exploration itself exposes the requirements that dominate the system's design, performance, and cost. One approach to identification of critical requirements is as follows:

1. **Look at the Principal Performance Requirements.** In most cases, the principal performance requirement will be one of the key critical requirements. Thus, for FireSat II, the requirements on how well it must detect and monitor forest fires would normally be principal drivers of the system design. For SCS, the need to work with existing equipment will likely be a critical requirement.

2. **Examine Table 4-18.** The next step is to look at the requirements list in Table 4-18 and determine which of these entries drive the system design, performance, or cost.

Table 4-18. Most Common Critical Requirements. See text for discussion.

Requirement	What it Affects	Where Discussed
Coverage or Response Time	Number of satellites, altitude, inclination, communications architecture, payload field of view, scheduling, staffing requirements	Secs. 10.2, 10.6, Chap. 29
Resolution	Instrument size, altitude, attitude control	Sec. 17.1
Sensitivity	Payload size and complexity, processing, thermal control, altitude	Chaps. 16, 17
Mapping Accuracy	Attitude control, orbit and attitude knowledge, mechanical alignments, payload precision, processing	Sec. 8.6
Signal Strength	Payload size and power, altitude, transmit power	Chap. 16
On-orbit Lifetime	Redundancy, weight, power and propulsion budgets, component selection	Secs. 3.4, 9.6, Chap. 30
Survivability	Altitude, weight, power, component selection, design of space and ground system, number of satellites, number of ground stations, communications architecture, system redundancy	Sec. 7.5

3. **Look at Top-level Requirements.** Examine each of the top-level requirements established when we defined the mission objectives (Sec. 3.3) and determine how we will meet them. For each, ask whether or not meeting that requirement fundamentally limits the system's design, cost, performance, risk, or schedule.
4. **Look for Hidden Requirements.** In some cases, hidden requirements such as the need to use particular technologies or systems may dominate the mission design.

For most FireSat II approaches, resolution and coverage are the principal critical requirements, and we could find them by any of the first three approaches listed above. The critical requirements depend on a specific mission concept. For the low-cost FireSat II of Chap. 13, they are coverage and sensitivity. For an alternative system design, that may not be the case. For SCS, we will be dominated by either the desired bandwidth or the ground equipment that we're forced to deal with to make the system workable on the ground.

References

Get Ref **For annotated bibliography of mission concept definition and exploration, see the book website.**

Elbert, Bruce R. 2003. *The Satellite Communication Applications Handbook.* Norwood, MA: Artech House.

Elbert, Bruce R. 2008. *Introduction to Satellite Communication. 3rd ed.* Norwood, MA: Artech House.

Fortescue, Peter W., John Stark, and Graham Swinerd. 2003. *Spacecraft Systems Engineering. 3rd ed.* Chichester, UK: John Wiley and Sons.

Gordon, Gary D. and Walter L. Morgan. 1993. *Principles of Communication Satellites.* New York, NY: Wiley Interscience.

Griffin, M. and J. R. French. 2004. *Space Vehicle Design.* Washington, DC: AIAA.

Kemble, Stephen. 2006. *Interplanetary Mission Analysis and Design*, with software disk. Chichester, UK: Praxis Publishing, Ltd. And Springer.

Lu, Ning. 1997. *Fractal Imaging.* San Diego, CA: Academic Press.

Maral, Gerard, and Michel Bousquet. 2010. *Satellite Communications Systems: Systems, Techniques and Technology. 5th ed.* Chichester, UK: John Wiley and Sons.

Pisacane, Vincent L. and Robert C. Moore. 2005. *Fundamentals of Space Systems. 2nd ed.* Oxford: Oxford University Press.

Plam, Yegor, Richard Van Allen, James R. Wertz, and Thomas Bauer. 2008. "Autonomous Orbit Control Experience on TacSat-2 using Microcosm's Orbit Control Kit (OCK)." 31st Annual AAS Guidance and Control Conference. AAS 08-008. Breckenridge, CO. Feb. 1–6.

Sayood, Khalid. 2005. *Introduction to Data Compression. 3rd ed.* San Francisco, CA: Morgan Kaufman Publishers.

Wertz, James R. and Gwynne E. Gurevich. 2001a. "Applications of Autonomous On-Board Orbit Control." 11th AAS/AIAA Space Flight Mechanics Meeting. AAS 01-238. Santa Barbara, CA. Feb. 11–15.

Wertz, James R. and Gwynne E. Gurevich. 2001b. "Autonomous On-board Orbit Control: Flight Results and Cost Reduction." JHU/APL Symposium on Autonomous Ground Systems for 2001 and Beyond. Laurel, MD. Apr. 25–27.

5 Mission Analysis and Mission Utility

James R. Wertz, *Microcosm, Inc./USC*

Chapter 4 discussed defining and characterizing alternative concepts and architectures for space missions. This chapter shows how we evaluate the ability of these options to meet fundamental mission objectives. We address *mission analysis*—how to quantify mission performance, *mission utility*—how to evaluate its utility to the customer or end user, and *mission selection*—how to select one or more concepts for further development or to decide that we cannot achieve the mission within current constraints or technology.

The narrow purpose of mission evaluation is to determine whether the system meets all of the requirements and specifications set for it. This is critically important (particularly to Congress or a group of investors who are putting up the large amounts of money that space missions normally require) and is largely the subject of Chap. 6. However, in the broad context of mission engineering, we are really concerned with two issues:

1. How well does the system perform (*performance analysis*)
2. How well does it meet the customer's or end user's objectives (*mission utility analysis*)

The distinction between performance and utility can be exceptionally important. This is clearly illustrated by two historical examples—the Space Shuttle and the Iridium LEO Communications Constellation.

The original goal of the Space Shuttle was to achieve "airplane-like" access to space and to drive down the launch cost to less than $10 million/flight in FY1972$, corresponding to roughly $50 million/launch in FY2010$. The actual cost per launch is not well-defined, but is likely well over $1 billion/launch, not counting any amortization of the original development cost. Irrespective of the exact costs, it is clear that the Shuttle was never able to achieve the dramatic cost reductions that were promised. As discussed in Sec. 2.1.7 and Chap. 13, high launch costs remain a major impediment to the large-scale expansion of the exploration and use of space.

Similarly, the Iridium LEO communications constellation declared bankruptcy in 2000, representing a loss of approximately $5.5 billion—most likely from a group of people that would have preferred to not lose that money. As discussed in Sec. 2.1.4, this represented a loss for the astronautics community as a whole. It indirectly increased costs for nearly all other programs and made it difficult or impossible to fund other constellations.

The important issue is that both Iridium and the Space Shuttle largely met their performance requirements.* (The Shuttle program had two failures resulting in loss of life, which represents a major and significant programmatic failure, even though we know that human spaceflight carries risks that can not realistically be avoided.) Both programs were exceptionally well-engineered, and were built by some of the best engineers and space organizations in the world. Nonetheless, while the performance assessment was very good, they failed to meet their fundamental mission objectives, i.e., to achieve an adequate level of mission utility. We, as a community, did not do what we should have done. If a surgeon performs a remarkable operation, but the patient dies, they should not take comfort in the great work that

* For the Space Shuttle the performance requirements are things like payload mass to orbit, injection accuracy, and loiter time on orbit, whereas the mission objective was to achieve "airplane-like" performance and dramatically drive down launch costs. For Iridium the performance requirements were availability, number of telephone calls supported, and ability to successfully complete a call. The objective was simple—to make money for the people who put up the initial investment.

they did. The only immediate goal of the surgery is to help the patient. If Iridium goes bankrupt or the Shuttle fails to drive down launch cost, then we didn't do a good job*. This is the fundamental purpose of mission utility analysis—to evaluate and quantify what it means to meet the needs of the end user.

Essentially all missions go through mission analysis and evaluation stages many times. The literature base describing this process has increased significantly in recent years. Fortescue et al. [2003], Pisacane and Moore [2005], Larson et al. [2009], and Chesley et al. [2008] discuss the process for generic missions; Larson and Pranke [1999] do so for human missions; Przemieniecki [1993, 2000] does this for defense missions; Kemble [2006] does so for interplanetary missions; and NASA [2007] provides an excellent process summary for NASA missions. Kay [1995] discusses the difficulty of doing this within the framework of a political democracy and Sarsfield [1998], Sandau [2006], and Wertz and Larson [1996] provide specific techniques applicable to reducing mission cost, which is also discussed in Chap. 13.

5.1 Introduction to Mission Analysis

Mission analysis is the process of quantifying the system parameters and resulting performance. *Mission utility analysis*, described in Sec. 5.4, is the process of quantifying how well the system meets its overall mission objectives. Recall that the mission objectives themselves are not quantitative. However, our capacity to meet them should be quantified as well as possible in order to allow us to make intelligent decisions about whether and how to proceed. *Mission requirements*, introduced in Chap. 3 and discussed in more detail in Chap. 6, are the numerical expressions of how well the objectives must be met. At their best, they represent a balance between what we want and what is feasible within the constraints on the system and, therefore, deriving them should be a central part of the mission analysis activity. In practice, requirements are often set by a process outside of the space mission and unrelated to what is real or achievable. Therefore, it is often the case that mission analysis is concerned with how and how well externally defined mission requirements can be met. Nonetheless, in principle, mission analysis should be the process by which we define and refine both the system definition and mission requirements in order to meet our broad objectives at minimum cost and risk.

A key component of mission analysis is documentation, which provides the organizational memory of both the results and reasons. It is critical to understand fully the choices made, even those that are neither technical nor optimal. We may choose to apply a particular technology for political or economic reasons, or may not have enough manpower to investigate alternatives. In any case, for successful analysis, we must document the real reasons so others can reevaluate them later when the situation may be different. Technical people often shy away from nontechnical reasons or try to justify decisions by exaggerating their technical content. For example, as a result of our preliminary FireSat II analysis, we may choose a circular orbit at 700 km at an inclination of 60 deg because this is a good mid-range starting point. If so, we should document this as the reason, rather than trying to further justify these parameters or simply leave the reason undefined. If we have documented the reason, then later we, or others, can refine the choice for the best altitude and inclination, rather than having to live by choices for which there is no documented justification.

5.1.1 The Mission Analysis Hierarchy

I like to think of the mission analysis process as a huge spreadsheet model of a space system. Along the top of the spreadsheet matrix are the various parameters and alternatives that one might assess, such as power, orbit, and staffing levels for ground stations. Along the left are the various system parameters that flow from the mission choices, such as the orbit period, or coverage parameters, and along the bottom row are the system's quantitative outputs, indicating its performance, effectiveness, cost, and risk. The matrix itself would capture the functional relationships among the many variables. We would like to wiggle any particular parameter—such as the altitude, or the number of people assigned to the ground station—and determine the effect on all of the other parameters. In this way, we could quantify the system's performance as a function of all possible variables and their combinations.

Fortunately for the continuing employment of mission analysts, the above spreadsheet model does not yet exist.† Instead, we analyze as many reasonable alternatives as possible so we may understand how the system

* What does "we" mean in this context? Obviously most aerospace engineers weren't directly involved in either Iridium or the Space Shuttle. Nonetheless, all of us collectively set the rules and define the "culture" in which we all work. It is this culture that has let it be acceptable in some sense, for the Shuttle to miss its recurring cost projections by a factor of 20 or so and for Iridium to go bankrupt, rather than make a good return on investment for those that put up the money. Our surgeon analogy continues to work here. Surgeons, collectively aren't responsible for the death of a single patient. But they do make the rules under which surgeons operate. If that death causes a reassessment of those rules, it's still not good, but at least the community is responding. The fundamental question for mission utility and space mission engineering is whether our community is responding appropriately and adequately to the fact that programs cost too much and take too long.

† In due course, system engineers may become technologically obsolete. The challenge to future system engineers will be to stay ahead of the computer models in being creative and innovative. One of the elements most often missed by automated processes is how to think about the problem in a totally different way. For example, can we drive down the cost of a human mission to Jupiter by first putting a settlement on the Moon and using those resources to build low-cost interplanetary systems? These are the types of questions that are very difficult to answer by simply adjusting parameters in a model.

behaves as a function of the principal design features, i.e., the system drivers (Chap. 4). This approach does not imply that we are uninterested in secondary detail, but simply recognizes that the mission analysis process, much like the space system we are attempting to analyze, is ultimately limited in both cost and schedule. We must achieve the maximum level of understanding within these limits.

If the resources available for concept exploration are limited, as is nearly always the case in realistic situations, then one of the most critical tasks is to intelligently limit the scope of individual analyses. We want to be able to compute approximate values for many parameters and to determine at what level of detail we should reasonably stop. In practice, this is made difficult by the continuing demand for additional detail and depth. Thus, we would like to be able to determine and make clear to others what elements of that detail will significantly affect the overall system performance and what elements, while important, can reasonably be left to a more detailed design phase.

We use two main methods to limit the depth of analysis in any particular area. The first is to clearly identify each area's system drivers by the methods in Sec. 4.4 and to concentrate most of the mission analysis effort on these drivers. The second is to clearly identify the goal of the system study and to provide a level of detail appropriate to that goal. This approach leads to a *mission analysis hierarchy*, summarized in Table 5-1, in which studies take on increased levels of detail and complexity as the activity progresses. The first three types of studies are meant to be quick with limited detail and are not intended to provide definitive results. The last three are much more complex ways to select an alternative to provide the best system performance. Each of these types of analysis is discussed below.

5.2 Studies with Limited Scope

The first three types of analyses in Table 5-1 provide methods for undertaking a *quick-look assessment*. They provide limited detail, but can frequently be done quickly and at low cost. Consequently, these quick-look assessments are important in any situation that is funding-limited or time-limited, which is very often the case in real mission analysis. We will briefly outline these methods here. However, nearly the entire book is devoted to the process of making initial estimates, which is the basic goal of limited scope studies. We want to be able to understand whether or not a particular project is feasible, and to get some idea of its size, complexity, and cost. Doing this requires that we be able to make numerical estimates and undertake limited studies in order to develop insight into the nature of the problem we are trying to solve.

The biggest difficulty with limited scope studies is the tendency to believe that they are more accurate than they really are. Thus, it is not uncommon to use a feasibility assessment or point design to establish the requirements for a mission in such detail that, in practice, the point design becomes the only alternative which can meet them. As long as we recognize the limited scope of these studies, they have a valuable place in the mission analysis hierarchy and represent one of the most important tools that we can use to understand the behavior of the system we are designing.

5.2.1 Feasibility Assessment

The simplest procedure in the mission analysis hierarchy is the *feasibility assessment*, which we use to establish whether a particular objective is achievable and to place broad bounds on its level of complexity. Frequently, we can do a feasibility assessment simply by comparison with existing systems. Thus, we are reasonably convinced that FireSat II is feasible because most FireSat II tasks could be performed by existing Earth resources satellites. Similarly, it is feasible to land people on the Moon and return them safely to Earth because we have done so in the past.

We can also determine whether a particular goal is feasible by extrapolating our past experience. Is it feasible to send people to Mars and bring them back safely? Here we need to look at the principal differences

Table 5-1. The Mission Analysis Hierarchy. During the preliminary design phase, these help us decide how detailed studies should be.

Analysis Type	Where Discussed	Goal	
Feasibility Assessment	5.2.1	To establish whether an objective is achievable and its approximate degree of complexity	Quick, limited detail
Sizing Estimate	5.2.2	To estimate basic parameters such as size, weight, power, and cost	
Point Design	5.2.3	To demonstrate feasibility and establish a baseline for comparison of alternatives	
Trade Study	5.3.1	To establish the relative advantages of alternative approaches or options	More detailed, complex trades
Performance Assessment	5.3.2	To quantify performance parameters (e.g., resolution, timeliness) for a particular approach	
Utility Assessment	5.4	To quantify how well the system meets overall mission objectives and satisfies the needs of the end user	

between a Mars mission and a Lunar mission. These differences include a longer flight time and higher gravity at Mars than on the Moon, and, therefore, a need for greater radiation protection during the mission and a higher lift-off velocity to leave Mars. These factors make the job more challenging and possibly more expensive than going to the Moon, but there is nothing about the Mars mission that makes it inherently impossible. Getting to Mars is feasible. The problem is being able to do so at modest cost and risk such that we are willing to both pay for the mission and accept the risk.

The third method of providing a feasibility assessment is to provide a very broad design of how such a mission might be accomplished. For example, in the 1970s, Gerard O'Neill of Princeton University proposed building large space colonies at the Lagrange points between the Earth and the Moon. (See Sec. 2.1.9 and O'Neill [1974].) No mission of this scope had ever been undertaken (and still hasn't), and it certainly was not a straightforward extrapolation of any of our normal space experience. O'Neill and his colleagues proceeded to establish the feasibility by developing a variety of alternative designs for such space colonies. While the work done was far in excess of a simple feasibility assessment, it clearly established that such colonies were feasible and gave at least an estimate of the scope of the problem.

5.2.2 Sizing Estimate

The purpose of the *sizing estimate* is to provide an estimate of basic mission parameters such as size, weight, power, or cost. We can do sizing estimates in much the same manner as the feasibility assessment: by analogy with existing systems. Thus, if we are aware of an Earth observation system that has resolution and information characteristics comparable to what we believe are needed for FireSat II, we can use these parameters to give us an initial estimate of the FireSat II parameters.

We can also provide a quantitative estimate of key mission parameters by scaling the parameters from existing missions or payloads in order to obtain estimates of the component sizes for our particular mission. This scaling process is described in Sec. 17.2.6 for space payloads, and in Sec. 14.5 for the spacecraft as a whole. The process of sizing by scaling existing hardware is an extremely powerful approach to estimating what it will take to achieve mission objectives. It is of use not only during the conceptual design process, but throughout the hardware design, definition, and development phases to evaluate the system design as it evolves. If scaling existing systems leads to the suggestion that a particular component should be twice as heavy as the current design suggests, this gives us reason to look very closely at the current design and to try to determine whether or not any factors have been overlooked. We assume that designers of previous systems did a reasonable job of optimizing their system. If the current design is significantly different, either better or worse, then we would like to understand the reasons for these differences. It may be that the technology has advanced to the point where a better design is possible or it may be that the current preliminary design has simply forgotten a key element. This process is a good way to gain confidence in the overall design as we proceed.

As the design develops, more and more accurate sizing estimates come from the scaling process. We proceed by breaking down the system into components and sizing individual components based on scaling estimates with prior systems. Thus, we may initially estimate the system as a whole divided into a spacecraft and payload. As the design becomes more detailed, we will break down the spacecraft into its subsystems and components and estimate the size, weight, and power of each element based upon scaling from prior systems or engineering estimates of the new system to be built. Similarly, we initially size the payload or ground station by comparison with existing systems and eventually by building a list of all the components and undertaking similar sizing estimates for each component. As introduced in Chap. 3, this process of creating a list of components and estimating parameters for each is known as budgeting and is described in more detail in Sec. 14.5.

5.2.3 Point Design

A *point design* is a design, possibly at a top level, for the entire system that is capable of meeting the broad mission objectives. We refer to it as a point design if we have not attempted to optimize the design to either maximize performance or minimize weight, cost, or risk. The point design serves two basic purposes. It demonstrates that the mission is feasible, and it can be used as a baseline for comparison of alternatives. Thus, if we can establish a point design for FireSat II that meets mission objectives with a spacecraft that weighs 500 kg and costs \$50 million, then we can use this as a comparison for later systems. If other systems cost more, weigh more, and don't perform as well, then we will abandon those alternatives in favor of the original baseline. If we continue to improve the design so that the cost and risk decrease, then we will let the baseline evolve to take into account the new approaches.

A point design is valuable because we can do it quickly and easily. There is no need to optimize any of the parameters associated with the design unless it is necessary to do so to meet mission objectives. This gives us a sense of whether it will be easy or hard to meet the mission objectives and what are likely to be the most difficult aspects. One of the biggest problems in a point design is taking it too seriously at a later stage. We are always likely to regard work that we have done as representing the best approach, even though we may not have been aware of alternatives. The key issue here is to make use of point designs but at the same time to recognize their limitations and to continue to do trades to reduce overall cost and risk and to look for alternative approaches to meet mission objectives better and at lower cost.

5.3 System Trade Studies and Performance Assessments (Step 8)

Step 8 of our overall Space Mission Engineering process defined in Table 3-1, is to conduct performance assessments and system trades. Deciding whether to proceed with a mission should be based on a strawman system concept or a point design that shows that the mission objectives can be met within the assigned constraints. Of course, the initial point design is probably not the best solution, and we would ordinarily consider a number of alternatives. This process of looking at alternatives is the *system trade process*. Generally there are three types of systems trades that are done, or should be done:

- Single effect trades (easy to do)
- Multiple effects trades (hard to do)
- New and unique approaches (very hard to do)

The system trade process evaluates different broad concepts to establish their viability and impact on performance, cost, risk, and schedule. We then combine the system trade results with the performance assessment (Sec. 5.3.2) and the mission utility analysis (Sec. 5.4) to provide input for concept selection (Sec. 5.7).

5.3.1 System Trade Studies

System trades consist of analyzing and selecting *system drivers*, i.e., key system parameters defined in Sec. 4.4, which largely determine mission performance, cost, risk, and schedule. We use these parameters to define a mission concept and mission architecture that can then be used for performance analysis and utility analysis as described in Secs. 5.3.2 and 5.4. The key system trades are those that define how the system works and determine its size, cost, and risk. Typically, the key system trades will be in one of the major areas defined in Table 5-2. Here the first question should always be: What are the real objectives of the mission? In addition, it would be wise to review the broad objectives of the community involved, as discussed in Chap. 2. What are the long-term goals and objectives of the community and how will this mission support those goals? For example, space telescopes of all sorts are typically out to find things that have never been seen before, which makes defining the system parameters a bit challenging. For military systems, our goal is ordinarily to provide support to the warfighter or gather intelligence about the enemy.

Table 5-2. Principal Areas for Key System Trades. See Table 5-3 for examples.

Area	Principal Issue	Where Discussed
Mission Objectives	What are we really trying to accomplish?	Sec. 4.1
Critical Requirements	What are the requirements that are hard to meet and, therefore, drive cost, risk, and schedule?	Sec. 4.4
Mission Concept	How do we get the information and data and how do we get the results to the end user?	Sec. 4.1
Subject	What do we want to look at or measure to get the information we want?	Sec. 15.2
Type and Complexity of Payloads	What spectral band do we work in and how do we measure it? How many payloads?	Sec. 15.1
Orbit	A specialized orbit or one of a continuum?	Chap. 10
Number of Spacecraft	A single satellite or a constellation?	Chap. 10

Table 5-3. Examples of Representative Key System Trades. Although these system trades are critical, we can't expect numerically precise answers to our system design problem.

Trade Area	FireSat II	SCS	James Webb Space Telescope	Aircraft Detection
Mission Objectives	Save lives and property or reduce fire fighting costs?	Support the warfighter?	Discover stuff we've never seen? If so, how do we build the telescope?	Traffic control or smuggling interdiction?
Critical Requirements	What's a forest fire? What's the needed resolution?	Small omni ground antenna?	How cold a detector? How large an aperture?	How small a plane do we need to detect and track?
Mission Concept	Identify forest fires on board or on the ground?	Circular orbits with fore and aft fixed crosslinks?	How do we deploy and control the mirror?	Is it a cooperative target? How do we cover the areas of interest?
Subject	Heat, fire, or smoke?	Likely a handheld receiver.	Something we've never seen and don't know.	Commercial planes or small private planes?
Payload Type and Complexity	What wavelength? How many spectral bands?	What band? How many?	How many sensors and instruments?	IR, visible, radar, RF?
Orbit	LEO or GEO	LEO, HEO, MEO, GEO	Lagrange point or closer and cheaper?	LEO, HEO, MEO?
Number of Spacecraft	1 or a constellation?	Probably a constellation	Probably only 1	1 or a constellation?

Table 5-3 shows typical examples of key system-trades for several representative missions. For essentially all missions, specification of the critical requirements will be a key system trade. For the FireSat II mission, the subject is probably the heat from the fire itself and the payload is probably an IR sensor. Thus, the principal system trades are probably the mission objectives, mission concept, the resolution and coverage requirements, the orbit, and whether it's a single satellite or a constellation. For a mission such as the James Webb Space Telescope, there will be only 1 telescope, the orbit is of marginal importance, and the subject is moderately well defined, if only very poorly known. Here the principal trades will be the resolution and pointing requirements, the payload, and the mission concept. Communications satellite systems are normally in geosynchronous orbit with a well-defined concept of operations. Here the only real trade is with the required traffic load, the subject, and the size and complexity of the payload.

Truly innovative approaches—those that really change how we think about a problem—typically involve finding a new option among these key system trades. Motorola's Iridium program and subsequent low-Earth orbit communications constellations represented a new way of thinking about using satellites for communications. These have a very different concept of operations and different orbits from traditional systems. Similarly, Chap. 13 presents an innovative approach to thinking about FireSat II that provides a totally different concept of operations and type of payload. Innovative solutions are never easy to come by. To try to find them, a good place to start is with the key system trade areas given in Tables 5-2 and 5-3.

We cannot normally do system trades in a straightforward numerical fashion. Choosing a different concept of operations, for example, will result in changes in most or all of the mission parameters. Consequently, the fact that Option A requires twice the power of Option B may or may not be critical, depending on the orbit and number of satellites for the two options. We need to look at the system as a whole to understand which is better.

The best approach for key system trades is a utility analysis as described in Sec. 5.4. We use the utility analysis to attempt to quantify our ability to meet mission objectives as a function of cost. We then select the option that fulfills our objectives at the lowest cost and risk. As described in Sec. 5.7, this is still not a straightforward numerical comparison, but does have quantitative components.

The simplest option for system trades is a list of the options and the reasons for retaining or eliminating them. This allows us to consider the merits and demerits at a high level without undertaking time-consuming trades. This also allows our list to be challenged at a later date. We should go back to our key system trades on a regular basis and determine whether our assumptions and conclusions are still valid. It is this process of examination and review that allows us to introduce technical innovation and new ideas. It is a process that must occur if we are to drive down the cost of space systems.

Single Effect Trades

For the purpose of trade studies, system drivers generally divide into two categories—those for which more is better (*single effect drivers*) and those with multiple effects. By far the easier to deal with are the "more is better" single effect drivers, for they simply require us to ask: "What is the cost of achieving more of the commodity in question?" For example, in a space-based radar, added power improves performance but costs more money. Thus, the designer will want to understand how much performance is available for how much power. A second example is coverage. For virtually any Earth-oriented system, including our FireSat II example, more coverage means better performance at higher cost. Increasing coverage ordinarily means adding satellites or, perhaps, increasing a single satellite's coverage by increasing its altitude or the range of its sensors. Therefore, we often do a coverage trade considering performance vs. number of satellites, substituting the latter for cost. Assessing performance as a function of power or coverage may take considerable work, but it is relatively easy to present the data for judging by the funding organization, the users, or other decision makers.

Multiple Effect Trades

System drivers and critical requirements that cause multiple effects demand more complex trade studies. The basic problem here is that pushing parameters one way will improve some characteristics and degrade others. In trades of this type, we are looking for a solution that provides the best mix of results. Examples of such trade studies include instrument design, antenna type, and altitude. Each antenna style will have advantages and disadvantages, so we must trade various possible solutions depending upon the end goals and relative importance of different effects.

In trades with multiple effects, selecting the correct independent parameter for each trade is critical. Consider, for example, selecting either a reflector or a phased-array antenna for a space-based radar [Brookner and Mahoney, 1986]. From the radar equation, we know that a principal performance parameter for a radar is the antenna aperture. All other things being equal, larger antennas will provide much better performance. Thus, for our example, we might choose to compare reflector and phased-array antennas of equal aperture. On this basis, we would choose the phased array because its electronic steering makes it more agile than a reflector antenna, which must be mechanically steered. But our choice becomes more complex when we recognize that weight typically limits large space structures more than size does. Generally, we can build a reflector larger than a phased array for a given weight. Based on weight, a reflector may have considerably more power efficiency and, therefore, be a better radar than a phased-array system. Thus, we would have to trade the better performance of a larger reflector vs. the better agility of a smaller phased array. Depending upon the application, the results may be the same as for an aperture-based trade

Table 5-4. System Trade Process for Parameters with Multiple Effects. The example is the altitude trade for the FireSat II mission. See also Fig. 5-1.

Step	FireSat II Example	Where Discussed
1. Select trade parameter (typically a system driver)	Altitude	Sec. 10.2
2. Identify factors which affect the parameter or are affected by it	Coverage Deployment strategy and coverage evolution Orbit period Time in view Eclipse fraction Response time Number of spacecraft needed Launch capability Resolution Radiation environment Communications Lifetime	Sec. 10.2.1 Sec. 10.6.2 Sec. 9.1.5, App. I Sec. 8.4 Sec. 8.2.4 Sec. 10.2.1.4 Sec. 10.6.1 Secs. 10.3.2, 26.1 Sec. 10.2.2.1 Chap. 7 Secs. 16.2, 21.1 Secs. 3.4, 9.4.4, Chap. 30
3. Assess impact of each factor	Can launch up to 1,800 km Best coverage above 600 km Resolution—lower is better Survivability—higher is better, but not much	—
4. Document and summarize results	Launch Coverage Resolution Survivability	Fig. 5-1
5. Select parameter value and possible range	Altitude = 700 km Range = 600 to 800 km	In text

or reverse. The important point is the critical nature of selecting the proper independent variable in system trades. To do so, we must find the quantities that inherently limit the system being considered. These could be weight, power, level of technology, cost, or manufacturability, depending on the technology and circumstances.

Table 5-4 summarizes the system trade process for parameters with multiple effects. Typically the trade parameter is one of our system drivers. We begin by identifying what performance areas or requirements affect or are affected by the trade parameter. For example, the altitude of the spacecraft will have a key effect on coverage, resolution, and survivability and will be limited by launchability, payload weight, communications, and radiation. We next assess the effect in each of these areas and document and summarize the results, generally **without** trying to create a numerical average of different areas. We use the summary to select the parameter value and a possible range. Although the process is complex and may not have a well-defined answer, it is not necessarily iterative unless we find that the results require fundamental changes in other system parameters.

Altitude trades are perhaps the most common example of a trade in which multiple influences push the parameter in different ways. We would normally like to move the satellite higher to achieve better coverage, better survivability, and easier communications. On the other hand, launchability, resolution, and payload weight tend to drive the satellite lower. The radiation environment dictates specific altitudes we would like to avoid, and the eclipse fraction may or may not play a crucial role in the altitude trade. We must assess each of these effects and summarize all of them to complete our trade study. One possible summary is a numerically weighted average of the various outcomes, such as three times the coverage in square nautical miles per second divided by twice the resolution in furlongs. Although this provides a convenient numerical answer, it does not provide the physical insight or conceptual balance needed for intelligent choices. A better solution is to provide the data on all of the relevant parameters and choose based on inspection rather than numerical weighting.

The FireSat II altitude trade provides an example of this process. For FireSat II, neither survivability nor communications is a key issue, but coverage does push the satellite upward. On the other hand, payload weight and good resolution tend to push the satellite lower. Figure 5-1 shows the results of a hypothetical FireSat II altitude trade. Notice that each parameter has various possible outcomes. Altitudes above or below a certain value may be eliminated, or we may simply prefer a general direction, such as lower altitude providing better resolution. Based on these results, we select a nominal altitude of 700 km for FireSat II and a possible range of 600 to 800 km. This selection is neither numerical nor purely qualitative. We have tried to balance the alternatives sensibly, but not in a way that we can numerically justify.

New and Unique Approaches

By far the most challenging system trades, and also those that have the most potential benefit, are trades that involve new and unique approaches to system design. This is where potential major breakthroughs come about that can dramatically alter the way we do business in

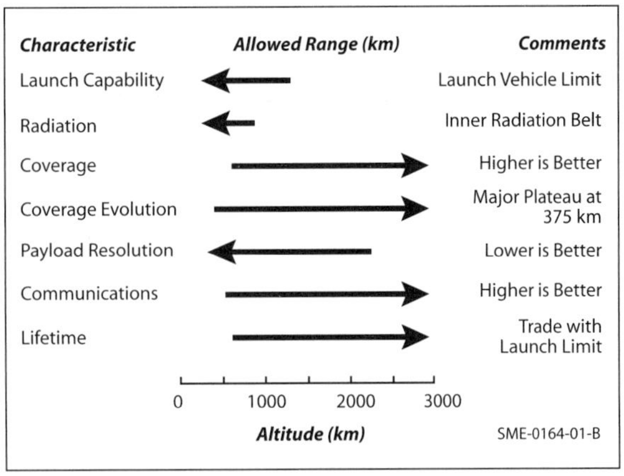

Fig. 5-1. Results of FireSat II Altitude Trade. See Table 5-4 for a list of altitude trade issues. Political constraints and survivability were not of concern for the FireSat II altitude trade.

space. Typically, it's very difficult to make major breakthroughs occur, in part because they may end up being more difficult and less advantageous than was first anticipated (i.e. the reusable Space Shuttle and its goal of dramatically reducing launch cost) and in part because it is difficult in the very conservative space community to move new and innovative approaches beyond the study phase and into real systems (such as the O'Neill space colonies described in Sec. 2.1.9).

An example of this, that also illustrates the potential pitfalls, is the Iridium communications constellation discussed earlier (in the chapter) and in Sec. 2.1.4. Traditionally, communications systems had been thought of as either geosynchronous or Molniya orbits. Iridium took a very different approach and used a LEO constellation instead which, unfortunately, did not work out as intended. On the other hand, both GlobalStar and ORBCOMM are now working successfully in LEO, and Iridium itself has regained sufficient business that an Iridium Next constellation is under development.

A new and unique approach that is working very well is the development of CubeSats, initially intended for educational purposes, but now expanding into highly functional small satellites for a variety of purposes. (See Secs. 2.1.8 and 25.4.)

In the communities that actually fund and build space systems, the acceptance of new approaches moves with all the rapidity of a glacier moving uphill. Nonetheless, we very much need new ideas and new approaches if we are to change the way business is done in space. As we saw in Chap. 1, space missions cost too much and take too long, and we need to find ways to reverse that trend. We will return to this, and discuss explicitly how to do it, in Chap. 13.

5.3.2 Performance Assessments

A *performance assessment* is a numerical analysis of how well the system will perform in specific areas. Computing the area search rate, the available data rate, or the resolution of an optical system are all the result of a performance assessment.

Quantifying performance demands an appropriate level of detail. Too much detail drains resources away from other issues; too little keeps us from determining the important issues or causes us to assess the actual performance incorrectly.

To compute system performance, we use three main techniques:

- System algorithms
- Analogy with existing systems
- Simulation

System algorithms are the basic physical or geometric formulas associated with a particular system or process, such as those for determining resolution in diffraction-limited optics, finding the beam size of an antenna, analyzing a link budget, or assessing geometric coverage. Table 5-5 lists system algorithms typically used for space mission analysis. System algorithms provide the best method for computing performance. They provide clear

Table 5-5. Common System Algorithms Used for Quantifying Basic Levels of Performance. These analyses use physical or geometrical formulas to determine how system performance varies with key parameters.

Algorithm	Used For	Where Discussed
Link Budget	Communications and data rate analysis	Sec. 16.2
Diffraction-limited Optics	Aperture sizing for optics or antennas; determining resolution	Sec. 17.1
Payload Sensitivity	Payload sizing and performance estimates	Sec. 17.2
Radar Equation	Radar sizing and performance estimates	Cantafio [1989]
Earth Coverage, Area Search Rates	Coverage assessment; system sizing; performance estimates	Chap. 8, App. C
Mapping and Pointing Budget	Geolocation; instrument and antenna pointing; image sensing	Sec. 8.6

traceability and establish the relationship between design parameters and performance characteristics. Thus, for FireSat II, we are interested in the resolution of an on-orbit fire detector. Using the formula for diffraction-limited optics in Chap. 17, we can compute the achievable angular resolution from the instrument objective's diameter. We can then apply the geometric formulas in Chap. 8 to translate this angular resolution to resolution on the ground. This result gives us a direct relationship between the altitude of the FireSat II spacecraft, the size of the payload, the angles at which it works, and the resolution with which it can distinguish features on the ground. Similarly, communications systems follow a very-well defined *link budget*, that can determine with good precision, just how fast we will be able to get data back from Jupiter, given the power, wavelength or frequency, and the diameter of the antennas on the ground and on the spacecraft.

System algorithms are powerful in that they show us directly how performance varies with key parameters. However, they are inherently limited because they presume the rest of the system is designed with fundamental physics or geometry as the limiting characteristic. For FireSat II, resolution could also be limited by the optical quality of the lens, by the detector technology, by the spacecraft's pointing stability, or even by the data rates at which the instrument can provide results or that the satellite can transmit to the ground. In using system algorithms, we assume that we have correctly identified what limits system performance. But we must understand that these assumptions may break down as each parameter changes. Finding the limits of these system algorithms helps us analyze the problem and determine its key components. Thus, we may find that a low-cost FireSat II system is limited principally by achieving spacecraft stability at low cost. In this case, our attention would be focused on the attitude control system and on the level of resolution that can be achieved as a function of system cost.

The second method for quantifying performance is by comparing our design with existing systems. In this type of analysis we use the established characteristics of existing sensors, systems, or components and adjust the expected performance according to basic physics or the continuing evolution of technology. The list of payload instruments in Chap. 15 is an excellent starting point for comparing performance with existing systems. We could, for example, use the field of view, resolution, and integration time for an existing sensor and apply them to FireSat II. We then modify the basic sensor parameters such as the aperture, focal length, or pixel size, to satisfy our mission's unique requirements. To do this, we must work with someone who knows the technology, the allowable range of modifications, and their cost. For example, we may be able to improve the resolution by doubling the diameter of the objective, but doing so may cost too much. Thus, to estimate performance based on existing systems, we need information from those who understand the main cost and performance drivers of that technology.

The third way to quantify system performance is simulation, described in more detail in Sec. 5.4.2. Because it is time-consuming, we typically use simulations only for key performance parameters. However, simulations allow much more complex modeling and can incorporate limits on performance from multiple factors (e.g., resolution, stability, and data rate). Because they typically provide much less insight, however, we must review the results carefully to see if they apply to the specific situation we have in mind. Still, in complex circumstances, a simulation may be the only acceptable way to quantify system performance. A much less expensive method of simulation is the use of commercial mission analysis tools or even Excel or MATLAB models.

5.4 Mission Utility and Figures of Merit— Is the Mission Worthwhile? (Step 9)

Is the mission worth doing? Does it meet the fundamental objectives of the end user or the people who paid to create it? Does FireSat II save lives and property and reduce fire fighting costs sufficiently to warrant flying the mission? *Mission utility analysis* is the process of trying to provide a quantitative assessment of the degree to which the system meets the basic objectives it is attempting to fulfill. This is used to (1) provide quantitative information for decision making, and (2) provide feedback on the system design. Ultimately, an individual or group will decide whether to build a space system and which system to build based on an overall assessment of whether the system can meet its mission objectives at an acceptable cost and risk and do so better than alternative approaches. As discussed in Sec. 5.7, this does not mean the decision is, or should be, fundamentally technical in nature. However, even though basic decisions may be political, economic, or sociological, the best possible quantitative information from the mission utility analysis process should be available to support them.

Mission utility analysis also provides feedback for the system design by assessing how well alternative configurations meet the mission objectives. FireSat II shows how this process might work in practice. Mission analysis quantifies how well alternative systems can detect and monitor forest fires, thereby helping us to decide whether to proceed with a more detailed design of several satellites in low-Earth orbit or a single larger satellite in geosynchronous orbit. As we continue these trades, mission utility analysis establishes, for example, the probability of being able to detect a given forest fire within a given time, with and without FireSat II, and with varying numbers of spacecraft. For FireSat II, the decision makers are those responsible for protecting the forests of the United States. We want to provide them with the technical information they need to determine whether they should spend their limited resources on FireSat II or on some alternative. If they select FireSat II, we will provide the technical information needed to allow them to select how many satellites and what level of performance to provide.

5.4.1 Performance Parameters and Measures of Effectiveness

The purpose of mission analysis is to quantify the system's performance and its ability to meet the ultimate mission objectives. Typically this requires two distinct types of quantities—performance parameters and measures of effectiveness. *Performance parameters,* such as those shown in Table 5-6 for FireSat II, quantify how well the system works, without explicitly measuring how well it meets mission objectives. Performance parameters may include coverage statistics, power efficiency, or the resolution of a particular instrument as a function of nadir angle and altitude. In contrast, *measures of effec-*

Table 5-6. Representative Performance Parameters for FireSat II. By using various performance parameters, we get a better overall picture of our FireSat II design.

Performance Parameter	How Determined
Smallest detectable fire	Analysis
Resolution	Analysis
Orbit average area coverage rate	Simulation
Fire location accuracy	Analysis
Temperature of the fire	Analysis
Average number of times per day the fire is observed	Simulation

tiveness (MoEs) or *figures of merit* (FoMs) quantify directly how well the system meets the mission objectives. For FireSat II, the principal MoE will be a numerical estimate of how well the system can detect forest fires or the consequences of doing so. This could, for example, be the probability of detecting a given forest fire within 6 hours, or the estimated dollar value of savings resulting from early fire detection. Table 5-7 shows other examples for FireSat II.

Table 5-7. Representative Measures of Effectiveness (MoEs) for FireSat II. These Measures of Effectiveness help us determine how well various designs meet our mission objectives.

Goal	MoE	How Estimated
Fire Detection	Probability of detection vs. time since start of fire (milestones at 6, 12, and 24 hours)	Simulation
Prompt Knowledge	*Time late*—time from observation to availability to the fire captain	Analysis + Budget
Containment	Probability of containment vs. time	Simulation
Save Property and Reduce Cost	Value of property saved plus savings in fire fighting costs	Simulation + Analysis
Save Lives	Estimate of the number of lives saved as a result of having FireSat II available	Scenario Evaluation

We can usually determine performance parameters unambiguously. For example, resolution is determined by an optical analysis as discussed in Sec. 17.3 and the level of coverage for any point on the Earth's surface is determined by analysis or simulation. The probability of detecting and containing forest fires (i.e., MoEs) better measure our end objective, but are also much more difficult to quantify. It may depend on how we construct scenarios and simulations, what we assume about ground resources, and how we use the FireSat II data in conjunction with other data sources to fight fires.

Clearly, performance parameters and MoEs are unique to each mission and depend on the particular objectives that we are trying to achieve and constraints that we must live with. Nonetheless, in general, we would like to minimize cost and risk, maximize the performance, and obtain the results in a timely manner. Building a satellite to help the warfighter in a specific war is of very little utility if the war is over by the time the satellite is launched. Table 5-8 lists some of the most common performance parameters that are likely to be useful in evaluating mission utility for any mission. Of course, many of these will not apply to a specific mission and we are likely to need some additional mission-specific parameters that aren't on the list, but the table provides a reasonable place to start.

Good measures of effectiveness are critical to successful mission analysis and design. If we cannot quantify the degree to which we have met the mission objectives, there is little hope that we can meet them in a cost-effective fashion. The rest of this section defines and characterizes good measures of effectiveness, and Sec. 5.4.2 shows how we evaluate them.

Good measures of effectiveness must be

- Clearly related to mission objectives
- Understandable by decision makers
- Quantifiable
- Sensitive to system design (if used as a design selection criterion)

MoEs are useless if decision makers cannot understand them. "Acceleration in the marginal rate of forest-fire detection within the latitudinal coverage regime of the end-of-life satellite constellation" will likely need substantial explanation to be effective. On the other hand, clear MoEs which are insensitive to the details of the system design, such as the largest coverage gap over one year, cannot distinguish the quality of one system from another. Ordinarily, no single MoE can be used to quantify how the overall system meets mission objectives. Thus, we typically want to provide several MoEs summarizing the system's capacity to achieve its broad objectives.

Measures of effectiveness generally fall into one of three broad categories associated with (1) discrete events, (2) coverage of a continuous activity, or (3) timeliness of the information or other indicators of quality. Discrete events include forest fires, nuclear explosions, ships crossing a barrier, or cosmic ray events. In this case, the best measures of effectiveness are the rate that can be sustained (identify up to 20 forest fires per hour), or the probability of successful identification (90% probability that a forest fire will be detected within 6 hours after ignition). The probability of detecting discrete events is the most common measure of effectiveness. It is useful both in providing good insight to the user community and in allowing the user to create additional measures of effectiveness, such as the probability of extinguishing a forest fire in a given time.

Some mission objectives are not directly quantifiable in probabilistic terms. For example, we may want continuous coverage of a particular event or activity, such as continuous surveillance of the crab nebula for extraneous X-ray bursts or continuous monitoring of Yosemite for temperature variations. Here the typical measure of

Table 5-8. Performance Parameters Applicable for Most Space Missions. For additional details, see Wertz [2008]. These are primarily technical measures that can be evaluated analytically or with a mission simulation.

1. Cost *Primary Performance Parameters* ***Non-Recurring Engineering (NRE)*** = full cost of developing the system ***Recurring Cost per Mission*** = ongoing cost of building and launching subsequent units, including launch, spacecraft bus, payload, and operations (often normalized to 1 year) *Secondary Performance Parameters* ***Cost per Year***—not meaningful if the goal is to achieve a particular objective such as return of samples from a comet ***Cost per Unit of Performance***—here "performance" should be one of the goal-oriented MoEs. ***Cost per data bit*** is a bad idea in most cases—it's results we want, not data volume.	**4. Mission Risk** ***Probability of Successful Deployment***—takes into account both launch failures and failure to work on orbit when first deployed ***Probability of a Successful Mission***—will be much higher if a back-up is available in case of a launch or on-orbit failure ***Ability to Reconstitute Assets***—note that the back-up system may well be of lesser capability than the primary one which it is replacing. Most important in military missions or human resupply.
2. Coverage ***Observations per Day***—may be per satellite or for the system as a whole, if there are multiple satellites ***Number of Spacecraft*** = number of spacecraft required to achieve a given level of coverage or frequency of observations. May change with time as more spacecraft are added to the system.	**5. Flexibility** ***Orbit Agility***—having a high delta V available provides much higher utility for many missions because of the capacity to adjust the orbit to meet changing mission needs ***Observation Time Flexibility*** —this allows the "driver" to adjust both conditions and arrival time at any given location ***Multi-Mission Utility*** = potential to use one asset for more than one mission
3. Data Quality or Quantity ***Resolution at Nadir***—See Sec. 17.3 for definitions and formulas. An alternative measure often used by image analysts is the ***National Imagery Interpretability Ratings Scale (NIIRS)*** that is based on the ability to interpret the resulting images (See Fiete [1999].) ***Bandwidth*** or ***Number of Simultaneous Users***—as discussed throughout the book, there is an ever-increasing demand for more bandwidth	**6. Responsiveness** ***Total Response Time (TRT)*** = total time from when a new request for data is made until the data is delivered to the end user, including launch and on-orbit check out ***Mean Response Time*** = mean time from when a new request for data is made to an on-orbit asset until the data is delivered to the end user ***Time Late*** = time from when an observation is made until the data is delivered to the end user. Measures how "stale" the delivered data is ***Development Time*** = total time to develop, build, and launch a new satellite

effectiveness is some type of coverage or gap statistics such as the mean observation gap or maximum gap under a particular condition. Unfortunately, Gaussian (normal probability) statistics do not ordinarily apply to satellite coverage; therefore, the usual measure of average values can be very misleading. Additional details and a way to resolve this problem are part of the discussion of coverage measures of effectiveness in Sec. 10.2

A third type of measure of effectiveness assesses the quality of a result rather than whether or when it occurs. It may include, for example, the system's ability to resolve the temperature of forest fires. Another common measure of quality is the timeliness of the data, usually expressed as time late, or, in more positive terms for the user, as the time margin from when the data arrives until it is needed. Timeline MoEs might include the average time from ignition of the forest fire to its initial detection or, viewed from the perspective of a potential application, the average warning time before a fire strikes a population center. This type of information, illustrated in Fig. 5-2 allows the decision maker to assess the value of FireSat II in meeting community needs.

The space mission engineer is unlikely to know from looking at Fig. 5-2 whether this FireSat II data will have a high level of utility to fire fighters. But it is likely that someone who manages fire fighting activities and distri-

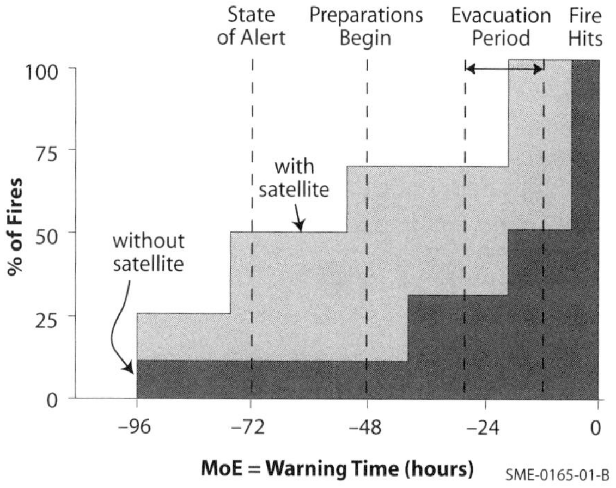

Fig. 5-2. Forest Fire Warning Time for Inhabited Areas. A hypothetical measure of effectiveness for FireSat II.

bution of fire fighting resources, will understand clearly the level of value that additional warning time brings. It may be that the level of advanced warning provided by FireSat II will allow equipment to be put in place and people evacuated in time to make a major difference in the cost and risk of fighting some fires, or it may be that the extra time has very little value if all that is needed is sufficient time for evacuation. Irrespective of the result, the type of information shown in Fig. 5-2 is what is needed to truly judge the utility of FireSat II and, therefore, whether it is worth the cost.

Because MoEs measure the ability of the system to satisfy the mission objectives, they are typically much more specific to each individual mission. In most cases, the objectives of an educational mission or an alt-space mission are very different than those of a military or a commercial mission, as discussed in Sec. 2.1. Most of the mission-specific MoEs fall into 4 broad categories reflecting the impact of the system on the ultimate mission objectives:

- ***Measures of Utility*** = how useful the mission is at meeting the objectives
- ***Measures of Success*** = how successful the mission is at meeting its objectives
- ***Impact on Outcome*** = whether the mission changes the ultimate outcome of events sufficiently to justify its cost
- ***Level of Preparedness*** = whether the mission allows us to be better prepared for future events

Table 5-9 gives some examples of these *goal-oriented MoEs* for several of the space mission communities identified in Chap. 2. As with performance parameters, the selection of specific MoEs depends on the mission objectives. In identifying MoEs, we want to look carefully at the mission objectives and ask what a good measure would be of the level at which the mission achieves these objectives.

5.4.2 Evaluating Mission Utility

In analyzing mission utility, we try to evaluate the measures of effectiveness numerically as a function of cost and risk, but this is hard to do. Instead, we typically use principal system parameters, such as the number of satellites, total on-orbit weight, or payload size, as stand-ins for cost. Thus, we might calculate measures of effectiveness as a function of constellation size, assuming that more satellites cost more money. If we can establish numerical values for meaningful measures of effectiveness as a function of the system drivers and understand the underlying reasons for the results, we will have taken a major step toward quantifying the space mission engineering process.

Recall that mission utility analysis has two distinct but equally important goals—to aid design and provide information for decision making. It helps us improve the mission design by examining the relative benefits of alternatives. For key parameters such as payload type or overall system power, we can show how utility depends on design choices, and therefore, intelligently select among design options.

Mission utility analysis also provides information that is readily usable by decision makers. Generally those who determine funding levels or whether to build a par-

Table 5-9. Goal-Oriented Measures of Effectiveness (GO-MoEs). Columns 2, 3, and 4 are representative space communities from Chap. 2. Column 5 is a specific example of a type of application mission.

Category	Military	Science	Education	Disaster Monitoring
Measures of Utility	How will the mission impact our ability to predict, protect, respond, retaliate, restore, rescue, contain, or limit collateral damage	Amount and importance of scientific data collected Ability to collect data not previously possible	Ability to design, build, test, and launch student experiments Cost of educational space experiments	Accuracy and speed of damage assessment Speed of getting the data to the people that need it
Measures of Success	Reduction in Casualties Reduction in combat duration	Detection of things never before detected Discovery of objects or processes that were previously unknown or not understood	Number of student experiments launched Number launched while the student is still a student	Rapidly locating and assessing damage Finding people in need of help or rescue in time to help or rescue them
Impact on Outcome	Change the outcome of the battle or war Tip the balance against future terrorist attacks	Prove or disprove theories Develop new scientific ideas or concepts Discover previously unknown phenomena	Quality of astronautics and space science education Number of students going into astronautics or space science	Number of lives saved Value of property saved Reduction in amount or duration of human suffering (e.g., getting food quicker to where it is needed)
Level of Preparedness	Ability to respond to changing world events or terrorist attacks Ability to prevent future conflicts by having advanced warning	Ability to respond to unexpected scientific events Ability to gain knowledge from transient events (e.g., nearby nova explosion)	Ability to educate the next generation of scientists and engineers Ability to demonstrate to children and the public the value of space science and astronautics	Ability to respond rapidly to the next major natural or man-made disaster Ability to prevent disasters (e.g., earthquake prediction; hurricane forecasting)

ticular space system do not have either the time or inclination to assess detailed technical studies. For large space programs, decisions ultimately depend on a relatively small amount of information being assessed by individuals at a high level in industry or government. A strong utility analysis allows these high-level judgments to be more informed and based more on sound technical assessments. By providing summary performance data in a form the decision-making audience can understand, the mission utility analysis can make a major contribution to the decision-making process.

5.4.2.1 *Mission Utility Simulation*

Typically, the only effective way to numerically evaluate mission utility is to use a mission utility simulation designed specifically for this purpose. This is **not** the same as a *payload simulator*, which evaluates performance parameters for various payloads. For FireSat II, a payload simulator might compute the level of observable temperature changes or the number of acres that can be searched per orbit pass. In contrast, the *mission simulator* assumes a level of performance for the payload and assesses its ability to meet mission objectives. The FireSat II mission simulator would determine how soon forest fires can be detected or the amount of acreage that can be saved per year.

In principle, mission simulators are straightforward. In practice, they are expensive and time consuming to create and are rarely as successful as we would like. Attempts to achieve excessive fidelity tend to dramatically increase the cost and reduce the effectiveness of most mission simulators. The goal of mission simulation is to estimate measures of effectiveness as a function of key system parameters. We must restrict the simulator as much as possible to achieving this goal. Overly detailed simulations require more time and money to create and are much less useful, because long run times keep us from running them enough for effective trade studies. The simulator must be simple enough to allow making large number of runs, so we can collect statistical data and explore various scenarios and design options.

The mission simulation should include parameters that directly affect utility, such as the orbit geometry, motion or changes in the targets or background, system scheduling, and other key issues, as shown in Fig. 5-3. The problem of excessive detail is best solved by providing numerical models obtained from more detailed simulations of the payload or other system components. For example, we may compute FireSat II's capacity to detect a forest fire by modeling the detector sensitivity, atmospheric characteristics, range to the fire, and the background conditions in the observed area. A detailed payload simulation should include these parameters. After running the payload simulator many times, we can, for example, tabulate the probability of detecting a fire based on observation geometry, time of day, and size of the fire. The mission simulator uses this table to assess various scenarios and scheduling algorithms. Thus, the mission simulator might compute the mission geometry, time of day, and fire size, and then use the lookup table to determine the payload effectiveness.

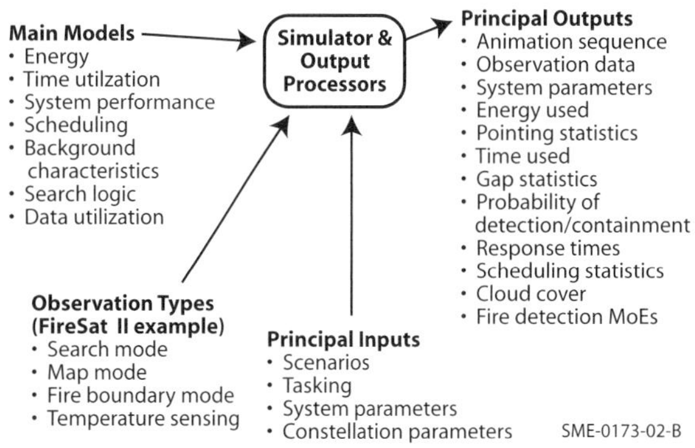

Fig. 5-3. Typical Mission Utility Simulation Inputs, Models, and Outputs for FireSat II.

With this method, we can dramatically reduce repetitive computations in each mission simulator run, do more simulations, and explore more mission options than with a more detailed simulation. The mission simulator should be a collection of the results of more detailed simulations along with unique mission parameters such as the relative geometry between the satellites in a constellation, variations in ground targets or background, and the system scheduling or downlink communications. Creating sub-models also makes it easier to generate utility simulations. We start with simple models for the individual components and develop more realistic tables as we create and run more detailed payload or component simulations.

In a constellation of satellites, scheduling is often a key issue in mission utility. The constellation's utility depends largely on the system's capacity to schedule resource use appropriately among the satellites. At the end of a single simulation run, the system should collect and compute the statistics for that scenario, generate appropriate output plots or data, and compute individual measures of effectiveness, such as the percent of forest fires detected in that particular run.

The next step is to run more simulations using new start times or otherwise varying the conditions for the scenarios. Changing the start times alters the relative timing and geometry between the satellites and the events they are observing, thus, averaging results caused by these characteristics. Collecting statistics on multiple runs is called a *Monte Carlo simulation*. For example, we might average the percentage of forest fires detected over different runs with different timing, but using the same scenario, to estimate the overall probability of detecting forest fires—our ultimate measure of effectiveness. The mission simulator should accumulate output statistics and prepare output plots over the Monte Carlo runs.

Frequently, in running mission simulations, we must choose between realistic and analytical scenarios. Realistic scenarios usually are too complex to help us understand how the system works but are still necessary to satisfy the end users. On the other hand, simple scenarios illuminate how the system is working but do not show how it will work in a real situation. The best answer is to use simple scenarios for analysis and realistic scenarios to assess mission performance. In the FireSat II example, we might begin by studying a single satellite to determine how it behaves and then expand to a more complex simulation with several satellites. We might also start evaluating a multi-satellite constellation by looking at its response to a simple situation, such as one fire or a small group of uniformly distributed fires. This trial run will suggest how the system performs and how changes affect it. We can then apply this understanding as we develop more realistic simulations.

A related problem concerns using a baseline scenario to compare options and designs. Repeating a single scenario allows us to understand the scenario and the system's response to it. We can also establish quantitative differences by showing how different designs respond to the same scenario. But this approach tends to mask characteristics that might arise solely from a particular scenario. Thus, we must understand what happens as the baseline changes and watch for chance results developing from our choice of a particular baseline scenario.

Finally, mission simulations must generate usable and understandable information for decision makers—information that provides physical insight. Two examples are strip charts of various system characteristics and animated output. A *strip chart* plot is similar to the output of a seismograph or any multi-pin plotter, in which various characteristics are plotted as a function of time. These characteristics might include, for example, whether a particular satellite is in eclipse, how much time it spends in active observation, and the spacecraft attitude during a particular time step. Plots of this type give a good feel for the flow of events as the simulation proceeds.

A valuable alternative for understanding the flow of events is looking at an animation of the output, such as a picture of the Earth showing various changes in the target, background, and observation geometry as the satellites fly overhead. Thus, as Fig. 5-4 illustrates, an animated simulation of FireSat II output could be a map of a fire-sensitive region with areas changing color as fires begin, lines showing satellite coverage, and indications as to when fires are first detected or when mapping of a fire occurs. Animation is not as numerical as statistical data, but it shows more clearly how the satellite system is working and how well it will meet broad objectives. Thus, mission analysts and end users can assess the system's performance, strengths, and short-comings, and the changes needed to make it work better.

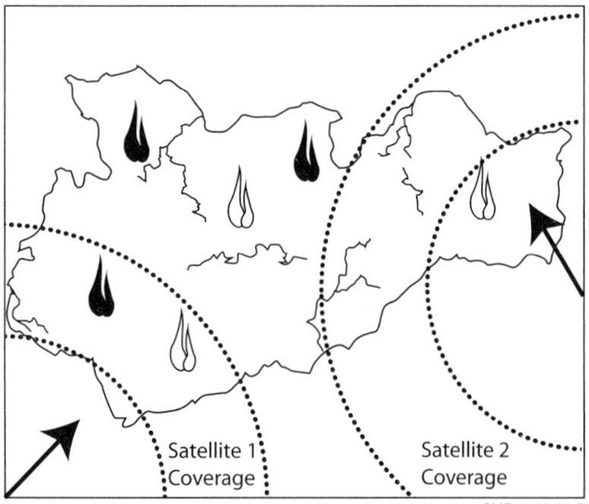

Fig. 5-4. Hypothetical Animation Output for FireSat II Mission Utility Simulator. Color displays are very valuable for animation sequences because we need to convey multiple parameters in each frame.

5.4.2.2 Scenario Evaluation—The Hawaii Disaster of 2025

Many of the MoEs in Table 5-9 are very difficult to evaluate numerically in large part because they aren't intended to be engineering oriented, but are meant to measure how well the mission objectives are being met. Realistically, there probably is no way to estimate via simulation the number of lives saved, the impact on the outcome of the war, or the importance of the resulting science. One of the best approaches to dealing with this is *scenario evaluation* in which we look at a real or hypothetical scenario and try to evaluate how that scenario would have been different had the system being evaluated been in place. Typically we would look to people who have been through the scenario if it's a real historical event, or similar ones if it's a hypothetical scenario, to estimate what the consequences would have been had the space system been in place. The advantage of using a real historical event or sequence of events is that at least for the baseline case, i.e., what happened without the system in place, the results are reasonably well understood. In addition, this type of evaluation is meaningful to decision makers because it is easy to discuss what actually happened and contrast that with what could have happened.

The scenario evaluation can be done either in conjunction with a simulation or, less precisely, by simply estimating the results. As an example, consider the great Hawaiian disaster of October 10, 2025 [Wertz, 2008]. On the evening of October 9, an earthquake and resulting tsunami struck in the ocean east of Japan with damage to all of the major airports and most homes, businesses, and infrastructure. Communications were badly disrupted and it was difficult to assess the damage or to find people that needed help, needed to be moved, had been washed out to sea, or were in imminent danger due to potential aftershocks. The tsunami also headed for Hawaii where evacuations of low ground began immediately. While major population centers were largely evacuated, it wasn't possible to get word to all of the residents and it was feared that many in rural areas may have been washed out to sea when the tsunami hit Hawaii.

By order of the President, HawaiiSat was launched from KSC 10 hours after the earthquake hit to provide both visible and IR images. The satellite carried an 0.5 meter diameter imager. Following a 4 deg inclination

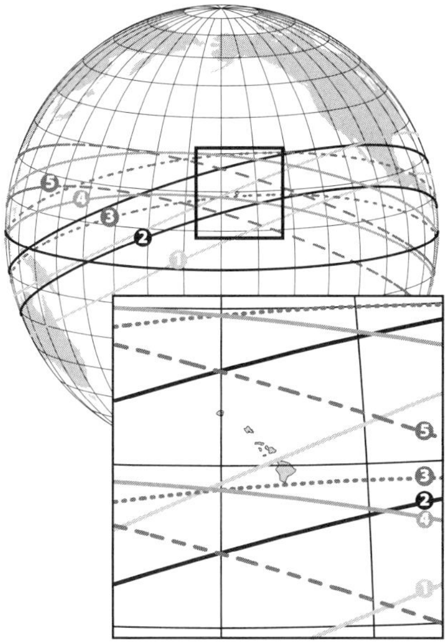

Fig. 5-5. Swath of the First 5 Orbits for the Hypothetical HawaiiSat Mission in October, 2025. Hawaii will be visible on 5 or 6 orbits/day with the observation times moving approximately 35 minutes earlier per day.

change at the equator, the satellite was placed in a 250 km altitude circular orbit at an inclination of 24.5 deg. The ground swath of HawaiiSat's first 5 orbits are shown in Fig. 5-5. The first images of the damage at a low elevation angle were returned on the first orbit about 80 minutes after launch. The second pass, 90 minutes later, flew almost directly over the islands and gave very good images of the damage and allowed the first estimate of the drift rate and direction of debris floating at sea by comparison with images from the first orbit. The next 2 orbits provided images at shallow angles for the big island and more nearly overhead for the rest of the islands. The fifth orbit again passed nearly overhead, 6 hours after the first orbit. 5 or 6 orbits of imaging occurred on subsequent days, moving about 35 minutes earlier per day.

The spacecraft parameter and cost estimates for the above system are based on the Frequent Revisit Surveillance mission discussed by Wertz et al. [2006] and Cox, et al. [2005, 2006]. Based on these parameters, the HawaiiSat performance parameters and MoEs are shown in Table 5-10.

While we don't yet have all of the numbers we need, it seems clear that a responsive disaster monitoring satellite could provide a significant capability to respond, restore, rescue, contain, and limit collateral damage. With this capability the government will be prepared to save lives and property.

In this type of scenario evaluation, some people will argue that existing on-orbit assets could do the job and that HawaiiSat wouldn't be needed. Others will argue that historically that doesn't happen and that existing assets are not in fact made available until well after the immediate need is past. Irrespective of which side of that argument prevails, the scenario evaluation approach, particularly when combined with real historical events and some mission simulations, can provide a great deal of insight into the utility of both existing and proposed systems and their strengths and weaknesses. This then leads to a more informed decision as discussed in Sec. 5.7.

Table 5-10. HawaiiSat Performance Parameters and MoEs.

Parameter	Value
Cost	
NRE	$40 M
Recurring Cost/Mission	$17.3 M
Coverage	
Observations/Day	5 to 6
Number of Spacecraft	1
Data Quality	
Nadir Resolution	0.3 m
Risk	
Deployment—Prob. of Success	90%
Mission—Prob. of Success	99%
Flexibility	TBD
Responsiveness	
Total Response Time	5 min
Mean Revisit Time	85 min for 6 to 7.5 hrs
Time Late	5 min
GO-MoEs	
Need a mission simulation and discussion with emergency response personnel to evaluate these critical measures	

5.5 Defining the Baseline Mission Concept, Revising Requirements, and Evaluating Alternatives (Steps 10–12)

Steps 10 to 12 in the Space Mission Engineering process from Table 3-1 are to define the baseline mission concept and architecture, revise the quantitative requirements and constraints, and evaluate alternatives. A *baseline mission*, like the point design defined in Sec. 5.2.3, is simply a mission definition that, in a broad sense, fulfills the overall mission objectives. By *mission definition* we mean what is being used for each of the 8 elements of the mission architecture plus the basic concept of operations. For FireSat II we want to know broadly how we're going to detect and monitor forest fires and how we're going to get that information to the end user. Ultimately, we are concerned with the firefighter in the truck and how he or she gets the data they need to do their job better and safer. Although we will work a great many technical details as we go through the definition of the mission, we should return often to the end user. Are we meeting their needs in a timely fashion at minimum cost and risk? If we aren't convinced that this is the case, then we should go back and work on the problem until we are. Space mission engineering is a highly iterative process and it is rarely the case that the first approach is the best, and our first ideas may not even work that well.

Table 5-11 summarizes the process for selecting the baseline, trading on requirements, and evaluating alternative mission concepts. We begin by going back to the broad mission objectives and constraints that define what the mission is all about (Sec. 3.3). What is it that we're trying to achieve? Are there major constraints on how we are allowed to do that, such as the use of a particular technology or building on prior experimental missions? Who are the people that will ultimately pay for the mission, who are the people that will use the data that it generates, and what are their goals and objectives? This leads us to Step 2 where we identify the space community or communities that are being served. Irrespective of the details of a particular mission, a mission being done for the education community will almost certainly have a different set of objectives and constraints than will a military mission or a science mission meant to explore the depths of the Universe.

Table 5-11. Process for Selecting A Baseline Mission and Evaluating Alternatives. See text for discussion. See Sec. 5.6 for specific examples for the FireSat II and SCS mission.

Step	Where Discussed
1. List mission objectives and constraints	Sec. 3.3
2. Identify the space community being served and the end users and their broad objectives and approaches	Sec. 2.1
3. Determine which is the most important criteria for the mission—performance, cost, risk, or schedule	Sec. 1.1, Chap. 3
4. For each element of the mission architecture plus the mission concept, select an approach consistent with Step 3. This is a ***Point Design*** and the ***Initial Baseline***.	Sec. 4.1 to 4.3, 5.2.3
5. List major alternative approaches	Chap. 4
6. Look for the critical requirements that drive performance, cost, risk, or schedule (may be different for alternative approaches)	Sec. 4.4
7. For the baseline and each major alternative, begin the process of the Trading on Requirements	Sec. 5.5
8. Select a ***Revised Baseline*** and Major Alternatives for further analysis	—
9. Document and Iterate. This is a highly iterative process and documenting the reasons for choices is key.	—

The third step is to determine the most important criteria for the mission—performance, cost, risk, or schedule. Is the group that is funding the mission dramatically risk averse, such that we want to use largely processes and hardware that have worked in the past, or are they open to new ideas and approaches that might be able to dramatically drive down cost or provide a new level of performance? Throughout much of the history of the space program, the emphasis on most missions was avoiding risk, largely irrespective of the consequences on cost and schedule. (A common quote in the space industry is "If it works, all else is forgiven.") As discussed in Chap. 1, this has brought us to a space program that, in many cases, we can no longer afford and that doesn't generate results quickly enough to have sufficient utility to many end users. An asteroid warning system is of very little use if it is cancelled because of excessive cost or delayed until after an asteroid hits New York. Because of budget constraints in nearly all space programs worldwide, there is now a strong tendency to ask whether we can do things differently, or adopt hardware or processes from one of the other space communities or non-space applications, in order to significantly reduce cost or schedule.

Having created the framework for what we're trying to achieve and the basic rules within which we need to work, the next step is to define an initial baseline mission that can do the job, although perhaps with less performance or at a higher cost, greater risk, or longer schedule than we would like. We do this by defining each of the 8 elements of the mission architecture:

- Subject
- Payload
- Spacecraft Bus
- Ground Segment
- Mission Operations
- Orbit
- Command, Control, and Communications Architecture
- Launch Segment

Each of these is defined in more detail in Table 4-1. In addition to the elements of the mission architecture, we need to define the broad mission concept—i.e., how all of the mission elements work together to meet the needs of the end user. As discussed in Secs. 4.2 and 5.6, the mission concept for FireSat II revolves primarily around how (and where) we identify a forest fire and distinguish it from a really big barbecue and how we get that information to the firefighter in the truck. The method of doing these assessments are defined in Chap. 4 and in the discussion of the quick, limited detail studies (feasibility assessment, sizing estimate, and point design) in Sec. 5.2.

In addition to the initial baseline, we also want to list the major alternatives. These will nearly always involve one of elements of the mission architecture or the mission concept. For FireSat II one of the major alternatives will be the orbit. Do we use one or more small satellites in LEO or a single large satellite in GEO? We will get at the process of numerically evaluating these alternatives shortly, but in this step we simply want to identify them. This is a part of the creative process of space mission engineering. What are the alternative approaches that we might use to increase performance or drive down cost, risk, or schedule? Are there processes or hardware from other space communities or from the non-space arena that might work well for this mission? Do the advances in computing power and image recognition and analysis software allow us to identify forest fires on-board the spacecraft and go directly from the spacecraft to the end user or the fire management station? We select as our initial baseline the approach that appears to be most consistent with what is important to this user—performance, cost, risk, or schedule.

In order to evaluate alternative approaches, we first identify the *critical requirements* that serve to drive the performance, cost, risk, and schedule. The process of identifying these critical requirements is defined in Sec. 4.4. Note that both the critical requirements and the system drivers may be different for different approaches. Two key issues here are to define the **reasons** for each requirement and to look for requirements that drive the cost, but don't improve performance, risk, or schedule. **Our goal is to adjust both the system parameters and the mission requirements to achieve our mission objectives at the minimum cost, risk, and schedule, or at least within a cost, risk, and schedule that we can afford, given that cost and schedule are likely to increase as the mission definition proceeds.**

The process of mission definition is much like an individual buying a new car. What we want to buy is a combination of what we would like and what we can reasonably afford and is likely to be strongly influenced by what is available in the marketplace. Is there new, lightweight mirror technology that can help us build a larger telescope at much lower mass and cost than was possible the last time we built one? Will new computer technology let us do more data processing on board such that we can simply send down the results and not all of the data needed to get there? What we want is to help the customer become an intelligent consumer.

The numerical processes for evaluating the major alternatives are the system trade studies, performance assessments, and mission utility analyses defined in detail in Secs. 5.3 and 5.4. The performance parameter trades are typically straightforward analyses that are relatively easy to do. These can help greatly when we are looking at a simple trade like orbit altitude or the amount of power or the resolution that is required to do the mission. Mission utility assessments are likely to be much harder, but also more useful. For FireSat II, when we compare the single geosynchronous satellite with multiple small satellites in LEO, the two alternatives will have very little in common, except the ability to detect forest fires. The system drivers and critical requirements will be different for both and they will have very different operational approaches and hardware. The only realistic way to make a comparison between them is to look at the mission utility that each can achieve as a function of cost, risk, and schedule.

5.6 Examples: FireSat II and SCS

As an example, we would like to go through the definition of a baseline system and the identification of major alternatives and system trades for both FireSat II and the SCS constellation defined in Sec. 3.2. As discussed in Sec. 3.3, the primary objective of FireSat II is **to detect, identify, and monitor forest fires throughout the United States, including Alaska and Hawaii in near-real time.** and for the Supplemental Communications System, SCS, it is **to provide low-cost, low-data-rate, real-time supplemental communications to existing military systems and aide in natural disaster relief with continuous connectivity to CONUS.** For both missions there are several possible secondary objectives, but these may change with the definition of the system and, therefore, are more important later when we begin the evaluation of alternatives. The principal constraints on both systems are those that are implied by the primary mission objectives—to be low cost and to be in place at the time that they are needed. In addition, we expect that military systems will want secure communications, while this is not likely to be of concern for the natural disaster relief mission.

For FireSat II, the principal community being served is the Earth applications community and the end user is the forest service and fire fighting community. Other than being regular users of GPS, they have no connection with space activity and no real interest in space per se. Thus, they will be interested in FireSat II only to the extent that it solves a problem that they can't otherwise solve (such as early detection of fires in remote areas) or solves problems more economically or substantially better than the traditional non-space solutions. If monitoring forest fires from space can get them data sufficiently quicker or better than other approaches such that they can more quickly contain fires, reduce fire fighting costs, and save property and lives (including reducing the risk to the firefighters themselves), then there will be some interest. But it is also likely that they will be wary of a system that costs 10's of millions of dollars or more (possibly much more) and that is well outside their area of expertise. There is likely to be a level of (possibly unspoken) concern on their part that FireSat II is more of a gimmick to support the space industry than a real and useful tool for identifying and fighting fires. This, in turn, means that clearly demonstrating mission utility to a group that fundamentally doesn't know or care about space will be critical.

In contrast, SCS is intended to serve two communities, both of which already use space assets and recognize a very real need for better communications in remote locations. The military community uses space assets for a great many functions and, along with the intelligence community, is one of the largest users, builders, and developers of space assets. The disaster relief community (part of the Earth applications community) works on a much lower budget, but has made good use of the Surrey-developed Disaster Monitoring Constellation, which provided the first images published in *Aviation Week* of the aftermath of Hurricane Katrina. In both cases, the end user is likely an individual in a remote area with limited communications equipment (much like the firefighter in the truck) who needs communications with the outside world as reliably and continuously as possible to save lives and accomplish their basic mission.

For all 3 groups involved (fire fighting, disaster relief, and military), low-cost is the most important criteria for both FireSat II and SCS. The fire fighting and disaster relief communities have very little budget to devote to "external" systems, such as space missions. The military community has substantial resources for communications, but already has large, expensive systems in place. The only reason for SCS is to provide additional communications at low cost. Because the systems will be low-cost and most likely SmallSats, they do not need to be as risk averse as traditional, large, multi-billion dollar satellites. Nonetheless, risk is important because the budget is limited and replacing the systems would be painful.

Defining an initial baseline for each system will require looking at each of the 8 mission elements and the mission concept. Assuming we have done this initial analysis using each of the chapters defined in Sec. 4.1, the preliminary results for FireSat II and SCS are shown in Table 5-12. In some cases, the likely lowest cost approach has been selected as the baseline (the payload and mission concept for FireSat II and the orbit for SCS) and in some cases a more traditional approach has been selected as the baseline (the ground station approach for both). So long as we continue the system trade and system evaluation process, the choice of the initial baseline isn't critical. The baseline will evolve as we continue to make trades and evaluate alternatives. The risk here is that we may try to fix the baseline in concrete and treat it as somehow better than the alternative approaches and this is what we very much need to avoid. After a few rounds through the system trade process we will learn more about which approaches are better and what the real goals and objectives are, assuming that the customer or end user are a part of the trade process, as they should be.

Our next step is to identify the critical requirements that will tend to drive performance, cost, risk, and schedule. These will tend to be different for the different alternatives. For the baseline FireSat II mission, the critical requirements for performance, cost, risk, and schedule are most likely the revisit interval since that drives the number of satellites, and the mission concept, since that determines the complexity of both ground and on-board processing. If we look at the GEO option for FireSat II, revisit interval won't really matter since we can see CONUS continuously. The requirements that will matter for GEO are the resolution (which could lead to needing a bigger telescope) and the need to cover

Table 5-12. Definition of the Initial Baseline and Major Alternatives for FireSat II and SCS. While alternatives exist for essentially all of the elements, we are only concerned here with the most important alternatives that will have a major impact on performance, cost, risk, schedule, or the mission concept.

Element	FireSat II Baseline	FireSat II Major Alternatives	SCS Baseline	SCS Major Alternatives
Subject	Heat from fire	—	Handheld receiver	Cell phone with wire antenna to boost signal
Payload	IR sensor	Possibly multiple spectral bands	Software defined radio; bands TBD	—
Spacecraft Bus	SmallSat bus, body-mounted arrays, integral propulsion, Earth pointing	May want steerable payload to look specifically at forests	200 kg SmallSat bus with deployable arrays and fixed crosslinks fore and aft	Mass of the spacecraft can be a continuous variable depending on the equipment and launch
Ground Segment	Dedicated ground station in CONUS	Commercial, pay-per-pass ground system	2 dedicated ground stations for redundancy	Commercial, pay-per-pass ground system
Mission Operations	Single facility doing both fire detection and commanding	Single facility doing commanding and monitoring of the on-board fire detection	Single facility doing both payload and constellation control	—
Command, Control, and Communications Architecture	Direct link from ground segment to FireSat II	—	Continuous link from ground station in CONUS to all of the satellites	—
Orbit	2 satellites in LEO orbit at inclination = 60 deg	1 satellite in GEO stationed over CONUS	3 satellites in circular, equatorial orbits at 20,000 km; supplemented with 3 more equatorial or 3 polar	TBD satellites in elliptical orbits—not as good, but more traditional
Launch Segment	Pegasus or Minotaur I	Secondary launch on a larger vehicle	All 3 satellites launched on a single EELV	Single launches on Pegasus or Minotaur 4
Mission Concept	Fire detection by trained analysts at mission ops facility; fire data relayed back through FireSat II and down to end user	On-board fire detection and monitoring sent directly to end user with data going from time-to-time to monitoring activity	Fixed crosslinks provide continuous connectivity to CONUS with only 1 hop from anywhere within 50 deg of the equator	—

northern Alaska, which may be too far north to be easily visible from GEO. If GEO becomes a viable option as the analysis proceeds, we may choose to argue that forest fires are less of a problem in northern Alaska and, therefore, the latitude that we need to reach can be limited.

For the SCS baseline constellation the critical requirements will be the capability of the hand held receiver, the spacecraft bus mass (which determines the size and power of the payload), and the need to overcome jamming for the military mission since this could dramatically reduce the available bandwidth. In the SCS alternatives we have chosen to list the possibility of doing something to boost the gain of an ordinary cell phone so that either military personnel or relief workers could use their cell phone which they are much more likely to have with them than some extraneous piece of equipment, particularly in the case of emergency relief operations. It would be an enormous asset if we could do this, but we don't know if it can be done. Therefore, we will need to devote analysis time, and most likely quite a bit of test time, to see what is possible and reasonable to do under adverse conditions in remote areas.

For both FireSat II and SCS we have listed commercial, pay-per-pass ground stations as a potential low-cost option to significantly drive down the ground system and operations cost. In this model, data can be brought down and commands sent back up via any of a series of commercial ground stations around the world, typically for a few hundred dollars per pass. Data is then put on a secure internet link and, if needed, encrypted on board the spacecraft before being transmitted. The satellite system then becomes simply another node on the secure internet. This has the potential of being both lower cost and more reliable than dedicated ground stations, but it tends to be a non-traditional approach (although service provided ground stations have been in operation for decades) and, therefore, may be **perceived** as too high a risk.

As part of evaluating alternatives we will make use of all of the various analytic techniques defined in Secs. 5.2, 5.3, and 5.4 including performance assessments, systems trades, and utility analysis. For FireSat II we can do system trade studies for many of the alternative approaches:

- Use of single vs. multiple spectral bands
- Earth pointing vs. steerable payload
- Choice of ground station approach
- Launch vehicle options (we want to keep more than 1 option available in order to allow negotiation for the lowest price)
- Basic mission concept of ground vs. on-board identification and monitoring of forest fires

The key need of the mission utility analysis will be twofold—to evaluate the results of multiple satellites in LEO vs. a single satellite in GEO and to convince ourselves, the customer, and the end user that FireSat II will really have substantial mission utility and be worth the estimated cost and risk. This will, of course, depend very much on what the cost turns out to be.

For SCS we can probably do a simple performance assessment for the issue of spacecraft mass and system trades for the

- Orbit selection
- Choice of ground station approach
- Launch vehicle options (as with FireSat II, we want to keep more than 1 option available in order to allow negotiation for the lowest price)

The cell phone option will probably require substantial analysis and testing to see whether it is workable and may go forward or may be discarded as impractical. Here the main purpose of a utility analysis is to clearly show the customer (and possibly Congress) that the end result is well worth the probable cost.

Having done our systems trades and utility assessment we then go back and either revise or confirm our initial baseline approach. Here we need to do two things. We need to document the choices we have made and the studies and analysis that have led to them so that they can be revisited from time to time as needed. Second, and perhaps equally important, is to not believe our results. There will be many more trades and analyses as we go forward. We haven't even started yet to take into account potential secondary objectives for either mission and these may take on a more important role, particularly if one or more of the secondary missions becomes involved in funding the program. For example, GPS did not have sufficient political support to be funded when it first came about. For this reason the Nuclear Detection System (NDS) was added and provided the margin needed to generate sufficient support in Congress for the system to come about. This means that we must continue to remain open to trades and alternatives as the system becomes better defined. And we must always go back to the needs of the end user—the firefighter in the truck, the soldier in an isolated area, or the relief worker in a remote disaster area somewhere in the world. Are we truly satisfying their needs at minimum cost and risk?

5.7 Deciding Whether a Mission Should Proceed

This section is concerned not with the detailed engineering decisions for a space mission, but with the broad trades involved in defining the overall mission—whether to proceed with it and what concept to use. Decisions for space missions fall into three broad categories: (1) go/no-go decision on proceeding with the mission; (2) selection of the mission concept; and (3) detailed engineering decisions, which are generally described throughout this book.

In principle, the go/no-go decision depends on only a few factors, the most important of which are:

- Does the proposed system meet the overall mission objectives?

- Is it technically feasible?
- Is the level of risk acceptable?
- Are the schedule and budget within the established constraints?
- Do preliminary results show this option to be better than nonspace solutions?

In addition to the above technical issues, a number of nontechnical criteria are ordinarily equally or more important in the decision-making process:

- Does the mission meet its political objectives?
- Are the organizational responsibilities acceptable to all of the organizations involved in the decision?
- Does the mission support the infrastructure in place or contemplated?

For example, a mission may be approved to keep an organization in business, or it may be delayed or suspended if it requires creating an infrastructure perceived as not needed in the long term. The mission analysis activity must include nontechnical factors associated with space missions and see that they are appropriately addressed.

The top-level trades in concept selection are usually not fully quantitative, and we should not force them to be. The purpose of the trade studies and utility analysis is to make the decisions as informed as possible. We wish to add quantitative information to the decisions, not quantify the decision making. In other words, we should not undervalue the decision-maker's judgment by attempting to replace it with a simplistic formula or rule.

Table 5-13 shows how we might try to quantify a decision. Assume that a system costs $500 million, but an improvement could save up to $300 million. To save this money, we could use option A, B, or C. Option A would cost $50 million, but the probability of success is only 70%; B would cost $120 million with 99% probability of success; C would cost $200 million with a 99.9% probability of success.

Which option should we select? The table gives the cost if successful, the cost if the improvement fails, and the expected values of both the cost and net savings. By numbers alone, we would select option B with an expected savings of $177 million. However, reasonable and valid cases can be made for both A and C. In option A, we risk only $50 million, and, therefore, are minimizing the total cost if the improvement succeeds or if it fails. In fact, the $620 million cost of failure for option B may be too much for the system to bear, no matter the expected savings. Option C provides a net savings of "only" $100 million, but its success is virtually certain. Although savings for this option are less dramatic, it does provide major savings while minimizing risk. In this case, we may assume the cost to be a fixed $400 million, with failure being so unlikely that we can discount it. Option B, of course, balances cost and risk to maximize the expected savings.

Table 5-13. Mathematical Model of a Hypothetical Decision Process for a New Space System (costs in $M). Numerically, we would choose B or A' if it were available. As discussed in the text, any of the choices may be best depending on the decision criteria.

Current Cost						$500M
Potential Savings if Improvement is Successful						$300M
Option	**Cost of Improvement**	**Probability of Success**	**Total Cost if Successful**	**Total Cost if Failed**	**Expected Total Cost**	**Expected Savings**
A	$50M	70%	$250M	$550M	$340M	$160M
B	$120M	99%	$320M	$620M	$323M	$177M
C	$200M	99.90%	$400M	$700M	$400.3M	$99.7M
A'	$50M	80%	$250M	$550M	$310M	$190M

Suppose, however, that option A had an 80% probability of success as shown in A', rather than the original 70% probability. In this case, the expected savings of A' would increase to $190 million, and would make it the preferred approach in purely mathematical terms. However, most individuals or groups faced with decisions of this sort are unlikely to change from option B to A' based solely on the increase in estimated probability to 80%. Their decisions are more likely to depend on perceived risk or on minimizing losses. Using non-mathematical criteria does not make the decisions incorrect or invalid, nor does it make the numerical values unimportant. We need quantitative information to choose between options but we do not have to base our decisions exclusively on this information.

As a second example, we can apply the results of utility analysis to concept selection for FireSat II. In particular, the number of satellites strongly drives the cost of a constellation. If we select the low-Earth orbit approach for FireSat II, how many satellites should the operational constellation contain? More satellites means better coverage and, therefore, reduces the time from when a fire starts until it is first detected. Consequently, one of our key parameters is the *time late*, that is, the time from when a fire starts until the system detects its presence and transmits the information to the ground. Figure 5-6 plots the hypothetical time late vs. the number of satellites for FireSat II. The details of such plots will depend on the latitude under consideration, swath coverage, altitude, and various other parameters. However, the characteristic of increasing coverage with more satellites eventually reaches a point of diminishing returns. This will normally be true irrespective of the coverage assumptions.

If we assume an initial goal for time late of no more than 5 hours, we see from the plot that a system of 6 satellites can meet this goal. Alternatively, a 4-satellite system can achieve a time late of 6 hours. Is the smaller time late worth the increased number of satellites and the money to

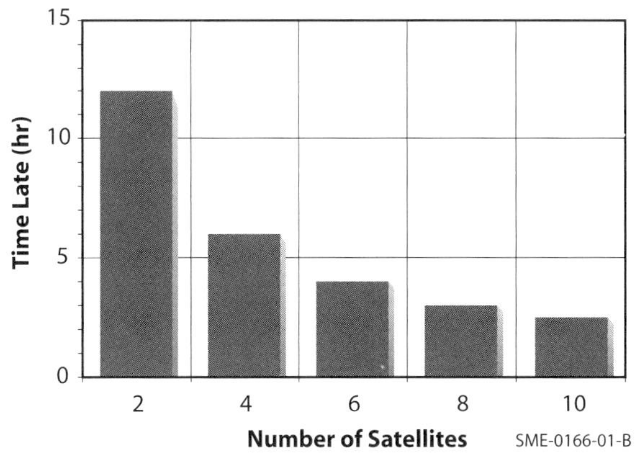

Fig. 5-6. Hypothetical Coverage Data for FireSat II. See text for definitions and discussion. As discussed in Sec. 10.10, growth in coverage typically comes in increments or plateaus. These are assumed to be 2-satellite increments for FireSat II.

build them? Only the ultimate users of the system can judge. The additional warning may be critical to fire containment and, therefore, a key to mission success. However, it is also possible that the original goal was somewhat arbitrary, and a time of **approximately** 5 hours is what is really needed. In this case, fire-fighting resources could probably be used better by flying a 4-satellite system with 6 hours time late and applying the savings to other purposes. Again, mission utility analysis simply provides quantitative data for intelligent decision making.

Of course, we must remember that the number of FireSat II satellites will depend not only on the utility analysis but also on politics, schedules, and resources. The public must see FireSat II as an appropriate response to the problem, as well as an efficient use of scarce economic resources compared to, for example, more fire fighters. In addition, a satellite system may serve several missions, with multiple mission criteria and needs. Just as we cannot apply only one criterion to some system drivers, we may not be able to balance numerically the several criteria for mission selection. Instead, the developers, operators, and users must balance them using the insight gained from the system trades and mission utility analysis.

Having undertaken a round of system trades, evaluated the mission utility, and selected one or more baseline approaches, we are ready to return to the issue of system requirements and their flow-down to various components. Chapter 6 treats this area, which is simply the next step in the iterative process of exploring concepts and defining requirements.

References

Get Ref **For annotated bibliography of mission analysis and utility, see the book website.**

Brookner, Eli, and Thomas F. Mahoney. 1986. "Derivation of a Satellite Radar Architecture for Air Surveillance." *Microwave Journal*. 29: 173–191.

Cantafio, Leopold J. 1989. *Space-Based Radar Handbook*. Norwood, MA: Artech House.

Chesley, Julie, W. Larson, M. McQuade, and R. Menrad. 2008. *Applied Project Management for Space Systems*. Boston, MA: The McGraw-Hill Companies.

Cox, Charles, Stanley Kishner and David Flynn. 2006. "Reconnaissance Payloads for Responsive Space." 4th Responsive Space Conference. AIAA RS4 2006-5003. Los Angeles, CA. Apr. 24–27.

Cox, Charles, Stanley Kishner, Richard Whittlesey and Fredrick Gilligan. 2005. "Reconnaissance Payloads for Responsive Missions." 3rd Responsive Space Conference. AIAA RS3 2005-5004. Los Angeles, CA. Apr. 25–28.

Fiete, Robert D. 1999. "Image quality and λFN/p for Remote Sensing Systems." *Optical Engineering*, vol. 38, no. 7. Jul. pp. 1229–1240.

Fortescue, Peter W., J. Stark and G. Swinerd. 2003. *Spacecraft Systems Engineering. 3rd ed.* Chichester, UK: John Wiley and Sons.

Kay, W. D. 1995. *Can Democracies Fly in Space?: The Challenge of Revitalizing the U.S. Space Program.* Westport, CT: Praeger.

Kemble, Stephen. 2006. *Interplanetary Mission Analysis and Design.* Berlin: Springer.

Larson, Wiley J., and Linda K. Pranke. 1999. *Human Spaceflight: Mission Analysis and Design*. New York: The McGraw-Hill Companies.

Larson, Wiley J., Douglas Kirkpatrick, Jerry Sellers, Lawrence Thomas, and Dinesh Verma. 2009. *Applied Space Systems Engineering*. Boston, MA: The McGraw-Hill Companies.

NASA. 2007 National Aeronautics and Space Association. *Systems Engineering Handbook*. Hanover, MD: NASA.

O'Neill, Gerard K. 1974. "The Colonization of Space." *Physics Today*, vol. 27, no. 9. Sept. pp. 32–40.

Pisacane, Vincent L. and Robert C. Moore. 2005. *Fundamentals of Space Systems, 2nd ed.* Oxford: Oxford University Press.

Przemieniecki, J. S. 1993. *Acquisition of Defense Systems*. Washington, DC: AIAA.

Przemieniecki, J. S. 2000. *Introduction to Mathematical Methods in Defense Analyses*. Reston, VA: AIAA.

Sandau, Rainer. 2006. *International Study on Cost-effective Earth Observation Missions*. London, UK: Routledge.

Sarsfield, Liam P. 1998. *The Cosmos on a Shoestring: Small Spacecraft for Space and Earth Science*. Santa Monica, CA: RAND.

Wertz, J. R. 2008. "ORS Mission Utility and Measures of Effectiveness." 6th Responsive Space Conference. AIAA/RS6 2008-1003. Los Angeles, CA. Apr. 28–May. 1.

Wertz, James R. and W. J. Larson.1996. *Reducing Space Mission Cost*. Torrance, CA: Microcosm Press and Springer.

Wertz, James R., Richard Van Allen, and Christopher J. Shelner. 2006. "Aggressive Surveillance as a Key Application Area for Responsive Space." 4th Responsive Space Conference. AIAA/RS4 2006-1004. Los Angeles, CA. Apr. 24–27.

6 Formal Requirements Definition

Jeffery J. Puschell, *Raytheon*

The intent of the formal requirements definition process is to describe a system that can actually do what it is intended to do. Space missions frequently begin with a broad set of qualitative, sometimes vaguely defined mission requirements—to find evidence of water on Mars, provide high speed Internet access for ships at sea, or improve navigation for military forces. Ultimately these mission needs flow by a creative and sometimes magical process called *requirements definition* into a large set of very specific quantitative requirements on all elements of a space system—e.g., the spacecraft must have 2 star trackers, each weighing less than 0.5 kg, using less than 1.3 W of average power, with an 8×13 deg field of view, capable of detecting 7th magnitude stars with an angular accuracy of 0.004 deg (1σ) using on-board pattern recognition processing over a 15 year lifetime in geosynchronous orbit. To be effective, these requirements must be tied to the highest level system performance and mission requirements and to lower level subsystem requirements through performance allocations and error budgets. In addition, space system performance requirements must be verifiable through ground-based hardware and software testing and analysis.

This requirements definition process often ends up defining the cost and complexity of the system, too. Consequently, the requirements definition process may be the single most important part of space mission engineering for establishing performance, cost, and risk of the system. To produce lower cost, more effective systems, we should put as much or more thought and care into defining the requirements as we do into designing the system to fulfill these requirements.

If most of the system cost is effectively determined at the end of detailed requirements definition, then the requirements definition process itself must become the principal focus in the process of reducing cost, especially near the beginning of system development. In early phases of space mission engineering, system optimization, with an eye toward cost reduction, comes about primarily by trading performance requirements versus cost and mission effectiveness. This process defines and revises requirements in an iterative process to minimize cost and risk of the system as a whole, while simultaneously meeting mission needs. Our broad mission objective may be to find evidence of water on Mars, but, to design a system to meet that need, that objective is translated into a set of performance requirements to map 95% of the surface of Mars at infrared wavelengths in one year at a resolution of 50 m. This translation of mission needs into requirements determines space system performance, cost, and risk. Will the scientific return of our mission be significantly degraded by a resolution of 75 m or 200 m mapped over three years? What are the cost implications of each of these changes? In the end, system requirements definition must be completed by design, manufacturing, supply chain and test system engineers working in close coordination with mission stakeholders. In some cases, it may be necessary to select detailed requirements that embody a sensible compromise between mission objectives and mission affordability. Only when we truly understand the nature of this compromise, i.e., what it costs to achieve a given level of mission performance, can we begin to make rational decisions on defining the system requirements.

Too often, detailed system performance requirements definition is left entirely to the end user of the system or to mission stakeholders. The government or organization that is financing the mission establishes detailed requirements and then asks candidate suppliers to bid on a system to meet those requirements at the lowest cost. However, defining technical performance requirements in advance of thoroughly trading performance requirements with cost means that the requirements will have been largely fixed before the impact on cost is completely understood. Furthermore, if requirements trade studies are made without benefit of validation that can be achieved only by building and testing candidate hardware and software in mission relevant environments, system level cost and risk versus performance cannot be thoroughly understood and the probability of significant cost and schedule growth increases within context of a fixed set of requirements. If a better process is to allow requirements to evolve as the system definition changes in response to better understanding of the detailed and validated relationship between mission value and system performance, cost and risk, then we should always be looking for ways to adjust the requirements to reduce cost and optimize mission value versus cost. This chapter introduces that process.

Requirements definition consists of two distinct but interrelated functions:

- A mission and customer-driven process to define mission objectives and relate those objectives to top level and detailed system and subsystem requirements and specifications
- An analytical process that breaks down requirements into constituent components with creation of error budgets, performance budgets, and cost budgets to track progress and ensure that the system objectives are met.

The following section, deals with the mission and customer-driven requirements definition process. Sections 6.2 and 6.3 focus on the process of allocating top-level system requirements to system components and mathematically analyzing associated allocation and error budgets. Specifications and requirements documents are discussed in Sec. 6.4. System engineering tools for capturing and managing relationships between requirements at all levels are discussed in Sec. 6.5. Section 6.6 discusses the role of standards in space system development. Finally, Sec. 6.7 examines whether requirements are really needed at all.

Table 6-1. Critical Issues in Requirements Development. Note that the reason is rarely included in the specification, but must be documented if requirements trades are to be performed. See text for discussion.

Critical Features of System or Subsystem Requirements:
• Should be based on the fundamental mission objectives
1. Mission or payload derived
2. Flow down from basic requirements
• Should be part of the system trade process
• Should state what is to be done (e.g., pointing, mapping, and timing), rather than how to do it (orbit, attitude, and on-board clock)
• Are the quantitative expressions of how well the objectives are met, recorded in the system specification
Types of Requirements:
• *Functional requirements* = how well it must perform
• *Operational requirements* = how it is to be used
• *Constraints* = what limitations are imposed on the system
Elements which Should be Documented for Each Requirement in the System or Subsystem Specification:
• *Function* = what is to be done
• *Performance requirement* = how well it has to be done
• *Verification* = how the performance is to be verified
1. Inspection 2. Test 3. Analysis
Key Element which Should be Documented (though typically omitted from the system specification):
• *Reason* = *why* it is required

6.1 The Requirements Definition Process

System requirements are the quantitative expression of an approach for meeting mission objectives. These requirements are recorded in a set of system requirements documents or system specifications. Frequently, space systems customers create system requirements by first developing a straw man or reference mission design, that is, a detailed design description that the defining organization believes is fundamentally capable of meeting mission objectives. Thus, if the broad goal is to look for evidence of water on Mars, a hypothetical system of satellites to provide mapping over some defined period of time may be described. If the objective is to create high speed global communications, a constellation consisting of a specific number of low-Earth orbit satellites each with a number of communications channels capable of meeting broad mission objectives may be described. The characteristics of this straw man design are then used to create system specifications, i.e., so many satellites are required at a specific altitude over the surface of Mars with instruments capable of making certain measurements with specified angular resolution. The fundamental problem with this approach is that although the original system designers may have been very clever and knowledgeable, they do not necessarily have all of the necessary or appropriate knowledge to determine how best to meet mission needs at the lowest possible cost. Consequently, if system requirements are expressed in terms of specific parameters of the reference design, i.e., so many satellites or star trackers with a specific field of view or limiting magnitude, then any further trades may be effectively eliminated. The defining organization has essentially created the system design and fixed the system cost and made it more difficult to reduce that cost.

On the other hand, if system requirements at all levels specify what needs to be achieved rather than how to achieve it, then the system trade process can continue and the customer may be able to take advantage of new knowledge, new developments or clever techniques from throughout the space system development community. For example, resolution on the ground may be specified rather than satellite altitude and instantaneous field of view of an instrument. This leaves open the trade for using a large number of satellites at a lower altitude, or a smaller number at higher altitudes, or perhaps even a smaller number at lower altitudes and taking longer to collect the required data. Similarly, for the star tracker, required field of view or resolution should not be specified, but simply the desired end result; a required attitude accuracy. Even better, given spacecraft attitude is of little interest to a typical end user, a better parameter to specify is geolocation knowledge or pointing knowledge. Requirements should be specified in mission relevant terms such as pointing and mapping rather than in system design terms of how to achieve mission requirements such as orbit and attitude. By specifying what we want, and not how to achieve it, we can leave open other options that have the potential of reducing cost and risk or perhaps improving performance at minimal increase in cost or risk, in order to obtain the best system at the lowest cost. These and other critical issues in the requirements development process are summarized in Table 6-1.

There are three basic types of requirements:

- *Functional requirements* that define what a system is supposed to do and how well it must do it
- *Operational requirements* that define how the system is to be used
- *Constraints* that define limitations imposed on the system such as operating environment and requirements imposed by other system elements to minimize electromagnetic interference

The requirements and constraints for any specific mission will be driven by fundamental mission objectives and by how the mission is implemented. Nevertheless, whether the mission is an international scientific research program, a commercial venture or an emergency program responding to urgent need, its requirements will likely be developed within the broad categories shown in Table 6-2 for the FireSat II mission that is discussed throughout this book.

Requirements are based primarily on fundamental mission objectives. What must the system do to satisfy mission objectives? Mission objectives drive requirements for the payload more than any other part of the system. Nevertheless, mission objectives impact other system elements, too. For example, spacecraft orbit, attitude stability and timing requirements flow from needs that can vary widely according to mission ranging from measuring the Earth's infrared radiation across the entire globe every day at 500 m resolution to providing high speed Internet access

Table 6-2. Example of Top Level Mission Requirements. We typically subdivide these top-level requirements into more specific requirements applicable to specific space missions.

Requirement	Factors which Typically Impact the Requirement	FireSat II Example
	FUNCTIONAL	
Performance	Primary objective, payload size, orbit, pointing	0.12 K sensitivity at 300 K 500 m resolution 500 m location accuracy
Coverage	Orbit, swath width, number of satellites, scheduling	Daily coverage of 750 million acres within continental US
Responsiveness	Communications architecture, processing delays, operations	Send registered mission data within 30 min to up to 50 users
Secondary Mission	As above	Land and sea surface temperature, high resolution water vapor imagery and crude winds over the continental US
	OPERATIONAL	
Duration	Experiment or operations, level of redundancy, altitude	Mission operational at least 10 yrs
Availability	Level of redundancy	98% excluding weather, 3-day maximum outage
Survivability	Orbit, hardening, electronics	Natural environment only
Data Distribution	Communications architecture	Up to 500 fire-monitoring offices + 2,000 rangers worldwide (max. of 100 simultaneous users)
Data Content, Form, and Format	User needs, level and place of processing, payload	Location and extent of fire on any of 12 map bases, average temperature for each 30 m^2 grid
	CONSTRAINTS	
Cost	Manned flight, number of spacecraft, size and complexity, orbit	< $20M/yr + R&D
Schedule	Technical readiness, program size	Initial operating capability within 5 yrs, final operating capability within 6 yrs
Regulations	Law and policy	NASA mission
Political	Sponsor, whether international program	Responsive to public demand for action
Environment	Orbit, lifetime	Natural
Interfaces	Level of user and operator infrastructure	Comm. relay and interoperable through NOAA ground stations
Development Constraints	Sponsoring organization	No unique operations people at data distribution nodes

across Africa to 0.3 m diameter receivers to providing 1 m navigation accuracy worldwide to commercial users. A commercial end user of navigation data does not care about the attitude stability of the satellites providing the basic information, only that her location is known to within the needed accuracy and timeliness.

Specific mission implementation approaches drive requirements definition, also. For instance, a specific mission implementation may require the ability to point the spacecraft solar arrays at the Sun, communicate with the ground station, or get within 2 km of a distant asteroid. These requirements are typically, though not necessarily, less stringent than the mission or payload derived requirements. However, many implementation driven requirements apply to all mission phases, whereas mission driven requirements frequently apply only to the operational phase. Thus implementation driven requirements, though often less stringent, may drive the range over which orbit and attitude systems, for example, must operate or the various conditions under which data must be provided. A typical implementation driven function would be to regain control of the spacecraft if it tumbles. This implies the need to have low accuracy attitude in a variety of orientations such that it is possible to recover the system when it is in a non-nominal mode. This might imply use of very coarse Sun sensors covering a large fraction of the sky, or an Earth sensor that is capable of picking up the Earth as the spacecraft tumbles as derived requirements related to specific implementations.

Constraints of various types drive requirements definition, too. For example, an infrared radiometer operating on board a dedicated remote sensing satellite in geosynchronous orbit will have radiation and electromagnetic interference constraints that are quite different from a radiometer operating on board a multifunctional satellite with high power communications transmitters in medium Earth orbit. A very different type of constraint is an international mission may be constrained to use a launch vehicle provided by the nation funding the mission, which could limit payload size and mass. Communications missions are constrained by their ability to secure the radio frequency licenses required to operate in customer nations, which can impact not only system design but also mission operating areas.

For each requirement, regardless of its origin or type, we want to select it to meet mission needs in a way that minimizes cost, schedule, and risk for the overall system development and operation. Once again, this argues in favor of making the requirements definition process itself part of the system trade process.

There are two basic types of trades:

- Trades on the overall level of performance
- Trades on how the performance is achieved

Most often the level of performance is defined as a specific number, such as radiometric sensitivity at a specific wavelength, spacecraft attitude accuracy or location knowledge accuracy. Frequently, these values are fixed by the nature of the system procurement and associated requirements definition process. That is, in order to be fair to all of the candidate suppliers, the defining agency picks a number which they believe to be appropriate and then asks suppliers to achieve this value at minimum cost. Neither the customer nor the supplier wants to change the number. The customer has gone to some lengths to specify this number, and would like to have it achieved, although of course, at very low cost. The supplier doesn't want to appear non-responsive to the customer's needs, and therefore will go to great lengths to achieve the specified performance, even if it drives up the cost or risk of the end system. A more effective approach for optimizing end system performance with respect to cost and schedule is to maintain an ongoing conversation in the early stages of system procurement on the implications of specific requirements on system performance, cost, and risk. To be most effective, this conversation must occur within context of validated, well understood relationships between performance and cost derived from hardware already flown or tested in mission relevant environments. It is this well-informed dialog and trading back and forth which too often are omitted in the requirements definition process.

The trades on how the performance is achieved are also critical. Ideally, these should allow the assessment and use of well understood alternative design options to reduce cost or to meet other elements of the system performance. Thus a system requiring high-accuracy pointing may specify the use of star trackers to achieve the required attitude accuracy. On the other hand, it may be possible to achieve an acceptable level of accuracy using a combination of Earth sensors and gyros to average the noise from the Earth's horizon. This is an example of a trade process that may be able to achieve the fundamental objectives of the mission at lower cost and risk.

Most people in the space business recognize that in order to minimize cost, requirements definition should be part of the overall system trade process, and yet this is rarely done for several reasons. As discussed above, suppliers do not wish to be perceived as non-responsive or less competitive and therefore frequently do not want to disagree with the customer over performance requirements or even suggest that certain requirements may not be achievable. But minimizing the cost of the system implies that we need to have this basic debate between desired performance and cost.

A second reason for not trading on requirements is that it frequently involves moving requirements, and therefore budget, between various elements of the system, which may be owned by different customer organizations. For example to achieve a required level of geolocation accuracy, we may want to consider changing from tight attitude requirements and loose orbit requirements to the other way around. That would end up putting additional requirements on the orbit, and therefore the ground system, in order to save money on the spacecraft. However, these distinct parts of the system are typically done by different organizations operating in very different ways. Therefore, to save money we may need to take money from one organization and give it to another. This can prove to be an unpopular process.

If it is politically difficult to trade on requirements, how do we go about doing it? The best approach is to make it a very explicit and open process. Almost every mission is divided into a series of phases as the definition of the system becomes more mature and complete. Each of these phases usually begins with a briefing or technical meeting defining the status of the system at that time. Thus, to define status of the program, we might have a Concept Design briefing or a kick-off for the Design and Development phase. This can occur at the system level, subsystem level or component level. The key issue for requirements trades is to have the first portion of each such briefing devoted explicitly to requirements trades. Ask the system engineer either for the prime contractor or the component manufacturer to explicitly define the source of the requirements that they are working to and indicate which of those requirements are principally responsible for impacting performance, cost, risk, and schedule. This allows the customer to examine trades on key requirements with the objective of reducing overall system cost with respect to achieving some set of mission objectives. The key point is that this process makes trading on requirements an open and defined engineering process subject to review and detailed examination in much the same fashion as the system design itself is examined and reviewed.

To complete effective system trades we need to identify the critical key performance requirements, i.e., those that drive mission performance, cost, risk and schedule. One approach for identifying key performance parameters is to examine top-level system requirements and develop different system concepts for meeting those requirements. Critical requirements will frequently depend on the specific implementation being considered and often concept exploration will help isolate the requirements that drive performance, cost and schedule. We then study the impact of changing each of the fundamental requirements. Regardless of how we define the key performance parameters exactly, the objective is to let the requirements evolve in order to achieve the mission objectives at minimum cost and risk. To do this we need to concentrate our system trades around the critical requirements, so that we are continuously examining and re-examining those requirements that have the highest impact on performance, cost and risk.

Specifications

Specifications document system requirements. Every documented requirement must include three things:

- *Function* = what is to be done
- *Performance requirements* = how well it is to be done
- *Verification* = how the performance is to be verified

We can verify performance of the system as a whole by allocating top-level requirements to subsystems and components and then verifying performance of each of the components to show that the final system will work as designed. In many cases, system level performance verification for some requirements occurs by testing the system as it is intended to fly, to the greatest extent possible.

A simple example of system level performance verification is to examine a top-level requirement to use a specific launch vehicle capable of launching a certain total spacecraft mass to the mission required orbit. This total mass is allocated to each of the various subsystems and, in turn, to the various components within those subsystems. This will be reflected in the specification documents for the components, and all of the masses will be added up in a single mass budget. The masses of the components will first be verified by analysis and ultimately by weighing all of them as the spacecraft is built. In doing this, we will determine that the final spacecraft will in fact meet its mass requirement.

One major element that is almost always missing from the typical specification document is the rationale for the requirement and its priority with respect to other requirements. Specification documents tend to be a demand from the customer to the supplier and therefore generally do not reflect the reasons why specific requirements are imposed. Nonetheless, if we are to continue the system trade process and make it a part of the overall process of system design, then we must know why specific requirements are imposed. Otherwise there is no way to go back and determine if a less stringent or more stringent requirement is appropriate. Consequently, even though it does not fit well within the contractual hierarchy, providing the reasons for the various requirements given in the specification is extremely important to the process of trying to drive down system cost.

In order to be useful in terms of whether the system can meet its broad requirements, each individual requirement must be capable of being verified. This verification is typically done in one of three ways: inspection, test or analysis. Thus, we may determine that a particular system has redundant components simply by inspection. Alternatively, we may test the star tracker to determine the resolution or we may verify adequate performance of a structural element by analysis. Whatever method we choose, we need to specify how all requirements are to be verified.

The general classes of system specifications are shown in Fig. 6-1. In smaller programs, many of these specification documents are not created in order to reduce the very substantial cost associated simply with documentation. On the other hand, failure to document those system characteristics that are critical to determining performance can ultimately drive up cost dramatically. Particularly important is the *Interface Requirements Document*, because it formalizes an interface between people or organizations that may not be working closely together. For example, it may be the job of the navigation computer to compute the position and

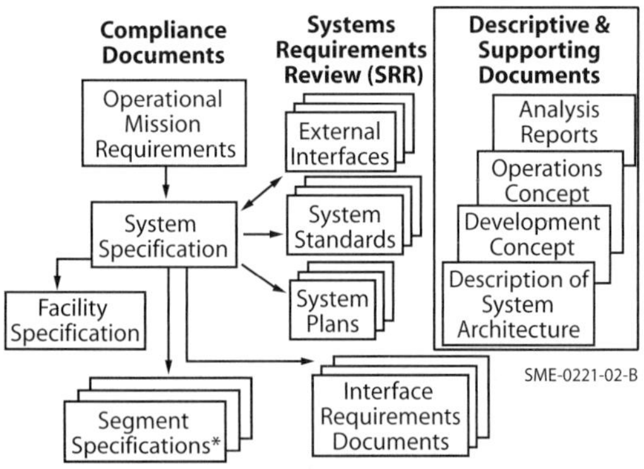

Fig. 6-1. Typical Specification Documents. While not all of these documents exist for all programs, the information contained in each should be recorded so that it is available for review and is agreed to by everyone involved in the project.

velocity of the spacecraft. How that computation is done is typically of little consequence to the end user. Nonetheless, it is important to specify how that information will be communicated to those systems which need it. The interface requirements document could specify, for example, the data rates, units, and word characteristics associated with the information generated by the navigation system.

As stressed above, a key issue in requirements definition, and therefore in creating specification documents, is to specify what is to be done and not how it is to be done. No mission requires star trackers. Missions require accurate geolocation and pointing knowledge that can be derived in part from accurate attitude data. How this is achieved across the system design should be left to organizations or individuals assigned the responsibility of achieving it.

6.2 Budgeting, Allocation, and Flow-Down

Having established the top-level system requirements, the next step in the requirements definition process is to budget, allocate, or flow-down these requirements to the components which make up the overall system. This section summarizes the broad process of doing that. The following section and App. G present a detailed mathematical description of how error budgets are analyzed. Section 8.6 provides a detailed numerical example for mapping and pointing budgets which are a principal area of interest for space mission engineering.

The budget is the numerical list of the components into which the top-level resource or requirement is divided along with the rules on how the components are to be combined to meet the system requirement. The margin is the planned difference between the system requirement and the sum of the components. Margin should be tracked and controlled at the system level to be available to meet implementation needs. Table 6-3 provides a list of items frequently budgeted in space missions. Generally almost anything that should be budgeted represents either a cost-driving resource or an element that is necessary to make the mission successful. For example, mass, power, and propellant are cost-driving commodities that are budgeted on virtually all missions. Communications systems would have a pointing budget to ensure that the communication antennas are correctly pointed and a link budget to ensure that there is adequate margin in the data transmission. An Earth observation mission would add a radiometric sensitivity budget to establish the accuracy with which spectral radiance emitted by the Earth can be measured. If the time limit for obtaining data is critical, as might be the case for military surveillance or emergency data processing, then a time budget would be established to monitor and control this.

Table 6-3. Items Frequently Budgeted in Space Missions. Overall budgets are typically established at the systems level and flow-down or allocated to the subsystems. See Wertz and Larson [1999] for a discussion of each of the budgets listed here.

Primary	Secondary
Weight	Subsystem Weight Power Propellant
Geolocation or System Pointing Errors	Pointing and Alignment Mapping, Attitude Control, Attitude Determination Position Determination
Timing	Coverage Communications Operations Processing
Availability	Reliability Operational Availability
Cost	Development Cost Deployment Cost Operations and Maintenance Cost

There are two basic types of space system budgets. *Commodity budgets* allocate any of the finite resources available on the spacecraft, such as mass, power, propellant or data rate. These budgets are straightforward; there exists an available amount and that quantity is allocated in some appropriate fashion among the subsystems that need it. Thus, the spacecraft mass will be allocated to all of the subsystems, including, for example, the attitude control system. The attitude control mass budget will then be allocated to the various components, which will in turn be allocated to the constituent parts of the components. Verification of the commodity budgets is also straightforward. We weigh each component and ultimately the spacecraft. Commodity budgets are often broken down further. For example, the mass budget may be broken down into different masses during different mission phases, and the power budget is frequently broken down into orbit average and peak power requirements.

The second and more complex type of budget is the *error budget* which breaks down the required accuracy on any measurement or control requirement, such as the mapping errors, pointing errors, or absolute timing errors. These are discussed in more detail in Secs. 6.3 and 8.6. The principal cause of complexity for these budgets,

Table 6-4. Simplified Pointing Error Budget for a Space Telescope. (All values in degrees.) In reality, there would be substantially more elements in the pointing budget as shown, for example, in Fig. 6.2. Note that if the errors had been summed literally, the total of 0.0155 deg would exceed the requirement and a major design enhancement would be required.

Random Errors	
Star Sensor Noise	0.002
Star Centroid Calculation	0.003
Pixel-to-pixel Variations	0.002
Thermal Variations	0.0015
RSS of Random Errors	0.0044
Bias Errors	
Star Sensor Mounting Errors	0.002
Payload Mounting Error	0.002
Payload Detector Mounting Error	0.003
RSS of Bias Errors	0.0041
Sum of Random and Bias Errors	0.0085
Requirement	0.010
Margin	0.0015

and a potential major cost driver for the system as a whole, is the process of how error budgets are to be added. If the elements that make up the error budget are random and uncorrelated then a root sum square (RSS) is the correct approach. If the error components are fully correlated, or if they are components that will physically add, then they should be added linearly. For attitude systems, for example, the most common result is to RSS the short-term noise, RSS the bias sources and then add the two results. However, in a worst-case situation the bias terms would add linearly. The correct approach to doing this is a mathematical question, discussed in more detail in Sec. 6.3.

Table 6-4 shows a simplified pointing error budget for a space telescope. In a real mission there would be substantially more elements in the budget, as shown in Fig. 6-2 on geopositioning error. However, this simple example illustrates one of the fundamental problems in error budgets. The user wishes to point the telescope to within 0.01 deg. If we RSS the random terms and bias terms separately, and then add the results, we're able to meet this requirement with some margin. On the other hand, if all of the terms were simply added linearly, the requirement would not be met, and we would have to either change the requirement or change the system design, presumably at significantly higher cost. In the end, how we treat error budgets depends on what the mission is trying to achieve. Is it a scientific mission in which we are trying to establish confidence levels? A military mission, where we are looking for the worst case that might be taken advantage of by an opponent? Or a commercial mission, in which we are trying to provide a customer with services of a given quality? In each case, we need to work with the user or the customer in order to determine their mission intent and create the most appropriate error budget and budgeting process.

Figure 6-2 shows an example of the allocation of a geopositioning error from a top-level mission requirement down to detailed component designs. As can be seen from the figure, this allocation is both complex and involves both the spacecraft and the mission control or data processing segments. Each step of the operation includes at least a small source of additional error. This may be round-off errors in the computer, errors in the uncertainty of coordinate transformation, or errors in physical hardware or their calibration. The importance of the budgeting process itself is to reach agreement on the list of error sources such that we can then find numerical values appropriate to each source, to ensure ourselves that the ultimate mission requirement will be met.

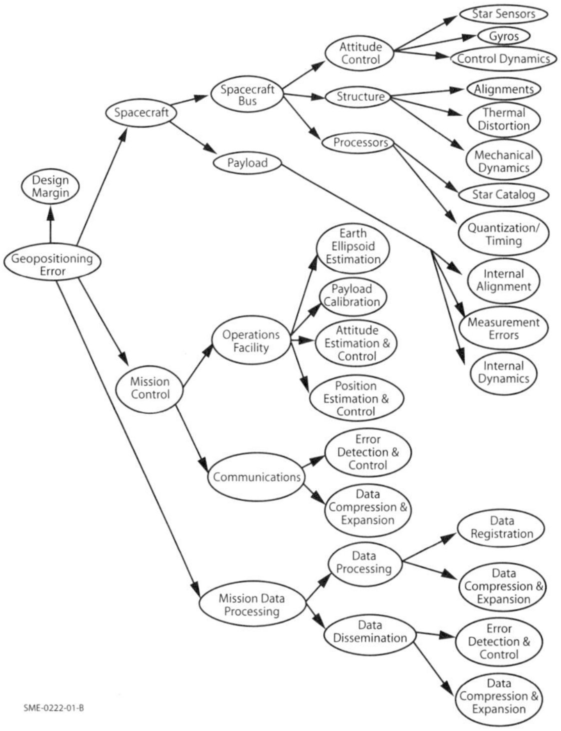

Fig. 6-2. Allocation of Geopositioning Error with Margin from Mission Requirements to Component Design Level.

Budgeting is both a mathematical process, as discussed in Sec. 6.3, and a political process in which various individuals and organizations agree on how much of any of the budgeted elements is to be incorporated within their particular subsystem. Each subsystem would of course like to have as much of the mass, power and precision budgets as possible in order to make their job less expensive and less complex. In principle, we should be willing to change the allocation among the various budgets in order to make the entire system perform as well as possible for a minimum cost. However, this may require shifting resources between competing organizations or making changes to contractual requirements. For example, it may be possible to do additional calibration on an Earth sensor in order to improve its accuracy to make up for a lack of accuracy in the GPS receiver. However, since these two components will typically be built by different manufacturers, changing this allocation could represent a contractual change for both manufacturers which could make it expensive for the prime contractor to achieve the end goal. Consequently, most system and subsystem engineers will work hard to both achieve an appropriate balance in the original budget and to provide sufficient margin to accommodate additional error sources that arise. This political process of balancing error budgets is summarized in Fig. 6-3. This chart was originally created by Mike Williams [1992], who coined the phrase "negotiation of terrible injustices" to give a sense of the political negotiations that go on during the budgeting and allocation process. It certainly suggests the nature of the political battles that can often ensue from the budgeting, allocating, and flow-down process.

Figure 6-4 provides a summary of a time budget for providing data in a forest fire detection mission. Here it is clear that timeliness is critical to the end user. Information on the fire's location is of very little interest a week after the data was collected. On the other hand, millisecond accuracy is also not necessary. This implies that there is a time-span in which data must be provided to be useful to the user, and that we can allocate this time to the various components of the system, including the orbital coverage of the spacecraft, the identification of the forest fire data, and the delivery of this data to the end user. Note also that there may be more than one timeline involved. For example, we may have one timeline from the time that a detectable fire starts until it is first seen by the system, and a second, probably much shorter, timeline from when a fire is detected by the system until that data is reported to a firefighter on the ground. Even here, there can be substantial contractual questions such as whether "detection" of a forest fire represents appropriate data being collected on board the spacecraft, or the process of identifying a specific forest fire which may occur somewhat later. The critical issue for system design is to create this budget such that issues can be defined and resolved as early in the process as possible. Consequently, the detailed budgeting process is an important one for the organizations involved, as well as for the system engineering process of ensuring that the mission objectives can be met.

6.3 Introduction to Error Analysis*

In this section we discuss how error budgets are to be handled numerically—i.e., how component errors are to be "summed" to yield the total error or system error. In a sense, the requirements allocation problem discussed in Sec. 6.2 is the inverse of the summation problem. Requirements allocation assigns to each component an allowable error. Here, we want to know how to combine the errors to check that the resulting system error meets requirements.

* Adapted from Geoffrey N. Smit, "Introduction to Error Analysis" Sec. 5.4 in Wertz [2001].

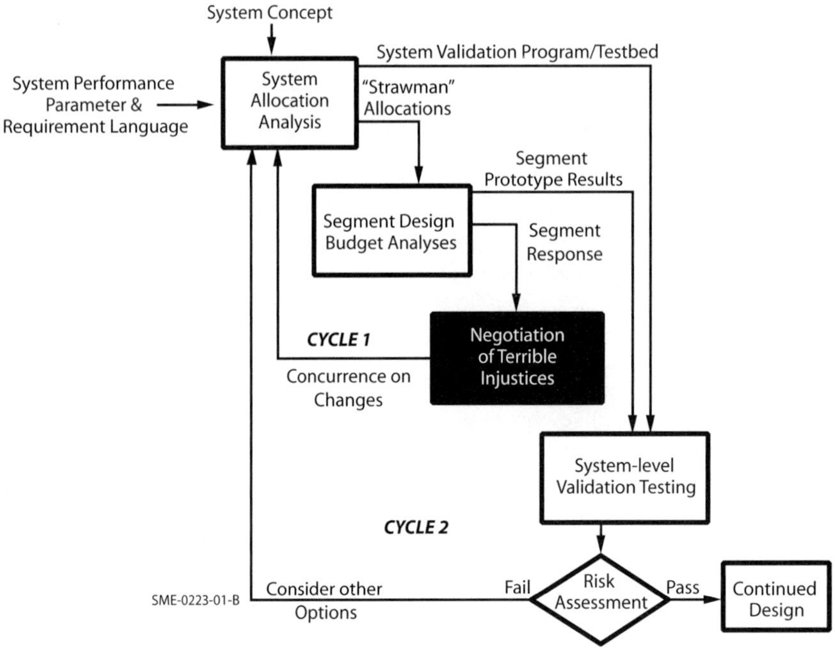

Fig. 6-3. Introduction to Error Analysis.

Table 6-4◀, Fig. 6-3, Eq. 6-0

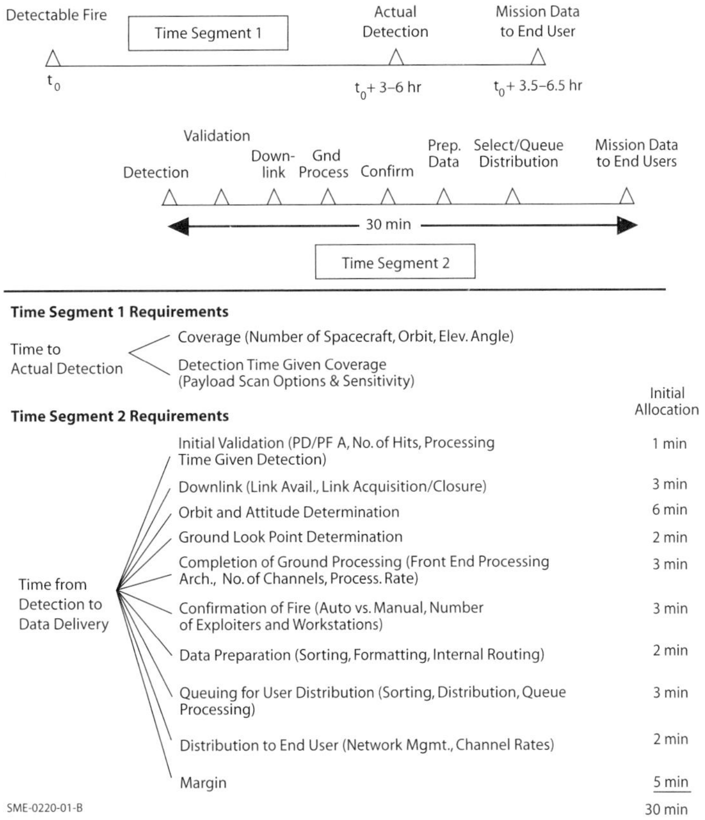

Fig. 6-4. Allocation of Data Timeline.

System error analysis involves the following steps:

1. **Modeling the system** and identifying the error sources i.e., the places where errors are introduced.
2. **Determining the sensitivity** of the system error to each of the error sources.
3. **Characterizing the distribution** for each of the error sources.
4. **Combining the sources** to determine the system error.

Accomplishing **Step 1** adequately is crucial and is system specific. In realistic systems, the models for error analyses can be dismayingly complex. Our treatment here will be as simple as possible, to bring out the main features.

Step 2 is really an integral part of Step 1, but we have separated it out for emphasis. Step 1 normally gives us a deterministic relationship between error sources and the system error. For want of a better term, we shall call this relationship the *error equation*. Typically, the system error will not be dominated by the effects from a single source. Usually, there are numerous error sources, and an efficient design will tend to balance their effects. In some situations, a system may have singularities leading to high sensitivity to a particular input. In the normal situation (no singularities, reasonably balanced response to the various errors), the error equation can be represented as a sum in which the output error is the algebraic sum of the inputs. (See, for this example, Taylor [1997].)

Step 3 involves knowledge of the types of components being used, and of the operating environment. Since many errors are inherently random, some sort of probabilistic characterization must be given. Usually, the component errors are specified in terms of standard deviations. For example, a star tracker may be accurate to 30 arcseconds (3σ), implying that the distribution is Gaussian and that about 99% of all readings will be within 30 arcseconds of the true direction. Ideally, the probability distribution of the errors could be given, but this level of information is usually not available.

From the error equation, we can easily bound the system error. If $e = e_1 + e_2 + \ldots + e_n$, where e is the system error and $e_1, e_2, \ldots, e_n$ are the component errors, then $|e| \le |e_1| + |e_2| + \ldots + |e_n|$. This bound can form the basis for an error budget. Normally, however, it will be too conservative, i.e., it will demand that we keep the e_i considerably smaller than is necessary to achieve a given bound on e. We must exploit the statistical nature of the errors to make the design affordable while still meeting the error budget.

Step 4 addresses the mathematical problem of estimating the statistical properties of the system error, given those of the components and the error equation connecting them. The summation calculation can be approached in various ways. The actual analysis undertaken and the degree of detail included will depend on the system and on the amount of information available:

- In some cases (e.g., when the probability distribution of the e_i are normal or uniform), the distribution of the sum can be evaluated analytically. (See Feller [1971], Meyer [1972], Papoulis [2002], and Parzen [1992].)
- When this is not possible (or efficient) the output distribution can be generated using a Monte Carlo simulation as described in Table 6-6.
- In many cases, generation of the system probability distribution may not be necessary or feasible, e.g., when the component distributions are unknown. It is possible to estimate the system standard deviation directly in terms of the component standard deviations. This not only makes fewer demands for detail in the input data, it is also far simpler, computationally. For most error budgeting, this is the preferred approach.

It is shown in App. G (where the terminology is defined) that if $e = e_1 + e_2 + \ldots + e_n$, then

$$\sigma^2 = \sum_i \sigma_i^2 + 2\sum_{i>j}\left[\mathrm{Cov}\left(e_i \cdot e_j\right)\right] \tag{6-1}$$

where σ is the standard deviation of e, σ_i is the standard deviation of e_i and $\mathrm{Cov}(e_i, e_j)$ is the covariance between e_i and e_j. If the covariances are zero (i.e., if the errors are independent), this reduces to

$$\sigma = \left(\sigma_1^2 + \ldots + \sigma_n^2\right)^{1/2} \tag{6-2}$$

This is called the root sum square or RSS. If the correlations are unity, so that the covariances equal the products of the corresponding standard deviations, then σ reduces to the sum of the σ_i. If the correlations are partial, we get a combination rule between the RSS and the sum. This is a standard result for the combination of standard deviations, and it forms the basis for most error analyses. (See Feller [1971], Meyer [1972], Papoulis [2002], and Parzen [1992].)

The procedure for undertaking an error analysis for the purpose of error budgeting is summarized in Table 6-5. A related procedure for a Monte Carlo error analysis is given in Table 6-6.

We have been describing the error addition process as though the system and the errors were static. In most cases this is not true, and the dynamics of the system and the time structure of the component errors should be accounted for to obtain an accurate error estimate. At the simplest level, this involves looking at the frequency spectra of the various errors, and noting that in some cases this allows us to reduce the effective system error variance. (See the boxed example.) On a more sophisticated level, the system dynamical equations can be manipulated to provide an equation for the propagation of the system error covariance matrix which is then optimized. The error budget is then formulated in terms of this optimal error. The degree of sophistication adopted will depend on how far along in the program we are and on the program's financial budget.

Note that there are two distinct "flows" in the error analysis and budgeting process:

- The desire for less conservatism, and hence more accuracy, leads us to increasing levels of sophistication in our modeling of the system.
- The need to keep the calculations manageable leads us to simpler ways of characterizing the errors. This aspect of the flow is often driven by a lack of data on the error performance of the components.

Frequency Distribution of Errors

Any system-level measurement, whether it involves calculating direction to an image pixel or reading spectral radiance from a radiometer, can be thought of as selecting a single sample from within a statistical ensemble of all possible measurements. This ensemble includes noise effects from all system elements. Each noise component may have its own temporal or frequency characteristics. The sampling process that leads to estimates of most probable measurement value, error and overall probability distribution function occurs as a time series of measurements. Therefore, sampling rate, collection duration and other details of how these measurements are collected over time may affect measurement value and estimated error.

For example, measurement samples taken closer together in time may be more similar in value than those taken farther apart in time. In those cases, estimated probability distribution of the measurement depends on the time scale used in collecting the samples. At any given time, only a limited part of the total statistical ensemble may actually be accessible in the sampling process. That region of accessibility can move around within the overall ensemble in a random manner that in itself represents a source of noise. Over relatively short time periods, a smaller measurement variance than the entire ensemble range will be found along with a slowly varying bias that can be tracked and eliminated from the error budget. In some cases, the slowly varying bias can be deterministic such as when it is due to thermal or lighting effects that are periodic with spacecraft orbit.

Consider the sources of error associated with calculating direction to an image pixel. These error sources include star sensor measurement error, star sensor mounting error, star catalog error, attitude computation error, payload sensor measurement error, pixel centroid error, payload sensor mounting error and coordinate transformation error. (See Table 5-19 of Wertz [2009].) We would expect errors like star sensor and payload mounting errors to vary much more slowly than others like star sensor measurement error resulting from electronic noise in the detector array. On the shorter time scales of the higher frequency errors, we are able to estimate these biases and correspondingly reduce the system error. See App. G on the book website for a more detailed and thorough discussion of frequency dependent noise.

Table 6-5. Creating Error Budgets. RSS = "Root Sum Square" = Square root of the sum of the squares of the individual components. (See Wertz [2001], Secs. 5.4, 5.5 and App. C for more detail.)

Step	Comments
1. Define the end-to-end measurement process.	Start with basic orbit, attitude, and payload measurements and compute the final output.
2. Identify sources of error in each step.	Break down each step into its lowest constituents.
3. Identify the statistical distribution of each error source.	Typically Gaussian or uniform if the measurements are quantized.
4. Assign a preliminary error value to each error source	If Gaussian, use 3σ error; if quantized use full range.
5. Estimate the maximum probable error by adding all error terms in worst case end-to-end geometry.	If this meets the requirement, quit and go to Step 12. If singularities occur, calculation and implementation may need refinement.
6. Estimate the minimum probable error by RSSing all error terms.	If this doesn't meet the requirement, then need to find a way to reduce error sources or find another solution.
7. If the requirement lies between (5) and (6), proceed to more accurate summation techniques.	Steps 8–11.
8. Determine the frequency associated with each of the error sources.	Over what time span is one measurement set not correlated with the previous one?
9. Divide the error sources into frequency regimes.	Typically, Gaussian noise at the sampling frequency, most error sources at orbit frequency, and some at other frequencies (for example, weather sampling or magnetic field errors).
10. Determine the error within each frequency regime as follows:	Within each frequency regime, there is the potential for errors to be correlated.
10a. Add the correlated errors*.	Look explicitly for where singularities can occur.
10b. RSS the uncorrelated errors and the sums of the correlated errors	Assumes these are statistically independent.
11. RSS the errors for different frequency regimes; this gives an analytic estimate of the total error.	Errors at different frequencies are orthogonal (cf Fourier analysis) and can be RSS'd.
12. Review the steps looking for missing sources of error, such as uncertainty in coordinate transformations. Also conduct an independent search for singularities.	Every coordinate transformation includes an error associated with the definition of the new coordinate frame in terms of the old one.
13. Document and Iterate.	—

* For partial correlations, summing is conservative, RSS is optimistic. For more accurate formulas, see App. G.

A key measurement problem is that correlated error sources can lead to singularities in the measurement process for which the error in the result can become unbounded (i.e., very large). For a geometrical discussion of the source and treatment of measurement correlation, see Sec. 8.6.

Table 6-6. Monte Carlo Error Analysis. This is a numerical approach requiring a large number of runs. Singularities become evident due to a dramatic increase in the spread of the solutions when noise or biases are added to the data. (See Sec. 8.6, Wertz [2001], and App. C for more detail.)

Step	Comments
1. Do steps 1–4 of the analytic approach	See Table 6-5.
5. Assign a representative value for each of the variables involved	Pick both representative values and extremes where singularities can occur.
6. Execute the computation, from initial measurements to final answer; adding error to each computation according to the assigned probability distribution	Near singularities, computations may fail due to an illegal operation (e.g., asin of a number greater than 1).
7. Evaluate the statistical results of multiple runs*	The statistical distribution of the result is the best estimate of the final error.
8. Check carefully for singularities, correlated measurements, and missing error sources†	Must cover the full range of measurements. If this is done, singularities become evident in the data due to very high noise levels.
9. Iterate and document	

* For ways to enhance the efficiency of this process. For example, see Robert et al. [2010].

† As in the case of an analytic assessment, measurement singularities can dramatically impact the final error and cause divergence in numerical solutions. (See Sec. 8.6)

Error sources can be categorized in various ways: random vs. systematic (or deterministic), additive vs. multiplicative, modeled vs. unmodeled. Some of the classifications commonly used, such as noise vs. bias, are often subjective. The basic idea is to distinguish between effects which can be removed by calibration or filtering and those which cannot and which must therefore be added to the error budget. This distinction will depend on several factors. Some error sources are inherently random (such as thermal noise in electronic systems and optical detectors), while others, such as misalignments, are systematic. In principle, the systematic part can be calibrated out. In practice there are always residuals due to limitations in the calibration technique or due to the myriad of details in the system behavior. The ability to compensate for error sources will depend on how accurately they have been modeled. In very high precision systems, we may be prepared to take into account a large number of details which would simply be ignored and lumped into "noise" in other systems. For example, a star tracker may distort under temperature changes. To some extent we can measure this effect and use an open loop calibration curve to take it out based on a temperature measurement. However, there are also hysteresis effects, so the distortion is not exactly repeatable. This would contribute to the residuals. A more complex model accounting for the thermal time history might be used to further reduce the residuals. There will always be a bound to the degree of detail that can be justified, and the unmodeled effects will usually be treated as "random."

The time scale over which measurements are being taken will also influence how we view different sources. What may appear as a slowly varying bias on one time scale, may look like noise on another. With this in view, the distinction between noise and bias is really based more on how they are treated in a given system. Normally, bias is estimated, either via a separate calibration procedure or some sort of filter, and subtracted out. Noise is usually filtered via a low pass filter. In general, error sources that are outside the frequency band being used for measurements can be removed by various kinds of filters. Error sources within the measurement band can sometimes be removed, provided we understand the system well enough. The errors which would be summed, as described in the rest of this section, would be those which cannot be removed or which are not economical to remove.

Finally, combinations of sensors, and the corresponding combinations of their errors, do not always result in a system error larger than that of the components. In fact, many configurations are set up to allow sensors to complement each other. A simple example would be to put several identical sensors in parallel and take their average. The variance of the output would be $(1/N)$ times the variance of an individual sensor reading. A more realistic example would be combining a gyro with a star sensor.

Table 6-6◀, Fig. 6-4◀, Eq. 6-2◀

6.4 Specifications and Requirements Documentation

Specifications and requirements documents are developed using organizational best practices that are generally consistent with commercial and international standards documented by the Electronics Industries Association (EIA), IEEE, International Organization for Standardization (ISO), and International Electrotechnical Commission (IEC) along with the draft US Department of Defense (DoD) Standard MIL-STD-499C on "System Engineering." The commercial and international standards include EIA-632 on "Processes for Engineering a System," IEEE 1220 on "Standard for Application and Management of the Systems Engineering," EIA-649 on "Configuration Management" and ISO/IEC 15288 on "Systems and Software Engineering—System Life Cycle Processes." The removal of most military standards, including the system engineering standard, as contractual requirements in US DoD developments has led to a different paradigm for verifying excellence in system engineering practice that includes organizational certifications for implementing standards in ISO 9000 and the use of Carnegie Mellon Software Engineering Institute's Capability Maturity Model® Integration (CMMI®) levels to encourage and document continuous process improvements in system development and delivery. The comprehensive *NASA Systems Engineering Handbook* (NASA/SP-2007-6105 Rev 1) provides an excellent guide to fundamental systems engineering concepts and techniques, including requirements definition and documentation. All of these best practices and documents emphasize the importance of mission and requirements development and management and place it at the beginning of sound system design processes.

Effective requirements documents must be consistent within the set of program documents, complete relative to the maturity of the system in development and traceable to the highest level mission and system requirements and specifications and to derived lower level requirements and specifications. A consistent performance requirement should be written only once, kept in a readily accessible place and positioned appropriately in the hierarchy of established requirements. System requirements documents and specifications become more complete as the system design and implementation matures. Nevertheless, at each stage of completeness, every level of requirement must satisfy the next higher level. As an example of completeness, the geolocation requirement of the FireSat II mission should address all error sources both in segment and interface documents. Requirements must be rigorously traceable as they are developed, allocated and decomposed or derived, to ensure they are unambiguous and verifiable. The method used for tracing requirements should be specified in program requirements documents. Section 6.5 discusses tools for documenting requirements and managing requirements traceability.

Requirements documents or specifications notionally fall into eight classes (Fig. 6-1) that are supported with descriptive documents and analyses that need to be current with the requirements baseline. The *system requirements document* (sometimes called "system requirements specification") should cover every aspect of what the system should do (functions) and how well it should do it (performance requirements). Normally, the system requirements document is developed before subsystem and component requirements documents, because it should establish the requirements basis for these lower level system elements. However, for any given system implementation approach, trade-offs may be required at the system level in response to cost, interface issues, performance limitations, or schedules related to subsystem design approaches.

Requirements reviews are necessary predecessors to system design reviews and important elements in program design reviews. Requirements-related issues must have the same weight as design issues in readiness decisions by a program to proceed to its next step of development. Requirements assessments may identify the need to reassess project drivers, including:

- Relax design constraints
- Reallocate requirements
- Request a change to funding profiles.

System test plans are derived from requirements documents and capture approaches for requirements validation and verification in qualification and acceptance processes. Test plans typically reflect test specifications and identify objectives, environments and levels of assembly at which tests are to be performed.

Requirements specifications are potentially subject to change. Therefore, they should be designated "preliminary" prior to reviews at each stage of design. During formal design phases, while requirements may have to be traded, the specifications must, like design documents, be subject to rigorous configuration management and change control.

In addition, when requirements specifications at a top level govern more than one system element, tailoring a spec to accommodate the specific character of a subsystem may be appropriate, especially if the requirements not directly associated with system performance.

Interface Management

Interface Requirements Documents (IRDs) define all physical, functional and operational interface requirements between different systems and between different elements or components in the same system to ensure hardware and software compatibility. An IRD consists of physical and functional requirements and constraints on hardware and/or software items. The IRD controls the interfaces between interrelated components of a system under development, as well as between the system under development and any external systems (either existing or under development) that comprise a complete architecture. Interfaces between systems must be carefully considered with the complete end-to-end system architecture, even in the early stages of system development. The system level IRD may be referred to or included in the system specification.

Interface Control Documents (ICDs) describe design solutions to specific interface requirements. ICDs are the key to integrating and maintaining relationships between different systems and different segments within the same system. An ICD defines the physical interface between two system elements, including the number and types of connectors, electrical parameters, mechanical properties and environmental constraints and the data interface including all input and output data sent between elements. ICDs covering critical interfaces, such as the spacecraft-to-ground segment for FireSat II, can become highly complex. Two guidelines are important in developing and refining interface documents. Each ICD normally covers only two segments, although multiple elements within segments may require consideration of relationships with other segments. In general, we should avoid designs necessitating such added complexity.

Interface agreements must be documented at every level of design, usually in ICDs. At the system level, project managers or system engineers control the ICDs, whereas individual integrated product team leads control the ICDs at lower system levels. Although the exact content and format of interface documents may vary significantly across different systems and development organizations, ICDs always address physical, data and electrical interfaces and interactions. In addition, other system characteristics such as gyro drift and star tracker performance, for example, including nonlinearities of the transfer function, output axis coupling or star tracker noise, require the same definition level in the ICD so that the mission ground station can correctly calibrate these system elements and use them effectively in processing mission data.

6.5 System Engineering Tools

Lloyd Purves, ***NASA GSFC***

A challenge to describing engineering software tools is that their current rate of change is very high. On a roughly annual timescale, individual software programs of this class can become obsolete and even cease to exist. Programs that continue to be useful see their user interfaces, and the platforms on which they run, change at equivalent rates.

As examples of ongoing change, the platforms for engineering software have evolved from mainframe computers, through minicomputers and desktop personal computers, and now largely consist of laptop computers. Moreover, elements of this software are currently beginning a migration to handheld smart phones. Over this time period, the user interface has progressed from alphanumeric punch cards and printouts, to monochromatic text terminals, to color graphics terminals using pointing devices like mice that interact with clickable, drop-down menus. Voice input and touch screens are now beginning to be used. The actual 3D objects produced by 3D printers (sometimes called stereo-lithography or rapid prototyping) can be considered a new kind of output from engineering design programs.

Although somewhat invisible to the user, there is also an ongoing evolution in the means by which the software for these programs is executed. While laptops typically still store and execute the software of these engineering programs, often the user needs to be connected to a key-server that insures that the user has a valid, unexpired license to use the software. Sometimes the software is not resident on the platform hosting the user interface. Instead, the user interface is often a web browser showing a page that is the portal to a website where the software is either:

- Temporarily downloaded to run on the platform supporting the user interface,
- Run on a computer associated with the website,
- Propagated to a remote, massively-parallel supercomputer,
- In extremely compute-intensive cases (such as searching for SETI signals), propagated to any internet-connected personal computer in the world whose owner in willing to allow his or her computer to be so utilized

Compare that rate of change with the current Soyuz-FG launch vehicle, which is still used as a primary means for supplying the International Space Station with crew and supplies. The Soyuz-FG is the latest of many upgrades of the R-7, a modified ICBM developed by the USSR and used in 1957 to launch the first space mission, Sputnik. The Soyuz still looks much like the original R-7 and utilizes the same basic propulsion system. There is every indication that the Soyuz, or another upgrade of it, will still be in use past 2017, meaning a more than 60-year lifetime.

However, despite the seeming rapid change of engineering software, it is important to understand that its underlying theory and mathematics evolve even more slowly than long-lived launch vehicles. CAD programs still use elements of Euclid's geometry, and trajectory simulators are built on the theories of Kepler, Newton, and Einstein. Thus, the fundamental capabilities of these programs evolve far more slowly than their hosting platforms, computing power, user interfaces and convenience features.

The software tools that are applicable to space mission analysis and design can be usefully divided into two basic groups.

1. A simple set of tools that can be used by a single systems engineer or mission designer, or a small group of generalists, to develop a rough, but frequently adequate, mission concept. The size of these efforts could range from a single week (for a single individual to develop a variant of a mission that he or she is already familiar with) to more than a labor year of effort for three or four generalists to develop a relatively unique and complex mission.

2. More complex and sophisticated software tools that are typically used by specialists, such as the use of NASTRAN by a structural analyst. On larger mission design efforts, typically involving 5 to 10 people working for 6 to 12 months, these more capable tools are frequently used to come up with much more accurate and complete mission concepts. If the mission concept is actually developed into a real mission, these tools will continue to be used throughout the development process, first to support more detailed design and finally to help analyze how closely the performance of hardware in testing comes to its design objectives.

Obviously, it is possible, as frequently happens, that some mixture of the above approaches will be employed. Possibilities include:

- Augmenting the work of generalists with a subset of specialists
- Bringing in needed specialists for short periods to solve specific problems
- Having some generalists with good enough discipline backgrounds that they also function as effective specialists in certain areas.

Simple Tool Sets

In his book, *Space Vehicle Design*, Michael Griffin says that one of the capabilities desirable in a systems engineer is the knowledge and ability to carry out a first order design of any spacecraft subsystem. In a somewhat larger context, it is equally possible for a systems engineer to develop a complete first-order mission design for relatively straightforward missions. Such end-to-end skills are equally useful when space mission design is undertaken by a small group, for the result can be much improved when each person has the knowledge to contribute to and check the design and analysis of any part of the mission.

The essential tools for such an end-to-end capability can be summarized as follows:

- The first and most essential ingredient is a handbook, essentially one such as SME, which covers all basic areas of space flight design in a consistent and quantitative way that is understandable to a person having an education and background equivalent to that of an engineer working on space missions. The values and formulas presented in such a handbook need to be presented in a form that can be conveniently programmed in software.

There are also more specialized handbooks, such as for propulsion and thermal design, and occasionally a systems engineer may want to go to them for additional detail.

- The most important software tool then is a software program that makes it simple to enter and use these formulas and data. Generally, a spreadsheet program, such as Excel, is adequate. Spreadsheets are also useful as simple databases, and documenting the traceability of requirements. The ability for one worksheet to make use of data on another further increases their versatility.
- Occasionally, a simple procedural language, such as Basic, can usefully augment the capabilities of a spreadsheet. Some procedural languages can be integrated with spreadsheets.
- Knowledge of the top-level information about related missions accomplished in the past is generally a requirement for developing any reasonable mission concept. Handbooks such as SME typically only have room to briefly describe a very small number of example missions. Many more missions are described in adequate detail in papers presented at space conferences such as those by the AIAA. Today, relevant papers from such conferences are typically searched for and accessed via Internet browsers such as Explorer, Safari, and Firefox. Downloading a desired paper can require a credit card and fee, but often, companies and educational and research institutions have blanket agreements to allow their users free access to such papers. Search engines such as Google and Bing can often find the abstracts to useful papers, as well as websites and other on-line articles that are free.
- Finally, there are a variety of software tools that are almost critical for effectively documenting and communicating mission designs. Examples are word processing programs, such as Word, and business graphics programs such as Power Point. Frequently, the output of such programs will be converted into a common format, such as PDF, which can then be read on basically any computer with a free, downloadable PDF reader. As a more powerful visualization tool, it would be reasonable to get a simple, inexpensive 3D CAD program that would be used to document the design with 3D solids. Individual snapshots from the CAD program can be converted to 2D PDF images, and some CAD programs can output a 3D geometry in a format that can be viewed in 3D by free, downloadable viewers. In general, a simple website building tool is also needed to document almost any study. This is because often the only practical way to organize and communicate all of the intermediate and final data from a mission design is via a website that can be hierarchically organized, password protected, and provide different access privileges, such as read and write, based on user identification.

Complex Tool Sets

Get More For a discussion of more complex tools see the book website.

6.6 The Role of Standards in Space Systems Development

Frederick A. Slane,
Space Infrastructure Foundation

Technical Standards Play an Increasingly Important Role

Space Standards are benchmark requirements for space systems, services, operations or other specific views documented by experts in the field, often, but not always, in response to lessons learned. From our example standard below we have the generalized purpose of a standard:

> "This...Standard establishes a common framework and provides a common basis for the interchange of...data. It allows implementing organizations...to proceed coherently with the development of compatible derived standards for the flight and ground systems that are within their cognizance. Derived...standards may implement only a subset of the optional features allowed by the...Standard and may incorporate features not addressed by this...Standard."

Get Stnd Standards are used throughout all life cycle phases and must be accounted for in the space development process. Note that the word "must" here is not regulatory. Simply put, standards effectively include current best practices. While one does not need a standard to do space mission engineering work, failure to consider openly available, current standards does leave the engineer liable in the event of failure.

Some standards are relatively obvious. For example, engineering data standards that are used for transfer among engineering tools. ISO 10303 includes the STEP standards like AP203 for transfer of mechanical drawing information and the relatively new AP233 for systems engineering data. STEP files are commonly used to transfer mechanical drawings between organizations and different CAD tools. Consider that many tools use proprietary data formats for the file structure, and these formats change with time. The result is that it is difficult to read files from even 10 years ago. Using standard formats to store this data will enable us to provide the long-term storage necessary for design information of flight and ground systems that last over multiple decades.

Other data standards include PDF, RTF, and JPEG. With JPEG or TIFF, we have the ability to store images and view them many years from now—try to view the original image data from Voyager or Lunar Orbiter! The value of this type of engineering standard is well understood. Another is the use of TCP/IP to support space systems. CCSDS uses TCP/IP as one base for their standards work.

Due to the evolving nature of all engineering and scientific knowledge the benchmark contained in standards does change over time (TCP/IP began migration to v.6 approximately in the mid-1990s). It is the responsibility of all of us to update the knowledge in open standards as new lessons are learned, with special emphasis on safety. It is also the responsibility of each of us to use standards as we should use any tool; with judgment on when and how to vary from the benchmark. While a student may blindly apply standards as the use of the tool is learned, the master is expected to know his or her tools and expertly apply them. To extend teaching from the martial arts, a master is not limited by his or her weapons, but uses what is at hand to extend his or her capabilities.

Unfortunately, many engineers and scientists are not familiar with engineering standards; until recently no engineering schools have included engineering standards as part of their curriculum [Bickart, 2007], and scientific curricula will never include something as coarse as engineering topics. Therefore, the scientists and engineers who are often leaders in space systems development or space organizations do not understand open technical standards. A practical and extended education on the topic of standards is needed for the student and the master. Inclusion of the topic of standards in this text is a needed first step.

A small tempest, perhaps a "tempest in a teapot," rages in the space industry today regarding the role of technical standards, their development and application. From the first successful space launch in 1957 each organization and each project within those organizations has created their own engineering basis. It is understandable that in the early stages of spaceflight this was so; there were few standard practices and many unknowns to deal with. Today, our knowledge base is much deeper, with personal, institutional, national and even regional bodies of space expertise. Our industry-wide technical knowledge base should be strong, and one indicator of that is an industry standards base, as is common in other industries. However, there still are those who maintain that open technical standards for space systems are more trouble than they are worth.

Interestingly, the global market value of the space industry in 2009 [The Space Report, 2010] was about $262B (US). This is 3.4 times what Home Depot reported in the same year ($76.9B US). The point of this comparison is that the space industry has barely reached a level of production and service delivery where standardization makes sense. So the question is not *if* we need standards for the space industry. Some capabilities we discuss in this text *require* high volume or significant interoperability. *Where* we need standardization is a much more relevant point of discussion than *if* we need standardization and standards. The question of where we need standards and standardization is answered not by technical arguments, but by economic arguments. The counter question, "Where do we *not* want standards or standardization?" is answered by policy or political arguments. Happily, we will not get into those arguments here, but you need to understand that as the space industry grows, as the components of space infrastructure become ubiquitous to society at large, as spacecraft become smaller, and as modularity in space systems increases, the economic argument for increased standardization and standards *at some level* also grows. Since we are a small industry, we enjoy high visibility and prestige in society, and our political masters find us often to be troublesome, we need the strength in self-governance standards provide.

The small tempest will subside, because we cannot go back to the "good old days" of space projects being run as personal fiefdoms. And the teapot will expand as our industry continues its steady growth. Establishing an intelligent standards base now is a challenge worth our best efforts.

What are the Right Standards to Develop and Use?

Standards cover many topics, and there is no set rule on content. Understanding the answers to the questions of Who? What? Why? Where? When? and How? is very important in space systems engineering and standards are useful in finding quick and reliable answers. It is also true that good standards are useful to a common interest group. The larger the group that actually uses the standard, the more useful it is. Generally standards can cover operations, systems and services areas of any mission. Special areas such as space data and information transfer have been very effective topic areas. Within or across these areas standards effectively address:

- Interfaces of all types
- Form, fit or function of types of components which are used regularly
- Processes or procedures with many contributors/users
- All aspects of verification, mostly dealing with testing
- Other areas

Standards are tools. They are often very technical tools, and they have a formal construction and language. A standards document is a listing, in concise language, of required items on a specific topic. **The points listed in a standard can be required ("normative") and are indicated by use of the word "shall." Some points in a standard are not required but are strongly sup-**

ported; these are indicated by words such as "should." Often a standard will list possible variations; each variation will include "shall" and "should" types of statements. To see how this works, it is helpful to look at an example. One is provided at the end of this section.

It is also important to understand that there are some things that standards are not. Standards are not

- Rigid lists of requirements invented by people with no expertise in the topic area
- Meant to be unduly burdensome
- Required (unless specified by contract)
- Replacements for responsibility for engineers or scientists to fully address technical issues in their projects
- Removers of options on how technical issues on projects are addressed
- Constraints on technology

Properly applied, standards are not cost drivers. (However, using standards can make it more difficult to recover program schedule by eliminating portions of the test program. Unfortunately the practice of eliminating "unnecessary" testing at the end of the development cycle is uncommon in the space industry.)

The Merits of Standards (how do they help make spacecraft better or cheaper)

There are many reasons for voluntary compliance technical standards. They are primarily a means of self-governance by a technical community or industry. For people within the community they are a means of clearly communicating essential information. For people outside the community they are a means of establishing expectations. Standards are enforced by being referenced in contracts as compliance documents.

Standards are applied to the products and services in an industry, and also to the expectations of organizations in how these products and services aggregate to satisfy customer needs (in other words, organizational processes). A fundamental need addressed by a standard is to identify, quantify and document a basic requirement, so a producer may deliver products and services that meet (or exceed) the "bar" of customer expectations or accepted by the industry. For example, an engineering standard for a spacecraft requires design and verification of the spacecraft to meet the vibration expected through the launch profile (Sec. 26.3). An operational example is the requirement to design space to ground communications consistent with the basic physics in the laws of astrodynamics (Chap. 9 or Sec. 10.5). Open standards are very new to the space industry, so the benefit of common language, definitions, interfaces, verification methods and so forth are not yet realized.

A challenge for people who create space standards is the proper decomposition of products and services in a manner acceptable to yield efficiency, cost effectiveness, acceptable risk, reliability, flexibility and so on. For this reason standards must continually evolve: we continue to learn better ways to build and we continue to learn from mistakes we have made.

Standards promulgate from the most general levels of any industry down to ever increasing levels of detail over time. As the industry matures, it is possible—it is a competitive requirement—to internally control efficiency. It also becomes necessary as an industry grows in size for external controls, such as acceptable levels of risk for manned spaceflight, be negotiated for consistency with risk from other industries. For example, manned spaceflight today assumes risk consistent with experimental aviation. Tomorrow our expectation of risk might be on par with commercial aviation.

Multiple space communities (Chap. 2) need many similar things and it makes sense that re-use between communities keeps cost down. Standards document acceptable, critical re-use characteristics for space products, space services, and space operations. Within the space community at large there are still some communities that are closed (vs. open) in their practices. The manned spaceflight community is, once again, our example, but we will look at the most exclusive manned spaceflight community—NASA: In the area of reliability it has taken monumental shifts in the global manned spaceflight market to force NASA to discuss systems, services or operational technical metrics, rather than the human rating certification process and the related manned system acquisition process.

The Demerits of Standards (ways they can be harmful)

On the demerit side, standards poorly applied tend to potentially drive cost by demanding that things be done which are unnecessary. They may slow breakthroughs by the forced application of standards that aren't applicable to new technology. (For example, on a project building all-composite, cryogenic tanks that have never been built before, people have tried to apply standards for composite overwrap pressure vessels. Due to technological differences these didn't really make sense.) The important point is that standards are developed by professionals for professionals. So in standards application, use professional judgment: if and when necessary tailor the requirements so things make sense. If needed seek professional help.

Tailoring Standards to Meet Specific Mission Needs

Tailoring is something that we do a great deal of to control cost. Since the requirement listed in a standard are created to address a topic in a notional or general sense, it is clear that almost no standard is a perfect fit for a given project. True, the requirements listed are meant to be a minimal set. A practicing engineer must be smart in applying any initial approach to solving program design, fabrication, test, operations, or disposal issues, and that is no less true for applying a standard baseline than it is for applying text book solutions.

Where Standards Come From

There are many standards (and more are coming). As the example standard demonstrated, the authority for creating a standardized set of requirements rests with some duly formed body. In the example it is the CCSDS, but there are many, many Standards Development Organizations (SDOs). For the space industry a few specific SDOs are listed below, and their function is discussed briefly. While the technical work in SDOs is done by focused expert groups, each standard is reviewed and approved by staff and an executive board.

Which standards are important depends on what you are trying to do. The primary international SDOs for space are:

- The Consultative Committee for Space Data Systems (CCSDS)
  - Originally formed as a collaboration of the space agencies of the world, CCSDS has recently expended its charter to include defense or commercial organizations. Participation is free, but registration is required. See their website for current communications architecture and standards. (CCSDS calls their standards "recommendations")
  - CCSDS maintains a close relationship with ISO and is associated with ISO as ISO TC20/SC13, the Subcommittee for Space Data Systems. Interestingly, CCSDS documents are downloaded for free, while the same document, purchased through ISO with an ISO coversheet, will cost in the range of $70 to $130.
- The International Organization for Standardization (ISO), Technical Committee 20 (Aircraft and Space), Subcommittees 13 (above) and 14, Space Systems and Operations
  - Chartered by the United Nations and comprised of national member bodies (e.g., the American National Standards Institute (ANSI)). Each participating country in a Technical Committee, Subcommittee or Working Group registers to participate. Participation is free. See their website.

The primary US professional SDO for space is:

- The American Institute for Aeronautics and Astronautics (AIAA)
  - This professional organization works through both Technical Committees (to participate in a TC AIAA membership is required) and Committees on Standards (to participate in a CoS AIAA membership is not required). See their website for AIAA standards.

Each of these SDOs develop what are called voluntary compliance standards (VCS). Compliance is only required as specified by the program/project contract. In creating a VCS an SDO assures documents are valid by requiring consensus of the participating experts developing the document, and a public review at the final stage. Consensus requires that all points of view presented be addressed. This means when an expert position is not included, a clear reason is given. In the public review phase, each comment is addressed and the disposition documented. The SDO staff is responsible for bringing discrepancies in the consensus process to the attention of the project lead and the SDO standards executive board.

The primary European regional SDO for space, which operates in a manner similar to NASA in standards development, is the European Cooperation for Space Standardization (ECSS). See their website for ECSS standards.

Of the many available standards, the Consultative Committee on Space Standards (CCSDS) provides several good examples. They are free to download and can be referenced in this text without special permission. The standard on Attitude Data Messages is a CCSDS Recommended Standard (a Blue Book), issued in May 2008. It is a good example to use while referencing Chap. 8. This example defines how the important data on mission geometry is communicated to and from the spacecraft and the ground control center. Because this standard exists, it is no longer necessary for each project to define these terms.

Take a moment to review the excerpt in the boxed example from CCSDS 504.0-B-1. Notice that the document has a publication date. This is important in answering when the standard should be used. Standards must be current to be relevant. A refresh rate of every 5 years is recommended, but as long as even 10 years acceptable. Notice also that the document uses an "authority" statement to identify who the user is meant to be. While this doesn't limit use to only those organizations, it does identify which body is trying to establish some form of self-governance and where the participating experts are from. The procedure for developing this standard follows an established process. This standard has more strength, more authority, within the CCSDS member country space agencies than in a purely commercial activity.

The Statement of Intent and the Forward help the user to understand how and why the standard was developed, when to use it and how to properly apply the requirements contained within. The process for developing open standards is by consensus, which is not a simple democratic process. The requirement for endorsement and use is voluntary by each organization. This type of standard development is termed "voluntary consensus." Resulting standards are "voluntary consensus standards."

It is important to note that standards do not generally define how to fulfill requirements. They simply state the requirement. That is not to say lower level requirements will not be part of this or another standards. Standards may also set conditions for successful use or application.

ATTITUDE DATA MESSAGES
RECOMMENDED STANDARD (excerpts)
CCSDS 504.0-B-1
May 2008

. . .

STATEMENT OF INTENT

The Consultative Committee for Space Data Systems (CCSDS) is an organization officially established by the management of its members. *The Committee meets periodically to address data systems problems that are common to all participants, and to formulate sound technical solutions to these problems* why the standard was developed. Inasmuch as participation in the CCSDS is completely voluntary, the results of Committee actions are termed **Recommended Standards** and are not considered binding on any Agency. This **Recommended Standard** is issued by, and represents the *consensus* not a simple democratic process of, the CCSDS members. Endorsement of this **Recommendation** is *entirely voluntary* use is voluntary. Endorsement, however, indicates the following understandings:

Whenever a member establishes a CCSDS-related **standard**, this **standard** will be in accord with the relevant **Recommended Standard**. Establishing such a **standard** does not preclude other provisions which a member may develop.

- Whenever a member establishes a CCSDS-related **standard**, that member will provide other CCSDS members with the following information:
  - The **standard** itself.
  - The anticipated date of initial operational capability.
  - The anticipated duration of operational service.
- Specific service arrangements shall be made via memoranda of agreement. Neither this **Recommended Standard** nor any ensuing **standard** is a substitute for a memorandum of agreement

No later than five years from its date of issuance, this **Recommended Standard** will be reviewed by the CCSDS to determine whether it should: (1) remain in effect without change; (2) be changed to reflect the impact of new technologies, new requirements, or new directions; or (3) be retired or canceled. In those instances when a new version of a **Recommended Standard** is issued, existing CCSDS-related member standards and implementations are not negated or deemed to be non-CCSDS compatible. It is the responsibility of each member to determine when such standards or implementations are to be modified. Each member is, however, strongly encouraged to direct planning for its new standards and implementations towards the later version of the Recommended Standard.

3 ATTITUDE PARAMETER MESSAGE (APM)

3.1 OVERVIEW

3.1.1 Attitude information may be exchanged between two participants by sending the attitude state (see reference [E4]) for a specified epoch using an Attitude Parameter Message (APM). The message recipient must have an attitude propagator available that is able to propagate the APM state to compute the estimated attitude at other desired epochs. For this propagation, additional ancillary information (spacecraft properties such as inertia matrix, torque vectors, and maneuver planning data, if applicable) shall be included with the message.

. . .

3.2.2 APM HEADER

3.2.2.1 Table 3-1 specifies for each header item:

a) The keyword to be used;

b) A short description of the item;

c) Examples of allowed values; and

d) Whether the item is obligatory or optional.

3.2.2.2 Only those keywords shown in Table 3-1 shall be used in an APM header.

Keyword	Description	Examples	Obligatory
CCSDS_APM_VERS	Format version in the form of 'x.y', where 'y' is incremented for corrections and minor changes, and 'x' is incremented for major changes.	1	Yes
COMMENT	Comments (allowed at the beginning of the APM Header after the APM version number). Each comment line shall	This is a comment	No

. . .

3.3 APM EXAMPLES

Figures 3-1 through 3-8 are examples of Attitude Parameter Messages [Note: only one is included here].

CCSDS_APM_VERS	= 1.0
CREATION_DATE	= 2003-09-30T19:23:57
ORIGINATOR	= GSFC
COMMENT	GEOCENTRIC, CARTESIAN, EARTH FIXED
COMMENT	OBJECT_ID: 1997-068A
COMMENT $ITIM	= 1999 DEC 18 $ original launch time
OBJECT_NAME	= TERRA
OBJECT_ID	= 1997-068A
CENTER_NAME	= EARTH

. . .

See website for complete standard.

A Final Note: If It's Broke—Fix It!

All open standards organizations are, in fact, open for professional participants. Since poorly written standards or standards requirements affect the entire industry it is important to fix what needs to be fixed. Additionally, standards developers generally want to share information in their specialty area and they make great collaborators on concepts for future (standards) work.

6.7 Are Requirements Needed?— Capability-Based vs. Requirements-Based Systems

A well known and long-standing problem in US space system acquisitions is that final program costs tend to be much higher than initial cost estimates. Testimony by the US Government Accountability Office (GAO) before the Senate in March 2010 described how estimated total costs for some recent space system acquisitions were two to three times greater than initial estimates (Fig. 6-5). Most of these very expensive systems have been or will be delivered late (Fig. 6-6) and some of them will be delivered with diminished capability. While there can be a variety of reasons for large cost growth, late deliveries and reduced technical performance, recent GAO assessments, National Research Council studies and reports by US Congressional committees have all noted that problems with how system requirements are actually defined and managed are among the root causes of poor program execution. Recommended improvements to the requirements definition process included implementing "requirements discipline…to prioritize stakeholder needs and consider the impact of programmatic changes on cost and schedule…understand impact of any change to program requirements…deny requests to change program requirements if their request would unacceptably impact cost, schedule, or system performance." Other recommendations included "…research and define requirements before programs are started and limit changes after they are started…use systems engineering to close gaps between resources and requirements before launching the development process." In 2008, one Congressional committee, the House Permanent Select Committee on Intelligence (HPSCI) recommended migrating away from a requirements-based acquisition approach towards a capabilities-based strategy to improve the US national space strategy. Are requirements the problem? If so, are requirements even needed? What is a capabilities-based system?

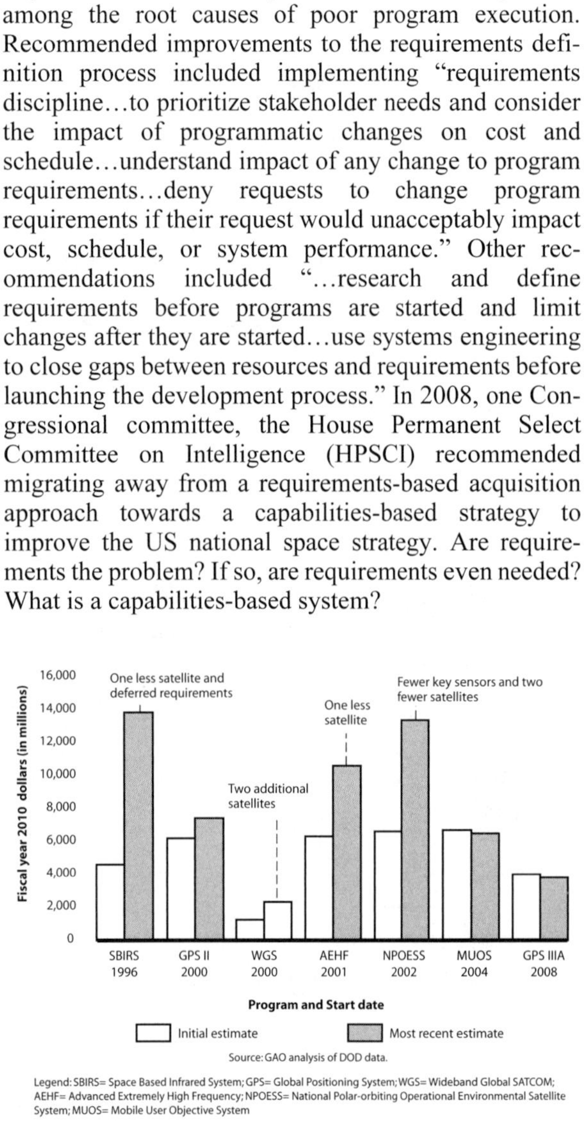

Fig. 6-5. Differences in Total Program Costs from Program Start and Most Recent Estimates (Fiscal Year 2009). (US Government Accounting Office GAO-10-447T)

The US became the world's preeminent space power by designing and building systems based on mission requirements driven by perceived importance and value of that mission much more than cost. For the most part, startling cost growth and program delays didn't matter to

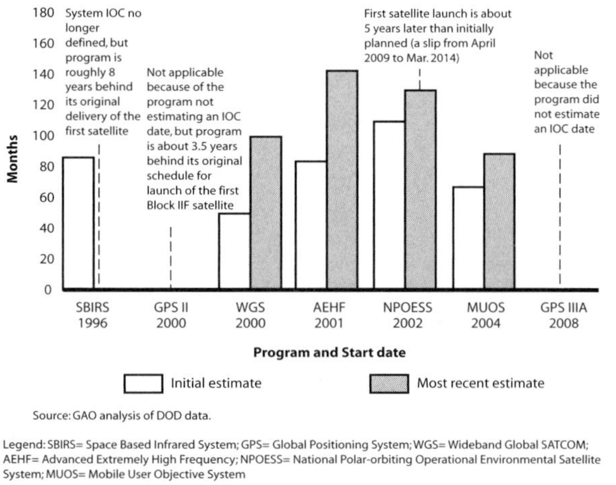

Fig. 6-6. Differences in Total Number of Months to IOC from Program Start and Most Recent Estimates. (US Government Accounting Office GAO-10-447T)

a wealthy nation focused on mission success in a highly competitive and threatening Cold War environment. The mission had overarching importance and the US dazzled the World with the success of Apollo, Corona, Viking and ultimately the Hubble Space Telescope. The NRO's Corona reconnaissance satellite program (Fig. 6-7) required 14 launches to achieve its first mission success back in the late 1950s and 1960s. Would a more cost-constrained and risk-adverse nation be so patient and focused on mission success?

Over time, in an era of American hegemony, a tendency developed to underestimate complexity of mission hardware and software and make optimistic assumptions about how simple it would be to develop and build new mission systems. In many cases, the relationship between mission requirements and capability was not completely understood—especially in early program phases—and the requirements definition process described here, which is based on detailed understanding of relationships between requirements, capability and cost was not followed. In a competitive environment, through a Darwinian process, bidders were motivated and encouraged to argue that mission goals could be achieved as cheaply as possible to maximize return for a given assumed budget. As a result, the relationship between mission objectives and cost in proposals tended to be poorly understood by proposer and reviewer alike, and initial cost estimates were overly optimistic and unrealistic to the point that it became impossible to implement missions within initial budgets.

In a sense, a capabilities-based process responds to this increasingly unacceptable circumstance of unbounded cost based on poorly understood mission-cost relationships by standing the requirements-based process on its head and asking the simple question of what mission requirements can we accomplish with hardware and software systems that we've got already? In this approach, we don't derive system performance

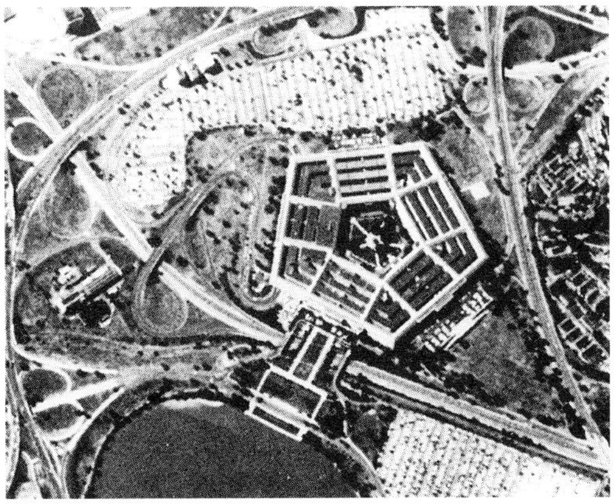

Fig. 6-7. The NRO's Corona Program. This program, declassified in 1995, involved satellites that returned film canisters to Earth in capsules, called "buckets," which were recovered in mid-air by specially equipped aircraft during their parachute descent. After 13 consecutive failures, the program enjoyed a relatively high success rate with 102 out of 144 Corona satellites returning usable imagery. (Courtesy of National Reconnaissance Office)

requirements from mission requirements. Instead, we take existing systems and either use them in new ways or piece them together into new systems and see what we can get for worthwhile missions. In that sense, capabilities-based systems take advantage of existing infrastructure to find new mission value, while delivering systems faster and at lower cost. We still need specifications to describe the system, but the mission requirements are derived from existing capability.

An example of a capabilities-based mission is the measurement of ionospheric and atmospheric physical characteristics like temperature and water vapor distributions made by looking at GPS satellites through the Earth's atmosphere with receivers onboard LEO satellites. This so-called GPS occultation technique has been implemented in a number of international systems like COSMIC (Constellation Observing System for Meteorology, Ionosphere and Climate), illustrated in Fig. 6-8, a joint US-Taiwan mission.

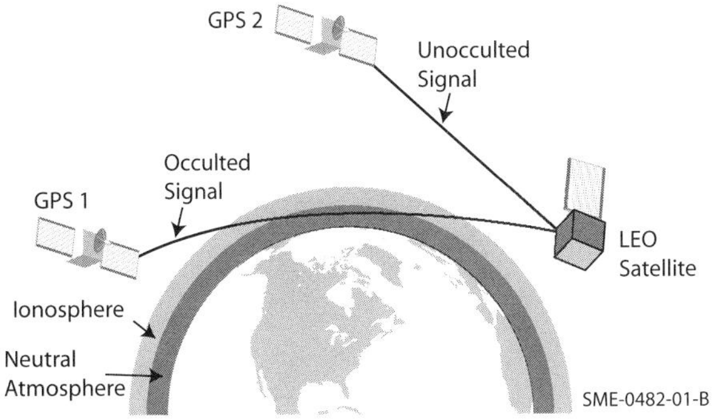

Fig. 6-8. COSMIC Measures Physical Properties of the Atmosphere and Ionosphere through precise measurement of phase delay and amplitude of GPS signals viewed through the atmosphere.

An obvious flaw in the capabilities-driven process is where do the existing capabilities come from if someone does not take bold steps to reach for and develop new technology that can be built into these lower cost systems? Who would build a GPS constellation to enable a COSMIC? Existing capabilities can come from at least two sources. The first is major system developments that are in fact driven by urgent mission needs. In some cases, hardware developed as part of these programs can be built into other systems and in other cases the systems themselves can be used for other purposes, as with GPS occultation. Another approach, possibly with more applicability, is to develop specific hardware and software in dedicated research and development programs that are embedded into broad national strategy roadmaps. Following "acquisition reform" in the 1990s, technology development was folded into operational system development to "save money." Unfortunately, like so many well-intended government initiatives to save money, this move had the exact opposite effect with technology being developed during operational system programs, even after Critical Design Review (CDR), with standing armies of engineers, accountants and program managers waiting for critical technology to be finished, which increased cost and schedule and decreased customer confidence.

Clearly, at least part of the right answer is to return a model that served us well for decades, which involves developing technology in agile research programs that are executed as part of a broader national strategy. In that case, proven, newer technology gets implemented at low risk and with much more predicable cost and schedule into operational systems. Despite the relative comfort and appeal of this approach, in some cases, it's just not good enough. The nation will always have urgent needs that demand technical solutions that go beyond demonstrated hardware and software, but not beyond laws of physics, engineering and production and so we will always have an engine for change that will lead to new capabilities. Even in those cases, though, key enabling technologies need to be developed and proven first before final authority to proceed to develop expensive operational systems makes sense.

Applicable Standards:
AIAA S-102-2010: Performance-Based Reliability Modeling Requirements
See website for reference.

References

For annotated bibliography of formal requirements definition, see the book website.

Bickart, T. E. 2007. "An IEEE Perspective on Standards in Education." *The Journal of the Standards of Engineering Society,* vol. 59, no.1. Jan–Feb. pp. 1–9.

Fellar, W. 1971. *An Introduction to Probability Theory and Its Applications. 3rd ed.* Hoboken, NJ: John Wiley and Sons.

Meyer, P. L. 1972. *Introductory Probability and Statistical Applications.* Reading, MA: Addison-Wesley.

Papoulis, A. 2002. *Probability, Random Variables, and Stochastic Processes. 4th Ed.* New York, NY: The McGraw-Hill Companies.

Parzen, E. 1992. *Modern Probability Theory and its Applications.* Hoboken, NJ: John Wiley and Sons.

Robert, C. P. and G. Casella. 2010. *Monte Carlo Statistical Methods.* New York, NY: Springer.

Taylor, J. R. 1997. *An Introduction to Error Analysis: The Study of Uncertainties in Physical Measurements, 2nd ed.* Sausalito, CA: University Science Books.

Space Foundation. 2010. *The Space Report.* Website.

Wertz, James R. 2001. *Orbit and Constellation Design and Management.* Hawthorne, CA: Microcosm Press and Springer.

Wertz, James R. 2009. *Orbit & Constellation Design and Management.* Hawthorne, CA: Microcosm Press and Springer.

Wertz, James R. and Wiley J. Larson. 1999. *Space Mission Analysis and Design. 3rd ed.* Hawthorne, CA: Microcosm Press and Springer.

Williams, Michael S. 1992. "Requirements Definition." *Space Mission Analysis and Design. 2nd ed.* Torrance, CA: Microcosm Press and Kluwer Academic Publishers.

7 The Space Environment

W. Kent Tobiska, *Space Environment Technologies**

* With contributions from D.J. Gorney, J.B. Blake, H.C. Koons, M. Schulz, *The Aerospace Corporation*
A.L. Vampola, R.L. Walterscheid, *The Aerospace Corporation*

7.1 The Space Environment and Space Weather

The *space environment* is ambiguously defined as the region beyond the Earth's atmosphere (usually the troposphere) where non-terrestrial energy sources begin to dominate and spacecraft operate. The near-Earth space environment includes the Earth's upper atmosphere, ionosphere, radiation belts, and magnetosphere. The deep space environment extends beyond to include interplanetary space (the *heliosphere*), other planetary and small body regions, and even galactic environments that affect our Solar System.

Space weather is the shorter-term variable impact of the Sun's photons, solar wind particles, and interplanetary magnetic field upon the Earth's environment that can adversely affect space systems. It includes, for example, the effects of solar coronal mass ejections, solar flares, solar and galactic energetic particles, as well as the solar wind. All of these affect Earth's magnetospheric particles and fields, geomagnetic and electrodynamical conditions, radiation belts, aurorae, ionosphere, and the neutral (i.e., non-ionized) thermosphere and mesosphere as well as space systems that interact with these domains. Disturbances to these regions cause unwanted effects on systems that have sensitive components.

Active or passive mitigation of space weather effects can most effectively be done when space weather information is produced automatically and then integrated into space systems and space operations. The systems most susceptible to space weather are related to communications, navigation, low Earth orbit satellite operations, and geosynchronous satellite operations.

Operational space weather is, in essence, a supply chain. It is a system of organizations, people, technology, activities, information and resources that move space weather products or services from suppliers to customers. The raw material of space environment data is processed by models into information and then refined into specialized products for delivery to end customers. Space weather's greatest value is when it is an integrated information layer within broader systems [Tobiska and Bouwer, 2010; Tobiska, 2009].

The near-Earth space and atmospheric environments strongly influence the performance and lifetime of operational space systems by affecting their size, weight, complexity, and cost. Some environmental interactions also limit the technical potential of these systems. They can lead to costly malfunctions or even the loss of components or subsystems [Tribble, 1995; Hastings and Garrett, 1996; DeWitt et al., 1993].

Operating in space can pose significant problems for many spacecraft systems. For example, in vacuum, most organic materials will *outgas*—i.e., generate spurious molecules that may act as contaminants to other surfaces. Even before reaching orbit, particles from the atmosphere may fall onto optical surfaces and degrade the performance of electro-optical instrumentation. Because there is no practical way to clean spacecraft surfaces once the vehicle reaches orbit, maintaining effective contamination control during design and development is a significant issue for most spacecraft [Tribble et al., 1996]. Ultraviolet (UV) degradation of materials, surface charging, deep dielectric charging (see Sec. 7.1.1), communication interference, and unexpected perturbations to orbits and attitudes are other types of effects that can be attributed to space weather.

Above 100 km, a spacecraft or rocket enters the very tenuous upper atmosphere called the thermosphere. In LEO (low-Earth orbit) orbits below 500 km, a spacecraft encounters the constituent species of the atmosphere, i.e., molecular nitrogen and oxygen, and atomic oxygen, hydrogen, and helium, at orbital velocities on the order of 8 km/s. Interactions between the satellite and the neutral atmosphere primarily affects the spacecraft's orbit by causing drag on the surfaces that has a cumulative effect on the orbital energy and orbital lifetime (See Sec. 9.4.4.). Additional effects include erosion of satellite surfaces due to adsorption of atomic oxygen resulting in thermal, electrical, and possibly structural surface property effects.

7.1.1 Solar Output

Energy is transferred to the Earth from the Sun via three main forms: electromagnetic radiation (photons), charged particles, and magnetic, electric, and gravitational fields. The source of this energy comes from the solar interior where nuclear fusion produces photons that eventually find their way from the core through the *Radiative zone* over the course of a million years. At the Radiative zone–Convection zone boundary (the *Tachocline*), the plasma cools enough to condense into highly ionized atoms and here the solar magnetic field is born.

Magnetic flux, charged particles (ions and electrons), and photons continue their way through the Convection zone to the surface, which is the coolest part of the Sun at ~5770K. Magnetic flux features erupt through the surface in the form of *sunspots* and sunspot groups. Above the surface, the *solar atmosphere* consisting of the *chromosphere*, *transition region*, and *corona* feel the effects of emergent magnetic flux episodes in the form of active regions, plage, flares, and coronal mass ejections (CMEs)†. In these features, solar atmospheric ions and electrons are accelerated by magnetic shearing and eruptions; in these processes, solar X-ray, extreme ultraviolet (EUV), and UV photons [IS0, 2007] are dynamically created by the plasma's ionized states and the ions' relaxation to lower energy states. The solar magnetic field reverses polarity every ~11 years as part of a 22 year solar magnetic cycle, observed since 1610 as the sunspot cycle. The intensities of the X-ray, EUV, and UV irradiances that are the most Earth-effective energies are associated with the sunspot cycle. The solar 10.7 cm radio flux, called the F10.7 *proxy*,‡ has variability that occurs in sync with energy processes in the solar atmosphere and has been used as an indicator for the solar EUV irradiances. Figure 7-1 shows the solar cycle 23–24 variation of the F10.7 proxy. Cycle 24 started in January, 2008.

The integration of spatial radiances from all points on the visible solar disk become the spectral solar irradiances that make their way to Earth in 8 minutes, causing thermospheric density increases, ionospheric enhancements, and spacecraft surface charging (photoelectric effect). The fast solar wind (500–800 km/s) originates in solar coronal holes* and overtakes the slow solar wind (200–500 km/s) that emanates from the active corona. The electrons and protons in the solar wind are bound on trajectories defined by the spiral-like structure of the Sun's magnetic field that extends throughout the heliosphere. They arrive at Earth within 2–3 days. Occasionally, extremely fast solar wind particles from CMEs (800–2,000 km/s), including Solar Energetic Protons (SEPs), blast through the solar wind and can arrive at Earth as early as ½ hour to a few hours after the eruptive event.

At Earth the fast solar wind from the coronal holes, also called *Co-rotating Interactive Regions* (CIRs), can cause minor ionospheric changes. The extremely energetic particles from CMEs can cause major and minor disturbances to the Earth's magnetic field, called *geomagnetic storms* and *substorms* (See Sec. 7.2.), by coupling with, and distorting, the external Earth magnetic field called the *magnetosphere*. On spacecraft, the

† **Plage:** Plage are bright regions in the Sun's middle atmosphere (chromosphere) usually near and above sunspots. These brightenings extend away from the bright chromosphere active regions above the sunspots and are the result of magnetic flux diffusing away from the active region into the quiet regions. They account for part of the EUV emission from the Sun seen at the Earth that causes thermospheric density increases and, thus, increases to satellite drag.
Flare: A solar flare is a large explosion in the Sun's atmosphere that affects all layers of the solar atmosphere (photosphere, chromosphere, and corona). It produces radiation across the electromagnetic spectrum at all wavelengths, from radio waves to gamma rays, although most of the energy goes into X-rays and EUV. Flares occur in active regions above sunspots and brighten along the strong magnetic field lines coming from the Sun's interior and extending into the corona. Flares occur on timescales of minutes to a few hours and their X-ray and EUV radiation affects Earth's ionosphere and thermosphere.
CME: A coronal mass ejection (CME) is a massive explosion in the solar atmosphere associated with a large flare where material (ions and electrons) from the Sun's atmosphere escape into space. CMEs inject a large quantity of energetic ions and electrons into the solar wind. This material, if it follows interplanetary field lines that connect the Sun to the Earth, can cause major disruptions to the Earth's magnetosphere, resulting in geomagnetic storms that cause intense heating of the Earth's polar atmosphere and affect satellite drag.

‡ The output of the Sun at a wavelength of 10.7 cm has often been called the F10.7 *index* or, more correctly, the F10.7 *proxy*, and is an indicator of solar activity. There is nothing magic about 10.7 cm, except that the solar output at this wavelength has been measured continuously since WWII and, therefore, is known to correlate to the Sun spot cycle and solar radio activity over an extended period. The reason that the F10.7 proxy is used for atmospheric drag calculations is that its variation generally replicates the actual heating process for the upper atmosphere, i.e., the absorption of solar EUV photons by oxygen and nitrogen. The more photons absorbed, the more active are the molecules and lower layers expand to higher altitudes, creating the effect of greater densities at higher altitudes. F10.7 has no direct relationship to this process but varies day to day in a manner similar to the solar photons that do affect the atmosphere densities and satellite drag [ISO, 2007].

* Coronal holes are regions where the corona is dark. These features were discovered when x-ray telescopes were first flown above the Earth's atmosphere to reveal the structure of the corona across the solar disc. Coronal holes are associated with open magnetic field lines and are often found at the Sun's poles.

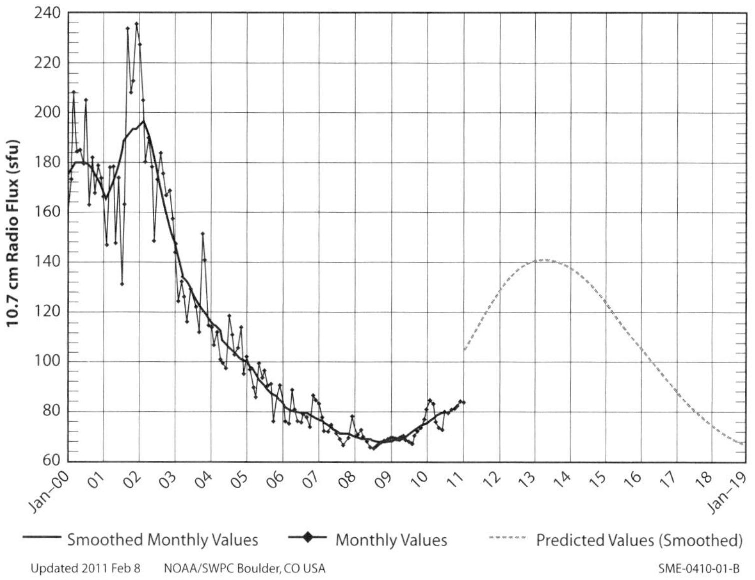

Fig. 7-1. F10.7 Solar Cycle Number 24 Progression from ISES and NOAA SWPC. Shown is the mean F10.7 daily flux in units of sfu = 10^{-22} W m^{-2} Hz^{-1}. (See also Fig. 9-16 in Sec. 9.4.4.)

charged particles in the storms and substorms can cause severe surface charging at geosynchronous orbit as well as deep dielectric charging/discharging. Deep dielectric discharging occurs when electrons of 2–10 MeV penetrate deep into satellite surfaces. Excess charge spreads out evenly on conducting surfaces but results in uneven potential distribution on dielectric surfaces. Potential differences can reach a threshold at which point discharge occurs. Deep dielectric charging occurs inside the surfaces of satellites and discharges can occur to circuits inside the spacecraft. In the outer Van Allen Radiation Belt these events inject increased populations of particles. The Earth's thermosphere experiences density enhancements that heat the upper atmosphere. The ionosphere sustains increased densities from electron precipitation into the polar region and ion drag through the neutral atmosphere (*Joule heating*), thereby affecting radio communications, radar signals, and GPS navigation.

From outside the Solar System, galactic cosmic rays (GCRs) (see Sec. 7.3) from supernovae and black holes reach the Earth, penetrate to the lower atmosphere, and impact nitrogen or oxygen, creating a spray of particles, including neutrons, that then scatter outside the atmosphere and decay to protons and electrons in the inner Van Allen Radiation Belt. The free neutron is in fact radioactive—within about 10 minutes it breaks up into a proton, which captures most of the energy, an electron, and a massless neutrino.

7.1.2 The Upper Atmosphere (Thermosphere and Ionosphere)

7.1.2.1 Thermosphere

The thermosphere (85–500 km altitude range) is the neutral atmosphere in Near-Earth space. EUV irradiance penetrates to different levels of the thermosphere depending upon the energy of photons of a given wavelength, the absorption cross sections of atoms and molecules, and the attenuation of the flux by the thermospheric density. Heating, and subsequent density changes, occurs when an EUV photon is absorbed by a particle. This is called *photoabsorption*. The route to thermal energy deposition proceeds through two major paths: 1) *photoionization* of molecules or atoms, where an electron is stripped from the particle and carries away most of the excess energy as kinetic energy, followed by ion-neutral and photoelectron reactions which convert stored chemical energy into kinetic, or thermal energy, or 2) *photodissociation* of a molecule, where the chemical bond between atoms is broken, with the initial photon energy being transferred into particle kinetic energy. The upper thermosphere is a heat source and is nearly isothermal. By either of these paths, heat produced at high thermospheric altitudes, i.e., above 200 km, is transported down to cooler atmosphere regions. Because the solar X-ray, EUV, and UV irradiances vary with flare (hours), solar rotation (27 days), active region evolution (3–6 months) and solar cycle (10–12 year) changes, this affects the densities of the thermosphere and ionosphere on the same time scales. Figure 7-2 shows the altitude-structured daily neutral density variability in the thermosphere with the decline of solar cycle 23, the episodic solar active region evolution, and the 27-day solar rotation.

In addition to solar X-ray, EUV, and far UV (FUV) heating, the Earth's neutral upper atmosphere absorbs energy in the polar regions as a result of electron precipitation along magnetic field lines and ion drag (*Joule heating*). Terrestrial dynamical processes (winds, waves, and tides) also play a role in transferring energy from region

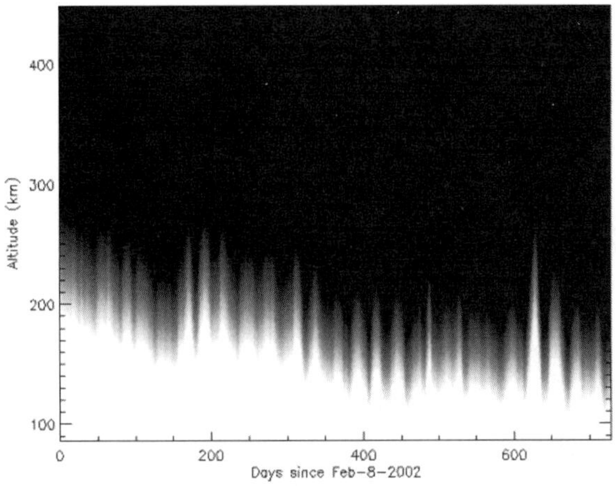

Fig. 7-2. Thermosphere Density for Two Years Starting February 8, 2002 is Modeled with daily SOLAR2000 EUV Irradiances in the 1DTD (1-dimensional, time dependent) Physics Model from Space Environment Technologies. The grayscale gradient indicates exponentially decreasing sub-solar daily densities (light to dark) with altitude from 100 to 450 km. The secular decreasing level of density at every altitude is from the decline of solar cycle 23, the sharp spikes are the density enhancements due to 27-day solar rotation, and the broader periodic density enhancements (several months) comes from solar active region evolution and decay.

to region, resulting in density enhancements or depletions. The main effect of thermospheric density changes is increased or decreased drag on a spacecraft (See Sec. 9.4.4.), attitude perturbations, and atomic oxygen erosion.

Atomic oxygen. Atomic oxygen is the predominant atmospheric constituent from 200 km to 600 km and has important effects upon space systems. Atomic oxygen can react with thin organic films, advanced composites, and metallized surfaces [Visentine, 1988], resulting in degraded sensor performance. For example, Kapton, a material commonly used for insulation and seals, erodes at a rate of approximately 2.8 μm for every 10^{24} atoms m^{-2} of atomic oxygen fluence [Leger et al. 1984]. *Fluence* is the total number of particles that has crossed a unit area. It is related to the *number density* (i.e., the number of particles per unit volume) of atomic oxygen and the satellite velocity.

Atomic oxygen forms when solar far ultraviolet radiation dissociates molecular oxygen. Above 110 km, atmospheric constituents reach a density distribution based on their influence by gravity; each constituent's density varies with altitude according to its *scale height*. The scale height of a constituent is the height change over which the density drops to e^{-1} of its value. In diffusive equilibrium, the scale height is inversely proportional to its molecular weight. Thus, the density of light constituents decreases less rapidly with altitude than the density of heavy constituents, and eventually the light constituents dominate the mixture of gases. Atomic oxygen is lighter than the molecular nitrogen and oxygen; therefore, near 200 km altitude, atomic oxygen becomes the most abundant constituent. The large solar-cycle variation in atomic oxygen means spacecraft materials can be selected based on phasing the mission to the solar cycle. Since there are large differences between solar cycles, material choices made on the basis of average solar maximum conditions may be inappropriate because of the possibility of more extreme solar maximum conditions.

7.1.2.2 Ionosphere

The thermosphere is coupled with the ionosphere where solar X-ray, EUV, and FUV photons have the ability to strip electrons from neutral species. The result is a plasma (*ionosphere*) that is created on the dayside of the planet, and is affected by the magnetic-electric field coupling to form the *Equatorial Anomaly*, and that disappears during the night. Figure 7-3 shows the total electron content (TEC) of the ionosphere. The two bands of electron density enhancement on either side of the magnetic equator are the *Equatorial Anomaly*. Just as the neutral thermosphere is modified primarily by the solar photons, secondarily by Joule heating and charged particle precipitation, and thirdly by winds, waves, and tides, so the same relative importance affects ionospheric variability. Ionosphere and neutral atmosphere coexist together but the densities of ionosphere species are about 6 orders of magnitude less dense than the neutral species. Ionosphere particles (constituents) are formed from the neutral when solar EUV and X-ray photons hit them and knock off electrons—those electrons then become the population of particles in the ionosphere but, when the Sun goes behind the planet, the electrons reattach to the ions, creating neutrals, and collapse the ionosphere.

The main features of the ionosphere include Chapman profiles for each of the ion species that are dominant in different regions. A Chapman profile (or Chapman layer) is the distribution of ionization as a function of height produced solely by absorption of solar radiation. It is named after Sidney Chapman, one of the principal scientists who made early investigations of the ionosphere. In 1931 he derived the simple case of a single gas with an

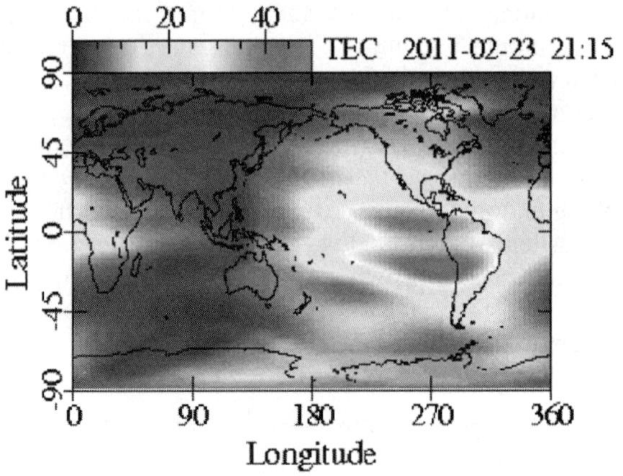

Fig. 7-3. The Ionosphere Total Electron Densities from the USU Space Weather Center GAIM System. Greatest electron densities occur during the dayside and the two bands on either side of the magnetic equator are called the Equatorial Anomaly.

absorption coefficient that is constant for all wavelengths. The Chapman layer theory assumes a single species gas with exponential distribution (therefore with constant scale height) and monochromatic radiation from the Sun for ion production rate, and that there is an equilibrium between the creation of free electrons and their loss by recombination [Goodman, 2005]. These assumptions represent a major simplification with respect to reality; however the Chapman theory is a fundamental baseline for ionospheric profile modeling. The regions of the ionosphere are:

- D-region: 50–85 km, dominated by H_2O^+, formed by solar wavelengths, λ, where $\lambda < 1$ nm (X-ray) or Lyman-α ($\lambda = 121.6$ nm); the main neutral constituent (or species) in the overlapping mesophere is N_2 (78%) followed by O_2 (21%)
- E-region: 85–140 km, dominated by O_2^+, $1 < \lambda < 10$ nm (XUV) or Lyman-β ($\lambda = 102.6$ nm) or CIII ($\lambda = 97.7$ nm); the E-F1 valley is the cross-over between the two regions
- F1-region: 140–250 km, is dominated by NO^+, $10 < \lambda < 91$ nm (EUV), F1 maximum electron density at ~200 km
- F2-region: 250–500 km, dominated by O^+, $10 < \lambda < 91$ nm (EUV), F2 maximum electron density at ~300 km
- Topside ionosphere: 500–1,500 km, dominated by the escape of H^+ and, occasionally, O^+ during periods of intense thermospheric heating due to major flares and geomagnetic storms. The principal neutral species in this exosphere altitude range is H and sometimes O, again depending on thermospheric heating due to flares and CMEs
- The plasmasphere: extending to approximately geosynchronous orbit (~36,000 km) with a falloff of cold (few eV) protons and electrons to interplanetary levels

These charged particles, called the plasma environment, can cause differential charging of satellite components both on the surface and interior of the vehicle. If severe, this charging can exceed breakdown electric fields and the resulting electrostatic discharges may be large enough to disrupt electronic components. More energetic space radiation, such as electrons with energies from about 200 keV to 1.5 MeV, can become embedded in dielectric components and produce electrostatic discharges in cable insulation and circuit boards. This *bulk charging* may disrupt a subsystem's signals or the operation of its devices. Even if mild, the charging may alter the electrical potential of the spacecraft relative to space and affect the operation of scientific instrumentation.

7.2 The Earth's Magnetic Field

The Earth's magnetic field is comprised of the main field created by the iron core dynamo within the planet and the magnetosphere components. The latter include the *ring current*, the *cross-tail current*, and the *magnetopause surface current*. Together, main field and magnetosphere comprise the magnetic system that can affect ground- and space-based systems.

The Earth's magnetic field is roughly dipolar and the combination of Maxwell's Equations, Ohm's Law, the Equation of continuity, and the hydrodynamic equation are used to describe its general character. The main magnetic field can be modeled by the World Magnetic Model (WMM) or the International Geomagnetic Reference Field (IGRF). Both models represent the field from the Earth's core out into space, and both are revised every 5 years. In particular, the IGRF is revised by the International Association of Geomagnetism and Aeronomy (IAGA) and is in its 10th generation (1900.0–2010.0). The IGRF, which is part of in ISO Earth Main Field Standard (ISO 16695) along with the WMM, has a regularly updated website [IGRF, 2011]. An example of the Earth main field is shown in Fig. 7-4. Here, the WMM total intensity at the 2000.0 epoch is shown with contour intervals in 2000 nT and a Mercator projection. The variation in field strength ranges from 24,000–66,000 nT (0.24–0.66 Gauss).

As the dipole field extends beyond the Earth's surface, the magnetic field lines are subjected to perturbations by the plasma of the solar wind. The interaction between the solar wind and the Earth's magnetic field causes the magnetic field on the night side of the Earth to stretch into a very elongated structure known as the magnetotail. Figure 7-5 shows an example of the Earth's magnetosphere system. A thin plasma sheet bifurcates the *magnetotail*, which is the portion of the magnetosphere opposite to the Sun behind the Earth and which extends over 1,000 Earth radii parallel to the velocity flow of the solar wind.

Through the interaction between the solar wind and the Earth's magnetic field, some of the solar wind's kinetic energy is converted to magnetic energy stored in the magnetotail. *Geomagnetic storms* are large disturbances in the near-Earth environment (especially in the geomagnetic field), which are caused by solar wind and interplanetary field structures that originate from solar disturbances such as coronal mass ejections. In these storms there is a strong increase of energetic ions (tens to hundreds of keV) in the ring current region just inside geosynchronous orbit. The *Disturbance Storm Time (Dst) index* is an indicator of the strength of the magnetospheric ring current as it is modulated by the solar wind, and as it perturbs the Earth's main magnetic field. There are also occasionally intense fluxes of relativistic (MeV) electrons that are injected into the outer Van Allen radiation belt. This perturbation on the Earth main field is registered as a decrease in the main field strength and Dst is reported in nT and with the range of +100 to –400. A geomagnetic storm is occurring when Dst reaches –75 and major storms can reach values as low as –300 nT or lower. Because this ground-based Dst measurement from 4 mid-latitude magnetic observatories is an excellent

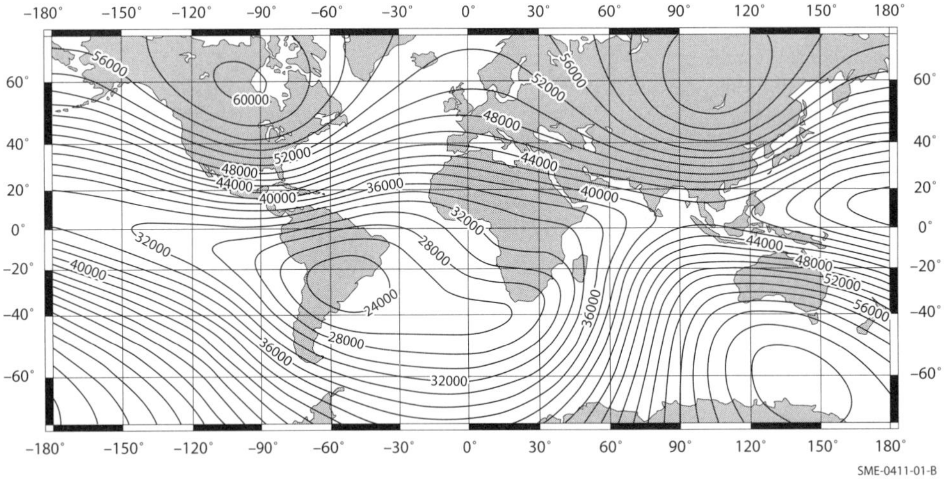

Fig. 7-4. The WMM2000 Earth Main Field Model is Shown with 2000 nT Contour Intervals.

indicator of solar wind influence on the magnetosphere, and hence of the energy from Poynting (electromagnetic) flux and (kinetic) particle precipitation in the polar regions, it provides a very good, time-resolved surrogate for the high latitude heating in the upper atmosphere that affects satellite drag.

Satellite drag calculation is moving toward the ISO and COSPAR methods (NRLMSIS for constituents and JB2008 for mass densities and drag calculations). Dst is used in JB2008 for increasing the atmospheric density (and drag) during geomagnetic storms. The older F10.7 is still useful but less accurate. F10.7 will continue to be used and as the new models become more available engineers can use them. Historically, F10.7 has been used as an indicator, a proxy, of the variable drag on a LEO satellite. Figure 9-17 in Chap. 9 shows the density vs. altitude for various F10.7 values. If those variable densities are translated into LEO satellite lifetimes, Fig. 9-18 shows the altitude as a function of dates for 9 hypothetical satellites launched over a 6-year period. F10.7 and Dst are decoupled; engineers need both and have to use a computation application that both incorporates atmospheric density models and contains the proper methods.

The charged particle motions are affected by the magnetic field's intensities and particle bounce, drift, and *magnetic mirroring* can occur. Magnetic mirroring is the bouncing of a charged particle along the field lines back and forward between the northern and southern geomagnetic hemispheres. The interaction of these particles with the magnetosphere causes magnetospheric variability, which then manifests as geomagnetic variations measured by magnetic observatories at the Earth's surface. The planetary geomagnetic indices of Kp and Ap (where

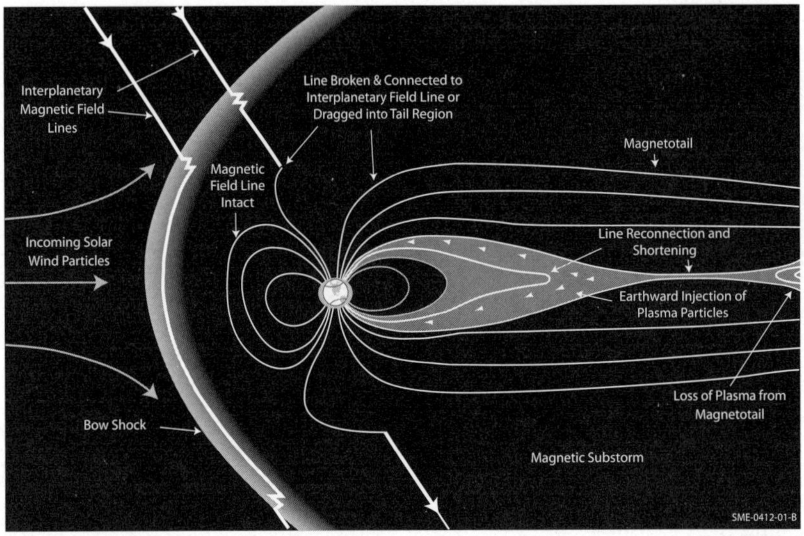

Fig. 7-5. The Magnetosphere System.

Ap is the daily average of 8 a-indices and Ap is the 3 hour index of geomagnetic activity, equivalent to Kp but on a scale of 0–400 instead of 0–9), and the disturbance storm time (Dst) index for the ring current all provide information about how the solar wind perturbs the magnetosphere, and hence the Earth's main field. They are also proxies for the influx of charged particles along magnetic field lines into the polar regions, i.e., particle precipitation, that combine with high latitude current systems to cause heating and auroral phenomena in the upper atmosphere. Figure 7-6 shows the occurrence of periods of geomagnetic storms during several solar cycles, where Ap* indicates values of Ap ≥ 40, while Fig. 7-7 shows the USGS and Kyoto Dst indices in 2009 with minor storm conditions.

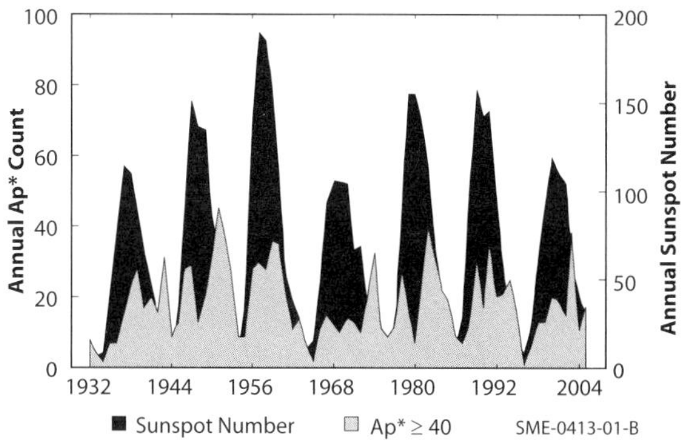

Fig. 7-6. Sunspot (black) vs Magnetic Storm (light gray) for Solar Cycles 17–23.

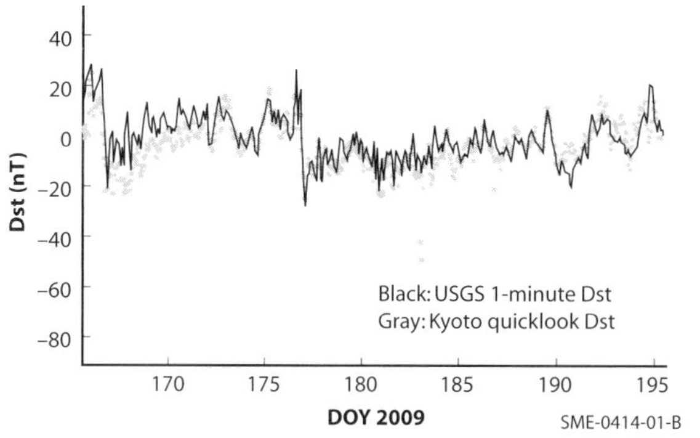

Fig. 7-7. USGS (black) and Kyoto (gray) Dst for Days 165–195 in 2009.

Because this energy cannot build up indefinitely, magnetic substorms dissipate it from time to time. *Magnetospheric substorms* are caused by the dynamic response of the magnetosphere to varying solar conditions. The energy input from the solar wind is governed by the orientation of the interplanetary field and, as long as the magnetospheric region remains stable, energy is stored as magnetic energy. At some critical point the magnetotail becomes unstable and the magnetic energy is released via the *substorm expansion phase*, which involves injection of energetic particles (electrons and ions—tens to hundreds of keV) into the vicinity of the geostationary orbit. These substorms are associated with strong electric currents in the auroral region, rapid fluctuations, and configuration changes of the magnetospheric magnetic field. These substorms produce an energetic plasma (5 to 50 keV) that is injected toward the Earth. This hot plasma can extend into geosynchronous orbits and has the ability to charge the surface of any spacecraft within it to high negative voltages.

The electrical potential of a spacecraft or one of its components is measured with respect to the plasma in which it is immersed where the net current flow is zero. That is, the following currents must cancel each other: (1) the electron current from the plasma to the vehicle, (2) the ion current from the plasma to the vehicle, (3) the secondary electron current, (4) the backscattered electron current, and (5) the photoelectron current. The voltage at the component's surface also depends on the material's capacitance with respect to the surrounding materials, especially the vehicle ground. Because materials have varying secondary emission coefficients and photoelectron currents, their equilibrium potentials also differ. An electrostatic arc occurs if the electric field exceeds the breakdown field along the surface of the material, through the material, or between adjacent materials.

Disturbed geomagnetic conditions near geosynchronous orbit can also lead to charge collection in dielectric (non-conducting) materials. This can result in either spacecraft surface or deep dielectric charging, both of which can also happen in LEO and MEO (medium-Earth orbit) environments. With charge buildup, *electrostatic discharge* (ESD) can occur as *Paschen discharge* and *arcing*[†] and the result can be a loss of system components or even catastrophic failure of a mission.

Electromagnetic interference (EMI) from such arcs can cause spacecraft to operate erratically. Surface charging detrimental to vehicle operation occurs mainly in orbits where electrons with energies of 10 to 20 keV dominate the electron current from the plasma to the vehicle. At low altitudes this charging occurs only at high latitudes where auroral electrons collide with the vehicle, which is passing through an otherwise cold, low-density plasma. For other low-altitude locations, low energy electrons usually develop enough current to keep electric fields below breakdown levels. In higher orbits, such as geosynchronous, surface charging occurs during magnetospheric substorms between the longitudes corresponding to midnight and dawn. Figure 7-8 shows an example of charging potential and deep dielectric discharge probability at GEO (geosynchronous-Earth orbit) using models built with the statistics of the SCATHA spacecraft. It approximates the

† ESD initiates when the potential between two parts of a spacecraft increases and a sparking potential is reached. Paschen discharge is the sparking potential between two electrodes (or oppositely charged surfaces) in a gas. The sparking potential is a product of the gas pressure and the distance between the electrodes. Arcing is ESD that occurs on a short time scale.

electron-flux distribution during a substorm by summing a cold and a hot Maxwellian distribution. The cold component can have a density of 0.2 cm^{-3} and a temperature of 0.4 keV; the hot component can have a density of about 2.3 cm^{-3} and a temperature of 25 keV. It is the hot component from the magnetosphere plasma sheet that can place additional charge on spacecraft surfaces in GEO, which can then result in surface charging events.

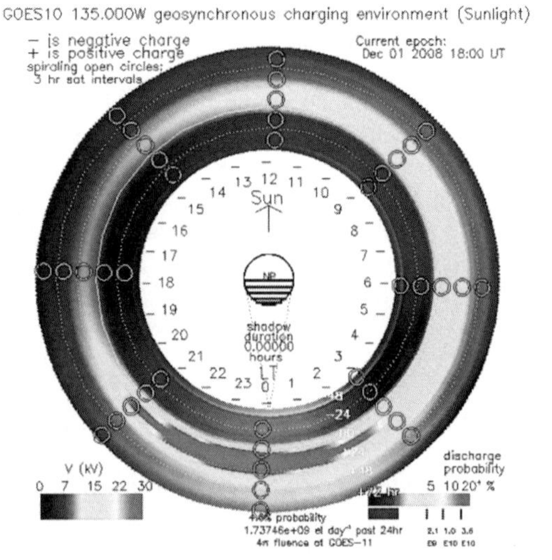

Fig. 7-8. The GEO Alert and Prediction System, GAPS [2011]. Surface Charging Potential and Deep Dielectric Discharge Probability for the GOES-10 Spacecraft on Dec. 1, 2008. The 3-hour Ap is correlated with the SCATHA measurements to provide estimates of the surface charging. The GOES 0.6 MeV electron densities are correlated with deep dielectric anomalies and provide an estimate of deep dielectric discharge probability.

The Fig. 7-8 plot shows the current epoch, real-time electron flux at the GOES satellite position, which is used as an indicator of the general level of electron flux for all GEO spacecraft. This north pole view of the GEO environment shows the local time along the GEO orbit. The inner ring is the –48 hour history of the potential, the solid white ring is the current epoch, and the outermost ring is the +72 hour forecast of the potential for spacecraft surfaces in GEO. Electron fluxes producing a potential of greater than 20 keV can result in increased surface charging events. Design considerations for spacecraft desire to keep the differential charging caused by this plasma well below breakdown potentials, or use materials that can tolerate the electrostatic discharges. GEO spacecraft design considerations for surface charging are detailed in NASA TP 2361 [Purvis et al., 1984].

Design guidelines are available to help reduce differential potentials on vehicle surfaces [Purvis et al., 1984]. For example, we can select candidate materials and conductive coatings, apply numerical or analytical models using their quantifiable characteristics, and determine their differential potentials in space. If one cannot prevent discharges by selecting alternative materials, it is useful to consider alternatives such as special filtering, cabling, or grounding. One can employ coupling models for electromagnetic interference simulation, and test the vehicle for electrostatic discharges in its flight configuration. It is important to note that while differential charging as discussed here is not seen in lower equatorial orbits, the spacecraft potential may be as much as 90% of the solar array voltage more negative than that of the surrounding plasma, depending on the configuration of the spacecraft electrical power supply. This may be a concern on scientific missions, where nonbiased measurements of the plasma environment are desired, and it may also give rise to arcing or other undesirable effects if high voltage power supplies are used [Tribble, 1995].

7.3 Radiation Belts

W. Kent Tobiska,
Space Environment Technologies
Nicola Sarzi-Amade, *Microcosm*

The *Van Allen radiation belts* are a permanent hazard to spacecraft. They consist of electrons and ions (mostly protons) having energies greater than 30 keV and distributed non-uniformly within the magnetosphere. As shown in Fig. 7-9, the energetic electrons preferentially populate a pair of toroidal regions centered on the magnetic shells $L \sim 1.3$ (inner zone) and $L \sim 5$ (outer zone).

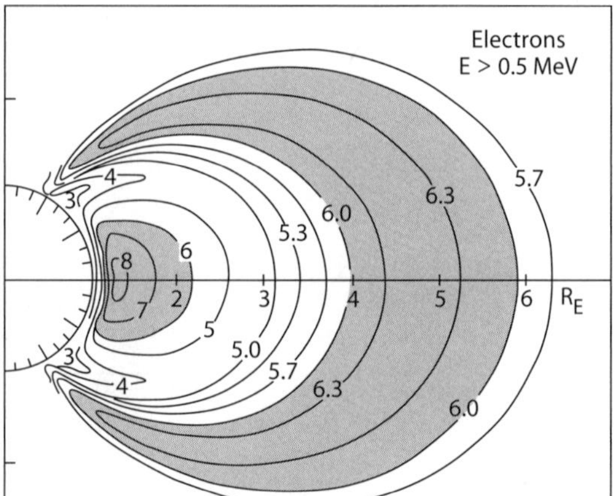

Fig. 7-9. Electron Belts of the Inner and Outer Zones. The numbers on the contours represent the $\log_{10}$ of the integral omnidirectional flux in units of particles $cm^{-2}s^{-1}$. The horizontal axis is the magnetic equator marked in units of Earth radii. Only electrons with energies above 0.5 MeV are included. Adapted from Vette et al., [1966] by Schultz and Lanserotti [1974].

A *magnetic L-shell* is the surface generated by rotating a magnetic field line around the dipole axis. It approximately satisfies the equation

$$R = L \cos^2 \lambda \tag{7-1}$$

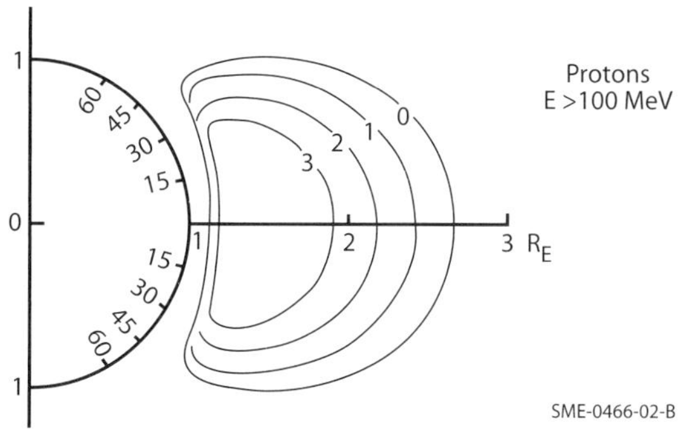

Fig. 7-10. High-Energy Protons in the Inner Zone. Axes and units are the same as on Fig. 7-9. (Note a somewhat different scale.) Data is the omnidirectional flux from the AP8MIN model. Only protons with energies above 100 MeV are considered.

where R is the distance in Earth radii from the idealized point dipole near the Earth's center, and λ is the magnetic latitude. Thus, the L value of a dipolar magnetic shell is its equatorial radius measured in Earth radii. A generalized concept of L, introduced by McIlwain [1961], takes account of the way higher harmonics of the main geomagnetic field perturb the motion of charged particles from their dipolar trajectories. Normally, one uses this concept instead of the dipole L value for mapping the trapped radiation environment. Standard models of the Van Allen belts are available from the National Space Science Data Center. The legacy model, which provides inner zone (L = 1.2–2.4) electron data is AE8, which has an average energy range of 40 keV to 5 MeV [Bilitza et al., 1988]. AE8 has two forms, AE8MIN and AE8MAX, which represent the time-averaged environments during solar minimum and maximum.

Outer-zone electron fluxes vary much more over time than inner-zone fluxes. Indeed, during a major magnetic storm, the equatorial intensity at a given energy and L value may grow by several orders of magnitude in less than a day. Between storms, such flux enhancements usually decay exponentially with an energy-dependent lifetime $\tau \sim 10$ E days at $L > 3$, where E is energy (MeV).

Available proton models are AP8MIN and AP8MAX, which also represent the solar minimum and maximum periods. At solar maximum, the increased atmospheric densities decrease the proton fluxes because the trapped protons collide with the atmosphere at low altitudes. The AP8 models cover the energy range from 100 keV to > 400 MeV. Figure 7-10 shows some of AP8MIN's typical contours for proton fluxes in (R, λ) space. Since the MIN model predicts slightly more flux than the MAX model, it can be used during solar maximum or as a conservative model for long-term missions.

New models for electrons (AE9) and protons (AP9) are in beta-testing with an anticipated release in 2011. Using the energetic proton models (e.g., AP8) is difficult because they are organized in terms of B (local magnetic field intensity) and L. Secular variations in the Earth's magnetic field drive the normally stable energetic protons toward lower altitudes and the models do not take this into account. Thus, if we project the magnetic field more than 10–15 years into the future, our calculations will be invalid for low-altitude orbits [Konradi and Hardy, 1987]. The present and future configurations of the inner-zone proton belt probably will not differ much, provided both are described in terms of L and λ.

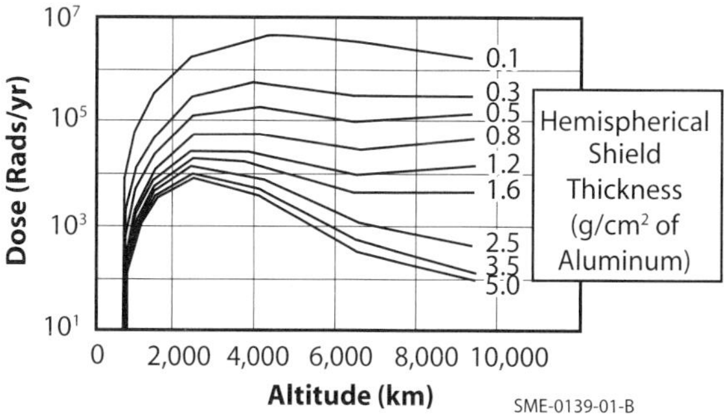

Fig. 7-11. Radiation Dose Rates as a Function of Altitude for Low-Altitude Polar Orbits. Dose rates are shown for several shielding depths.

One can determine the appropriate amount of shielding for future spacecraft by computing the dose rate for the desired orbit as a function of shield thickness. To do so, we must apply a radiation transport computation to the time-averaged space environment. Figure 7-11 shows how various shielding depths affect radiation doses in low-altitude polar orbits. Figure 7-12 shows results for geosynchronous satellites. A *rad* is that amount of radiation which deposits 100 ergs ($= 6.25 \times 10^7$ MeV) per gram of target material (100 mils of aluminum is equivalent to 0.686 g cm^{-2}). The *total radiation dose* consists of three components: proton dose, electron dose and *bremsstrahlung X-ray dose* produced by the interaction of electrons with the shielding material. In low-Earth orbits, energetic protons in the inner radiation belt contribute most to the total radiation dose. Radiation dose strongly depends on altitude; below 1,000 km the dose increases at approximately the 5th power of the altitude. At geosynchronous altitude the greater than 5 MeV proton dose is negligible and the bremsstrahlung dose dominates the electron dose for shield thicknesses greater than 1 cm.

Figure 7-12 illustrates that protons trapped near a geosynchronous orbit do not have enough energy to penetrate 10 mils of aluminum. Nevertheless, many trapped protons and heavier ions in this region of space have energies around 10–200 keV. These lower-energy ions can harm space systems differently than penetrating radiation. By depositing their energy in the spacecraft skin, the lower-energy ions can cause a temperature rise sufficient to significantly enhance the infrared background. Heat loads of up to 0.5 Wm^{-2} are possible. These same low-energy ions can degrade the effectiveness of paints and protective glass by breaking chemical bonds in their surface layers. Unfortunately, we cannot shield against these effects.

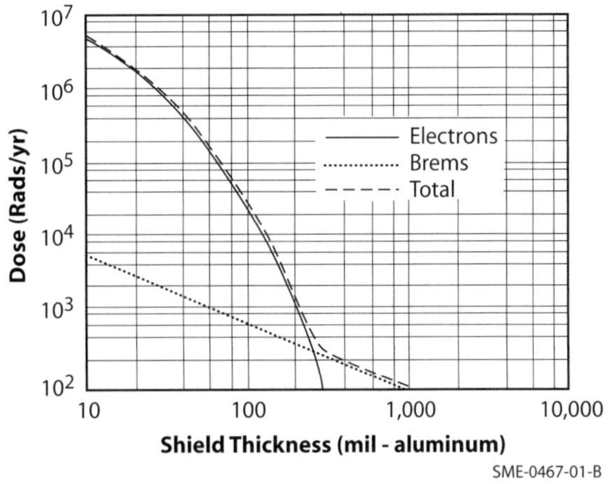

Fig. 7-12. Radiation Dose Rate in Geosynchronous Equatorial Orbit for Various Shield Thicknesses.

Solar Particle Events

Solar particle events (SPEs) occur in association with solar flares. SPEs are rapid increases in the flux of energetic particles (~1 MeV to above 1 GeV) lasting from several hours to several days. On the average, only a few SPEs occur per year; however, they have important consequences for space systems and for humans in space. For example, they degrade solar array elements, increase background noise in many types of electro-optical sensors, and cause illnesses in astronauts.

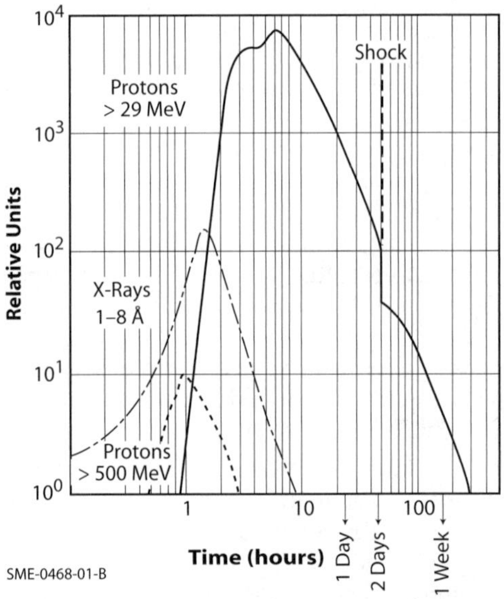

Fig. 7-13. Typical Time Evolution of a Solar Particle Event Observed on Earth.

Figure 7-13 shows the typical evolution over time of a solar particle event observed near Earth. The profile of a solar particle event depends on the time evolution of the originating solar flare, how long the energetic particles take to diffuse within the solar corona and how the particles propagate within the interplanetary medium. Protons of relativistic energies arrive at Earth within minutes after the flare's occurrence. Lower energy (~10's of MeV) protons are slowed by diffusion within the solar corona and by interactions with the interplanetary medium. After a solar particle event occurs, proton fluxes decay to background noise values over several days. The practical importance of an individual event depends on its maximum intensity, its duration, and the relative abundance of the highest-energy components and heavy nuclei.

The frequency of proton events peaks within a year or two of sunspot maximum and diminishes greatly during the few years surrounding sunspot minimum. Nevertheless, intense events can occur virtually any time within the solar cycle except at solar minimum.

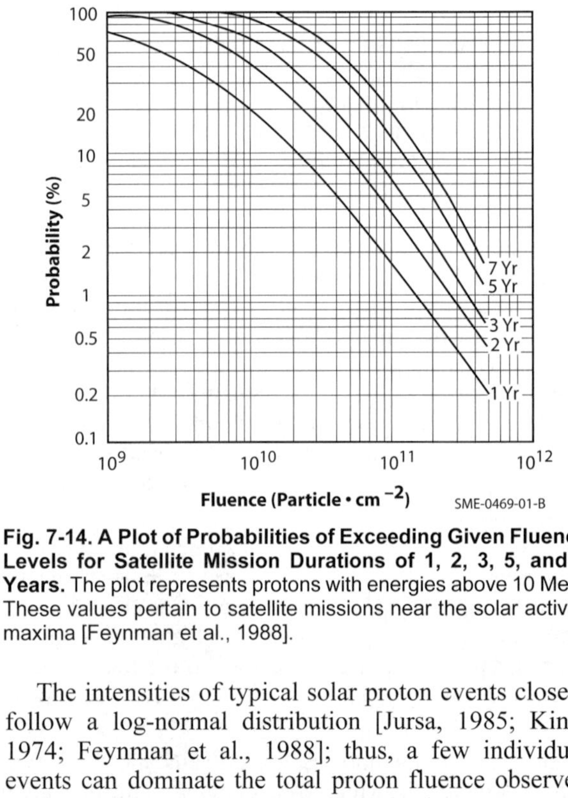

Fig. 7-14. A Plot of Probabilities of Exceeding Given Fluence Levels for Satellite Mission Durations of 1, 2, 3, 5, and 7 Years. The plot represents protons with energies above 10 MeV. These values pertain to satellite missions near the solar activity maxima [Feynman et al., 1988].

The intensities of typical solar proton events closely follow a log-normal distribution [Jursa, 1985; King, 1974; Feynman et al., 1988]; thus, a few individual events can dominate the total proton fluence observed over a complete solar cycle. A typical solar proton event above 10 MeV has a fluence of $10^{8.27}$ cm^{-2}, whereas an extreme (3σ) event would contribute $10^{(8.27 + 3 \times 0.59)}$ cm$^{-2} \approx 1.1 \times 10^{10}$ cm^{-2}. Figure 7-14 shows the probability of the proton fluence (energy >10 MeV) exceeding a given value over time intervals of 1–7 years (typical of the durations of many satellite missions). Solar array outputs typically degrade by a few percent following exposure to fluences above ~10^9 cm^{-2} at energies over ~1 MeV, but actual degradation rates depend on cell type, cover glass thickness, and cell age.

Galactic Cosmic Rays

Galactic cosmic rays (GCR) are particles which reach the vicinity of the Earth from outside the Solar System. The number and type of nuclei in these particles are pro-

Table 7-0, Fig. 7-14, Eq. 7-1◀

portional to those in Solar System material. Cosmic rays pose a serious hazard because a single particle can cause a malfunction in common electronic components such as random access memory, microprocessors, and hexfet power transistors. When a single passing particle causes this malfunction, we call radiation effects *single-event phenomena,* or *SEP.*

A galactic cosmic ray loses energy mainly by ionization. This energy loss depends chiefly on the square of the particle's charge, Z, and can be increased if the particle undergoes nuclear interactions within an electronic part. Thus, the lower-Z (and more abundant) ions deposit as much energy in a device as the less abundant, higher-Z ions. When the galactic cosmic ray generates electron-hole pairs (i.e., excited electrons that move to a higher energy state) in a depletion (i.e., insulating) region of an electronic device, the electric field in that region sweeps away the pairs [Vampola, 1996].

Single-event phenomena include three different effects in electronic components. The first is the so-called *bitflip,* or *single-event upset (SEU),* which neither damages the part nor interferes with its subsequent operation. The second is *single-event latchup (SEL).* In this case, the part hangs up, draws excessive current, and will no longer operate until the power to the device is turned off and then back on. The excessive current drawn in the latched condition can destroy the device if the power supply cannot handle the current. When latchup demands too much current for the power supply, it may drag down the bus voltage, or even damage the supply. The third effect is *single-event burnout (SEB).* This causes the device to fail permanently.

The frequency of single-event phenomena for a given part depends on three things: the external environment; how the incident energy spectrum and particle intensity change as a particle passes through the spacecraft to the sensitive device; and how the electronic device responds to ionizing radiation. These are difficult to evaluate because of the complex interactions between the radiation environment and the device's circuit elements. On-orbit failure rates can be predicted primarily for single-event upsets in memory devices, with well-defined sensitive volumes, in which the galactic cosmic rays produce electron-hole pairs. A useful equation developed by Petersen [1995] expresses the upset rate R as follows:

$$R = 200\ \sigma_L / L^2_{0.25} \tag{7-2}$$

where R is the number of upsets or errors per bit day, σ_L is the limiting cross section (sensitive area) of the device in cm^2, and $L_{0.25}$ is the *linear energy transfer* (LET) at 25% of the limiting cross section in units of MeV mg^{-1} cm^{-2}. If experimental cross section data is not available, but device modeling data is, then geometric data can be used in conjunction with the predicted critical charge, and now

$$R = 2 \times 10^{-10}\ abc^2 / Q_c^2 \tag{7-3}$$

where R is the number of errors per bit day, a and b are device surface dimensions in mm, c is the device depth in mm, and Q_c is the critical charge in pC. These two equations have been shown to predict upset rates in the geosynchronous orbit for solar minimum conditions with reasonable accuracy. Scale factors for estimating error rates for other orbits and other calculation methods may be found in Petersen [1995].

Single-event upset rates in complex devices such as microprocessors, or single-event latchups or burnouts in any devices, cannot be reliably predicted. One must resort to predictions based on simulated accelerator test observations and flight performance of similar devices.

Galactic cosmic rays can also generate background noise in various satellite subsystems such as star sensors, infrared detectors, and components employing charge-coupled devices. In addition to increased noise signals, these rays create spurious events, which can masquerade as real signals. The spurious signals can affect satellite subsystems depending on the genuine signals' frequency of occurrence, time duration, and repetition, as well as the sophistication of the sensor system. Galactic cosmic rays are a potential source of background noise, which must be taken into account when designing a satellite system.

7.4 Microgravity

James R. Wertz, *Microcosm, Inc./USC*

Microgravity, also called *zero-g, weightlessness,* or *free fall,* is the nearly complete absence of any of the effects of gravity. In the microgravity environment in space objects don't fall, bubbles don't rise, particles don't settle out of solution, and convection currents don't occur. Yet in low-Earth orbit, where all of these things happen, the gravitational force is about 90% of its value at the Earth's surface. Indeed, it is the Earth's gravitational field that keeps the satellite in its orbit.

In space, microgravity comes about because a satellite is in *free fall*—i.e., it is continuously falling through space and all of the parts of a satellite are falling together. In a circular orbit the forward velocity of the satellite (perpendicular to the direction to the Earth) is just enough that the continual falling of the satellite toward the Earth keeps it at the same distance from the Earth's center. Moving in a circular orbit requires a continuous acceleration toward the center, just as does twirling a rock tied to a string.

The term "microgravity" is used in the space environment because, in practice, zero gravity cannot actually be achieved. Two objects traveling very near each other in orbit will not travel in quite the same path due to differences in the gravitational forces or external nongravitational forces acting on them. Two objects held side by side and dropped from a tall building will both accelerate toward the center of the Earth and, as they fall, will converge slightly toward each other. From the point of view

Table 7-1. Equations for Microgravity Level. ω is the orbital angular velocity. $\omega_{LEO} = (\mu/a^3)^{1/2} = 0.061$ deg/sec, assuming spacecraft at 475 km. *x, y,* and *z* are the distances from the spacecraft center of mass.

Source	x direction (velocity)	y direction (orbit normal)	z direction (nadir)
Aerodynamic Drag	$\ddot{x} = -0.5(C_D A/m)\rho a^2 \omega^2$	$\ddot{y} = 0$	$\ddot{z} = 0$
Gravity Gradient	$\ddot{x} = -x\omega^2$	$\ddot{y} = -y\omega^2$	$\ddot{z} = 2z\omega^2$
Centrifugal (due to spacecraft rotation in inertial frame)	$\ddot{x} = x\omega^2$	$\ddot{y} = 0$	$\ddot{z} = z\omega^2$
Sinusoidal Vibration Along X Axis of Frequency f and Amplitude A	$\ddot{x} = A(2\pi f)^2$	—	—
Coriolis Force from Material Moving in the Spacecraft Frame	$\ddot{x} = 2\dot{z}\omega$	$\ddot{y} = 0$	$\ddot{z} = -2\dot{x}\omega$

of the objects, there is a small component of Earth gravity that pulls them toward each other. An orbiting spacecraft under the influence of atmospheric drag or solar radiation pressure will feel a very small force due to this external pressure. This force can mimic the effect of gravity, causing heavy particles in solution to settle toward the front end of a spacecraft under the influence of atmospheric drag, just as loose cargo in a car appears to be "pulled" toward the front when the car suddenly brakes. Similarly, a rotating spacecraft produces "artificial gravity" due to centrifugal force. Finally, *tidal forces,* sometimes called *gravity-gradient* forces, come about because of very small differences in the force of gravity over an extended object. For a spherical bubble drifting in orbit, the force of gravity on the lower edge of the bubble will be stronger than at the center of mass and weaker at the far edge of the bubble. This very small difference in forces results in "tides" which will distort the shape of the bubble and elongate it toward and away from the direction to the Earth.

For most practical applications, microgravity effects in low-Earth orbit can be reduced to the level of 10^{-6} g (= 1 μg). A level of 10^{-7} g can be achieved over a very small region near the center of mass of the spacecraft. Table 7-1 provides formulas for the most common forces in the microgravity environment. In this table, z is the direction toward nadir and $\ddot{z}$ is the acceleration in the nadir direction. ω is the angular velocity of the satellite in its orbit. Note that for a nadir-pointing spacecraft, the spacecraft rotates in inertial space at a rate of one rotation per orbit and thus adds to the acceleration environment due to the centrifugal force of this rotation. In low-Earth orbit, the lowest microgravity level can be achieved in an inertially-oriented spacecraft rather than a nadir-oriented spacecraft. The last row in Table 7-1 is the *coriolis force* which is an apparent sidewise force that occurs whenever objects move (e.g., fluid flow in a tube) in a rotating reference frame, such as a nadir-oriented spacecraft.

Table 7-2 uses the formulas in the previous table to compute the conditions under which 1 μg is achieved. This gives an idea of the scale over which specific microgravity values can be obtained. Microgravity levels could be substantially lowered by conducting microgravity experiments well away from the vicinity of the Earth or other massive objects.

Microgravity leads to a wide variety of chemical and manufacturing processes that cannot occur on the surface of the Earth. Heavier particles in a solution do not settle out and bubbles do not rise to the surface. This allows uniform, universal mixing and permits chemical reactions to occur that could not occur on Earth because settling would hinder completion of the reaction or hardening of the material. Surface tension and other inter-molecular forces can take over that would otherwise be dominated by settling due to gravity. Similarly, convection does not occur in space and heated materials do not churn or boil. This allows differential heating to take place to provide other chemical reactions. Because settling does not occur, very large crystals can be formed in space which have a variety of industrial applications.

Table 7-2. Microgravity Levels. Each entry gives the conditions under which a microgravity level of 1 μg will be achieved, assuming a gravity-gradient stabilized spacecraft at 700 km. CM = Center of Mass.

Source	x direction	y direction	z direction
Aerodynamic Drag	Altitude of 360 km at solar max, 260 km at solar min for $m/C_D A = 65$ kg/m^2	—	—
Gravity Gradient	7.3 m from CM	7.3 m from CM	3.6 m from CM
Centrifugal	7.3 m from CM	—	7.3 m from CM
Sinusoidal Vibration	$A = 2 \times 10^{-9}$ m at 10 Hz	—	—
Coriolis Force	$\dot{z} = 4.6$ mm/s	—	$\dot{x} = -4.6$ mm/s

Table 7-2, Fig. 7-14◀, Eq. 7-3◀

Containerless processing and working in the vacuum of space can lead to extremely pure chemicals for use in both pharmaceuticals and manufacturing. Microgravity has a wide variety of applications that are only beginning to be explored and exploited.

7.5 Orbital Debris—A Space Hazard

David B. Spencer, *Pennsylvania State University*
Ronald A. Madler, *Embry-Riddle University*

Orbital debris is any non-operational object in orbit. This can be further broken down between *naturally occurring debris* (e.g. micrometeoroids, asteroid particles) and *human-generated debris* from both normal and abnormal spacecraft operations. As an object is launched into orbit, each launch creates payloads, rocket bodies, and mission-related debris. *Mission-related debris* includes: large trackable objects, such as fairings and interstage adapters; small trackable objects, such as Ed White's glove from Gemini 4; and small debris not detectable from the Earth, such as explosive bolt fragments and lens caps [Johnson and McKnight, 1987].

The high expected collision velocity between orbiting objects is one reason to be concerned about space debris. Another is that we cannot detect, much less track and predict an orbit for objects smaller than approximately 10 cm for LEO (about the size of a softball) and 1 meter for GEO. The United States Space Command (USSPACECOM) is tracking over 15,000 objects by late 2010 through its Space Surveillance Network (SSN), a job for which it was not originally intended. This secondary mission of the worldwide network of radar, optical and data processing facilities is to track, identify, and catalog data on the largest orbiting objects. Although many of these objects may not seriously threaten space operations, it is known that a significantly larger number of untrackable objects smaller than 10 cm exist in low-Earth orbit as a result of satellite breakups and operational practices. Because these objects can't be effectively tracked, they can't be avoided by maneuvering. These fragments will threaten spacecraft for tens, hundreds, and even thousands of years. The GEO region is of special concern because it has no natural mechanism that removes debris. Nevertheless, various scientific and space operations organizations (such as NASA, the Air Force, ESA (European Space Agency), and the Russian Space Agency) have been collecting statistical data on untrackable, yet detectable, objects since the early 1990s to aid the modeling of the debris environment and the sources of debris.

All the man-made orbital material in space has come from human activity, so the orbital debris issue is really about how that mass is distributed and managed (i.e., distribution of objects and their orbits). We can quantify how crowded space has become by using the *spatial density,* i.e., the number of objects per volume of space. Figure 7-15a estimates the spatial density of objects in LEO and GEO as a function of altitude for January 2011,

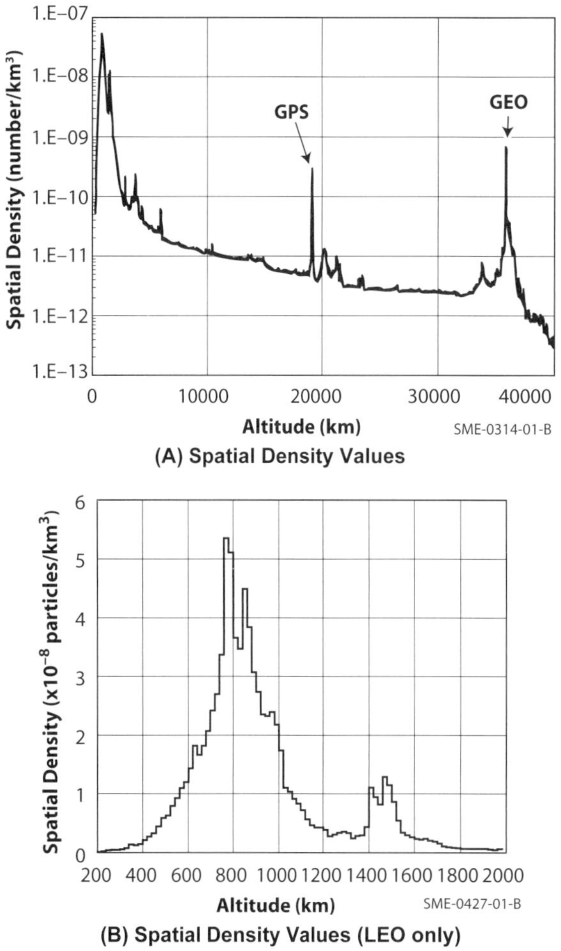

Fig. 7-15. (A) Spatial Density Values of All Catalogued Objects for January 2011, (B) Spatial Density Values of All Catalogued Objects for January 2011 (LEO Only). Densities in GEO are approximately 10 times less than in LEO. The probability of a spacecraft getting hit by something big is small, while the chance of getting hit by something small is big. See text for discussion. [Courtesy of Orbital Debris Program Office, NASA/JSC.]

while Fig. 7-15b zooms into the lower altitude region. The GEO data represents the spatial density within 1 deg of the equatorial plane. The smallest trackable objects may weigh tens to hundreds of grams. We cannot shield against objects of this size. In GEO the average spatial density is one to two orders of magnitude less than LEO. The **average** relative velocity in LEO between orbiting objects is 9 to 10 km/s with maximum values above 14 km/s due to eccentric and retrograde orbits. In comparison, the relative velocity between debris and satellites in GEO ranges between almost nothing (coplanar objects moving in the same direction) to 2.5 km/s (objects with significant different inclination/right ascension combinations). The distribution of objects around the geosynchronous band is grouped by inclination in Fig. 7-16. Note that most objects are in nearly equatorial orbits, although a few objects are inclined by

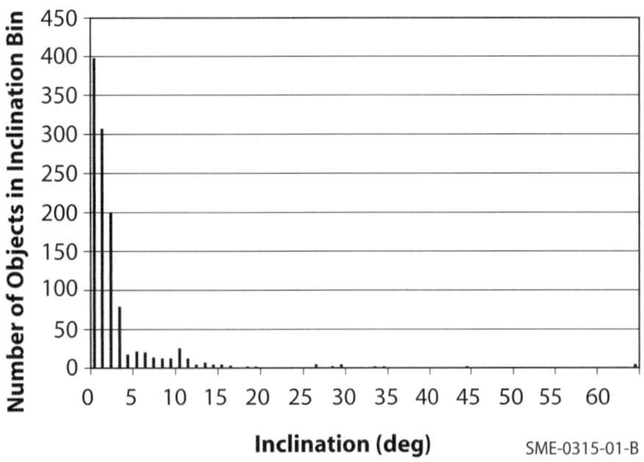

Fig. 7-16. Inclination Distribution of Objects Near the Geosynchronous Belt (as of 1/1/11).

as much as 64°. The difference in relative velocities is due mainly to the lower orbital velocities and smaller inclination distribution of objects in GEO. The key to understanding the damaging effects of a debris impact is understanding the kinetic energy. For example, a 1 kg object impacting something at 10 km/s has the equivalent energy of 25 sticks of dynamite. A Ferrari traveling at 200 mph has the equivalent kinetic energy of a 1.5 kg object moving at 3 km/s. This kinetic energy comparison, coupled with the lower spatial density values in GEO, make the collision hazard much smaller in GEO than LEO.

Note that the LEO density is averaged over all latitudes and that the true density varies with latitude because space objects have various inclinations. Over time, the spatial densities and flux rates will change due to natural decay (see Sec. 9.4.4), new launches, and fragmentation. Presently the only sink for objects in LEO is natural decay, which is dependent on altitude and solar activity as shown in Figs. 9-15 and 9-19, with the exception of controlled reentry of satellites. End-of-life burns are becoming a common removal mechanism for controllable objects in orbit, such as the controlled reentry over the Pacific Ocean of the Russian Mir space station).

Get Stnd For NASA missions, the NASA Safety Standard [NASA, 2007], requires end-of-life maneuvers that result in reentry within 25 years or objects being "reorbited" out of the high traffic orbital regimes, including LEO, GEO, and semisynchronous orbit, but no more than 30 years after launch. Many other spacecraft operators have similar practices. Chapter 30 provides further discussion on the end-of-life process.

7.5.1 Orbital Debris Environment

Meteoroids and orbital debris are now well recognized as a potential hazard to spacecraft. This is largely due to recent fragmentations in low-Earth orbit and the resulting media coverage. Debris awareness during mission design and operations is necessary for mission success and also to lower the risk to present and future spacecraft. An early example of the design implications of orbital debris was the RADARSAT program, where concerns about meteoroids and orbital debris caused the program to add 17 kg of shielding to increase their probability of success from 50% to 87% over the five year mission [NRC, 1995]. In addition to debris impact hazards, end-of-life satellite disposal requirements may be a driving requirement in mission design. Taking into account debris hazard and mitigation requirements early in the design process will allow for a more robust mission design and lessen the risk due to orbital debris. This section will provide a brief overview of the orbital debris environment as well as the implications of orbital debris for mission and spacecraft design. Table 7-3 provides a summary of the process for determining the mission impacts due to debris.

Table 7-3. Mission Design Considerations for Orbital Debris.

Step	Notes
Define Operational Regime	LEO, MEO and GEO will have very different environments, concerns and requirements.
Define Applicable Policies	US Government, commercial, and international vehicles fall under different regulatory regimes.
Determine Applicable Models	Programs may have defined or preferred environment models and procedures depending upon customer and policies.
Review Resources	Extensive resources are available from national and international members of the Interagency Debris Committee. Many references are publicly available.
Determine Hazard and Policy Compliance	
Lessons Learned	Several papers discuss lessons learned by satellite operators.

The hazard due to the natural environment was foreseen as early as the 1940s due to the high expected collision velocity. Meteoroid impact speeds can average about 20 km/s but can be as high as 70 km/s. At these speeds even small particles have high kinetic energies and can thus cause significant damage.† While these particles are not trackable, they can cause a cumulative degradation of surfaces of a spacecraft, which may require additional protection to be designed into the spacecraft.

Over the full spectrum of sizes of orbital debris, collision hazards have varying effects on the spacecraft. This hypervelocity‡ impact damage can range from surface erosion and degradation to damage of mission-critical systems or breakup of the spacecraft. Small impacts on a spacecraft may not even be noticeable unless the space-

† A 1 mm meteoroid at 20 km/s has as much kinetic energy as a person swinging a baseball bat.

‡ A hypervelocity impact is defined as having a higher impact velocity than the speed of the shockwave through the object being hit.

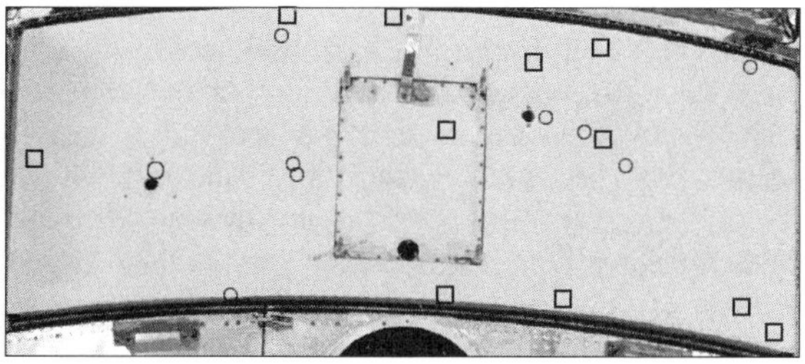

Fig. 7-17. Small Particle Impacts on Radiator on Hubble Space Telescope. Circles indicate impacts identified from the 2002 servicing mission, while squares identify new impacts observed during the post-mission inspections, (Courtesy Orbital Debris Program Office, NASA/JSC.)

craft is recovered. A visual examination of the Hubble Space Telescope, as seen in Fig. 7-17, shows small impacts that occurred during 16 years of exposure. None of these impacts affected the performance of the telescope and it is likely that they would have gone unnoticed had a close visual examination not been conducted. However, it was purely by chance that these impacts occurred in non-critical areas—had an impact occurred at a critical location, performance could have been affected.

The first confirmed on-orbit collision between two tracked objects occurred in 1996 between the Cerise satellite and a piece of debris [Alby et al. 1997]. This impact separated the gravity gradient boom from the spacecraft. A more recent collision between IRIDIUM 33 and COSMOS 2251 destroyed both spacecraft and is an example of a catastrophic impact that has left many large objects and an unknown amount of untrackable debris still in orbit such that the remaining debris will pose a hazard for many years to come [ODQN, 2009]. As of 2010, 203 satellite fragmentations and collisions have generated a large growth of debris and create an additional hazard for space missions [Liou, 2010]. An international awareness has developed of the long-term impact of fragmentations and mission operations on mission hazard, which has led to debris mitigation guidelines that have been accepted by most spacefaring nations.

It is important for space mission designers to assess the impact of their design on the space environment early in the design process. Figure 7-18 outlines the lifecycle of a space mission. There are several phases of a space mission where orbital debris issues need to be addressed. During the launch phase, launch vehicles are delivering payloads to their operational orbits. During this phase, the system is subject to potential collision hazards with existing orbital objects. During satellite operations, assessments of the hazard to the space environment from the spacecraft and hazards to the spacecraft from the space environment should be made. Lastly, at the end-of-life of the mission, considerations as to disposal options should be addressed. Each of these steps should be analyzed in context with any national, international or satellite owner/operator debris mitigation guidelines. Should the designs not meet the desired debris environmental effects, the designer iterates the design until a satisfactory solution is found. At the present time, there are not universal debris mitigation regulations, only guidelines, and it is in the best interest of the satellite operator to operate a "clean" spacecraft, as the spacecraft is subject to self-induced hazards. Additionally, many satellite operators use the same orbit for replenishment, so it is in their best interest to minimize the effects of decommissioned spacecraft on their replacements.

Small natural objects in space are known as *meteoroids* and are in orbit around the Sun. Meteoroids are composed mainly of debris from comets and asteroids and are continually passing through space. Having various sources, meteoroids consist of a variety of materials with densities ranging from 0.2 to 8 g/cm^3. Average values of 2 g/cm^3, 1 g/cm^3, and 0.5 g/cm^3 for masses less than 10^{-6} g, between 10^{-6} and 0.01 g and above 0.01 g, respectively, have been recommended [Anderson, 1994 and NASA, 1991]. The meteoroid environment is usually expressed in terms of an average flux of objects per area per unit time. The actual meteoroid flux consists of sporadic meteoroids and streams of meteoroids. The former have no identifiable parent object or pattern; the latter have a common parent object and orbit. Streams typically occur whenever the Earth encounters debris along the orbital path of a comet. Occasionally, the Earth will pass through an especially dense region of a natural debris stream, causing meteor storms which may threaten spacecraft operations. The risk from storm particles over several hours can match that of the background meteoroid environment for a year. Meteoroid models generally do not take meteor storms into account although some do, but manned missions presently do consider this threat.

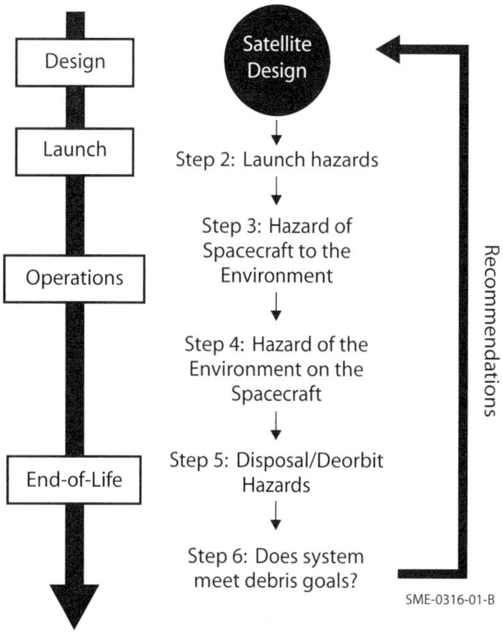

Fig. 7-18. Satellite Design Lifecycle for Orbital Debris Assessment.

Table 7-3◀, Fig. 7-18, Eq. 7-3◀

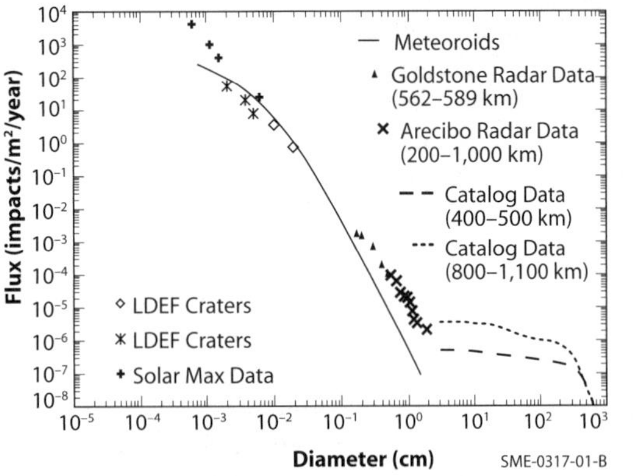

Fig. 7-19. Comparison of the Fluxes of Meteoroids and Orbital Debris for Low Altitude Orbits (adapted from the NRC, 1995). This figure shows that human-generated orbital debris has much higher impact rates than meteoroids for large and small debris diameters.

The flux of meteoroids is less than the flux of orbital debris in LEO for most sizes, but is on the same order as man-made debris between 0.001 and 0.1 cm. Figure 7-19 compares the fluxes of meteoroids and orbital debris. Meteoroid hazard becomes comparable to the hazard due to man-made orbital debris at about 1 mm in size, yet can damage unprotected surfaces due to the high relative velocities. As meteoroids come in close proximity to the Earth (especially in close proximity to where satellites fly), they pose a collision hazard. Estimates put the amount of meteoroids entering the Earth's atmosphere between 20,000 and 60,000 metric tons of material per year [Love and Brownlee, 1993]. Most of these meteoroids are small and light and rarely are recovered. An advantage of meteoroids over man-made orbital debris is that individual objects are not in orbit around the Earth, so that individual particles are a hazard for only a very short time. However, the average velocity of a meteoroid is about 17 km/s [Kessler, 1969], which means that the amount of kinetic energy involved in a collision with a natural object is substantially greater than a collision with a man-made object, but the duration of this risk is longer for man-made objects.

Computer models have been developed over the years to model the natural environment. One of the more widely used models was created by Grün et al [1985]. In this empirical model, they estimate the flux of natural debris at 1 AU. Grün's empirical micrometeoroid flux model for a given size particle, m, is based on in situ measurements, and has the form

$$F_1(m,r_0)=(c_1m^{\gamma_1}+c_2m^{\gamma_2}+c_3)^{\gamma_3}+(c_4m^{\gamma_4}+c_5)^{\gamma_5}$$

where $r_0 = 1AU$ and the constants, $c_1 = 4\times10^{29}$,

$c_2 = 1.5\times10^{44}, c_3 = 1.1\times10^{-2}, c_4 = 2.2\times10^{3}, c_5 = 15$

and the exponents,

$$\gamma_1 = 1.85, \gamma_2 = 3.7, \gamma_3 = -0.52, \gamma_4 = 0.306, \gamma_5 = -4.38 \tag{7-4}$$

The units on this model are (number/m^{2}s). The terms in the first bracket represent the small particles ($m \le 10^{-10}$ g) and the second part describes the large particle flux. The exponents control the slopes of the particle populations. This model was originally developed for interplanetary space, and is usable for all regions, including the region around Earth's orbit.

While the Grün model provides a model that allows a designer to estimate the meteoroid flux, it does not take into account sporadic meteoroids. NASA has supported development of a new meteoroid environment model (MEM) [Jones, 2004] that identifies sporadic meteoroids from sources such as comets, provides users with accurate fluxes and directionality for spacecraft from 0.2 AU to 2 AU. The model also incorporates observation data and compares that with theoretical models. The computer models are available through NASA's [2011], Meteoroid Environment Office website.

Table 7-4. Space Object Origination (as of October 6, 2010, Cataloged by the US Space Surveillance Network). (Adopted from ODQN—October 2010, Courtesy of NASA/JSC.)

Country or Organization	Payloads	Rocket Bodies & Debris	Total
China	98	3,395	3,493
CIS	1,406	4,600	6,006
ESA	39	44	83
France	49	426	475
India	41	133	174
Japan	113	76	189
USA	1,124	3,701	4,825
Other	479	115	594
TOTAL	3,349	12,490	15,839

The US satellite catalogue is maintained by tracking data from the SSN. As of October 6, 2010, there were 15,839 catalogued objects in Earth orbit. We know that there exists a much larger population of smaller objects. This has been confirmed by many measurement campaigns with more sensitive radars and evaluation of objects returned from space. Studies have shown that there is approximately an order of magnitude more objects in the 1 cm size than what exists in the catalog [OSTP, 1995]. The 1 cm size is significant because it is the largest size fragment that we can effectively shield against. Thus, there are a significant number of objects that we cannot track, but which can cause substantial spacecraft damage [Spencer et al., 2000].

The man-made debris population has become an important satellite operations issue over the past few decades. The increasing utilization of space has created additional risk to satellites from collision. The orbital debris population has been created by all users of space. The contribution to the orbital population broken down by countries and organizations is shown in Table 7-4. This table shows the origins of rocket bodies and debris as well as payloads.

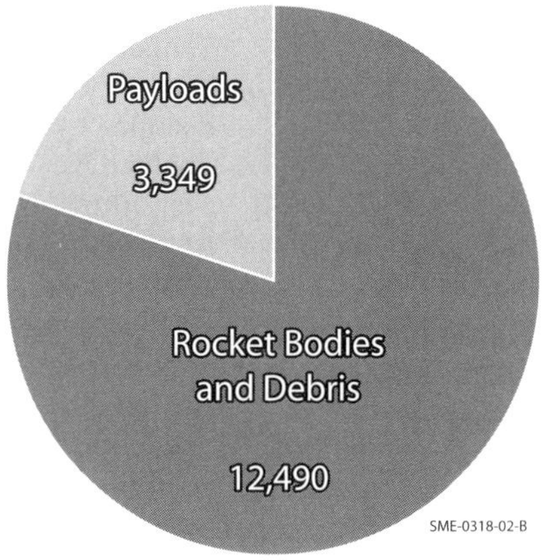

Fig. 7-20. Catalogued Low-Earth Orbit Population.

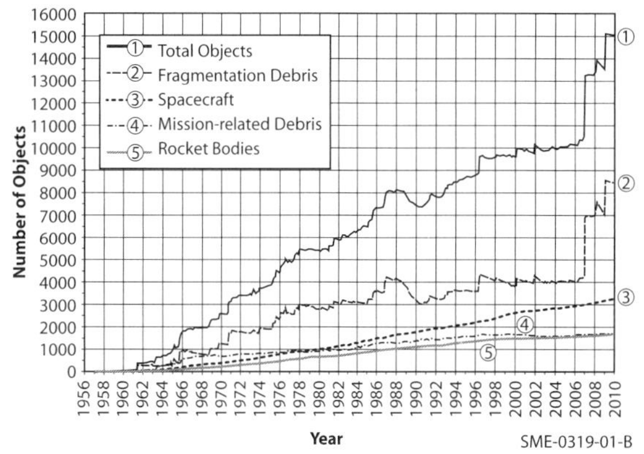

Fig. 7-21. Historical Growth of the Space Population. (Courtesy of Orbital Debris Program Office, NASA/JSC.)

Man-made objects in orbit consists of operational and derelict spacecraft, operational debris, break-up debris and rocket bodies. Derelict spacecraft are intact spacecraft that are no longer functioning. Operational debris includes items that were designed to be released during some phase of operations. Examples of this include lens covers, yo-yo despin devices, and explosive bolt pieces. The break-up debris constitutes the majority of catalogued objects in space, and come from both explosions and collisions. Rocket bodies are the delivery vehicle for spacecraft. As seen in Fig. 7-20, nearly 80% of this population is rocket bodies and debris.

Historically, the orbital population has grown. Figure 7-21 shows this cumulative growth since the beginning of the space age in 1957. Note that the population of active satellites has grown nearly linearly over the past couple of decades. The significant increase in the total population has come from fragmentation debris (break-up events are evident from this figure by identifying step increases in the fragmentation debris curve). At present trends, one theory projects a "runaway" scenario—known as the Kessler syndrome or collisional cascading [Kessler and Cour-Palais, 1978], where the debris from one breakup collides with another satellite and then, debris created, in turn, collides with another satellite, and so on. Concerns as to whether this scenario is plausible is one of the driving factors in managing the space debris environment.

The significant increase in the orbital debris population can be traced back to several fragmentation events. The Orbital Debris Program Office at NASA/JSC has compiled a list of the top 10 fragmentation producing events, and this is shown in Table 7-5. Approximately 1/3 of the orbiting objects in the catalog come from these 10 events.

Spacecraft designers handle the orbital debris environment in various ways. For the very small objects which are untrackable, the spacecraft designers may try to design the spacecraft with sufficient shielding to survive an impact. At the other end of the size spectrum, large objects in space are tracked using two forms of sensors: radar and optical. Geographically spread out radar sites perform the majority of tracking of objects in low Earth orbit. As the altitude increases, optical sensors track more of the objects. In the region in between shielding and tracking there is a vulnerable region where there are on-going efforts to close the gap between what can be shielded against and what can be tracked. Figure 7-22 graphically represents the approximate boundaries between these regions.

Table 7-5. Top 10 Historical Breakups (As of May 2010). (Source: Orbital Debris Quarterly News [July 2010, NASA/JSC])

Common Name	Year of Breakup	Altitude of Breakup	Catalogued Debris	Tracked Debris in Orbit	Cause of Breakup
Fengyun-1C	2007	850 km	2841	2756	Intentional Collision
Cosmos 2251	2009	790 km	1267	1215	Accidental Collision
STEP 2 Rocket Body	1996	625 km	713	63	Accidental Explosion
Iridium 33	2009	790 km	521	498	Accidental Collision
Cosmos 2421	2008	410 km	509	18	Unknown
SPOT 1 Rocket Body	1986	805 km	492	33	Accidental Explosion
OV 2-1/LCS 2 Rocket Body	1965	740 km	473	36	Accidental Explosion
Nimbus 4 Rocket Body	1970	1075 km	374	248	Accidental Explosion
TES Rocket Body	2001	670 km	370	116	Accidental Explosion
CBERS 1 Rocket Body	2000	740 km	343	189	Accidental Explosion
		TOTAL	7903	5172	

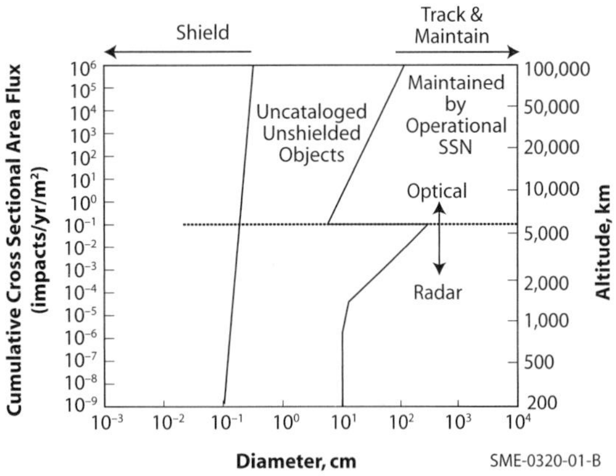

Fig. 7-22. Shielding, Tracking and Cataloguing Thresholds.

To assess the collision risk between a spacecraft and the orbital debris environment, computer models must be employed. There are two types of modeling techniques available: deterministic and stochastic. *Deterministic models* treat orbital debris objects as individual pieces, and examine the close approach possibilities. Many of these deterministic models are limited due to uncertainties in object locations, and, depending on the confidence level in close approach predictions, typically called *conjunctions* or *conjunction events*, spacecraft operators can chose to take a number of actions that range from doing nothing to performing a collision avoidance maneuver. While in the majority of potential collision events a spacecraft operator chooses to do nothing, there are cases where the operators choose to perform a collision avoidance maneuver. Table 7-6 shows collision avoidance maneuvers that were performed in 2009.

Stochastic models, on the other hand, treat the debris environment as a continuum of objects, much like gas particles in an enclosed volume. Here, the concern isn't a distinct object versus another distinct object collision, but a collision between a distinct object and a "cloud" of objects.

Several organizations have developed software that is available for use. The most widely used software packages are those developed by NASA and ESA. As this software is being continually updated, the reader is directed to these agency websites for information on the most up-to-date features.

There are several different categories of software that would be of interest to different technical communities. The spacecraft mission designer would be interested in software to assess the effects of the orbital debris environment on their spacecraft and the effects of their spacecraft on the orbital debris environment. The environment community would be interested in predicting the short-term and long-term behavior of the orbital debris environment. The observation community would be interested in models that convert information about what is observed into information about the current environment. The operations community would be interested in improving methods of predicting close approaches between objects, and reducing the number of false alarms that predict a close approach or a collision.

Many of these modeling efforts have led to international collaboration, and to the development of debris mitigation guidelines. Since the early 1990s, the Inter-agency Space Debris Coordination Committee (IADC) has led the effort to coordinate orbital debris measurements, modeling, protection and mitigation activities underway in various national space agencies. In addition to other organizations, such as the ISO [2010], (International Organization for Standardization), the IADC [2010] has developed debris mitigation guidelines and standards that are being accepted as standard design practices throughout the world [IADC, 2002]. This work has led to the development of United Nations' guidelines on orbital debris mitigation [UN, 2010]. As new technologies become available, these recommended practices and guidelines are continually being updated.

Get Stnd

7.5.2 Implications of Orbital Debris for Orbit and Spacecraft Design

The space mission that has undertaken the most extensive assessment of the effects of the orbital debris environment is the International Space Station (ISS). The ISS has a unique mission both in duration and in

Table 7-6. Collision Avoidance Maneuvers in 2009 (Source: ODQN, Jan. 2010).

Spacecraft	Maneuver Date	Object Avoided
TDRS 3	27 January	Proton rocket body
ISS	22 March	CZ-4 rocket body debris
Cloudsat	23 April	Cosmos 2251 debris
EO-1	11 May	Zenit rocket body debris
ISS	17 July	Proton rocket body debris
Space Shuttle	10 September	ISS debris
PARASOL (France)*	29 September	Fengyun-1C debris
Aqua	25 November	Fengyun-1C debris
Landsat 7	11 December	Formosat 3D
* Operating in NASA-led Earth observation network		

payload. The mission is currently planned to operate until at least 2020 and the payload is the most valuable of cargos—humans. With these two considerations, an extensive assessment of the risk posed to the ISS from the orbital debris environment has been conducted [NRC, 1997]. Orbital debris environment models are used to assess the risk, and determine the collision hazard posed by the orbital debris environment. Small object collision risk can be assessed statistically, while large object collision risk can be assessed deterministically.

Statistical Collision Hazard

The stochastic modeling treats the orbital debris environment as a statistical distribution of particles. We can approximate the probability, P_c, of a piece of debris impacting a space system using the kinetic theory of gases:

$$P_c = 1 - e^{(-SPD \bullet AC \bullet T \bullet VREL)} \tag{7-5}$$

where *SPD* is the spatial density of debris objects (i.e., average number of objects per volume in space), *AC* is the collision cross-sectional area, *T* is the mission duration, and *VREL* is the relative velocity between the satellite and debris population. Detailed analysis should use a more accurate debris environment model (for example, early development of NASA and ESA models can be found in Kessler et al. [1996], and Klinkrad et al. [1997], respectively), as well as a more refined representation of the spacecraft's cross-sectional area. Also space satellite designers must take the meteoroid environment into account. Meteoroids dominate the hazard for sub-millimeter up to millimeter size, and can penetrate thin honeycomb structures and other delicate structures. Debris flux from natural and man-made sources can simply be added together to create a total flux.

NASA's standard orbital debris model uses the yearly averaged flux, *F*, and a reference surface of a randomly rotating plate. Thus, the orbital debris flux, which is a statistical estimate of the debris density, becomes the number of impacted objects per unit surface during a unit of time. The cumulative particle fluence, *N*, on specific spacecraft surfaces can be found by using the "k-factor method" [Anderson, 1994] along with the flux value,

$$N = \int_t^{t+T} \sum_i k_i F A_i \, dt \tag{7-6}$$

where *i* represents each surface of the spacecraft, $k_i F$ is the actual flux on the surface *i,* and A_i is the area of each surface. The Poisson process to calculate the probability of exactly *n* impacts (P_n) occurring on the spacecraft in the time period is

$$P_n = \frac{N^n}{n!} e^{-N} \tag{7-7}$$

The flux can be derived empirically [Anderson, 1994] for a randomly tumbling surface as:

$$F(d,h,i,t,S) = H(d)\ \varphi(h,S)\ \psi(i) \left[F_1(d) g_1(t) + F_2(d) g_2(t)\right] \tag{7-8}$$

where *F* is the flux in impacts/m^2/yr, and *d* is the debris' diameter in centimeters (cm), for which acceptable values are 10^{-4} to 500 cm. The date is *t* (in years), and *h* is the altitude in km, valid when less than 2,000 km. The term *S* is the 13-month smoothed solar-radio flux, $F_{10.7}$, for the previous year (expressed in 10^4 Jy), and *i* is the inclination in degrees. The factor is the ratio between the flux on a spacecraft in an orbit of inclination *i*, and the flux on a spacecraft at 50 deg. inclination.

Because the damage caused by an impact with an object is a function of the kinetic energy, the velocity of a particular impact can be found using NASA's standard model for the velocity distribution *f(v)* as

$$f(v) = \left\{2vv_0 - v^2\right\}\left\{ \begin{aligned} &G\,exp\left(-\left(\frac{v - Av_0}{Bv_0}\right)^2\right) \\ &+F\,exp\left(-\left(\frac{v - Dv_0}{Ev_0}\right)^2\right) \end{aligned} \right\} + \left\{HC(4vv_0 - v^2)\right\} \tag{7-9}$$

where *v* is the collision velocity in km/s. The remaining terms are either constants or functions of inclination, and are detailed further in Anderson [1994].

Lastly, the number of impacts on a given spacecraft surface over the mission lifespan can be found by integrating the flux over the surface,

$$N_{impacts}(d) = T_{mission} \int_{Surface} F(d) n_A dA \tag{7-10}$$

where *F* is the total flux at the particle size of interest *d*, *A* is the exposed surface area, n_A is the local surface's normal vector corresponding to the area element *dA*, and $T_{mission}$ is the mission lifetime [Rainey, 2004]. Based on evaluation of the satellite catalog of objects in low Earth orbit, the collision probability for a 10 m^2 object is shown as a function of altitude in Fig. 7-23 [Ailor et al., 2010].

Deterministic Collision Hazard

In addition to shielding, spacecraft operators worry about whether there is an expected *conjunction* (close approach) in the next few days. The Center for Space Standards and Innovation (CSSI) has developed a service known as SOCRATES (Satellite Orbital Conjunction Reports Assessing Threatening Encounters in Space) [CSSI, 2011]. This service provides information on when and where potential conjunctions will occur in the next week. Satellite operators can then use this information to decide whether there is sufficient confidence in a future conjunction to warrant the operator executive collision avoidance maneuver. For example, SOCRATES

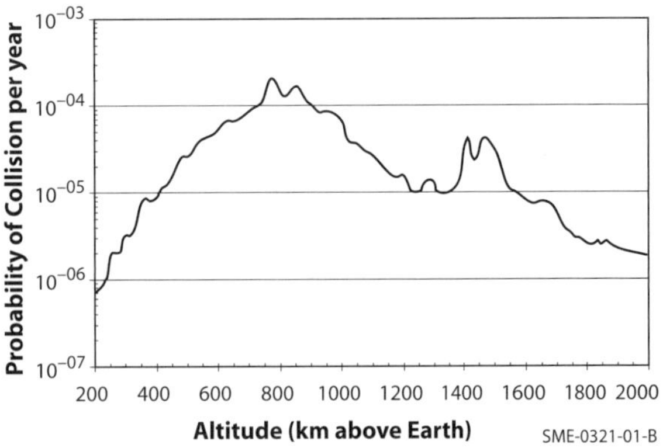

Fig. 7-23. Collision Probability for a 10m² Object in Low Earth Orbit. [Ailor, Womack, Peterson, and Lao 2010.]

identified that there was a close approach between the Iridium 10 satellite and a Delta 1 rocket body on January 15, 2011 at 10:13:04.632 UTC. The two objects were forecast to pass within 116 m of each other, traveling at a relative velocity of 14.729 km/s. The probability of collision was estimated to be less than 0.3%. Based on this low probability, Iridium chose not to perform a collision avoidance maneuver.

Damage Assessment

Impacts with orbital debris can damage spacecraft in various ways. Figure 7-24 shows three levels of damage from hypervelocity impacts. The first picture (a) is a scanning electron microscope image of an area eroded by impacts with very small objects (on the order of microns). This is the most frequent impact on spacecraft. This type of object typically degrades performance, such as decreasing a solar panel's efficiency or interferes with an image taken from a camera. The second picture (b) shows an object penetrating the surface in a hypervelocity impact. Depending on the location of the impact on a spacecraft, the effects can range from small (penetrating an antenna or solar panel) to catastrophic (penetrating a space suit or a fuel tank). The colliding object's size for this level of damage varies—overall damage depends on the impact velocity, the physical characteristics of the object it is hitting, and what the impacting object is made of. The last picture (c) shows a spacecraft-like structure destroyed in a hypervelocity test. Although statistically rare in space, a collision of this intensity would likely be fatal to both colliding objects, as what happened to both the Iridium 33 and COSMOS 2251 on February 10, 2009.

Spacecraft designers generally take into account the possibility of collision with objects in orbit. Risk reduction techniques can range from judicious placement of sensitive components (using other parts of the spacecraft to shield such things as pressurized tanks) to adding shielding to the spacecraft. For example, the International Space Station uses what is known as a stuffed Whipple shield. The Station uses multiple customized shields to protect sensitive structures, especially habitable components and associated support components. An example stuffed Whipple shield is shown in Fig. 7-25 [NRC, 1997]. This shield uses a sandwich of Nextel and Kevlar inserts between the exterior and interior aluminum walls. This design was thoroughly tested on the ground to survive an impact of a 3.5 g aluminum sphere traveling at 7 km/s.

Design Considerations and Debris Mitigation

There are several analysis software packages used to perform orbital debris assessments. NASA has developed a software package, *Debris Assessment Software* (DAS), which was designed to help NASA programs in performing orbital debris assessments [Opiela et al., 2007]. While the software has a NASA focus (including discussion of NASA standards and orbital debris mitigation practices), the software can be used for non-NASA programs, and the results can be used to assess a program's compliance with their own debris policies. Although the overall orbital debris collision hazard analysis partially drives the design of space missions, and is a significant consideration that any mission designer should take into account. In many cases, debris mitigation and debris protection adds to the

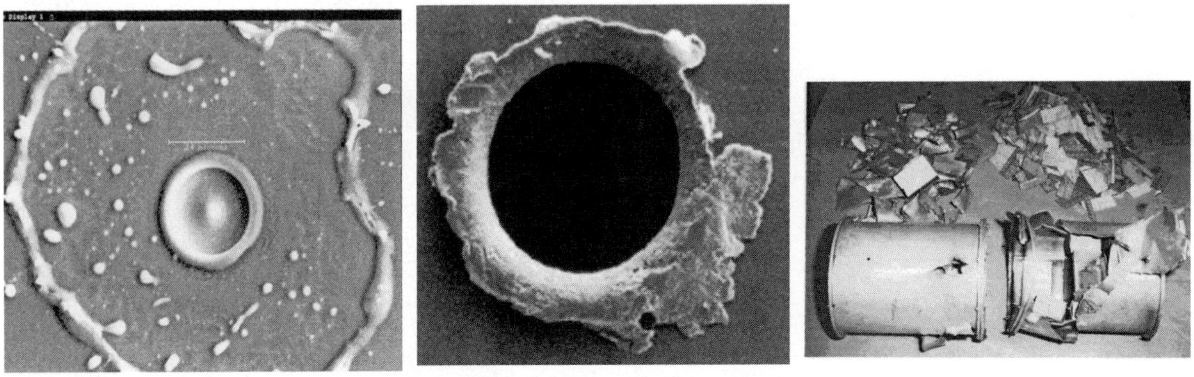

Fig. 7-24. Erosion (Left), Penetration (Middle), and Catastrophic Effects from Impacts with Debris (Right). (Courtesy of NASA)

overall cost (both in added mass and added financial considerations). However, the cost of doing nothing can be a premature end to a satellite mission. A balanced approach should be undertaken where the best design practices are performed to minimize the impact of the space mission on the orbital debris environment and to minimize the impact of the environment on the space mission. The overall goal should be to make the spacecraft safe by focusing on well thought out design and operation practices, not to simply meet some arbitrary standard or guideline.

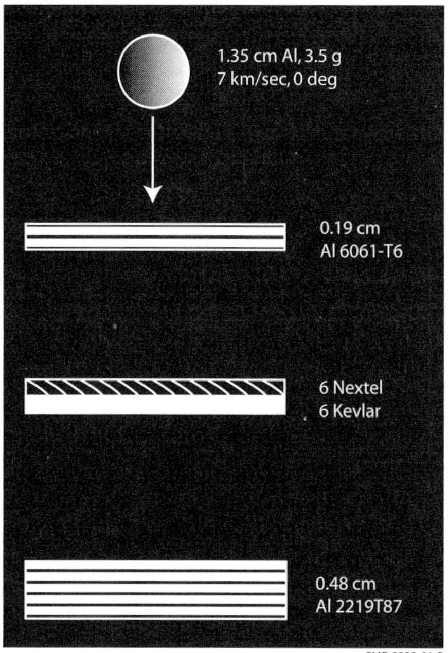

Fig. 7-25. A Stuffed Whipple Shield Used by the International Space Station. This shield design is a multi-layer shield with various distances between the layers. Non-structural insulation can fill the voids between the layers. (Courtesy of NASA)

References

For annotated bibliography of the space environment, see the book website.

Ailor, W.H., J. M. Womack, G. E. Peterson, and N. Y. Lao. 2010. "Effects of Space Debris on the Cost of Space Operations." IAC-10.A6.2.10. *International Astronautical Congress.* Prague, Czech Republic. Sept.

Alby, F., E. Lansard and T. Michal 1997. "Collision of Cerise with Space Debris." Second European Conference on Space Debris, ESOC. ESA SP-393 Darmstadt, Germany. May 17–19. pp. 589–596.

Anderson, B. J. ed 1994. *Natural Orbital Environment Guidelines for Use in Aerospace Vehicle Development.* NASA TM 4527, Jun./2000 Added to updated NASA-HDBK-1001

Bilitza, D., K. Rawer, and S. Pallaschke. 1988. "Study of Ionospheric Models for Satellite Orbit Determination." *Radio Science.* Vol. 23, Issue 3, pp. 223–232.

CSSI. 2011. SOCRATES, *Satellite Orbital Conjunction Reports Assessing Threatening Encounters in Space.* Website

DeWitt, Robert N., D. Duston, and A. K. Hyder. 1993. *The Behavior of Systems in the Space Environment.* Dordrecht, The Netherlands: Kluwer Academic Publishers.

Feynman, J., T. Armstrong, L. Dao-Gibner, and S. Silverman. 1988. "A New Proton Fluence Model for E>10 MeV." in *Interplanetary Particle Environment.* Pasadena, CA. Jet Propulsion Laboratory. pp. 58–71

Geosynchronous Alert and Prediction System (GAPS). 2011. Website

Goodman, John M. 2005. *Space Weather & Telecommunications.* New York, NY: Springer.

Grün, E., H. A. Zook, H. Frechtiq, and R. H. Giese. 1985. Collisional Balance of the Meteoritic Complex. Icarus 62:244-272.

Hastings, D. and H. Garrett. 1996. *Spacecraft-Environment Interactions.* New York: Cambridge University Press.

IADC. 2002. *IADC Space Debris Mitigation Guidelines.* Interagency Space Debris Coordination Committee. IADC-02-01. Oct.

IGRF. 2011. *International Geomagnetic Reference Field.* Website.

ISO. 2007. "Space Environment (Natural and Artificial) —Process for Determining Solar Irradiances". International Organization for Standardizations, ISO 21348.

ISO. 2010. *Space Systems—Space Debris Mitigation Requirements.* International Organization for Standardization, ISO 24113.

Johnson, N. L. and D. S. McKnight. 1987. *Artificial Space Debris.* Malabar, FL: Orbit Book Company.

Jones, J. 2004 "*Meteoroid Engineering Model—Final Report.*" NASA Space Environment and Effects Program, SEE/CR-2004-400. Jun.

Jursa, Adolph S., ed. 1985. *Handbook of Geophysics and the Space Environment.* US Air Force Geophysics Laboratory. Air Force Systems Command.

King, J. H. 1974. "Solar Proton Fluences for 1977-1983 Space Missions." *J. Spacecraft and Rockets.* 11:401.

Kessler, D. J. 1969. "Average Relative Velocity of Sporadic Meteoroids in Interplanetary Space." *AIAA Journal* 7(12):2337-2338.

Kessler, D. J. and G. G. Cour-Palais. 1978. "Collision Frequency of Artificial Satellites: The Creation of a Debris Belt." *Journal of Geophysical Research.* 83:63.

Kessler, D. J., E. G. Stansbery, J. Zhang, M. J. Matney, P. Eichler, R. C. Reynolds, and P. D. Anz-Meador. 1996. "A Computer-Based Orbital Debris Environment Model for Spacecraft Design and Observations in Low Earth Orbit." NASA Technical Memorandum 104825, Nov.

Klinkrad, H., J. Bendisch, H. Sdunnus, P. Wegner, and R. Westerkamp. 1997. "An Introduction to the 1997 ESA MASTER Model." Second European Conference on Space Debris. ESOC. ESA SP-393. Darmstadt, Germany. March 17–19. pp. 217–224.

Konradi, A and A. C. Hardy. 1987. "Radiation Environment Models and the Atmospheric Cutoff." *J. Spacecraft and Rockets.* 24:284

Leger, L. J., J. T. Visentine, and J. F. Kumineca. 1984. "Low Earth Orbit Oxygen Effects on Surface." AIAA 22nd Aerospace Sciences Meeting. Reno, NV. Jan. 9–12.

Liou, J. C. 2010. "A Parametric Study on Using Active Debris Removal for LEO Environment Remediation." IAC-10.A6.2.5.

Love, S. G. and D. E. Brownlee. 1993. "A Direct Measurement of the Terrestrial Mass Accretion Rate of Cosmic Dust." *Science 22,* vol. 232, no. 5133. pp. 550–553.

McIlwain, C. E. 1961. "Coordinates for Mapping the Distribution of Magnetically Trapped Particles." *J. Geophys. Res.* 66:3681-3691.

NASA. 2011. Meteoroid Environment Office. Website.

NASA. 2007. *NASA Safety Standard Guidelines and Assessments for Limiting Orbital Debris.* NASA-STD-8719.14. Aug. 28.

NASA. 1991. Space Station Freedom Program Office. *Space Station Program Natural Environment Definition for Design.* NASA SSP 30425. Rev. A. Jun.

NRC. 1997. *Protecting the Space Shuttle from Meteoroids and Orbital Debris.* National Research Council, Committee on Space Shuttle Meteoroid/Debris Risk Management. Washington, DC: National Academy Press.

NRC.1995. *Orbital Debris: A Technical Assessment.*National Research Council, Committee on Space Debris. Washington, DC: National Academy Press.

ODQN. 2009. *Orbital Debris Quarterly News.* Apr.

Opiela, J. N., E. Hillary, D. O. Whitlock, and M. Hennigan. 2007. *Debris Assessment Software User's Guide: Version 2.0.* NASA Johnson Space Center. JSC 64047. Nov.

OSTP. 1995. US Office of Science and Technology Policy. *Interagency Report on Orbital Debris.* Nov.

Petersen, E. L. 1995. "SEE Rate Calculation Using the Effective Flux Approach and a Generalized Figure of Merit Approximation." *IEEE Trans. Nuclear Science.* vol 42, no. 6. Dec. 6.

Purvis, C. K., H. B. Garrett, A. C. Whittlesey, and J. J. Stevens. 1984. "Design Guidelines for Assessing and Controlling Spacecraft Charging Effects." NASA Technical Paper 2361.

Rainey, L. 2004. *Space Modeling and Simulation:Roles and Applications Throughout the System Lifecycle.* Aerospace Press. Reston,VA: AIAA.

Schultz, M. and L. J. Lanzerotti. 1974. *Particle Diffusion in the Radiation Belts.* Heidelberg: Springer-Verlag.

Spencer, D. B., C. B. Hogge, W. S. Campbell, M. E. Sorge, and S. R. McWaters. 2000. "Some Technical Issues of an Optically-Focused Small Space Debris Tracking and Cataloguing System." *Space Debris. 2(3): 137-160.*

Tobiska, W. K. 2009. Operational Space Weather Entering a New Era. *Space Weather, 7.* S10003.

Tobiska, W. K. and S. D. Bouwer. 2010. "Distributed Networks Enable Advances in U.S. Space Weather Operations." *J. Adv. Space Res.* "Space Environment (Natural and Artificial)—Process for Determining Solar Irradiances." International Standards Organization (ISO). Geneva.

Tribble, A. C. 1995. *The Space Environment: Implications for Spacecraft Design.* Princeton, NJ: Princeton University Press.

Tribble, A. C. B. Boyadjian, J. Davis, J. Haffner, and E. McCullough. 1996. *Contamination Control Engineering Design Guidelines for the Aerospace Community.* NASA CR 4740. May.

UN. 2010. *"Space Debris Mitigation Guidelines of the Committee on the Peaceful Uses of Outer Space."* United National Office for Outer Space Affairs.

Vampola, A. L. 1996. "The Nature of Bulk Charging and Its Mitigation in Spacecraft Design." WESCON. Anaheim, CA. Oct. 22–24.

Vette, J. I., A. B. Lucero and J. A. Wright. 1966. *Models of the Trapped Radiation Environment.* Inner and Outer Zone Electrons, vol. II. NASA SP-3024. Greenbelt, MD.

Visentine, J. T. ed. 1988. *Atomic Oxygen Effects Measurements for Shuttle Missions STS-8 and 41-G,* vols. I-III. NASA TM-100459. Greenbelt, MD.

8 Space Mission Geometry

James R. Wertz, ***Microcosm, Inc./USC***

Most spacecraft observations including both payload sensing and orbit and attitude measurements are angles—i.e., they are measurements made on the sky as seen by the spacecraft, called the *celestial sphere*. This chapter provides an introduction to measurements and observations on the celestial sphere. It begins by explaining why spherical geometry is important to this process and establishes the relationship between spherical geometry and vector analysis with which many analysts are more familiar. It then introduces basic algorithms and provides several sample applications. Wherever possible, we provide summary formulas in both vector and spherical forms that can be readily applied to practical problems.

While this chapter introduces the concepts and mathematics associated with spacecraft sensing and angular measurements, the fundamental purpose of the chapter is to evaluate the space mission geometry, i.e., what the spacecraft sees and how other observers see the spacecraft and its motion, for a particular mission. This mission geometry evaluation process is summarized in Table 8-1 and discussed further in Table 8-2 and Table D-1 in App. D.

There is a substantial literature base on orbit and attitude dynamics and the general equations of motion for spacecraft. There is no comparable literature base for the theory of angular measurements made by spacecraft. Consequently, background information must be assembled from a variety of sources. *Spherical Astronomy* [Green, 1985] provides a good summary of spherical geometry, but only from an astronomical perspective. *Spacecraft Attitude Determination and Control* [Wertz, 1978], provided the first detailed discussion of mission geometry, but only for attitude analysis. (These techniques are broadly applicable, however, and form the basis for much of the current work). An extension and update to this work is *Orbit & Constellation Design & Management* [Wertz, 2009], called OCDM in this chapter. This work extends the description of space mission geometry to all types of directions-only measurements, provides the background for all of the results presented in this chapter, and extends classical spherical geometry to "full-sky spherical geometry" in which any or all of the angles and arc lengths can cover the full range of 0 to

Table 8-1. The Space Mission Geometry Evaluation Process. See Table 8.2 for additional mission geometry topics, summary tables, and where derived and Table D-1 for a list of both geometry background and application areas and where they are discussed. Earth coverage over time by satellites is discussed in Sec. 10.2.

Step	Where Discussed
Evaluate target and ground station coverage and apparent motion as seen from the spacecraft (also sky coverage for systems that are looking away from the central body)	Secs. 8.4, 10.2
Determine sensor field-of-view in space and on the ground	Secs. 8.2.2, 8.2.3, 8.3.4
Determine Sun angle and eclipse conditions	Secs. 8.1, 8.2.4
Evaluate satellite motion as seen from the Earth	Sec. 8.4
Evaluate relative motion of satellites in a constellation or if intersatellite links are needed	Sec. 8.5
Develop mapping and pointing budgets	Sec. 8.6

Table 8-2. Mission Geometry Areas of Analysis. OCDM = *Orbit & Constellation Design & Management* [Wertz, 2009]. See also Table D-1.

Subject	Where Discussed	Summary Tables	Derivation
Fundamentals of mission geometry — what the spacecraft sees	Secs. 8.0, 8.1	App. D, Inside rear cover	OCDM Sec. 6.1*
Appearance of the Earth from space	Sec. 8.3.2	—	OCDM Sec. 9.1.2
Ground track computations	Sec. 8.4	—	OCDM Secs. 8.3.3, 9.3
Earth coverage = Target and ground station appearance and motion	Secs. 8.4, 10.5	Tables 8-11, 8-12, App. C, Inside rear cover	OCDM Secs. 9.1, 9.2, 9.5
Motion of the satellite as seen from Earth	Sec. 8.4	—	OCDM Sec. 9.4
Array Sensor field-of-view (FOV)	Secs. 8.2.2, 8.2.3	Table 8-8	OCDM Sec. 6.3.1
Shapes and angles projected onto the Earth and as seen from space	Sec. 8.3.3	—	OCDM Sec. 9.1.3
Projection of FOV onto the Earth	Sec. 8.3.4	Table 8-10	OCDM Sec. 9.1.4
*Sun geometry** (Sun interference, eclipses, power and thermal analysis)*	Secs. 8.1.1, 8.2.4	—	OCDM Sec. 6.1
Relative and apparent motion of other satellites	Sec. 8.5	Table 8-13	OCDM Chap. 12
Spacecraft-to-spacecraft viewing	Sec. 8.5	—	OCDM Sec.10.1
Constellation design and analysis	Sec. 10.9, OCDM Chap. 13	Table 10-24	OCDM Chap. 13
Measurement singularities and accuracy analysis	OCDM Chap. 7	—	OCDM Chap. 7
Mapping and pointing budgets	Sec. 8.6	Tables 8-16, 8-17, Figs. 8-53, 8-54	OCDM Sec. 5.5

* *Full Sky Geometry* is spherical geometry in which the angles and arc lengths can go from 0 to 360 deg, thus resolving the quadrant ambiguities that make classical spherical geometry challenging to implement. The basic formulas are derived and applications discussed in OCDM Chap. 6.
** Also used for inertial targets (i.e., space telescopes).

360 deg. This alleviates the problem with classical spherical trig of having to keep track of multiple quadrants in trying to solve spherical triangles. *Space Mission Analysis and Design, 3rd edition* [Wertz and Larson, 1999] gives an overview of the application of spherical geometry to problems of space mission analysis but provides only a top-level introduction. Shuster [1993] gives an excellent and complete assessment of coordinate transformations and their applications. Similarly, Seidelmann [2006] provides a very complete discussion of both coordinate frames and time systems used in essentially all astronomical and astronautical measurement systems. This has been updated in an excellent summary by Kaplan [2005]. From a historical perspective, Nathaniel Bowditch's *American Practical Navigator* [2010] provides one of the most complete discussions of spherical geometry as applied to terrestrial navigation. A large number of authors from the mid-twentieth century [Brink, 1942; Palmer et al., 1950; Small, 1952; and Newcomb, 1906] provide derivations of the general rules of spherical geometry. Note, however, that these rules are less complete and substantially less useful for computer implementation than those which are introduced here and given in detail in App. A of OCDM.

8.1 Introduction to Space Mission Geometry

As listed in Table 8-2, many space mission analysis problems (orbit, attitude, and payload related) are fundamentally geometrical. In analyzing the behavior of spacecraft sensors and the data they produce, we are more interested in what the sensors see than the forces which move either the spacecraft or the objects that we are looking at. For example, in analyzing star camera data, we are interested in where the stars are relative to some object we are observing, but have little interest in their distances or the forces that keep the stars moving about the center of the galaxy.*

Most spacecraft sensors measure only angles. Fundamental to this angles-only geometry is the concept of the *celestial sphere*, illustrated in Fig. 8-1, which is the apparent bowl of the sky, such as that seen by anyone on a dark starry night in a large open area. We know that the distances to the Moon, planets, and stars are dramatically different. But this is not relevant to looking at them with our eye or a camera nor to building clock drives for telescopes or analyzing astronomical photographs. Points on the celestial sphere such as stars, planets, or the outline of the horizon, represent directions in space irrespective of distance. Just as unit vectors, which are also used to represent direction, have a length of one, the celestial

* I apologize to our astronomy customers and colleagues. We really are interested in the motion of the stars. It's just that this motion makes relatively little difference for most practical problems in space mission engineering. Note, however, that the assumption that the stars are essentially fixed begins to break down as we try to achieve more accurate measurements. As high accuracy becomes more and more important, the relative motion of the stars themselves and of the inertial coordinate frame becomes a critical part of spacecraft measurements.

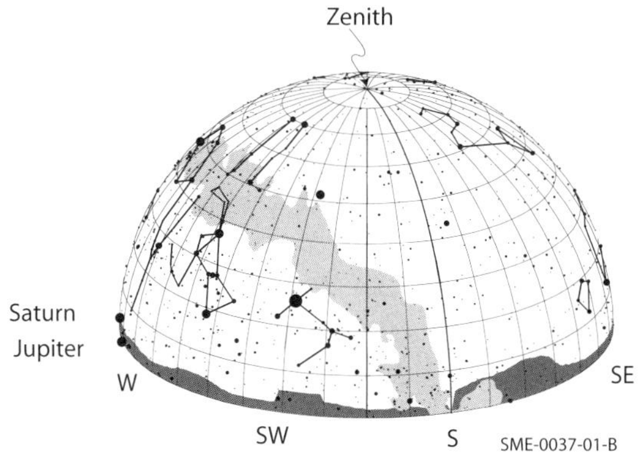

Fig. 8-1. The Celestial Sphere is the Bowl of the Sky Centered on the Observer who is Assumed to be at the Center. Points on the sphere, such as planets or the outline of the Milky Way, represent directions in space, irrespective of distance.

sphere is assumed to have a radius of one so that only the angular coordinates on the sphere are relevant.

Another way to think of Fig. 8-1 is as the dome of a planetarium as seen from the outside. The planetarium projector and, more importantly, the observer, are at the center of the sphere. We would like to put ourselves at the center of the sphere as well, but that is significantly more difficult to draw. The principal inconvenience in looking at the celestial sphere from the outside is that east and west are reversed in orientation. Thus, in Fig. 8-1, east is to the right of south and, for those who are amateur astronomers, Orion and Canis Major are reversed in their orientation as we would normally see them from "inside" the celestial sphere. If you think of the view from inside the sphere, east will be to the left of south and west will be to the right, as they should be.

How we choose to display the celestial sphere, the Earth, or any spherical surface depends on our objectives. No representation is perfect. Figure 8-2 illustrates the two most common alternatives. On the left is a typical latitude-longitude plot of the Earth's surface common in many ground station displays. On the right is an orthographic projection which we call a *globe plot*. We have drawn the same satellite ground trace on both. The lat-long plot has the advantage of allowing us to see the entire Earth at one time but the disadvantage of distorting shapes and sizes. Is the ground trace on the left a circle? In looking at it, we cannot easily tell because of the distortions introduced by the plot itself. The shapes of figures in a lat-long plot tell us more about the plot projection than about the shapes we're looking at. In the globe plot on the right, we only see half of the surface of the world. But shapes and directions are much more easily distinguished. It is clear in the plot on the right that the orbit is basically circular and we can easily envision the Earth rotating under the orbit in inertial space such that the orbit traces out a slowly moving spiral over the Earth's surface.

Figure 8-3 illustrates comparable alternative representations of the celestial sphere showing a rainbow in the sky and a large, nearby balloon with a gondola attached. As always, the observer is assumed to be at the center of the sphere such that he or she is looking at the balloon and rainbow against the background of the sky. In Fig. 8-3A, it is clear that both the rainbow and the balloon are round. We could easily measure both the diameter and the location of the center. Figure 8-3B contains the identical information plotted in an azimuth-elevation plot such that the horizon is along the bottom, and the *zenith*, or point directly overhead, is at the top. The fundamental problem with the Az-El plot is that it simply doesn't convey as much information to the person who is looking at it. Is the balloon round? Which has the larger diameter, the balloon or the rainbow? We could, of course, analyze Fig. 8-3B to determine at least some of the answers. The arc of the rainbow is 100 deg across; the

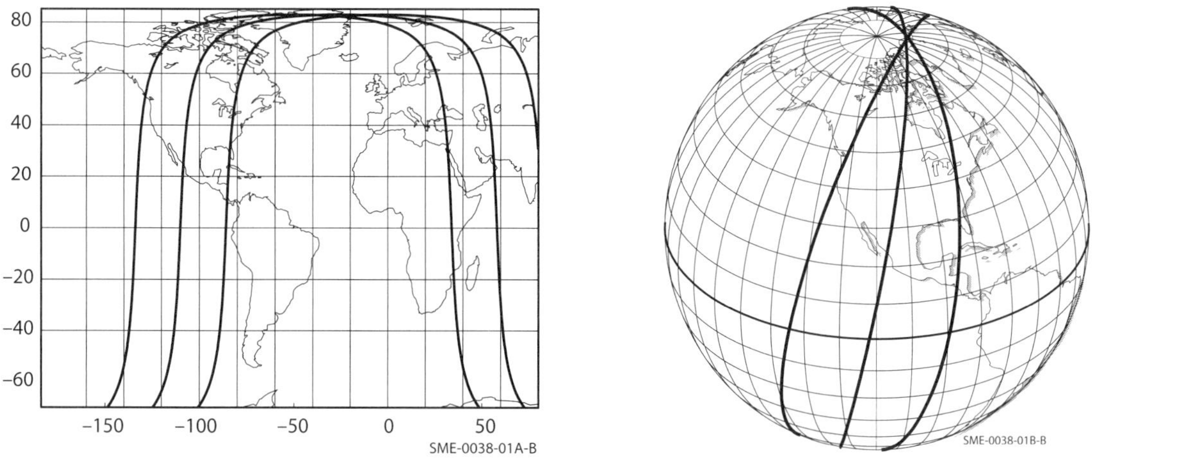

(A) Latitude-Longitude Plot **(B) *Orthographic Projection* or *Globe Plot***

Fig. 8-2. Alternative Representations of the Earth's Surface. Our objective is to use the globe plot on the right not as a projection of the surface, but as a "drawing" of a globe. We want to do our arithmetic on the surface of the globe itself and not on any projection.

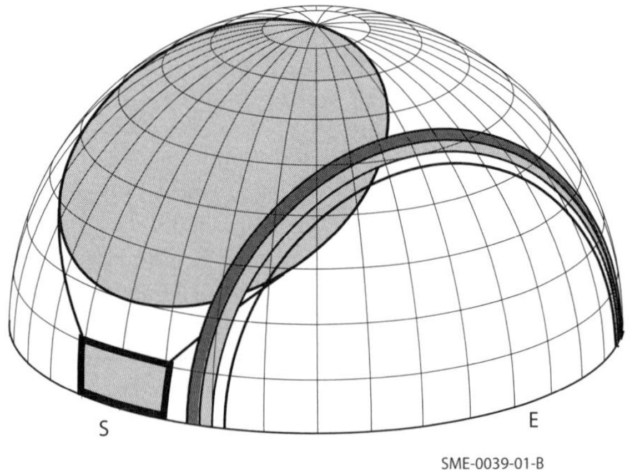

(A) Globe Plot of a Balloon and a Rainbow

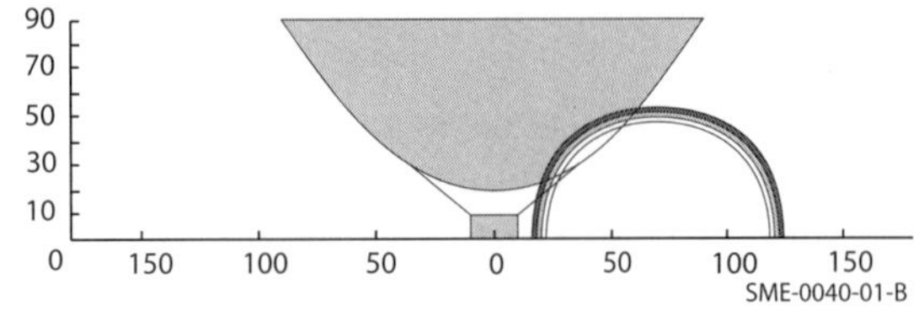

(B) Two-Dimensional Azimuth/Elevation of the Same Scene

Fig. 8-3. The Celestial Sphere Provides Distortion-Free Geometry on the Sky. The key to using the plot in (A) is to think of it as a sphere with the observer at the center and to work on the curved surface of the sphere.

diameter of the balloon, if we believe it to be round goes from an elevation of 20 deg to 90 deg and, therefore, is only 70 deg in diameter. Thus, the rainbow is larger. Nonetheless, this is not immediately apparent from the plot and it takes some work to find what we can see immediately by simply looking at the picture in Fig. 8-3A.

The key issue is that we don't want to use a projection at all. We want to work directly on the curved surface of the Earth or of the celestial sphere. This allows us to completely avoid both the conceptual and arithmetic distortions associated with projections. Consequently, we want to think of the globe plot as a "picture" of a sphere and work directly on the sphere itself. For example, look at the intersections of the latitude and longitude lines in Fig. 8-2B. In the center of the drawing they are at right angles to each other. At the edges, they intersect at very oblique angles. However, if we think of this figure not as a flat projection, but as a drawing of a globe, and see it as round and three dimensional, then it is easy to perceive that on the curved surface of the globe, the intersections are still at right angles at the edge, and will appear that way when we rotate the globe to move them nearer the center of the figure. Working on the globe itself provides truly distortion free geometry, and is the **only** way to achieve this.*

* For a discussion of alternative projections, see, for example, Canters and Decleir [1989].

Most scientists and engineers are familiar with vector analysis and the use of unit vectors to represent directions. Two such unit vectors are shown in a typical representation of a three dimensional Cartesian coordinate frame in Fig. 8-4A. One of the difficulties with this type of representation is that it is difficult to interpret unambiguously. For example: What is the radius of the small circle, and is it centered to the left or the right of the X-Z plane? Given the coordinates of the points, we could find the answer, but it is difficult to interpret from the drawing. Another way to conceptualize the celestial sphere is to think of it as a plot of the tips of all possible unit vectors centered on the origin of a coordinate frame. This idea of the celestial sphere is illustrated in Fig. 8-4B where the coordinate axes and vectors are identical to those in Fig. 8-4A, but we have now added a sphere of unit radius centered on the origin. In the spherical plot, we are interested only in the points on the surface representing the tips of the axes and the unit vectors. In this plot, it is clear that the small circle has a radius of 10 deg, and its center is 15 deg over and 30 deg up from the X axis. While the points plotted in Fig. 8-4A and Fig. 8-4B are identical, we can learn considerably more from the spherical coordinate plot in Fig. 8-4B.

We will use globe plots frequently throughout the chapter and the book. However, in most cases, we will

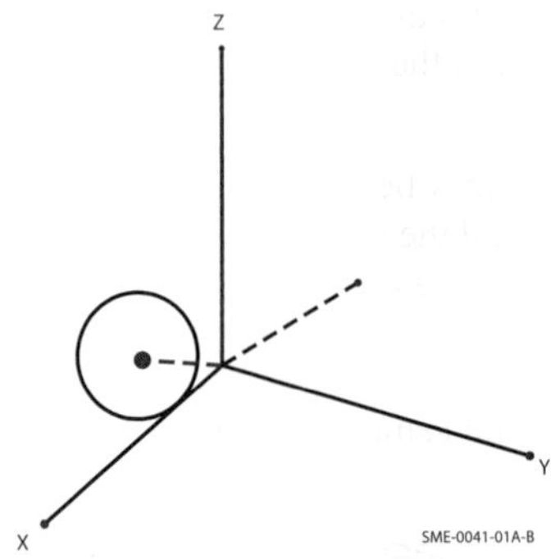

(A) Unit Vector in 3-D Space

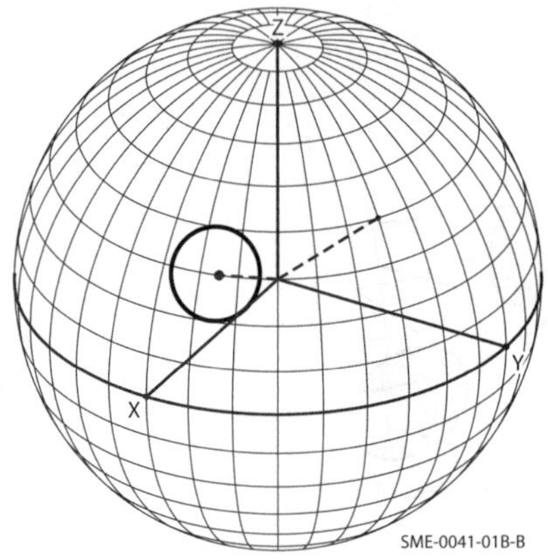

(B) Point on Unit Sphere

Fig. 8-4. Alternate Representations of Unit Vectors. Global geometry plots provide an unambiguous interpretation of directional geometry.

omit the origin, the axes and other lines inside the sphere and draw simply the points on the surface of the sphere itself. Nonetheless, these points represent directions in space just as the unit vectors do. The celestial sphere is simply a good way to think about directional geometry much as vectors are a good way to think about forces and velocity. Doing the mathematics as vectors or in spherical geometry gives the same results. We are interested here in the angular measurements themselves, and the information they contain, not in how they are processed.

Finally, we have discussed thus far principally the celestial sphere as seen by an observer on the ground. However, our principal interest is what is seen from space. Consequently, as illustrated in Fig. 8-5, we need to introduce the concept of the *spacecraft-centered celestial sphere*, showing the direction to objects seen from a spacecraft. The principal difference between this and one for an observer on the ground is that on the ground we are looking only at the sky overhead, and the celestial "sphere" is really just a hemisphere overhead. Spacecraft, on the other hand, see the entire sky, although portions of it may be blocked by the Earth or another planet. While the globe plot approach eliminates the distortion of map projections, it only shows half the sky. Therefore, in most of our plots, we will try and show the half of the sky containing the objects of most interest for the problem at hand. But we need to keep in mind that there is always a second half as well and that for the spacecraft, the celestial sphere is the sky both "above" and "below" the spacecraft.

The differences between the spacecraft-centered celestial sphere and the tradition Az-El plots can be seen in Fig. 8-6. The figures on both the top and bottom show the Earth as seen from a low-Earth orbiting spacecraft. How large is the Earth? Is it round? Where is the center? Both plots contain the same information, but these questions are not easily answered from an Az-El plot because of the distortion of the plot itself. In effect, we are seeing the consequences of the plot rather than the reality of what is seen. In the globe plot, these problems go away. We have eliminated the distortion by plotting directly on the sphere. Here it is clear that the disk of the Earth is indeed round, has a radius of approximately 60 deg, and is centered about 35 deg above the equator of the plot.

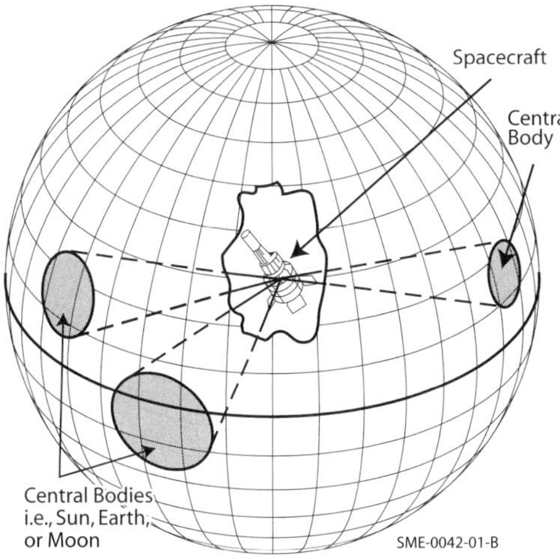

Fig. 8-5. The Spacecraft-Centered Celestial Sphere is the Bowl of the Sky Centered on the Spacecraft. The "observer" at the center may be an instrument, the center of the spacecraft, or any point in space.

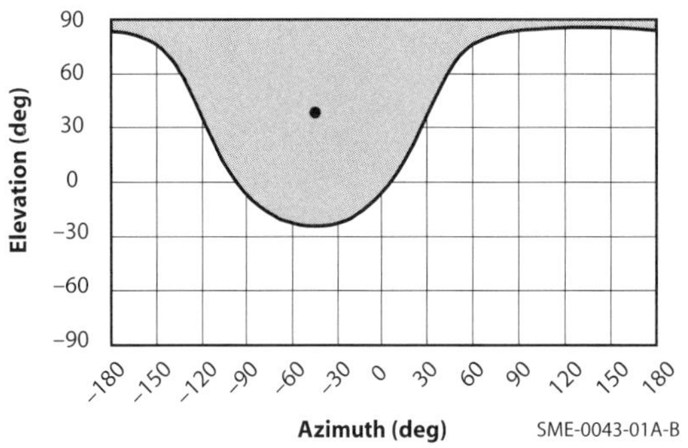

(A) Az-El Plot

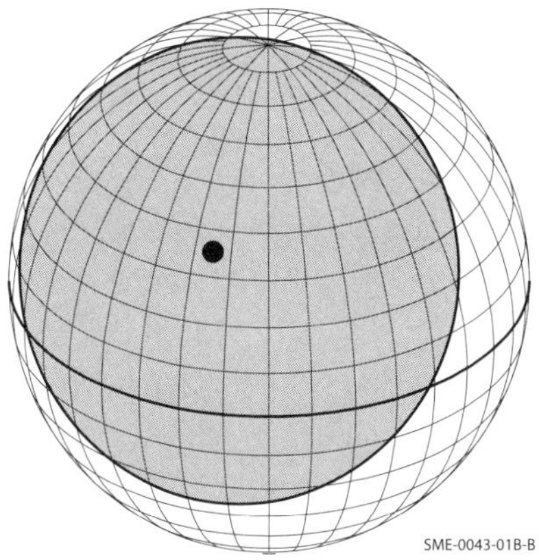

(B) Globe Plot

Fig. 8-6. The Disk of the Earth as Seen From Low-Earth Orbit. Globe plots of the sky provide distortion-free geometry as seen from the spacecraft.

As with unit vectors, the underlying coordinate frame for globe plots can represent a variety of coordinate frames, either fixed or moving, depending on the problem we are interested in analyzing. For the celestial sphere for an observer on the Earth, the two most common coordinate frames are one with the equator along the horizon and the pole at the zenith, or one which is aligned with celestial coordinates with the North Star at the pole and the celestial equator along the globe's equator. Both of these can be used in spacecraft-centered celestial coordinates as well. In addition, common coordinate frames for space mission analysis include spacecraft-fixed coordinates, in which the axes are fixed in the spacecraft frame of reference, and axes which are momentarily fixed relative to the stars, relative to the direction of the Earth, or relative to some target being observed.

8.1.1 Sample Problem: Eclipse Analysis

As an example of the utility of the spherical geometry approach, we will analyze the eclipse duration for a satellite in low-Earth orbit. Specifically, assume we have a satellite in a circular orbit at an altitude of 1,000 km and inclination of 32 deg relative to the equator. We would like to determine the frequency and duration of eclipses for the satellite. Figure 8-7A shows a standard isometric view of the eclipse problem. This type of approach would allow us to set up a simulation using the various equations introduced in Chap. 9. We could then run the simulations for different seasons and node crossing times, and determine a statistical distribution. However, we get no numerical estimates from the drawing itself, and no physical insight into what is happening until we have completed the simulation and subsequent analysis.

Figure 8-7B provides better insight by plotting the problem on the spacecraft-centered celestial sphere in inertial coordinates. By inertial coordinates we mean that the sphere is attached to the fixed stars, such that the celestial pole (near the North Star) is at the pole of the coordinate system and the celestial equator is along the coordinate equator. The *ecliptic*, or path of the Sun in the sky, is inclined 23.5 deg to the equator, and is also shown on the plot. The orbit plane is inclined at 32 deg to the equator. Note that the orbit plane is the plane of the spacecraft's orbit for an observer at the center of the Earth. However, for an observer on the spacecraft, it can also be thought of as the orbit of the Earth around the spacecraft.

If I am sitting on the spacecraft, I see the Earth going around me relative to the background stars, in the same path as an observer at the center of the Earth would see the spacecraft move against the same stars, only 180 deg out of phase. At any given time the apparent disk of the Earth is a circle on the celestial sphere, centered at a

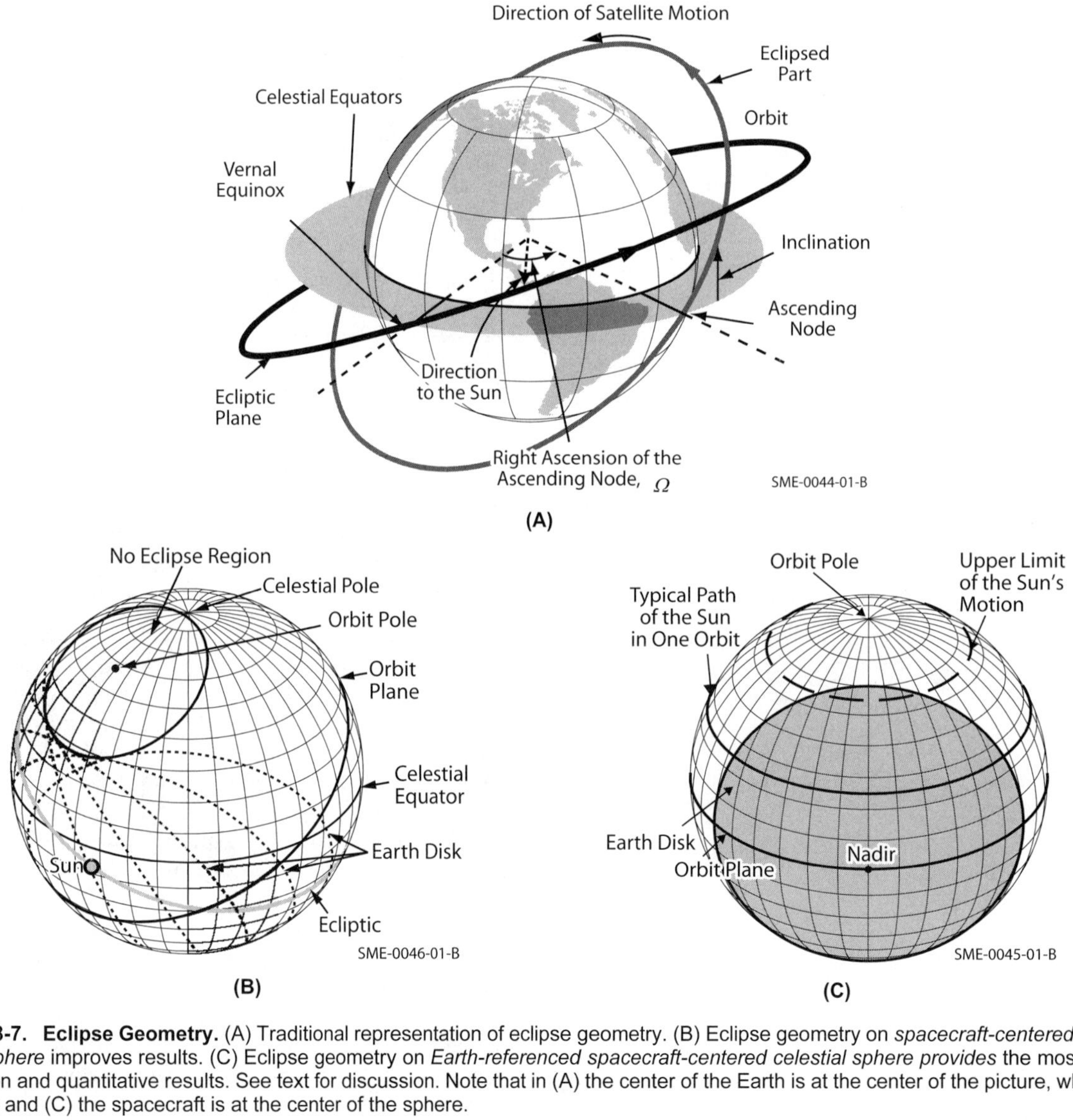

Fig. 8-7. Eclipse Geometry. (A) Traditional representation of eclipse geometry. (B) Eclipse geometry on *spacecraft-centered celestial sphere* improves results. (C) Eclipse geometry on *Earth-referenced spacecraft-centered celestial sphere provides* the most information and quantitative results. See text for discussion. Note that in (A) the center of the Earth is at the center of the picture, whereas in (B) and (C) the spacecraft is at the center of the sphere.

point somewhere along the orbit plane. As we will determine in Sec. 8.3, the angular radius of the Earth as seen from 1,000 km altitude is approximately 60 deg [see Eq. (8-26)]. The outline of the disk of the Earth at a series of locations along the orbit is shown by the sequence of dotted circles of 60 deg radius centered on the orbit plane. As the Earth moves around the spacecraft (as seen from the spacecraft) it will sweep across the sky and from time to time cover the Sun, thus causing an eclipse to occur from the perspective of the spacecraft. It is the frequency and duration of these eclipses that we would like to determine. Notice on Fig. 8-7B that as the Earth moves along the orbit plane, there will be a region in the vicinity of the orbit pole which is never covered by the disk of the Earth. This "no eclipse region" centered on the orbit pole and a similar one, centered at the opposite pole, will be 30 deg in radius, because the angular diameter of the Earth is 60 deg at this altitude. Whatever is in either of these "polar caps" will not be eclipsed, including the Sun, Moon, and some set of stars. For the sample plotted in Fig. 8-7B, the Sun is not in the "no eclipse region," and therefore, an eclipse will occur at some period during the orbit.

We can learn somewhat more about the eclipses from Fig. 8-7B. The Sun moves along the ecliptic which is inclined 23.5 deg to the celestial equator. The orbit plane is at 32 deg to the equator but may be oriented with the node (i.e., where the orbit plane crosses the equator) at various places along the equator, depending both on how the spacecraft was launched and the motion of the node as described in Chap. 9. Wherever the node is, the orbit plane will still be inclined at 32 deg to the equator. Since the ecliptic is inclined at 23.5 deg to the equator, the most that the ecliptic can be inclined to the orbit plane will be 23.5 + 32 = 55.5 deg. The Earth's angular radius at the assumed altitude is 60 deg. Consequently, at this altitude and inclination, the Sun can never be in the "no eclipse region" surrounding either orbit pole. Thus, at 1,000 km and 32 deg inclination, there will **always** be an eclipse on every orbit, at all seasons, irrespective of the longitude or time at which the satellite is launched. Although it would still be difficult to calculate the duration of a particular eclipse, we have gained substantial insight just by the way we have constructed the figure.

We can further increase our insight into the eclipse problem by making the simple coordinate transformation shown in Fig. 8-7C. Here, we plot the Earth and Sun on the spacecraft centered celestial sphere in *Earth referenced coordinates*, i.e., in coordinates centered on the spacecraft in which the direction of the Earth remains fixed. Many spacecraft fly with one axis fixed toward the direction of the Earth, and one axis toward the orbit pole. This is the coordinate frame we would like to use, although, since we are only interested in eclipse geometry, we don't care whether the spacecraft itself is in this attitude or not. On the figure, the orbit pole is at the pole of the plot, and the orbit plane is along the equator. *Nadir*, or the direction of the center of the Earth, is marked by a dot on the plane. Because our coordinate frame is fixed in the direction of the Earth, the apparent disk of the Earth is fixed and has been shaded in the figure.

In this figure we are at the center of the sphere sitting on the spacecraft, facing the Earth, and watching the Sun and the stars go by behind it. The coordinate frame we have chosen has an axis fixed in inertial space in the direction of the orbit pole. In order to maintain the other axis in the direction of the Earth, the coordinate frame is rotating in inertial space, at one rotation per orbit in order to keep the Earth's disk fixed in the coordinate frame. In this coordinate frame, objects fixed in space will appear to rotate once per orbit as seen in Fig. 8-7C. The stars, the Moon, and the Sun will all move in small circles centered on the orbit pole as the coordinate frame rotates to follow the Earth. The typical path of the Sun in one orbit is shown as the heavy solid line. The Moon and the stars all follow similar paths. Depending on where the Sun is along the ecliptic, and the orientation between the ecliptic and the orbit plane, the Sun will move slowly (over the course of months) up and down on the plot but can never get more than 55.5 deg above or below the orbit plane, as shown by the dashed line at 35 deg from the orbit pole.

As the Sun moves in this coordinate frame, eclipses occur whenever the Sun is behind the disk of the Earth, i.e., within the shaded region. The maximum eclipse occurs when the Sun is in the orbit plane and will cover 120 deg of the orbit or 1/3 of the orbit period. Since the orbit period at this altitude is approximately 105 min (see Sec. 9.1 or the tables on the inside rear cover), the maximum eclipse duration for a satellite in a circular orbit at 1,000 km will be 35 min. The minimum eclipse will occur when the Sun is at the upper limit of the Sun's motion, at the dashed line. Here, the Sun covers 60 deg in azimuth as can be seen by the figure. Consequently, the minimum eclipse duration will be approximately half of the maximum duration, or about 17 min.

Using Fig. 8-7C, we can calculate not only the maximum and minimum duration of the eclipses, but also get substantial physical insight into how they occur. Notice that in the vicinity of the orbit plane, the eclipses remain long and only gets to be shorter as we get very close to the extremes. Therefore, if we were to ask for the average eclipse duration, we would not be far off by saying that it was 35 min. The average eclipse duration is very close to the maximum. We have now gained substantial physical insight into the problem. If we were to increase the orbit inclination by 5 deg, the minimum eclipse would drop to zero, but there would be little impact on the average eclipse. Simply by constructing the plot, we are able to gain considerable insight into the problem, and to provide at least some quantitative estimates. We will use a plot very similar to this to calculate eclipse durations in the example in Sec. 8.2.4, after we've introduced spherical geometry computations.

8.1.2 Coordinate Systems

In principle, any coordinate system will work for space mission geometry problems. However, as we have

Table 8-3. Common Coordinate Systems Used in Space Applications. Figure 8-8 shows the most common ones. See Table 8-6 in Sec. 8.2 for further information on the first two rows.

Coordinate Name	Fixed with Respect to	Center	Z Axis or Pole	X Axis or Ref. Point	Applications
Celestial (Inertial)	Inertial space*	Earth† or spacecraft	Celestial pole	Vernal equinox	Orbit analysis, astronomy, inertial motion
Earth-Fixed	Earth	Earth	Earth pole = celestial pole	Greenwich meridian	Geolocation, apparent satellite motion
Spacecraft-Fixed	Spacecraft	Defined by engineering drawings	Spacecraft axis toward nadir‡	Spacecraft axis in direction of velocity vector‡	Position and orientation of spacecraft instruments
Local Horizontal (RPY)**	Orbit	Spacecraft	Nadir	Perpendicular to nadir and orbit pole (toward velocity vector)	Earth observations, attitude maneuvers††
Ecliptic	Inertial space	Sun	Ecliptic pole	Vernal equinox	Solar System orbits, lunar/solar ephemerides

* Actually rotating slowly with respect to inertial space. See text for discussion.
† Earth-centered inertial coordinates are frequently called *GCI (Geocentric Inertial)*.
‡ For on Earth-oriented mission.
** Also called *LVLH (Local Vertical/Local Horizontal)*, *RPY (Roll, Pitch, Yaw)* or *Local Tangent Coordinates*.
†† An important and environment characteristic of roll pitch, yaw coordinates is that they do not commute (i.e., the result depends on the order in which they are specified). For a complete discussion See OCDM, pg. 154-5.

seen in the previous section, selection of the proper reference coordinates is often critical to developing a good physical understanding, obtaining analytic expressions for key mission parameters, and reducing the probability of error.

To define a *coordinate system* for space applications, we must first specify two characteristics: the location and motion of the origin and what the coordinate system is fixed with respect to (i.e., its attitude and attitude rate). Typically, we choose the Earth's center as the origin for problems in orbit analysis or geometry on the Earth's surface and the spacecraft's position for problems concerning the apparent position and motion of objects as seen from the spacecraft or analysis of payload observations. Occasionally, coordinates are centered on a specific spacecraft instrument when we are interested not only in viewing the outside world but also in obstructions of the field of view by other spacecraft components. Typical ways to fix the rotational orientation of a coordinate system are with respect to inertial space, to the direction of the Earth or some other object being viewed, to the spacecraft, or to an instrument on the spacecraft. Table 8-3 lists the most common coordinate systems used in space mission engineering and their applications. These are illustrated in Fig. 8-8. If you are uncertain of the coordinate system to select, I recommend beginning with the following:

- Earth-centered inertial for orbit problems
- Spacecraft-centered local horizontal for missions viewing the Earth
- Spacecraft-centered inertial for missions viewing anything other than the Earth

For a more detailed discussion of coordinate systems and a complete set of coordinate transformations, see OCDM Sec. 6.1.2 and App. B.

Unfortunately, the inertial coordinate system which everyone uses, called *celestial coordinates*, is not truly fixed with respect to *inertial space*—that is, the mean position of the stars in the vicinity of the Sun. Celestial coordinates are defined by the direction in space of the Earth's pole, called the *celestial pole*, and the direction from the Earth to the Sun on the first day of spring, when the Sun crosses the Earth's equatorial plane going from south to north. This fundamental reference direction in the sky is known as the *vernal equinox* or *First Point of Aries*.* Unfortunately for mission engineers, the Earth's axis and, therefore, the vernal equinox precesses around the ecliptic pole (the pole of the Earth's orbit) with a period of 26,000 years. This *precession of the equinoxes* results in a shift of the position of the vernal equinox relative to the fixed stars at a rate of 0.014 deg/year. Because of this slow drift, celestial coordinates require a date to accurately define the position of the vernal equinox. The most commonly used systems are *2000 coordinates* and *true of date*, or *ToD*. The latter coordinates use the same epoch as the orbit parameters and are traditionally used for spacecraft orbit analysis. The small corrections required to maintain ToD coordinates are conveniently done by standard computer subroutines. They are important for precise numerical work, but are not critical for most problems in mission analysis.

Once the underlying coordinate system has been defined most work is done in either rectangular (x, y, z) or

* The position of the vernal equinox in the sky has been known since before the naming of the constellations. When the zodiacal constellations were given their current names several thousand years ago, the vernal equinox was in Aries, the Ram. Consequently the zodiacal symbol for the Ram, ♈, or sometimes a capital T (which has a similar appearance), is used for the vernal equinox. Since that time the vernal equinox has moved through the constellation of Pisces and is now slowly entering Aquarius, ushering in the "Age of Aquarius."

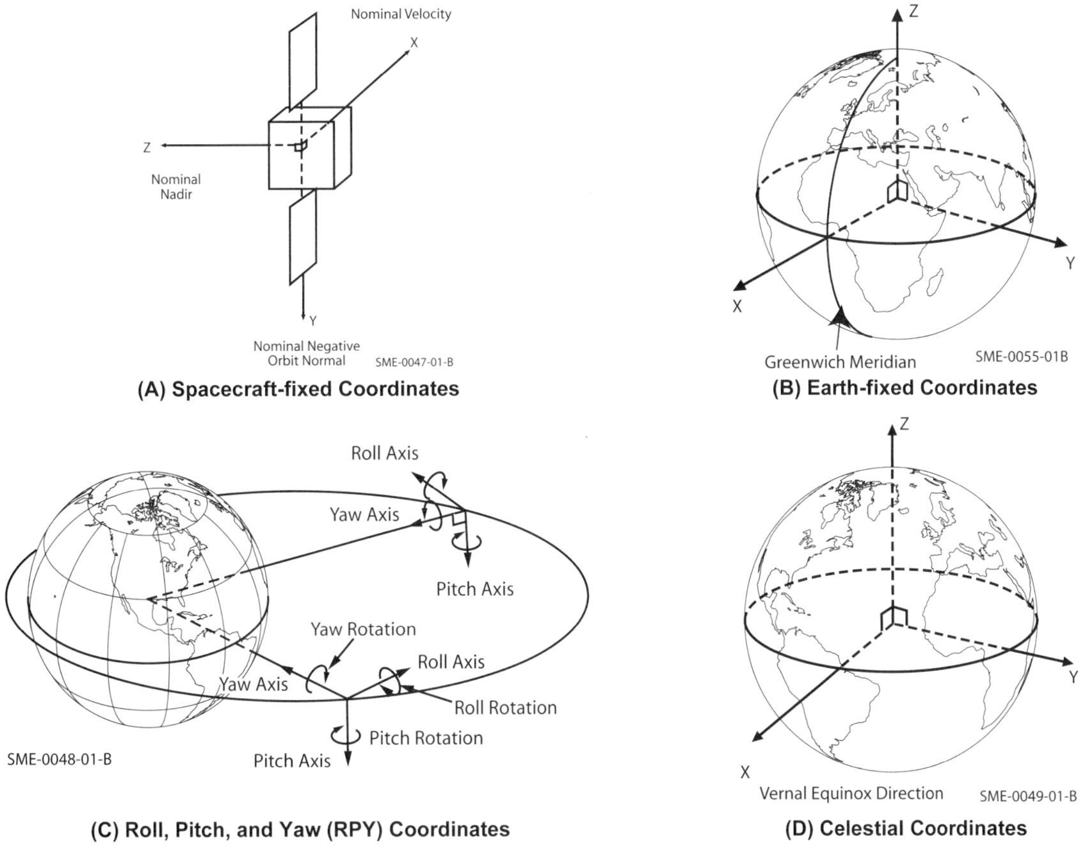

Fig. 8-8. Coordinate Systems in Common Use. See Table 8-4 for characteristics.

spherical (ϕ, θ) coordinates or some combination of the two. A given problem may be easier in one or the other, but so long as the computations are done correctly and we do not introduce new singularities, the accuracy of the solution will be the same in either set of coordinates. Transforming between them is both conceptually and numerically straightforward. As shown in Fig. 8-9, the +X axis is normally toward the reference point on the equator, and the +Z axis is toward the positive or North pole. The great circles through the poles and perpendicular to the equator are called *meridians*. The meridian through any point on the sphere determines the *azimuth coordinate*, ϕ, of that point. *Azimuth* is the equivalent of longitude on the Earth's surface, and is measured along the equator. The azimuth is also equivalent to the rotation angle measured counterclockwise about the pole from the reference point to the point in question. The second coordinate which determines the position of any point on the sphere is the *elevation*, θ, or latitude component. It is the arc-length distance above or below the equator. The *co-latitude* or *co-elevation* is the arc length from the positive pole to the point in question. Small circles at a constant elevation are called *parallels*. Because a parallel of constant elevation is not a great circle (except at the equator), the arc length along a parallel will be larger than the arc-length separation between two points. (For example, 1 deg of arc length on the surface of the Earth

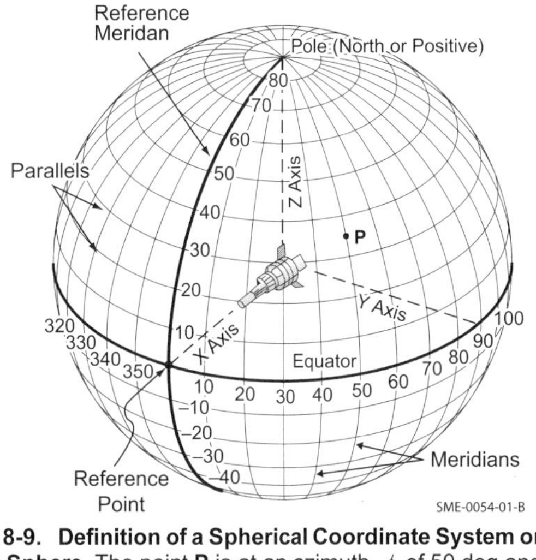

Fig. 8-9. Definition of a Spherical Coordinate System on the Unit Sphere. The point **P** is at an azimuth, ϕ, of 50 deg and elevation, θ, of 35 deg, normally written as (50°, 35°).

is about 111 km. Thus, at the equator 2 points 1 deg apart will be 111 km apart, but two points 1 deg apart in longitude that are the same latitude, but not at the equator, will be less than 111 km apart and will be very close to each other near the pole.) As Table 8-4 shows, several spherical coordinate systems in common use have special names for the azimuth and elevation coordinates.

Table 8-4. Coordinate Names in Common Spherical Systems.

Coordinate System	Azimuth Coordinate	Elevation Coordinate (Z Axis)	Applications	Typical Origin
Celestial Coordinates	Right ascension	Declination	Inertial measurements, astronomy	The observer
Earth-Fixed	Longitude	Latitude	Earth applications	Earth center
Spacecraft-Fixed	Azimuth or clock angle	Elevation	Spacecraft measurements, attitude analysis	Reference mark on spacecraft
Local Horizontal	Azimuth	Elevation*	Directions relative to central observer	The observer
Ecliptic Coordinates	Celestial longitude	Celestial latitude	Planetary motion	The Sun

* Also used are *zenith angle* = angle from point directly overhead to point in question = 90 deg minus elevation angle; and *nadir angle* = angle at the observer from the center of Earth to point in question = 90 deg minus elevation angle minus Earth central angle (See Sec. 8.3.1).

The following equations transform the azimuth, ϕ, and elevation, θ, to the corresponding unit vector coordinates (x, y, z):

$$x = \cos\phi \cos\theta \tag{8-1a}$$

$$y = \sin\phi \cos\theta \tag{8-1b}$$

$$z = \sin\theta \tag{8-1c}$$

Similarly, to transform from unit vectors to the corresponding spherical coordinates, use:

$$\phi = \text{atan2}(x, y) \tag{8-2a}$$

$$\theta = \text{asin}\,(z) \tag{8-2b}$$

where atan2 is the computer function with output defined over 0 to 360 deg and the asin function is evaluated over –90 deg to +90 deg.

8.1.3 Basic Spherical Geometry and Unit Vector Formulas

Section 8.1.1 discussed the broad concept of the celestial sphere and explained why we want to use it. This section reintroduces the celestial sphere as a formal mathematical construct, and describes how we go about working on it. App. D provides the specific rules for spherical geometry. We discuss here the major differences between plane and spherical geometry, and introduce spherical triangles as the principal computational tool.

Figure 8-10 illustrates the use of the celestial sphere to represent directions to objects in space. These objects may be either very close, such as other components of the spacecraft, or very far, such as the surface of the Earth, planets, or stars. As can be seen from the spherical triangle in Fig. 8-10, there are three types of objects on the celestial sphere. Points, lines, and angles on the sphere represent directions, arc lengths and rotation angles as seen from the observer at the center. *Points on the celestial sphere* represent directions in space, such as the direction to the Sun, Moon, or the rotation axis of the spacecraft. The direction opposite a given direction is called the *antipode* or *antipoint* and frequently has a –1 superscript. Thus S^{-1} is the direction opposite the Sun, and is called the *antisolar point. Nadir* is the direction to the center of the Earth. The direction opposite nadir is called the *zenith.* Points on the sphere may represent either directions to real objects or simply directions in space with no object associated with them, such as the direction parallel to the axis of the Earth (the *celestial pole*) or parallel to the +Z axis of the spacecraft coordinate system.

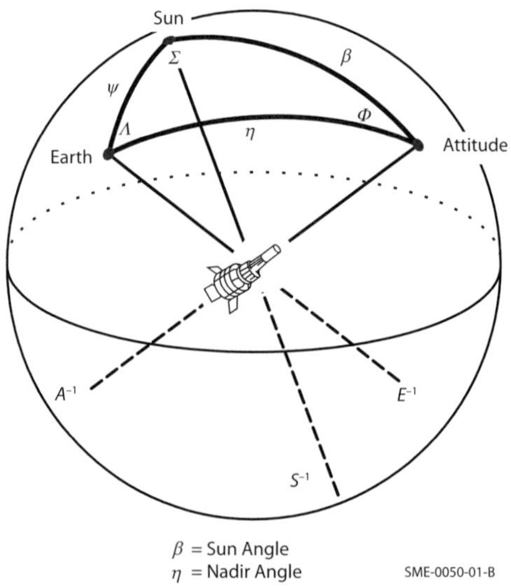

Fig. 8-10. The Spacecraft-Centered Celestial Sphere Specifies Direction in Space. The sides of the triangle are arc lengths. The angles of the triangle are rotation angles.

Specifying a direction in space requires two independent numbers such as the azimuth and elevation of a star in a spherical coordinate system.* "Straight lines" on the celestial sphere are great circle arcs. A *great circle* on the celestial sphere is any circle which divides the sphere into two equal hemispheres. Any part of a great circle is called an *arc* or *arc segment* and is equivalent to a straight line segment in plane geometry. Thus, the shortest path connecting two stars on the celestial sphere is the *great circle arc* connecting the stars. Any two points

* In contrast, orientation or attitude requires three numbers—the direction to the center, and the rotation about the axis.

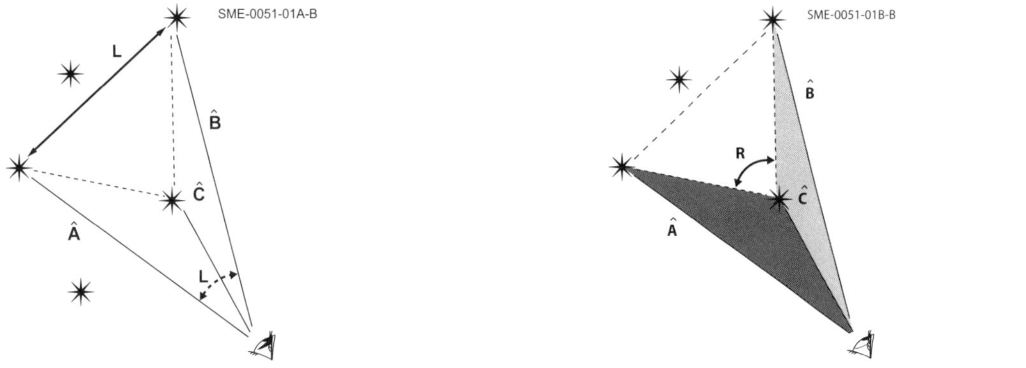

(A) Arc Length Measurement, L, from, Â to B̂ (B) Rotation Angle Measurement, R, from, Â to B̂ about Ĉ

Fig. 8-11. Distinction between Arc Length and Rotation Angle Measurements.

which are not antipoints of each other determine a unique great circle arc on the celestial sphere.

Given three points in the sky, such as the direction to the Sun, the Earth and the spin axis of a spinning spacecraft, we can connect them with great circle arcs (η, β, and ψ in Fig. 8-10) to construct a *spherical triangle.* **The angles Λ, Σ, and Φ at the vertices of the spherical triangle are called *rotation angles* or *dihedral angles.*** The lengths of arc segments and the size of rotation angles are both measured in degrees. However, as shown in Fig. 8-11, these are distinctly different measurements. The arclength represents the side of the spherical triangle, and is equal to the angular separation between two points as seen on the sky, such as the angle between the Sun and the center of the Earth. The rotation angle, which is always measured about a point on the sphere represents the angle in a spherical triangle and is equal to the dihedral angle between two planes for the observer in the center. For example, assume that we see the Earth, Sun, and Moon on the spacecraft sky. The arc length between the Sun and the Moon is the angular separation between them as seen by the observer at the spacecraft. The rotation angle about the Earth between the Sun and the Moon is equal to the angle between two planes. The observer, Earth, and Sun form the first plane, and the observer, Earth and Moon form the second.

An alternative way to think about the difference, is that a rotation angle is the angle between the hour hand and the minute hand on a clock, or about 90 deg at 12:15. The angular length of the minute hand or the hour hand as I look at the clock are both arc length measurements. Both types of angles are important for spacecraft applications, and we must clearly understand the distinction between them. Table 8-5 lists the properties of these two basic measurement types.

Most work in spherical geometry is done with great circle arcs which are the equivalent of straight lines in plane geometry. However, another important figure on the celestial sphere is the *circle* which is the locus of all points equidistant from a given point. (The center and all of the points on the circle are assumed to be on the celestial sphere.) If the radius of the circle is 90 deg, the circle divides the sphere into two equal hemispheres and the circle is a *great circle*, as discussed above. Otherwise it is a *small circle.* In this context a "small circle" is not necessarily small. It could have a radius of 89.9 deg, for example. We could also construct a small circle with a radius of 110 deg, which would be the same as a small circle centered on the antipode of the center with a radius of 180 – 110 = 70 deg. The lines of constant latitude on the surface of the Earth are small circles, except for the equator which is a great circle, and the poles themselves which are points.

In plane geometry, straight lines which are parallel do not intersect. However, this is not possible with great circles on the sphere. Consider, for example, the equator on a globe and any two lines of constant longitude, which are great circles perpendicular to the equator. Irrespective of the separation between the lines of longitude, they always intersect at the two poles. Any two great circles on the sphere will either lie on top of each other, or intersect at two points 180 deg apart. The orange slice-shaped figure formed by the intersection of two great circles is called a *lune.* The lune has two sides, both of which are 180 deg long. The rotation angle between the sides, at either of the intersection points is equal to the angle between the two planes that form the great circles and pass through the center of the sphere.

Because great circle arcs (which are the spherical equivalent of straight lines) always intersect, triangles in spherical geometry are substantially more common than in plane geometry problems, and take a more important role in computations on the sphere. Nearly all problems in spherical geometry can be reduced to the solution of spherical triangles. Thus, spherical trigonometry becomes the principal computational method for most space mission geometry problems. These computations are described further in OCDM Sec. 8.3, and the rules of spherical trigonometry are given in App. D in this volume. Note that one of the most common errors in spherical trigonometry is to construct a "triangle" in which one of the sides is a small circle arc rather than a great circle arc. Just as all of the sides of a plane triangle must be straight lines, all of the sides of a spherical triangle

Table 8-5. Properties of Arc Lengths and Rotation Angles. See also Fig. 8-11.

ARC LENGTHS

- Angle between two directions
- Segment of a great circle on the celestial sphere
- Side of a spherical triangle
- Measured in degrees
- Analogous to a distance measurement in plane geometry
- For unit vectors $\hat{\mathbf{A}}$ and $\hat{\mathbf{B}}$, arc length = arccos ($\hat{\mathbf{A}} \cdot \hat{\mathbf{B}}$)
- Examples:
  - — Angular distance from Sun to center of Earth
  - — Angular radius of the Earth as seen by the spacecraft
  - — Latitude of a point on the Earth
- Expressed as "Angle from **A** to **B**" or "Arc length between **A** and **B**"

ROTATION ANGLES

- Angle about a point on the sky from one arc to another
- Dihedral angle between two planes
- Angle in spherical triangle
- Also measured in degrees
- Analogous to an angular measurement in plane geometry
- For unit vectors $\hat{\mathbf{A}}$, $\hat{\mathbf{B}}$, and $\hat{\mathbf{C}}$,

  rotation angle from $\hat{\mathbf{A}}$ to $\hat{\mathbf{B}}$ about $\hat{\mathbf{C}}$ = $\arctan\left[\dfrac{\hat{\mathbf{C}}\cdot\left(\hat{\mathbf{A}}\cdot\hat{\mathbf{B}}\right)}{\hat{\mathbf{A}}\cdot\hat{\mathbf{B}}-\left(\hat{\mathbf{C}}\cdot\hat{\mathbf{A}}\right)\left(\hat{\mathbf{C}}\cdot\hat{\mathbf{B}}\right)}\right]$
- Examples:
  - — Difference in longitude between two points on the Earth
  - — Angle between the orbit plane and the Earth's equator (i.e., the orbit inclination)
  - — Angular amount that the Earth rotates on its axis in a fixed amount of time
- Expressed as "Rotation angle from **A** to **B** about **C**"

The arc length and rotation angle between two points are equal if and only if the rotation angle axis is 90 deg from both points.

must be great circle arcs. We cannot apply plane trigonometry directly to a piece of pie. Similarly,

The sides of spherical triangles can ***not*** *be small circles.*

Although most of the work in mission geometry is done with spherical triangles and small and great circles, there are other more complex figures as well. The *dual-axis spiral* is described in Sec. 10.4, the *analemma* is introduced in Sec. 8.5, and the *rhumb line* is discussed in OCDM Sec. 6.3.

Another concept in spherical geometry that is different from plane geometry is illustrated in Fig. 8-12, in which we have constructed a spherical triangle using the equator and two lines of longitude. The intersections of the longitude lines with the equator are both right angles, such that the sum of the angles of the triangle exceeds 180 deg by an amount equal to the angle at the pole. The sum of the angles of any spherical triangle is always larger than 180 deg. The amount by which this sum exceeds 180 deg is called the *spherical excess* and is directly proportional to the area of the spherical triangle. Thus, small triangles on the sphere have a spherical excess near zero, and are very similar to plane triangles. Large spherical triangles, however, are very different as in Fig. 8-12 with two right angles.

A *radian* is the angle subtended if I take a string equal in length to the radius of a circle, and stretch it along the circumference. Similarly, if I take an area equal to the square of the radius, and stretch it out on the surface of a sphere (which requires some distortion, since the surface of a sphere cannot fit on a flat sheet), the resulting area is called a *steradian.* Since the area of a sphere is $4\pi r^2$, there are 4π steradians in a full sphere, and 2π steradians in a hemisphere. **These units are convenient for area problems, because in any spherical triangle the spherical excess, expressed in radians, is equal to the area of the triangle expressed in steradians.** In general, the area, *A,* of any spherical polygon (a figure with sides which are great circle arcs) expressed in steradians is given by:

$$A = \Sigma - (n-2)\,\pi \tag{8-3}$$

where n is the number of sides, and Σ is the sum of the rotation angles expressed in radians. This is used, for ex-

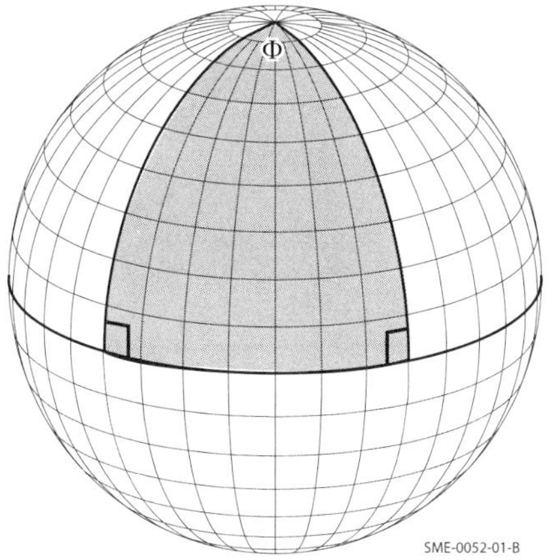

Fig. 8-12. The Sum of the Angles in a Spherical Triangle is Always Greater than 180 deg. The sum of the angles minus π radians is called the *spherical excess* and equals the area of the triangle in steradians.

ample, in measuring the angular area subtended by an array sensor, such as a digital camera on the spacecraft.

Figure 8-13 shows a variety of spherical triangles. Note that all of the triangle sides are great circle arcs. Figure 8-13A is a nearly plane triangle, for which the sum of the angles is approximately 180 deg and plane geometry is a close approximation. Figure 8-13B is called a *right spherical triangle* because the angle at B is a right angle. Just as right plane triangles have particularly simple relationships among the angles and sides, right spherical triangles also have exceptionally simple relationships between the sides and angles. These are expressed by *Napier's rules* which are written out in App. D. Right spherical triangles are common in mission geometry problems, and provide simple, straightforward solutions for many problems associated with angular measurements.

In spherical trigonometry, there is a second type of special and particularly simple spherical triangle shown in Fig. 8-13C. Here, side A-B has an arc length of 90 deg. This is called a *quadrantal spherical triangle*. An equally simple set of rules applies to the relationship among the angles and sides in quadrantal spherical triangles. These are also summarized in App. D. Between them, right and quadrantal spherical triangles provide solutions to most of the problems encountered in mission analysis.

Figure 8-13D shows an *obtuse isosceles triangle* with two equal rotation angles larger than 90 deg. Clearly, this cannot exist in plane geometry. A similar strange triangle for plane geometry is Fig. 8-13E which shows an *equilateral right triangle* in which all three angles and all three sides are 90 deg. This triangle represents 1/8 of the surface of the celestial sphere, and has an area of 0.5 π steradians, which can be seen either by examination or from the spherical excess rule. Finally, Fig. 8-13F shows a very large spherical triangle. Note that this triangle is remarkably similar in appearance to the small triangle in 8-13A. This is because the triangle can be thought of either as a small triangle with three angles of approximately 60 deg, or as a very large one, with three angles of

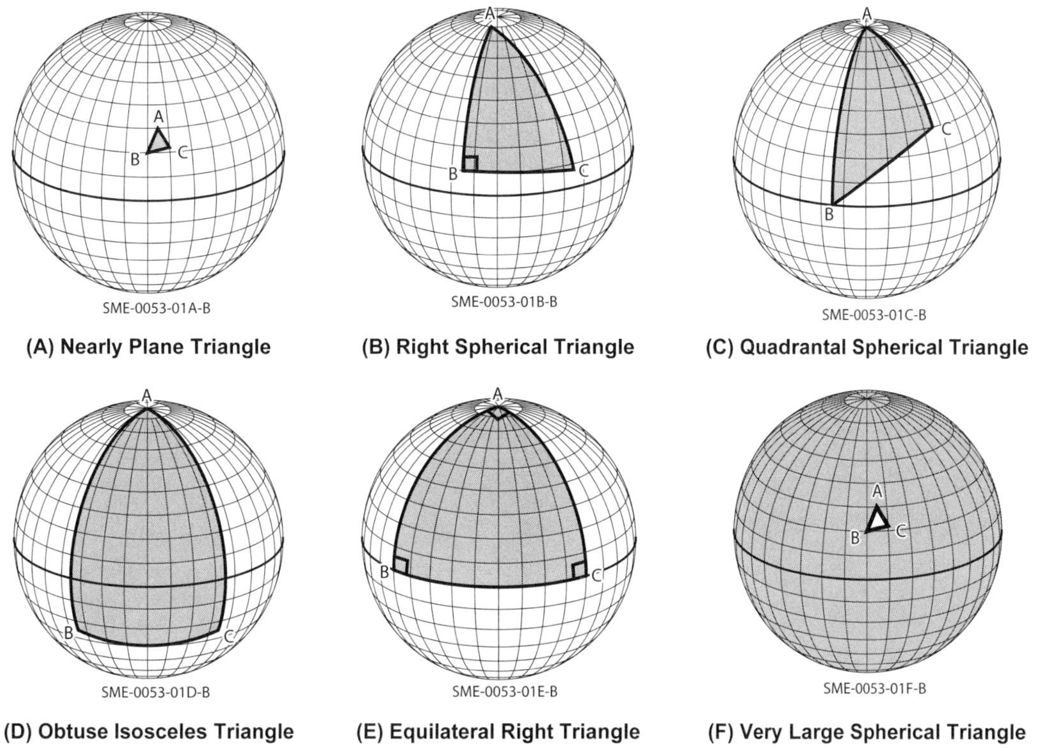

Fig. 8-13. Types of Spherical Triangles. See text for discussion.

approximately 300 deg. That is, the area between A, B, and C can be thought of either as the inside of a small triangle or as the outside of a large one which covers all of the surface of the sphere except for the small area between A, B, and C. In this large spherical triangle, the rules of spherical geometry still apply and can be used in very convenient fashions as described further in OCDM.

The ideas above lead to defining three major areas of geometry on the surface of the sphere:

- *Spherical trigonometry* is concerned with the solution of triangles on the celestial sphere. It is used for almost all computations
- *Spherical geometry* is concerned with triangles plus great and small circles and their intersection. This expands spherical trigonometry to cover angular area and circles contained in one hemisphere, such as a typical antenna pattern.
- *Global geom*etry is concerned with more complex figures on the sphere, and relationships covering the entire sphere. This expands spherical geometry to include problems covering the entire celestial sphere, such as constellation design for satellites or the ground track of a satellite in a circular orbit. This ground track is called a *dual axis spiral* because the satellite is rotating about the orbit pole and the orbit pole is rotating once per day with respect to the surface of the Earth (See Sec. 10.4.)

8.2 Applications

8.2.1 Solving Mission Geometry Problems

The key to most spherical geometry problems is to define the coordinate system correctly. Given the correct set of coordinates, most problems can be solved algebraically very quickly, using the techniques described below.

Figure 8-14 shows a general spherical geometry coordinate system. To define the coordinates, we start by defining the orientation of either pole. For geographic coordinates, this would ordinarily be the Earth's poles. For a coordinate frame attached to the stars, it is often taken to be the *celestial pole* which is the projection of the Earth's pole onto the celestial sphere. For an observer on the surface of the Earth, the pole is frequently taken as the *zenith* or point straight overhead. For spacecraft-fixed coordinates, the pole is typically the +Z axis defined by some mark inscribed on the spacecraft body. It is also convenient to use spacecraft-centered coordinates defined relative to the orbit plane, such that the pole is in the direction of the angular momentum of the spacecraft in its orbit, i.e., the positive orbit pole.

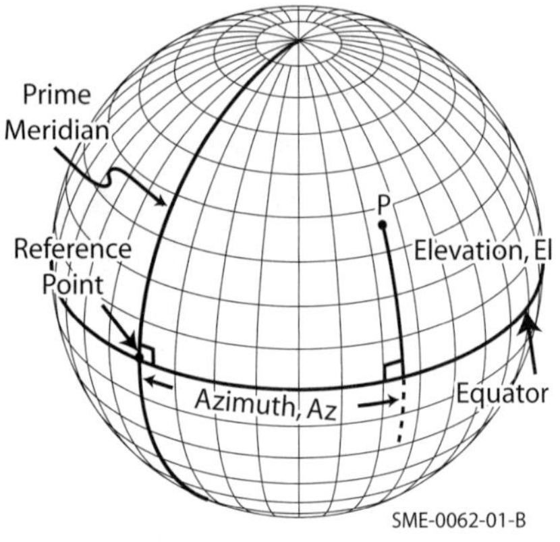

Fig. 8-14. The Spherical Geometry Coordinate System. See Table 8-6 for definitions of principal components. (See also Fig. 8-9.) P is at (65 deg, 35 deg).

Table 8-5◀, Fig. 8-14, Eq. 8-3◀

The *equator* of the coordinate system is the great circle which is 90 deg from the two poles. In order to fully define the coordinates we need to define where to start our azimuthal coordinate measured along the equator. This is determined by a *reference point* along the equator, or equivalently, by a *prime meridian,* which is one of the lines of constant azimuth going through a well-defined point, not necessarily on the equator. In geographic coordinates, the prime meridian goes through the Royal Greenwich Observatory, near downtown London, and is often called the *Greenwich meridian*. It represents the starting point for longitude on the surface of the Earth. On the celestial sphere, relative to the stars, we use one of the two *equinoxes*, or intersections between the ecliptic (the path of the Sun) and the equator. The one chosen as the zero point on the sky is the *vernal equinox*, which is the location of the Sun on the first day of spring. (The other intersection is called the *autumnal equinox*.) See Table 8-3 for other common systems.

The two coordinates in a general spherical coordinate system are called *azimuth*, measured along the equator, and *elevation*, measured above and below the equator. In geographic coordinates, these are called *longitude* and *latitude*, and in celestial coordinates on the sky, they are *right ascension* and *declination*. *Meridians* are the arcs of great circles running from pole to pole, and latitude lines are small circles at a constant latitude. Naming conventions are summarized in Table 8-6.

Virtually all problems in spherical geometry are done by solving spherical triangles, both because great circles always intersect, and because any three components, including the three rotation angles provide a solution. The specific algebraic rules for solving all types of spherical triangles are summarized in App. D. The rules to be applied to specific types of figures are as follows.

- **Right spherical triangles**: If one of the rotation angles is a right angle, and any two of the remaining components (rotation angles or sides) are known, then the three unknown components can be determined immediately by Napier's rules* which are a very simple set of relationships between the sines and cosines of the various components. These are explicitly defined for all possible combinations of right spherical triangles in App. D.

Table 8-6. Names of Principal Components in Common Spherical Coordinate Systems. See Table 8-3 for other coordinate systems.

Component	Coordinate System		
	Generic	Geographic	Celestial
Fixed with Respect to	Various	Earth	"Fixed" stars
Pole	Pole	North and South poles	Celestial poles (projection of Earth's poles onto the sky)
Equator	Equator	Equator	Celestial equator
Reference Meridian	Prime meridian	Greenwich meridian	0 of right ascension
Reference Point	Not named	Not named	Vernal equinox
Azimuthal Coordinate	Azimuth	Longitude	Right ascension
Vertical Coordinate	Elevation	Latitude	Declination

- **Quadrantal spherical triangles:** If one of the sides is equal to 90 deg, and any two of the remaining components are known, then the three unknown components can be determined by rules analogous to Napier's rules for right spherical triangles.
- **Oblique (general) spherical triangles**: Use either the law of cosines or law of sines set out in App. D. The law of cosines is preferred, since the inverse cosine is uniquely defined between 0 and 180 deg.
- **Area of any figure**: Use the spherical excess rule for polygons and the formulas in App. D for the areas of small circles or fractions of small circles.

To illustrate the applications of spherical geometry, we will present two sample problems:

- The field of view of a "square" Sun sensor
- Eclipse duration in a circular orbit (corresponding to the sample problem set out conceptually in Sec. 8.1.1.)

8.2.2 Example 1: Field of View of a "Square" Sun Sensor

Sensors used on spacecraft are often said to have square or rectangular fields of view, i.e., an "8 × 8 deg star sensor" or "128 × 128 Sun sensor." Unfortunately, "square" and "rectangular" are not as well defined as we might like in terms of sensor fields of view on the sky. If the edge of a sensor field of view is defined by a straight line, such as an array of pixels on a focal plane, then this straight line will be projected onto the spacecraft sky as an arc of a great circle. Two parallel edges on the field of view will be projected as two great circle arcs on the sky. We can, for example, think of these two edges as being projected out along two meridians, or lines of longitude in a celestial coordinate system. However, since these are great circle arcs, they do not remain the same distance apart, and would ultimately intersect if extended far enough. Thus, a square or rectangular field of view when projected onto the spacecraft sky does not have edges which remain a fixed distance apart. In this section we define what is meant by a "square" field of view, and determine the parameters of such a field of view projected onto the sky and then extend the computations to rectangular fields of view in Sec. 8.2.3.

To make our example specific, we will look at a "128 deg square" field of view Sun sensor, and ask what is the actual field of view projected onto the sky. Figure 8-15 shows how such a sensor could be constructed. We begin with a flat square array 8.2 cm on a side. We mount the array parallel to an opaque sheet and 2 cm behind it. As shown in the figure, we put a pinhole in the center of the opaque sheet such that it is directly above the center of the array. We use a pinhole because this provides perfect geometrical optics, i.e., there are no dis-

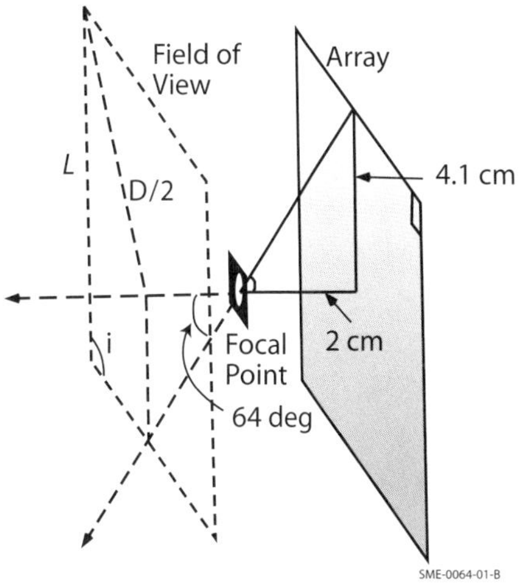

Fig. 8-15. Construction of a "128 × 128 deg" Sun Sensor. The "128 deg" is measured between opposite sides, through the center.

* Not too surprisingly, Napier's rules were introduced by the Scottish mathematician and Baron of Merchiston, John Napier, who also invented logarithms and in 1617 introduced the decimal system as it is used today. During the early part of the 20th century Napier's rules for spherical triangles were taught as a part of high school mathematics and a variety of convenient mechanisms for memorizing them were introduced. Needless to say, relatively few of today's high school students are required to do so.

tortions introduced by the pinhole itself and we are interested in creating a "perfect" sensor, although, perhaps, not a very practical one. As the array looks through the pinhole out into the sky, the angle from the central axis to the center of any one of the edges will be equal to atan (4.1 /2.0) = 64 deg, such that the field of view of the sensor is 128 deg across as measured through the center, perpendicular to any edge. This is what we traditionally mean by "128 deg square" field of view. What we would like to determine for this perfect sensor is:

- The length, L, of each side
- The angle of intersection, i, between two adjacent sides
- The length of the diagonal, D, and
- The projected area, A, of the sensor on the sky.

To show how the problem is done, we will solve it using plane geometry, vectors, and spherical geometry.

The plane geometry solution is shown in Fig. 8-16. Here the arithmetic is particularly simple. In the plane geometry approximation, the distance across the center is 128 deg. Therefore the length of each side, L, is 128 deg. The angle of intersection at the corners is 90 deg, the area, A, is 128^2 = 16,384 deg^2 (equals 39.7% of the celestial sphere) and the diagonal, D, is $128\sqrt{2} = 181.0$ deg. Clearly, there is a very fundamental problem with this solution. Although our sensor may not be a practical one, it is certainly capable of being constructed. And yet, if it is constructed, it is highly unlikely that the field of view on the sky would be more than 180 deg across, since this means that the sensor would be seeing behind itself. The solution using plane geometry is simple to compute, but, unfortunately, wrong.

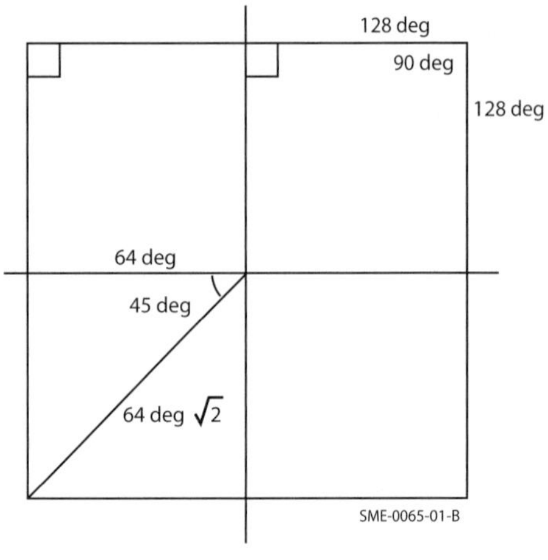

Fig. 8-16. Plane Geometry Solution to Sun Sensor Problem. The answer is simple, but, unfortunately, wrong.

Figure 8-18 illustrates a vector solution to the Sun sensor problem. Here we construct unit vectors to the center of the field of view, to the center of one edge, and to one of the corners. We then use the vector algebra illustrated in the figure to determine the angles among the various vectors and the rotation angle formed at the corner of the sensor. The solution presented in the figure is computationally correct, but is both awkward and complex. In addition, the area of the field of view is not easily computed using vectors. Finally, the solution provides us with almost no physical insight into the shape of the field of view, or the implications of the shape for either measurements or creating overlapping fields of view with other sensors.

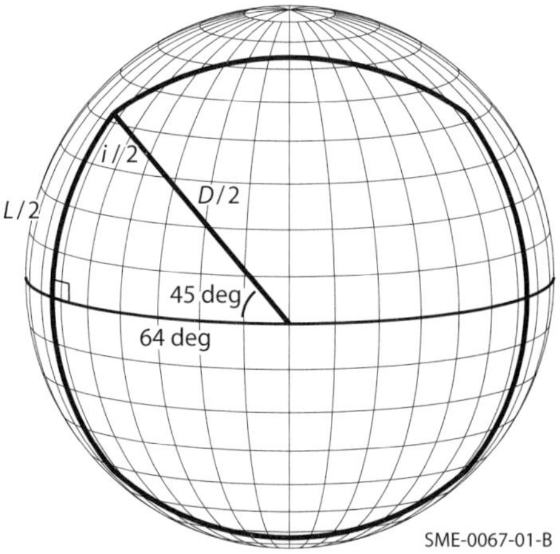

Fig. 8-17. Spherical Geometry Solution to "128 Deg Square Sun Sensor" Problem. Solution is complete, correct, and simple.

Figure 8-17 shows the spherical geometry solution to the Sun sensor problem. The sphere represents the celestial sphere as seen by the sensor. We construct the edges of the field of view by first defining the center axis as a point on the equator, then going 64 deg along the equator in either direction and drawing the meridians at right angles to the equator. These lines represent the sides of the field of view. The top and bottom are produced by rotating about the center by 90 deg and constructing two similar lines. This is the real shape of the sensor field of view projected onto the sky.

To determine the values of the parameters of interest, we first construct the diagonal going from the center to one of the corners, and the line from the center to the middle of one of the edges. The length of this line is 64 deg by the definition of our problem. The rotation angle at the center between the two edges of the triangle is 45 deg by symmetry, and the line through the center to the middle of the edge intersects the edge at a right angle, again by definition of our problem. Consequently, we have formed a right spherical triangle in which two of the components are known. Using Napier's rules from App. D, we simply write down the formulas for the various components:

$$\tan(L/2) = \sin 64 \text{ deg} \ \tan 45 \text{ deg}$$
$$L = 83.9 \text{ deg} \quad (8\text{-}4)$$

$$\cos(i/2) = \cos 64 \text{ deg} \ \sin 45 \text{ deg}$$
$$i = 143.9 \text{ deg} \quad (8\text{-}5)$$

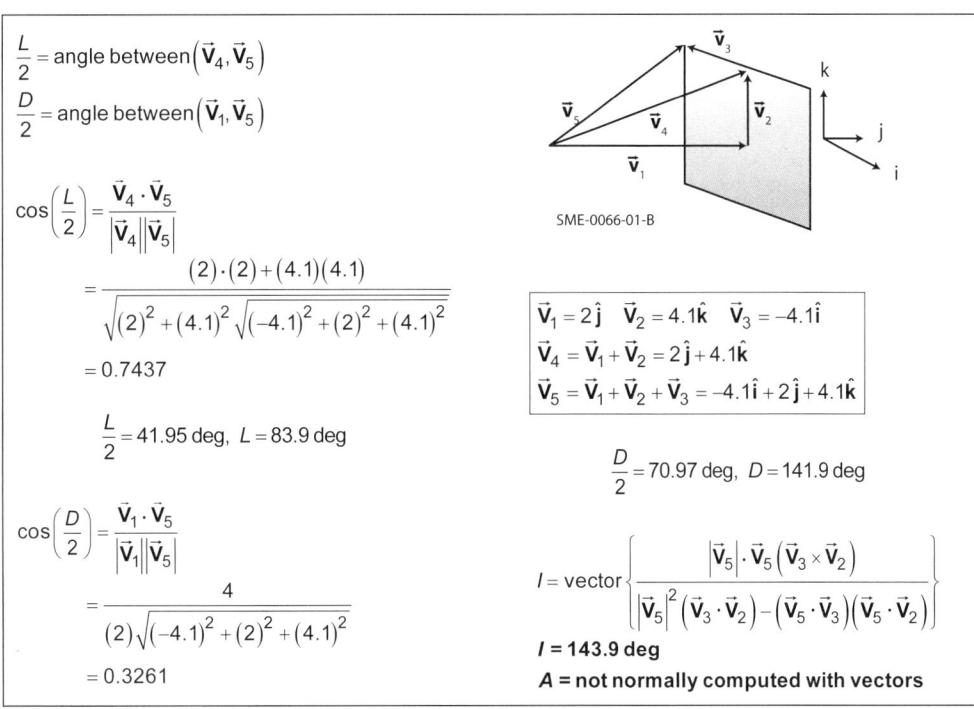

$$\frac{L}{2} = \text{angle between}\left(\vec{V}_4, \vec{V}_5\right)$$

$$\frac{D}{2} = \text{angle between}\left(\vec{V}_1, \vec{V}_5\right)$$

$$\cos\left(\frac{L}{2}\right) = \frac{\vec{V}_4 \cdot \vec{V}_5}{\left|\vec{V}_4\right|\left|\vec{V}_5\right|} = \frac{(2)\cdot(2)+(4.1)(4.1)}{\sqrt{(2)^2+(4.1)^2}\sqrt{(-4.1)^2+(2)^2+(4.1)^2}} = 0.7437$$

$$\frac{L}{2} = 41.95 \text{ deg}, \quad L = 83.9 \text{ deg}$$

$$\cos\left(\frac{D}{2}\right) = \frac{\vec{V}_1 \cdot \vec{V}_5}{\left|\vec{V}_1\right|\left|\vec{V}_5\right|} = \frac{4}{(2)\sqrt{(-4.1)^2+(2)^2+(4.1)^2}} = 0.3261$$

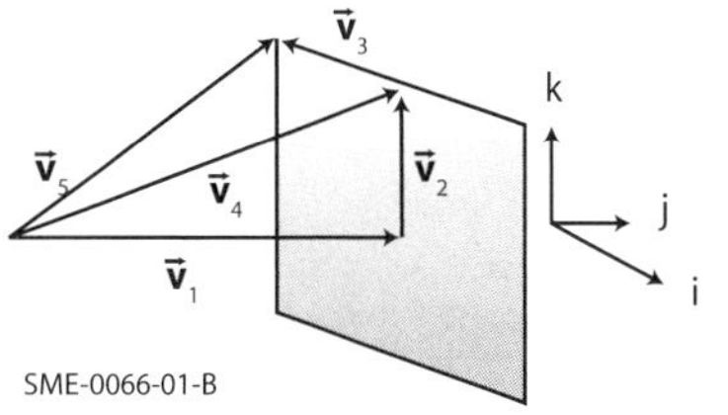

$$\vec{V}_1 = 2\hat{\mathbf{j}} \quad \vec{V}_2 = 4.1\hat{\mathbf{k}} \quad \vec{V}_3 = -4.1\hat{\mathbf{i}}$$
$$\vec{V}_4 = \vec{V}_1 + \vec{V}_2 = 2\hat{\mathbf{j}} + 4.1\hat{\mathbf{k}}$$
$$\vec{V}_5 = \vec{V}_1 + \vec{V}_2 + \vec{V}_3 = -4.1\hat{\mathbf{i}} + 2\hat{\mathbf{j}} + 4.1\hat{\mathbf{k}}$$

$$\frac{D}{2} = 70.97 \text{ deg}, \quad D = 141.9 \text{ deg}$$

$$I = \text{vector}\left\{\frac{\left|\vec{V}_5\right| \cdot \vec{V}_5\left(\vec{V}_3 \times \vec{V}_2\right)}{\left|\vec{V}_5\right|^2\left(\vec{V}_3 \cdot \vec{V}_2\right) - \left(\vec{V}_5 \cdot \vec{V}_3\right)\left(\vec{V}_5 \cdot \vec{V}_2\right)}\right\}$$

***I* = 143.9 deg**

***A* = not normally computed with vectors**

Fig. 8-18. Vector Solution to Sun Sensor Problem. The answer is correct, but both incomplete (since the area cannot be computed) and complex.

$$\tan(D/2) = \tan 64 \text{ deg} \;\; \cos 45 \text{ deg}$$
$$D = 141.9 \text{ deg} \tag{8-6}$$

From Eq. (8-3), the Spherical Excess (8-7)

$$= 4 \times 143.9 \text{ deg} - 360 \text{ deg} \tag{8-8}$$
$$= 215.6 \text{ deg}$$
$$= 3.763 \text{ rad}$$

$$A = 3.763 \text{ steradians}$$
$$= 29.9\% \text{ of the sphere} \tag{8-9}$$

Here the solution is exact, simple, and gives us good physical insight into how the solution will vary with different defining parameters. The sensor is 128 deg across at the middle, but the edges are only 84 deg long. In addition, two edges which are at right angles on the focal plane array intersect at an angle of 144 deg on the celestial sphere. While the rows and columns of the physical array may be orthogonal, the projected fields of view onto the sky are not orthogonal and indeed, are highly correlated.* Rows and columns near the edge of the sensor are no longer independent measurements. The large scale of the Sun sensor exaggerates the size of the effect. Nonetheless, sensors with smaller fields of view typically require much higher accuracy which may require the spherical geometry of the sensor field of view be taken into account. Typical magnitudes of plane geometry errors for various size fields of view are given in Table 8-7. Whether the differences between plane and spherical geometry are important for any given application will depend upon the required accuracies. This table allows us to judge whether a plane geometry approximation is appropriate. In any case, the correct computations in spherical geometry are extremely simple.

8.2.3 Example 2: Measurements Made by a Rectangular Array Sensor

As shown in Fig. 8-19, there are two basic types of rotation angle measurements:

- Type I—rotation about a known axis from a known reference direction to the unknown direction
- Type II—rotation about an unknown axis between two known points

A remarkably large number of sensors produce rotation angle measurements—rotating sensors, nearly all sensors on spinning spacecraft, and many fixed 3-axis sensors such as a two-dimensional array. As discussed in OCDM Sec. 7.1, the type of measurement is determined

* *Independent* or *uncorrelated* measurements are ones that do not depend on each other. In an ordinary rectangular coordinate frame, such as the layout of array sensor, the *x* and *y* measurements are orthogonal and uncorrelated — changing the value of *x* has no impact on the value of *y*. When this same array coordinate frame is projected onto the celestial sphere, that is no longer true and the measurements are said to be *correlated* or related to each other. As we move along the top row of the array for example, both the *x* and *y* values on the celestial sphere will change. If two measurements are *fully correlated*, they are simply two different ways of measuring the same thing, such as specifying a location on the Earth by giving the latitude and the distance from the North Pole. This gives us two measurements of the north-south location and no measurement of the East-West location.

Table 8-7. Representative Errors Using Plane Geometry Approximation for Sensor Fields of View. The subscript "plane" means a plane geometry approximation. The subscript "true" means the actual spherical geometry value. In the "128 deg Square Sun Sensor" in Fig. 8-17, L is the SIDE and *i* is the ANGLE.

FOV size (deg)	128 × 128	64 × 64	32 × 32	16 × 16	8 × 8	1 × 1	0.1 × 0.1
Application	Sun sensor; Earth at LEO	Sun sensor	General photographs	Earth at GEO	Star sensor	Small telescope	Larger telescope
Equivalent 35 mm Camera Lens	7 mm	25 mm	50 mm	85 mm	200 mm	1.7 m	17 m
$SIDE_{plane}$ (deg)	128.00	64.00	32.00	16.00	8.00	1.00000	0.1000
$SIDE_{true}$ (deg)	83.90	55.84	30.82	15.85	7.98	0.99996	0.9999996
$ANGLE_{plane}$ (deg)	90.00	90.00	90.00	90.00	90.00	90.0000	90.000
$ANGLE_{true}$ (deg)	143.88	106.31	94.36	91.11	90.28	90.0044	90.000044

by the solution loci on the celestial sphere. It is the shape of the loci that determines how the measurements should be processed, the arithmetic associated with analyzing and combining measurements, and the impact of sensor or mission geometry on the accuracy.

As we will demonstrate shortly, the Type I rotation angle is the basic measurement made by an array processor. In Sec. 8.2.2, we showed the projection of 128 × 128 deg field of view Sun sensor onto the celestial sphere, largely because the size of the sensor dramatically increased the impact of the spherical geometry effects and therefore made the nature of the results more apparent. Nonetheless, the same fundamental geometry and formulas apply to star sensors, payload array sensors, cameras, and any other instrument which uses a generally rectangular array with its field of view projected onto the sky. Because this is such a fundamental type of instrument, we will provide all the relevant formulas for a generic rectangular array.

As illustrated in Fig. 8-20, the basic assumption throughout is that the array is perfectly rectangular, i.e., has straight edges on the focal plane, and that the optical system itself is perfect, i.e., it behaves like a pinhole camera. Of course, a real camera adds distortion and absorbs light differently in various parts of the field of view. The effects that we are concerned with here are purely geometrical, i.e., taking a flat focal plane and projecting it onto the "curved" surface of the celestial sphere. Consequently, these effects apply to any sensor that uses a flat focal plane. This should be the starting point for any systematic calibration because it will minimize the magnitude of the variations. Larger arrays will be used to illustrate the effects more clearly, but numerical values will also be given for smaller fields of view.

Figure 8-21 shows the view projected onto the celestial sphere for the rectangular physical array illustrated in Fig. 8-20. Specifically, we assume that the focal plane array is perfectly rectangular and flat, with dimensions $2x_a$ by $2x_b$; that is, x_a is the distance from the center of the array to the edge of the array along the long axis, and x_b is the distance from the center to the edge along the

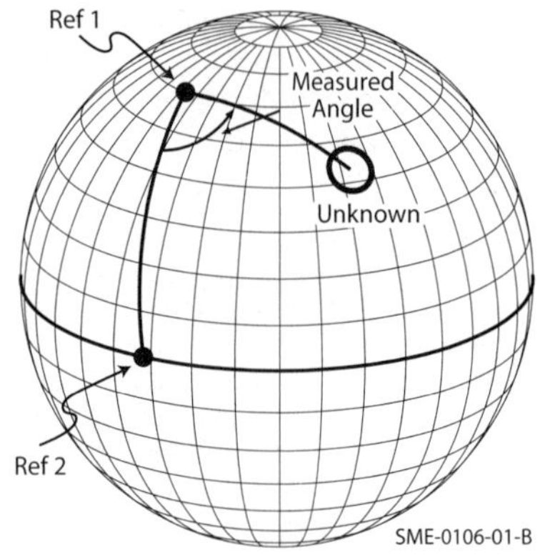

(A) Type I

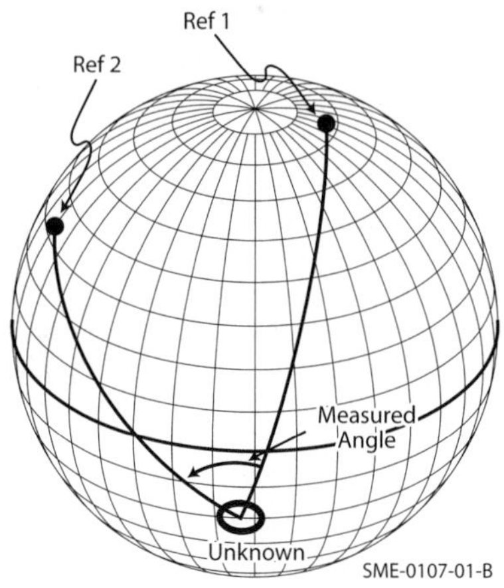

(B) Type II

Fig. 8-19. Two Types of Rotation Angle Measurements. (A) In *Type I* the measurement is made about a known reference axis from a second reference to the unknown direction. (B) In *Type II* the measurement is made about the unknown axis from one known reference to another.

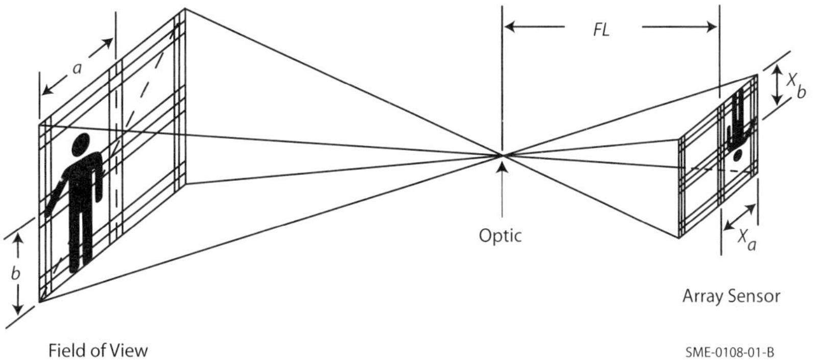

Fig. 8-20. Geometry of an Array Sensor. A rectangular sensor on the right looks through a perfect optical system. Pixels on the right are projected into space on the left and the stick figure in space is projected onto its corresponding location on the array. The projection onto the celestial sphere is shown in Fig. 8-21.

short axis. Since our camera or detector is assumed to be focused at infinity, the array is at a distance from the camera's focal point equal to the focal length, FL. Consequently, we can determine the angular dimensions of the array on the celestial sphere, a and b, by:

$$\tan a = x_a / FL \tag{8-10a}$$

$$\tan b = x_b / FL \tag{8-10b}$$

where a and b are now the angular dimensions projected onto the sky corresponding to the linear dimensions x_a and x_b. For example, a normal 35 mm camera produces a negative on the focal plane with an image size 36 mm × 24 mm. (It is called a 35 mm camera because the film is 35 mm wide, in the 24 mm direction because of the sprocket holes on either side.) This means that x_a = 18 mm and x_b = 12 mm. Projected onto the sky using a normal 50 mm focal length lens, a = atan (18/50) = 20 deg and b = atan (12/50) = 13.5 deg such that the total field of view on the sky is 40 deg wide by 27 deg high, measured through the center perpendicular to the edges.

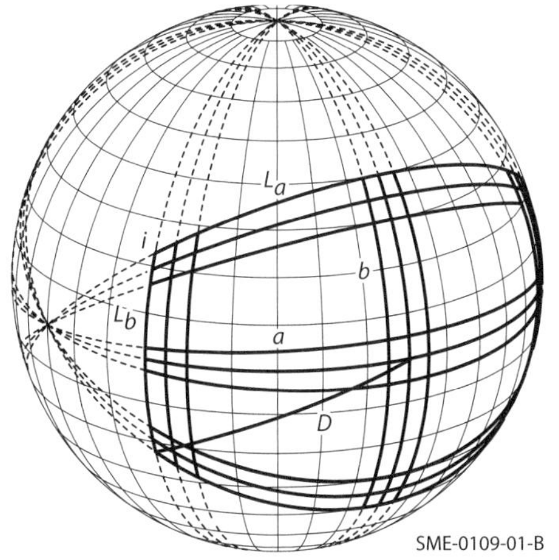

Fig. 8-21. Projection of a Rectangular Array onto the Celestial Sphere. The assumption here is that the projection is a perfect optical system. This is the image seen on the left in Fig. 8-20.

Given a and b in Fig. 8-21, we want to determine the formulas for the edge lengths L_a and L_b, the angle of intersection of the edges at the corner, i, the distance from the corner to the center (i.e., half the diagonal), D, and the area of the rectangular array. We also wish to calculate the basic parameters for the pixel size and shape at any place within the array. **Note**: Depending upon our application, we may think of a and b either as the dimensions of the entire array or as the coordinates of a given point on the array. Thus, x_a and x_b can be either the size of the physical array on the focal plane or can be the two coordinates of some pixel within that array whose position, size and shape we are trying to calculate.

Section 8.2.2 provided the geometry and formulas for a square array. Here we will describe the general formulas for a rectangular array with the notation shown in Fig. 8-22. The important characteristic here is that a straight line on the focal plane projects onto the sky as a great circle arc. Thus the rows and columns in our perfectly rectangular array project onto the sky as a series of

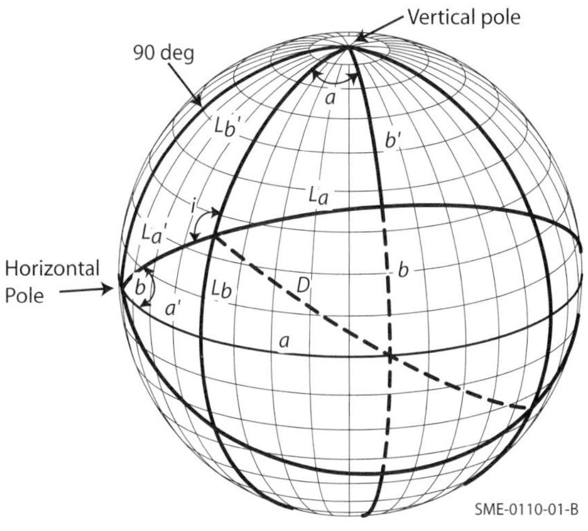

Fig. 8-22. Definition of Parameters for a Rectangular Array.

great circle arcs. The rows are all orthogonal to the middle column in the array and will project onto the sky as orthogonal to the great circle going vertically through the sensor, as shown in Fig. 8-21. Consequently, extending these great circle arcs on either side, they will all meet at a pole 90 deg on either side of the center of the sensor. Similarly, the columns on the physical focal plane array project as great circle arcs which meet at two poles, 90 deg above and below the projection of the center of the camera. By identifying a particular row in the array, we are identifying one of the horizontal great circle arcs. A particular column represents one of the vertical great circle arcs. Consequently, the row-column specification on the focal plane array corresponds to specifying two great circle arcs on the sky. The angle b represents the angular displacement of the point in question above or below the horizontal center line. The angle a represents the angular displacement of the column right or left of the vertical center line. These angles are measured along the two central axes and, therefore, are equal to the rotation angle measured at the pole of those central axes. Consequently, the measurement b implies that the pixel in question lies at a rotation angle b about the horizontal sensor pole upward from the reference axis. Similarly, a specification of a for the point in question means that the point lies along the great circle arc at rotation angle a, measured about the top or bottom pole relative to the reference axis. Thus, a and b are Type I rotation angle measurements.

Once we have recognized the nature of the array geometry, doing the arithmetic to calculate the various values is straightforward. First, note that we have constructed multiple quadrantal spherical triangles since the arc length between the horizontal and vertical poles is 90 deg, as is the arc length between either pole and the center of the field of view. Given the known quantity a, the angle in the quadrantal triangle, a', is just 90 deg – a, and similarly, $b' = 90$ deg – b. Consequently, we know two of the three rotation angles in the quadrantal triangle, and the remaining rotation angle and sides can be easily computed. We can then use the right spherical triangle between the corner of the rectangle and the center to determine the length of the diagonal. Given this triangle, we simply write down by inspection the formulas for the various components as follows:

$$\cos i = \sin a \ \sin b \tag{8-11}$$

$$\tan L_a = \tan a \ \cos b \tag{8-12}$$

$$\tan L_b = \tan b \ \cos a \tag{8-13}$$

$$\cos D = \cos L_a \cos b = \cos L_b \cos a \tag{8-14}$$

$$A = 4i - 2\pi \text{ (steradians)} \tag{8-15}$$

For a sensor array, we are interested not only in the general coordinates of various components in the array, but also in the size, shape, and area of individual pixels projected onto the sky. Here the geometry is shown in

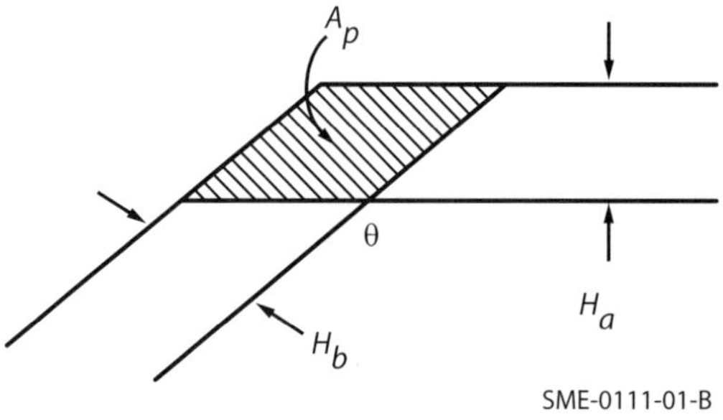

Fig. 8-23. Field of View of a Single Pixel Within a Rectangular Array.

Fig. 8-23. Because the spherical geometry effects are very small near the center, pixels near the center of the array have the shape that one would expect from plane geometry. However, this becomes more distorted as pixels get further from the center. In particular, the angular height of a pixel **along the central axes** is given by:

$$H_{a_\Delta} = \left(\Delta_{x_a} / FL\right) \cos^2 a \tag{8-16}$$

$$H_{b_\Delta} = \left(\Delta_{x_b} / FL\right) \cos^2 b \tag{8-17}$$

where H_{a_Δ} and H_{b_Δ} are the angular dimensions of the pixel in radians along the a and b directions, respectively, Δ_{x_a} and Δ_{x_b} are the linear dimensions of the pixels on the array, and FL is the focal length of the optical system. This is due simply to each pixel covering a smaller and smaller angle as it gets further from the optical axis; i.e., when I am in the center horizontally and move above or below the central horizontal axis, the angular height of each pixel will get shorter. If, in addition, I also move horizontally along a row the height of the pixel will get shorter still (by the cosine of the angle off the central axis) just as longitude lines come closer together as I move from the equator to the pole.

In addition, the angle at which the edges of the pixel intersect gets further from a right angle as it approaches the diagonal corners. In this case, the correlation angle, θ, or angle at which the edges of the pixel intersect is the same angle at which the sides of the image intersect. It is therefore equal to the angle i above. The area of the pixel, A_p, can be computed with a plane geometry approximation. Thus the pixel equations are as follows:

$$H_a = H_{a_0} \cos^2 a \cos L_b \tag{8-18}$$

$$H_b = H_{b_0} \cos L_a \cos^2 b \tag{8-19}$$

$$\cos\theta = \cos i = \sin a \ \sin b \tag{8-20}$$

$$A_p = H_{a_0} H_{b_0} \cos L_a \cos L_b \cos^2 a \ \cos^2 b / \sin\theta \tag{8-21}$$

where H_a is the angular height of the pixel in the a direction, H_{a_0} is the angular height of the pixel along the ref-

The Meaning of "Distortion" in Projecting the Celestial Sphere onto a Flat focal Plane Array

It is important to clearly understand what is meant by "distortion" in this context. Assume that we take a picture of a brick wall from some distance away with the optical axis of the camera pointed precisely perpendicular to the wall. In our "perfect" camera with no "optical irregularities," the picture we take of the brick wall will be an exact, though reduced, duplicate of the wall itself. The rows of bricks will line up precisely with the edges of the film. On the print, each brick will have the same area, and so on. However, for a brick that is 45 deg off the central axis both horizontally and vertically the angular area subtended by that brick, from the right hand column in Table 8-8, is 19.2% of the angular area of a brick on the optical axis. This means that I will have less than 20% of the light and less than 20% of the image intensity relative to those bricks directly in front of the camera. Another way to think of it is that the light coming from a brick in the corner of the field-of-view, which appears very small when we look at it, must be spread out to cover the same area on the negative as the light from a brick right in front of us that covers a much larger angular area.

That parallel lines get "closer together" as they get further away is known to anyone that does much drawing or photography. This is usually expressed as "parallel lines converge at infinity" and is most easily seen in railroad tracks or the edges of a highway. Again, this is expressed mathematically in the columns labeled H_a and H_b in Table 8-8.

Finally, the correlation between "orthogonal" directions seen off-axis is much less apparent in everyday life, but can be observed. Try standing very close to a wall and looking at the corner where two walls and the ceiling come together. This intersection represents three orthogonal axes. As your eye gets very close to the wall, the two perpendicular edges of the wall you're next to begin to form nearly a straight line at the corner. A bug walking at the corner will appear to be moving in nearly the same direction if he is going up the seam between the two walls or toward you along the seam between the wall and the ceiling. This is a manifestation of the correlation between orthogonal components expressed in the "i" column in Table 8-8.

Although these effects are apparent only in extreme cases, they are still present in any array image. Whether they are important depends on the precision required. Thus, Table 8-8 should be used as a guide to the size of the effects so that you determine what needs to be taken into account in any given problem.

erence axis through the center of the sensor, and A_p is the area of the pixel.

Table 8-8 gives both the array size and pixel size and shape for a variety of rectangular arrays. This gives a sense of the geometric distortion that comes about, not from any optical irregularities, but simply from the process of projecting the celestial sphere onto a flat image plane.

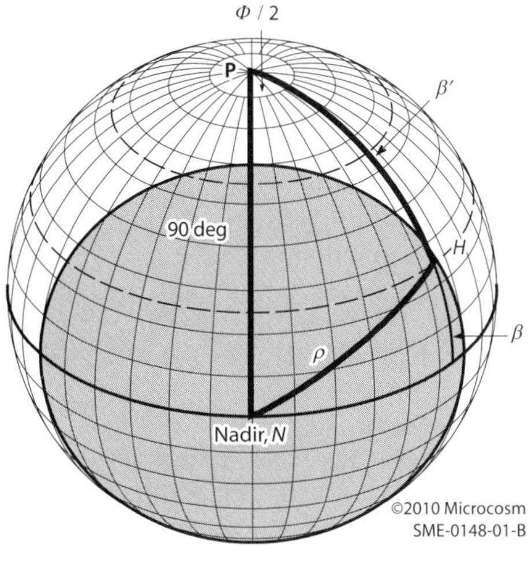

Fig. 8-24. Computation of Eclipse Duration. Compare with Fig. 8-7C in Sec. 8.1.1.

Note that by the time I've gotten to the corner of a 60 deg × 60 deg sensor, the half-length of the sides is only 41 deg and the correlation angle at which the sides intersect is nearly 140 deg, such that a "rectangular" pixel is very distinctly diamond shaped. The distance from the center of the sensor is only 68 deg. Equally important, the pixel that was 1 deg by 1 deg at the center is now only 0.2 deg × 0.2 deg. In addition to its rather elongated shape, the angular area has now been reduced to 5% of the area of one of the pixels at the center. It is this effect that produces the dimmer image at the sides and corners of photographs or electronic images.

Whether or not the spherical geometry calculations are necessary for your particular problem can be determined by examining the size of the effects shown in Table 8-8. Notice, however, that the correct spherical geometric equations in Eqs. (8-11) through (8-21) are extremely simple, such that doing the computation correctly, rather than incorrectly in plane geometry, is very straightforward.

8.2.4 Example 3: Calculating the Duration of an Eclipse

This example returns to the eclipse problem illustrated in Fig. 8-7 in Sec. 8.1.1. The computational geometry is shown in Fig. 8-24. Recall that the altitude of the satellite was 1,000 km, which implies that the angular radius of the Earth $\rho = 59.8$ deg [see Eq. (8-26) in Sec. 8.3.1].

Table 8-8. Coordinates and Dimensions on the Celestial Sphere for a 1 deg × 1 deg Pixel (Measured at the Center of the Array). See Fig. 8-22 and Fig.8-23 for the definition of variables. The most important parameters are *i* for which a value different from 90 deg indicates a correlation between the sensor rows and columns and A_p (the projected area of the pixel) which shows the reduction in coverage by pixels away from the center. Note that this assumes a pixel size that gives a 1 deg × 1 deg field of view on the optical axis of the sensor. The dimensions and area in the 3 right columns can be proportionally adjusted for other pixel sizes.

a	b	L_a	L_b	D	$\theta = i$	H_a	H_b	A_p
0	0	0.00	0.00	0.00	90.00	1.00	1.00	1.000
5	0	5.00	0.00	5.00	90.00	0.99	1.00	0.989
5	5	4.98	4.98	7.05	90.44	0.99	0.99	0.977
10	0	10.00	0.00	10.00	90.00	0.97	0.98	0.955
10	5	9.96	4.92	11.14	90.87	0.97	0.98	0.945
10	10	9.85	9.85	14.00	91.73	0.96	0.96	0.913
15	0	15.00	0.00	15.00	90.00	0.93	0.97	0.901
15	5	14.95	4.83	15.74	91.29	0.93	0.96	0.892
15	10	14.78	9.67	17.78	92.58	0.92	0.94	0.863
15	15	14.51	14.51	20.75	93.84	0.90	0.90	0.818
30	0	30.00	0.00	30.00	90.00	0.75	0.87	0.650
30	5	29.91	4.33	30.28	92.50	0.75	0.86	0.644
30	10	29.62	8.68	31.12	94.98	0.74	0.84	0.627
30	15	29.15	13.06	32.48	97.44	0.73	0.81	0.600
30	30	26.57	26.57	39.23	104.48	0.67	0.67	0.465
45	0	45.00	0.00	45.00	90.00	0.50	0.71	0.354
45	5	44.89	3.54	45.11	93.53	0.50	0.70	0.352
45	10	44.56	7.11	45.44	97.05	0.50	0.69	0.345
45	15	44.01	10.73	45.99	100.55	0.49	0.67	0.335
45	30	40.89	22.21	49.11	110.70	0.46	0.57	0.281
45	45	35.26	35.26	54.74	120.00	0.41	0.41	0.192
60	0	60.00	0.00	60.00	90.00	0.25	0.50	0.125
60	5	59.91	2.50	60.03	94.33	0.25	0.50	0.125
60	10	59.62	5.04	60.13	98.65	0.25	0.49	0.124
60	15	59.13	7.63	60.29	102.95	0.25	0.48	0.122
60	30	56.31	16.10	61.29	115.66	0.24	0.42	0.111
60	45	50.77	26.57	63.43	127.76	0.22	0.32	0.089
60	60	40.89	40.89	67.79	138.59	0.19	0.19	0.054

For specificity we will calculate the duration of the eclipse when the Sun is 25 deg out of the orbit plane, i.e., $\beta = 25$ deg in Fig. 8-24.

We use the pole, **P**, of the coordinate system, which is also the orbit pole, as one of the corners of a spherical triangle. This is one of the most common spherical geometry computation techniques, and the pole of the coordinate system is often chosen such that it can be a corner of a spherical triangle. The second corner is the point, **H**, at which the Sun crosses the horizon of the Earth's disk, i.e., at the beginning or end of the eclipse, and the third point is the direction to nadir, **N**, or the center of the Earth. The angle from the orbit pole to nadir is 90 deg by definition, so we have constructed a quadrantal spherical triangle. The angular radius of the Earth, $\rho = 59.8$ deg, is known. Similarly, the side $\beta' = 90\,\text{deg} - \beta = 65$ deg is also known. Consequently, we can use Napier's rules for quadrantal triangles to determine any of the three rotation angles. In particular, we would like to determine $\Phi/2$ at the orbit pole, which is given by:

$$\cos(\Phi/2) = \cos\rho / \sin\beta' \tag{8-22}$$

If $\beta' = 65\,\text{deg}$, then $\Phi/2 = 56.3$ deg and $\Phi = 112.6$ deg. This is the rotation angle covered by the Sun as it passes behind the disk of the Earth. Since the orbit is assumed to be circular with the spacecraft moving at a constant angular rate, the eclipse duration will be $112.6/360 =$ 31.3% of the orbit. With an orbit period of 105 min, this gives an eclipse duration of 32.9 min for this example. The formulation is extremely simple, and can be easily evaluated for other angles of the Sun out of the orbit plane. In addition, we could take into account the 0.5 deg diameter of the Sun itself, or the angular height of the Earth's atmosphere, and calculate, for example, the time at which eclipse begins, when it reaches full darkness, or the length of twilight at either end. None of these computations requires complex simulations or detailed orbit analysis. Simple geometrical calculations give us good insight into both the duration and character of eclipses seen from space.

For eccentric orbits the situation is more complex, because the eclipse fraction varies depending upon where the eclipse occurs relative to apogee and perigee. Nonetheless, we can relatively easily determine the eclipse extremes that occur at apogee and perigee. First, note that even though the orbit is noncircular, the projection of the orbit plane onto the celestial sphere, and therefore, the apparent path of the Earth will still be a great circle. The differences from a circular orbit are twofold. The Earth moves at a nonuniform rate along this great circle and the apparent size of the Earth's disk changes with changing altitude. As shown in Fig. 8-25 the no-eclipse region about either pole will change from circular to an approximately oval shape with a much larger no-eclipse region in the direction of apogee. The maximum eclipse at both apogee and perigee will, of course, occur when the Sun is in the orbit plane, and is given by:

$$E_{A/P} \approx \left(\frac{\rho_{A/P}}{180}\right)\left(\frac{R_E + H_{A/P}}{a}\right) \qquad (8\text{-}23)$$

$$a = R_E + (H_A + H_P)/2 \qquad (8\text{-}24)$$

where $E_{A/P}$ is the fraction of the orbit period spent in eclipse at apogee and perigee when the Sun is in the orbit plane, $\rho_{A/P}$ is the angular radius of the Earth at apogee or perigee in degrees, R_E is the radius of the Earth, $H_{A/P}$ is the height of apogee and perigee and a is the semimajor axis. The angular radius of the Earth can be evaluated using Eq. (8-25) in Sec. 8.3.1. The effect of the Sun not being in the orbit plane can be determined using Eq. (8-22), just as for circular orbits. Note that the excursion range is not as large as one might anticipate, since at apogee the Earth's disk is much smaller, but the spacecraft is moving more slowly, thus providing some compensation. For example, in an extremely elliptical orbit with perigee at 500 km and apogee at geosynchronous altitude of 35,768 km, the maximum eclipse at perigee is 10.6% of the orbit period, vs. 8.3% at apogee. However, as the Sun moves out of the orbit plane, it will enter the no-eclipse region at apogee far more quickly than at perigee.

8.3 Looking at the Earth from Space

This section is intended as a cookbook for Earth coverage. Our goal is to provide a practical set of formulas and algorithms for analyzing Earth coverage from space. We will use the preceding sections for both motivation and derivations as appropriate. Formulas for a single ground station or target pass and what the spacecraft sees are covered here. Formulas for the ground track over the Earth and coverage over time are discussed in the Earth Coverage section in 10.6.

Throughout the section, we give vector formulations wherever they are significantly different from the spherical geometry formulation. To make the text easier to follow, the vector formulations have been put in inline notes, separated from the remainder of the text by a rule at the top and bottom, and a substantial philosophical gulf. Those who have reviewed the preceding two sections may safely ignore the inline notes. On the other hand, those who remain staunchly unconverted (direct descendants of those who refused to look through Galileo's telescope, no doubt) will find the necessary formulas in the inline notes and can ignore the rest of the text.

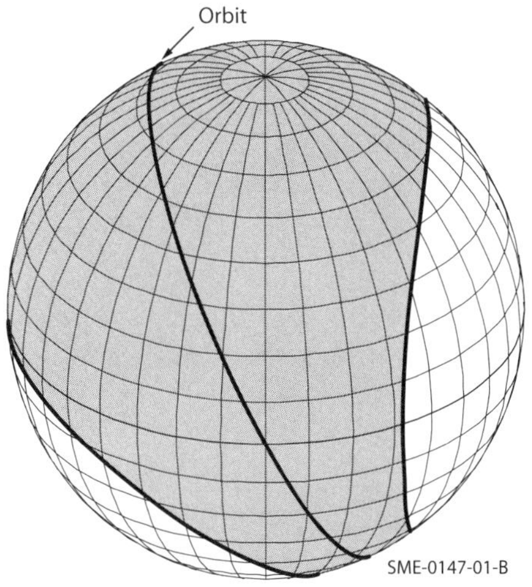

Fig. 8-25. Motion of the Disk of the Earth in an Eccentric Orbit. Shaded area is the portion of the celestial sphere blocked by the disk of the Earth. Compare with Fig. 8-7B in Sec. 8.1.1.

A spherical Earth model is used throughout the chapter. For problems which represent pure coordinate transformations, the spherical approximation to the Earth's surface is exact so long as geocentric coordinates are used for the Earth. For problems involving the physical surface of the Earth, Earth's oblateness may need to be taken into account, depending upon the accuracy required. In low-Earth orbit, Earth oblateness can shift the position of the horizon by as much as a few tenths of a degree on an angular radius of 60 to 70 deg. Consequently, oblateness may be important for data analysis, but is rarely of concern for mission analysis or planning. Alternative methods for taking oblateness into account are discussed in OCDM Sec. 8.1.5.

8.3.1 Transforming Between Earth and Spacecraft Coordinates

The most common problem in space mission geometry is to transform back and forth between Earth coordinates and the view as seen from the spacecraft. This section provides all of the fundamental formulas in both spherical geometry and vector forms for making this transformation. An example of problems of this type is to use the given coordinates of a target on the Earth to determine its coordinates in the spacecraft field of view. Another is to determine the intercept point on the surface of the Earth corresponding to a given direction in spacecraft coordinates or a given location in the field of view of a spacecraft camera.

Figure 8-26 shows the relationship between geometry on the Earth's surface and as seen from the spacecraft. A vector from the spacecraft will be tangent to the surface of the Earth at the *true* or *geometric horizon.* (The *effective horizon* introduced in Sec. 10.6 will be nearer to the spacecraft subsatellite point due to both foreshortening and atmospheric absorption.) The area inside the horizon is called the *access area*; it represents all of the surface of the Earth that the spacecraft can communicate with or

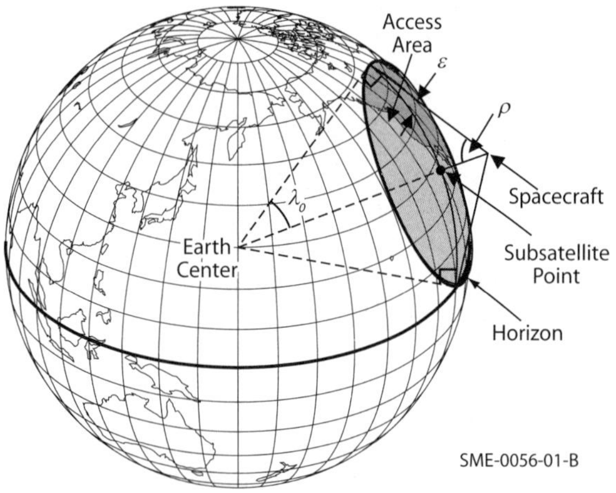

Fig. 8-26. Relationship Between Geometry as Viewed from the Spacecraft and from the Center of the Earth.

observe at this time. For a spherical Earth, the true horizon will be a small circle. The angular radius of this circle is called the *maximum Earth Central Angle*, λ_0, when measured from the center of the Earth, and the *angular radius of the Earth*, ρ, when measured from the spacecraft. The axis of the two cones formed by the horizon and either the Earth's center or the spacecraft is the *spacecraft position vector* when it goes from the center of the Earth to the spacecraft, and the *nadir vector* when it goes from the spacecraft to the center of the Earth. This line intersects the surface of the Earth at the *subsatellite point, SSP*. Finally, the direction toward the center of the Earth is called *nadir*, and the opposite direction is called *zenith.* Thus, for an observer standing at the subsatellite point, the center of the Earth is in the nadir direction and the spacecraft is at the zenith. (Nadir and zenith are well defined for an observer on the spacecraft or on the Earth's surface, but not for an observer at the center of the Earth).

For both conceptual and computational purposes, it is convenient to define an access area coordinate frame on the Earth's surface corresponding to the nadir-centered coordinate frame on the spacecraft. As shown in Fig. 8-27, the elevation component is the Earth Central Angle, λ, measured from the SSP and the azimuthal angle, Φ_E, is the rotation angle measured about SSP from a reference direction to the point in question. Depending upon the particular problem, the reference direction may be either North or the projection of the velocity vector down onto the Earth's surface. The transformation between latitude and longitude and access area coordinates is straightforward and is given in the boxed example at the end of this section.

Our fundamental geometry problem has now been reduced to transforming back and forth between access area coordinates on the surface of the Earth and spacecraft coordinates centered on nadir. This is particularly easy to do for the azimuthal component, since it is the same azimuth angle measured in either frame of reference, i.e., the azimuth is the angle between two planes—one containing the spacecraft, the center of the Earth, and the pole, and the other containing the spacecraft, the center of the Earth, and the target. In order to keep the rotation right handed, as seen from the spacecraft and on the Earth's surface, we introduce a minus sign so that:

$$\Phi_{spc} = -\Phi_E \tag{8-25}$$

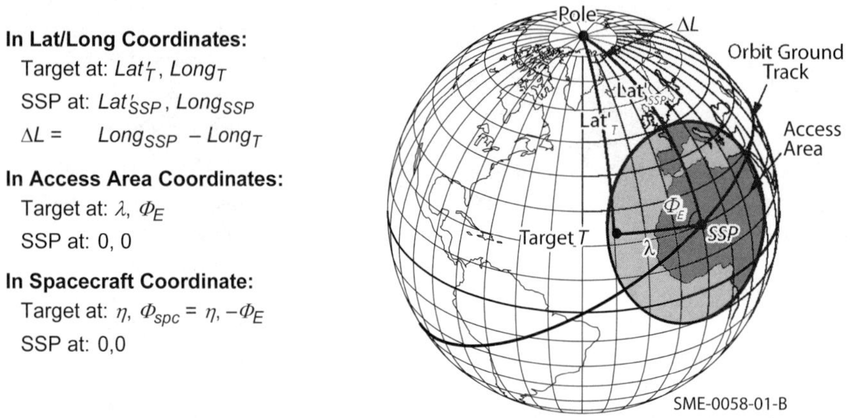

Fig. 8-27. Definition of the Access Area Coordinate Frame. See the box at the end of Sec. 8.3.1 for transformation equations.

where Φ_{spc} is the azimuthal angle about nadir from the reference direction to the target point, and Φ_E is the same angle measured on the surface of the Earth about the subsatellite point.

The remaining problem is to transform the radial component. Depending on the problem at hand, it is convenient to measure this radial component either in terms of angles at the satellite, at the Earth's center, or at the target point on the surface of the Earth. As shown in Fig. 8-28, the *nadir angle,* η, is measured at the spacecraft from the subsatellite point (= nadir direction) to the target. The Earth central angle, λ ,is measured at the center of the Earth from the subsatellite point to the target, and the *grazing angle* or *spacecraft elevation angle*, ε, is the angle measured at the target between the spacecraft and the local horizontal. First, we find the angular radius of the Earth, ρ, and the maximum Earth Central Angle, λ_0, from:

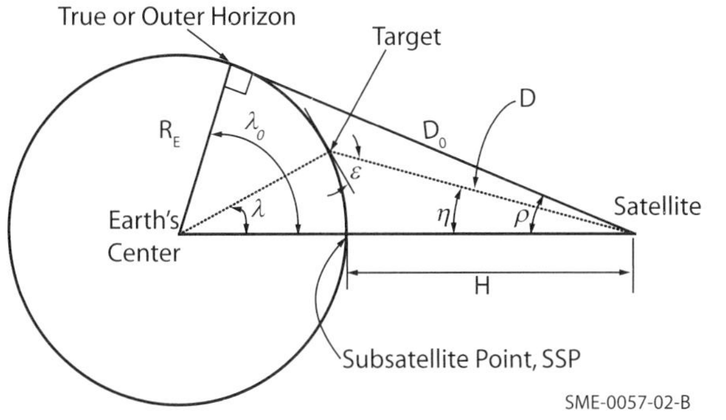

Fig. 8-28. Definition of Angular Relationships Between the Satellite, Target, and Earth's Center.

$$\sin\rho = \cos\lambda_0 = \frac{R_E}{R_E + H} \tag{8-26}$$

where R_E is the radius of the Earth = 6,378.136 6 km and H is the altitude of the spacecraft. Next, if λ is known, we find η from:

$$\tan\eta = \frac{\sin\rho\ \sin\lambda}{1-\sin\rho\ \cos\lambda} \tag{8-27}$$

Or, if η is known, we find ε from:

$$\cos\varepsilon = \frac{\sin\eta}{\sin\rho} \tag{8-28}$$

Or, if ε is known, we find η from:

$$\sin\eta = \cos\varepsilon\ \sin\rho \tag{8-29}$$

Finally, the remaining angle is determined from:

$$\eta + \lambda + \varepsilon = 90\text{ deg} \tag{8-30}$$

The distance D, to the target, is:

$$D = R_E\,(\sin\lambda / \sin\eta) \tag{8-31}$$

and the distance to the true horizon D_0 is given by:

$$D_0 = R_E / \tan\rho \tag{8-32}$$

Vector Formulation

For the corresponding vector equations, see the boxed example at the end of this subsection.

As an example, consider a satellite at an altitude of 1,000 km. From Eq. (8-26), the angular radius of the Earth, ρ = 59.8 deg. From Eqs. (8-26) and (8-32), the horizon is 30.2 deg in Earth Central Angle from the subsatellite point and is at a line-of-sight distance of 3,709 km from the satellite. We will assume a ground station at Hawaii (D_r=22 deg, L_r = 200 deg) and a subsatellite point at δ_S = 10 deg, L_S = 185 deg. From Eqs. (8-33) and (8-34), the ground station is a distance λ = 18.7 deg from the subsatellite point, and has an azimuth relative to North = 48.3 deg. Using Eqs. (8-27) and (8-31) to transform into spacecraft coordinates, we find that at the spacecraft from the subsatellite point to the target is 56.8 deg up from nadir (η) at a line of sight distance, D, of 2,444 km. From Eq. (8-30), the elevation of the spacecraft as seen from the ground station is 14.5 deg. The substantial foreshortening at the horizon can be seen in that at ε = 14.5 deg we are nearly half way from the horizon to the subsatellite point (λ = 18.7 deg vs. 30.2 deg at the horizon).

The spherical Earth approximation is adequate for most mission geometry applications. However, for precise work, we must apply a correction for oblateness as described in OCDM Sec. 8.15. The Earth's oblateness has two distinct effects on the shape of the Earth as seen from space. First, the Earth appears slightly oblate rather than round, and second, the center of the visible oblate Earth is displaced from the true geometric center of the Earth. Except when we are specifically dealing with oblateness, we will use spherical coordinates throughout this chapter, both on the Earth and in the spacecraft frame. Computationally, we can treat both oblateness and surface irregularities as simply the target's altitude above or below a purely spherical Earth or, equivalently, as a small variation in the radius of the Earth. That the Earth's real surface is both irregular and oblate is immaterial to the computation and, therefore, the results are exact.

8.3.2 Earth Features Viewed from Space

What does the surface of the Earth look like from space? This is a key question, not only for understanding what an astronaut sees, but for developing an understanding of how to design space missions and analyze data from them. We are so used to looking at projections onto the Earth that it is easy to forget that it is the geometry as seen from the spacecraft that has a major impact on the capacity of the spacecraft to fulfill its objectives.

Transformations Between Latitude/Longitude, Access Area Coordinates, and Spacecraft Nadir Coordinates

To transform between the various coordinate sets, we first define coordinates for the subsatellite point and for the *target* (i.e., the point on the surface of the Earth we wish to determine or point at). As shown in Fig. 8-27 in the text, the geocentric coordinates (latitude and longitude) for these points are:

Target Point, **T**, at $(Lat_T, Long_T)$
Subsatellite Point (*SSP*), **S**, at $(Lat_{SSP}, Long_{SSP})$
$\Delta L \equiv Long_{SSP} - Long_T$

In Area Access coordinates:

Target Point, **T**, at (λ, Φ_E)
Subsatellite Point, **S**, at $(0, 0)$

and, in Spacecraft Nadir coordinates:

Target Point, **T**, at $(\eta, \Phi_{spc}) = (\eta, -\Phi_E)$
Subsatellite Point, **S**, at $(0, 0)$

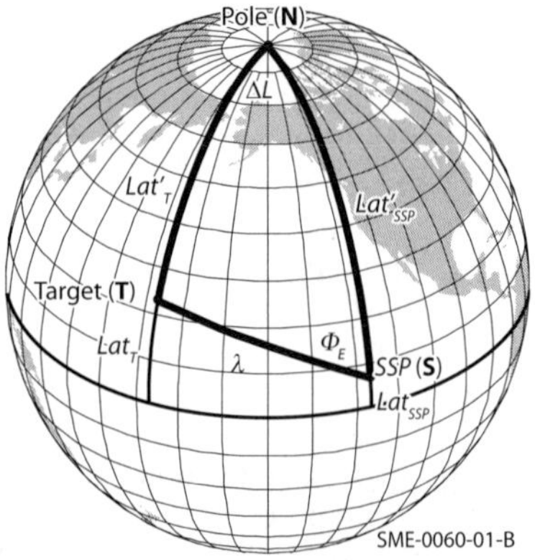

Fig. 8-29. Relationship Between the Target and the Subsatellite Point on the Earth's Surface.

Using spherical coordinates on both the Earth's surface and the spacecraft, and given the latitude and longitude for the target and *SSP*, we have:

$$\lambda = \text{acos}\,[\cos Lat'_T \cos Lat'_{SSP} + \sin Lat'_T \sin Lat'_{SSP} \cos \Delta L\,] \quad (8\text{-}33)$$

$$\Phi_E = \text{acos2}\left[\frac{\cos Lat'_T - \cos Lat'_{SSP} \cos\lambda}{(\sin Lat'_{SSP} \sin\lambda)}, H(\Delta L)\right] \quad (8\text{-}34)$$

where $Lat' \equiv (90 \text{ deg} - Lat)$ is the angle measured from the pole and is frequently more convenient to use. The acos function is evaluated over range 0 to 180 deg, and the acos2 and *hemisphere function, H,* are defined in App. D.4.* Given the area access coordinates (λ, Φ_E), we have:

$\eta = \text{atan}\,[\sin\rho \sin\lambda\,/(1 - \sin\rho\,\cos\lambda)]$
point is on visible side if $\lambda < (90 \text{ deg} - \rho)$ (8-35)

$$\varepsilon = \text{acos}\,(\sin\eta\,/\,\sin\rho) \quad (8\text{-}36)$$

$$\lambda = 90 \text{ deg} - \eta - \varepsilon \quad (8\text{-}37)$$

$$Lat'_T = \text{acos}\,[\,\cos\lambda \cos Lat'_{SSP} + \sin\lambda \sin Lat'_{SSP} \cos\Phi_E\,] \quad (8\text{-}38)$$

$$\Delta L = \text{acos}\left[\frac{\cos\lambda - \cos Lat'_T \cos Lat'_{SSP}}{H(Lat'_{SSP}) \sin Lat'_{SSP} \sin Lat'_T}\right] - 90 \text{ deg}\left[H(Lat'_{SSP}) - 1\right] \quad (8\text{-}39)$$

Vector Formulation

To do the problem using vectors, we first define the vector quantities shown on Fig. 8-29 as follows:

T = target vector from the center of the Earth to the target point

S = spacecraft position vector from the center of the Earth to the spacecraft, and

O = observation vector from the spacecraft to the target.

Given **T** and **S**, we determine the observation vector, **O**, from the spacecraft by:

$$\mathbf{O} = \mathbf{T} - \mathbf{S} \quad (8\text{-}40)$$

Given the observation unit vector, $\hat{\mathbf{O}}$, from the spacecraft, first determine the distance to Earth's surface, *D*:

$$D = -(\mathbf{S}\cdot\hat{\mathbf{O}}) \pm \sqrt{(\mathbf{S}\cdot\hat{\mathbf{O}})^2 - |\mathbf{S}|^2 + R_E^{\,2}} \quad (8\text{-}41)$$

where R_E is the Earth radius (6,378.136 km), and the smaller value of *D* corresponds to the intersection on the visible portion of the Earth. Then,

$$\mathbf{O} = (D\cdot\hat{\mathbf{O}}) \quad (8\text{-}42)$$

$$\mathbf{T} = \mathbf{S} + \mathbf{O} \quad (8\text{-}43)$$

To compute the observability parameters, ρ, η, ε, λ, and Φ_E.

$$\eta = \text{acos}(-\hat{\mathbf{S}}\cdot\hat{\mathbf{O}}) \quad (8\text{-}44)$$

$$\rho = \text{asin}\,(R_E\,/\,|\mathbf{S}|) \quad (8\text{-}45)$$

$$\varepsilon = \text{acos}(\hat{\mathbf{T}}\cdot\hat{\mathbf{O}}) - 90 \text{ deg} \quad (8\text{-}46)$$

$$\lambda = \text{acos}(\hat{\mathbf{S}}\cdot\hat{\mathbf{T}}) \quad (8\text{-}47)$$

The point is visible if $\lambda < (90 \text{ deg} - \rho)$. Finally,

$$\Phi_E = \text{acos}\left[(\hat{\mathbf{S}}\times\hat{\mathbf{N}})\cdot(\hat{\mathbf{S}}\cdot\hat{\mathbf{T}})\,/\,|\hat{\mathbf{S}}\times\hat{\mathbf{N}}|\cdot|\hat{\mathbf{S}}\cdot\hat{\mathbf{T}}|\right] \quad (8\text{-}48)$$

where $\hat{\mathbf{N}}$ is the unit vector from the center of the Earth to the celestial pole.

* For complete treatment of full-sky spherical geometry see Wertz [2009], Chap. 8 and App. A.

Figure 8-30 is a photo of the Earth taken by the Apollo 17 astronauts on their way to the Moon. Northern Africa, Arabia, the Red Sea, and the Mediterranean are all clearly visible at the top of the photo. The Antarctic polar ice cap is visible at the bottom although it blends in with the clouds somewhat. The brightest feature by far is the cloud tops such that weather patterns become much more visible than features on the surface. There is also good contrast between the desert in northern Africa and the vegetation in central Africa. Although this view is nearly a "full Earth," the terminator, or sunrise/sunset line, can be seen by the slightly fuzzier, right-hand edge of the Earth's disk. Also, notice the bright spot in the clouds just above and to the left of center. This is the specular reflection of the Sun off the clouds where the angle of incidence equals the angle reflection. Finally, notice that around the perimeter you don't see any detail, even where it is cloud-free. This is an example of the geometrical foreshortening that dominates much of spacecraft viewing of the Earth.

To clearly illustrate the geometrical effects, Fig. 8-31 shows the geometry on the surface of the Earth and as seen from spacecraft for a satellite at 1,000 km over Mexico's Yucatan Peninsula at the southern edge of the Gulf of Mexico. The left side shows the geometry on the surface of the Earth. The right side shows the geometry as seen by the spacecraft projected onto the spacecraft-centered celestial sphere, i.e. what the spacecraft really sees. As computed in Sec. 8.3.1, the maximum Earth central angle will be approximately 30 deg from this altitude, such that the spacecraft can see from northwestern South America to Maine on the East Coast of the U.S. and Los Angeles on the West Coast. The angular radius of the Earth as seen from the spacecraft will be 90 – 30 = 60 deg as shown in Fig. 8-31B. Because the spacecraft is over 20 North latitude, the direction to nadir in spacecraft-centered celestial coordinates will be 20 deg south of the celestial equator. (The direction from the spacecraft to the Earth's center is exactly opposite the direction from the Earth's center to the spacecraft.)

Even after staring at it a bit, the view from the spacecraft in Fig. 8-31B looks strange. First, recall that we are looking at the spacecraft-centered celestial sphere **from the outside**. The spacecraft is at the center of the sphere. Therefore, the view for us is reversed right-to-left relative to the view as seen by the spacecraft. Consequently, the Atlantic is on the left and the Pacific on the right. Nonetheless, there still appear to be distortions in the view. Mexico has an odd shape and South America has almost disappeared. All of this is due to the very strong foreshortening at the edge of the Earth's disk. Notice, for example, that on the Earth, Jacksonville, FL, is about halfway from the subsatellite point to the horizon. This means that only 1/4th of the area seen by the spacecraft is closer to the subsatellite point than Jacksonville. Nonetheless, as seen from the perspective of the spacecraft (Fig. 8-31B and B′), Jacksonville is 54 deg from nadir, i.e., 90% of the way to the horizon with 3/4ths of the visible area beyond it.

Fig. 8-30. Photo of the Earth from Apollo 17 on the Way to the Moon. See text for discussion. (Photo courtesy of NASA)

The rectangle in the upper left of Fig. 8-31B is the field of view of a 35 mm camera with a 50 mm focal length lens (a normal lens that is neither wide angle nor telephoto). The camera person on our spacecraft has photographed Florida and the eastern seaboard of the U.S. to approximately Maine. The region photographed on the Earth is shown in Fig. 8-31A′ and 8-31B′ and an enlargement of a portion of the photo from Georgia to Maine is shown in Fig. 8-31B″. Note the dramatic foreshortening as Long Island and Cape Cod become little more than horizontal lines (Fig 8-30B″), even though they are some distance from the horizon. This distortion does not come from the plotting style, but is what the spacecraft sees. We see the same effect standing on a hilltop or a mountain. (In a sense, the spacecraft is simply a very tall mountain, even when the spacecraft is Apollo 17 on the way to the Moon.) Most of our angular field of view is taken up by the mountain top we are standing on. For our satellite, most of what is seen is the Yucatan and Gulf of Mexico directly below. There is plenty of real estate at the horizon, but it appears very compressed.

As shown quantitatively in Fig. 8-51 in Sec. 8.6.2 we can point an antenna approximately equally well at Cancun on the Yucatan below us or at Boston, on the horizon. However, as shown in Fig. 8-50, mapping can be done extremely well directly below us, but is nearly impossible near the horizon. From the perspective of the satellite, we can draw an excellent map of the Yucatan or the Gulf of Mexico. We can point our antenna at Boston. But we can not realistically map Boston or Massachusetts from the current location of the satellite.

8.3.3 Directions, Shapes, and Areas

Figure 8-31 provides a good conceptual view of the geometry as seen from space. However, for analysis and computation, it is most convenient to work in terms of

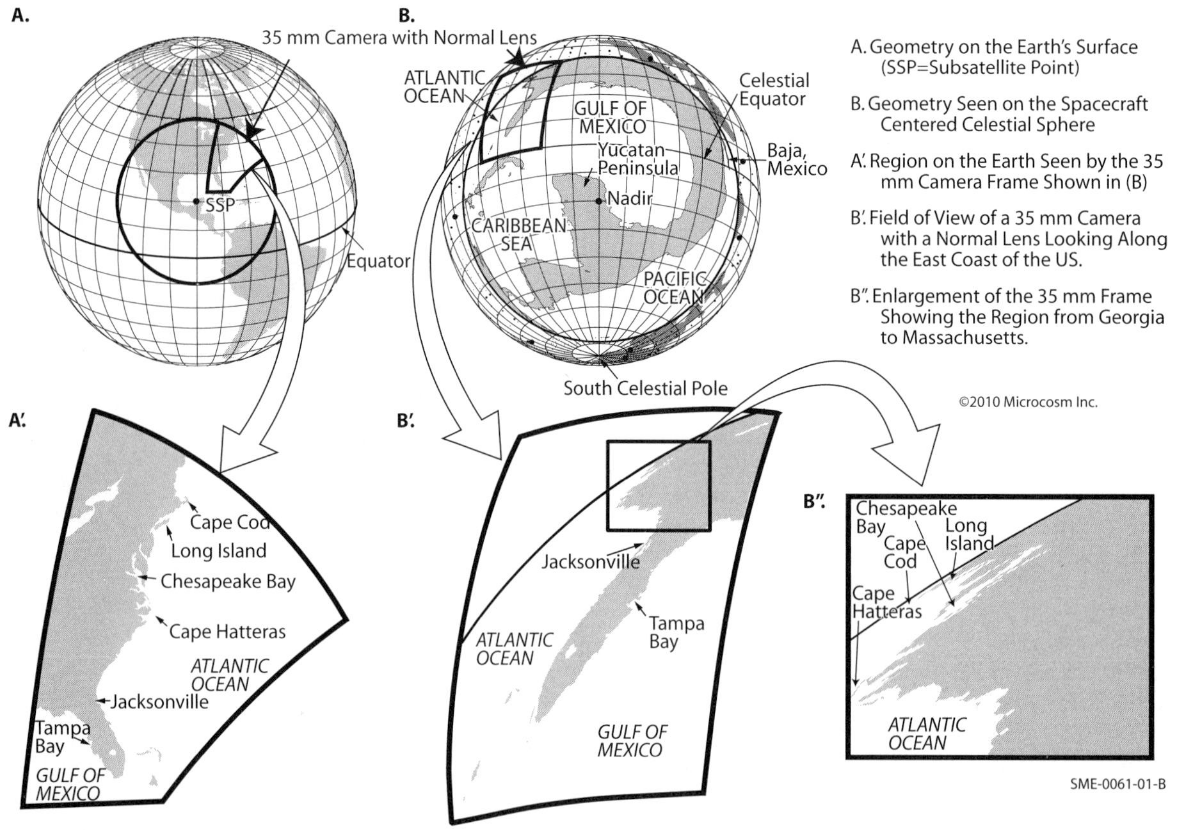

Fig. 8-31. Viewing Geometry for a Satellite at 1,000 km over the Yucatan Peninsula at 90 deg West Longitude and 20 deg N Latitude. (A) Geometry projected onto the Earth's surface. (B) Geometry of (A) as seen on the spacecraft-centered celestial sphere. See text for discussion.

points, directions, shapes and areas on the Earth's surface, and to ask how these are viewed from the spacecraft. The formulation for transforming points was given in Sec. 8.3.1. Directions, shapes and areas are described below. For viewing geometry computations, it is very convenient to introduce horizontal and vertical to refer to directions when looking at the Earth. Specifically, *horizontal* refers to the direction parallel to the Earth's horizon, either in the spacecraft coordinate frame, or on the surface of the Earth. Similarly, *vertical* refers to the direction perpendicular to the horizontal, i.e., toward or away from nadir or radial with respect to the subsatellite point. With these definitions, horizontal and vertical mean the same for the spacecraft, the access area coordinate system, and an observer standing at the subsatellite point. (See Fig. 8-32.)

Although horizontal and vertical remain the same as seen from the spacecraft and in the access area coordinate system, angular directions relative to horizontal and vertical do not. As shown in Fig. 8-32, directions are most conveniently described relative to the horizontal. If we define θ as the angle relative to the horizontal on the surface of the Earth and θ' as the angle relative to the horizontal as seen from the spacecraft, then these are related by:

$$\tan \theta' = \tan \theta \sin \varepsilon \tag{8-49}$$

where ε is the elevation angle at the point in question. We can see from this equation another effect of foreshortening. As ε goes to 0 near the horizon, any line that isn't purely horizontal becomes nearly vertical. Thus, essentially all curves on the spacecraft centered celestial sphere, when projected onto the Earth, will intersect the horizon nearly perpendicular to it. Similarly, essentially all curves on the surface of the Earth near the horizon will become nearly horizontal when seen from the spacecraft. This can be seen clearly by looking at the shape of the coastline near the horizon in Fig. 8-31B''.* For a discussion of the projection of lines from the spacecraft onto the Earth or lines on the Earth as see by the spacecraft, see OCDM Sec. 9.1.

Finally, the projection of area is also of interest. Given a number of deg^2 on the Earth's surface, what angular area in deg^2 does this represent as seen from the spacecraft? In general, the only solution is to integrate the pro-

* The effect is easily seen by taking a square piece of paper and drawing a diagonal between 2 opposite corners. Hold the paper so that you're looking at a very shallow angle and the angle between the line and the side nearest you will appear to be much less than 45 deg.

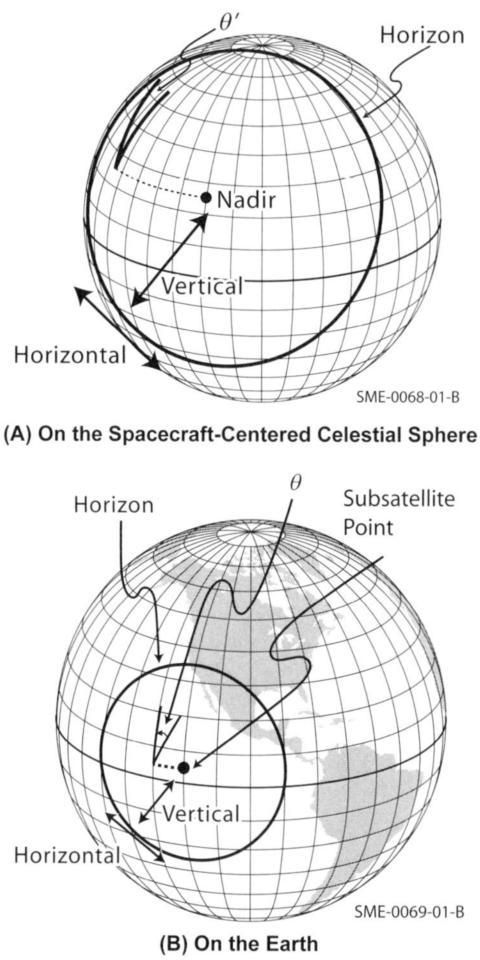

Fig. 8-32. Directions are Most Conveniently Described Relative to the Horizontal, or Equivalently, with Respect to the Subsatellite Point or Nadir.

jected area. However, there are several convenient approximations that make estimating the angular area reasonably easy. For shapes which have a high degree of symmetry about nadir, exact formulas are readily available. These formulas are given in Table 8-9 with the definition of variables shown in Fig. 8-32.

Finally, there is a convenient approximation that can be made as accurate as desired for odd shaped areas. Angular segments, *i*, on the Earth centered on nadir, project into annular segments as seen from the spacecraft and the exact area, A_i, of each is easily computed.

$$A_i = \Phi_i(\cos\lambda_i - \cos\lambda_{i+1}) \tag{8-50a}$$

where Φ_i defines the width of the segment, λ_i is the inner radius, and λ_{i+1} the outer radius. The total area, A, is then simply

$$A = \Sigma A_i \tag{8-50b}$$

Since Φ_i is the same on the Earth and as seen from the spacecraft, the comparable formulas for the angular area on the spacecraft centered celestial sphere, A_i, are:

$$A_i' = \Phi_i\left(\cos\eta_i - \cos\eta_{i+1}\right) \tag{8-51a}$$

$$A' = \Sigma A_i' \tag{8-51b}$$

where η_i is related to λ_i by the previously derived equations:

$$\tan\eta_i = \frac{\sin\rho\,\sin\lambda_i}{1-\sin\rho\,\cos\lambda_i} \tag{8-52}$$

If η_i is known, we find ε_i from:

$$\cos\varepsilon_i = \frac{\sin\eta_i}{\sin\rho} \tag{8-53a}$$

If ε_i is known, we find η_i from:

$$\sin\eta_i = \cos\varepsilon_i\,\sin\rho \tag{8-53b}$$

Finally, the remaining angle is obtained from:

$$\eta_i + \lambda_i + \varepsilon_i = 90\text{ deg} \tag{8-54}$$

Consequently, as shown in Fig. 8-33, any arbitrary area can be conveniently transformed by simply breaking it down into appropriately sized annular segments.

Vector Formulation

In the unit vector formulation, there is no convenient method for working with directions shapes, or areas on the celestial sphere except as collections of points. Consequently, all of the computational work in a vector approach would be done using the point transformations given in Sec 8.3.1. The only additional computational element required is to determine when a point on the Earth is beyond the horizon. This occurs whenever:

$$\hat{\mathbf{x}}\cdot\hat{\mathbf{s}} < \sin\lambda \tag{8-55}$$

where $\hat{\mathbf{x}}$ is the unit vector from the Earth's center to the point in question, $\hat{\mathbf{s}}$ is the unit vector from the Earth's center to the subsatellite point, and λ is the angular radius of either the true horizon or the effective horizon, as appropriate.

8.3.4 Projection of Sensor Fields of View onto the Earth

We now wish to work the Earth geometry problem the other way from Sec. 8.3.2, and project shapes as seen from the spacecraft (i.e., on the spacecraft-centered celestial sphere) down onto the Earth. Once again, points transform as given in Sec. 8.3.1, and directions transform as given in Sec. 8.3.3. For convenience, the transformation equations used for projecting onto the surface of the Earth are as follows:

$$\Phi_{spc} = \Phi_{Earth} = \Phi \tag{8-56}$$

$$\cos\varepsilon = \sin\eta\,/\cos\rho \tag{8-57}$$

$$\lambda = 90\text{ deg} - \eta - \varepsilon \tag{8-58}$$

$$\tan\theta = \tan\theta'/\sin\varepsilon \tag{8-59}$$

Table 8-9. Formulas for the Areas of Shapes Symmetric About Nadir. See Fig. 8-32 for the definition of variables. See Eqs. (8-27) to (8-30) for transformation between η and λ. For area computations, $\Phi_{Earth} = \Phi_{spc} = \Phi$. **Note that for area formulas, all angles should be expressed in radians and angular areas in steradians.**

Shape	Area on the Surface of the Earth	Area on the Spacecraft-Centered Celestial Sphere
Entire Access Area	$2\pi\,(1 - \cos \lambda_0)$ $= 2\pi\,(1 - \sin \rho)$	$2\pi\,(1 - \cos \rho)$ $= 2\pi\,(1 - \sin \lambda_0)$
Area within Effective Horizon	$2\pi\,(1 - \cos \lambda)$	$2\pi\,(1 - \cos \eta)$
Pie Shaped Piece	$\Phi\,(1 - \cos \lambda)$	$\Phi\,(1 - \cos \eta)$
Annulus Centered on Nadir	$2\pi\,(\cos \lambda_1 - \cos \lambda_2)$	$2\pi\,(\cos \eta_1 - \cos \eta_2)$
Annular Segment Centered on Nadir	$\Phi\,(\cos \lambda_1 - \cos \lambda_2)$	$\Phi\,(\cos \eta_1 - \cos \eta_2)$

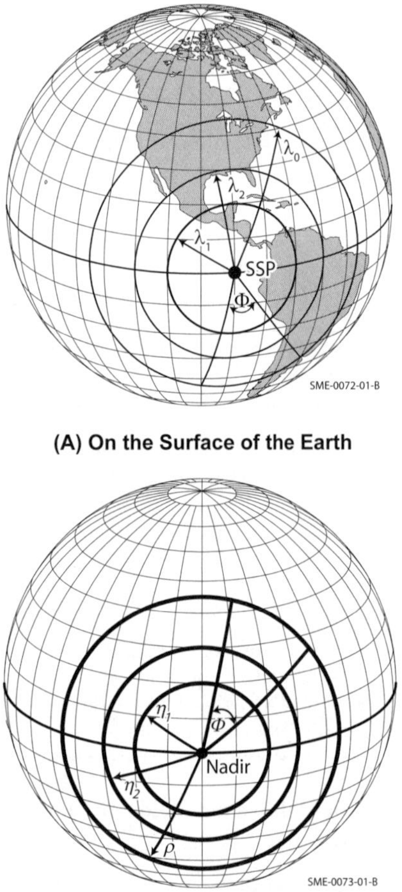

(A) On the Surface of the Earth

(B) On the Spacecraft-Centered Celestial Sphere

Fig. 8-33. Definition of Variable for Annular Shapes Centered on Nadir. See Table 8-9 for area formulas.

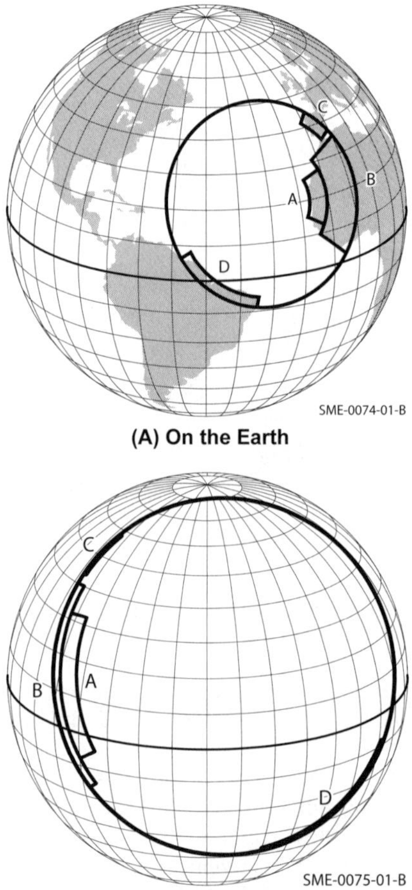

(A) On the Earth

(B) On the Spacecraft-Centered Celestial Sphere

Fig. 8-34. Areas are Conveniently Transformed From Earth to Spacecraft Coordinates by Using Annular Segments for Which the Area can be Transformed Exactly.

where Φ is the azimuthal orientation of the point in question and is the same both from the spacecraft and on the surface of the Earth, ε is the elevation angle at the target point from the horizontal up to the spacecraft, η is the nadir angle measured at the spacecraft from the subsatellite point to the target, ρ is the angular radius of the Earth determined from Eq. (8-26), λ is the Earth Central Angle measured at the center of the Earth from the subsatellite point to the target, θ is the direction relative to the horizontal measured on the Earth's surface, and θ' is the direction relative to the horizontal measured on the spacecraft-centered celestial sphere. The equations in vector form are given in the box at the end of Sec. 8.3.1; there is no convenient vector form for determining the direction relative to the horizontal.

Most practical shapes (i.e., instrument fields of view and antenna patterns) are lines, circles, or rectangles, as

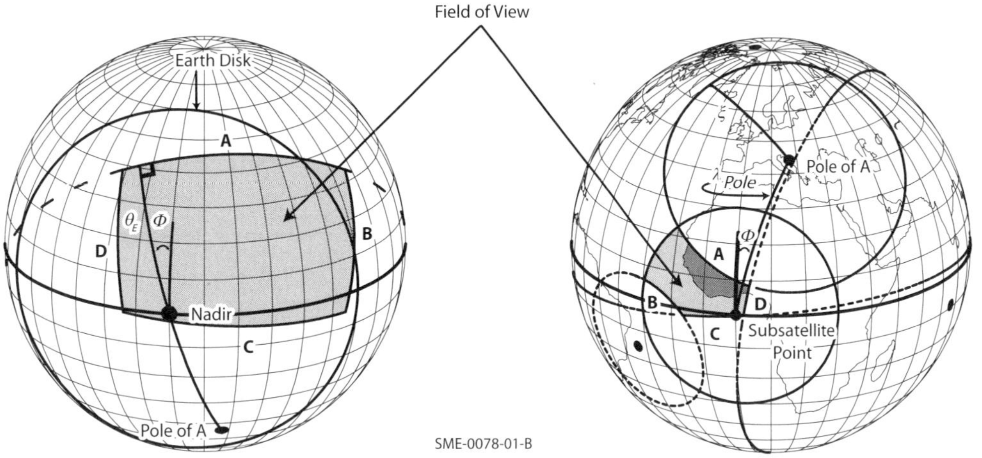

(A) On the Spacecraft-Centered Celestial Sphere **(B) On the Earth**

Live Calc

Fig. 8-35. Projection of a Rectangular Field of View as seen from the Spacecraft onto the Earth. The field of view is equivalent to that of a 50 mm lens on a 35 mm camera. (A) as seen from the spacecraft, (B) as projected onto the Earth's surface. See Table 8-10 for Live Calc.

seen from the spacecraft. Examples include the field of view of a conical scanner, a circular antenna pattern, or an array sensor pointed at the Earth. The rectangular array is discussed here and the circular FOV is discussed in OCDM Sec. 9.1.4.

The edge of any rectangular or linear field of view from a spacecraft instrument projects onto the sky as a great circle arc and projects into space as a plane surface. The pole of the great circle on the celestial sphere is in the direction of the vector normal to the plane in space. This great circle is characterized by two numbers: the azimuthal orientation, Φ, of the pole relative to some reference and either θ_p, the angle from nadir to the pole, or θ_E, the angle from nadir to the arc of the great circle (= the edge of the field of view). Note that θ_E is measured along the great circle arc connecting nadir and the pole and is perpendicular to the great circle representing the edge. If the coordinates of the pole of the great circle representing the edge in any coordinate frame are (α_p, δ_p) and the coordinates of nadir in the same coordinate frame are (α_N, δ_N) then:

$$\sin \theta_E = \cos \theta_p = \sin \delta_p \sin \delta_N + \cos \delta_p \cos \delta_N \cos (\alpha_p - \alpha_N)$$

$$\theta_E = | 90 \text{ deg} - \theta_p | \quad (8\text{-}60)$$

where θ_E is the angle from nadir to the nearest point on the edge.

The plane representing the edge of the field of view will miss the Earth altogether if:

$$\theta_E > \rho \quad \text{(great circle misses Earth)} \quad (8\text{-}61)$$

where ρ is the angular radius of the Earth. If $\theta_E = 0$, then the plane passes through nadir and the projection of the plane onto the surface of the Earth will be a great circle through the subsatellite point. If $0 < \theta_E < \rho$, then the plane intersects the spherical surface of the Earth in a small circle. Therefore, in general, **the edges of a rectangular field of view from the spacecraft will intersect the surface of the Earth in a set of four intersecting small circles**. A small circle on the surface of the Earth is fully defined by the center and radius. As always, the azimuthal orientation of the center of the small circle is the same as seen from the spacecraft and as projected onto the surface of the Earth. (Note that the azimuth changes sign if we wish to maintain a right-handed coordinate system in both cases.) The distance λ_{pole} from the pole of the small circle to nadir is given by:

$$\lambda_{pole} = 90 \text{ deg} - \theta_E = \theta_p \quad (8\text{-}62)$$

and finally, the radius of the small circle, ξ, is given by:

$$\cos \xi = \frac{(R_E + H) \sin \theta_E}{R_E} \quad (8\text{-}63)$$

where R_E is the radius of the Earth and H is the altitude of the spacecraft.

An alternative approach to projecting the field of view is to project the corners of the field of view onto the Earth using the point transformation equations at the end of Sec. 8.3.1 and the radius of the small circle defined by Eq. (8-63) to construct the four sides. We could also use any three points along the small circle such as two of the corners and either the nearest point to nadir or the point at which the small circle intersects the horizon.

The equations above were used to construct Fig. 8-35, which shows the projection of a rectangular field of view down onto the surface of the Earth. Note that the azimuthal orientation of all of the points remains the same on both the spacecraft-centered celestial sphere and on the surface of the Earth (to within the sign change for opposite directions), but that the radial distortion caused by

Table 8-10. Planes or Edges Projected onto the Surface of the Earth. Altitude = 1,000 km. Therefore, ρ = 59.8 deg and λ_0 = 30.2 deg. All values in deg.

On Spc Dist. from Nadir to Edge (θ_E)	On Spc. Dist. from Nadir to Pole (θ_p)	On Earth Radius (ξ)	On Earth Dist. from Edge to SSP (λ_{Pole})	On Earth Dist. from Edge to Horizon ($\lambda_0 - \lambda_{Pole}$)
0	90	90.00	0.00	30.18
5	85	84.21	0.79	29.39
10	80	78.41	1.59	28.59
15	75	72.58	2.42	27.76
20	70	66.69	3.31	26.87
25	65	60.73	4.27	25.91
30	60	54.66	5.34	24.84
35	55	48.43	6.57	23.61
40	50	41.96	8.04	22.14
45	45	35.12	9.88	20.30
50	40	27.61	12.39	17.79
55	35	18.63	16.37	13.81
56	34	16.46	17.54	12.64
57	33	14.03	18.97	11.21
58	32	11.18	20.82	9.36
59	31	7.45	23.55	6.63
59.5	30.5	4.64	25.86	4.32

projection onto the surface of the Earth transforms the great circle arcs on the spacecraft-centered celestial sphere into small circle arcs on the surface of the Earth.

Most sensors will have fields of view which are more symmetric with respect to nadir than that in Fig. 8-35, and the angular parameters with respect to nadir can frequently be determined by inspection. The approximately rectangular shape is largely retained when the field of view is oriented toward nadir. The more strongly curved edges occur when the edge of the sensor lies near or crosses the edge of the disk of the Earth. Thus, in Fig. 8-35, sides C and D pass relatively close to nadir and, therefore, are nearly great circles when projected onto the Earth. Side A is further from nadir and has a distinctly curved edge on the Earth. Side B is nearly parallel to the horizon and, as seen from the spacecraft, crosses the horizon at a very shallow angle. However, when projected onto the Earth it still crosses the horizon at essentially a right angle and is strongly curved. Since a corner of the FOV is off the Earth, the projection onto the Earth has a fifth side consisting of the horizon itself. Of course each of the rows and columns within the FOV could also be represented by corresponding small circles projected onto the Earth. Table 8-10 shows the angular radius for various small circles and the distance from the edge of the small circle to the subsatellite point for straight lines projected onto the surface of the Earth from an altitude of 1,000 km. As we approach the edge of the disk of the Earth, the curvature of the projection becomes very strong.

8.4 Computing Parameters for a Single Target or Ground Station Pass

We define a *target* as an object on or near the Earth's surface that we wish to observe or track. A *ground station* is an antenna fixed on the Earth with which we wish to communicate. However, for purposes of the relative geometry and motion there is essentially no distinction between them and we will use the two terms interchangeably throughout this section. Overall, it makes very little difference whether the target is stationary or moving over the surface of the Earth, such as airplanes flying in and out of a busy airport. The satellite velocity is far greater than any Earth targets, such that nearly all targets are essentially stationary in terms of coverage analysis as seen from spacecraft.* (We can pick out moving targets using Doppler radar but they do not move very far in the time that the satellite is observing them.) The only realistic exception is rocket launches, which, of course, approach orbital velocities.

8.4.1 Circular LEO Orbits

This section looks at the characteristics of a ground station pass for a satellite in low-Earth orbit. We begin by looking at the qualitative characteristics of this pass and then compute the relevant parameters for the pass based

* For the motion of a satellite in geosynchronous orbit that is nearly fixed with respect to the Earth's surface, see Sec. 9.5.1.

on the assumption that the ground trace is a great circle arc. Finally, we compute the ground station parameters using the substantially more accurate approximation of the ground trace as a small circle centered on the instantaneous rotation axis.

Figure 8-36A shows the geometry of a ground station pass as seen on the surface of the Earth. Three representative orbit passes are drawn, one which passes directly overhead the ground station at Hawaii, one which passes within 5 deg of the ground station, and one which passes within 15 deg of the ground station. The appearance of these three orbits on the ground station-centered celestial sphere is shown in Fig. 8-36B. The general parameters for the shape of this orbit are defined in OCDM Sec. 6.3.4. The satellite which passes directly over the station will travel along a great circle arc which passes through the zenith. The others will have the appearance of an orbit viewed from nearby. Although the satellite moves uniformly along the orbit path in Fig. 8-36A, it does not move uniformly across the sky as seen from the ground station (Fig. 8-36B). Generally, the spacecraft will appear to travel slowly when it is near the horizon due to both the greater distance and the substantial foreshortening. It will move most rapidly in apparent angular velocity as it passes the point nearest the ground station. It then repeats the process in a symmetric fashion and leaves slowly over the "forward horizon" (i.e., in the direction the satellite is moving).

Because the apparent satellite path is not a simple geometrical figure, it is best computed using a simulation program. A variety of commercial tools are available to do this. These programs also work with elliptical orbits so they are convenient, along with the appropriate formulas from this chapter, for evaluating specific orbit geometry. Unfortunately, a simulation does not provide the desired physical insight into the apparent motion of satellites, nor does it provide a rapid method for evaluating geometry in the general case, as is most appropriate when first designing a mission or trying to determine the most common parameters for a ground station pass. For these problems, we are interested in bounding or approximating the apparent motion rather than in computing the detailed path precisely.

Throughout this section, we use the notation shown in Fig. 8-37, which shows the geometry of a ground station pass where we have approximated the ground track by a great circle centered on the orbit pole. (Later in this section, we will correct that approximation by shifting to a ground track centered on the instantaneous rotation axis.) The small circle centered on the ground station represents the subsatellite points at which the spacecraft elevation, ε, seen by the ground station is greater than some *minimum working elevation angle* ε_{min}. The nature of the communication or observation will determine the value of ε_{min}. For ground station communications, the satellite typically must be more than 5 deg above the horizon, so ε_{min} = 5 deg. The size of this circle of accessibility strongly depends on the value of ε_{min}, as emphasized in

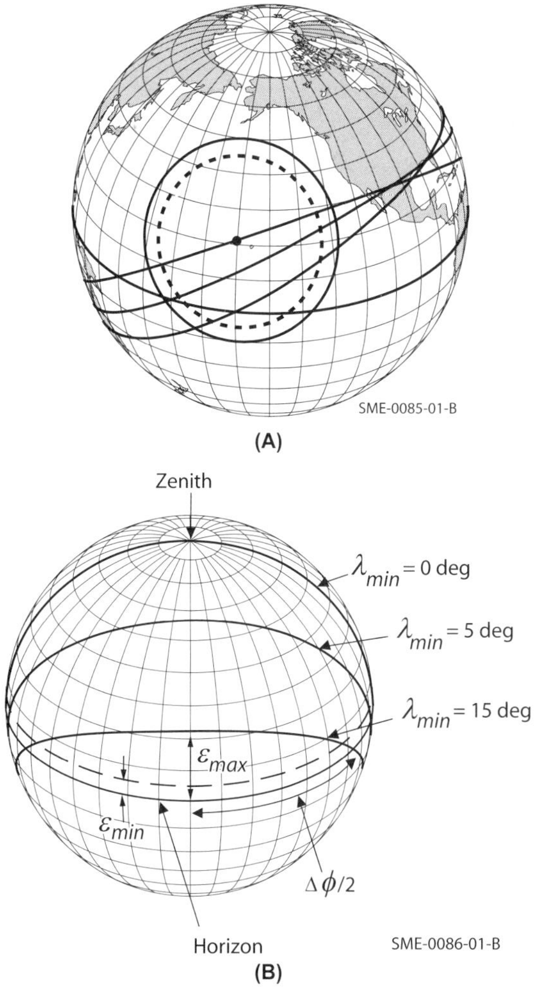

Fig. 8-36. Apparent Motion as Seen From the Earth of a Satellite in 1,000 km Circular Orbit. (A) Geometry on the Earth's surface. (B) Geometry on the ground station-centered-celestial sphere.

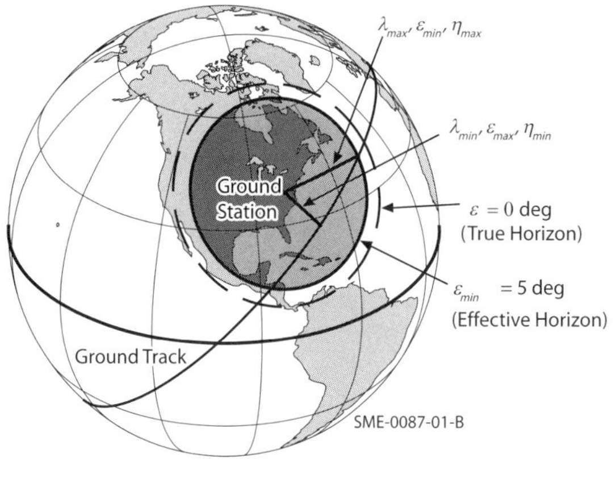

Fig. 8-37. Geometry of Satellite Ground Track Relative to an Observer on the Earth.

Table 8-10◀, Fig. 8-37, Eq. 8-63◀

the discussion of Fig. 8-31 and shown in the tables on the inside rear cover. In Fig. 8-37 we have assumed a satellite altitude of 1,000 km. The dashed circle surrounding the ground station is at $\varepsilon = 0$ deg (that is, the satellite's true outer horizon), and the solid circle represents $\varepsilon_{min} = 5$ deg. In practice we often select a specific value of ε_{min} and use that number for the entire analysis. However, you should remain aware that many of the computed parameters are extremely sensitive to this value.

Given a value of ε_{min}, we can define the *maximum Earth Central Angle*, λ_{max}, the *maximum nadir angle*, η_{max}, measured at the satellite from nadir to the ground station, and the *maximum range*, D_{max}, at which the satellite will still be above ε_{min}. These parameters, as determined by applying Eqs. (8-4) to (8-31), are given by:

$$\sin \eta_{max} = \sin \rho \, \cos \varepsilon_{min} \tag{8-64}$$

$$\lambda_{max} = 90 \text{ deg} - \varepsilon_{min} - \eta_{max} \tag{8-65}$$

$$D_{max} = \mathrm{R_E} \frac{\sin \lambda_{max}}{\sin \eta_{max}} \tag{8-66}$$

where ρ is the angular radius of the Earth as seen from the satellite; that is, $\sin \rho = \mathrm{R_E}/(\mathrm{R_E} + H)$. We will call the small circle of radius λ_{max} centered on the target the *effective horizon*, corresponding in our example to $\varepsilon_{min} = 5$ deg, to distinguish it from the *true* or *geometrical horizon* for which $\varepsilon = 0$ deg. Whenever the subsatellite point lies within the effective horizon around the target or ground station, then communications or observations will be possible. The duration, T, of this contact and the maximum elevation angle, ε_{max}, of the satellite will depend on how close the ground station is to the satellite's ground track on any given pass.

As described in Chap. 9, the plane of a spacecraft's orbit and, therefore, the ground track, is normally defined by the inclination, i, and either the right ascension, Ω, or longitude, L_{node}, of the ascending node. Except for orbit perturbations, Ω, which is defined relative to the stars, remains fixed in inertial space while the Earth rotates under the orbit. On the other hand, L_{node} is defined relative to the Earth's surface and, therefore, changes by 360 deg in 1,436 min, which is the rotation period of the Earth relative to the stars. (Recall that orbit perturbations affect the exact rotation rate of the node.) Because of this orbit rotation relative to the Earth, it is convenient to speak of the *instantaneous ascending node* which is L_{node} evaluated at the time of an observation or passage over a ground station. For purposes of geometry it is also often appropriate to work in terms of the *instantaneous orbit pole*, or the pole of the orbit plane at the time of the observation. The coordinates of this pole are:

$$lat_{pole} = 90 \text{ deg} - i \tag{8-67}$$

$$long_{pole} = L_{node} - 90 \text{ deg} \tag{8-68}$$

A satellite will pass directly over a target or ground station (represented by the subscript gs) on the Earth's surface if and only if:

$$\sin (long_{gs} - L_{node}) = \tan lat_{gs} / \tan i \tag{8-69}$$

There are two valid solutions to the above equation, corresponding to the satellite passing over the ground station on the northbound leg of the orbit or on the southbound leg. To determine when after crossing the equator the satellite passes over the ground station for a circular orbit, we can determine μ, the arc length along the instantaneous ground track from the ascending node to the ground station, from:

$$\sin \mu = \sin lat_{gs} / \sin i \tag{8-70}$$

Again, the two valid solutions correspond to the northbound and southbound passes.

Figure 8-37 defines the parameters of the satellite's ground station pass in terms of λ_{min}, the minimum Earth central angle between the satellite's ground track and the ground station. This will be 90 deg minus the angular distance measured at the center of the Earth from the ground station to the instantaneous orbit pole at the time of contact. If we know the latitude and longitude of the orbit pole and ground station (gs), then the value of λ_{min} will be given by:

$$\sin \lambda_{min} = \sin lat_{pole} \sin lat_{gs} + \cos lat_{pole} \cos lat_{gs} \cos (\Delta long) \tag{8-71}$$

where $\Delta long$ is the longitude difference between gs and the orbit pole. At the point of closest approach, we can compute the minimum nadir angle, η_{min}, maximum elevation angle, ε_{max}, and minimum range, D_{min} as:

$$\tan \eta_{min} = \frac{\sin \rho \sin \lambda_{min}}{1 - \sin \rho \cos \lambda_{min}} \tag{8-72}$$

$$\varepsilon_{max} = 90 \text{ deg} - \lambda_{min} - \eta_{min} \tag{8-73}$$

$$D_{min} = \mathrm{R_E} \frac{\sin \lambda_{min}}{\sin \eta_{min}} \tag{8-74}$$

At the point of closest approach, the satellite will be moving perpendicular to the line of sight to the ground station. Thus, the *maximum angular rate* of the satellite as seen from the ground station, $\dot{\theta}_{max}$ will be:

$$\dot{\theta}_{max} = \frac{V_{sat}}{D_{min}} = \frac{2\pi(\mathrm{R_E} + H)}{P D_{min}} \tag{8-75}$$

where V_{sat} is the orbital velocity of the satellite, and P is the orbit period from Chap. 9 or the inside rear cover.

Finally, it is convenient to compute the *total azimuth range*, $\Delta\phi$, which the satellite covers as seen by the ground station, the *total time in view, T*, and the azimuth, ϕ_{center}, at the center of the viewing arc where the elevation angle is a maximum:

$$\cos\frac{\Delta\phi}{2} = \frac{\tan\lambda_{min}}{\tan\lambda_{max}} \tag{8-76}$$

$$T = \left(\frac{P}{180 \text{ deg}}\right) \text{acos}\left(\frac{\cos\lambda_{max}}{\cos\lambda_{min}}\right) \tag{8-77}$$

where the arc cos is in degrees. ϕ_{center} is related to ϕ_{pole}, the azimuth to the direction of the projection of the orbit pole onto the ground, by

$$\phi_{center} = 180 \text{ deg} - \phi_{pole} \tag{8-78}$$

$$\cos\phi_{pole} = (\sin lat_{pole} - \sin\lambda_{min} \sin lat_{gs}) \,/\, (\cos\lambda_{min} \cos lat_{gs}) \tag{8-79}$$

where $\phi_{pole} < 180$ deg if the orbit pole is east of the ground station and $\phi_{pole} > 180$ deg if the orbit pole is west of the ground station.

Table 8-11 summarizes the computations for ground station coverage and provides a worked example. As indicated above, T is particularly sensitive to ε_{min}. If we assume a mountain-top ground station with $\varepsilon_{min} = 2$ deg, then the time in view for the example increases by 15% to 14.27 min.

Thus far, we have ignored the impact of the rotation of the Earth on ground station coverage. While this is a reasonable simplification for some cases, the assumption becomes less valid as the altitude of the satellite becomes higher. In addition, the rotating Earth under the satellite changes not only the velocity of the satellite relative to the Earth's surface but also its direction of motion. The dual-axis spiral formulation developed in OCDM Chap. 8 and summarized here, provides the mechanism to readily take this rotation into account. The geometry of doing so is shown in Fig. 8-38. Fundamentally, we want to replace the great circle centered on the orbit pole with a small circle of appropriate radius centered on the instantaneous rotation axis.* This will correctly model the direction, the velocity, and the curvature of the orbit as it passes the ground station, all of which are slightly different than the motion over a non-rotating Earth.

We begin by noting that the *instantaneous rotation axis* or *Euler axis*, **E**, lies on the great circle containing the orbit pole and the Earth's pole, with a latitude given by

* We can think of the satellite as being fixed in a rigid coordinate frame rotating in inertial space. Similarly, the surface of the Earth is also a rigid coordinate frame rotating about a different axis in inertial space. The most general motion of two rigid, rotating coordinate frames is a rotation about an *instantaneous rotation axis* or *Euler axis*, **E**, that is fixed instantaneously, but moving over time in both the orbit frame and the Earth frame. (Similarly, the wheel on a car is rotating instantaneously about the point of contact with the ground, but that point is continuously moving with respect to both the wheel and the ground.) See OCDM Chap. 8 for a detailed discussion and development of the relevant equations.

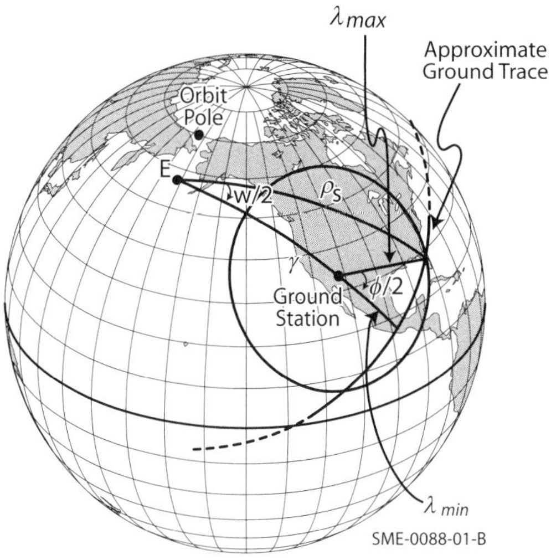

Fig. 8-38. Geometry for Using the Instantaneous Rotation Axis to Compute Ground Station Parameters.

$$\delta_E = \text{lat}_E = \text{atan}\left(\frac{\omega_{Earth} + n\cos i}{n \sin i}\right) \tag{8-80}$$

where $n = 6 / P$ is the mean motion of the satellite in deg/sec, P is the period in minutes, i is the orbit inclination, and ω_{Earth} is the inertial rotation rate of the Earth on its axis = 0.004 178 075 deg/sec. [To take the node regression rate into account see OCDM Eq. (9-66).]

There is a potential complication here in that the instantaneous rotation axis should be evaluated at the time when the satellite passes at the minimum distance from the ground station. Since we cannot compute this time precisely, we would in principle be left to an iterative process to determine the right time to evaluate both the orbit pole for the previous calculation and the instantaneous rotation axis for this calculation. However, the orbit pole and the instantaneous rotation axis are rotating about the Earth's pole at a rate of approximately 0.004 deg/sec. Consequently, providing the correct time to evaluate the position of the rotation axes to within even a few minutes is sufficiently accurate for most analysis purposes.

Having determined the position of the pole, we now determine the angular rotation rate, ω_E, about the instantaneous rotation axis, **E**, and the arc length distance, ρ_S, from **E** to the subsatellite point by:

$$\omega_E = n(\sin i / \cos\delta_E) \tag{8-81}$$

$$\rho_S = \text{acos}(\sin\delta \sin\delta_E + \cos\delta \cos\delta_E \cos\Delta\alpha) \tag{8-82}$$

We then use the standard formula for arc lengths on the surface of the Earth to determine γ, the distance from the instantaneous rotation axis to the ground station:

$$\cos\gamma = \sin\delta_E \sin\delta_{gs} + \cos\delta_E \cos\delta_{gs} \cos(\alpha_E - \alpha_{gs}) \tag{8-83}$$

Table 8-11. Summary of Computations for Ground Station Passes for LEO Circular Orbits. Example computations are based on the following: Circular orbit at H = 1,000 km, i = 50 deg, orbit pole at 40 deg N, 150 deg E, ground station in Phoenix at 33.5 deg N, 248 deg E, and minimum allowable elevation angle ε_{min} = 5 deg. "same" indicates that either the formula or value listed is the same for both approximations.

	"Nonrotating Earth"			"Rotating Earth"		
Parameter	**Formula**	**Eq.**	**Ex.**	**Formula**	**Eq.**	**Ex.**
Approximation	Great circle centered on instantaneous orbit pole			Small circle centered on instantaneous rotation axis		
Accuracy	Evaluation point only			Point plus 1st and 2nd derivatives of path and velocity		
Earth ang radius, ρ	$\sin \rho = R_E / (R_E + H)$	8-26	59.8 deg	same		same
Period, P	$P = 2\pi \sqrt{a^3 / \mu}$	9-4b	105 min	$P = 2\pi \sqrt{a^3 / \mu}$	9-4b	same
Max nadir ang, η_{max}	$\sin \eta_{max} = \sin \rho \cos \varepsilon_{min}$	8-64	59.4 deg	same		same
Max Earth cen ang, λ_{max}	λ_{max} = 90 deg $- \varepsilon_{min} - \eta_{max}$	8-65	25.6 deg	same		same
Max distance, D_{max}	$D_{max} = R_E (\sin \lambda_{max} / \sin \eta_{max})$	8-66	3,194 km	same		same
Min Earth cen ang, λ_{min}	$\sin \lambda_{min} = \sin lat_{pole} \sin lat_{gs} + \cos lat_{pole} \cos lat_{gs} \cos (\Delta long)$	8-71	15.4 deg	$\lambda_{min} = \lvert \rho_S - \gamma \rvert$	8-84	13.7 deg
Min nadir ang, η_{min}	$\tan \eta_{min} = (\sin \rho \sin \lambda_{min}) / (1 - \sin \rho \cos \lambda_{min})$	8-72	54.1 deg	same		51.9 deg
Max elev ang, ε_{max}	ε_{max} = 90 deg $- \lambda_{min} - \eta_{min}$	8-73	20.5 deg	same		24.4 deg
Min dist, D_{min}	$D_{min} = R_E (\sin \lambda_{min} / \sin \eta_{min})$	8-74	2,095 km	same		1,914 km
Max ang rate, $\dot{\theta}_{max}$	$\dot{\theta}_{max}$ = [360 deg $(R_E + H)] / (P D_{min})$	8-75	12.1 deg/min	$\dot{\theta}_{max} = [2\pi (R_E + H)] / (P D_{min})$	8-75	13.2 deg/min
Az range, $\Delta\phi$	$\cos (\Delta\phi / 2) = (\tan \lambda_{min} / \tan \lambda_{max})$	8-76	109.5 deg	$\cos (\Delta\phi / 2) = \dfrac{\cos \gamma \cos \lambda_{max} - \cos \rho_S}{\sin \gamma \sin \lambda_{max}}$	8-86	118.9 deg
Az of center of pass, ϕ_{center}	$\cos \phi_{center} = \dfrac{\sin \lambda_{min} \sin lat_{gs} - \sin lat_{pole}}{\cos \lambda_{min} \cos lat_{gs}}$	8-78	128.1 deg	same Eq. substituting $\sin lat_E$ for $\sin lat_{pole}$	8-77 8-78	125.1 deg
Time in view, T	$T = (P / 180 \text{ deg}) \operatorname{acos} (\cos \lambda_{max} / \cos \lambda_{min})$	8-77	12.05 min	$T = W / (60 \cdot \omega_E)$ $\cos (W / 2) = \dfrac{\cos \lambda_{max} - \cos \rho_S \cos \gamma}{\sin \rho_S \sin \gamma}$	8-85a 8-85b	13.34 min

where as usual, α and δ are the longitude and latitude of the instantaneous rotation axis and the ground station. Having computed ρ_S and γ, the off ground track angle, or minimum Earth central angle, λ_{min}, is given by:

$$\lambda_{min} = \lvert \rho_S - \gamma \rvert \tag{8-84}$$

as can be seen from Fig. 8-38. Also from the figure, we can immediately determine both the azimuth range as seen from the ground station, $\Delta\phi$, and the arc through which the satellite moves, W, as measured about the instantaneous rotation axis. By the definition of the rotation rate about E, this lets us determine immediately the time in view, T. Specifically:

$$T = W / \omega_E \tag{8-85a}$$

where:

$$\cos (W / 2) = \frac{\cos \lambda_{max} - \cos \rho_s \cos \gamma}{\sin \rho_s \sin \gamma} \tag{8-85b}$$

and

$$\cos (\Delta\phi / 2) = \frac{\cos \gamma \cos \lambda_{max} - \cos \rho_s}{\sin \gamma \sin \lambda_{max}} \tag{8-86}$$

These equations allow us to obtain a substantially more precise yet still analytic estimate of the ground station pass parameters. The revised equations and an example of their application are provided in Table 8-11. It is important to recognize the basis for this revised formulation. Previously we represented the ground track by a great arc through the subsatellite point, but not quite tangent to the actual ground track. We are now representing it by a small circle which is both tangent to and has the same curvature and rotation velocity as the real dual-axis spiral ground track.

8.4.2 Elliptical Orbits

The computation of viewing parameters for satellites in elliptical orbits are conceptually similar but computationally more complex than for circular orbits. At perigee, the access area is small, and the satellite is moving rapidly. At apogee, the access area is large, and the satellite moves more slowly. Consequently, substantially larger areas of the Earth will see the satellite at apogee for longer periods of time. Figure 8-39 shows the apparent motion as seen from the Earth for a spacecraft in a geosynchronous transfer orbit. The parameters for any specific ground station pass will be typically done by simulation because of the complexity of the analytic formulation. However, we can apply the elliptical orbit parameters defined in Sec. 9.3.2 and the coverage equations from Table 8-11 to compute the extrema at apogee and perigee and also representative parameters for other ground station passes for which the parameters

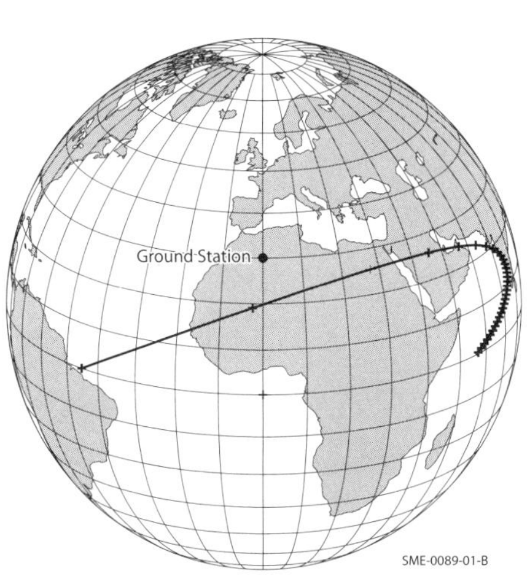

(A) On the Earth's Surface

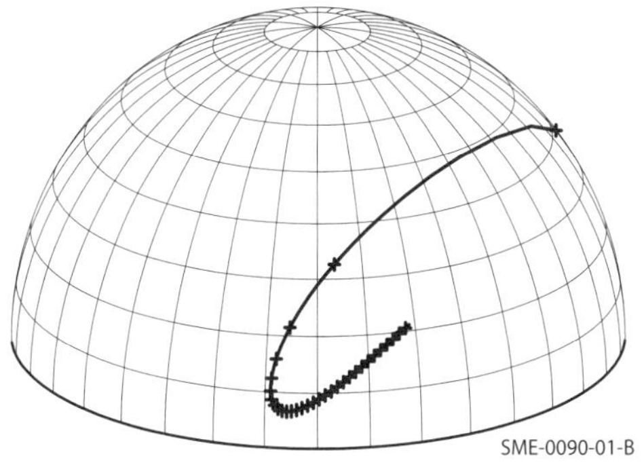

(B) On the Ground Station Celestial Sphere

Fig. 8-39. Apparent Motion of a Satellite in a 200 km × 26,000 km GEO Transfer Orbit.

are known. These computations using the previous equations are shown in Table 8-12 for a satellite in a Molniya orbit and ground station passes at apogee and at perigee.

8.5 Satellite Relative Motion

Thus far, we have been concerned primarily with the motion of satellites relative to the surface of the Earth, or the apparent motion as seen from Earth. However, as illustrated in Fig. 8-40, the motion of satellites relative to each other is also of interest. This is important for constellation analysis and design, operations planning and analysis, and intersatellite communications, such as data transfer between satellites or low-Earth orbit communications constellations.

What does the motion of one spacecraft look like as seen from another? In some sense, the answer is easy. We integrate the equations of motion for both the target and the observer, difference the two, plot the results against the background of fixed stars, and the computer will have done all the work for us. This is the traditional approach. It works well for detailed analysis in an operations environment but is entirely unsuccessful at providing the physical insight and broad overview critical for conceptual mission design, constellation design and analysis, mission and operations planning, or the analysis of alternative approaches. Consequently, we are interested here not in a precise numerical answer but in broad characteristics and general limits on the motion, so that we can understand how to design, plan, and analyze the process of spacecraft interacting with each other.

Fig. 8-40. INTELSAT Communications Satellite Seen from the Space Shuttle Orbiter. Because the satellite is about to be captured, the orbits have been nearly perfectly matched and the two vehicles are moving very slowly with respect to each other. In most cases, satellites cross paths moving at relative velocities on the order of 7 km/sec or 30 times the speed of normal commercial jet airliners. (Photo courtesy Johnson Space Center.)

Because the relative motion of spacecraft, particularly on a large scale, is normally done by computer simulation, there have been very few analytical studies of the characteristics of this motion. The one exception to this is the case of two spacecraft orbiting very near each other. Here the equations of motion can be considerably simplified and are reduced to what are frequently called *Hill's equations* or the *Clohessy-Wiltshire equations*. These are summarized in OCDM Sec. 10.2.3.

The relative motion of satellites naturally breaks down into three broad areas. First, there is the large-scale relative motion due to individual satellites not being in the same orbit. This creates the gross motion of one satellite relative to another that is needed for constellation design, coverage

Table 8-12. Summary of Computations for Ground Station Passes for Elliptical Orbits. "At Perigee" refers to a ground station pass centered on perigee and uses the subscript P. "At Apogee" refers to a ground station pass centered on apogee and uses the subscript A. Because of the large arc at apogee that can see the ground, the time in view computation there is valid only for small eccentricities. Sample calculations are based on a satellite in an elliptical orbit at 63.4 deg inclination, 500 km perigee, and 40,000 km apogee. The orbit pole is assumed to be at 26.6 deg N, 150.0 deg E. The ground station is at 33.5 deg N, 248.0 deg E. All formulas are based on the "non-rotating Earth" approximation.

	At Perigee			At Apogee		
Parameter	**Formula**	**Eq.**	**Ex.**	**Formula**	**Eq.**	**Ex.**
Earth ang radius, ρ	$\sin \rho_{max} = R_E / (R_E + H_P)$	8-26	68.0 deg	$\sin \rho_{min} = R_E / (R_E + H_A)$	8-25	7.90 deg
Semimajor axis, a	$a = R_E + (H_A + H_P)/2$	8-23	26,628 km	$a = R_E + (H_A + H_P)/2$	8-23	26,628 km
Period, P	$P = 2\pi\sqrt{a^3/\mu}$	9-4b	721 min	$P = 2\pi\sqrt{a^3/\mu}$	9-4b	721 min
Mean motion, n	$n = (180/\pi)\sqrt{\mu/a^3}$	9-17	0.008 32 deg/s	same		same
Orbital angular velocity, ω	$\omega_{max} = na/(R_E + H_P)$ $\omega_E = n(\sin i / \cos \delta_E)$	8-80	0.032 2 deg/s	$\omega_{min} = na/(R_E + H_A)$ $\omega_E = n(\sin i / \cos \delta_E)$	8-80	0.004 78 deg/s
Max nadir angle, η_{max}	$\sin \eta_{maxP} = \sin \rho_{max} \cos \varepsilon_{min}$	8-95	67.5 deg	$\sin \eta_{maxA} = \sin \rho_{min} \cos \varepsilon_{min}$	8-95	7.87 deg
Max Earth central angle, λ_{max}	$\lambda_{maxP} = 90\text{ deg} - \varepsilon_{min} - \eta_{maxP}$	8-65	17.5 deg	$\lambda_{maxA} = 90\text{ deg} - \varepsilon_{min} - \eta_{maxA}$	8-64	77.1 deg
Max distance, D_{max}	$D_{maxP} = R_E(\sin \lambda_{maxP} / \sin \eta_{maxP})$	8-66	2,078 km	$D_{maxA} = R_E(\sin \lambda_{maxA} / \sin \eta_{maxA})$	8-65	45,385 km
Min Earth central angle, λ_{min}	$\sin \lambda_{min} = \sin lat_{pole} \sin lat_{gs} + \cos lat_{pole} \cos lat_{gs} \cos(\Delta long)$	8-71	8.2 deg	same		same
Min nadir angle, η_{min}	$\tan \eta_{minP} = \dfrac{\sin \rho_{max} \sin \lambda_{min}}{1 - \sin \rho_{max} \cos \lambda_{min}}$	8-72	58.2 deg	$\tan \eta_{minA} = \dfrac{\sin \rho_{min} \sin \lambda_{min}}{1 - \sin \rho_{min} \cos \lambda_{min}}$	8-71	1.3 deg
Max elevation angle, ε_{max}	$\varepsilon_{maxP} = 90\text{ deg} - \lambda_{min} - \eta_{minP}$	8-73	23.5 deg	$\varepsilon_{maxA} = 90\text{ deg} - \lambda_{min} - \eta_{minA}$	8-72	80.5 deg
Min distance, D_{min}	$D_{minP} = R_E(\sin \lambda_{min} / \sin \eta_{minP})$	8-74	1,075 km	$D_{minA} = R_E(\sin \lambda_{min} / \sin \eta_{minA})$	8-73	40,076 km
Max angular rate, $\dot{\theta}_{max}$	$\dot{\theta}_{max} = \omega_{max}(H_P + R_E)/D_{minP}$	8-74	0.206 deg/s	$\dot{\theta}_{max} = \omega_{min}(H_A + R_E)/D_{minA}$	8-74	0.005 53 deg/s
Azimuth range, $\Delta\phi$	$\cos(D\phi_P/2) = (\tan \lambda_{min} / \tan \lambda_{maxP})$	8-75	125.4 deg	$\cos(\Delta\phi_A/2) = (\tan \lambda_{min} / \tan \lambda_{maxA})$	8-75	176.2 deg
Azimuth of center of pass, ϕ_{center}	$\cos \phi_{center} = \dfrac{\sin \lambda_{min} \sin lat_{gs} - \sin lat_{pole}}{\cos \lambda_{min} \cos lat_{gs}}$	8-77 8-75	116.5 deg	same		same
Time in view, T	$T_P = (2/\omega_{max})\,\text{acos}(\cos \lambda_{maxP} / \cos \lambda_{min})$	8-76	982 sec.	$T_A = (2/\omega_{min})\,\text{acos}(\cos \lambda_{maxA} / \cos \lambda_{min})$	8-76	N/A*

* At apogee, the approximation given is valid only for low eccentricities.

computations, or how to fill in holes in coverage. Superimposed on this is the small-scale relative motion due to varying orbit perturbations on each satellite and individual satellites not being in precisely the intended orbit. This produces almost a "Brownian motion" within the constellation that causes each satellite to move around relative to its ideal location. This small-scale motion, discussed in detail in OCDM Chap. 10, impacts the size of the stationkeeping box that we can create in a constellation and, therefore, impacts coverage and crosslink communications. Finally, in addition to how satellites actually move, we are interested in how they appear to move as seen from an observer satellite. This is important for understanding how to design and point antennas, lasers, or cameras for communications or observations.

For the large-scale relative motion of co-altitude satellites in circular orbits there are two key parameters, as illustrated in Fig. 8-41. The *relative inclination*, i_R, is the angle at which the orbits of the two satellites intersect. This is **not** the same as the difference between the inclinations of the two orbits since orbits at the same inclination but different nodes will intersect at non-zero angles, as shown in Fig. 8-42. The second parameter is the *relative phase*, ϕ_R, which is the angular separation between the two satellites at the time they pass through one another's orbit plane. As can be seen from Fig. 8-41, this will occur four times per orbit—once when satellite 1 crosses the plane of satellite 2 and later when satellite 2 crosses the plane of satellite 1. It then occurs twice more at the other intersection of the orbits, 180 deg away.

Table 8-12, Fig. 8-40◀, Eq. 8-86◀

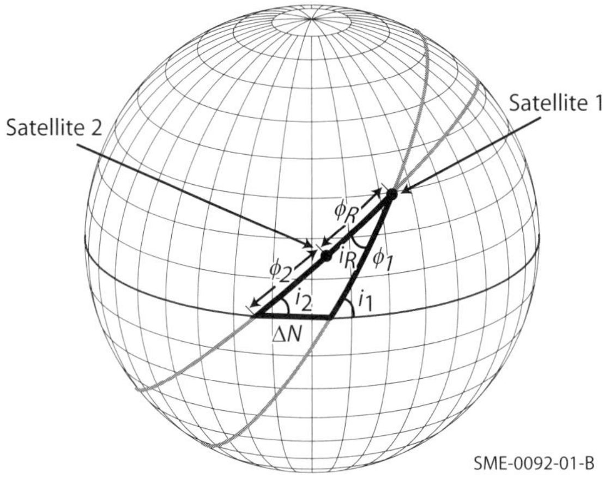

Fig. 8-41. The Relative Motion of Co-Altitude Satellites in Circular Orbits Depends on Only Two Parameters—the Relative Inclination, i_R, and the Relative Phase, ϕ_R.

The relative phase and relative inclination fully define the relative motion between the satellites. This is perhaps the most important message of this section:

> **The relative motion of co-altitude satellites in circular orbits depends only on the relative phase and relative inclination.**

It does not depend on the specific inclination or on the satellite's being at a common inclination. Once we have calculated i_R and ϕ_R, we can ignore the actual inclinations and use these parameters to calculate all of the characteristics of the relative motion of the satellites.

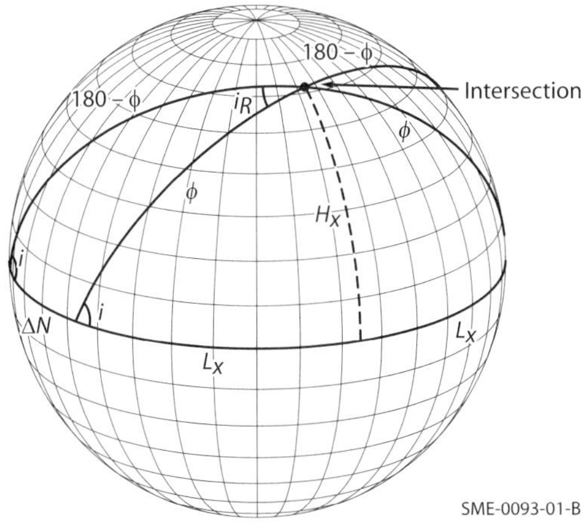

Fig. 8-42. Intersection of Two Orbits with the Same Inclination. The intersection point will be midway between the pairs of ascending and descending nodes. For one satellite the arc length, ϕ, from the ascending node to the intersection point will be less than 90 deg. For the other it will be 180 deg – ϕ.

In most constellations, the actual inclination of any two satellites is the same, i.e., $i_1 = i_2 = i$. (See Fig. 8-42.) In this case, there are particularly simple expressions for i_R and ϕ_R:

$$\cos i_R = \cos^2 i + \sin^2 i \cos\Delta N \tag{8-87a}$$

$$\phi_R = (T_2 - T_1)n + \Delta\phi \tag{8-87b}$$

where

$$\Delta\phi = 180 \text{ deg} - 2\phi \tag{8-87c}$$

$$\tan\phi = \frac{\tan(90 \text{ deg} - \Delta N / 2)}{\cos i} \tag{8-87d}$$

ΔN is the angular separation along the equator between the two ascending nodes, $T_2 - T_1$ is the time between satellites 1 and 2 crossing their respective ascending nodes, n is the mean motion or angular frequency of both satellites, ϕ is defined on Fig. 8-42, and $\Delta\phi$ is an intermediate variable that represents the difference in arc length from the point where the two orbits intersect to their respective ascending nodes.

In terms of classical orbit elements, Eq. (8-87b) can be replaced by:

$$\phi_R = L_{0_2} - L_{0_1} + \Delta\phi \tag{8-88a}$$

where the *spacecraft longitude*, L_{0_1} is defined by:

$$L_{0_i} \equiv M_{0_i} + \omega_i \tag{8-88b}$$

where ω_i is the argument of perigee and M_{0_i} is the anomaly at a common epoch for the two orbits. For nearly circular orbits ω_i and M_{0_i} will not be well-defined but L_{0_i} will be.*

In the more general case in which the inclinations of the two satellites are different ($i_1 \neq i_2$), the relative inclination and relative phase are somewhat more complex:

$$\cos i_R = \cos i_1 \cos i_2 + \sin i_1 \sin i_2 \cos\Delta N \tag{8-89a}$$

$$\phi_R = (T_2 - T_1)n + \Delta\phi \tag{8-89b}$$

where

$$\Delta\phi = \phi_2 + \phi_R - \phi_1 \tag{8-89c}$$

$$\cos\phi_1 = \left[\frac{\cos i_2 - \cos i_R \cos i_1}{\sin i_R \sin i_2}\right] \tag{8-89d}$$

$$\cos\phi_2 + \cos\phi_R = -\left[\frac{\cos i_1 - \cos i_R \cos i_2}{\sin i_R \sin i_2}\right] \tag{8-89e}$$

Here ϕ_1 is the arc length from the ascending node of satellite 1 to the intersection of the orbits and ϕ_2 is the arc length from the ascending node of satellite 2 to where satellite 2 will be when satellite 1 is at the intersection of the orbits.

---

* If the orbit is circular, we simply use the spacecraft longitude, L_{0_i}, with respect to node as the defining element.

We can use the above equations to determine the motion of a satellite relative to any arbitrarily defined *base satellite*. Any satellite in a constellation may be chosen as the base satellite. If the constellation is highly symmetric, it will not matter which satellite is chosen as the base.

To simplify the analysis, we use the *relative motion reference frame* defined in Fig. 8-43. This is an Earth centered frame of reference, co-rotating with the base satellite, with the equator of the frame aligned with the orbit plane and the coordinate pole at the orbit pole. In comparing the motion of two satellites, it doesn't matter which is the base satellite. Changing the base satellite simply flops the relative motion pattern to the other side and reverses the sequence of motion, leaving the pattern unchanged. The purpose of using the relative motion reference frame is to remove the rotation of the base satellite relative to the Earth and concentrate on the motion relative to the satellites themselves. (For most constellation designs we want complete coverage of the Earth so our location with respect to the surface doesn't matter. However, we can easily go back to motion over the surface of the Earth if this becomes important.) Depending on what is convenient, we can think of the surface of the Earth-centered sphere containing the base satellite as representing either the direction as seen from the center of the Earth or the sphere with radius equal to the common altitude, i.e. the sphere which contains the actual motion of the satellites.

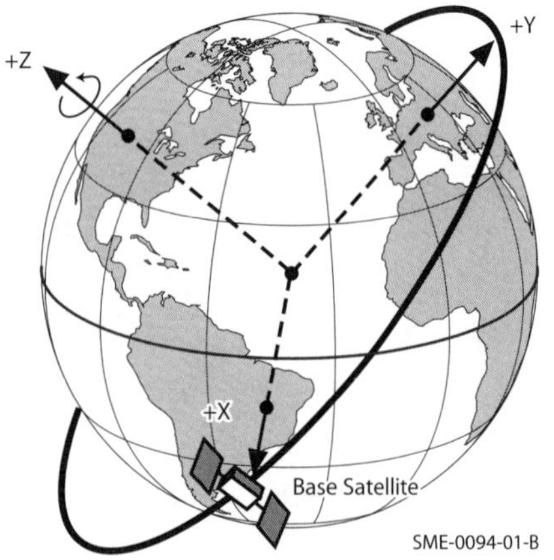

Fig. 8-43. Coordinate Frame of Reference Used for Relative Motion Analysis.

For circular co-altitude orbits, the relative motion of any satellite with respect to the other is an *analemma* or figure eight in the relative motion frame. As shown in Fig. 8-44 the half height of the analemma equals the relative inclination and the distance along the equator from the base satellite equals the relative phase. Thus, if the orbit planes remain the same but the satellites change position within the orbit, then the relative motion analemma will remain unchanged, but will be located at a different distance, ϕ_R. The equations of motion for the analemma are given most easily in parametric form:

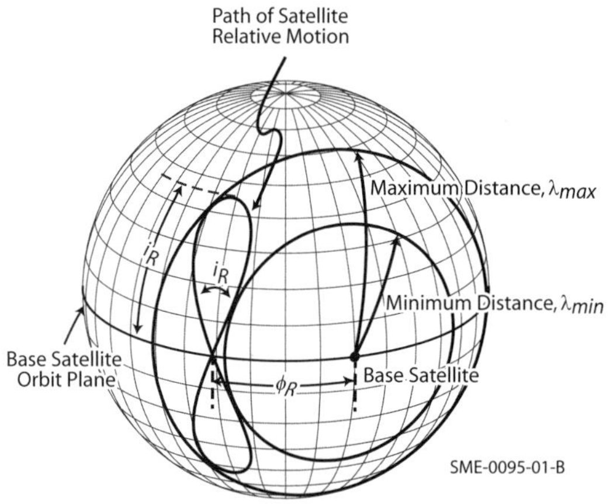

Fig. 8-44. The Relative Motion of Two Co-Altitude Satellites in Circular Orbits as Seen in the Relative Motion Frame. Here the motion is simply an analemma offset from the base satellite by the relative phase and with height equal to the relative inclination.

$$\sin \delta = \sin i_R \sin nt \tag{8-90}$$

$$\alpha = nt - \text{atan}(\cos i_R \tan nt) \tag{8-91}$$

where t is the time, n is the angular frequency of both satellites, δ is the elevation component in the relative motion frame, and α is the azimuthal component, relative to the point where the analemma crosses the equator (i.e., α and δ are the azimuth and elevation coordinators in Fig. 8-44). At the orbit plane, the left and right sides of the analemma cross at an angle equal to the relative inclination. Consequently, the angle that each curve makes with respect to the base orbit plane as it crosses this plane is 90 deg $- i_R/2$. The minimum angular separation, λ_{min}, from the base satellite will be the radius of a small circle centered on the base satellite and tangent to the inside of the analemma. This is given by:

$$\sin(\lambda_{min}/2) = \sin(\phi_R/2)\cos(i_R/2) \tag{8-92}$$

Similarly the maximum distance, λ_{max}, is the radius of the larger small circle tangent to the outside of the analemma given by:

$$\cos(\lambda_{max}/2) = \cos(\phi_R/2)\cos(i_R/2) \tag{8-93}$$

The shape of the relative motion analemma is a one parameter family of curves depending only on the relative inclination between the two orbits. A few representative analemmas are shown in Fig. 8-45. Recall that the height of the analemma equals the relative inclination. If the two satellites are in the same orbit plane, the height will be 0 and the analemma reduces to a point offset from the base satellite by an amount equal to the spacing be-

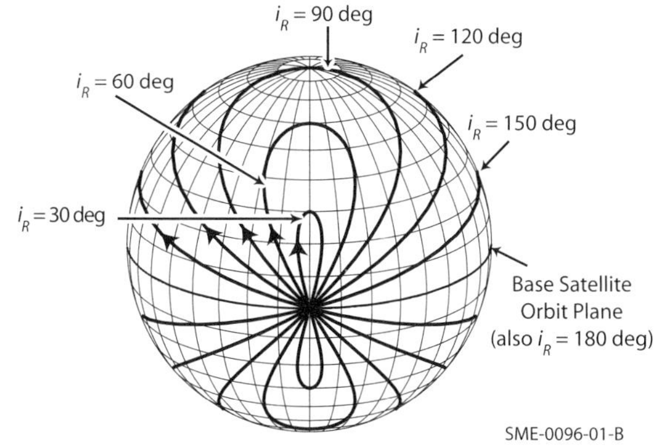

Fig. 8-45. Representative Relative Motion Analemma for Co-altitude Satellites. The shape of the relative motion analemma for co-altitude satellites depends only on the relative inclination, i_R, which is listed on each curve. i_R = 180 deg is a satellite in the same orbit as the base satellite, but moving in the opposite direction.

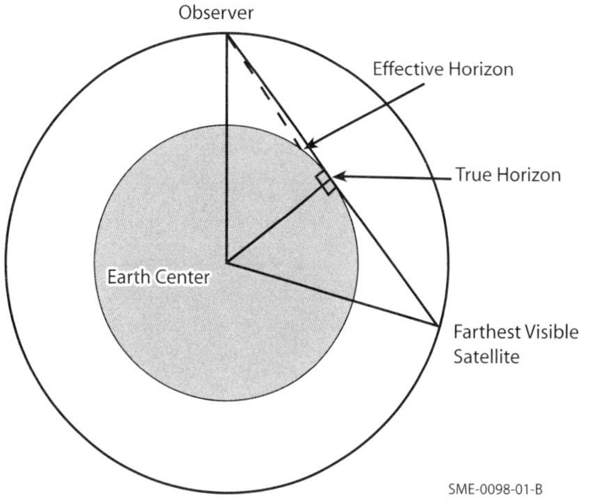

Fig. 8-46. Determining Regions of Intersatellite Visibility. Whenever two satellites are within twice the maximum Earth central angle (true horizon), they will be able to see each other.

tween the two satellites. For very small values of the relative inclination, the analemma is nearly a vertical line with very little sideways motion. As the analemma gets larger, it also gets "fatter" and covers a larger azimuth range. If the two orbits are at right angles to each other, the analemma crosses the equator at 45 deg and just reaches the pole of the coordinate system. When the relative inclination is larger than 90 deg, the two satellites are traveling in opposite directions and the analemma sweeps through all azimuth angles. Finally, when the relative inclination becomes 180 deg, the analemma reduces to a great circle along the coordinate equator, with the two satellites moving in the same plane but in opposite directions, such that they pass each other twice per orbit.

We can use the relative motion analemma to determine when 2 satellites can see each other. Ignoring atmospheric refraction and absorption, satellites will be able to just see each other when the line joining them is tangent to the surface of the Earth. As shown in Fig. 8-46, this will occur at twice the maximum Earth central angle seen by a single satellite. This is another way of saying that whenever two satellites can see the same point on the surface of the Earth, they must be able to see each other. Thus, on our relative motion reference frame we can draw a circle centered on the base satellite with a radius equal to twice the Earth central angle corresponding to the true horizon. Whenever the second satellite is within this circle, it will be above the horizon and visible to the base satellite. Whenever it is outside this circle, it will be below the horizon and the satellites cannot see each other.

As shown in Fig. 8-47, we can extend this concept to determine the nadir angle, η, as seen from either satellite to the other. For any co-altitude satellite at Earth central angle, λ, the nadir angle from each satellite to the other is given by:

$$\eta = 90 \text{ deg} - \lambda / 2 \qquad (8\text{-}94)$$

As must be the case, all co-altitude satellites will be seen within 90 deg of nadir.

In addition to the relative motion of the two satellites, we are also interested in the apparent motion, that is, how does one satellite move in the spacecraft-centered celestial sphere of the other satellite. This problem is similar in many respects to transforming between geometry on the surface of the Earth and geometry as seen by the satellite, with similar results. Like the Earth projection

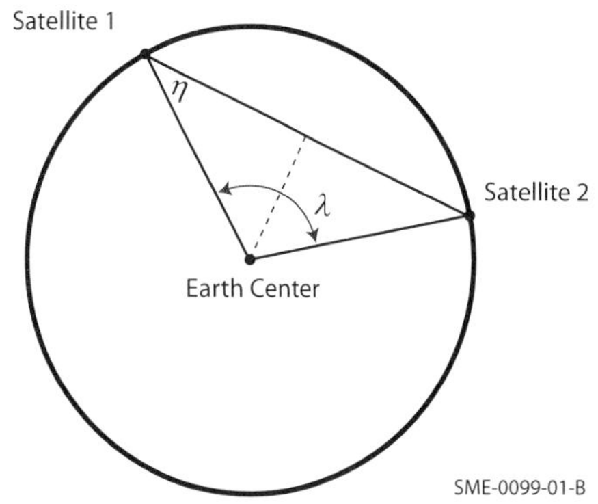

Fig. 8-47. Relationship Between Geometry as Seen from the Satellite and as Seen from the Earth's Center.

problem, azimuths measured relative to the base satellite don't change. They are the same in Earth-centered and spacecraft-centered coordinates. However, the Earth central angle, measured in the relative motion frame, is transformed into the nadir angle measured in the spacecraft frame according to Eq. (8-94). This allows us to transform any of the relative motion analemmas into the apparent motion, as seen from the base satellite.

Fig. 8-48 shows this relative motion and apparent motion for a series of satellites in a plane at a relative inclination of 25 deg with respect to the base satellite's orbit plane. We have put 11 satellites in the inclined plane such that they are 32.7 deg apart and have spaced them so that the relative phase of the closest one is as large as possible, i.e., 16.4 deg. The relative motion analemmas are shown is Fig. 8-48A. All of the analemmas are the same and are simply spaced out along the equator of the coordinate frame. The visibility limit is also shown. Figure 8-48B shows the same analemmas transformed into the spacecraft-centered celestial sphere, centered on the base satellite. The general effect is to bend each analemma about the nadir direction and elongate the analemma for those which are nearest to the base satellite.

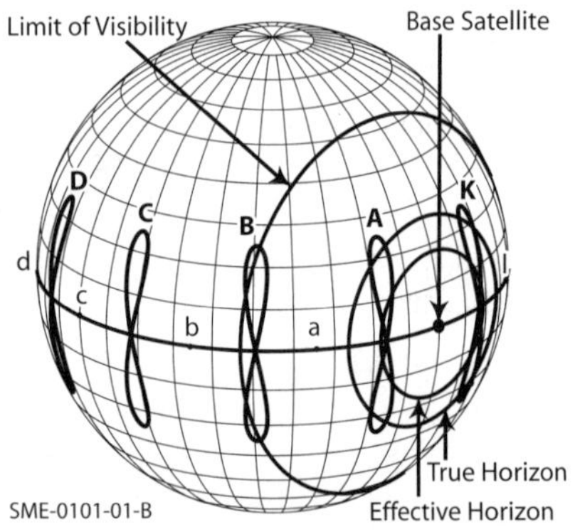

(A) In Relative Motion Frame (Earth at the Center).

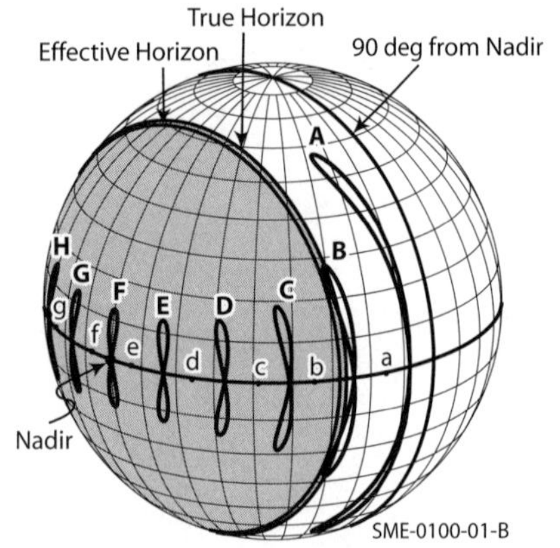

(B) On Spacecraft-Centered Celestial Sphere
(Base Satellite at the Center).

Fig. 8-48. Relative Motion vs. Apparent Motion. Satellites A to K are assumed to be in a common plane at i_R = 25 deg with respect to the base satellite orbit plane. See text for discussion.

To get a better feel for the relative motion, we can think of the background sphere in Fig. 8-48A as the sphere containing the constellation of circular orbits and rotating such that the "base satellite" remains fixed on the x axis. The orbit plane of the base satellite is the equator of the plot and the orbit pole is the pole of the plot. The 10 other satellites in the orbit plane of the base satellite are the dots, a through i, spread out along the equator. The next plane over in our constellation is at a relative inclination, i_R, of 25 deg and contains 11 satellites. The paths of these 11 satellites in this coordinate frame are the 11 analemmas, A through K. The nearest plane on the other side would have a similar series of 11 analemmas, although the phase of the satellites within each analemma would be different. Planes that are further away would have a larger relative inclination and, therefore, larger analemmas. Nonetheless, all of the relative motion analemmas for all of the other satellites will be centered on the equator in the plot. While the figure would get "busy" if we tried to plot them all, this process gives us a good way to understand the relative motion of all of the other satellites in the constellation.

In Fig. 8-48B, we are looking at the motion as seen by an observer sitting on the base satellite. The other satellites in the same plane are simply at fixed locations in front or behind. The closest satellites (a and l) are always visible and the rest are always invisible. The closest satellite in the neighboring plane (A or K), oscillates back and forth across the base orbit plane moving mostly parallel to the horizon. The furthest satellite in this adjacent plane (F), moves in a very small apparent analemma but is never visible because it is always behind the Earth's disk, as are the 3 satellites on either side of it. Thus, of the 11 satellites in the adjacent plane, 2 are always visible, 7 are always invisible, and 2 are invisible part of the time and visible, but very near the horizon, most of the time.

From the plot, we can determine a number of **general characteristics of the apparent motion of satellites:**

- All co-altitude satellites are within the hemisphere centered on nadir (i.e., below the *horizontal plane* which is the great circle perpendicular to nadir and is the limit of apparent satellite positions when they are very close to the base satellite).
- Satellites near the base satellite will appear near the horizontal plane; those far from the base satellite will appear near nadir and will be obscured by the Earth disk.
- The visible motion is confined to an annulus or band between the horizontal plane and the Earth's horizon. Any satellite which is over a location on the Earth less than twice as far away as the true geometric horizon will be visible and in this band.
- Generally, the motion is back and forth, approximately parallel to the horizon; the center of this back and forth motion is the base satellite orbit plane.

As an example of this motion, satellite A is the one in the neighboring plane closest to the base satellite. In the relative motion frame (Fig. 8-48A), the analemma is near the base satellite and is well within the limit of visibility at all times. In the apparent motion frame (Fig. 8-48B), the motion is basically horizontal, moving back and forth across the base satellite's orbit plane with relatively little elevation change.

Satellite B is the next closest satellite in the adjacent plane. Here the satellite is principally within the limit of visibility but goes outside of that limit for brief periods. In the apparent motion frame, this means that the satellite lies very near the Earth's horizon. It is above the horizon most of the time, and for brief periods dips below the horizon and becomes invisible. The remaining satellites remain below the horizon at all times and are invisible to the base satellite. The apparent motion is still an analemma but is obscured by the disk of the Earth. Combining Eqs. (8-92), (8-93), and (8-94), we can determine the maximum and minimum nadir angles for any other satellite as follows:

$$\sin \eta_{min} = \cos(\lambda_{max} / 2) = \cos(\phi_R / 2) \cos (i_R / 2) \quad (8\text{-}95)$$

$$\cos \eta_{max} = \sin(\lambda_{min} / 2) = \sin(\phi_R / 2) \cos (i_R / 2) \quad (8\text{-}96)$$

In addition, we can determine the following expression for the maximum azimuth angle, α_{max}, as seen from the base satellite as:

$$\tan \eta_{max} = \tan (i_R / \sin \phi_R) \quad (8\text{-}97)$$

Finally, Table 8-13 summarizes the results of our assessment of the large scale relative motion for co-altitude satellites. For a discussion of the small scale relative motion see OCDM, Sec. 10.1.2.

Table 8-13. Results of Large-Scale Relative Motion for Co-altitude Satellites.

- For co-altitude satellites in circular orbits, the large-scale relative motion depends only on the relative inclination and relative phase of the satellites
- The general motion is an analemma centered on the base satellite orbit plane
  - Height is equal to relative inclination
  - Position of central point is equal to the relative phase
- The apparent motion as seen from one of the satellites "bends" the analemma about the nadir direction
  - Visible motion is confined to a band between the Earth's horizon and the horizontal plane perpendicular to nadir
  - Generally, the motion is back-and-forth, approximately parallel to the horizon, and centered on the orbit plane
  - Any satellite will be visible when it is over a location on the Earth less than twice as far as the true (geometric) horizon

8.6 Mapping and Pointing Budgets

As discussed in Sec. 1.3, most space missions are not concerned with orbit, attitude, and timing per se, but rather with the more fundamental aspects of mapping and pointing. In this context, *pointing* means orienting the spacecraft, camera, sensor, or antenna to a target having specific geographic coordinates or inertial direction. *Mapping* is determining the coordinates of the *look-point* of a camera, sensor, or antenna. Satellites used only for communications will generally require only pointing. Satellites having some type of viewing instrument, such as weather, ground surveillance, or Earth resource satellites, will ordinarily require both pointing (point the instrument at Los Angeles) and mapping (determine the geographic location of the feature in pixel 1096).

In order to create a mapping and pointing budget, we must first understand the sources of error in determining the mapping and pointing, and then evaluate how to quantify these error sources, and how the errors should be added to create the final budget. The components of pointing and mapping budgets for an Earth-oriented observation mission are shown in Fig. 8-49 and defined in Table 8-13.* Mapping and pointing errors are related to the knowledge of the spacecraft position and attitude in space. However, even if these are known precisely, other errors will be present. For example, an error in the observation time will result in an error of the computed location of the target, because the target frame of reference moves relative to the spacecraft. A target fixed on the Earth's equator will rotate with the Earth at 464 m/s. A 10 sec error in the observation time would produce an error of 5 km in the computed geographic location of the target. Errors due to the target altitude come about because of the projection of the direction of the target onto a location on the surface of the Earth. For example, if the spacecraft has an elevation angle of 45 deg as seen from the target, and if the assumed altitude of the target is off by 1 km, then there will be a 1 km error in "placing" the target on the geographic surface of the Earth. Since the roughness of the surface of the Earth has a variation of several kilometers relative to a perfect spheroid, this implies that observations must be made nearly vertically, or if we wish geographic accuracies much greater than this, the target altitudes must be well known.

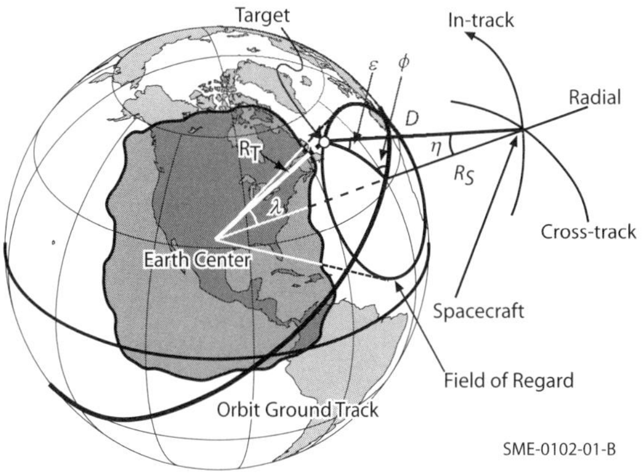

Fig. 8-49. Definition of Pointing and Mapping Error Components for an Earth-oriented Observation Mission.

* Errors associated with an inertially pointed mission are similar, but do not include any of the error sources associated with projecting the position onto the Earth.

Table 8-14. Sources of Pointing and Mapping Errors. Sensing axis orientation errors include errors in (1) attitude determination, (2) instrument mounting, and (3) stability for mapping control for pointing.

Spacecraft Position Errors:		
ΔI	In- or along-track	Displacement along the spacecraft's velocity vector
ΔC	Cross-track	Displacement normal to the spacecraft's orbit plane
ΔR_S	Radial	Displacement toward the center of the Earth (nadir)
Sensing Axis Orientation Errors		
$\Delta\eta$	Elevation	Error in angle from nadir to sensing axis
$\Delta\phi$	Azimuth	Error in rotation of the sensing axis about nadir
Other Errors:		
ΔR_T	Target altitude	Uncertainty in the altitude of the observed object
ΔT	Clock error	Uncertainty in the real observation time (results in) uncertainty in the rotational position of the Earth)

Pointing errors differ from mapping errors in the way they include inaccuracies in attitude control and angular motion. The pointing error must include the entire control error for the spacecraft. On the other hand, the only control-related component of the mapping error is the angular motion during the exposure or observation time. This short term jitter results in a blurring of the look-point of the instrument or antenna. Except for this blur, it is attitude knowledge, rather than attitude control that is important for observation missions and therefore mapping. We may achieve an accuracy goal for either pointing or mapping in many ways. For example, we may know the position of the spacecraft precisely, and the attitude only poorly. Or we may choose to allow a larger error in the position, and make the requirements for determining the attitude more stringent. The ideal mathematical process for minimizing the cost is as follows:

> **If the components of an error budget are continuously variable then the minimum system cost is obtained by adjusting each component until the differential cost of improvement is the same for all components.**

Assume, for example, that we wish to minimize the cost of achieving a given pointing accuracy, and that with the current design, we can improve the pointing accuracy by adjusting the orbit accuracy at a cost of \$100,000/mrad. Also assume that we could improve the pointing accuracy by improving the attitude accuracy at a cost of only \$50,000/mrad. In this case, we should adjust our error budgets so as to be less stringent in terms of orbit accuracy and more stringent in terms of attitude accuracy until the differential cost of improvement for both was \$75,000/mrad. In a sense, we are selling orbit accuracy for \$100,000/mrad, in order to buy attitude accuracy for only \$50,000/mrad. Continuing to do this so long as one component costs more than another in terms of improvement allows us to continually reduce the cost of achieving a given level of performance.

In practice the above process seldom works. Ordinarily, we cannot improve accuracy continuously. Normally, we have some components for which very little adjustment in accuracy is possible, and others for which there are very large steps in both performance and cost as we change the methods or techniques that we are using. Even if we can make nearly continuous adjustments, we seldom know precisely how much money it costs to achieve a given level of performance. In practice, the mission designer attempts to balance the components, often by relying on experience and intuition as much as analysis. In any case, the overall goal remains correct. We should try to balance the error budget so the incremental cost of improvement in any of the components results in approximately comparable cost.

Table 8-15. Construction of Mapping and Pointing Error Budgets. This process is essentially the same for all types of spacecraft error budgets.

Optimal Solution (How It Should be Done)
Adjust each error component until the differential cost of improvement (\$ per milliradian or \$ per km) is the same for each
Doesn't work in practice because performance improvements are not continuously variable.
Practical Solution (How it Works in Practice)
Allocate the budget equally among all components
Divide the components into three categories A. Those allowing very little adjustment (e.g., position) B. Those that easily meet the allocation (e.g., time) C. Those allowing increased accuracy at increased cost (e.g., attitude)
Adjust both the requirement and category (C) components to meet the cost vs. performance trade

A more practical technique for creating an error budget is summarized in Table 8-15. We begin the process by writing down all of the components of the budget. We then spread the total available budget equally among all of the components. For example, if there are five error sources relevant to the problem, then if we are going to add the errors linearly we would assign each source 1/5 of the error and if we are going to use a root sum square then we would assign each source the square root of 1/5 of the error. This provides a starting point for allocating the errors. Our next step is to look at the range of options available to us and divide the error sources into the following categories:

A. Those allowing very little adjustment
B. Those easily meeting their error allocation
C. Those allowing increased accuracy at increased cost

Table 8-16. Mapping and Pointing Error Formulas. ε is the elevation angle of the spacecraft as seen from the target, *lat* is the latitude of the target, ϕ is the target azimuth relative to the ground track, λ is the Earth central angle from the target to the satellite, D is the distance from the satellite to the target, R_T is the distance from the Earth's center to the target (typically ~ R_E, the Earth's radius), and R_S is the distance from the Earth's center to the satellite. See Fig. 8-49.

Error Source	Error Magnitude (units)	Magnitude of Mapping Error (km)	Magnitude of Pointing Error (rad)	Direction of Error
Attitude Errors:(1)				
Azimuth	$\Delta\phi$ (rad)	$\Delta\phi D \sin\eta$	$\Delta\phi \sin\eta$	Azimuthal
Nadir Angle	$\Delta\eta$ (rad)	$\Delta\eta D / \sin\varepsilon$	$\Delta\eta$	Toward nadir
Position Errors:				
In-Track	ΔI (km)	$\Delta I (R_T/R_S) \cos H$ (2)	$(\Delta I/D) \sin Y_I$ (5)	Parallel to ground track
Cross-Track	ΔC (km)	$\Delta C (R_T/R_S) \cos G$ (3)	$(\Delta C/D) \sin Y_C$ (6)	Perpendicular to ground track
Radial	ΔR_S (km)	$\Delta R_S \sin\eta / \sin\varepsilon$	$(\Delta R_S/D) \sin\eta$	Toward nadir
Other Errors:				
Target Altitude	ΔR_T (km)	$\Delta R_T / \tan\varepsilon$	—	Toward nadir
S/C Clock	ΔT (s)	$\Delta T V_e \cos(lat)$ (4)	$\Delta T (V_e/D) \cos(lat) \cdot \sin J$ (7)	Parallel to Earth's equator

Notes:
(1) Includes attitude determination error, instrument mounting error, stability over exposure time (mapping only), and control error (pointing only). The formulas given assume that the attitude is measured with respect to the Earth.
(2) $\sin H = \sin\lambda \sin\phi$.
(3) $\sin G = \sin\lambda \cos\phi$.
(4) V_e = 464 m/s (Earth rotation velocity at the equator).
(5) $\cos Y_I = \cos\phi \sin\eta$.
(6) $\cos Y_C = \sin\phi \sin\eta$.
(7) $\cos J = \cos\phi_E \cos\varepsilon$, where ϕ_E = azimuth relative to East.

For example, determining the position of the spacecraft is a normal spacecraft operational function, done either by the ground station or by GPS. Whichever method is chosen, the level of accuracy is essentially fixed and cannot be adjusted without a dramatically high cost. (Launching a new and more accuracy GPS constellation is not a practical solution for most missions). Consequently, we assign these errors to category A and accept whatever error is inherent in the process. Timing errors frequently fall into category B, since modern spacecraft clocks can easily maintain an accuracy of tens of milliseconds which represents a small motion on the part of the spacecraft. Therefore, the error associated with the timing will typically be much smaller than the allocation and we will accept the more accurate values in order to allow a looser budget in another category. Attitude determination errors ordinarily fall into category C. Here, we could use a gravity-gradient stabilized system at very low cost, but accurate to only a few degrees, or a horizon sensor system, accurate to 0.05–0.10 deg at moderate cost, or an expensive star sensor system, accurate to better than 0.01 deg.

This process not only allows us to balance cost between appropriate components, but also to go back to the mission definition process and find the real requirements. For example, achieving a mapping accuracy of 100 m on the ground might triple the cost of the space mission, by requiring highly accurate attitude determination, a new system for orbit determination, and a detailed list of target altitudes. Reducing this accuracy requirement to 500 m might lower the cost enough to make the mission possible within established budget constraints. This is an example of trading on mission requirements as discussed in more detail in Chaps. 3 and 6. Requirements trading is extremely important to a cost-effective mission, but we often omit this step in the normal process of defining and allocating mission requirements. However, it is this evaluation of the cost of achieving a particular level of performance that allows technical information and technical decision-making to flow back into the requirements definition process.

To carry out the trade process defined above, we need to know how an error in each of the components listed in Table 8-14 relates to the overall mapping and pointing errors. Table 8-16 gives the formulas relating the errors in each of the seven basic components to the overall mapping and pointing errors. The notation here is the same as in Fig. 8-49. For any specific mission conditions, these formulas relate the errors in the fundamental components to the resulting pointing and mapping accuracies. This set of formulas provides the basic algebraic information which we use to transform attitude, position, and other error sources into specific mapping and pointing requirements for a given mission.

8.6.1 Representative Mapping Budget

To illustrate the process of constructing detailed mapping and pointing budgets, we will look at specific numerical examples of a moderate accuracy satellite, flying at an altitude of 1,000 km. The Excel model on the website allows you to transform this example to the parameters of your particular mission.

The errors associated with mapping, depend strongly on how close to the horizon we choose to work. Working in a very small region directly under the spacecraft gives excellent mapping accuracy and resolution, but provides

Table 8-17. Representative Mapping and Pointing Error Budgets. See Figs. 8-50 and 8-51 for plots.

Source	Error in Source	Error Budgets: Mapping Error (km) ε = 10 deg	Mapping Error (km) ε = 30 deg	Pointing Error (deg) ε = 10 deg	Pointing Error (deg) ε = 30 deg
Attitude Errors:					
Azimuth	0.06 deg	2.46	1.33	0.051	0.045
Nadir Angle	0.03 deg	8.33	1.78	0.030	0.030
Position Errors:					
In-Track	0.2 km	0.17	0.17	0.002	0.005
Cross-Track	0.2 km	0.16	0.17	0.004	0.007
Radial	0.1 km	0.49	0.15	0.002	0.003
Other Errors:					
Target Altitude	1 km	5.67	1.73	—	—
S/C Clock	0.5 sec	0.23	0.23	0.005	0.008
Root Sum Square		10.39	2.84	0.060	0.055

very poor coverage. On the other hand, working near the horizon provides very wide coverage, but poor mapping accuracy. Thus, we must trade resolution and mapping accuracy for coverage. The mapping accuracy for a particular mission will depend on the spacecraft's elevation angle at the edge of the coverage region. In almost all cases the mapping accuracy would be much better looking straight down, and the limiting accuracy will be closest to the horizon. To see how this works in practice, Table 8-17 provides representative mapping and pointing error budgets which are then plotted for an altitude of 1,000 km in Fig. 8-50 as a function of spacecraft elevation angle as seen from the ground, using the equations listed in Table 8-16. The total mapping error is the RSS of the individual components. Generally, uncertainty in target altitude and attitude determination contribute the most to the errors in mapping accuracy. In most cases, improving the other factors will have only a second-order effect. Consequently, determining the target altitude and spacecraft attitude are high priorities in assessing a mission's mapping performance and cost.

The uncertainty in target altitude typically contributes most to determining a geographic location on the Earth. The oblateness of the Earth has the largest effect on target altitude. It causes a variation in distance from the center of the Earth of approximately 25 km between the poles and the equator. However, we can account for this factor analytically at a very low cost, so it does not usually contribute to the error. The next plateau is for airplanes, clouds or other atmospheric features. The uncertainty in target altitude for these will typically be 10 km or larger, unless we have some a priori estimate of the altitude. For features fixed on the Earth's surface, the uncertainty in target altitude reduces to approximately 1 km, unless data analysis includes a detailed map of target altitudes. Figure 8-50 incorporates this 1 km error in target altitude as the dominant source of error. To do significantly better would require one of two options. First, the spacecraft could work only very near nadir and therefore have very poor coverage. Alternatively, it could include the elevation of the target region as a part of the data reduction process, therefore requiring a large database and making the data processing more complex.

8.6.2 Representative Pointing Budget

Unlike mapping, pointing depends only weakly on the spacecraft's elevation angle. This can be seen in Fig. 8-51, which is based on the same parameters as Fig. 8-50. For missions which require only pointing, working in a region near the horizon is almost as easy as pointing to a target or ground antenna at nadir. In this case the working limit on the spacecraft's elevation angle will depend on other factors, such as the transmission of the atmosphere for a selected wavelength, or possible obstruction by local geography. For example, ground stations ordinarily limit their work to approximately 5 deg above the horizon because of the reduced transmission of the atmosphere at lower elevation angles.

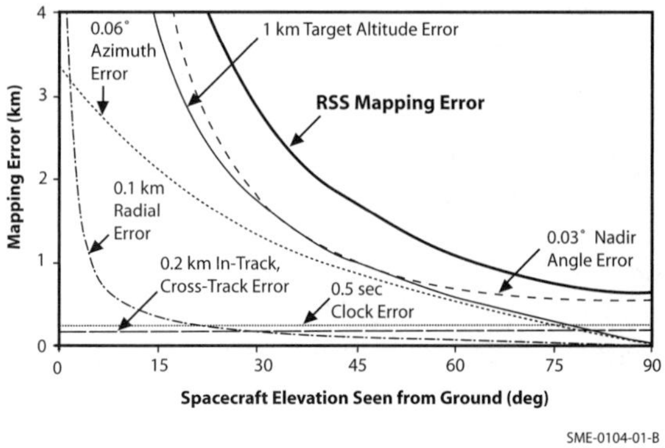

Fig. 8-50. Mapping Error as a Function of Elevation Angle for a Spacecraft at 1,000 km. Errors are from Table 8-17.

Pointing requirements normally arise from the spacecraft's housekeeping function, or from the need to point a particular instrument or antenna toward a ground target. Housekeeping requirements, such as solar array pointing and orbit maneuvers ordinarily demand pointing accuracies of 0.25–1 deg. Consequently, for most missions, the need to point the mission sensor or antenna is more important. Here again, two cases exist. If we wish to point the sensor at a single target, then we will generally try to point the center of the sensor at the target. By doing so, we establish a pointing requirement to place the target within the field of view. If the payload sensor's field of view is four times the 3σ pointing error, then the target will lie within the field of view with a 6σ probability, or virtual certainty. For example, if a sensor has a 1 deg square field of view, an overall pointing requirement of 0.25 deg will assure that the target will be within the field of view on essentially every observation.

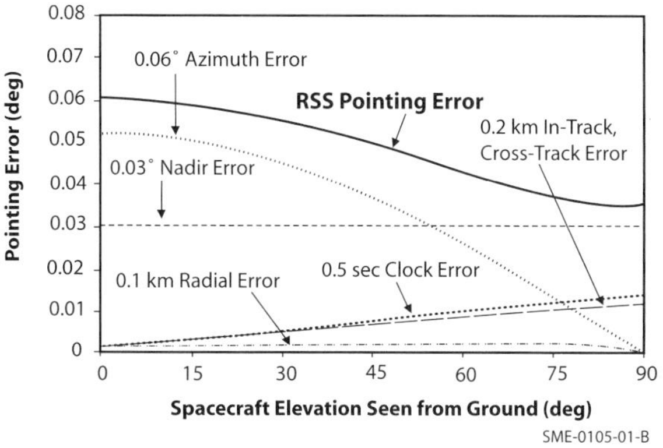

Fig. 8-51. Pointing Error as a Function of Elevation Angle for a Spacecraft at 1,000 km Altitude. Compare with Fig. 8-50. Note that mapping error is very sensitive to elevation angle while pointing error is not.

In pointing, we may also want to eliminate overlapping coverage. For example, if we wish to take a series of pictures, we must overlap the pictures by more than the pointing error to ensure continuous coverage of the ground. This requirement in turn implies that the spacing between pictures must equal the field of view size, less the pointing error. With a large pointing error, we must accept having fewer pictures in a given time, and increased resource cost in terms of time, power, and data rate for a given level of coverage. It is common to have a pointing requirement of 10%–20% of the field of view diameter. Driving the pointing under 10% of the field of view diameter will only slightly improve overall coverage. On the other hand, a pointing error worse than 20% of the field of view size can require substantial overlap, thus significantly diminishing the system's coverage and resource utilization.

8.6.3 Minimizing Cost

The first approach for minimizing cost is to eliminate entirely elements from the overall budget, thereby improving performance at essentially no cost. The key issue here is to look at the budget components and see which ones could be eliminated. For example, consider the pointing budget for a spacecraft whose goal is to remain nadir pointed. We can do this by using either star sensors or Earth sensors. However, star sensors are sensing the orientation with respect to inertial space, and therefore require an additional coordinate transformation which includes uncertainties in the position of the spacecraft in order to determine where nadir is and, therefore, remain nadir pointed. This is eliminated by using an Earth sensor to provide measurements directly with respect to the item we would like to be pointed toward. This implies that I could end up with a system that achieves lower accuracy using the high-cost star sensors than using low-cost Earth sensors. In general, I can maximize accuracy and minimize cost by using sensors that detect directly the object that I am interested in measurements with respect to.

The second principal way to reduce cost is to look at the overall problem of system requirements specification. If you do not meet the initial requirement, then the classic response is to go back and tighten up on the specifications. However, in a cost-conscious system, this is the wrong answer. The process needs to involve an iterative trade between what we want (the initial requirement) and what we can afford (what the engineering budget comes back with). In the end, the organization putting up the money must come up with a decision on how to proceed and whether or not meeting the accuracy objectives is worth the differential cost of doing so.

A key issue is to look for creative mechanisms for defining accuracy that may be able to meet the needs of the end user while still holding down cost. For example, as discussed above, accuracy is a strong function of elevation angle for a mapping error budget. This results in a very undesirable trade. If we increase the elevation angle to improve the accuracy, we will dramatically reduce coverage, which could drive up the number of spacecraft that are required. On the other hand, working at low elevation angles to achieve wide coverage with a small number of spacecraft provides extremely poor mapping accuracy at the edges of the swath. In cases such as this, a possible alternative is a "flexi-spec" in which different accuracies are required at different elevation angles. For example, in examining Fig. 8-50, we might set a mapping requirement of 3 km at an elevation angle of 25 deg, and 1 km at an elevation angle of 60 deg. This means that the user will get very wide and frequent coverage, with limited accuracy, and much higher accuracy, but at a less frequent rate, from the narrow swath. Certainly, this is less desirable than achieving high accuracy at all times. However, we may be able to reduce the number of spacecraft required by a factor of two or three and, therefore, dramatically drive down the cost of the system, if we can find a way to make use of poorer accuracy data at a higher frequency, and more accurate data at a lower frequency. This is representative of the types of trade that need to be made in modern systems, in order to drive down the overall system cost and maximize the performance.

References

For annotated bibliography of space mission geometry, see the book website.

Bowditch, Nathaniel. 2010. *The American Practical Navigator*. Pub. No. 9. Bethesda, MA: National Imagery and Mapping Agency.

Brink, Raymond W. 1942. *Spherical Trigonometry*. New York: Appleton-Century-Croft, Inc.

Canters, Frank and Huge Decleir. 1989. *The World in Perspective: A Directory of World Map Projections.* New York: John Wiley and Sons.

Green, R.M. 1985. *Spherical Astronomy*. Cambridge: Cambridge University Press.

Kaplan, George H. 2005. *Naval Observatory Circular No. 179, The IAU Resolutions on Astronomical Reference Systems, Time Scales, and Earth Rotation Models.* Washinton, DC: U.S. Naval Observatory.

Newcomb, Simon. 1906. *A Compendium of Spherical Astronomy with Its Applications to the Determination and Reduction of Positions of the Fixed Stars*. New York: The Macmillan Co; Ithaca, NY: Cornell University Library

Palmer, Claude I., Charles W. Leigh, and Spofford H. Kimball. 1950. *Plane and Spherical Trigonometry with Tables*. New York: The McGraw-Hill Companies.

Seidelmann, Kenneth P. 2006. *Explanatory Supplement to the Astronomical Almanac*. Mill Valley, CA: University Science Books.

Shuster, Malcolm D. 1993. "A Survey of Attitude Representations." *Journal of Astronautical Sciences*. vol. 41, no. 4. Oct–Dec. pp. 439–517.

Small, Lloyd L. 1952. *Trigonometry, Plane and Spherical.* New York: NcGraw Hill.

Wertz, James R. 1978. *Spacecraft Attitude Determination and Control*. Dordrecht, The Netherlands: D. Reidel Publishing Company.

Wertz, James R. and Wiley J. Larson. 1999. *Space Mission Analysis and Design. 3rd ed.* Hawthorne, CA and New York: Microcosm Press and Springer.

Wertz, James R. 2009. *Orbit & Constellation Design and Management: Spacecraft Orbit and Attitude Systems.* Hawthorne, CA: Microcosm Press.

9 Orbits and Astrodynamics

James R. Wertz, ***Microcosm, Inc./USC***

This chapter is a general introduction to orbits and defines the terminology used in orbit analysis and mission planning. It provides physical motivation for the principal effects important to orbit and mission design, formulas or approximations for all of the basic astronautical computations, and formulas needed for orbit and constellation design and the computation of ΔV budgets. As listed in the annotated bibliography on the book website, many books in celestial mechanics and orbit analysis are widely available. Those which provide the most comprehensive mathematical background are Battin [1999] and Seidelmann [2006]. High accuracy coordinate and time systems are very well explained by both Seidelmann [2006] and Kaplan [2005]. The best current book on orbits and astrodynamics, including both derivations of most of the equations presented here and free orbit software, is Vallado [2007]. The problem of selecting an orbit for a particular space mission (vs. the mathematical properties of an orbit described in this section and by the above references) is discussed in Chap. 10 and in more detail in Wertz [2009].

The *orbit* or *trajectory* is the path of a spacecraft or natural body through space. We will use orbit and trajectory interchangeably, although some authors prefer to use *orbit* to mean only a closed circular or elliptical path and *trajectory* to refer to other shapes such as hyperbola or paths which intersect the surface of the Earth. *Astrodynamics* is the mathematical analysis of orbits and their properties. An orbit is ordinarily specified by a *state vector* which can be the position and velocity of the spacecraft at some specified time or *epoch*, or a number of other equivalent forms described in Sec. 9.1.5. In principle, the state vector at any one time allows us to predict the position and velocity of the spacecraft at all future times. The list of successive positions of a satellite or planet is known as its *ephemeris* (plural *ephemerides*). Planetary ephemerides are published annually by the Government Printing Office. They are either in tabular form, such as *The Astronomical Almanac*, or more typically in machine readable form.

A *Keplerian orbit* is one in which gravity is the only force; the central body is spherically symmetric; the central body's mass is much greater than that of the satellite; and the central body and satellite are the only two objects in the system. Although this appears to be a large number of constraints, Keplerian orbits provide a remarkably good approximation for most spacecraft motion. A *perturbation* is a deviation from Keplerian motion of which there are two types. *Secular perturbations* are those for which the effects build up over time. *Cyclic perturbations* are periodic such that the effects cancel after one cycle or orbit.

Generally, this chapter addresses astrodynamics from a mission analysis and design perspective such that we can understand the underlying physics and make use of approximations and top-level formulas to evaluate most orbit effects. The detailed mathematical basis of astrodynamics is available from most volumes listed in the bibliography.

9.1 Keplerian Orbits

Predicting the motion of the Sun, Moon, and planets was a major part of the scientific revolution of the 16th and 17th centuries. Galileo's discovery of the satellites of Jupiter in 1610 provided a break with Aristotelian science and a strong argument for Copernicus' heliocentric theory. Danish astronomer Tycho Brahe determined the positions of the planets to about 1 minute of arc (1/60 deg) and the length of the year to about 1 sec with the unaided eye. Brahe's German assistant, Johannes Kepler, used these precise observations to derive empirically the rules of planetary motion which would later be justified by Newton.

It was the search for the underlying cause of the motion of celestial objects that motivated much of Newton's development of mechanics. In 1665, he determined that if gravity were an inverse square force it could account both for objects falling at the Earth's surface and for the motion of the Moon. However, he did not publish the detailed theory until 1687 in *Philosophiae Naturalis Principia Mathematica*. A major cause of this 22-year delay was Newton's inability to show that spherically symmetric objects (e.g., the Earth) behave gravitationally as though all the mass were concentrated at the center, the proof of which required development of the calculus. Having achieved this, Newton was able to combine his second law of motion, $\mathbf{F} = m\mathbf{a} \equiv m\ddot{\mathbf{r}}$, with his law of gravitation, $\mathbf{F} = -(G(Mm)/r^3)\mathbf{r}$, to obtain the two-body equation of motion which closely approximates the motion of spacecraft and planets:

$$\ddot{\mathbf{r}} = -\left(GM/r^3\right)\mathbf{r} \equiv -\left(\mu/r^3\right)\mathbf{r} \tag{9-1}$$

where **F** is the force between two objects of mass m and M, **r** is the vector between them, **a** is the acceleration of the small body, G is Newton's constant of gravitation, and $\mu \equiv GM$ is the measure of the gravitational effect of the large body. Accurate orbit work includes the effect of the non-spherical symmetry of the Earth, perturbations due to other bodies, and non-gravitational forces—but nearly all of the basic foundations of orbit theory are direct extrapolations of Newton's work as foreseen by Newton himself.

Using gravitational theory and his laws of mechanics, Newton was able to derive Kepler's three laws of planetary motion. These laws apply to any two point masses (or spherically symmetric objects) moving under their mutual gravitational attraction. Kepler's laws in the form derived by Newton are:

- **Kepler's First Law:** *If two objects in space interact gravitationally, each will describe an orbit that is a conic section with the center of mass at one focus. If the bodies are permanently associated, their orbits will be ellipses; if not, their orbits will be hyperbolas*

- **Kepler's Second Law:** *If two objects in space interact gravitationally (whether or not they move in closed elliptical orbits), a line joining them sweeps out equal areas in equal intervals of time.*

- **Kepler's Third Law:** *If two objects in space revolve around each other due to their mutual gravitational attraction, the sum of their masses multiplied by the square of their period of mutual revolution is proportional to the cube of the mean distance between them; that is,*

Consequences of the Equation for Orbital Motion. Although Eq. (9-1) is a relatively simple set of equations, they provide very interesting consequences for satellite motion. First, notice that the right-hand side of Eq. (9-1) does not contain any properties of the spacecraft (m canceled in the two preceding equations). This implies that the acceleration and subsequent motion of objects in space does not depend on any physical properties of the objects themselves, so long as we ignore non-gravitational forces. A feather follows the same orbit as a bowling ball or a large spacecraft. Consequently, when the astronaut lets go of their pen, it follows the same trajectory that the spacecraft is following and appears to float next to the astronaut because they are both falling together with the same acceleration. This is the phenomenon often called *weightlessness* or *zero g*. However, gravity has not gone away and objects are certainly not weightless. An object sitting on a tall platform attached to the Earth, but at the altitude of the Space Shuttle, would weigh about 95% of what it does on the surface of the Earth. Gravity is very strong and objects are falling very rapidly. It's just that they are falling together, such that the motion relative to each other is very slow. The result is the astronaut and the pen floating gently at 7 km/s relative to the Earth's surface.

There is a second more subtle implication of these equations. In Newton's second law, m is the *inertial mass* which is the property of an object which resists acceleration or gives it momentum. A feather or ping pong ball has relatively little inertial mass whereas a freight train has a great deal. On the other hand, the m in the law of gravitation is the *gravitational mass*, which is a measure of the gravitational charge or how strong gravity acts. This is equivalent to the electrical charge on an object which determines how strong the electrical forces are. Objects with a similar mass can have very different electrical charges and, consequently, behave very differently in the presence of electrical fields. For some reason, this isn't true of gravity. Objects with the same inertial mass all have the same gravitational charge and all of them behave the same in the presence of a gravitational field. It is this very strange equivalence of gravitational and inertial mass that led Einstein, in the early 20th century, to develop the theory of relativity which implies, in part, that gravity is more a property of space than a property of objects, as electrical forces are. The theory of relativity plays a very minor role in the orbits of planets (particularly Mercury) and spacecraft designed specifically to test gravitational theories. For all but remarkably demanding applications, relativistic effects may be totally ignored in spacecraft calculations. Nonetheless, it is interesting that the seeds of relativity lie in the very foundations of Newtonian mechanics.

$$\left(m+M\right)P^2 = \frac{4\pi^2}{G}a^3 \tag{9-2}$$

where P is their mutual period of revolution, a is the mean distance between them, m and M are the two masses, and G is Newton's gravitational constant.

The more massive of the two objects, M, is called the *primary* and the other, m, is called the *secondary*, or *satellite*. The *barycenter* is the location of the center of mass between the two objects. Kepler's empirical relations presented in two works in 1609 and 1619 were essentially the same as those derived by Newton, except that the constant of proportionality in the third law was obtained empirically and the shape of the orbits specified in the first law was an ellipse (one of 4 possible conic sections) because his experience was limited to planets.

In 1673, Christian Huygens introduced the quantity $(1/2)\ mV^2$ which he called the *vis viva* or "living force," to explain the motion of the compound pendulum. This concept was further developed by Gottfried Leibnitz in terms of "living" and "dead" forces which later came to be known as kinetic and potential energy. The application of this theory to celestial mechanics led to the fourth fundamental relationship for two objects rotating under their mutual gravitational attraction, the *vis viva equation*:

$$\mathcal{E} = \frac{V^2}{2} - \frac{\mu}{r} = -\frac{\mu}{2a} \tag{9-3}$$

where $\mathcal{E}$ is the total *specific energy* (i.e., energy per unit mass), and $V^2/2$ and $-\mu/r$ are the kinetic energy and potential energy, respectively, of the satellite, r is the instantaneous separation of the objects, and V is the magnitude of the relative velocity.

For some time there was bitter controversy between the followers of Huygens and Leibnitz, who believed that $\mathbf{F}\Delta x = (1/2)mV^2$ was the correct measure of the effect of a force, **F**, and the followers of Galileo and Newton, who believed that $\mathbf{F}\Delta t = \Delta(mV)$ was the proper measure. The controversy was resolved in 1743 when Jean D'Alembert published his *Traité de Dynamique*, which showed that both measures were correct and that they were not equivalent. (For a discussion of this controversy see, for example, Girvin [1948] or Dugas [1988].)

9.1.1 Kepler's First Law

Recall from the introduction that a *Keplerian orbit* is one in which gravity is the only force; the central body is spherically symmetric, the central body's mass is much greater than that of the satellite; and the central body and the satellite are the only two objects in the system. Kepler's first law states that the orbits of celestial objects are *conic sections*, i.e., figures produced by the intersection of a plane and a cone (Fig. 9-1 and Table 9-1) or any quadratic function in a plane. If the objects are permanently associated, this figure will be an *ellipse*, as

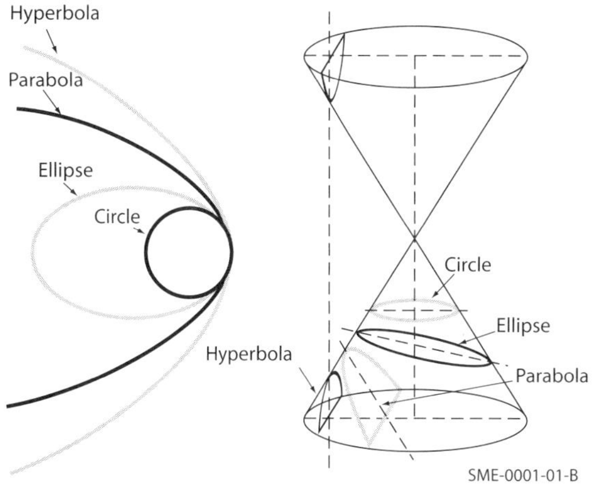

Fig. 9-1. The 4 Conic Sections Result from the Intersection of a Plane and a Right Circular Cone. Two special cases occur when the angle between the plane and axis of the cone is either 90 deg (resulting in a circle) or equal to the angular radius of the cone (resulting in a parabola).

shown in Fig. 9-2. Geometrically, an ellipse is defined by two points known as *foci*; the ellipse is then the locus of all points such that the sum of the distances from each point on the ellipse to the two foci is $2a$, where a is called the *semimajor axis* and is half the long axis or *major axis* of the ellipse. The semimajor axis is also the mean distance between either focus and points on the ellipse and is often listed this way in tables of orbit parameters. In Fig. 9-2, the quantity c is half the distance between the foci, and the *semiminor axis*, b, is half the short axis or *minor axis* of the ellipse. One of the foci is the center of mass or *barycenter* of the two objects; the other focus is of only geometric interest and is an empty point in space. Finally for some computations it is convenient to define the *semiparameter*, p, which is the distance from the focus to the orbit measured perpendicular to the major axis.

Table 9-1. Orbit Properties for the 4 Conic Sections. In practice only elliptical and hyperbolic orbits occur. Circular and parabolic orbits are special cases, but are convenient approximations for many orbits.

Conic	Total Energy, $\mathcal{E}$	Semimajor Axis, *a*	Eccentricity, *e*
Circle	< 0	= radius (> 0)	= 0
Ellipse	< 0	> 0	$0 < e < 1$
Parabola	= 0	∞	= 1
Hyperbola	> 0	< 0	> 1

The shape of an ellipse is uniquely specified by a single parameter, such as the ratio of the semimajor and semiminor axes. The parameter normally used to specify this shape is the *eccentricity, e*, defined as the ratio $c/a = (a^2 - b^2)^{1/2}/a$. The eccentricity also serves as a convenient ratio to parameterize all the conic sections as listed in Table 9-1. Specifically, $e = 0$ for a circle; $0 < e < 1$

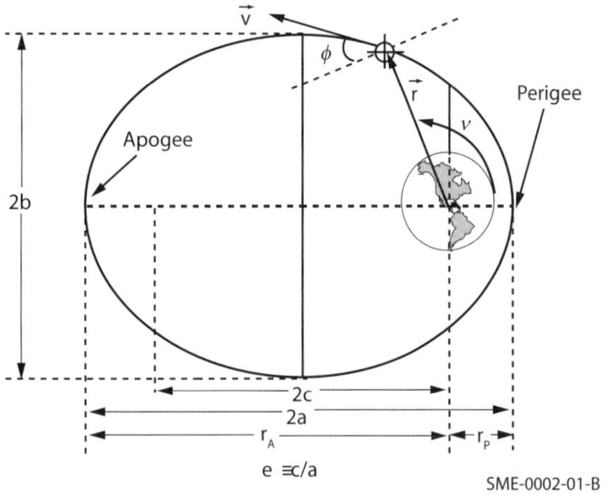

Fig. 9-2. Geometry of an Elliptical Orbit with Eccentricity $e \equiv c/a$ = 0.6. Both the satellite and the primary go around their mutual center of mass. However, for most practical problems (except double stars), this center of mass is nearly the same as the center of mass of the primary.

for an ellipse; $e = 1$ for a *parabola*; and $e > 1$ for a *hyperbola*. In the last case, the nearest point on the curve to the focus is between the focus and the center of the two branches of the hyperbola. These 4 classes of curves are illustrated in Fig. 9-3 and their properties are summarized at the end of the section.*

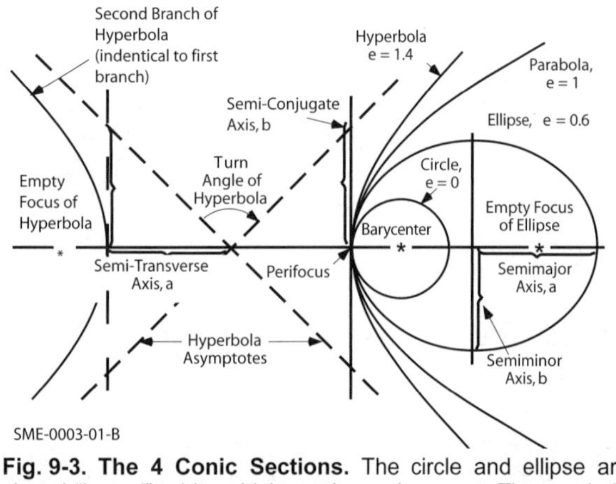

Fig. 9-3. The 4 Conic Sections. The circle and ellipse are closed "bound" orbits which continuously repeat. The parabola and hyperbola are open, "unbound" orbits such that the satellite passes perifocus only once and then recedes to infinity.

Both the circle and parabola represent special cases of the infinite range of possible eccentricities and therefore will never occur in nature. Orbits of objects which are gravitationally bound will be elliptical and orbits of objects which are not bound will be hyperbolic. Thus, an object approaching a planet from "infinity," such as a spacecraft approaching Mars, travels on a hyperbolic trajectory relative to the planet and will swing past the planet and recede to infinity, unless some non-gravitational force (a rocket firing or a collision with the planet) intervenes. Similarly, a rocket with insufficient energy to escape a planet must travel in an elliptical orbit in the absence of non-gravitational forces. Because the ellipse is a closed curve, the rocket will eventually return to the point in space at which the engine last fired.

* Alternatively, we may define a conic section as the locus of all points which maintains a fixed ratio between the distance to the focus and the perpendicular distance to a fixed line called the *directrix*. The directrix is perpendicular to the major axis of any conic section. The ratio of the distance to the focus and to the directrix is the *eccentricity*, *e*.

9.1.2 Kepler's Second Law

As shown in Fig. 9-4, Kepler's second law is a restatement of the conservation of angular momentum. The angular momentum is proportional to the magnitude of the radius vector, *r*, multiplied by the perpendicular component of the velocity, $V_\perp$. In any infinitesimal time interval δt, the area swept out by a line joining the barycenter and the satellite will be $(1/2)mV^2$. Hence, the area swept out per unit time is proportional to the angular momentum per unit mass which is a constant.

9.1.3 Kepler's Third Law

Kepler's third law applies only to elliptical orbits and relates the orbital period to the semimajor axis. In the case of Earth satellites, and very nearly in the case of the planets orbiting the Sun, we may ignore the mass of the secondary and write:

$$a^3 = \left[\mathrm{G}(M+m)/4\pi^2\right]P^2 \approx \left(\mathrm{G}M/4\pi^2\right)P^2$$
$$\equiv \left(\mu/4\pi^2\right)P^2 \qquad \text{or} \qquad (9\text{-}4a)$$

$$P = 2\pi\sqrt{a^3/\mu} \qquad (9\text{-}4b)$$

Table 9-2. Values of $\mu \equiv$ GM for the Earth, Sun, Moon, and Mars. (See App. B for other values.)

Central Body	μ (m^3/s^2)	$\mu/4\pi^2$ (m^3/s^2)
Earth	$3.986\ 004\ 356 \times 10^{14}$	$1.009\ 666\ 698 \times 10^{13}$
Moon	$4.902\ 800\ 15 \times 10^{12}$	$1.241\ 893\ 786 \times 10^{11}$
Earth & Moon	$4.035\ 032\ 357\ 5 \times 10^{14}$	$1.022\ 085\ 636 \times 10^{13}$
Mars	$4.282\ 837\ 522 \times 10^{13}$	$1.084\ 855\ 418 \times 10^{12}$
Sun	$1.327\ 124\ 400\ 41 \times 10^{20}$	$3.361\ 645\ 377 \times 10^{18}$

The values of $\mu \equiv$ GM for the Earth, Moon, Sun, and Mars are given in Table 9-2 and for the major objects in the Solar System in App. D. Note that μ can be measured with considerable precision by astronomical observations. However, the values of M are limited by the accuracy of G to about 0.06%. (This is the most poorly known of the fundamental physical constants.) Therefore, the use of G is normally avoided and calculations are best

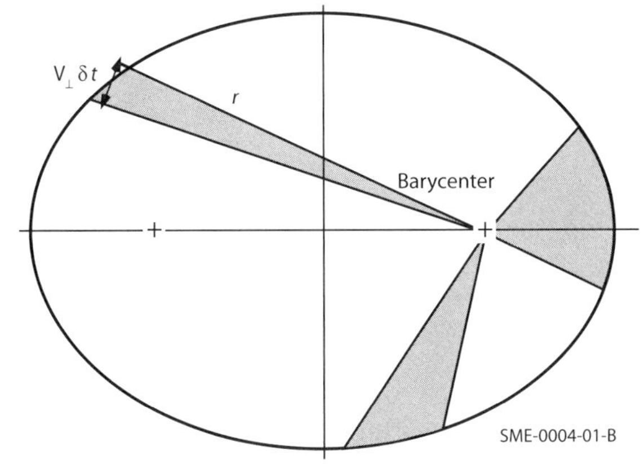

Fig. 9-4. Kepler's Second Law. Because the shaded areas are equal the time required for the satellite to sweep out each area is equal. The area swept out is directly proportional to both the time interval and the satellite's angular momentum.

done in terms of μ and the ratio of the masses of Solar System objects.

As long as the mass of the secondary is small, such that Eq. (9-4a) holds, then the constant of proportionality in Kepler's third law may be evaluated directly from observing orbiting objects. For example, the *astronomical unit*, or *AU*, is a unit of length equal to the semimajor axis of the Earth's orbit about the Sun; thus, in units of years and AU, $\mu/4\pi^2 = 1$ for the Sun and, therefore, $a^3 = P^2$ in units of astronomical units and years for the planets and any other satellites of the Sun. Similarly, for satellites of the Earth, Moon, or planets at different altitudes, the ratio of the periods may be determined from the expression

$$P = P_0\left(\frac{a}{a_0}\right)^{3/2} \tag{9-5a}$$

where P_0 and a_0 are any known period and semimajor axis. For Earth satellites:

$$P = 1.658\,669 \times 10^{-4}(6{,}378.136\,6 + H)^{3/2} \quad H \text{ in km} \tag{9-5b}$$

$$P = 4.180\,432 \times 10^{-4}(3{,}443.918\,3 + H)^{3/2} \quad H \text{ in NMi} \tag{9-5c}$$

where P is in minutes and H is the mean altitude.

9.1.4 Vis Viva Equation

If we again assume that the mass of the secondary is small, the *vis viva* equation may be rewritten as

$$V^2 = GM\left(\frac{2}{r} - \frac{1}{a}\right) \tag{9-6a}$$

$$\frac{1}{2}V^2 - \frac{GM}{r} = -\frac{\mu}{2a} \equiv \varepsilon \tag{9-6b}$$

where the *total specific energy, ε,* is the total energy per unit mass (kinetic plus potential) of the orbiting object. Thus, the semimajor axis is a function **only** of the total energy. Because the potential energy is a function only of position, the semimajor axis for a satellite launched at any point in space will be a function only of the launch velocity and not the direction of launch. (The shape and orientation of the orbit will, of course, depend on the launch direction). The orbit is hyperbolic if $\varepsilon > 0$ and elliptical if $\varepsilon < 0$. The special case between these, zero total energy, is an orbit with infinite semimajor axis. The velocity in this case is called the *parabolic velocity*, or *velocity of escape*, V_e. At any distance, R, from the center of a spherically symmetric object we have:

$$V_e \equiv \sqrt{(2\mu)/R} \equiv \sqrt{(2GM)/R} \tag{9-7}$$

A satellite launched with this velocity in any direction will not return, assuming that there are no other forces and the satellite doesn't run into the planet.

The vis viva equation may be used to obtain two other velocities of particular interest. If $R = a$, then

$$V_c = \sqrt{\mu/R} \tag{9-8}$$

is the *circular velocity,* or the velocity needed for circular orbit of radius R. Finally,

$$V_h \equiv \sqrt{2\varepsilon} = \sqrt{V^2 - 2\mu/R} \tag{9-9}$$

is the *hyperbolic velocity*, or the velocity of an object infinitely far away from the primary. Here V is the instantaneous velocity in the hyperbolic orbit at an arbitrary distance R from the center of the massive object. Values of the circular velocity and escape velocity for the Earth, Moon, Mars, and the Sun are shown in Table 9-3.

Table 9-3. Values of the Circular Velocity and Escape Velocity for the Earth, Sun, Moon, and Mars. Constants are evaluated at the surface, except for the last row. (See website or App. C.1 for other values.)

Central Body	Equatorial Radius (km)	Circular Velocity (km/s)	Circular Period (min)	Escape Velocity (km/s)
Earth	6,378.136 6	7.905	84.49	11.180
Moon	1,738	1.680	108.36	2.375
Mars	3,390	3.551	100.19	5.021
Sun (at surface)	695,990	436.7	166.91	617.5
Sun (at Earth's orbit)	1.496×10^8	29.78	5.260×10^5	42.12

9.1.5 Keplerian Orbit Elements and Terminology

For a purely Keplerian orbit, if we know the position and velocity at any given instant, we can integrate the equations of motion to determine the position and velocity at all future times. Consequently, a Keplerian orbit can be fully specified by giving the three components of the position and three components of the velocity at any instant. This numerical specification of an orbit is called the *orbit elements*. The position and velocity at any instant is convenient for computer applications but provide relatively little insight into the fundamental characteristics of the orbit. A convenient set for conceptualization are the classical or *Keplerian elements* described below. (Unfortunately, in many cases, these are inconvenient for numerical computation.) The information needed to fully specify a Keplerian orbit is:

- The orbit size and shape (2 parameters)
- The orientation of the orbit plane in space (2 parameters)
- The rotational orientation of the semimajor axis within that plane (1 parameter)
- Where the satellite is on the orbit (1 parameter)

In addition to the orbit elements, we need to know the value of $\mu = GM$ for the central body in order to calculate the motion of the satellite over time.

Orbit Size and Shape. For either hyperbolic or elliptical orbits, *perifocus* is the point on the orbit where the secondary is closest to the center of mass (Fig. 9-5). The *periapsis* or *perifocal distance* is the distance between the center of mass and the perifocus. This is equal to $a-c = a(1 - e)$ for an elliptical orbit of semimajor axis, a, and eccentricity, e. Unfortunately, the terminology here is both well established and awkward because different words are used for the point of closest approach to different primaries. Thus, we have *perihelion* (closest approach to the Sun), *perigee* (closest approach to the Earth), *pericynthiane* or *perilune* (closest approach to the Moon), *perijove* (closest approach to Jupiter) and even *periastron* (closest approach of two stars in a binary pair).

Perihelion and perifocal distance are measured from the center of mass, but *perigee height*, frequently shortened to "perigee" in common usage, is measured from the surface of the Earth. (See Fig. 9-6.) This terminology arises because we are interested primarily in the height above the surface for low-altitude spacecraft. The most unambiguous procedure is to use perigee height or perigee altitude whenever the distance is being measured from the surface;* however, this is frequently not done.

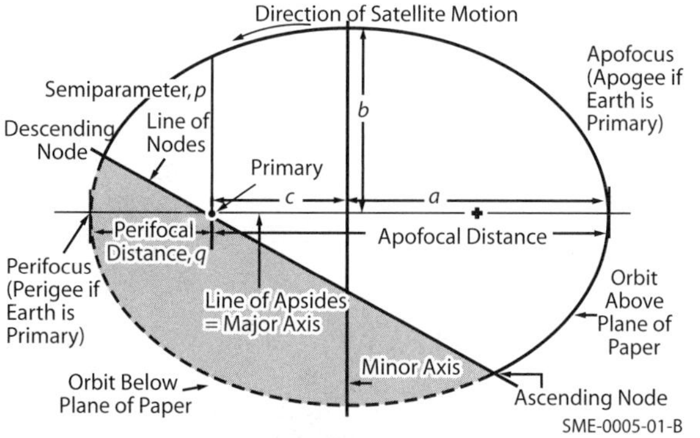

Fig. 9-5. Orbit Terminology for an Elliptical Orbit. The orbit is tilted, or inclined, with respect to the plane of the paper such that the dashed segment is below the paper which is assumed to be the reference plane.

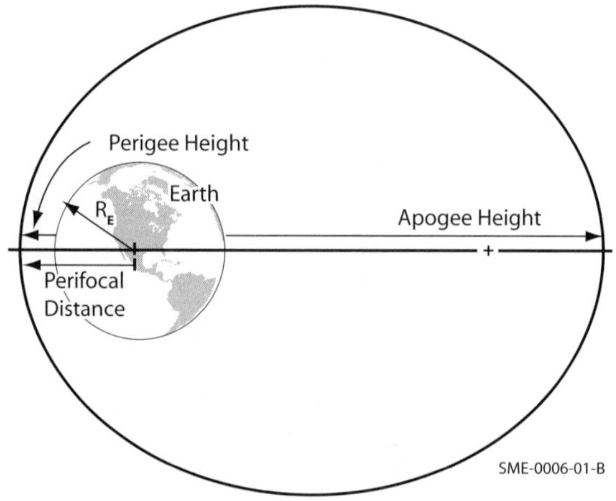

Fig. 9-6. Definition of Perigee Height and Apogee Height.

In elliptical orbits, the most distant point from the primary is called *apofocus*; the *apoapsis* or *apofocus distance* is $a+c = a(1+e)$. Again, the words *aphelion*, *apolune*, and *apogee* or *apogee height* are used, the latter being measured from the Earth's surface. The straight line connecting apogee, perigee, and the two foci is called the *line of apsides,* which is the same as the major axis of the ellipse. If, h_p, h_A, and R_E are the perigee height, apogee height, and radius of the Earth, respectively, then for an Earth satellite, the semimajor axis is:

$$a = R_E + (h_p + h_A)/2 \tag{9-10}$$

The size and shape of any Keplerian orbit can be defined equivalently by either the semimajor axis and eccentricity or the apogee height and perigee height. Both methods are in common use depending on the application.

Orientation of the Orbit Plane. As shown in Fig. 9-7, the *inclination, i,* is the angle between the orbit plane and a reference plane which also contains the center of mass. The most commonly used reference planes are the *equatorial plane* (the plane of the Earth's equator) for Earth's satellites and the *ecliptic* (the plane to the Earth's orbit about the Sun) for interplanetary orbits.

* Throughout this book when discussing distances relative to the Earth, we use "height" exclusively for distances measured from the Earth's surface; e.g., apogee height, perigee height, or height of the atmosphere.

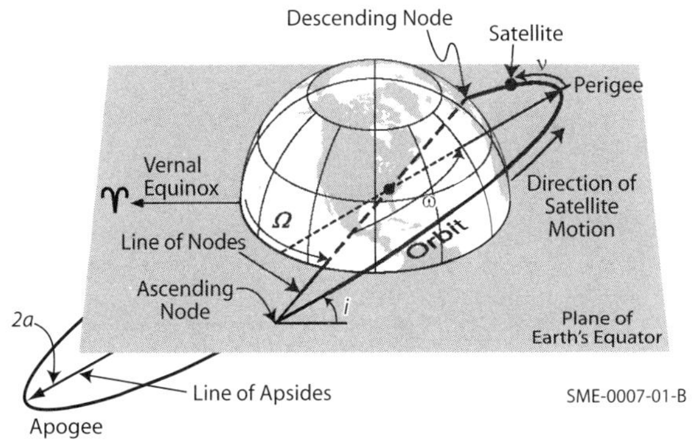

Fig. 9-7. Keplerian Orbit Elements. ♈ marks the direction of the vernal equinox. The line of nodes is the intersection between the equatorial plane and the orbit plane. Ω is measured in the equatorial plane, and ω is measured in the orbit plane.

Both the rotation of the Earth on its axis and the revolution of the Earth around the Sun are in a counterclockwise direction as seen from the North Pole. Most satellites travel in this same direction and are said to be in a *prograde* orbit which has an inclination between 0 and 90 deg. Satellites traveling in a direction opposite the rotation of the Earth are in a *retrograde* orbit and have inclinations between 90 deg and 180 deg.

The intersection of the orbit plane and the equatorial plane through the center of mass is the *line of nodes*. For an Earth satellite the *ascending node* is the point in its orbit where the satellite crosses the equator going from south to north. The *descending node* is the point where it crosses the equator going from north to south.

To fully define the orbit plane, we need to specify both its inclination and the orientation of the line of nodes around the equator. Because the Keplerian orbit is approximately fixed in inertial space,* we need to define this rotational orientation with respect to inertial space rather than with respect to the surface of the Earth. The reference point that is ordinarily used for inertial space is the ascending node of the Earth's orbit about the Sun. This is the location of the Sun in the sky on the first day of spring. It is called the *vernal equinox* or *first point of Aries*. This is the zero point for *right ascension* in the sky which is the equivalent of longitude measured on the surface of the Earth. (See Table 8-4 in Sec. 8.1.2) Consequently, the orientation of the ascending node on the sky is defined by the *right ascension of the ascending node, Ω* (often called RAAN in computer code), which is the angle in the equatorial plane measured eastward from the vernal equinox to the ascending node of the orbit. At times, it is also convenient to specify the *longitude of the ascending node* measured on the surface of the Earth from the Greenwich meridian to the ascending node. However, this parameter is changing continuously as the Earth rotates underneath the orbit.

The vernal equinox is universally used as the zero point for coordinates in inertial space, i.e., relative to the "fixed" stars. Unfortunately, this is an exceptionally inconvenient reference because it is moving very slowly through the sky due to the precession of the Earth's axis as described in Sec. 9.2. The motion is remarkably slow with a period of approximately 26,000 years. Nonetheless, it implies that all inertial coordinate systems have a date or *epoch* attached to them. Modern almanacs list the locations of stars in *2000 coordinates*, which means that they are expressed in a coordinate system in which the vernal equinox has been precessed to January 0 of the year 2000.

Equally unfortunately, nearly all satellite orbit systems use what are called *true-of-date coordinates* in which the vernal equinox is precessed to the time of specification of the orbit called the *orbit epoch*. This correction to the fundamental coordinate system is extremely small and is easily done by standard computer routines. However, it means that it is very difficult to verify orbit computations with simple hand calculators because there are always small differences in the answer due simply to differences in the coordinate system specification. The principal merit of this approach is that it provides continued employment for astrodynamicists.

Orientation of the Orbit within the Plane. Having specified the orientation of the orbit plane, we now need to specify the rotational orientation of the major axis (line of apsides) within that plane. This is normally done by defining the *argument of perigee*, ω, which is the angle at the center of mass of the Earth measured in the orbit plane in the direction of the satellite's motion from the ascending node to perigee. (See Fig. 9-7.)

Position of the Satellite within the Orbit. Finally, we need some mechanism to specify where the satellite is in its orbit. The *true anomaly*, ν, is the angle measured at the center of mass between perigee and the satellite. This gives us a series of three angular measurements. The right ascension of the ascending node is measured eastward from the vernal equinox to the ascending node of the orbit. The argument of perigee is then measured from the ascending node in the direction of the motion of the satellite to perigee, and, finally, the true anomaly is measured in the direction of motion from perigee to the location of the satellite.

Unfortunately, the true anomaly is difficult to calculate. Consequently, those who were first studying the mathematics of orbital motion introduced the *mean anomaly, M,* as 360 $(\Delta t/P)$ degrees where P is the orbital period and Δt is the time since perigee passage. Thus, $M = \nu$ for a satellite in a perfectly circular orbit. The mean anomaly at any time is a trivial calculation and of no physical interest. The quantity of real interest is the true anomaly which is difficult to calculate. The *eccentric*

* Friction with the Earth's surface drags the atmosphere around as the Earth rotates on its axis. This friction is negligible in orbit. Thus, a satellite orbit remains approximately fixed in inertial space (except for orbit perturbations described in Sec. 9.4) as the Earth rotates once per day underneath the orbit. This causes satellites not in an equatorial orbit to view most of the Earth's surface twice daily—once on the upward portion of the orbit and once on the downward portion.

anomaly, E, was introduced as an intermediate variable relating the two.* The mean and eccentric anomalies are related by *Kepler's equation* (not related to Kepler's laws):

$$M = E - e \sin E \tag{9-11}$$

where e is the eccentricity. E is then related to ν by *Gauss' equation*:

$$\tan\left(\frac{\nu}{2}\right) = \left(\frac{1+e}{1-e}\right)^{1/2} \tan\left(\frac{E}{2}\right) \tag{9-12a}$$

or

$$\tan\left(\frac{E}{2}\right) = \left(\frac{1-e}{1+e}\right)^{1/2} \tan\left(\frac{\nu}{2}\right) \tag{9-12b}$$

$E/2$ and $\nu/2$ are used because these quantities are always in the same quadrant.

The above approach was used for historical computations. In modern computer programs, the true anomaly is determined by simply integrating the equations of motion and taking into account other forces, as well as the purely central body forces which produce Keplerian motion. Alternatively, for a Keplerian orbit the mean anomaly and true anomaly can be determined by the following recursive formula:†

$$E_{i+1} = E_i + \frac{M - E_i + e\sin E_i}{1 - e\cos E_i} \tag{9-13}$$

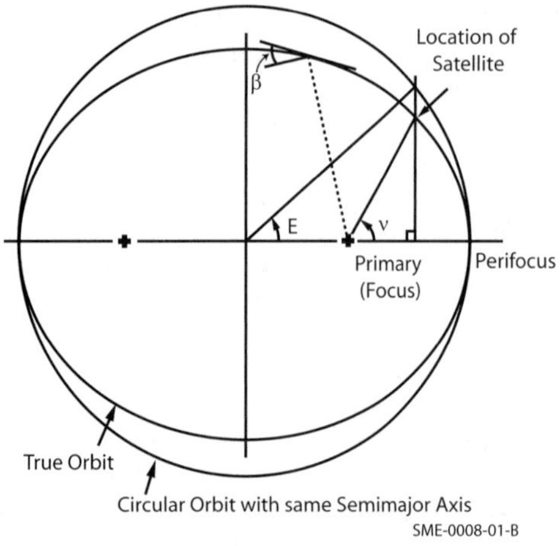

Fig. 9-8. Definition of the True Anomaly, ν, and Eccentric Anomaly, *E*. The *flight path angle, β,* is the angle between the velocity vector and the perpendicular to the radius vector.

For small eccentricities, ν may be expressed directly as a function of M by expanding in a power series in e to yield:

$$\nu = M + 2e\sin M + \frac{5}{4}e^2\sin 2M - \frac{1}{4}e^3\sin M + \frac{13}{12}e^2\sin 3M + \mathcal{O}\left(e^4\right)^{\ddagger} \tag{9-14}$$

Finally, it is often convenient to discuss variations in the orbital elements in terms of the *mean angular rate,* often called the *mean motion, n,* which is simply the rate of change of the mean anomaly. If n is in rad/s, then

$$n \equiv \mathrm{d}M/\mathrm{d}t = 2\pi/P \tag{9-15}$$

$$M = M_0 + n(t - t_0) \tag{9-16}$$

where P is the period, and M_0 is the mean anomaly at epoch t_0. From Eq. (9-4a), we have

$$n = \sqrt{\mu/a^3} \tag{9-17}$$

where $\mu \equiv GM$ and a is the semimajor axis. Thus, n and M are easily determined from fundamental orbit parameters and can then be used as the basis for computing the true anomaly and the variations in the elements due to orbit perturbations as discussed in Sec. 9.4.

Summary. The elements of an orbit are the parameters needed to fully specify the motion of a satellite. Table 9-4 and Figs. 9-7 and 9-8 show the classical elements or Keplerian elements for an Earth satellite (planetary elements are slightly different and are defined in Sec. 9.2). The semimajor axis and eccentricity define the size and shape of the orbit; the inclination and right ascension of the ascending node define the orbit plane. The argument of perigee defines the rotation of the orbit within the plane, and finally, the true anomaly or mean anomaly specifies the position of the satellite in its orbit at the epoch time at which the orbit is specified.

Unfortunately, the Keplerian elements are poorly defined under conditions that commonly occur for Earth satellites. For near circular orbits, perigee will be very poorly defined and consequently, both the argument of perigee and true anomaly will not be well-defined. In this case, the *longitude of the satellite* measured from the ascending node is often used. If the orbit plane is near the equatorial plane, then the ascending node will also be poorly defined and, in this case, the basic angle will be measured from the vernal equinox. For a hyperbolic orbit, the period is undefined and is replaced by the *aerial velocity* or area per unit time swept out by a line joining the satellite and the planet (i.e., the angular momentum per unit mass). The equations for this are in Table 9-4.

In practice, a variety of orbit perturbations, described in Sec. 9.4, cause continuing changes and oscillations in the orbit elements. The *mean orbit elements* given in

* E is defined as the angle measured at the center of the orbit between perigee and the projection of the satellite perpendicular to the major axis onto a circular orbit with the same semimajor axis as shown in Fig. 9-8.

† This convenient formula is from David Diaz, Microcosm.

‡ $\mathcal{O}$ in Eq. (9-14) and subsequent equations stands for "of order" and refers to subsequent terms of expansion. Thus, Eq. (9-14) includes all terms of order e^3 or lower and excludes terms of order e^4 and higher.

Table 9-4. Properties of Keplerian Orbits. See Fig. 9-2, 9-3, 9-5, 9-6, and 9-8 for illustration of the variables.

Quantity	Circle	Ellipse	Parabola	Hyperbola
Defining Parameters	a = semimajor axis = radius	a = semimajor axis b = semiminor axis	p = semi-latus rectum q = perifocal distance	a = semi-transverse axis ($a < 0$) b = semi-conjugate axis
Parametric Equation	$x^2 + y^2 = a^2$	$x^2/a^2 + y^2/b^2 = 1$	$x^2 = 4qy$	$x^2/a^2 - y^2/b^2 = 1$
Eccentricity, e	$e = 0$	$e = \sqrt{a^2 - b^2}/a \quad 0 < e < 1$	$e = 1$	$e = \sqrt{a^2 - b^2}/a \quad e > 1$
Perifocal Distance, q	$q = a$	$q = a(1 - e)$	$q = p/2$	$q = a(1 - e)$
Velocity, V, at Distance, r, from Focus	$V^2 = \mu/r$	$V^2 = \mu(2/r - 1/a)$	$V^2 = 2\mu/r$	$V^2 = \mu(2/r - 1/a)$
Total Energy Per Unit Mass, ε	$\varepsilon = -\mu/2a < 0$	$\varepsilon = -\mu/2a < 0$	$\varepsilon = 0$	$\varepsilon = -\mu/2a > 0$
Mean Angular Motion, n	$n = \sqrt{\mu/a^3}$	$n = \sqrt{\mu/a^3}$	$n = 2\sqrt{\mu/p^3}$	$n = \sqrt{\mu/(-a)^3}$
Period, P	$P = 2\pi/n$	$P = 2\pi/n$	$P = \infty$	$P = \infty$
Anomaly	$\nu = M = E$	Eccentric anomaly, E $\tan\frac{\nu}{2} = \left(\frac{1+e}{1-e}\right)^{1/2} \tan\left(\frac{E}{2}\right)$	Parabolic anomaly, D $\tan\frac{\nu}{2} = D/\sqrt{2q}$	Hyperbolic anomaly, F $\tan\frac{\nu}{2} = \left(\frac{1+e}{1-e}\right)^{1/2} \tanh\left(\frac{F}{2}\right)$
Mean Anomaly, M	$M = M_0 + nt$	$M = E - e \sin E$	$M = qD + (D^3/6)$	$M = (e \sinh F) - F$
Distance from Focus, $r = q(1 + e)/(1 + e\cos\nu)$	$r = a$	$r = a(1 - e\cos E)$	$r = q + (D^2/2)$	$r = a(1 - e\cosh F)$
$r\,dr/dt \equiv r\dot{r}$	0	$r\dot{r} = e\sqrt{a\mu}\,\sin E$	$r\dot{r} = \sqrt{\mu}\,D$	$r\dot{r} = e\sqrt{(-a)\mu}\,\sinh F$
Areal Velocity, $\frac{dA}{dt} = \frac{1}{2}r^2\frac{d\nu}{dt}$	$\frac{dA}{dt} = \frac{1}{2}\sqrt{a\mu}$	$\frac{dA}{dt} = \frac{1}{2}\sqrt{a\mu(1-e^2)}$	$\frac{dA}{dt} = \frac{1}{2}\sqrt{\frac{\mu q}{2}}$	$\frac{dA}{dt} = \frac{1}{2}\sqrt{a\mu(1-e^2)}$ © 2011 Microcosm, Inc.

Note: μ = GM is the gravitational constant of the central body; ν is the true anomaly, and $M \equiv n(t - T)$ is the mean anomaly, where t is the time of observation, T is the time of perifocal passage, and n is the mean angular motion. See App. C for additional formulas and a discussion and listing of terminology and notation.

most general purpose tables define the average motion over some span of time. For more precise calculations, it is preferable to use *osculating elements* which are the elements of a true Keplerian orbit instantaneously tangent to the real orbit. Thus, the *osculating elements* fluctuate continuously as various forces (e.g., atmospheric drag and perturbations from other planets) alter the simple shape defined by Kepler's laws.

Keplerian orbits are not sufficiently accurate for spacecraft ephemerides or for calculations which require a precise knowledge of the spacecraft's position or velocity; however, they are accurate enough to estimate overall mission characteristics in most regions of space. The normal procedure for adding additional detail to orbit analysis is to treat orbits as Keplerian with additional perturbations produced by any of the various interactions which may be important. Approximations for the most important perturbations are discussed in Sec. 9.4.

9.2 Orbits of the Moon and Planets

Orbits of the planets and other natural objects in the Solar System exhibit considerable regularity. With the exception of cometary orbits, they are all nearly circular, coplanar, and regularly spaced.

Although perturbations due to third bodies (mostly Jupiter) must be taken into account for computing accurate planetary ephemerides, the description of planetary orbits in terms of Keplerian elements describes most orbital characteristics quite well. The position of the center of mass of the Solar System relative to the Sun depends on the position of all the planets but is typically somewhat below the surface of the Sun in the general direction of Jupiter. For most practical purposes we can regard the Sun as the center of mass of the Solar System and, therefore, as at one focus for all planetary orbits.

To define the Keplerian elements for the orbits of either planets or interplanetary spacecraft we must establish a reference plane for the solar system. The standard plane chosen for this is the *ecliptic* or the plane of the Earth's orbit about the Sun. This plane is inclined to the Earth's equatorial plane by 23.44 deg, an angle known as the *obliquity of the ecliptic*. The intersection of the plane of the ecliptic and the plane of the Earth's equator define two opposite directions in space known as the *vernal* and *autumnal equinoxes* represented by the symbols, ♈ and ♎, respectively. The vernal equinox is the direction of the Sun (viewed from the center of the Earth) as it crosses the equatorial plane from south to north on the first day of spring. It serves as the reference direction for coordinate systems using either the equatorial or ecliptic plane. Perturbative forces on the Earth cause the rotational axis of the Earth to move in a cone of 23.44 deg radius about a vector perpendicular to the ecliptic plane. This *precession of the equinoxes* has a period of 25,700 years. This implies that all celestial or "inertial" coordinate systems will have a date attached to them called the *epoch* for the coordinate system.

Because the Earth's orbit is not perfectly Keplerian, and because of the drift of the vernal equinox, the orbital period of the Earth about the Sun (and similarly the periods of the other planets) depends on how it is measured. The *sidereal year*, about 365.26 days, is the period of revolution of the Earth relative to the fixed stars. The *tropical year* is the Earth's period relative to the vernal equinox, and is about 20 minutes shorter than the sidereal year. This is the basis of the civil calendar, since for calendar purposes we are interested in the seasons, which are determined by the position of the Sun relative to the Earth's equatorial plane. Finally, the *anomalistic year*, 5 minutes longer than the sidereal year, is the period of the Earth relative to perihelion. Recall that *perihelion* is the perifocal point when the Earth is closest to the Sun. The drift in the inertial position of perihelion is due to perturbations from the other planets.

The orbital elements of the planets and other Solar System objects are analogous to the Earth satellite elements defined in Table 9-4 with the Earth's equatorial plane replaced by the ecliptic plane.* Thus the semimajor axis and eccentricity retain the same definitions. The inclination of planetary orbits is measured relative to the ecliptic so the inclination of the Earth's orbit is zero. The *longitude of the ascending node, Ω*, is the angle from the vernal equinox to the ascending node of the planet's orbit measured eastward (i.e., in the direction of motion of the Earth in its orbit) along the ecliptic plane. The *argument of perihelion, ω*, is the angle from the ascending node to perihelion measured along the planet's orbit in the direction of its motion. In some tables, ω is replaced by the *longitude of perihelion*, $\tilde{\omega}$, defined as $\Omega + \omega$. Note that this is not a true angular measure because Ω and ω are measured in different planes. Finally, the mean anomaly of satellite orbits is replaced by the *time of perihelion passage*, which is one of the times, usually the most recent, when the planet was at perihelion. Numerical values for the planetary orbital elements are given in App. C.

Planetary orbits within the Solar System are fairly uniform in both shape and orientation; with the exception of Pluto and Mercury, the orbital inclinations are all less than 3.5 deg and the eccentricities are less than 0.1. The semimajor axes of the planetary orbits are also nearly regular and are approximately given by an empirical relationship known as *Bode's Law* in which the semimajor axes of the planets and asteroid belt in AU are approximately 0.4, 0.7, 1.0, 1.6, 2.8, 5.2, and so on.†

Get More For both interplanetary spacecraft and for determining the brightness of the planets as seen by Earth-orbiting spacecraft, we are interested in the orientation of the planets relative to the Earth and Sun, as well as the orientation relative to the fixed stars. The various geometrical orientations of the planets relative to the observer and the Sun are called *planetary configurations*, or *aspects*, and are discussed on the book website.

A critical characteristic for interplanetary flight is the length of time it takes for planets to return to the same relative orientation, known as the *synodic period, S*, which is more formally defined as the interval between successive oppositions of a superior planet or successive inferior conjunctions of an inferior planet. The relation between the synodic period and the sidereal period, P, relative to the fixed stars is shown in Fig. 9-9. In this example, the innermost planet has made one and one-third revolutions in the period of time that the outer planet has made one-third of a revolution.

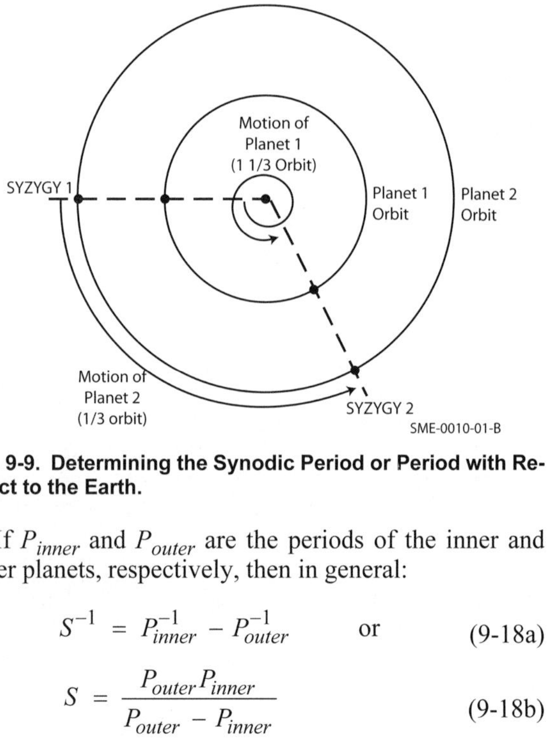

Fig. 9-9. Determining the Synodic Period or Period with Respect to the Earth.

If P_{inner} and P_{outer} are the periods of the inner and outer planets, respectively, then in general:

$$S^{-1} = P_{inner}^{-1} - P_{outer}^{-1} \quad \text{or} \tag{9-18a}$$

$$S = \frac{P_{outer} P_{inner}}{P_{outer} - P_{inner}} \tag{9-18b}$$

For an observer on the Earth, if S and P are both expressed in years, then for superior planets the synodic period is given by:

* Note that *longitude* in the Solar System is measured in the ecliptic plane from the vernal equinox and is not the same as longitude on the surface of the Earth or right ascension in the sky which is measured along the celestial equator.

† Bode's Law states that the semimajor axis of the planets is given approximately by the empirical expression $a = 0.4 + 0.3 \times 2^n$, where n is the series of integers, 0, 1, 2, … Bode's Law did reasonably well at predicting the orbit of Uranus, which had not yet been discovered, but didn't do well for Neptune or Pluto.

Table 9-4◀, Fig. 9-9, Eq. 9-18b

$$S^{-1}_{superior} = 1 - P^{-1}_{outer} \quad \text{or} \tag{9-19a}$$

$$S_{superior} = P_{outer} / (P_{outer} - 1) \tag{9-19b}$$

and for an inferior planet by:

$$S^{-1}_{inferior} = P^{-1}_{inner} - 1 \quad \text{or} \tag{9-20a}$$

$$S_{inferior} = P_{inner} / (1 - P_{inner}) \tag{9-20b}$$

For planets at very different distances from the Sun, the synodic period will be slightly longer than the period of the inner planet. For planets which are close together the synodic period will become longer since the two planets revolve about the Sun at nearly the same rates and, therefore, pass each other very slowly. For example, oppositions of Mars occur approximately every 780 days. Because planetary orbits are not circular, the actual synodic periods vary by several weeks. Synodic periods of the various planets are shown in Table 9-5. Specific oppositions for Mars are shown in Table 9-6 along with the associated launch opportunities.

Planetary configurations are important for interplanetary flight as well as for observations because they define the opportunities for planetary travel. For example, as discussed in Sec. 9.6.1, trips to Mars along a minimum energy trajectory will leave the Earth about 97 days before opposition, and will arrive at Mars about 162 days after opposition (see Table 9-6), although various factors may cause the actual flight times, (particularly the arrival), to vary by several weeks. Because an opposition of Mars occurred on March 17, 1997, we would expect flights that left Earth on about December 10, 1996, to arrive at Mars about August 26, 1997. The two spacecraft flown during this launch opportunity, Mars Pathfinder and Mars Global Surveyor, were launched on December 4, 1996, and November 7, 1996, and arrived at Mars on July 4, 1997, and September 11, 1997, respectively. Similarly, because of the Mars opposition on October 13, 2020, we can expect flights to Mars at that time to leave Earth about July 8, 2020, and arrive at Mars about March 24, 2021.

Table 9-5. Synodic Periods of the Planets.

Planet	Synodic Period (Days)	1st Opposition after 2000
Mercury	115.9132	February 12, 2001
Venus	583.9178	March 29, 2001
Mars	779.9317	June 13, 2001
Jupiter	398.8854	January 1, 2002
Saturn	378.0914	December 3, 2001
Uranus	369.6563	August 15, 2001
Neptune	367.4861	June 30, 2001
Pluto*	366.7326	June 2, 2001

*Pluto is officially a *dwarf planet* as discussed in App. D.

The orbits of the natural satellites in the Solar System are generally less uniform than the orbits of the planets primarily because perturbations cause substantial variations in satellite orbits. For example, the perigee location for the Moon makes one complete revolution about the Moon's orbit in only 8.85 years, and the line of nodes rotates fully around the orbit in 18.6 years. Thus, in analogy with the various types of years, the month is defined in several ways, depending on the measurement reference. For most purposes the fundamental intervals are the *sidereal month*, relative to the fixed stars, about 27.32 days, the *synodic month* from new moon to new moon, about 29.53 days and the *nodical* or *draconic month* between successive ascending nodes, about 27.21 days. Other periods are listed in App. C.

Live Calc

Table 9-6. Earth-Mars Oppositions and Launch Opportunities, 1994–2035. Launch opportunities assume a Hohmann Transfer (see Sec. 9.6.1).

Launch Opportunity	Opposition	Arrival Date	Launch Opportunity	Opposition	Arrival Date
11/7/94	2/12/95	7/24/95	2/15/16	5/22/16	10/31/16
12/9/96	3/16/97	8/25/97	4/20/18	7/26/18	1/4/19
1/16/99	4/23/99	10/2/99	7/8/20	10/13/20	3/24/21
3/8/01	6/13/01	11/22/01	9/1/22	12/7/22	5/18/23
5/23/03	8/28/03	2/6/04	10/10/24	1/15/25	6/26/25
8/2/05	11/7/05	4/18/06	11/14/26	2/19/27	7/31/27
9/17/07	12/23/07	6/2/08	12/18/28	3/25/29	9/3/29
10/24/09	1/29/10	7/10/10	1/25/31	5/2/31	10/11/31
11/27/11	3/3/12	8/12/12	3/22/33	6/27/33	12/6/33
12/31/13	4/7/14	9/16/14	6/10/35	9/15/35	4/24/36

Table 9-7. Orbit Classification by Distance from the Earth. This classification is convenient since it represents approximately the difficulty of getting there and, therefore, the cost and time. See text for additional discussion of each.

Name	Location	Uses	Examples
LEO (Low-Earth Orbit)	< 3,000 km (most < 900 km)	All applications (cheapest to get to)	Space Telescope, ISS, LandSat, Iridium
MEO (Medium-Earth Orbit)	3,000 km to GEO	Communications, navigation, some observation	GPS
HEO (Highly Elliptical Orbit),* also called *Molniya Orbits	Typically perigee in LEO and apogee near GEO	Communications	Russian Comm Satellites
GEO (Geosynchronous)	35,856 km	Communications, weather	TDRS, Intelsat, DBS (radio, TV), BrazilSat
Super-Synchronous	Above GEO, below the Moon	Limited	Vela
Lunar and Lagrange Point	At or near Moon distance (350,000 km)	Science, potentially manufacturing	Apollo, Lunar Orbiter, Lunar Prospector
Interplanetary, Deep Space	Beyond the Moon, within the Solar System	Exploration	Viking, Mars Pathfinder, Galileo, Mars Rovers
Interstellar	Outside the Solar System	Exploration	Pioneer 10,11

9.3 Spacecraft Orbit Terminology

Objects launched into space are categorized by their orbit. *Ballistic missiles, sounding rockets* and *suborbital vehicles* travel in elliptical orbits which intersect the surface of the Earth. This is frequently called a *ballistic trajectory* because it is also the path of a baseball, bullet, or cannonball. The ballistic missile and sounding rocket are distinguished by their functions. The missile is used to strike some specific target, whereas the sounding rocket or suborbital vehicle is used to make measurements in or above the Earth's atmosphere. The sounding rocket may either impact the surface, burn up in the atmosphere, or be recovered by parachute.

The semimajor axis of a satellite orbit must be at least as large as the radius of the planet, whereas the semimajor axis for a sounding rocket or suborbital vehicle may be as small as approximately half the radius of the planet.* Because the total energy of a spacecraft depends only on the semimajor axis, the energy of a sounding rocket is normally, though not necessarily, much less than that of an Earth satellite. However, sounding rockets and ballistic missiles frequently reach altitudes well above those of low-Earth satellites because they travel in very elongated elliptical orbits.

Any object which travels in an elliptical orbit around a planet is called a *satellite* of that planet. As shown in Table 9-7, Earth satellites are typically classified by their distance. The principal differences between the orbit altitudes is the energy or velocity required to achieve them and the radiation level in that environment. Most Earth satellites are in *low-Earth orbit*, or *LEO*, below the Van Allen radiation belts, which start somewhat above 1,000 km. This orbit is both easy to get to and has a much lower radiation density than higher orbits and, therefore, has the potential for more economical satellites. The next most common is *geosynchronous orbit* or *GEO*, at an altitude of 35,786 km at which the satellite's orbit period is just equal to the Earth's rotation period so the satellite remains approximately fixed over a location on the Earth's equator. This is the single most used satellite orbit. Between LEO and GEO is a broad regime known as *medium-Earth orbit* or *MEO*, which typically contains relatively few satellites because of high levels of radiation in the Earth's Van Allen belt. A few satellites are in *super-synchronous orbits* above GEO, but below the Moon. Finally, a few Earth satellites are at approximately the distance of the Moon, in what are called *Lagrange point orbits*. As discussed further in Sec. 9.5, the *Lagrange points* are five points relative to the Earth and Moon at which the satellite will maintain the same orientation relative to the Earth-Moon system.

If the velocity of an object is greater than the escape velocity of a planet it will be an *interplanetary probe*, or deep space spacecraft traveling in a hyperbolic trajectory relative to the planet and, after it has left the vicinity of the planet, traveling in an elliptical orbit about the Sun. Finally, if an object attains a velocity greater than the Sun's escape velocity, it will be an *interstellar probe*. Pioneer 10, swinging past Jupiter in December 1973, gained sufficient energy in the encounter, as described in Sec. 9.5, to become the first man-made interstellar probe.

All known satellites or probes are assigned an international designation by the World Warning Agency on behalf of the Committee on Space Research, COSPAR, of the United Nations. These designations are of the form 2015-27c, where the first number is the year of launch, the second number is a sequential numbering of launches in that year, and the letter identifies each of the separate objects launched by a single vehicle. Thus, 1997–069c

* Assume all the mass of the Earth is concentrated at its center and a high platform is built to the former location of New York City. An object dropped from the platform will *not* go all the way to the former location of Australia, but will swing very rapidly around the central mass (with perigee essentially at the former center of the Earth) and return to apogee at the platform tip. [Use Eq. (9-5a) with $V = 0$.] Therefore, the semimajor axis will be about half the radius of the Earth and the total energy will be a factor of two less than that for a circular orbit at the Earth's surface.

was the third of five Iridium satellites orbited on the 69th launch of 1997 (a Delta II launched from Vandenberg Air Force Base on Nov. 9, 1997).

In addition to the international designation, most satellites are assigned a name by the launching agency. For NASA, spacecraft in a series are given a letter designation prior to launch, which is changed to a number after a successful launch. Thus, the second Synchronous Meteorological Satellite was SMS-B prior to launch, and SMS-2 after being successfully orbited. Because of launch failures or out of sequence launches, the lettering and numbering schemes do not always follow the pattern A = 1, B = 2, and so forth. For example, in the Interplanetary Monitoring Platform series, IMP-B failed on launch, IMP-E was put into a lunar orbit and given another name and IMP-H and -I were launched in reverse order. Thus IMP-I became IMP-6 and IMP-H became IMP-7. The satellites may also be assigned names in different series; IMP-6 was also Explorer-43 and IMP-7 was Explorer-47.

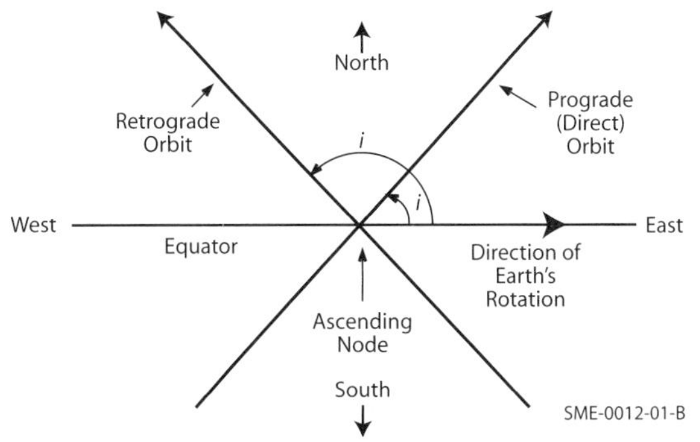

Fig. 9-10. Inclination, *i*, for Prograde and Retrograde Orbits. Satellite is moving from south to north.

The *trajectory* of a spacecraft is its path through space; if this path is closed (i.e., elliptical), then the trajectory is formally an *orbit*. Thus, correct usage would refer to a satellite in elliptical orbit or a probe on a hyperbolic trajectory. Although this distinction is maintained at times, orbit and trajectory are often used interchangeably. Throughout this book we will use "orbit" as the generic term for the path of a spacecraft.

For satellites it is frequently convenient to number the orbits so that we can refer to "a maneuver on the 17th orbit." In standard NASA practice, that portion of the orbit preceding the first ascending node is referred to as *orbit 0*, or *revolution 0*. *Orbit 1* or *revolution 1* goes from the first ascending node to the second ascending node, and so forth. (Note that *revolution* refers to one object moving about another in an orbit, whereas *rotation* refers to an object spinning about an axis.)

When spacecraft are launched, the initial stages of the launch vehicle are typically jettisoned or returned to Earth. However, the final stage may remain inactive and attached to the spacecraft during the coasting phase or parking orbit. The final stage is then ignited or reignited to *inject* the spacecraft, or place it into its proper orbit. The orbit in which the satellite conducts normal operations is referred to as the *mission orbit*, and is typically either *Earth-referenced*, if the principal purpose of the satellite is to observe or communicate with the Earth, or *space-referenced* if its principal purpose is to be or look somewhere in space. A *transfer orbit* is one that is used to transport a spacecraft from one orbit or location to another, as in the case of an Apollo transfer orbit to the Moon or the Mars Rovers orbit to Mars. Finally, at the end of its useful life, a satellite is typically *deorbited* or brought back to Earth, usually burning up in the atmosphere. If the satellite is too high to de-orbit, then an alternative at end of life is to raise the satellite into a parking orbit above the mission orbit such that it will not interfere with other satellites.

A satellite which revolves above the Earth in the same direction that the planet rotates on its axis is in a *prograde* or *direct orbit*. If it revolves in a direction opposite to the rotation, the orbit is *retrograde*. As shown in Fig. 9-10, the inclination of an Earth satellite orbit is measured from east toward north. Therefore the inclination of a prograde satellite is less than 90 deg, and the inclination of a retrograde satellite is greater than 90 deg. In a *polar orbit* $i = 90$ deg. Most satellites are launched in a prograde direction, because the rotational velocity of the Earth provides a part of the orbital velocity. Although this effect is not large (0.46 km/s for the Earth's rotational velocity at the equator compared with a circular velocity of around 7.5 km/s), the available energy is typically the limiting feature of a space mission. Thus, all factors that change the energy which must be supplied by the launch vehicle are important.

9.4 Orbit Perturbations, Geopotential Models, and Satellite Decay

Recall that Kepler's laws are based on a spherically symmetric mass distribution and do not take into account non-gravitational forces or the gravity of other bodies. Consequently, real orbits never follow Kepler's laws precisely, although at times they come very close. Keplerian orbits provide a convenient analytic approximation to a true orbit. In contrast, a *definitive orbit* is the best estimate that can be obtained with all available data of the actual path of a satellite. Because formal analytic solutions are almost never available for real orbit problems with multiple forces, observed orbits are generated numerically based on both orbit theory and observations of the spacecraft. Thus, definitive orbits are only generated for times that are past, although the information from the definitive orbit is frequently extrapolated to the future to produce a predicted or *propagated* orbit.

A *reference orbit* is a relatively simple, precisely defined orbit (usually, though not necessarily, Keplerian) which is used as an initial approximation to the spacecraft's motion. *Orbit perturbations* are the deviations of the true orbit from the reference orbit and are typically classified according to the cause, e.g., perturbations due to the Earth's oblateness, atmospheric drag, or the grav-

Table 9-8. Summary of Forces Acting on a Spacecraft in Earth Orbit.

Source	Regime	Effect in LEO
Earth (point mass)	Dominant force for orbits between Earth and Moon*	Results in Keplerian orbit of satellite about the Earth's center of mass
Earth (higher-order geopotential)	Significant perturbing force at GEO and below; declines rapidly with increasing altitude	Depends on specific orbit; orbit plane rotation of up to 14 deg/day is possible
Sun/Moon (point mass)	Dominant force for interplanetary flight; minor perturbing force in Earth orbit	Low level perturbations; orbit plane rotation of up to 0.007 deg/day
Atmosphere	LEO only, decays exponentially with altitude	Reentry occurs rapidly below 120 km Atmosphere negligible above 1,000 km
Solar Radiation Pressure	Minor perturbing force for normal spacecraft	Small eccentricity growth
Relativistic Effects	Near very massive objects	Negligible
Incidental Forces (leaks, RF, explosive bolts)	Very minor perturbing force for normal spacecraft	Negligible in most circumstances

*The Sun's perturbing force is less than 0.01 times the central force below 370,000 km; the Earth perturbing force is less than 0.01 times the central solar force above 2.5×10^6 km.

itational force of the Moon. In this section we describe the causes of orbit perturbations, the principal effects caused by them, and, where possible, formulas to determine the approximate magnitude of specific effects. More detailed methods for the numerical treatment of perturbations may be found in any of the references in the annotated bibliography on the book website.

Effects which modify simple Keplerian orbits are shown in Table 9-8. These may be divided into four classes: non-gravitational forces (principally atmospheric drag and solar radiation pressure), third body interactions, non-spherical mass distributions, and relativistic mechanics. For some orbits the first two effects dominate the motion of the spacecraft, as in satellite re-entry into the atmosphere or motion about both the Earth and the Moon. Although the effects of non-spherical mass distributions never dominate spacecraft motion, they do provide the major perturbation relative to Keplerian orbits for most intermediate altitude satellites, i.e., those above the atmosphere and below where effects due to the Moon and Sun become important. Additionally, the nonspherical mass distribution becomes much more important for orbits about small bodies such as comets or asteroids where the basic object itself may be fundamentally nonspherical. Finally, relativistic mechanics may be completely neglected in essentially all applications except those specifically intended to test elements of relativity. The largest orbit perturbation in the Solar System due to general relativity is the rotation of the perihelion of Mercury's orbit by about 0.012 deg/century or 3×10^{-5} deg/orbit. Although a shift of this amount is measurable, it is well below the magnitude of other effects which we will consider.

The relative importance of the various orbit perturbations will depend upon the construction of the spacecraft, the specific orbit it's in, and even the level of solar activity. Nonetheless, the Keplerian orbit is an excellent approximation for most astrodynamic problems, with a few important exceptions. For Earth orbits these are:

- Atmospheric drag in low-Earth orbit (less than 1,000 km)
- Rotation of the ascending node and perigee due to Earth's oblateness
- Resonance and Lunar-Solar effects at geosynchronous altitudes

Each of these effects is discussed below. For interplanetary orbits, places where perturbations are important or may dominate include:

- Atmospheric drag in low orbits about planets with an atmosphere or in the vicinity of comets where the gravitational forces are very weak
- Oblateness effects near rapidly rotating planets, such as Jupiter
- Higher order nonspherical effects near small bodies such as natural satellites or asteroids
- Multiple body effects in regions where gravitational forces approximately balance, e.g., between the Earth and the Moon or the Earth and the Sun (often called Lagrange point orbits, see Sec. 9.5)

The impact of each of the major perturbation is discussed in the following subsections.

9.4.1 Nonspherical Mass Distribution

The Earth is very nearly spherically symmetric. However, the rotation of the Earth causes it to assume approximately an equilibrium configuration of an oblate spheroid with an equatorial bulge and flattening at the poles. The difference between the equatorial radius, a, and the polar radius, c, is 21.4 km which produces a *flattening factor* or *ellipticity*, $f \equiv (a-c)/a$ of 1/298.257. As illustrated in Fig. 9-11 this is imperceptible as seen in almost any photograph or illustration.

In addition, the Earth has a slight pear shape at the equator (approximately 100 m out of round) and a variety of minor mass anomalies such as continents, mountain ranges, and San Francisco. Mathematically, this is

Lagrange Planetary Equations. As a practical matter, most current orbit computations are done by simply integrating the equations of motion to obtain a numerical approximation of the motion of the spacecraft. This process works extremely well for computer calculations but provides little physical insight into the effects which are occurring. We began the discussion at the front of the chapter by applying $\mathbf{F} = m\mathbf{a}$ and letting $\mathbf{F}$ be the gravitational force due to a spherically symmetric central body. We can generalize this approach to take additional forces into account by writing:

$$\begin{aligned} m\mathbf{a} &= \mathbf{F}_{\text{central body}} + \mathbf{F}_{\text{spherical harmonics}} + \mathbf{F}_{\text{Sun}} + \mathbf{F}_{\text{Moon}} + \cdots \\ &= -m\nabla U = -m\nabla(\text{central body} + \text{perturbations}) \\ &= -m\nabla(\mu/r) - m\nabla R \end{aligned} \tag{9-21a}$$

Therefore:

$$\mathbf{a} = -\left(\mu r^{-3}\right)\mathbf{r} - \nabla R \tag{9-21b}$$

where as usual, m is the mass of the spacecraft, $\mathbf{a}$ is the vector acceleration, U is the potential energy of the orbit, $\mu \equiv GM$ for the central body and R is the potential function of the perturbation, i.e., representing all of the forces other than the symmetric central body force. R is called the *disturbing potential* and provides a convenient mechanism for evaluating the impact of various forces acting on a spacecraft minus the central body effects.

We can use the above decomposition of the forces to derive *Lagrange's planetary equations* for the variation of the Keplerian orbital elements with time. (The derivation is given in most of the astrodynamics books listed in the bibliography.) The results are:

$$\frac{da}{dt} = \frac{2}{na}\left(\frac{\partial R}{\partial M}\right) \tag{9-22a}$$

$$\frac{de}{dt} = \frac{\left(1-e^2\right)^{1/2}}{na^2 e}\left\{\left(1-e^2\right)^{1/2}\left(\frac{\partial R}{\partial M}\right) - \left(\frac{\partial R}{\partial \omega}\right)\right\} \tag{9-22b}$$

$$\frac{di}{dt} = \frac{1}{na^2\left(1-e^2\right)^{1/2}\sin i}\left\{\cos i\left(\frac{\partial R}{\partial \omega}\right) - \left(\frac{\partial R}{\partial \Omega}\right)\right\} \tag{9-22c}$$

$$\frac{d\omega}{dt} = \frac{1}{na^2}\left\{-\frac{\cos i}{\left(1-e^2\right)^{1/2}\sin i}\left(\frac{\partial R}{\partial i}\right) + \frac{\left(1-e^2\right)^{1/2}}{e}\left(\frac{\partial R}{\partial e}\right)\right\} \tag{9-22d}$$

$$\frac{d\Omega}{dt} = \frac{1}{na^2\left(1-e^2\right)^{1/2}\sin i}\left(\frac{\partial R}{\partial i}\right) \tag{9-22e}$$

$$\frac{dM}{dt} = n - \frac{1-e^2}{na^2 e}\left(\frac{\partial R}{\partial e}\right) - \frac{2}{na}\left(\frac{\partial R}{\partial a}\right) \tag{9-22f}$$

where $R(a, e, i, \omega, \Omega, M)$ is the disturbing potential and n is the mean motion. Note that here a is the semimajor axis and not the acceleration, and M is the mean anomaly (measured relative to the moving perigee) and not the mass of the central body. In the absence of any orbit perturbations all of the partial derivatives are zero, so that only M changes with time as is appropriate for a Keplerian orbit. The advantage of Lagrange's planetary equations is that they allow us to analytically assess the effects of any disturbance on a Keplerian orbit.

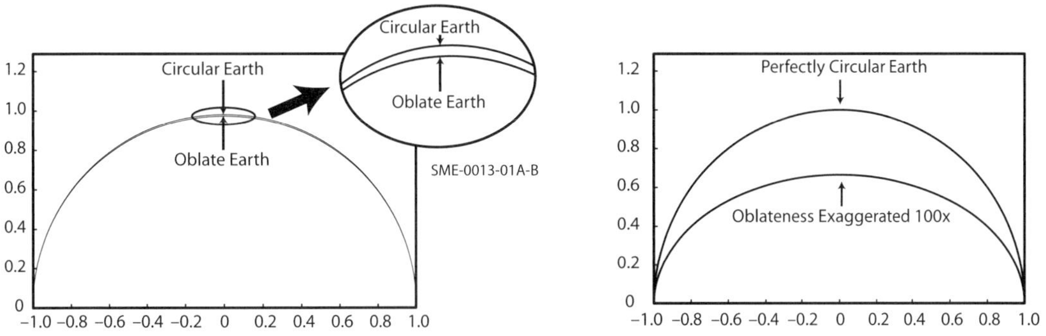

Fig. 9-11. The Difference Between a Spherical Earth and an Oblate Earth is Very Small.

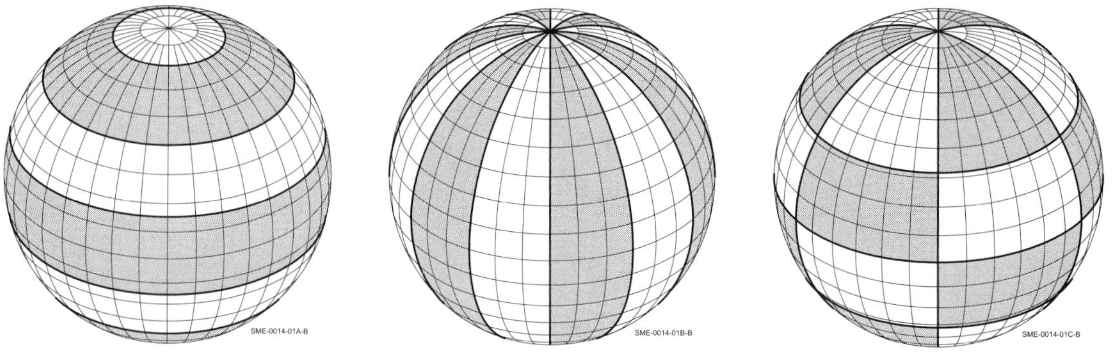

Fig. 9-12. Basis of Spherical Harmonic Expansions. Boundaries between shaded regions are where the expansion changes sign. Thus, J_2 represents a change of sign on either side of the equator and, therefore, is the principal term representing the equatorial bulge.

dealt with by expanding the geopotential function at the point (r, θ, ϕ) in a series of spherical harmonics:

$$U(r,\theta,\phi) = \sum_{n=0}^{\infty} \left(\frac{r}{R_E}\right)^{n+1} J_n P_{n0}(\cos\theta) + \sum_{n=1}^{\infty}\sum_{m=1}^{n} \left(\frac{r}{R_E}\right)^{n+1} \times \left[C_{nm}\cos m\phi + S_{nm}\sin m\phi\right] P_{nm}(\cos\theta) \quad (9\text{-}23)$$

where J_n is defined to be C_{n0}, $\mu = GM$ is the Earth's gravitational constant, R_e is the Earth's equatorial radius, P_{nm} are Legendre polynomials, r is the geocentric distance, θ is the latitude, and ϕ is the longitude. Terms with $m = 0$ are called *zonal harmonics* and J_n are the zonal harmonic coefficients. The zonal harmonics are independent of the longitude and have n sign changes over the full range of latitude on the Earth. As shown in Fig. 9-12A, they divide the Earth into a series of longitude independent zones analogous to the temperate and tropic zones. Terms with $n = m$ are called *sectoral harmonics* since they divide the Earth into sectors which are independent of latitude as shown in Fig. 9-12B. Finally, terms with $m \neq 0$ and $m \neq n$ are called *tesseral harmonics* from the Latin *tessera* for tiles, since these divide the world into a tiled pattern as shown in Fig. 9-12C.

A *geopotential model* of the Earth is a set of coefficients in the spherical harmonic expansion. For example, one of the more widely used is the *Goddard Earth Model 10b* or *GEM10b* which is a 21 × 21 geopotential model, meaning that it is a 21 × 21 spherical harmonic expansion. These geopotential models are determined by analyzing tracking data for a large number of satellites. The need for higher accuracy orbit determination has led to more complex geopotential models. Models that are 50 × 50, 70 × 70, 100 × 100, up to 2160 × 2160 are currently in use, although of course most of the terms in higher order models will be extremely small.

The J_0 term in the spherical harmonic expansion represents the point mass or spherically symmetric distribution for which the potential falls off as $1/r$. The J_1 term changes sign at the equator and therefore represents the difference in mass between the northern and southern hemispheres. The J_2 term has two changes in sign between the north and south poles and represents the mass distribution of the equatorial bulge. This is, by far, the largest of the geopotential terms. (The words "J_2" and "Earth oblateness" are frequently used interchangeably.) Beyond J_2, coefficients become small quickly as can be seen by looking at the first several terms:

$$\begin{aligned} J_0 &= 1 \\ J_1 &= 0 \\ J_2 &= 0.001\,082\,635\,9 \\ J_3 &= -0.000\,002\,54 \\ J_4 &= -\,0.000\,001\,61 \end{aligned} \quad (9\text{-}24)$$

$J_0 = 1$ by definition. In addition, because the coordinate frame is defined as going through the center of mass, $J_1 \equiv 0$. The oblateness term, J_2, is much larger than any of the other perturbations and has important effects for the orbit in that it causes both the right ascension of the ascending node and the argument of perigee to rotate at rates of several degrees per day. Because of the importance of these effects for orbit design they will be described in more detail in Secs. 9.5.2 and 9.5.3.

In addition to rotating the orbit, the principal effect of the non-spherical mass distribution is to cause small changes in the shape of the orbit. Rather than a perfect ellipse in a well-defined inertial plane, actual spacecraft move in a shape more like that of a potato chip, with maximum deviations from a Keplerian orbit on the order of 3 km, as shown in Figs. 9-13 and 9-14. Again this difference in shape is dominated by the equatorial bulge and, consequently, has a pattern in the various components that is nearly sinusoidal.

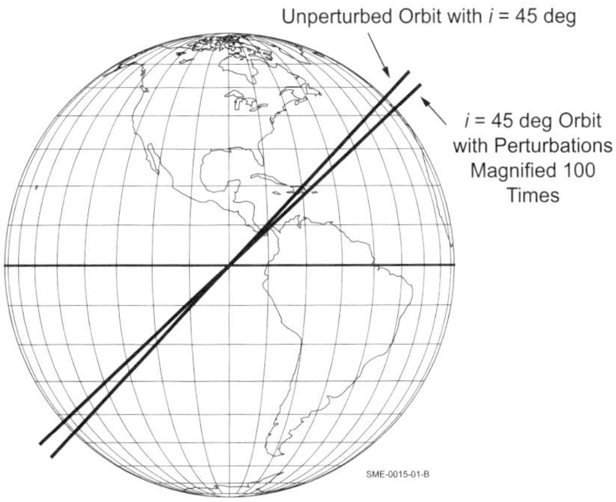

Fig. 9-13. Greatly Exaggerated Shape of a "Circular" Low-Earth Orbit.

Typically the effects of the higher order harmonics are extremely small, except for special circumstances. For example, in geosynchronous orbit, a satellite remains largely over one location on the Earth; therefore, the sectoral harmonics are felt continuously and pull the satellite in an east-west direction. Similarly, in a repeating ground-track orbit, the satellite flies over the same locations on the ground, day after day, and it is possible for resonances to build up when the satellite continuously passes, for example, to the right of the Himalayas, such that the effects of tesseral terms can be substantially magnified. As central bodies become less spherically symmetric the impact of the higher order harmonics becomes more important. For example, the Moon has a variety of mass concentrations or *mascons* which cause large variations in the orbits of lunar spacecraft and make it difficult to predict the orbits even though atmospheric drag plays no role. Orbits around asteroids or other very small objects will also be dominated by higher order harmonics both because of the distinctly nonspherical shape and the smallness of the point mass gravitational forces.

9.4.2 Third Body Interactions

The gravitational forces of the Sun and the Moon cause periodic variations in all of the orbit elements. The effect is generally similar to that of the Earth's equatorial bulge as described in Sec. 9.5.3, i.e., the Sun and the Moon apply an external torque to the orbits and cause the angular momentum vector to rotate. This effect is extremely small and in LEO is dominated by the orbit rotations caused by the Earth's oblateness. However, as described in Sec. 9.5.1 the effect becomes important in geosynchronous orbit and is the dominant source of the need for stationkeeping in GEO.

For nearly circular orbits, the Lagrange planetary equations can be used to determine the approximate rotation rates for the ascending node, Ω, and the argument of perigee, ω, due to the Sun and the Moon. These are:

$$\dot{\Omega}_{MOON} = -0.003\,38(\cos i)/n \tag{9-25}$$

$$\dot{\Omega}_{SUN} = -0.001\,54(\cos i)/n \tag{9-26}$$

$$\dot{\omega}_{MOON} = 0.001\,69\left(4 - 5\sin^2 i/n\right) \tag{9-27}$$

$$\dot{\omega}_{SUN} = 0.000\,77\left(4 - 5\sin^2 i/n\right) \tag{9-28}$$

where i is the orbit inclination, n is the number of orbit revolutions per day, and $\dot{\Omega}$ and $\dot{\omega}$ are in deg/day. The equations neglect the variations caused by the changing orientation of the orbital plane with respect to the Moon's orbit and the ecliptic plane and, therefore, are only average values.

9.4.3 Solar Radiation Pressure

Solar radiation pressure causes periodic variations in all of the orbit elements. The effect is strongest for satellites which have low mass and large cross-sectional areas, such as balloons or spacecraft with a large solar sail. The magnitude of the acceleration a_r in m/s^2 due to solar radiation pressure is:

$$a_r = -4.5 \times 10^{-6} A/m \tag{9-29}$$

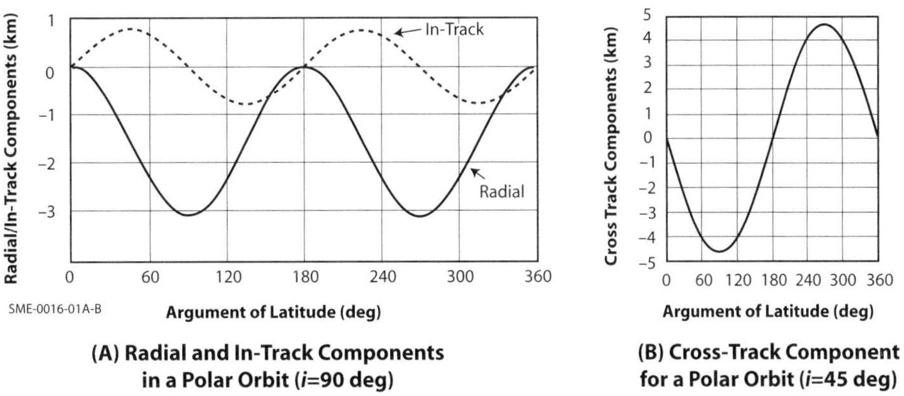

Fig. 9-14. Effect of Nonspherical Earth on the Satellite Orbit. The three curves are the difference between the position of a real satellite and a satellite in a perfectly circular orbit about a point-mass Earth. *In-track* is the direction of the velocity vector; *cross-track* is toward the normal to the orbit.

where A is the cross-sectional area of the satellite normal to the Sun in m^2 and m is the mass of the satellite in kg. This formula applies to an absorbing surface. A mirror normal to the Sun would have twice the acceleration. For satellites below approximately 800 km altitude the acceleration from atmospheric drag is typically much greater than from solar radiation pressure. Above 800 km however, the acceleration from solar radiation pressure can become an important perturbing force. It is frequently the dominant perturbing force for interplanetary spacecraft simply because the other perturbations become dramatically small.

9.4.4 Atmospheric Drag and Satellite Decay

Atmospheric drag is the principal nongravitational force acting on most satellites in low-Earth orbit. Drag acts opposite the direction of the velocity vector, thus slowing the satellite and removing energy from the orbit. This reduction of energy causes the orbit to get smaller, leading to increases in the drag until eventually the altitude becomes so small that the satellite reenters the atmosphere. Below approximately 120 km, the satellite lifetime is extremely short and it will reenter quickly. Above 600 km the lifetimes due to drag will typically exceed spacecraft operational lifetime of approximately 10 years, although drag may still be important for orbit maintenance or maintaining the structure of a constellation.

Although the physics of atmospheric drag is very well understood, drag is nearly impossible to predict with even moderate precision and, therefore, is a major source of the unpredictability of satellite positions at future times and of when and where they will reenter the atmosphere. There are two reasons for this difficulty in predicting drag:

- Drag can vary by as much as an order of magnitude due to the attitude of the spacecraft and, particularly, the orientation of the solar arrays, with respect to the velocity vector.
- The atmospheric density at satellite altitudes varies by as much as two orders of magnitude depending upon the solar activity level which itself varies dramatically.

The net result is that the lifetime and impact point of satellites are extremely difficult to predict and satellite lifetimes themselves vary dramatically depending on a variety of circumstances and conditions. In this section, we provide a brief summary of the physical basis for drag and its effect on satellite orbits, a discussion of the atmosphere and the causes of the variability, and simple mechanisms for bounding the drag level to be expected for satellites in various low-Earth orbits.

The equation for acceleration due to drag, a_D, is:

$$a_D = -(1/2)\,\rho(C_D A/m)V^2 \qquad (9\text{-}30)$$

where ρ is the atmospheric density, C_D is the dimensionless *drag coefficient* of the satellite (typically $C_D \approx 2.2$ as discussed below), A is the cross-sectional area, m is the satellite mass, and V is its velocity. The quantity $m/C_D A$ is called the *ballistic coefficient* and is typically in the range of 25 to 100 kg/m^2 for satellites.*

The atmospheric density, ρ, decreases approximately exponentially as altitude increases:

$$\rho \approx \rho_0 e^{-\Delta h/h_0} \qquad (9\text{-}31)$$

where ρ and ρ_0 are the density at any two altitudes, Δh is the altitude difference, and h_0 is the atmosphere *scale height*, by which the atmospheric density drops by 1/e. The scale height is typically between 50 and 100 km at satellite altitude. The scale height and density at various altitudes are given just inside the rear cover. For circular orbits, drag will act approximately continuously, and the orbit will spiral downward. Because of the exponential character of the atmosphere, drag for elliptical orbits will act predominantly at perigee and, therefore, will lower apogee while having relatively little effect on the perigee height. As shown in Fig. 9-15, this divides the drag effect on elliptical orbits into two distinct phases. In the first phase, the elliptical orbit is circularized by reducing apogee and having only a small effect on perigee. As the orbit becomes more circular, drag operates over the entire orbit and the orbit spirals inward more quickly. For elliptical orbits the approximate changes in semimajor axis, a, and eccentricity, e, per orbit are:

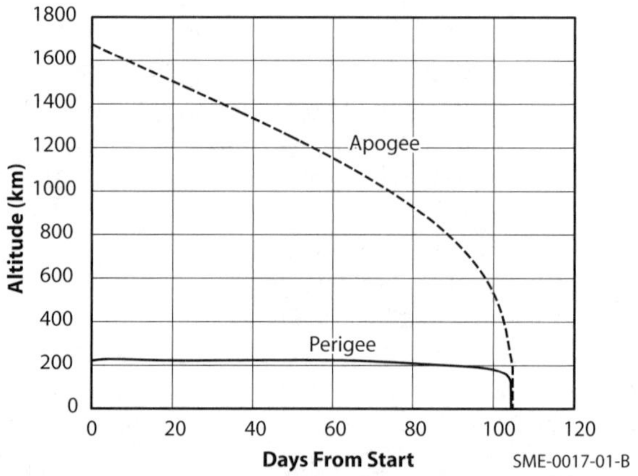

Live Calc

Fig. 9-15. Evolution of an Elliptical Orbit Due to Drag. Orbit began with a perigee height of 215 km and apogee height of 1,680 km.

$$\Delta a_{rev} = -2\pi(C_D A/m)\,a^2\rho_p \exp(-c)\,[I_0 + 2eI_1] \qquad (9\text{-}32)$$

$$\Delta e_{rev} = -2\pi(C_D A/m)\,a\rho_p \exp(-c)\,[I_1 + e(I_0 + I_2)/2] \qquad (9\text{-}33)$$

where ρ_p is the atmospheric density at perigee, $c \equiv ae/h$,

* Note that some authors define the ballistic coefficient as $C_D A/m$. It's important to check the units on the relevant equations.

h is the atmospheric scale height, and I_j are the modified Bessel functions of order j and argument c.

For circular orbits, Eqs. (9-32) and (9-33) can be substantially simplified, to yield:

$$\Delta a_{rev} = -2\pi(C_D A/m)\rho a^2 \quad (9\text{-}34)$$

$$\Delta P_{rev} = -6\pi^2(C_D A/m)\rho a^2/V \quad (9\text{-}35)$$

$$\Delta V_{rev} = \pi(C_D A/m)\rho aV \quad (9\text{-}36)$$

$$\Delta e_{rev} = 0 \quad (9\text{-}37)$$

where P is the orbit period, and V is the satellite velocity. Thus, the computation of effective drag is straight forward with the minor complication that the key parameters (atmospheric density and ballistic coefficient) are largely unknown.

The spacecraft drag coefficient, C_D, depends primarily on four factors:*

- Shape
- Attitude
- Surface condition: smooth (*specular reflection*), rough (*diffuse reflection*), or sticky (*absorption* or *skin friction*)
- Multi-collision effects (*form drag*)

Form drag is very important at low speeds and low altitudes but is negligible for satellites. This is fortunate, because form drag is very difficult to compute.

Ignoring multi-collision effects, the coefficient of drag C_D can be computed using the following expressions:

$$C_D = \frac{4}{A}\int_S \cos^3\psi\, dS \quad \text{Specular Reflection} \quad (9\text{-}38)$$

$$C_D = 2 + \frac{1}{A}\int_S \cos^2\psi\, dS \quad \text{Diffuse Reflection} \quad (9\text{-}39)$$

$$C_D = 2 \quad \text{Absorption} \quad (9\text{-}40)$$

where A is the cross-sectional area, S is the surface area, and ψ is the angle between the velocity vector and normal to the surface. The integral is taken over the entire forward-facing surface, so that ψ is always between 0 deg and 90 deg. Note that $dA = \cos\psi\, dS$. For any satellite, C_D can be divided into three components:

$$C_D = \alpha C_{DS} + \beta C_{DD} + \gamma C_{DA} \quad (9\text{-}41)$$

$$\alpha + \beta + \gamma = 1 \quad (9\text{-}42)$$

where C_{DS} is the drag coefficient for specular reflection, C_{DD} is the drag coefficient for diffuse reflection, and C_{DA} is the drag coefficient for absorption. The drag coefficients C_{DS}, C_{DD}, and C_{DA}, can usually be computed from the shape and attitude of the spacecraft. The component fractions, α, β, γ, however, must be determined by experiment. For most satellites, C_D is dominated by absorption or specular reflection. Table 9-9 gives values of C_D for various common shapes and attitudes.

* The discussion of drag coefficients is due to Leo Early.

Table 9-9. Drag Coefficients for Common Shapes, Attitudes, and Surface Conditions. See text for discussion. (Formulas due to Leo Early.)

Shape	Surface	Drag Coefficient
Flat Plate, Face First	Specular Diffuse	4 3
Flat Plate, Angle of Incidence α	Specular Diffuse	$4\sin^2\alpha$ $2 + \sin\alpha$
Sphere	Specular Diffuse	2 8/3 = 2.667
Circular Cylinder, Side First	Specular Diffuse	8/3 = 2.667 $2 + \pi/4 = 2.785$
Octagonal Cylinder, Side Face First	Specular	$2\sqrt{2} = 2.828$
Octagonal Cylinder, Side Edge First $\alpha = \cos 22.5°$ $\beta = \cos 67.5°$	Specular	$4\frac{\alpha^3+\beta^3}{\alpha+\beta} = 2.586$
Octagonal Cylinder, Side First, Average Over All Side-first Orientations	Specular	$C_D A = 2.812\, A_{\text{face first}}$
Circular Cone, Half-angle α, Point First	Specular Diffuse	$4\sin^2\alpha$ $2 + \sin\alpha$

The mass of the satellite is ordinarily very well known. However, the ballistic coefficient depends on both C_D and the cross-sectional area, A, perpendicular to the velocity vector. The fundamental difficulty is that most spacecraft have large deployable solar arrays which are very thin and thus have a high cross-sectional area perpendicular to their face and very low cross-sectional area when flying edge-on. Typically the solar arrays rotate to track the Sun and antennas, instruments, and other appendages rotate to track ground targets, geosynchronous relay satellites, or targets in space. Consequently, the cross-sectional area "into the wind" can vary by approximately a factor of ten, as shown in Table 9-10 for a number of representative low-Earth orbit satellites.

The next fundamental problem in calculating atmospheric drag is the extreme variation in atmospheric density. Variations in solar activity, particularly over the course of a solar cycle, cause both a variety of geomagnetic effects and heating of the upper atmosphere due primarily to extreme ultraviolet radiation which is not monitored from the Earth. When the atmosphere is heated, it expands and becomes denser at any given altitude. This seems counter-intuitive because heating a gas causes it to expand and to become less dense. The explanation here is that heating the atmosphere causes it to expand and rise, such that portion of the atmosphere which was previously at 200 km is now at 250 km and represents a much denser atmosphere for a satellite at that altitude.

Figures 9-16 through 9-19 provide a means of estimating satellite lifetimes based on a general evaluation of atmospheric densities. Fig. 9-16 shows the historical record of solar activity. What is plotted is the mean daily F10.7 index of radio flux from the Sun. The *F10.7 index*

Table 9-10. Typical Ballistic Coefficients for Low-Earth Orbit Satellites. Values for cross-sectional area and drag coefficients are estimated from the approximate shape, size, and orientation of the satellite and solar arrays. [XA = cross-sectional area].

Satellite	Mass (kg)	Shape	Max. XA (m^2)	Min. XA (m^2)	Max. Drag Coef.	Min. Drag Coef.	Max. Ballistic Coef. (kg/m^2)	Min. Ballistic Coef. (kg/m^2)	Type of Mission
Oscar-1	5	box	0.075	0.0584	4	2	42.8	16.7	Comm.
Intercos.-16	550	cylind.	3.16	2.7	2.67	2.1	82.9	76.3	Scientific
Viking	277	octag.	2.25	0.833	4	2.6	128	30.8	Scientific
Explorer-11	37	octag.	0.18	0.07	2.83	2.6	203	72.6	Astronomy
Hubble	11,000	cylind.*	112	14.3	3.33	4	192	29.5	Astronomy
OSO-7	634	9-sided	1.05	0.5	3.67	2.9	437	165	Solar Physics
Pegasus-3	10,500	cylind.*	264	14.5	3.3	4	181	12.1	Scientific
Landsat-1	891	cylind.*	10.4	1.81	3.4	4	123	25.2	Remote Sensing
ERS-1	2,160	box*	45.1	4	4	4	135	12.0	Remote Sensing
LDEF-1	9,695	12-face	39	14.3	2.67	4	169	93.1	Environment
Vanguard-2	9.39	sphere	0.2	0.2	2	2	23.5	23.5	Scientific
SkyLab	76,136	cylind.*	462	46.4	3.5	4	410	47.1	Scientific
Echo-1	75.3	sphere	731	731	2	2	0.515	0.515	Communications
Extrema							437	0.515	

* With solar arrays

is simply a measure of the radio flux at a wavelength of 10.7 cm measured in units of 10^{-22} watts/m^2/Hz. This is a convenient measure largely because data for the F10.7 index is available for historical periods beginning in 1945. The peaks in the F10.7 index correspond approximately to solar maxima, to levels of high solar activity, and, therefore, to levels of high atmospheric density. Several things are immediately clear from the plot. First, there is an 11-year RF solar cycle corresponding essentially to the sun spot cycles which have been observed for centuries. In addition, it is clear that there are very large month-to-month variations and that while the overall solar cycle can be predicted, the level at any specific time cannot be predicted with any reasonable accuracy. In addition, some solar cycles have levels which are much higher than other solar cycles. Consequently, while the average F10.7 index over an extended period of time is well known, predicting the level at any specific future time is highly uncertain.

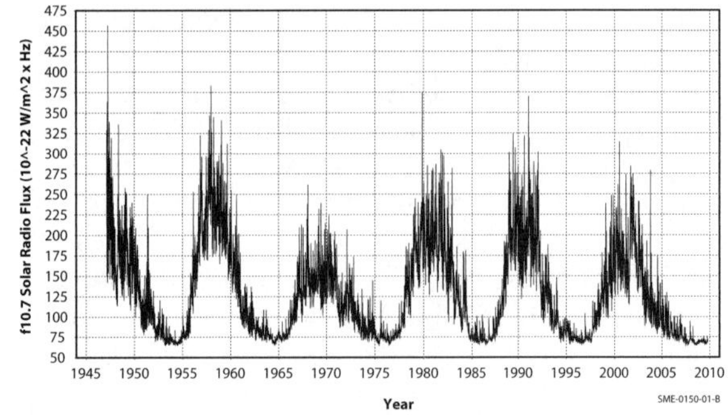

Fig. 9-16. Observed Daily Mean Radio Flux at 10.7 cm. This flux is called the F10.7 index.

Figure 9-17 shows atmospheric density versus altitude corresponding to various values of the F10.7 index. These densities were obtained from the MSIS atmospheric model. Below approximately 150 km, the density is not strongly affected by solar activity. However, at satellite altitudes in the range of 400–800 km, the density variations between solar maximum and solar minimum are approximately two orders of magnitude. Because of these large density variations, satellites will decay far more rapidly during periods of solar maximum and more slowly during solar minimum.

To demonstrate the wide fluctuations in spacecraft lifetimes, we "de-orbited" nine satellites in a computer model, with the results shown in Fig. 9-18. All of the satellites were started at an initial altitude of 700 km in circular orbits. Three were started in 1956 at the beginning of solar maximum, three were started in 1959 near the peak of solar activity, and three were started in 1962 at the beginning of the subsequent solar minimum. Within each set, one satellite had a ballistic coefficient of 20 kg/m^2, one was at 65 kg/m^2, and one at 200 kg/m^2, corresponding roughly to light, moderate and dense satellites respectively. The histories of the nine satellites are shown on the graph. The bars at approximately 400 km altitude mark the periods of solar maxima where the F10.7 index was above 150.

Several characteristics of satellite decay are easily seen in Fig. 9-17. Satellites decay very little during solar minimum and then rapidly during solar maximum. For any one satellite, each solar maximum period will generally produce greater decay than the previous maximum because the satellite is lower. It will also depend on the level of the particular solar maximum. The effect of the

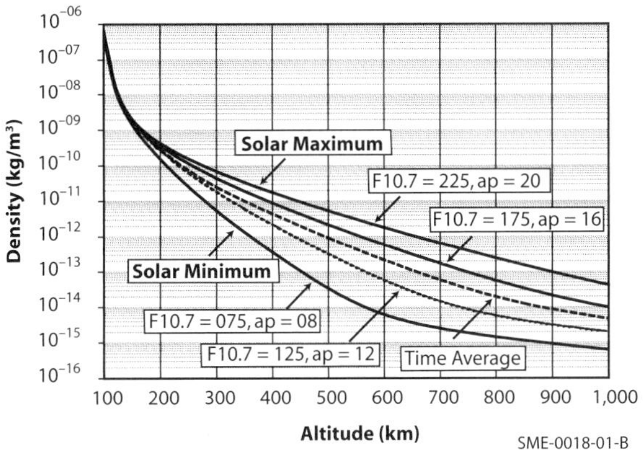

Fig. 9-17. Density vs. Altitude for Various F10.7 Values.

solar maximum also depends on the satellite ballistic coefficient. Those with a low ballistic coefficient respond quickly to the atmosphere and tend to decay promptly. Those with high ballistic coefficients push through a larger number of solar cycles and decay much more slowly. In the end the time for satellite decay is generally measured better in solar cycles than in years. All 9 satellites reentered during periods of solar maxima. For the range of ballistic coefficients shown, the lifetimes varied from approximately one-half of a solar cycle (5 years) to 17 solar cycles (190 years). Predicting in advance where any of the satellites come down would be remarkably difficult.

For a specific satellite whose parameters and current or expected orbit are known, the best way to predict the orbit lifetime is to integrate the equations of motion in an orbit propagator with realistic atmospheric models and assumptions about the satellite cross section. Alternatively, if the altitude is high such that orbit propagation over the satellite lifetime will take excessive computer time, we can simply integrate the equations for the change in altitude to provide approximate lifetime predictions, as was done for Fig. 9-18.

A third alternative, shown in Fig. 9-19, is to estimate a range of lifetimes based on the satellite ballistic coefficient and the approximate time of launch with respect to the solar cycle. The three sets of curves show satellite lifetime as a function of initial circular altitude for satellites with three different ballistic coefficients. The spread of the curves near the center represents the difference between solar maximum and solar minimum. At high altitudes and long lifetimes the curves come together because the satellite will see a large number of solar cycles and it will make very little difference when the satellite starts. Satellites in the midrange go through only a few solar maxima, so the lifetimes will depend strongly on when in the solar cycle the satellite is launched. Notice the steep bends in the curves at multiples of the 11 year solar cycle. As the satellite starts out lower and lower, the atmospheric variations are less, so the curves tend to come together again. Thus, a satellite launched at 100–200 km will decay very quickly irrespective of solar maximum or solar minimum. This chart provides a convenient mechanism for estimating the satellite lifetime range. The actual lifetime will depend on detailed design parameters, the details of the actual orbit, and the launch date relative to the solar cycle.

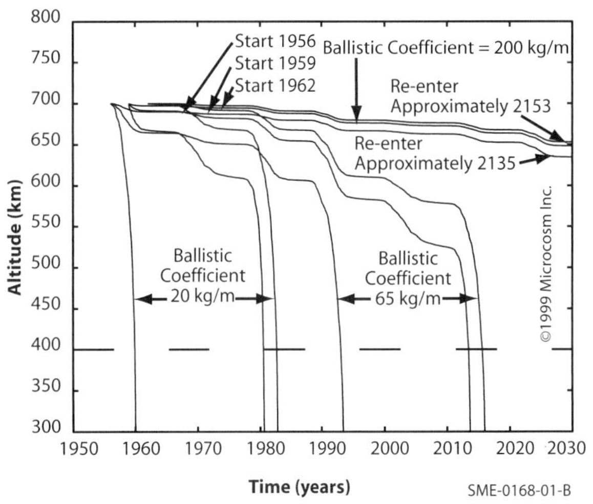

Fig. 9-18. Altitude as a Function of Date for 9 Hypothetical Satellites Launched Over a 6-year Period.

9.5 Specialized Orbits

Spacecraft orbits fall into two broad groups. First, there is a continuum of orbits with varying eccentricities and altitudes ranging from low-Earth to higher orbits, to eventually interplanetary and interstellar orbits. Typically, most such orbits are nearly Keplerian and are conveniently described and analyzed by the techniques in Sec. 9.2. In addition, superimposed on this orbit continuum is a set of specialized orbits summarized in Table 9-11. Within this group, geosynchronous orbits and the repeating ground track come about simply because of the relationship between the orbit period and the rotation period of the Earth. All the rest of the specialized orbits are the result of special effects arising from one of the major orbit perturbations described in Sec. 9.4. This section describes each of these specialized orbits. For each we discuss the physical effect which produces it, the basic equations which govern it, and why these orbits are important. Specific applications of these orbits are discussed in Secs. 10.4 and 10.5.

Whenever possible, expressions for the characteristics of specialized orbits are given in three forms:

- Analytic expression applicable to any central body
- First order approximation applicable to any central body
- Expression where constants have been evaluated for satellites in Earth orbit

The purpose is to allow the equations to be used for any planet or other central body and to allow them to

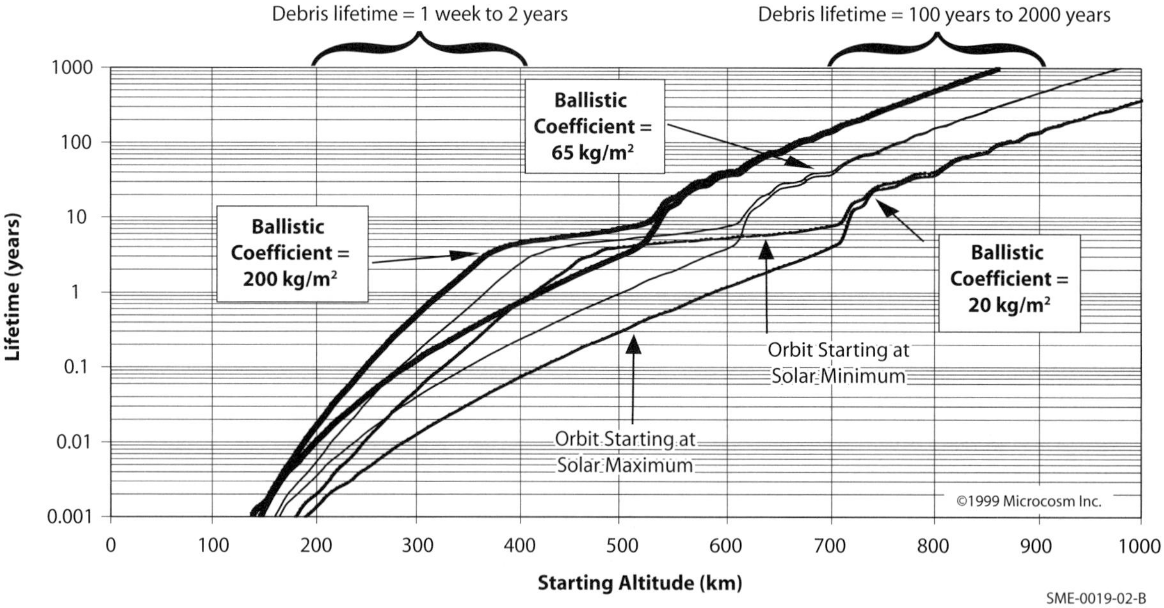

Fig. 9-19. Satellite Lifetime as a Function of Altitude, Relationship to the Solar Cycle, and Representative Ballistic Coefficient. For each ballistic coefficient, the upper curve represents launch during solar minimum and the lower curve represents launch during solar maximum. Note that below approximately 500 km essentially everything will decay and re-enter at the next solar maximum.

Table 9-11. Specialized Orbits and Their Cause.

Specialized Orbit	Characteristic	Cause	Physics Discussed	Applications Discussed
Geostationary	Maintains nearly fixed position with respect to the surface of the Earth	Orbit period = 1 day	Sec. 9.5.1	Sec. 10.4.2.1
Repeating Ground Track	Ground trace repeats after k orbits in n days	Orbit period = n / k days, where n and k are integers	Sec. 9.5.2	Sec. 10.4.2.4
Sun Synchronous	Orbit plane maintains approximately fixed orientation relative to the Sun	Torque due to equatorial bulge causes orbit to rotate 360 deg in 1 year	Sec. 9.5.3	Sec. 10.4.2.2
Repeat Coverage Orbit	Provides coverage of a single location on successive orbits	Inclination chosen to be several deg higher than the target latitude	Sec. 10.4.2.6	Sec. 10.4.2.6
Molniya	Apogee and perigee don't rotate at i = 63.4 deg	Greater equatorial force balanced by lesser polar force so that net in-plane; 0 net rotation	Sec. 9.5.4	Sec. 10.4.2.3
Lagrange Point	Maintains fixed position with respect to 2 bodies (e.g., Earth-Moon, Earth-Sun)	Forces between the 2 bodies balance to cause motion with their common period about the barycenter	Sec. 9.5.5	Sec. 10.5
Frozen Orbit	Orbit with fixed, low eccentricity for which apogee doesn't rotate	Balance of higher order harmonics	Sec. 9.5.6 Vallado [2007]	Sec. 10.4.2.5
Statite	Maintains fixed position relative to the Earth and Sun	Gravity balanced by solar radiation pressure	Sec. 18.7.2, Forward [1989]	Sec. 18.7.2, Forward [1989]

be evaluated quickly for Earth orbits. In addition, a complete numerical evaluation for circular Earth orbits at various altitudes for most of these expressions are contained in the appendices.

9.5.1 Geosynchronous Orbit

Geosynchronous orbit or *GEO* is both the simplest and most used of the specialized orbits. Approximately half of the spacecraft launched are geosynchronous spacecraft intended principally for Earth observation and communications. The period of satellites in low-Earth orbit is approximately 90 min. As the altitude increases, the orbit period also increases, according to Kepler's third law. At an altitude of 35,786 km, the period becomes 1,436 min, which is just the rotation period of the Earth relative to the fixed stars, called the *sidereal day*. Consequently, a satellite in a circular orbit at 0 inclination at this altitude will remain indefinitely fixed over a point on the Earth's equator.* In practice, of course, the orbit is never exactly circular nor at zero inclination and, consequently, will move relative to the surface of the Earth. For a perfectly circular orbit of inclination, i, the path of the satellite as seen from the center of the Earth will be a narrow *analemma* or figure 8 with the following dimensions:

$$\text{height}_{inc} = \pm i \tag{9-43}$$

$$\text{width}_{inc} = \pm\left(\frac{i}{4}\right)\sin i \tag{9-44}$$

This is illustrated in Fig. 9-20A. A small eccentricity, e, in geosynchronous orbit with $i = 0$ will produce a back and forth motion with 1 cycle per orbit. The amplitude of this, in radians, will be:

$$\text{width}_{ecc} = \pm 2e \tag{9-45}$$

In most cases the sidewise component of the eccentricity effect will be larger than that of the inclination effect such that the resulting figure will be an approximately oval shape of height $\pm i$ and width $\pm 2e$ (Fig. 9-20B).

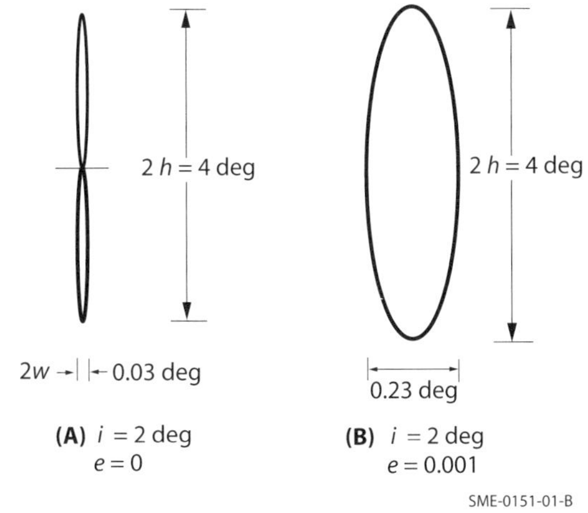

Fig. 9-20. Apparent Daily Motion of a Satellite in Geosynchronous Orbit. Horizontal scale is exaggerated to show the shape.

In addition to the daily oscillations due to small variations in the orbit elements, perturbations continuously act to change the orbit. The largest perturbation in GEO is a north-south drift or inclination change caused by the gravitational interaction with the Sun and the Moon. If not corrected, this perturbation will cause the inclination to vary between 0 and 15 deg over a period of approximately 55 years. As shown in Fig. 9-21, the general motion of the orbit pole under the effect of solar lunar perturbations will be a circle of approximately 7.5 deg radius centered at a point between the ecliptic pole and the equatorial pole. Because the Sun and the Moon are effectively point gravitational masses and are moving continuously with respect to the Earth and the geostationary satellite, the motion is a complex spiral. The approximate worst case changes in velocity per year are given by:

$$\Delta V_{Moon} = 102.67 \cos\alpha \ \sin\alpha \ \text{(m/s per year)}$$
$$\approx 36.93 \text{ m/s per year, for } i = 0 \tag{9-46}$$

$$\Delta V_{Sun} = 40.17 \cos\gamma \ \sin\gamma \ \text{(m/s per year)}$$
$$\approx 14.45 \text{ m/s per year, for } i = 0 \tag{9-47}$$

where α is the angle between the orbit plane and the Moon's orbit, and γ is the angle between the orbit plane and the ecliptic. The net effect of these forces is an inclination drift for satellites in GEO of approximately 0.9 deg/year.

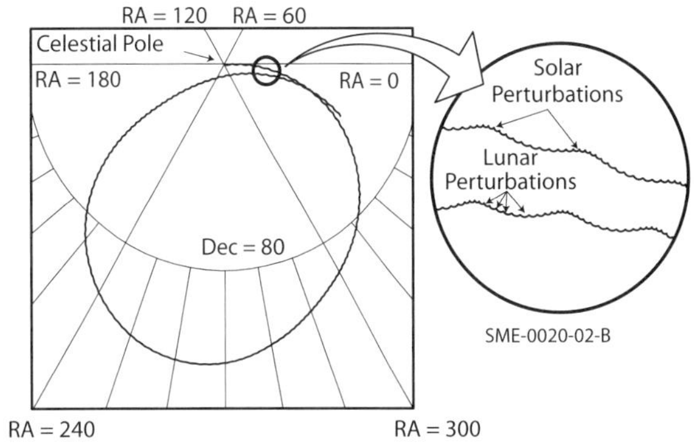

Fig. 9-21. Motion of the Orbit Pole Over 60 Years for a Satellite in Geosynchronous Orbit. The celestial pole is at the coordinate intersection near the top of the plot in the center. The long term motion is roughly a circle of 15 deg radius centered on a right ascension of 270 deg and a declination of 82.5 deg. As can be seen in the figure, the real motion is substantially more complex because of the motion of the Sun and Moon relative to the spacecraft. The large "waves" are due to the Sun and have a 6 month periodicity. The smaller ones (best seen in the enlarged view) are semimonthly "waves" due to the Moon. In general, geosynchronous satellites drift about 0.9 deg per year in inclination. RA = right ascension, Dec = declination.

In addition, there is an east-west drift caused by the out of roundness of the Earth's equator (i.e., the J_{22} sectoral term in the spherical harmonic expansion of the geopotential). If uncorrected, this transverse acceleration would result in a sinusoidal motion about either of 2 stable longitudes located at approximately 75 deg and 255 deg East longitude. The ΔV in m/s/year required to compensate for the East-West drift is given by:

$$\Delta V = 1.715 \sin(2|l_D - l_S|) \tag{9-48}$$

where l_D is the desired longitude and l_S is the closest stable longitude. Typically, the ΔV required for East-West stationkeeping is approximately 10% of that required for North-South stationkeeping.

* Geosynchronous orbit was first described mathematically in 1928 by a Slovene rocket engineer, Herman Potocnik. The potential for GEO communications satellites was first described by the popular science and science fiction writer, Arthur C. Clarke in the October 1945 issue of *Wireless World* [Clarke, 1945]. Clarke often commented on the potential impact had he chosen to patent GEO communications satellites (For more details, see, for example, Gruntman [2004].)

None of the above perturbations serve to change the radius of the geostationary orbit. Whereas atmospheric drag provides a housekeeping function in low-Earth orbit, there is no natural perturbation which provides a similar process for removing satellites from the geostationary ring. Consequently, a satellite in GEO which dies will drift in inclination and drift back-and-forth in longitude among the other geosynchronous satellites. Similarly, if one of the spacecraft in GEO explodes or collides with another satellite, the resulting debris cloud will also remain in geosynchronous orbit. Thus, geosynchronous orbit is both a unique resource and a fragile environment because of the potential for debris to accumulate. The key to this problem is to raise spacecraft 500 km above geosynchronous orbit when they have finished their useful life. At this altitude, they will remain essentially indefinitely with no perturbations to bring them back into the geostationary arc. Such a maneuver takes an extremely small amount of propellant. The largest difficulty with spacecraft disposal is that it must be done while the spacecraft itself is still operating so that thrusters can be commanded to make the appropriate maneuver.

The synchronous altitude for any central body can be obtained immediately from Kepler's Third Law by setting the orbit period, P_{sync}, equal to the rotation period of the central body relative to the fixed stars, D^*, called the *sidereal day* for that body. Thus:

$$P_{sync} = D^* \tag{9-49}$$

$$a_{sync} = (\mu / 4\pi^2)^{1/3} (D^*)^{2/3} \tag{9-50}$$

$$H_{sync} = a_{sync} - R_{planet} \tag{9-51}$$

where as usual $\mu \equiv GM$ for the planet, a_{sync} is the semimajor axis of the synchronous orbit, R_{planet} is the equatorial radius of the planet, and H_{sync} is the synchronous altitude. Values of the synchronous altitude for principal bodies in the Solar System are listed in Table 9-12.

Live Calc

Table 9-12. Synchronous Orbits for Major Solar System Objects.

Central Object	Sidereal Period (days)	Equatorial Radius (km)	Synchronous Altitude (km)
Earth	0.99726	6,378.136 6	35,786
Moon	27.322	1,738	86,715
Sun	25.38	695,990	24,588,000
Mercury	58.6462	2,439.7	240,453
Venus	243.01	6,051.9	1,530,500
Mars	1.02596	3,397	17,031
Jupiter	0.41354	71,492	88,565
Saturn	0.44401	60,268	51,981

9.5.2 Repeating Ground Track Orbits

In a *repeating ground track orbit*, the spacecraft returns after one or more days to the same location with respect to the surface of the Earth such that the path of the spacecraft then repeats itself. For this to occur, an integral number of orbit periods, j, must equal an integral number of days, k. For example, if a spacecraft makes exactly 15.25 orbits per day, then it will make $j = 61$ orbits in $k = 4$ days and will have a 4 day repeating ground track. Every 4th day, the satellite will follow the same path and, therefore, will see the same geometry relative to features on the ground and will move across the sky in the same apparent path as seen by a ground observer. An example of a 2-day repeating ground track orbit is shown in Fig. 9-22.

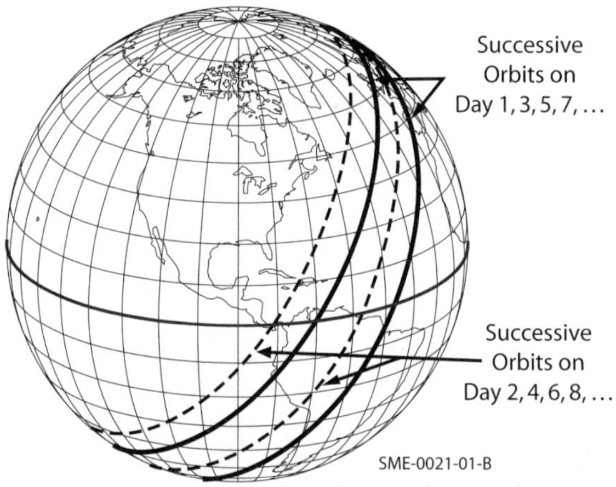

Fig. 9-22. A 2-day Repeating Ground Track Orbit will cross the Equator on the second day midway between where it crossed on the first day and then repeat the day 1 crossings on day 3. The pattern repeats at 2-day intervals.

The actual period for a repeating ground track is made more complex by the presence of orbit perturbations which cause the orbit itself to rotate. We want the orbit period to be a harmonic rotation of the Earth relative to the orbit plane, rather than the fixed stars. Consequently, we need to take into account the rotation of the orbit (in node, perigee, and mean anomaly) due to the oblateness of the Earth. Because the oblateness effects are a function of the altitude, solving the altitude for a given ground track repeat pattern is an iterative process. Our initial estimate H_0, although inaccurate, is the repeating ground track altitude ignoring the effects of oblateness:

$$H_0 = \mu^{1/3} \left(\frac{2\pi j}{D^* k} \right)^{-2/3} - R_E \tag{9-52a}$$

$$\equiv k_1 (j/k)^{-2/3} - R_E \tag{9-52b}$$

$$k_1 \equiv \mu^{1/3} \left(2\pi / D^* \right)^{-2/3} \tag{9-52c}$$

$$\approx 42{,}164.173 \text{ km} \tag{9-52d}$$

Table 9-12, Fig. 9-22, Eq. 9-52d

where $D^* \approx 86{,}164.10035$ sec is the sidereal rotation period of the Earth (i.e., relative to the fixed stars), R_E is equatorial radius of the Earth, and $\mu = GM$ is the Earth's gravitational constant. We then determine the rotation rate of the Earth, $\dot{L}$, and the rotation rate of the three orbit parameters due to oblateness as follows:

$$\dot{L} = 360 \text{ deg/day}^* \tag{9-53}$$

$$\dot{\Omega} = -2k_2 a^{-7/2} \cos i \left(1 - e^2\right)^{-2} \tag{9-54}$$

$$\dot{\omega} = k_2 a^{-7/2} \left(5\cos^2 i - 1\right)\left(1 - e^2\right)^{-2} \tag{9-55}$$

$$\dot{M} = k_2 a^{-7/2} \left(3\cos^2 i - 1\right)\left(1 - e^2\right)^{-3/2} \tag{9-56}$$

where

$$k_2 = 0.75 \left(\frac{360}{2\pi}\right) J_2 \mu^{1/2} R_E^2 \tag{9-57a}$$

$$\approx 1.029\,553\,297 \times 10^{14} \text{ km}^{3.5} \text{ deg/day}^* \tag{9-57b}$$

where $\dot{\Omega}$ is the rate of change of the ascending node, $\dot{\omega}$ is the rate of change of perigee, $\dot{M}$ is rate of change of the mean anomaly, J_2 is the Earth's oblateness, e is the orbit eccentricity, i is the inclination, and a is the estimate of the semimajor axis. For the first iteration, we take $a \approx H_0 + R_E$. All of the angular rates are expressed in deg/sidereal day ≡ deg/day*. We next estimate the mean angular motion, n, for the repeating ground track as:

$$n = (j/k)\left(\dot{L} - \dot{\Omega}\right) - \left(\dot{\omega} + \dot{M}\right) \tag{9-58}$$

Finally, the revised estimate for the repeating ground track altitude, H, is:

$$H = \mu^{1/3} \left(\frac{n\pi}{180D^*}\right)^{-2/3} - R_E \tag{9-59}$$

If necessary, we can then recompute a and iterate again from Eq. (9-54) on. Note that for prograde orbits, $\cos i$ is positive, for retrograde orbits, $\cos i$ is negative, and that a must be in km if the value of k_2 in Eq. (9-57b) is used. Values for the above constants for different objects in the Solar System are given in App. B.

The principal advantage of this type of orbit is that the ground track and, therefore, the geometry relative to the surface of the Earth repeats. This in turn, means that we can view the surface of the Earth from the same viewpoint on a recurring basis and, therefore, compare one image or data set with another taken at a later time from the same orientation. This makes the interpretation of changes and variations far easier. In addition, the geometry of the satellite's path as seen by the ground also remains the same such that a ground station can follow the path of the satellite more easily since it will follow the same path on a recurring basis. The principal demerit of the repeating ground track is that it has the potential for resonance effects with the Earth's higher order harmonics. If we pass just to the left of a major mass concentration such as the Himalayas today, then we will do so again tomorrow, and the day after, and so on. Thus, perturbations have the potential to accumulate over time, and resonance effects can build up which will significantly distort the orbit. Consequently, repeating ground tracks are useful for observations, but should generally be avoided unless there is a specific reason for using them.

There are a very large number of potential repeating ground track orbits. For the Earth, there are 15 orbits per day at an altitude of 482.25 and 14 per day at an altitude of 817.14. However, in between these we have 14.33 orbits per day, 14.5 per day, 14.75 per day, 14.8 per day, and so on. This set of representative repeating ground track orbits is shown in Table 9-13.

An interesting subgroup of the repeating ground track orbits are those for which the inclination and, therefore, node rotation rate is adjusted such that the repeat occurs on precise multiples of the *civil orbits* day of 24 hours. For these orbits, the ground track not only repeats, but does so at the same time each day, every other day, or on a weekly basis depending upon the orbit parameters.

Live Calc

Table 9-13. Representative Repeating Ground Track Orbits. A large number of such orbits are possible.

Altitude (km)	Inclination (deg)	Period (min)	Orbits per Day	Repeat Pattern
817.14	28	101.24	14.0	14 orbits/day
701.34	28	98.80	14.33	43 orbits/3 days
645.06	28	97.63	14.50	29 orbits/2 days
562.55	28	95.91	14.75	59 orbits/4 days
546.31	28	95.57	14.8	74 orbits/5 days
482.25	28	94.25	15.0	15 orbits/day

9.5.3 Sun-Synchronous Orbits

Because the gravitational force is conservative, the total energy and mean values of the semimajor axis, apogee and perigee heights, and eccentricity do not change due to oblateness or other higher order terms in the Earth's geopotential. Nonetheless, secular variations in some of the orbit elements can occur. Perhaps the easiest of these to visualize is the rotation of the orbit due to the torque produced by the Earth's oblateness. In this context, it is easiest to visualize the Earth as a point mass plus a ring of additional mass along the equator representing the equatorial bulge (the J_2 term). The gravitational effect of the equatorial bulge is to continuously try to pull the orbit plane downward toward the equatorial plane. However, the result of this force is not a change in the inclination, but a rotation of the right ascension of the ascending node.

The reason for this effect is the angular momentum of the orbit. In this regard, we can think of the orbit as a

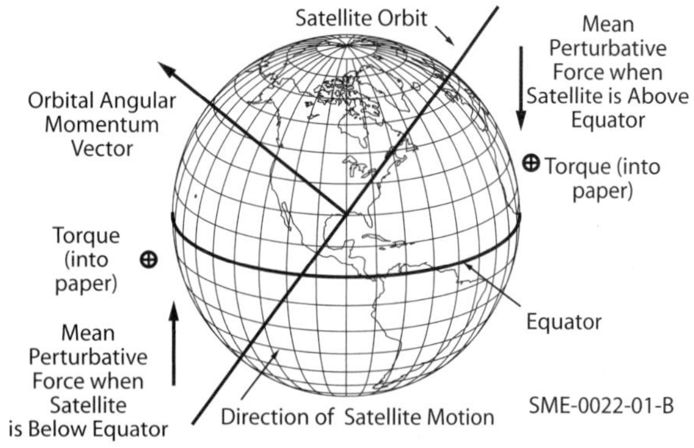

Fig. 9-23. Regression of the Nodes Due to Oblateness. The equatorial bulge of the Earth produces a torque on the orbit, causing prograde orbits to rotate from east to west (i.e. regress). Retrograde orbits rotate from west to east due to oblateness.

rotating wheel with its axis along the normal to the orbit plane. Recall from freshman physics that when a bicycle wheel is rotated rapidly and one end is allowed to drop, it does not fall, but rather *precesses*, i.e., the axis rotates in a horizontal direction. A similar result applies to the spacecraft orbit. As shown in Fig. 9-23, when the spacecraft is north of the equator, the oblate Earth is pulling it down thus producing a torque into the paper. Similarly, when the spacecraft is south of the equator, the equatorial bulge is pulling it up and, again, there is a torque into the paper. This continuous torque causes the angular momentum vector to move in the direction of the torque, i.e., to rotate about the Earth's pole. For a satellite in a prograde orbit, this rotation is in the westward direction opposite the direction of the Earth on its axis. Consequently, this motion is called the *regression of the nodes*. So long as the other orbit elements do not change, the orbit will rotate indefinitely in inertial space and the node will continue to change while the inclination remains constant.

To evaluate the rate of node rotation, we will return to the Lagrange planetary equations (Eq. 9-22e) and evaluate the impact of the J_2 term. When only the secular variations due to J_2 are considered, the right ascension of the ascending node, Ω, at time t is given by:

$$\Omega = \Omega_0 + \frac{d\Omega}{dt}\left(t - t_0\right) \quad (9\text{-}60a)$$

$$= \Omega_0 - \frac{3}{2}J_2 n\left(\frac{R_E}{a}\right)^2\left(1-e^2\right)^{-2} \times \left(\cos i\right)\left(t - t_0\right) \quad (9\text{-}60b)$$

$$\approx \Omega_0 - \frac{3}{2}J_2\sqrt{\mu}\,R_E^2\,a^{-7/2}\left(1-e^2\right)^{-2} \times \left(\cos i\right)\left(t-t_0\right) + \mathcal{O}\left(J_2^2\right) \quad (9\text{-}60c)$$

$$\approx \Omega_0 - 2.064\,74\times10^{14}\,a^{-7/2}\left(1-e^2\right)^{-2} \times \left(\cos i\right)\left(t-t_0\right) + \mathcal{O}\left(J_2^2\right) \quad (9\text{-}60d)$$

where in the last form, $t - t_0$ is in days, Ω is in degrees, a is the semimajor axis in km, e is the eccentricity, i is the inclination, and Ω_0 is Ω at the epoch time t_0. In the final two forms, n is approximated by n_0 which may produce an error as large as 0.1% in the $d\Omega/dt$ term.

For example, in a circular low-Earth orbit at 500 km, we may further evaluate Eq. (9-60d) to yield $\dot{\Omega} = -7.652 \cos i$. Consequently, for low inclination orbits, the node can rotate up to 7.7 deg per day. This represents a significant motion of the orbit plane over the lifetime of most satellites, since the orbit could rotate through 360 deg in only about 45 days.

For a polar orbit, $i = 90$ deg, $\dot{\Omega} = 0$ and the orbit plane remains fixed in inertial space. For a polar orbit, if the Sun is in the orbit plane on any given date, then it will be in the vicinity of the orbit pole 3 months later and back in the orbit plane after 6 months when the Earth has moved 180 deg in its orbit.

If the orbit inclination is more than 90 deg, i.e., a retrograde orbit, then $\cos i$ will become negative and $\dot{\Omega}$ will become positive. In this case, the orbit progresses and rotates in the same direction as the Earth is rotating on its axis or as the Earth is going around the Sun. A particularly interesting case occurs whenever the product of the three terms in a, e, and i in Eq. (9-45) has the value of -4.7737×10^{-15} km$^{-3.5}$. In this case, the rotation rate of the node will be 0.9856 deg per day or 1 rotation per year. This is called a *Sun-synchronous orbit* because the orientation of the orbit plane will remain nearly fixed relative to the Sun as the Earth moves in its orbit. In a Sun-synchronous orbit, we are using the natural perturbation caused by the Earth's oblateness to pull the orbit around in inertial space at a rate of 1 rotation per year, so that we can maintain an approximately constant Sun angle. As shown in Table 9-14, the specific inclination in which this occurs will vary slightly depending upon the altitude of the satellite.

Live Calc

Table 9-14. Inclination for Sun-Synchronous Orbits at Varying Altitudes.

Mean Altitude (km)	e = 0	e = 0.1		
	i (deg)	i (deg)	h_P (km)	h_A (km)
0	95.68	—	—	—
200	96.33	—	—	—
400	97.03	—	—	—
600	97.79	—	—	—
800	98.60	98.43	82	1,518
1,000	99.48	99.29	262	1,738
2,000	104.89	104.59	1,162	2,838
3,000	112.41	111.94	2,062	3,938
4,000	122.93	122.19	2,962	5,038
5,000	138.60	137.32	3,862	6,138
5,974	180.00	168.55	4,738	7,209

Table 9-14, Fig. 9-23, Eq. 9-60d

The effect of oblateness on the rotation of the orbit remains essentially constant throughout the year. Consequently, the orbit pole will move at a uniform rate at a fixed angle relative to the celestial pole. On the other hand, because of the eccentricity of the Earth's orbit, the Sun moves at a nonuniform rate going faster at perihelion and more slowly at aphelion. In addition, the Sun moves along the ecliptic inclined at 23.5 deg to the Earth's equator. This means that relative to the celestial pole, the Sun moves north and south through a total angle of 47 deg and additionally moves more rapidly along the equator at some times of the year than at other times. (The general character of this motion including the reasons for different speeds along the equator are explained in detail in Chap. 10 of Wertz [2009].) The net result is that throughout the year, the Sun moves in an analemma or figure 8 relative to the position of the orbit as shown in Fig. 9-24.

The general path of the Sun relative to the orbit plane will be an analemma with a half height equal to 23.5 deg. The width of the analemma will be 2.5 deg due simply to the obliquitity of the ecliptic. When the eccentricity of the Earth's orbit is taken into account, the analemma will be 3.8 deg across in the southern hemisphere and only 1.3 deg in the northern hemisphere.

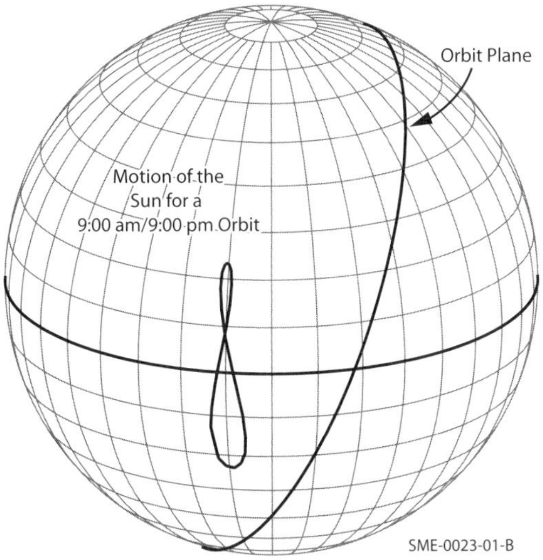

Fig. 9-24. Changing Position of the Sun Relative to the Orbit Plane in a Sun-Synchronous Orbit. The position of the Sun remains approximately fixed. However, since the J_2 perturbation is being used to balance the non-uniform revolution of the Earth about the Sun, and because the Sun isn't in the equatorial plane, the relative position will change somewhat throughout the year. For a detailed discussion, see Wertz [2009], Chap. 10.

Sun-synchronous orbits are typically labeled by the approximate orientation of the Sun relative to the orbit. If the Sun is approximately in the orbit plane, it is called a *noon-midnight orbit* because it will be either noon or midnight at the subsatellite point. If the Sun is near the orbit pole, it is called a *twilight orbit* or *6 am–6 pm orbit*, since the Sun will be nearly at right angles to the direction to the Earth. In twilight orbits, the Sun is always in the vicinity of the orbit pole and, therefore, there are almost no eclipses and the available power is at a maximum. In addition, the lighting on the ground below has very long shadows and, therefore, good contrast. The applications of the Sun-synchronous orbits are discussed in Sec. 10.6.

Finally, it is convenient to compute the local mean time* at the subsatellite point of the spacecraft. For any satellite in a circular orbit, the local mean time, T, at which the satellite is over latitude λ is given by:

$$T = \frac{1}{15}\left[-\alpha_s + \Omega + \arcsin\left(\frac{\tan\lambda}{\tan i}\right)\right] + 12 \tag{9-61a}$$

$$\approx \frac{1}{15}\left[-\frac{360}{365.24}\Delta D + \Omega + \arcsin\left(\frac{\tan\lambda}{\tan i}\right)\right] + 12 \tag{9-61b}$$

where α_s is the right ascension of the mean Sun, Ω is the right ascension of the ascending node of the orbit, i is the orbit inclination, ΔD is the number of days from the vernal equinox to the time Ω is evaluated, the angular quantities in square brackets are in degrees, and T is in hours. For Sun-synchronous orbits, $\alpha_s - \Omega$ is constant and, therefore, the local mean time is a function only of the latitude and does not change from orbit to orbit.

9.5.4 Molniya Orbits

In addition to causing rotation of the nodes, the oblateness of the Earth also causes the major axis of the orbit connecting apogee and perigee to rotate within the orbit plane. The reason for this is shown in Fig. 9-25. The $1/r^2$ force corresponding to a perfectly spherically symmetric mass distribution will cause the spacecraft to move in an elliptical Keplerian orbit such that the spacecraft would return exactly to its starting conditions and the orbit would repeat itself over and over in inertial space. If the force is stronger than $1/r^2$, the orbit will curve more strongly and the spacecraft will return to perigee sooner than it otherwise would have, thus causing perigee to rotate in a positive direction. Similarly, if the force is weaker than $1/r^2$, the orbit will rotate more slowly than a Keplerian orbit, the spacecraft will take longer than one period to return to perigee and the orbit will rotate opposite the direction of motion. For the case of the oblate Earth, the gravitational force over the equator is stronger than $1/r^2$ and weaker than $1/r^2$ in the vicinity of the poles. In a low inclination orbit, the spacecraft will feel a stronger force at all times and perigee will advance. In a polar orbit, the forces will be stronger over the equator and weaker when the spacecraft is over the pole. The

* The *local mean time* is the solar time that would be the case if the Sun moved at a uniform rate along the equator rather than at a varying rate along the ecliptic. Thus local mean time does not take into account either time zones or the eccentricity and obliquity of the ecliptic.

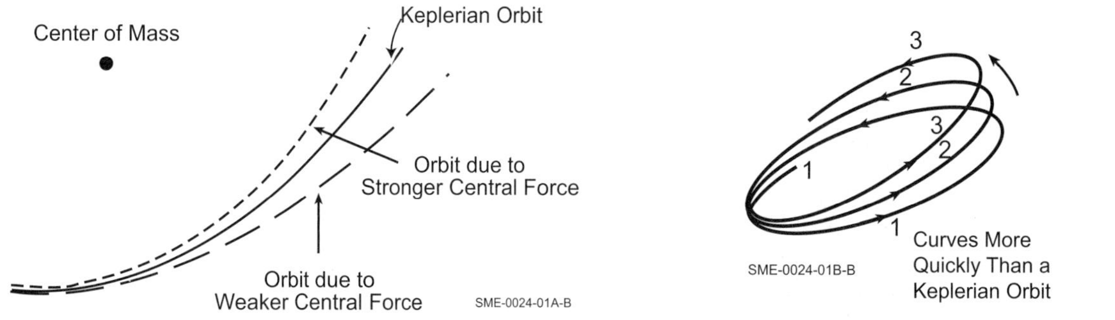

(A) Effect of Non-point Mass Forces **(B) Rotation of Line of Apsides Connecting Apogee and Perigee for an Equatorial Orbit**

Fig. 9-25. Physical Basis for Rotation of Eccentric Orbits. Near the equator the force will be greater than the $1/r^2$ force from the Earth point mass and the orbit will rotate faster than the closed Keplerian orbit. Near the pole it will be less and the orbit will be more open.

net effect is that in a polar orbit perigee rotates backwards but not as rapidly as it rotates forward for an equatorial orbit.

Once again, we can use the Lagrange planetary Eqs. (9-22d) to evaluate the rate at which the argument of perigee, ω, rotates:

$$\omega = \omega_0 + \frac{d\omega}{dt}(t - t_0) \tag{9-62a}$$

$$= \omega_0 + \frac{3}{2} J_2 n \left(\frac{R_E}{a}\right)^2 \left(1 - e^2\right)^{-2} \times \left(2 - \frac{5}{2}\sin^2 i\right)(t - t_0) \tag{9-62b}$$

$$\approx \omega_0 + \frac{3}{2} J_2 \sqrt{\mu}\, R_E^2\, a^{-7/2} \left(1 - e^2\right)^{-2} \times \left(2 - \frac{5}{2}\sin^2 i\right)(t - t_0) + \mathcal{O}\left(J_2^2\right) \tag{9-62c}$$

$$\approx \omega_0 + 2.064\,74 \times 10^{14}\; a^{-7/2} \left(1 - e^2\right)^{-2} \times \left(2 - \frac{5}{2}\sin^2 i\right)(t - t_0) + \mathcal{O}\left(J_2^2\right) \tag{9-62d}$$

where in the last term $t - t_0$ is in days, ω is in degrees, a is the semimajor axis in kilometers, e is the eccentricity, i is the inclination, and ω_0 is the value of ω at the epoch t_0. For example, we can evaluate the expression for a circular orbit at 500 km to obtain $\dot{\omega} = 3.826\,(4 - 5\sin^2 i)$. This implies that for an equatorial orbit, the line of apsides or major axis will rotate in the direction of motion by up to 15.3 deg per day and for polar orbits it will rotate opposite the direction of motion by as much as –3.8 deg per day.

The rotation of perigee can be even more rapid than the rotation of the line of nodes. For example, in a low eccentricity, low inclination orbit that begins with apogee over the northern most latitude, apogee will have rotated to the equator after only a week, and in 2 weeks will be at the southern most latitude. At this high rate of rotation, it would be difficult to find good utility for highly elliptical orbits except perhaps to successively sample different regions of space. Notice, however, that there is a term in the expansion $(4 - 5\sin^2 i)$ that goes to 0 at an inclination of 63.435 deg. For an elliptical orbit at this *critical inclination*, the line of apsides does not rotate. Consequently, nearly all spacecraft in highly elliptical orbits intended for long-term applications are at the critical inclination of 63.435 deg, or at the complementary angle of 116.565 deg which also does not rotate.

The Soviet Union started using critically inclined orbits very early in the space age. Specifically, a *Molniya* orbit (Russian for lightning) is a semisynchronous, highly elliptical orbit with a 12-hour period at the critical inclination such that perigee does not rotate. Perigee is typically placed in the southern hemisphere so that the satellite remains above the northern hemisphere for approximately 11 hours per orbit. Recall that in highly elliptical orbits, the satellite moves much more slowly at apogee than at perigee. Much of the former Soviet Union was not visible from geosynchronous orbit. Molniya orbits, on the other hand, were at a high inclination and the spacecraft moved very slowly at apogee and, therefore, was in view for an extended period. Thus, 2 or 3 spacecraft in a Molniya orbit could provide communications for northern latitude regions well beyond the reach of geosynchronous satellites. Consequently, most of the Soviet communications satellites were placed in Molniya orbits. The basic parameters of representative Molniya orbits are shown in Table 9-15.

The rate of perigee rotation depends on the value of J_2 and, therefore, will be different for different central bodies. Note, however, that the critical inclination of 63.4 deg is a function only of the fact that the expansion is in terms of spherical harmonics and thus will be the same for all planets. Consequently, Molniya-like orbits about any of the planets will be inclined at 63.4 deg to the planet's equator.

9.5.5 Lagrange Point Orbits

Most specialized orbits are defined with respect to a single central body such as the Earth or the Moon. *Lagrange point orbits,** however, are defined with respect to 2 large co-orbiting bodies such as the Earth and the Moon or the Sun and the Earth. This is often called the *circular restricted three-body problem*, which refers to the two large bodies being in circular orbits about each other and the mass of the spacecraft or small body being much less than the mass of the other two objects. For convenience, we will define the Lagrange points for the Earth-Moon system. However, they can be applied to any pair of co-orbiting large bodies.

Table 9-15. Characteristics of Representative Molniya Orbits.

Rev Per Day	Period (sec)	Semimajor Axis (km)	Inc (deg)	Alt at Apogee (km)	Alt at Perigee (km)	Eccen-tricity
1	86,164	42,164	63.4	53,622	17,951	0.423
2	43,082	26,562	63.4	39,863	504	0.740
3	28,721	20,270	63.4	33,659	504	0.660

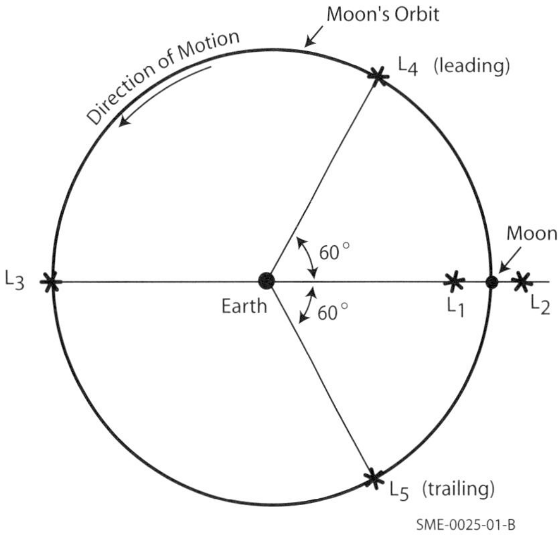

Fig. 9-26. Earth-Moon Lagrange Point Orbits. In the general literature, the L_4 and L_5 locations are always regarded as the ones off the Earth-Moon line; however, the specific nomenclature for each individual point (i.e., which one is which) varies widely among authors. The numbering scheme here is the one used by NASA and, therefore, applied to space missions associated with the Lagrange points. A similar set of points apply to the Sun and Earth and any other sets of two co-orbiting bodies.*

As shown in Fig. 9-26, the *Lagrange points*† or *libration points* for the Earth and the Moon are the five points such that an object placed at one of them will remain there indefinitely relative to the Earth-Moon system. All five of the Lagrange points are in the plane of the Moon's orbit. The 3 Lagrange points on the Earth-Moon line are positions of unstable equilibrium, i.e., any small change causes the object to drift away. However, L_4 and L_5 which form equilateral triangles with the Earth and the Moon in the plane of the Moon's orbit are positions of stable equilibrium. A satellite placed in the vicinity of L_4 or L_5 with an appropriate velocity will continue to orbit in that vicinity indefinitely.

The Moon orbits the Earth with a period of one month. If the Moon were not present, a satellite placed closer to the Earth, say at L_1, would rotate with a period shorter than a month and one placed at L_2 would rotate with a period longer than a month. For the satellite at L_1, "putting the Moon back" decreases the central force and, therefore, increases the period. Similarly, the satellite at L_2, the Moon increases the central force and decreases the period. L_1 and L_2 are simply the points at which the change is just sufficient to make the period exactly equal to the Moon's orbital period. Similarly, at L_3 the sum of the forces due to the Earth and the Moon are just enough to cause the satellite to rotate in a period of one month. The source of the stable equilibria at L_4 and L_5 is a bit more difficult to conceptualize. Although we usually think in terms of the Moon revolving around the Earth, in fact, both the Earth and the Moon revolve around their common *barycenter*, or mutual center of mass. (For the Earth-Moon system the center of mass is displaced from the center of the Earth approximately 4,700 km toward the Moon, i.e., still below the Earth's surface.) The effect of the Moon's gravitational force on the L_4 and L_5 Lagrange points is to displace the net gravitational force away from being directed toward the center of the Earth, changing the direction just enough so that the total force on the small satellite is directed toward the barycenter of the Earth-Moon system and, again, produce a period of revolution equal to that of the Moon.

Ehricke [1960] provides the following approximations for the locations of the Lagrange points for a spacecraft of negligible mass. For L_1 and L_2:

$$L_1 : \rho_1 = R_B \left[1 - \left(\frac{m}{3M} \right)^{1/3} \right] \tag{9-63}$$

$$L_2 : \rho_2 = R_B \left[1 + \left(\frac{m}{3M} \right)^{1/3} \right] \tag{9-64}$$

where M is the larger mass (Earth in our example), m is the smaller mass (the Moon), R_B is the distance from the

* Named after the 18th century French mathematician and astronomer Joseph Lagrange, who was also the principal inventor of the metric system.

† The naming convention for the Lagrange points is particularly bad. First, the numbering scheme varies widely between authors. Fig. 9-26 shows the scheme adopted by NASA. Second, the two central bodies are often left unstated. L_1 and L_2 missions most often refer to the Sun-Earth Lagrange points, while L_4 and L_5 most often refer to the Earth-Moon ones. The best approach is to be unambiguous, i.e., "the L_1 Lagrange point between the Earth and the Sun."

barycenter to the smaller mass, and ρ is the distance from the barycenter to the spacecraft. For L_3:

$$L_3 : \rho_3 = R_M\left[1+\left(\frac{7m}{12M}\right)^{1/3}\right] \quad (9\text{-}65)$$

Here M and m are as above, but R_M is now the distance from larger mass to the smaller mass and, similarly, ρ_3 is the distance from the larger mass to the spacecraft. Because L_4 and L_5 form equilateral triangles with the two masses, the distance of these two locations from both M and m is just equal to R_M. For a more detailed discussion of Lagrange point missions and orbits, see for example, Farquhar, et al. [1994, 1998] or Vallado [2007].

9.5.6 Other Specialized Orbits

Circular low-Earth orbits are not inherently stable. Higher order harmonics cause the eccentricity to oscillate about a small nonzero value as shown in Fig. 9-27. To avoid this, we can put a spacecraft in an orbit with a low eccentricity and an argument of perigee of 90 deg or 270 deg and the orbit will be stable. This is called a

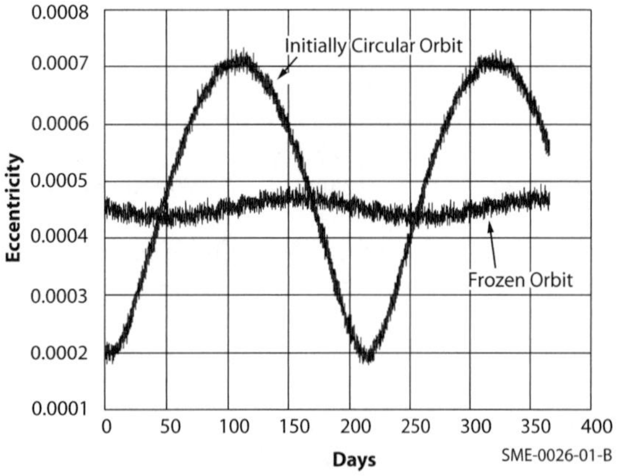

Fig. 9-27. Eccentricity Oscillation in an Initially Circular LEO Orbit. Central line shows the eccentricity in a comparable frozen orbit. Orbit shown is at 650 km at an inclination of 57 deg.

frozen orbit. Frozen orbits can be used with any low-Earth orbit. They are not so much a specialized orbit as a mechanism for maintaining a more stable orbit and avoiding a low level oscillation. The argument of perigee, ω_f, and eccentricity, e_f, for frozen orbits are as follows:

$$\omega_f = 90 \text{ deg} \quad \text{or} \quad 270 \text{ deg} \quad (9\text{-}66)$$

and

$$e_f \approx -\frac{J_3}{2J_2}\left(\frac{R_E}{a}\right)\sin i \sin\omega_f \quad (9\text{-}67a)$$

$$\approx +\,7.459\,335\left(\frac{\sin i \sin\omega_f}{a}\right) \quad (9\text{-}67b)$$

Table 9-15◀, Fig. 9-27, Eq. 9-67b

where, as usual, i is the inclination, R_E is the equatorial radius of the Earth, J_2 and J_3 are the second and third terms in the spherical harmonic expansion of the geopotential, and a is the semimajor axis, expressed in km in Eq. (9-67b). For a polar orbit of 500 km, $e_f \approx 0.00108$. (Including higher order terms will add about 0.00010 to this value.) In addition, both the eccentricity and argument of perigee will be frozen at the critical inclination of 63.4 deg or 116.6 deg and any values of e or ω.

In 1989, Bob Forward invented and patented the *statite* [Forward, 1989]. It is not called a satellite because it is not in an orbit but is an object fixed with respect to the Earth and Sun using solar radiation pressure to balance gravity. Because solar radiation pressure tends to be remarkably small, the statite is required to be very light weight, have an extremely large cross-sectional area, and be at a substantial distance from the Earth or other gravitating bodies. Thus far, no spacecraft have been placed in statite "orbits."

In 2005, Microcosm introduced the *Repeat Coverage Orbit* (RCO), as a more appropriate choice than Sun synchronous orbits for short or moderate duration missions or coverage of specific events or regions of the world [Wertz, 2005]. The RCO gives up global coverage in exchange for much better coverage of a specific region. (The RCO can provide 4 or 5 successive orbits of coverage every day for a particular latitude region vs. typically less than once a day for Sun synchronous orbits.) Because it best discussed as a part of Earth coverage, the RCO is described in more detail in Sec. 10.4.2.6.

9.6 Orbit Maneuvers

Thus far we have discussed primarily orbits which are either constant or slowly varying with time. In this section we discuss the physics and provide basic equations for orbit maneuvers intended to move the spacecraft from one orbit to another, typically for the purpose of getting somewhere, such as transfer orbits to a geosynchronous orbit or to the Moon or Mars. (Orbit maintenance and stationkeeping are discussed in Sec. 18.4.) This section discusses the basic physics of such orbits. Chapter 10 discusses the principal advantages and disadvantages of the various alternatives and reasons for selecting them.

9.6.1 Transfer Orbits

One of the fundamental goals of space missions is to get from one place to another—from the Earth to Mars, from low-Earth orbit to a higher orbit, or from the Earth to the Moon and back. The basic mechanism for doing this is the *transfer orbit*. The simplest and most common orbit transfer is between co-planar circular orbits. While most orbit transfers are not precisely co-planar, it is a good approximation to many transfer problems, and gets us started on the analysis and design of transfer orbits.

Putting mass and, therefore, propellant into space is remarkably expensive. Consequently, nearly all transfer orbits are intended to minimize the propellant required to

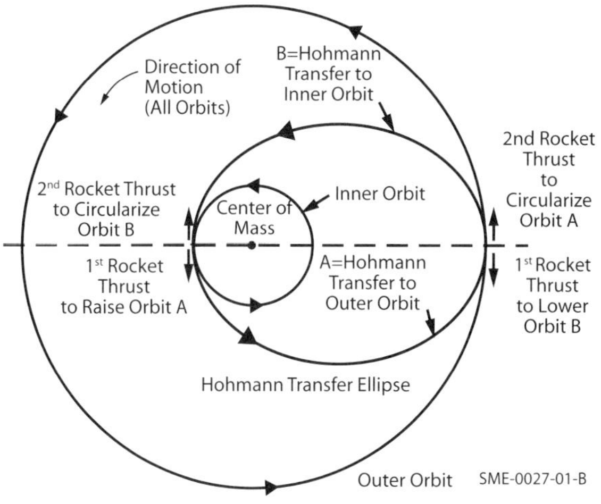

Fig. 9-28. The Hohmann Transfer Trajectory. This is normally the lowest energy approach for going between 2 co-planar circular orbits.

achieve the desired end orbit. The most fundamental and most often used is the *Hohmann transfer trajectory*, which is normally the lowest energy transfer between two co-planar circular orbits. This approach is based on the analytical results published in 1925 by Walter Hohmann, who was at the time the city architect of Essen, Germany. As shown in Fig. 9-28, the Hohmann transfer is an elliptical orbit with perigee tangent to the inner orbit and apogee tangent to the outer orbit, 180 deg away. If we're starting in a low orbit and wish to transfer to a higher one, we need to add energy. The most efficient way to do this is to increase the velocity of the spacecraft without changing its direction. Consequently, we point our rocket in the direction of motion (i.e., with the rocket exhaust going out the back, opposite the direction of motion). We then fire the rocket engine 180 deg from where we wish to end up and simply add ΔV to the current circular velocity. This creates an elliptical orbit with perigee where the engine fired. At this first firing, we provide just enough ΔV to raise apogee to the radius of our higher circular target orbit. When the spacecraft arrives at apogee, 180 deg later, we again fire the rocket engine in the direction of motion in order to raise perigee to the value of the apogee altitude, circularizing the orbit at the target altitude. The fundamental equations for the Hohmann transfer are as follows:

$$a_T = \frac{1}{2}(a_L + a_H) \tag{9-68}$$

$$\Delta V_L = \sqrt{\mu}\left[\left(\frac{2}{a_L} - \frac{1}{a_T}\right)^{1/2} - \left(\frac{1}{a_L}\right)^{1/2}\right] \tag{9-69}$$

$$\Delta V_H = \sqrt{\mu}\left[\left(\frac{1}{a_H}\right)^{1/2} - \left(\frac{2}{a_H} - \frac{1}{a_T}\right)^{1/2}\right] \tag{9-70}$$

$$T = \frac{1}{2}P_T = \pi\, a_T^{3/2}\mu^{-1/2} \tag{9-71}$$

where a is the semimajor axis, ΔV is the change in velocity, T is the transfer time, P is the orbit period, the values of μ for principal Solar System objects are given in Table 9-2 and the subscripts L, H, and T refer to the lower circular orbit, higher circular orbit, and Hohmann transfer orbit, respectively. For transfers between orbits at nearly the same altitude, the equations for the ΔV and transfer time may be further simplified to:

$$\Delta V_L \approx \Delta V_H \approx \frac{1}{2}(V_L - V_H) \tag{9-72}$$

$$T \approx \frac{1}{4}(P_L + P_H) \tag{9-73}$$

where the subscripts have the same meaning as above. Finally, if the initial orbit is circular and the magnitude of a single ΔV burn is known, then:

$$\Delta a = 2a\frac{\Delta V}{V} = 2\Delta V a^{3/2}\,\mu^{-1/2} \tag{9-74}$$

$$\Delta H = 2\Delta a \tag{9-75}$$

where Δa is the change in semimajor axis due to the single burn and ΔH is the corresponding change in altitude which will occur 180 deg away from where the burn was made.

A Hohmann transfer orbit from a higher orbit to a lower orbit is simply the reverse of the above process. The first burn is opposite the direction of motion and lowers perigee to the altitude of the inner orbit. When perigee is reached, 180 deg later, a second ΔV is applied, also opposite the direction of motion, to lower apogee and circularize the orbit. Thus it takes the same total ΔV to go from a high orbit to a low one as from a low orbit to a high one. Although we may at times use mechanisms such as atmospheric drag to slow the spacecraft, the fundamental problem of going to a lower energy orbit is just as difficult as going to a higher energy orbit.

Another interesting characteristic can be seen from Eqs. (9-68) to (9-73). If we start in a circular orbit with a velocity of 7 km/s and **add** 1 km/s in a two-burn Hohmann transfer then we will end up in a higher orbit with a velocity of 6 km/s. By adding energy to the orbit, more of the energy has been transferred into potential energy, and the total kinetic energy has been reduced. Similarly, if we go from a high orbit to a lower one, we will reduce the velocity and the total energy, but will end up in a lower orbit at a higher velocity and higher kinetic energy.

Most practical orbit transfers are relatively close to a Hohmann transfer because of the need to maximize efficiency. Nonetheless, as shown in Fig. 9-29 and listed in Table 9-16, alternative direct transfer orbits are used from time to time. Fig. 9-29A shows the classical Hohmann transfer. Fig. 9-29B shows a high-energy transfer which takes less time, but requires a higher ΔV. In the first burn, the ΔV will be higher because apogee will be

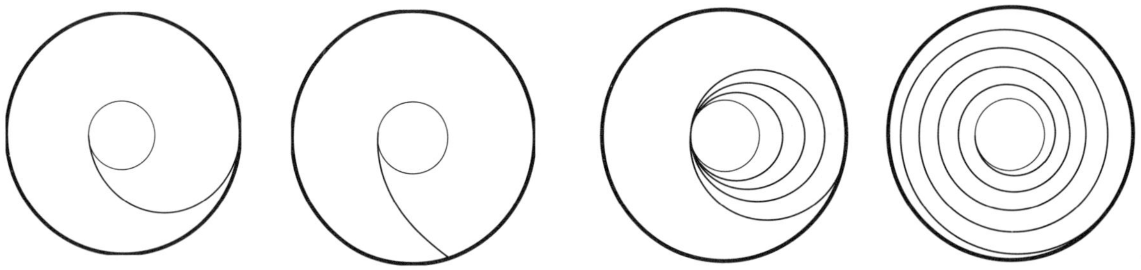

Fig. 9-29. Alternative Direct Transfer Orbits. See Table 9-16 for characteristics and Table 10-23 in Sec. 10.5.1 for advantages and disadvantages.

above the higher orbit. In the second burn, the ΔV will also be higher because we will need to change both the magnitude and the direction of the velocity. There are two practical applications for the high-energy transfer. One is for simply hitting a target in the higher orbit rather than matching velocities with it, since the second ΔV is not necessary in this case. The other application is when transfer time is critical and more rapid transfers are necessary. (See the discussion of rapid round trip transfers in Sec. 10.7.3.)

Both the Hohmann transfer and high-energy transfer assume impulsive burns, i.e., rocket engines which are large enough that the ΔV is applied over a short period of time. Alternatively, as described in Sec. 10.5, there can be significant advantages to using smaller rocket engines and applying the ΔV over a longer period such that the burn time is no longer short relative to the orbit period. Two specific cases are of practical interest. Fig. 9-29C shows the orbit path for a low-thrust chemical transfer in which rocket engines from the size of a few pounds to a few hundred pounds of thrust are used. In this case, the ΔV for a large orbit transfer cannot be applied in a single orbit, but must instead be applied over several orbits. First, a series of burns is made at successive perigees, such that the perigee height remains essentially unchanged, but the apogee height is raised by each maneuver until it ultimately reaches the desired final apogee. Then one or two burns are used at apogee to raise perigee to the circular orbit height. (Fewer burns are needed at apogee than at perigee because the spacecraft is moving at a lower velocity there.) For the low-thrust chemical transfer, the time for the transfer covers several orbits, and can be determined by adding up the orbit periods using Eqs. (9-4) and (9-5). The total ΔV that is required is identical to the ΔV used in the Hohmann transfer. Consequently the low-thrust chemical approach has the same optimal transfer efficiency as the Hohmann transfer, but a significantly lower thrust and, therefore, lower acceleration using a smaller engine and providing smaller disturbance forces on the spacecraft.

Finally, Fig. 9-29D shows the characteristics for electric propulsion transfer. Electric propulsion thrusters are much smaller than chemical ones, with thrust levels that are only a small fraction of a pound. Consequently, it is not practical for any large transfer to be done with burns only at perigee because the transfer time would be excessively long. In this case, the ΔV is applied continuously for the entire period of the orbit transfer. Because the thrust is very low, transfer from low-Earth orbit to geosynchronous orbit still takes many months rather than the few hours required for a Hohmann transfer. In addition, because apogee and perigee are being raised simultaneously, the electric propulsion transfer is significantly less efficient than the Hohmann transfer for large maneuvers, such as transfer to GEO. Specifically, the total ΔV required to transfer between coplanar circular orbits via spiral electric propulsion is given by:

$$V_T = V_L - V_H \tag{9-76}$$

Table 9-16. Physical Characteristics of the Alternative Transfer Trajectories Shown in Fig. 9-29. (See Table 10-23 in Sec. 10.5.1 for advantages and disadvantages.)

Transfer Type	Orbit Type	Typical Acceleration	ΔV	Typical Transfer Time
A. Hohmann (minimum energy)	Hohmann transfer	1 to 5 g	Eqs. (9-69), (9-70)	*T*= 1/2 orbit period, *P* is given by Eqs. (9-71) and (9-73)
B. High Energy	Elliptical or hyperbolic	1–10 g	> Hohmann	<*T*
C. Low Thrust Chemical	Hohmann transfer segments	0.02 to 0.5 g	Same as Hohmann	3 to 4 times *P* = 6 to 8 times *T*
D. Electric Propulsion	Spiral transfer	0.0001 to 0.001g	Eq. (9-76)	60 to 120 times *P*

where the parameters have the same definitions as above. Note once again that we are adding velocity to the orbit to get to a lower final velocity but higher energy orbit. For the ultra low-thrust transfer, transfer time is longer and the ΔV is greater. Nonetheless electric propulsion is inherently much more efficient than chemical propulsion and, therefore, can use a much lower propellant mass. (I_{sp}, a measure of propellant efficiency, is 5 to 10 times higher for electric propulsion systems than for chemical propulsion.) See Sec. 10.5 for further discussion of the advantages and disadvantages of the different methods of orbit transfer.

9.6.2 Plane Change and Phase Shifts

The previous section described transfer orbits which changed the total energy of the orbit itself. However, we may wish to change the orbit without changing the semimajor axis or the total energy. The two most common transfers in which this is done are changing the orbit plane (i.e., the inclination or the right ascension of the ascending node) or leaving the orbit the same and simply changing where we are in the orbit (i.e., moving forward or backward relative to an imaginary satellite which remains in the original orbit position).

Changing the orbit plane is required when the desired orbit plane is different from where we are initially. For example, in going from the Earth to Mars, we need to change the plane of the spacecraft from the Earth's orbital plane, i.e., the ecliptic, to the orbit plane of Mars. Similarly, for a spacecraft launched from anywhere not on the equator and, therefore, at a nonzero inclination, we need to make a plane change in order to put the spacecraft into geosynchronous orbit. In both of these examples, as in many plane change maneuvers, the need for the plane change occurs at the same time that the semimajor axis is to be changed. Consequently, combined plane-change and orbit-raising maneuvers are common.

As shown in Fig. 9-30, plane change maneuvers are simply a matter of vector addition. We have a velocity vector, $\mathbf{V}_i$, which defines the initial orbit plane, and need to obtain a different velocity, $\mathbf{V}_f$, to define a different orbit plane and potentially a different semimajor axis.

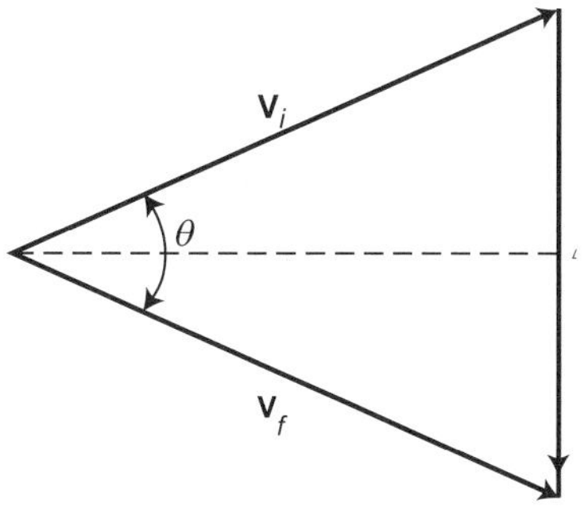

Fig. 9-30. Plane Change ΔV. Plane change maneuvers are simply problems in vector addition.

Combining a plane change with an altitude change is more efficient in terms of the total ΔV than doing the two maneuvers separately. (See Fig. 9-31.) Also, the ΔV required to undertake a plane change will be proportional to the velocity itself. Consequently, because spacecraft velocities are very large, plane change maneuvers typically require a very large ΔV, sometimes as much or more than the original orbital velocity. This implies that plane change maneuvers are highly energy intensive and will usually be undertaken only when absolutely necessary. Normally plane changes are done only once in the course of a mission and everything possible is done to reduce the ΔV required for the plane change. For example, the bielliptic transfer uses less ΔV than a standard two-burn transfer when launching to GEO from a latitude greater than about 35 deg.

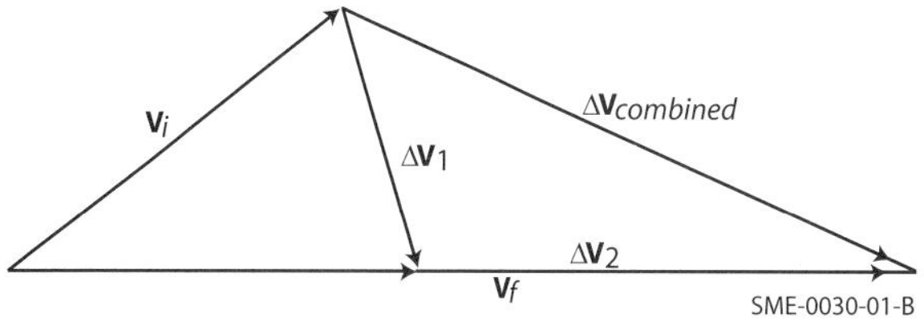

Fig. 9-31. Combining Plane Change and Orbit Raising Reduces the Total ΔV Required. The savings will be $|\Delta V_1| + |\Delta V_2| - |\Delta V_{combined}|$.

Because the plane change is simply a vector sum, we can determine the total ΔV required as a function of the initial and final velocities as:

$$\Delta V = \left(V_i^2 + V_f^2 - 2V_i V_f \cos\theta\right)^{1/2} \tag{9-77}$$

where V_i is the initial velocity, V_f is the final velocity, and θ is the required angular change. If $V_i = V_f$, then the magnitude of the required ΔV reduces to:

$$\Delta V = 2V_i \sin\left(\frac{\theta}{2}\right) \tag{9-78}$$

As an example, we find the total change in velocity to transfer from a 250 km parking orbit at 28.5 deg inclination to a geosynchronous equatorial orbit as follows:

r_i = 6,628 km	r_f = 42,159 km
i_i = 28.5 deg	i_f = 0 deg
V_i = 7.75 km/s	V_f = 3.07 km/s
ΔV_A = 2.44 km/s	ΔV_B = 1.83 km/s
ΔV_{total} = 4.27 km/s	

Completing a Hohmann transfer followed by a simple plane change would require a velocity change of 5.425 km/s, so the Hohmann transfer with a combined plane change of apogee of the transfer orbit represents a savings of 1.15 km/s. As we see from Eq. (9-77), a small plane change ($\theta \geq 0$) can be combined with an energy change for almost no cost in ΔV or propellant. Conse-

Table 9-17. Methods for Reducing the ΔV Required for Orbit Plane Change. It may be possible to combine techniques to increase the amount of plane change. See Table 10-22 in Sec. 10.5.1 for a discussion of the advantages and disadvantages of each. See text for discussion.

Method	Mechanism for Reducing ΔV	Computations
Do ΔV at Lowest Velocity (Highest Altitude)	Smallest velocity is easiest to change.	Eqs. (9-77), (9-78)
Combine ΔV with Orbit Raising	Vector sum is less than sum of components	Eqs. (9-77), (9-78)
3-Burn Transfer	Go to high altitude where plane change ΔV is low and then lower orbit	Eqs. (9-77), (9-78)
Use Differential Node Rotation	Allow natural perturbations to change plane	Eq. (9-61a)
Aero-Assist Trajectory	Use aerodynamic forces to change direction	[Albee et al., 1998]
Planetary Fly-By	Elastic "collision" with a planet changes direction	Sec. 9.6.3

quently, in practice, we do geosynchronous transfer with a small plane change at perigee and most of the plane change at apogee. (See Table 9-18).

As shown in Table 9-17 there are a number of mechanisms that are used to reduce the total ΔV needed for orbit plane changes. In addition to combining the ΔV with orbit raising, it is clear from the above equations that we should also do plane change maneuvers at the lowest velocity and, therefore, at the highest altitude in the orbit. Consequently, plane change maneuvers are typically done predominately at apogee.* If the plane change is very large, then it may be more efficient to use a *bi-elliptic* or *three burn transfer* rather than a two burn Hohmann transfer with plane change. In this case, we use the first burn to take the spacecraft to a very high altitude above the desired final orbit where the apogee velocity is very low. Here the plane change ΔV is small. At the high altitude we do a combined maneuver to raise perigee to the end altitude and change the plane. We then do a third and final burn to circularize the orbit at the final altitude. In this process we have used more than the minimum required energy to change altitude, but have still saved propellant by substantially reducing the ΔV required for the plane change.

Another technique for changing the ascending node of the orbit is to make use of the node rotation caused by the Earth's oblateness. If satellites are at different altitudes the node rotation rate will be different; the orbits will slide relative to each other in an East-West sense. Consequently, we can change that ascending node by changing the altitude, allowing differential node rotation to work, and then returning the altitude to its original value after the node has shifted as far as needed. Depending on the speed of the desired node rotation, we can use this mechanism to change the node with very small amounts of propellant.

We can also use the atmospheres of the Earth or other planets as a means of changing the orbit plane, using *aero-assist trajectories* in which aerodynamic forces on the spacecraft are used to provide a turn maneuver. Such maneuvers can be efficient, but also place additional stress on the spacecraft by applying significant aerodynamic forces. For example, Mars Global Surveyor used an aero-assist trajectory to adjust its orbit around Mars, but larger than anticipated aerodynamic forces caused the mission to be delayed to reduce further stress on the solar arrays [Albee, et al., 1998].

If we are going to change the altitude of the spacecraft then a small amount of plane change can be obtained at very low cost. This implies that when combining orbit raising and plane change it is most efficient to do some plane change at both apogee and perigee with most done at apogee. The process is optimized by iterating on the amount of plane change done at apogee and perigee to determine the total ΔV. An example of the potential savings is shown in Table 9-18.

Table 9-18. Alternative Approaches for Going from a 250 km Circular Orbit at 28.5 Deg Inclination to an Equatorial Geosynchronous Orbit. Because the last alternative uses the least propellant, it is essentially always used in practice.

Approach	Total ΔV (km/s)
Plane Change at 250 km Followed by Hohmann Transfer to GEO	7.696
Hohmann Transfer to GEO Altitude Followed by Separate Plane Change	5.425
Combined Maneuver, All Plane Change at Perigee	6.483
Combined Maneuver, All Plane Change at Apogee	4.273
Combined Maneuver, 4.0 deg Plane Change at Perigee, 24.5 deg Plane Change at Apogee	4.265

In addition to plane changes, spacecraft are frequently required to adjust their relative phasing in the orbit. Unlike plane changes, this requires very little ΔV and can be accomplished easily. To make the spacecraft drift relative to its nominal position we simply raise or lower the orbit to a slightly different altitude and, therefore, change the orbit period and in-track velocity. When we are done

* Part of the plane change will be done at perigee because a small amount of plane change takes very little ΔV. The correct ratio is determined by trial and error with Eq. (9-77) evaluated at apogee and perigee.

shifting it as far as we would like, we return the spacecraft to its original altitude. The transfer into a *drift orbit* can be done either using a two burn Hohmann transfer, or a single burn so that the drift orbit is elliptical, with apogee or perigee remaining at the initial altitude. In either case, the drift rate, ω_{drift}, in deg/orbit, is given by:

$$\omega_{drift} = 1{,}080\,\frac{\Delta V}{V} \tag{9-79}$$

where ΔV is the applied velocity change (in either one burn or both burns) and V is the nominal orbit velocity. The total ΔV required to shift phase depends only on the drift velocity and, therefore, the time for making the phase change. Thus in total:

$$\Delta V_{total} = \Delta V_{start} + \Delta V_{stop} \tag{9-80a}$$

$$= \left(\omega_{drift}\,V\right)/540 \tag{9-80b}$$

where ω_{drift} is in deg/orbit. For a satellite in geosynchronous orbit, $V = 3.0747$ km/s and consequently:

$$\Delta V_{total} = 5.6939\,\omega_{drift} \tag{9-81}$$

where ΔV is in m/s and ω_{drift} is in deg/day. Sample calculations of the ΔV required as a function of time are given in Table 9-19.

Live Calc

Table 9-19. Drift Rate and Total ΔV Required to Shift a Geosynchronous Satellite 60 deg in Longitude. In general, rapid maneuver requirements correspond to high propellant usage.

ω_{drift} (deg/day)	ΔV (m/s)	Time to Shift 60 deg (days)
1	5.7	60
2	11.4	30
6	34.2	10
10	56.9	6
30	170.8	2
60	341.6	1

9.6.3 Planetary Assist Trajectories

For interplanetary spacecraft, we can perform both plane change and velocity change maneuvers by one or more interactions with other planets or with the Earth. The general process of a planetary fly-by is shown in Fig. 9-32 [Minovitch, 1963]. We assume the spacecraft is initially in an orbit about the Sun a long way from any planet. With respect to the planet, the spacecraft approaches on a hyperbolic trajectory. It swings by the planet at "periplanet" and leaves on the other leg of the hyperbolic trajectory at the same velocity **with respect to the planet** at which it came in. The total angle through which the spacecraft orbit velocity has changed is known as the *turn angle*, ψ, and is the angle between the two asymptotes of the hyperbola. Because the orbit has undergone an angular change, this can be used to either change

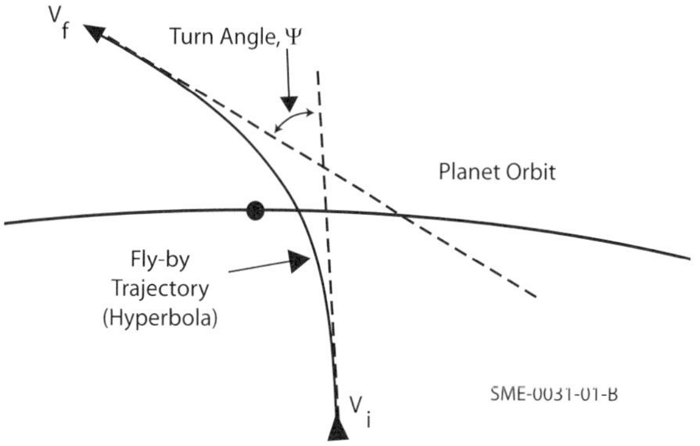

Fig. 9-32. Geometry of a Planetary Fly-By. The spacecraft velocity with respect to the planet remains the same incoming as outgoing. However, the vector sum of the planet and spacecraft velocities can be used to increase energy, decrease energy, or change direction.

the orbit plane or increase or decrease the energy. Because Jupiter has a very large mass and, consequently, can produce a large turn angle, it is the planet most commonly used for fly-bys. Depending upon our objective, we can use a fly-by of Jupiter to increase the spacecraft velocity and therefore increase the mass or reduce the transfer time to the outer planets, to decrease the velocity and allow the spacecraft to go to the vicinity of the Sun, or to change the plane of the spacecraft's orbit to allow us to explore space in the direction of the ecliptic poles.

A planetary fly-by is equivalent to an elastic collision between a baseball and a bat. The velocity of the baseball with respect to the bat is the same coming from the pitcher as leaving toward the outfield. The difference is that the baseball has picked up the velocity of the bat in the interaction, or in the case of a pop up, has principally changed direction.* Conceptually, we can think of the spacecraft as bouncing off the planet without having to undergo the excessive acceleration associated with actually hitting the surface.

The turn angle, ψ, obtained in a planetary fly-by is:

$$\sin(\psi/2) = 1/e \tag{9-82}$$

where e is the eccentricity of the hyperbolic trajectory. This may also be expressed in a form more convenient for analysis as:

$$\sin(\psi/2) = \left(1 + \frac{V_\infty^2 q}{\mu}\right)^{-1} \tag{9-83}$$

where q is the perifocal distance or distance of closest approach to the planet, V_∞ is the hyperbolic velocity or the velocity of the spacecraft with respect to the planet when

* Hans Meissinger [1970] was the first to point out that the Earth could be used for a planetary fly-by. [Hollenbeck, 1975.] Continuing our baseball analogy, this is similar (though not mathematically equivalent) to throwing the baseball up in the air and then hitting it with the bat when it comes down.

Live Calc

Table 9-20. Representative Turn Angle, ψ, and Velocity Change, ΔV, for Fly-by Missions to the Planets. The assumed hyperbolic verocity, V_∞, is the velocity of approach for a Hohmann transfer orbit. R_p is the radius of the planet and q is the perifocal distance or distance of closest approach.

	Assumed	$q = R_p$ (Grazing)		$q = 2R_p$		$q = 10\ R_p$	
Planet	V_∞ (km/s)	ψ (deg)	$\lvert\Delta V\rvert$ (km/s)	ψ (deg)	$\lvert\Delta V\rvert$ (km/s)	ψ (deg)	$\lvert\Delta V\rvert$ (km/s)
Mercury	9.6	10.2	1.7	5.4	0.9	1.1	0.2
Venus	2.7	123	4.8	104	4.2	50	2.3
Earth	3.5	114	5.8	92	5.0	40	2.4
Moon	0.8	109	1.3	87	1.1	36	0.5
Mars	2.6	81	3.4	58	2.5	18	0.8
Jupiter	5.6	159	11.0	150	10.8	116	9.5
Saturn	5.4	146	10.3	133	9.9	86	7.4
Uranus	4.7	132	8.6	114	7.9	61	4.8
Neptune	4.1	141	7.7	127	7.3	78	5.1
Pluto	3.7	5.57	0.36	2.86	0.18	0.58	0.04

it is infinitely far away, and as usual $\mu \equiv GM$ for the planet. The magnitude of the velocity change, ΔV, resulting from the fly-by is a function of the turn angle between the two asymptotes and is given by:

$$|\Delta V| = 2V_\infty \sin(\psi/2) \qquad (9\text{-}84)$$

Table 9-20 lists the values of the turn angle and velocity change for fly-bys of the principal objects of interest in the Solar System.

9.6.4 Spacecraft Disposal

Orbital debris is potentially a major problem for space missions, particularly in regions of high spacecraft density such as low-Earth orbit or geosynchronous orbit. Consequently, spacecraft disposal is becoming a key element of mission design. NASA guidelines require that spacecraft in low-Earth orbit be removed from orbit within 25 years of the end of their useful life. Of course it is desirable to remove them from orbit much more rapidly, but it may require more propellant to do so.

There are two basic ways to deorbit a satellite in low-Earth orbit. The first approach is to lower perigee to a low enough value, approximately 75 km, that the orbit will decay and the spacecraft will reenter essentially immediately. The second approach is to reduce perigee to the point where atmospheric drag will cause the satellite to decay within an appropriate period of time, though not immediately. With this approach we will have an approximate idea of how long reentry will take, but have no way of knowing or controlling when or where it will occur. Rough estimates of the re-entry time required for representative orbits and spacecraft parameters are given in Table 9-21.

The ΔV required for a satellite to drop from an initial circular altitude H_i to a reentry perigee altitude H_e is given by:

$$\Delta V_{deorbit} \approx V\left[1 - \sqrt{\frac{2(R_E + H_e)}{2R_E + H_e + H_i}}\right] \qquad (9\text{-}85a)$$

$$\approx V\left[\frac{0.5(H_i - H_e)}{2R_E + H_e + H_i}\right] \qquad (9\text{-}85b)$$

where V is the initial satellite velocity and R_E is the radius of the Earth.

Table 9-21. Spacecraft Disposal Options. Lifetime assumes a ballistic coefficient of 100 kg/m².

	From 600 km Circular		From 1,200 km Circular	
Perigee	ΔV (m/s)	Approx. Lifetime (days)	ΔV (m/s)	Approx. Lifetime (days)
50	157	0.0	304	0.0
75	149	0.0	297	0.0
100	142	0.1	290	0.3
125	134	0.7	282	2.6
150	127	7.2	275	26.4
200	112	47	261	174
250	97.8	152	247	615

For high altitude orbits deorbiting the spacecraft is impractical because of the large ΔV required. Nonetheless, there is still a strong desire to remove spent spacecraft from their operational orbit, particularly if they are part of a constellation with many satellites at that altitude or part of an orbit region, such as GEO, where there are a large number of different satellites. In this case the preferred option is to raise the orbit by several hundred kilometers above the nominal value. In the regime where atmospheric drag is no longer relevant, the spacecraft will be left in an orbit where the orbit elements oscillate, but where the spacecraft will remain for thousands or hundreds of thousands of years, effectively eliminating it as a threat to other spacecraft. The disposal orbit is placed above the operational orbit so that spent spacecraft do not interfere with new operational spacecraft being brought up from the Earth. Spacecraft in disposal orbits still represent a theoretical threat to other spacecraft passing through that regime. However, this threat is dramatically reduced relative to the threat that is present if they remain in the operational orbit. In the future it may be possible to retrieve or destroy old spacecraft, but this is not a practical option at the present time.

The ΔV needed to raise a spacecraft to a higher altitude is typically very low. For example, in geosynchronous orbit the ΔV requirement is given by:

$$\Delta V_{disposal} = 0.0365\,(\mathrm{m/s})/\mathrm{km} \qquad (9\text{-}86)$$

Thus, an increase of 500 km above geosynchronous altitude requires a ΔV of only 18 m/s, as opposed to a deorbit ΔV of 4,000 m/s. The principal problem with any of the spacecraft disposal options is that they must be done at a time when both commanding and thruster firings can still be achieved by the spacecraft, and, therefore, at least critical spacecraft subsystems are still operating and propellant remains available.

9.7 Summary—The Rules of Practical Astronautics

9.7.1 Important Characteristics of Spacecraft Orbits

1. **Spacecraft in an elliptical orbit will always return to the location in space where the last maneuver was made.** Because the elliptical orbit is a closed figure, the spacecraft will always return to the location in space where we gave it the last ΔV. Thus, we cannot lower perigee by firing at perigee, unless we apply sufficient ΔV to change perigee into apogee. Similarly, we can't launch directly from the Earth's surface into an Earth orbit. We must first get into space and then apply sufficient ΔV to put the spacecraft into an orbit.
2. **Lower orbits have less energy, but greater velocity than higher orbits.** Higher orbits have a greater potential energy, but less kinetic energy than lower ones.
3. **The semimajor axis depends only on the total energy of the orbit.** This means that to change the size of the orbit, at least a portion of the applied ΔV must be along the velocity vector.
4. **For orbits to stay synchronized, they must be at the same altitude and inclination.** Because of the node rotation due to J_2, orbits at different inclinations or altitudes will drift with respect to each other, potentially quite rapidly. The exception here is a circular, equatorial orbit, for which the drift of the orbit doesn't matter.
5. **Elliptical orbits will almost always be at the critical inclination of 63.4 deg.** If this isn't the case, perigee will rotate relatively rapidly due to J_2.

As shown in Chap. 10, these characteristics will be important for both orbit and constellation design. In addition, they lead to what I call "Wertz's Practical Rules of Astronautics." Summarized below are the key elements of orbit maneuvers and orbit transfer.

9.7.2 Ten Rules of Practical Astronautics

1. **To go forward in the orbit, slow down; to go backward speed up.** That is the practical result of characteristic 2 above. When the spacecraft slows down, it goes into a lower orbit with a shorter period and, therefore, moves faster than when it was higher. The spacecraft can drift forward as far as desired and then be raised back to the previous altitude (and slowed down) by speeding up.
2. **Add ΔV deep in a gravity well when the velocity is highest.** The energy increases for a given ΔV is directly proportional to the velocity, so adding ΔV is most efficient when the spacecraft is going fast.
3. **Change direction when the velocity is lowest.** An inclination or plane change "at infinity" costs essentially no ΔV. An exception to this rule is number 4.
4. **Let Mother Nature help with plane changes.** Changing the plane typically takes a large ΔV, potentially even more than launching the spacecraft. With patience, Mother Nature can do quite a bit for free with planetary fly-bys, aerodynamic forces (in the upper atmosphere), or differential node rotation.
5. **Changes well in advance are far cheaper.** If you want to fly over a particular location at a particular future time or move to a different location in GEO, it takes almost no ΔV if done far in advance of when you want to get there and a huge ΔV if you want to do it quickly. If you want to deflect an asteroid from hitting Earth, it's essentially impossible just before impact and pretty easy years in advance.
6. **Use high thrust to get off a planet; use low thrust in space.** To get to orbit, you need large engines and high thrust to overcome gravity losses. However, once you're in orbit, high thrust is of little or no value and is potentially damaging to the payload (due to the high forces), expensive to control, hard to measure, and hard to fine tune for precision adjustments. In addition, big engines are heavy, expensive, and known to blow up from time to time, as in the case of Clementine.
7. **Stage early and often.** It's remarkably inefficient to carry the rocket stage itself to Jupiter, to GEO, or even to a high LEO orbit. To the extent possible, get rid of the launch vehicle and upper stages as early as possible and let the spacecraft fly itself around.

Table 9-21◀, Fig. 9-32◀, Eq. 9-86

8. **For round trip travel, there are major discontinuities in the round trip time as a function of the transfer ΔV.** This will be discussed in Sec. 10.8.2, but under the right conditions, a small increase in ΔV can reduce interplanetary round trip times by more than a year and time can be an important factor in the success of round trip missions.
9. **Design both orbits and constellations with orbit debris in mind.** As discussed in Sec. 7.5, orbit debris can be a major long-term hazard, particularly in GEO or high LEO orbits. The right initial orbit design and operations can do a great deal to mitigate this problem.
10. **Clean up after yourself.** To keep debris from bothering other spacecraft, dispose of stuff when you're done with it—both spacecraft and stages. Burn it up, retrieve it, or put it in an orbit where it won't bother anyone for 10,000 years or so. Even better, find a way to use spent vehicles to look for water on the Moon, find out the composition of asteroids and comets, or build habitats out of external tanks. Just don't leave it lying around in orbit.

Using astronautics wisely can dramatically reduce launch cost and propellant usage and keep space available for future missions.

Applicable Standards:
ANSI/AIAA S-131-2010:
Astrodynamics Standard—Propagation Specifications, Technical Definitions, and Recommended Practices
See website for reference.

References

For annotated bibliography of orbits and astrodynamics, see the book website.

Albee, A. L., F. D. Palluconi, and R. E. Arvidson. 1998. "Mars Global Surveyor Mission: Overview and Status." *Science.* Mar. 13. 279:1671–2.

Battin, Richard H. 1999. *Introduction to the Mathematics and Methods of Astrodynamics*. Reston, VA: AIAA.

Clarke, Arthur C. 1945. "Extra-Terrestial Relays—Can Rocket Stations Give World-Wide Coverage." *Wireless World.* Oct. pp. 305–307.

Dugas, René. 1988. *A History of Mechanics*. Translated by J. R. Maddox. Neuchatel, Switzerland: Éditions du Griffon.

Ehricke, Krafft A. 1960. *Space Flight: Environment and Celestial Mechanics*. New York: Van Nostrand Company.

Farquhar, R. W. 1994. "Utilization of Libration-Point Orbits, Lunar Gravity-Assist, and Earth-Return Trajectories." 34th Israel Annual Conf. on Aerospace Sciences. Haifa, Israel. Feb. 16–17.

Farquhar, R. W. 1998. "The Flight of ISEE-3/ICE; Origins, Mission History, and a Legacy." AIAA/AAS Astrodynamics Specialist Conf. AIAA 98-994. Boston, MA. Aug. 10–12.

Forward, R. L. 1989. "Statite: Spacecraft that Utilizes Light Pressure and Method of Use." U.S. Patent No. 5,183,225. Issued Feb. 2, 1993.

Girvin, H. F. 1948. *A Historical Appraisal of Mechanics*. 2007 Reprint. Seattle, WA: Girvin Press.

Gruntman, M. 2004. *Blazing the Trail; The Early History of Spacecraft and Rocketry.* Reston, VA: AIAA.

Hollenbeck, G. R. 1975. "New Flight Techniques for Outer Planet Missions." AAS/AIAA Astrodynamics Specialist Conf. AAS #75-087. Nassau, Bahamas. Jul. 28–30.

Kaplan, G. H. 2005. *Naval Observatory Circular No. 179, The IAU Resolutions on Astronomical Reference Systems, Time Scales, and Earth Rotation Models.* Wash, DC: US Naval Observatory.

Meissinger, H. F. 1970. "Earth Swingby—A Novel Approach to Interplanetary Missions Using Electric Propulsion." AIAA 8th Electric Propulsion Conference. AIAA 70-1117. Stanford, CA. Aug. 31–Sept. 2.

Minovitch, M. A. 1963. "Determination and Characteristics of Ballistic Interplanetary Trajectories Under the Influence of Multiple Planetary Attractions." Tech Report No. 32-464, JPL.

Seidelmann, K. P. 2006. *Explanatory Supplement to the Astronomical Almanac*. Mill Valley, CA: University Science Books.

Vallado, David A. 2007. *Fundamentals of Astrodynamics and Applications. 3rd ed.* Hawthorne, CA and New York: Microcosm Press and Springer.

Wertz, J. R. 2005. "Coverage, Responsiveness, and Accessibility for Various Responsive Orbits." 3rd Responsive Space Conf. Los Angeles, CA. Apr. 25–28.

Wertz, J. R. 2009. *Orbit & Constellation Design & Management.* Hawthorne, CA: Microcosm Press and Springer.

10 Orbit and Constellation Design—Selecting the Right Orbit

James R. Wertz, ***Microcosm, Inc./USC***

Chapters 8 and 9 introduced the geometry and physics of spacecraft orbits as well as formulas for computing viewing and orbit parameters. Those chapters are fundamentally computational in that there is a well defined answer to how the satellite will move in response to a given set of forces or what portion of the Earth I can see with a camera oriented in a specific direction. In contrast, orbit selection and design is a much fuzzier process. The question that we are trying to deal with is not how the spacecraft will move, but what orbit should we put it in. This is, of course, a mix of mission objectives, cost, available launch vehicles, and operational requirements to support the mission. There is no precise answer or correct solution.

In most cases, orbit design consists of choosing among a continuum of orbits and some specialized orbits, such as GEO or Sun synchronous, that come about because of specific orbit characteristics. In addition, the orbit selection process itself is typically complex, involving trades between many parameters. The orbit normally defines the space mission lifetime, cost, environment, viewing geometry, and, frequently, the payload performance. Nonetheless, the single most common trade is between the velocity required to achieve an orbit as a measure of cost vs. the coverage to be achieved as a measure of performance.

Section 10.1 addresses the overall orbit selection and design process. Section 10.2 discusses ways of evaluating orbit performance and Sec. 10.3 discusses the idea of orbit cost and introduces the orbit cost function as a comparative measure of what it costs for different orbits. Sections 10.4 and 10.5 then describe the design of Earth-referenced orbits and space-referenced orbits, respectively. Section 10.6 provides a summary of constellation design. Finally, Sec. 10.7 describes the design of interplanetary orbits. For a discussion of interstellar travel and interstellar orbits, see Sec. 12.8 of Wertz [2009].

There are relatively very few references on orbit and constellation design, per se. By far the most extensive is Wertz [2009], which forms the basis for much of the material here.

10.1 The Orbit Selection and Design Process

Orbit and constellation selection and design is a process rather than a set of specific computations. Throughout the chapter, we will use a series of process tables to summarize the fundamental steps and how to undertake them. These should be treated as guides to the issues involved rather than complete definitive recipes. There are a wide variety of mission types, each of which will be unique in the orbit selection process. Nonetheless, the tables here should be used as a starting point to create a process appropriate for your particular mission.

Table 10-1 summarizes the steps in the overall orbit selection and design process. Each step is discussed below, and later with greater detail in the sections listed in the table. Effective orbit design requires clearly identifying the reasons for orbit selection, reviewing these reasons regularly as mission requirements change or mission definition improves, and continuing to remain open to alternatives. Several different designs may be

Table 10-1. The Single Satellite Orbit Selection Process. See Table 10-24 in Sec. 10.6.1 for Constellation Design.

Step	Where Discussed
1. Establish Orbit Types	Sec. 10.1
2. Determine Orbit-Related Mission Requirements	Secs. 10.4.1, 10.5.1
3. Evaluate Orbit Performance	
A. Earth coverage	Sec. 10.2.1
Specialized orbits	Secs. 9.5, 10.4.2
Single satellite vs. constellation	Sec. 10.1
B. Other ways the orbit impacts performance	Sec. 10.2.2
C. Do mission orbit design trades	Secs. 10.4.3, 10.5.3, 10.5.4
4. Evaluate Orbit Cost	
A. Evaluate launch options and launch cost	Secs. 10.3.3, 11.3.6, 26.1
B. Look at low-cost options, if possible	Sec. 13.5.7
C. Add disposal options	Secs. 30.1, 30.2
D. Create delta V budget	Sec. 10.3.1
E. Evaluate the orbit cost function—launch cost vs. available on orbit mass	Sec. 10.3.2
5. Document Selection Criteria, Key Orbit Trades, Selected Orbit Parameters, and Allowed Ranges	Sec. 10.1
6. Iterate as Needed	Sec. 10.1

credible. Thus, communication systems may work effectively through a single large satellite in geosynchronous orbit, or a constellation of small satellites in low-Earth orbit. We may need to keep both options for some time before selecting one for a particular mission.

Step 1. Establish Orbit Types

To design orbits we first divide the space mission into segments and classify each segment by its overall function. In terms of orbit requirements, each segment falls into one of four basic orbit types, listed in Table 10-2. The first two entries are operational orbits in which the spacecraft is intended to spend a large fraction of its operational life, and to do most of the useful work of the mission. In contrast, the bottom two entries are simply means of getting the spacecraft where we want it, when we want it there. Typically, the requirements for the latter two are much less stringent, with the exception that it may be necessary to get the spacecraft where we want it with very precise timing, such as the requirement to attempt to land a probe at a particular location on the surface of Mars.

An example of the changing orbit types throughout the mission would be a geosynchronous communication satellite initially launched along with a transfer stage into a low-Earth orbit. (See Fig. 10-1.) Once ejected from the launch vehicle, the spacecraft stays briefly in a parking orbit to provide test and checkout of the spacecraft and transfer vehicle subsystems. The next mission segment is a transfer orbit that moves the spacecraft from the parking orbit to a geosynchronous equatorial orbit. Frequently, to preserve propellant, the spacecraft is initially put into a drift orbit near GEO such that any errors in the transfer process can be taken out by small adjustments associated with achieving the desired geosynchronous station location. The spacecraft then enters its operational orbit in the geostationary ring where it will spend the rest of its active life. While the spacecraft itself is still functional and before its stationkeeping propellant runs out, we must move it out of the geostationary ring to avoid possible collisions with other satellites and to free the orbital slot for a replacement. Putting the nearly dead

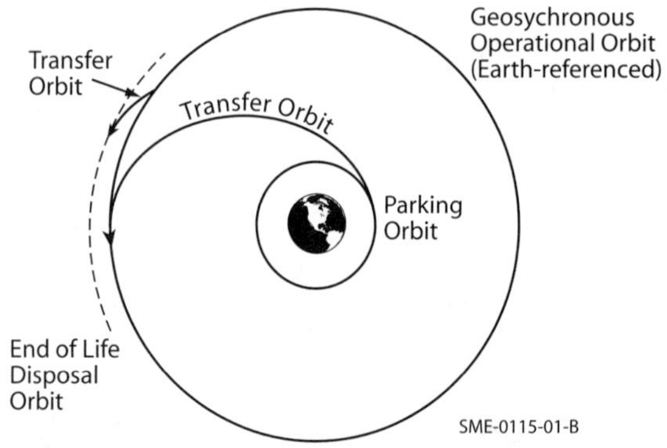

Fig. 10-1. Typical Orbit Phases. At end-of-life, the spacecraft should be either de-orbited or moved into a higher orbit where it will not interfere with other spacecraft.

spacecraft into a final disposal orbit a few hundred kilometers above the geostationary ring requires a relatively small amount of propellant (but not 0). Going above the geostationary ring rather than below avoids the potential for collisions with other satellites during subsequent geosynchronous transfers.

Table 10-2. Principal Orbit Types. For orbit design it is convenient to divide the mission into a series of orbit types based on the varying requirements as the mission progresses.

Type	Definition	Examples	Where Discussed
Earth-Referenced Orbit	An operational orbit which provides the necessary coverage of the surface of the Earth or near-Earth space (also applicable to the Moon and planets)	Geosynchronous orbit, low-Earth communications or observation constellations	Sec. 10.4, Sec. 13.5.6
Space-Referenced Orbit	An operational orbit whose principal characteristic is being or pointing somewhere in space, such that specific orbit parameters may not be critical	Hubble Space Telescope orbit, Chandra X-Ray Observatory, space manufacturing orbit	Sec. 10.5.3
Transfer Orbit	An orbit used for getting from place to place	Geosynchronous transfer, inter-planetary transfer to Mars	Sec. 10.5.4
Parking Orbit	A temporary orbit providing a convenient location for satellite check-out, storage between activity or at end-of-life, or used to match conditions between phases	After launch, while awaiting proper conditions for orbit transfer; end-of-life 500 km above geosynchronous	Sec. 10.5.4

Step 2. Establish Orbit-Related Mission Requirements

For each mission segment defined in Step 1, we next define the orbit-related requirements. They may include orbital limits, individual requirements such as the altitude needed for specific observations, or a range of values constraining any of the orbit parameters. Secs. 10.4.1 and 10.5.1 discuss in detail the requirements for designing operational orbits. Ordinarily, these multiple requirements drive the orbit in different directions. For example, resolution or launch capability tend to drive the orbit to low altitudes, but coverage, lifetime, and survivability drive the spacecraft to higher altitudes. Consequently, the operational orbit trades are typically complex, involving the evaluation of multiple parameters in selecting a reasonable compromise that meets mission objectives at minimum cost and risk.

Selecting parking, transfer, and space-referenced orbits is normally conceptually much simpler, although it may be mathematically complex. Here, the normal trade is meeting the desired constraints on a mission, such as lifetime, thermal, or radiation environments, at the lowest possible propellant cost. Section 10.5.4 discusses these types of orbits in more detail.

Step 3. Evaluate Orbit Performance

For all orbits, we are interested in the performance we can achieve (Step 3) vs. the cost of achieving it (Step 4). As discussed in Sec. 10.4, most missions are Earth-referenced, i.e., looking back at the Earth and here there is an immediate conflict. The best coverage occurs as we move up in altitude and can see more of the Earth at any one time (and, therefore need less satellites), but the best resolution occurs as we move down in altitude. It's like taking pictures of a facility or people. We like views from a distance to get a broad perspective, but like close-ups for detail. This suggests an elliptical orbit that provides both near and far views, but this comes with its own set of problems. Orbits that aren't Earth-referenced typically have fewer conflicting requirements, as dissussed in Sec. 10.5, although there still may be a need for high precision, such as landing on a distant planet or rendezvous with a spacecraft or celestial object.

Step 3A. Earth Coverage

Coverage is a key requirement for any Earth or planet referenced mission and can be challenging to evaluate. As discussed in Sec. 10.2.1, coverage is not uniform but is also not a random variable and, therefore, statistical results that are often used can prove very misleading. Section 10.2.1 discusses some of the "traps" of evaluating coverage and relatively simple approaches to resolving these issues.

Specialized Orbits. In selecting the orbit for any mission phase, we must first determine if a specialized orbit applies. *Specialized orbits* (Sec. 9.5) are those with unique characteristics, which set them apart from the broad continuum of orbit parameters. (See Table 10-12 in Sec. 10.4.2 and Table 10-18 in Sec. 10.5.) Geosynchronous orbits, Sun-synchronous orbits, Molniya orbits, and Lagrange point orbits are typical examples. We examine each of these specialized orbits to see if its unique characteristics are worth its cost. This examination precedes the more detailed trades, because specialized orbits constrain parameters such as altitude or inclination, and, therefore, often lead to very different solutions for a given mission problem. Consequently, we may need to carry more than one orbit into more detailed design trades, such as keeping open a geosynchronous option and a low-Earth orbit option as possibilities for further trade studies.

Single Satellite vs. Constellation. The principal advantage of a single satellite is that it reduces cost by minimizing the mission overhead. One satellite will have one power system, one attitude control system, one telemetry system, and require only a single launch vehicle. A constellation or multiple spacecraft, on the other hand, may provide better coverage, higher reliability if a satellite is lost, and greater survivability. We may also need a constellation to provide the multiple conditions needed to carry out a mission, such as varying lighting conditions for observations, varying geometries for navigation, or continuous coverage of all or part of the Earth for communications.

To meet budget limits, we often trade a single large satellite with larger and more complex instruments against a constellation of smaller, simpler satellites. This decision may depend on the technology available at the time of system design. As discussed in detail in Sec. 13.1, Wertz and Larson [1996], and Wertz et al. [2010], small satellites have become more capable through miniaturized electronics and on-board processing. Consequently, we may be able to construct constellations of small, low-cost satellites, frequently called *SmallSats* or *LightSats*, that weren't previously economically feasible. Another issue for large constellations is the operational problem of providing continuous navigation and orbit control. The introduction of low-cost, GPS-based navigation and autonomous orbit control (Sec. 19.2) can resolve many of these problems and promote larger constellations of small satellites in the future.

Step 3B. Other Ways the Orbit Impacts Performance

The orbit is one of the principal drivers of mission performance, as discussed in Secs. 10.2.2 and 10.4.3. The orbit impacts nearly every aspect of the system performance, including aperture and power requirements, drag and stationkeeping, the radiation environment, and the viewing angles and distance to various targets. As discussed in Sec. 9.6, orbit changes are very expensive in most cases, such that the spacecraft will typically remain very nearly in its initial operational orbit for the entire mission life. (There are some exceptions; such as changing phase in an operational orbit which has a very modest delta V cost.)

Step 3C. Do Mission Orbit Design Trades

The next step is to select the mission orbit by evaluating how orbit parameters affect each of the mission requirements defined in Chap. 5 and Sec. 10.4.1. As shown in Table 10-11 in Sec. 10.4.1, orbit design in Earth orbit depends principally on altitude. The easiest way to begin is by assuming a circular orbit and then conducting altitude and inclination trades. This process establishes a range of potential altitudes and inclinations, from which we can select one or more alternatives. Documenting the results of this key trade is particularly important, so we can revisit the trade from time to time as mission requirements and conditions change. We then evaluate the use of eccentric orbits as discussed in Sec. 10.4.3.

A relatively new criterion for orbit design is the problem of orbital debris and collision avoidance. As discussed in Sec. 7.5, orbital debris is a potential major problem for spacecraft. One of the principal solutions to this problem is to fly the spacecraft in a relatively low orbit. Below roughly 500 km, the life of any object is limited to a solar cycle of 11 years or less, as can be seen from Fig. 9-18 in Sec. 9.4.4. This means that debris cannot accumulate below this altitude. Traditionally satellites have been placed at higher altitudes specifically so that they will have a long orbit life. Satellites at lower altitudes will need some orbit maintenance, but have much better resolution in a smaller instrument and cannot contribute to the orbit debris problem simply because drag will remove any possible debris at the time of the next solar maximum.

Step 4. Evaluate Orbit Cost

Step 3 gives us a sense of how well the orbit is doing at performing the fundamental needs of the mission. However, often lost in the discussion of orbits is that there is a significant cost to the choice of orbits as well. For example, putting spacecraft in GEO requires launching approximately 5 times the spacecraft mass into LEO and putting spacecraft on the surface of the Moon requires launching approximately 10 times that mass into LEO. It may be that we have no choice but to launch into a specialized orbit such as GEO so that we can provide direct broadcast TV into some part of the world. But if we do have a choice, then we need to ask ourselves, will we do better with a 1,000 kg satellite in GEO or a 5,000 kg satellite in LEO? Unfortunately, that question is rarely asked.

Step 4A. Evaluate Launch Options and Launch Cost

Section 26.6 discusses current satellite launch options, including selection issues associated with different alternatives. In addition, Isakowitz et al. [2004] provides detailed numerical summaries of currently available launch vehicles worldwide. The launch vehicle contributes strongly to mission cost, and ultimately limits the amount of mass that can be placed in any given orbit. During early mission definition, we must provide enough launch margin to allow for later changes in launch vehicles or spacecraft mass. New designs require more margin than existing ones, with 20% being typical for new missions. In order to keep cost down and maintain schedule, it is highly desirable to design our spacecraft so as to be compatible with more than one launch vehicle, as discussed in Sec. 13.5.7.

Step 4B. Look at Low-Cost Launch Options, if Possible

While launch is not the major cost element for most space missions, it tends to drive mission cost, and often the schedule as well. Therefore, if possible, it is desirable to look at low-cost options to a dedicated launch, as discussed in Sec. 13.5.7. In addition, some low-cost alternatives may offer observation opportunities that are simply not available with orbiting spacecraft. At the very beginning of X-Ray astronomy, which has to done above the atmosphere, it was clear that there were many discrete sources of X-Rays in the sky, but no way of knowing what they were due to the very poor angular resolution of detectors prior to the Chandra X-Ray telescope. A suborbital flight with an X-Ray detector on board was timed such the Crab Nebula would be occulted by the Moon during the very brief flight. As soon as the Crab Nebula disappeared behind the Moon, the brightest X-Ray source in the sky turned off and first source of extraterrestrial X-Rays was identified.

Step 4C. Add Disposal Options

Although given little consideration in many early missions, spacecraft disposal has become critical to mission design because of the orbital debris problem. This represents potentially major legal, political, and economic issues. Spacecraft disposal options are discussed in detail in Chap. 30. Spacecraft that will reenter the atmosphere must either do a controlled reentry over the ocean or break up into pieces harmless to the Earth's surface.

If the spacecraft will not reenter the atmosphere in a reasonable time, we must still dispose of it at the end of its useful life so it isn't hazardous to other spacecraft. This problem is particularly acute in geosynchronous orbit where missions compete strongly for orbit slots. (See Cefola [1987] for an excellent analysis of the requirements for removing satellites from geosynchronous orbit.) As pointed out in Sec. 7.5, a collision between two spacecraft not only destroys them but also causes a debris cloud that is dangerous to their entire orbital area. Consequently, this is a major concern for satellite constellations as well.

Spacecraft beyond geosynchronous orbit are ordinarily allowed to continue to drift in interplanetary space at the end of their useful life. If a spacecraft is not specifically designed to encounter a planetary surface, then normal practice calls for preventing collisions with planets or moons in order to avoid the potential of biological contamination. At the end of their normal mission, Pioneers 10 and 11 became the first spacecraft to begin the exploration of interstellar space and continued to send back signals for an extended time on the environment that they encountered. (See Sec. 10.7.)

Step 4D. Create a Delta V Budget

To numerically evaluate the cost of an orbit, we first create a ΔV budget for the orbit, as described in Sec. 10.3.1. This then becomes the basis for the spacecraft propellant budget and a component of the Orbit Cost Function as described in Step 4E.

Step 4E. Evaluate the Orbit Cost Function

Section 10.3.2 discusses the *orbit cost function,* which is a mechanism for defining the approximate cost of orbit transfer in terms of the mass that must be put in low-Earth orbit to achieve the end mission orbit. Consequently, it provides a cost multiplier to be used in conjunction with launch cost estimates from other sources.

Steps 5 and 6. Document and Iterate

A key component of orbit or constellation design is documenting the mission requirements used to define the orbit, the reasons for selecting the orbit, and the numerical values of the selected orbit parameters. With this documentation, the baseline selection can be reevaluated from time to time as mission conditions change. Because mission design nearly always requires many iterations, we must make the iteration process as straightforward as possible and readdress orbit parameters throughout the mission design to ensure that they continue to meet all of the mission objectives and requirements at minimum cost and risk.

10.2 Orbit Performance—Evaluating Earth Coverage and Payload Performance

For a large number of spacecraft, Earth coverage is the fundamental element of performance. The number of satellites we need or the utility of the data depends on coverage. Thus, coverage is often a key parameter in orbit and constellation design. Most typically, this is done by computer simulation and statistical analysis of the results. However, one of the most important coverage characteristics is that

> ***Earth coverage is not a Gaussian parameter and statistical data can give very misleading results.***

I would like to give a specific example of this problem. Several years ago, a systems engineering group that I was a part of was asked to do a constellation coverage analysis. Continuous coverage was not necessary, but the customer was concerned with minimizing the duration of the gaps in coverage, consistent with keeping down the number of satellites in the constellation, and, therefore, the cost. Mindful of the fact that maxima are often a very poor measure of system performance, we chose instead to use as our most relevant measure of performance, the *mean gap duration*, i.e., the average length of coverage gaps under a variety of circumstances and constellation designs. We collected, analyzed, and plotted a variety of mean gap statistics as well as some additional statistical data based on our simulations of coverage performance. In one particular constellation design, we had a mean gap of approximately 40 min, which we determined was probably longer than the customer wanted. Consequently, we added a satellite to each of the orbit planes in the constellation configuration, rephased the satellites to provide the best coverage possible, and re-ran our statistical analysis. The result, with 50% more satellites, was that the mean gap went from approximately 40 min to more than an hour. Budgets were not quite so tight in those days when rockets were still pulled by horses; nonetheless, it seemed highly unlikely that our customer would be willing to pay for 50% more satellites in order to have longer gaps in coverage.

Although our computations were correct, it was clear that something had gone terribly wrong with our analysis. What had happened was actually straightforward. Our original constellation had a number of large and small gaps with an average duration of 40 min. We had improved the coverage by adding satellites and had actually filled in quite a few of the smaller gaps. What was left was a small number of larger gaps such that the average gap duration was longer, even though the total of all of the gaps was significantly reduced.

When obvious errors such as the above occur, it becomes clear that something has gone wrong and the problem can be identified and corrected. Unfortunately, that rarely happens. We collect statistical data on constellation coverage not because it has any type of a Gaussian distribution, but because we **always** collect statistical data from simulations. Often, the results look "good" and do not have any manifest problems. Nonetheless, statistical analysis of coverage is based on an assumption that is simply not true, and, therefore, must be approached with substantial care.

I would not propose that you avoid statistical data in coverage analysis. In any case, that is almost impossible to do. What is important is to use several of the other coverage analysis tools described in this section to provide substantial physical insight into the nature of the coverage that is being provided. It is this insight into what is occurring that provides the checks and balances to be able to draw conclusions that are truly valid.

10.2.1 Evaluating Earth Coverage

Earth coverage refers to the part of the Earth that a spacecraft instrument* or antenna can see at one instant or over an extended period. As Fig. 10-2 shows, the *instantaneous field of view*, typically called the *FOV* or *footprint*, is the actual area the instrument or antenna can see at any moment. In contrast, the *access area* is the total area on the ground that could potentially be seen at that moment by turning the spacecraft or instrument. In the case of an instrument that covers the entire visible surface of the Earth, these two would always be the same. For most operational instruments they are not.

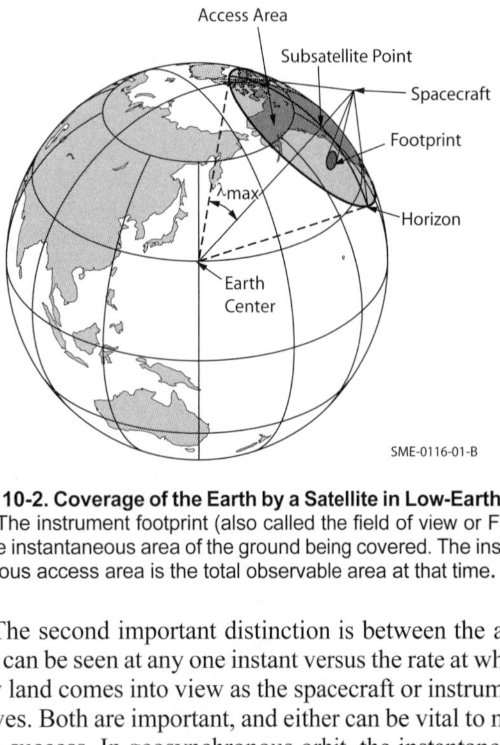

Fig. 10-2. Coverage of the Earth by a Satellite in Low-Earth Orbit. The instrument footprint (also called the field of view or FOV) is the instantaneous area of the ground being covered. The instantaneous access area is the total observable area at that time.

The second important distinction is between the area that can be seen at any one instant versus the rate at which new land comes into view as the spacecraft or instrument moves. Both are important, and either can be vital to mission success. In geosynchronous orbit, the instantaneous area is typically most important because the spacecraft is nearly stationary relative to the Earth's surface. In low-Earth orbit, satellites are moving rapidly over the surface, so the rate at which new land appears is often critical.

The two distinctions above lead to four parameters for Earth coverage:

* Throughout this section we will use *instrument* to refer to any spacecraft sensor or antenna for which we want to compute coverage.

- *Footprint Area* (*FA*, also *FOV area* or *instantaneous coverage area*) = area that a specific instrument or antenna is viewing at any instant.
- *Instantaneous Access Area* (*IAA*) = all the area that the instrument or antenna could potentially see at any instant.
- *Area Coverage Rate* (*ACR*) = the rate at which the instrument or antenna is sensing or accessing new land.
- *Area Access Rate* (*AAR*) = the rate at which new land is coming into the spacecraft's access area.

For an instrument that covers all of the area available to it as the spacecraft moves along, the coverage rate and access rate will be the same. For instruments operating only part of the time or continuously selecting the region to be examined, the coverage rate and access rate may be dramatically different. Generally the access area and access rate depend only on the orbit and limiting geometry of the system, so we can easily compute them with only a minimal knowledge of the detailed system design. On the other hand, the actual area coverage rate during spacecraft operations may well depend on the spacecraft control system, power, and management systems, as well as the details of mission operations.

Coverage assessment conveniently divides into two areas: first, an analytic assessment to provide approximate formulas for coverage parameters as a function of mission variables as described in Secs. 10.2.1.1 to 10.2.1.3; second, numerical simulations to provide coverage Figures of Merit for more detailed studies. These are discussed in Sec. 10.2.1.4.

10.2.1.1 Analytic Approximations

In this section, we present analytic approximations for various Earth coverage parameters. All of the formulas here take into account the spherical surface of the Earth, but do not account for oblateness, orbit eccentricity, or the rotation of the Earth underneath the orbit. These effects, plus coverage by multiple satellites, are ordinarily accounted for in numerical simulations as described in Sec. 10.2.1.4. Analytic expressions for coverage taking the Earth's rotation into account are given in Table 8-11 in Sec. 8.4.1 and Wertz [2009]. Analytic approximations appropriate for elliptical orbits are given in Table 8-12 in Sec. 8.4.2 and Wertz [2009].

All of the formulas here are derived directly from the single-satellite geometry described in Sec. 8.3. In particular, we will use the notation developed there and summarized in Fig. 8-28 in Sec. 8.3.1. In this section we will parameterize coverage in terms of the Earth Central Angle, λ.† However, we can use Eqs. (8-25) to (8-29) to

† λ may be thought of either as an angle at the Earth's center or as a distance measured along the Earth's surface and, therefore, may be expressed in either degrees or kilometers. We will use these two views interchangeably as convenient for the problem at hand.

transform each of the formulas below into one for either the spacecraft-centered nadir angle, η, or spacecraft elevation angle, ε, seen from the ground.

As Fig. 10-2 shows, the instrument footprint is normally a beam projected onto the Earth's surface with a circular cross section substantially smaller than the access area. The nomenclature and computational geometry for the footprint are in Fig. 10-3. (For instruments that see very large portions of the Earth, we can use the access area formulas below. For the projection of rectangular FOVs, corresponding to a typical focal plane array, onto the surface of the Earth, see Eqs. (8-59) to (8-62) in Sec. 8.3.4.)

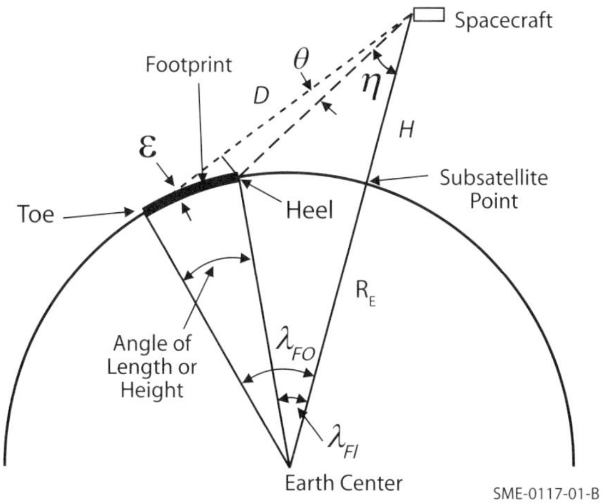

Fig. 10-3. Computational Geometry for Footprint Parameters. Note that ε is always measured at the toe because that is where performance is the worst.

The length (also called the height) of the footprint, L_F, is given by:

$$L_F = K_L\,(\lambda_{FO} - \lambda_{FI}) \tag{10-1a}$$

$$\approx D\,(\sin\theta / \sin\varepsilon) \tag{10-1b}$$

where the variables are defined in Fig. 10-3 and, for λ expressed in degrees, the conversion factor, K_L, is

$K_L = 1$	for length in deg
$K_L = 111.319\,543$	for length in km
$K_L = 60.107\,744\,7$	for length in nmi

Note: the linear approximation given in Eq. (10-1b) is computationally convenient but can be very inaccurate, particularly near the horizon where ε is small. (For a satellite at an altitude of 1,000 km with a 1 deg diameter beam, the error in Eq. (10-1b) is 400% at $\varepsilon = 1$ deg, 10% at $\varepsilon = 15$ deg, and 1% at $\varepsilon = 60$ deg). However, the alternative computation of Eq. (10-1a) is much less convenient. To find the footprint length for a given spacecraft elevation angle at the toe of the beam, ε, we begin by computing η and λ at the toe, then subtract the beam width, θ, from η to determine η at the heel, compute λ at the heel, and finally subtract to get the footprint length from Eq. (10-1a). An alternative that improves the approximation somewhat is to the center rather than the toe of the beam. Because the toe represents the worst-case link budget, it is most often used for performance computations and therefore is commonly used for geometry calculations as well.

The *footprint width*, W_F, is given by:

$$W_F = R_E\,\text{asin}\,(D \sin\theta / R_E) \tag{10-2a}$$

$$\approx D \sin\theta \tag{10-2b}$$

where R_E = 6,378.136 km is the radius of the Earth, θ is the beam width, and D is the distance from the spacecraft to the toe of the footprint.* Here the error in the approximation in Eq. (10-2b) is proportional to $1 - (W_F / \sin W_F)^{\dagger}$ and is generally small relative to other errors. Thus, Eq. (10-2b) is adequate for most practical applications.

Finally, if we assume that the projection on the ground is an ellipse, then the footprint area, F_A, is given by:

$$F_A \approx (\pi/4) L_F W_F \tag{10-3}$$

Assuming that L_F was computed by Eq. (10-1a), the error in ignoring the curvature of the Earth in Eq. (10-3) is again proportional to $1 - (W_F / \sin W_F)$ and is negligible for most applications.

The *instantaneous area* coverage rate for the beam is defined by:

$$ACR_{instantaneous} \equiv F_A / T \tag{10-4}$$

where T is the exposure time or dwell time for the instrument. The *average area coverage rate*, ACR_{avg}, will also be a function of the *duty cycle*, *DC*, which is the fraction of the total time that the instrument is operating, and the average between the footprint, O_{avg}, which is the amount by which two successive footprints cover the same area (typically about 20%):

$$ACR_{avg} = \text{DC}\,(1 - O_{avg})\,F_A / T \tag{10-5}$$

Computing the instantaneous access area, IAA, will depend on the shape of the potential coverage area on the ground. Figure 10-4 shows several typical shapes. The most common of these is Fig. 10-4A, which assumes that the instrument can work at any point on the Earth for which the spacecraft elevation is above ε. This corresponds to a small circle on the Earth of radius λ centered on the current subsatellite point. However, some instruments, such as radar, cannot work too close to the subsatellite point. As Fig. 10-4B shows, these instruments have both an outer horizon, λ_1, and an inner horizon, λ_2.

For instruments with an access pattern as shown in Fig. 10-4A, the instantaneous access area, *IAA*, will be just the area of the small circle, that is,

$$IAA = K_A (1 - \cos\lambda) \tag{10-6}$$

---

* See Sec. 8.3.4 for a discussion of the projection of non-circular fields of view onto the Earth.

† Here W_F should be in radians as seen from the center of the Earth.

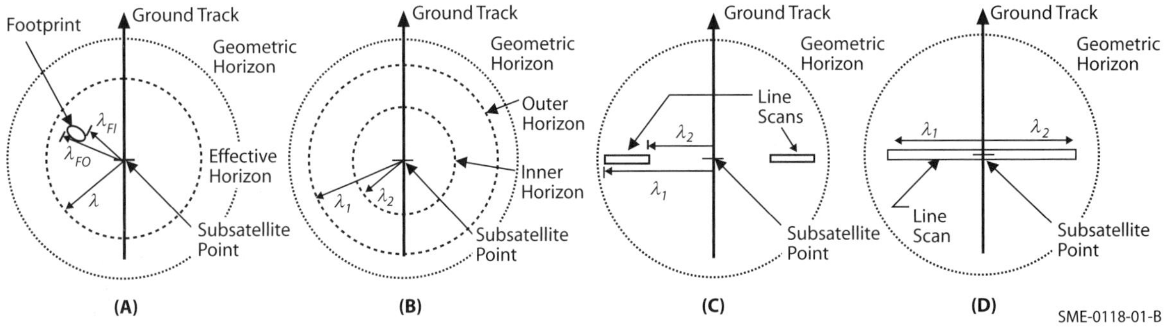

Fig. 10-4. Typical Spacecraft Access Areas. See Table 10-3 for formulas. See Sec. 8.3.4 for sensor FOV analysis.

where

$K_A = 2\pi \approx 6.283\ 185\ 311$ for area in steradians

$K_A = 20{,}626.4806$ for area in deg^2

$K_A = 2.556\ 041\ 87 \times 10^8$ for area in km^2

$K_A = 7.452\ 225\ 69 \times 10^7$ for area in nmi^2

The instantaneous access areas or access lengths for the other patterns in Fig. 10-4 are given in Table 10-3, which also summarizes all of the coverage formulas for these patterns. These access area formulas take into account the curved surface of the Earth and are accurate for any access area size or satellite altitude to within very small corrections for the Earth's oblateness.

We now wish to determine the length of time a particular point on the Earth is within the satellite access area and the access area rate at which land enters or leaves the access area. Consider a satellite in a circular orbit at altitude H. The orbit period, P, in minutes is given by:

$$P = 1.658\ 669 \times 10^{-4} \times (6{,}378.14 + H)^{3/2},\ H \text{ in km} \quad (10\text{-}7)$$

$$P = 4.180\ 432 \times 10^{-4} \times (3{,}443.9 + H)^{3/2},\ H \text{ in nmi} \quad (10\text{-}8)$$

We define the *maximum Earth Central Angle*, λ_{max}, as the radius of the access area for the observation in question. Twice λ_{max} is called the *swath width* and is the width of the coverage path across the Earth. As shown in Fig. 10-5, the coverage for any point **P** on the surface of the Earth will be a function of λ_{max} and of the off-ground-track angle, λ, which is the perpendicular distance from **P** to the satellite ground track for the orbit pass being evaluated. The fraction of the orbit, F_{view}, over which the point **P** is in view is:

$$F_{view} = \phi / 180 \text{ deg} \quad (10\text{-}9)$$

where:

$$\cos\phi = \cos\lambda_{max} / \cos\lambda \quad (10\text{-}10)$$

Therefore the *time in view, T*, for the point **P** will be

$$T = PF_{view} = \left(\frac{P}{180 \text{ deg}}\right) \text{acos}\left(\frac{\cos\lambda_{max}}{\cos\lambda}\right) \quad (10\text{-}11)$$

See Sec. 8.4 for a detailed discussion of the computation of all relevant parameters for a single target or ground station pass, including the corrections that take into account the rotation of the Earth during the pass.

Live Calc

Table 10-3. Coverage Formulas for Patterns Shown in Fig. 10-4. See text for definition of variables. In pattern D, the minus sign applies if λ_2 is on the same side of the ground track as λ_1. The approximation for footprint area is invalid when $\varepsilon \approx 0$. The ACR formulas for patterns C and D assume that the instrument is side-looking. P is the orbit period.

Pattern	Typical Application	Footprint Area (*FA*)	Instantaneous Access Area (*IAA*) or Length (*IAL*)	Area Coverage Rate (*ACR*)	Area Access Rate (*AAR*)
A	Omni-antenna, Ground-station Coverage, General Sensing	$(\pi D K_L / 4) \sin\theta \times (\lambda_{FO} - \lambda_{FI}) \approx (\pi D^2/4) \times \sin^2\theta / \sin\varepsilon$	$IAA = K_A (1 - \cos\lambda)$	$\frac{F_A(1-O_{avg})DC}{T}$	$\frac{2K_A \sin\lambda}{P}$
B	Doppler Radar	As above	$IAA = K_A (\cos\lambda_2 - \cos\lambda_1)$	As above	$\frac{2K_A \sin\lambda}{P}$
C	Synthetic Aperture Radar	As above	$IAL = 2 K_L (\lambda_1 - \lambda_2)$ $\approx 2K_L D \frac{\sin\theta}{\sin\varepsilon}$	$\frac{2K_A(\sin\lambda_1 - \sin\lambda_2)}{P}$	$\frac{2K_A(\sin\lambda_1 - \sin\lambda_2)}{P}$
D	Scanning Sensor	As above	$IAL = K_L (\lambda_1 \pm \lambda_2)$	$\frac{K_A(\sin\lambda_1 \pm \sin\lambda_2)}{P}$	$\frac{K_A(\sin\lambda_1 \pm \sin\lambda_2)}{P}$

Table 10-3, Fig. 10-4, Eq. 10-11

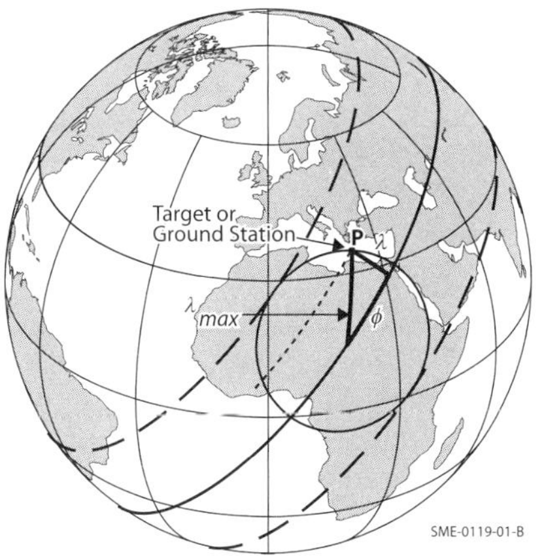

Fig. 10-5. Earth Coverage Geometry. λ is the *off ground-track angle* and $2\lambda_{max}$ is the *swath width*. **P** is the target or ground station.

Finally, the area access rate as the satellite sweeps over the ground for the access area of Fig. 10-4A is:

$$AAR = (2\,K_A \sin\lambda)\,/\,P \qquad \text{(Pattern A)} \qquad (10\text{-}12)$$

Formulas for other patterns are in Table 10-3. Again note that because of the curvature of the Earth's surface, this area access rate is **not** equal to the width of the access area times the subsatellite velocity.

As an example of the above computations, consider a spacecraft at 2,000 km altitude with a 1 deg diameter beam looking perpendicular to the ground track at an elevation angle of 10 deg as seen from the ground. Our linear estimate of the footprint height is 446 km from Eq. (10-1b).* However, from Eq. (10-1a) we see that the true height is 355 km. From Eqs. (8-26), (8-27), and (8-30) in Sec. 8.3.1 we determine λ_{FO} = 31.43 deg and λ_{FI} = 28.24 deg. The footprint width from Eq. (10-2b) is 77 km. From Eq. (10-3) the footprint area is 21,470 km^2. The accuracy of the area is proportional to 1 (77/6,378)/sin (77/6,378) = 0.002%. The ground track velocity is the circumference of the Earth divided by the orbit period [from Eq. (10-7)] = 40,075 km/127 min = 315.6 km/min = 5.26 km/s. Multiplying this by the footprint height of 355 km gives a crude estimate of the area coverage rate of 1,867 km^2/s. Using the more accurate formula in Table 10-3 (Pattern D) and the values of λ above, we obtain a more accurate value of ACR = $2.556 \times 10^8 \times$ (sin 31.43 deg – sin 28.24 deg)/(127 × 60) = 1,620 km^2/s which implies an error of 15% in the less accurate approximation.

10.2.1.2 Identifying Coverage Patterns

As previously indicated, Earth coverage is not a statistically distributed parameter. Coverage tends to come in "chunks." Thus, at any given time, whether there is Earth coverage at some point on the Earth's surface is very strongly correlated with whether there was coverage at the last time step. Consequently, we need not only statistical data generated from simulations but also other types of analyses that can begin to identify coverage patterns and how coverage works in both a qualitative sense and analytical approximations.

One of the most useful approaches for analyzing coverage patterns is simply the *ground track plot* or *ground trace*, i.e., the trace of the subsatellite point over time. (For a detailed discussion of ground track plots and relevant formulas and examples, see Wertz [2009], Sec. 9.3.) A typical ground track plot is shown in Fig. 10-6 for a satellite in an orbit at an altitude of 1,000 km and inclination of 60 deg. In previous plots, we have drawn the access area on the surface of the Earth corresponding to the area that is visible for a specific satellite. In this figure, we draw a circle of the same size centered not on the position of the satellite, but on a specific target or ground station, in this case, Miami. For a satellite at 1,000 km and minimum elevation angle of 5 deg, the maximum Earth Central Angle is 25 deg, i.e., any point on the ground within 25 deg of the subsatellite point is within view. Conversely, whenever the subsatellite point for a spacecraft is within 25 deg of a specific target or ground station, then that target can be seen by the spacecraft. Therefore, the small circle of 25 deg radius centered on Miami encloses all possible subsatellite points for which a satellite at 1,000 km altitude can see Miami with a minimum elevation angle at the target greater than 5 deg.†

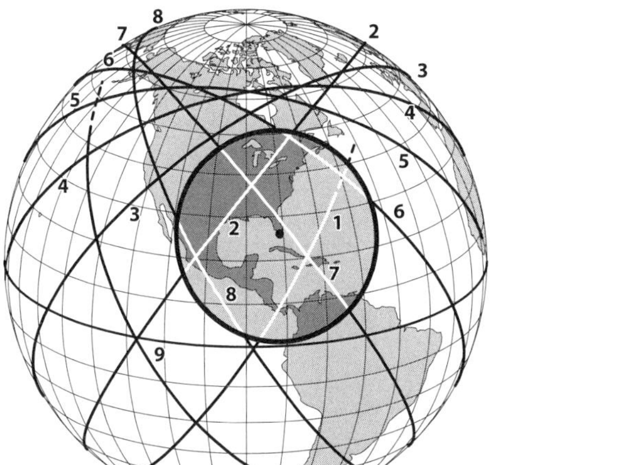

Fig. 10-6. Ground Track for 8 Successive Orbits (Out of 14 per Day) for a Satellite in a 1,000 km Circular Orbit. The heavy circle covers subsatellite points for which the satellite will be at an elevation angle, ε, of 5 deg or higher.

* As indicated previously, this estimate would be substantially improved if the 10 deg elevation angle was at the center of the beam. However, we would then need to keep track of beam-center parameters for the geometry and beam-edge parameters for performance estimates.

† Another way to think of the construction of this plot is to consider a cone of 85 deg radius centered on Miami, with its axis toward the zenith. The intersection of this cone with a sphere 1,000 km above the Earth produces the small circle shown in the figure. In this equivalent representation, the small circle represents all possible locations of the satellite that can see Miami with the appropriate conditions.

By simply looking at the plot, it is clear what the nature of the coverage will be. Notice that the orbits on the plot are numbered consecutively and that coverage of Miami is provided on orbits 1 and 2 and is then not available on orbits 3, 4, and 5 but is available again on orbits 6, 7, and 8. For this example, there will be 2 or 3 orbits of coverage followed by 3 or 4 orbits with no coverage and then another 2 or 3 orbits of coverage after which the process repeats. The specific coverage will depend on how the orbit lies with respect to the particular target. The orbit period at this altitude is approximately 105 min. A pass that goes directly over Miami will provide coverage for approximately (50/360) × 105, or a bit less than 15 min. Thus, an "orbit of coverage" will consist of somewhat less than 15 min of coverage, followed by a bit more than 90 min of no coverage.

What happens if we move our ground station either north or south? As the ground station moves toward the equator, the coverage patterns become more symmetric, with coverage occurring twice per day at times centered 12 hrs apart. As we move toward the pole, coverage becomes more "one-sided" in terms of its daily distribution. There will be a larger number of orbits in a row that provide coverage, and then a longer gap with no coverage, with the process repeating on a daily basis. If we get close enough to the pole, there will be either no coverage if the radius of the coverage region is less than 90 deg minus the inclination, or a short region of coverage on every orbit.

We can learn a great deal about the nature of coverage and how it is distributed by simply looking carefully at a ground track plot for the orbit. One way to demonstrate this coverage as a function of latitude is a *coverage histogram* or *tombstone plot* as shown in Fig. 10-7. The horizontal axis is time and the various lines which look like a strip chart recorder are the coverage for points at the longitude of Miami and at 10 deg steps in latitude. When the line is up, there is coverage; when it is down, there is no coverage. Here you can see clearly the general characteristic of what we have discussed, including the symmetry of coverage that occurs near the equator and the asymmetry that occurs as we approach the poles. The extensive coverage at 40 deg latitude in this example is the basis for the Repeat Coverage Orbit discussed in Sec. 10.4.2.6.

We can also use the information from Fig. 10-6 to immediately calculate one statistical parameter. The access area represents just less than 5% of the surface area of the world. Consequently, in general, the mean coverage for any single point on the surface of the Earth will be 5%. Five percent of the Earth is covered at any one time, and over the course of time a random point will be covered approximately 5% of the time. While this is true, it does remarkably little to reflect the reality of the curves in Fig 10-7 or the understanding we can gain by looking at Fig. 10-6.

10.2.1.3 Analytic Coverage Computations

Figure 10-5 in Sec. 10.2.1.1 shows the geometry for a single ground station or target pass. Note that this is the

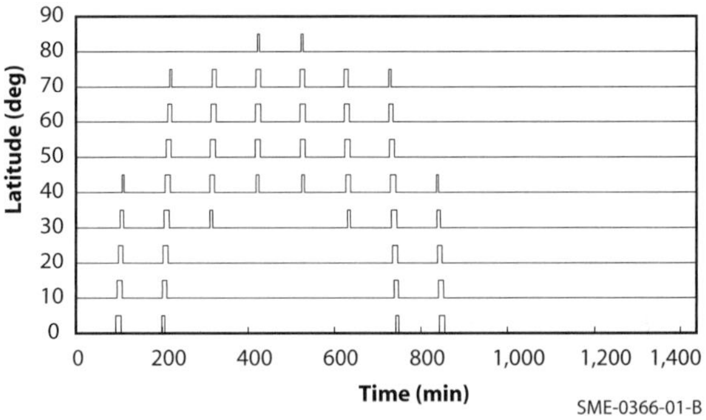

Live Calc

Fig. 10-7. Histograms of Coverage Over a Day for Ground Stations at the Same Longitude Shown in Fig. 10-6, but Varying Latitudes. Note the asymmetry as the ground station moves toward the pole. See text for discussion.

same computational geometry that was done in detail in Sec. 8.4.1. Consequently, all of the tables and computations in that section are applicable to Earth coverage for a single point. These computations were summarized in Table 8-11 in Sec. 8.4.1 and are available on the book website for that table.

It is also of interest to compute the coverage as a function of latitude, L. Conceptually, this is most conveniently done by thinking of the orbit and coverage pattern as fixed, and the Earth as rotating underneath as shown in Fig. 10-8.

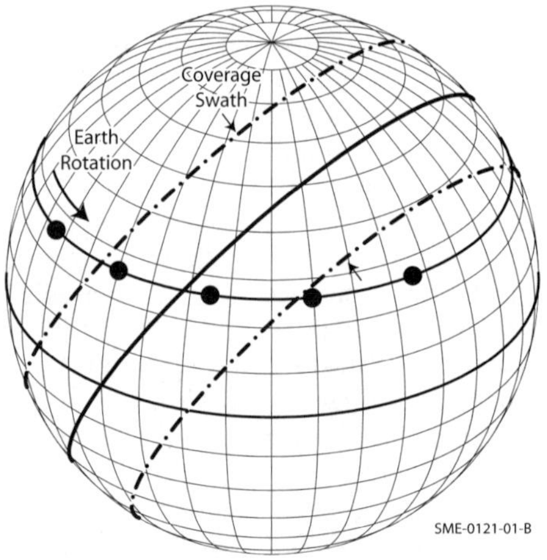

Fig. 10-8. Alternative View of a Rotating Ground Track. For some computations it is convenient to think of the orbit coverage pattern as fixed in inertial space and the Earth rotating under it. The large dots represent locations of a ground target on successive passes.

The large dots show the position of a ground station or target on successive orbits. Here we can see both the discrete nature of coverage and the derivation of the continuous analytic formulas. If the ground swath is thinner then the spacing between successive dots, then we may or may not get coverage on a given ascending or descending pass. If it is wider than one space but less then two spaces, then we will get coverage on either 1 or 2 passes at each ascending and descending node. Thus, we could divide the world into latitude bands with each band having a discrete set of possible coverage patterns, corresponding approximately to the histogram of Fig. 10-7.

To obtain a continuous analytic approximation, we note that the arc length along the small circle connecting the dots is directly proportional to the percent coverage at that latitude.* Specifically, we assume that there is a satellite in a circular orbit at inclination i and that observations can be made at any off-ground-track angle less then or equal to λ_{max} on either side of the ground track. We also assume that L is positive, i.e., in the northern hemisphere. (The extensions are straightforward for the southern hemisphere or nonsymmetric observations.) As shown in Fig 10-9 there will be either no coverage, a single long region of coverage, or two shorter regions of coverage depending on the latitude and inclination as shown in Table 10-4.

Table 10-4. Coverage vs. Latitude.

Latitude Range	No. of Coverage Regions	Percent Coverage
$L > \lambda_{max} + i$	0	0
$i + \lambda_{max} > L > i - \lambda_{max}$	1	$\phi_1/180$
$i - \lambda_{max} > L > 0$	2	$(\phi_1 - \phi_2)/180$

where:

$$\cos\phi_{1 \text{ or } 2} = \frac{\pm\sin\lambda_{max} + \cos i \sin L}{\sin i \cos L} \qquad (10\text{-}13)$$

where the minus sign applies for ϕ_1 and the plus sign for ϕ_2. Here ϕ is one-half the longitude range over which coverage occurs. The formula in the third column above represents the fraction of all points at a given latitude in view of the satellite during one orbit. This is approximately equal to the fraction of orbits that will cover a given point at that latitude.

As an example, consider a satellite in a 62.5 deg inclined orbit which can see to an off-ground-track angle, λ_{max} = 20 deg. At a ground station latitude of 50 deg, the percent coverage will be 49.3%. On any orbit, 49% of the points at a latitude of 50 deg will be within view of the satellite at some time. Conversely, a given point at 50 deg latitude will be covered at some time on approximately 49% of the satellite orbits.

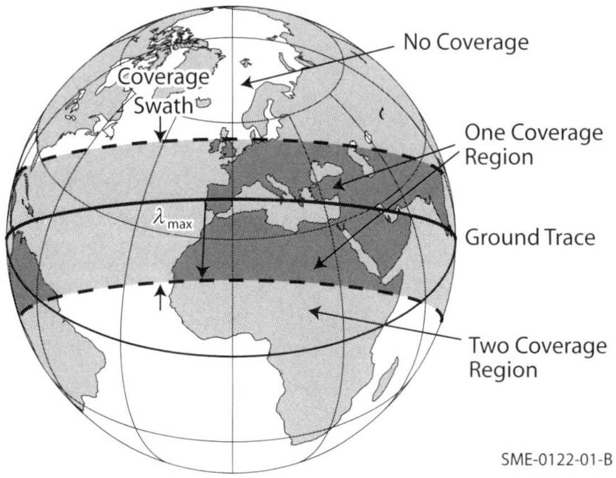

Fig. 10-9. Single Orbit Coverage is a Function of Latitude, Orbit Inclination, and Swath Width. See text for formulas.

Because there is only one coverage region, the covered orbits will occur successively during the day. If the satellite orbit period is 2 hrs, then our hypothetical ground station at 50 deg latitude will typically see the satellite on six successive orbits followed by six orbits of no coverage. The number and duration of coverage passes on a given day will depend on where the ground station is located with respect to the orbit node.

Figure 10-10 shows a representative plot of Earth coverage as a function of latitude, based on the above equations. For latitudes below $i - \lambda$, there will be two distinct coverage regions. In this area, the coverage increases somewhat as we go further from the equator, because the orbit is tilting more and therefore covering more of a given latitude line. At a latitude of $i - \lambda$, we transition from two coverage regions to a single coverage region which is extremely long. This can be seen in Fig. 10-9 and occurs where the underlying latitude line is just tangent to the southernmost edge of the coverage

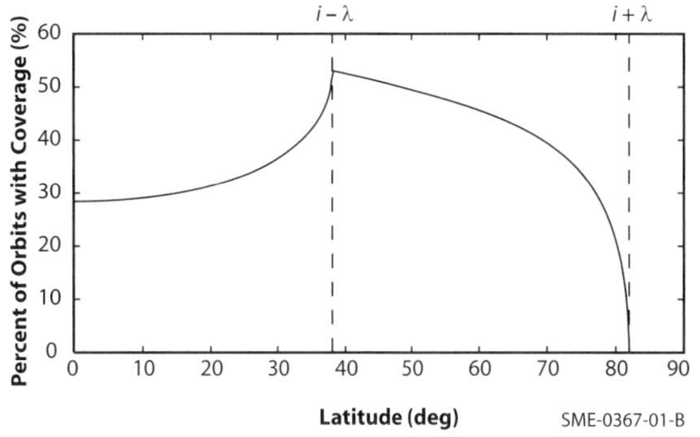

Live Calc

Fig. 10-10. Representative Plot of Earth Coverage as a Function of Latitude. Note that the chart gives the percentage of orbits which provide coverage, but does not reflect the coverage distribution, which is equally important. The satellite is assumed to be in a circular orbit at 1,000 km, an inclination of 60 deg and a minimum elevation angle of 10 deg.

* We need to emphasize once again that coverage is not a statistical variable. If the orbit is a 1-day repeating ground track, then the targets will appear in the same locations with respect to the orbit every day. In this case, coverage will be a function of both latitude and longitude and each Earth location will have its own fixed coverage pattern. If the orbit is not a repeating ground track, then the "percent coverage" rules are applicable.

band. This is the latitude with the highest coverage and is frequently missed in histograms such as those described above. As we proceed further north, coverage drops as the single coverage region gets smaller until coverage disappears entirely at a latitude of $i + \lambda$.

There are several conclusions that can be drawn from this curve. First of all, coverage varies significantly with latitude and we can design our orbit inclination to provide the greatest coverage where it is most needed. For example, a communications constellation might choose to use an inclination such that the coverage is maximized over the mid northern latitudes, where the principal population densities occur. Our second conclusion is that the coverage curve from Fig. 10-10 is interesting and informative but does not tell the whole story. It does not provide the information on the distribution of coverage that we get from either the ground track plot or the coverage histogram. While useful, it needs to be combined with other types of information in order to provide a clear understanding of coverage patterns.

10.2.1.4 Numerical Simulations

The analytic formulas presented above provide an easy and rapid way to evaluate Earth coverage and provide good physical insight into the nature of that coverage. However, to provide additional numerical details, simulations are nearly always required. The numerical simulations themselves are relatively straightforward. Simply set up representative points you are interested in or a grid of points covering the Earth, "fly" the spacecraft over the grid for one or more days, and collect the results. The difficult part is interpreting the meaning of the results and avoiding both computational problems and interpretations which misrepresent the real coverage.

There are four principal numerical interpretation problems that the user should be aware of in developing and using point coverage simulations. These are:

Spacing of Grid Points:

If we use a grid of points in our numerical simulation, we frequently want to compare coverage performance at different latitudes. To do this, we need to have grid points covering approximately equal areas over the surface of the globe. If the grid points are at equal intervals of latitude and longitude (every 10 deg, for example) then the number of points per unit area will be much greater near the poles, thus incorrectly weighting polar data in the overall global statistics. This problem is easily resolved by either using grid points at a constant latitude spacing with the number of points at each latitude proportional to the cosine of the latitude, or by adjusting the weighting of the points in creating the global statistics.

Gaps at the Beginning and End of the Simulation:

If the system being simulated is not intended for continuous global coverage, then there will be gaps in coverage for which the statistics are usually important. However, these statistics can be biased by gaps which occur at the beginning and end of the simulation run. For example, if the simulation covers exactly 24 hr and there is a 4-hr gap in coverage during the period when the simulation begins, then this may be misinterpreted as two 2-hr gaps. The easiest solution to this problem is to run the simulation long enough that start and end data have minimal impact on the overall statistics.

Incorrect Step Size:

In a time stepped simulation, the simulation itself does not see a continuous coverage distribution but rather a series of steps. If the steps are far apart in order to make the simulation easy to run it is possible to step "over" some of the grid points such that coverage which actually exists is missed. The principal requirement to avoid this happening too much is to keep the simulation step small relative to the dimensions of the coverage regions.

Incorrect Interpretation of Results:

As we have discussed previously, Earth coverage is not a statistically distributed phenomenon. Consequently, statistical figures of merit can prove extremely misleading. The principal solution to this problem is twofold. First, we should use more than one figure of merit for evaluating coverage so that multiple pieces of information are available and can be compared. The second approach is to use any of the more analytic approaches to understand the coverage such that we can be sure that the statistical data reflects a true assessment of the nature of the coverage.

Our most important step in creating a coverage simulation is to find the appropriate way to accumulate coverage statistics and to evaluate the quality of coverage. This is done by way of *coverage figures of merit* which are the numerical mechanisms for comparing the coverage of satellites and constellations. We would like to find a figure of merit which is physically meaningful, easy to compute in a numerical simulation, and fair in comparing alternative orbits and constellations. In the end, no one coverage figure of merit will prove successful by itself and a combination of techniques is most appropriate. The most common coverage figures of merit are:

Percent Coverage:

The *percent coverage* for any point on the grid is simply the number of times that point was covered by one or more satellites divided by the total number of simulation time steps. The advantage of percent coverage is that it shows directly how much of the time a given point or region on the ground is covered. However, it does not provide any information about the distribution of gaps in that coverage.

Table 10-4◀, Fig. 10-10, Eq. 10-13◀

Maximum Coverage Gap (= *Maximum Response Time*):

The *maximum coverage gap* is simply the longest coverage gap encountered for an individual point. When looking at statistics over more than one point, we can either average the maximum gaps or take their maximum value. Thus, the worldwide *mean maximum gap* would be the average value of the maximum gap for all the individual points, and the worldwide *maximum gap* would be the largest of any of the individual gaps. This statistic conveys some worst-case information, but it incorrectly ranks constellations because a single point or a small number of points determine the results. Thus, the maximum coverage gap, or maximum response time, is a poor figure of merit.

Mean Coverage Gap:

The *mean coverage gap* is the average length of breaks in coverage for a given point on the simulation grid. To compute mean gap statistics, we must have three counters for each point on the simulation grid. One counter tracks the number of gaps. A second tracks total gap duration. The third tracks the duration of the current gap and is reset as needed. During the simulation, if no satellite covers a given point on the grid, we increment the gap length counter (3) by one time step. If the point is covered but was not covered the previous time (indicated by a value of the gap length counter greater than 0), then we have reached the end of an individual gap. We increment the counter for the number of gaps (1) by one and add the gap duration to the total gap counter (2) or incorporate it in other statistics we want to collect. The final mean coverage gap is computed by dividing the total gap length by the number of gaps. As noted above, what happens at the beginning and end of the simulation influences all statistics relating to gap distribution.

Time Average Gap:

The *time average gap* is the mean gap duration averaged over time. Alternatively, it is the average length of the gap we would find if we randomly sampled the system. To compute the time average gap, two counters are required, one for the current gap length, and one for the sum of the squares of gap lengths. During the simulation, if no satellite covers a given point on the grid, add one to the current gap length counter. If the point is covered, square the current gap length, add the results to the sum of the squares counter, and reset the current gap length counter to zero. (If the current gap length counter was previously 0, then no change will occur in either counter.) The time average gap is computed at the end of the simulation by dividing the sum of the squares of the gaps by the duration of the simulation.

Mean Response Time:

The *mean response time* is the average time from when we receive a random request to observe a point until we can observe it. If a satellite is within view of the point at a given time step, the response time at that step will be 0.* If the point in question is in a coverage gap, then the response time would be the time until the end of the coverage gap. In principle, response time should be computed from a given time step to the end of a gap. But by symmetry we could also count the time from the beginning of the gap—a computationally convenient method with the same results. Thus, the response time counter will be set to 0 if a point is covered at the current time step. We advance the response time counter by one time step if the point is not now covered. The mean response time will then be the average value of all response times for all time steps. This figure of merit takes into account both coverage and gap statistics in trying to determine the whole system's responsiveness. As shown below, the mean response time is most often the best coverage figure of merit for evaluating overall responsiveness.

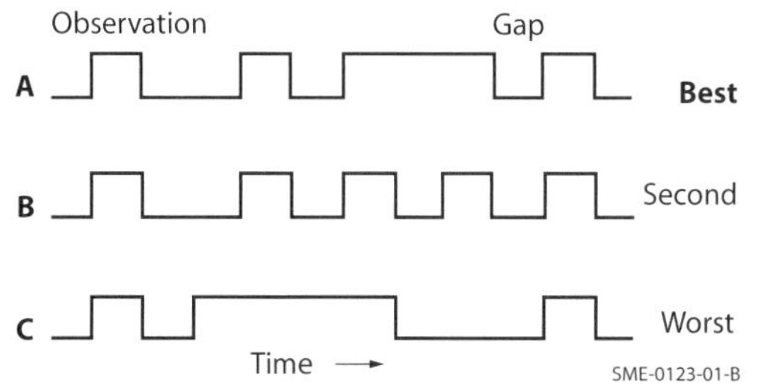

	Percent Cov.	Max Gap	Mean Gap	Time Average Gap	Mean Response Time
A	60	2	1.33	0.6	0.5
B	50	2	1.25	0.7	0.6
C	60	3	2.00	1.0	0.7

Fig. 10-11. Simulation of Coverage Figures of Merit. See text for explanation.

To illustrate the meaning and relative advantages of these figures of merit, Fig. 10-11 diagrams a simplified coverage simulation for 3 satellite systems: A, B, and C. These could, for example, be 3 sample FireSat II constellations. Our goal is to see events as quickly as possible, and therefore, minimize gaps. Constellation B is identical to A, except for one added gap, which makes B clearly a worse

* One advantage of response time as a figure of merit is that delays in processing or communications (for both data requests and responses) can be directly added to the coverage response time. This results in a *total response time,* which measures the total time from when users request data until they receive it. We can also evaluate minimum, mean, and maximum total response times which have much more operational meaning than simple gap statistics and are still easy to compute.

Table 10-5. Advantages and Disadvantages of Different Approaches to Evaluating Coverage. See text.

Approach	Advantages	Disadvantages	Example
Ground Trace Plot	Very simple to do; provides excellent physical insight	Does not provide quantitative results; hard to compare systems	Fig. 10-6
Coverage Histogram	Simple to calculate; gives excellent insight into multiple coverage characteristics; best overall evaluation approach	Difficult to compare systems; can not be reduced to a single number; may miss key features at locations not evaluated	Fig 10-7
Analytic Coverage Functions	Simple to calculate; gives good insight into percent coverage	Provides no information about gaps or coverage distribution	Fig. 10-10
Numerical Simulations and Coverage Figures of Merit	Relatively easy to determine via simulation; provides simple numerical answers that can be easily compared (but may be misleading)	Requires coverage simulation; many parameters to select; provides statistical information on inherently nonstatistical data; can lead to very misleading results and conclusions	Fig. 10-11

solution than A. C has the same overall percent coverage as A, but the gaps are redistributed to create a rather long gap, making C the worst constellation for regular coverage.

The table at the bottom of Fig. 10-11 shows the numerical values of the figures of merit defined above. The percent coverage correctly ranks constellation A better than B, but because it does not take gap statistics into account, it cannot distinguish between A and C. Similarly, the maximum gap cannot distinguish between A and B, even though B is clearly worse by having an additional gap. In this case, the maximum gap tells us which constellation is worse but cannot distinguish between two constellations that are clearly different.

The mean gap statistic is even more misleading. By adding a short gap to constellation B, the average length of the gaps has been decreased, and consequently, this figure of merit ranks constellation B **above** constellation A. (As discussed in the introduction to Sec. 10.2 this can happen in real constellation statistics. By adding satellites we may eliminate some of the very small gaps, thus **increasing** the average gap length, even though more satellites provide more and better coverage.)

Finally, the time average gap and mean response time in the fourth and fifth columns correctly rank the three constellations in order of preference by taking into account both the percent coverage and gap statistics. Consequently, both of these are better figures of merit than the other three. I believe the mean response time is the stronger figure of merit because it provides a more useful measure of the end performance of the system and because it can be easily extended to include delays due to processing, communications, decision-making, or the initiation of action. However, because each figure of merit represents different characteristics we should evaluate more than one. Specifically, I recommend evaluating mean response time, percent coverage, and maximum gap, and qualitatively (not quantitatively) weighing the results in that order, keeping strongly in mind the caveat at the beginning of Sec. 10.2.

In summary, we have seen that there are four broad techniques available for evaluating Earth coverage:

- Ground track plots
- Coverage histograms
- Analytic coverage assessment (single location or vs. latitude)
- Numerical figures of merit

Table 10-5 summarizes some of the relative advantages and disadvantages of each of these approaches. In the end, there is no substitute for developing physical insight into the nature of the coverage and finding the most effective way to express that for each individual problem.

10.2.1.5 Earth Coverage for Geosynchronous Orbits

By definition, geostationary orbits maintain an approximately fixed location over the Earth. Small amounts of motion due to a low inclination, small eccentricity, or stationkeeping maneuvers have essentially no impact on the coverage area of the satellite. Consequently, the area of Earth covered is essentially fixed and is a function only of the minimum working elevation angle of the system. Figure 10-12 is a plot of the percent coverage of the surface of the Earth as a function of latitude for various minimum elevation angles. These coverage regions are drawn on the Earth in Fig. 10-13. For inclined geosynchronous orbits, all of the mechanisms of the low-Earth orbit analysis are applicable as discussed in Secs. 10.2.1.1 to 10.2.1.4. In addition, the motion of an inclined geosynchronous satellite relative to the surface of the Earth is a relative motion analemma as described in Sec. 8.5.

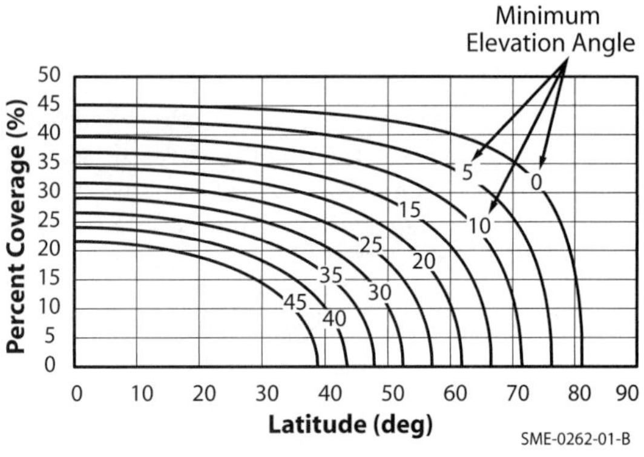

Live Calc

Fig. 10-12. Coverage from Geostationary Orbit as a Function of Minimum Elevation Angle.

Table 10-5, Fig. 10-12, Eq. 10-13◀

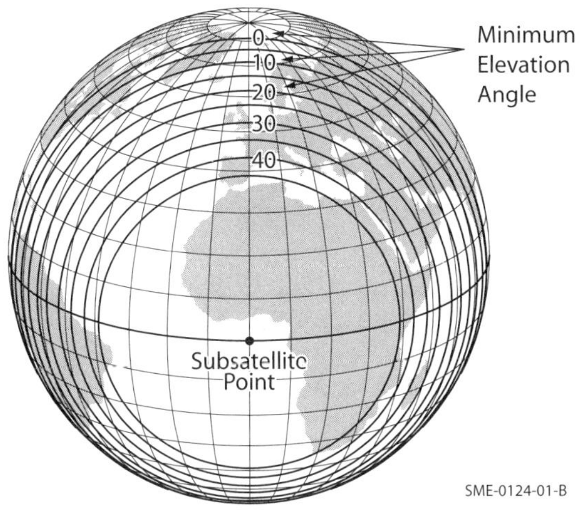

Fig. 10-13. Coverage from Geostationary Orbit Projected onto the Earth.

10.2.1.6 Coverage Analysis Example

Get More: See the book website for a detailed coverage example and simplified method of analyzing coverage.

10.2.2 Payload Performance vs. Altitude

As discussed in Sec. 5.3, the orbit, and particularly the altitude, affect a great many system parameters. (See Table 5-4 in Sec. 5.3.) The effect of the altitude of the satellite on the performance of the payload depends largely on whether we are looking down (observation payloads discussed in Sec. 10.2.2.1), illuminating the surface and looking at the return (radar and laser payloads, discussed in Sec. 10.2.2.2), or communicating (communications payloads, discussed in Sec. 10.2.2.3).

10.2.2.1 Observation Systems

Most observation payloads looking back at the Earth operate in visible or IR regions of the spectrum because the atmosphere is largely transparent at these wavelengths and the resolution is good. (See Chap. 17.) The key issue for most observation systems will be the *resolution*, i.e., the fineness of the detail that we can see on the Earth's surface, which depends on the size of the instrument and the altitude, as shown in Fig. 10-14. It also depends on the quality of the optical instrument, but space instruments are sufficiently expensive that they are essentially all diffraction-limited, i.e., effectively perfect optics. (The effects of diffraction on the image are discussed in Chap. 17.) Another critical characteristic is that the *brightness* (the amount of light per square degree) of an object on the Earth depends on the Sun angle and cloud cover, but does **not** depend on the distance. The amount of light from any object arriving at a camera lens, falls off as the square of the distance. (At twice the distance, the light fills a sphere which is twice as large and, therefore, has 4 times the surface area so the light per square meter is 1/4th as much.) But the angular size of the

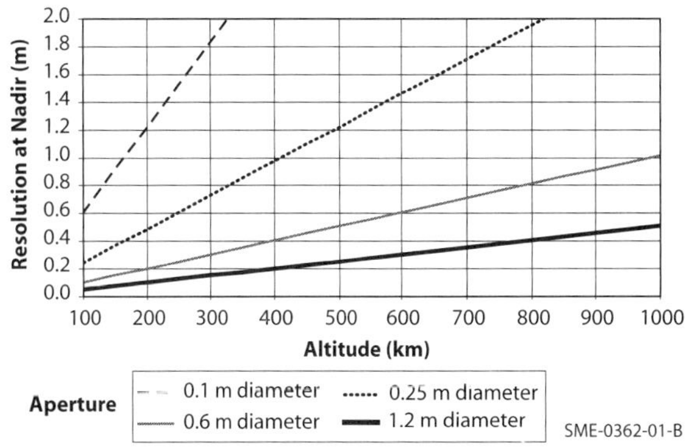

Live Calc: **Fig. 10-14. Resolution vs. Altitude at Visible Wavelengths for Satellites in Low-Earth Orbit.** The resolution in the IR will be 4 to 6 times worse because of the longer wavelength.

object is only 1/2 what it was and the angular area it subtends is also 1/4th as much. Therefore, the light per unit of angular area, or brightness, is independent of distance. This is clear when we take photos or simply look at the world around us. People that are twice as far away are half as high, but just as bright as those that are closer. Therefore, as the satellite gets higher, we don't need more light gathering power, but the resolution, i.e., the size of smallest object that we can see, gets worse.

Note that atmospheric attenuation, described in Chap. 17, is very strong, but does not change as the altitude changes. Spacecraft are above essentially all of the atmosphere, so that the amount of air that the light goes through depends on the elevation angle as seen from the ground, but not on the range to the spacecraft. Therefore, atmospheric attenuation depends on the elevation angle and the wavelength, but not on the distance or altitude.

10.2.2.2 Radar and Laser Systems

Space-based radar and space-based lasers are generally very high power devices because of the large distances involved in space missions. Nonetheless, they have been used throughout the space program to serve a variety of purposes. There are a number of advantages to the use of both radar and lasers in space, as discussed in Chap. 17. First, we can control both the amount of illumination and the spectral characteristics in order to get as much information as possible. In addition, we can adjust the wavelength to provide cloud penetration as in the case of using radar to map the surface of Venus. The largest detriment to this approach is that we must carry our own source of radar or laser illumination, which typically requires very high levels of power.

The dependence of radar power on distance depends on how the radar is used, as shown in Table 10-6. Space-based radar works in a series of *dwells*, or looks, in which a burst of energy is sent out by the radar antenna and typically received by the same antenna after bouncing off the target. Since the same antenna is used for both transmit and receive, the beam size or angular diameter of the field of view of the radar,

Table 10-6. Power Requirements as a Function of Range for Differing Beam and Target Sizes. See text for discussion.

Beam Size	Target Size	# of Dwells Required	Power per Dwell	Power for Whole Target
Large	Small	1	r^4	r^4
Small	Large	$1/r^2$	r^2	Independent of r
= Target	= Beam	1	Independent of r	Independent of r

will be the same for both transmit and receive. The beam size is inversely proportional to the size of the antenna, thus large antennas correspond to narrow beams and small antennas correspond to large beams, just as it is for parabolic radio antennas.

Ordinarily, we think of the beam size as being much larger than the target we are looking at. For example, in using radar to search for spacecraft, we will use a large beam to search for spacecraft with a small angular diameter (row 1 in Table 10-6). Assuming that we hit the target with the radar beam, a single dwell or look is sufficient to see the target. However, the required power per dwell increases as r^4, where r is the distance between the radar and the target. As the target gets farther away, the area covered by the radar beam increases as r^2, which means we must increase the power as r^2 to provide a given level of illumination at the target. With a given level of illumination, the surface brightness of the target in terms of the reflected radar energy will be independent of distance. However, the angular diameter of the target as seen from the radar antenna will fall off as $1/r^2$ such that the total intensity will fall off as $1/r^2$. This implies a need to further increase the power by r^2 to account for the smaller angular size. The net effect is that the power required with a large radar beam and a small target increases as r^4. Because the distances involved for a space-based radar are typically very large, they are ordinarily very high-power devices.

Next, consider what happens if the target is much larger than the beam size (row 2 in Table 10-6). This would occur, for example, if we want to make a radar map of the state of Texas. As we increase the distance between the target and the radar, the area covered on the ground becomes larger by r^2. In order to maintain a fixed level of illumination per square meter, we must increase the power per dwell proportional to r^2. However, we do not have the same problem in the receive antenna. The size of the receive beam is the same as the size of the area being illuminated. The surface brightness is constant, therefore, the energy return will also be constant. From the point of view of the radar, it is very much like looking at the surface of the Earth illuminated by the Sun. There is a constant illumination level irrespective of distance (due to the increased transmitter power in proportion to r^2); therefore, the surface brightness remains the same and the exposure time or received energy also remains the same. Consequently, the total power required per dwell increases only as r^2 rather than as r^4. What's more, is that the area covered by each dwell also increases as r^2 and, therefore, the number of dwells required to cover the state of Texas is reduced by $1/r^2$. Consequently, the total power required to make a radar map from space of the state of Texas is independent of the distance so long as the radar beam remains smaller than the size of the state.*

Finally, consider the case in which the target and the beam are the same size (row 3 in Table 10-6). Note that for a target of fixed size, this means that the antenna must get bigger as I get farther away in order to make the beam smaller so that it remains the same angular size as the target. In this case, the power per dwell required to provide a given level of illumination is independent of distance. All of the energy transmitted by the beam is falling on the target and none is being wasted. Consequently, the energy per square meter at the target is independent of distance (it is simply the energy in the beam divided by cross-sectional area of the target in m^2). As in the case above, I'm looking at a uniformly illuminated target, so once again, the required power per dwell will be independent of distance. Because the target and the beam are the same size, I require only a single look to see it and, consequently, the power required to view the entire target is independent of distance. Of course the practical limitation here is that as I get farther and farther away, I must use larger and larger diameter antennas in order to make the beam as small as the size of the target. If I do this, however, I can create a radar for which the power requirement is independent of distance.

The above results seem strange at first glance. The physical reason that the power required is independent of distance is that I am being efficient in using all of the energy that I am transmitting. None of it is wasted by spilling out into space. This is illustrated conceptually in Fig. 10-15. The same logic applies to laser illumination or the use of a flashlight and a pair of binoculars on the surface of the Earth.

10.2.2.3 Communications Systems

Communications systems follow essentially the same logic as radar systems, but without the need for observ-

* Another way to think of this is as follows. I need to illuminate the whole state with so many W/m^2 and, therefore, so many Watts. (There is a reasonably well-defined number of m^2 in Texas, even though that number is large.) I am being efficient in only taking a "picture" of those m^2 that are currently being illuminated. Therefore, I only need the prescribed total number of Watts, irrespective of how far away the "camera" and the "light source" are.

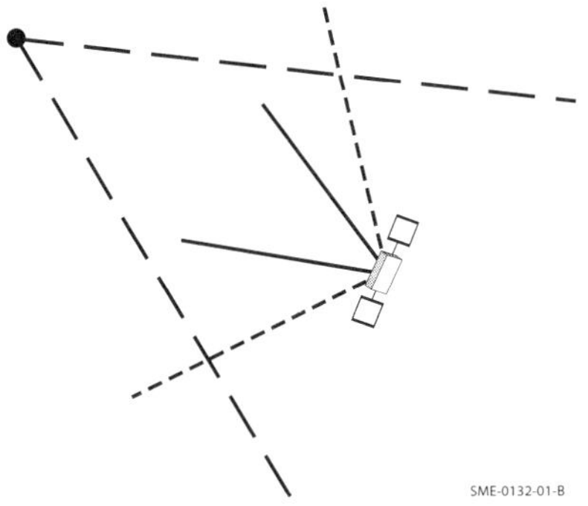

(A) Power Proportional to r^4

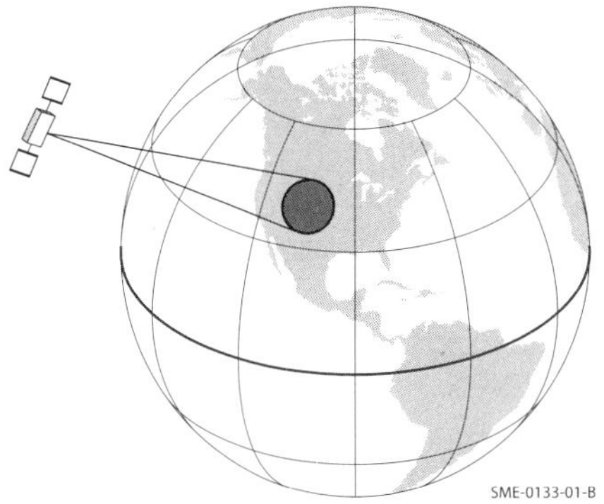

(B) Power Independent of r

Fig. 10-15. Power Requirements for Radar or Laser Illumination of Surfaces. (A) A broad illuminator and a small target. (B) A narrow illuminator and a large target. See text for discussion.

ing the reflected return signal. Normally, we have a large beam and a small target, as when we're trying to send signals to a spacecraft or a spacecraft at Jupiter is trying to send signals to Earth. In this case, the power required increases as r^2, where r is the distance to the target. However, there are circumstances where this is not the case. For a direct broadcast satellite in geosynchronous orbit, we design the size and shape of the antenna to just cover the region of interest, say the United States and southern Canada. If we were able to hold the spacecraft fixed at half the geosynchronous altitude, or we didn't mind the motion, then if we reduced the diameter of the antenna by half, the coverage area would be the same and it would take the same amount of power on the spacecraft.

The same logic holds for the GPS constellation. Here we want to provide a given number of W/m^2 from 4 non-collinear spacecraft over the entire surface of the Earth. If we change the constellation altitude, the number of satellites required will change, but, if the in coverage remains about the same, the total power required from the whole constellation will not change. The total number of Watts to cover the Earth does not change, no power is lost in space itself, and, therefore, the power needed by the constellation will be the same irrespective of altitude, although the size of the spacecraft antenna will change so as to just cover the Earth.

10.3 Orbit Cost—Delta V Budget and the Orbit Cost Function

The key characteristic of any orbit is performance vs. cost. What is the performance we can obtain vs. the cost required to put the payload into that orbit? In these terms, GEO is an "expensive" orbit in that approximately 5 kg must be launched into low-Earth orbit for every kilogram that ultimately arrives in geosynchronous orbit. The purpose of this section is to look at alternative launch and orbit options and quantify the assessment of cost as much as possible.

10.3.1 The Delta V (ΔV*) Budget

As discussed in Sec. 10.1 (Table 10-2), a space mission is a series of different orbits. For example, a satellite may be released in a low-Earth parking orbit, transferred to some mission orbit, go through a series of rephasings or alternative mission orbits, and then move to some final orbit at the end of its useful life. Each of these orbit changes requires energy. The *ΔV budget* is traditionally used to account for this energy. It is the sum of the velocity changes, or ΔVs, which must be imparted to the spacecraft throughout mission life. In a broad sense the ΔV budget represents the cost for each mission orbit scenario. In designing orbits and constellations, we must balance this cost against the utility achieved.

We use the ΔV budget to create a propellant budget and estimate the propellant mass, m_p, required for the space mission. (See Table 10-7 and Sec. 14.5.2.) For preliminary design, we estimate the propellant mass, m_p, needed for a space mission by using the *rocket equation* to determine the total required spacecraft plus propellant mass, $m_i \equiv m_0 + m_p$, in terms of the dry mass of the spacecraft, m_0, the total required ΔV, and the propellant exhaust velocity, V_0:

$$m_i = m_0 e^{\left(\Delta V / V_0\right)} \equiv m_0 e^{\left(\Delta V / I_{sp} g\right)} \tag{10-14}$$

where the *specific impulse*, $I_{sp} \equiv V_0 / g$, and g is the acceleration of gravity at the Earth's surface.† Typical exhaust velocities for chemical propellants are in the range of 2 to 4 km/s and up to 30 km/s for electric propulsion systems. We can see from Eq. (10-14) that a total ΔV much smaller than the exhaust velocity (i.e. a few hundred meters per second) will require a propellant mass that is a small fraction of the total mass. If the total ΔV required

* ΔV is also often written as delta V. Both notations are used in the book.

† Note that g in the definition of I_{sp} is best thought of as a units conversion factor. It does **not** depend on the actual acceleration of gravity where the rocket happens to be operating.

Table 10-7. Creating a ΔV Budget.

Item	Where Discussed	FireSat II Example	SCS Example
Basic Data Required			
Initial Conditions	Secs. 10.5.1, 13.5.7	200 km, 55 deg inc	20,500 km, 0 deg inc
Mission Orbit	Secs. 10.4, 10.5	700 km, 55 deg inc	21,000 km, 0 deg inc
Mission Duration (each phase)	Sec. 3.4	8 years	10 years
Orbit Maintenance Requirements	Secs. 9.5, 9.6	Altitude maintenance	Phase maintenance
Drag Parameters	Sec. 9.4.4, Table 9-9	BC = 25 kg/m^2 $\rho_{max} = 1.47 \times 10^{-13}$ kg/m^3	N/A
Orbit Maneuver Requirements	Sec. 9.6	None	Initial rephasing
End-of-Life Requirements	Chap. 30	Positive deorbit	raise 300 km
ΔV Budget (m/s)			
Orbit Transfer	Sec. 9.6, Eqs. (9-68)–(9-75), Fig. 10-16		
1st Burn	Eq. (9-69)	141 m/s	18 m/s
2nd Burn	Eq. (9-70)	139 m/s	17 m/s
Altitude maintenance			
LEO	Sec. 9.4.4, Fig. 10-17, Eq. (9-36)	21 m/s at solar max	N/A
GEO North/South	Eqs. (9-46, 9-47)*	N/A	N/A
GEO East/West	Eq. (9-48)*	N/A	N/A
Orbit Maneuvers			
Rephasing, Rendezvous	Eqs. (9-79)–(9-81)	N/A	5 m/s**
Node or Plane Change	Eqs. (9-77), (9-78)	N/A	N/A
Spacecraft Disposal	Eqs. (9-85)–(9-86), Fig. 10-17	183 m/s	20 m/s
Total ΔV		484 m/s	60 m/s
ΔV Savings	Tables (9-17)–(9-19), Sec. 9.6.3, Also see text.	N/A	N/A
Margin	Secs. 14.3.2, 26.1.2	In propellant budget	In propellant budget

* For GEO missions, N/S stationkeeping represents about 50 (m/s)/yr and E/W stationkeeping is at most about 10% of the N/S amount.
** Assigned value based on continuous adjustment of in-track phase

is equal to the exhaust velocity, then we will need a total propellant mass equal to $(e - 1) \approx 1.7$ times the mass of the spacecraft. Propulsion systems require additional structure such as tanks, so a ΔV much greater than the exhaust velocity is difficult to achieve. It may make the mission effectively impossible, or require some alternative, such as staging or refueling. The fractional mass of the spacecraft that must be devoted to propellant depends directly on the ΔV that must be supplied during the life of the mission. Consequently, calculating ΔVs is a basic step in assessing the cost of a particular orbit.

The process for constructing a ΔV budget is summarized in Table 10-7. First we assemble the needed data: the launch vehicle's initial conditions, the mission orbit or orbits, the mission duration, required orbit maneuvers or maintenance, and the mechanism for spacecraft disposal. We then transform each item into an equivalent ΔV requirement using the formulas given in Sec. 9.6 and listed in Table 10-7. Each of these formulas is discussed in more detail in the location referenced.

What is the ΔV cost of putting a satellite into orbit at varying altitudes? Figure 10-16 shows representative orbit acquisition and de-orbit ΔV requirements for a satellite dropped off at 185 km altitude. As can be seen from the figure, a plane change of 30 deg tends to dominate all of the other characteristics. Figure 10-17 shows the altitude maintenance ΔV for spacecraft at varying altitudes and with a ballistic coefficient of 100 kg/m^2. Recall from Eq. (9-36) that the ΔV requirement is inversely proportional to the ballistic coefficient such that ΔVs required for spacecraft with different ballistic coefficients can be easily estimated from the figure.

The higher the mission orbit, the more propellant it takes for both orbit acquisition and de-orbit, but the less it takes for orbit maintenance. This represents the ΔV cost which must be compared to the overall utility of the orbit to make an intelligent selection decision. Figure 10-18 shows the total ΔV budget as a function of altitude for representative LEO orbits. Depending on the desired lifetime of the mission and the phase during the solar cycle, there exists an optimal altitude that balances orbit acquisition and orbit maintenance. However, this may or may not be useful for orbit design because of the dramatically high variability in the atmospheric density

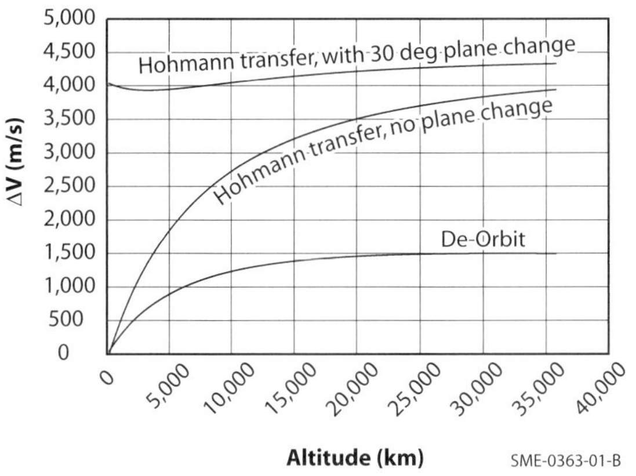

Live Calc

Fig. 10-16. Representative Orbit Transfer and De-Orbit ΔV Requirements. Assumes satellite is dropped off at 185 km altitude and raised via a 2-burn Hohmann transfer. De-orbited is assumed to be an elliptical orbit with a perigee altitude of 50 km.

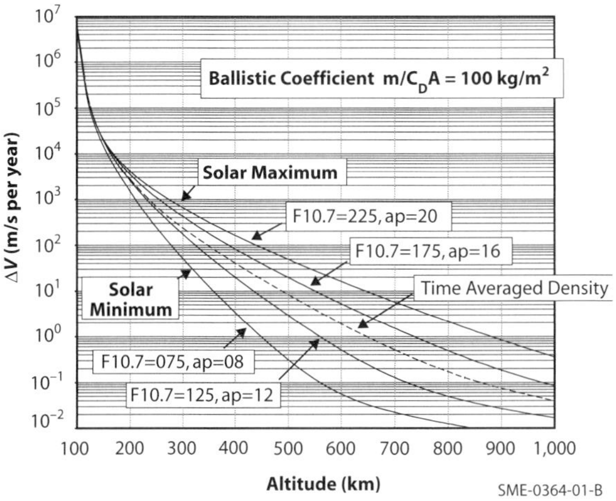

Live Calc

Fig. 10-17. Altitude Maintenance ΔV for a Ballistic Coefficient of 100 kg/m^2. The required ΔV will be inversely proportional to the ballistic coefficient. See Sec. 9.4.4 for a discussion of ballistic coefficients, solar activity, and atmospheric density.

(Sec. 9.4.4 and Fig. 10-17) and the other requirements on the orbit altitude. Beyond plane change requirements, the principal factors which will increase the ΔV cost in low-Earth orbit are a low altitude and long mission lifetime. The atmosphere increases in density exponentially as the altitude decreases, thus dramatically increasing drag as altitude comes down. In addition, large solar arrays or other appendages represent a large cross sectional area that will increase drag. A low mass per unit area, i.e., a large, lightweight satellite will also have higher drag than a small, dense satellite. Note that the shape and surface characteristics typically play only a secondary role (See Sec. 9.4.4). They impact the drag coefficient somewhat but usually play a relatively minor role in overall ΔV requirements, except at low altitude where it may become important.

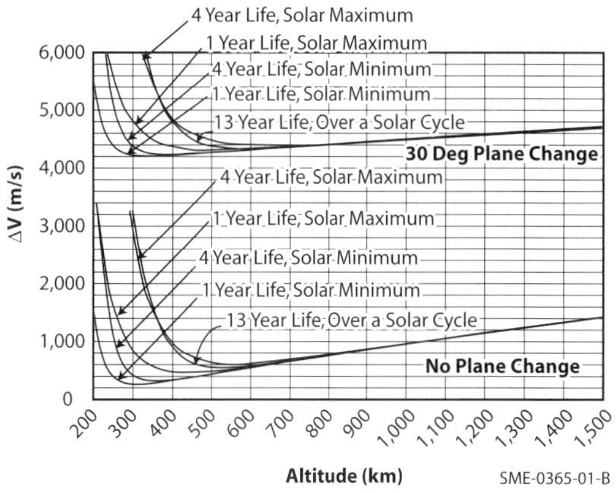

Live Calc

Fig. 10-18. ΔV Budget as a Function of Altitude for Low-Earth Orbits.

The ΔV budget has a strong impact on the propulsion requirements and, therefore, on the final cost and achievability of a space mission. Nonetheless, other factors can vary the propellant requirements relative to a nominal ΔV budget. For example, although rocket propulsion usually provides the ΔV, we can obtain very large ΔVs from a flyby of the Moon, other planets, or even the Earth itself [Kaufman et al. 1966; Meissinger, 1970]. As discussed in more detail in Sec. 9.6.3, a spacecraft in a planetary flyby leaves the vicinity of some celestial body with the same velocity relative to the body as when it approached, but in a different direction. This phenomenon is like the elastic collision between a baseball and a bat, in which the velocity of the ball relative to the bat is nearly the same, but its velocity relative to the surrounding baseball park can change dramatically. We can use flybys to change direction, to provide increased heliocentric energy for solar system exploration, or to reduce the amount of energy the satellite has in inertial space. For example, one of the most energy-efficient ways to send a space probe near the Sun is to use a flyby of Jupiter to reduce the intrinsic heliocentric orbital velocity of the Earth associated with any spacecraft launched from here.

A second way to produce a large ΔV without burning propellant is to use the atmosphere of the Earth or other planets to change the spacecraft's direction or reduce its energy relative to the planet. The manned flight program has used this method from the beginning to dissipate spacecraft energy for return to the Earth's surface. It can also be used to produce a major plane change through an *aeroassist trajectory* [Austin et al., 1982; Mease, 1988]. This has been used, for example, on Mars orbiter missions.

The *solar sail* is a third way to avoid using propellant. A large, lightweight sail uses solar radiation pressure to slowly push a satellite the way the wind pushes a sailboat. Of course, the low-pressure sunlight produces **very** low acceleration. Hence, very large solar sail areas are required as discussed in Sec. 18.7.

The aerospace literature discusses many alternatives for providing spaceflight energy because of its impor-

Table 10-7◀, Fig. 10-18, Eq. 10-14◀

tance for a variety of missions. Nonetheless, experimental techniques (i.e., those other than rocket propulsion and atmospheric braking) are risky and costly, so that normal rocket propulsion will ordinarily be used to develop the needed ΔV, if this is at all feasible.

To convert the ΔV budget described in Table 10-7 into a propellant budget, we must consider other characteristics as well. These include, for example, inefficiencies from thrusters misaligned with the desired ΔV direction, and any propulsion diverted from ΔV to provide attitude control during orbit maneuvers or desaturation of momentum wheels.

For most circumstances, the ΔV budget does not include margin because it results from astrodynamic equations with very little error relative to most other errors in system design. Instead, we maintain the margin in the propellant budget itself, where we can reflect other elements such as residual propellant. (See Sec. 14.5.) An exception is the use of ΔV to overcome atmospheric drag. Here the ΔV depends upon the density of the atmosphere, which is both highly variable and difficult to predict. Consequently, we must either conservatively estimate atmospheric density or incorporate a ΔV margin for low-Earth satellites to compensate for atmospheric variability.

10.3.2 The Orbit Cost Function

Given that we can estimate the total launch cost or specific launch cost for putting mass into low-Earth orbit, how can we translate this into the mass available in a mission orbit. Equivalently, what is the ultimate cost per kilogram to get where we want to go and achieve our mission objectives? To address this, we define the *Orbit Cost Function*, *OCF*, as the ratio of the mass available in a 185-km circular orbit due East from the launch site to that available in the mission orbit, or at the end of mission life. This can be thought of either as a multiplier on the cost of putting a spacecraft into its mission orbit, or, for a given launch vehicle, an inverse multiplier for the amount of payload that can be put into that mission orbit. Section 10.3.3 will look at the practical applications of using the *OCF* as a means of estimating launch costs and available mass.

The *OCF* depends on how the spacecraft is launched. For example, direct injection into Jupiter transfer orbit has a total *OCF* on the order of 10. Using a Venus swingby followed by an Earth swingby can reduce this to approximately 6. In this case, we can use the *OCF* to measure the performance gain associated with the swingbys and compare that with the time lost to determine whether the swingbys are worthwhile for a particular mission. Thus, the use of a Venus swingby for the Jupiter mission represents an increase in the available mass at Jupiter or a decrease in launch cost by a factor of approximately $10/6 \approx 1.7$. The question for the mission designer is then whether the added complexity and added time associated with these swingbys is worth the savings that are obtained.

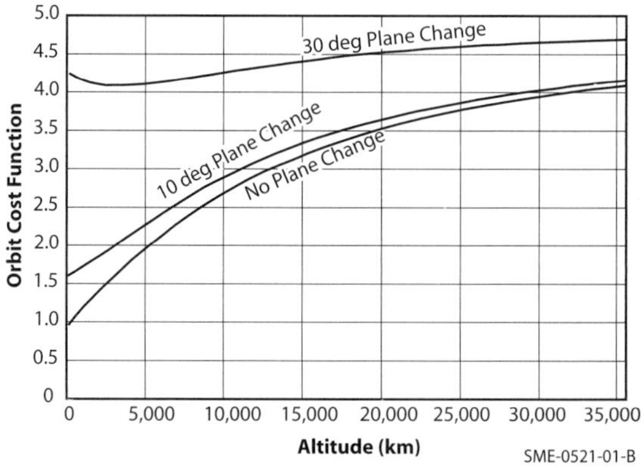

Live Calc

Fig. 10-19. Orbit Cost Function for Various Earth Orbiting Missions. The curves assume starting at a 185 km circular orbit and a circular orbit at the final mission altitude. The curves are for orbit acquisition only.

The orbit cost function is related to the required ΔV by:

$$OCF = (1+K)e^{\Delta V/V_0} - K = (1+K)e^{\Delta V/gI_{sp}} - K \quad (10\text{-}15)$$

where K is the fraction of the propellant mass assigned to tankage and other propellant hardware, typically 10%. I_{sp} is the specific impulse, g is the constant of gravity at the Earth's surface, and V_0 is the exhaust velocity of the propulsion system. An I_{sp} of 300 sec (typical for a bipropellant system) gives a V_0 value of 2.94 km/s. Depending on the purpose of the evaluation, we may choose to compare the Orbit Cost Function for simply getting to the mission orbit, through the useful life, or through de-orbit or disposal. If we calculate the *OCF* corresponding to the ΔV for multiple segments, then the cumulative cost function, $OCF_{A+B+C...}$, is just the product of the individual *OCF*s. Thus, if there is a series of mission phases or maneuvers *A, B, C...*, with OCF_A corresponding to ΔV_A, and so on, then

$$\Delta V_{A+B+C...} = \Delta V_A + \Delta V_B + \Delta V_C + ... \quad (10\text{-}16a)$$

and

$$OCF_{A+B+C...} = OCF_A \times OCF_B \times OCF_C \times ... \quad (10\text{-}16b)$$

Figure 10-19 shows the Orbit Cost Functions for typical Earth orbiting missions as a function of altitude and plane change. For more complex orbits, or interplanetary missions, the *OCF* is computed by first calculating the required ΔV, and then accounting for added tank mass and any other additional requirements such as the extra power required for electric propulsion. The *OCF* is tabulated for various Earth-oriented and interplanetary missions in Table 10-8.

We can also construct the Orbit Cost Function for a launch vehicle alone from the data supplied by the manufacturers. For example, Fig. 10-20A shows the mass as a function of orbit parameters as provided by the launch vehicle manufacturer for the Delta 7925 launch vehicle.

Table 10-8. Typical Orbit Cost Functions for Various Earth-Orbiting and Interplanetary Missions. Interplanetary missions assume a Hohmann transfer. *OCF* assumes I_{sp} of 300 sec and 10% tank mass.

Mission	Incremental ΔV			Cumulative Orbit Cost Function		
	Getting There	Mission Life	Disposal	Getting There	Mission Life	Disposal
200 km @ 90°	0.75	12.66	0.045	1.32	107.01	108.83
407 km @ 51.6°	0.39	0.192 0	0.104	1.16	1.24	1.29
500 km @ 28.7°	0.24	0.43 2	0.130	1.47	1.49	1.57
500 km Sun-synchronous	0.89	0.43 2	0.130	1.39	1.41	1.48
500 km @ 90°	0.89	0.043 2	0.130	1.39	1.41	1.48
1,000 km @ 28.7°	0.51	0.000 2	0.257	1.21	1.21	1.33
1,000 km Sun-synchronous	1.38	0.000 2	0.257	1.66	1.66	1.82
GTO (200 × 35,786 km)	2.80	0.411 4	0.024	2.75	3.20	3.23
GEO	4.95	0.521 5	0.018	5.82	7.06	7.11
Lunar Fly-by	3.14			3.10		
Lunar Orbit	3.23			3.20		
Lunar Lander	7.07			12.06		
Mars Fly-by	3.61			3.65		
Mars Orbit	5.69			7.51		
Mars Lander	9.30			25.86		
Mission Life ΔV = ΔV required for 10 years						

The Orbit Cost Function is the ratio of the mass that can be launched due East to 185 km low-Earth orbit to the masses shown in figure. This is plotted in Fig. 10-20B. As a specific example, the Delta II 7920 can put 5,140 kg into a 185 km circular orbit at 28.7 deg inclination and 3,220 kg into a Sun synchronous orbit at 800 km and 98.6 deg. Thus, the *OCF* for the Sun-synchronous orbit is 5,140/3,220 ≈ 1.60.

Typically, the highest mass to the final orbit can be achieved by using on-board propulsion. The reason for this is that we can then avoid putting the vehicle upper stage into the final spacecraft orbit. For example, if we launch a spacecraft to Jupiter using the traditional approach of a large upper stage, then the upper stage vehicle itself will also be put in the Jupiter transfer orbit. Using onboard propulsion, we will put only the spacecraft and some additional tankage into this very high energy orbit. An example of a high cost approach to orbit transfer is the Hubble Space Telescope, which was launched on board the Space Shuttle and is re-boosted from time to time by the Orbiter at the same time instruments are changed out. The reasons for this approach were to avoid entirely an on-board propulsion system and the potential for contamination from thruster firings as well as to avoid the possibility of propellant slosh providing even a low level of vibration to the telescope. In this case, a higher cost approach to orbit acquisition and maintenance was used to meet the mission requirements for near-zero disturbances and absolute minimization of potential contamination.

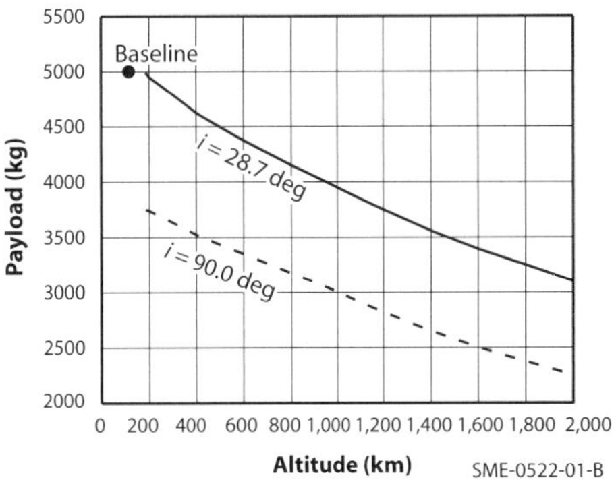

(A) Payload Mass

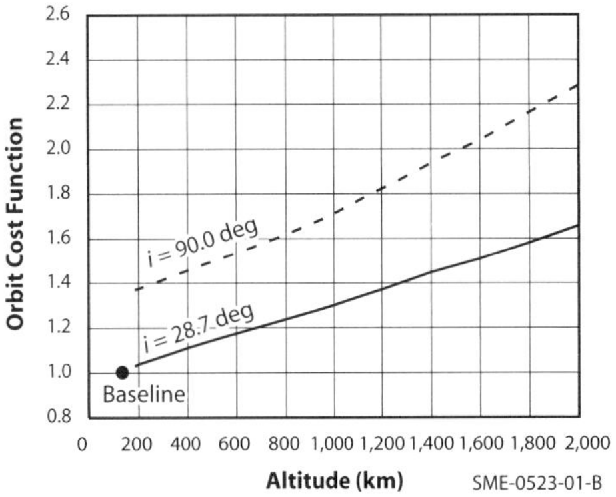

(B) Orbit Cost Function

Fig. 10-20. Performance Data for the Delta 7925 Launch Vehicle (3 m fairing). (A) Mass vs. orbit as provided by the launch vehicle manufacturer. (B) The Orbit Cost Function is simply the ratio of the mass that can be launched due East to a 185 km LEO orbit to the mass that can be put in the mission orbit. See text for discussion.

Table 10-9 compares alternative scenarios for a low-cost Jupiter mission based on (a) the traditional approach of using the launch vehicle upper stage for final injection to the transfer orbit, (b) using a Venus-Earth-Earth swing-by as was done for the Galileo mission, and (c) using on-board propulsion to provide direct transfer to the target planet in a modified launch mode as proposed by Meissinger, et al. [1997, 1998]. The planetary swing-by approach provides 4 to 5 times the payload mass at Jupiter, but at the cost of increasing the transfer time from 2.3 years to over 6 years. The on-board propulsion approach increases the payload available from the traditional approach by 50% to 100%, but with no increase in transfer time.

Finally, the selection criteria for launch vehicles for interplanetary missions are similar to those for Earth orbit missions, but use a different set of parameters to characterize vehicle performance. As discussed further in Sec. 10.7, launch requirements are defined in terms of the velocity or energy of the spacecraft at the point at which it has just escaped the gravitational pull of the Earth. The velocity at this time is called the *hyperbolic*

Table 10-9. Alternative Launch Scenarios for a Low-Cost Jupiter Mission. The number below each vehicle is the baseline mass in a due east orbit at 185 km. See text for discussion.

	At Jupiter Arrival			In Jupiter Orbit		
	Traditional Direct	Venus-Earth-Earth	MLM Direct*	Traditional Direct	Venus-Earth-Earth	MLM Direct*
Taurus XL/S (1,400 kg)	M = 62 kg T = 840 days C = 22.6	M = 316 kg T = 2,240 days C = 4.4	M = 143 kg T = 840 days C = 9.8	M = 49 kg T = 840 days C = 28.6	M = 249 kg T = 2,240 days C = 5.6	M = 109 kg T = 840 days C = 12.8
Delta II 7925 (5,089 kg)	M = 280 kg T = 840 days C = 18.2	M = 1,004 kg T = 2,240 days C = 5.1	M = 443 kg T = 840 days C = 11.7	M = 221 kg T = 840 days C = 23.0	M = 792 kg T = 2,240 days C = 6.4	M = 330 kg T = 840 days C = 15.4
Delta II 7925 H (6,107 kg)	M = 336 kg T = 840 days C = 18.2	M = 1,205 kg T = 2,240 days C = 5.1	M = 520 kg T = 840 days C = 11.7	M = 265 kg T = 840 days C = 23.0	M = 950 kg T = 2,240 days C = 6.4	M = 397 kg T = 840 days C = 15.4

M = mass at destination; T = transfer time; C = Orbit Cost Function; MLM = modifed launch mode
** US Patent No. 6,059,235, Microcosm Inc.*

excess velocity, V_∞, and the energy per unit mass at this time is called the reference launch energy, $C_3 \equiv V_\infty^2$. Typical values of C_3 are 12 km²/sec² for missions to Mars and 75 to 85 km²/sec² for missions to Jupiter, corresponding to V_∞ values of 3.5 and 8.7 to 9.2 km/sec, respectively. Figure 10-21 shows the payload mass of representative launch vehicles as a function of the C_3 provided. Because of the strong effect of the upper stage mass and staging process, there is no simple standard form of the rocket equation applicable to all of the vehicles. The data presented is based on detailed performance analysis by the vehicle manufacturers.

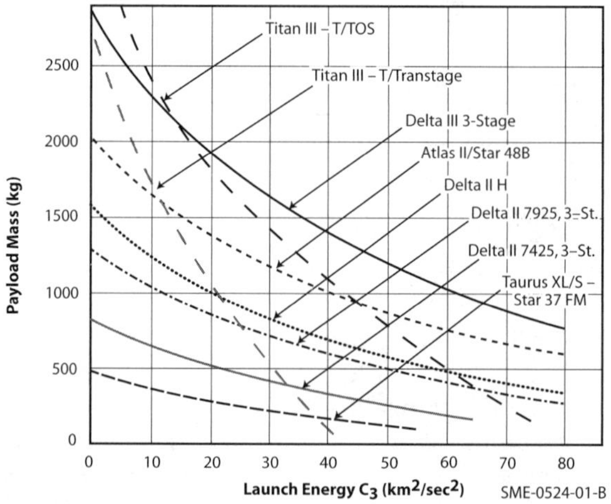

Fig. 10-21. Representative Range of US Launch Vehicle Escape Mission Performance. Data should be compared with mass to LEO from Table 11-23 to determine the Orbit Cost Function.

10.3.3. Estimating Launch Cost

What does it cost to put a payload in orbit? In general, there are two answers, depending on how we view the problem. On the one hand, having selected a launch vehicle and possibly an upper stage or orbit transfer mechanism, the cost is a fixed dollar value. Changing the mass of the spacecraft will have no impact unless we ultimately are forced to use a larger vehicle, or find that we can launch on a smaller one. Once we have selected a launch vehicle, there is little point in reducing weight beyond what is needed to accommodate that vehicle.

The second view is to look at the launch capacity per kilogram, or *specific launch cost*. Generally, as shown in Fig. 10-22 launching twice as much mass will cost twice as much. From this perspective, reducing the mass of some portion of the spacecraft can allow us to either reduce the launch cost by potentially using a smaller vehicle, or alternatively, to increase the spacecraft mass in some other area, i.e., by flying an additional payload instrument or more propellant to allow a longer mission at the final destination.

There are two factors which make the specific launch cost inappropriate or at least a poor measure of effectiveness for launch cost. First is the quantization in launch vehicles. Launchers are not available in an infinite variety of sizes, so that once we have chosen a vehicle, the cost per kilogram is immaterial. Second, there are economies of scale as vehicles get bigger, as shown in Fig. 10-22. In general, launching a spacecraft which

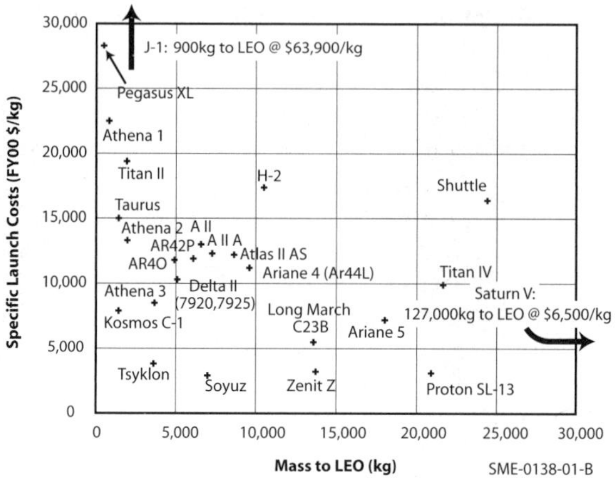

Fig. 10-22. Specific Launch Costs. Data from Tables 11-23 and 13-17. A II= Atlas II.

Table 10-10. Estimating Launch Cost. Specific launch costs will depend on additional factors, such as the vehicle selected and the negotiating leverage of the organization buying the launch. Thus, this process is more accurate at estimating relative cost than absolute cost.

Step	Where Discussed
1. Establish orbit parameters	Sec. 10.1–10.5
2. Establish spacecraft mass	Chap. 14
3. Estimate Orbit Cost Function for direct ascent and on-board propulsion, if applicable	Sec. 10.3.2
4. Obtain corresponding LEO mass	Result of (2) × (3)
5. Obtain rough estimate of launch cost from specific launch costs in Table 11-23	Secs. 10.3.3, 11.2.8
5A. For dedicated launch, select vehicle, or vehicles based on LEO mass or direct injection	Sec. 11.2.8, Chap. 26, Isakowitz et al. [2004]
6. Determine launch cost and available mass margin	See text.

is 10 times as massive will cost less than 10 times as much, because of the efficiency associated with larger vehicles. Many of the commercial low-Earth orbit communications constellations have chosen to use a variety of launch vehicles and typically launch several spacecraft on a single large vehicle. This allows them to take advantages of the economies of scale and, at the same time, implies that the cost per kilogram continues to be an important measure. As the mass of an individual spacecraft is reduced, this effect is multiplied by the number of spacecraft per vehicle and can allow either additional propellant on board each of the spacecraft, or potentially, allow an additional spacecraft to be put on a given launcher.

Despite the shortcomings, the specific launch cost is a useful concept in mission design. It allows us to get a rough estimate of the cost of getting our payload into low-Earth orbit at a time before launch vehicle options have been selected. The biggest shortfall of the specific launch cost model is that it only gives the cost of getting into low-Earth orbit. To use this concept effectively, we need to be able to apply it to multiple orbit types—to low-Earth orbit, geosynchronous orbit, Sun-synchronous orbits, interplanetary, and so on, so that we have an effective means of comparing orbit cost. This is the purpose of the Orbit Cost Function defined in Sec. 10.3.2. We can make use of this function to assess the relative costs between, for example, high-inclination posigrade orbits and Sun-synchronous orbits which are retrograde.

Table 10-10 summarizes the step-by-step process of estimating the launch cost for a particular mission. Overall, it is an iterative process of selecting launch parameters, spacecraft mass, and launch cost. We need to adjust all of these factors to achieve our mission objectives at minimum cost and risk.

We begin the launch cost estimation process by determining the orbit parameters for the mission. We then estimate the spacecraft dry mass consisting of the operational payload and the spacecraft bus exclusive of the tankage required for any propellant used in orbit transfer. Next, we establish the Orbit Cost Function based on the ΔV budget as defined in Sec. 10.3.1. If possible, we would like to do this for both direct ascent using the launch vehicle and for using on-board propulsion. This process allows us to compute a corresponding mass into low-Earth orbit for our particular mission. Given an amount of mass in low-Earth orbit, we can then estimate the launch cost from the specific launch cost given in Fig. 10-22 or using the costs for an appropriate vehicle or range of vehicles listed in Table 11-23 in Sec. 11.2.8. For dedicated launch, we can then do a preliminary selection of a specific vehicle or range of vehicles based upon either the mass in low-Earth orbit or direct injection. This gives us the first estimate of our launch cost and available mass margin. We then proceed to iterate the process as appropriate. For example, we may be able to reduce our mass estimates somewhat in order to obtain a smaller, lower-cost launch vehicle. Alternatively, if we have large margins, we may choose to increase the system mass in order to provide more payload or greater propellant for other mission activities.

There are a number of potential error sources in estimating launch costs. First, the cost of launch is a negotiated figure based in large part on the law of supply and demand. Thus, a user with a large number of payloads may be able to negotiate a lower price in exchange for a long-term contract. However, the capacity to negotiate a lower price depends on the existence of at least some level of competition within the launch vehicle arena. Thus, if the political decision is made to use only national launch vehicles, then typically, the competitive environment is substantially reduced and we can expect to pay significantly more for a given launch. Commercial launches, on the other hand, are usually not constrained to use vehicles from any particular nation or organization and, therefore, are in a better position to negotiate favorable prices based strictly on performance.

In addition to price negotiation, there is also the potential for dual payload launches. For example, we may choose to use a somewhat larger vehicle with substantial launch margin, and use that launch margin to include a secondary payload, which can cover a significant fraction of the cost of the launch vehicle. Third, there are overall evolutionary trends in launch costs that will impact the price which vehicle manufacturers can charge for vehicles of a given size. The net effect of these factors is to imply that the relative costs obtained by the above process will have a higher level of accuracy than the absolute costs.

For some missions, it is also useful to run the cost estimation process "backwards." To do this, we first select a representative launch vehicle, determine the mass available in low-Earth orbit, and use the Orbit Cost Function to estimate the mass available in the final mission orbit. This is a mechanism for sizing the payload to meet the capacity of a launch vehicle that falls within the budget constraints appropriate to the mission.

In general, the Orbit Cost Function provides a much easier mechanism for including launch and orbit transfer costs in system trades than the traditional approach of selecting a vehicle and making the process work within this constraint. We would like to include the mission orbit itself as a part of the system trade process and determine the impact of the mission orbit on the overall mission cost. The Orbit Cost Function is an analytic mechanism doing this.

10.4 Selecting Earth-Referenced Orbits

Earth-referenced orbits are typically among the most complex in terms of mission design for two reasons. First, there are a variety of specialized orbits that are design options that need to be evaluated and assessed. Second, the orbit parameters impact a large number of requirements in varying ways, such that no one orbit is ideal for all aspects of a mission. For example, a higher orbit typically provides better coverage, but is more expensive to get to in terms of the Orbit Cost Function (OCF), has lower resolution for observations, requires more power for communications, and is in a more adverse radiation environment.

Most of the steps in the orbit design process for Earth-referenced missions are the generic ones, defined in Table 10-1 in Sec. 10.1. The key issues that are specific to Earth-referenced missions are the orbit-related mission requirements, specialized Earth-referenced orbits, and the potential use of eccentric orbits. These are discussed in the three subsections below.

10.4.1 Mission Requirements for Earth-Referenced Orbits

As listed previously in Table 10-1 in Sec. 10.1, the first step in the orbit selection process after dividing the mission into phases is to accumulate the orbit-related mission requirements. The mission requirements which normally have the greatest effect on Earth-referenced orbits are listed in Table 10-11. The principal conclusion here is that for Earth-orbiting missions, a large number of mission requirements are orbit-dependent. The second most important conclusion from the table is that the orbit parameter that is most important in orbit selection is the altitude, with the secondary parameter being the inclination. Altitude is the main determining factor in nearly all of the orbit-related mission requirements. The altitude is the primary determinant of most aspects of coverage, performance, spacecraft environment, launch cost, and even the end-of-life options available to the spacecraft. Consequently, the most common trade here is one of coverage as a measure of performance versus ΔV or *OCF* as a measure of cost.

Another key factor in altitude selection is the satellite's radiation environment. As described in Sec. 7.3, the radiation environment undergoes a dramatic change at an altitude of approximately 1,000 km (See Fig. 7-11). Below this altitude, the atmosphere quickly clears out charged particles such that the radiation density is relatively low. Above this altitude are the Van Allen Belts, where the high level of trapped radiation can greatly reduce the lifetime of spacecraft components. Consequently, most Earth-referenced mission orbits separate naturally into *low-Earth orbit* (LEO), below 1,000 km, and *geosynchronous orbit* (GEO), which is largely above the Van Allen Belts. Mid-range altitudes have coverage characteristics that may make them particularly valuable for some missions. However, the added shielding or reduced life stemming from this region's increased radiation environment also makes them more costly. Nonetheless, the increased coverage to be obtained at higher altitudes has tended to push up the minimum altitude defined as LEO. For example, LEO communications constellations have been considered at altitudes of up to 1,500 km. At these altitudes, not only is the radiation environment harsher, but the potential options for end-of-life are also more difficult. Low-Earth orbit spacecraft are often de-orbited or allowed to reenter at the end of their useful life. Above 1,000 km, this process occurs extremely slowly when driven only by drag and requires

Table 10-11. Principal Mission Requirements that Normally Affect Earth-Referenced Orbit Design. See Sec. 10.1 for a discussion of the orbit design process.

Mission Requirement	Parameter Affected	Where Discussed
Coverage Continuity Frequency Duration Field Of View (Or Swath Width) Ground Track Area Coverage Rate Viewing Angles Earth Locations Of Interest	Altitude Inclination Node (only relevant for some orbits)	Chap. 8, Sec. 10.2
Sensitivity or Performance Exposure or Dwell Time Resolution Aperture	Altitude	Sec. 10.2.2, Chaps. 16, 17
Environment and Survivability Radiation Environment Lighting Conditions Hostile Action	Altitude (Inclination usually secondary)	Secs. 7.5, 8.2.4
Launch Capability Launch Cost On-Orbit Weight Launch Site Limitations	Altitude Inclination	Sec. 10.3.3, Chap. 26
Ground Communications Ground Station Locations Use Of Relay Satellites Data Timeliness	Altitude Inclination	Sec. 8.4, Chaps. 28, 29
Orbit Lifetime	Altitude Eccentricity	Fig. 9-18 (Sec. 9.4.4)
Legal or Political Constraints Treaties Launch Safety Restrictions International Allocation	Altitude Inclination Longitude in GEO	Secs. 12.3

Table 10-12. Specialized Orbits Used for Earth-Referenced Missions. Typically the orbit design process consists of deciding whether any of the specialized orbits should be used followed by a general trade on other orbits. Section 9.5 provides the physical basis for each orbit; this section discusses applications.

Orbit	Characteristic	Applications	Applications Discussed	Physics Discussed
Geosynchronous (GEO)	Maintains nearly fixed position over equator	Communications, weather, surveillance	Sec. 10.4.2.1	Sec. 9.5.1
Sun Synchronous	Orbit plane rotates so as to maintain approximately constant orientation with respect to Sun	Earth resources, weather	Sec. 10.4.2.2	Sec. 9.5.3
Molniya (also called HEO)	Apogee/perigee do not rotate	High latitude communications	Sec. 10.4.2.3	Sec. 9.5.4
Frozen Orbit	Minimizes changes in orbit parameters	Any orbit requiring stable conditions	Sec. 10.4.2.4	Sec. 9.5.6, Vallado [2007]
Repeating Ground Track	Subsatellite trace repeats	Any orbit where constant viewing angles are desirable	Sec. 10.4.2.4	Sec. 9.5.2
Repeat Coverage Orbit	Coverage of multiple successive orbits	Whenever multiple successive views are needed	Sec. 10.4.2.6	Sec. 10.4.2.6

Table 10-13. Advantages and Disadvantages of Specialized Earth-Referenced Orbits.

Orbit	Advantages	Disadvantages
Geosynchronous	Continuous viewing of one region; fixed ground antenna	Poor polar region coverage, very high cost, very long range
Sun-Synchronous	Maintains roughly constant Sun angle relative to orbit plane	High cost
Molniya (HEO)	Provides extended coverage of high latitude regions	High cost; widely varying ranges, Earth size, and rates drive up spacecraft cost; high radiation
Frozen Orbit	Maintains stable conditions for near-circular orbits	None
Repeating Ground Track	Coverage repeats	Orbit perturbations can resonate
Repeat Coverage Orbit	Best coverage of a specific latitude band	Doesn't provide whole Earth coverage; time of day of coverage changes

a very substantial ΔV if it is to be done by an on-board propulsion system. Consequently, in the regime above 1,000 km, the end-of-life option often regarded as the most desirable is to raise the spacecraft 50 to 100 km higher in order to remove it from the constellation structure. Note however, that this process creates one or more "graveyard" regimes in which a large number of spent non-functioning spacecraft could accumulate. Of course, one constellation's graveyard orbit could be another constellation's operational orbit.

10.4.2 Specialized Earth-Referenced Orbits

After having defined the orbit related mission requirements, the next step in finding an appropriate Earth-referenced orbit is to determine if any of the specialized orbits listed in Table 10-12 are appropriate. The advantages and disadvantages of these alternatives are summarized in Table 10-13 and discussed in more detail below. Chapter 9 provides a detailed discussion of the physical basis of each of these orbit types. For purposes of mission design, we need to examine each of these specialized orbits individually to see if its characteristics will meet the mission requirements at a reasonable cost. Space missions do not need to be in specialized orbits, but these orbits have come into common use because of their valuable characteristics for many missions. Because they do constrain orbit parameters such as altitude and inclination, we first determine whether or not to use one of the specialized orbits before doing the more detailed design trades in Table 10-1 in Sec. 10.1.

It is frequently the existence of specialized orbits which yields very different solutions for a given space mission problem. For example, a geosynchronous orbit may provide the best coverage characteristics but may demand too much propellant, instrument resolution, or power, or have too high an Orbit Cost Function. The trade of value vs. cost can lead to dramatically different solutions depending on mission needs. A Sun-synchronous orbit is typically 30% more expensive than a low-inclination prograde orbit. Nonetheless, for many observation satellites such as Earth resources or weather, the advantage of being able to see locations on the ground at the same time of day and under the same lighting conditions on a continuing basis outweighs the additional cost of this type of orbit.

10.4.2.1 Geosynchronous Orbits (GEO)

Prior to the introduction of low-Earth orbit communications constellations, geosynchronous orbit represented the single most used orbit in space. It accounted for approximately 50% of satellite launches during the 1990s. The physical properties of geosynchronous orbit and orbit perturbations are discussed in Sec. 9.5.1; in addition, Pocha [1987] and Soop [1994] provide very detailed discussions of geosynchronous orbit design and stationkeeping approaches. Chapter 16 discussed the design of geosynchronous communications satellites. GEO satellite applications and design are also discussed in detail by Gordon and Morgan [1993] and Maral and Bousquet [2010].

The principal applications for geosynchronous orbit are communications (both two-way and direct broadcast), weather, and Earth surveillance. However, as shown in Chap. 16, GEO is getting full. There are now relatively few orbital slots available over regions of particular interest, such as the mid-Atlantic or mid-Pacific areas used for communications between North America, Europe, and Japan. Similarly, slots over Europe and North America used for internal communications are also becoming full.

Overcrowding and the potential for satellite collisions represent major problems for geosynchronous orbit, as discussed in detail by Reijnen and De Graaff [1989]. In a sense, space is large and the potential for collisions between satellites is small. Nonetheless, the cost of getting spacecraft to GEO is extremely high and there is no current potential for being able to retrieve or actively recover either spent spacecraft or debris. In addition, there are essentially no natural perturbations that will remove debris from geosynchronous orbit. Consequently, any sequence of either spacecraft explosions or inadvertent collisions which produce a significant debris cloud in GEO may make the orbit effectively unusable for the foreseeable future. (An interesting potential alternative to GEO using solar radiation pressure for orbit maintenance is the cylindrical orbit discussed in Sec. 18.7.2.)

Because there is currently no mechanism for removing debris from GEO, the only approach for protecting it is to not allow actions which have the potential for generating debris. This means that spacecraft should be removed from geosynchronous orbit while they are still responding to commands and while there is still propellant available to do so. Thus, in order to preserve this unique resource, we must be willing to turn off operational spacecraft prior to the use of their last few grams of propellant. The graveyard orbit for geosynchronous spacecraft is to put them in an orbit approximately 200 km above GEO. At this altitude, natural perturbations will cause the inclination to oscillate as discussed in Sec. 9.5.1. However, these oscillations in orbit elements will not bring the spacecraft back into the geosynchronous ring in any reasonable amount of time, i.e., within several hundred thousand years. In addition, the ΔV required to raise the altitude is extremely small. Increasing the altitude by 200 km requires a ΔV of only 7.4 m/sec.

As discussed in Sec. 9.5.1, the principal perturbative forces in GEO are solar/lunar perturbations, which cause a general North/South drift or change in inclination, and the effect of the out-of-roundness of the Earth's equator, which cause a very slow drift in the East/West direction. In both cases, the effects are extremely predictable and essentially continuous. Consequently, this represents an excellent application for electric propulsion for orbit maintenance. A nearly continuous low level of thrust can be used to maintain the spacecraft in geosynchronous orbit. Typically, the North/South stationkeeping is required for operational purposes so that the spacecraft can keep its target regime on Earth in view, and equally important, so that Earth antennas can be pointed at the spacecraft without having to be continuously steered. The East/West stationkeeping, while requiring only 10% of the ΔV of North/South stationkeeping, is perhaps more important in that it prevents either physical or communications interference with satellites in a neighboring orbital slot. Without nearly continuous East/West stationkeeping, geosynchronous satellites would continuously slide through the orbit slots assigned to other spacecraft, thus providing both significant communications interference and even the potential for satellite collisions.

Synchronous orbits are possible around other planets and satellites as well, although, like the Earth, they may be significantly influenced by various perturbations. Both the formulas to determine these orbits and the characteristics of synchronous orbits for a variety of other central bodies are listed in Table 9-12 in Sec. 9.5.1.

10.4.2.2 Sun-Synchronous Orbits

As discussed in Sec. 9.5.3, a *Sun-synchronous orbit* is one in which the perturbation due to the Earth's oblateness causes the orbital plane to rotate in inertial space at a rate equal to the average rate of the Earth's rotation about the Sun. Consequently, in a Sun-synchronous orbit, the position to the Sun relative to the orbit plane remains approximately constant. The general motion of the Sun relative to the orbit plane is shown in Fig. 9-27 in Sec. 9.5.3. From an applications perspective, the Sun-synchronous orbit has the principal advantage of maintaining approximately constant Sun angles. This means that for Earth resources satellites, for example, the angle of illumination will be approximately constant as photographs of a given region are taken over time. Consequently, it is significantly easier to interpret the photos and look for changes over time. In addition, visual observations are best done when the shadows are long, i.e., in the morning or late afternoon. Thus, 9 am–9 pm and 3 am–3 pm orbits are often chosen for Earth observations.

Sun-synchronous orbits have also been used by some missions as a means of reducing the battery size or eliminating a second gimbal in the solar array drive because of the nearly constant Sun angle. Thus, rather than requiring a 2-axis gimbal, a single-axis gimbal is sufficient and the cost of the spacecraft can be marginally reduced. This is an example of an application of the Sun-synchronous orbit which is probably inappropriate in most circumstances. The Sun-synchronous orbit requires an additional cost of approximately 30% to obtain this orbit. This cost is far in excess of the benefit achieved by having only a single gimbal in the solar array drive. In addition, it also adds another element of risk to the mission by creating a new failure mode. If the launch vehicle or propulsion system are unable to achieve or to maintain a Sun-synchronous orbit, then a failure of the mission is possible. If the system could operate under non-Sun-synchronous conditions, then there would have been no reason for the orbit in the first place. Consequently, choosing a Sun-synchronous orbit for purely spacecraft bus functions is an incorrect engineering choice in most circumstances.

Live Calc

Table 10-14. Representative Sun-Synchronous Orbits for Other Central Bodies.

Central Body	Altitude (km)	Inclination (deg)	Period (min)
Mars	1,000 5,000	94.85 144.52	147.2 388.4
Jupiter	1,000 5,000	90.08 90.09	181.5 196.7
Saturn	1,000 5,000	90.04 90.05	257.8 283.5
Uranus	1,000 5,000	90.01 90.02	183.3 232.4
Neptune	1,000 5,000	90.02 90.04	166.0 206.1

Sun-synchronous orbits are also possible around other central bodies. Representative parameters for these orbits are given in Table 10-14. The advantages of these orbits are similar to their advantages when used on the Earth. That is, a constant level of illumination allows us to compare photographs taken at different times in order to more accurately determine physical changes that may be taking place on the planet or moon that we are orbiting. For example, Sun-synchronous orbits would be appropriate for examining seasonal variations on Mars, or variations as a function of volcanic activity or electromagnetic storms in the vicinity of Jupiter's moon, Io. Note that in the case of other planets and satellites, Sun-synchronous orbits are significantly less expensive to achieve. Generally, the orbit plane in which the spacecraft arrives can be adjusted by very small ΔVs applied during the orbit transfer. Consequently, the high cost associated with Sun-synchronous orbits on the Earth is not necessarily a problem for other central bodies. However, the parameters associated with Sun-synchronous orbits for other central bodies, such as the required altitude or inclination may make them inappropriate for other reasons, such as viewing distance or excessive perturbations. Note that for the gas giants, the oblateness is large and the revolution rate about the Sun is slow such that Sun-synchronous orbits are essentially polar.

10.4.2.3 Molniya (HEO) Orbits

A *Molniya orbit* is a *Highly Elliptical Orbit* (HEO) inclined at the critical inclination of 63.4 deg (or 180 – 63.4 = 116.6 deg) in order to prevent apogee and perigee from rotating. The fundamental equations and physical properties for Molniya orbits were discussed in Sec. 9.5.4. The basic application of these orbits is for communications or observations at high northern latitudes where geosynchronous spacecraft are ineffective or inaccessible. Consequently, Molniya orbits have been used for communications in Russia and the former Soviet Union for an extended period of time.

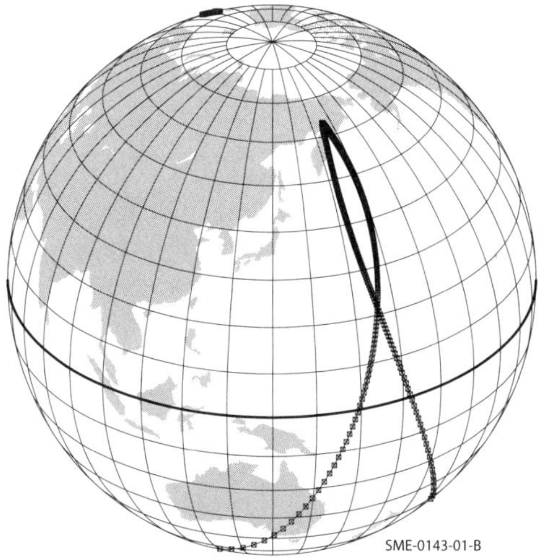

Fig. 10-23. A Molniya Orbit with a 12-Hour Period. With two satellites in this orbit, one of them will always be within 24 deg of apogee in true anomaly and with three satellites one will always be within 15 deg.

The properties of representative Molniya orbits for the Earth are summarized in Table 10-15 and a typical orbit ground track is shown in Fig. 10-23. Note that there are tick marks along the orbit at equal time intervals that clearly illustrates the long period of time that the spacecraft remains over high northern latitudes. Because each of the satellites tends to "hang" at apogee, it is straightforward to use two or three satellites in orbits of this type to provide good coverage of far northern or far southern regimes. Unfortunately, there are a number of disadvantages of the Molniya orbit, such as the non-stationary ground track with respect to the Earth, and the fact that it travels through the Van Allen radiation belts on a continuing basis, and consequently has a severe radiation environment. Nonetheless, the Molniya orbit provides the best mechanism for providing extended coverage in high latitude regions, and therefore, is appropriate for any type of communication, observation, or sampling system that requires coverage of this type. (The statite, a

Live Calc

Table 10-15. Properties of Representative Molniya Orbits. (See also Table 9-15 in Sec. 9.5.4.)

Period Hours	Eccentricity	Apogee Height (km)	Perigee Height (km)	Fraction of Orbit with 90° < True Anomaly < 270°	Fraction of Orbit with 120° < True Anomaly < 240°
2	0.1713	3,062	300	60.9%	43.4%
6	0.6016	20,471	300	85.8%	73.6%
12	0.7490	40,164	300	92.7%	84.9%
24	0.8419	71,426	300	96.3%	91.7%
36	0.8794	97,647	300	97.5%	94.3%
48	0.9004	121,051	300	98.1%	95.6%
72	0.9240	162,674	300	98.8%	97.0%

potential alternative using solar radiation pressure, is discussed in Sec. 18.7.2.)

The period and eccentricity of the Molniya orbit depend on the gravitational parameters of the Earth. However, as discussed in Sec. 9.5.4, the fact that it is at the critical inclination of 63.4 deg, does not depend on any parameters of the Earth. Consequently, Molniya orbits about any of the other planets or satellites will also be at an inclination of 63.4 deg relative to the equator of that central body. Thus, we might choose a Molniya-style orbit for monitoring the polar regions of Mars or providing communications or observations for scientific activities at the poles and the Moon.

10.4.2.4 Repeating Ground Track Orbits

A *Repeating Ground Track* is simply an orbit in which the ground trace of the satellite will repeat itself after one or more days. This can be very convenient for Earth observations and communications in that the general characteristics of the flight path with respect to a ground target or observer on the ground is a repeating pattern. Recall from Sec. 9.5.2 that a repeating ground track comes about when we go through an integral number of orbits in a sidereal day, taking into account the orbit rotation due to the oblateness of the Earth. Consequently, the fundamental requirement for a repeating ground track is:

$$H = \mu^{1/3}\left(\frac{n\pi}{180}\right)^{-2/3} - R \qquad (10\text{-}17)$$

$$n = (j/k)(360 - \dot{\Omega}) - (\dot{\omega} + \dot{M}) \qquad (10\text{-}18)$$

where

$$\dot{\Omega} = -2K_2 a^{-7/2}\cos i\left(1-e^2\right)^{-2} \qquad (10\text{-}19)$$

where the initial estimate of a for Eqs. (10-20 and 10-21)

$$\dot{\omega} = K_2 a^{-7/2}\left(5\cos^2 i - 1\right)\left(1-e^2\right)^{-2} \qquad (10\text{-}20)$$

$$\dot{M} = K_2 a^{-7/2}\left(3\cos^2 i - 1\right)\left(1-e^2\right)^{-3/2} \qquad (10\text{-}21)$$

is just the repeating ground track value of the semimajor axis in the absence of the oblateness correction, i.e., $a_{initial} = K_1(j/k)^{-2/3}$, where j and k are integers. As discussed in Sec. 9.5.2, $\dot{\Omega}$ is the node rotation rate $\dot{\omega}$ is the argument of perigee rotation rate, and $\dot{M}$ is the mean anomaly rotation rate due to oblateness. As usual, the parameters, a, e, and i are the semimajor axis, eccentricity, and inclination of the repeating ground track orbit and R is the radius of the central body. Values of K_1 and K_2 for various objects in the solar system are given in Table 10-16. (See Sec. 9.5.2 for the formulas for these constants.) Note that with the constants in the table, the rotation rates are all expressed in deg/sidereal day ≡ deg/day*, where "sidereal day" is the rotation period **of the body the satellite is orbiting about** relative to the fixed stars. The satellite completes j orbits in k sidereal days.

The principal merit of a repeating ground track is that we continue to sample the same region of the planet's surface on a repeating basis. This is useful, for example, in planet observations where we are interested in determining changes from one time to the next. For the Earth, this can be particularly important for evaluating changes in vegetation, water levels, pollution parameters, population growth, or deforestation. The principal demerit of a repeating ground track orbit is that it also flies through the variations in the planet's geopotential in the same fashion on successive orbits. Thus, if the spacecraft flies just to the left of the Himalayas on one day, it will do so on successive days as well. This allows the potential of resonance effects to build up, comparable to vibrations in a physical structure, which can greatly magnify the impact of the perturbations and cause significantly larger variations in the motion of the satellite. Consequently, a repeating ground track should be chosen only if there is an operational reason to do so, since it may require significant propellant utilization to counter the cumulative perturbative forces.

For the Earth, an interesting subgroup of the repeating ground track orbits are those for which the inclination, and therefore node rotation rate, is adjusted so that the repeat occurs on precise multiples of the civil day of

Table 10-16. Repeating Ground Track Parameters for Representative Central Bodies.

Body	Radius, R (km)	Sidereal Day (sec)	μ (km^3/sid day^2)	K_1 (km)	K_2 ($km^{3.5}$/sid day)
Mercury	2,439	$5.067\,032 \times 10^{6}$	$5.656\,674 \times 10^{17}$	$3.666\,292 \times 10^{6}$	$2.013\,338 \times 10^{11}$
Venus	6,052	$2.099\,606 \times 10^{7}$	$1.435\,799 \times 10^{20}$	$5.988\,628 \times 10^{7}$	$8.887\,296 \times 10^{12}$
Earth	6,378.136	$8.616\,410\,04 \times 10^{4}$	$2.959\,310\,16 \times 10^{15}$	$2.959\,310\,16 \times 10^{15}$	$1.029\,549\,648 \times 10^{14}$
Moon	1,738	$2.360\,591 \times 10^{6}$	$2.732\,032 \times 10^{16}$	$8.023\,799 \times 10^{5}$	$7.590\,274 \times 10^{10}$
Mars	3,397.2	$8.864\,266 \times 10^{4}$	$3.382\,663 \times 10^{14}$	$2.081\,545 \times 10^{4}$	$3.126\,615 \times 10^{11}$
Jupiter	71,492	$3.572\,986 \times 10^{4}$	$1.618\,757 \times 10^{17}$	$8.884\,214 \times 10^{4}$	$2.274\,883 \times 10^{16}$
Saturn	60,268	$3.780\,000 \times 10^{4}$	$5.421\,019 \times 10^{16}$	$6.405\,589 \times 10^{4}$	$1.043\,377 \times 10^{16}$
Uranus	25,559	$5.616\,000 \times 10^{4}$	$1.827\,396 \times 10^{16}$	$5.804\,523 \times 10^{4}$	$7.947\,793 \times 10^{14}$
Neptune	24,764	$6.635\,520 \times 10^{4}$	$2.998\,011 \times 10^{16}$	$7.651\,243 \times 10^{4}$	$3.185\,514 \times 10^{14}$
Pluto	1,151	$5.518\,109 \times 10^{5}$	$2.740\,457 \times 10^{14}$	$6.566\,573 \times 10^{4}$	N/A
Phobos	11.3	$2.755\,384 \times 10^{4}$	$5.385\,410 \times 10^{5}$	$1.115\,318 \times 10^{1}$	N/A
Deimos	6.3	$1.090\,749 \times 10^{5}$	$1.889\,503 \times 10^{6}$	$4.241\,016 \times 10^{1}$	N/A
Io	1,821.3	$1.528\,535 \times 10^{5}$	$1.392\,519 \times 10^{14}$	$2.226\,665 \times 10^{4}$	N/A
Europa	1,565	$3.068\,220 \times 10^{5}$	$3.015\,221 \times 10^{14}$	$4.583\,899 \times 10^{4}$	N/A

24 hours. For these orbits, the ground track not only repeats but does so at the same time each day, every other day, or on a weekly basis, depending on the orbit parameters chosen. We call an orbit of this type a *civil orbit* because it is one in which the spacecraft is keeping time with civil functions, rather than requiring the many users on the ground to keep track of a spacecraft ephemeris. Thus, for example, for relaying data to the home office, we could catch the "5:10 to London" on a daily basis such that we could transmit data at the same time each day and have it received at a fixed, later time.

10.4.2.5 Frozen Orbits

As discussed in Sec. 9.5.6, frozen orbits come about because circular orbits are not inherently stable. On the other hand, stable or frozen orbits are available with very low values of eccentricity, such that they are nearly circular for most practical applications. Frozen orbits can be used with essentially any low-Earth orbit and are largely used as a means of maintaining a more precise orbit and reducing the propellant requirements for orbit maintenance. For applications in which a circular orbit is desirable, a frozen orbit will somewhat reduce the propellant utilization and has no significant drawbacks. For additional details on creating a frozen orbit, for example, Vallado [2007].

10.4.2.6 Repeat Coverage Orbits

A *Repeat Coverage Orbit* (RCO) is a prograde orbit that provides multiple successive orbits of coverage for a specific location on the Earth [Wertz, 2005]. Most of the other specialized orbits make use of particular orbit perturbations, such as J_2, to create unique conditions. In contrast, the RCO simply takes advantage of the coverage characteristics brought about by the Earth rotating under the orbit plane as discussed in detail in Secs. 10.2.1.2 and 10.2.1.3.

Figure 10-24A shows the coverage swath of a typical satellite in a low Earth orbit as the Earth rotates under it. The most coverage will occur at a latitude, L, equal to the orbit inclination, i, minus half the swath width, λ_{max}. This is also clear from Fig. 10-10 in Sec. 10.2.1.3. Equation 10-13 in the same section gives the coverage formula. Figure 10-24B shows 5 successive orbits that provide coverage of a specific location, shown as a small black square. Here, you can see what happens as the Earth rotates under the satellite or, equivalently, as the ground swath moves approximately 22 deg westward on each orbit. This is the same coverage pattern that was in the hypothetical HawaiiSat example in Sec. 5.4.2.2. The tombstone plots, equivalent to Fig. 10-7, for a slightly different example are shown in Fig. 10-24C. Notice that at 40 deg latitude, there are 8 successive orbits that provide coverage. This type of plot is particularly useful in designing a small constellation of RCO satellites.

The coverage vs. latitude for a *Repeat Coverage Orbit* is shown in Fig. 10-25 and compared with that of a Sun-synchronous orbit, SSO. Note that the RCO provides substantially more coverage than the SSO, particularly at mid and low latitudes. However, the RCO coverage is tuned to the specific latitude of interest while the SSO coverage is from one SSO orbit. Thus, with the RCO, we are giving up global coverage in order to provide better coverage of a specific latitude band of interest.

In the RCO, all of the revisits occur one after another. The time of day of the first pass will depend on the time of day when the satellite was launched and the difference in longitude between the launch site and the target. On

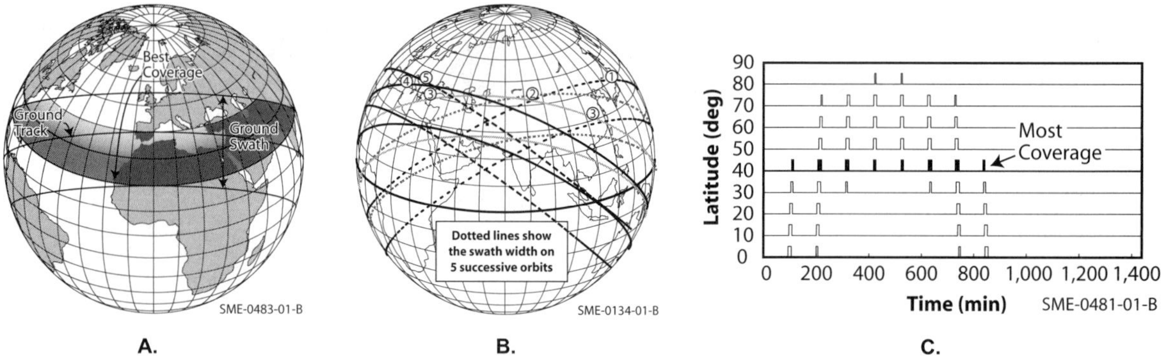

Fig. 10-24. The Repeat Coverage Orbit. (A) The maximum coverage occurs at a latitude equal to the inclination minus half the swath width. (B) Five successive orbits provide coverage of a target at 32 deg N latitude. (C) A tombstone plot showing the region of maximum coverage. For additional plots and Excel calculation models, see Figs. 10-7, 10-9, and 10-10.

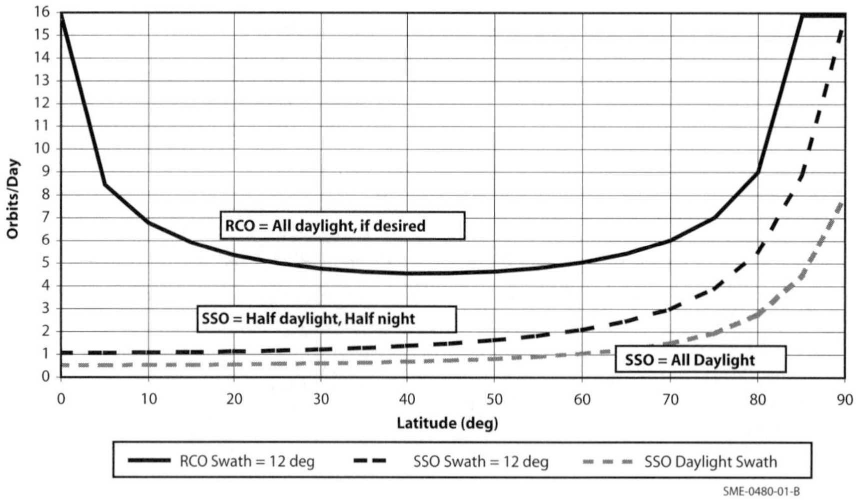

Fig. 10-25. Coverage vs. Latitude for Single Satellites in an RCO and an SSO. The SSO is a single orbit intending to cover the entire world. The RCO is adjusted to each individual latitude.

successive days, the combination of node rotation due to J_2 and the revolution of the Earth around the Sun will move the sequence of passes over a given location forward in time by:

$$\Delta T \approx 3.9424 + 8.1896 \times 10^{14}\, a^{-7/2}\, (1 - e^2)^{-2} \cos i \qquad (10\text{-}22a)$$

where ΔT is the amount earlier that each pass occurs in min/day, a is the semimajor axis in km, e is the eccentricity, and i is the inclination. (The first term is due to the revolution of the Earth around the Sun and the second term is due to node rotation caused by J_2, as shown in Eq. (9-60d).) For a circular orbit at an altitude of 500 km, this becomes

$$\Delta T \approx 34.289 \cos i \qquad (10\text{-}22b)$$

Thus, for mid-latitude orbits, the time of day of the sequence of passes gets earlier by approximately 30 min/day.

Table 10-16, Fig. 10-25, Eq. 10-22b◀

Depending on the latitude, a constellation of 3 or 4 satellites can provide coverage of a given location every 90 min, 24 hours/day. Similarly 6 or 8 satellites could provide coverage every 45 min, 24 hrs/day, and 24 or 32 satellites could provide 24 hrs/day coverage approximately every 10 min.

To choose a Repeat Coverage Orbit, we first select the latitude, L, (or latitude band) of interest and determine the width of the ground swath width, $2\lambda_{max}$, for the satellite, as discussed in Sec. 10.2.1.3. We then select an inclination, i, somewhat less than $L + \lambda_{max}$. Recall from Fig. 10-10 that the coverage drops off rapidly below $i - \lambda_{max}$. Also note that most launch vehicles can put approximately 30% more payload into a prograde orbit due east from the launch site than into a Sun-synchronous orbit such that the launch cost will be less for the RCO than for the SSO or, equivalently, we can launch a somewhat larger satellite, or more of them, into an RCO with a given launch vehicle. The RCO is an excellent option for observation satellites, if we are able to limit the latitude band of interest.

10.4.2.7 Eccentric Orbits for Earth Coverage

Eccentric orbits can be thought of in either of 2 ways. On one hand, they add a level of complexity that increases the design cost of the spacecraft and the mission by requiring the spacecraft to work at multiple altitudes and at differing rotation rates if one side is to remain facing the Earth. On the other hand, eccentricity adds a degree of freedom in the design that can be used to adjust the orbit to best meet specific mission needs. Eccentric orbits can be used to minimize the number of satellites, maximize the coverage with respect to areas of interest, or combinations of these purposes. The use of eccentric orbits has been studied at length by Draim [1997, 1998, 2004, 2008, 2009], who has made an extremely strong case for using eccentric orbits to achieve maximum mission performance with a minimum number of satellites [Draim et al., 1999, 2008].

For any specific mission, the question becomes whether this additional level of performance is worth the increased cost and complexity of the spacecraft and mission parameters. As discussed in Sec. 10.6.2, one of the most interesting examples of the use of eccentric orbits is using only 4 spacecraft to provide complete, continuous coverage of the surface of the Earth.* Other interesting examples include the proposed Ellipso and Cobra communications constellation which uses eccentric orbits, potentially in combination with a supplemental equatorial orbit in order to optimize a low-Earth orbit communications system with small numbers of satellites and optimized coverage for both geographic location and times of day [Draim, 1999, 2001, 2002]. As in the case of Molniya orbits, virtually all satellites in elliptical orbits will need to be at the critical inclination of 63.4 deg in order to prevent the line of apsides from rotating. Since this rotation rate can be up to 14 deg per day, it is important to maintain the critical inclination with good precision in order to maintain apogee and perigee over an extended mission life. This implies that orbit maintenance will typically be necessary for satellites in long term elliptical orbits. However, the ΔV requirements to maintain these parameters are very modest. For a discussion of elliptical orbits vs. circular orbits for communications, see Wertz [2007].

10.5 Selecting Transfer, Parking, and Space-Referenced Orbits

In a space-referenced orbit, our objective is typically to be in space for manufacturing, low-gravity or high-vacuum experiments, or to observe celestial objects from above the Earth's atmosphere. These orbits are used by celestial observatories such as Space Telescope, Chandra, or JWST. In these orbits we typically have only a minimal concern with our orientation relative to the Earth. Consequently, we select such orbits to use minimum energy, while maintaining the orbit altitude and possibly to gain an unobstructed view of whatever celestial objects we may be observing. As listed in Table 10-17, the mission requirements that normally affect the design of such orbits tend to be less stringent than for Earth-referenced orbits. We are looking for a reasonable environment, easy accessibility, and good communications, all of which can be satisfied by a wide range of orbits. Consequently, the orbit design process is typically much more straightforward than it is for Earth-referenced orbits. Of course, some space-referenced mission orbits are designed specifically to sample space, such as magnetic field or solar wind explorers. In these cases, the orbit design is chosen to sample the region of interest on a schedule appropriate to the science return.

Table 10-17. Principal Requirements that Normally Affect the Design of Space-Referenced Orbits. Typically none of the requirements is as stringent as for Earth-referenced orbits.

Requirement	Where Discussed
Accessibility (ΔV or OCF)	Sec. 10.3
Orbit Decay Rate and Long Term Stability	Sec. 9.4.4
Ground Station Communications, Especially for Maneuvers	Sec. 8.4, 10.2.1
Radiation Environment	Sec. 7.3
Thermal Environment (Sun angle and eclipse constraints)	Secs. 8.2.4, 22.2

As listed in Table 10-18, there are a few specialized space-referenced orbits that need to be considered in much the same fashion as specialized Earth-referenced orbits. The Sun-synchronous orbit was discussed previously in Sec. 10.4.2.2. This type of orbit may be appropriate for maintaining a constant Sun angle with respect to a satellite instrument such as an orbiting solar observatory.

Perhaps the most interesting and most widely used of the space-referenced orbits are the Lagrange point orbits, described in Sec. 9.5.5. These are orbits which use the gravitational attraction of two orbiting bodies such as the Earth and the Moon or the Earth and the Sun to maintain the spacecraft in a constant orientation relative to the two bodies. The locations of Lagrange point orbits are shown in Fig. 10-26 and Fig. 9-29 in Sec. 9.5.5. Because of their long-term stability, these orbits have a wide variety of potential applications as summarized in Table 10-20.

Recall from Sec. 9.5.5 that the L_4 and L_5 Lagrange points are stable, such that objects orbiting these points will remain there indefinitely. In contrast, L_1, L_2, and L_3 are unstable equilibrium points such that an object placed there will ultimately drift away. However, it takes a relatively small amount of propellant to maintain a spacecraft in a *halo orbit* about one of the Lagrange points. In

* This orbit has been patented by Draim, [1987a].

Table 10-18. Specialized Space-Referenced Orbits.

Orbit	Characteristic	Application	Where Discussed
Sun-Synchronous	Orbit rotates so as to maintain approximately constant position with respect to Sun	Solar observations; Missions concerned about Sun interference or uniform lighting	Secs. 9.5.3, 10.4.2.2
Lagrange Point Orbit	Maintains fixed position relative to Earth/Moon system or Earth/Sun system	Interplanetary monitoring; potential space manufacturing	Secs. 9.5.5, 10.5
Statite	Solar radiation pressure balances gravity	Interplanetary monitoring and communications	Forward [1989], Sec. 18.7.2

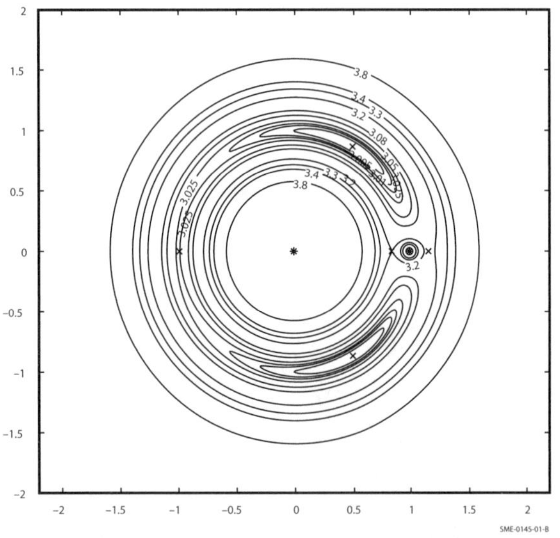

Fig. 10-26. Lagrange Point Orbits. These orbits are stable with respect to the 2-body system they are part of and are convenient locations for observations, communications, and manufacturing. (See also Fig. 9-29 in Sec. 9.5.5.)

Table 10-19. Principal Requirements that Normally Affect the Design of Transfer Orbits. Typically none of the requirements is as stringent as for Earth-referenced orbits.

Requirement	Where Discussed
Transfer ΔV	Sec. 9.6, Table 10-7
Transfer Time	Sec. 9.6
Departure and Arrival Conditions	Sec. 9.6.1
Ground Station Communications, Especially for Maneuvers	Secs. 8.4, 10.2.1
Radiation Environment	Sec. 7.3
Thermal Environment (Sun Angle and Eclipse Constraints)	Secs. 8.2.4, 22.2
Required Navigation and Control Accuracy	Sec. 19.2

any case, the halo orbit is necessary in most cases in order to provide communications. For example, a spacecraft at the L_2 Lagrange point on the far side of the Moon will be useful for communications with any lunar far side stations but would need to be in a halo orbit in order to provide line of sight communications back to the Earth.

Similarly, solar monitoring stations have been maintained for extended periods at the Earth-Sun L_1 Lagrange point in order to provide advance warning for solar storms. Again the halo orbit is required in order to keep the spacecraft away from a direct line with the Sun, which would prevent communications with the spacecraft due to the high level of radio noise from the solar disk.

The long term stability of the Earth-Moon L_4 and L_5 Lagrange points make these an ideal location for very large space colonies or space manufacturing facilities. Because they are at the distance of the Moon, the gravity-gradient forces will be extremely small such that a very large region of extremely low microgravity is possible. In addition, massive facilities are possible there, because no ΔV is necessary to maintain the orbit and there is no drag to provide orbit decay, as occurs for the International Space Station. Material for constructing a large facility at the L_4 and L_5 Lagrange points can be brought at relatively low ΔV cost from the surface of the Moon. The extensive work by Gerard O'Neill* and his colleagues in the 1960s and 1970s has clearly established the feasibility and potential utility of large colonies at these locations. [Heppenheimer, 1977; O'Neill, 1976a,b; O'Leary, 1982a,b; Faughnam et al., 1993]. Unfortunately, the continuing high cost of launch has prevented any of these from advancing beyond the mission study phase.

Lagrange point orbits are also possible with respect to other pairs of celestial bodies. For example, spacecraft at the L_4 or L_5 Lagrange point with respect to Jupiter or the Sun could be used for monitoring the asteroid belt, Similarly, a Lagrange point orbit between any of the major planets and their larger moons could be used as a stable orientation with which to observe that planetary system. Thus, long-term stable (or nearly stable) observation platforms could be created at any of several of the Lagrange points within the systems of Jupiter, Saturn, Uranus, or Neptune.

* O'Neill originated the concept as part of his undergraduate physics classes at Princeton in 1969. After several years working on technical details, he first published the concept of colonizing space itself at L_4 or L_5, rather than on a planetary surface, in the journal *Physics Today* in Sept., 1974 [O'Neill, 1974]. Substantial public enthusiasm led to the creation of the L-5 Society in 1975. In 1987 the L-5 Society merged with the National Space Institute to form the National Space Society.

Table 10-20. Potential Applications of Lagrange Point Orbits. E-S = Earth-Sun, E-M = Earth-Moon, H = Halo orbit.

Lagrange Point	Application
E-M L_4, L_5	Space Manufacturing
E-M L_4, L_5	Space Observatory
E-M L_4, L_5	Lunar Communications
E-M L_4, L_5	Large Space Colonies
E-M L_2 H	Lunar Far Side Communications
E-S L_1 H	Monitoring solar activity
E-S L_3 H	Observing events not visible from Earth

10.5.1 Design of Transfer and Parking Orbits

Typically, the *parking orbit*, or *storage orbit*, is a low-Earth orbit high enough to reduce atmospheric drag, but low enough to be easy to reach. We may store satellites in these orbits, referred to as *on-orbit spares*, for later transfer to a higher altitude, or may use them as a place for test and check-out following launch or waiting for the appropriate transfer conditions to occur. Consequently, the principal issues for parking orbits are accessibility and matching the orbit conditions on either end to what is needed. For example, a Mars probe may be launched into low-Earth orbit for test and check-out while awaiting the appropriate opportunity to begin the Mars transfer phase.

The fundamental purpose of a *transfer orbit* is to get the spacecraft where it wants to be, when it wants to be there. Ordinarily, the design process is straightforward, and we'll want to do this with a minimum cost in terms of ΔV or propellant utilization. The physics of transfer orbits and the equations that govern them were described in Sec. 9.6.1. The principal requirements that normally affect the design of transfer orbits are shown in Table 10-19. As with space-referenced orbits, these are typically less stringent requirements than for Earth-referenced orbits, although there is often a requirement to match the desired end conditions with high precision in order to minimize the propellant cost of any corrective ΔV.

A further requirement that can arise in manned flight is for orbit transfer options that are "forgiving." For example, the Apollo program used a *free return trajectory* such that if the burn required to go into lunar orbit did not occur on the backside of the Moon, then the spacecraft would return to the Earth with no further ΔV. This was critical for the successful rescue of Apollo 13, in which the propulsion system in the command module was effectively destroyed by an explosion and the free return was necessary in order to bring the astronauts back to the vicinity of the Earth such that the lunar module propulsion system could be used to provide the appropriate deorbit ΔV for recovery of the astronauts.

Similarly, in potential human Mars missions, there is a high premium for reducing the transfer time because of the high cost of maintaining people in orbit for extended periods. In addition, in any manned planetary mission, we need to plan the transfer time such that a return to Earth can be achieved in an appropriate time. Both of these requirements lead to somewhat higher energy transfers for human flight than the traditional Hohmann transfer.

As shown in Table 10-21, there are specialized transfer orbits that are available to the mission designer. The physics of these transfers was discussed in Chap. 9. For each of the specialized transfer orbits, the fundamental objective is to reduce the ΔV required to achieve a particular set of mission objectives. Lunar or planetary flybys, for example, are used to provide additional energy by providing effectively an elastic collision between the spacecraft and some other celestial object. Aeroassist trajectories are used principally to provide either a plane change or braking, as in the case of the Mars orbiter program.

As was discussed in Sec. 9.6.2, the ΔV required for simultaneous plane changing and orbit raising can be reduced by combining these maneuvers such that the total ΔV is the vector sum rather than the linear sum of the individual maneuvers. However, in cases where the plane change is extremely large, this ΔV can be further reduced by using a 3-burn transfer, in which the spacecraft is first raised to an altitude significantly higher than the final orbit altitude. At extremely high altitude, the velocity will be very low and consequently a plane change can be done with very small ΔV. Thus the plane change is accomplished at the high altitude and the orbit is then returned to the final altitude. Similar to the 3-burn transfer, Miller and Belbruno [1991], has evaluated and patented several trajectories which make use of the Moon to further reduce the ΔV required for plane change maneuvers. The principal demerit of this approach is that it requires a fairly extended time for the maneuver, although substantial ΔV savings are possible in the case of large plane changes. The principal advantages and disadvantages of alternative plane change mechanisms are given in Table 10-22.

Table 10-21. Specialized Transfer Orbits.

Orbit	Characteristic	Application	Where Discussed
Lunar or Planetary Fly-By	Same relative velocity approaching and leaving flyby body	Used to provide energy change or plane change	Sec. 9.6.3
Aeroassist Orbit	Use atmosphere for plane change or braking	Used for major energy savings for plane change or reentry	Sec. 9.6.2
3-Burn Transfer (= bi-elliptic transfer)	Go to altitude above final orbit to reduce plane change ΔV	Reduce total ΔV for orbits with large plane change	Sec. 9.6.2,

Table 10-22. Alternative Plane Change Mechanisms. See Table 9-17 in Sec. 9.6.2 for physical mechanisms and computations.

Orbit	Advantages	Disadvantages	Typical Application
Do ΔV at Lowest Velocity (highest altitude)	Smallest velocity is easiest to change	May not be a low-velocity orbit segment	Orbit transfer
Combine ΔV with Orbit Raising	Vector sum is less than sum of components	Works best when large in-track ΔV is required	Orbit transfer
3-Burn Transfer	Plane change can occur at essentially no ΔV cost	Requires going to a higher altitude and then returning	Large plane change with moderate to high altitude final orbit
Use Differential Node Rotation	No propellant cost	Time delay	Storage of satellites in a parking orbit
Aero-Assist Trajectories	No propellant cost	Requires precision maneuver and aerodynamic surfaces; may be heating	Planetary exploration
Planetary Fly-by	No propellant cost	Requires planetary swing-by and typically long delays	1-Outer planet exploration 2-Out of ecliptic mission (using Jupiter) 3-Trips to near the Sun (using Jupiter)

Table 10-23. Characteristics of the Alternative Direct Transfer Orbits Shown in Fig. 9-29 in Sec. 9.6.1. See Table 9-16 for transfer characteristics.

Type	Typical Accel.	Orbit Shape	Advantages	Disadvantages	Applications
High Energy	1g to 10g	Elliptical & hyperbolic	Rapid transfer	Uses more energy than necessary + Hohmann disadvantages	Human flight, military intercept
Minimum Energy, High Thrust (Hohmann)	1g to 5g	Hohmann transfer	Traditional High efficiency Rapid transfer Low radiation exposure	Rough environment Thermal problems Can't use S/C subsystems	Used for nearly all orbit transfers
Low Thrust Chemical	0.02 to 0.10g	Hohmann transfer segments	High efficiency Low engine weight Low orbit deployment & check-out Better failure recovery Can use spacecraft subsystems	Moderate radiation exposure 3 to 4 day transfer to GEO	Use when needed to reduce cost, weight, risk, or disturbances
Electric Propulsion	0.0001 to 0.001g	Spiral transfer	Can use very high I_{sp} engines = major weight reduction Low orbit deployment & check-out Can have reusable transfer vehicle	2 to 6 month transfer to GEO High radiation exposure Needs autonomous transfer for cost efficiency	Rarely used. Has been proposed for GEO and interplanetary transfer

The various alternatives for direct orbit transfers have been described in detail in Sec. 9.6.1. (See specifically Fig. 9-32 and Table 9-16.) Table 10-23 lists the relative advantages and disadvantages of using these alternative transfer methods and the principal applications to which they apply. High-energy direct transfers are useful principally when the transfer time is critical, as in human flight or some military missions. Typically, the ΔV penalty associated with high-energy transfer is small for minor increases in transfer time, but becomes very large for any major reduction in transfer time, such that very short transfers are prohibitively expensive in terms of ΔV. The other alternatives of successive burns using low-thrust chemical or a spiral transfer using electric propulsion both take significantly longer than the Hohmann transfer and are of use principally when transfer time is not a major constraint. The low thrust chemical transfer offers the significant advantage of providing a much more benign environment for the spacecraft, since the principal disturbance forces and maximum loads frequently occur during orbit transfer. In addition, low thrust transfer allows the spacecraft to be fully deployed prior to transfer, such that it can be tested and checked out before being put in a totally inaccessible orbit. Electric propulsion transfer has the merit of extremely high efficiency but can take a very long time. Consequently, electric propulsion is an extremely efficient approach for orbit maintenance but has not yet been widely used for orbit transfer.

In the design of orbit transfer, it is important to keep in mind the distinction between the basic requirements for launch vehicles and the requirements for in-orbit transfer. In launch vehicle design, high thrust is absolutely imperative in order to get to space as quickly as possible and minimize gravity losses that occur when thrusting is not done at right angles to the central body. In a number of launch attempts in the early space program, the thrust to weight ratio was very close to 1, such that the launch vehicle lifted a short distance off the pad, got out of the ground effect, held itself briefly in the air, and then fell back to Earth. Thus, a driving characteristic for launch vehicles is the need for a high thrust system.

In contrast, once we have gotten into space, high thrust is no longer important and can be a major detriment to an in-orbit transfer system. A high thrust transfer stage frequently imparts the largest loads the spacecraft will ever see. Thus it has a strong potential for damaging the spacecraft. In addition, in any high thrust system, performance is critical and all maneuvers must be done with precision both in terms of the maneuver itself and the timing of the maneuver. Typically, any failures of high thrust transfer will lead directly to mission failure. Similarly, because the forces are extremely large, high thrust orbit transfer stages need their own separate control system to control the very large disturbance torques that are generated. Consequently, the transfer stage is nearly a separate spacecraft with a very large propulsion and control system. However, in the on-orbit environment, much of this performance is either wasted or detrimental. An on-board propulsion system, for example, can provide the ΔV appropriate to orbit transfer but do so at much lower thrust levels. For most orbit transfers, the time required for the burn is small relative to the transfer time and is unimportant in successfully completing the maneuver. If the orbit transfer is done by a sequence of low thrust burns, then individual burns become far less critical and an error or misfire on one burn may be able to be corrected on subsequent burns. Consequently, low thrust orbit transfer tends to be significantly more fail-safe than high thrust transfer. In addition, the disturbance torques imparted by a low thrust system are far less, such that it may be possible to control the transfer using the control system already on board the spacecraft itself. This can significantly reduce the amount of ancillary equipment that needs to be flown, thus reducing both the weight and cost of the mission. The use of on-board propulsion can have a dramatic impact on the mass available in the mission orbit, or, alternatively, on the launch cost because the entire mass of the transfer stage doesn't need to be sent all the way to the mission orbit.

The important point here is to make a clear distinction between the requirements for launch and the requirements for orbit transfer once we have achieved low-Earth orbit. These frequently are regarded as nearly the same process because they are often assigned to a single organization which has the responsibility for putting the spacecraft in its final mission orbit. While this has some possible organizational advantages, it typically provides a system which is less robust, higher risk, more expensive, and lower performing than would be the case using a low thrust system once we have achieved orbit. The critical issue here is to regard in-orbit transfer not as simply an extension of the launch process, but as a separate mission phase. As always, we want to achieve the overall mission objectives at minimum cost and risk. In many cases, we may be able to substantially reduce both cost and risk by making use of straightforward, low-cost, low-thrust technology for in-orbit transfer.

10.6 Summary of Constellation Design

A *constellation* is a set of satellites distributed over space intended to work together to achieve common objectives. If the satellites are close together, such as a flying interferometer, or spacecraft next to each other exchanging data or material, then it is called a *cluster* or *formation*, rather than a constellation. Because constellations are inherently very expensive, most are used for communications, navigation, or similar functions that take advantage of the global Earth coverage provided by satellites and difficult to achieve by other means.* The constellation design process tends to be complex with no agreed upon solution by the community as a whole. A thorough discussion of this process is beyond the scope of this volume and is covered in detail in Wertz [2009]. Here we provide a summary of the constellation design process and the broad rules for constellation design.

One of the most important results of decades of constellation studies has been that no absolute rules exist for constellation design. For example, the Multi-Satellite System Program (MSSP), was a proposed constellation of satellites in random low-Earth orbits in order to create a survivable communications system. (See Wertz [2009], Sec. 13.2.) One of the most interesting characteristics of the low-Earth orbit communications constellations is that constellation builders have invested billions of dollars and come up with distinctly different solutions. For example, a higher altitude means fewer satellites, but a much more severe radiation environment, such that the cost of each satellite will be higher, and the life potentially shorter. Both solutions are being used by commercial constellations. Similarly, circular orbits provide a simple, low-cost satellite design. However, elliptical orbits allow an additional degree of freedom, which allows the constellation to be optimized for multiple factors, but requires a more complex satellite operating over a range of altitudes and velocities, and passing through heavy radiation regimes. (See, for example, Draim et al. [1996, 1999].) Again, both solutions are being used by modern constellations. Because the constellations' size and structure strongly affect system cost and performance, we must carefully assess alternative designs and document the reasons for trades that are made. It is this list of reasons that allows the constellation design process to continue in order to achieve the system objectives at minimum cost and risk.

10.6.1 The Constellation Design Process

The overall process of constellation design is summarized in Table 10-24. The key requirement in this process is to understand the mission objectives and what is needed to fulfill the mission, particularly with respect to coverage. This means understanding both the coverage

* In contrast, the F6 program is intended to create a resource-sharing formation specifically to reduce cost and vulnerability and allow low-cost augmentation or replenishment.

Table 10-24. The Constellation Design Process. See also Tables 10-25, 10-27, and 10-28. See Wertz [2009] for a more extensive discussion.

Step	Where Discussed Here	Where Discussed OCDM
1. Establish constellation-related mission requirements, particularly • Latitude-dependent coverage • Goals for growth and degradation plateaus • Requirements for different modes or sensors • Limits on system cost or number of satellites	Secs. 8.4, 10.2.1, 10.6.1	Chap.5 Secs. 12.1, 13.1
2. Do all single satellite orbit trades except coverage	Table 10-1 (Sec. 10.1), Sec. 10.2	Chap. 12, Sec. 13.3
3. Do trades between swath width (or maximum Earth central angle), coverage, and number of satellites. *Evaluate candidate constellations for:*	Secs. 8.4, 10.6.2	Chap. 9, Secs. 13.3, 13.6, 13.7
• Coverage Figures of Merit vs. Latitude and mission mode	Sec. 10.2.1	Chap. 9, Secs. 13.1–13.3
• Coverage excess		Sec. 13.7
• Growth and degradation		Sec. 13.6
• Altitude plateaus		Sec. 13.6
• End-of-life options	Sec. 9.6.4, Chap. 30	Secs. 2.6.4, 13.6
Consider the following orbit types: • Walker Delta pattern (GlobalStar, GPS) • Polar constellations with seam (Iridium) • Equatorial (TDRS, GEO Comm, MEO Comm [Wertz, 2007]) • Equatorial supplement (Ellipso) • Elliptical (Molniya, Ellipso, Cobra)		
4. Evaluate ground track plots for potential coverage holes or methods to reduce the number of satellites	Sec. 10.2	Sec. 9.5.1.2
5. Adjust inclination and in-plane phasing to maximize the intersatellite distances at plane crossings for collision avoidance		Sec. 13.5
6. Review the Rules of Constellation Design.	Sec. 10.6.3 (Table 10-30)	Sec. 13.7
7. Document reasons for choices and iterate.		

needs for the mission, and the spacecraft needs to provide that coverage, such as swath width or constraints on lighting, power, or communications. Can the system operate in the Van Allen belts? A second key part of the requirements is the growth and degradation goals. Are outages acceptable if a satellite dies on orbit? How soon is a replacement required? How soon will the constellation as a whole be replaced and upgraded?

The principal factors to be defined during constellation design are listed in Table 10-25, along with the major selection criteria for each. These factors have been discussed in detail earlier in the chapter. A key point to keep in mind here is that constellation design consists of more than just orbit elements. The minimum working elevation angle is perhaps the single most critical parameter in defining constellation coverage. Collision avoidance parameters, including the method for stationkeeping and size of the stationkeeping box are key to insuring the integrity of the constellation over its lifetime. While we often think of a constellation as a single, coherent pattern, it may be that some combination of patterns will satisfy our mission objectives at a lower cost and risk. This approach has been adapted, for example, by Ellipso with a mix of inclined eccentric and circular equatorial orbits.

Typically the purpose of creating a constellation is to provide Earth coverage, or at times, coverage of near-Earth space. The demerit of a constellation is that you need multiple satellites and, therefore, multiple reaction wheels, communication systems, and so on. A typical goal of constellation design is to provide the needed coverage with a minimum number of satellites. Consequently, the principal system trade is most frequently coverage as a measure of performance vs. number of satellites as a measure of cost. Nonetheless, it is important to bear in mind that the number of satellites is not necessarily an accurate representation of system cost. For example, raising the altitude of the constellation will normally result in needing fewer satellites. However, as the altitude increases, the launch cost for each satellite increases, and the radiation hardening requirements increase dramatically as we enter the Van Allen radiation belts. Minimizing the number of satellites may or may not minimize the system cost and it is the cost which is typically of most interest to constellation sponsors, both government and commercial.

Specifying a constellation by defining all of the orbit elements for each satellite is complex, inconvenient, and overwhelming in its range of options. A reasonable way to begin is by looking at constellations with all satellites in circular orbits at a common altitude and inclination. This means that the period, angular velocity, and node rotation rate will be the same for all of the satellites. This leads to a series of trades on altitude, inclination, and constellation pattern involving principally the number of satellites, coverage, launch cost, and the environment

Table 10-25. Principal Factors to be Defined During Constellation Design.

Factor	Effect	Selection Criteria	Where Discussed Here	Where Discussed OCDM
PRINCIPLE DESIGN VARIABLES:				
Number of Satellites	Principal determinant of cost and coverage	Minimize number consistent with meeting other criteria	Chap. 8, Sec. 10.6.2	Chap. 9 Sec. 13.3
Constellation Pattern	Determines coverage vs. latitude, plateaus	Select for best coverage	Sec. 10.6.2	Sec. 13.1
Minimum Elevation Angle	Principal determinant of single satellite coverage	Minimum value consistent with payload performance and constellation pattern	Secs. 8.4, 10.6.2	Secs. 9.1, 13.3
Altitude	Coverage, environment, launch, and transfer cost	System level trade of cost vs. performance	Secs. 10.2.2, 10.4.1	Chap. 9, Secs. 12.4, 13.3
Number of Orbit Planes	Determines coverage plateaus, growth and degradation	Minimize consistent with coverage needs	Secs. 10.6.2, 10.6.3	Sec. 13.6
Collision Avoidance Parameters	Key to preventing constellation self destruction	Maximize the intersatellite distances at plane crossings	Sec. 10.6.3	Sec. 13.5
SECONDARY DESIGN VARIABLES:				
Inclination	Determines latitude distribution of coverage	Compare latitude coverage vs. launch costs*	Sec. 10.2, Fig. 10-10	Sec. 13.3
Between Plane Phasing	Determines coverage uniformity	Select best coverage among discrete phasing options*	Sec. 10.6.2	Sec. 13.1
Eccentricity	Mission complexity and coverage vs. cost	Normally zero; non-zero may reduce number of satellites needed	Table 8-12, Sec. 8.4.2, Sec. 10.4.2	Sec. 13.3
Stationkeeping Box Size	Coverage needed; cross-track pointing	Minimize consistent with low cost maintenance approach		Sec. 13.4
End-of-Life Strategy	Elimination of orbital debris	Any mechanism that allows you to clean up after yourself	Sec. 9.6.4, Chap. 30	Secs. 2.6.4, 13.6
* Fine tune for collision avoidance				

(primarily drag and radiation). We then examine the potential of elliptical orbits and the addition of an equatorial ring. After exploring the consequences of some of the choices, we will summarize the key trades and Rules for Constellation Design in Sec. 10.6.3.

10.6.2 Coverage and Constellation Structure

For most constellations, Earth coverage is the key reason for using multiple satellites. A constellation can provide observations and communications more frequently than a single satellite can. Given this objective, the normal trade in constellation design is coverage as a measure of performance versus the number of satellites as a measure of cost. Thus, we normally assume that a 5-satellite constellation will be less expensive than a 6-satellite one, but this assumption may be wrong. The larger constellation may be at a lower altitude or inclination and, therefore, cost less to launch or have a less harsh radiation environment. Alternatively, we may be able to have a smaller constellation with elliptical orbits, for which increased spacecraft complexity could offset the lower cost due to the number of satellites.

A principal characteristic of any satellite constellation is the number of orbit planes in which the satellites reside. Symmetry in constellation structure requires an equal number of satellites in each orbit plane. This means that an eight-satellite constellation may have either one, two, four, or eight separate orbit planes. But because moving satellites between planes uses much more propellant than moving them within a plane, it is highly advantageous to place more satellites in a smaller number of planes. Moving satellites within an orbit plane requires only a slight change in the satellite altitude. This changes the period so we can slowly rephase the satellite within the constellation, and then return it to the proper altitude to maintain its position relative to the rest. Thus, we can rephase many times using relatively little propellant. If a satellite fails or a new satellite is added to a given orbit plane, we can rephase the remaining satellites so that they are uniformly spaced. The consequence of this is to provide a significant premium to constellations which contain more satellites in a smaller number of orbit planes.

The number of orbit planes relates strongly to a coverage issue often overlooked in constellation design: the need to provide the constellation performance plateaus and graceful degradation. Ideally one would like to achieve some performance level with the very first satellite launched and to raise that level of performance with each succeeding satellite. Generally, however, performance tends to come in plateaus as we put one more satellite into each orbit plane of the final constellation. If a constellation has 7 orbit planes, we will achieve some performance with the first satellite, but the next major performance plateau may not come until one satellite is in each of the 7 planes. We would expect this constellation to have plateaus at 1, 7, 14, 21, (and so on) satellites. Again, constellations with a small number of orbit planes have a distinct advantage over many-plane ones. A single-plane constellation produces performance plateaus with each added satellite, whereas one with 2 planes would have plateaus at 1, 2, 4, 6, 8, (and so on) satellites. Thus, more complex constellations will require more satellites for each performance plateau.

Frequent performance plateaus have several advantages. First, because individual satellites are extremely expensive, we may want to build and launch one or two satellites to verify both the concept and the constellation's ultimate usefulness. If a constellation is highly useful with just 1 or 2 satellites, it offers a major advantage to the system developer.

Another advantage is that coverage requirements are rarely absolute. More coverage is better than less, but we may not know at the time the constellation is designed how useful added coverage will be. For example, we may design the FireSat II system for 30-min revisits, then later revise the response strategy so 45-min revisits can provide nearly equal performance. Communications constellations are normally thought of as having a very rigid requirement of continuous global coverage. Even here, however, they may want more coverage or greater redundancy over regions of high population density.

A constellation of 1 or 2 planes can be more responsive to changing user needs than a system with multiple planes. Because we often design constellations many years before they are launched, we may not be able to correctly balance performance vs. cost. Both needs and budgets follow political constraints and economic priorities over much shorter periods than a constellation's lifetime. Thus if an 8-satellite constellation is highly useful with only 6 satellites, budget constraints may delay the launch of the remaining 2. At the same time, the constellation may expand to 10 satellites if the first set generates substantial demand for more performance or greater capacity. This responsiveness to political and performance demands provides perhaps the largest advantage to constellations with a smaller number of orbit planes.

Finally, a smaller number of orbit planes leads to more graceful degradation. In an 8-satellite, 2-plane constellation, if one satellite is lost for any reason, we may rephase the constellation at little propellant cost and thereby maintain a high performance level corresponding to a 6-satellite plateau. This rephasing and graceful degradation may be impossible for constellations with a large number of orbit planes.

Another important characteristic is the orbit inclination. In principle, one could design satellite constellations with many different inclinations to get the best coverage. In practice this is extremely difficult because the rate of nodal regression for a satellite orbit is a function of both altitude and inclination. Consequently, satellites at a common altitude but different inclinations will regress at different rates, and a set of orbit planes which initially have a given geometric relationship with respect to each other will change that relationship with time. Otherwise, we would have to expend propellant to maintain the relative constellation spacing, a technique that is extremely expensive in terms of propellant and is achievable for only a short time or under unique circumstances. Thus, we usually design constellations to have all the satellites at the same inclination. A possible exception is to have all satellites at a single inclination except for a set of satellites in a 0 inclination (equatorial) orbit. Regression of the nodes is not meaningful for the equatorial orbit, so we can maintain constant relative phasing indefinitely between satellites in equatorial and inclined orbits. An example of such a constellation is satellites in three mutually perpendicular orbit plane—2 polar and 1 equatorial.

As shown in Fig. 10-27, the spacing between satellites in a single orbit plane determines whether coverage in that plane is continuous and the width of the continuous coverage region. Assume that λ_{max} is the maximum Earth central angle as defined in Sec. 5.3.1 and that there are N satellites equally spaced at $S = 360/N$ deg apart in a given orbit plane. There is intermittent coverage throughout a swath of half-width λ_{max}. If $S > 2\ \lambda_{max}$, the coverage is intermittent throughout the entire swath. If $S < 2\ \lambda_{max}$, there is a narrower swath, often called a *street of coverage*, centered on the ground trace and of width 2 λ_{street}, in which there is continuous coverage. This width is given by:

$$\cos \lambda_{street} = \cos \lambda_{max} / \cos(S/2) \qquad (10\text{-}23)$$

If the satellites in adjacent planes are going in the same direction, then the "bulge" in one orbit can be used to offset the "dip" in the adjacent orbit as shown in Fig. 10-28. In this case, the maximum perpendicular separation, D_{max}, between the orbit planes required for continuous coverage is,

$$D_{maxS} = \lambda_{street} + \lambda_{max} \qquad (10\text{-}24)$$

(moving in the same direction)

If the satellites are moving in opposite directions, then the bulge and dip cannot be made to line up continuously and, therefore,

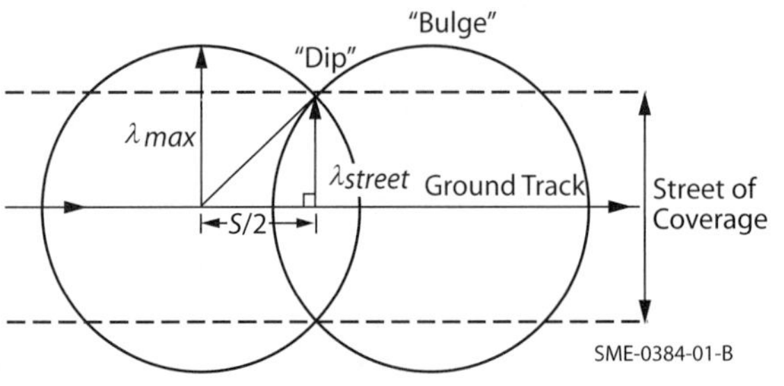

Fig. 10-27. The "Street of Coverage" is a Swath Centered on the Ground Track for which there is Continuous Coverage.

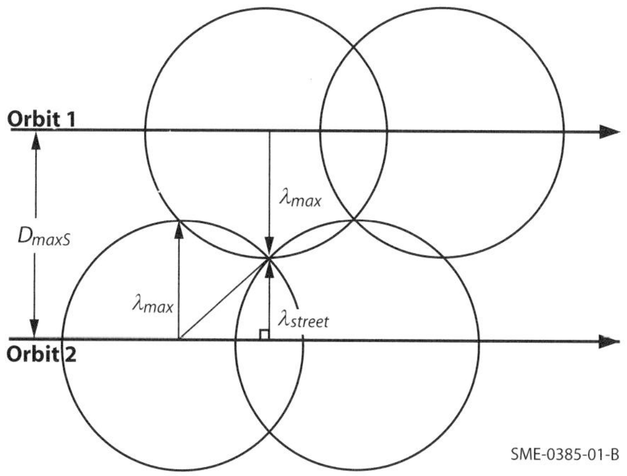

Fig. 10-28. Coverage in Adjacent Planes. If the satellites in the planes are moving in the same direction, the coverage pattern can be designed to provide maximum.

$$D_{maxO} = 2\lambda_{street} \quad \text{(moving opposite directions)} \tag{10-25}$$

This leads to a polar constellation often called *Streets of Coverage*, illustrated in Fig. 10-29, in which M planes of N satellites are used to provide continuous global coverage. At any given time, satellites over half the world are going northward and satellites over the other half are going southward. Within both regions, the orbit planes are separated by D_{maxS}. Between the two halves there is a seam in which the satellites are going in opposite directions. Here the spacing between the planes must be reduced to D_{maxO} in order to maintain continuous coverage.

This pattern clearly shows another critical characteristic of constellations—**coverage does not vary continuously and smoothly with altitude**. There are discrete jumps in coverage that depend primarily on λ_{max} which, in turn, depends on the minimum elevation angle, ε_{min}, and the altitude. (See Table 8-11 in Sec. 8.4.1.) If we keep ε_{min} fixed and lower the constellation altitude, then we will reach an altitude plateau at which we will need to add another orbit plane, and N more satellites, to cover the Earth. The Iridium communications constellation was originally intended to have 77 satellites in a streets of coverage pattern. (The element iridium has an atomic number of 77.) By slightly increasing the altitude and decreasing the minimum elevation angle, the number of orbit planes was reduced by one, and the number of satellites required for continuous coverage was reduced to only 66. (Unfortunately, Dysprosium is not a compelling constellation name.)

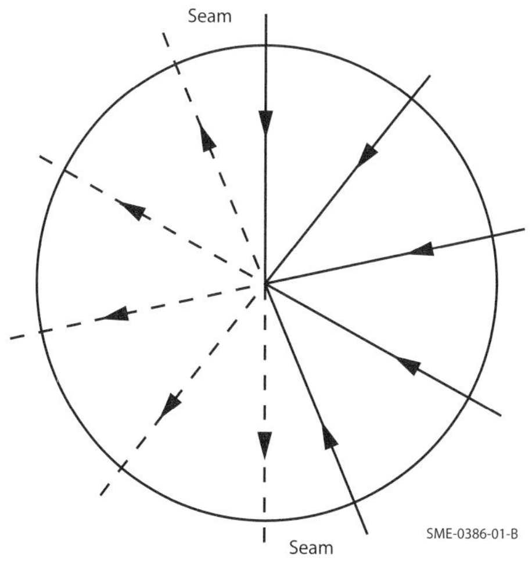

Fig. 10-29. "Streets of Coverage" Constellation Pattern. View seen from the north pole Northward portions of each orbit are drawn as solid lines and southward portions are dashed. To achieve full coverage, orbit planes on either side of the seam must be closer together than the others.

As the altitude changes, the fundamental constellation design changes and, consequently, the number of satellites and coverage characteristics change in steps. As a result, we cannot provide a meaningful chart, for example, the number of satellites vs. altitude without examining different constellation designs at different altitudes. While we may use this sort of chart to estimate constellation size, it would not provide realistic data for orbit design.

Requirements other than coverage can also be important in constellation design, but most are directly related to coverage issues. For example, we may need several satellites to cover a point on the ground or in space at the same time. Navigation with GPS requires that four satellites be in view with a reasonably large angular separation. A similar requirement is cross-link connectivity among satellites in the constellation. Cross-link connectivity is geometrically the same issue as overlapping coverage. At any time when the coverage of two satellites overlaps (that is, they can both see at least one common point on the ground), then the two satellites can see each other and we can establish a cross-link. Thus, forming cross-links is equivalent to the problem of multiple coverage.

Even apparently simple design problems can be very difficult, with solutions depending on various mission conditions. Perhaps the simplest constellation design problem is the question "What is the minimum number of satellites required to provide continuous coverage of the Earth?" In the late 1960s, Easton and Brescia [1969] of the United States Naval Research Laboratory analyzed coverage by satellites in two mutually perpendicular orbit planes and concluded we would need at least 6 satellites to provide complete Earth coverage. In the 1970s, J.G. Walker [1971, 1977, 1984] at the British Royal Aircraft Establishment expanded the types of constellations considered to include additional circular orbits at a common altitude and inclination. He concluded that continuous coverage of the Earth would require 5 satellites. Because of his extensive work, Walker constellations are a common set of constellations to evaluate for overall coverage. More recently in the 1980s, John Draim [1985, 1987a, 1987b] found and patented a constellation of 4 satellites in elliptical orbits which would provide continuous Earth coverage. A minimum of four satellites are required at any one instant to

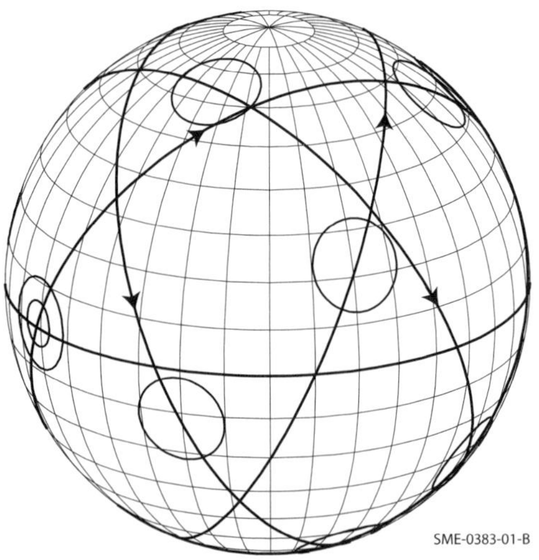

Fig. 10-30. A 15/5/1 Walker Constellation at 65 deg Inclination. Circles are centered on each of the 15 satellites. The double circle is on a satellite at its ascending node.

provide full coverage of the Earth. Consequently, while the above progression looks promising, the 1990s did not yield a 3-satellite full Earth coverage constellation or the 2000s a 2-satellite constellation.

While extensively studying regular, circular orbit patterns, Walker [1984] developed a notation for labeling orbits that is commonly used in the orbit design community and frequently used as a starting point for constellation design. Specifically, the *Walker delta pattern* contains a total of t satellites with s satellites evenly distributed in each of p orbit planes. All of the orbit planes are assumed to be at the same inclination, i, relative to a reference plane—typically the Earth's equator. (For constellation design purposes, this need not be the case. But orbit perturbations depend on the inclination relative to the equator and, therefore, the equator is the most practical standard reference plane.) Unlike the streets of coverage, the ascending nodes of the p orbit planes in a Walker pattern are uniformly distributed around the equator at intervals of 360 deg/p. Within each orbit plane the s satellites are uniformly distributed at intervals of 360 deg/s.

The only remaining issue is to specify the relative phase between the satellites in adjacent orbit planes. To do this we define the *phase difference*, $\Delta\phi$, in a constellation as the angle in the direction of motion from the ascending node to the nearest satellite at a time when a satellite in the next most westerly plane is at its ascending node. In order for all of the orbit planes to have the same relationship to each other, $\Delta\phi$ must be an integral multiple, f, of 360 deg/t, where f can be any integer from 0 to $p - 1$. So long as this condition holds, each orbit will bear the same relationship to the next orbit in the pattern. The pattern is fully specified by giving the inclination and the three parameters, t, p, and f. Usually such a constellation will be written in the shorthand notation of i: $t/p/f$. For example, Fig. 10-30 illustrates a Walker constellation of 15/5/1 at i = 65 deg. Table 10-26 gives the general rules for Walker delta pattern parameters.

Table 10-26. Characteristics of a Walker Delta Pattern Constellation. See Walker [1984].

T/P/F—Walker Delta Patterns
t = Number of satellites.
p = Number of orbit planes evenly spaced in node.
f = Relative spacing between satellites in adjacent planes.
Define $s \equiv t/p$ = Number of satellites per plane (evenly spaced).
Define Pattern Unit, $PU \equiv$ 360 deg/t
Planes are spaced at intervals of s PUs in node.
Satellites are spaced at intervals of p PUs within each plane.
If a satellite is at its ascending node, the next most easterly satellites will be f PUs past the node.
f is an integer which can take on any value from 0 to (p–1).
Example: 15/5/1 constellation shown in Fig. 10-30.
15 satellites in 5 planes (t = 15, p = 5).
3 satellites per plane ($s \equiv t/p$ = 3).
PU = 360/t = 360/15 = 24 deg.
In-plane spacing between satellites = $PU \times p$ = 24 × 5 = 120 deg.
Node spacing = $PU \times s$ = 24 × 3 = 72 deg.
Phase difference between adjacent planes = $PU \times f$ = 24 × 1 = 24 deg.

While Walker constellations are important to constellation design, they are not the only appropriate options and do not necessarily provide the best characteristics for a given mission. Walker intended to provide continuous multiple coverage of all the Earth's surface with the smallest number of satellites. This plan may or may not meet all the goals of a particular program. For example, equally distributed coverage over the Earth's surface may not be the most beneficial. We may wish to provide global coverage with the best coverage at the poles, mid-latitude regions, or the equator. In these cases, we may want constellation types other than Walker orbits.

If the regions of interest do not include the poles, then an equatorial constellation may provide all of the coverage with a single orbit plane, which leads to flexibility, multiple performance plateaus, and graceful degradation. Thus, for example, if all of the regions of interest were within 50 deg of the equator, we would want to consider a constellation having several equatorial satellites with enough altitude to provide the appropriate coverage at the smallest spacecraft elevation angle [Wertz, 2007].

If all or most regions of interest are above a given latitude, a directly polar constellation would allow all satellites to see the region of the pole on every orbit. Thus, if all targets of interest were within 50 deg of the pole, a polar constellation with a single orbit plane could provide excellent coverage. If most targets were in the polar region with lesser interest in the equatorial regions, a two-plane polar constellation could provide continuous or nearly continuous coverage of the pole while providing reduced but good coverage of the equatorial regions. Conversely, if most of the targets were at lower latitudes an excellent choice would be a ring of equatorial satel-

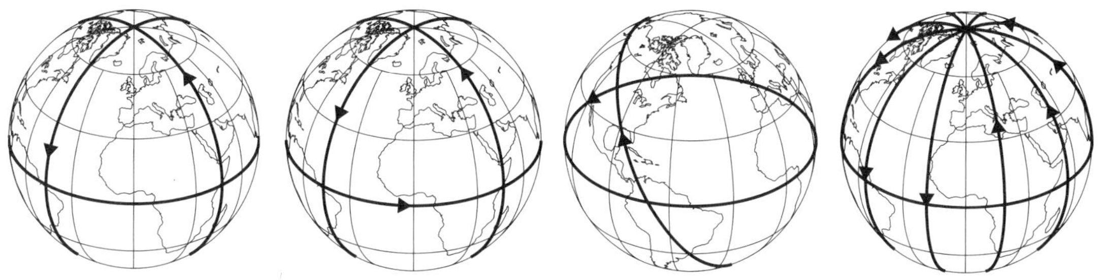

Fig. 10-31. Examples of Typical Non-Walker Constellations. All orbits are assumed to be circular.

lites, augmented by a ring with fewer satellites covering the polar regions if needed [Wertz, 2007]. One might also consider a mix of polar or high inclination satellites with some satellites at the equator to provide the added coverage needed there.

Another class of non-Walker constellations consists of two planes at right angles to each other. If both planes are perpendicular to the equator it will be a polar constellation. Although it will have substantial symmetry, it is not one of the Walker delta patterns. The two planes can also be tipped relative to the equator to achieve any inclination from 90 to 45 deg. Again the ascending nodes are such that they are not Walker constellations except when the inclination is 45 deg, in which case they reduce to a Walker two-plane configuration. Figure 10-31 shows examples of several non-Walker constellations.

A final example of non-Walker constellations is the Molniya orbits used for Russian communication satellites. Sections 9.5.4 and 10.4.2.3 describe them in more detail. These constellations can fully cover high northern latitudes while requiring less energy than circular high-altitude orbits.

10.6.3 Overview

Constellation design is complex, requiring us to assess many issues and orbit characteristics. When we pick a preliminary design, this complexity demands that we document the reasons for the design and remain aware of alternatives as orbit design continues. Unfortunately, systematic reassessments of constellation design are difficult under typical budget constraints and the constellation pattern is often locked in very early in mission design.

Perhaps the most important coverage issue to remember in terms of constellation design is that compiling statistical data on orbit coverage may not provide useful physical insight into the constellation design problem and can, in many cases, be dramatically misleading. The mission designer must always be aware that in constellation design, statistical data is being used to represent a dramatically non-Gaussian process. Examples of this problem have been given throughout the book—particularly at the beginning of Sec. 10.2.

There are two fundamentally different types of constellations —those that demand continuous coverage and those that do not. The former group represents the more straightforward design problem. What is the minimum number of satellites (or minimum total system cost) needed to provide the necessary single or multiple coverage? For example, GPS wants continuous coverage of the entire world by a minimum of four satellites. What is the minimum cost system to do this?

An interesting figure of merit for continuous coverage constellations is the *excess coverage*—i.e., the total instantaneous coverage available as a percentage of the total required. For N satellites in circular orbits at a common altitude with coverage defined as being within λ_{max} of the subsatellite point, the total instantaneous coverage, COV, is given by:

$$COV = N\,(1 - \cos \lambda_{max}) \,/\, 2K \qquad (10\text{-}26)$$

where K is the coverage multiplicity that is needed (i.e., K = 4 for GPS). Our goal is to drive COV toward 1.

For the 24-satellite GPS constellation, the satellites are all at half GEO (a = 26,562 km) and the assumed minimum elevation angle is 5 deg. From Eqs. (9-4) and (9-5), we find that λ_{max} = 71.2 deg and COV = 2.03. This means that it takes approximately twice as many satellites as would be needed if the coverage were static and could be perfectly distributed. Iridium is a communications constellation with 66 satellites at 780 km. Here $K = 1$ and the minimum working elevation angle is 9.5 deg corresponding to λ_{max} = 19.0 deg and COV = 1.80. Although the two constellations are very different in use and in coverage pattern, the excess coverage in the implemented constellations is nearly the same.

For constellations that do not demand continuous coverage, the most representative figure of merit is typically the mean and maximum response time as a function of the number of satellites (see Sec. 10.2.1.4). This is a substantially more difficult trade because it now needs to be worked iteratively with the basic objectives of the constellation and may require extended interaction with the end user to determine how those needs are best met.

With numerical simulation, we can evaluate some of the Figures of Merit defined in Sec. 10.2.1. (That section discusses how to lay out the simulation for unbiased results.) Generally the results of such a simulation are best expressed as Figures of Merit vs. latitude for the various performance plateaus. Thus, a typical decision plot might include mean response, percent coverage, and maximum gap as a function of latitude for the various constellations being considered. Often, we must also evaluate coverage data for different instruments on board a spacecraft. Each instrument has its own coverage area and, therefore, a different swath width will apply for each principal observation type. Thus, the coverage associated with one instrument may differ dramatically from that associated with another instrument or operating mode. Alternative operating modes or instruments will likely lead us to prefer distinctly different constellation designs. We may then choose either different satellites or a compromise between the alternative instruments or modes.

Ultimately, constellations are expensive. Therefore, all of our system trades should be based on cost vs. performance. The principal issues that dominate constellation design are listed in Table 10-27. Generally, we evaluate each constellation design for four criteria:

1. Baseline Coverage vs. Latitude

The coverage associated with different instruments or operating modes is best expressed as coverage vs. latitude. (See Secs. 8.4 and 10.2.1.) I regard the mean response time as the best overall measure of coverage, although percent coverage and maximum gap can also be important in some applications. We must use the maximum gap measure carefully because this single point should not be allowed to drive the design of an entire constellation as it will typically not provide the best overall performance for the cost.

2. Growth, Replenishment, and Degradation

As described in OCDM Sec. 13.6, this is a key issue in practical constellation design. It will be different for each constellation type. In evaluating growth, replenishment, and degradation, we should assume that rephasing within the orbit plane can be done at very modest propellant cost, and that changing orbit planes is not feasible.* (See Sec. 9.6.2.)

3. Existence of Altitude Plateaus

We should evaluate each constellation to see if plateaus exist in which the number of orbit planes or other

* If we are willing to allow months for putting the satellites in place, differential node rotation due to a different altitude can be used to move the ascending node.

Table 10-27. Principal Issues that Dominate Constellation Design. See also Tables 10-24, 10-25, and 10-28.

Issue	Why Important	What Determines It	Principal Issues or Options	Where Discussed Here	Where Discussed OCDM
Coverage	Principal performance parameter	Altitude, minimum elevation angle, inclination, constellation pattern	Gap times for discontinuous coverage; Number of satellites simultaneously in view for continuous coverage	Secs. 8.4, 10.2.1	Chap. 9, Sec. 13.3
Number of Satellites	Principal cost driver	Altitude, minimum elevation angle, inclination, constellation pattern	Altitude, minimum elevation angle, inclination, constellation pattern	Chap. 8, Sec. 10.6.2	Sec. 13.3
Launch Options	Major cost driver	Altitude, inclination, spacecraft mass	Low altitude, low inclination costs less	Chap. 26	Secs. 12.3, 13.3
Environment	Radiation level and, therefore, lifetime and hardness requirements	Altitude	Options are below, in, or above Van Allen radiation belts	Chap. 7	Fig. 2-12, Sec. 12.4
Orbit Perturbations (Stationkeeping)	Causes constellations to disassociate over time	Altitude, inclination, eccentricity	Keep all satellites at common altitude and inclination to avoid drifting apart	Sec. 9.6	Secs. 2.4, 13.4
Collision Avoidance	Snowball effect can destroy entire constellation	Constellation pattern, orbit control	No option—must design entire system for collision avoidance	—	Sec. 13.5
Constellation Build-Up, Replenishment, and End-of-Life	Determines level of service over time and impact of outages	Altitude, constellation pattern, build-up and sparing philosophy	Sparing: on-orbit spares vs. launch on demand; End-of-life: Deorbit vs. raise to higher orbit	End-of-life: Sec. 9.6.4, Chap. 30	Secs. 2.6.4, 13.6
Number of Orbit Planes	Determines performance plateaus	Altitude, inclination	Fewer planes means more growth plateaus and more graceful degradation	Sec. 10.6.2	Secs. 2.6.2, 13.6
Legal or Political Constraints	Limits options, locations in GEO, frequency use	Law, policy, international treaties and agreements	Need to be sure all needed permissions can be secured and time needed to do so	Sec. 12.3	—
Viewing and Lighting Conditions	Determines visibility of targets and objects of interest	Distance, surface properties, Sun angle	May drive orbit selection, viewing direction, or observation timing	Viewing conditions: Sec. 8.3	Chap. 11

Table 10-27, Fig. 10-31◀, Eq. 10-26◀

key characteristics make a discrete step. Plateaus may be different for different instruments and operating modes, but usually are functions of the swath width for each instrument or operating mode.

4. Collision Avoidance

Finally, one of the most important characteristics of any constellation is collision avoidance. The reason for this is not merely the loss of the satellites that collide, because we anticipate losing satellites for many reasons in any large constellation. The fundamental problem is the debris cloud that rcsults from any satellite collision. The velocity imparted to the particles resulting from the collision is small relative to the orbital velocity. Consequently, the net effect of a collision is to take two trackable, possibly controllable satellites and transform them into thousands of untrackable particles that spread out with time in the same orbit regime as the original satellites. Because the energy is proportional to mv^2, even a small piece of a satellite carries an enormous amount of kinetic energy at orbital velocities. Because the debris cloud remains in the area of the constellation, it dramatically increases the potential for secondary collisions, which, in turn, continues to increase the amount of debris and the possibility of making the orbit "uninhabitable." The implication for constellation design is that we should go to great lengths to design the constellation and the spacecraft to avoid collisions, explosions, or generation of extraneous debris.

10.6.4 The Rules for Constellation Design

It is clear from the above discussion, and particularly the example of the MSSP program at the beginning of Sec. 10.6, that there are no absolute rules for constellation design. It is not a systematic process, where we can simply take, for example, all possible Walker constellations and enumerate how well they do, and then select an absolute winner for the best constellation. The constellation design process is much fuzzier than that. The key is to look at the fundamental mission objectives and determine how these objectives can best be met at minimum cost and risk.

Ordinarily, our goal would be to minimize the number of satellites while achieving the appropriate level of coverage. Nonetheless, this may not be the lowest cost approach. For example, we may be able to achieve our coverage objectives with 20 satellites in the Van Allen radiation belts, where 25 would be required below the belts. The key question then becomes whether the lower cost and longer life per satellite for the lower constellation is worth the additional number of satellites. The constellation design process per se cannot answer that question. It can only be answered within the broader context of mission, system, and spacecraft design.

While there are not absolute rules, there are broad guidelines that assist in the process of constellation design. These are summarized in Table 10-28. In the end, constellation design is coupled only moderately to astrodynamics, and strongly to the process of meeting mission objectives at minimum cost and risk.

10.7 Design of Interplanetary Orbits

Ron Noomen, *Delft University of Technology*

This section on interplanetary orbit design is application-oriented. Clearly, spacecraft on interplanetary missions obey the same universal laws of nature as spacecraft orbiting the Earth. This means that the types of trajectories of such vehicles are similar to those of missions restricted to the direct vicinity of the Earth; we can therefore similarly apply the well-known concepts of Kepler orbits and so on. As a matter of fact, the formulas that we use nowadays for the description of satellite orbits were based on observations of planets, i.e., motions on the scale of the Solar System: it was the works of people like Brahe, Kepler, and Newton which lead to our knowledge of orbital mechanics as it is now. Rather than going through a detailed discussion on the theory of orbital mechanics, this chapter will **"only"** focus on the process of designing interplanetary orbits. For more specific information, refer to Chap. 9 in this book and a range of excellent texts, e.g., Cornelisse et al. [1979], Battin, [1999], Chobotov, [2002], Vallado, [2007].

Although the title of this section might suggest differently, we will use the term "interplanetary" irrespective of whether our vehicle travels to another planet, the Moon, an asteroid, a comet, or a mathematical position in space, like a Lagrange libration point. Along the same lines, we will consider Pluto as a planet, although officially it lost this status in 2006 and should be referred to as a dwarf planet.

The design of interplanetary missions goes back a long time. The first man-made vehicle to orbit the Earth was Sputnik-1, launched on October 4, 1957. Since the extra energy needed to step from a closed orbit around the Earth (an ellipse) to an escape orbit (a parabola or hyperbola) is relatively modest (at least, compared to what is needed to achieve a stable Earth orbit), it comes as no surprise that the first attempts to fly missions beyond the Earth took place in the year after Sputnik-1. Table 10-29 gives a summary of milestones in interplanetary spaceflight. It clearly shows that it is a discipline with many new and exciting developments. A more detailed overview of interplanetary missions can be found on the website.

One of the key factors in spaceflight is propulsion, in particular the thrust needed to accelerate the vehicle such that it can overcome Earth's gravity and atmospheric drag, and achieve the required velocity to sustain a steady flight in a certain orbit. During the first four decades of its existence, spaceflight solely relied on chemical high-thrust propulsion, where the energy to provide this thrust is stored in and delivered by chemical rocket engines. Such rocket engines are known for their high reliability, large thrust range, but also their modest efficiency (see Chap. 18). The latter aspect is expressed by the so-called specific impulse, I_{sp}, which has typical values of 200–450 sec. for this kind of propulsion. Alternatively, more efficient low-thrust engines have been in development since many decades, but the very first real applica-

Table 10-28. Rules for Constellation Design. While there are no absolute rules, these broad guidelines are applicable to most constellations. See also Tables 10-24, 10-25, 10-27.

Rule	Where Discussed Here	Where Discussed OCDM
1. ***To avoid differential node rotation, all satellites should be at the same inclination, except that an equatorial orbit can be added.***	Secs. 9.4.1, 9.5.3	Sec. 13.1
2. ***To avoid perigee rotation, all eccentric satellites should be at the critical inclination of 63.4 deg or (180–63.4)deg.***	Secs. 9.4.1, 9.5.4	Sec. 13.1
3. ***Collision avoidance is critical, even for dead satellites, and may be a driving characteristic for constellation design.***	Secs. 7.5, 10.6.3	Sec. 13.5
4. ***Symmetry is an important, but not critical element of constellation design.***	Sec. 10.6.2	Secs. 13.0, 13.1
5. ***Altitude is typically the most important of the orbit elements, followed by inclination. 0 eccentricity is the most common, although eccentric orbits can improve some coverage and sampling characteristics.***	Table 10-6, Sec. 10.4.1	Sec. 13.1
6. ***Minimum working elevation angle (which determines swath width) is as important as the altitude in determining coverage.***	Secs. 8.3.1, 10.2, Fig. 10-12	Sec. 9.1, 13.1
7. ***Two satellites can see each other if and only if they are able to see the same point on the ground.***	Fig. 8-46 (Sec. 8.5)	Sec. 10.1.1
8. ***Principal coverage Figures of Merit for constellations:*** • Percentage of time coverage goal is met • Number of satellites required to achieve the needed coverage • Mean and maximum response times (for non-continuous coverage) • Excess coverage percent • Excess coverage vs. latitude	Sec. 10.2.1.4	Secs. 9.5.1.4, 13,1
9. ***Size of stationkeeping box is determined by the mission objectives, the perturbations selected to be overcome, and the method of control.***	—	Sec. 13.2
10. ***For long-term constellations, absolute stationkeeping provides significant advantages and no disadvantages compared to relative stationkeeping.***	Sec. 19.2	Sec. 13.2
11. ***Orbit perturbations can be treated in 3 ways:*** • Negate the perturbing force (use only when necessary) • Control the perturbing force (best approach if control is required) • Leave perturbation uncompensated (best for cyclic perturbations)	—	Sec. 13.2
12. ***Performance plateaus and the number of orbit planes required are a function of the altitude.***	Sec. 10.6.2	Sec. 13.1
13. ***Changing position within the orbit plane is easy; changing orbit planes is hard; implies that a smaller number of orbit planes is better.***	Sec. 9.6.2	Sec. 13.4
14. ***Constellation build-up, graceful degradation, filling in for dead satellites, and end-of-life disposal are critical and should be addressed as part of constellation design.***	Sec. 9.6.4, 10.6, Chap. 30	Sec. 13.4
15. ***Taking satellites out of the constellation at end-of-life is critical for long-term success and risk avoidance. This is done by:*** • Deorbiting satellites in LEO • Raising them above the constellation above LEO (including GEO)	Sec. 9.6.4, Chap. 30	Sec. 13.4

Table 10-29. Most Prominent Successful "Firsts" in Interplanetary Spaceflight.

Satellite	Event Date	Achievement
Luna-2	September 14, 1959 (impact)	First Lunar mission
Mariner 2	December 14, 1962 (Venus flyby)	First planetary fly-by
Pioneer 10	July 1972	First to travel through asteroid belt
Mariner 10	February 5, 1974 (Venus GA)	First planetary gravity-assist
International Sun/Earth Explorer-3 (ISEE-3)	August 12, 1978	First mission to Lagrange point
Magellan	August 10, 1990 (Venus orbit insertion)	First use of aerobraking
Deep Space 1	October 1998	First mission with low-thrust propulsion as primary propulsion technique
Near Earth Asteroid Rendezvous (NEAR)	April 30, 2000 (asteroid Eros)	First to orbit and land on asteroid

Table 10-29, Fig. 10-31◀, Eq. 10-26◀

tions as a primary propulsion technique were not flown until 1998 [NASA, 2010a] and 2003, [ESA, 2010a]. The ion engines used in these missions had I_{sp} values of 3,100 sec and 1,640 sec, respectively, which can still be considered as relatively conservative: the I_{sp} of (near) future low-thrust propulsion engines may range between 5,000 and 10,000 sec. This means that low thrust is to be considered as a very likely propulsion technique for virtually any future interplanetary mission. However, this section will restrict itself to high-thrust missions, if only since a treatment of the ins and outs of low-thrust interplanetary trajectory design would require quite a number of pages. For an introduction to low-thrust orbits and their design, refer to Petropoulos and Longuski [2004], and Izzo [2006], amongst others.

Another key element of interplanetary missions is the geometry of the problem: the location of the Earth and other celestial bodies involved, relative to the spacecraft. For first-order calculations, it is customary to consider the problem to be 2-dimensional, i.e., all bodies move about the Sun in one plane, the *ecliptic* (which is the orbital plane of the Earth). Realizing that the inclinations of the orbits of most other planets are quite small (apart from Mercury and Pluto, all planets have inclinations of a few degrees at most), this is a very reasonable approach. However, in order to achieve the most accurate trajectory, one should take one step further and work with a 3-dimensional problem formulation. This section will address both possibilities.

With the risk of being contradictory, the highest possible accuracy is not always what one is after in preliminary mission design. This would require including the most accurate models for the positions of the celestial bodies, covering all possible forces acting on the vehicle, use of accurate propagators, and so on. As a consequence, this would be a time-consuming activity. Rather, in first-order design, preference is given to fast, accurate-but-not-perfect algorithms. In doing so, a designer can gain several orders of magnitude on CPU-time, get a very reasonable first-order optimal solution, and later on, refine this with a fully detailed model of all aspects, only for a last iteration. In this section, we will mainly focus on fast, analytical techniques, and merely address some aspects that are relevant to "the real thing."

Finally, for those readers who have whetted their appetite after having read this section: an international competition is being organized on an almost yearly basis since 2005, in which teams are invited to design an optimum trajectory according to specific requirements: the Global Trajectory Optimization Competition (GTOC). The initial competition, GTOC1, was organized by the Advanced Concepts Team of the European Space Agency [ESA, 2010b], and the winner of each particular round is required to organize the competition for the year thereafter. Previous versions dealt, for example, with the design of an optimal trajectory through a series of asteroids, or a mission to such heavenly bodies followed by a return to the Earth. Experience teaches that these assignments are extremely difficult to solve, if only for the large number of unknowns in the problem and the fact that solutions have to be handed in within a month after release of the assignment. On the other hand they are extremely motivating for students, and very good projects to work on off-line, in order to study, develop, and fine-tune the various elements of interplanetary mission design.

10.7.1 Design Process

In order to structure the search for an optimal interplanetary trajectory, one should follow a series of well-defined steps. These are summarized in Table 10-30; a brief explanation of each element is given below.

Table 10-30. The Orbit Design Process. See text for discussion of each step.

Step	Where Discussed
1. Quantify Relevant Mission Parameters	Sec. 10.7.1
2. Obtain Model for Planetary Ephemerides	Sec. 10.7.1
3. Analyze Direct Hohmann Flight	Sec. 10.7.2
4. Analyze Alternative Direct Keplerian Orbit	Sec. 10.7.2
5. Assess (Round Trip) Travel Times	Secs. 10.7.2, 10.7.3
6. Identify Possible Multi-leg Scenarios	Sec. 10.7.2
7. Analyze Multi-leg Scenarios Using Lambert Targeting	Sec. 10.7 web article
8. Iterate	

Step 1. Quantify Relevant Mission Parameters

Any design process starts with an assessment of what is actually required. Questions to be answered are: what is the departure planet? What is the target? Do we go for a direct flight, or will we possibly allow fly-by's of planets in-between? Is the mission objective to arrive at the destination only, or do we want to return to the departure planet? Do we have specific constraints, like departure and arrival conditions (time, geometry), maximum allowable ΔV, maximum allowable time-of-flight? Usually, such aspects are set by the customer, but some aspects can also be traded during the design process. In this section, we are interested in the parameters which are related to orbital mechanics only; however, these may very well affect other mission parameters such as required propellant mass.

Step 2. Obtain Model for Planetary Ephemerides

One of the aspects that need to be fulfilled is the availability of a model that specifies the positions of the planets involved, as a function of time. Depending on what is actually required, one can do with a simple 2-dimensional model, where the orbits of the planets are assumed to lie within a single plane and described by simple Kepler orbits (i.e., coplanar orbits). This is a reasonable first-order assumption, since the inclinations of the orbits of most of the planets in our Solar System have a value of a few degrees at most; it can become a different story when wanting to study missions to and from asteroids. So one step further is to work with a 3-dimensional model with

Kepler orbits, now also involving the orientation parameters inclination and the longitude of the ascending node (see App. C). To simulate reality as closely as possible, one can go for a fully detailed 3-dimensional representation, where perturbations acting on the trajectories of the planets are also taken into account. For the latter purpose, JPL's DE405 model [Standish, 1998] or later versions thereof can be used.

Step 3. Analyze Direct Hohmann Flight

The classical optimal solution, at least in terms of required ΔV, to a direct transfer problem between two coplanar orbits is the Hohmann transfer orbit. Such an orbit tangentially touches the orbits of the departure planet and that of the target planet (see Sec. 9.6). Here, it is assumed that the velocity changes are obtained instantaneously (i.e., the position of the spacecraft is unaffected, and the maneuver is achieved with an idealized rocket engine that can provide an infinite acceleration), and that the velocities directly before and after each maneuver are parallel. Although definitions may differ, it is also customary to assume that this transfer takes place between two circular orbits. The Hohmann transfer between two orbits around the Earth has already been discussed in Sec. 9.6; a similar concept can be applied for interplanetary purposes (although some elements do differ). Section 10.7.2 will provide more details.

Step 4. Analyze Alternative Direct Keplerian Orbits

Attractive as they may be from an energy point of view, Hohmann transfers are also reputed for having a long trip time. In order to overcome this problem, one can investigate whether faster transfers between two planets are possible, with limited consequences for the required ΔV. This is also covered in Sec. 10.7.2.

Step 5. Assess (Round Trip) Travel Times

Timing of events (launch, maneuvers, rendezvous) is already crucial in missions around the Earth, but for interplanetary missions it is even more stringent: the positions of the celestial bodies involved are prominent elements in the design, and dictate the geometry of potential transfers. For a trip to Mars, for example, you don't want to reach Mars' orbit without the planet being there! This problem becomes worse in the case of missions along a series of celestial objects, or round trips, in which we want to return to our original point of departure. The problem will be treated in Sec. 10.7.3.

Step 6. Identify Possible Multi-leg Scenarios

Direct transfers between two planets are attractive, if only for the ease with which the various options can be analyzed. However, the energy that can be provided by launchers, upper stages and on-board engines is restricted, meaning that we will be confronted with limitations as to what can be achieved with a direct (single-leg) flight. Fortunately, nature provides a free tool to increase the energy of a spacecraft without paying any cost: a planetary fly-by. This necessitates a more complex mission design, where a vehicle travels to one or more planets first before reaching its destination. In order to analyze the possible application of such a scenario, one first has to identify the candidate (series of) fly-by planets. The quantitative analysis of each of such proposed scenarios is dealt with in the next step. Both will be discussed in Sec. 10.7.2.

Step 7. Analyze Multi-leg Scenarios Using Lambert Targeting

When the trajectory proposal encompasses a series of legs between pairs of planets (such as Galileo's VEEGA trajectory: launch at the Earth, followed by fly-by's along Venus, Earth, and Earth again, before arriving at Jupiter), the analysis of the advantages and disadvantages of such an option cannot be done with straightforward Hohmann orbits anymore. In this case, the problem is tackled by means of solving a series of Lambert problems, which allows a straightforward evaluation of ΔV and time-of-flight, amongst others. This is the standard approach applied for any mission design; it can be used for a wide variety of missions: one-way, round trip, different departure and target conditions. The theory will be discussed briefly in the web article for this section.

Step 8. Iterate

It is very likely that the first result is not optimal: the required ΔV is too high, the trip takes too long. So, one may have to take a fresh look at the initial requirements (as defined under Step 1) and modify them such that a more satisfactory result can be obtained. When the techniques to analyze the interplanetary transfer problem have been coded in a general-purpose computer program, this should not be a problem at all.

10.7.2 One-Way Missions

The following sections will address most of the issues listed in Table 10-30. First, we will take a look at fundamental aspects that play a role for one-way missions, and in the next section we will treat round-trip missions.

In Sec. 9.6, the theory of the Hohmann transfer orbit was discussed, in particular for transfers between circular orbits around the Earth. Inspecting Fig. 9-28 in Sec. 9.6.1, the main characteristics of such a transfer are clearly visible: (1) it is a transfer between two circular, coplanar orbits (the circularity requirement is traditional, if only for providing unique solutions for the parameters of the Hohmann transfer orbit), (2) it is tangent to both the departure orbit and the target orbit, and (3) it is an ellipse. Its *pericenter* and *apocenter* exactly touch the departure and target orbits (note that the concept can be used for a transfer to an inner target orbit as well), so the value of the semi-major axis of the transfer orbit (and hence the corresponding energy) is minimal. This concept can also be applied to interplanetary spaceflight, albeit that the situation is slightly more complicated. Therefore, we take one step back and address the geometry for the most general trajectory between arbitrary objects around the Sun first. The situation is sketched in Fig. 10-32.

First of all, positions and velocities are given in a heliocentric system, i.e., with respect to an inertial reference frame with its center at the Sun. The spacecraft has

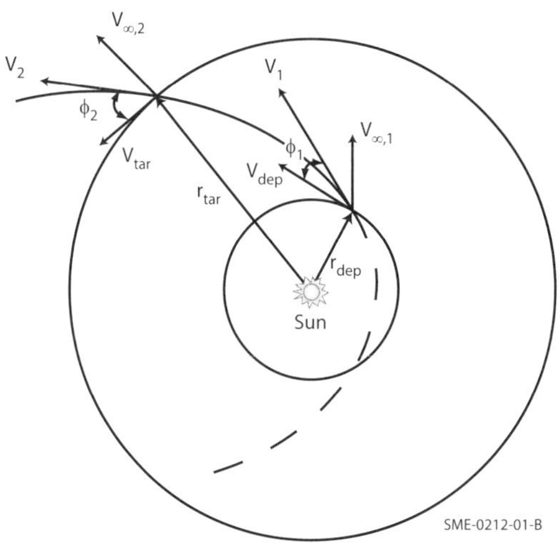

Fig. 10-32. Geometry of an Arbitrary Interplanetary Transfer Between Two Planets, and Definition of the Parameters Involved.

velocities V_1 and V_2 (at different epochs), whereas the departure planet and the target planet have velocities V_{dep} and V_{tar}, respectively. The relative velocities $V_{\infty,1}$ and $V_{\infty,2}$ of our spacecraft can be obtained by vectorially subtracting the heliocentric velocities of the spacecraft and the planet, respectively.

Secondly, Fig. 10-32 shows that we are dealing with (at least) 4 different objects: the central body (i.e., the Sun), the departure and target planets, and our spacecraft. However, when making a first-order design of an interplanetary trajectory, it is customary to describe this by a succession of 2-body problems: the so-called patched conics approach. According to this approach, the motion of our vehicle in each segment is considered to be dominated by the gravitational pull of a perfectly symmetrical central body, whereas all other forces (e.g., third-body attractions, solar radiation pressure, atmospheric drag) are ignored. So, each segment can be described by the equations of a Kepler orbit. In our interplanetary transfer problem (Fig. 10-32), we work with a series of 3 consecutive 2-body problems: (1) the satellite around the departure planet (planetocentric), (2) the satellite around the Sun (heliocentric), and (3) the satellite around the target planet (planetocentric again). The planetocentric phases take place within the *Sphere of Influence (SoI)* of the respective planets; these basically indicate the limit where the gravitational dominance of one celestial body (e.g., the departure planet, Earth) is taken over by another one (e.g., the Sun). Without derivation (which can be found in Cornelisse et al. [1979], for example), the average dimension of the *SoI* of a planet can be computed with the following equation:

$$r_{SoI} = r_{planet}\left(\frac{m_{planet}}{m_{Sun}}\right)^{0.4} \qquad (10\text{-}27)$$

where r_{planet} is the distance between the particular planet and the Sun (not to be confused with the radius of the former), and m_{planet} and m_{Sun} are the masses of the planet and the Sun, respectively. The resulting dimensions of the *SoI*'s for the planets in our Solar System are summarized in Table 10-31.

Live Calc **Table 10-31. Dimensions of the Sphere of Influence of the Planets in Our Solar System.** The SoI values are based on the average distance between the planet and the Sun, and may vary slightly when evaluated at actual planetary positions.

Planet	Sphere of Influence [AU]	Sphere of Influence [% of Average Distance from Sun]
Mercury	0.0008	0.2
Venus	0.004	0.6
Earth	0.006	0.6
Mars	0.004	0.3
Jupiter	0.322	6.2
Saturn	0.365	3.8
Uranus	0.346	1.8
Neptune	0.579	1.9
Pluto	0.021	0.1

It is clear that the size of any *SoI* is marginal compared to the size of our Solar System. Therefore, we can consider the heliocentric part of the transfer to (effectively) take place between the exact positions of the departure and target planets. In addition, the planetocentric part takes place on a local scale and involves a hyperbola around the planet of interest (since of course, the spacecraft has to escape/enter the gravity field of the departure/target planet).

Hohmann Transfers

The geometry of an interplanetary Hohmann transfer is a special case of the general geometry as sketched in Fig. 10-32. In the Hohmann case and evaluated at the departure epoch, the heliocentric velocity $\boldsymbol{V_1}$ of the satellite is parallel to the velocity $\boldsymbol{V_{dep}}$ of the departure planet; at the arrival epoch, the same thing holds for the velocities $\boldsymbol{V_2}$ and $\boldsymbol{V_{tar}}$ of the satellite and the target planet, respectively (note the vector notations). In essence we end up at the geometry for a Hohmann transfer between orbits around the Earth (see Fig. 9-28). In order to quantify the relevant characteristics of an interplanetary Hohmann transfer, we can apply the series of calculations summarized in Table 10-32. In this table, μ_S, μ_{dep} and μ_{tar} represent the gravitational parameter of the Sun, the departure planet and the target planet, respectively; r_{dep} and r_{tar} represent the radius of the orbits of the departure planet and target planet around the Sun, respectively (both assumed to be circular); and r_0 and r_3 represent the radius of the (circular) orbit around the departure planet and the target planet, respectively. The last column gives an example for the case of a Hohmann transfer from the Earth to Mars.

An important element of Table 10-32 are the maneuvers ΔV_0 and ΔV_3. The first one is responsible for the transition from a circular orbit around the departure planet to

Live Calc

Table 10-32. Summary of the Procedure to Compute the Characteristics of an Interplanetary Hohmann Transfer. The meaning of the parameters is explained in the main body of the text. The example values hold for a trip from the Earth (at 1.0 AU) to Mars (at 1.52366 AU), with circular parking orbit altitudes of 185 and 500 km, respectively.

Step	Parameter	Expression	Example
1	V_{dep} (heliocentric velocity of departure planet)	$V_{dep} = \sqrt{(\mu_S / r_{dep})}$	29.785 km/s
2	V_{tar} (heliocentric velocity of target planet)	$V_{tar} = \sqrt{(\mu_S / r_{tar})}$	24.130 km/s
3	V_{c0} (circular velocity around departure planet)	$V_{c0} = \sqrt{(\mu_{dep} / r_0)}$	7.793 km/s
4	V_{c3} (circular velocity around target planet)	$V_{c3} = \sqrt{(\mu_{tar} / r_3)}$	3.315 km/s
5	a_{tr} (semi-major axis of transfer orbit)	$a_{tr} = (r_{dep} + r_{tar}) / 2$	188.77 10^6 km
6	e_{tr} (eccentricity of transfer orbit)	$e_{tr} = \lvert r_{tar} - r_{dep} \rvert / (r_{tar} + r_{dep})$	0.208
7	V_1 (heliocentric velocity at departure position)	$V_1 = \sqrt{[\mu_S (2 / r_{dep} - 1 / a_{tr})]}$	32.729 km/s
8	V_2 (heliocentric velocity at target position)	$V_2 = \sqrt{[\mu_S (2 / r_{tar} - 1 / a_{tr})]}$	21.481 km/s
9	$V_{\infty,1}$ (excess velocity at departure planet)	$V_{\infty,1} = \lvert V_1 - V_{dep} \rvert$	2.945 km/s
10	$V_{\infty,2}$ (excess velocity at target planet)	$V_{\infty,2} = \lvert V_2 - V_{tar} \rvert$	2.649 km/s
11	V_0 (velocity at pericenter of hyperbola around departure planet)	$V_0 = \sqrt{(2\mu_{dep} / r_0 + V_{\infty,1}^2)}$	11.408 km/s
12	V_3 (velocity at pericenter of hyperbola around target planet)	$V_3 = \sqrt{(2\mu_{tar} / r_3 + V_{\infty,2}^2)}$	5.385 km/s
13	ΔV_0 (maneuver at pericenter around departure planet)	$\Delta V_0 = \lvert V_0 - V_{c0} \rvert$	3.615 km/s
14	ΔV_3 (maneuver at pericenter around target planet)	$\Delta V_3 = \lvert V_{c3} - V_3 \rvert$	2.070 km/s
15	ΔV_{tot} (total velocity change)	$\Delta V_{tot} = \Delta V_0 + \Delta V_3$	5.684 km/s
16	T_{tr} (transfer time)	$T_{tr} = \pi \sqrt{(a_{tr}^3 / \mu_S)}$	0.709 yr

a hyperbola, whereas the second one causes the reverse, but now around the target planet. Knowing the characteristics of hyperbolas, the two maneuvers translate into excess velocities $V_{\infty,1}$ and $V_{\infty,2}$, respectively. Note that the required amount of propellant is determined by the magnitudes of ΔV_0 and ΔV_3, and not by the relative velocities $V_{\infty,1}$ and $V_{\infty,2}$. This represents a fundamental difference between Hohmann transfers on a heliocentric scale and Hohmann transfers between orbits around a particular planet (e.g., the Earth; see Fig. 9-28). Depending on the exact conditions, the difference between such a ΔV and the excess velocity V_∞ may in fact be easily in the order of a few kilometers per second, with significant consequences for the amount of propellant to be spent.

Timing

Of course, a Hohmann transfer has to physically connect 2 objects orbiting the Sun: the spacecraft leaves from a physical departure body, with a velocity tangent to the heliocentric velocity of that body, and should exactly arrive at the target object in its orbit around the Sun. In order to assess the timing of such a transfer, the geometry of the departure planet, an arbitrary (i.e., non-Hohmann) transfer orbit and the target planet is depicted in Fig. 10-33 (including the definition of the relevant parameters). Figure 10-33 refers to a trip from the Earth to Mars, but of course any combination of planets will be valid.

Here, the transfer starts at epoch t_1 whereas the vehicle is expected to arrive at epoch t_2. In addition, the angular positions of the 3 objects involved are expressed by a parameter ν, and an arbitrary epoch t_0 is taken as a reference to express the positions of the planets. In our case specifically, the connection between the 2 planets is a Hohmann transfer, with the time-of-flight denoted as T_H, and a transfer angle π (see Sec. 9.6.1). We then can write the positions at the departure epoch:

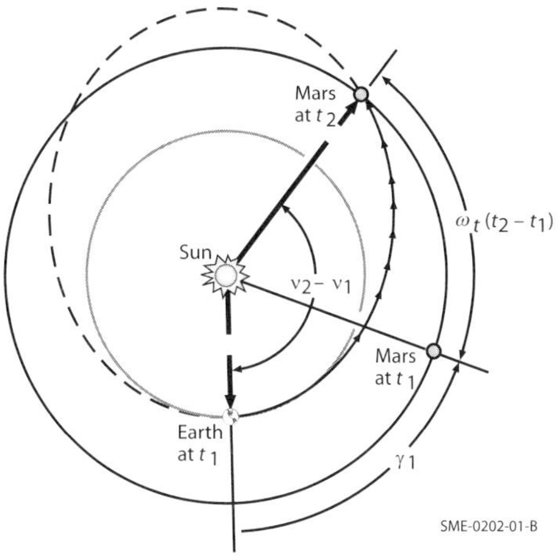

Fig. 10-33. The Geometry of Departure Planet, Arbitrary Transfer Orbit, and Target Planet [Wertz, 2009].

$$\begin{aligned} \nu_E(t_1) &= \nu_E(t_0) + \omega_E(t_1 - t_0) \\ \nu_M(t_1) &= \nu_M(t_0) + \omega_M(t_1 - t_0) \\ \nu_{spc}(t_1) &= \nu_E(t_1) = \nu_E(t_0) + \omega_E(t_1 - t_0) \end{aligned} \tag{10-28}$$

where ω_E and ω_M are the average orbital angular rates of the Earth and Mars, respectively.

And, similarly, the positions at the arrival epoch:

$$\begin{aligned} \nu_E(t_2) &= \nu_E(t_1) + \omega_E T_H \\ \nu_M(t_2) &= \nu_M(t_1) + \omega_M T_H \\ \nu_{spc}(t_2) &= \nu_{spc}(t_1) + \pi = \nu_M(t_2) \end{aligned} \tag{10-29}$$

From these 6 equations, it can easily be derived that

$$\nu_E(t_1) = \nu_M(t_2) - \pi = \nu_M(t_1) + \omega_M T_H - \pi \tag{10-30}$$

or

$$t_1 = t_0 + \frac{\nu_M(t_0) - \nu_E(t_0) + \omega_M T_H - \pi}{\omega_E - \omega_M} \tag{10-31}$$

and

$$t_2 = t_1 + T_H \tag{10-32}$$

As an example, take the situation Earth to Mars: at the epoch January 1, 2000, 12 hrs (i.e., J2000), the planets have a longitude of 100.46° and 355.45° in their orbits, respectively (ignoring any effect of differences in inclination, $\nu(t_0)$ can be taken identical to these values) [Cox, 2000], [Seidelmann, 1992]. Substituting these values in the equations above, with orbital periods of 1.0000 and 1.8807 years for the Earth and Mars, respectively, and a Hohmann transfer time of 0.709 years, gives as the first Hohmann transfer opportunity the epoch of departure, t_1, 456.4 days after January 1, 2000 (i.e., April 1, 2001), and the epoch of arrival, t_2, 715.2 days after January 1, 2000 (i.e., Dec 16, 2001). Of course, the same option repeats after exactly one synodic period (2.135 years, see Table 9-5). It must be emphasized that these considerations are valid for an ideal case where the planets move in circular, coplanar orbits; a more realistic simulation will be discussed in Table 10web-1.

Faster Trajectories

Using the recipe given in Table 10-32, one can compute the parameters of a Hohmann transfer between any pair of planets in a straightforward manner. Attractive as it is from an energy and computational point of view, a Hohmann transfer does have a number of drawbacks: (1) the launch epoch is very strict, with little or no room for deviations (at least ideally; pericenter and apocenter are by definition on opposite sides of the central body, with consequences for the departure and arrival epochs), (2) the time-of-flight may be too long for some applications, and (3) although it represents the most energy-efficient direct transfer, the total ΔV required for a direct trip to distant planets may simply be too large to be delivered by even the most powerful combination of launcher, upper stage and on-board engine (an indirect trajectory, involving planetary flybys, could provide a solution; more on this later in this section).

In order to compensate for the first 2 drawbacks, one might consider to leave the departure planet (e.g., Earth) under conditions which are different from those of a Hohmann transfer; a similar flexibility can be introduced for the arrival geometry. This is the most general situation as sketched in Fig. 10-32. Clearly, our vehicle now follows an elliptical orbit with dimensions that exceed those of a Hohmann transfer orbit. As shown in Fig. 10-32, it can reach the orbit of the target planet on its way out, before reaching apocenter; in such a case we speak of a so-called Type-I transfer, which is clearly faster than a Hohmann transfer. In case the orbit of the target planet is reached after having passed the apocenter, we speak of a Type-II transfer, which has a longer transfer time compared to a Hohmann transfer. Both options (Type-I, Type-II) can have advantages and disadvantages (travel time, ΔV, departure, and arrival geometry, possibilities for continuation to another planet), so both should be considered.

A summary of the recipe to analyze such options is given in Table 10web-2.

Multiple Legs

As mentioned earlier, a Hohmann trajectory is the most attractive transfer from one planet to another from an energy point of view. However, it may bring drawbacks in terms of flight time, geometry, and required total ΔV (still). An alternative could be to refrain from entering in a circular orbit around the target planet and instead make a simple pass by it; however, this may not be rewarding enough (scientifically, financially) and jeopardize the entire mission. As an alternative, it is possible to gain energy from one or more planetary fly-by's around planets along the way (also known as Gravity Assists, abbreviated GA's; see Sec. 9.6.3): the energy is available for free, and the flight time might be reduced considerably. Ideally, on-board propellant would have to be taken along only for insertion in the orbit around the target planet and maintenance thereof. The first thing to do is to propose one or more scenarios of celestial bodies that one wants to pass along consecutively. This can be based on a plot of the positions of the planets during the interval of interest: the positions of the departure planet at this moment (e.g., "leave Earth in 2015") and the target planet at arrival (e.g., "be at Saturn within 5 years") will typically suggest a logical order of possibly useful GA planets.

It will be clear that a succession of Hohmann transfers would be difficult to use for such a purpose, if only for the strict requirements on geometry of the positions of the planets involved. Instead, the Lambert technique as presented in the book website in the web article is typically applied in these cases. Consider for instance a mission to Saturn, for which one wants to perform a GA at Jupiter. In such a case, the mission is a succession of 2 legs (Earth-Jupiter and Jupiter-Saturn). If the designer assumes epochs for launch, Jupiter GA, and Saturn arrival, it is possible to compute the parameters of the two connecting Kepler orbits, determine the excess velocity vector V_∞ before and after the Jupiter GA, and determine the ΔV's required at the Earth and at Saturn. Ideally, the required excess velocities before and after the Jupiter GA would be equal in magnitude (remember: they should be equal in case of a perfect hyperbola around the GA planet), and the gravity field of the GA planet should be strong enough to achieve the required bending angle (see Eq. 9-83).

However, the satellite heliocentric velocities directly before and directly after the GA result from solving two almost independent Lambert problems (they only share the epoch of the GA, and hence the position of the GA planet), so it is very unlikely that the magnitudes of the excess velocities are identical (irrespective of whether they are expressed in a heliocentric or a planetocentric frame). If these excess velocities indeed differ in magnitude, one needs to apply a ΔV when passing through the pericenter of the hyperbola around the GA planet: we have a so-called powered GA. Another possibility would be the situation when the gravity field of the GA planet is not strong enough (or the conditions prohibit the spacecraft from coming close enough to the surface of that planet—think of Jupiter's radiation belts) to bend the excess velocity from its original direction to the one required for the 2nd leg. In such a case, the mission also needs a ΔV, which is typically applied when the vehicle is about to leave the *SoI* of the GA planet; again we speak of a powered GA. The results (the summation of the 4 possible maneuvers: Earth escape, 1st maneuver during GA, 2nd maneuver during GA, Saturn capture) can be used in an optimization, in which the propellant usage can be minimized. As an example, a mission from the Earth to Neptune might be flown using a Venus-Venus-Earth-Jupiter-Saturn (VVEJS) sequence (required ΔV in parenthesis): launch from the Earth on May 25, 2012 (1.5972 km/s), GA around Venus (0.0010 km/s), Venus GA again (0.0030 km/s), GA around the Earth (0.0094 km/s), GA around Jupiter (0.4172 km/s), GA around Saturn (0.0081 km/s), and arrival at Neptune on December 18, 2029 (3.7831 km/s for orbit insertion at 4000 km altitude); the total ΔV amounts to 5.8190 km/s, whereas the total flight takes 17.6 years. For comparison: a direct Hohmann transfer would require a ΔV of 15.7 km/s and a transfer time of 30.6 years; this ΔV is far too large to be delivered by current launchers and upper stages alone.

In order to save propellant mass, one might also consider another option: fly a so-called *Aero Gravity Assist (AGA)*. In such a case, the vehicle performs a GA around a planet with an atmosphere, and uses the aerodynamic forces to achieve a larger total turn angle than would have been possible if flying a hyperbola only (lift, pointed downward unlike what we want with airplanes, forces the vehicle to follow a curved trajectory at a given altitude; with respect to the planetocentric frame, the vehicle will also loose some velocity because of drag). This exotic topic will not be treated here, however.

10.7.3 Round-Trip Missions

In many cases, one is not only interested in flying a mission to a distant object (a planet, an asteroid), but also in returning the vehicle to the Earth. Examples are sample retrieval missions like Stardust [NASA, 2010b], and Hayabusa [ISAS, 2010], to mention a few. It is obvious, right from the beginning, that this will complicate the mission considerably. First, it will require a larger amount of propellant: now it is also necessary to depart from the target planet, and a braking maneuver might be needed to end up in a parking orbit (for instance, for a rendezvous with the International Space Station) around the Earth—although the latter might be avoided if a direct entry into the Earth's atmosphere is employed, and a subsequent landing is made somewhere on the Earth's surface. Second, the total trip time can increase considerably: one can fly a one-way mission to Mars in 0.71 years using a Hohmann transfer (Table 10-33), but a back-and-forth mission using 2 Hohmann transfers would require a total mission time of 2.66 years (0.71 years for each leg plus another 1.24 years waiting at Mars for a favorable alignment of the two planets).

Timing

As for an analytical treatment of this round trip problem, see Wertz [2003], Wertz [2004], and Sarzi-Amade and Wertz [2009]. Here, we will treat the simple case in which (1) the departure and target planets move in circular, coplanar orbits around the Sun, (2) there is a single leg outbound and a single leg back, and (3) the transfers (outbound and return) are done by means of simple Hohmann trajectories. Other cases are extensively discussed in the references just mentioned.

The geometry of the problem is sketched in Fig. 10-34, for the case in which we perform a trip to an outer planet and back. In this example, an Earth-Mars-Earth trip is considered, but of course the relevant parameters can be referred to any combination of planets.

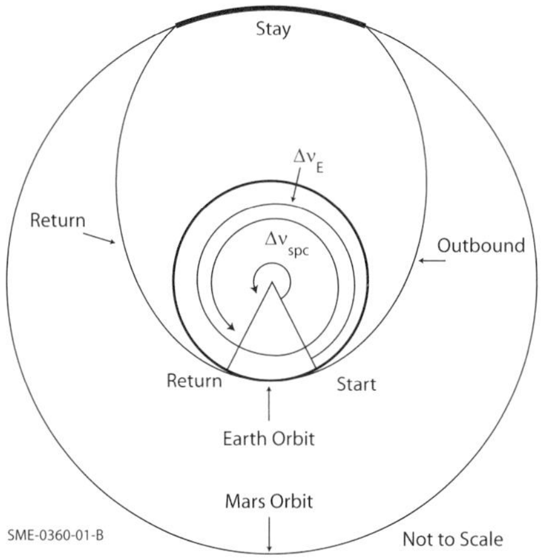

Fig. 10-34. Geometry of Round Trip Flight [Wertz, 2003]. Note: the transfers depicted here are non-Hohmann.

During the time of the mission, the Earth is assumed to cover an angle Δv_E, whereas the spacecraft covers an angle Δv_{spc}. In order to rendezvous at the Earth again at the end of the mission, the relation between the two angles must be the following:

$$\Delta v_E = \Delta v_{spc} + 2\pi W \tag{10-33}$$

where W is an integer number (which can be positive or negative). Without derivation (see Wertz, [2003]), the fastest round trip to Mars following a dual-Hohmann transfer is achieved when $W = 1$ (the case with $W = 0$ would require departure from Mars before even having arrived there). For the fastest possible trip to Venus, instead, we would have $W = -1$. In addition, the total transfer time T can be expressed as the summation of 2 Hohmann transfer times T_H plus a stay time at the target planet T_S:

$$T = 2T_H + T_S \tag{10-34}$$

If the angular velocities of the Earth and Mars around the Sun are expressed as ω_E and ω_M, respectively, one can express the total angle Δv_E covered by the Earth as:

$$\begin{aligned}\Delta v_E &= \omega_E T = \Delta v_{spc} + 2\pi W \\ &= \pi + \omega_M T_S + \pi + 2\pi W\end{aligned} \tag{10-35}$$

(Any Hohmann transfer covers an angle of π radians; ω_E and ω_M are constant since we assume circular orbits.) By solving these equations, we get a solution for the total trip time T and the stay time T_S:

$$T = \frac{(W+1)2\pi - 2\omega_M T_H}{\omega_E - \omega_M} \tag{10-36}$$

$$T_S = T - 2T_H = \frac{(W+1)2\pi - 2\omega_E T_H}{\omega_E - \omega_M} \tag{10-37}$$

Obviously, the stay time has to be a positive number, so this condition defines the possible values for the parameter W for any combination of planets. Clearly, the fastest round trip can be achieved when W is chosen such that the stay time is smallest (in the case of a Hohmann trajectory, the transfer time is a given). Table 10-33 gives some numerical values for a number of back-and-forth trips from the Earth to some relevant planetary targets. Fig. 10-35 gives similar information for arbitrary distances between the target and the Sun. As expected, the curve for the one-way Hohmann transfer time shows a gradual increase with distance. The curves for stay time and total time, on the other hand, show regular jumps, which essentially represent integer increases of the parameter W, in order for the geometry to be favorable for the return leg (the stay time increases with $2\pi/(\omega_E - \omega_M)$ for each step in W). For targets at distances larger than about 2 AU, it is clear that the Earth needs to make more revolutions in order to make the round trip possible (for example, the minimum value for the parameter W increases to 5 for a trip to Jupiter). Clearly, objects that have a semi-major axis which approaches 1 AU (e.g., near-Earth asteroids) would be difficult targets for a Hohmann approach since their angular velocity is comparable to that of the Earth, and so the stay time would become quite large, awaiting a favorable return geometry; consequences for the total trip time are obvious.

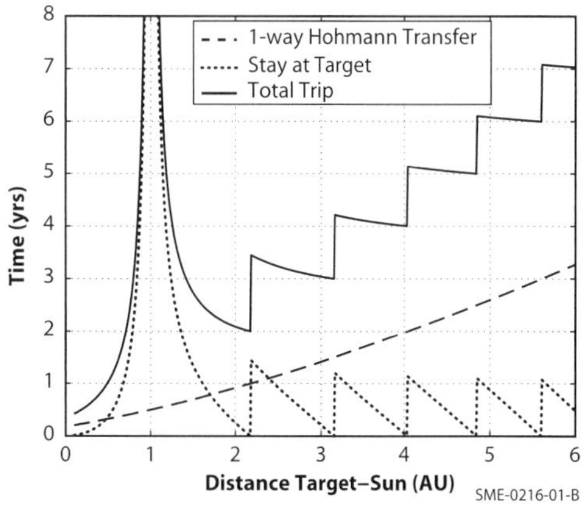

Fig. 10-35. Hohmann Transfer Times, Stay Times, and Round Trip Times for Missions Between the Earth and Targets at Arbitrary Distances.

As shown in Wertz [2003], one may opt to go for a longer stay time while maintaining the total trip time at nearly the same values as shown in Table 10-33. However, in such a case, the transfer time itself has to be shortened. Obviously, this results in a non-Hohmann

Live Calc

Table 10-33. Hohmann Transfer Times, Stay Times, and Round Trip Times for Missions Between the Earth and Neighboring Planets.

Target	Mean Orbit Radius* [AU]	Angular Motion [rad/s]	Hohmann Transfer Time [yrs]	Stay Time [yrs]	Total Trip Time [yrs]	W [–]
Mercury	0.387	8.267×10^{-7}	0.289	0.183	0.761	–1
Venus	0.723	3.236×10^{-7}	0.400	1.279	2.078	–1
Mars	1.524	1.059×10^{-7}	0.709	1.244	2.661	1
Jupiter	5.203	1.667×10^{-8}	2.731	0.587	6.050	5
Saturn	9.537	6.760×10^{-9}	6.047	0.939	13.032	12

* rounded off to 3 digits behind the dot; see appendices for full value.

Table 10-34. Four Scenarios for a Mission to Mars, Plus their Main Characteristics. In all cases, the vehicle leaves the Earth somewhere in the time frame 2013–2015. The planet positions have been represented using JPL's DE200 ephemerides [Standish, 1982]. All scenarios start in a parking orbit around Earth at 185 km altitude. Scenario 1 does not enter into an orbit around Mars, whereas scenarios 2–4 enter in an orbit at 500 km around Mars. Scenarios 3 and 4 return to Earth, where scenario 4 ends up at the orbit of the ISS at 340 km altitude.

Scenario	ΔV [km/s]	Total ΔV [km/s]	Dates	Total Travel Time [days]
Mars Flyby	3.616 (Earth dep.)	3.616	Jan 2, 2014 (Earth dep.) Nov. 28, 2014 (Mars arr.)	330
Mars Orbit Insertion	3.649 (Earth dep.) 2.341 (Mars arr.)	5.989	Dec 4, 2013 (Earth dep.) Sep 24, 2014 (Mars arr.)	294
Mars Orbit Insertion, Return to Earth (direct landing)	3.649 (Earth dep.) 2.341 (Mars arr.) 1.920 (Mars dep.)	7.999	Dec 4, 2013 (Earth dep.) Sep 24, 2014 (Mars arr.) Dec 13, 2015 (Mars dep.) Oct 8, 2016 (Earth arr.)	1039
Mars Orbit Insertion, Return to Earth (rendezvous with ISS)	3.649 (Earth dep.) 2.341 (Mars arr.) 2.041 (Mars dep.) 3.987 (Earth arr.)	12.018	Dec 4, 2013 (Earth dep.) Sep 24, 2014 (Mars arr.) Dec 25, 2015 (Mars dep.) Aug 12, 2016 (Earth arr.)	982

transfer, at the expense of larger ΔV requirements. Another option is to extend the stay time by adding the synodic period; in that case one would simply wait until the departure geometry is favorable again.

As for the departure and arrival epochs (for both the outbound leg and the inbound leg), the same formulas given for one-way Hohmann trips can be used (see Table 10-32).

Lambert Approach

The numerical approach, as presented on the book website is more flexible since it uses a (first order) succession of 2-body formulations, and can involve direct trajectories, or multiple legs. Again, the basis for this approach is a succession of Lambert problems plus an optimization technique. The recipe is, in essence, the one that was proposed already for one-way missions: assume a range of epochs for departure from the Earth, possible GA's, arrival epoch at the target, epoch of departure from that target, possible GA's again, and arrival date at the Earth; compute the parameters of the various legs, including propellant usage, stay time, and so on; and optimize. By defining an objective function (i.e., the factor in the optimization that can be quantified and that needs to be minimized or maximized) that not only includes the required propellant expenditure but also the total trip time, one can end up at a trajectory design that performs (slightly) worse in terms of propellant usage, but does better in terms of time-of-flight. Do not forget: time-of-flight has consequences for degradation, radiation hazards, operational costs, and other characteristics.

As an example, Table 10-34 gives an overview of 4 fundamentally different missions to Mars, plus the main characteristics of each option. The first 2 concepts are one-way missions, and the last 2 are round trips. Clearly, bringing a sample back to the Earth does not exactly come for free (higher ΔV, longer time-of-flight). The situation becomes even more demanding when the return vehicle has to rendezvous in Earth orbit, rather than (for instance) plunge into the ocean directly (as was the case with the Apollo missions).

References

Get Ref

For annotated bibliography of orbit and constellation design, see the book website.

Austin, R. E., M. Cruz, and J. French. 1982. "System Design Concepts and Requirements for Aeroassociated Orbital Transfer Vehicles." AIAA Paper 82-1379. AIAA 9th Atmospheric Flight Mechanics Conf.

Battin, R. H. 1999. *Introduction to the Mathematics and Methods of Astrodynamics*. Reston, VA: AIAA.

Cefola, P.J. 1987. "The Long-Term Orbital Motion of the Desynchronized Westar II." AAS Paper 87-446. AAS/AIAA Astrodynamics Specialist Conf. Aug. 10.

Chobotov, V. A. 2002. *Orbital Mechanics. 3rd ed.* Reston, VA: AIAA Publishing.

Conway, B. A. 2010. *Spacecraft Trajectory Optimization*. New York, NY: Cambridge University Press.

Cornelisse, J., H. Shoyer, and K. Wakker. 1979. *Rocket Propulsion and Spaceflight Dynamics*. Pittman.

Cox, A. N. 2000. *Allen's Astrophysical Quantities. 4th ed.* New York, NY: Springer-Verlag.

Draim, John. 2009. "Sixteen-Hour Droplet Constellations for Northern Hemisphere Coverage." Paper 3.3.2. 27th Intern. Communication Satellite Systems Conference (ICSSC). Edinburgh, Scotland: Jun 1–4.

Draim, J. and P. Cefola. 2008. "Beyond GEO II—Raindrop Elliptical Orbit Constellation for Frequency Re-Use." AIAA-2008-5415. 26th ICSSC. San Diego, CA: Jun 10–12.

Draim, J. 2004. "Satellite Constellations, The 2004 Breakwell Memorial Lecture." 55th Intern. Astronautical Congress. Vancouver, BC, Canada: Oct. 6.

Draim, J. 2002. "The Orbital Perturbation Environment for the COBRA and COBRA Teardrop Elliptical Constellations." AAS 02-173, vol. 112, Adv. in the Astro. Sci. San Diego, CA: Univelt.

Draim, J. 2001. "Constellation of Elliptical Orbit Satellites With Line of Apsides Lying In or Near The Equatorial Plane." WO/2001/013525. World Intellectual Property Organization. Feb. 22.

Draim, John E., Cecile Davidson, and David Castiel. 1999. "Evolution of the ELLIPSO™ and ELLIPSO 2G™ GMPCS Systems." IAF-99-M.4.02. 50th International Astronautical Congress. Amsterdam, Netherlands. Oct. 4–8.

Draim, J. 1998. "Optimization of the ELLIPSO™ and ELLIPSO 2G™ Personal Communications System, Mission Design & Implementation of Satellite Constellations."

Draim, J. 1997. "Optimization of the Borealis™ and Concordia™ Sub-Constellations of the ELLIPSO™ Personal Communications System." *Acta Astronautica*, vol. 40, Issues 2-8, pp 183–193. Jan–Apr.

Draim, J. 1987a. "A Common-Period Four-Satellite Continuous Global Coverage Constellation." *JGCD.* 10:492-499.

Draim, J. 1987b. "A Six-Satellite Continuous Global Double Coverage Constellation." AAS Paper 87-497. AAS/AIAA Astrodynamics Specialist Conference.

Draim, J. 1985. "Three- and Four-Satellite Continuous Global Coverage Constellation." *JGCD.* 6:725-730.

Easton, R. L. and R. Brescia. 1969. Continuously Visible Satellite Constellations. NRL Report 6986.

ESA. 2010a. Website.

ESA. 2010b. Website.

Faughnam, Barbara. 1993. *Space Manufacturing Nine-The High Frontier Accession Developments and Utilizations*. Reston, VA: AIAA Publishing.

Feoktistov, V. 2006. *Differential Evolution in Search of Solutions*. New York, NY: Springer-Verlag.

Goldberg, E. 1989. *Genetic Algorithms in Search, Optimization and Machine Learning.* Old Tappan, NJ: Addison-Wesley Publishing.

Gooding, R. H. 1990. "A Procedure for the Solution of Lambert's Orbital Boundary-Value Problem." Celestial Mech. and Dynam. Astro, vol. 48, pp. 145–165.

Gordon, Gary and Walter Morgan. 1993. *Principles of Communications Satellites.* Hoboken, NJ: Wiley.

Heppenheimer, T. A. 1977. *Colonies in Space: A Comprehensive and Factual Account of the Prospects for Human Colonization of Space.* Stackpole Books.

ISAS. 2010. Website.

Izzo, D. 2006. "Lambert's Problem for Exponential Sinusoids." *JGCD*, vol. 29, no. 5, pp 1242–1245. Reston, VA: AIAA.

Kaufman, B., C. R. Newman, and F. Chromey. 1966. *Gravity Assist Optimization Techniques Applicable to a Variety of Space Missions*. NASA GSFC. Report No. X-507-66-373.

Kemble, S. 2006. *Interplanetary Mission Analysis and Design.* New York, NY: Springer.

Kennedy, J. and R. Eberhart. 1995. "Particle Swarm Optimization." IEEE International Conference on Neural Networks. Pp. 1942–1948. Piscataway, NJ.

Kirk, D. E. 1998. *Optimal Control Theory, An Introduction.* Mineola, NY: Dover Publications, Inc.

Kirkpatrick, S., C. D. Gelatt, and M. P. Vecchi. 1983. "Optimization by Simulated Annealing." *Science.* 220 (4598) 671-680.

Lawler, E. L. and D. E. Wood. 1966. *Branch-and-Bound Methods: A Survey.* Ann Arbor, MI: U of M Press.

Maral, G. and M. Bousquet. 2010. *Satellite Communications Systems: Systems, Techniques and Technologies. 5th ed.* Hoboken, NJ: Wiley.

Mease, K. D. 1988. "Optimization of Aeroassisted Orbital Transfer: Current Status." *JAS. 36:7-33.*

Meissinger, Hans F. 1970. "Earth Swingby-A Novel Approach to Interplanetary Mission Using Electric Propulsion." AIAA-70-117. AIAA 8th Electric Propulsion Conference. Stanford, CA. Aug. 31–Sept. 2.

Meissinger, H. F., S. Dawson, and J. R. Wertz. 1997. "A Low-Cost Modified Launch Mode for High-C_3 Interplanetary Missions." AAS Paper No. 97-711, presented at the AAS/AIAA Astrodynamics Specialist Conference, Sun Valley, Idaho, Aug. 4–7.

Meissinger, H. F., and S. Dawson. 1998. "Reducing Planetary Mission Cost by a Modified Launch Mode." Presented at the Third IAA International Conference on Low-Cost Planetary Missions, Pasadena, CA, Apr 27–May 1.

Michalewicz, Z. 1996. *Genetic Algorithms and Data Structures = Evolution Programs, 3rd ed.* New York, NY: Springer.

Munkres, J. 1957. "Algorithms for the Assignment and Transportation Problems." *Journal by the Society for Industrial and Applied Mathematics,* vol. 5, no. 1.

Myatt, D. R., V. M. Becerra, S. J. Nasuto, S. J. Bishop and D. Izzo. 2003. *Advanced Global Optimisation for Mission Analysis and Design.* Ariadna 03/4101, ESA ACT and University of Reading

NASA. 2010a. Website.

NASA. 2010b. Website.

O'Leary, Brian. 1982a. *Space Based Manufacturing From Nonterrestrial Materials.* Ames Research Center.

O'Leary, Brian. 1982b. *Space Utilization,* vol. I and vol. II. Boca Raton, FL: CRC Press.

O'Neill, Gerald. 2000. *The High Frontier: Human Colonies in Space, 3rd ed.* Toronto: Apogee Books.

O'Neill, G. 1976a. Presentation on Satellite Solar Power to the State Energy Resources Conservation and Development Commission. Sacramento, CA.

O'Neill, G. 1976b. "Solar Power from Satellites." Senate Subcom. on Aero. Tech. and Nat. Needs. Wash, DC.

O'Neill, G. 1974. "The Colonization of Space." *Physics Today.* Vol. 27, No. 9, pp. 32–40. Sept.

Petropoulos, A. E. and J. M. Longuski. 2004. "Shape-Based Algorithms for Automated Design of Low-Thrust, Gravity-Assist Trajectories." AIAA. *Journal of Spacecraft and Rockets,* vol. 41, no. 5, pp. 787–796.

Pocha, J. J. 1987. *An Introduction to Mission Design for Geostationary Satellites.* Space Technology Library. Dordrecht, Netherlands: D. Reidel Publishing.

Price, K. V., R. M. Storn, and J. A. Lampinen. 2005. *Differential Evolution—A Practical Approach to Global Optimization.* New York, NY: Springer-Verlag.

Ross, I. M. and C. N. D'Souza. 2005. "Hybrid Optimal Control Framework for Mission Planning." *Journal of Guidance, Control, and Dynamics,* vol. 28, no. 4.

Sarzi-Amade, N. and J. R. Wertz. 2009. "Astrodynamics Constraints on Mars Round-Trip Mission Design." AAS 09-352. AAS/AIAA ASC. Pittsburgh, PA: Aug. 9–13.

Seidelmann, P. K. 1992. *Explanatory Supplement to the Astronomical Almanac.* Mill Valley, CA: University Science Books.

Sergeyvsky, A. B. and R. A. Cunniff. 1987. *Interplanetary Mission Design Handbook,* vol. I, part 5. NASA, JPL Publication 82-43.

Soop, E. M. 1994. *Handbook of Geostationary Orbits.* Dordrecht: Kluwer Academic Publishers.

Standish, E. M. 1998. JPL Planetary and Lunar Ephermides. DE405/LE405. JPL Interoffice Memorandum 312F-98-48.

Standish, E. M. 1982. "Orientation of the JPL Ephemerides. DE200/LE200, to the Dynamical Equinox of J2000." *Astronomy and Astrophysics,* vol. 114, pp. 297–302.

Vallado, David A. 2007. *Fundamentals of Astrodynamics and Applications, 3rd ed.* Hawthorne, CA: Microcosm Press and New York, NY: Springer.

Walker, J. G. 1984. "Satellite Constellations." *Journal of the British Interplanetary Society.* 37:559-572.

Walker, J. G. 1977. *Continuous Whole-Earth Coverage by Circular-Orbit Satellite Patterns.* Royal Aircraft Establishment technical Report No. 77044.

Walker, J. G. 1971. "Some Circular Orbit Patterns Providing Continuous Whole Earth Coverage." *Journal of the British Interplanetary Society.* 24:369-384.

Wertz, J. R., R. Van Allen, and Tina Barcley. 2010. "NanoEye—Military Relevant Surveillance for Less Than $5 Million Total Recurring Cost." AIAA-RS8-2010-1008. AIAA 8th Responsive Space Conference. Los Angeles, CA. Mar. 8–11.

Wertz, J. R. 2009. *Orbit and Constellation Design and Management.* Hawthorne, CA: Microcosm Press and New York, NY: Springer.

Wertz, J. R. 2007. "Circular vs. Elliptical Orbits for Communications Satellites." RS Conference. RS5-2007-2005. Los Angeles, CA. Apr.23–26.

Wertz, J. R. 2004. "Rapid Interplanetary Round Trips at Moderate Energy." IAC-04-Q.2.a.11. IAF. Vancouver, BC, Canada. Oct. 4–8.

Wertz, J. R. 2003. "Interplanetary Round Trip Mission Design." IAC-03-Q.4.06. 54th IAC. Bremen, Germany. Sep. 29–Oct. 3.

Wertz, J.R. 2005. "Coverage, Responsiveness, and Accessibility for Various Responsive Orbits." 3rd Responsive Space Conf. Los Angeles, CA. Apr. 25–28.

Wertz, J. R. and W. Larsen. 1996. *Reducing Space Mission Cost.* Space Technology Library. El Segundo, CA: Microcosm Press and Dordrecht, Netherlands: Kluwer Academic Publishers.

Wilke, D. N. 2005. *Analysis of the Particle Swarm Optimization Algorithm.* MSc Thesis, University of Pretoria, South Africa.

Winston, W. J. 2004. *Operations Research, Applications and Algorithms, 4th ed.* Duxbury.

11 Cost Estimating

Henry Apgar, ***MCR Technologies***

Cost estimating is the iterative process of calculating the expected cost of a space mission. Just as the space systems engineer predicts performance parameters for his evolving space system design, he can also predict development, production, and operations costs. Since any prediction entails some uncertainty, cost predictions need to be stated in risk terms, e.g., within uncertainty bounds or with an associated confidence level. Just as space systems engineers need to understand technical and program parameters (capacity, reliability, operating life) which drive design, so do they need to understand the engineering and program requirements (size, complexity, technology) which drive cost. Typical cost drivers are: size (weight in kilograms for hardware and lines of code for software), complexity (choice of material, power, bandwidth), availability of the technology (technology readiness level, degree of design completion), and schedule (time available for development).

The scope and depth of the cost estimating process depends on the intended purpose of the estimate. A rough order magnitude (ROM) estimate for a preliminary space system design will entail some opinion and judgment, but we seek estimating credibility to support design decisions and so we base our estimates on known facts and calculated expected cost values. A proposal price estimate depends on a well-crafted and documented prediction of future cost and the associated cost-risks. An engineering trade study, on the other hand, may require only a top-level understanding of the difference in cost between design alternatives. A cross-check estimate should require less time, less information, and fewer resources.

Technically, all estimates are based on *analogy*. That is, what will be the differences or application of changes from an earlier design or mission for which we already know and understand the relevant costs? The estimating process can be systematized by developing statistical *cost estimating relationships* (CERs) with known cost data from those earlier designs. CERs are equations which relate the **dependent** variable (e.g., dollars, labor or hours) to one or more **independent** variables (size, complexity, resources, and time). An aggregate of CERs is often called a *parametric cost model*. Similar to the application of engineering design models, cost models emulate the design process, production activities, and operations of space systems.

Since a space mission cost model emulates the materials and activities consumed during the space mission development, production, and operation, we strive to assure proper application of the chosen model to the space mission being designed. Section 11.2 in this chapter provides several parametric models, each applicable to a different phase (development, production, operations) of the program. The aggregate of costs from all program phases is popularly known as the *life cycle cost*.

Some help in understanding these terms and their relationship to space mission analysis and design may be found in NASA [2010] and ISPA [2007]. A list of cost-related acronyms is given in Table 11-1.

Cost estimates support the engineering and design process. Awareness of most likely cost, concern with cost targets from program inception, and sensitivity to the relative cost between design alternatives contribute to the acceptance and utility of the space system design. *Most likely cost* is the same as the mode of all likely cost outcomes and is the value which would occur most often in a Monte Carlo simulation of final cost.

Cost estimating has assumed a more proactive role in space systems development with the availability of parametric cost estimating tools, early awareness of system

Table 11-1. Cost Estimating Acronyms.

AUC	Average Unit Cost	***MM***	Man Months
BOM	Bill of Materials (basis for bottoms-up estimate)	***NICM***	NASA Instrument Cost Model
CAIV	Cost As an Independent Variable, an affordability initiative	***O&M***	Operating and Maintenance, a program phase, alternately called Operations and Support (O&S)
CADRE	Cost Analysis Data Requirements	***O&S***	Operating and Support, a program phase, alternately called Operations & Maintenance (O&M)
CARD	Cost Analysis Requirements Description	***OTS***	Off-the-shelf, designating a component which requires no development effort
CBS	Cost Breakdown Structure, variation of WBS	***PME***	Prime Mission Equipment (hardware and software), what most CERs will estimate
CER	Cost Estimating Relationship, building block of the parametric cost estimating model	***ROI***	Return on Investment
COCOMO	Cost Construction Model	***ROM***	Rough Order Magnitude, a type of cost estimate, typically when little information is available
COTS	Commercial off-the-shelf	***SEE***	Standard Error of the Estimate (of regression in deriving a CER)
DSI	Delivered Source Instructions (similar to SLOC) (software)	***SLOC***	Source Lines of Code, input parameter for most software estimating models
DTC	Design to Cost, an affordability initiative	***SSCM***	Small Satellite Cost Model
ESLOC	Equivalent Source Lines of Code, captures the labor impact of modifying (rather than developing) code	***T1***	See TFU
FTE	Full Time Equivalent (one person working full time for one year)	***TFU***	Theoretical First Unit; the starting point for production "learning," sometimes known as T1
ICE	Independent Cost Estimate	***TRL***	Technology Readiness Level, a measure of the state of development—a cost driver
KPP	Key Performance Parameter (traded against cost in trade studies)	***USCM8***	Unmanned Spacecraft Cost Model, version 8
LOOS	Launch and orbit operations support	***WBS***	Work Breakdown Structure
MDAL	Master Data and Assumptions List	***WLC***	Whole Life Cost (similar to Life Cycle Cost)
MUPE	Minimum unbiased percentage errors (method of developing CERs)		

cost drivers, and responsibility of the engineer to design affordable products. Engineers are especially involved in the application of *affordability initiatives* such as Design to Cost (DTC) and Cost as an Independent Variable (CAIV), where product design converges on a cost goal. Section 11.2.12 identifies the CAIV initiative as a process for reducing cost. Such initiatives effectively support lower cost space missions through better understanding of the life cycle cost drivers. Careful evaluation of Return on Investment (ROI) analyses and cost/performance trade studies are more effective than simply trying to make the system "cheaper."

The "laws of estimating" are different philosophically from the "laws of nature." For estimating, there can be no absolute right answer to the question, "How much will it cost?" With estimating, we are predicting a future event in a world of fiscal, political, and technological uncertainty.

11.1 Introduction to Cost Estimating

11.1.1 Groundrules and Assumptions

Our first step is to establish the estimating groundrules and assumptions which can be extracted from the mission description and the development plan.

Estimating groundrules are statements about the form and content of the estimate (e.g., "*...costs include a competitive development by two contractors up through system test, and are stated in 2012 dollars*"). Groundrules also establish the scope of the estimate, distinguishing specifically between costs that are included and those excluded from the analysis. For example, an estimate may not address operating costs at this time, or it may not include the cost of establishing new test facilities.

Estimating assumptions are suppositions about what will happen at some future time. Assumptions can be established globally for the system or program (e.g., laser technology that meets the requirement will be available before the start of system development; contractor A will be the system designer; all software will be written in C++); or they can be established for the specific cost elements (e.g., a VLSI chip will be used to implement the function; five test units will be needed for test evaluation; a software development lab will be established). Assumptions may change throughout the estimating process; thus, careful recording and tracking of assumptions and their changes to cost estimate versions are necessary. Assumptions help to identify significant cost drivers and indirectly the choice of a parametric cost estimating model.

Examples of estimating groundrules and assumptions can be seen in Sec. 11.4, particularly Tables 11-34 through 11-39, where we estimate the FireSat II and SCS system costs.

11.1.2 Types of Estimates

We typically develop our first ROM estimate before we can expect (1) a good *bill of materials* (BOM—a list of all materials, parts, and components) and (2) a description of development, production, and operations activities by labor classification. This is an estimating process commonly called a "bottoms-up" or "detailed cost estimating" process. Instead, we must rely on broad design concepts and subsystem-level design parameters, also known as cost drivers. This process is commonly called a "top-down" or "parametric cost estimating" process.

The parametric cost estimating process is supported by cost estimating tools described in this chapter, including cost estimating models and normalized historic databases. Models are comprised of CERs, which are statistically-based cost-predicting algorithms derived from these databases.

Models typically focus on specific cost elements, such as spacecraft hardware, payload software, or launch vehicle operations. CERs typically are derived at the subsystem or component level and relate cost to one or more cost drivers, such as weight, power, and amount of additional design required. Apgar [2009] and Fox [2008] provide an introduction to the selection of cost drivers for space mission CERs.

The distinction between non-recurring and recurring costs helps to choose the appropriate model or CER, as well as to correctly place (or map) cost predictions within the project work breakdown structure (WBS). CERs predict non-recurring cost or recurring costs, or sometimes both.

It is important to ascertain that model and CER definitions are consistent with WBS definitions. The following distinction is typically made between non-recurring and recurring costs:

- ***Non-recurring costs*** are associated with the labor and material associated with designing, developing, fabricating, and testing a space vehicle qualification test model plus program-peculiar ground support equipment (GSE). This is often identified as the prototype approach and does not produce a flight unit. For those programs that use the alternative *protoflight* approach, the qualification test unit will later be refurbished to become the first flight unit. This requires an additional 30% (approximate) non-recurring cost for the refurbishment.
- ***Recurring costs*** are associated with the labor and material of fabricating, manufacturing, integrating, assembling, and testing of follow-on space vehicle flight hardware plus the effort associated with launch and orbital operations in support of the program. Cost databases typically accumulate recurring program costs in total, rather than by specific production units. As a result, historical recurring cost data must be adjusted to reflect a theoretical first unit (TFU) cost, or T1, for the purpose of developing the recurring CERs. By default, a cumulative average learning curve of 95% is typically applied, both in CER development and cost prediction. (See Sec. 11.3.2 on Cost Improvement for more information on learning rate.) For the prototype approach, the T1 then is the first flight unit; for the protoflight approach, the T1 is actually the second flight unit.*

11.1.3 Elements of Cost

Elements of cost are essentially the hardware, software, and operations elements of the space system, plus necessary management and administrative elements (wrap factors) as identified by the project WBS. Collectively, then, the WBS elements describe the entire project and provide a disciplined structure for developing the cost estimate, budgeting the project, and tracking costs as the project proceeds.†

To facilitate matching CERs to WBS elements, and for instructional purpose, we have adopted an ad-hoc WBS numbering system for all models, CERs, and factors described in SME-SMAD. The engineer will most likely encounter a project-specific WBS early in the development process. The SME-SMAD example facilitates a standard cost estimating model.

The estimator typically obtains the WBS from the system designer. The estimator must be able to translate, or map, between similar WBS structures, since the industry has not achieved the goal of a standard WBS. The estimator may find slightly different WBS structures for:

- Legacy programs which are the source of historical cost data, useful for analogy estimating.
- Special purpose cost estimating models, such as USCM8, which are based on a pre-determined WBS.
- The new program which he must estimate; in SME-SMAD, the WBS for FireSat II and SCS will be provided.

* It may seem unusual to identify costs for a single spacecraft, in the prototype approach, as *recurring* costs; however, the convention has been established for cost models that the manufacturing costs beyond the qualification test model are generally regarded as recurring. In multiple-unit production, the first unit is often identified as the theoretical first unit (TFU or T1) cost. An example of this convention is seen in Sec. 11.2.2. On the other hand, Sec. 11.2.5 describes a single CER model for predicting the total cost of development and production of one protoflight unit. The engineer must determine the definitions and bounds of a set of CERs before using them.

† This product-oriented (versus function-oriented) WBS structure is similar to an expanded version called the cost breakdown structure (CBS); the difference is that the CBS includes additional elements for profit, cost of money, and budget reserve. For this chapter, we will use only the term WBS.

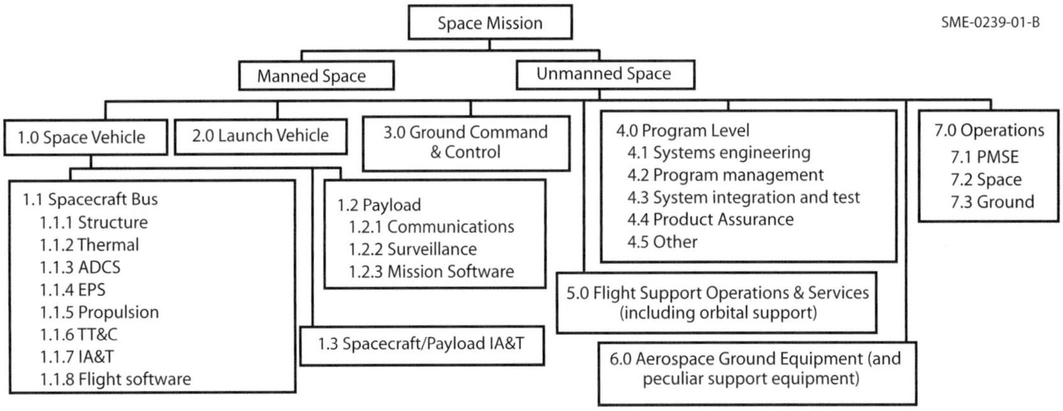

1.0 Space Vehicle—the housing or platform for carrying a payload and other mission-oriented *prime mission equipment* (PME) into space.

1.1 Spacecraft Bus—the space vehicle less the payload.

1.1.1 Structure—basic structural items including enclosures, deployable components, supporting structure, launch vehicle interface.

1.1.2 Thermal—structure and devices for maintaining temperature control; passive devices include paints, coatings and blankets, and space radiator; active devices include pumped-loop systems, heaters controlled by thermostats, mechanical devices, and refrigerators; passive systems cost less than active systems.

1.1.3 Attitude Determination and Control (ADCS) —hardware and software which stabilize and orient spacecraft using sensors and actuators; primary cost drivers are the pointing accuracy, control stability, and maneuvering requirements.

1.1.4 Electrical Power Subsystem (EPS)—hardware includes solar arrays, batteries, wiring harness, and power management electronics.

1.1.5 Propulsion—hardware and software which provides thrust for attitude control and orbit correction; orbit insertion may require an apogee kick motor (AKM).

1.1.6 Tracking, Telemetry, and Command (TT&C); Typically Includes Data Handling (DH)—consists of command/telemetry electronics, onboard computers, transponders, transmitters, receivers, data storage components, antennae, and associated electronics.

1.1.7 Integration, Assembly, and Test (IA&T)—the vehicle IA&T identifies the cost of integrating, assembling, and testing all space subsystems into an operable spacecraft bus. This does not include the costs of integrating the bus with the payload.

1.1.8 Flight Software—computer program for controlling the spacecraft.

1.2 Payload—the software and hardware associated with conducting the space mission.

1.2.1 Communications Payload—consists of hardware similar to the TT&C.

1.2.2 Surveillance Payload (sensors)—includes optics.

1.2.3 Mission Software—computer program for controlling the payload.

1.3 Integration of Bus with Payload—planning and executing the interface, including engineering, testing, and checkout; consideration of signal and power connections.

2.0 Launch Vehicle—typically a negotiated price for placing the spacecraft into orbit. The costs associated with mating the spacecraft with the launch vehicle, performing integrated system test and checkout, and tracking launch vehicle performance during ascent are (included in WBS 5.0):

3.0 Ground Command & Control—the ground hardware and software necessary for communicating between controlling and tracking facilities, monitoring the health and status of space vehicles, commanding the space vehicle's hardware, and adjusting the space vehicle's orbit.

4.0 Program Level—prime contractor and subcontractor costs for systems engineering, program management, systems integration and test, and product assurance; usually predicted as a percentage of prime mission equipment (PME) costs; normally does not include government costs or other customer oversight.

4.1 Systems Engineering (Sometimes Combined with Program Management)—the technical effort of directing and controlling an integrated engineering effort to include e.g., requirements analysis, program planning, reliability, maintainability, or human factors; excludes design engineering.

4.2 Program Management—the business and administrative planning, organizing, directing, coordinating, and controlling the program.

4.3 System Integration and Test (and Acceptance) —the application of prototype or production hardware to validate engineering performance data.

4.4 Product Assurance—the quality control function.

5.0 Flight Support Operations and Services (Sometimes Called Launch and Orbital Operations Support [LOOS]) —these are contractor costs associated with prelaunch planning, trajectory analysis, launch site support, launch vehicle integration with spacecraft, and initial on-orbit operations for the first 30 days after launch.

6.0 Aerospace Ground Equipment (AGE), Ground Support Equipment (GSE), Peculiar Support Equipment (PSE)—test and support equipment for integration, assembly, and acceptance testing of spacecraft before launch; excludes common support equipment.

7.0 Operations—the on-going steady state support to operate the space mission to include mission operations, ground operations, sustaining engineering, flight hardware spares and maintenance, program/project management and integration, and communication services.

Fig. 11-1. SME-SMAD Space Project WBS Provides the Estimate Framework. Model descriptions and discrete CERs throughout this chapter will apply this WBS numbering scheme.

Table 11-2. SME-SMAD Space Program WBS and Reference to Suggested Cost Estimating Tools in SME-SMAD. The estimator typically needs to apply CERs and factors from a suite of cost prediction models because there are few models available which can estimate the entire project.

SME-SMAD WBS Element (from Figure 11-1)	Model/Database/Factors and where to find them (section number) in SME-SMAD									
	Top-down Estimating 11.1	USCM8 11.2.2	SSCM05 11.2.3	QuickCost 11.2.4	NICM 11.2.5	COCOMO 11.2.6	Ground 11.2.7	Launch 11.2.8	Factors 11.2.9	Operations 11.2.10
1.0 Spacecraft	N, R			N+R						
1.1 Spacecraft Bus		N, R	N+R							
1.1.1 Structure		N, R	N+R							
1.1.2 Thermal		N, R	N+R							
1.1.3 ADCS		N, R	N+R							
1.1.4 EPS	N	N, R	N+R							
1.1.5 Propulsion	N, R	N, R	N+R							
1.1.6 TT&C		N, R								
1.1.7 IA&T		N, R								
1.1.8 Flight Software	N					N, R				
1.2 Payload			N+R		N+R					
1.2.1 Communications		N, R								
1.2.2 Surveillance	N, R									
1.2.3 Mission Software						N, R				
1.3 Spacecraft IA&T		N, R	N+R							
2.0 Launch Vehicle								R		
3.0 Ground C&C	N, R						N+R		R	
4.0 Program Level		N, R	N+R		N+R				N, R	
5.0 Flight Support Ops		N, R	N+R					R		
6.0 AGE			N+R							
7.0 Operations										R

Notes from the Table:
N = Non-recurring CERs
R = Recurring CERs
N+R = Hybrid CERs defining both non-recurring and recurring costs in a single algorithm

The key for successful mapping of different WBS structures, and to assure configuration control for your estimate, is to establish a WBS definition for each WBS element. A top-level unmanned space WBS example is shown in Fig. 11-1, with the unique SME-SMAD WBS number system to facilitate correlation between WBS, hardware definitions, and CERs. Note that certain elements have been omitted from this example, such as: reentry vehicle, launch operations and mission support, system test, training, spares, et al. A more comprehensive guide is DoD [2005], which provides a detailed WBS with element definitions. Hardware and software estimates are generally combined under the appropriate subsystem title; in some program WBSs, software elements may be grouped separately from hardware elements.

The SME-SMAD Space Mission WBS elements are defined in Fig. 11-1. These definitions are consistent with Chaps. 3 and 4. Individual program definitions and specific CER definitions may differ based on peculiar requirements or specialized data collection; this presents an estimating challenge to the engineer to ensure the applied CER reasonably estimates the corresponding WBS element.

The space systems engineer relies upon one or more estimating tools (models, databases, factors) and then ensures these tools are compatible with the project WBS structure and its definitions. Table 11-2 provides a starting point for selecting appropriate tools described in this chapter. Apgar [2004] provides a guide to the development and review process for space missions parametric cost prediction models.

11.1.4 Phases of the Estimate

Program phases of the estimate should be defined by the program manager. The aggregate of all costs for all phases is typically identified as *life cycle cost (LCC),* or

Table 11-3. Cost Estimating Process Steps. This is a relevant guide to the application of sequential steps described in this chapter, as appropriate to predicting future costs

Cost Estimating Process Steps	Where Discussed
1. Establish the estimate purpose, including the estimating groundrules and assumptions.	11.1.1
2. Establish the work breakdown structure (WBS) to identify elements of cost for all program phases (development, production, O&M). Determine the estimate detail and the lowest WBS level for which estimates are required.	11.1.3
3. Apply an estimating method and tool set for each lowest-level WBS element for each phase, based on availability of cost driver information. The choice of estimating method may depend upon the understanding of the cost drivers and the availability of information defining them. Products of this step are "most-likely estimates" for: • Hardware Development including prototype units. (11.2.2–11.2.5) • Software Development and Maintenance. (11.2.6) • Hardware Production of subsequent flight units, based on spacecraft first unit cost (T1) and cost improvement (learning curve) theory. (11.2.2–11.2.5, 11.3.2) • Operations and Support, for the space launch and facilities. (11.2.7–11.2.10) • Program-level elements (e.g., management, engineering), for each phase. (11.2.9) • Availability of off-the-shelf (OTS) hardware and computer software, for which purchase price may be used in lieu of the CER prediction. (11.2.1) • Operations Cost (11.2.10)	11.2
4. Establish a range of estimates around each element's "most-likely estimate" and then roll-up the element estimates to the top-level most-likely estimate with a confidence level. Consider likelihood of future cost growth. The result should be the estimate cumulative probability versus the range of top-level estimate values (an S-Curve), as generated by a Monte Carlo simulation. An alternative product would be an estimate range for each subsystem or system.	11.2.11
5. Inflate (or deflate) the estimate to reflect dollars in another base year, necessary for comparative cost trade studies and for budget purposes.	11.3.3
6. Spread the estimate of cost (allocate the dollars) by year—for the purpose of budgeting.	11.3.4
7. Document the estimate result and the estimating process to satisfy the estimate purpose. Consider credibility and affordability issues. Plan for subsequent performance/cost trade studies, affordability initiatives, and estimate updates.	11.3.1, 11.3.2, 11.3.7

sometimes *whole life cost (WLC)*. LCC includes all costs from system planning through end-of-life. The estimator needs to be sensitive to the three generic cost phases (common to DoD and NASA) comprising LCC since each phase generally depends on a unique cost prediction model. There are few models which can estimate more than one phase. The three generic phases and their associated costs are:

- **Development** costs which include design, analysis, and test of breadboards, brassboards, prototypes, and qualification units, comprising hardware and software elements. These are generally *non-recurring costs* and are determined on a program basis.
- **Production** costs which include manufacturing of hardware components and assembling them into flight units and then launching them. The estimation process is typically characterized by estimating the *theoretical first unit (TFU) cost* and then extrapolating the cost of additional units by assuming a human learning rate or cost improvement factor.
- **Operations** costs, alternatively identified as Operations and Support (O&S) costs, which include ongoing operations and maintenance, spacecraft replacement units, software updates, and ultimate system salvage. For unmanned missions, most of these costs are consumed by the ground station. These are generally recurring costs and are determined on an annual basis.

11.1.5 Cost Estimating Process Steps

A recommended set of steps to execute this estimating process is shown in Table 11-3, with reference to detailed explanations elsewhere in this chapter. Variations on this process may be necessary to accommodate unique system requirements, peculiar estimating models, and availability of cost driver information. Your support to defining the low-cost and low-risk space mission depends upon your ability to accurately predict the development, production, and operations cost of any proposed space architecture. This process will organize your efforts.

11.2 Estimating Tools

11.2.1 Top-Down Estimating Process Using Models, CERs, and Factors

The parametric cost estimating model is the most common example of top-down estimating and is the preferred estimating tool for space system estimates in the pre-design phase of the program. Properly developed models, with statistically-sound CERs derived from representative and validated cost data, are expected to provide credible estimates for several decades, assuming there are no revolutionary technology changes. Even with evolutionary changes in the way certain space components are designed and built, the CERs can be adjusted if one understands the technology.

SME-SMAD provides convenient, and sometimes simplified, versions of contemporary parametric cost estimating models, all keyed to the SME-SMAD WBS described in Sec. 11.1.3 and all converted to a common parameter set (same year dollars and application of metric-system measurements). You may find same-name CERs from different models which provide slightly different estimates for the same WBS element; this is normal when the model CERs have been derived from different sets of historic data and, possibly, with different definitions (e.g., development estimates including protoflight hardware).

There are three categories of parametric models, identified below, and the user needs to assess their relative advantages in application and investment of training time.

1. **Publicly-available special purpose models** are generally developed by government agencies, federally-funded research centers, cost analysis support contractors, and public universities because of their likely access to primary (and often proprietary) source cost data, e.g. prime contractors. Such models typically are built around a complete WBS—such that the estimator can develop a full program acquisition cost estimate. The models' software and user manuals are typically available at no cost to qualified users. Examples include USCM8, NICM, and COCOMO 81 and these three models are described in this chapter (Sec. 11.2) and on the SME-SMAD website.

2. **Publicly-available general purpose models** are developed by private companies who provide software, training, and consulting services to licensed users. These users, then, are expected to calibrate these general purpose models to their specific product experience and program WBS. Model examples include PRICE and SEER models; these models are not discussed in SME-SMAD but the reader is encouraged to investigate their application to his needs.

3. **Private special purpose models** are generally developed by contractors for their own use since they are typically based on proprietary data for the purpose of generating proposal cost estimates and evaluating product design alternatives. These models are not identified or discussed in SME-SMAD.

There is no single space mission parametric cost model which constitutes such a wide range of CERs that it can provide estimates for the full life cycle WBS or even for multiple technologies within the single category of spacecraft payloads. To develop a full life cycle system estimate, one must apply multiple models and then aggregate the estimates. Refer to Sec. 11.2.11 for guidance on aggregating probabilistic estimates using a Monte Carlo approach. Although there is some statistical inaccuracy involved, the user could arithmetically sum the CER predictions of "most likely cost" (aka the point estimate) to achieve the system or mission-level "most likely cost."

The inclusion (or exclusion) of models in SME-SMAD does not imply endorsement (or lack of endorsement) of any particular model. The descriptions have been streamlined and annotated to fit the format and purpose of the SME-SMAD. Interested readers are encouraged to seek the full version of each model from the web sites or published reports identified in the references. Models in SME-SMAD were chosen primarily on their representing a class of models (hardware, software, or facilities).

The models presented here consistently predict costs either in (a) calendar year 2010 US Dollars or in (b) labor hours, which is a proxy for cost. To convert estimates to "other year" dollars, refer to Sec. 11.3.3 for the appropriate inflation adjustment factor.

We use the standard cost notations for CERs where \$K means thousands of dollars and \$M means millions of dollars. All size variables are in the metric (meters, kilograms) system. Some CERs include the cost of program level costs and some do not; the reader is cautioned to assure he understands a CER's definition before using it.

We have numbered individual CERs and have matched these numbers to the appropriate WBS element as previously shown in Fig. 11-1 to facilitate organizing the total mission cost estimate. This will prove useful where the model developers assigned inconsistent names to the CERs, such as aerospace ground equipment (AGE) vs. ground support equipment (GSE). Some models provide alternate CERs, with a different set of cost drivers, for the same WBS element, providing a choice to the engineer when choosing among cost driver metrics.

Good estimating practice considers model predictions to be starting points for an estimate. That is, the engineer still needs judgment to distinguish between disparate model predictions, and whether the model input metrics properly define his design, and whether the design assumptions (regarding technology, for example) match the model assumptions. Adjustments can be made, for example, for: very much or very little design legacy, quality excursions, and off-shore production. These models are based on cost data from international (not limited to US) developers and manufacturers and from US Government sources.

Cost estimating models are aggregates of CERs, which are statistically-based equations that relate cost to one or more non-cost drivers. Figure 11-2 depicts a database comparing Electrical Power Subsystem (EPS) development cost to the spacecraft bus dry weight, based on actual cost and technical data. The best fit statistical CER for this data set would be a non-linear (note the logarithmic axes) expression of the form $Y = aX^b$, where Y is cost (either dollars or labor hours) and X is weight or some other cost driver. Traditionally, weight of the spacecraft or one of its subsystems has proven to be a good predictor of cost.

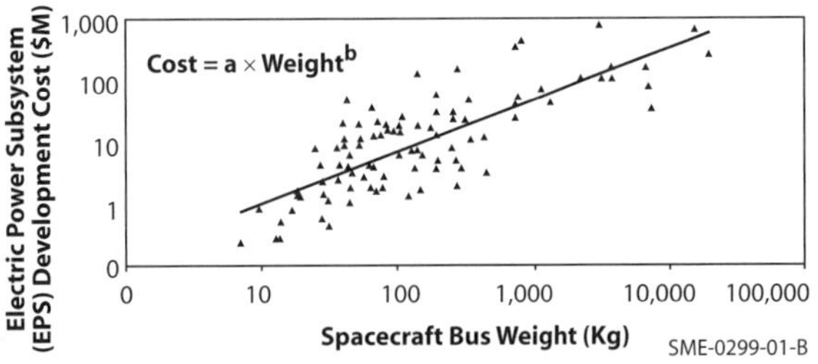

Fig. 11-2. Example of a Development Cost vs. Weight Database. This dataset provides the basis for deriving a statistical CER.

Factors can be simplified versions of CERs where the cost driver is typically a previous estimate, such as total hardware cost. Examples are shown in Table 11-4, where the amount of development effort required to complete the development can be applied as a scaling factor to the full-scale development estimate.

Table 11-4. Development-Completion Factors Useful in Development Estimates. This table provides factors for adjusting the full-development cost estimate to identify only the cost to complete the development.

Electronics Effort Previously Completed	Development Completion Factor; 1 minus this factor is then the multiplier of the full-scale estimate
Block Diagram Complete	0.10
Partitioning Complete	0.20
Schematic Design Complete	0.50
Parts Selection Complete	0.55
Breadboard Constructed	0.60
Breadboard Tested	0.70
Drawings Signed Off	0.85
Qualification Test Completed	1.00
Source: [PRICE Systems, 1999]	
For example, if the total development is initially estimated to cost $1M, then the estimate to complete the development after breadboard testing could be predicted as $1M × (1–0.70) = $300K.	

Factors provide the manager with a quick check on estimates and also provide engineers the basis for a rough order of magnitude (ROM) estimate before the cost drivers have been identified and quantified.

Table 11-5 provides a range of unmanned and manned spacecraft non-recurring (development) and recurring (Theoretical First Unit TFU or T1) hardware costs per kilogram of dry weight. Weight is not the only cost driver for our SME-SMAD cost models but, over time, weight has proven a reliable predictor of costs.

Table 11-6 provides typical software productivity metrics in (delivered) source lines of code (SLOC) per man-month.

Another set of spacecraft factors at the **subsystem** level is shown in Table 11-7, along with typical spacecraft bus weights for engineers who are not sure how much a typical subsystem weighs.

Table 11-5. Development and Production Factors for Space Vehicles and Major Subsystems. These simple factors provide the basis for top-level rough-order-magnitude (ROM) estimates for SME-SMAD WBS elements.

SME-SMAD WBS Element	Develop. Cost (in FY2010$K) per kg	T1 (TFU) (in FY2010 $K per kg)
WBS 1.0 Earth Orbital Space Vehicle (typical)	311	71
• WBS 1.0—Communication Space Vehicle	429	90
• WBS 1.0—Mapping/ Meteorological	277	52
• WBS 1.0—Observatory	129	33
• WBS 1.0—Positioning/ Navigation	475	55
• WBS 1.0—Reconnaissance	402	82
• WBS 1.0—Science	238	63
WBS 1.0 —Planetary Space Vehicle (typical)	1,167	161
• WBS 1.0—Inner Planetary	1,022	84
• WBS 1.0—Outer Planetary	1,056	171
• WBS 1.0—Planetary Lander	2,390	317
• WBS 1.0—Probe	550	69
• WBS 1.0—Crewed Space Vehicle	698	55
WBS 1.1.5—Engines	1,500	33
WBS 1.1.5—Liquid Rocket Stage	176	12
WBS 1.1.5—Solid Rocket	156	8
For example, the predicted non-recurring development cost for a small communications spacecraft, weighing 175 kg, should be 429 × 175 = $75M (in 2010 dollars), while the recurring T1 production cost should be 90 × 175 = $16M (in FY2010 dollars). All factors assume space vehicle or rocket engine dry mass (no fuel).		

11.2.2 Unmanned Space Vehicle Cost Model (USCM8)

The Unmanned Space Vehicle Cost Model, version 8, (USCM8) was developed by Tecolote Research for the US Air Force, Space and Missile Systems Center (SMC/FMP), [Tecolote Research, 2002]. The CERs were derived, using statistical regression techniques, from 44 satellites (23 military, 12 NASA, and 9 commercial) to support parametric cost estimates of unmanned, earth-orbiting space vehicles with a communications (mission equipment) payload. The CERs were derived to represent minimum unbiased percentage errors (MUPE).

Each CER is consistent with engineering expectations. This chapter provides only the subsystem CERs; component CERs are also available from the model's website. An update to this model (version 9) is scheduled for release in 2011.

In addition to CERs for large spacecraft development (non-recurring cost) and T1 production (recurring cost), the model provides a set of non-recurring and recurring CERs for estimating aerospace ground equipment (AGE), launch operations & orbital support (LOOS) and a communications (mission equipment) payload. CERs for other payloads (navigation or sensor payloads, for

Table 11-6. Productivity Factors for Software Development Cost in Man-months (MM). Note the references to the SME-SMAD WBS; this table must next be converted to dollars using applicable labor rates.

SME-SMAD WBS Element	Avg. Prod. in Source Lines of Code (SLOC) per man-month (MM) (a)	Typical Application
WBS 1.1. Flight Software	111 SLOC/MM	For controlling spacecraft
WBS 3.0 Ground Software	340 SLOC/MM	For ground operations
WBS 3.0 Instrument Operations	362 SLOC/MM	For controlling sensors
WBS 3.0 Image Processing	161 SLOC/MM	Highly algorithmic

(a) Based on 152 hours/MM and includes requirements analysis, design, coding, integration and test, QA, CM, and task management.

For example, the predicted development of 10,000 SLOC of flight software (WBS 1.1.8) should require 10,000/111 or 90 man-months of labor. This can be converted to 13,770 man-hours of labor, considering the typical labor month has 152 billable hours.

Table 11-7. Estimating Factors for Spacecraft Subsystems. Using this table, in FY2010 dollars, the predicted T1 cost for a small spacecraft electrical power system weighing 175 kg is: 25.5 × 175 = $4,462 K (in 2010 dollars)

SME-SMAD WBS Element (Component)	T1 (TFU) Prod. Cost in FY2010 $K/kg	Typical Comp. Weight in Kilograms (kg)	Typical T1 (TFU) Prod. Cost in FY2010 $K
WBS 1.0 Spacecraft Bus			
1.1.1 Structure	22.8	205	4,674
1.1.2 Thermal Control	22.8	40	912
1.1.3 ADCS	165.9	65	10,784
1.1.4 EPS	25.5	251	6,400
1.1.5 Propulsion	44.1	75	3,308
1.1.6 TT&C	82.5	45	3,712
1.1.6 C&DH	97.8	46	4,500

example) can be obtained from payload-specific models, as described in Sec. 11.2.5. However, there is some additional risk in aggregating estimates from multiple models, so assure the groundrules and assumptions are consistent.

For this model, non-recurring cost CERs predict the cost of: design and development, manufacturing and test of one space vehicle qualification model, and acquisition of program peculiar support equipment. Recurring cost CERs predict the cost of: fabrication, manufacturing, integration, assembly, and test of the space vehicle flight hardware. Recurring cost CERs also include efforts associated with the LOOS.

The model estimates are for contractor and subcontractor costs including fee (cost to the government) but does not include government program office costs. We will need to determine the design values for subsystem weight and other input parameters.

We can arithmetically sum the most likely costs from each element, although a more precise estimate will be obtained by aggregating the cost ranges from each element using a Monte Carlo simulation, as explained in Sec. 11.2.11.

The subsystem non-recurring CERs are presented in Table 11-8. These non-recurring costs are presumed to include one qualification (prototype) unit plus a typical amount of software development. Many estimators, however, prefer to estimate software development and maintenance costs independently from hardware, as described in Sec. 11.2.6. These development cost estimates assume a new design and not a modified design. If there is substantial design legacy, and the effort is more of a modification than a new design, the estimate needs to be reduced, probably by the amount of legacy or development effort which need not be repeated. For a starting point, consider the design completion adjustment factors previously presented in Table 11-4.

The cost driver input range, as used by the CER developer, appears in the table. The estimator is cautioned when using a cost driver value outside this range (more than 25% above or below) without considering scope and technology differences. For example, a significantly lighter component may cost *more* per pound due to more expensive materials or additional labor to reduce its weight, thereby altering the normal cost per pound relationship.

The Standard Error of the Estimate (SEE) of the resulting CER prediction, also shown in the table, is based on a statistical analysis of the actual data and the resulting CER (SEE) may be expressed as a percent or absolute value. For each MUPE regression exercise, the model's SEE (in %) is calculated as a measure of how well the CER function fits the data. The SEE is the root-mean square of the percentage error residuals about the regression line, corrected for degrees of freedom and is calculated as shown here in Eq. (11-1):

$$SEE_{\%} = \sqrt{\frac{1}{n-p} \sum_{i-1}^{n} \left[\frac{y_i - f(x_i)}{f(x_i)} \right]^2} \qquad (11\text{-}1)$$

where n = number of pairs of data points and p = number of parameters in CER, and x_i and y_i are the independent and dependent variables (cost value) for the ith data point, respectively.

The tables include program level (administrative, management, and systems engineering) CERs based on "wrap factors," which are percentage multipliers of the non-recurring or recurring costs previously estimated. These costs are not included in the hardware prime mission equipment (PME), CERs and, therefore, must be calculated separately and added to the aggregate total.

USCM8 makes a distinction for recurring CERs between standard and non-standard (unique) spacecraft bus costs. The standard bus distinction refers to an existing bus which can be produced directly on an existing

Table 11-8. USCM8 Non-recurring Subsystem CERs in FY2010 Thousand s of Dollars. These CERs predict the cost of development plus one qualification unit. See Tables 11-34 and 11-37 for application of these CERs.

SME-SMAD WBS Element (Non-recurring subsystem)	CER Y = non-recurring cost in FY2010 thousands of dollars for development plus one qualification unit.	Cost Driver(s)	Cost Driver Input Range	SEE
1.1 Spacecraft				
1.1 Spacecraft Bus (alternate CER when no component information is available)	Y = 108 X1	X1 = Spacecraft Weight (kg)	114–5,127 kg	47%
1.1.1/1.1.2 Structure and Thermal Control	$Y = 646\ X1^{0.684}$	X1 = Structure + Thermal Weight (kg)	59–501 kg	22%
1.1.3 Attitude Determination & Control System (ADCS)	Y = 324 X1	X1 = ADCS Weight (kg)	35–524 kg	44%
1.1.4 Electrical Power System (EPS)	Y = 64.3 X1	X1 = EPS Weight (kg)	47–1,065 kg	41%
1.1.5 Propulsion (Reaction Control)	$Y = 20.0\ X1^{0.485}$	X1 = Total RCS tank volume (cubic centimeters)	Not given	35%
1.1.6 Telemetry, Tracking, & Command (TT&C)	Y = 26,916	Y = Average TT&C Cost (since there is no statistical CER for this element)	*CER* based on S-Band telemetry	Not given
1.2 Payload				
1.2 Communications Payload (based on weight and number of channels)	Y = 339 X1 + 5,127 X2	X1 = Communications Subsystem Weight (kg) X2 = Number of Communication Channels	160–395 kg 2–32 channels	40%
1.2 Communications Payload (alternate CER based on weight alone)	Y = 618 X1	X1 = Communications Subsystem Weight (kg)	160–395 kg	38%
1.3 Spacecraft Integration, Assembly, and Test				
1.3 Integration, Assembly, & Test (of bus and payload into spacecraft)	Y = 0.195 X1	X1 = Spacecraft Bus + Payload Non-recurring Cost ($K)	3,600–545,000 $K	42%
4.0 Program Level				
4.0 Program Level (for a Communications Satellite)	Y = 0.236 X1	X1 = Space Vehicle and IA&T Non-recurring Cost ($K)	7,850–353,804 $K	23%
4.0 Program Level (for an other than Communications Satellite)	Y = 0.357 X1	X1 = Space Vehicle and IA&T Non-recurring Cost ($K)	7,850–353,804 $K	50%
6.0 Aerospace Ground Equipment (AGE)				
6.0 Aerospace Ground Equipment (AGE)	$Y = 0.432\ X1^{0.907} \times 2.244^{X2}$	X1 = Spacecraft Bus Non-recurring Cost ($K); X2 = 0 for comm sats and X2 = 1 for non-comm sats	7,850–353,804 $K	37%

product line without extensive engineering development. The non-standard (unique) bus (applied in this chapter) refers to a bus requiring substantial development, or that requires new production tooling, or for which a product line does not exist. Both versions of CERs appear on the USCM8 website. There is no similar distinction for non-recurring CERs.

The subsystem recurring production T1 or TFU (theoretical first unit cost) CERs are presented in Table 11-9. Estimates using these CERs may be assumed to be the delivered cost for the first flight unit after the test validation model. The cost of each additional similar unit may be extrapolated using learning curve theory, as explained in Sec. 11.3.2.

Table 11-10 shows estimating examples as a step-by-step calculation of several subsystem CERs from Tables 11-8 and 11-9. Input parameter values (cost drivers) are assumed for each example and are based on a space vehicle design within the scope of the database. For this example, we assume a 95% cumulative average learning curve to be consistent with the derivation of the USCM8 CERs. We will assume a space vehicle flight unit quantity of five; therefore, the average unit cost is 0.89 × T1 based on a factor from Table 11-30. All estimates are in 2010 dollars.

11.2.3 Small Satellite Cost Model (SSCM)

Over the past two decades, the level of functionality possible in small spacecraft increased dramatically due to the availability of space-compatible computational power. Smaller spacecraft are those weighing less than 500 kg, whereas larger spacecraft (better estimated with USCM8 CERs) typically weigh several thousand kg. Smaller spacecraft may be less expensive per kg than

Live Calc

Table 11-9. USCM8 Spacecraft Bus Recurring T1 CERs in FY2010 Thousands of Dollars. These CERs predict the manufacturing cost of the first flight unit. See Tables 11-34 and 11-37 for application of these CERs.

SME-SMAD WBS Element (Recurring subsystem T1)	CER Y = Recurring T1 cost in FY2010 thousands of dollars	Cost Drivers	Cost Driver Input Range	SEE
1.1 Spacecraft				
1.1 Spacecraft Bus (alternate CER when no component information is available)	$Y = 283.5\ X1^{0.716}$	X1 = Spacecraft Weight (kg)	288–7,398 kg	21%
1.1.1/1.1.2 Structure and Thermal Control (a)	Y = 22.6 X1	X1 = Structure + Thermal Weight (kg)	59–501 kg	21%
1.1.3 Attitude Determination & Control System (ADCS)	$Y = 795\ X1^{0.593}$	X1 = ADCS Weight (kg)	27–524 kg	36%
1.1.4 Electrical Power Supply (EPS)	Y = 32.4 X1	X1 = EPS Weight (kg)	111–1,479 kg	31%
1.1.5 Propulsion Apogee Kick Motor (AKM)	Y = 29 X1 + 0.024 X2	X1 = AKM Weight (kg) X2 = Burn-time (seconds)	81–966 kg	22%
1.1.6 Telemetry, Tracking, & Command (TT&C)	$Y = 883.7\ X1^{0.491} \times 1.13^{X2}$	X1 = TT&C weight (kg) X2 = Geosynchronous Transfer Orbit (1 = yes; 0 = no)	12–76 kg for S-band	18%
1.2 Payload				
1.2 Communications Payload	Y = 189 X1	X1 = Communications Payload Weight (kg)	38–928 kg	39%
1.3 Spacecraft Integration, Assembly, and Test				
1.3 Integration, Assembly, & Test (IA&T) of bus and payload into space vehicle	Y = 0.124 X1	X1 = Spacecraft Bus + Payload Recurring Cost ($K)	35,367–142,044 $K	34%
4.0 Program Level				
4.0 Program Level (for a Communication Satellite)	Y = 0.234 X1	X1 = Space Vehicle (Spacecraft Bus + Payload + IA&T) Recurring Cost ($K)	13,287–268,225 $K	12%
4. Program Level (for an other than communication satellite)	Y = 0.320 X1	X1 = Spacecraft (Spacecraft Bus + Payload + IA&T) Recurring Cost ($K)	13,287–268,225 $K	40%
5.0 Flight Support				
5.0 Launch Operations & Orbital Support (LOOS)	Y = 5,850	Y= Average LOOS cost in $K	Not given	Not given

(a) Current version of USCM8 provides a combined structure/thermal CER.

larger spacecraft due to shortened development times by using standard designs, lower launch costs by using smaller launch vehicles, and cheaper production cost due to smaller size if their component complexities are similar. The Aerospace Corporation [1996], developed a parametric cost model for predicting development and first unit cost for smaller Earth-orbiting and near-planetary spacecraft. SSCM does not distinguish between non-recurring and recurring cost, as is done in USCM8, and so these CERs predict the aggregate of non-recurring and recurring costs. SSCM CERs are based on 53 individual satellites, of which most are smaller than 100 kg. These CERs represent MUPE and are presented in Table 11-11. This is not the latest version of SSCM CERs (since that version of the model is not available for public release); these are the same CERs in Wertz [1999]. Government agencies may request release of the latest version; for more information, go to Aerospace Corporation's website.

Another model suitable for estimating small spacecraft, although not described in SME-SMAD, is the NASA—Air Force Cost Model (NAFCOM) [SAIC, 2010].

In Eq. (11-2), we provide a single example, similar to multiple USCM8 examples, for the aggregate of development and one protoflight unit in 2010 dollars for the thermal control system.

11.2.4 QuickCost

A more simple approach to predicting cost for an unmanned robotic space vehicle was developed for NASA projects in 2010 from historic cost data. The single-CER QuickCost model, version 4.2, was created by Hamaker [2011], the former Director of the Hq NASA

Table 11-10. USCM8 Spacecraft Bus Non-recurring and Recurring Estimate Examples, Keyed to SME-SMAD WBS Elements and Estimating Examples.

1.1.1/1.1.2 STRUCTURE/THERMAL SUBSYSTEM

Non-recurring $Y = 646\ X1^{0.684}$

where

- $X1$ = Structure + Thermal Weight = 175 kg
- $Y = 646 \times 175^{0.684}$
- Y = \$22,104 K

Recurring T1 $Y = 22.6\ X1$

where

- $X1$ = Structure Weight + Thermal Weight = 175 kg
- $Y = 22.6 \times 175$
- Y = \$3,955 K

The average unit cost for a lot of five units = 0.89×3995 = \$3,556 K

1.1.3 ATTITUDE DETERMINATION AND CONTROL SUBSYSTEM

Non-recurring $Y = 324\ X1$

where

- $X1$ = ADCS Weight = 280 kg
- $Y = 324 \times 280$
- Y = \$90,720 K

Recurring T1 $Y = 795\ X1^{0.593}$

where

- $X1$ = ADCS Weight = 280 kg
- $Y = 795 \times 280^{0.593}$
- Y = \$22,466 K

The average unit cost for a lot of five units = $0.89 \times 22{,}462$ = \$19,991 K

1.1.4 ELECTRICAL POWER SUBSYSTEM

Non-recurring $Y = 64.3\ X1$

where

- $X1$ = EPS Weight = 556 kg
- $Y = 64.3 \times 556$
- Y = \$35,751 K

Recurring T1 $Y = 32.4\ X1$

where

- $X1$ = EPS Weight = 556 kg
- $Y = 32.4 \times 556$
- Y = \$18,014 K

The average unit cost for a lot of five units = $0.89 \times 18{,}014$ = \$16,032 K

1.1.6 TELEMETRY, TRACKING AND COMMAND SUBSYSTEM

Non-recurring Y = \$26,916 K

Recurring T1 $Y = 883.7\ X1^{0.491} \times 1.13^{X2}$

where

- $X1$ = TT&C Weight = 109 kg
- $X2$ = Orbit (1 = Geo Orbit, 0 = Non-Geo Orbit)
- $Y = 883.7 \times 109^{0.491} \times 1.13^{1}$
- Y = \$9,993 K

The average unit cost for a lot of five units = $0.89 \times 9{,}967$ = \$8,871 K

1.2 COMMUNICATIONS PAYLOAD

Non-recurring $Y = (339\ X1) + (5{,}127\ X2)$

where

- $X1$ = Communications Payload Weight = 226 kg
- $X2$ = Number of Channels = 17
- $Y = (339 \times 226) + (5{,}127 \times 17)$
- $Y = 76{,}614 + 87{,}159$
- Y = \$163,773 K

Recurring T1 $Y = 189\ X1$

where

- $X1$ = Communications Payload Weight = 226 kg
- $Y = 189 \times 226$
- Y = \$42,714 K

The average unit cost for a lot of five units = $0.89 \times 42{,}714$ = \$38,015 K

1.3 INTEGRATION, ASSEMBLY, AND TEST (IA&T)

Non-recurring $Y = 0.195\ X1$

where

- $X1$ = Spacecraft Total Non-recurring Cost = \$196,600 K
- $Y = 0.195 \times 196{,}600$
- Y = \$38,317 K

Recurring T1 $Y = 0.124\ X1$

where

- $X1$ = Space Vehicle First Unit Cost = \$127,650 K
- $Y = 0.124 \times 127{,}650$
- Y = \$15,829 K

The average unit cost for a lot of five units = $0.89 \times 15{,}829$ = \$14,088 K

4.0 PROGRAM LEVEL for Communications Satellite

Non-recurring $Y = 0.236\ X1$

where

- $X1$ = Space Vehicle Total Non-recurring Cost = \$398,900 K
- $Y = 0.236 \times 398{,}900$
- Y = \$94,140 K

Recurring T1 $Y = 0.234\ X1$

where

- $X1$ = Space Vehicle Total Recurring Cost = \$272,600 K
- $Y = 0.234 \times 272{,}600$
- Y = \$63,788 K

5.0 LAUNCH OIPERATIONS & ORBITAL SUPPORT (LOOS) for Communications Satellite

Recurring T1 Y = \$5,850 K

6.0 AEROSPACE GROUND EQUIPMENT (AGE) for Communications Satellite

Non-recurring $Y = 0.421\ X1^{0.907} \times 2.244^{X2}$

where

- $X1$ = Spacecraft Total Non-recurring Cost = \$196,600
- $X2$ = Mission Type (0 = Comm Sat, 1 = Non-Comm Sat)
- $Y = 0.421 \times (196{,}600^{0.907}) \times (2.244^{0})$
- $Y = 0.421 \times 63{,}282 \times 1$
- Y = \$26,642 K

Live Calc

Table 11-11. SSCM Earth Orbiting Total Non-recurring Cost (development plus one protoflight unit) CERs in FY2010 Thousands of Dollars. Useful for spacecraft weighing less than 500 kg. It is presumed that these CERs include the cost of contractor program management, systems engineering, product assurance, and I&T. See Tables 11-35 and 11-38 for application of these CERs.

SME-SMAD WBS Element	CER Y = total non-recurring cost of development plus one protoflight flight unit in FY10 $K	Cost Driver(s)	Cost Driver Input Range	Standard Error of Estimate (absolute) FY10 $
1.1 Spacecraft				
1.1 Spacecraft Bus (alternate CER when no component information is available)	$Y = 1{,}064 + 35.5\ X^{1.261}$	X = Spacecraft Bus Dry Weight (kg)	20–400 kg	3,696
1.1.1 Structure	$Y = 407 + 19.3\ X \times \ln(X)$	X = Structure Weight (kg)	5–100 kg	1,097
1.1.2 Thermal Control	$Y = 335 + 5.7\ X^2$	X = Thermal Control Weight (kg)	5–12 kg	119
1.1.3 Attitude Determination & Control System (ADCS)	$Y = 1{,}850 + 11.7\ X^2$	X = ADCS Dry Weight (kg)	1–25 kg	1,113
1.1.4 Electrical Power Supply (EPS)	$Y = 1{,}261 + 539\ X^{0.72}$	X = EPS Weight (kg)	7–70 kg	910
1.1.5 Propulsion (Reaction Control)	$Y = 89 + 3.0\ X^{1.261}$	X = Spacecraft Bus Dry Weight (kg)	20–400 kg	310
1.1.6a Telemetry, Tracking, & Command (TT&C)	$Y = 486 + 55.5\ X^{1.35}$	X = TT&C Weight (kg)	3–30 kg	629
1.1.6b Command & Data Handling (CD&H)	$Y = 658 + 75\ X^{1.35}$	X = Command & Data Handling Weight (kg)	3–30 kg	854
1.2 Payload				
1.2 Payload	$Y = 0.4\ X$	X = Spacecraft Bus Total Cost ($K)	2,600–69,000 ($K)	
1.3 Spacecraft Integration, Assembly, and Test				
1.3 Integration, Assembly, & Test (IA&T)	$Y = 0.139\ X$	X = Spacecraft Bus Total Cost ($K)	2,600–69,000 ($K)	
4.0 Program Level				
4.0 Program Level	$Y = 0.229\ X$	X = Spacecraft Bus Total Cost ($K)	2,600–69,000 ($K)	
5.0 Flight Support				
5.0 Launch & Orbital Operations Support (LOOS)	$Y = 0.061\ X$	X = Spacecraft Bus Total Cost ($K)	2,600–69,000 ($K)	
6.0 Aerospace Ground Equipment				
6.0 Ground Support Equipment (GSE)	$Y = 0.066\ X$	X = Spacecraft Bus Total Cost ($K)	2,600–69,000 ($K)	

1.1.2 THERMAL CONTROL SUBSYSTEM

Non-recurring $Y = 335 + 5.7X^2$

where

$X1$ = Thermal Control Weight = 12 kg

$Y = 335 + 5.7 \times 12^2$

$$Y = \$1{,}156\ K \tag{11-2}$$

Cost Analysis Division, for budgetary exercises and top-level trade studies. The CER is based on a relatively large number of cost drivers, which are likely to be available to system planners and systems engineers early in the design process.

As shown in Table 11-12, the CER predicts, in 2010 dollars, full program cost (contractor plus government) for development plus the first flight unit. See notes below the table for full description of the costs predicted and for some useful factors which can be applied to other models.

An example of using QuickCost to predict the cost of an automated scientific satellite is shown in Table 11-13.

The shaded column recommends an appropriate cost driver value.

The table of the QuickCost input and output includes a cell giving the regression model result of $268 million in 2010 dollars (which is the median cost or 50% confidence level).

11.2.5 *NASA Instrument Cost Model (NICM)*

The NASA Instrument Cost Model (NICM), Version IIIC, was developed by the Jet Propulsion Laboratory in 2010 from 159 data points obtained from instrument contractors [Habib-agahi, 2010]. The model predicts the cost of development plus one flight unit of each of five payload instrument types. The five alternative subsystem-level CERs are shown in Table 11-14. The costs include contractor fee. Select one of these CERs for the payload subsystem estimate, depending on the technology (e.g.,

Live Calc

Table 11-12. QuickCost Non-recurring plus Recurring (T1) CER in FY2010 Dollars. Note the reference to the SME-SMAD WBS. See Tables 11-13, 11-36, and 11-39 for application of these CERs.

SME-SMAD WBS Element	CER and Cost Drivers Y = total cost of development plus one protoflight flight unit in 2010 dollars		Cost Driver Data Range	Standard Error of Estimate (percentage)
1.0 Space Vehicle for Unmanned Robotic Mission	$Y = 2.829 \times (\text{Dry Mass}^{0.457}) \times (\text{Power}^{0.157}) \times (2.718^{(0.171 \times \text{Data \%})}) \times (2.718^{(0.00209 \times \text{Life})}) \times (2.718^{(1.52 \times \text{New})}) \times (2.718^{(0.258 \times \text{Planetary})}) \times 1/(2.718^{(0.0145 \times (\text{Year}-1960))}) \times (2.718^{(0.467 \times \text{InstrComp\%})}) \times 1/(2.718^{(0.237 \times \text{Team})})$			41%
	Dry Mass	Dry mass of spacecraft bus and instruments in kg	76 to 14,475 kg	
	Power	LEO equivalent beginning of life power (BOLP) in watts	90 to 10,000 Watts	
	Data%	Data Rate Percentile (fraction) relative to the state-of-the-art at Authority to proceed (ATP) (enter 0.5 for median data rate missions, <0.5 for lower data rates, >0.5 for higher data rates)	0 to 100%	
	Life	Advertised Design Life (in months)—advertised design life excluding extended operations	6 to 180 months	
	New	Percent New (fraction): 0.2-0.3 = Simple Mod, 0.3–0.7 Extensive Mod, 0.7–1.0=New, >1.0 for New Technology	28% to 130%	
	Planetary? (0 =no, 1=yes)	0 for earth orbital, 1 for planetary	0 and 1	
	Year	ATP date in 4 digit calendar year minus 1960	1961 to 2005	
	InstrComp%	Instrument complexity percentile (fraction)—relative to "average" instrument complexity (enter 0.5 for median complexity, <0.5 for lower complexity >0.5 for higher complexity)	0% to 100%	
	Team	Team Experience: 1 = Unfamiliar, 2 = Mixed, 3 = Normal, 4 = Extensive	1 to 4	

Notes to the Table: 1. CER provides cost in millions of 2010 dollars including Phase B through Phase C/D (NASA program phases). 2. Cost includes all contractor cost through fee (10%) and NASA full cost support (~17%). 3. Cost includes spacecraft bus and instruments DDT&E plus TFU (first flight unit). 4. Includes all flight and ground software cost. 5. Cost excludes launch services (add \$150M to \$250M typical if EELV Delta IV or Atlas V variants used). 6. Add 2% for Phase A if desired (rough rule of thumb). 7. Add 9% for Ground Station if desired (e.g., rough rule of thumb for the cost of retrofitting existing facility, terminals, software). 8. Add 5% per year for each year of Mission Operations and Data Analysis (MO&DA) (rough rule of thumb).

Table 11-13. Example of Using QuickCost Model with Typical Input Parameters and Risk-Adjusted Predictions.

Cost Driver:	Example Value	Cost Driver Range
Dry Mass (kg)	664	kg mass of total spacecraft bus and instruments
Power (watts)	653	In LEO equivalent beginning of life watts
Data Rate Percentile (fraction)	0.50	Relative to the state-of-the-art at ATP (enter 0.5 for median data rate missions, <0.5 for lower data rates, >0.5 for higher data rates)
Design Life (months)	36	Advertised design life excluding extended operations
Percent New (fraction)	0.68	0.2–0.3=Simple Mod, 0.3–0.7=Extensive Mod, 0.7–1.0=New, >1.0 for New Technology
Planetary? (0=no, 1=yes)	0	0 for Earth orbital, 1 for planetary
ATP Date Year	1987	Authority to Proceed date in 4 digit Calendar Year
Instrument Complexity Percentile (fraction)	0.50	Relative to "average" instrument complexity (enter 0.5 for median complexity, <0.5 for lower complexity, >0.5 for higher complexity
Team Experience	2.0	1=Unfamiliar, 2=Mixed, 3=Normal, 4=Extensive
Year Dollar of Output	2010	Calendar Year entered as 4 digits (20XX)
Regression Model Result	\$268	DDT&E + TFU (Phases B/C/D) in Millions Dollars including fee, including full cost for full cost years

Table 11-13, Fig. 11-2◀, Eq. 11-2◀

planetary optical, Earth orbiting optical, microwave, particles, or fields).

NICM is where the CER predicts the development and single-unit fabrication without management and systems engineering "wrap" factors. These additional costs can be calculated from the Wrap CERs in Table 11-15. It is likely that these same wrap factors could also be used to predict program-level costs associated with other models.

Example of using NICM CERs:

- 1.2.2 Optical planetary instrument payload:
  - Sensor Cost = Y = 328 × $M^{0.426}$ × $P^{0.414}$ × $DL^{0.375}$
  - Where M = instrument mass = 20 kg
  - P = power = 30 Watts
  - And, DL = Design Life = 24 months
  - Y = 328 × $20^{0.426}$ × $30^{0.414}$ × $24^{0.375}$
  - Y = 328 × 3.58 × 4.09 × 3.29 = 15,685
  - Therefore, estimated PME cost = $15,685K in FY10$.
- 4.1 Management Cost (Wrap Factor)
  - Y = 0.07124 × $S^{1.0317}$= 0.07124 × $15{,}685^{1.0317}$ = 1,518
  - Therefore, estimated management cost = $1,518K in FY10$.

Similarly we can calculate the estimated cost for the other wrap factors (systems engineering, product assurance, and I&T).

Table 11-14. NICM Non-recurring Hardware Development Plus One Protoflight Unit Cost for Remote Sensing Instrument Payload in FY2010 Thousands of Dollars. These are alternative instrument (non-communications) payloads; select one CER from the table. See Table 11-34 (item 1.2) for application of CER 1.2.2.

SMAD WBS Element	CER Y in FY2010 thousands of dollars for development plus production of one protoflight unit	Cost Drivers [plus Data Range]
1.2.2 Optical Planetary (for instruments visiting planets other than Earth) Payload (e.g. cameras, spectrometers, interferometers)	Y = 328 × $M^{0.426}$ × $P^{0.414}$ × $DL^{0.375}$ R^2 = 0.76 SEE = 39%	M = Instrument Total Mass in kilograms (kg). [1–75 kg] P = Maximum Instrument Power in watts (W). [1–75 W] DL = Design Life in months [10–150 months]
1.2.2 Optical Earth-Orbiting (instruments on spacecraft in geocentric orbits) Payload (e.g., cameras, spectrometers, interferometers)	Y = 1,163 × $M^{0.328}$ × $P^{0.357}$ × $DR^{0.092}$ R^2 = 0.89 SEE = 35%	M = Instrument Total Mass in kilograms (kg). [10–350 kg] P = Maximum Instrument Power in watts (W) [0. 5–400 W] DR = Total Data Rate in kilo bits per second (kbps). [0.1–30,000 kpbs]
1.2.2 Active and Passive Microwave Payload (e.g., radars, altimeters, scatter meters,sounders, GPS receivers)	Y = 23,620 × $M^{0.284}$ × $P^{0.325}$ × $DR^{0.090}$ × $T^{-1.296}$ R^2 = 0.88 SEE = 37%	M = Instrument Total Mass in kilograms (kg). [10–50 kg] P = Maximum Instrument Power in watts (W). [10–600 W] DR = Total Data Rate in kilo bits per second (kbps). [0.1–1,000 kbps] T = Instrument Technology Readiness Level (TRL) [4–9]
1.2.2 Particles Payload (e.g., plasma detectors, plasma wave detectors)	Y = 980 × $M^{0.327}$ × $P^{0.525}$ × $DL^{0.171}$ R^2 = 0.65 SEE = 29%	M = Instrument Total Mass in kilograms (kg). [1–40 kg] P = Maximum Instrument Power in watts (W). [1–40 W] DL = Design Life in months. [10–150 months]
1.2.2 Fields Payload (e.g., electric field detectors, magnetic field detectors)	Y = 1,130 × $M^{0.184}$ × $P^{0.238}$ × $DL^{0.274}$ R^2 = 0.87 SEE = 28%	M = Instrument Total Mass in kilograms (kg). [0.1–35 kg] P = Maximum Instrument Power in watts (W). [0.1–25 W] DL = Design Life in months. [1–100 months]

Table 11-15. Estimate Wrap Factors for NICM in Same Currency as Hardware Cost Estimate from Table 11-14. Note the references to the SME-SMAD WBS.

SMAD WBS Element	CER Y in FY2010 thousands of dollars for program-level cost elements	Cost Drivers
4.2 Management	Y = 0.07124 × $S^{1.0317}$ R^2 = 0.85.	S = Sensor Cost from CER in Table 11-14 (WBS 1.2.2)
4.1 Systems Engineering	Y = 0.4931 × $S^{0.8645}$ R^2 = 0.75	S = Sensor Cost from CER in Table 11-14 (WBS 1.2.2)
4.4 Product Assurance	Y = 0.1427 × $S^{0.9422}$ R^2 = 0.91	S = Sensor Cost from CER in Table 11-14 (WBS 1.2.2)
4.3 Integration and Test (I&T)	Y = 0.1457 × $S^{1.0071}$ R^2 = 0.87	S = Sensor Cost from CER in Table 11-14 (WBS 1.2.2)

11.2.6 Software Cost Estimating Model—COCOMO 81

Since software development costs have increasingly become a percentage of lifetime space mission costs, it is no longer acceptable to predict them as a percent of hardware costs. To satisfy the need of the estimator to accurately predict software costs, unique software cost estimating models have been developed. The Cost Construction Model (COCOMO81) was first described in Boehm [1981]. The model was originally based on 63 completed software development programs. A major refinement to the model, identified as COCOMO II, was subsequently described in a sequel book [Boehm, 2000]. These and other software estimating tools are maintained by the University of Southern California (USC) Center for Systems and Software Engineering. More information, including software versions of the suite of COCOMO models, can be found on the USC website.

The software estimating sub-process is shown in Fig. 11-3 and described in the following sections.

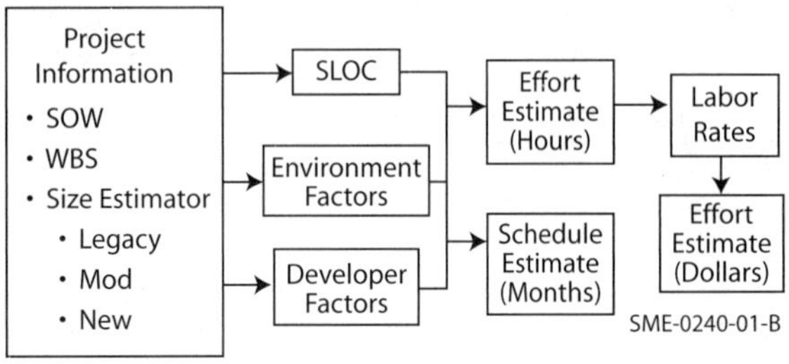

Fig. 11-3. Software Estimating Process.

This chapter describes COCOMO 81,* presented as a set of effort and schedule CERs and factors, and usable on a hand-held calculator. These CERs support the prediction of the most likely (point estimate) effort (cost) and time (schedule) required for a software product developed under the traditional waterfall development process. Other software models (but with more complex algorithms) emulate other development processes, such as the agile or incremental process.

Effort Estimate

Software development effort for flight software and for mission software subsystems, as well as software for each hardware component, in man-months, can be predicted with Eq. (11-3). Note that the result in man-months must then be multiplied by the applicable monthly labor rate to establish the year-currency estimate cost.

To use this equation to predict the development effort, you must first predict the number of SLOC and assign a rating to each of the Effort Adjustment Factors (EAFs).

* We chose to represent available software models with this one example, COCOMO 81, because it is time-tested, easy to apply with a hand-held calculator, and requires a smaller number of Effort Adjustment Factors (EAFs) than some of the more recent models, such as COCOMO II.

BASIC COCOMO 81 Development Effort (Man Months) Equation

SME-SMAD WBS 1.1.8 and 1.2.3

$$\textbf{Effort (MM)} = 3.312\ (\text{KSLOC})^{1.2} \times \pi\text{EAF} \qquad (11\text{-}3)$$

Where:

Effort = cost in man-months of full development cycle, including requirements validation, architecture design, detail design, coding, and testing (then transformed to monthly currency cost when multiplied by monthly labor rate).

KSLOC = thousands of delivered source lines of code (SLOC)—note that the original model reference identified this cost driver by a similar parameter: delivered source instructions (DSI). This parameter can represent (a) all new code or (b) a mix of new and reused code with a weighted metric called "equivalent SLOC." (ESLOC).

π**EAF** = cumulative effort adjsutment factor (EAF_1 x EAF_2 x EAF_3 x ... EAF_n). (See Table 11-17 for defining EAF)

The primary cost driver in Eq. (11-3) is software **size**, measured in thousands of delivered source lines of code (SLOC). A simple definition of SLOC is: a software statement that must be ***designed***, ***coded***, and ***tested.*** When counting SLOC, we should consider all programmed instructions including those contributed by pre-processors, compilers, and assemblers. This includes job control language, format statements, and data declarations but excluding comment lines, blank lines, unmodified utility software, and non-delivered support software such as test drivers.

There are alternate ways to characterize software size, such as the number of function points (FP), operating points (OP), and number of requirements. Using these would require different CERs.

The first challenge, then, is to establish the SLOC metric. During the mission design phase, this size metric is typically not known with any degree of certainty. Several approaches will work:

- The most direct approach is based on analogy to similar software development programs, considering software function, application, and quality. Table 11-16 displays some typical space software SLOC values from other programs, but we need to be careful about using such information from someone else's database. Note the calculation for equivalent SLOC (ESLOC), as explained later.

- Expert opinion is useful if more than one expert can be engaged.

- A structured Delphi approach, using multiple experts and possibly a pair-wise comparison.

Note that the software effort exponent in Eq. (11-3) is greater than unity, thereby driving this non-linear relationship to increasing man-months faster than the software module size increases and displaying a cost per SLOC increasing with size. Contrast this behavior to

Table 11-16. Example of Sizing (SLOC) and Calculation of ESLOC for Space Flight Software Components. Note how the calculated ESLOC (40,545) in this example is less than the sum of new SLOC and Reused SLOC; it is the ESLOC value (using the weighting factors from Table 11-8) that is used for the software development effort CER Eq. (11-3). This real-life example is from space probe software programmed in C.

Flight Software Component	New SLOC (C Language)	Reused SLOC	% Redesign	% Reimplementation	% Retest	Equivalent SLOC (ESLOC)
Executive	5,000	5,000	30%	30%	75%	7,175
Communications	2,000	8,000	20%	20%	50%	4,320
Command & Data Handling	3,000	22,000	25%	25%	50%	10,150
Power Control	1,000	4,000	20%	20%	50%	2,160
Attitude & Control	2,000	18,000	30%	30%	50%	8,480
Thermal Control	1,000	9,000	20%	20%	50%	3,610
X-Band Uplink & Downlink	1,000	10,000	20%	20%	75%	4,650
TOTAL	15,000	76,000				40,545
Example: Communications—2,000 + 8,000 (20% x 0.4 + 20% x 0.3 + 50% x 0.3) = 4,320						

Table 11-17. COCOMO 81 Effort Adjustment Factors (EAF). Only four of the more common COCOMO 81 EAFs are described here.

	Effort Adjustment Factor (EAF) Based on Expected Impact for each Project Attribute					
Project Attribute	**Very Low**	**Low**	**Nominal**	**High**	**Very High**	**Extra High**
Required Software Reliability (RELY)	(0.75)—slight inconvenience	(0.88)—easily recoverable losses	(1.00)—recover able losses	(1.15)—high financial loss	(1.40)—risk to human life	No factor
Product Complexity (CPLX) (note 1)	(0.70)—simple expressions, simple statements, simple arrays	(0.85)—moderate level expressions, no edits, no intermediate files	(1.00)—simple nesting, standard math and statistical routines	(1.15)—high nesting, basic numerical analysis special purpose routines	(1.30)—partial differential equations, communications handling, command processing	(1.65)—multiple resource scheduling, highly coupled and dynamic relationships
Programmer Capability (PCAP) (note 2)	(1.42)—4 months experience (15th percentile)	(1.17)—1 year experience (35th percentile)	(1.00)—3 years experience (55th percentile)	(0.86)—6 years experience (75th percentile)	(0.70)—12+ years experience (90th percentile)	No factor
Required Develop. Sched. (SCHED) (note 3)	(1.23)—75% of nominal time	(1.08)—85% of nominal time	(1.00)—100% of nominal time	(1.04)—130% of nominal time	(1.10)—160% of nominal time	No factor

NOTES: 1. Product complexity factors shown are an extrapolation from expanded tables in the COCOOM 81 Reference Manual which describe multiple sub factors for the complexity attribute. 2. Lesser experience typically requires a longer time to develop the product; sometimes this increase in man-months is offset by lower labor costs; the reference to "nominal time" would be the shortest time for an experienced team. 3. Note how adjust factors increase for both compressed and extended development schedule requirements, thus confirming that the COCOMO default effort estimates are based on a minimum effort schedule; some software model default effort estimates are alternatively based on a minimum schedule effort.

most *hardware* CERs where corresponding components are usually less than unity, illustrating economy of scale where cost per pound generally decreases with size. The constant coefficient (3.312) was derived from the data used to develop the CER.

For example, the nominal effort (assuming a nominal cumulative adjustment factor) to develop 10,000 new SLOC would be predicted by Eq. (11-3) as: $3.312\,(10)^{1.2} = 52.5$ man-months. If the cost per man-month (including salary and fringe benefits) were $25,000, then the monetary cost would be $52.5 \times 25{,}000 = \$1{,}312$K, or about $131 per SLOC. Note that the predicted cost to develop twice as many SLOC, i.e., 20,000, would be about $148 per SLOC—reflecting the "diseconomy of scale" associated with software development.

For better estimating accuracy and closer emulation to the software development process, COCOMO 81 relies on the cumulative effect of fifteen environment and developer EAFs which, when multiplied together, identified by π**EAF** in Eq. (11-3), provide a scaling or adjustment to the **nominal** effort equation.

Each adjustment factor is described by a series of rating levels that expresses the impact on development effort. These ratings are categorized between Very Low and Extra High, with a nominal value requiring no adjustment. Table 11-17 summarizes four of the available fifteen attributes, with a corresponding numerical value to be used in calculating π**EAF**. (Note, for example, that a very high software reliability attribute would increase the nominal effort development estimate to account for: the more detailed test plans and procedures; higher quality assurance, configuration management, and documentation standards; extensive stress tests; and IV and V interfaces required for human space flight.) In the effort example, we saw that 10,000 new SLOC could be developed in 52.5 man-months if all the adjustment factors were nominal (value of 1.0). If, however, the software were required for a manned space mission, where the required software reliability was very high and we were able to assign programmers with an average of 6-years of experience, the predicted effort may increase to $3.312\,(10)^{1.2} \times 1.4 \times 0.86 = 63.2$ man-months.

Schedule Estimate

Software development schedule duration in months may now be predicted, from the prior man-months prediction of effort, using Eq. (11-4), the *Basic COCOMO Schedule Equation*. To use this equation, you must first predict the development effort in man-months. Note how the development duration does not increase as fast as effort, suggesting that multiple software developers can work together in parallel activities, rather than in serial activities.

SME-SMAD WBS 1.1.8 and 1.2.3

Duration (in months) = 4.376 (MM)$^{0.32}$

Where:

Duration = Schedule time, in calendar months, to complete software development, including requirements analysis, coding, assembly, testing, and documentation

MM = effort in man-months derived from Eq. (11-3)

(11-4)

In the first effort example, we saw that 10,000 new SLOC could be developed for a cost of 52.5 man-months if all the adjustment factors were nominal. The predicted development time could then be calculated as: $4.376 \times (52.5)^{0.32} = 15.5$ months. This equates to an average staff loading of 3.4 persons. Is this reasonable as a sanity check on our estimate?

Estimates Based on Equivalent SLOC

Not every software development requires the development of all new SLOC; and, some allowance must be made for the integration and testing effort of legacy (reused and modified) SLOC. When legacy software is reused or modified, and often combined with new software, the software estimator typically calculates an "equivalent number" of SLOC (ESLOC), based on the activities (design, implementation, and test) planned for each software module. Then, he applies the calculated ESLOC parameter to the effort CERs as substitutes for the SLOC parameter (or KESLOC in this example).

Table 11-18. ESLOC Weighting Factors for Reused and Modified SLOC.

Redesign	Reimplementation	Retest
0.4	0.3	0.3

COCOMO recommends the weighting factors to the SLOC count as shown in Table 11-18 as a starting formula, but actual weighting factors depend on the organization's experience, the type of software being implemented, and the cost prediction model used.

Commercial off-the-shelf (COTS) products are not included in this equivalent SLOC process because the end user typically has no idea how many SLOC characterize a typical commercial software product. However, the estimator needs to determine the purchase price and needs to estimate the cost of integration software. He also needs to be aware of any auto-generated code as well as code to be ported from another software system.

As an example, calculate the ESLOC for the aggregate of the following software packages:

- 10,000 new SLOC
- 6,000 SLOC reused as is; but, requires 80% retest
- 3,000 SLOC modified; requires 25% redesign, 50% reimplementation, and 100% retest

Using these weighting factors, one should calculate ESLOC to be 13 KESLOC, not 19 KESLOC, which would be the arithmetic total, as shown in Table 11-19. The difference is due to the reduced development effort associated with reusing some of the SLOC.

Software Maintenance Effort

For post-launch ground operations, the software maintenance cost can contribute 50% to 75% of the life cycle software cost. The annual effort to maintain software can be predicted either by the appropriate level-of-effort (LOE) of manpower assigned to operate and support the software or by a parametric approach based on the number of SLOC to be modified each year. This can be considered a recurring cost under SME-SMAD WBS element 1.1.8, 1.2.3, 7.2, and 7.3.

LOE predictions can be based on the number of SLOC which can be managed and maintained by one person. The metrics are subjective and depend upon the following considerations:

- What is included?—failures only or new applications, also
- Who does the maintenance?—users or separate software development facility

Refer to Sec. 11.2.10 for more information.

A parametric approach, which seems more practical, can be based on a productivity ratio defining the number of SLOC modifications per man-month of dedicated maintenance effort. COCOMO defines this metric as Annual Change Traffic (ACT) which is the ratio of

Table 11-19. Solution to ESLOC Example.

Software Source	Original KSLOC	KESLOC			
		Redesign	Reimplementation	Retest	Subtotal
New	10	n/a	n/a	n/a	10.00
Reused—As Is	6	n/a	n/a	6 KSLOC × 80% retest × 0.3 = 1.44	1.44
Modified	3	3 KSLOC × 25% redesign × 0.4 = 0.30	3 KSLOC × 50% reimplementation × 0.3 = 0.45	3 KSLOC × 100% retest × 0.3 = 0.90	0.30 + 0.45 + 0.90 = 1.65
TOTAL	19.00				13.09

SLOC modified each year to SLOC delivered and ranges from 0.05 for mathematical and logical operations to 0.15 for more complex, non-real-time software. This metric works best after the initial software "bugs" have been repaired.

So, for example, if our previous example of 10,000 lines of complex software were to be maintained, the "steady state" annual maintenance requirement might cost 15% per year of the 19.0 man-months or 2.85 MM per year—equivalent to 0.24 persons to maintain the software. How does this prediction compare with the LOE of 25,000 to 50,000 SLOC per man-year?

More Information

More information on using COCOMO 81 (Intermediate version) may be found in Boehm [1981] and in the USC COCOMO 81 Reference Manual. Some useful space software estimating rules of thumb are shown in Table 11-20, but there are wide variations in these metrics.

Table 11-20. Software Development Estimating Rules of Thumb in 2010 Dollars per SLOC. These factors may need adjustment if your labor rates are unusually low or high.

Space Platform	FY10$/SLOC
Manned Flight	$800
Unmanned Flight	$550
Ground	$300

11.2.7 Facility Costs

Facility costs are not normally included in the prediction of space program costs and so do not appear in the SME-SMAD Project WBS. However, facility costs could be important to the project planner who is concerned with the impact on facility planning and consequential trade studies.

Facility construction cost information may be found in the much-used Air Force Construction Cost Handbook [USAF, 2003]. Extrapolations from this historical data are typically made on the basis of size and geographic location. Portions of the database, useful for facility estimates, are shown in Table 11-21. This data is useful for sizing (typical facility size), factor development (range of costs per square foot), and analogy estimating (total cost). Space engineers should scale and extrapolate predicted costs from these actual costs.

Typical location cost-adjustment factors are shown in Table 11-22.

Table 11-21. Space-Related Ground Facility Cost Factors. This data must also be adjusted for geographic location if other than Washington DC as shown in Table 11-22.

Facility Type	Typical Size (m^2)	Avg. Const. Cost in Wash DC per m^2 in 2010 $
Communications Facility	474	$2,170
Control Tower	465	$8,346
Hazardous Material Storage	3,716	$1,557
High Tech Laboratory	3,716	$3,993
Missile Assembly	929	$3,341
High Bay Assembly	3,250	$2,622
Headquarters Building	3,700	$2,410
Satellite Communications Center	550	$6,471

Table 11-22. Facility Cost Environmental Adjustment Factor (Multipliers) for Facility Costs. These are examples only; a complete list may be found in USAF [2003].

Location	Adjust Factor	Location	Adjust Factor
Marshall Center, AL	0.85	*Germany*	1.22
Cape Canaveral, FL	0.97	*Fort Irwin, CA*	1.27
Washington, DC	1.00	*Australia*	1.30
JPL, CA	1.13	*Japan*	1.62
Vandenberg, CA	1.19	*Hawaii*	1.70

For example, a high bay assembly building of 4,000 square meters, to be built at Cape Canaveral, would likely cost: 4,000 × 2622 × 0.97 = $10.173 M in 2010 dollars.

11.2.8 Launch Costs

The recurring cost of space launch is best predicted from previous cost history. The space mission engineer should select one or more candidate launch vehicles, based on capacity payload and current availability, and then negotiate the launch price. Estimators may approximate this cost from historical cost information such as presented in Table 11-23.

Selecting the appropriate launch vehicle, as described in Chap. 26, is conditioned by the required orbit (LEO or

Table 11-23. Historical Launch Vehicle Costs for Predicting SME-SMAD WBS 2.0 Cost. Launch costs are typically negotiated; these factors are best used for planning and worst case budgeting.

Mass Class (a)	Vehicle Name	Country of Origin	Capacity Payload in kg to Orbit LEO (b)	GTO (c)	Average Launch Cost (FY2010 $K) (d)	Launch Cost in FY2010 $K per kg Placed into Orbit (e) LEO (b)	GTO (c)
			Small				
Small	***Athena 2***	USA	2,065	590	$32,688	$15.8	$55.4
Small	***Cosmos***	Russia	1,500	N/A	$18,387	$12.1	N/A
Small	***Pegasus XL***	USA	443	N/A	$18,454	$41.5	N/A
Small	***Falcon 1e***	USA	1,010	N/A	$10,900	$10.8	N/A
Small	***Minotaur IV***	USA	1,650	N/A	$22,000	$13.3	N/A
Small	***Rockot***	Russia	1,850	N/A	$18,454	$9.9	N/A
Small	***Shtil***	Russia	430	N/A	$272	$0.7	N/A
Small	***START***	Russia	632	N/A	$10,215	$15.9	N/A
Small	***Taurus***	USA	1,380	448	$25,878	$18.8	$57.7
			Medium and Intermediate				
Inter.	***Ariane 44L***	Europe	10,200	4,790	$153,225	$15.0	$32.0
Inter.	***Atlas 2AS***	USA	8,618	3,719	$132,795	$15.4	$35.7
Medium	***Delta 2***	USA	5,144	1,800	$74,910	$14.6	$41.7
Medium	***Dnepr***	Russia	4,400	N/A	$20,430	$4.6	N/A
Inter.	***Falcon 9***	USA	10,450	4,540	$56,750	$5.4	$12.5
Medium	***Long March 2C***	China	3,200	1,000	$30,645	$9.5	$30.6
Inter.	***Long March 2E***	China	9,200	3,370	$68,100	$7.4	$20.2
Inter.	***Soyuz***	Russia	7,000	1,350	$51,075	$7.4	$37.9
			Heavy				
Heavy	***Ariane 4G***	Europe	18,000	6,800	$224,730	$12.5	$33.1
Heavy	***Atlas 5***	USA	20,050	8,200	$172,000	$8.6	$25.3
Heavy	***Delta 4 Heavy***	USA	22,560	13,130	$215,000	$9.5	$16.4
Heavy	***Long March 3B***	China	13,600	5,200	$81,720	$6.0	$15.7
Heavy	***Proton***	Russia	19,760	4,630	$115,770	$5.9	$25.1
Heavy	***Space Shuttle***	USA	28,803	5,900	$408,600	$14.2	$69.2
Heavy	***Zenit 2***	Ukraine	13,740	N/A	$57,885	$4.2	N/A
Heavy	***Zenit 3 SL***	Multinational	15,876	5,250	$115,770	$7.2	$22.1

NOTES: (a) The FAA Office of Commercial Space Transportation has divided all vehicles into four mass classes: small, medium, intermediate, and heavy, based on their payload capacities in pounds to LEO (<5,000, <12,000, <25,000, >25,000); in the table, all weights have been converted to kg. (b) Low Earth Orbit (c) Geosynchronous Transfer Orbit; these costs do not include the additional cost of apogee kick motors or other payload injection means. (d) These costs (in 2010 thousands of dollars) include the launch vehicle and related launch services. Where necessary, the costs were converted to dollars from other currencies. (e) Assuming maximum use of the payload weight capacity in the calculations, these are minimum values.

GTO), the total payload weight (with allowance for weight growth), country of manufacture (see large cost differences between Western and non-Western countries), and trajectory (usually dependent on designated launch site), and whether the mission is to be manned or unmanned. This table illustrates the sensitivity of launch cost to mass class, orbit, and country of origin (Western vs non-Western). From a cost estimator's point of view, it is interesting to note that cost per kg decreases with capacity, thereby confirming our general cost presumption about economies of scale.

Note, also, that this cost information has been derived from multiple sources [Futron Corporation, 2002; AIAA, 2004; NASA, 2006], and may not reflect the recent competitiveness observed in the launch vehicle industry where price drops of 20% or more have occurred over the past few years.

The discussion up to this point has focused on the recurring cost of launch systems, which is what most users will be interested in for costing a particular mission. Additionally, TRANSCOST is a parametric cost model for estimating the development (non-recurring) cost of space launch systems and is currently in version 8.1 [Koelle, 2010]. This tool is more appropriate for use by new launch vehicle designers. (See also Sec. 10.3.3.)

11.2.9 Additional Cost Factors

Certain cost factors or wrap factors, representative of those activities not directly associated with "touch labor" or with specific hardware or software elements, are typically used to estimate "adders" or wrap factors to the prime mission equipment (PME) costs—both non-recurring and recurring. PME are the hardware and software "deliverables."

Typical factors are shown in Table 11-24. The estimator might consider the range of factors (minimum, maximum) for each element; for example, a higher project management factor would be appropriate for small projects or for projects which require coordination among several team members or subcontractors. As with

Table 11-24. Cost Factor Percentages to Calculate Wrap Factors. These are additions to PME costs, where PME is total cost of spacecraft and payload costs. Consider the range of factors and the reasons for not always choosing the average factor. Not all of these factors would apply to every estimate.

SME-SMAD WBS Element	Minimum Factor	Average Factor	Maximum Factor	Reasons for Using the Maximum Factor
3.0 Annual Operations and Support for Ground Station	1%	5%	27%	Many subsystems and platforms, contractor support
4.1 System Engineering	15%	20%	35%	Frequently changing requirements, multiple interfaces
4.2 Project Management	10%	15%	35%	Small project; multiple team members or working locations
4.3 System Integration & Test	1%	15%	33%	Many components, conflicting requirements, changing baseline
4.4 Product Assurance	1%	3%	6%	Anticipated short life, harsh operating environment
4.5 Configuration Management	1%	4%	20%	Detailed control level, multiple users
4.5 Contractor (or subcontractor) Fee	10%	12%	15%	Contractor assumes project risk, such as with fixed price contract
4.5 Data Management	1%	2%	5%	Multiple data clients, multiple IT platforms
4.5 Development Support Facility	1%	4%	11%	Real time support, multiple operating locations
4.5 Hardware/Software Integration	10%	16%	24%	When hardware or software components are still being developed
4.5 Integrated Logistics	1%	6%	15%	Multiple operating platforms, multiple operating agencies
4.5 Safety & Mission Assurance (S&MA)	7%	7%	8%	When human life is at risk
4.5 Site Activation	1%	3%	6%	Remote area, crowded environment, harsh climate

most factors or rules of thumb, these are "starting points" for the estimate and should be tempered with judgment, other information, or other methods (e.g., level of effort) of estimating. It is common to evaluate these factor-derived costs by converting the dollars to man-months of labor to see if the estimate is reasonable.

For example, if the development cost for a one-year project were estimated to be \$2 million without project management and the average project management factor of 15% were used to estimate a cost of \$300K, then it would be reasonable to ask if one full-time senior project manager at \$300K per year would be adequate. The real challenge with this level-of-effort approach comes when we estimate the cost for fractions of persons.

11.2.10 Operations Costs

Mission operations costs are integral to total life cycle cost but are too often overlooked during the development phase of the project. A discussion of operations cost drivers may be found in Larson [2006]. Understanding the cost impact of mission requirements, logistics, and concept of operations may require investigation of the following parameter sets and alternatives:

- Defense/Commercial/Experimental/Communications/Microsatellite
- Manned/Unmanned
- US/Russian/European/Japanese Cooperation
- Communication Architecture and Criticality
- Earth/Interplanetary/Lunar Orbits
- Number of Missions/Spacecraft/Orbits
- Number of Ground Stations/Sites
- Levels of Automation and Staffing (Space and Ground Segments)

Estimating Process

Consistent with the estimating process defined in Sec. 11.1.5, we begin with establishing the operations phase ground rules and assumptions; these will be explained in Chap. 29, particularly Table 29-1. Consider, especially, the duration and complexity of the mission, as well the staffing levels. The long-term steady-state labor costs to operate the space system are best predicted by a level-of-effort (LOE) analysis; that is, by planning for the number of operators required, their labor costs, and their schedule of support (full-time versus part-time) to the operations phase.

Next, we expand the SME-SMAD WBS Element 7.0, Operations, as previously identified in Fig. 11-1, into the following sub elements (or a similar subset), consistent with the level of information available and the desired detail of the estimate:

7.1 Program Management and System Engineering (PMSE)

7.2 Space Segment
  - 7.2.1 Payload Software
  - 7.2.2 Bus Software
  - 7.2.2 Communication System

7.3 Ground Segment
  - 7.3.1 Mission Operations
    - Monitor and Control
    - Anomaly resolution

- Data retrieval, processing, dispersion
- Rehearsals/Training
- Disposal/Termination

7.3.2 Ground Software
- Work Stations
- Simulation Test-beds

7.3.3 Ground Hardware
- Mission Control Center
- Antennas/Reference Stations

7.3.4 Facilities

Finally, we must apply cost factors, parametric cost estimating CERs, or historic analogies to each WBS sub element, considering the following definitions of these Operations WBS sub elements:

WBS Element 7.1, Program Management and System Engineering (PMSE) includes business management, business development, data management, operations, logistics/support analysis/planning, scheduling, and office administration. PMSE may be estimated either as a level of effort (number of personnel required per year) or as a factor of total operations costs. A general rule of thumb, depending on mission duration and complexity, is to predict PMSE at 10% to 20% of the annual space and ground operations costs.

WBS Element 7.2, Space Segment, includes maintaining the software of the space vehicle. Software maintenance activities include code corrections, code adaptations, code perfections, and occasional enhancements. The three major software subsystems to be maintained are the payload (mission software), the space vehicle (bus software), and the communication software. The bus software communicates the vehicle's position, movements, and status while the payload software communicates valuable data and information related to the mission. Software sustainment and maintenance may be estimated as a level of effort (number of personnel required per year).

WBS Element 7.3, Ground Segment, includes most of the costs for space mission operations. The key components are the mission operations costs, ground software sustainment costs, ground hardware maintenance costs, and the facilities.

WBS Element 7.3.1, Mission Operations, includes the cost of operating personnel, who are responsible for:

- Monitor and Control—the number of personnel and hours required to monitor space vehicle, including orbital corrections, scheduled systems checks, shut downs, and planned space software upgrades and corrections.
- Anomaly Resolution—extra personnel to resolve complex issues outside the planned or typical orbital adjustments.
- Data Retrieval, Processing, Dispersion—the man hours needed to retrieve, process, format, and disperse data to and from the satellite; this includes both the payload and the bus data and may be dispersed to multiple end users or teams.
- Rehearsals/Training—planned rehearsals and training for multiple missions in accordance with launch schedules and key milestones.
- Disposal/Termination—personnel hours for planning and terminating.

WBS Element 7.3.2, Ground Software, includes communication with the space vehicle from the ground. Costs include simulation and test-bed software to analyze new software, proposed orbits, and anomaly resolutions. Ground software maintenance includes corrections, adaptive code, perfections, and some enhancements. Ground software may include some related hardware elements such as work stations and displays to monitor and control the space systems. A system test-bed may include hardware to simulate software that mimics all aspects of the space system and mission. However, the cost of these hardware elements should have been included in the program development cost estimate.

WBS Element 7.3.3, Ground Hardware, includes monitoring and control stations, reference stations, antennas, networks, and mobile units required for mission operations. However, the cost of these hardware elements should be included in the program acquisition cost estimate. A general rule of thumb predicts annual ground hardware maintenance cost at 7% to 20% of the hardware acquisition (production phase) costs.

WBS Element 7.3.4, Facilities, include structures that house operations equipment and personnel required to perform space systems operations. Annual dollars per square meter factors may be applied to predict rent, maintenance, taxes, insurance, and fees. If the operations center is not charged to this project, then ignore this cost element. See Sec. 11.2.7 for more information.

Estimating Models

NASA developed several parametric cost prediction models which can be used as the primary basis, or as a cross-check, for operations costs. One of these models is the Exploration Architectures Operations Cost Model (ExAOCM) [Shishko, 2006] for estimating lunar outpost operations costs. This model traces its heritage to NASA's Model Evaluation of Space Station Operations Cost (MESSOC), which dealt with the costs of mature operations for a LEO space station. Another model, TRANSCOST [Koelle, 2010], is a commercially available model of space transportation costs. A description and application of these models is beyond the scope of SME-SMAD.*

ExACOM was developed by the Jet Propulsion Laboratory (JPL) under NASA sponsorship for the Constellation Program. It runs in MS Excel and can predict operations cost by fiscal year in accordance with the program WBS. Access to the model is controlled by Hq NASA, Cost Analysis Division.

Operations costs have not received as much attention

* Some of the material in Sec. 11.2.10 was contributed by Robert Shishko, Ph.D., Principal Systems Engineer/ Economist; Jet Propulsion Laboratory, California Institute of Technology.

and detailed analysis within the space costing community as have development and production costs. However, operations costs are often a substantial contributor to total life cycle costs, especially for human spaceflight programs. Early system design decisions can exert a tremendous influence on operating costs and, therefore, we must ensure that the operating cost drivers have been properly identified and the operating costs of all alternatives have been considered in the selection of the preferred alternative.

To estimate operations costs, we follow the same steps as for development and production costs. We must first establish an operations WBS, understand the operations concept, select the proper cost model or other estimating method, and develop the cost estimate. Mission operating costs are inherently time-based, and must be spread over time and inflated.

Operations costs include mission operations, ground operations, training, sustaining engineering, sustainment of the mission control center, flight hardware spares and maintenance, program/project management and integration, and communication services.

In addition to parametric modeling and LOE analysis, discrete event simulation has been used with some success to estimate the workforce and costs associated with aspects of ground operations. For each sub-function, we develop an equation relating the program/project's approach to the number of personnel needed and then to cost. With L as the length of crew training in years, a simple equation for the cost of trainers in year t is:

Mission Ops Trainers Cost Estimate

Trainer Cost **=** $\alpha + \beta \times NC_t$

$$NC_t = \sum_{\tau=t+1}^{\tau=t+L} \left(Number\ of\ crewed\ flights_{\tau}\right)$$

Where:

α = fixed trainer cost for training curriculum maintenance and updates, participation in procedure development, mission planning, training system engineering studies

β = variable trainer cost per crew in training.

NC_t = number of crews in training

(11-5)

The parameters, α and β, are usually obtained using expert judgment and are based on the program/project's operations concept for crew training.

A more sophisticated algorithm would model the dynamic flow of flight crews through the training system, taking into account the type of training (e.g., classroom lectures, flight simulators), the number of trainers for each training activity, the need for refresher training, the unique training requirements of each mission, and the constraints on the availability of trainers and training assets.

Estimating Example

Here we present an example of a **WBS 7.0 Operations** cost prediction, using the principles and information previously presented plus some representative analogy information. This example is for a low to moderately complex scientific reconnaissance mission, similar to FireSat II using readily available information.

Operational staffing levels must be determined for each year of operations, and are typically lower for prelaunch years, peaking during the more active data collection and processing years, and lower again during the maturing years. A convenient analogy data point would be the number of operators employed for a similar program. However, adjustments should be considered for pertinent cost drivers, such as: whether an interactive payload operation will be supported, the degree of automation to be acquired, the number of spacecraft to be supported, whether the team also controls the ground antenna, and whether some of the support can be provided by an external organization.

Table 11-25 provides an example of a relatively large and dedicated support team responsible for a complex mission experiencing frequent contact with the spacecraft, operating 24 hours per day and 7 days per week, with a separate engineering support staff. The term, full time equivalent (FTE), is a metric for a full-time worker employed for one year. Obviously, the operating plan cannot realistically predict each operator will be engaged in his function, and his function alone, for exactly 2,000 hours per year, and so we assume that most staff are cross-trained to be able to back-up other operators.

Less complex missions are easier to automate, leading to smaller staffs which do not work as many shifts. Smaller staffs typically will expect more cross-training between the staff and might also engage an existing and separate organization for engineering (payload) support which can support additional missions, thereby requiring less than half the number of assigned FTEs each year. Members of smaller staffs, however, need to be more experienced (more expensive) so that they can support multiple functions.

Once we have predicted the operations staffing level, we must next determine the annual cost for each FTE, considering salary, overhead (typically 75–150%), administrative costs, contractor fee (if any), and other support costs (such as travel). Labor cost estimates may be different for contractors, government, and university staff, due to variations in the accounting methods. Salaries vary by location. Overhead rates can vary significantly when staff members are provided pre-arranged working space and tools. For reference, consider Table 11-26 which provides typical FY2010 FTE costs, for equivalent mission operations staff (which are less expensive than for development engineers and development technicians).

Since the earlier discussion of software estimating in Sec. 11.2.6 focused primarily on development phase costs, we need a new set of factors relevant to operations phase software maintenance costs. Consider factors to characterize the number of software lines of code (SLOC) which can be maintained by one person for one year (one FTE), as shown in Table 11-27. Note, however, that it is unlikely we could employ a fraction of a

Table 11-25. Typical Highly Complex Mission Operations Staffing Levels. [AIAA, 2003].

Staff Position	FTE	Shift (Hours/Days)	Comments
Operations Staff			
Operations Manager	1	8/5	
Flight Operations Supervisor	1	8/5	Cross-trained for Spacecraft and Payload Controller position.
Spacecraft Controller	4	24/7	
Payload Controller	4	24/7	
Ground Controller	4	24/7	
Spacecraft Operations Engineer	2	8/5	Cross-trained for Spacecraft Controller and Payload Analyst position.
Payload Analyst	1	8/5	Cross-trained for Spacecraft Analyst job
Mission Planner	2	8/7	Share Orbit Analysis
Data Analyst	2	8/7	
Orbit Analyst	1	8/5	Share Mission Planning
Operations Engineer	2	8/5	
Engineering Support Staff			
Engineering Manager	1	8/5	
Ground Systems Engineer	1	8/5	
Systems Engineer	1	8/5	
Technician	1	8/5	
Testbed/Simulator Engineer	2	8/7	
Flight Software Engineer	1	8/5	
Ground Software Engineer	2	8/5	
System Database Administrator	1	8/5	

Table 11-26. Annual Labor Costs for One FTE, Considering Salary and Overhead. This information was adjusted from Department of Labor statistics for similar engineering and technician skills and adjusted for 150% overhead (excluding administrative costs, contractor fee, and travel). (Data from various sources.)

Labor Category	Typical Annual Salary in FY2010 Dollars	Typical FTE Cost in FY2010 Dollars
Engineers and Managers: *Spacecraft controllers, payload controllers, operations engineers, software engineers, systems engineers*	$80K	$200K
Technicians: *Database administrators, data analysts,*	$60K	$150K

software engineer so we need to round up or down to the best number of whole FTE (unless we can share staff with another mission).

Next, we demonstrate the operations cost model with an example, using some of the factors and analogy data already presented. Table 11-28 takes us through the steps for calculating the most likely cost prediction for each sub element of WBS 7.0 Operations.

Table 11-29 summarizes our cost prediction for a single mission year; the total cost will be the aggregate prediction for all mission years. The number of operating staff typically will be different for each year and the number of SLOC to be maintained may change from one year to the next. This estimate summary is based on the following assumptions:

- Total FTE staff consists of 8 engineers & 4 technicians, none experienced in software maintenance.
- Software to be maintained:
  - Space—100,000 SLOC.
  - Ground—25,000 SLOC (the amount to be adapted from a much larger ground software package intended to manage multiple missions).
- Hardware acquisition cost was $1,400K.
- Facility lease of 1,000 square meters; annual local rent will be $1.25K per square meter.

11.2.11 Cost-Risk Assessment Model

Until now, we assumed that component and subsystem cost predictions may be arithmetically summed to equal the mission system cost. Statistically, however, the arithmetic sum of element most likely cost predictions, typically understate the system most likely cost prediction.

This simplified arithmetic summation process is often necessary when there is no single CER which effectively predicts the total cost. However, there are some statistical errors in this aggregation process since the cost uncertainty spread is unique to each CER and we may fail to capture the uncertainty metrics.

A more rigorous method, not further described in

Table 11-26, Fig. 11-3◀, Eq. 11-5◀

Table 11-27. Range of Software Maintenance Effort Estimating Factors for Space Mission Operations (SLOC Maintained per Person-Year). [Galorath Incorporated, 2011].

	Low	Most Likely	High	Typical Functions
Flight Software—Unmanned	7,800	16,000	25,600	Command & Control, Communications, Signal Processing, Diagnostics
Flight Software—Manned	5,400	12,000	19,400	Command & Control, Communications, Signal Processing, Diagnostics
Ground Control Software	17,000	28,200	39,600	Ground Command & Control, Mission Planning, Data Handling
Ground Support Software	18,800	30,700	44,700	Offline Testing, Simulation, General Support

Table 11-28. Mission Operations Cost Prediction Model.

WBS Element 7.0 Operations	Cost Category	Assumptions, Factors, Calculations	Annual Cost ($K 2010)
7.1 PMSE	Labor	X% of the other Ops Costs (10% to 20%)	A = X% × (B+C+D+E+F)
7.2 Space Segment Software Maintenance	Labor	$N_{SLOC,FSW}$/16,000 x FTE_{ENG}	B
7.3 Ground Segment			
7.3.1 Mission Operations	Labor	$N_{ENG} \times FTE_{ENG} + N_{TECH} \times FTE_{Tech}$	C
7.3.2 Ground Segment Software Maintenance	Labor	$N_{SLOC,GSW}/28{,}200 \times FTE_{ENG}$	D
7.3.3 Ground Hardware Maintenance	Labor	Y% of H/W Acquisition Cost (7% to 20%)	E
7.3.4 Facilities	Facility Lease	Z m^2 × W (price/m^2 floor space)	F
TOTAL ANNUAL OPERATIONS PHASE COST			T_{ann} = A+B+C+D+E+F
TOTAL MISSION OPERATIONS COST =	$N_{years} \times T_{ann}$		

Table 11-29. Example of Predicting Annual Unmanned Space Mission Operations Cost in 2010 Dollars Using Level-of-Effort Estimating Techniques.

WBS Element 7.0 Operations	Cost Category	Assumptions, Factors, Calculations	Annual Cost ($K 2010)
7.1 PMSE	Labor	15% of other costs (as high as 20%)	742
7.2 Space Segment Software Maintenance	Labor	100,000 SLOC/16,000 ~ 6 FTE @ $200K	1,200
7.3 Ground Segment			
7.3.1 Mission Operations	Labor	8 engineers @ $200K + 4 technicians @ $150K	2,200
7.3.2 Ground Segment Software Maintenance	Labor	25,000 SLOC/28,200 ~ 1 FTE @ $200K	200
7.3.3 Ground Hardware Maintenance	Labor	7% of $1,400K	98
7.3.4 Facilities	Facility Lease	1,000 square meters @ $1.25K per square meter	1,250
TOTAL ANNUAL OPERATIONS PHASE COST			5,690

SME-SMAD, requires simulation software which can be incorporated into a Microsoft Excel spreadsheet. Such software incorporates a Monte Carlo summation achieved through running multiple summation iterations, each considering the cost range for every element. Cost ranges are typically determined by the uncertainty in the input parameter of each CER, such as the uncertainty of weight growth when weight is the principle cost driver. If there is some expectation that the design weight may grow, for example, the CER could be applied individually to estimate the lowest possible value, the most-likely value, and the highest possible value of weight in order to derive a range of estimates.

The process works like this:

1. Calculate a range of costs for each estimate, emulated by a triangular distribution as shown in Fig. 11-4. Lower and Upper Bound estimates

depend on optimistic and pessimistic assumptions about one or more cost drivers, thereby requiring three estimates for each element. By definition, the mode (most likely cost) estimate represents the result which would occur the greatest number of times in a multi-event simulation.

2. Enter the three costs for each WBS element into the Monte Carlo simulation spreadsheet, likely an add-on to MS Excel such as @-Risk or Risk Plus and run the aggregating program many times (several thousand would be appropriate).
3. Plot the probability and then the cumulative probability of the resulting system-level estimate.

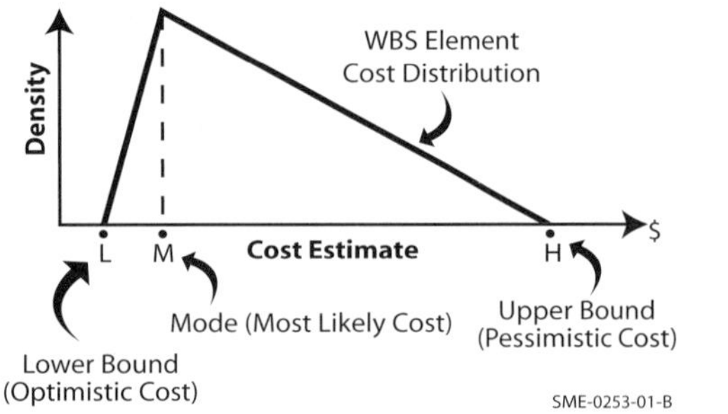

Fig. 11-4. Assumed Triangulation of the Cost Range for Each WBS Element.

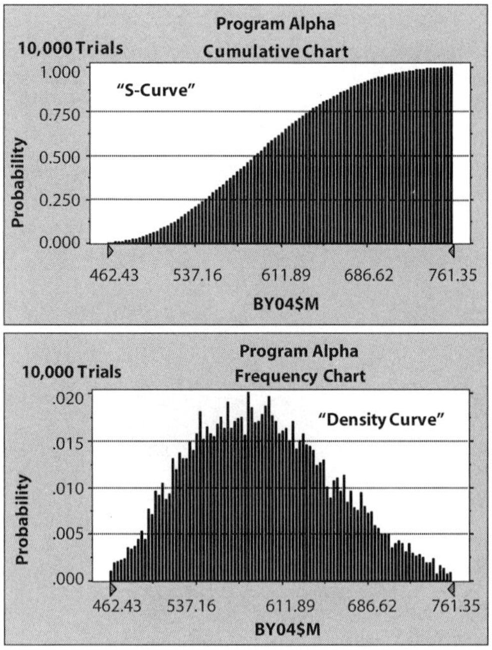

Percentile	Value
10%	516.81
20%	538.98
30%	557.85
40%	575.48
50%	592.72
60%	609.70
70%	629.19
80%	650.97
90%	683.01

Statistics	Value
Trials	10,000
Mean	596.40
Median	592.72
Mode	---
Standard Deviation	63.18
Range Minimum	450.19
Range Maximum	796.68

Fig. 11-5. What a System-Level Risk-Adjusted Cost Estimate Looks Like, Showing the Instant Probability and the Cumulative Probability. In this figure, you can see the system-level mode value is $593 and the range extends between $517M (at the 10% confidence level) and $683M (at 90% confidence level).

After the element most-likely cost estimates have been aggregated through a Monte Carlo simulation approach, the final estimate looks like the plots in Fig. 11-5 after 10,000 trials.

From the "S-Curve," we can determine that there is a 50% probability that the true cost will not exceed $593M and that there is an 80% probability that the true cost will not exceed $651M. If we were budgeting at 50% confidence and funded at the 80% confidence, we would enjoy a $58M management reserve to spend on risk mitigation to reduce our cost risk.

This process, as applied to cost estimating, is described in several publications, including Garvey [1999], Tecolote Research [2007], Book [2008], and Book [1999].

An alternate approach to describing the uncertainty of a cost estimate is to state the range of expected costs, corresponding roughly to the lower bound and upper bound defined in Fig. 11-4.

11.2.12 Cost Trade Studies

A primary purpose for developing a space system cost estimate is to support engineering trade studies, often in support of affordability initiatives. A trade study might help the system architect determine, for example, the most affordable option or the best value option among design alternatives. Figure 11-6 illustrates a performance/cost trade where the vertical scale indicates the range of acceptable key performance parameters (KPP) such as communications bandwidth or service life, and the horizontal scale the range of cost. Boundaries (dotted lines) on the vertical scale represent the threshold (minimum required) KPP and the more expensive objective value representing the most performance the user is willing to buy.

Boundaries (solid line) on the horizontal scale represent the maximum cost the user can afford and the lower cost which typically represents his budget.

Of the four design alternatives, only alternatives 1, 2, and 3 satisfy the cost requirement and only alternatives 2, 3, and 4 can satisfy the performance requirement. Likely, alternative 3 would be judged the most effective choice because it lies within both ranges and it costs only a little more than alternative 2 but offers significantly more performance—good ROI.

Refinements of this approach is promoted by the US DoD as Design to Cost (DTC) and Cost as an Independent Variable (CAIV) affordability initiatives. An overview description of CAIV can be found in Apgar [2001]. Comparative cost estimates are a useful product while parametric models are the tool of choice.

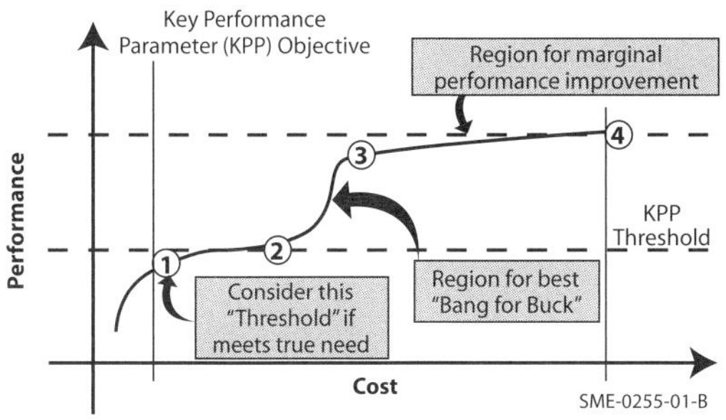

Fig. 11-6. Performance/Cost Trade Space.

11.3 Other Considerations in the Cost Estimate

11.3.1 Cost Realism

Cost realism is not the same as accuracy or precision. Realism refers more to the perception of the estimate, i.e., how likely is the estimate to closely predict the future event. This issue is more than statistical correctness; it also describes the inherent quality of the prediction.

Cost realism occurs when the estimator uses commonly accepted estimating procedures, applies proven estimating tools which have been calibrated to the product or service being estimated, and when he demonstrates estimating cross-checks and "second opinions." Cost realism results when an independent cost estimate (ICE) compares well with the primary estimate. Shown in Fig. 11-7, multiple risk adjusted and overlapping estimates give the manager or customer a more comfortable feeling about the estimate and thereby assigns a high degree of cost realism to the estimate.

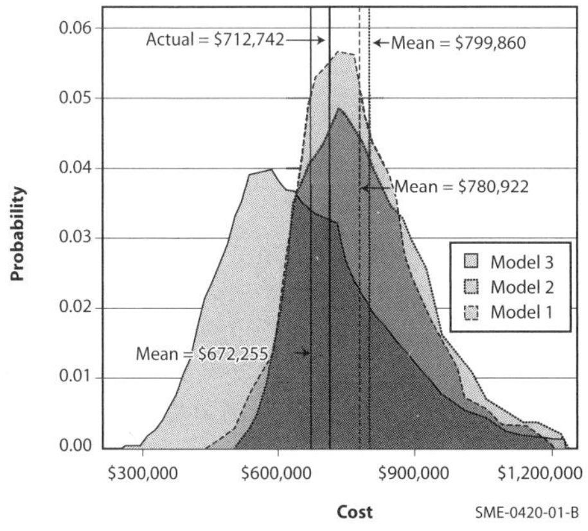

Fig. 11-7. Realism Improves When Using Multiple Cost Models and Then Comparing Results. This figure demonstrates the plotting of cost-risk distributions (as described in Sec. 11.2.10) from multiple models in overlapping manner comparison.

11.3.2 Cost Improvement

Cost improvement refers to the observable phenomenon by which workers become more efficient and productive as they continuously produce more units of a nearly-identical design and technology with a similar production process. Essentially, the second unit tends to go faster and cheaper than the theoretical first unit (T1), particularly with higher complexity products requiring a substantial labor (less automation) contribution. The original concept, learning theory, was developed in the airplane industry in the 1930s with observations on high-quantity production lines.

Cost improvement is also identified as *cost progress*, *experience curves*, or *learning curves*. These terms are somewhat interchangeable but the user must be careful to determine if the improvement rate refers to the entire subsystem or just the labor portion.

Cost improvement has been adapted to the space industry but has actually been quantified in only a few programs. Its main application has been with those parametric models, such as the recurring CERs of USCM8, which predicts the T1 cost. The T1 then must be factored ("down the learning curve") to predict average unit cost (AUC) for quantities beyond the first. Cost improvement rates (learning factors) are usually derived by fitting a curve through historical lot costs and then projecting lot costs backward to determine T1, as shown in Fig. 11-8. When starting with a different T1, indicating a modified product or a changed production process, another learning curve may then be used to apportion the costs to any follow-on unit.

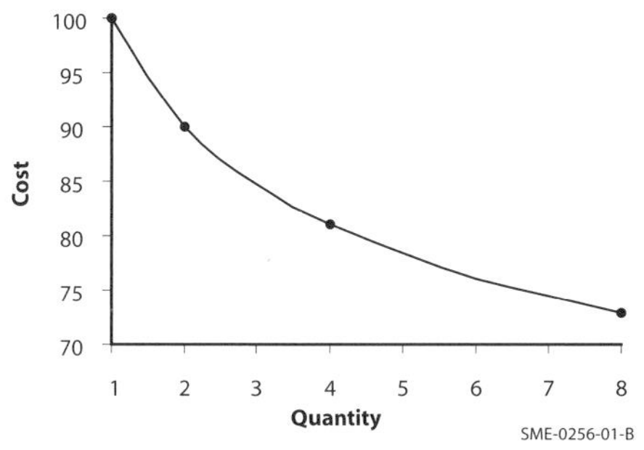

Fig. 11-8. Learning Rate is Determined Empirically.

Spacecraft production today is not as efficient as airplane production, primarily because each satellite tends to differ from its predecessor, because spacecraft typically are one-of-a-kind products, and because there are typically many changes from one spacecraft to the next in a series. Therefore, cost improvement adjustments must be applied with reasonable care. Further discussion on the selection and application of learning theory to space mission products is found in Fox [2008].

The basic cost improvement formula, essentially a CER based on quantity and learning rate as cost drivers, is of the form shown in Eq. (11-6). This is the classic learning curve theory.

For example, when T1 = \$1.00M (as determined by our recurring cost model), the expected learning curve slope is 95%, and the number of units (lot size) being built at the same time is 5, we can calculate three distinct costs:

Table 11-29◀, Fig. 11-8, Eq. 11-5◀

Total Lot Cost = T1 × N$^{(1+\ln S/\ln 2)}$
Where:
T1 = the theoretical first unit production cost (e.g., as predicted by recurring CER in Table 11-8)
N = quantity (lot size)
S = learning curve slope in % or decimal form, (e.g., 95% OR 0.095; an empirical parameter)

(11-6)

- *Total lot cost* = $T1 \times N^{(1 + \ln S/\ln 2)} = 1 \times 5^{(1 + \ln 0.95 / \ln 2)} = 1 \times 5^{[1 + (-0.0513 / 0.6931)]} = 1 \times 5^{(1 - 0.0740)} = 1 \times 5^{0.9260} = 4.438$ = \$4.44M (for 5 units)
- Average Unit Cost = \$4.44M / 5 units = \$0.89M
- Unit (marginal) Cost for 5th unit = $Total_5 - Total_4 = (1 \times 5^{0.9260}) - (1 \times 4^{0.9260}) = 4.438 - 3.610$ = \$0.83M

Although the estimator needs to assess whether the learning effect is to be applied to the entire product (element) or only to the labor component of that product, USCM8 assumes the rate is applied to the entire product.

Making similar calculations for 95% learning rate, for each unit numbered 1 through 5, we can develop a convenient set of data (Table 11-30), which is useful for quick learning curve calculations.

Table 11-30. Cost Improvement Factors Due to 95% Learning Rate.

Unit #	Total Lot Cost (a)	Avg Unit Cost (AUC) (b)	Unit (marginal) Cost (c)
1	\$1.00M	\$1.00M	\$1.00M
2	\$1.90M	\$0.95M	\$0.90M
3	\$2.77M	\$0.92M	\$0.87M
4	\$3.61M	\$0.90M	\$0.84M
5	\$4.44M	\$0.89M	\$0.83M

(a) From Eq. (11-6). (b) Total lot cost divided by number of units; note how the AUC is reduced by the learning rate whenever N doubles.(c) Difference in total lot cost between N units and N-1 units

11.3.3 Inflation

For consistency in referring to cost estimates, and to minimize confusion in the review of cost estimates, costs should be stated in constant-year dollars. Trade studies and cost-benefit analyses should also be developed in constant-year dollars. Then-year dollars (or real inflated dollars) may be necessary for funding analysis or budget analysis. Inflation adjustments are necessary in the following situations:

- When aggregating subsystem or component estimates from multiple models and the model CERs predict cost in different "years"
- When incorporating historic cost data from multiple sources, in different years, before assembling them into a normalized database as the basis for developing CERs
- When applying aggregated estimates to a single program estimate in a different year
- When transforming costs from constant-year to then-year and vice versa

Although generally not significant, you should notice whether annual inflation tables are based on calendar-year (starting in January) or fiscal-year (starting in some other month).

To adjust from one to another year dollars, or to convert between constant-year dollars and then-year dollars, use one of the many inflation tables available. Such tables sometimes provide multiple conversion factors, each tailored to development, production, and operations dollars.

An example conversion table in government fiscal year (running from October 1 through September 30) is shown in Table 11-31. This table allows conversion of historic data (back to 1985) to FY2010 and conversion from the model output year-dollars (all CERs and tables in this chapter predict cost in FY2010 dollars) to the preferred common year for analysis purposes.

Updates to this table may be found on the SME-SMAD website. For example:

- To convert historic data in FY2000 dollars to FY2010 dollars, multiply by 1.332
- To convert an estimate in FY2010 dollars to FY2015 dollars, divide by 0.913

Table 11-31. Inflation Factors Relative to the Year 2012 Based on Projects by the Office of the Secretary of Defense (Mar. 2011). See text for discussion.

Fiscal Year	Inflation Factor to Base Year 2012	Fiscal Year	Inflation Factor to Base Year 2012
1995	0.6408	2016	1.0857
1996	0.6558	2017	1.1089
1997	0.6723	2018	1.1326
1998	0.6913	2019	1.1568
1999	0.7102	2020	1.1815
2000	0.7285	2021	1.2067
2001	0.7516	2022	1.2324
2002	0.7717	2023	1.2588
2003	0.7979	2024	1.2856
2004	0.8240	2025	1.3131
2005	0.8583	2026	1.3411
2006	0.8867	2027	1.3698
2007	0.9108	2028	1.3990
2008	0.9375	2029	1.4289
2009	0.9501	2030	1.4594
2010	0.9701	2031	1.4906
2011	0.9850	2032	1.5224
2012	1.0000	2033	1.5549
2013	1.0201	2034	1.5881
2014	1.0413	2035	1.6221
2015	1.0630	2036	1.6567

Beyond 2012, the rates shown are based on an extrapolated constant rate of inflation. New projections are available annually.

Table 11-32. Example of Cost Spreading on Both Base-Year and Then-Year Costs.

Year of Expenditure	Percentage of Funding Each Year	Base Year Cost	Cumulative Cost (BY)	Inflation Factor	Then Year Cost	Cumulative Cost (TY)
2007	8.54%	85.4	85.4	1.084	92.6	92.6
2008	16.42%	164.2	249.7	1.107	181.8	274.4
2009	18.68%	186.8	436.5	1.130	211.1	485.5
2010	17.05%	170.5	607.0	1.154	196.7	682.2
2011	13.47%	134.7	741.6	1.178	158.6	840.8
2012	9.59%	95.9	837.5	1.203	115.4	956.2
2013	6.39%	63.9	901.4	1.228	78.5	1,034.7
2014	4.17%	41.7	943.1	1.254	52.3	1,087.0
2015	2.83%	28.3	971.4	1.280	36.2	1,123.2
2016	2.10%	21.0	992.4	1.307	27.5	1,150.6
2017	0.76%	7.6	1,000.0	1.335	10.1	1,160.8
		1,000.0	1,000.0		1,160.8	1,160.8

11.3.4 Cost Spreading

A cost estimate phasing (spread by year) model was developed by Burgess [2004] using a Weibull distribution function. Full explanation of this model is more complex than appropriate for SME-SMAD. A simplified version of this model is shown in Eq. (11-7), with default values for the Weibull function; normally, these parameters are based on calibration to an organization's expenditure experience, including the percent funding expended at specific schedule phase points. Analysts are advised to query the original paper, which is cleared for public release and can be downloaded from the Defense of Defense Cost Analysis Symposium (DoDCAS) website.

$$E(t) = d[Rt + 1 - e^{(-\alpha t^{\wedge}\beta)}]$$

$$d = \text{Estimate}/[(R + 1 - e^{(-\alpha)}]/\text{Total Cost}$$

Where:

$E(t)$ = that portion of the total cost estimate apportioned to a cumulative portion of the program (through one or more years)

$R = 0.00148 \times$ (program duration in months)

t = the ratio of cumulative time (years) divided by total time (years)

$\alpha = -0.414 + 0.0729 \times$ (number of units) $+ 0.0488 \times$ (months duration) $+ 0.0145 \times$ percent of estimate which is non-recurring

$\beta = 1.71$ (the Weibull shape parameter)

(11-7)

Since total cost is estimated in the user-specified base year (BY) dollar value, the Phasing Model first spreads the expenditures in base year dollars and then applies the appropriate inflation factor to adjust the base year effort value to then-year (TY) dollars.

An example of spreading a $1M estimate over eleven years starting in 2007, in both base year and then year costs with influence of inflation, is shown in Table 11-33.

11.3.5 Technology Readiness Levels

Another consideration in predicting development cost is the magnitude of the engineering effort to progress from a lower Technology Readiness Level (TRL) to a higher one. TRLs are defined in Chap. 1 and Sec. 1.3.4.

The cost prediction models in this chapter can generally predict the engineering and development costs to progress from level 6 to level 9. For planned development efforts with a greater or lesser "spread," e.g., starting from a TRL level other than level 6, the engineer may need to adjust his cost model prediction accordingly.

The key to successful development cost estimating is to calibrate this list to your real space program experience.

There have been numerous studies to characterize the difference in cost due to the maturity of technology, instrument maturity and space flight history. Most recently, Jet Propulsion Laboratory, [JPL, 2009] performed an assessment for the JIMO program and included several TRL correction factors. Relevant for this effort are those contributed by Smoker [2005], Malone [2011] and Hamaker J. [2008]. Table 11-33 presents a set of model factors which can be applied to correct the parametric model estimates to the appropriate TRL.

Note that the default case is when we assume the hardware to be developed is at TRL 6—then there is no adjustment required to the result from a development CER. If, however, the technology starting level is less than TRL 6, indicating more than typical engineering development is required, then the adjustment is greater than 1.0.

As an example of estimate correction based on TRL: An engineering development estimate from a reputable cost model predicts the engineering cost will be $2.0M.

Table 11-33. TRL Adjustment Factors for Development Estimates.

TRL	Factor	TRL	Factor
1	4.0	*6*	1.0
2	3.0	*7*	0.8
3	2.0	*8*	0.7
4	1.5	*9*	0.5
5	1.3		

However, since the starting point for the development is judged to be TRL 4 (because the hardware development has not progressed beyond the breadboard stage) and the goal is TRL 9 (mission ready), the multiplier is 1.5 and the corrected estimate will be 2.0 × 1.5 = $3.0M.

11.3.6 Establishing Cost Estimate Requirements

The US DoD Cost Analysis Requirements Description (CARD), the NASA Cost Analysis Data Requirements (CADRe) document, and the UK MoD Master Data and Assumptions List (MDAL) are to the space systems cost estimator what the system specification is to the space system architect. These documents typically provide the quantitative and narrative description of the technical, physical, and performance features pertinent to costing the system being acquired and of the acquisition program-necessary parameters that serve as the basis of estimate (BoE) for cost modelers.

A typical cost estimating requirements document would include:

1. System Overview
2. Risk
3. Operational Concept
4. Quantity Requirements
5. Manpower Requirements
6. Activity Rates
7. Milestone Schedule
8. Acquisition Strategy/Plan
9. Development Plan
10. Facilities
11. Track to Prior CARD
12. Contractor Cost Data Reporting Plan

Even if your project does not formalize the system requirements in time for you to develop your estimate, you should be seeking similar information in order to determine the scope of your estimate, which estimating tools are most suitable, and what cost driving parameters you must obtain.

11.3.7 Documenting the Final Estimate

Documenting the estimate is just as important as the engineering notebook which documents the evolving hardware and software design. It is important to provide a "thread" to demonstrate how each sequential estimate was created and what caused the estimate to change over time. A suggested outline of the risk-adjusted space mission estimate description would include the following topics:

1. Executive Summary: A high-level summary of the estimate, summarizing purpose, scope and result of estimating cost and schedule
2. System Description: Technical information in sufficient detail to understand and evaluate the technical cost drivers
3. Acquisition Strategy: A description of the acquisition and deployment cost drivers
4. Groundrules and Assumptions: Aspects of the analysis framework that will have significant impact if they are changed
5. Estimating Methodologies: An overview of the primary and secondary methods for deriving the cost estimates by WBS element
6. Detailed Cost Estimate Derivation: A complete description of the calculation of the cost estimate in sufficient detail to allow replication; often in the form of bases of estimate (BoEs)
7. Uncertainty Analysis: A detailed description and quantification of uncertainties in the system's cost and schedule estimates
8. Conclusions and Recommendations: A summary of key insights and important findings, including a discussion on affordability

11.4 Example Space Mission Cost Estimates

John Collins, *Microcosm*

In this section, we will apply the space mission cost models presented earlier in the chapter, to both the FireSat II and SCS missions, and estimate full mission cost for each, including costs for: spacecraft bus non-recurring and recurring cost for the appropriate number of flight units (2 units for FireSat II and 3 units for SCS), payload development, program level costs, IA&T, ground support equipment, launch and orbital ops support, launch vehicle, and flight software. The cost models to be applied for each mission are USCM8, SSCM, NICM, and QuickCost. Comparisons will be made of the costs generated by each model and an estimate will be selected based on which model best approximates the mission class represented by FireSat II and SCS.

The purpose of presenting the results in this way is to both show how to apply each of these mission cost models as well as the value of creating several cost estimates using different cost models. For each example cost estimate given, all input parameters that are used in calculating the cost estimates will be explicitly shown. The cost numbers are generated using the CERs presented for each cost model earlier in the chapter, namely: USCM8 CERs presented in Tables 11-8 and 11-9; SSCM CERs presented in Table 11-11, and the QuickCost CER presented in Table 11-12. Estimated costs are given, along with cost uncertainty for each cost element. The QuickCost model generates a conglomerate single cost estimate and uncertainty based on numerous inputs and uses a single CER to compute cost.

11.4.1 FireSat II

We now apply the various cost models presented in this chapter to the FireSat II mission, to assess the applicability of the various models to FireSat II and evaluate which model may provide the best cost estimate based on FireSat II mission and spacecraft characteristics. First, a traditional large spacecraft cost model will be employed to

Table 11-34. FireSat II Space, Ground, and Launch Segment Costs in FY10$K. Cost estimates based on the CERs in Tables 11-8 and 11-9 using the USCM8 Cost Model and in Table 11-14 for the NASA Instrument Cost Model (NICM). Input Data from FireSat II Spacecraft Mass and Power budgets is from Table 14-28.

Cost Component	CER Input Parameter	Value	Units	RDT&E (NRE) Cost (FY10$K)	1st Unit Cost (FY10$K)	2nd Unit Cost (FY10$K)	Total Cost (FY10$K)	Std Error ($K)
1.1 Spacecraft Bus								
1.1.1 Structure and Thermal**	mass	29.1	kg	6,480	657	591	7,728	1,658
1.1.3 ADCS**	mass	11.6	kg	3,767	3,405	3,065	10,237	3,987
1.1.4 Electrical Power System**	mass	20.9	kg	1,346	678	610	2,634	951
1.1.5 Propulsion**	N/A†							
1.1.6 TT&C and Data Handling**	mass	8.1	kg	26,916	1,680	1,512	30,108	5,419
1.1.7 Integration, Assembly, & Test (IA&T)	S/C Bus and P/L NRE Cost	73,722	FY10$K	14,376	9,142	8,227	31,745	11,943
1.1.9 Flight Software‡	source lines of code	38,100	N/A	20,955	0	0	20,955	6,287
Spacecraft Bus Total Cost				73,840	15,562	14,005	103,407	15,201
1.2 Payload					NRE + 1st Unit Cost			
1.2.2 IR Sensor*		mass(kg)	pwr(W)	Data (kbps)				
1.2.2.1 Fabrication	mass, power, total data rate	30.2	65.0	100	24,120	21,708	45,929	16,040
1.2.2.2 Management	sensor cost	24,120	FY10$K		2,366	2,129	4,496	899
1.2.2.3 Systems Engineering	sensor cost	24,120	FY10$K		3,030	2,727	5,758	1,439
1.2.2.4 Product Assurance	sensor cost	24,120	FY10$K		1,921	1,729	3,650	730
1.2.2.5 Integration and Test	sensor cost	24,120	FY10$K		3,775	3,398	7,173	1,793
IR Sensor Total Cost					35,212	31,691	67,006	16,245
2. Launch Segment	2 Minotaur Launches	50,000	FY10$K	0	25,000	25,000	50,000	5,000
4. Program Level	S/C Bus, P/L, & IA&T NRE Cost	88,098	FY10$K	36,473	28,191	25,372	90,036	29,587
5. Launch and Orbital Ops Support (LOOS)		5,850	FY10$K	0	5,850	5,265	11,115	3,335
6. Ground Support Equipment (GSE)	S/C Bus NRE Cost	38,509	FY10$K	13,627	0	0	13,627	5,042
Total Space Segment Cost to Contractor				123,940	78,966	71,070	273,975	
10% Contractor Fee				12,394	7,897	7,107	27,398	
Total Space Segment Cost to Government				136,334	86,863	78,177	301,373	
Total Cost of Deployment							**351,373**	**37,842**

* IR Sensor CER (1.2.2) is from the NASA Instrument Cost Model (NICM), see Table 11-14. **Spacecraft bus subsystem masses shown include a fraction of the spacecraft mass margin of 14 kg. † FireSat II propulsion system is taken into account in the ADCS CER (1.1.3). The 13.1 kg mass value for ADCS mass includes propulsion system hardware mass. The typical USCM CER for propulsion systems are for reaction control systems and apogee kick motors, not standard spacecraft propulsion systems. ‡ Software cost CER (1.1.9) taken from Table 11-20, unmanned flight CER.

understand what a typical cost estimate for this type of mission would be if traditional procurement and system development practices were employed in developing and launching two FireSat II spacecraft. Table 11-34 depicts a mission cost estimate using the USCM8 cost model (Sec. 11.2.2) for all mission elements except the payload, and the NASA Instrument Cost Model (Sec. 11.2.5) for the IR sensor payload. The total mission cost estimate for FireSat II, with 2 spacecraft, is $351.4 M (FY2010), with an uncertainty of $37.8 M. This is not unusual for a traditional military surveillance spacecraft procurement, and actually is less than traditional costs only because the spacecraft here are much smaller than traditional surveillance spacecraft with IR sensors. This example estimate will serve as the "traditional large mission" cost estimate.

Table 11-35 shows the FireSat II mission cost as estimated using the Small Satellite Cost Model (SSCM) from the Aerospace Corp, as described in Sec. 11.2.3. This full mission cost model is geared toward missions like FireSat II that are small spacecraft (under 400 kg spacecraft dry mass) and have relatively rapid development timelines. The cost that SSCM yields is $116 M total, with an uncertainty of $9.5 M, including an allocation of $50 M for launching both spacecraft on two separate Minotaur launches. This total mission cost is 33.3% of that estimated in Table 11-34 with the USCM8 and NICM models.

Table 11-36 displays a third cost estimate for the FireSat II mission utilizing the QuickCost cost model from NASA, showing a total mission cost of $186 M with a standard error of $56 M. This estimate is 61.3% higher than the SSCM estimate shown in Table 11-35, but is understandably larger because the QuickCost model has much larger spacecraft in its database than does the SSCM database. The QuickCost estimate is 53.7% of the USCM8/NICM cost estimate for FireSat II.

Table 11-35. FireSat II Space, Ground, and Launch Segment Costs in FY10$K. Cost estimates based on the CERs in Table 11-11 using the SSCM Cost Model that includes cost estimates for both the spacecraft bus and payload, program level costs, launch and orbital operations support, and ground support equipment. Input Data from FireSat II Spacecraft Mass and Power budgets is from Table 14-28.

Cost Component	CER Input Parameter	Value	Units	RDT&E plus 1st Unit Cost (FY10$K)	2nd Unit Cost (FY10$K)	Total Cost (FY10$K)	Std Error ($K)
1.1 Spacecraft Bus							
1.1.1 Structure*	mass	26.7	kg	2,103	1,893	3,996	2,084
1.1.2 Thermal*		2.3	kg	366	329	695	226
1.1.3 ADCS*	mass	7.0	kg	2,419	2,178	4,597	2,115
1.1.4 Electrical Power System*	mass	20.9	kg	3,553	3,198	6,752	1,729
1.1.5 Propulsion*	spacecraft bus dry mass	69.8	kg	723	651	1,373	589
1.1.6a TT&C*	mass	3.5	kg	786	707	1,493	1,195
1.1.6b Command & Data Handling	mass	4.7	kg	1,255	1,130	2,385	1,623
1.1.7 Integration, Assembly, & Test (IA&T)	spacecraft bus total cost	11,206	FY10$K	1,558	1,402	2,960	888
1.1.9 Flight Software†	source lines of code	38,100	N/A	20,955	0	20,955	6,287
Spacecraft Bus Total Cost				33,718	11,488	45,206	7,522
1.2 Payload							
1.2.2 IR Sensor	spcrft bus total cost	11,206	FY10$K	4,482	4,034	8,517	2,555
2. Launch Segment	2 Minotaur Launches	50,000	FY10$K	25,000	25,000	50,000	5,000
4. Program Level	spcrft bus total cost	11,206	FY10$K	2,566	2,310	4,872	1,463
5. Launch & Orbital Ops Support (LOOS)	spcrft bus total cost	11,206	FY10$K	684	615	1,299	390
6. Ground Support Equipment (GSE)	spcrft bus total cost	11,206	FY10$K	740	666	1,405	422
Total Space Segment Cost to Contractor				41,507	18,497	60,004	
10% Contractor Fee				4,151	1,850	6,000	
Total Space Segment Cost to Government				45,658	20,346	66,004	
Total Cost of Deployment						**116,004**	**9,517**

* Spacecraft bus subsystem masses shown include a fraction of the spacecraft mass margin of 14 kg.
† Software cost CER (1.1.9) taken from Table 11-20, unmanned flight CER.

Table 11-36. FireSat II Space, Ground, and Launch Segment Costs in FY10$K. Cost estimates based on the single QuickCost CER in Table 11-12. All FireSat II inputs are within the QuickCost model ranges of applicability for the various inputs, although at the low end. Input Data from FireSat II Spacecraft Mass and Power budgets is from Table 14-28.

Parameter	Applicable Range	Value	RDT&E plus 1st Unit Cost (FY10$K)	2nd Unit Cost (FY10$K)	Total Cost (FY10$K)	Std Error ($K)
Dry Mass of Bus and Payload (kg)	76 to 14,475 kg	100				
Power (LEO BOL, W)	90 to 10,000 W	183				
Data% (Data rate percentile [fraction] relative to state-of-the-art ATP)	0 to 100%	50%				
Life (Advertised design life, months)	6 to 180 mo	36				
New (% New [fraction], 0.2–0.3 simple mod, 0.3–0.7 extensive mod, 0.7–1.0 New, >1.0 new tech)	20% to 130%	90%	71,833	64,649	136,482	55,958
Planetary (0 = no, 1 = yes)	0 or 1	0				
Year (authority to proceed date in 4 digit calendar year)	1961 to 2025	2011				
InstrComp% (Instrument complexity percentile [fraction], relative to avg. instrument complexity)	0 to 100%	50%				
Team (Team Experience, 1 = Unfamiliar, 2 = Mixed, 3 = Normal, 4 = Extensive)	1 to 4	3				
Launch Cost (FY10$K)—Assume 2 Minotaur Launches	2 Launches –$50M (FY10)	50,000			50,000	5,000
Total Mission Cost					**186,482**	**56,181**

Table 11-36, Fig. 11-8◀, Eq. 11-7◀

Of the three separate cost estimates for FireSat II discussed in this section, the SSCM estimate in Table 11-35 is the estimate that should be closest to the actual mission costs, based on the type of missions in the SSCM database and similarity with the FireSat II mission.

11.4.2 Supplemental Communications System (SCS)

This section describes 3 cost estimates for the SCS, consisting of three 200 kg spacecraft launched into a 20,500 km circular, equatorial orbit with a mission lifetime of 5 years. Table 11-37 shows a SCS mission cost estimate using the USCM8 cost model, which includes a cost estimate for both the spacecraft bus and communications payload. The total mission cost is $441.5 M (FY2010) with uncertainty of $55.6 M. This will serve as the SCS traditional large space mission type cost estimate for purposes of comparison with other mission cost models.

Table 11-38 shows the SCS mission cost as estimated using the SSCM. The cost that SSCM yields is $165.7 M total with an uncertainty of $11.3M, including an allocation of $50 M for launching all three spacecraft on a single Falcon 9 launch. This total mission cost is 37.5% of that estimated in Table 11-37 with the USCM8 model. This percentage is fairly close to the previous results for the FireSat II mission, comparing the USCM8 and SSCM model results together. For both FireSat II and SCS examples, SSCM yields a mission cost estimate that is about 1/3 of the mission cost generated by USCM8. Again, this reflects the new type of procurement and spacecraft development and test processes employed in the small satellite arena vs. the much more complex and more costly processes employed traditionally for larger spacecraft

Table 11-39 displays a third cost estimate for the SCS mission utilizing the QuickCost cost model from NASA, showing a total mission cost of $435.8 M with a standard error of $158.3 M. This estimate is fairly close to the USCM8 mission cost from Table 11-37, and may reflect the fact that the QuickCost database does not include many communications satellite spacecraft, if any, as NASA's mission database is primarily scientific spacecraft with science instrument payloads. For the same spacecraft dry mass, a science mission will generally yield a higher cost than a communications satellite would, and so the cost generated by the QuickCost model is understandably higher than what would be expected for a communications spacecraft.

Just as concluded in Sec. 11.4.1 for FireSat II, of the three separate SCS mission cost estimates discussed in this section, the SSCM estimate in Table 11-38 is the

Live Calc

Table 11-37. SCS Space-Ground, and Launch Segment Costs in FY10$K. Cost estimates based on the CERs in Tables 11-8 and 11-9 using the USCM8 Cost Model, which includes a CER for the communications payload. Input Data from SCS Spacecraft Mass budget is from Table 14-26.

Cost Component	Parameter	Value	Units	RDT&E (NRE) Cost (FY10$K)	1st Unit Cost (FY10$K)	2nd & 3rd Unit Cost (FY10$K)	Total Cost (FY10$K)	Std Error ($K)
1.1 Spacecraft Bus								
1.1.1 Structure and Thermal*	mass	56.1	kg	10,164	1,269	2,240	13,674	2,973
1.1.3 ADCS*	mass	26.0	kg	8,421	5,486	9,688	23,595	9,168
1.1.4 Electrical Power System*	mass	34.3	kg	2,206	1,112	1,963	5,281	1,858
1.1.5 Propulsion*	N/A†							
1.1.6 TT&C and Data Handling*	mass	14.6	kg	26,916	2,235	3,946	33,096	5,957
1.1.7 Integration, Assembly, & Test (IA&T)	S/C Bus and P/L NRE Cost	85,406	FY10$K	16,654	10,590	18,700	45,944	16,953
1.1.9 Flight Software‡	source lines of code	22,918	N/A	12,605	0	0	12,605	3,781
Spacecraft Bus Total Cost				76,966	20,692	36,537	134,195	20,821
1.2 Payload								
1.2.1 Comm Payload	payload mass	61.0	kg	37,698	11,529	20,357	69,584	26,761
2. Launch Segment	1 Falcon 9 Lnch	50,000	FY10$K	0	0	50,000	50,000	5,000
4. Program Level	S/C Bus, P/L, & IA&T NRE Cost	102,060	FY10$K	42,253	32,659	57,668	132,580	42,193
5. Launch and Orbital Ops Support (LOOS)		5,850	FY10$K	0	5,850	10,330	16,180	4,854
6. Ground Support Equipment (GSE)	S/C Bus NRE Cost	47,708	FY10$K	16,550	0	0	16,550	6,123
Total Space Seg Cost to Contractor				173,467	64,880	114,562	352,909	
10% Contractor Fee				17,347	6,488	11,456	35,291	
Total Space Segment Cost to Government				190,814	71,368	126,018	388,200	
Total Cost of Deployment							**438,200**	**54,918**

*Spacecraft bus subsystem masses include a fraction of the spacecraft mass margin of 5 kg. † SCS propulsion system is taken into account in the ADCS CER (1.1.3). The 26.0 kg mass value for ADCS mass includes propulsion system HW mass. typical USCM CER for propulsion systems are for reaction control systems and apogee kick motors, not standard spacecraft propulsion systems. ‡ Software cost CER (1.1.9) taken from Table 11-20, unmanned flight CER.

Table 11-37, Fig. 11-8◀, Eq. 11-7◀

Table 11-38. SCS Space, Ground, and Launch Segment Costs in FY10$K. Cost estimates based on the CERs in Table 11-11 using the SSCM Cost Model that includes cost estimates for both the spacecraft bus and payload, program level costs, launch and orbital operations support, and ground support equipment. Input Data from SCS Spacecraft Mass budget is from Table 14-26.

Cost Component	Parameter	Value	Units	RDT&E plus 1st Unit Cost (FY10$K)	2nd and 3rd Unit Cost (FY10$K)	Total Cost (FY10$K)	Std Error ($K)
1.1 Spacecraft Bus							
1.1.1 Structure*	mass	47.8	kg	3,977	7,022	10,999	3,034
1.1.2 Thermal*		8.3	kg	729	1,288	2,017	329
1.1.3 ADCS*	mass	12.5	kg	3,671	6,482	10,154	3,078
1.1.4 Electrical Power System*	mass	34.3	kg	5,611	9,908	15,519	2,517
1.1.5 Propulsion*	spacecraft bus dry mass	131.0	kg	1,492	2,634	4,126	857
1.1.6a TT&C*	mass	8.3	kg	1,455	2,569	4,024	1,740
1.1.6b Command & Data Handling	mass	6.2	kg	1,546	2,730	4,276	2,362
1.1.7 Integration, Assembly, & Test (IA&T)	spacecraft bus total cost	18,481	FY10$K	2,569	4,536	7,105	2,131
1.1.9 Flight Software†	source lines of code	22,918	N/A	12,605	0	12,605	3,781
Spacecraft Bus Total Cost				33,655	37,169	70,825	7,301
1.2 Payload							
1.2.2 Comm Payload	spcrft bus total cost	18,481	FY10$K	7,392	13,053	20,446	6,134
2. Launch Segment	1 Falcon 9 Launch	50,000	FY10$K	0	50,000	50,000	5,000
4. Program Level	spcrft bus total cost	18,481	FY10$K	4,232	7,473	11,705	3,512
5. Launch & Orbital Ops Support (LOOS)	spcrft bus total cost	18,481	FY10$K	1,227	1,991	3,118	935
6. Ground Support Equipment (GSE)	spcrft bus total cost	18,481	FY10$K	1,220	2,154	3,374	1,012
Total Space Segment Cost to Contractor				46,499	59,849	106,348	
10% Contractor Fee				4,650	5,985	10,635	
Total Space Segment Cost to Government				51,149	65,834	116,983	
Total Cost of Deployment						**166,983**	**11,409**

* Spacecraft bus subsystem masses shown include a fraction of the spacecraft mass margin of 5 kg. † Software cost CER (1.1.9) taken from Table 11-20, unmanned flight CER.

Table 11-39. SCS Space, Ground, and Launch Segment Costs in FY10$K. Cost estimates based on the single QuickCost CER in Table 11-12. All SCS inputs are within the QuickCost model ranges of applicability for the various inputs, although at the low end. Input Data from SCS Spacecraft Mass budget is from Table 14-26.

Parameter	Applicable Range	Value	RDT&E plus 1st Unit Cost (FY10$K)	2nd and 3rd Unit Cost (FY10$K)	Total Cost (FY10$K)	Std Error ($K)
Dry Mass of Bus and Payload (kg)	76 to 14,475 kg	192				
Power (LEO BOL, W)	90 to 10,000 W	614				
Data% (Data rate percentile [fraction] relative to state-of-the-art (ATP)	0 to 100%	50%				
Life (Advertised design life, months)	6 to 180 mo	60				
New (% New [fraction], 0.2–0.3 simple mod, 0.3–0.7 extensive mod, 0.7–1.0 New, >1.0 new tech)	20% to 130%	90%	139,489	246,303	385,792	158,175
Planetary (0 = no, 1 = yes)	0 or 1	0				
Year (authority to proceed date in 4 digit calendar year)	1961 to 2025	2012				
InstrComp% (Instrument complexity percentile [fraction], relative to avg. instrument complexity)	0 to 100%	80%				
Team (Team Experience, 1 = unfamiliar, 2 = Mixed, 3 = Normal, 4 = Extensive)	1 to 4	3				
Launch Cost (FY10$K)—Assume Falcon 9 Launch for 3 SCS Spacecraft	1 Launch–$50M (FY10)	50,000			50,000	5,000
Total Mission Cost					**435,792**	**158,254**

Table 11-39, Fig. 11-8◀, Eq. 11-7◀

estimate that should be closest to the actual mission costs, based on the type of missions in the SSCM database and similarity with the SCS mission.

11.4.3 Summary

Table 11-40 summarizes all the cost estimates generated for both FireSat II and SCS, as discussed in Secs. 11.4.1 and 11.4.2. In each case, the SSCM yields a cost estimate that is more consistent with the class of mission for each. The other estimates with USCM8 and QuickCost yield estimates which are too high since the databases of missions for each model are generally larger, more expensive missions with much longer development cycles. Therefore, for the same input parameters, they yield total mission costs which are substantially higher than the SSCM model, which has a database of small missions much more consistent with the FireSat II/SCS mission class. It may even be the case that SSCM is not representing FireSat II or SCS as accurately as the cost estimator would like in terms of their relatively small sizes and very short development cycles. These actually are both on the low end of the mass range for spacecraft in the SSCM database. Carrying out more detailed bottoms-up cost estimates for each mission may yield more accurate mission costs which may be less than the estimates generated with the SSCM.

Table 11-40. Summary of Alternate Mission Cost Estimates for FireSat II and SCS Using Three Cost Models.

Cost Model	FireSat II	SCS
USCM8	\$362.1 ± 39.2 M	\$441.5 ± 55.6 M
SSCM	\$120.5 ± 9.6 M	\$165.7 ± 11.3 M
QuickCost	\$194.3 ± 59.4 M	\$435.8 ± 158.3 M

References

For annotated bibliography of cost estimating, see the book website.

Aerospace Corporation. 1996. *Small Satellite Cost Model (SSCM).* El Segundo, CA: The Aerospace Corp.

AIAA. 2003. "Satellite Mission Operations Best Practice." *AIAA Space Operations and Support Technical Committee (SOSTC).* Apr. 18.

Apgar, H. 2001. "Cost As an Independent Variable (CAIV)—A Process and Methodology." *Economics of Space Conference.* Long Beach, CA: AIAA.

Apgar, H. 2004. "Gaining Approval for Your Parametric Estimating System." *AIAA Space Conference.*

Apgar, H. 2009. "Space System Cost Drivers—A Survey and Assessment." *AIAA Space Conference.* Pasadena, CA: AIAA.

Boehm, B. 2000. *Software Cost Estimation with COCOMO II.* Upper Saddle River, NJ: Prentice Hall.

Boehm, B. 1981. *Software Engineering Economics.* Englewood Cliffs, NJ: Prentice Hall.

Book, S. 2008. "Combining Probabilistic Estimates to Reduce Uncertainty." *NASA Cost Analysis Symposium.* Portland, OR: NASA.

Book, S. 1999. "Why Correlation Matters in Cost Estimating." *32nd DoD Cost Analysis Symposium.* VA: US Dept of Defense.

Burgess, E. 2004. "Time Phasing Methods and Metrics." *Annual DoD Cost Analysis Symposium.* VA: US Dept. of Defense.

DoD. 2005. *Work Breakdown Structures for Defense Material Items,* MIL-HDB-881A, Appendix F: Space Systems.

Fox, B. 2008. *Guidelines & Metrics for Assessing Space System Cost Estimates.* Santa Monica, CA: RAND Corp.

Futron Corporation. 2002. *Space Transportation Costs: Trends in Price per Pound to Orbit 1990-2000.*

Galorath Incorporated. 2011. Website.

Garvey, P. 1999. *Probability Methods for Cost Uncertainty Analysis—A Systems Engineering Perspective.* New York: Marcel Dekker.

Habib-agahi, H. 2010. NASA *Instrument Cost Model (NICM) Version IV.* Pasadena, CA: NASA JPL.

Hamaker, J. 2011. QuickCost—Suite of Space Project Cost Estimation Models. *Proceedings of the Joint 2011 ISPA-SCEA National Conference.* Albuquerque, NM: ISPA-SCEA.

Hanmaker, J. 2008. *TRL Calibrations for NASA Programs.* Wash., DC: NASA

ISPA. 2007. *Parametric Cost Estimating Handbook.* Washington, DC.

JPL. 2009. "TRL Impact on Cost as Estimated for the JIMO Effort." March.

Koelle, D. 2010. *Handbook of Cost Engineering for Space Transportation Systems* (Rev. 3a) with TRANSCOST 8.1. Ottobrunn, Germany.

Larson, W. 2006. *Cost Effective Space Mission Operations, 2nd ed.* NY: McGraw Hill.

Malone, P. 2011. "The Application of TRL Metrics to Existing Cost Predition Models." *IEEE Aerospace Conf.*

NASA. 2008. *Cost Estimating Handbook (CEH).*

PRICE Systems. 1999. *Your Guide to PRICE H.* Mt. Laurel, NJ: PRICE Systems LLC.

SAIC. 2010. NASA—*Air Force Cost Model (NAFCOM).* NAFCOM.

Shishko, R. 2006. "The Application of Architecture Frameworks to Modeling Exploration Operations Costs." *16th Annual INCOSE International Symposium,* Orlando, FL. Jul.

Smoker, R. 2005. *Approach to Use of Selected Acquisition Measurement of TRLs and Associated System Cost Growth.* El Segundo, CA: MCR Federal.

Tecolote Research. 2007. *Air Force Cost Analysis Agency Cost Risk Analysis Handbook.* DC: United States Air Force.

Tecolote Research. 2002. *Unmanned Space Vehicle Cost Model (USMC).* El Segundo, CA: U S Air Force, Space and Missile Systems Center.

Wertz, J. R. and W. J. Larson, eds. 1999. *Space Mission Analysis and Design, 3rd ed.* Hawthorne, CA: Microcosm Press and New York: Springer.

USAF. 2003. *Historical Air Force Construction Cost Handbook. Washington,* DC.

12 Space System Financing and Space Law

12.1 Sources of Space Financing

John M. Jurist, *University of North Dakota*
David Livingston, *The Space Show*

12.1.1 Developing Business Strategies

An accepted rule of thumb in the commercial arena for high risk investments is that they should return at least 18% and preferably 25% annually on invested capital [Jurist et al. 2005]. This means that an established investor will expect his or her investment to increase in value by that amount every year. This return must be built into any plan to attract investment capital as a means of financing a space business. Otherwise, the potential investment is not attractive.

Developing a business strategy is simple in concept but often difficult in its execution. The strategy must be converted into a plan to make money for investors in the business. That business plan is normally used to attract investment and is generally the initial iteration of a continuously evolving plan to implement the stated strategy.

The plan should delineate how to get from the current status quo to the desired end state in a step by step fashion. It must be clear and readily understood by management and potential investors. The reader of such a plan should be able to use it to visualize the day to day activities of the management team members. Details of creating an effective business plan are beyond the scope of this textbook.

12.1.2 Finance Source Summary

The next sections describe the various following sources and methods of funding, as well as associated considerations that may be relevant to space finance. They are summarized in the adjacent boxed section:

Potential Sources of Finance

Government
- Procurement
- Contracted R&D
- Small Business Innovation Research (SBIR)
- Small Business Administration (SBA) Loans
- Grants

Corporate
- Stock
- Funding with income stream
- Debt financing
- Public/private partnership financing
- Venture capital (VC)
  - Primarily for startups
  - Return expected within short time
  - Active participation

Angel Investors
- Individuals
- Family, friends, and fools (FFF)
- Similar to venture capital

Convertible Instruments and Debentures

Non-Profits
- Limited opportunities
- Grants

Prizes

12.1.3 Government

The US government is a major source of space funding either directly or indirectly. Governmental funding is typically negotiated in a procurement contract. This is an agreement between the government and a supplier or vendor to provide goods or services in exchange for government money. Multiple mechanisms used in these contracts include fixed price, cost plus a fixed fee, and cost plus a fixed percentage contract. Various hybrid arrangements can also be created. Contracted R&D

services are frequently sought by the US government. Basically, a statement of work to be performed, a budget, a reporting arrangement, and various performance and payment milestones to monitor progress are negotiated between the supplier and the funding agency and, depending on budget appropriations consistent with congressional actions, may be funded. Contracted R&D can also be performed by a subcontractor to a larger corporation.

The Office of Technology within the *Small Business Administration (SBA)* administers the Small Business Innovation Research (SBIR) Program and the Small Business Technology Transfer Research (STTR) Program. SBA does not directly fund projects funded under these programs.

The *Small Business Innovation Research (SBIR)* program is a set-aside program (2.5% of a government agency's extramural budget) for domestic small business concerns to engage in research and development that can be potentially commercialized or exploited by commercial interests as an addition to the US economy. If those ideas meet the research and research and development needs of the specific government agency, they may be funded. SBIR is a competitive 3-phase award system which provides qualified small business concerns with opportunities to propose innovative ideas:

- Phase I is a feasibility study to evaluate the scientific and technical merit of an idea. Awards are for up to six months and up to $150,000
- Phase II expands on the Phase I results and further pursues the development of the idea. Awards are for up to 2 years and up to $1,000,000
- Phase III is for the commercialization of the results of Phase II and requires the use of private sector or non-SBIR federal funding. Although US government agencies cannot fund Phase III SBIR projects, they may provide technical assistance

A small business is defined as a for-profit business located within the US and operating primarily within the US with no more than 500 employees. Non-profits are not eligible. The business must be owned and controlled by one or more US citizens or permanent resident aliens in the US. It may be an individual proprietorship, partnership, limited liability company, corporation, joint venture, association, trust, or cooperative. Joint ventures can have no more than 49% participation by foreign business entities.

A significant requirement is that the principal researcher's primary employment must be with the small business during the duration of the project. Innovations to be developed under SBIR cannot be patented or have patents pending. Part of an SBIR award may be subcontracted:

- For Phase I, a minimum of 2/3 of the research and analytical effort must be performed by the proposing firm
- For Phase II, a minimum of 1/2 of the research and analytical effort must be performed by the proposing firm

Small Business Technology Transfer Research (STTR) is different in that it specifically involves partnership of ideas and technologies between a for-profit business and a non-profit organization. All federal agencies with annual extramural R&D budgets exceeding $1 billion devote 0.3% of their extramural R&D budgets to STTR. Extramural R&D is that funded by a government agency but performed by the grantee—usually an academic or commercial organization. Projects funded under the STTR program consist of 3 phases:

- Phase I is a feasibility study that determines the scientific, technical, and commercial merit and feasibility of a selected concept. Phase I projects are competitively selected from proposals submitted against solicitations. Each solicitation contains topics seeking specific solutions to stated Federal government needs. The Phase I selection process is highly competitive; with perhaps 10% of submitted Phase I proposals receiving awards
- Phase II represents a major research and development effort, culminating in a well defined deliverable prototype—a technology, product, or service. The Phase II selection process is also highly competitive. Only successful Phase I contractors may submit Phase II proposals as there are no separate Phase II solicitations
- In Phase III, the small business or research institution is expected to obtain funding from the private sector and/or non-STTR government sources to develop the prototype into a viable product or service for sale in the government or private sector

The STTR program is open to any organized team consisting of a small business and a research institution. The goal is expansion of the public/private sector partnership to include joint venture opportunities for small business and the nation's premier non-profit research institutions by funding meritorious joint proposals. The most important role of STTR is to foster the innovation necessary to meet the scientific and technological challenges facing the US. The research institution may be any US non-profit research institution, federally funded research and development center, university, or college. The small business must perform at least 40% of the Phase I and Phase II work. The research institution must perform at least 30% of the Phase I and Phase II work. Up to 30% of the work may be subcontracted. The principal investigator must be primarily employed with either the small business or the research institution for the Phase I and II efforts. The Department of Defense generally issues 2 STTR solicitations each year.

The SBA oversees a wide variety of programs and services intended to support small businesses in addition to those described above.

The SBA does not fund grants to start or expand small businesses, but does offer a variety of loan programs. SBA grants are instead intended to expand or strengthen organizations that provide small business management, technical, or financial assistance and are usually awarded to state and local governments, intermediary lending institutions, and non-profit organizations. Because the conventional commercial loan market may not offer many small businesses the capital access needed to grow and remain strong, SBA manages multiple financial programs for small businesses. These include SBA-backed loans and government contracting opportunities. Additionally, SBA offers disaster assistance and a wide variety of training programs.

12.1.4 Corporate

Corporate funding allows a variety of approaches with various advantages and disadvantages. The advantages and disadvantages for R&D funding may differ from those for other purposes.

A corporation can issue stock at a reasonable market value. Stock purchases do not have to be paid back by the company like loans, but the buyers expect a return—either as dividends (money paid back to investors from corporate earnings) or as capital gains (increased value of stock over time). Issuance of public stock is regulated by the Securities and Exchange Commission (SEC) and state corporation commissions. The issuance of private stock for closely-held corporations is governed by a series of SEC and state regulations specific to private stock investments at both the federal and the state level. A private stock offering may need to qualify in every state involved in the business, serving as residences for potential investors, or where the offer is made. How the corporation is actually structured may also depend on which state will serve as the corporate home since states have differing rules, taxes and fees, often based on the number of outstanding shares and the classification of those shares.

Stock can come in the form of common stock, preferred stock, warrants, and even convertible preferred stock. Founders and key corporate employees can take advantage of Letter Stock, which is not registered and cannot be sold or transferred until it is registered. Registering stock is complicated and can happen only if certain other conditions exist. Rather than defining all the types and classifications of stock, it suffices to state that all forms of stock represent a fractional share in the company rather than debt. The equity represented by stock is at risk if the company fails. If the stock is classified as preferred or guaranteed, it has some asset protection behind it, mainly for dividend payments. It would have a slightly preferred status over common stock in a bankruptcy liquidation of the corporation

Corporate R&D can potentially be funded out of an internal revenue stream. However, this approach must compete with other potential uses of the revenues, such as paying off outstanding loans or paying shareholder dividends.

A corporation with adequate credit can simply borrow the money needed to finance a space project. Traditional loan sources frequently require securing the loan with corporate assets, or, in the case of smaller closely held corporations, personal guarantees of the shareholders. Unlike a stock issue, loans must be paid back. Principal amounts are carried as liabilities for the term of the loan and interest payments are treated as expenses. Generally, principal repayments are made out of pretax dollars.

Numerous combinations of public and private financing sources and mechanisms exist. They can be difficult to negotiate—especially if closely held corporations are involved.

Venture capitalists (VCs) exist to fund smaller companies in order to realize large gains as companies in which they invest grow and profit. Although specific conditions of investment vary, venture capitalists usually expect returns of at least 20% annually on their investments. Many small startup companies attempt to acquire funding for expansion from a VC source. A small company will assume that it can readily access this capital pool only if the corporate principals do not understand opportunity cost and the necessary foundation of venture capitalism. While VC pros may take financial positions in companies that they might not normally consider, a candidate space company must still face competition from an extremely large pool of competitive terrestrial opportunities. Furthermore, terrestrial investment opportunities have a long and established history of working with the VC industry. Space companies do not. Space projects generally take longer than the time horizon of a typical VC. That VC usually expects significant returns (18%/yr–25%/yr) on his or her investment within a 2–5 year time frame.

There is a high potential price to pay when accepting VC money and support. If things do not follow the business plan, or they head south, company managers may have their lives made miserable by the active involvement of the VC. This may even lead to the forced break up of the company. When accepting VC money and support, company management must willingly allow the participation of outside team members, a change in the company vision, and VC representation on the board of directors. In extreme circumstances, the company must accept replacement of management and the board of directors as well as other restrictive and possibly dramatic changes. How many NewSpace company management teams are open to VC management influence and takeover if the company does not perform as promised? How many management teams of space companies understand the true scarcity of capital due to lucrative alternative investments (opportunity costs) and otherwise competitive market forces among terrestrial business ventures competing for the same investment dollars? How many management teams really understand that it is not usually about the rocket science or space objective, rather it is mostly about the return on investment (ROI), payback period, risk assessment for both business and political risks, and internal rates of return (IRR)? These terms are defined in Sec. 12.2.

To focus on space and space objectives rather than the fundamentals that make a business venture attractive for capital acquisition is to delay NewSpace industrial development. Although wealthy players and benefactors are important, a handful of them with their private investments do not constitute an industrial development program.

Angel investors generally have a personal interest in the goals of the candidate company that transcends simply maximizing investment returns. They generally want to participate in the early formation and growth of a startup. In a NewSpace company, the typical angel is a "space cadet"—often times with more enthusiasm than sound business judgment. Angel investors often seek to place their funds in companies with a high "coolness factor" in order to gain bragging rights. Yet they expect eventual returns on their investments unless they are completely ego-driven. A typical example of the latter might be the owner of sports teams who earned his or her fortune in other venues. In a sense, angels are similar to VCs by typically wanting an eventual return, but they differ in their willingness to accept longer time horizons before seeing returns.

Often corporate startups, whether space-related or otherwise, begin with an individual. That individual frequently has significant technical training and a bright idea but often lacks business experience or understanding of the intricacies of running a new and growing business. Failure rates of these startups are correspondingly high.

Traditional funding sources first sought by an individual entrepreneur who lacks the means of financing his or her company from personal funds or personally guaranteed credit lines are from family, friends, and fools (FFF). After that, "outside investors" are commonly sought.

Convertible instruments can be used for corporate funding. One of several forms is the convertible loan, in which a funding source puts money into a company to fund a project. That money is treated contractually as a loan that can be converted into stock at some future date and at a negotiated price or simply treated as a loan depending on circumstances. Those circumstances must be spelled out in detail in the instrument documentation and agreed upon by all parties. In the US, a debenture is an unsecured corporate bond. Other countries may treat them differently. A debenture is a medium or long term debt incurred by borrowing money. In legal terms, a debenture is the document that creates and describes the debt. Debentures are usually transferable by the holder, who has no voting rights. Interest paid to debenture holders is charged against corporate profits (pre-tax dollars) rather than being treated as a deductable expense in the company's financial statements.

Non-profit corporations and foundations are treated differently than typical for-profit corporations by the government. Generally, they must have a charitable purpose or a charter to improve society in some sense. They frequently fund R&D for projects that are congruent with their specific societal interests.

Opportunities for standard for-profit companies to obtain funding from non-profits are very limited because of tax laws that limit the non-profit's ability to engage in businesses that are operated for profit.

Project funding from non-profits generally are in the form of grants. The non-profits or foundations generally require an application that explains the nature of the intended project, the methodology to be used, the goals of the project, plans for reporting progress, and a budget. If approved and funded, money is transferred to the grantee and the project can begin.

Ever since the Ansari X-Prize was offered and won by Scaled Composites of Mojave, California for creating SpaceShipOne and flying it to apogees of over 100 km under specified conditions, prizes seem to be proliferating in the NewSpace arena. They can be offered by private non-profits, (as was the X-Prize) by a foundation, or they can be offered by governmental agencies, such as NASA's Lunar Lander Challenge. This contest was redesignated the Northrop-Grumman Lunar Lander Challenge in deference to that corporation's partial sponsorship of the prizes. The NASA Office of the Chief Technologist has extended the Lunar Landing Challenge concept by issuing a set of "Centennial Challenges" with associated prizes. As a general rule, the prizes are offered to the first team (or first few teams) that succeed at some difficult task while complying with a specified set of preconditions. Recently, Masten Space Company of Mojave won the Lunar Lander Challenge. Prizes are not usually cost effective for the winner and are certainly not cost effective for the losers. The $10 million Ansari X-Prize reportedly cost $30 to 40 million to win. Winning is therefore more about ego-feeding and prestige than money, although winning a prize may increase a small company's attractiveness to potential angel investors.

12.2 GAAP, Amortization, and Return on Investment (ROI)

John M. Jurist, ***University of North Dakota***
David Livingston, ***The Space Show***

12.2.1 Useful Parameters and Terms

General Accepted Accounting Practices (GAAP)

Private sector business accounting follows a set of rules that control and govern how corporate financial reports are made. The rules are set by the Financial Accounting Standards Board (FASB) [2010] and are recognized by both the Securities and Exchange Commission (SEC) and the American Institute of Certified Public Accountants (CPAs). These organizations can and do vary in accounting rules depending on the type of business. Special accounting rules may apply that are unique to a specific industry. These rules exist because financial activity can be reported in a way that can potentially impact the bottom line of a company, its stock value, and its business operations by misleading the person reviewing the accounting statement. The rules are intended to minimize the potential for being misled.

The accounting rules are detailed in the GAAP [GASB, 2010]. This term has a unique meaning among accounting, business and auditing professionals. Frequently a financial report contains a professional opinion about the financial health of the company being reported on or being audited. The American Institute of CPAs' Code of Professional Conduct does not allow its members to provide an opinion on the financial health of a company unless the report meets GAAP. A corporate annual audit report or audited financial statement frequently contains a statement such as:

> **In our opinion, the financial statements referred to above present fairly, in all material respects, the consolidated financial position of ABC Company as of December 31, 2010 and the changes in their net assets and their cash flows for the year then ended are in conformity with accounting principles generally accepted in the United States of America.**

A company's accountants and auditors must be able to provide this "clean" statement in order to accurately reflect the financial health of the company for the reporting period in question. It is important to note that financial statements, accounting and audit rules may differ in different foreign countries, even if the parent corporation is an American company.

While management is not expected to know all the detailed accounting rules that are in play for the company and its industry sector, management must know that outside professional and legal rules govern the financial conduct and reporting for the company.

Engineers and other specialists within the company do not work in a vacuum sheltered from these rules and principles. It is possible, for example, that an engineering decision may need to be made based on how the consequence of the decision is financially reported by the company. Engineers and specialists should have some familiarity with the broad overlay of GAAP.

The rules for non-profit corporations and for government accounting related to reporting grants and contract work differ somewhat from GAAP. Relevant staff members may need to become familiar with more specialized accounting rules in addition to GAPP including rules that may affect foreign subsidiaries or operations.

GAAP rules allow uniform reporting of corporate financial conditions. Analytical comparisons of different entities require the use of some terms, tools, and methodologies that are also used by corporate management in fulfilling their duties. Several of these are discussed below.

Interest

Interest is the value of money expressed in percentage terms over time. If one invests a certain amount of cash and the investment is worth more cash at some later date, the difference is interest. With a loan, an individual is expected to pay interest back to the lender along with the original amount of the loan (principal). If a bank savings account pays interest of 3%/yr, a dollar placed into that account today will be worth $1.03 in 1 yr.

Dividends

Dividends are funds paid to investors in a corporation out of corporate profits. They are usually evaluated by investors in percentage terms relative to the original amount invested or as specified cash amounts per share of stock owned. The US tax code occasionally treats dividend income differently from interest income.

Capital Gains

If a company is profitable, some of the profits are paid to the US and state governments as corporate income taxes. Other portions of the profits may be paid to investors as dividends or to retire debts. If some of the profits are retained by the company, the company increases in value. That value is reflected by the potential sale of shares of stock for a higher price than their original purchase price. The difference in purchase price and sales price of stock is a *capital gain*. If the stock has been held for a long period of time, the gain is a long-term gain. If the stock was bought and sold over a short period of time, the gain is a short-term gain. The US tax code treats long-term capital gains differently from short-term capital gains at various times and defines long and short term differently according to the whims of the US Congress.

Payback Time

A simple way to evaluate a potential investment is to determine how long it takes to get money back from investment revenues. This is called the payback method. For example, if a company invests $1,000,000 and it takes 5 years to get it back, the payback is $200,000/yr. After 5 years, any additional returns shift to profit on the investment. In this example, management must decide if getting all the invested money back in 5 years is acceptable. The payback method ignores inflation, imputed interest, or the decreased value of money as time passes. Put another way, payback time ignores the time value of money impacting cash flow and investment return. It also ignores risk, and it ignores accounting rules that may prevent the complete classification of cash flows from the project as being treated as a return of the investment principal.

When value of an investment over time is considered, the concept of time value of money becomes compelling. The basic concept behind the time value of money is a proposition: "Would you rather have a dollar today or a dollar 10 years from today?" The rational choice is to take the dollar today because the real value of a dollar in 10 years is unknown and probably reduced given inflation. Next, what would the effective interest rate have to be to make the amount 10 years from now equivalent in value to the dollar today? This is discussed in detail in the following sections.

Time value oriented investment tools are far more useful than calculations of simple payback time. Nevertheless, the payback method has its use, particularly for space investments because many of them are very long term. This is especially significant when comparing potential space investments to other terrestrial investment opportunities of similar risk. For example, knowing that you will not get your money back on an investment for 10 years, assuming the investment goes according to plan, tells you right away that you are engaged in something long term. If you are not prepared to invest and wait for your return over that period of time, you would typically not go any further in the analysis of that particular investment opportunity. Using the simple payback method is a very useful first step in evaluating the basics of any investment project or venture, but more sophisticated methods are used for those projects or ventures that pass the payback time test.

Net Present Value (NPV)

A commonly used analytical tool is NPV. NPV is based on a very simple concept: How much money does it take today (present value) to be equal to a specified amount at some time in the future (future value) if it were returning a specific rate of interest from now until that future date? That interest rate is called the discount rate and is the cost of money. NPV allows the measurement of a time series of cash flows in terms of the present value of the investment at an accepted discount rate.

Present value is defined by the following formula:

$$PV = FV / (1+i)^t \tag{12-1}$$

In this formula, FV is the value of some cash in some future year or future value, i is the discount rate or effective interest rate, and t is the number of years between now and the specified future year. Restating this formula for FV will yield the future value of a current asset PV invested at an annual interest rate of i for t years. This formula is commonly used to show returns on savings accounts offered by banks. Interest rates may be fixed by contract as they often are in savings accounts, or they may fluctuate according to financial market conditions.

For example, if a person has a savings account that contractually pays interest at 3%/year and wants to have \$10,000 in the account in 10 years, the amount that is required to be put into the account today (PV) is $\$10{,}000/(1.0+0.03)^{10}$ or \$7,440.94.

In terms of a simple individual savings account, future value defines how money saved today will grow over time at a known return. In business terms, Net Present Value or NPV is the difference in the present value of future incomes less future expenses as applied to specific investments or projects.

There are several ways to calculate NPV, but a common formula is:

$$NPV = \sum_{t=1}^{Total\ years} \frac{R_t}{(1+i)^t} \tag{12-2}$$

Table 12-0, Fig. 12-0, Eq. 12-2

In this formula, R_t is the net cash flow (revenues less expenses) in some single future year, i is the discount rate or effective interest rate, and t is the number of years between now and each specified future year. The total NPV is the sum of the present values calculated over all years under consideration.

Assigning an appropriate discount rate or cost of money is critical. NPV shows the value for future cash flows discounted back to present value using the cost of capital or some other parameter that represents the minimum acceptable return for the project or investment. NPV includes an assessment of risk built into discount rate. The riskier the venture, the more heavily the project is likely to be discounted, thus suggesting that larger returns are required in order to compensate for the risk.

Internal Rate of Return (IRR)

Internal Rate of Return or IRR is another common investment analysis tool. IRR shows the sum of the NPVs of all the cash flows over all years related to the proposed investment or project as zero based on a defined discount rate. IRR is used to select projects that have returns in excess of the cost of capital. When using IRR, one usually incorporates an anticipated cost of capital rather than some other discount rate. Risk is also factored into the discount rate. If the venture is extremely risky, the cost of capital will be much higher than were the investment less risky. Generally, in an investment, there is an initial outflow of money in the first year that is to be offset by the future net inflows discounted to the present year. The IRR is the effective interest or discount rate such that the present values of the outflows and the inflows, including capital, add up algebraically to zero.

The concept of IRR can be illustrated by a simple example. Assume a project to develop a sounding rocket will cost \$10,000,000 today and the discount rate or cost of money is 5%/yr for this prospective project. Then, assume that the net sales (revenues from sales less manufacturing and sales costs) are expected to be \$1,500,000/yr for 3 years, starting in the 2nd year, and \$2,000,000/yr for the rest of the 9 year project.

Table 12-1 shows the projected annual cash flows over the 9 year duration of the project, the PV of each annual cash flow at the 5%/year discount rate, and the NPV of each cash flow at the IRR of 8.503%/yr.

The initial cash outlay is returned in the 7th year of the project (payback time). The total net return on the project over its lifetime is \$4.5 million. The anticipated and significant effects of time are shown in the Present Value column. Assuming that the 5% discount rate approximates the market cost of money over the 9 year duration of the project, investing the \$10 million would return, if all goes well, a net gain of \$1,564,802 in beginning year dollars. According to the last column in the table, the total NPV over all years of the project is zeroed out at a discount rate of just over 8.5%. Therefore, the contemplated project is expected to return an IRR of a bit over 8.5% assuming accurate cash flow calculations. At this coarse level of analysis, the proposed project appears to

Table 12-1. Illustrative Sounding Rocket Project Cash flow Analysis.

Discount	0.05	per year	
IRR	0.085033816	per year	
Year	*Cash Flow*	*Present Value (PV)*	*PV at IRR*
1	$ (10,000,000)	$ (10,000,000)	$ (10,000,000)
2	$ 1,500,000	$ 1,428,571	$ 1,382,445
3	$ 1,500,000	$ 1,360,544	$ 1,274,104
4	$ 1,500,000	$ 1,295,756	$ 1,174,252
5	$ 2,000,000	$ 1,645,405	$ 1,442,969
6	$ 2,000,000	$ 1,567,052	$ 1,329,884
7	$ 2,000,000	$ 1,492,431	$ 1,225,661
8	$ 2,000,000	$ 1,421,363	$ 1,129,606
9	$ 2,000,000	$ 1,353,679	$ 1,041,079
Totals	$ 4,500,000	$ 1,564,802	$ 0

be a good deal since the IRR is greater than the discount rate unless one can find a better use for the $10 million. That is, an alternative with a higher IRR. Deliberately forgoing a project with a higher IRR for one with a lower IRR causes an *opportunity cost* to be incurred.

Return on Investment (ROI)

ROI is the annualized return or earnings expressed as a percentage of the total investment. For a simple savings account, ROI would be the stated interest rate to be paid on the account (less fees charged to the account, if any). Several tools are available to determine the value of a series of cash flows for a business. This facilitates evaluation of a potential investment and the likely ROI. Using the various ROI tools also allows comparison of likely ROI to the cost of money.

Earnings Before Interest and Taxes (EBIT)

EBIT allows analysis of profitability before applying interest and tax expenses to the gross earnings. Tax rates, accounting rules, and even interest earned can skew the net earnings number, so examining gross earnings before these expenses are taken out allows measurement of a company's profitability at a gross level. Earnings are not generally tied to one particular investment or project, but are totaled across the entire company. As an evaluation tool, EBIT facilitates comparison of relative profitability and efficiency despite variation in the tax, financial, and accounting structures of different companies.

12.2.2 Government Accounting

Standards for financial reporting and accounting for government contracts and grants is a highly specialized subset of GAAP. There is a formally defined set of Federal Financial Accounting Standards approved by the Government Accounting Standards Board [GASB, 2010].

12.2.3 Effects of Program Lifetime

Program lifetime can be altered with sometimes profound effects on total budgets. A powerful method of dealing with the interactions between program lifetime and projected cost is discussed below.

Critical Path Analysis and Program Evaluation and Review Technique (PERT) are management methodologies that formalize decision making in complex projects. PERT was first used during the late 1950s in the development of the Polaris submarine launched ballistic missile [Durrwachter, 2010].

In Fig. 12-1, a simplified flowchart for a hypothetical launch vehicle project is shown. The initial step of providing preliminary funding from internal sources is followed by 3 independent steps that can be performed in parallel:

- Vehicle Characterization
- Market Analysis
- Study Regulatory Process

According to PERT rules and the structure of the flowchart, all 3 of these steps must be completed before the following step of Cost Analysis can be started. Assume that the 3 tasks will require 2 wks, 12 wks, and 4 wks to complete, respectively. The time-limiting step is Market Analysis at 12 wks. Vehicle Characterization consumes 2 wks and has a slack of up to 10 wks and Study Regulatory Process has a slack of up to 8 wks without delaying the project under this scenario. The critical path in any project is the longest possible continuous pathway from the beginning of a project to its completion. It defines the total calendar time required for the project. Time delays along the critical path will delay project completion. The critical path is the longest parallel path (Market Analysis) in this simplified illustration.

Table 12-1, Fig. 12-0, Eq. 12-2◀

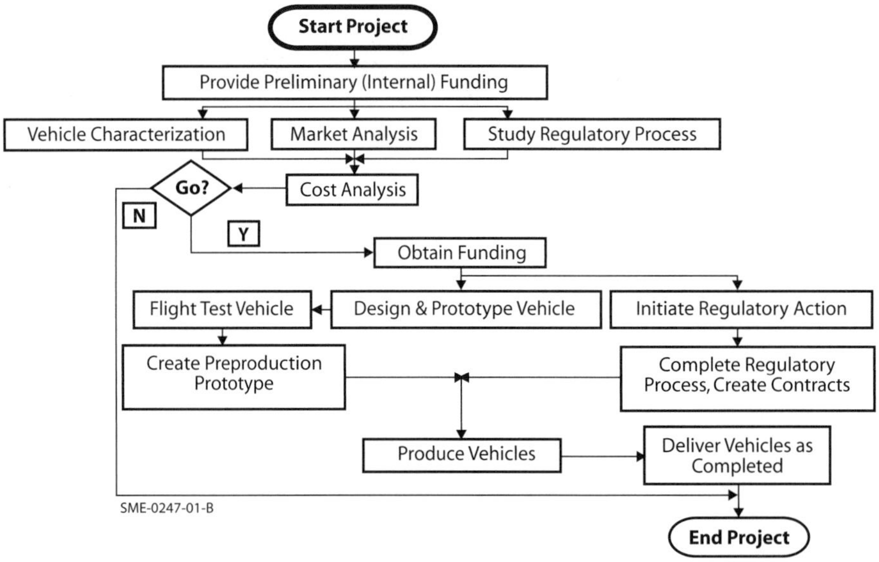

Fig. 12-1. Illustrative PERT Chart.

If resource limitations are responsible for the 12 wk requirement for the Market Analysis, managers could potentially divert resources from the two shorter tasks to reduce the time required for the time-critical Market Analysis and also consume some of the slack in the other 2 tasks. Of course, that assumes that resources can be interchanged freely and that adding additional resources reduces the time required to complete a task.

For each task or step, a minimum or optimistic, maximum or pessimistic, and most likely (best estimate) time and cost are specified for completion of that task or step. Frequently, 10th, 50th, and 90th percentile times and costs are estimated and used for each task or step. If the optimistic time is defined as the 10th percentile time, the probability of completing the project step within that time is 10%. If the pessimistic time is defined as the 90th percentile time, the probability of completing the project step within that time is 90%. The expected time (or cost) is given by the formula:

$$T_e = \left(T_o + 4 \times T_b + T_p\right) / 6 \tag{12-3}$$

In this formula, T_e is the expected time, T_o is the optimistic time, T_b is the best estimate or most likely time, and T_p is the pessimistic time for a given task. Filler steps (slack) can be used as dummy tasks for clarity of the overall process. Slack is the time that a task can be delayed without causing a delay in overall project completion. Tasks or steps can be redefined with experience or as initially unanticipated problems arise. This is where the power of PERT becomes obvious. Software, such as Microsoft's Project, is available and is especially valuable for simplifying the analysis tasks or for dynamic reanalysis of changing conditions associated with the project. PERT is ideally suited for management of complex one time projects—especially if the project must be dynamic in that multiple changes are expected during the lifetime of the project. This property makes PERT useful for managing complex research and development projects. PERT can also monitor project compliance with schedules as part of the management or compliance monitoring process.

If a project has a "drop dead date," PERT can be used to examine the effects of changing tasks, changing their order, or running them in parallel on the final completion date. Dollars can be traded for time with some tasks. In other words, throwing money at a project by paying overtime or adding personnel can accelerate completion of some specific tasks. However, this is not always the case. Nine women cannot make a baby in one month. Delaying or stretching out a project can increase total project costs as well. Koelle [2007] developed an empirical relationship between relative cost and deviation (either acceleration or stretch-out) from the optimal time schedule in the aerospace industry. This is illustrated in Fig. 12-2.

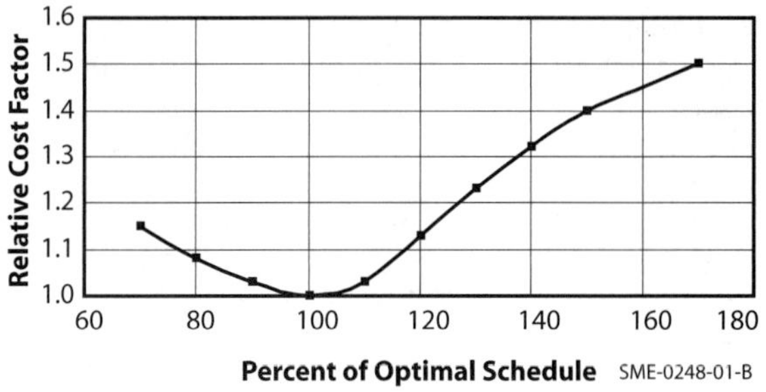

Fig. 12-2. US Aerospace Industry Cost Trends Versus Schedule Duration [Koelle, 2007].

PERT can be used to meet fixed project costs by iteratively refining or redefining tasks and their associated costs. With increasing experience, repetitive tasks, including

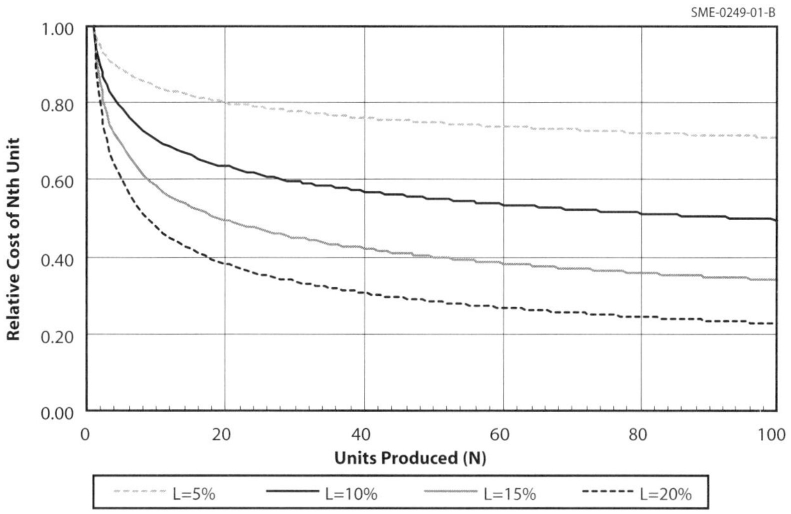

Fig. 12-3. Cost of Producing the nth Unit as a Function of Number of Units Produced and Learning Factor.

production, can gradually become more efficient. Empirical observations have shown that associated production efforts, as quantified by the surrogates of cost, man hours, or both, decrease by approximately constant percentages for each doubling of production. A learning or experience curve can frequently be applied to production costs of automobiles or other non space-related products, aircraft, or spacecraft. In addition, it can even be applied to such things as, for example, maintenance hours per flight hour of aircraft.

For aerospace production, the learning factor typically reduces production costs by 10%–15% for each doubling. If a learning factor of 12% is used, a production run of 6 vehicles should cost 4.93 times the cost of producing the 1st vehicle (TFU).

In simplistic terms, one of the several formulations of the learning or experience curve is described by the following power law equation:

$$C_n = C_1 \left(1.0 - L/100\%\right)^{\log n/\log 2} \qquad (12\text{-}4)$$

Here, C_n is the cost or labor needed to produce the nth unit and C_1 is the cost of producing the first unit (usually described as TFU). L is the learning factor in percent.

Figure 12-3 illustrates the cost of units produced relative to that of the TFU for learning factors ranging from 5% to 20%. Underlying assumptions in the figure are that all units are identical and produced without major changes in production equipment or technology. These factors and major unit redesigns can produce discontinuities in the cost versus production number curves. Readers interested in more details should consult the relevant literature.

Six Sigma is another popular management tool that has been in use since the early 1980s. It is based on statistical tools and people specifically trained in the method to gain expertise in solving organizational problems. Companies interested in the Six Sigma approach have their staff trained and certified with sophisticated and progressive certification levels. Six Sigma projects follow specific paths with specific protocols.

Figure 12-4 illustrates the historical Consumer Price Index compiled by the US Bureau of Labor Statistics. Comparison of this graph with Fig 1-14 shows that aerospace industry labor costs inflated more than consumer prices in the US—particularly in the mid-1970s.

Interest accounts for 2 factors: The time cost of money as reflected by currency inflation and the risk associated with promises of future payment. NPV methodology has been discussed in terms of a discount rate or effective interest rate. That rate must compensate for inflation (decreased value of money with time) and also for perceived risk of a default in payment. Acceptable cash in hand is worth more than a promise of cash to be delivered in the future because events may transpire to prevent delivery on that promise.

Projects involving development of a product such as a launch vehicle, especially if funded by governmental sources, have a significant probability of being cancelled. Cancellation of such projects is usually supported by a contract clause allowing termination "for the convenience of the US government." That "convenience" may result from the vendor failing to meet project milestones or from changing procurement needs, budgetary changes imposed by Congress, or other non-technical factors. Financial planning for a specific project, whether involving space or not, should include compensation for the risk of cancellation. That risk may be addressed by building it into the pricing structure or it may be addressed explicitly by incorporation of cancellation terms into the project contract. Cancellation terms are especially important in government contracting because funding is subject to the whims of congressional appropriations—and the US Congress is sometimes perceived as being fickle. Cancellation can damage a contractor as it ripples into risks of dispersion of experienced design

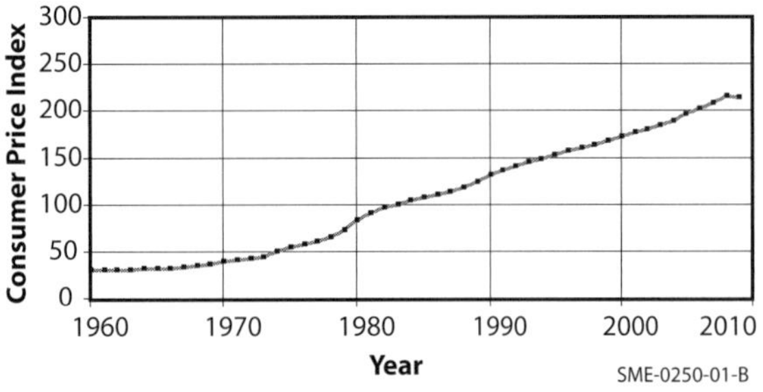

Fig. 12-4. Consumer Price Index Trend From 1960 Forward. Modified from CPI [US Bureau of Labor Statistics, 2010].

and fabrication teams, effects on plant size, specialized capital equipment acquisition, and assorted contractual agreements.

Projects may fail, and some perception of risk of failure should be considered in financial planning. Risk of project failure for technical reasons has been significant in an historic sense. Sometimes a project is initiated which is eventually seen as "a bridge too far."

12.2.4 Role of Insurance

Insurance is a way of protecting against relatively low or medium probability risks of unforeseen events with large economic consequences. In the space industry, insurance is needed by the launch provider in case of a catastrophic failure resulting in loss of payload, damage to uninvolved parties, or failure to properly place the payload. The payload provider needs insurance in case of a launch failure. The end customer also needs insurance against any failures to have a functional payload available for use. In the space industry, insurance is frequently offered as a percentage of the launch cost—often in the 8%–10% range.

Space launches involve three components of insurance. Those components are intended to provide protection against loss of payload, loss of vehicle, and liability coverage for potential damage to third parties from, for example, falling debris. Computation of insurance costs is extremely complex and dependent on specific circumstances. Regardless of how insurance is priced for the customer, costs are obtained by generally following an analysis similar to that described below. Specifics related to past events (actuarial data) are considered to be proprietary by insurance companies. The following discussion largely relates to liability coverage, but also discusses self insurance to cover potential loss of vehicle.

An insurance premium component typically consists of the product of three factors for each specified risk of loss:

- An underwriting multiplier to provide revenue to the insurer
- A risk factor, and
- The *Maximum Probable Economic Loss (MPL)* associated with the specified failure

These premium calculations are summed over each identified risk when there are multiple risks associated with a given activity.

The underwriting multiplier is typically 3. It can be reduced by up to 25% by auctioning to the lowest cost bidder [Jurist et al., 2005]. Therefore, an auction or bidding process could potentially reduce the multiplier to 2.25.

The risk factor is typically given by $(1+f)/(1+s)$, where f is the number of losses or failures and s is the number of successful events.

If 100 launches of a given vehicle results in 4 failures ($f=4$) and 96 successes ($s=96$), then the risk factor is $(1+4)/(1+96)$, or 0.0515. Larger programs with lower failure rates have lower risk factors. With increased program size, the risk factor approaches the ratio of failures to successes, and with decreased program size, the risk factor increases to reflect lack of experience. If the same statistical failure rate of 4 failures in 100 attempts holds for a program of 1,000 launches, the larger program will have 40 failures and 960 successes. In this case, the risk factor will be reduced from 0.0515 to 0.0427. As the program size increases without bound to even more launches, the risk factor will approach 0.0417. The way to minimize the risk factor is to design the launch program for maximum launch reliability and maximize the number of launches.

Assuming a total of 5 successful test and demonstration flights of a new launcher with zero losses as it enters commercial service, the risk factor is initially $(1+0)/(1+5)$, or 0.167. If there are two failures during the 5 test and demonstration flights, the risk factor for insurance purposes will be $(1+2)/(1+3)$, or 0.750. The value is greater than 1 if there are more failures than successes. The risk factor can be recalculated based on accumulated experience every time the insurance contract is renewed. If additional experience extends the string of successes, insurance premiums should be appropriately reduced.

The maximum probable third party damage or economic loss with a catastrophic failure is related to the energy dissipated in the loss event and to the value of damaged properties in the failure event debris field. This loss depends on vehicle mass, velocity, and location at the time of the failure. Examples of MPL will be given later.

One can minimize MPL by:

- Assuring that the vehicle trajectory does not overfly valuable properties (i.e., launch over uninhabited areas),
- Minimizing vehicle mass from launch to mission completion, and
- Minimizing potential velocity of the failed vehicle (or its fragments)

Minimizing potential velocity of vehicle fragments has been accomplished historically by command destruct mechanisms that blow the failing vehicle into small pieces so that air drag effectively decelerates the fragments and reduces their impact kinetic energy. Positive control of the vehicle and defaulting to an automatic abort mode if vehicle communications are lost will also reduce the potential damage to uninvolved parties.

Launch vehicles, including RLVs, can be initially tested with reduced propellant loads to reduce vehicle mass and maximum burnout velocities. This reduces maximum kinetic energy and potential flight range and also reduces the MPL factor for insurance purposes.

Incremental testing of each vehicle or spacecraft design during the development phase should provide meaningful failure statistics. For a hypothetical reusable vehicle development project, this occurs as vehicle kinetic energy is progressively increased. Finally, benign failure modes should be designed into each vehicle or spacecraft to reduce the probability of catastrophic loss. For vehicles, this will entail low vehicle empty weights and provision for dumping of environmentally benign propellant loads in the event of an abort or trajectory deviation.

The US government requires a minimum MPL of $3 million on liability coverage for commercial launches [Jurist, 2009]. For a single low mass, low fuel capacity vehicle such as those competing in the recent Northrop-Grumman Lunar Lander Challenge, the total insurance premium for a projected 2 day flight window was recently quoted as $22,000 [Breed, 2008]. Commercial orbital launcher cost factors use a liability MPL of about $1,000/kg of gross takeoff mass.

An underwriting multiplier of 2.25, an MPL of $3 million, and a risk factor of 0.167 for a string of 5 successful test flights with no failures yields a third party liability insurance premium of approximately $1,125,000 for the subsequent flight. Assume that the vehicle developer can establish a probability of loss of vehicle of 0.1% (1 in 1,000 flights)—either by analytical means or by direct flight experience. Then, the asymptotic risk factor would approach 0.001001 after many thousands of successful flights to establish the track record. This would eventually, after many thousands of successful flights, reduce the per flight insurance premium to $6,757.

A better strategy while accumulating risk data based on flight experience for a presumably reliable vehicle design would be to self-insure for liability. For example, one might place a security deposit of $6 million (twice the optimistic MPL) with an independent escrow agency. That amount can be retired over 10 years at an 18% annual interest rate with annual payments of $1,335,000 annually. This equates to $133,500 per flight for 10 flights/yr and $13,350 per flight for 100 flights/year assuming no payouts for third party losses.

However, the probability of escaping a payout over 10 years at 100 flights/year with a 99.9% reliable vehicle is only 37% ($0.999^{1,000} = 0.37$). The loss of two partly reusable Space Shuttles in about 126 flights gives a loss risk of about 0.016 compared to the postulated, and highly optimistic, loss rate of 0.001 used in this example.

Since the flight tests and demonstration flights need to be insured with no revenue stream, self-insurance for liability makes even more sense. Of course, the risk in self insuring against liability is the possibly catastrophic consequences of a string of "bad luck" events in which losses occur more frequently than the average predicted rate. A high deductible blanket insurance policy could be purchased to cover part of the MPL and the remainder escrowed and retired as described previously. Discussion of the optimization of such a business strategy is beyond the scope of this section.

A rational approach is to produce spare vehicles to "self insure" against vehicle loss if a probability of loss of 0.001 can be attained. This would add a minimum of 0.1% to the cost of vehicles produced and successfully launched and it would allow replacement of lost vehicles from the spare inventory. Insurance against vehicle loss for vehicle replacement is a single factor in the overall insurance cost and does not affect the costs for third party liability "insurance" based on MPL.

12.2.5 Price vs. Demand

Sale price has an effect on demand for many products. Gasoline might serve as a useful example. Cutting price at a given outlet may increase its sales at the expense of other nearby outlets as consumers become aware of the change and act upon it. In addition, sustained lower prices encourage more driving and more discretionary gasoline consumption. How this factor may come into play with space access and the NewSpace industry is presently unclear.

A market is *inelastic demand* when demand remains unchanged with changes in price. A market is described as *elastic demand* when demand increases as price decreases. The equilibrium elasticity, E, is defined as the percentage increase in demand divided by the corresponding percentage decrease in price for small changes. If $E > 1$, the total revenues increase as price decreases at equilibrium. If $E < 1$, total revenues decrease as price decreases. If $E = 0$, demand is unchanged with price changes and revenues decrease in direct proportion to any decrease in price. Equilibrium time is significant since markets take time to respond to changes in price structures.

This concept is illustrated in Figs. 12-5 and 12-6 for a hypothetical reusable suborbital sounding rocket [Jurist, 2009]. The figures show annual launch demand (in payload mass) and total annual revenues as a function of launch price and various hypothetical values of E. Both figures are based on current suborbital sounding rocket launch numbers. The threshold for elastic demand is assumed to be $250/kg with negligible market response time. In the region of inelastic demand ($250–$1,000/kg), total revenues decrease as price decreases to the elastic threshold, and then increase with further price decreases if $E > 1$.

If launch demand remains inelastic, the provider is motivated to keep prices as high as possible without going to the extreme of killing demand by making the launches unaffordable.

Standard economic practice is to put price on the vertical axis of the graph with revenue or demand on the

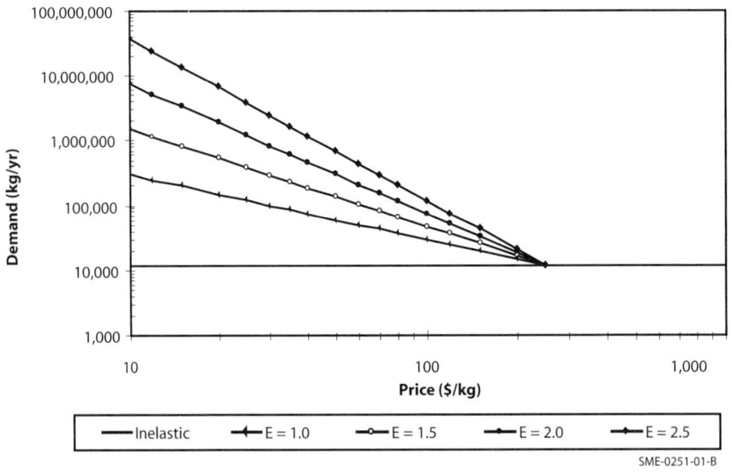

Fig. 12-5. Annual Launch Demand as a Function of Delivered Price.

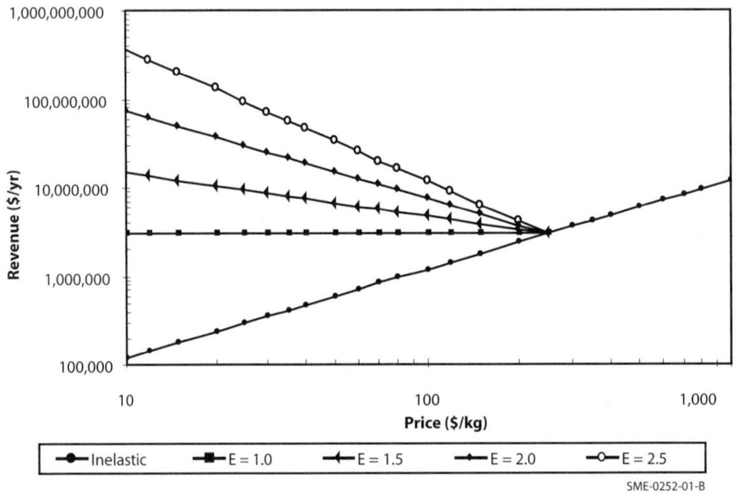

Fig. 12-6. Annual Launch Revenues as a Function of Delivered Price.

horizontal axis, but standard scientific and engineering practice is to put the independent variable (price in this case) on the horizontal axis. Engineering practice is used in these figures.

As mentioned previously, the response time to changes in price structure may be significant. With space operations, the entire system response time includes definition of the mission requirements, assembly of procurement documentation (such as requests for proposals or RFPs), negotiation of contracts, definition of contract compliance monitoring, mechanisms for dealing with delivery delays, R&D, vehicle or system production and testing. The entire response time is commonly measured in years or even decades.

The absence of solid documentation of market size for a potential vehicle or payload implies a "build it and they will come" mentality. Financial success of such an approach requires the reliable creation of demand for the product. This approach is frequently described as the "Field of Dreams Approach to Space Development."

Determination of market size allows the definition of product lifespan, and production rates to optimize profitability or minimize costs. In the context of a launch vehicle, launch rates and program lifetime would determine the production rate, plant size, degree of automation, planning for learning curve influences on production economics, and other factors.

12.2.6 Project Life Cycle

The life cycle of a space project may contain many stages as well as reiterations of many of those stages. Adequate business planning needs to develop a realistic budget for each stage. Additionally, some estimate of the uncertainties in that stage's budget for contingencies that may arise must be made. Finally, the time for completion of each stage, and the overlap in time, if any, that impacts adjacent stages must be estimated. This is where PERT and Critical Path Analysis becomes very valuable in allowing dynamic modifications to be made to the plan. Some of the life cycle stages are listed in the boxed section:

Life Cycle Stages
• Concept or response to RFP • Feasibility study • Trade studies • Detailed conceptualization • Initial cost estimation • Detailed planning (PERT or some other method) • Detailed cost estimation • Financing • Assignment of assets to the project • Acquisition of needed assets • Performing the necessary R&D • Testing at subsystem and system levels • Fabrication of the first preproduction prototype • Production planning • Production asset and facility assignment • Acquisition of additional assets • Production • Testing and quality assurance • Shipping • Testing at destination • Evaluation of performance, and • Consideration of the next generation

The rest of this textbook considers the stages outlined in the boxed section in much more detail.

12.3 Law and Policy Considerations

James D. Rendleman and Milton "Skip" Smith,
Sherman & Howard, L.L.C.

Civil and military, as well as national and multinational commercial space capabilities are vital enablers for successful 21st century militaries, economies, diplomatic communication and collaboration. Given their strategic importance, engineers should not be surprised to find that legal and policy concerns intrude on all elements of the space system mission design process. The complete span of international legal, policy, and diplomacy implications should, therefore, be fully considered when planning for and executing space activities.

Engineers crafting a space system must anticipate these issues in order to avoid potential "show stoppers"—adverse decisions that could be directed by government leaders, customers, suppliers, legislators or courts, and the international community. A perfect engineering solution is useless unless and until it can be implemented. Engineers also need to appreciate the time it may take to comply with applicable laws. A good example of this is Space Shuttle mission 51C to retrieve the Palapa and Westar VI satellites. These satellites remained in low-Earth orbit because the motors which should have transferred them to geostationary orbit failed to operate. Hughes and NASA engineers worked out the technical solutions in a little more than six weeks. The lawyers then spent more than six months resolving the legal questions concerning ownership, salvage rights, insurance coverage, and release of liability between the insurance carriers, Western Union Company and the Indonesian government. Hughes Aircraft Company and NASA had to agree on technical roles, liability, and compensation before the recovery effort could begin. The recovery efforts were successful, but legal fights related to the original launches continued for another 10 years.

International space law and domestic aspects of US space law and policy were forged within the crucible of the most dangerous parts of the Cold War. Comprehensive diplomatic, law and policy activities have since been executed to achieve important strategic objectives throughout the Space Age. In some ways, space activities provided a tremendous opportunity for competing powers to offer olive branches to each other on cooperative activities. Indeed, the International Space Station (ISS) was an important post-Cold War expression of the integration of Russia and the former Soviet Union into the Commonwealth of Nations. The ISS has been cited by many national representatives as a wonderful expression of the promise that such cooperation can provide.

President Eisenhower's administration developed the first comprehensive treatment of US space policy. Presidents since have followed suit, accompanied by a number of targeted policy pronouncements on more narrow space-related topics. Each of these national pronouncements was carefully considered, and reflects priorities of their time—to emphasize desires to fly national security and civil missions on the Space Shuttle, unhook national security missions from the Shuttle system after the Challenger explosion, energize a nascent commercial launch and remote sensing industry, encourage global use of the US Global Positioning System, and, affirmatively state US interests to protect its access to space capabilities following the September 11 attacks. A number of these considerations have also been incorporated into US law, and they affect how national security, civil, and commercial space programs are structured and funded.

This chapter reviews the major international agreements impacting space activities and then turns to US national laws impacting space activities. Thereafter, specific topics, such as satellite communication and space debris, that have particular relevance to space activities are addressed [International Institute of Space Law, 2011].

12.3.1 Foundations of International Space Law

US law and policy place great emphasis on diplomacy and international engagement; it is a centuries-old practice that has secured borders, enhanced commerce, and brokered and resolved disputes. Assuming space operators pay heed to customary and treaty-based provisions of international law and to best practices encouraged by the international space community, such efforts afford the space community a respectable measure of confidence they can all have assured access to space capabilities.

So what are the foundations of international law that affect space activities? Treaties and other bilateral agreements to which sovereign states are signatories, and which govern issues of interest; and, second, multinational agreements among sovereigns. International agreements are governed, not by contract law, but by the *Vienna Convention on the Law of Treaties* [1969]. While the United States has not ratified the Vienna Convention, it accepts the bulk of its rules as customary international law, which is a third foundation of international law. The fourth formulation is general principles common to mature legal systems; and the fifth, subsidiary "municipal" determinations of law, see Burney [2008], (e.g., national laws and decisions such as those rendered by the US Supreme Court).

With relatively few treaty restrictions governing military and other space activities, some might think the US is faced with a dilemma—should it only abide by a permissive "letter of the law" standard or the "spirit of the law"? If only the letter of the law, what approach should it want to see adopted by current or fledging space nations? Actually, the choice is not between the letter and spirit of the law; on the whole, the United States, abides by both standards. Decades of senior policy-makers within the executive and congressional branches of the US government have recognized the importance of the space domain and the rule of law. They have assessed risks associated with not providing measured and calm global leadership to preserve access to the domain consistent with law, and have made innumerable decisions in accord with those assessments. While diplomatic engagement has been helpful, there is an element of risk in relying solely on it to assure access to space capabilities. Enforcement mechanisms for violating treaties and agreements relating to space are rather limited. There are no specific enforcement mechanisms in place to address violations of space related treaties, and this increases the risk of depending on such documents and handshakes to protect or assure access to space. Violations of treaties and other agreements should nominally be responded to through economic means and diplomatic consultation and, if necessary, other sanctions, assuming a nation or some part of the global community agree to them. In turn, the United States encourages thoughtful law and policy-making by other members of the global community.

Despite their minimalist nature, space-related treaties, conventions, and agreements help regularize space activities. They help protect capabilities of systems that have been or are about to be placed on orbit. Bi-lateral and multi-lateral arms control treaties also preserve some of the *sanctuary* aspects of space by prohibiting "interference" with "national technical means" (NTMs) such as missile warning and reconnaissance satellites used to verify treaty compliance. Confidence building procedures have been agreed to and these have improved opportunities for transparency between potential adversaries, perhaps improving dialogue to prevent any dispute from escalating into armed conflict or to a nuclear catastrophe. Other treaties and conventions such as those involving the International Telecommunications Union (ITU) address vexing spectrum management issues which have profound impacts on military, civil, and commercial space systems. The ITU presently attempts to equitably reconcile the explosion of information technologies and exponential user growth and needs, all within nature's limited useable bandwidth in the electromagnetic spectrum.

Of course, space missions are inherently an international activity. Satellites can overfly the sovereign territory of every nation on Earth. Mission designers must, therefore, consider the potential for objections as they develop their systems. Views of space-faring nations sometimes diverge from those of developing nations, and economic competitors or potential military adversaries may disagree on particular issues in order to gain near- and long-term advantages. Differences of opinions can arise from different cultures, economic status, political imperatives, and world views.

Each nation approaches international space policy and legal issues differently. For example, some nations argue for a legal definition of the demarcation between a country's air space and outer space should be defined as beginning at 100 kilometers above sea level. This is known as the Kármán Line, calculated by and named for Theodore von Kármán. This demarcation has been accepted by the Fédération Aéronautique Internationale (FAI) [2004]. The United States does not agree with this definition and rejects the need for it. It refuses to officially accept a specific "boundary" and, instead, employs a functional approach to assert space-related free passage and transit rights. In the US view, if boundaries for the definition of space are strictly defined by treaty or through customary international law, this could affect important space-related rights. The reader is reminded that the Soviet Union reserved the right to shoot or bring down aircraft in its "airspace", and did so with alarming and tragic deadly effect. The United States and its allies might be forced to employ deterrence strategies and prepare for conflict if a state wanting adoption of the Kármán Line also threatens spacecraft that cross below it above their territory. Given these considerations, the United States has not agreed to the definition.

Similarly, a number of the world's equatorial nations have argued (in vain) that their air and space sovereignty rights extend upwards to about 36,000 km (geostationary orbit). These nations seek to assert rights to control access and obtain compensation from space-faring nations who use the slots above their territory. No major space-faring nation agrees with this claimed right.

12.3.2 Outer Space Treaty

The *Treaty on Principles Governing the Activities of States in the Exploration and Use of Outer Space, Including the Moon and Other Celestial Bodies, 1967,* the "*Outer Space Treaty*" [1967], is the grandparent of international and US space law. The classic treatise on space policy [Christol, 1982]. The Treaty serves as an important foundation of the entire US military, civil and commercial space program. It forms the basis for most international space law, including its important legal principles and prohibitions, and incorporates important elements of what was emerging as customary international space law in the 1960s.

The Treaty was consummated at a time when US policy makers concluded space offered unique benefits for the military and political dimensions of the Cold War national security strategy. They hoped to fashion an agreement to preserve access to the domain and these motivations and the document have endured and continue to serve the US and its allies' national interests. Assuming the mantel of the world's leading space-faring nation, the US helped lead the way on discussions relating to the treaty's formation, crafting the treaty instruments and forging a global consensus to set a tone and worldview that space activities should be prosecuted for peace and the benefit of mankind. Other material is in the annual reports of the *Colloquium on the Law of Outer Space*, [AIAA, 2011].

Signatories of the *Outer Space Treaty*, have agreed to a document that supports freedom of access to space by all space venturing powers, with language that provides: "Outer space ... shall be free for exploration and use by all States without discrimination of any kind...." *Treaty on Principles Governing the Activities of States in the Exploration and Use of Outer Space, including the Moon and Other Celestial Bodies* (Outer Space Treaty), Article I. The treaty states in pertinent part: Article I—The exploration and use of outer space, including the moon and other celestial bodies, shall be carried out for the benefit and in the interests of all countries, irrespective of their degree of economic or scientific development, and shall be the province of all mankind. Outer space, including the moon and other celestial bodies, shall be free for exploration and use by all States without discrimination of any kind, on a basis of equality and in accordance with international law, and there shall be free access to all areas of celestial bodies. There shall be freedom of scientific investigation in outer space, including the moon and other celestial bodies, and States shall facilitate and encourage international co-operation in such investigation. Article III—States Parties to the Treaty shall carry on activities in the exploration and use of outer space, including the moon and other celestial bodies, in accordance with international law, including the Charter of the United Nations, in the interest of maintaining international peace and security and promoting international co-operation and understanding. Article IV—States Parties to the Treaty undertake not to place in orbit around the earth any objects carrying nuclear weapons or any other kinds of weapons of mass destruction, install such weapons on celestial bodies, or station such weapons in outer space in any other manner. The treaty also declares nations should have "freedom of scientific investigation in outer space." Addressing topics that affect the potential for space conflict, the Outer Space Treaty provides that international law applies. "...Article III [of the Outer Space Treaty] incorporates the application of international law, and specifically the Charter of the United Nations, in outer space, making it a vital part of the *corpus juris spatialis*" [Blount, 2008]. This incorporation of *international law*, not just the United Nations Charter, is important.

Under the *Outer Space Treaty,* nations agree to share the global space commons, and every major space faring nation is now a signatory.

Rights (and obligations) of non-signatories can be found in international customary law. Customary international law "... consists of rules of law derived from the consistent conduct of States acting out of the belief that the law required them to act that way" [Rosenne, 1984]. *Outer Space Treaty* signatories can look to both treaty and customary law sources, as customary law may be applied whether or not a state is a treaty party. The vast majority of the world, including the United States, accepts in principle the existence of customary international law (although there are often differing opinions as to what rules are contained in it).

The *Outer Space Treaty* lays down widely accepted legal principles for outer space, codifying important, preexisting customary international law principals and precedent relating to space. For example, the launch of the Sputnik satellite system over a half-century ago established the legal precedence and customary international law for free passage of space systems and overflight rights over national territories while on-orbit. The Eisenhower Administration's objective to confirm universal acceptance of this concept of satellite free passage and over-flight rights was achieved years later when these principles were included as part of the *Outer Space Treaty*. In the meantime, customary law related to such issues was developed as statements of such principles were presented and discussed within various global community and United Nations' forums. They can be found in a number of disparate documents including the 1958 National Aeronautics and Space Act, and UN General Assembly resolutions.

The *Outer Space Treaty* provides:

- All nations may scientifically investigate space, with international cooperation encouraged
- No nation may claim sovereignty over outer space, including the Moon and other celestial bodies. As an illustration, when Neil Armstrong placed an American flag on the Moon, he did not do so to claim new territory, as Columbus and other explorers did when they arrived in the New World
- The laws relating to space activities will follow the established principles and rules of international law and the U.N. Charter
- No signatory will place nuclear weapons or any other weapons of mass destruction in orbit around the Earth, or on the Moon, or on other celestial bodies. Note, however, this restriction does not ap-

ply to nuclear power sources; comparably, the 1963 *Treaty Banning Nuclear Weapon Tests in the Atmosphere, in Outer Space and Under Water*, also known as the *Limited Test Ban Treaty* (LTBT), prohibits "any nuclear weapon test explosion, or any other nuclear explosion" (emphasis added) in the atmosphere, underwater, or in outer space

- The *Outer Space Treaty* does not specifically prohibit testing weapons in outer space itself (as opposed to on celestial bodies); instead it proscribes the stationing of nuclear weapons on orbit. However, with the LTBT, testing and subsequent use of nuclear weapons in response to attacks on space systems would appear to be banned, unless employed in a possible narrow exception that allows such devices to be employed to preserve the "survival of a State." Employing nuclear weapon systems against conventional space systems probably could not be shown to support such a survival objective
- Nations must use the Moon and other celestial bodies exclusively for "peaceful purposes," but they may use military personnel in scientific research. The United States defines *peaceful* as "non-aggressive," thus permitting defensive measures
- Astronauts are *envoys of mankind* and must be returned to their home nation when rescued
- Nations bear international responsibility for their activities in outer space, whether done by governmental agencies or private citizens. Thus, the US must authorize and continuously supervise all space activities of its citizens. This requirement is unique to space activities, resulting from a compromise between the United States and the former Soviet Union. The Soviets had insisted that only governments should be permitted to go into space, whereas the United States insisted on permission for private entrepreneurs. The *Commercial Space Launch Act of 1984* was enacted and amended by the United States in part to carry out the its obligations under the *Outer Space Treaty* and *Liability Convention*. Even though the Treaty provides that States bear international responsibility for government and private space activities and must supervise and regulate national activities in space, some argue there is no effective enforcement mechanism in the Treaty to respond to a failure by a State to perform actions consistent with responsibilities established under the document.
- Launching nations are liable for direct damages to citizens of other nations caused by national and private launch activities
- A State Party to the Treaty retains jurisdiction, and control rights over their spacecraft, space objects and personnel. In addition, ownership rights of objects launched into outer space, and their component parts, is not affected by their presence in outer space. Unless these rights are relinquished, some argue that peacetime retrieval, alteration of orbit, or any other form of interference with foreign space objects would be unlawful without prior consent under treaty and customary international law, no matter how desirable the end result. If strictly interpreted, only a launching State can exercise *jurisdiction and control* of its space objects, even after satellites are defunct and long abandoned, and even if they threaten a particular orbital regime or another satellite with debris.* Any entity attempting to remove space junk could run into a claim from a State that the removal is a violation of international law†
- Nations must conduct space activities so as to avoid harming or adversely affecting space activities of other nations. The 1963 *Project West Ford* influenced this provision when the United States placed 480 million copper dipoles into orbit 2,000 miles above the Earth in an attempt to create an artificial ionosphere to enable radio messages to bounce from coast to coast. The in-house name for the project was *Needles*, which proved to be an unfortunate choice. Complaints came in from the astronomical community asserted by astronomers who were convinced the belt of copper needles would ruin their view of the universe. They also argued the experiment might lead to even worse experiments. The Soviets wryly observed and commented "What if one of the needles pierces the heart of a cosmonaut or puts out someone's eye when it reenters the atmosphere?"
- If one State's space activities pose a potential to cause harm or interference to space activities conducted by another State, consultations should be initiated before they proceed. Consistent with the point, military mission planners should review the 1977 *Convention on the Prohibition of Military or any Other Hostile Use of Environmental Modification Techniques*, or *Environmental Modification Convention* [1977], if they anticipate large-scale effects. The *Environmental Modification Convention* prohibits all military or hostile environmental modification techniques that might cause long-lasting, severe or widespread environmental changes in Earth's atmosphere or outer space. "Each State Party to this Convention undertakes not to engage in military or any other hostile use of

* As of 1989, jurisdiction and control of a State over its space objects was considered "permanent."

† "Ownership of space objects is also permanent, as Article VIII implies that the State of registration may not be divested of title to its space objects, (cit.om.) regardless of the use or condition of the space object. (cit.om.) Moreover, the rights of ownership include the rights of possession, use and disposal, thereby denying a right of encroachment without the consent of the State of registration.(cit.om.)" [Baker, 1989].

environmental modification techniques having widespread, long-lasting or severe effects as the means of destruction, damage or injury to any other State Party." "Widespread" is defined as "encompassing an area on the scale of several hundred square kilometers"; "long-lasting" is defined as "lasting for a period of months, or approximately a season"; and "severe" is defined as "involving serious or significant disruption or harm to human life, natural and economic resources or other assets" [Understanding, Environmental Monitoring Convention, 1977]. The *Environmental Modification Treaty* focuses on proscribing employing military weapons, tactics and techniques that deliberately change natural processes. The 1992 version of the *Environmental Modification Convention* limited its purposes to military conflict*

- Stations on the Moon and other celestial bodies shall be open mutually to representatives of other nations after reasonable advance notice. The *Antarctic Treaty*, in contrast, allows unannounced inspection of stations, installations, and equipment; therefore we must not confuse these provisions with those of the *Outer Space Treaty*. The *Moon Treaty of 1979* has extensive inspection provisions but little force or effect, because no major space-faring nation has ratified it. The "common heritage of mankind" provisions, which envision sharing profits with all nations even though they have not contributed, is a major sticking point

12.3.3 Liability Convention

The 1972 *Convention on International Liability for Damage Caused by Space Objects* (the "Liability Convention") expands on a topic noted in the *Outer Space Treaty* that "launching states" are liable to other states for damage caused by space objects (including debris). States are liable only for direct damage caused by a space object (i.e., loss of life; personal injury or other impairment of health; or loss of or damage to property). If damage is caused to another space object in outer space, liability is based on fault. If damage is caused by a space object on earth or to an aircraft in flight, liability is absolute.

The *Liability Convention* was crafted to protect the interests of non-space-faring nations, so it held space-faring nations absolutely liable if they caused injury or damage on Earth. Absolute liability simply means that someone who is injured may claim compensation just by proving damage and who did it, without having to demonstrate negligence or fault. If damage occurs in space, however, the Convention provides that space-faring nations must prove fault in order to recover damages.

The procedure for settling claims calls first for negotiations by the nations involved. The only claimant under the *Liability Convention* is another nation, bringing a claim on its own behalf or on behalf of its citizens. If these negotiations fail, a three member claims commission is formed. Each nation involved appoints one member. The two appointed members then appoint a third, the chairman.

Notably, there can be more than one "launching State"—a launching state is any state that launches an object, procures the launch of an object, or from whose territory or facility an object is launched. If there is more than one launching State, joint and several liability rules would apply. States may make indemnification agreements and apportion liability among themselves. Since allied nations supporting space conflict activities could be construed as launching states, liability issues and allocation of liability issues should be resolved before engaging in such activities.

In the end, the *Liability Convention*'s real limitations on space activities arise out of its provision for liability associated with causing damage to third-parties. These liability issues must be evaluated, addressed and mitigated by law-abiding states before performing activities that could cause damage to third-parties. Planners must account for payment of damages or plan to limit such problems.

The first case involving a claim under the *Liability Convention* arose out of the reentry of Cosmos 954 over the Northwest Territory of Canada on January 24, 1978. The reentry scattered radioactive debris from the Cosmos' nuclear reactor over 124,000 km^2. The two nations did not submit their claims and defenses to a claims commission, because negotiations between Canada and the Soviet Union were successful. The search and recovery effort entitled *Operation Morning Light* cost Canada almost $14M Canadian dollars, but the claim was settled for $3M. Canada elected not to assert claims for personnel and equipment costs. The Soviets argued that Canada was too meticulous in the clean up operations and that if this event had occurred in Siberia, it would not have expended that much effort. Additionally, the Soviets asserted that it had offered to help clean up, but Canada rejected the offer. Thus, Canada had not mitigated its damages. The amicable settlement set a positive precedent for resolving claims in the future.

* US attempts at environmental modification during the Southeast Asia conflicts were opposed by dissidents in Congress. As a result, in 1973 the US Senate passed a resolution urging President Nixon to initiate negotiations leading to a multilateral treaty. In 1974 US-USSR bilateral negotiations began. In 1975, the USSR and the US submitted separate but identical texts of a draft convention to the UN. The draft was then finalized in the Conference of the Committee of Disarmament (CCD) and adopted by the UN General Assembly on 10 December 1976. The Environmental Modification Convention opened for signature in May 1977 and entered into force 5 October 1978.

The US Delegation Statement provides: "The Environmental Modification Convention is not an Environmental Protection Treaty; it is not a treaty to prohibit damage to the environment resulting from armed conflict. Rather, the Environmental Modification Convention fills a special, but important niche reflecting the international community's consensus that the environment itself should not be used as an instrument of war."

Under the *Liability Convention*, the US must pay when her space activities injure citizens of other nations or their property. The Federal Tort Claims Act also provides that US citizens may also recover damages for personal injury and property loss caused by US procured government activities. Losses caused by US commercial space operators may be recovered in state and sometimes federal courts. In order to manage the potential liability arising out of space activities, and ensure that appropriate compensation is paid, the government through its FAA licensing activities requires insurance be obtained before authorizing a commercial launch. Government launches, both military and civil, do not have formal insurance coverage, as the government is a self-insurer. If the government suffers a loss, it only allocates more funds for replacement systems and mitigating damages from the public coffers.

12.3.4 Registration Convention and Rescue and Return Agreement

The 1975 *Convention on Registration of Objects Launched into Outer Space* (the "Registration Convention") requires a launching State to advise the U.N. Secretary General of the following: name of the launching nation, description or registration number, date and location of launch, basic orbital parameters (nodal period, inclination, apogee, and perigee) and general function of the space object, as soon as practicable. A nation need not update this information but may do so if it wishes. States often delay filing the requisite information.

The 1968 *Agreement on the Rescue of Astronauts, the Return of Astronauts and the Return of Objects Launched into Outer Space*, (the "*Rescue and Return Agreement")*, sets forth rights and obligations of states concerning the rescue of persons in space. It expands on the rescue provisions in the *Outer Space Treaty*. The Agreement requires that any state party that becomes aware that the personnel of a spacecraft are in distress must notify the launching authority and the Secretary General of the United Nations. In addition, any state party to the agreement must provide all possible assistance to rescue the personnel of a spacecraft who have landed within that state's territory, whether because of an accident, distress, emergency, or unintended landing. If the distress occurs in an area that is beyond the territory of any nation, then any state party that is in a position to do so shall, if necessary, extend assistance in the search and rescue operation.

The *Outer Space Treaty* states simply that *astronauts* are to be rendered assistance by parties to the treaty. It does not define the term "astronaut" and fails to clarify whether this applies to spacecraft personnel such as a space "tourist". The Rescue and Return Agreement expands on the term by referring to the "personnel of a spacecraft" rather than "astronauts."

Finally, the *Rescue and Return Agreement* provides that if a space object or its parts land in the territory of another state party, the state where the object lands is required (upon the request of the launching authority) to recover the space object and return it to the launching authority. The *Rescue and Return Agreement* provides that the launching state must compensate the state for the costs incurred in recovering and returning the space object. The Agreement does not describe the condition of the object or parts that are to be returned.

12.3.5 International Cooperation

Interest in international space cooperation is not new. International cooperation has been an important and long-standing hallmark of the US national space policies. The United States engages in a wide range of such activities.

Cooperation allows space-faring States to combine resources and reduce risk, improve efficiency, expand diplomatic engagement, enhance prestige, improve political sustainability of space projects, and provide workforce stability. Cooperative participants expect international projects will generate a calculus that one plus one will equal three—that diverse resources, skills, and technologies of the partners will provide synergy, adding up to more than the sum of their parts [Mukai, 2008]. Given the benefits sought, sentiments to support international cooperation and collaboration are growing and evolving, much more so than in past policy declarations. NASA, commercial, and European space activities have already achieved considerable success with their cooperative endeavors [Dale, 2006].

Fans of the new US National Space Policy may think that the number of times "international cooperation" or "cooperation" is mentioned is very important. The reality, however, often is that cooperative programs are expensive, difficult to resource, and hard to manage. Given the challenges, shrewd partners know that the direction to engage in cooperation is not worth much unless tied to money and programs. Some potential and even current international partners are taking a judicious *wait and see* attitude to the new direction. Changing business plans to respond to changing US international cooperation initiatives involves risks.

12.3.6 US National Space Policy

The US National Space Policy provides the President's statement of the "highest priorities for space, and reflects our principles and goals to be used in shaping the conduct of our space programs and activities" [Rose, 2010].* The policy has been updated a number of times. It sets forth a number of perspectives one would expect on such an important topic. A careful reading of the current document shows it continues the key principles of national

* Rose has been serving as point man for the Administration on the new policy. He has been traveling to a wide variety of venues to speak to and relate its key messages for the US and global community.

space policy that were crafted long ago. The document is circulated within the US Government agencies to achieve consensus and moves the discussion forward incrementally. The decision to do this is wise. Revolutionary transmutations in policy and national interests should be driven by major shifts in the international scene, such as those foisted upon decision makers by wars, new countries, breakthroughs in technologies, or other significant events. No recent shift or significant event has occurred with regard to the space domain, so the continuing incremental evolution in policy is appropriate.*

Past versions of the US National Space Policy emphasized that the sustainability, stability, and free access to, and use of, space is vital to US national interests. The 2010 US National Space Policy endorses this view and contends that space systems are vital to secure access to and satisfy important communication, navigation and timing, weather, remote sensing, missile warning and defense needs. It also tips the hat to needs of the United States to secure its industrial base, improve the science, technical, engineering and math expertise of the population, and ensure the professionalism of its space community. Importantly, much of the new policy's foundational points are based on principles of international cooperation—*mitigate the dangers of space debris*, *improve space situational awareness (SSA)*, *achieve collision avoidance*, and *pursue pragmatic bilateral and multilateral transparency and confidence-building measures (TCBMs)* to mitigate the risk of mishaps, misperceptions, and mistrust (that could lead to space or terrestrial warfare.).

It is US policy to comply with the four basic international space treaties.† Each US space policy has supported the proposition that all nations have the right to explore and use space for peaceful purposes, and for the benefit of all humanity, in accordance with international law.

Importantly, the United States considers that its space systems possess the rights of passage through, and conduct of operations in, space without interference. It reserves the right to defend itself from threats and attacks against its space systems in each of the last three policies in one form or another. It has been longstanding US policy that purposeful interference with space systems, including supporting infrastructure, will be considered an infringement *on its rights*. Reflecting the expanding international flavor of the policy, the new US National Space Policy broadens this assertion by stating that purposeful interference with space systems will be considered an infringement of a *nation's rights* [National Space Policy, 2010]. Consistent with exercising its inherent right of self-defense or lawful collective self-defense, the policy asserts that the United States will "deter others from interference and attack, defend our space systems and contribute to the defense of allied space systems, and, if deterrence fails, defeat efforts to attack them" [National Space Policy, 2010].

The new policy also continues to emphasize the need to address the dangers posed by space debris. Warnings about space debris and mitigating its hazards have been part of US space policies for decades and understandably so. The 1980s saw the United States migrating to use only the Space Shuttle to support its national security and civil spacelift needs. In undertaking this responsibility, NASA concluded that the growing space debris threat endangered its astronauts and therefore commenced studies and analysis to better understand the risk. This concern was then embodied in early national space policies that emphasized the need to mitigate the generation of space debris. Consistent with this long-standing policy, the United States has been a strong proponent of activities conducted within the United Nation's *InterAgency Space Debris Coordination Committee (IADC)*. The IADC has been used as a vehicle to develop recommended space debris mitigation guidelines and obtain global space community compliance with the techniques space-faring nations should employ when launching, operating, and safely retiring and de-orbiting space objects. Unfortunately, compliance by the international community has been inconsistent to date.

12.3.7 Import and Export Controls and Technology Transfer Constraints

Unfortunately, achieving increasingly interoperable platforms, planning, and operations can be difficult and complicated because US law and policy imposes controls on the release of sensitive technologies and operations. Specific information on important technologies and information relating to some space operations and technologies may be determined by the US Government to be non-releasable to allies, close partners, and sometimes one or more members of a coalition. (Other nations also secure their technologies for diplomatic, military and economic reasons.)

Law and policy considerations run the gamut of international military space relationships: foreign military sales, direct commercial sales and programs, cooperative programs, officer exchanges and liaison officer relationships, visits including data releases and briefings, and

* Space warfare zealots might argue the January 11, 2007 Chinese anti-satellite (ASAT) intercept was a watershed space security event. Perhaps so, but kinetic ASAT capabilities have been tested and even operational since the late 1960s.

† The four international treaties are: (1) the 1967 *Treaty on Principles Governing the Activities of States in the Exploration and Use of Outer Space, Including the Moon and Other Celestial Bodies* (the "Outer Space Treaty"); (2) the 1968 *Agreement on the Rescue of Astronauts, the Return of Astronauts and the Return of Objects Launched into Outer Space* (the "Rescue Agreement"); (3) the 1972 *Convention on International Liability for Damage Caused by Space Objects* (the "Liability Convention"); and (4) the 1975 *Convention on Registration of Objects Launched Into Outer Space* (the "Registration Convention"). For various reasons, the United States and the other major space-faring States have refused to ratify a fifth international treaty, the 1979 *Agreement Governing the Activities of States on the Moon and Other Celestial Bodies* (the "Moon Treaty").

operational activities including exercises and intelligence information. They must be continually assessed. Any proposed international space operation, cooperative effort, or technology transfer must be examined and assessed in its entirety. US government officials are charged to weigh the political and military advantages expected to accrue to the United States against the damage that could potentially result from the possible compromise of the information disclosed.

Important portions of releasability law and policy arise out of the *Arms Export Control Act (AECA)* [AECA, 1976], which provides the authority to control the export of defense articles and services. It governs the sale and export of defense articles and services and related technical data. The AECA is an important part of the statutory scheme to ensure US compliance with technology control regimes and agreements that seek to stop and slow the proliferation of missile technologies and the technologies that can be used to deliver weapons of mass destruction. Under the AECA, spacecraft, space related articles and services are designated to be subject to export control. The designated articles comprise part of the *US Munitions List (USML)*, which is contained within the *International Traffic in Arms Regulations (ITAR)*. The Munitions List specifically includes rockets, spacecraft, space electronics, and guidance equipment. *Defense services* are also included, defined as furnishing help to foreigners "in the design, engineering, development, production, processing, manufacturing, use, operations, overhaul, repair, maintenance, modification or reconstruction of articles." Included is the furnishing to foreigners of any technical data-whether in the United States or abroad. Finally, no one may provide foreigners "technical data", meaning information classified or related to defense articles, without a license or approval issued by the Department of State. Under these regulations, an export does not have to cross a border. For example, an export occurs when an individual discloses technical data concerning a spacecraft or rocket to foreigners, even if the disclosure is part of a potential sale and occurs within the US.

The AECA requires that exports of space articles, services and related technical data meet US national security interests. It also requires the proposed recipients offer assurances to the United States before transfers are made: First, the recipient nation must agree to not transfer the articles, services, or data to third parties without prior US government consent; second, the recipient must agree to use the articles, services, or data only for purpose for which they were furnished; third, the recipient must agree to maintain the security of the defense article and services and provide substantially the same degree of security as the US Government.

There is a substantial paperwork component associated with each of these releasability compliance regimes. The rules are driving some small suppliers out of the export marketplace as they usually lack the economies of scale to properly respond to export legal requirements. International partners are also wary of the legal rules and procedures. Nearly all members of the space community, foreign and domestic, consider the rules to be burdensome and onerous. The requirement for assurances, and the potential for US criminal liability arising out of them, is generally agreed to have cost the US space industry billions of dollars in sales in the international marketplace. The US communications satellite industry has lost market share to international competitors who claim their systems, products and services are ITAR-free.

Of course, other US laws, regulations, and policies apply to exports of space data, hardware, and services, such as the release of classified information.* For example, another control involves patents containing military technology. When the Departments of Defense and Energy review an export application, either department may classify the information to keep it secret, thus preventing export without additional security controls. In addition, dual use military/civilian use commodities and technical data on the *Commodities Control List (CCL)* fall under the licensing requirements of the Export Administrative Act of 1979. The Commerce Department runs this program, has published a series of detailed regulations, and licenses exports under them.

Unless a project has federal funding, the restriction on imports into the United States is not a substantial issue unless the import requires sharing of data proscribed by ITAR or other export constraints. If federal funding is involved, the *Buy American Act* and domestic preference provisions in various other acts and regulations could affect purchases. The *Buy American Act* restricts foreign involvement in US Government satellite launches. In general, the *Buy American Act* prohibits buying foreign goods but does not apply to services. NASA has held that a supplier of space services may not use foreign goods to provide the service. Under the Act, a product is not *foreign* if more than 50% of the cost of all components comes from domestic sources. The DoD may buy from NATO countries, and there are other exceptions. Given the global economy and on-going specialization in various technologies, the Act's provisions and rules can give American mission planners headaches, especially if waivers to the law and relief from policy constraints are needed. Waivers have been granted, however, to enable launches of important civil space missions. (See also Federation Acquisition Regulation (FAR) Part 25.)

* The *Export Administration Act of 1979* (EAA) governs the export of most dual-use unclassified articles and services (having both civilian and military uses) not covered by the AECA. The EAA controls exports on the basis of their impact on national security, foreign policy, or supply availability. With the expiration of EAA in 1994, the President declared a national emergency and exercised authority under the International Emergency Economic Powers Act (P.L. 95-223; 50 U.S.C. 1701 et seq.) to continue the EAA export control regulations then in effect by issuing EO 12924 on August 19, 1994.

12.3.8 Commercial Space Launch Act of 1984

Mission planners must consider the *Commercial Space Launch Act of 1984*. As amended, it requires the Department of Transportation's (DOT) Office of Commercial Space Transportation (a branch of the Federal Aviation Administration, generally referred to as FAA/AST, or AST) to approve and license all commercial expendable vehicles if launched from US territory or by a US citizen or corporation outside the US. AST approves any commercial rocket launch operations—that is, any launches that are not classified as model, amateur, or "by and for the government." The Act proclaimed two objectives: 1) to encourage, facilitate, and promote commercial space launches by the private sector; and 2) to foster the development of licensing requirements in consultation with other US Government agencies.

The creation of a new single regulatory agency within the FAA to handle this was hoped to speed development of the then-nascent US commercial launch industry. AST licenses private space vehicles and spaceports within the United States. In contrast, NASA, a research and development agency, neither operates nor regulates the commercial space transportation industry. It only launches satellites and spacecraft on vehicles developed by private companies.

Before issuing a launch license the AST requires both a mission review and a safety review. The first review focuses on the payload itself and the flight plan to ensure that the mission is in accord with US policy and meets US responsibilities under international treaties. Regulations require AST to review how missions affect national interests. This authority could be used to block missions, and the *Commercial Space Launch Act* gives AST considerable power over commercial activity. Still, Congress has declared privately conducted commercial launches to be consistent with the national security and foreign policy interests of the United States. Thus, US policy seeks to encourage commercial space activities.

The AST also reviews commercial operator launch safety efforts, including:

- Procedures for safety controls for launch sites and flight corridors
- Range safety expertise
- Procedures for ground and flight safety
- Range tracking and instrumentation
- Vehicle safety systems
- Proposed vehicle design

Given the damage that could occur, and US international obligations to conduct space activities safely and responsibly, mission designers have found that these reviews have been conducted conservatively. Missions using proven government launchers and national launching facilities usually receive quick approval. A mission proposing to use a new and untested vehicle or launch site will encounter close scrutiny.

The AST also establishes liability insurance requirements for commercial launch activities taking into account the requirements of international law and US obligations under it. In general, insurance is required to cover the Maximum Probable Loss (MPL) amount, which is not to exceed \$500M. Above that, the US Government provides indemnification for third party loses up to \$1.5B plus the MPL. Also the US Government covers losses of its own property above the MPL.

The AST must coordinate commercial launches with all other interested agencies within the Federal Government, particularly the Department of Defense and the Department of State.

The present US Commercial Space Policy requires maximum utilization of commercial launch capability by the federal government. This includes planning missions in such a way that they match the space transportation capabilities of US commercial launch providers. The main exceptions to this requirement are national security or international collaborative efforts relating to science and technology, or space exploration. As part of its efforts to support development of the private launch industry, Congress provided in the *Commercial Space Launch Act* that excess or unused Government launch property should be made available to private launch companies through lease or sale agreements. Specifically, the Secretary of Transportation was directed to "take such actions as may be necessary to facilitate and encourage the acquisition (by lease, sale, transaction in lieu of sale, or otherwise) by the private sector of launch property of the United States which is excess or is otherwise not needed for public use" [USC, 1984].

12.3.9 Satellite Communication Law

The provision of communication services is the most commercially profitable use of space, with important applications in telephone, telegraph, television, and data transmissions. As a consequence, considerable attention is paid to law and policy issues that pose a potential to affect the business activities of communication satellite systems. Importantly, the *International Telecommunication Union (ITU)* is chartered by treaty to regulate the use of satellite orbits and frequencies. The ITU has extensive Radio Regulations that govern the use of orbits and frequencies.

Once a satellite is registered with the ITU, no subsequent system may interfere with its signal transmission. Generally, a similar replacement satellite will retain the rights of a registered satellite.

Since 1973, orbital positions have been associated with particular frequencies and technical characteristics. The unique properties of the stationary orbit over the equator (the "geostationary-satellite orbit" or "GSO") permits "stationary" positioning of a satellite.

The GSO is a limited resource because satellites need separation between them to limit radio frequency interference. The required separation depends on many factors including the frequencies used, geographic area served, and technical and operating characteristics.

Table 12-1◀, Fig. 12-6◀, Eq. 12-4◀

There have been a number of concerns over the reservation of orbital slots, and frequencies based on the "first-come, first-served" regulatory regime. In particular, developing nations have been worried that no slots will be left for them. An ITU compromise was crafted that left the conventional part of C and K_u radio frequency bands allocated to the Fixed Satellite Service on a "first-come, first-served" basis. At the same time, an allotment scheme provided all nations with orbital slots and associated K_a band frequencies, *World Radiocommunication Conferences (WRC)**, organized by the ITU, review, and, as necessary, revise the Radio Regulations governing the use of the radio-frequency spectrum and geostationary and non-geostationary satellite orbits. The ITU is required to perform these activities "in order to avoid harmful interference between the radio communication services of different countries" [ITU, 2011]. The nations also occasionally hold multilateral planning meetings to resolve area conflicts between themselves.

According to the ITU, "Equitable access to spectrum and orbital resources is of special concern, given the uneven needs of developed and developing countries. As a consequence, the principle of *a priori* planning of spectrum and orbit resources is considered in conjunction with a series of plans established by radio communication conferences" [ITU, 2011]. In exercising its registration function, the ITU's Radio Regulation Board and Radiocommunication Bureau do not evaluate the particular nation's reasons for making a particular assignment. They only seek to ensure that the national assignment conforms to identified services for the assigned frequency and that transmissions do not interfere with other broadcasts. Nations then determine how they will parcel out the allocated frequencies.

If a proposed satellite could cause interference, the sponsoring nation resolves issues under negotiation procedures established by the ITU. The ITU conducts much of its technical activities through the Radio Regulation Board and Radiocommunication Bureau. In the United States, the FCC allocates orbital slots and frequencies upon formal application. The approval process may take 3 to 5 years for a new communications service or up to a year for an existing satellite.

Enforcement mechanisms for violating the ITU treaties and agreements are rather limited. The ITU has been described as a "gentlemen's club" depending on the "goodwill of its members. There is no mechanism for forcing an administration into compliance with the rules" [de Selding, 2010].†

* Prior to 1993 these were called the World Administrative Radio Conference (WARC).

† When commenting on Iranian jamming of European communication satellites: "Rancy, a veteran international-frequency regulator who chaired the ITU's World Radiocommunication Conference in late 2007, said that while he hoped ITU pressure would affect Iran's behavior, he was not counting on an immediate stop to the practice."

12.3.10 Intellectual Property Rights

Outer space activities utilize sophisticated technologies about which intellectual property and patent law play an important role to protect rights to the benefits of inventions, scientific discoveries, industrial designs, and protection against unfair competition. Space activities have been shifting from state-owned activities to private and commercial activities and this has heightened the emphasis on protecting property rights, whether in tangible or intangible form. Private financing has to be motivated by expectations that research and development and other investments can be recovered and profited on.

Patent law and intellectual property rights in the United States stem from the first national patent law enacted in 1790. It was based upon the US Constitution (1787), article 1, section 8, paragraph 8 that states, "Congress shall have power to... promote the progress of science and useful arts by securing for limited times to authors and inventors the exclusive right to their respective writings and discoveries." That limited period in the US is usually 20 years from the date of filing for a patent with the US Patent and Trademark Office.

According to the World Intellectual Property Organization, "A patent is an exclusive right granted for an invention, which can be a product or a process that provides a new and inventive way of doing something, or offers a new and inventive solution to a problem. A patent owner has exclusive rights to prevent third parties not having the owner's consent from the acts of making, using, offering for sale, selling, or importing for these purposes the patented invention... The patent owner may give permission (license) to other parties to use the invention on mutually agreed terms. The owner may also sell the right to the invention to a third party, who will then become the new owner of the patent. Once a patent expires, the protection ends, and the invention enters the public domain. Patent owners are obliged, in return for patent protection, to publicly disclose information on their invention in order to enrich the total body of technical knowledge in the world. This body of public knowledge promotes further creativity and innovation by others. In this way, patents provide not only protection for the owner, but valuable information and inspiration for future generations of researchers and inventors" [IBWIPO, 2004].

The United States has enacted law relating to protecting invention for space activities; the 1990 law, found at 35 USC § 105, provides in pertinent part:

Any invention made, used, or sold in outer space on a space object or component thereof under the jurisdiction or control of the United States shall be considered to be made, used or sold within the United States for the purposes of this title, except with respect to any space object or component thereof that is specifically identified and otherwise provided for by an international agreement to which the United States is a party, or with respect to any space object or component thereof that is carried on the registry of a foreign state in accordance with the Convention on Registration of Objects Launched into Outer Space.

Any invention made, used or sold in outer space on a space object or component thereof that is carried out on the registry of a foreign state in accordance with the Convention on Registration of Objects Launched into Outer Space, shall be considered to be made, used or sold within the United States for the purposes of this title if specifically so agreed in an international agreement between the United States and the state of registry.

Mission designers should be aware of two patent cases. Hughes Aircraft Company/Williams in 1973 obtained a patent relating to the spin stabilization of satellites to assure obtaining and maintaining satellite attitude on orbit. Hughes Aircraft Company sued the US Government for infringement of its patent, because the government used the concept without paying for it, and transferred it to third parties. It was not until 1983 that a multi-billion-dollar decision against the Government was handed down after the United States and others had launched 108 satellites, which were held to have infringed the patent rights of Hughes Aircraft Company. The lesson is clear; patent infringement may have very significant economic consequences for mission designers and systems engineers.

The second case stems from a matter where TRW obtained a "patent" for a particular system orbital architecture. It claimed rights to an "orbital shell" above the Earth from 5,600 to 10,000 nautical miles, to be reserved for TRW exclusively, for all communications applications to mobile handsets. Soon after the patent was granted TRW sued ICO Global Communications Ltd. to prevent them from launching satellites into the proscribed altitudes. The case was dismissed because there was no present infringement, and TRW and ICO separately resolved their issues. Nevertheless, this is a troublesome patent, because it flies directly in the face of the Outer Space Treaty provisions on non-appropriation of space by any nation including its private entities. The patent could be fatally flawed, especially if it is interpreted to give any property rights to a spatial location.

12.3.11 Insurance

The *Outer Space Treaty* requires a nation to *authorize* and *continually supervise* all of its space activity, including those of its citizens acting privately, to assure they conform to treaties and international law obligations. The treaty also imposed liability for space activity, and this provision was amplified by the *Liability Convention*. In order to satisfy these mandates, commercial space activities are required under US law to procure insurance to address the potential for damages. There are a number of different types of insurance that apply to space activities:

- ***Pre-Launch.*** Pre-launch coverage insures against the risks from damage during shipment of the launcher and the satellite, as well as during integration and movement to the launch pad
- ***Government Equipment.*** The government requires launches on commercial expendable vehicles to provide insurance for loss to government launch equipment and facilities
- ***Third-Party Liability.*** Launch vehicle and space operations may cause injury to others on launch, on-orbit, and through the reentry. The risk on reentry is small because these objects generally burn up in the atmosphere during reentry. If they do not, they would typically strike the ocean or one of the uninhabited areas that make up most of the Earth's surface. Because of this low risk, coverage is less expensive though still required by AST for launch vehicles and satellites and by NASA for commercial satellites. There are comparable risks for other launch and on-orbit activities, which are described in greater detail below
- When NASA was the only means of access to space for commercial satellites, their regulations required an insurance policy of $500M, with the government assuming the risk above that amount. This initial limit was a practical one because the insurance community could not insure a greater amount. Now that commercial launch vehicles are becoming the prime means of transportation into space, Congress has established and extended a similar cap of $500M, until the world's insurance community can provide greater coverage. The purpose of this provision of this amendment to the *Commercial Space Launch Act* was to attempt to level the commercial space launch playing field. This amount was based upon the prior NASA policy of requiring $500M coverage, adjusted for inflation
- Private operators of launch vehicles must also concern themselves with liability claims from citizens of the US and around the world. The AST regulations require coverage against this risk before issuing a launch license
- ***Launch Failure.*** The most expensive insurance coverage insures the satellite value from the moment of lift-off to on-orbit checkout. The prices for this coverage range from 5% to 30% of the satellite value depending on the perceived or actual risk, and availability of indemnification monies in the commercial space marketplace. Man-rated vehicle such as the Space Shuttle have enjoyed some discounts because the insurance community had higher confidence in their reliability. However, the insurance marketplace can change based on problems in the space community. Premiums rose dramatically with the loss of the Shuttle Challenger in 1986 and several significant failures of expendable launch vehicles shortly thereafter. In fact, during that timeframe, the space insurance community paid out 3 times more in loss claims than they took in through premiums. Once the United States and

Ariane launch vehicle programs were back on track, premiums moderated. Mission designers may want to choose launch vehicles and satellites with a history of proven success. Otherwise, insurance could be prohibitively priced

- ***Loss to Others on the Flight.*** Under provisions of NASA launch contracts, the risk of damage to a payload by another payload or by NASA's actions is addressed and mitigated by use of a *hold harmless clause*. This contractual clause requires that all parties to the launch agree not to sue each other regardless of what happens. This practical remedy came about because it is very difficult to calculate the risk of such problems and determine the premium. Given their size and perception that they are a deep pocket for any liability issues, large spacecraft and launch vehicle integrators monitor these agreements and insurance requirements for the system
- ***On-Orbit Performance.*** Insurance can also be obtained to address concerns on whether a satellite will continue to perform its mission activities for its planned lifetime. Launch failure insurance terminates after on-orbit checkout. Satellite owners obtain on-orbit performance coverage if they do not have sufficient resources to "self insure" the risks. Banks that finance communications systems usually demand the coverage. An alternative risk mitigation strategy may involve placing satellites on orbit to back-up the satellite losses

Unfortunately, space launch campaigns and on-orbit operations are relatively new activities. There have not been enough total launches to derive actuarially correct figures. Therefore, the price of insurance tends to depend on "feel" and various intangibles. Failures drive prices up, and successes decrease them. Interestingly, these variations occur whether or not a failure was insured.

12.3.12 Remote Sensing

The use of commercial remote sensing satellites is part of a trend toward global transparency. High-resolution satellite imagery of the globe is available now and provides the space industry an opportunity to make profits from a wide variety of consumers. US Governmental policies permit and encourage such systems. US national policy is to "advance and protect US national security and foreign policy interests by maintaining the nation's leadership in remote sensing space activities, and by sustaining and enhancing the US remote sensing industry. Doing so will also foster economic growth, contribute to environmental stewardship, and enable scientific and technological excellence" [Commercial Remote Sensing Policy, 2003]. To do this, the US Government is supposed to "Rely to the maximum practical extent on US commercial remote sensing space capabilities for filling imagery and geospatial needs for military, intelligence, foreign policy, homeland security, and civil users" [Commercial Remote Sensing Policy, 2003].

Of course, not all uses of remote sensing information are benign, and the provision of information shifts power from the former holders of secrets to the newly informed, which has implications for national sovereignty, for the ability of corporations to keep proprietary information secret, and for the balance of power between state and non-state actors. Sovereignty is directly challenged by new satellite systems, and this has important policy implications. If permitted to image territories anywhere in the world and sell such imagery to anyone, governments lose a significant degree of control over information about their territory. As noted in the literature.

Under international law, countries have no grounds for objecting to being imaged from outer space. The existing standards, the result largely of long-standing US efforts to render legitimate both military reconnaissance and civilian imaging from space, are codified in two UN documents. The Outer Space Treaty of 1967 establishes the notion that outer space cannot be claimed as national territory, legitimating satellite travel in space over any country's territory. And despite years of efforts by then-Soviet bloc and developing countries to claim a right of prior consent in order to review and possibly withhold any data about their territory, in 1986 the UN General Assembly adopted a set of legal principles on civilian remote sensing that make no mention of any right of prior consent. Instead, the principles merely require that "As soon as the primary data and the processed data concerning the territory under its jurisdiction are produced, the sensed State shall have access to them on a nondiscriminatory basis and on reasonable cost terms" [Florini and Dehqanzada, 1999].

Publically available imagery has improved from ten, to five, to one, and to 0.5 meter resolution. Higher resolution imagery is being demanded. If a country being imaged asks for a copy, it is entitled to buy one at the going rate. Military installations could be imaged. Industrial concerns may find themselves being observed by competitors. This can be considered a form of corporate espionage, but satellite imaging is legal.

Pursuant to the *1992 Land Remote Sensing Policy Act*, responsibilities have been delegated from the Secretary of Commerce to the Assistant Administrator for NOAA Satellite and Information Services (NOAA/NESDIS) for the licensing of the operations of private space-based remote sensing systems [USC, 5601]. In accordance with the Act, the *15 CFR Part 960* regulations concerning the licensing of private remote sensing space systems have been issued. Given national security and diplomatic sensitivities and pursuant to regulation, it is thus unlawful for any person who is subject to the jurisdiction or control of the United States, directly or through any subsidiary or affiliate, to operate a private remote sensing space system without possession of a valid license issued under the Act and the regulations.

The ability to image the globe is not unfettered and can be limited by the terms of the license and in accord with *15 CFR Part 960*. Consistent with the requirement that licensees operate their systems in a manner that protects national security concerns, foreign policy and international obligations, the Kyl-Bingaman Amendment requires that "[a] department or agency of the United States may issue a license for the collection or dissemination by a non-Federal entity of satellite imagery with respect to Israel only if such imagery is no more detailed or precise than satellite imagery of Israel that is available from commercial sources" [National Defense Authorization Act, 1997]. So the Department of Commerce must make findings as to the level of detail or precision of satellite imagery of Israel available from non-US commercial sources. NOAA requires an applicant to submit a plan explaining how its proposed system will be able to restrict the collection and/or dissemination of imagery of Israeli territory at a level of resolution determined by the Commerce Department. As an additional licensing requirement, licensees are required, "upon termination of operations under the license, to make disposition of any satellites in space in a manner satisfactory to the President," in accordance with Section 202(b)(4) of the *Land Remote Sensing Policy Act*. Applicants are also required to provide at the time of application a plan for post-mission disposition of remote sensing satellites.

12.3.13 Space Debris

As discussed in Sec. 7.5, the global expansion of space technologies, and especially the availability of diverse small spacecraft technologies and providers, is leading to a rapid expansion in the population of active spacecraft, and associated space debris. As of 2011, the DoD tracks over 22,000 objects in orbit. Of these objects, 928 are operating satellites with 437 owned by the United States, Russia 95 and China 58. Of the operating satellites, 449 are in low earth orbit (LEO), 59 in medium earth orbit, 381 in geosynchronous orbit (GEO) and 39 in elliptical orbits.

Space Situational Awareness (SSA) is crucial to monitoring space, and is absolutely essential to mission success and protection of space assets [Space Foundation, 2008]. It enables a space power to "detect, identify, assess, and track space objects and events to support space operations. SSA is also critical to space support operations, such as placing satellites in orbit," or performing anomaly or recovery operations [del Monte, 2007].* A basic and fundamental component of establishing SSA is space surveillance. Space surveillance is the "observation of space and of the activities occurring in space." Space surveillance tasks can be accomplished through a variety of ground and space-based radar and electro-optical sensors. Space-faring nations can use their awareness to avoid space hazards, or advise other nations on those dangers and perhaps on the means and ways to avoid producing them. Surveillance enables deterrence and defense activities against man-made and environmental threats, and promotes stability in the interactions among space operators.

A perfect surveillance system would provide "continual awareness of orbiting objects; real-time search and targeting-quality information; threat detection, identification, and location; predictive intelligence analysis of foreign space capability and intent in a geopolitical context; and a global reporting capability for friendly space systems" [Space Foundation, 2008]. If all operators had contemporaneous and exquisite awareness of their satellites, and threats to them, they could then react and maneuver their spacecraft out of harm's way if such a collision was imminent. Unfortunately, that perfect level of surveillance and awareness is nothing but science fiction. The current US and other space surveillance systems cannot observe everything in orbit continuously, nor can they provide any real-time services. The limited number of sensors, their locations, their fidelity, and plain fundamental physics do not enable that level of capability. The system only tracks satellites when they pass over or near one of its radar or optical sensors.

Owner/operators should expect to possess positional information on their satellites that are often an order of magnitude more accurate and timely than that gathered by US and other space surveillance systems. And that knowledge is even more significant when one takes into account their knowledge of maneuver plans. Despite this advantage, no single operator knows the location of all space objects with the best fidelity; and few have insight into what other non-US surveillance sensor networks observe and report. Even the organization with access to the most comprehensive catalog of SSA information, US Strategic Command (USSTRATCOM), which publishes

---

* The attributes of the SSA definition have been examined in a number of venues. For example, an ESA User Expert Group performing an SSA requirement study preliminarily defined Space Situational Awareness (SSA) "as a comprehensive knowledge of the population of space objects, of existing threats/risks, and of the space environment. According to del Monte, the study concluded that SSA is the understanding and maintained awareness of (a) the Earth orbital population, (b) the space environment, and (c) possible threats. "(a) Earth orbital population. Detection and/or tracking of man-made objects (e.g., US SSN Catalog, comprising spacecraft, rocket bodies, mission-related objects, and fragments); identification and characterization of detected objects (e.g., launching nation, owner, operator, object status, and function); determination of orbit state and covariance information; identification of spacecraft maneuvers; determination of spacecraft attitude; determination of antenna/instrument pointing. "(b) Space environment—Detection and/or tracking natural objects (e.g., near-Earth objects [NEO]); detect and understand man-made, induced environment; detect and understand interferences; forecast space weather and its effects; predict the natural particulate environment and its effects (meteoroids). "(c) Possible threats—Predict and assess the risk to humans and property on ground and in air space due to re-entries; detect and assess adversary use or preparations for adversary use of or upon space systems (e.g., ground- or space-based); detect on-orbit explosions and release events (accidental or intentional); predict and/or detect on-orbit collisions (accidental or intentional); predict and detect permanent or temporary disruption of mission and service capabilities."

the information about these objects through its SSA Sharing Program, doesn't know where all orbiting objects are, all the time. Even though it has more global sensor coverage and an ability to track smaller objects, the USSTRATCOM's SSA system would profit by obtaining owner/operator information and maneuver plans.

To be sure, the 22,000 orbiting objects described above are only those that can be tracked within the capability of USSTRATCOM's sensors, which have difficulty tracking objects smaller than the size of a grapefruit or 10 cm. Compounding the challenges, there may be millions more objects on orbit and up to 330 million objects of 1 mm to 1 cm size and 560,000 objects of 1 cm to 10 cm (see Sec. 7.5). The probability of collision by satellites with one or more of these small objects is almost a certainty given any amount of time on orbit. And small objects can be very destructive.

Another issue confronting satellite operators is that even if they know where all the threatening objects are and their ephemerides, they may not have sufficient time, fuel or maneuvering capability to avoid them. One must also consider the variety of collision scenarios. For example, two live, maneuverable satellites could both perform maneuvers to avoid a possible collision. Unless these maneuvers are coordinated, they could end up making the situation worse rather than better and wasting valuable fuel. Of course, this is not a new problem or one that operators are unaware of, but the recent growth in on-orbit debris has made solving or mitigating the problem more urgent.

In addition, the control of satellites is already a challenging task, given the space environment the satellites operate in and the distances involved in the communications chain, 500 to 35,000 km. Satellite operations are based on the ability to communicate with and control satellites, hopefully without hindrance from man-made objects or actions. Indeed, some satellites, such as Galaxy 15, have stopped responding to commands from ground operators. Galaxy 15, dubbed "Zombiesat" by the media, began to drift, while its receiver and transmitter equipment continued to function. The combination of uncontrolled drifting, with an active communications payload, meant that Galaxy 15 posed serious radio interference concerns to other satellite operations in the geosynchronous orbit (GEO) belt. Since its communications payloads receive and transmit functions were still working, the satellite could pickup and re-broadcast C-band signals intended for other active C-Band satellites. So as it drifted through the GEO belt near other satellites, Galaxy 15 could pickup and re-broadcast C-band emissions, potentially causing multi-path interference for other satellite operations. Rigorous and sophisticated operations, data sharing and coordination among several satellite system operators were necessary to mitigate the satellite's threat to other operating satellites, before it could be recovered by the operator.

Satellites fail in the active GEO belt, on an average about one per year, [Choc and Jehn, 2010], as documented in an annual report published by the European Space Agency. There are a variety of causes and scenarios for these failures. These failures leave satellites in active orbits and they then present danger to other systems.

Under the recently adopted United Nations Space Debris Mitigation Guidelines, which are based on the more extensive United Nations Interagency Space Debris Coordinating Committee (IADC) Guidelines, spacecraft operators are supposed to perform an end-of-life disposal maneuver to remove their satellite from the GEO region. This usually involves boosting it at least 250 km (155 miles) above the GEO belt. Unfortunately, the guidelines don't resolve problems associated with spacecraft left on orbit during the early years of the space age. Compliance with the IADC guidelines for new spacecraft is still spotty at best. Of the 21 GEO spacecraft that reached end-of-life in 2009, only 11 were disposed of properly. Several were moved, but not into an orbit high enough to ensure that they do not cause problems in the near future. Three spacecraft were abandoned in the active belt and are now librating about the 75 deg East libration point. Four rocket bodies, used to place payloads in geosynchronous orbit, also orbit within the protected zone [Weeden, 2010].

The continuing and expanding numbers of space debris and orbiting systems is heightening safety of flight concerns among space-faring states. Some argue we are nearing the point where whole sectors of the space domain are saturated and thus lost to safe and secure operations. Experts forecast that the debris may eventually and continually collide with other debris and active space objects; these collisions will then multiply and create even greater numbers of objects that could damage other spacecraft (see Sec. 7.5).

In addition to being what some would argue is one of the most physically congested regions, with significant space debris and satellite collision threats; the GEO belt is also a region in space that suffers from significant electromagnetic radio frequency inference (RFI) between satellites. This interference threat exists in part because many satellites in GEO are all relatively close and most broadcast and receive in the same frequency bands. The Galaxy 15 incident described above serves as a representative example of the threat radio frequency interference poses to on-orbit systems. Inadvertent and intentional jamming and RFI have caused problems for satellites for many years.

Space debris is a significant environmental issue. Mission designers must plan missions to prevent or abate space debris as much as possible. They may also want to design satellites to survive the risk of collision with debris. Finally designers should consider designing systems that support an effective SSA system to ascertain and attribute on-orbit events so that appropriate responses can be developed and implemented by affected space-operators and, if necessary, interested States.

12.3.14 Environmental Concerns

Space systems introduce pollution contamination in various degrees into different parts of the space environment. A spacecraft and its launch system produces exhaust gases, and a mix of cooling water, sand and dust when launching. Chemical releases from spacecraft on orbit could have a depleting effect on the ozone layer, and reduce the density of electrons in the ionosphere, potentially distorting radio communications. Reentry involves the production of metal vapors into the upper atmosphere. Space activities could introduce biological pollutants into the space environment.

The *Partial Test Ban Treaty* prohibits nuclear explosions in the atmosphere and in space. The *Convention on the Prohibition of Military and Other Hostile Use of Environmental Modification Techniques* also helps protect the environment.

The United States still has obligations under Article IX of the *Outer Space Treaty,* which provides for international protection of the outer-space environment. Thus, it must comply with either the letter of the Act's provisions or their essence. If a proposed mission "has been done before," environmental questions may quickly be resolved. But if the mission includes something new, then approval may take some time, depending on how strongly the mission affects outer space or, especially, any celestial body.

The *National Environmental Policy Act* (NEPA) and its implementing regulations established US policy promoting the enhancement of the environment. It sets up procedural requirements for all US Government agencies to prepare Environmental Assessments (EAs) and Environmental Impact Statements (EISs) describing the environmental effects of proposed actions. NEPA's requirements apply to all Federal agencies procuring and operating space systems. These agencies must integrate environmental values into their decision-making processes by considering the environmental impacts of their proposed actions and the reasonable alternatives to those actions. NASA follows the NEPA regulations promulgated by the Council on Environmental Quality (CEQ) and has developed agency-specific NEPA policies and regulations to ensure compliance with the NEPA statute, implementing regulations, and related Executive Orders.

The NEPA is an "umbrella" legislation and its processes often involves coordinating compliance with the following laws:

- ***Clean Air Act***—The Clean Air Act, incorporated as Title 42-Chapter 85 in US law, provides regulations to protect and improve the US's air quality as well as the ozone layer
- ***Clean Water Act***—The Clean Water Act regulates the restoration and maintenance of the integrity of the nation's waters and wetlands, and provides assistance for the improvement of wastewater treatment
- ***National Historic Preservation Act***—The National Historic Preservation Act promotes Federal leadership for the preservation of historically significant, cultural resources and to "foster conditions under which our modern society and our prehistoric resources can exist in productive harmony"
- ***Endangered Species Act***—The Endangered Species Act regulates the conservation of threatened or endangered animals, plants and habitats

Under NEPA, the responsible agency must analyze the potential environmental effects. If more than one agency is involved, a lead agency supervises the preparation of the environmental documentation. For a private or commercial launch, AST would require an environmental impact assessment under its mandate from the *Commercial Space Launch Act.*

An EA helps determine the need for an impact statement on a particular program. It must include enough information to allow one to determine whether the proposed action is major and whether it significantly harms the environment of the "global commons." It must assess the environmental effects and the need for the proposed action plus available alternatives. Unless security restrictions intervene, the assessment is usually made available to the public upon request. There is no need to obtain public comment. An EA is less formal and rigorous than an EIS. Typically, the EA applies to:

- Spacecraft development projects in space science and in space and terrestrial applications
- Specific experimental projects in space and energy technology
- Development and operations of new space transportation systems
- Advanced development of new space transportation and spacecraft systems

In contrast, there is a need to file an EIS when an action is "expected to have a significant impact on the quality of the human environment." The draft statement should be thorough enough to permit analysis and comment. If it is complete enough after agency review, it goes to the public for comment. At this time, the Department of State, the Council on Environmental Quality, and other federal agencies have a chance to comment. For the proposed action and reasonable alternatives, the EIS: (1) considers purpose and need; (2) provides a detailed description; (3) analyzes the environmental effects; (4) briefly describes the affected environment of the space "global commons"; and (5) compares the alternatives' effects on the space "global commons."

If something is not known because it is unavailable or scientifically uncertain, the EIS must say so. Public hearings are not required, but may be appropriate, depending on circumstances. After agencies and the public have commented, the EIS is revised as necessary, further analyzing any issues they have raised. It is then published in the *Federal Register* before forwarding it to the US Government decision maker for final action.

Normally, an EIS is required for research and development activities associated with developing and operating new launch vehicles, space vehicles likely to release large amounts of foreign materials into the

Earth's atmosphere or into space, and certain systems for nuclear propulsion and generating power.

In some cases, space activities may affect the environment of a foreign nation or a resource designated as one of global importance. If so, slightly different procedures would be required. First, an environmental survey or review would need to be prepared. An environmental survey is a cooperative action and may be bilateral or multilateral. Whether or not a review is conducted depends on consultations which determine if the proposed action would do significant harm. The content is flexible, but generally includes (1) a review of the affected environment, (2) the predicted environmental effects, and (3) significant known actions that governmental entities are taking to protect or improve the environment against the proposed action.

The US Government prepares an environmental review unilaterally. In effect, it is an internal action, by which one or more governmental agencies surveys the important environmental issues associated with the proposed action. It contains essentially the same information as an environmental survey.

12.3.15 Lasers, Particle Beams, and Nuclear Power

Lasers and particle beams illuminating into, through, and from space have occurred since the beginnings of laser technology. Use of laser systems is contemplated and used for a wide variety of needs: communications, calibration, ranging, active and passive tracking and space surveillance, power transfer, targeting, and negation purposes. Laser communications present great opportunities to increase data through-puts and security. Unfortunately, while not all lasing is malicious, the use of laser capabilities poses the potential to damage systems and payloads on orbit, spacecraft personnel, and ground-based populations, depending on the design and employment of the system. It is alleged that some countries have secretly fired powerful laser weapons to disable imagery satellites by "blinding" their payloads [Harris, 2006].

Laser beam propagation to and from the ground to space has executed the cognizance of various government agencies, namely: the Occupational Safety and Health Administration (OSHA) responsible for protecting workforce personnel; the Federal Aviation Administration (FAA) responsible for protecting pilots and aircraft; and the Laser Clearinghouse of US Strategic Command (USSTRATCOM) responsible for protecting space assets.

The Laser Clearinghouse (LCH) and laser owner/operators (LO/Os) are required to work together to provide safe and responsible laser activities, as required by Department of Defense Instruction (DODI) 3100.11. US Government LO/Os with non-waived lasers require Joint Functional Component Command (JFCC) —Space authorization to conduct laser activities according to US Strategic Command Instructions. DoD LO/Os must obtain predictive avoidance open firing windows from the LCH or the Joint Space Operations Center (JSpOC) prior to conducting laser activities [Cheyenne Mountain Operations Center, 2008].

The use of nuclear power in space has enabled the extension of space activities into regions that would not have been possible with non-nuclear power sources. The cold, hostile, and poorly lit environments of the outer planets require a rugged, solar-independent power source that can survive and function for long periods of time. Missions closer to the Sun have environments that can be too harsh for conventional power sources. As the need for nuclear power increases, it will not be banned from space, but its use will be closely regulated.

The main design requirement on US space nuclear power systems has been safety. Extensive safety testing and analyses have been conducted beginning with the very first nuclear power systems (SNAP-3B). Formal safety analysis and independent safety reviews are required before each launch. With the enactment of NEPA, an independent EA is also conducted. The primary safety requirement for radioisotope power sources is to contain or immobilize the radioisotope fuel so that there is no interaction with humans and the environment. Designs are assessed through a wide combination of safety tests. The primary safety requirement is to maintain the reactor in a subcritical condition.

Design for safety must include both system and mission design. The methods to reduce risks from nuclear materials include containing them within radioisotope thermoelectric generators, diluting and dispersing them with reactors, delaying their effects by boosting them into a higher orbit, and possibly retrieving them using a vehicle like the Space Shuttle.

The US safety program includes an Interagency Nuclear Safety Review Panel composed of three coordinators appointed by the Secretary of Defense, the Administrator of NASA, and the Secretary of Energy. The Nuclear Regulatory Agency, the Environmental Protection Agency, and the National Oceanic and Atmospheric Administration also participate in these reviews. The safety review ascertains whether the benefits of using nuclear power are worth the risks. The policy of the United States in using radioisotope thermoelectric generators following an aborted SNAP-A mission in April 1964 was to design the container so that all nuclear material would survive intact, regardless of the nature of the accident. The policy makers specifically envisioned reentry and impact on earth. This effort had important consequences. On May 18, 1968, the range safety officer aborted the launch of NIMBUS-81 at an altitude of 30 km over the Santa Barbara Channel. The generator capsules were recovered without incident. Those who launched SNAP 10A with a nuclear reactor in 1965 launched the reactor in a subcritical mode, designed it to remain subcritical at or after impact should it reenter the atmosphere before start-up, and delayed its start-up until it had reached orbit. It is in an almost circular polar orbit, which has a decay life of 4,000 years. Additionally, this reactor package was designed to come apart on reentry.

References

For annotated bibliography of space system financing and space law, see the book website.

AECA. 1976. Arms Export Control Act of 1976, Sec. 38, as Amended, P. L. 94-329. The AECA's 22 USC: 2778.

AIAA. 2011. *Colloquium the Law of Outer Space.* Report by International Institute of Space Law. Washington, DC: AIAA.

Baker, Howard A. 1989. *Space Debris: Legal and Policy Implications*. Dordrecht, Netherlands: Martinus Nihoff Publishers.

Blount, P. J. 2008. "Limits on Space Weapons Incorporating the Law of War into the Corpus Juris Spatials." IAC-08-E8.3.5. 115L Colloquium. IAC, Glasgow, UK. Oct. p. 1.

Breed, Paul. 2008, interview on *The Space Show,* Nov. 3.

Burney, N. 2008. "International Law: A Brief Primer for Information Purposes Only." Art. 38.

Cheyenne Mountain Operations Center. 2005. "Laser Clearing House Reports Handbook", Rev A1. CMOC/J3S, 15 March.

Choc, R. and R. Jehn. 2010. *Classification of Geosynchronous Objects.*, issue 12. Feb.

Christol, Carl Q. 1982. *The Modern International Law of Outerspace*. New York, NY: Pergamon Press.

Convention on the Prohibition of Military or Any Other Hostile Use of Environmental Modification Techniques. 1977, Entered Into Force May 18. 1978, Art. 1. Oct. 5.

Dale, Shana. 2006. Remarks at AAS/AIAA Seminar on the Importance of International Collaboration in Space Exploration. Nov. 1.

de Selding, P.B. 2010. "France Seeks ITU Help to Halt Satellite Signal Jamming by Iran." Space News. Jan. 8.

Del Monte, Luca. 2007. "A European Approach to Space Situational Awareness." 4th European Space Weather Week. Brussels. Nov. 5–9.

Durrwachter, William E.: 2010, E-mail communication with John M. Jurist, Aug. 22.

Environmental Modification Convention. 1977. Bureau of International Security and Nonproliferation.

FAI. 2004. "The 100km Boundary for Astronautics." Doc. Federation Aeronautique Internationale Press Release. Jun. 24.

Financial Accounting Standards Board (FASB). 2010. Website.

Florini, Ann M. and Yahya A. Dehqanzada. 1999. "No More Secrets?: Policy Implications of Commercial Remote Sensing Satellites" Carnegie Endowment or International Peace. Paper No. 1. Jul.

Government Accounting Standards Board (GASB). 2010. Website.

Harris, Francis. 2006. "Beijing Secretly Fires Lasers to Disable US Satellites." The Telegraph. Sept. 26.

IBWIPO. 2004. "Intellectual Property and Space Activities." International Bureau of the World Intellectual Property Organization. Geneva, Switzerland. Apr. Pg. 2.

International Institute of Space Law (IISL). 2011. Website.

ITU. 2011. "Radio Communication Sector." International Telecommunications Union. Apr. 5.

Jurist, John M., Sam Dinkin and David M. Livingston. 2005. "When Physics, Economics and Reality Collide: The Challenge of Cheap Orbital Access," Presented at the *American Institute of Aeronautics and Astronautics Space 2005 Conference,* AIAA-2005-6620, Sept.

Jurist, John M. 2009. "Astropolitics." Peer Review Journal, vol. 7. Jan–Apr. pp. 32–49.

Koelle, Dietrich E. 2007. *Handbook of Cost Engineering for Space Transportation Systems (Rev. 2)*, Report No. TCS-TR-184. Ottobrunn, Germany.

Mukai, Toshifumi. 2008. "International Cooperation: When 1+1=3." *Ask Magazine*, NASA. Pg. 8.

National Defense Authorization Act for Fiscal Year 1997. 1997. Sec. 1064, Public Law No. 104-201.

National Space Policy of the United States of America. "Principles," p. 3. 28 Jun.

The Outer Space Treaty. 1967.

Rose, Frank A. 2010. "International Cooperation: Furthering US National Space Policy and Goals." USSTRATCOM Space Symposium. Omaha, NE. Nov. 2.

Space Foundation. 2008. "Space Situational Awareness"—Panel Focus at Strategic Space and Defense: Sept. 22.

USC. 1984. Title 49, App. 2614.

U.S. Commercial Remote Sensing Policy. 2003. Fact Sheet, Apr. 25. Pg. 1.

U.S.C. 5601 et seq as Amended by Public Law 105-303.

Understandings, 1977. Environmental Monitoring Convention.

US Bureau of Labor Statistics. 2010. "Historical CPI-U Data from 1913 to the Present."

Vienna Convention on Law of Treaties. 1969. 1155 U.N.T.S. 331,8. *International Legal Materials 679.*

Weeden, Brian. 2010. "Dealing with Galaxy 15: Zombiesats and On-Orbit Servicing." *The Space Review.* May 24.

13 Reducing Space Mission Cost and Schedule

James R. Wertz, *Microcosm, Inc./USC*

This chapter focuses on perhaps the most fundamental problem facing space missions today—they cost too much and take too long. (See Sec. 1.1.) Obviously no one sets out to design a space mission that costs too much and takes too long, yet fixing this problem has proven remarkably elusive. A number of major and important activities in space, such as the human exploration of Mars and the Wide Field Infrared Survey Telescope (WFIRST) have been delayed for a decade or more due to budget pressure. On the other hand, there are a great many missions flying, largely using small spacecraft*, that are very low cost and also have high reliability. What we would like to find is what these small, low-cost missions can teach us about reducing the cost and schedule on all space missions.

There is a substantial bibliography on reducing space mission cost on the website. Several of the books are somewhat older, but remain the standard reference works on this topic. Wertz and Larson [1996] provide an overview of the entire subject, with some updates in Wertz and Dawson [1996] and Wertz, et al. [2011]. Sarsfield [1998] gives the results of a RAND study on low-cost science missions and London [1994] provides an overview of both the reasons for high launch costs and methods to overcome them. AMSAT has created a number of documents providing detailed recipes for building low-cost communications satellites [Davidoff, 1998; Ford, 2010]. Fleeter [2000] gives a detailed description of the use of smallsats to reduce cost and schedule. While not directly related to reducing cost, Harland and Lorenz [2005], provide an excellent discussion of space system failures, which is, of course, a key element of mission design that may, or may not, be related to attempts to reduce cost. Also important are the two principal annual conferences on this topic listed in the bibliography—the Utah State University SmallSat Conference in Logan, Utah, in August and the Reinventing Space Conference in Los Angeles in April or May. There are also several international SmallSat conferences.

Most of the specific missions cited in this section are SmallSat missions simply because that is where most of the experience base resides in methods for reducing cost and schedule. (See Sec. 25.3 for a discussion of SmallSats and 25.4 for CubeSats.) What we would like to do is take this experience base and make it applicable to more traditional larger missions (including science, military, interplanetary, commercial, and human spaceflight) by using any or all of the following:

- Applying some of the processes and methods first developed and tested on small satellite programs to larger, more traditional programs
- Using small satellites to test new technology in space much faster and at lower cost than would otherwise be possible
- Redefine the missions themselves so that they can be done, at least in part, by one or multiple small satellites

I teach a course in "Reinventing Space—The Design of Low Cost Space Missions" biannually at the University of Southern California where the question of applicability to

* What constitutes a "small" spacecraft is intentionally a bit nebulous here. In the context of this chapter, "small" represents more a state of mind than physical size. A small spacecraft is one that has a limited budget and schedule, constrained objectives, one, or at most a few, payloads, and a willingness to be less risk averse than a traditional large spacecraft. As discussed in more detail in Sec. 2.1.8, these spacecraft are typically less than 500 kg, but it is more a matter of how they are built than the actual physical size.

large missions arises often. At the end of the course, I apply the methods developed primarily on smallsats to the largest space program that seems practical in the near-term, a 1000-person permanent colony on the Moon. I am convinced that such a "Luniveristy" can be created for substantially less than the cost of the ISS. [Wertz, 1999]. The point here is not to begin a push for large-scale lunar colonies, but simply to point out that the goal of this chapter is to use methods, processes, and technology developed largely for smallsat missions to dramatically reduce the cost of the space mission enterprise as a whole.

13.1 The Need to Reinvent Space

What is "Reinventing Space"? In my view, this means combining the current dramatic advances in microelectronics, software, and material science with the goal-oriented, much more driven spirit of the Apollo, Explorer, or Corona missions to create smaller, lower-cost, more responsive systems capable of doing more and doing it more quickly and at lower cost. In short,

> ***Reinventing Space*** **is using modern technology and old-fashioned drive, determination, and some willingness to accept risk to do much more, much faster, with fewer resources.**

In practice, this means creating what I call *Mission Diversity*, i.e., a mix of large, typically very expensive programs and much smaller, quicker, more flexible space systems—the PT boats of space. In some respects, reinventing space is similar to the call by NASA Administrator Dan Goldin in the late 1990's for "faster, better, cheaper" space missions, with two critical differences:

- The problem today is substantially more acute
  - For example, in 2007 the top 10 DoD space programs were overrun by over $32 billion and it continues to get worse because of the Space Spiral shown in Fig. 1-2 in Sec. 1.1.
  - The economic decline prior to 2010 has created an unprecedented worldwide demand to reduce cost
  - To be relevant today, systems must be responsive in hours or days, not months, years, or decades
- The technology is available to make it happen
  - Microelectronics are greatly increasing the capability of small, low-cost systems
  - Computer technology and software are allowing major advances in on-board processing
  - Advanced materials technology is creating a new realm of lighter, stronger spacecraft and launch vehicles

In addition, it is likely that failing to aggressively attack this fundamental problem will mean that the United States will lose its dominant position in space. It is already the case that most commercial space launches are now done from Europe, Russia, India, or China. The US is rapidly losing its primary position in human spaceflight and this is likely to continue. Other nations have long-standing, very active programs to build both small launch systems and increasing capable small satellites, taking full advantage of modern technology to create increasingly competent systems that will be capable of being launched quickly and in large numbers. If the downward Space Spiral of Fig. 1-2 continues, the American space program has the potential of significantly falling behind other global space programs, while remaining the most expensive in the world.

Much of traditional mission assurance for space systems focuses on parts reliability and the capability of a system to work in space for a decade or more. Unfortunately, as discussed in Sec. 13.4, parts reliability does not prevent the most likely causes of mission failures or lack of data, such as:

- Launch failures (OCO, Challenger)—on the average, approximately 10% of launches fail
- System failures (USA 193)
- Collisions (Iridium 33/Cosmos 2251) which typically leave thousands of untrackable debris particles
- Operator errors (Huygens Titan probe wind experiment, Viking 1 Mars lander)
- Assembly errors (Genesis)
- Data unavailable due to cost or schedule overruns
  - Extended delays (Chandra, JWST, NPOESS)
  - Program cancellation due to cost (T-Sat, Constellation, Human mission to Mars)

For most traditional large satellite programs, the consequences of any of the above is that the asset isn't available for any current need and will take years or decades and a great deal of money to replace. In addition, 15 years after the successful launch of a large, perfectly assembled satellite with no orbit failures, no collisions, and no fatal operator errors, we have:

- A satellite built with 25-year old technology to meet 25-year old mission needs and trying to cover the entire world, and
- No production line and no one who knows how to build a replacement.

13.1.1 The Need for Low-Cost, Responsive SmallSat Missions*

The arguments for creating mission diversity by adding substantially more smallsats and responsive, smallsat launch capability to the broad mix of satellite systems

* For a more detailed discussion of this topic see Wertz [2010].

fall primarily into the following categories, each of which is discussed below:

- They create the potential to reduce long-term space mission cost by billions
- They reduce mission risk and fragility
- They can be put into operational orbits that aren't feasible with more traditional missions and effectively mitigate the growing problem of orbital debris
- They increase efficiency in the use of both human and financial resources
- They enable missions that aren't otherwise affordable or feasible
- They make newer, better technology available to users
- They can be far more responsive to world events and the needs of the end user
- They create a more economically sustainable business model for the space industry

The Potential to Reduce Long-Term Space Mission Cost by Billions. As discussed in Sec. 2.1.8 and in more detail in Sec. 25.3, there are many smallsat missions with a high level of utility and high reliability that are flying, being built, and being planned. Unlike more traditional satellites, smallsats are evolving rapidly. A smallsat that uses technology more than a few years old is effectively a dinosaur waiting to be replaced by systems much faster, much cheaper, and much more capable.

Nonetheless, this very substantial technological progress would appear to have very little impact on long-term space mission cost for several reasons. Some communities, such as human spaceflight, don't see the relevance of smallsats unless we are able to microminiaturize people, which is still a ways off. Also, the cost of the major space programs in DoD, NASA, the intelligence community, and the large international programs are dominated by the cost of the "programs of record" that are typically very large spacecraft built and flown over decades. Until we find a way to reduce the cost of large programs, it appears that any resulting savings will be small. But changing how the large programs are built and flown is very difficult because of the Space Spiral that we have discussed. The cost of these programs and of the associated launch vehicles continues to escalate with little potential for being reduced. By the time the programs get to the level of the NASA Director, the Secretary of the Air Force, or Congress, the only alternative to accepting high cost is to cancel the program and this has now occurred on a number of very expensive, high profile systems.

This issue is perhaps best addressed by an airplane analogy. Assume that an air fleet is dominated by 747s with very expensive equipment on board and we are trying to find a way to reduce cost. We can't change the 747 or any of the equipment without risking the entire mission and we can't afford to do that. The right answer is to begin off-loading some of the 747's tasks to small, cheaper, quicker-to-build airplanes and to begin testing on the small planes the technology that can ultimately reduce cost on the larger ones. This also reduces mission risk by having smaller systems available that can be put in place quickly, should there be any problems with the 747 fleet. Eventually, we arrive at a balanced fleet that can do far more with a combination of newer and better technology in small systems and a smaller number of large, expensive systems that are still cheaper than previously because they have less to do, can use more modern technology to get it done, and have back-ups available should problems arise. Returning to our space example, low-cost small spacecraft can't deliver astronauts to the Moon or the Space Station, but they can bring water, peanut butter sandwiches, medicine, and a left-handed torque wrench when it's needed. If we can do some entire missions, and parts of other missions, far quicker and at much lower cost, we can expand what we can do in space, be more responsive to the needs of the end user, and do more with fewer resources. Specifically, we can reasonably expect cost savings (or equivalently, increases in what can be done) of billions of dollars by reducing launch costs, reducing the "time to market," offloading some onto more economical, smaller systems, bringing newer technology to bear, and using small systems to test the processes and technologies needed to reduce cost on more traditional spacecraft [Wertz, 2010].

A key issue for space systems is that launch is a driver of mission cost. It is typically not the most expensive element for large missions, which has led some observers to conclude that launch cost is relatively unimportant in terms of reducing overall mission cost. But that isn't the case. It doesn't make sense to launch a $5 million satellite on a $25 million launch vehicle. So long as a dedicated launch costs $25 million or more, the mission (payload, spacecraft bus, launch, and initial operations) will typically cost $75 million to $100 million or more, because it doesn't make economic sense for them to be much cheaper.

Similarly, mission responsiveness is driven by both the cost and responsiveness of launch systems. The Soviets/Russians have had systems in inventory and launch-on-demand (within hours) for over 30 years. The Soviets launched 29 payloads in 69 days to support and monitor the 1982 Falklands War that was sufficiently far south that there was relatively little coverage from traditional observation satellites [Cooper, 1992]. But for most US missions, $50 million to $100 million satellites are too expensive to build to inventory, and this is typically not done.

Weather, particularly winds aloft, is one of the most common causes of launch delays. This further increases cost by requiring a "standing army" of launch operations personnel. Again, the Soviets/Russians have had all weather launch capability for decades, such that this is not a major concern for them.

From a purely economic perspective, large satellites need nearly all of the money spent up front before there is a return on investment. This is both economically adverse and tends to enforce the approach of being very risk-averse, because there is no way to fix a problem once the system has been launched. For SmallSat systems, money is spent and results are generated more-or-less continuously over the life of the program as systems are continually being built and launched. This is both cheaper (money spent later costs less, due to the cost of money) and more amenable to a build, test, fly approach in which corrections can be introduced during the program, and new technology can be rapidly inserted.

Satellites with high utility costing $5 million to $10 million can have a strong, positive, near-term impact on the ability of space to support the modern warfighter, respond to natural or man-made disasters, recover from on-orbit failures, or test space systems rapidly and at low cost. But **operational** systems in this price range cannot come about unless there is a dedicated, responsive launch at comparable cost. While launch itself is not the highest cost element for most missions, the high cost and long timelines of current launch systems prevent us from creating low-cost, truly responsive missions.

Reducing Mission Risk and Fragility. As defined in Sec. 24.3, mission risk is the product of reliability and the cost of failure. Lower cost missions are inherently lower risk because fewer resources are at stake. Most current large space systems are inherently fragile because any failure can lead to major consequences and the loss of a single spacecraft can lead to a lost capability that can be replaced only after many years and at very high cost. Alternatively, if one of many small spacecraft is destroyed by a collision with invisible debris, for example, there is a loss of capability, but that loss is mitigated by having multiple spacecraft on orbit and an inventory of others that can be launched in a short time. Given the rapid evolution of small spacecraft, it is likely that the replacement on the ground waiting to be launched will have a greater capability than the on-orbit asset that was lost. In a fleet of 20 small spacecraft, we can plan for launch and on-orbit failures and take that into account in our program by building 10% or 20% more spacecraft than are needed. (This is done in virtually all constellations.) If most or all of a capability is in a small number of large spacecraft, the risk is higher and far more difficult to mitigate.

As pointed out with specific examples in the introduction to Sec. 13.1 above, there is no failure-free system. **Reduced risk and high mission assurance come instead from system robustness—i.e., having sufficient back-ups and options available to ensure mission success even when failures do occur.** In addition, current space systems are designed primarily to have a high parts reliability, but parts failures aren't typically why missions fail. By driving up cost and schedule, we are making the system less reliable from the point of view of the end user. As discussed in Sec. 13.4, many current space systems are effectively being designed to have a "reliability of zero," because they are not launched on time—not a good scenario from the perspective of the end user.

There is often a presumption that what you "buy" with high cost space systems is a greater level of reliability, at least for the spacecraft itself, but even this may not be true. There is no statistical data available on the reliability of low-cost vs. high-cost spacecraft. However, anecdotal evidence and historical experience suggest that small, low-cost spacecraft may be equally as reliable as larger, more complex spacecraft.

For SmallSats, we would expect a decrease in reliability because of lower quality parts, fewer, lower-cost procedures, lack of redundancy, and more willingness to accept risk. On the other hand, we would expect an increase in reliability for SmallSats vs. traditional larger satellites because there are fewer parts, simpler designs, larger margins, less emphasis on an optimized design, and a higher level of personal responsibility [Wertz, 2010]. For example, on a SmallSat there may be only one person responsible for building the power system. If that system fails, everyone knows whose fault it was. This means that the power system engineer who designed, built, integrated, and tested the entire power system for that spacecraft has as their very first goal that the power system will not fail. They feel that personal responsibility and work very hard to ensure success.

The potential for better operational orbits that aren't feasible with more traditional missions and which can also mitigate the growing problem with orbital debris. Orbit design for low-cost, responsive, smallsat is fundamentally different than that of more traditional missions because the basic mission objectives are different. Specifically, traditional space missions are very expensive and have a long on-orbit lifetime. Therefore, the orbits are designed for worldwide coverage because it isn't known at the time of launch what area of the world may need coverage, and the area needing coverage is likely to change many times over the life of the mission. Consequently, traditional mission orbit objectives are:

- Global coverage
- Long life
- Use whatever launch vehicle it takes to get there

In contrast, operational SmallSat mission orbit objectives are significantly different:

- Coverage of a specific region, event, or set of events—i.e., localized in both time and space
- Willing to give up long life to get good performance at low cost
- Want low-cost launch commensurate with the satellite cost
- Want to minimize creation and accumulation of orbital debris

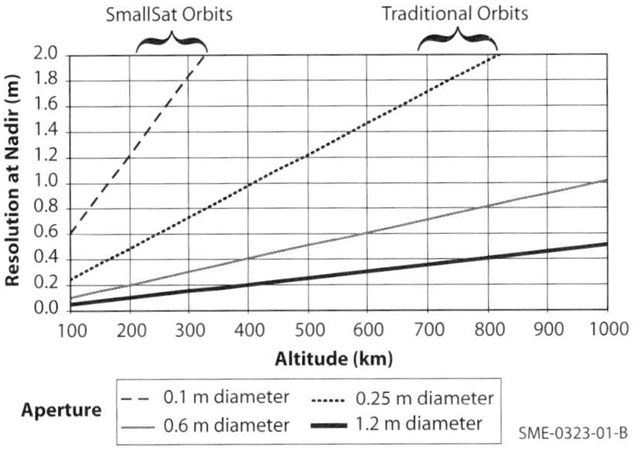

Fig. 13-1. Resolution vs. Altitude for Low Altitude SmallSat Orbits and Higher Altitude Orbits Used for More Traditional Systems [Wertz, 2010].

Most operational SmallSat mission orbits fall into one of 2 broad categories—observations and communications. For SmallSat observation missions, a low altitude, prograde *Repeat Coverage Orbit* (Sec. 10.4.2.6) provides better coverage and better resolution with lower collision probability and rapid debris decay such that orbital debris cannot accumulate. For SmallSat communications missions, circular orbits at 15,000 to 20,000 km altitude and 0 or 90 deg inclination provides both continuous coverage and one-hop communications to CONUS. These orbits provide better coverage, lower vulnerability to attack, and fewer collision opportunities than highly elliptical orbits (HEOs), which have often been considered the best choice for SmallSat communications systems [Wertz, 2007]. See Sec. 10.4.2.7 and Wertz [2005, 2007, 2010] for a discussion of the advantages and disadvantages of these types of orbits.

Because traditional observation satellites are expensive, they are normally placed into high-altitude orbits typically in the range of 700 to 900 km in order to provide both a wide swath and long mission life. In contrast, for SmallSat missions we would like to fly in the 200 to 400 km range with sufficient delta V to allow a 1 to 3 year life and substantial maneuvering. This approach provides comparable resolution using a much smaller telescope, as shown in Fig. 13-1 [Wertz, 2010]. For example, Hubble Space Telescope (2.4 m aperture) initially cost \$2.5 billion in FY10\$ and, if looking at the Earth, would provide 0.22 m resolution at 800 km altitude. Essentially the same resolution can be achieved with a 1 m instrument at 300 km or an 0.5 m instrument at 150 to 200 km, but at a cost of millions, rather than billions of dollars per mission.

While low altitude can be important for observation missions, it is even more important for missions with active sensors, such as a wind lidar or space-based radar. Resolution falls off as the square of the distance, but the power requirement for an active sensor falls as the distance to the 4th power. (See Chap. 15.) This means that going from 600 km to 300 km means a power reduction by a factor 16 and going to 200 km reduces the power by a factor 81. Flying at low altitudes can have a dramatic impact on cost, although it will also reduce coverage.

Low altitude works well for systems intended to provide focused coverage over a defined region, rather than needing to provide coverage of the entire world. In addition, *agile spacecraft,* i.e., ones with substantial on-board delta V, can adjust the altitude and coverage parameters as needed to optimize resolution, coverage, lifetime, and maneuvering to confuse the enemy. This high level of agility is more easily achieved on a lightweight SmallSat than with a large spacecraft. NanoEye, for example, has a 20 kg dry mass with 50 kg of propellant and is intended to provide approximately 2 km/sec of delta V, a much higher level of agility than would be possible with a traditional large and heavy system. [Van Allen et al., 2011].

It has been suggested that the orbital debris problem, made more visible by the Iridium 33/Comos 2251 collision in 2009, is an argument for large, multi-purpose space assets, rather than smaller, shorter-lived satellites or constellations. The essence of this argument is that fewer satellites leads to fewer collisions which leads to less debris. However, this is an incorrect argument for several reasons.

First, active satellites are only a very small part of the debris material in low Earth orbit. In LEO there are roughly 900 active satellites vs. approximately 500,000 debris particles larger than 1 cm, which is large enough to destroy virtually any spacecraft, as discussed in Sec. 7.5, and is about 10 times smaller than the smallest particle that can be tracked. Significantly increasing the number of active satellites doesn't change the amount of "dangerous stuff" in orbit by much at all.

Second, SmallSats have a smaller collision cross section and, therefore, are less likely to collide with other satellites. Traditional LEO satellites have a cross section of 20 to 200 m^2, largely due to the deployable solar arrays. On the other hand, SmallSats are typically 0.5 to 5 m^2 in cross section and CubeSats are about 0.01 m^2. Because of the much larger surface area to volume ratio, small satellites often do not have deployable arrays. Because of the small cross section, SmallSats have a lower probability of hitting another satellite.

Most important, operational SmallSats are typically at low altitudes where the debris cloud decays and re-enters over months or a very few years. As shown in Fig. 13-2, single large satellites are typically at high altitudes where the debris cloud decays over 100's or 1000's of years. Of course, SmallSats deployed with large satellites and into the same orbit could begin to create a debris problem, which is a possible argument against using rideshare for SmallSat deployment.

In terms of space debris, altitude is far more important than the number of spacecraft. Even large numbers of SmallSats at low altitude will **not** create a long-term debris hazard, simply because any debris will decay and re-enter in a short time. Low altitude is essentially "self-cleaning," even without an active deorbit system, which adds another failure mode for large, high-altitude spacecraft.

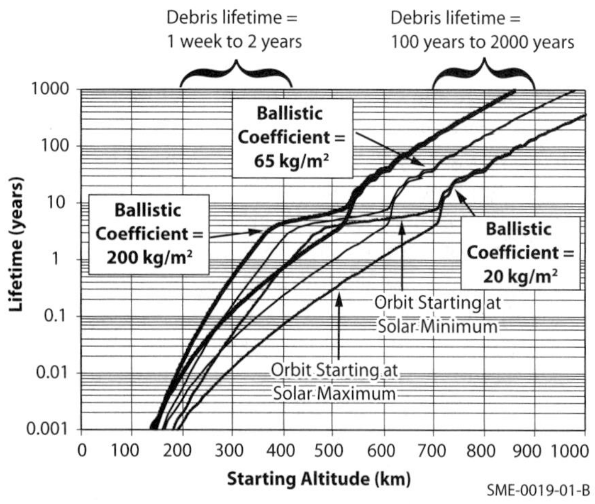

Fig. 13-2. Operational SmallSats Will Typically Inhabit a Regime Where Orbital Debris Cannot Accumulate. (Underlying chart is Fig. 9-22 from Sec. 9.4.4.)

Increased Efficiency in the Use of Scarce Resources. Smallsats can be more responsive to current needs than more traditional missions, simply because they are quicker and lower cost to build and can be built to inventory if needed. However, they are difficult to get funded because they don't have the political clout of larger missions which create large numbers of jobs. On the other hand, once funded they are less likely to be canceled, because of both their lower cost and quicker schedules. In most countries, funding decisions on both new and ongoing programs are made on an annual basis. In addition, in the United States, a major review of space goals, objectives, and programs is likely every 4 or 8 years when administrations change. This means that major programs which may well stretch out over several changes of administration, are subject to several major programmatic reviews in their lifetime, any of which can result in the program getting cancelled or stretched out. (It rarely occurs that a new administration comes in and puts emphasis on speeding up ongoing programs or gives them extra money to finish sooner or do a better job.) This means that a program that can be completed in a few years has a distinct advantage of being less likely to be cancelled. While canceling some programs may be appropriate as perceived needs change over time, it is certainly a waste of both human and economic resources. Smaller programs let us make progress in small steps with much less risk of large backward steps that occur when major programs have schedule overruns, or worse, are cancelled after extensive resources have been spent.

Enabling Missions that Aren't Otherwise Affordable or Feasible. There are many missions that are relevant and important, but which won't occur or will be greatly stretched out in time if they are too expensive. An obvious example is student and training missions. These are extremely important if we are to give younger engineers a sense of what real missions and real mission problems are like. But they simply won't occur if the costs are too high and are of little value unless they are launched while the student is still a student, or at least while they're still working in astronautics.

A 2006 Futron study [Foust, et al. 2008; Wertz, 2010], identified over 30 markets for smallsats* in 4 principal areas:

- Military (the largest market)
- Civil/commercial remote sensing
- Civil/commercial communications
- Other

In total, the Futron study defined an overall addressable market of 39 to 76 satellites/year. At an average total cost of \$7.5 million per spacecraft, this represents an overall market of \$290 million to \$570 million per year. Raising the cost to \$8 million/spacecraft, to account for inflation since the time of the study, provides an estimated current market value (payload, spacecraft, and launch, excluding operations) of \$312 million to \$608 million per year. It is clear from the Futron study that, while specific numbers and missions are uncertain, the smallsat market is very robust and could begin to reinvigorate the space business enterprise, **if** there is dedicated, responsive launch at a cost commensurate with the spacecraft cost.

In another example, the DoD Space Experiment Review Board (SERB) list currently contains 62 approved and validated payloads or spacecraft needing a ride to orbit. 59 of these provide sufficient information to estimate the Equivalent Mass to the Reference Orbit (EMRO). In order to estimate the launch requirements, payloads on the SERB list were first converted to an estimated spacecraft mass, then the spacecraft mass was converted to an EMRO by multiplying by the Orbit Cost Function (OCF), defined in Sec. 10.3.2. Complete spacecraft on the SERB list were simply multiplied by the OCF. The overall mass distribution is shown in Fig. 13-3.

The results of the analysis are as follows:

- 36 of the entries could be launched by a Very Small Launch Vehicle (VSLV = 100 kg to a due east orbit)
- 14 additional entries could be launched by a Small Launch Vehicle (SLV = 450 kg to a due east orbit).
- 9 entries are too large (or in too energetic an orbit) to use a small launch vehicle and would require a larger Light Launch Vehicle (LLV = 1800 kg to a due east orbit).

Some of the SERB missions could be launched as piggyback payloads with another mission. Most, however,

* For the Futron study, a small satellite was defined as less than 100 to 200 kg total mass with a payload mass fraction greater than 50%; 200 W orbit average power, 500 W peak; 1–2 year mission life; and total spacecraft cost of \$5 million to \$10 million with low-cost launch options available. It is clear that there are a great many additional smallsat missions that don't meet all of these criteria.

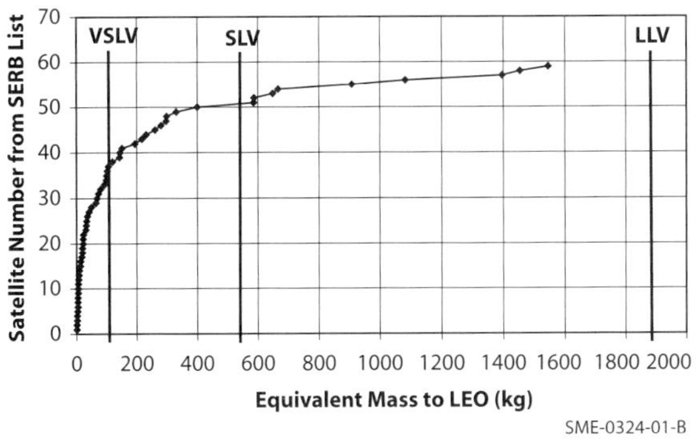

Fig. 13-3. Satellites in the SERB List Sorted by Equivalent Mass to LEO. (Data compiled by Nicola Sarzi-Amade, Microcosm.)

have specific orbit requirements that would require a dedicated launch. This indicates that at any given time, there is a substantial backlog of payloads and systems to be put in orbit from even a single space community, if there were an opportunity to do so.

Making Newer, Better Technology Available to Users. As we have previously discussed, smallsat technology is evolving rapidly and will continue to do so for some time as changes in the electronics marketplace and materials technology begin to make their way into space technology.* The result of this is a continuing influx of new technology and a greater willingness to use this technology because the risk (i.e., the resources and time at stake) is far less. If we are launching 5 to 10 low cost observation satellites per year, then there is relatively little risk associated with introducing a new sensor technology into the satellite stream. If, for any reason, it proves unsuccessful, there are still a number of on-orbit satellites using the prior sensor technology that are still providing data. In addition, a new spacecraft which either reverts to the older technology or finds a way to fix the new technology can be available and launched in a short time. It is a very different process and mindset relative to what occurs for traditional space systems.

An example of this process is the computer technology flown by Surrey Satellite Technology Limited (SSTL). Surrey typically launches a few satellites per year and flies a new computer with nearly every mission flown. At the same time, they also fly the computer flown and validated on the last mission such that they are continuously flying the latest in computer technology but still mitigating risk by flying one that is known to work. This means that Surrey is flying low-cost smallsats with current computer technology vs. large traditional satellites that may well be flying computer technology that is 2 decades or more old. The difference in performance between the new, small low-cost system, and the old, large, very expensive system may not be as great as one would otherwise expect.

Creating Missions that are Far More Responsive to World Events and the Needs of the End User. There is a continuing demand for more responsive solutions to modern issues—in part because of the nearly instant global communications that make problems apparent to the world virtually as soon as they happen. Traditional space systems can respond only if they are already on orbit, have on board the relevant instrumentation, and are in an orbit that provides the appropriate coverage. In contrast, the Chinese are developing launch-on-demand systems [Office of the Secretary of Defense, 2007] and the Soviets/Russians have had systems in inventory and launch-on-demand (within hours) for over 30 years [Cooper, 1992].

At the present time, if critical US military assets are destroyed by a system failure, collision with invisible debris, or enemy attack, they cannot be replaced in a time that would be applicable to any current needs. Because of their irreplaceable character and high cost, they also become inviting targets for a potential enemy attack. However, if some subset of their capability can be replaced within hours or days by inexpensive smallsats, they become a less valuable target and, because of low cost and rapid replacement, the back-up smallsats are also uninviting targets.

Perhaps most important, low-cost smallsats and launch-on-demand allow us the capacity to respond to world events and either natural or man-made disasters in time to help solve problems and potentially save lives and reduce suffering. If we can launch satellites quickly in direct response to a hurricane, tsunami, earthquake, or major terrorist attack, we might be able to find and rescue people who are stranded, washed out to sea, cut off by rubble, or in the path of a moving forest fire or rising flood. For these systems, our goal is not to evaluate what happened, but to find ways to help save lives, protect property, and reduce hardship while there is still a chance to help.

Creating an Economically Sustainable Business Model. One of the problems that arises with the traditional approach of high cost, long lived systems is that they don't provide an economic basis for a sustained industrial base. The Space Shuttle was intended to meet the needs for human spaceflight and large payloads for the indefinite future. But, once the Shuttle was designed, built, and delivered, there was no way to maintain the skill base required to design and build it. There was no continuous production process that would provide for changes, upgrades, maintenance, and incorporation of new technology. The same is true of other large systems that are intended to live for a decade or more on orbit and for which only a relatively small number are needed. Similarly, the cancellation or completion of a single large program can have a major impact on even large aerospace companies.

* Moore's Law suggests that the speed of modern electronics doubles every 2 years. This means that a program using 10 year old computer technology is operating roughly 32 times slower than one using more modern technology. A program that takes 10 years to design and build and then lives on-orbit for 15 years is operating at roughly 1/4000th (0.00025) of the speed and throughput currently available.

In contrast, a mix of spacecraft sizes provides a much more robust economic basis to build on. Building a larger number of satellites with shorter lifetimes not only reduces the overall cost, but leads to a more sustainable manufacturing process as satellites can be built more-or-less continuously with some speed up and slow down to meet the changing demand for any particular type of satellite. New technology can be incorporated as it becomes available, the people who understand how the satellite is built are still around, and the component manufacturers can produce a small, but continuing stream of components, rather than one set every 5 or 10 years, which is often the case currently.

Unfortunately, the scientists, engineers, and technicians who form the underlying space systems knowledge base are not commodities that can be easily "stored" for the next time they are needed. SmallSats and SmallSat launches can provide a continuous flow of business that can allow SmallSat manufacturers to continue to grow over an extended period of time.

13.1.2 The Need for Mission Diversity

Although there are significant cost advantages, SmallSats should not be viewed as a replacement for traditional, larger satellite systems because of their inherent limitations. Of these, perhaps the most fundamental is the limitation due to physical scale. Nearly all observation spacecraft use diffraction-limited optics, such that the only way to improve angular resolution is to make them larger. (Linear resolution can be improved by flying lower as discussed in Sec. 13.1.1, and it is possible that better resolution can be achieved by using multiple small satellites in formation, although this creates a challenging control problem.) Similarly, high data rates require a large power-aperture, and high power implies the need for large solar arrays and a large satellite. Physically large satellites and launch systems will continue to be required for human spaceflight. Of course, this doesn't mean that small responsive satellites cannot play an important role in human spaceflight or other large satellite missions by offloading tasks that could otherwise increase mission cost.

In addition, because SmallSats are inherently near-term and low cost, it doesn't make sense to spend billions in R&D for their development. If a particular problem requires billions of dollars in research investment, then it is likely that it will be implemented in a more traditional, unique, large spacecraft system. SmallSats built to inventory with launch-on-demand have significant economic and technological advantages over traditional large satellites for some applications and can help larger systems significantly reduce cost by offloading tasks, providing a level of back-up in case of system failures, and serving as a testbed to validate both technologies and processes needed to significantly reduce cost of the larger systems.

It is clear that smallsat systems can be lower cost, more flexible, and more responsive to both changing technology and changing user needs than traditional satellites. They can significantly reduce overall space program costs. However, they cannot replace traditional large satellites in all applications. It is clear that what is needed for a much lower cost, much robust and responsive space program is *mission diversity* in which we have a mix of larger traditional satellite programs (but with newer, lower-cost technology and a reduced work load) and lower cost, newer smallsats. This not only dramatically reduces space program costs, it allows us to do more with limited resources. Ultimately, there is far more that needs to be done in space than there is money or time available to do it. Having the right mix of large and small satellite programs is a major step toward becoming both more efficient and more capable.

13.2 It's Possible, But It Isn't Easy

It has been clear for some time that is very important to the future of the space program to substantially reduce space mission cost and schedule and that many competent people have worked hard to reduce both cost and schedule and constrain cost and schedule overruns. It has proven very difficult to do, which makes it clear from experience that it isn't an easy task, but is it possible?

Essentially all space programs are run so as to try to create the lowest cost system consistent with the mission objectives, requirements, and constraints. As mentioned at the opening of the chapter, no one sets out to create a program that costs too much and takes too long. In addition, it should be clear that if we build the same system that we built last time and build it the same way, it will cost the same to within minor variations. This means that genuinely reducing cost is not a matter of buying the same spacecraft that we bought last time for a lot less money. Dramatically reducing cost requires that the system be fundamentally "different" in some aspects. So the real question is not "can we buy the same spacecraft for a lot less money?" (for which the answer is "probably not"), but, rather "can we achieve these broad mission objectives for a lot less money than we would expect to pay for a traditional space mission?"

There are three different lines of evidence that suggest that dramatic cost reduction is indeed possible. First, because the USCM8 cost model presented in Chap. 11 and previously in SMAD continually overestimated the cost of small spacecraft, the Aerospace Corp. created the Small Satellite Cost Model (SSCM), also presented in Chap. 11, specifically for the purpose of more correctly estimating smallsat costs. As discussed in Sec. 2.1.8 (Fig. 2-15), the behavior of the SSCM and the introduction of CubeSats (Sec. 25.4) suggests that there may be a need for an even newer Very Small Satellite Cost Model that continues trying to model the trend of ever lower cost, smaller, more competent systems. Second, there is direct evidence from the cost data presented in the *Reducing Space Mission Cost* (RSMC) book [Wertz and Larson, 1996]. Table 13-1 shows the actual cost of each of the 10 case study missions as a percentage of the projected cost from the USCM8/SMAD cost model,

Table 13-1. Actual Cost for the 10 Case Study Missions in RSMC as a Percentage of the Projected Cost from the USCM8/SMAD Cost Model for Traditional Space Systems as Given in SMAD III [Wertz and Larson, 1999]. The actual dollar cost, inflated to $FY10, is shown in the right-most column. Data from RSMC [Wertz and Larson, 1996], which also provides an explanation of the cost data and extended discussion of each of the missions with the actual data cost data and explanations of the data. The other columns show the actual cost as a percentage of the model's projected cost.

	Bus	Payload	Space Seg.	Launch	Grnd Seg	Ops + Main	Total Prog	Total Program Cost (FY10$M)
AMSAT								
AO-13	2.8%	in spcraft	1.8%	0.4%	N/A	N/A	1.0%	1.87M
AO-16	0.9%	in spcraft	0.5%	0.2%	N/A	N/A	0.3%	0.30M
Average	1.8%	in spcraft	1.1%	0.3%	N/A	N/A	0.7%	
Other LEO								
Ørsted	31.8%	27.1%	29.8%	12.1%	4.2%	33.9%	19.6%	27.8M
Freja	28.2%	18.5%	24.1%	7.2%	0.7%	4.1%	9.0%	37.0M
SAMPEX	82.2%	41.1%	64.7%	93.9%	14.2%	109.2%	51.1%	109.6M
HETE	16.3%	59.4%	35.1%	42.2%	1.4%	in payload	14.4%	45.5M
RADCAL	12.3%	in spcraft	8.2%	73.3%	in spcraft	N/A	14.7%	25.1M
ORBCOMM	42.7%	in spcraft	24.9%	18.1%	0.2%	6.1%	4.2%	23.7M
PoSAT-1	4.4%	1.9%	3.3%	1.6%	0.7%	4.2%	2.2%	3.2M
Average	31.1%	28.9%	26.9%	35.5%	3.6%	31.5%	16.5%	
Interplanetary								
Clementine	88.5%	24.0%	72.2%	32.1%	1.9%	54.1%	36.3%	128.4M
Pluto Express	19.8%	18.0%	19.7%	7.6%	in spcraft	14.0%	15.8%	429.0M
Average	54.2%	21.0%	46.0%	19.9%	1.9%	34.0%	26.1%	
Avg - All Exc. AO	**36.3%**	**27.1%**	**31.3%**	**32.0%**	**3.3%**	**32.2%**	**18.6%**	
Avg - All Missions	30.0%	27.1%	25.8%	26.2%	3.3%	32.2%	15.3%	

adjusted for inflation. From this table, it is clear that there are large cost reductions for all of the elements of the space mission—i.e., the spacecraft bus, payload, launch, ground segment, and operations. This must be true in order to have large cost reductions for the entire program. If it were not the case, the elements where cost savings weren't possible would become the dominant cost and keep the full mission cost from coming down by a significant factor. Finally, there is the anecdotal evidence from individual missions other than those in RSMC. These include missions such as BremSat [Wertz and Dawson, 1996, 1997], TacSat-3 and Low-Cost Wind Lidar [Wertz, 2010], NanoEye [Van Allen, et al. 2010], NASA's Small Explorer program, and the various SmallSat and CubeSat missions described in Sec. 25.3 and 25.4.

Because we will likely never build both a low-cost smallsat and a traditional satellite with the identical mission objectives, there is no way to prove conclusively that cost reduction is real. Perhaps the most that we can conclude is that the "preponderance of the evidence" suggests that it's possible to dramatically reduce cost (i.e., by a factor of 2 to 10 or more) without significantly impacting reliability. However, it does require changing strongly the way we do business in space.

Nearly everyone would agree that it's desirable to reduce cost and increase responsiveness by a large fraction, and it appears to be possible, so why is it so hard? For one, inertia and culture can be two of the strongest forces in any organization. Dramatically reducing cost and schedule requires not just a different type of spacecraft in some way, but it also requires "doing business differently" to allow that spacecraft to be built quickly and at low cost. However doing business differently is hard. The culture of how we do business in space has come about over decades in response to specific successes and, more often, specific problems that have occurred in prior programs. For example, we may do a specific set of tests because in past experience failures occurred when those tests weren't done. The space culture is a result, in part, of our space experience.

We talked in the opening paragraph of the book about NASA Administrator Dan Goldin's attempt to change the culture by instituting a policy of "faster, better, cheaper." Surely, if anyone can cause the culture to change, the Administrator of NASA would seem to have a good chance. But, in the end, the old culture won. ("Faster, better, cheaper—pick any two.") Culture can be among the hardest forces to overcome—it will take great delight in pointing out every failure of a low-cost program and will point out that a low-cost program that fails is not as valuable as a high-cost one that works successfully on-orbit for many years. No matter how much one points out that occasional failures can be acceptable and taken into account if the program is sufficiently low cost, there is still an underlying belief that "failure is not an option," and that every program must be built such that the failure probability is driven to as near zero as possible, irrespective of the cost consequences. This is reinforced by both the funding hierarchy and Congress that notice, and then quickly forget, major cost reductions in programs, but remember system failures for a much longer time when deciding whether to fund the next phase of a program or a new program intended to be done more quickly and at much lower cost. It is further exacerbated by the response of the media and the public, i.e., all of us who ultimately pay for the public space program. Failures, especially very expensive ones that involve spectacular explosions, become front page photos on major newspapers and headlines on the evening news. On the other hand, it is typically quite a long time between front-page stories in the *Washington Post* about small, low-cost, high reliability spacecraft built by any small company. Small successes are not as newsworthy as expensive failures.

The cultural problem is reinforced by ideas that most of us share. A cheap product is expected to fall apart quickly, whereas an expensive product is expected to be one of high quality that lasts a long time. Of course, in reality that may depend on the application. A Ferrari is much more expensive than a Ford and is typically thought of as a "better" car. At winning races, the Ferrari **is** likely to be the better car. Every extra ounce is removed to provide higher performance. But, if our objective is to take the kids safely to school every morning and make trips to the grocery store with high reliability, it's possible that the Ford can do that job better, with higher reliability. Cost is not necessarily a good measure of long-term reliability and what system is "better" depends, at least in part, on your objectives.

All of this implies that to make major changes in the cost and responsiveness of space systems will require that we change, at least in part, both what we buy and how we buy it. Low-cost, quick and responsive programs are not consistent with the traditional space culture and will require a lot of work to make them happen. Unless there is a well-formulated "plan of attack," and a process for implementing it with management approval and support, the inertia and culture within the space community will largely prevent it from happening. Reversing the space spiral of Fig. 1-2 is possible, but hard.

In my opinion, the first lesson in creating a new way of doing business in space is that to successfully reduce cost, we have to talk about real cost and make cost data known. One way to ensure competitive pricing, is to tell the community what the government paid for something last time. If we paid $1 million each for reaction wheels of a specific size and make that data known, the next time we ask for reaction wheels of that size it is unlikely that we will get any bids over $1 million. While this seems obvious, there is a strong tendency to not want to do it. Cost and price data is sensitive and much of it is proprietary. In addition, cost data is hard to compare across programs and components. For example, our $1 million price may or may not include testing, spare parts, shipping, and a special, all-composite, light-weight housing. It may or may not include non-recurring development cost. In addition, cost data is frequently hidden to make costs appear lower. For example, it is virtually unknown what a Space Shuttle launch actually costs. Revealing costs may make it harder to get a program funded. Nonetheless,

> **Reducing space mission cost is hard if we know what the costs are, and virtually impossible if we don't.**

As discussed in Sec. 13.1.1, small spacecraft have a disproportionate advantage for reducing cost. Unlike many other areas, small organizations also appear to have an advantage. In automobile production, low cost cars are built by large companies and the expensive, unique cars are typically built by smaller organizations. In space, the reverse is the case. The most expensive spacecraft are built by large companies and the small, low-cost spacecraft are typically built by small companies. Why is this? The major advantages that large organizations traditionally use to drive down cost—such as large factories with the associated economies of scale, large research and support groups, and extensive (and expensive) facilities and operations—are typically not applicable to reducing spacecraft costs and may, in some cases, be handicaps. It would be challenging for an organization that is used to multi-billion dollar contracts to survive on a modest number of multi-million dollar contracts. On the other hand, small organizations could thrive and prosper on these and, in addition, have a number of characteristics that are advantageous to reducing cost. They tend to be innovative in their approach. Rapid decision-making is relatively easy. They live in a world where cost is always critical and they don't have to support a large and hungry infrastructure.

This dichotomy also suggests one of the biggest hurdles for government organizations that want to drive down cost. Governments are used to dealing with and depending on large organizations and spreading the decision-making process over years or decades and a great many organizations and people. But small organizations that are capable of dramatically driving down cost, simply can't survive that process. It can often take the government nearly as long to make a decision on spending a few million dollars as it does to spend a few hundred million dollars. If a small satellite program is ongoing and the government decides to take a funding break for 6 months or a year, it not only drives up the cost of the program, it's possible that nobody will be there at the small company to answer the phone when someone calls back to get things going again. Creating multiple small spacecraft creates a much more sustainable economic model for businesses, but only if the government supports the start of that process with moderately level or growing funding. (Once there is an ongoing small production line, it's likely spacecraft would be bought by multiple organizations and the ups and downs of the government procurement process would likely be much less of a problem.)

13.3 Counterproductive Approaches to Reducing Cost

One of the key issues in reducing mission cost is being creative and inventive in terms of new technology, new processes, new ways of doing business, and an understanding of how these will work in practice. This leads to the fundamental question of what it is that creates creativity and inventiveness—money or ideas? Where do new inventions, new ideas, and new ways of applying approaches and technology come from? Large organizations, such as those in the pharmaceutical industry and often the government, would argue that it comes from spending large amounts of money on R&D. Others would argue that it comes largely from small companies and individuals who are creative and can think differently about a problem—such as the movie dramatizing the invention of the intermittent windshield wiper blade for cars by an individual inventor working in his garage. Historically, it seems clear that both processes can work and, to an extent, we need an element of both. It is likely that no amount of research will yield truly breakthrough results without someone in the organization with a creative streak that can look at a problem from a different perspective. Similarly, small organizations can come up with great ideas and inventions, but typically need some level of funding to get them started and nourish ideas until they can blossom into real and useful inventions. This is a part of the reasoning behind the creation of the Small Business Innovative Research (SBIR) program that has helped many small businesses develop new ideas in space, astronautics, and a great many other fields.

All of the above suggests that if we really want to reduce cost, we should ensure that those organizations that have been successful at doing so or are likely to be able to help, indeed have the opportunity to continue. Therefore,

> **A litmus test for any new approach, regulation, or policy intended to reduce space mission cost or schedule should be: Would it encourage or discourage participation by small businesses, individuals, or other groups that have been successful in the past?**

If a proposed approach tends to discourage any participation by those groups or individuals who really understand how to reduce cost and schedule, have ideas on how to do it, or who have done it in the past, then it is unlikely to be successful and is more likely to drive up costs and schedule by inserting unproductive rules, regulations, and processes into the way we do business. If the heads of the major government space agencies convene a meeting with the CEOs of the 3 or 4 major aerospace prime contractors, it is unlikely to result in creating new ways of doing business that are faster, better, cheaper, and less comfortable for the major aerospace companies.

An example of a potentially counterproductive approach is cost-sharing (or risk-sharing) as a means of reducing cost. Creative, low-cost organizations rarely have excess internal funds to carry additional burden or risk and this implies that they likely cannot share in program cost. Organizations that are willing to cost share typically plan to recover that cost plus any prior cost-sharing activity not ultimately funded plus additional return due to cost-sharing risk. This suggests that demanding cost-sharing, particularly in the up-front development, on something for which the principal user is likely to be the government will probably make the ultimate item more expensive rather than less expensive and, in addition, damage those organizations who may have good ideas or worked on low cost approaches. On the other hand, cost-sharing may be appropriate and helpful for space technology if the end product involves technology that has many applications in the commercial world, such as batteries.

Using this approach implies that we can construct a list of potentially counterproductive "cost-cutting" approaches that have a high potential of increasing, rather than decreasing, cost. Some of these are shown in Table 13-2. Although all of these have the potential to reduce costs in some respects, it is more likely that they will increase costs by tending to eliminate or marginalize those individuals or organizations that are most likely to be helpful to the problem.

There is a good analogy here with software development. Software is extremely expensive and many attempts have been made to reduce its cost. However, lowering software development cost by reducing the up-front planning and design has almost always proven counterproductive. Beginning to write code in the first day or month of a software project may be psychologically satisfying, but in the end it is likely to substantially increase costs for development and maintenance as people try to fix software that wasn't well designed in the first place. (See Secs. 3.1 and 20.2.)

In most programs, additional resources should also be allocated to operations planning. This should be done in two distinct stages. First, operations planning should be a major part of the mission engineering process. How are we going to realistically operate this mission to achieve our end objectives? Not taking operational issues into account can significantly increase the life-cycle cost. Second, detailed planning and ground operations systems development needs to begin well in advance of the launch of the first satellite. (See Sec. 29.1.) In many programs, there is a strong tendency to put off problems. Costs are constrained at essentially all stages and it is frequently seen as more productive to simply proceed and resolve problems at a later stage. Ultimately, these become operations problems that tend to dramatically drive up the cost of mission operations.

Another area which typically receives inadequate support and funding is exploring options. Too often, in the name of reducing both cost and schedule, we curtail looking at options as "serious" engineering gets underway. However, options for reducing mission cost should be explored with substantial care during mission definition and continued throughout the mission life. The prag-

Table 13-2. Potentially Counterproductive Approaches to Reducing Space Mission Cost. Each of these approaches has the potential to significantly increase cost rather than reduce it.

Approach	Intended Benefit	Potential Negative Impact
Consolidated, Centralized Acquisition for Multiple Programs	Provides greater accountability; gives appearance of reducing waste	Restricts competition; likely to force out small organizations and innovative approaches; likely to institutionalize the high cost approaches
Contractor Sharing of Development Costs	Reduces cost to the government **if** the major customer base is the private sector (e.g., personal computer development)	Forces out the small player; acquisition will be driven by investment economics—will require very large ROI, since the government is a high-risk customer
Contractor Cost Sharing in Up-Front Studies	Reduces study cost	Forces out the small, innovative contractor; contractor costs will be recovered in higher indirect rates
Cost Guarantee on R&D Programs	Limits government cost commitment; good for achieving accountability, but **not** cost reduction	Forces out the small contractor and doesn't permit taking risks that could dramatically reduce cost
Doing Work In House	Eliminates subcontracting cost; can be effective **if** the group has experience with low-cost efficient production; provides good training for government engineers	May drive up costs due to lack of efficiency and knowledge; may be largely an excuse to maintain a large infrastructure; on-the-job training can be expensive
Reducing the Amount of Up-Front Systems Engineering	Shortens program schedule and avoids over-engineering a strawman design	Ignorance is rarely of value in reducing cost or improving performance; principal problem is not adequately addressing alternatives
Delaying Operations Planning	Postpones up-front costs when budgets are small and tight	Can significantly increase operations cost and risk and drive up life-cycle cost
Not Selling the Program to the Funding Community and End Users	Reduces both money and effort devoted to non-engineering activities	Program may get canceled as people and priorities change. A canceled program is rarely cost effective
Not Spending on Knowledge Capture at Mission End	Cuts off expenditures when all (or more) of the money has been spent	A very small investment can be extremely valuable in reducing cost for future programs. Not doing that loses this opportunity

matic approach is clear. Given the current state-of-the-program, is it cheaper to proceed with the current plan or choose a lower-cost option, taking into account the time and cost of changing to a new baseline? In initial mission design, the cost of changing is very low. As we go further downstream in a program, re-engineering becomes more and more expensive. The cost of looking at options, however, does not change significantly and, if costs can be reduced, changes may be worthwhile, even late in the program development cycle. Even if the cost of implementing changes is judged too expensive or too time-consuming, it may still be appropriate to evaluate options such that follow-on programs can take advantage of the knowledge gained.

What we have called by the fancy title of *mission utility analysis* (Sec. 5.4) is really a matter of selling the program. This is an extremely important process, which does not necessarily reduce cost directly, but does so indirectly in a number of ways. First, it keeps the effort focused on the mission objectives. Is the program achieving what the customer intended and what the end user needs? Second, keeping the program firmly sold helps reduce the start-stop syndrome of many programs, which is a major source of cost and schedule overruns. Third, keeping the program sold keeps the program alive so that it can achieve the original objectives, assuming that they are still worth doing. Programs can be cut or eliminated at any stage, and cancelled programs are rarely cost effective.

In the government arena, selling a program can have a negative connotation of convincing the government or the public to do something that isn't in their best interest. However, analyzing mission utility is really about establishing, as quantitatively as possible, the benefits of the program and how it can meet the objectives of whoever is providing the funding. This is a positive and critical step for any new mission or at any time mission funding decisions are being reviewed.

Finally, we should provide adequate funding at the end of mission life. At this time, basically all of the money has been spent and there is no further potential for cost savings or schedule reduction. Still, spending some money on assessing and recording "lessons learned," while they're still fresh, can cut costs and improve performance of subsequent programs.

13.4 Cost vs. Reliability—Focusing on the Mission Objectives

Michael S. Hurley Jr., ***Naval Research Laboratory***
William E. Purdy, ***Purdy Engineering***

The space industry's understanding of, and approach to, reliability can be one of the most important drivers of a program's cost and schedule. This section discusses what reliability is and what it is not, while highlighting common misunderstandings that often mislead designers and managers. Misunderstanding and misapplication of reliability can lead a program to set aside real mission objectives and effectively design and manage programs to a "reliability of zero." For instance, if extreme reliability requirements result in schedule delays and cost overruns leading to program cancellation, the achieved reliability is zero.

The reliability analysis presented in Chap. 24 is a quantitative analysis of the likelihood of part failures; for example, if a specific relay fails, then a given capability is lost. This section presents a complementary mission-oriented view of reliability with an emphasis on system availability to users. We examine historical space systems and on-orbit data to confirm key points. Ultimately, this section strives to advance the industry-wide understanding that is necessary to better achieve reliable space systems, available to users when needed.

The concept of reliability is heavily influenced by perspective. Personnel in space-system program offices and associated system developers almost always consider reliability to be a set of requirements. Those requirements specify a number that the system's reliability analysis must meet along with related processes and paperwork to assure the product properly made. These reliability requirements are met at design reviews or other development milestones; they will be met (or not) completely independent of cost, schedule, and actual on-orbit performance. On the other hand, from an end-user perspective, anything that makes the system unavailable when it is expected is considered unreliable, regardless of whether the reliability requirements were satisfied in a design or acquisition phase. Similarly, if a program delivers late, then the effective reliability is zero for every day (usually every year) it is late. If a program's cost doubles, those additional funds are unavailable for a second space system. These examples collectively give a sense of the important concept of availability: assuring a capability is available to users when required. Availability is further discussed in Sec. 13.4.4.

Ironically, efforts to achieve high reliability by analysis and processes can prove counterproductive. If a parts-reliability number is used as a mission design requirement, the reliability number can drive program decisions harder than real mission objectives. We have witnessed many programs implement hard (inflexible) reliability requirements, with little consideration for cost or schedule, as if meeting these requirements were a mission objective unto themselves. Although budget overruns and schedule delays are common, often resulting in an effective reliability of zero for many years (or permanently if canceled), cost and schedule are rarely considered to be related to a system's reliability. So it is essential to have a crisp understanding of reliability and to keep one's focus on achieving the mission objectives.

13.4.1 Understanding What Reliability Is and Is Not

True reliability, in our case on-orbit reliability, is a measure of how well a system performs in its operational environment. Regardless of the number of parts, design reviews, quality inspections, or acquisition processes, used to develop the system, in the end the on-orbit system may prove highly reliable or terribly unreliable. According to the Reliability Analysis Center, reliability is "the probability that an item can perform its intended function for a specified interval under stated conditions without failure." Unfortunately, nearly all space-system development only has estimated numbers to deal with and a perceived sense of what the system's reliability will be. In contrast, the aircraft industry has 10,000,000 commercial flights per year enabling them to measure operational reliability and iteratively improve their designs and processes.

What is the Reliability Prediction?

The *reliability prediction* is a calculated likelihood of avoiding part failures that induce loss of a spacecraft or mission. In other words, one minus the reliability number equals the probability of mission loss or degradation due to a part failure. See Chap. 24 of this book for a full description and calculations. The reliability analysis pulls upon mean time between failure data for standardized parts and electrical connections. In the US, MIL-HDBK-217 [DoD, 1991] is the guideline for performing such analyses. The analysis considers the failure of electronic parts, connections, and moving mechanical assemblies in the system. **It is especially important to understand the contributors to on-orbit reliability that are and are not considered in this reliability prediction, as shown in Table 13-3.**

Table 13-3. Failure Modes Included, and Not Included, in Reliability Predictions.

Failure Modes Considered in the Reliability Prediction	Failure Modes NOT Considered in the Reliability Prediction
• Electronic part failure	• Design failure
• Solder joint failure	• Software failure
• Connector or pin failure	• Operator error
• Moving mechanical elements such as bearing failure	• Improper build, assembly & workmanship
	• Late launch or launch failure
	• Program cancellation due to cost overruns

Limitations of Reliability Prediction

MIL-HDBK-217 revision F, section 3 [DoD, 1991] provides some of the best explanations of limitations on predicting reliability.

The direct extractions are shown in italics.

3.3 Limitations of Reliability Predictions – This handbook provides a common basis for reliability predictions, based on analysis of the best possible data at the time of issue. It is intended to make reliability prediction as good a tool as possible. However, like any tool, reliability prediction must be used intelligently, with due consideration of its limitations. The first limitation is that the failure rate models are point estimates which are based on available data.

Even when used in similar environments, the differences between system applications can be significant. ***Predicted and achieved reliability have always been closer for ground electronic systems than for avionic systems****, because the environmental stresses vary less from system to system on the ground and hence the field conditions are, in general, closer to the environment under which the data was collected for the prediction model. However, failure rates are also impacted by operational scenarios, operator characteristics, maintenance practices, measurement techniques and differences in definition of failure.* ***Hence, a reliability prediction should never be assumed to represent the expected field reliability as measured by the user ... note that none of the applications discussed above requires the predicted reliability to match the field measurement****.*

So the reliability handbook itself points out that it was never intended to be an accurate predictor of operational reliability or the probability of success. On-orbit data strongly confirm this point, as discussed in Sec. 13.4.2. It should be noted that the MIL-HDBK-217F, while still the recognized industry standard, is officially obsolete. It is no longer maintained or updated by the US government; its last update was in 1991. The handbook's analytical process is still sound but much of its parts data, upon which the quantified calculations are based, are badly outdated. The lack of ongoing support for the military handbook, coupled with the rapidly evolving world of electronics, creates a serious problem for developers to obtain statistically valid data sets from relevant environments for quantitative calculations.

One should also be aware of how politically charged a single reliability number can become for a program. For example, a single reliability number is often presented to outside organizations in an attempt to provide a simplified understanding of how likely the system is to work. At a System Requirements and Design Review (SRDR), we witnessed a program office order that the reliability analysis be completed by the Preliminary Design Review (PDR) and at the same time announce that the reliability for the space system including launch will be 90%! While this 90% number may have been useful to create perceived on-orbit reliability for sponsors or others necessary to politically support the program, clearly this pre-determined "analysis" did not add value to the design or final operations. Such political emphasis and simplified understanding can be major obstacles to properly applying reliability analysis and balanced processes to space systems.

Value of Reliability Prediction

MIL-HDBK-217 revision F, section 3 [DoD, 1991] also provides some of the best explanations of the value added by predictions of reliability.

3.2 The Role of Reliability Prediction— ***Reliability prediction provides the quantitative baseline needed to assess progress in reliability engineering****. A prediction made of a proposed design may be used in several ways. Once a design is selected, the reliability prediction may be used as a guide to improvement by showing the highest contributors to failure. If the part stress analysis method is used, it may also reveal other fruitful areas for change (e.g., over stressed parts). The impact of proposed design changes on reliability can be determined only by comparing the reliability predictions of the existing and proposed designs. The ability of the design to maintain an acceptable reliability level under environmental extremes may be assessed through reliability predictions. The predictions may be used to evaluate the need for environmental control systems.*

So, reliability prediction analysis is a quantitative approach for comparing and improving designs. This prediction analysis, along with associated reliability analyses such as the failure modes and effects analysis (FMEA) and parts stress analysis over temperature are excellent for identifying weak links in a design and making improvements. Design improvements include electronics parts substitution, implementation of select redundancy, changes in thermal design requirements, and simplification to reduce complexity.

13.4.2 On-Orbit Reliability—History and Examples

Tafazoli [2008] studied more than 4000 spacecraft launched in the past 25 years and identified 156 on-orbit failures that occurred on 129 different spacecraft from 1980 to 2005. In this study he observed that 41% of all failures happen within 1 year of on-orbit activities. See Table 13-4. He also observed that the data suggest insufficient testing and inadequate modeling of the spacecraft and its environment. The study concludes that the reliability lessons learned are that adequate testing, redundancy, and flexibility are the keys to producing a reliable spacecraft. An example of flexibility would be the ability to upload new software to run new attitude control modes to work around a failed sun sensor. Notice

Table 13-4. Spacecraft Failures Over Time [Tafazoli, 2008].

Failure Distribution Grouped by Years On-Orbit				
0–1	1–3	3–5	5–8	>8
41%	17%	20%	16%	6%

that only 1 of these 3 characteristics, redundancy, is even included in reliability prediction. For students or those new to this field, refer to Chap. 24 to better understand the reliability prediction and what is (and is not) included in its calculation. Although testing and flexibility are not included in reliability predictions, programs must consider them carefully to realize a reliable on-orbit space system.

A second assessment of on-orbit spacecraft failure history is provided in a study by Robertson and Stoneking [2003], which investigated 750 spacecraft from 1990 to 2002 reporting 63 failures. See Fig. 13-4. Like Tafazoli's study, the data also show the majority of failures (48%) occur in the first 10% of design life. Failures then drop to a much lower rate and continue to drop slowly for the remainder of the planned life.

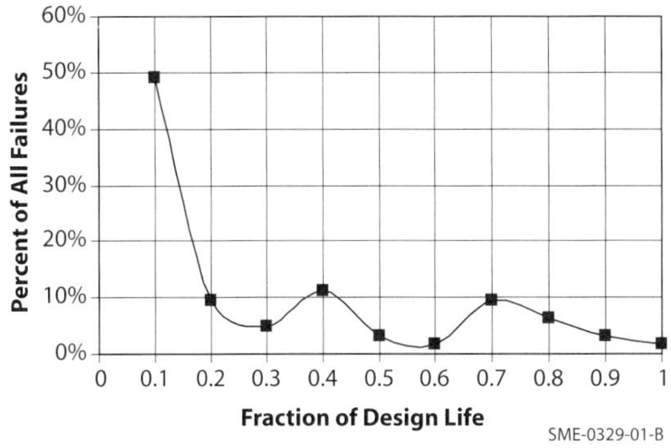

Fig. 13-4. Spacecraft Failure by Fraction of Design Life. (Graphic courtesy of Robertson and Stoneking [2003].)

The commonly used reliability Eq. (13-1) is often called P_S, for Probability of Success, with a value of 1.0 representing no failures, equivalent to 100% reliability. Examples of P_S calculations over time are shown in Table 13-5 in Sec. 13.4.3.

$$P_s = e^{-\lambda t} \neq On\text{-}Orbit\ P_s \tag{13-1}$$

P_S = Probability of Success (used interchangeably with Reliability)

λ = Failures In Time (FIT) per billion hours

1 FIT denotes 1 failure per billion hours

t = time in hours (1 billion hours = 114,100 years)

The historical on-orbit data do not match the reliability equation's predictions. This equation fundamentally misses the fact that most failures occur early in the life, especially in the first year (or first 10%) of life as shown by the on-orbit failure data above. In contrast, the reliability equation predicts a near constant rate of failures every year because a constant failure rate (λ) over time is typically used. This inconsistency highlights that failures most frequent in early operations, such as design failures, are not considered in the reliability equation (recall Table 13-3). Tafozili's and Robertson's results indicate that infant mortality holds true for spacecraft. The belief that the preponderance of failures in the first year is driven by design or workmanship faults that expose themselves early in a mission is corroborated in a variety of reports. [Tafazoli, 2008; Robertson and Stoneking, 2003; Sarsfield, 1998; Bloomquist, 1984]

Also once functioning, spacecraft life often far exceeds predictions as we will see later in Sec. 13.4.4. This is largely because, in the absence of a measured failure rate, a constant failure rate is often used in reliability calculations even though on-orbit data show failure rates decrease for spacecraft over time. Sarsfield's [1998] work in this area provides an excellent example of failure rates decreasing with time for the Voyager spacecraft. This is a case where measured on-orbit data do exist for a given system and therefore, the reliability calculations can be used effectively to match the on-orbit failures. When such data exist for and comparable applications and environments, which is sometimes the case when multiple, similar geosynchronous communications satellites are built and launched serially, then reliability analysis can be used effectively to predict the on-orbit failures beyond the first year.

Launch Vehicle Contribution to On-Orbit Reliability of Space Systems

A related and key factor in all space systems is the launch vehicle. While it is not the intent of this section to discuss launch vehicle reliability in depth, we want to highlight that the measured reliability of proven launch vehicles is only 90–95%. Research shows, "Of the 4,378 space launches conducted worldwide between 1957 and 1999, 390 launches failed (the success rate was 91.1%), with an associated loss or significant reduction of service life of 455 satellites (some launches included multiple payloads)" [Chang, 2001]. Regardless of the attempted reliability for all other aspects of the spacecraft, the space-system reliability cannot exceed the launch vehicle's reliability, and a launch failure results in $R = 0$. Users, of course, do not care about the source of mission loss; all the user knows is that the capability they were depending on is not available.

One must consider the impacts of a single launch failure on overall system capability. The bigger the spacecraft, the bigger the impacts to the cost, the schedule, and the users. Consider the implications of a single launch failure on a constellation of 2 large and highly capable spacecraft versus the impact of a single launch failure on a constellation of 4 less capable spacecraft. In this theoretical case, a single launch vehicle loss creates far more loss of availability to the constellation of 2 large satellites. Furthermore, the true reliability of the rocket that the mission cares about is not well known to the mission designer unless that rocket has a long track record of similar missions from which meaningful assessment of reliability can be calculated. The bottom line is that launch vehicle reliability is a huge component of mission availability, which must be recognized by the mission designer. The mission designer should consider things like the constellation design (one or multiple), spacecraft

Table 13-5. Reliability Prediction Analysis Using Eq. (13-1) Compares the Expected Probability of Success as a Function of Reliability Level and Launch Delay.

Case	Predicted Reliability	Delivery Date; Year Started	Probability of Success at End of Year					Comment
			1	2	3	4	5	
1	90%	0	98%	96%	94%	92%	90%	High Reliability, deliver on time
2	70%	0	93%	87%	81%	76%	70%	Medium Reliability, deliver on time
3	17%	0	70%	50%	35%	25%	17%	Low Reliability, deliver on time
4	90%	4	0%	0%	0%	98%	96%	High Reliability, deliver late

sparing, and reasonably pairing the resources put toward the spacecraft with the cost and reliability class of the launch vehicle.

13.4.3 Linking Reliability to Schedule

A reliability prediction and on-orbit reliability are inextricably linked to the variable of time. As discussed earlier, the user's perspective on reliability cares not if the satellite will work eventually in the distant future, but only that it is available when promised.

A reliability requirement is typically defined as a probability of success, P_s, at some number of years after launch. This equates to R_1 at year 1, R_2 at year 2, and so on. Let's examine the probability of success for a single spacecraft from a user's perspective. Our user has been promised a space-based capability to start in year 1 and continue through year 5. Table 13-5 was created using the predicted reliability of Eq. (13-1) for four different bounding cases: High, medium, and low-reliability systems delivered on schedule and a fourth case of a high-reliability system delivered three years late in year 4. Case four shows the problematic situation of the user being delivered a wonderfully reliable spacecraft, but 3 years late. For the full first three years the user has no capability; a reliability of zero has been achieved. This is no different from a launch failure followed by the building of a second spacecraft over the following 3 years. The users are the ultimate arbiter of value, and the authors suspect that most users would prefer cases one, two, or even three over case four. Although not many sponsors would agree to the case-three spacecraft requirement, "The spacecraft shall have a predicted reliability of 17% at the end of 5 years."

13.4.4 Considerations for Small and Large Satellites and Systems

Early in the design, or even proposal process, a mission designer must make decisions on a mission-fulfillment approach using small satellites, large satellites or a mixture of both. This decision has far reaching implications on mission cost, schedule, and availability, which play out much differently for small versus large satellites with advantages and disadvantages for both. Neither approach is universally better; the trade-off must be made for each specific mission.

Considerations for Small Satellites

Small satellites and systems have some inherent benefits toward addressing reliability both mathematically and in real terms. At a macro level, the quantity of small satellites tends to be larger and the cost, smaller. Missions that require more than one satellite typically degrade gracefully; and single small-satellite failures tend to have no appreciable effect on a National scale, as the investment and capability are inherently modest. Small satellites also tend to have shorter development schedules. The shorter time between design and on-orbit operations inherently allow newer, often better technologies to be used.

The predicted reliability levels for generally single-string, small satellites would indicate that they are highly unlikely to last more than a couple of years. However, many single string satellites that survive the 1st year last for 5 to 10 years. NASA's Earth Observation-1 (EO-1) satellite is a single-string system that launched in November 2000 and is still operating in 2010, which is statistically unlikely based upon conventional reliability analysis misused as an on-orbit reliability prediction. The EO-1 spacecraft bus had a predicted reliability, or probability of success (P_s), of 75% for 1 year, which equates to 6% for 10 years. Note, this is only the bus reliability—the predicted payload reliability reduces these numbers much further. The WindSat/Coriolos mission is an example of a moderate (but not high) reliability mission. The WindSat payload is a 22 channel radiometer designed mostly single-string. It was launched in 2003 with a reliability prediction that gave it only a 3% chance to still be working in 2010, 7 years after launch. Yet WindSat is still operating 24/7 in 2011. The Coriolis spacecraft upon which the WindSat payload resides is fully redundant; yet in 8 years it has not experienced a failure on its primary side, thus functioning as if it were single string and lasting 8 years.

An interesting case study of an alternative approach to reliability comes from small-satellite builder, Surrey Satellite Technology LTD (SSTL). Company data on 20 satellites from 1981 to 2003 show an average Mean Time To Failure (MTTF) for their satellites of 6.4 years, yet the average design life was only 2.1 years.* In the last 10 years, with the incorporation of better battery technology, their satellites' MTTF has improved to 7 years. In

* Data courtesy of SSTL.

Table 13-5, Fig. 13-4◀, Eq. 13-1◀

Table 13-6. Advantages of Small and Large Satellites.

Small Satellite Advantages	Large Satellite Advantages
• Larger quantities affordable • Single string reliability historically higher than reliability analysis indicates • Reduced cost and capability impact of a single loss • More rapid design cycles allow implementation of current, typically better technologies	• Enable capabilities limited by physics in small satellites, e.g., large aperture for high signal gain • Greater design oversight affordable • More extensive quality assurance affordable • Can perform technology R&D within program to support future capability growth • Redundancy and large margins often easier accommodate within mass and cost budgets

contrast to typical space industry practices which emphasize high reliability parts, SSTL uses commercial parts extensively and avoids quantified reliability analysis. In their words they prefer to "Concentrate efforts on improving reliability, not quantifying it" and do this largely by starting with mission objectives, performing Failure Modes and Effects Analysis (FMEA) to uncover modes which may prevent these objectives from being met, and then focusing resources on preventing these potential failures. Bottom line, in addition to the inherent benefits of small satellites such as larger numbers (for a given cost), shorter schedules, and more current technology, their on-orbit performance often substantially exceeds their reliability-analysis prediction. This is especially true if they were well tested and designed with high margins and flexibility.

Considerations for Large Satellites and Systems

Larger systems allow for enabling capabilities, such as larger aperture and higher power, simply not physically possible on smaller systems due to physics. Large satellites and systems also have some inherent benefits toward addressing reliability. In particular, larger systems and programs can afford and justify more thorough quality assurance, testing (such as parts radiation testing), and independent reviewers. The extensive use of redundancy and large margins can be more affordable within mass budgets and financial budgets on large platforms because they take a relatively small percentage of overall program resources. Large margins and extensive redundancy can provide the confidence necessary for mission users to plan for very long satellite lifetimes. Large communications satellites built, following these principals, are often designed for 15 year missions.

Technology can help by making the job much easier or by fundamentally enabling the mission. However, new technology is often viewed negatively by acquisition programs due to the risk of undiscovered flaws. The Technology Readiness Level (TRL) concept provides a sound process to mature a new technology into a flight qualified item; however, this concept can be misused by programs to eliminate valuable technologies by requiring that "TRL-7 technologies or greater." This type of blanket requirement eliminates new technologies entirely instead of creating a sound plan to develop and qualify the technology on a time frame consistent with the program's schedule. A blanket TRL requirement can also pressure space programs to pretend that needed technologies are at a higher TRL than they are to get a mission go-ahead. This situation causes an artificial feeling of comfort, often resulting in a lack of focus and lack of resources needed early in the program to ensure that development does not affect the schedule. We have watched programs worry extensively over a decision to use a new "high risk" technology while at the same time deleting the test units to save cost and schedule, although the latter created a much higher risk.

Large programs, with extensively designed and calculated reliability numbers need to remain alert and not allow themselves to become fooled by this number. Even the highest reliability commercial communication spacecraft with a P_S >95% for five years and >90% for 10 years regularly have their mission lives substantially reduced. The "Satellites & Launches Trend Down" article by the Teal Group [Caceres, 2004] "estimates that during 2001–2003, an average of about a dozen satellites failed or malfunctioned each year." The rate of a dozen per year was similar from 1991–2000, but there were more satellites on-orbit in the 1990s. The study details over 12 high-reliability geosynchronous spacecraft which experienced failures that reduced their mission life substantially or ended the mission within the first year. These failures covered a broad range of companies and spacecraft types. So programs with high-reliability calculations need to be vigilant in all practices, such as thorough testing and designing in flexibility to assure on-orbit reliability is realized.

Summary of Considerations for Large and Small Satellites

Large satellite programs are well suited to large-aperture, high-power and very long-life missions. Small satellites are well suited for quicker-response missions and shorter development schedules inherently make use of current, usually better technology. Small satellites in high-quantity constellations can be quite robust against individual launch or satellite failures in contrast to small-quantity constellations of large satellites being very sensitive to individual losses. A mix of both small and large space systems can best address the wide range of space missions, users, and reliability needs. (See Table 13-6.)

13.4.5 Considerations for Achieving On-Orbit Availability

It has been shown that reliability analysis is great for improving a design but is fundamentally misapplied as a predictor of spacecraft success on orbit. So let's consider availability and how best to achieve it with limited resources.

There are many availability definitions and analytical methodologies in the literature [NASA, 1998] that bring the aspect of time into the reliability assessment as well as other considerations such as service interruptions and the time to restore service. The simplest representation for **availability** is the ratio of the expected amount of the up time of a system (the time the system is working properly and available to users) divided by the total time on-orbit.

Focusing on the simple up-time versus down-time equation reflects the user's perspective of **'did I get the capability I required at the time I required it?'** which is in fact the true purpose of the mission. This availability-based viewpoint allows the mission designer to consider other mission impacts including schedule delays, launch failure, design problems, and software failures. Clearly, the likelihood of faults such as design failures is incalculable; yet history shows many on-orbit problems that were in fact design problems rather than hardware failures. Optimizing mission availability requires the mission designer to consider many qualitative factors to best fulfill the mission's objectives and satisfy users' needs.

Availability depends upon many factors: meeting mission performance, surviving the environments, avoiding parts failures, proper manufacture such that the spacecraft is built as designed, staying on budget (or at least close enough that the project is not cancelled), meeting the schedule promised to users, proper operations, and robust software.

These factors are addressed by space programs through a variety of practices. Every program must select, prioritize and pay for a combination of these availability practices that best support their mission. These practices include good design, thorough testing, large margins and design/operational flexibility, redundancy, use of mass-produced components (although this is rarely available in the low production world of spacecraft), reliability analysis, manufacturing and process controls (including quality assurance and acquisition processes), preparation of mission simulators, budgeting for operations training, and constellation design. The best availability depends on the program having budget and schedule for every practice selected but the question mission designers must answer is *"how much can the program afford for each practice?"*

We have provided our opinions on the relative contributions of each of these practices to each of the elements of availability in Table 13-7. As this is a matter of judgment, one can argue with any of the individual positions. However, the value of this analysis is in the observation of the broad trends between practice and result. **An important take away from this table is that there are at least 9 important practices programs can use to address failure modes and improve on-orbit reliability and that each practice has resource and schedule impacts as well.** To be used effectively, an honest assessment of the relative merits for each practice must be considered in light of the unique circumstances of each mission.

Let's study each practice and its impact on on-orbit reliability in the table above.

Good Design: Good design is essential to meeting mission performance and surviving the environment. The simplicity of a good design has important availability benefits through schedule control because of the efficiency with which a good design can be built and tested and because of the reduced quantity of time-consuming test failures. As a design element, software derives great reliability benefits from good design. Because nothing is free, the effort required for good design requires time and funding, increasing schedule and cost. Still, the broad trend is that good design pays many reliability dividends, particularly reducing the likelihood of infant mortality, indicating that a program gets much value for the application of resources towards good design.

Thorough Testing: Testing is crucial in finding problems on the ground before they become reliability problems on orbit. Good testing pays large dividends, including exposing problems in meeting thermal and launch environments, and in finding flaws in manufacturing and software. Additionally, when one follows the "test like you fly" adage, flight operation's reliability improves from using and refining the operational ground software and procedures. Testing carries the broad trend of large reliability benefits with low negative impacts. Programs are often tempted to cut testing towards the end of the development cycle because at this point in a program even modest cost and schedule problems tend to have accumulated into larger problems. This often proves to be a false savings as shown by the preponderance of infant mortality failures. Ensuing failure investigations frequently determine these failures could have been caught with the proper ground test. Sometimes one has to ask, "Can we afford not to spend this money?"

Flexibility and Margins: A spacecraft with inherent flexibility in its operation—either through forms of redundancy or a design that can perform core functions multiple ways—allows continued operations in the face of component failures or operations errors. Similarly, large margins allow a spacecraft to continue operations in the face of specific types of failures. Let's examine how the power subsystem design affects the spacecraft:

- Case 1 is a spacecraft with modest power margins and a single array on a single gimbal. A gimbal failure will disable this spacecraft and end its mission.

Table 13-6◀, Fig. 13-4◀, Eq. 13-1◀

Table 13-7. Author's Opinions—Effects of Development Practices on True Spacecraft Reliability.

	Failure Modes							
Practice to Address Failure Mode	**Meets Mission Performance**	**Survives Environments —Stress & Thermal**	**Avoidance of Parts Failure, Radiation, & Wear Out**	**Built as Designed**	**Meets Budget**	**Meets Schedule**	**Operator Error**	**Software Failure**
Good Design	++ strong benefit	++ strong benefit	+ weak benefit via simplicity and robustness	NA	– moderately higher cost	++ strong benefit via simplicity	+ weak benefit via simplicity	++ strong benefit
Good Testing	++ strong benefit	++ strong benefit	+ catch infant mortality	++ strong benefit	– moderately higher cost	– moderately longer schedule	++ if test like you fly	++ strong benefit
Flexibility & Margins	NA	++ ability to survive after component failures	+ margins enable work around for some part failures	NA	– moderately higher cost	+ weak benefit	++ more likely can recover from op errors	NA
Redundancy	NA	++ ability to survive after component failures	++ strong benefit	NA	– – high cost of parts & complexity	– increased build and test schedule	NA	NA
Use of Mass Production Components if Available	NA	+ part capabilities known in advance	++ measured reliability data exists & learning curve complete	+ weak benefit	++ production efficiency	++ production efficiency or truly off the shelf	+ ops of component often well understood	depends on specific component type
Reliability Analysis	+ circuit improvements	+ parts thermal stress analysis	++ strong benefit	NA	– or – – because of cost of Hi-REL parts if chosen	– or – – because of lead time of Hi-REL parts if chosen	NA	NA
Rigorous QA Controls	NA	NA	++ strong benefit	++ strong benefit	– or – – pending level chosen	– moderately longer schedule	+ QA & config control of ops procedures	++ strong benefit through software QA
Mission Simulation & Training	++ "flying" scenarios before launch, increases on-orbit availability	NA	NA	+ find undesired features	– cost for mission simulator & training	+ often enables parallel testing	++ strong benefit	++ wring out errors & inefficiencies in both ground & flight SW
Constellation Design (multiple S/C) or launch on demand replacement	NA	NA	NA	NA	– or – – cost pending specifics of the mission	++ strong benefit	++ learning curve ops benefits if multiple spacecraft	+ problems on first spacecraft fixed for others

Key: ++ Strong Benefit, + Weak Benefit, NA not applicable, – Weak Negative, – – Strong Negative

- Case 2 is the same spacecraft with large power margins and a single array on a single gimbal. A gimbal failure will limit the capability of this spacecraft, but the high margins may create enough power without gimballing the array to continue operations with modest degradation.
- Case 3 is the same spacecraft with large power margins but, instead of a single large array on a single gimbal, it has two half size arrays on two gimbals. Should a gimbal failure occur, the high margins, coupled with the second gimbaled array, are likely to give ground operators the flexibility needed to maintain most, if not all, of the mission capability.

These three cases illustrate the benefits and costs of margins and flexibility. More margins increase cost and mass for the solar array, as does a second gimbaled array.

Broadly speaking, the benefits and costs of flexibility and margins will be unique for each mission and each subsystem. A program's reliability will benefit from a continuous search for opportunities to provide flexibility and margins wherever available within a tolerable cost.

Redundancy: Redundancy can significantly increase reliability by providing insurance against bad parts or environmental failure. It is also one of the most expensive options in terms of financial cost, weight, modest increases in production and test schedules, and software complexity. Redundancy will not protect against fundamental design flaws; the redundant item will have the same flaws as the primary item. We have frequently witnessed spacecraft redundancy extend operational mission life by many years. We have also seen several cases where entire missions were lost, or greatly degraded, due to the blind application of redundancy as a hard requirement. The latter case has been especially prevalent for mechanisms. Often mechanisms become extremely complex when driven to redundancy such that they can be made more reliable by rigorously testing a simple non-redundant design. The most important point is to use redundancy smartly, not as a rigid requirement, to maximize its benefit-to-cost ratio.

***Use of Mass-Production Components*:** Aircraft and automotive reliability gains tremendous improvement from the fact that mass-production components are available for key functions. Mass-produced components have typically completed their learning curve, so that most or all reliability weaknesses have been removed. Mass production provides great benefits in manufacturing by consistently producing the intended design and driving down the cost and schedule. Unfortunately, very few spacecraft components are mass-produced, other than electronics piece parts and similar items.

Reliability Analysis: Reliability prediction analysis, along with associated reliability analyses such as the failure modes and effects analysis (FMEA) and parts-stress analysis over temperature, are excellent for identifying weak links in a design and making improvements. If misused as a predictor of true spacecraft reliability, the analytical predictions often drive programs towards very expensive and long lead, "class 1" maximum-reliability parts. Proper reliability analysis can be one of the most economical practices for improving spacecraft reliability. However, its misuse as a predictor of on-orbit spacecraft reliability can lead to great cost and schedule expense with little-to-no true reliability increase; and it can potentially even lead to major reliability decreases such as program cancellation.

Rigorous Manufacturing, QA, and Processes: Manufacturing a spacecraft using rigorous production-process control provides strong reliability by avoiding problems resulting from bad parts slipping into the build. It also ensures that the built spacecraft meets the engineered design, and implementation through software-quality assurance. These practices are always necessary at some level, as they can prevent costly errors at the system level and catch some items that testing is simply unable to screen. The price one pays for strict process control is cost and schedule increases that can be surprisingly large; for example in major acquisition programs large teams of people are dedicated to providing extensive process documentation. The degree of process control is best decided on the basis of careful consideration of the costs and benefits relative to the unique circumstances of a program's reliability needs.

Mission Simulation and Training: Sound flight operations carry large increases in on-orbit reliability through increased spacecraft availability and avoidance of mission-ending operations failures. The preparation of a realistic mission simulator, supported by sufficient training, provides these benefits at relatively low cost. The decision to design and build the simulator is often a substantial program decision made relatively early in the program. We have consistently seen programs that chose not to develop a good simulator pay much greater costs downstream due to technically inaccurate testing, schedule delays to support operations testing, and poor spacecraft availability during the first year on orbit—because operators are still learning how to fly the spacecraft instead of having learned using a simulator prior to launch. Schedule delays often result from programs being forced to test ground software and mission operations using the flight satellite for lack of a mission simulator alternative. For almost all spacecraft programs, we recommend producing a simulator that, at a minimum, enables commands and telemetry to be sent, and represents attitude determination and control events (i.e., slews, and ground contacts). A simulator and associated training costs are almost always worth the operational availability benefits.

Constellation Design and Launch-On-Demand: The mission designer has many options that drive availability to consider in a constellation design. Simplistically, one can (1) build only the number of satellites needed, initiating the build of additional spacecraft only as dictated by circumstances; (2) build and launch on-orbit spares; or (3) build spares and store them for launch on demand. The pre-planned building of spares provides benefits to availability issues should any spacecraft be lost; however, the cost is significant. On the other hand the lack of spares saves cost; however, the time to build a replacement once a failure occurs has significant impacts on availability. A strong point to consider in this analysis is that the cost of the last unit built of a limited production run is generally below the cost of the initial units and can be a relatively small percentage of overall program cost. Spare satellites can be viewed as insurance for availability and more spares are better if a program can afford them. Additionally, an advantage for constellations containing multiple similar satellites is that on-orbit lessons learned on one satellite can be applied to the others provided that satellites are designed with sufficient flexibility. For instance, if you find out that an attitude control device does not have sufficient life capability on one satellite, software patches for contingency attitude control modes can be created and installed throughout

Table 13-7◀, Fig. 13-4◀, Eq. 13-1◀

the constellation, making all the other satellites robust against this now known defect.

13.4.6 Conclusion

- Focusing on meeting mission objectives and maintaining a user perspective are essential to success. Remember that schedule delays and large cost overruns, both notorious in space systems, provide an effective reliability of zero whenever the system is not available to users as expected.
- Reliability analysis can be one of the most economical practices for improving true spacecraft reliability through improved design. However, this analysis is fundamentally misapplied as a predictor of spacecraft success on orbit. Both MIL-STD-217F and on-orbit data confirm the use of these calculations to predict on-orbit reliability is inappropriate and inaccurate. Misuse of reliability analysis as a predictor of on-orbit spacecraft performance can lead to great cost and schedule expense with little-to-no true reliability increase—and potentially even major reliability decreases such as program cancellation. Examples include implementing full redundancy as a hard requirement and mandating all class 1 electronics parts.
- The concept of system availability to users allows broader consideration of program practices, such as design with high margins and flexibility, which enable programs to better address on-orbit reliability. Foundationally this starts by focusing on mission objectives and eliminating failure modes that could prevent these objectives from being met.
- We recommend each reliability practice receive an honest assessment of the question, "Is the increase in on-orbit reliability provided by this specific practice worth the inherent cost and schedule increase?" Each space-mission developer should create a program availability plan that considers its unique program circumstances and resource limitations. This plan must carefully consider all failure modes, discussed in Sec. 13.4.5, and evaluate all 9 practices to address these failure modes.

13.5 Principal Methods for Reducing Cost and Schedule

As shown in Fig. 13-5, our goal is to find ways to reverse the Space Spiral, defined in Sec. 1.1, of ever increasing cost, fewer missions, longer schedules, and demand for higher reliability. Essentially any process that breaks that cycle and begins to reverse it—i.e., that lowers cost, shortens schedules, increases the number of missions, or reduces the demand for higher reliability—will help the process. However, it's clear that breaking through the barriers of inertia and culture discussed in Sec. 13.2 requires that we take moderately large steps that make a significant and visible change. Also as discussed in Sec. 13.4, the "reliability" of Fig. 13-5 is largely parts reliability and numerical reliability computations. Actual ***mission reliability***, i.e., whether the end user will have the data they need when they need, is increased by lower cost, shorter schedules, and more missions because the system becomes much less sensitive to individual failures, delays, or program cancellations.

The following sections discuss some of the major steps that can be taken to drive down cost and schedule. However, two broad caveats apply to most of these items. First, because reducing cost and schedule is hard, it is unlikely that any single step will have a large enough effect to make a major change. While even small steps help, really turning the Space Spiral around and beginning to make large reductions in cost and schedule will require a concerted effort and combining multiple elements to have an effect large enough to be truly helpful to a program or to the space community more broadly. Second, it is clear that almost any step can have either positive or negative effects (and possibly both) depending on how it is implemented. For example, we have

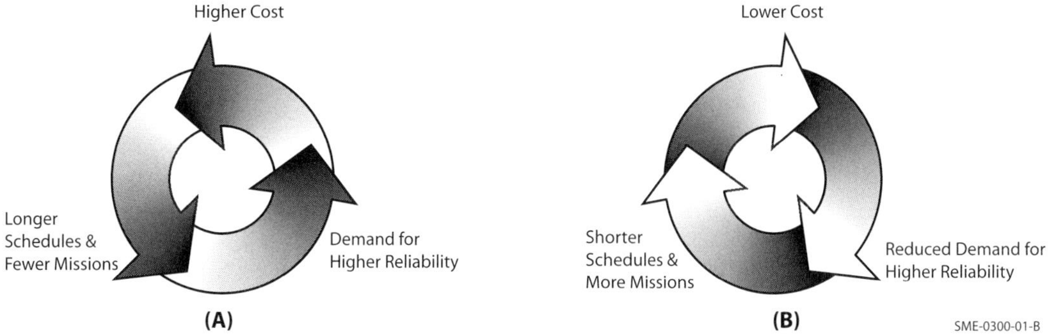

Fig. 13-5. Our Objective is to Find Ways to Reverse the Space Spiral in (A). As shown in (B) any actions that reduce cost, shorten schedules, increase the number of missions or reduce the demand for higher reliability will do this.

Table 13-8. Summary of Attitude-Related Approaches to Reducing Mission Cost and Schedule. The right attitude and personnel (Sec. 13.5.2) are truly critical for any of the other approaches to succeed. In this and the subsequent tables on reducing cost and schedule, the most important or productive approaches are shaded. In this table, all of them are important.

ATTITUDE

Reducing Space Mission Cost—Attitude		© 2010, Microcosm, Inc.
Technique or Action	**Mechanism**	**Comment**
A1. Recognize that it's Possible and Achievable	Eliminates major impediment of being unwilling to attempt to reduce cost	Biggest single impediment to reducing cost is the view expressed by "Faster, Better, Cheaper—Pick any Two." There are a great many successful, reliable, responsive, highly capable, low-cost space missions.
A2. Recognize that Low Cost is NOT Low Reliability	Eliminates major argument of wanting only "high reliability"	a) Low cost spacecraft are equally or more reliable than high cost spacecraft. b) Lower cost can dramatically improve reliability for the end user by: allowing multiple spacecraft on orbit, shortening the schedule, and reducing the probability the program will be cancelled.
A3. Recognize that Low Cost is Important	Assigns importance to low-cost and keeps it from being the last thing on the list of goals	Reducing cost has to be a high priority such that we are willing to give up something to achieve it. "We may want to explore Mars at a resolution of 10 m. But exploring Mars at a resolution of 20 m may be better than not exploring Mars at all."
A4. Recognize that Change is Critical to Reducing Cost	Reduces the opposition to "new ways of doing business"	We cannot buy or build the same spacecraft as last time with the same rules and processes and expect it to cost less.
A5. Recognize that Reducing Cost is Hard Work and Takes Real Engineering	Allows the allocation of resources and effort that are needed to achieve cost objectives	Like anything else of value, reducing cost is hard work and takes dedication, real engineering, and time, money, and attention devoted to it. There's a price to achieving low cost.
A6. Recognize that the Need to Change is Not a Criticism of Prior Programs or Practices	Reduces resistance to cost reduction programs	The Space Shuttle was a remarkable engineering achievement built by some of the best engineers in the world, but it didn't satisfy its end objective of greatly reducing launch cost. We have processes and rules in place for very good reasons, but collectively they, have created a space program that we cannot afford.
A7. Recognize that Virtually Any Technique Can Either Increase or Decrease Cost	Forces thinking about and evaluating changes within the context of individual programs—critical for successfully reducing cost	Cost reduction approaches must be implemented wisely with common sense. Virtually any of the techniques below can drive cost up if not implemented appropriately but this should not be used as an excuse for not doing them.

emphasized throughout Chaps. 1–5 the value of strong up-front mission engineering. This is a critical part of reducing both cost and schedule. Nonetheless, a blanket rule that requires a 2-year up-front mission engineering phase before anything can be implemented would be counter-productive by preventing new technologies from coming on board quickly, generally slowing down small, quick turn-around programs, and likely increasing their cost. Each of the recommendations must be implemented with some sense of balance to achieve the desired results.

13.5.1 Attitude

Large organizations would prefer to depend on processes and rules to reduce cost, but, as in most human activities, attitude and having the right people are critical to being successful. Table 13-8 summarizes the truly critical "attitude adjustments" that are needed to significantly reduce space mission cost and schedule. (People issues are discussed in Sec. 13.5.2.)

As discussed in Sec. 13.2, the largest single impediment to dramatically reducing cost and schedule is an attitude throughout the community most often expressed as "faster, better, cheaper—pick any two." This expresses the idea that we've done as well as we can do. In order to do better in one or two areas, we must do worse elsewhere, even though in virtually every other area of technology forward progress is real and moves at a much more rapid pace than in astronautics. The fact that technology advances and we have learned how to do things better over time should not be taken as a criticism of prior programs or prior management. Even though the space processes and technology that we have today have been created by some of the most capable and hard working engineers and managers in the world, this does not mean that we can't do better as time goes on.

Perhaps equally challenging is the idea that, so long as it works in the end, cost and schedule don't really matter. This is addressed quite well in the discussion on managing to a "reliability of zero" in Sec. 13.4. It doesn't matter to the soldier that was killed whether it was a remarkably capable system when it was finally launched, or would have been a great system when it was cancelled if in the end, the system wasn't there when it was supposed to be.

Table 13-9. Summary of Personnel-Related Approaches to Reducing Mission Cost and Schedule. Ultimately, it is people, not rules, that reduce cost and schedule. (For a more extended discussion, see Wertz and Larson [1996].)

PERSONNEL

Reducing Space Mission Cost—Personnel		© 2010, Microcosm, Inc.
Technique or Action	**Mechanism**	**Comment**
PI1. Improved Interpersonal Communications	Dramatically reduces errors and omissions. Conveys understanding as well as data.	Large programs use formal, structured communications through specified channels. Small programs use personal communications by creating close working relationships and personal responsibility.
PI2. Small Team	Clear, nearly instantaneous communications; strong sense of personal responsibility	Can be a problem if a key person drops out, but in practice this rarely happens.
PI3. Co-Located Team	Improves communications; reduces sense of "we vs. them"	Best communications are face-to-face, but AMSAT and some others don't seem to need it.
PI4. Empowered Project Team	Rapid decision-making; strong sense of personal responsibility; can make "sensible" decisions	Eliminates a major function of the large, formal management structure. Encourages personal "ownership" of problems and issues, often expressed as "I own that problem."
PI5. Reward Low Cost (both people and organizations)	Provides positive incentive to both people and organizations	Traditionally, if organizations spend less, they are rewarded by a reduced budget next year. Instead, they should get a larger budget next year or have half the savings put into an end-of-year bonus or party fund. (Rewards don't need to be monetary.)

In order to reduce cost and schedule, these have to be important to the system engineers, the program management, and the procuring organization. Finally, if you believe that something can't be done, or shouldn't be done, or isn't worth giving up something else to achieve, then it is likely that you won't be able to achieve it. Reducing cost and schedule is hard work and takes real effort and real engineering. **Reducing cost has a price.**

13.5.2 Personnel

Table 13-9 summarizes the second major pillar of reinventing space—personnel. Both the government and large organizations would much prefer to depend on rules, regulations, and processes, but the reality is that wars are won, inventions made, new businesses created, and creative ways to change how we do business in space are developed by motivated individuals who are out to get the job done. This means that individuals and small teams must be empowered to get things done and must be motivated to do them.

Personnel and groups must be rewarded for major reductions in cost and schedule. For example, the reward for not spending all of your department's computer budget by the end of the year is typically having a smaller computer budget next year. Amazingly, in most departments, the computer budget is always spent by the end of the year. A much better approach would be to split the savings between the organization, to reduce the overall budget, and fund the department end-of-year party.

Rewards don't need to be money. Give whoever came up with the idea for significantly reducing cost or schedule the parking space next to the door and let the department manager park in the back lot. (Actually, it would probably be best to give the department manager a bit of a reward as well. In the end, you want both the individuals and their managers to be pleased with the result.) Many small satellite builders take great pride in building high quality, low-cost satellites in a very short time. It is something they have learned how to do that much bigger, better-funded organizations do not know how to do. Recognizing this excellence can be a reward in itself. **The real secret to reducing space mission cost is to empower individuals and small teams, motivate them to reduce cost, reward them for achieving it, and get out of their way.**

13.5.3 Programmatic

Table 13-10 shows the primary programmatic approaches for driving down space mission cost. Traditionally, operational systems are very large with limited potential for changes to reduce cost or schedule, but these systems are both expensive and "fragile."

As discussed in Sec. 13.1.2, smallsats can help overcome this problem in multiple ways in the near term, and a mix of small satellites and traditional satellites can provide a robust capability with better performance, more flexibility, and greater mission assurance, at much lower cost. Another key programmatic approach is reducing the cost of failure. If we build a test engine that is so expensive, it can't be allowed to fail, we will never really learn what the failure mechanisms are. A major advantage of smallsats is that failures in test or early in the program are less of a problem than with traditional large satellites. The very reliable Soviet launch systems had multiple failures in early launches. These failures were used to improve the design and essentially eliminate nearly all failure modes. The demerit of this approach is that, unfortunately, failures early in a program tend to jeopardize funding for later phases or later missions.

Table 13-10. Summary of Programmatic Approaches to Reducing Mission Cost and Schedule. There are a large number of programmatic approaches that can help the problem. (See also Wertz and Larson [1996].)

P R O G R A M M A T I C

Reducing Space Mission Cost—Programmatic		©2010, Microcosm, Inc.
Technique or Action	**Mechanism**	**Comment**
Pg1. Operational SmallSats	Allows low-cost operational satellites	Smaller, much lower cost spacecraft are becoming more competent and can do far more in the future. Can dramatically reduce mission risk by allowing satellite replacement and multiple satellites on orbit.
Pg2. Low Cost, Rapid Test Missions	Greater potential for breakthroughs and more rapid technology insertion	Allows genuine tests (i.e., possibility of failure), instead of just on-orbit demonstrations. Creates potential for major, near-term breakthroughs.
Pg3. Use Small Business Effectively	Small businesses are a major source of cost reduction technology and processes	Typically, small businesses are not used for creative processes, both because of the contracting difficulties and the perception that small businesses don't understand the "real world" of space missions.
Pg4. Buy Multiple Spacecraft	Uses both learning curve and continuity of production line	Much like buys of aircraft or ground vehicles.
Pg5. Provide Continuous, Stable Funding (i.e., avoid programs stops and starts)	Does not reduce cost, but avoids cost and schedule overruns	Stopping and restarting a program dramatically drives up cost and increases schedule well beyond the length of the schedule break. Typically not recognized by the program office. 3 key steps: a) Make major decisions away from funding boundaries b) If possible, provide multi-year funding c) Key programs funded while decisions are being made
Pg6. Make Cost Data Known	Drives more competitive cost proposals	It is very hard to reduce cost when cost data is known, and virtually impossible when it's not.
Pg7. Reduce the Cost of Failure	Allows both ambitious goals and calculated risk in order to make major progress	Fear of failure feeds cost growth spiral. Major breakthroughs require accepting the possibility of failure—particularly in test or in early mission trials. Example: development of Soviet launch vehicles.
Pg8. Build to Inventory	Reduces mission risk and permits higher system risk	Can dramatically reduce mission risk by allowing satellite replacement. Less of a target for enemy attack. Mission becomes less susceptible to system failures or orbital debris.
Pg9. Minimize Formal Documentation	Reduces programmatic overhead for creating, reviewing, and maintaining documents	Critical to document **reasons** for key decisions and as-built design. Minimizing documentation also allows documents to be given importance and maintained. AMSAT uses redlined schematics to document as-built design.
Pg10. Compress the Schedule	Less overhead costs and less time to spend money	Must be done with care—requires (a) reducing the amount of work required and (b) providing expedited decision making.

This is an example of the culture that we have all created preventing us from doing things that we all understand are important to reducing cost.

Making cost data known is also key to reducing long term cost, as discussed in Sec. 13.2.* Often it is the government which most strongly resists this step. For example, although we had the strong support of senior Aerospace Corp. personnel, we were not allowed to publish the current version of their Small Satellite Cost Model, SSCM, in this volume. (See Sec. 11.2.)

Buying multiple spacecraft simultaneously and launching from inventory is one of the major mechanisms to drive down cost, schedule, **and** mission risk. Here, it is important that we understand the meaning of "schedule" in terms of the end user. When buying a car, we don't really care how long it takes to build that car. We only care about how long it takes to get one after we have made the decision to purchase it. While buying from inventory is certainly not the same as building something quickly, this distinction is somewhat lost on the end user that simply needs to get their mission data as soon as they can. Similarly, if we want our new car to

* Note that here we use cost and price interchangeably. Making the profit (= price – cost) known may be counterproductive by keeping some suppliers out of the market and focusing attention on a relatively small budget element that has little potential for adjustment and won't bring about the large cost changes that are needed. Basically, beating on companies to minimize profit is not a good long-term substitute for finding ways to actually getting things done more economically.

have a new class of radio that just became available, we aren't concerned whether that radio was built into the car at the original assembly line, or was added by the dealer at some later stage in the process. What the end user wants is rapid functionality.

Buying multiple spacecraft, or at least one off of an assembly line allows us to take advantage of the learning curve (Sec. 1.3) to reduce cost per unit, often by a great deal. This involves not only learning, but tooling, spares, and production equipment. It also allows us to maintain a more-or-less steady manufacturing flow in an environment where use rates can change greatly. Inventory is effectively a buffer to draw from when launches or systems fail, are attacked by an enemy, or simply are in greater demand.

When using an assembly line, we aren't forced into a mode where everything has to work perfectly the first time. In addition, it means that we have people available (engineers, technicians, and supply chain managers) that understand the system, how it's built, and what the major problem areas are. We can fix problems that arise in early production (i.e., the Soviet approach) and can insert new technology as it becomes available. The use of an assembly line is a standard approach for aircraft, ships, and ground vehicles of all kinds. A key issue in nearly all other areas of government procurement is that once a manufacturing line is closed down, it is very expensive to start it up again. In traditional space systems, we effectively restart the assembly line with nearly every procurement.

Finally, the lack of funding continuity is one of the most damaging elements for a program and a major source of cost overruns. The causes of this are discussed in more detail in Sec. 13.6. Here we want to point out that, in large part, this is a management problem and not a funding problem. Basically, it requires rapid decisions in conjunction with planning ahead. Apparently, from the perspective of the program manager, it's worse to try and explain why you spent money on the early phases of a program that was later canceled than to stop the program and then explain cost and schedule overruns that can be blamed on the contractor or other outside factors. There is no doubt that some vacillation will be unavoidable, often because of funding profits, but much of it can be controlled.

13.5.4 Government/Customer

Table 13-11 shows the government (or other large customer) approaches to reducing cost and schedule. Of course one of the principal actions the government can take is to foster and encourage the other approaches described throughout this section. By making cost and schedule reduction a priority, being willing to allow some new ways of doing business to accomplish it, and devoting time and resources to creating lower-cost, much more rapid systems, a great deal can be accomplished.

Perhaps one of the more counter-intuitive approaches that the government can use to reduce cost and schedule is to decentralize space system procurement (item G2). On a fairly regular basis, calls for government reform point out "waste and inefficiency" presumably created by having multiple organizations working on a problem. Thus, there are regular calls for a "launch czar" or a "spacecraft czar" to reduce inefficiency by consolidating all of one activity into a single person or organization. In fact, this is likely to drive up cost, increase schedule, and be counterproductive relative to what we would like to achieve. We all recognize the value of competition in industry. With competition, multiple approaches are tested and we pick the ones that are best for our particular circumstances. But this same idea works within the government. If one person is in charge of launch, we will quickly eliminate all secondary programs in the name of efficiency, concentrate all of the work in a few large contracts (probably with the major primes), and, of course, make reliability the most important feature since if we have fewer systems it is more important that they work every time. This is a prescription for feeding the Space Spiral that we discussed at the beginning of the section. If, instead of a single launch czar, there are programs for small, responsive launch systems from the Army, Navy, Air Force, MDA, and NASA (and perhaps even separate ones from Marshall Space Flight Center, Goddard, and Ames), then we have the roots of a competitive environment in which low cost and fast response become what it takes to make your program proceed. If we need a launch vehicle that can put 10,000 kg into LEO, we could start designing that from the outset or we could start with multiple agencies working on ideas for putting 500 kg into LEO, select the most promising 3 or 4 of those to work on 2,000 kg to LEO vehicles, and so on. This approach gets us multiple small launchers that provide competition to hold down cost and develops and tests in flight alternate technologies that can be used to drive down cost on larger vehicles. Rather like airplanes or ships or computers, it doesn't necessarily make sense to have one supplier working with one government agency to solve the diverse needs of the space community.

The government controls most of the R&D spending in space technology. Unfortunately, there is a strong bias within the R&D community toward challenging new technology and away from practical systems capable of being implemented and able to reduce cost or schedule or both. For example, the *Small Business Innovative Research* (SBIR) program would be an excellent vehicle for small companies, for which a major strength is finding innovative approaches to reducing cost or doing things more quickly. Microcosm undertook a survey of both DoD and NASA space-related SBIR topics in 1996 for the book *Reducing Space Mission Cost* [Wertz and Larson, 1996] and again in 2010 for this volume. The rather discouraging results are shown in Table 13-12. It is likely that much more rapid advances in reducing cost and schedule would be possible if the government chose to sponsor more R&D oriented toward reducing cost, without demanding that it advance technology at the same time.

Another SBIR approach is to make more extensive use of SBIR Phase IIIs (G6). By law, the SBIR Phase III

Table 13-11. Summary of Government or Customer Approaches to Reducing Mission Cost and Schedule. Many of these involve implementing approaches described elsewhere in this section. (Notes in parentheses in the rightmost box of the first row refer to methods from other tables, i.e., Pg5 refers to Programmatic method 5.)

GOVERNMENT

Reducing Space Mission Cost—Government / Customer		© 2010, Microcosm, Inc.
Technique or Action	**Mechanism**	**Comment**
G1. Implement Actions Specifically to Reduce Cost	Demonstrates a real interest in reducing cost and willingness to take action to achieve it	Among those listed elsewhere that can be done directly by the government or major customer: a) Foster an attitude of wanting and rewarding cost reduction (A1 to A7) b) Force trading on requirements (SE1) c) Reward low cost (Pl5) d) Provide funding continuity (Pg5) e) Make cost data available (Pg6) f) Reduce the cost of failure (Pg7) g) Develop a low-cost small launch vehicle (L5) h) Create low-cost smallsat programs for both test and operations (Pg 1 and Pg2)
G2. Decentralize Space System Procurement	Allows innovation and options that would not be allowed under a centralized procurement approach	Innovation often comes from small businesses and "secondary" organizations within the government. These should be encouraged as a way of providing positive and valuable "competition of ideas" within the government.
G3. Sponsor R&D to Reduce Cost	Main mechanism for finding lower cost solutions	Need to make reducing cost an alternative and acceptable objective for R&D, without demanding that it simultaneously "advance technology."
G4. Sponsor Knowledge Preservation and Dissemination	Actually using lessons learned rarely occurs, but is important to reducing cost	Space technology has dramatically fewer books, commercial software, or university programs than any other comparable major discipline. Knowledge is being lost at a rapid rate.
G5. Revise SBIR Objectives	An excellent source of innovative ideas for reducing cost	Currently, less than 4% of SBIR topics are directed specifically toward reducing cost. Can provide both innovative solutions and simpler, faster contracting mechanism via Phase IIIs.
G6. Use SBIR Phase III	Sole-source contract	Sole-source contract mandated by law. Can shorten schedule by a year or more. Contracting process short and simple.
G7. Assign the Task of Reducing Cost to an Individual or Organization	Allows cost reduction to be a part of the official hierarchy of organizational objectives	Typically, reducing cost is not in anyone's "job jar," which means that it is a secondary priority in a system where not all first priority tasks get done.
G8. Create a Program Intended Specifically to Reduce Cost	Allows cost reduction to be a part of the official hierarchy of organizational objectives	Similar to item above, but allows contractor participation. Can create specific objectives with a near-term schedule that can impact both near-term and longer-term, larger missions.

Table 13-12. Survey of the Principal Objectives of Space-Related Small Business Innovative Research (SBIR) Topics in 1996 and Again in 2010. (Study done by Microcosm for RSMC and again for this book.)

	1996		2010	
Principal Objective	**No. of Topics**	**Percentage**	**No. of Topics**	**Percentage**
New Software	33	15%	38	22%
Improvements to Existing Software or Technology	67	30%	20	12%
New Technology	113	51%	108	63%
Reduce Cost	**8**	**4%**	**6**	**3%**
Total	221	100%	172	100%

meets all of the competition in contracting requirements, is strongly encouraged by Congress, and has been endorsed within DoD [Finley, 2008]. This means that ideas developed under the SBIR program can go directly to being funded and built via a sole-source contract without another round of studies and competition, which can save more than a year and a large amount of funding and time in the competition and contracting process. Unfortunately, this isn't a popular law within the government bureaucracy because it eliminates another round of competition and contracting, and is often ignored.

Perhaps the most important thing that the government can do to reduce cost is either assign the task of reducing cost to an individual or organization (G7) or create a program intended specifically to reduce cost and schedule and fund some small programs to do that (G8). In both

Table 13-13. Summary of Systems Engineering Approaches to Reducing Mission Cost and Schedule. These approaches have proven to be extremely successful on many past and current low-cost, high-reliability missions.

Reducing Space Mission Cost—Systems Engineering		© 2010, Microcosm, Inc.
Technique or Action	**Mechanism**	**Comment**
SE1. Trading on Requirements	Allows a balance between cost and benefit	Makes are traditional competition difficult. Allows the government to become an "intelligent consumer."
SE2. Concurrent Engineering	Allows schedule compression; increases feedback between groups	High non-recurring cost. Can achieve "local optimization," but reduces willingness to consider truly different approaches.
SE3. Design-to-Cost	Adjusts requirements and approach until cost goal has been achieved	Has been used, but not often (Discovery, New Frontiers). Arbitrary cost goals are unlikely to be successful.
SE4. Large Margins	Reduces testing; better flexibility; reduces cost of engineering, manufacturing, and operations	Margins traditionally kept small to maximize performance. Requires balanced implementation—forcing large margins in all components may drive up cost.
SE5. Fly New Computer Plus Same Computer Flown on Last Mission	Allows use of newer technology with higher capability without the associated risk.	Allows use of newest computer technology—both lower cost and more capability with very low risk. Can be used for other hardware as well. Approach used by SSTL.
SE6. Avoid "Design for a Reliability of 0"	Places much greater emphasis on cost and schedule as critical	Recognize that from a user perspective, every day that the system is late, it has a reliability of 0. A program that is cancelled due to cost or schedule overruns has a reliability of 0 to the end user.
SE7. Devalue Optimization	Allows multiple cost reduction methods	"Optimized solutions" prevent standardization and use of non-space equipment or processes and require that everything be uniquely designed for each specific application.
SE8. Use the Existing Knowledge Base	Reduces cost, schedule, and risk	Reinventing the wheel is rarely economical. According to John Mather, "6 months in the laboratory can save you a week in the library." Specific approaches to building on existing knowledge: a. Books and literature b. Courses and conferences c. Commercial software tools d. Become a part of the low-cost community e. Take advantage of the knowledge of others

cases this allows reducing cost and schedule to become a part of the official hierarchy of organizational objectives, to be reported on at meetings, to get some assigned budget, and to flow regular status reviews up the management chain. All of this makes it clear that this is something the organization genuinely wants to accomplish and will be judged on how well it is being achieved.

13.5.5 Systems Engineering

Systems engineering approaches to reducing cost and schedule are summarized in Table 13-13. Perhaps the most fundamental of these is trading on requirements (SE1), an approach that has proven exceptionally successful in low-cost programs. The process for doing this is shown in Table 13-14 and is discussed in detail in terms of mapping and pointing accuracy in Sec. 8.6. (See Table 8-15 and Sec. 8.6.3.) The critical issue is to find areas where there is increased performance available at increased cost and then balance need vs. cost. In many respects, this is equivalent to the process of an individual buying a car. We don't write out a set of specifications and send them around to car dealers to find out who can give us this car at the best price. Instead, we look in our wallet and typically find that there is a bit less budget available than we would prefer. We then go around to various dealers and find out what is available at what price, knowing that there will be a certain amount of negotiation later on. Ultimately, we try to find a reasonable compromise between what we want and what we can afford. Our goal in space is the same—we would like to make the government into an intelligent consumer that can balance cost, schedule, performance, and risk.

We have talked in Sec. 13.2 about the problem of culture and the difficulties it raises in trying to do business economically. This is an excellent example. The government wants to give an impression of being fair to all of the contractors. Assume they evaluate multiple proposals and

Table 13-14. Process for Trading on Requirements. The example shown is for geolocation accuracy as discussed in Sec. 8.6. (See Table 8-15 and Sec. 8.6.3.)

Step	Example	How Traditionally Done
1. ***Document Reason for Requirements***	Geolocation accuracy for science data reduction	Not done
2. ***State Functional Rather than Technical Requirements***	Provide geolocation to within 500 m at nadir	Not done (i.e., attitude determination required = 0.05 deg, 3 σ)
3. ***Identify System Drivers for the Requirement***	Attitude sensor accuracy	Not done
4. ***Identify Principal Options***	(a) \$500K Earth sensor @ 0.10 deg (b) \$2,000K star sensor @ 0.01 deg	(a) \$500K Earth sensor @ 0.10 deg (b) \$2,000K star sensor @ 0.01 deg
5. ***Determine Consequences in Terms of Mission Performance***	(a) geolocation to 1 km (b) geolocation to 100 m	(a) N/A (b) Meets requirement with margin
6. ***Select Preferred Option***	Discuss cost with customers and users. Is it worth \$1.5 mil more per spacecraft to achieve geolocation of 100 m vs. 1 km?	Option (b) is only acceptable choice

select contractor A to build the next Mars lander. They work through the detailed design, trading on requirements as they go to get the most effective product at the best price. But when they're done the lander doesn't look very much like their original requirements and now contractor B comes back and says "if we had known that was what you wanted, we could have done it much cheaper," and, of course, that may be true. While we want to find ways around cultural (or legal) impediments, we also want to be sure that we understand why they exist so that we can find the right balance.

Trading on requirements typically demands other changes in the way we do business in space:

- Setting functional, rather than technical requirements (i.e., stating **what** we want done, not **how**)
- Documenting the source of requirements, so we know **why** they are needed
- Trading explicitly on the principal driving requirements
- Being willing to give up some level of performance in order to reduce cost or schedule

These are all things that we would do in normal buying decisions, but are much harder to do in a formal, rule-based system.

Another approach often used in low-cost systems is to use larger design margins (SE4). Traditional space systems are typically optimized for performance and, therefore, minimize margins. Everything is made as light and as thin and as small as possible, largely because space systems cost \$10,000 kg to get to orbit and every fraction of a kg matters if we want to squeeze out as much performance as possible. But the net effect can be a system that is nearly impossible to build or change. Returning to our car analogy, assume we find the car we want, but we would like to put in a better radio because we will be making many long trips and the better radio gets more stations in remote areas. No problem. The radio is an extra \$300. Of course, the new radio is heavier, so we will have to redesign the dashboard to be able to hold it. It also uses more power, so we'll need a larger generator. And then there's the heavier wiring for the rear speakers. And because everything has gotten heavier we can't meet our acceleration performance spec, so we will need a new engine. Fortunately, in the real world, cars are designed with lots of margin. For our spacecraft, large margins reduce cost, and the potential for cost and schedule overruns in quite a few ways:

- Less testing required
- Normal manufacturing tolerances acceptable
- Fewer rejects and reworks
- Fewer failures in both test and operations
- More robust design means less redesign
- Potential for standardized components
- Higher level of component and design reuse
- Can use more commercial grade components
- Can accept less certainty about the environment
- Reduces operations cost for planning and analysis

Most high quality products use large design margins to overcome the vicissitudes of the environment. In space, optimizing the design by driving margins as small as possible is one of the principal reasons that standardization has been dramatically unsuccessful. (In most cases, standardization means flying more capability and more mass than you actually need. Therefore, in space systems we tend to want the standard product, but with 3 of the 5 features removed to save mass and optimize performance.) Of course, this problem is made worse by the logic that says we must optimize performance so as to get the most bits (or whatever else it is we're buying) per spacecraft dollar. This leads not only to building Ferraris for every mission, but to customizing each individual Ferrari for the particular mission at hand. It results in a remarkably expensive way to observe, communicate, or predict the weather.

Finally, a key element of reducing cost is to make use of the knowledge base of what people have learned before. Low-cost, high-reliability missions have been around since the beginning of the space program and are getting more competent very rapidly with modern advances in microelectronics, processors, and composite materials. There is very little value in trying to reinvent what has been done before. It is important to learn what has worked and what hasn't worked in terms of reducing cost and schedule in prior programs and why. This means taking advantage of the knowledge of others, becoming a part of the low-cost, responsive space community, and making use of conferences, courses, and the existing literature base. The major sources of information are listed in the tables in Sec. 1.6. The references and bibliographies on the book website, along with web references to where to buy or download individual references, provide background information.

Get Ref In addition a specific "Bibliography of Reducing Space Mission Cost" is included on the website section for this chapter. This does not imply that every mission will want to follow every process developed for other missions. In many respects, each mission and organization is unique and will tailor what has been learned to their particular circumstances. But reinventing those rules is not the right approach.

13.5.6 Mission

Table 13-15 provides a summary of mission-related approaches to reducing mission cost and schedule. One of the most important elements of reducing mission cost is considering the possibility of alternative orbits. (See Sec. 13.1.1.) Traditional Earth surveillance missions want to last for a decade or more and, therefore, need to blanket the entire Earth with every sensor that will be needed in the future. (Because the spacecraft themselves are individually very expensive and effectively irreplaceable, the system as a whole tends to cost many billions.) If we are able, instead, to respond directly to world events, this cost can be dramatically reduced by both reducing the amount of coverage that is needed, but also by doing things, such as flying low, that can provide excellent performance at reduced cost with systems that are not intended to last for decades. This also lets us introduce new technology as it becomes available and employ that technology in those specific circumstances where it's needed. (See Sec. 13.1.1)

Similar considerations can apply to other missions as well. The orbit for science missions is often chosen as the best orbit for that mission irrespective of cost, in part because the "cost" of an orbit tends to be intangible. This is the reason for introducing the *orbit cost function* in Sec. 10.3.2 which is the ratio of the mass required in low Earth orbit (LEO), due east from the launch site to the total spacecraft mass needed in any given operational orbit. For example, going to GEO requires putting into LEO about 5 times the mass required in GEO. Going to the surface of the Moon requires about 8 times the mass in LEO that will ultimately end up on the surface of the Moon. This implies an orbit cost function of about 5 for GEO and 8 for the surface of the Moon. It may be that GEO or one of the Lagrange points is the ideal place for a scientific instrument due to excessive interference from the Earth. However, if we could get the same effect in LEO by tripling the mass of the spacecraft by adding shielding of baffling equal to the twice the spacecraft mass, we could potentially be much better off. We would still be launching only a bit more than half the mass of

Table 13-15. Summary of Mission-Related Approaches to Reducing Cost and Schedule. Cost reduction starts with the preliminary mission definition and design that largely determines many of the system costs.

MISSION

Reducing Space Mission Cost—Mission		© 2010, Microcosm, Inc.
Technique or Action	**Mechanism**	**Comment**
M1. Change the CONOPS to Use Existing Data Communications	Much lower cost. Systems are maintained at little or no cost to end user	Make the satellite simply another node on the Internet. Use commercial providers to get the data to and from the spacecraft.
M2. Fly Low	Low altitude is a dramatically lower cost substitute for large aperture for observations or high power for active payloads	a) Resolution is proportional to distance/aperture (small numbers are better). b) For SAR or lidar, power required is proportional to R^4 c) Also avoids the orbit debris problem. Requires propellant for drag make-up.
M3. Use Repeat Coverage Orbit	Much better coverage for a predefined location than SSO	Gives up global coverage for much better coverage of a specific latitude range. Coverage is tuned to provide 4 to 6 successive orbits of coverage at the latitude of interest.
M4. Use Orbit Cost Function as a Measure of Orbit Cost	Allows cost vs. benefit trade on the orbit selection	Orbit Cost Function is the ratio of the payload available at 185 km due east from the launch site to the payload available in a given operational orbit.
M5. Short Mission Design Life	Reduces redundancy and complexity	Most missions live much longer than their design life. Also short design life allows introduction of newer technology on a regular basis.

the more traditional mission, shielding or baffling are typically much lower cost than most other spacecraft components, we're in a very benign radiation environment and more uniform thermal environment, and we're in a regime where it is at least possible to get at the spacecraft in the future if something goes wrong. I don't want to imply that all scientific spacecraft should be in LEO, but that option should be a part of the cost reduction trade for many missions.

Finally, we should consider the use of "service provided" systems (i.e., existing, commercial ground stations) to reduce the overall mission cost, as discussed in Sec. 13.5.9 below. This typically provides better coverage, lower operating cost, and little or no up-front ground system development cost. The central issue here is that reducing mission cost and schedule is not just a low-cost payload, spacecraft bus, and operations, but starts with the entire mission design as discussed in Chaps. 1–5.

13.5.7 Launch

As discussed in Sec. 13.1.1, although launch is typically not the largest element of cost in most missions, it nonetheless drives mission cost. It simply isn't worth launching a $2 million spacecraft on a $10 or $20 million launch vehicle. In addition, the lack of launch-on-demand, which the Soviets/Russians have had for decades and the Chinese are developing, prevents us from creating responsive, low-cost systems that would be capable of taking some of the workload off large, very expensive satellites and could prevent them from having to cover all the world all the time.

The major approaches to reducing launch cost are shown in Table 13-16. The single most effective approach to reducing both cost and schedule is not to launch to orbit at all. Depending on the goals of the experiment, test, or mission, there are multiple alternatives to a dedicated orbital launch. These are shown in Table 13-17. Balloon flights can provide hours or days at high altitude at very low cost. If 0-g is important, drop towers and drop tubes can provide excellent 0-g conditions for 5–10 sec by dropping a payload of up to 1,000 kg inside a vacuum tube. (See Fig. 13-6.) The data and payload are available essentially immediately and the experiment can typically be repeated twice per day. Periods of 0-g up to about 20–25 seconds (and even longer periods of lunar gravity or Mars gravity) are available from aircraft parabolic flights. Up to 40 parabolas a day can be flown, but perhaps the major benefit is that the experimenter and a few others can fly along, watch what happens, and make adjustments and corrections in real time. (See Fig. 13-7.)

The next step up from parabolic flights are suborbital flights on a sounding rocket. These can provide up to 12 minutes of excellent 0-g and an altitude of up to 1,200 km. This means you can get to LEO altitudes and above with vacuum and a full view of the Earth and space, just as you would in LEO. The only thing missing is the orbital velocity and a large chunk of the price tag.

Fig. 13-6. Drop Tower at ZARM in Bremin, Germany. Drop towers provide 5–10 sec of very good 0-g and can typically do 2 "flights" per day with instant access to the payload after the test. (Photo courtesy ZARM.)

Fig. 13-7. Parabolic Flight. While the quality of 0-g is not as good as drop towers or sounding rockets, a major advantage is the experimenter can ride along, see what is happening, and make corrections on the next parabola only a few minutes away. (Photo courtesy 0-g Corp.)

For going all the way to orbit at lower cost for small payloads, the principal options are rides as secondary payloads or shared launches. The ASAP (*Ariane Structure for Auxiliary Payloads*) Ring on the Ariane V provides accommodations for up to 6 spacecraft of 100 kg each and multiple slots can be used. The ASAP ring has been in use for many years and has provided the ride to orbit for many low-cost satellites. More recently, the ESPA (*EELV Secondary Payload Adapter*) ring has been developed which provides similar services for the Atlas and Delta vehicles (see Fig. 13-8). The ESPA ring is qualified to mount a 6,800 kg primary satellite using the EELV standard interface plane (SIP) bolt pattern, and six 180 kg secondary satellites on a Delta IV or Atlas V vehicle. The standard secondary interface is a 0.38 m diameter bolt circle with 24 fasteners. The ring is about 1.5 m in diameter and 0.61 m tall, it is made of half-inch thick

Table 13-16. Summary of Approaches to Reducing Launch Cost and Schedule. While launch is typically not the principal element of space mission cost, it largely drives the mission cost. (For a more extended discussion of launch costs, see London [1994, 1996]. The Reinventing Space website [2011] also includes multiple papers on this topic.)

LAUNCH

Reducing Space Mission Cost—Launch		© 2010, Microcosm, Inc.
Technique or Action	**Mechanism**	**Comment**
L1. Use Alternatives to Orbital Missions	Dramatically reduces "launch" cost	Use balloons, drop towers, parabolic flights, or suborbital flights as low-cost testing alternatives.
L2. Design for Multiple Launch Vehicles	Increases competition; reduces schedule risk	Used by all of the commercial constellations. Serves to protect schedule as well as reduce cost.
L3. Use ASAP or ESPA Rings	Significantly lower cost	Does not allow selection of orbit or launch time. Not applicable for operational missions.
L4. Rideshare	Shares launch cost	Only works if systems have compatible orbits and schedules.
L5. Low-Cost Small Launch	Allows operational smallsats plus tests of technology for larger missions	Low-cost small launchers (several sizes) are critical to a long-term cost reduction program. Payloads are getting smaller and launchers are getting bigger.
L6. Build Small Launchers to Inventory	Reduces mission risk and permits higher system risk	Can dramatically reduce mission risk by allowing satellite replacement. Less of a target for enemy attack. Mission becomes less susceptible to system failures or orbital debris.

Get Info

Table 13-17.Space Principal Alternatives to a Dedicated Launch to Orbit. The main way to reduce launch costs is to use one of these alternatives to a dedicated orbital launch. (Updated from London [1994, 1996].)

Option	Characteristics	Weight Limits	Principal Constraints	Approximate Cost	Sources
Balloon Flights	Hours to days at ≈ 30 km altitude	Up to 70 kg for low-cost flights	Not in space, not 0-g, weather concerns	\$5K to \$15K	U. of Wyoming, USAFA, NSBF
Drop Towers	1 to 10 sec of 0-g with immediate payload recovery	Up to 1,000 kg	Brief "flight," 5 to 50 g landing acceleration, entire experiment package dropped	~ \$10K per experiment	ZARM, JAMIC, NASA LeRC and MSFC, Vanderbilt U.
Drop Tubes	1 to 5 sec of 0-g with immediate sample retrieval	<0.01 kg	Brief "flight," 20 to 50 g landing acceleration, instrumentation not dropped with sample	~ \$0.02K per experiment	ZARM, JAMIC, NASA LeRC and MSFC, Vanderbilt U.
Aircraft Parabolic Flights	Fair 0-g environment, repeated 0-g cycles	Effectively unlimited	Low gravity is only 10^{-2} g	\$6.5K to \$9K per hour	NASA LeRC and JSC, Novespace, Zero-g, ESA
Sounding Rockets	Good 0-g environment, altitude to 1,200 km, duration of 4 to 12 minutes	Up to 600 kg	Much less than orbital velocities	\$1M to \$2M	NASA GSFC, NRL, ESA/Sweden, OSC, EER, Bristol Aerosp.
Secondary Payloads	Capacity that is available in excess of primary's requirements	Up to ~ 1,000 kg	Subject to primary's mission timeline and orbit	<\$10M	Ariane, OSC, MDA, Russia
Shared Launches	Flights with other payloads having similar orbital requirements	Up to ~ 5,000 kg	Integration challenges launch timing and orbit must be compatible	Up to ~ \$60M	Ariane, OSC, Russia

aluminum and weighs 125 kg. Modified versions of the adapter are available depending on payload and launch vehicle requirements. ESPA rings may also be stacked to provide additional capacity.

ESPA provides the required thermal, mechanical, and electrical interfaces to the secondary payloads (SPL). SPL's can be deployed from the ESPA at a predetermined point along the primary mission trajectory or after primary spacecraft separation. Once it is separated from the launch vehicle, ESPA can be used as a satellite bus structure, as it was done for the NASA LCROSS mission [Maly, et al. 2009], for which ESPA was the structural hub of a free-flyer satellite, with interior mounting of a large hydrazine tank.

An ESPA ring is being developed to radially deploy CubeSats from an ESPA port after the SPL has separated from the port. [Maly, et al. 2009]. This structure houses a 3U P-POD. The "P-POD shooter" uses the volume on

Table 13-17, Fig. 13-7◀, Eq. 13-1◀

Fig. 13-8. EELV Secondary Payload Adapter (ESPA) Ring (Courtesy of MOOG CSA Engineering).

the interior of the ring. It mounts to the cylinder wall inside an ESPA port, and the port remains available for SPL mounting.

The *Small Launch ESPA* is a scaled version of the EELV ESPA. [Maly, et al. 2009]. It accommodates radial mounting for up to 6 low-profile small satellites on standard 0.2 m or 0.38 m diameter interfaces. It is suited for CubeSats and satellites below 180 kg. It can accommodate secondary payloads up to 100 kg on Minotaur IV and Delta II.

Depending on the specific mission needs, there are quite a few alternatives to a dedicated launch to orbit. Of course, each approach has both strengths and limitations, but all of them can provide potentially large reductions in both cost and schedule.

For larger spacecraft there are fewer options for reducing cost and schedule, although the use of some of the alternatives above for testing elements of the system may be able to find problems early in the program and, therefore, avoid more expensive fixes later. Perhaps the best option for reducing both cost and schedule, or at least helping to prevent overruns, is to design the spacecraft for multiple launch vehicles. The cost of launch is typically negotiated between whoever is buying the launch and the launch provider. Clearly, there is more potential for negotiation if more than one launch provider is possible. Designing for multiple launch vehicles is usually not hard or expensive because the payload environments of all of the launch vehicles are typically similar, except for the Minotaur that provides up to 13 g's of axial acceleration because it is made from decommissioned ICBMs for which the loads were not a principal design consideration.

An equally important reason for designing for multiple launch vehicles is to protect the schedule. Recall that launch systems have approximately a 90% success rate. When a launch failure occurs, there is a significant downtime until the next launch of that system (see Sec. 26.1.6). In addition, if your payload was the next in line at the time of the failure, it may have been moved further back by higher priority launches when the launch system resumes operations. For this reason, nearly all of the constellation builders use multiple launch providers. This also provides a continuing negotiating position. Thus, if a constellation needs to launch 50 satellites, they may choose Launch Provider A for 15, Launch Provider B for 15, and reserve the last 20, depending on the performance of the first ones. Note that constellations may also use launch vehicles of different sizes by launching multiple satellites on a larger launcher. This can work out well or badly. Iridium launched its entire constellation without a launch failure. Unfortunately, GlobalStar lost 12 satellites on a single Zenit 2 launch failure [Harland and Lorenz, 2005].

As discussed in Sec. 13.1.1, a key to reducing both cost and schedule for systems of all sizes is the development of a low-cost, small, responsive launch vehicle. (See also Wertz [2010].) This is needed for both operational smallsats and for rapid testing of both technology and processes applicable to larger systems. It also provides for the rapid introduction of new technology, which is evolving particularly quickly in small spacecraft. Building launch vehicles to inventory, as needed for launch-on-demand, is primarily an issue of whether it is worth the interest cost on the money required to build the vehicle for the time period from when it is completed until it is launched [Wertz, 2010]. Thus, at 10% interest, holding the vehicle in inventory for 6 months would increase the build cost by 5% and the total launch cost by less than that, say 4%, plus an incremental cost for storage and maintenance.

This book does not address the design and development of launch systems. However, London [1994] provides an excellent overview of why launch systems cost as much as they do and ways to reduce launch system cost. Wertz [2000] provides a cost model intended to compare reusable vs. expendable launch vehicles, which has been updated to model the added cost of launch-on-demand systems [Wertz, 2004]. A number of papers on low-cost launch systems are available at the Reinventing Space website [Reinventing Space, 2011].

13.5.8 Spacecraft Technology

As shown in Table 13-18, reducing the cost of spacecraft is largely a matter of finding lower cost, lighter, or more competent components. One of the better ways to do this is to have the spacecraft do more of the functions in software and less in hardware. (See Chap. 20.) This has multiple advantages, such as:

- Lower mass
- Lower recurring cost
- Much higher functionality
- **Can be changed, upgraded, and fixed on orbit**

and also disadvantages:

- High non-recurring development cost
- Development process is difficult to manage

Table 13-18. Summary of Approaches for Reducing Spacecraft Cost and Schedule. Note that all of the systems engineering approaches of Sec. 13.5.5 are key to reducing spacecraft cost as well. (See Table 13-8. For additional discussion, see Secs. 25.3 and 25.4 and Fleeter [1996, 2000]. The Reinventing Space website [2011] also has many papers on this topic. For a detailed discussion of building low-cost communications satellites, see Davidoff [1998, now out of print] or Ford [2010].)

SPACECRAFT

Reducing Space Mission Cost—Spacecraft Technology		© 2010, Microcosm, Inc.
Technique or Action	**Mechanism**	**Comment**
Sp1. Use Plug-and-Play Technology	Dramatically reduces cost and schedule for I&T	Has not been used much to date because it isn't minimum mass. Substantial work currently ongoing.
Sp2. More Extensive Use of Software	Minimizes mass and often allows use of a general-purpose processor	Can update and revise on-orbit as needed. Allows spacecraft to become a general purpose unit with specialized functions implemented in software.
Sp3. Use COTS Software	Immediately available; dramatically lower cost; tested through use	Possible drawbacks: May need modification and thorough testing. Typically not optimal for the application.
Sp4. Use COTS Hardware	Immediately available; dramatically lower cost; tested through use; less need for spares	Reduces both cost and risk when combined with large margins.
Sp5. Use CubeSat Hardware	All of the above plus built for space use	A specific example of COTS hardware for space applications. Most CubeSat hardware is in stock and available for immediate delivery.
Sp6. More Microelectronics	Lighter weight and lower cost than either mechanical parts or analog electronics	Takes advantage of dramatic recent growth in microelectronics. Key issue will be radiation tolerance—not a problem for low Earth orbit, but could be for higher orbits.
Sp7. Use Commercial Battery Technology	Both much lower cost and higher power density	Takes advantage of continuing advances in battery technology due to widespread use personal electronics of all sorts.
Sp8. Use More Composite Materials	Can be lighter, stronger, and lower cost	Can build much lighter, stronger structures with shorter schedules than metal tanks and structures. Potential problems include low thermal conductivity and near-zero coefficient of thermal expansion—very different than metals.
Sp9. Use Non-space Equipment	Takes advantage of existing designs, testing through use, and mass production	Typically not optimal. Often must be space qualified or put through major test program. Takes advantage of advances in design and extensive testing through use. Example: Carpenter tape antennas and hinges.
Sp10. Standardized Components and Interfaces	Reduces both cost and schedule. Avoids reinventing the wheel.	Has been remarkably unsuccessful in older space applications because it is sub-optimal in terms of weight and power. May be able to use these more in the future.
Sp11. Avoid Large Engines for In-Space Applications	Reduces cost, mass, and need for additional control components	Large engines in space often require separate control system and represent largest threat to the on-orbit spacecraft. Small thrusters can be controlled by spacecraft control system and recovery from errors may be possible.
Sp12. Hosted Payloads	Shares spacecraft bus and launch	Potential to increase cost and delay schedule if added payload creates conflicting requirements or forces a larger launch vehicle.

- Subsystem interfaces that are all in the spacecraft computer are difficult to control

The ability to fix the software on orbit is a key consideration for reducing cost and increasing reliability. This implies the need to ensure that mission operations has procedures and processes in place to change out the on-orbit software. Doing more in software also suggests that there is a major advantage to being able to fly the latest computer available. (Item SE5 above.) In effect, the spacecraft becomes a general purpose processor with most of the work being done in software. Because both software and on-board processors are evolving very rapidly, this also implies a large advantage to lower cost, short-lived spacecraft. It is likely that you have much more processing capability in your cell phone than many traditional on-orbit spacecraft. This means that newer spacecraft will typically be more competent than older spacecraft, such that the value of an on-orbit asset continues to decline. Some of the features that we can reasonably expect from future software controlled spacecraft, include:

- Software-defined radio
- Pre-processing of images such that only the needed information is sent to the ground (i.e., FireSat II sends the fire location, size, and intensity direct to the end user in the field)

Table 13-18, Fig. 13-8◀, Eq. 13-1◀

- More responsive systems, such that the spacecraft can send more detailed data if and when it is requested by the end user
- Autonomous on-board control of both orbit and attitude such that the spacecraft always knows where it is and where it's looking
- Precise control of spacecraft motion based on dynamic analysis such that all motions are both rapid and nearly jitter free

These features don't reduce cost directly, but rather allow low-cost small spacecraft to be much more capable, such that they can do the job of older, larger, much more expensive systems.

Another processor-related function intended specifically to reduce cost is the use of more plug-and-play electronics. Here the goal is to make an interface between the various spacecraft components and subsystems that will be essentially similar to the USB port on your computer in which multiple different items can be plugged in and begin to function immediately. This greatly reduces the time and cost associated with spacecraft integration and test. In addition, this allows the potential, for example, of a new more capable or more relevant payload to be put into a spacecraft that is in storage waiting for a need to be launched.

Using CubeSat hardware components, even if the satellite itself is not a CubeSat, is also a good way to drive down both cost and schedule. (For a discussion of CubeSats, see Secs. 2.1.8 and 25.4.) The two main advantages here are that CubeSat components are very low-cost and are maintained in stock and bought off-the-shelf, such that you can have them available with days. This not only reduces the cost and schedule of the component themselves, but also effectively eliminates, or greatly reduces, the need for spares because components can be obtained from inventory at any time. CubeSat components also make use of more modern technology, such as lithium-ion batteries, and that technology is tested on orbit much more rapidly because CubeSats themselves are launched more often and more quickly than traditional satellites.

Note that essentially all of the systems engineering approaches discussed in Sec. 13.5.5 serve to drive down the spacecraft bus cost. In addition, the effect of these processes is often multiplied when they are used together. For example, assume there is an existing optical instrument that is light weight and low cost. If we can use an existing instrument, it can drive down cost, risk, and schedule by a large amount. Of course, this instrument may or may not meet all of the mission requirements when flown in a traditional spacecraft. However, we can use a combination of trading on requirements (Item SE1); mission approaches, such as flying low (Item M2); and spacecraft approaches, such as the use of CubeSat components (Sp5) to create very capable, but also very low-cost space systems. This is the approach used for developing NanoEye, which can provide high-resolution imagery in a spacecraft with a projected recurring cost of less than $2 million [Van Allen, et al. 2010]. Typically, reducing the cost of a single component, i.e., buying lower cost reaction wheels, will have only a very small effect on the cost of the spacecraft and even less effect on the cost of the mission. Significantly reducing the cost and schedule of the mission as a whole typically requires that we use multiple, synergistic approaches to create a system that can meet our end objectives at very low cost and risk in a short period of time. For a much more extensive discussion of reducing spacecraft cost and schedule see Wertz and Larson [1996]. A large number of papers on this topic are also available on the Reinventing Space website [Reinventing Space, 2011].

There is at least one area in which low-cost spacecraft builders and traditional manufacturers would agree—test as much as possible and, if possible, test it like it flies. As discussed in Secs. 23.3 and 23.4, testing is critical to finding both integration flaws and design flaws, often associated with the interaction between various components. Low cost satellite manufacturers will try to find low-cost ways to conduct testing and will orient the testing toward specific questions that must be answered—i.e., will the spacecraft survive the launch loads, will it overheat in the vacuum environment, will it work in the radiation environment? As much as possible, low cost tests will be designed to verify these characteristics. Traditional systems will tend to use a more formal approach and have a "required" series of tests. (Note that thermal vacuum testing has the merit of driving out gasses that have been trapped in the material such that the test article will outgas less on orbit.) Testing is an important part of the regime for both low-cost and high-cost systems.

13.5.9 Operations

Traditionally, mission operations have been an expensive and complex activity; run from a mission operations center; requiring multiple people; and 24 hour coverage, 7 days a week. This, in turn, implies either 4 or 5 operations teams and, the management and communications needed to make them work smoothly together as discussed in Sec. 29.2. As summarized in Table 13-19, there are a number of approaches to reduce this cost.

The most direct approach to reducing operations costs is to reduce the operations crew to a single shift of 40 hours/week. This reduces the number of people, overhead, management, and communications costs. It also requires that the spacecraft be capable of "taking care of itself" for an extended period, including probably long weekends. Ordinarily, this is much easier with small spacecraft that have large design margins and are capable of at least maintaining themselves in nearly any orientation. Many small spacecraft are operated by one person on a very part-time basis often by using a safe mode combined with paging from the ground station. [Marshall, et al. 1996.]

Another approach for reducing operations cost is the use of service-provided ground stations. Here we are making use of existing ground stations located around the world that are both manned and maintained in order

Table 13-19. Summary of Approaches for Reducing Mission Operations Cost and Schedule. Multiple approaches are now available for reducing the cost of mission operations. (For a more extended discussion, see Marshall, et al. [1996] and many papers from the Reinventing Space website [2011].)

OPERATIONS

Reducing Space Mission Cost—Operations		© 2010, Microcosm, Inc.
Technique or Action	**Mechanism**	**Comment**
O1. Use Service-Provided Ground Systems	Lower cost with little or no non-recurring cost	Substantial redundancy and large area of coverage. Disadvantage is that your mission may have to share priority with others.
O2. Share Ground System Across Programs	Shares cost among two or more user organizations	Critical to compromise on requirements rather than simply combine all requirements from multiple programs.
O3. Use Iridium or GlobalStar Modem	Very low cost, continuous communications link	Low data rate, but nearly continuous coverage. Only applicable to LEO.
O4. Use Autonomous Orbit Control	Reduces personnel requirement on the ground	Also reduces propellant cost and provides precise timing for future coverage. Allows planned coverage with precision.
O5. Fully Autonomous Systems, On-board and in Operations	May allow one-shift coverage and less-frequent commanding	Autonomous systems may allow ground operations by a single shift or even one person maintaining the ground system, computers, and software. May increase non-recurring cost.
O6. Fly the Spacecraft Over the Internet	Simplifies operations by making spacecraft just another InterNet site	Can use secure Internet or encrypted data to protect data and commanding. Means spacecraft can be controlled from virtually anywhere.
O7. Use AMSAT Resources for Science Data Return	Lower cost by having an unpaid network	Has worked successfully in astronomy for decades. Can reduce both cost and provide high reliability by having multiply redundant ground segments.
O8. Common Software for Test and Operations	Reduces both cost and schedule. Avoids reinventing the wheel	May be less efficient and less user friendly than the operations group would prefer.

to communicate with multiple spacecraft. This also provides a high level of redundancy and excess coverage. The main disadvantage is that you have to share priority with others. However, this can be overcome by complementing the service-provided system with dedicated remote antennas built specifically for your system. When used in conjunction with a service-provided system, these remote sites are not required to have near-100% reliability, because the other ground stations provide back-up and coverage in areas beyond the reach of 1 or a few dedicated remote antennas. Generally, the cost of the service-provided system is in the range of several hundred dollars per data pass, which is usually a great deal less than maintaining a dedicated ground system.

In conjunction with service-provided systems, there is the potential for simply flying the spacecraft over the Internet. This is done by using the service-provided system for communications between the satellite and the ground. The ground station then puts the data on the Internet, which is then downloaded by as many end users as need it. (A variety of encryption techniques are available that keep the data secure, if needed.) Commands are sent to the spacecraft via the same process and, again, can be encrypted to avoid others intentionally or inadvertently taking over the spacecraft. In this way, the spacecraft becomes effectively just another node on the Internet that you can talk to, get data from, and control from any location where Internet access is available.

One of the more cumbersome and critical ground station functions is maintaining the spacecraft orbit, particularly in low LEO where atmospheric drag is high. This can be accommodated by using a GPS receiver on board for navigation and autonomous on-board orbit control. [Conger, et al. 2002; Wertz, 2003; Plam, et al. 2008.] A secondary advantage of this approach is that you will know in advance (years in advance, if desired) just where your spacecraft is located at any given time to about 1 km in-track and more precisely in cross-track and radial.

Finally, another approach is to use AMSAT resources for science data return. This approach of making use of the amateur community has worked in astronomy for decades as amateur astronomers make most of the observations of variable stars for which it is simply too expensive to tie up the manpower and resources of professional astronomers. This would not only provide data return at much lower cost, it would also create a high level of interest in multiple communities where amateurs were collecting useful science data and genuinely helping in the exploration of space.

13.5.10 Summary

In summary, there are several broad lessons from looking at the multiple approaches for dramatically reducing space mission cost and schedule:

- Significantly reducing overall mission cost and schedule typically requires using multiple techniques that complement each other. Unless there is a single large cost or schedule driver, making a change in only one approach or one part of the system is unlikely to have a major impact on the system as a whole

- Reducing cost and schedule is not just a matter of finding a low-cost spacecraft bus or payload. It is a mission problem involving the full range of mission engineering issues in order to provide the end user the data they need, when they need it, at low cost and with high reliability
- Truly reducing overall space mission cost significantly will require at least some investment in and development of both low-cost small spacecraft and low-cost, small, responsive launch systems
- The greatest impact comes from mission diversity in which small spacecraft are used for some operational activities and also as a test-bed to rapidly and economically develop both processes and technology for reducing cost, schedule, and workload for larger missions

The issue of mission diversity is important. Using a naval analogy, having even a few less battleships and a lot more PT boats changes the nature of the game. Diversity will allow us to do things we simply couldn't do before with a flexibility and responsiveness that isn't possible today in space. The right combination of assets will make us much less susceptible to enemy attack or the vagaries of launch failures, system failures, or collisions with orbital debris. It also makes the overall space mission enterprise much lower cost which gives us the potential of undertaking projects that today we simply cannot afford to undertake.

Our ultimate objective is to find ways to reverse the Space Spiral as shown in Fig. 13-6. What we would like to do is make use of the vast knowledge and experience base on reducing mission cost from throughout the world to begin to create much lower cost missions which will allow both shorter schedules and more missions, which will allow a reduced demand for 0 failures (that was unrealistic in the first place), which will allow further reductions in mission cost, and so on. In a real sense, we want to reinvent space—to return to the drive and excitement of the early space program, but with the advantages of modern technology and the experience base that 50 years of space exploration have brought.

13.6 Avoiding Cost and Schedule Overruns

This topic is particularly challenging because, in some respects, overruns in cost and schedule are one of the biggest problems in the space program and, in another respect, they aren't a bad thing at all. As we will see, they erode credibility and rob other programs of the funding to keep them going. On the other hand, in R&D programs, they are a necessary consequence of attempts to dramatically reduce cost and schedule, and these attempts are critical to the future of the space program.

An obvious solution to avoiding cost and schedule overruns is to never undertake anything challenging, to never push on reducing cost, reducing schedule, or trying to achieve more with less. I call this approach *Objectives Erosion*—it is basically the bureaucratic response to perceived "Requirements Creep." In the Objectives Erosion approach, if there are consistent cost and schedule overruns, then the obvious solution is to ask for less performance, for a higher price, in a longer time, until eventually we have programs that do nothing, or at least nothing new, for dramatically high cost, in a time frame such that the program is no longer useful.

While this might, or might not, be the right solution for the space community, it is not one that I'm willing to recommend. It is my belief that we need to dramatically reduce cost and schedule on space programs and to try to do much more, faster, and, most likely, with fewer resources. If we set a goal of major reductions in cost and schedule, we will not always get there. But we will never get there if we don't try.

As an example, let's assume that, using the cost models of Chap. 11, we estimate that a particular program will take 5 years and cost $100M. We apply as many of the cost reduction techniques from Sec. 13.5 as are appropriate and believe that we can accomplish the mission in 2 years and $20M or, if we add margin, 2.5 years and $25 million. In fact, the program ends up taking 3 years and $40M. Have we done well, or have we done badly? From the point of view of the contracting officer, we have done badly and our award fee should be cut to zero. We overran the schedule by 25% and the cost by 60%. In this view, we are either cheating or incompetent and the program manager should be hung in effigy and never allowed to manage another program. But, from a different perspective, we have saved the government 2 years and $60M. We should get a thank-you letter from the Secretary of Defense and twice the normal award fee. It is likely that if we had not set aggressive goals and had not pushed hard to get the cost and schedule down as far as possible, the program would have taken longer and cost even more. After 50 years of experience in space, we have very good cost models that project what it would cost if we built the system using the traditional approach. In my view, a new approach to reduce cost and schedule should be judged in part on whether it can accomplish what it set out to do (i.e., meet the stated cost and schedule goals) and in part on how it does relative to a traditional approach based on standard cost models.

Because there is a difference of opinion across the community and no guaranteed answers, I will provide both a "traditional approach" to avoiding cost and schedule overruns and an "alternative approach" (i.e., mine). Cost and schedule overruns are important issues that are worth serious discussion of alternative approaches to see what is best for any given program.

In 2007, the 10 largest DoD space programs were collectively overrun by $32 billion. Also in 2007, major weapon systems programs were over budget by $295 billion (26%), up from $42 billion in 2000 [Deloitte Consulting, 2008]. The schedule delays are not as well documented, but certainly average many years.

NASA programs suffer similar problems and often cause delays in follow-on programs. The Chandra X-Ray

Observatory was most likely delayed 10 to 15 years by cost and schedule overruns on Hubble Space Telescope. The James Webb Space Telescope started at $2 billion and is currently at $6.5 billion, if it can meet its delayed launch date of 2015, which seems unlikely.

This history of cost and schedule overruns is dramatically damaging to follow-on programs and to the credibility of both government and contractor personnel. This situation is particularly hard if you're trying to reduce cost, because it is difficult for people to believe any estimates that are below traditional values, much less any projections that are well below. But if we don't have at least some cost and schedule overruns, then we're not trying hard enough to reduce cost and contain the schedule. As in other elements of reducing mission cost, we need to find a reasonable balance—with R&D and development programs that have some cost and schedule overruns (and some underruns) and operational programs that are built on time and within budget.

In spite of different approaches to overruns, there are some aspects that I believe most observers would agree on. Cost and schedule overruns are much too widespread to be a result of bad program management, contractors that intentionally mislead the government, or poor individual decisions. In general, program managers are very experienced and very good at what they do. Everybody is working hard to meet cost and schedule, yet somehow we have trouble actually doing it. It may be that our estimates are too low or our expectations too high, but overruns are a fact of life on most programs, particularly in R&D activities.

The overrun problem is something much more fundamental than bad estimating or bad management and, most likely, has multiple causes that may well feed off each other. For example, in space systems there is a culture of "all is forgiven" if things work right in the end. Therefore, if there are cost and schedule overruns, there is more pressure to be sure you get it done "right," which, of course, leads to even more cost and schedule overruns. The problem is—What about the science you didn't get or the soldiers who died because the system wasn't in place when it was needed. Cost and schedule overruns are systematic problems that are somehow "built in" to the process or the culture. This is what we need to find and change.

13.6.1 Traditional Causes and Solutions

As we have pointed out previously, the Apollo program went from a challenge to Congress by President Kennedy to landing a man on the Moon in 8 years. Similarly, the Manhattan Project to create the atomic bomb was completed in 30 months. The CORONA project to create the first photographic reconnaissance satellite went from contractor selection to launch in less than 12 months [Nowinski and Kohler, 2006]. Historically, complex programs went much quicker than they do today.

Despite that, some observers see a strong correlation between system technical complexity and cost and schedule overruns. In 2007, technical complexity produced an average 8.7% cost overrun relative to the baseline budget, as shown in Fig. 13-9. Many programs rely on leading edge technologies that are still maturing. Sophisticated software and other advanced technologies deliver greater functionality, but require a much higher level of integration and interoperability. When large weapons systems were less complex, the development cycle was shorter. Modern jet fighter programs take in excess of 13 years and satellite systems routinely require 10 years or more [Deloitte Consulting, 2008].

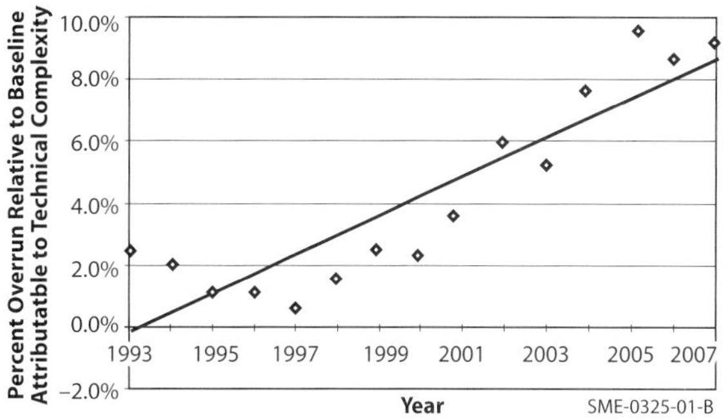

Fig. 13-9. Technical Complexity as a Cause of Increasing Cost Overruns (from Deloitte Consulting [2008]).

Recommended solutions to the problem of technical complexity include the following [Deloitte Consulting, 2008]:

- Divide programs into less complex work packages with shorter durations. Time is a clear predictor of budget and schedule risk. The longer the program, the greater the risk
- Don't approve contracts for system development and demonstration until the underlying technology is proven. Technology maturity is critical to program success, and should, therefore, be required prior to committing billions of dollars to development contracts
- Require the DoD and armed services to set a program's critical design requirements and priorities. Defense contractors cannot be expected to make the appropriate affordability trade-offs and "stand-in" for the customer
- Improve defense contractor capabilities in systems engineering, integration, and testing
- Provide more slack time in the schedule to react to unanticipated technical challenges
- Create budgets that reflect technical complexity risk and realistic assumptions

While many of these recommendations have merit, I believe the idea of "technical complexity" is rather subjective in this context. It is difficult to imagine tasks inherently more technically complex than the Manhattan Project or Apollo. In addition, the recommendations aren't consistent with the lessons learned from Apollo. If we required all of the underlying technology to be fully

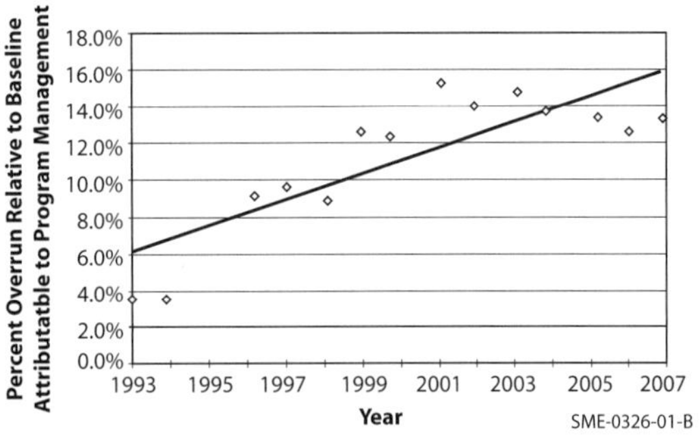

Fig. 13-10. Inadequate Program Management Contributes to Overruns (from Deloitte Consulting [2008]).

developed before proceeding, we would still be thinking about how to get to the Moon and would have spent a lot more money.

In addition to technical complexity, program management is also often given "credit" for many of the cost overruns as shown in Fig. 13-10. Other causes frequently cited include frequent program management turnover, unstable program requirements, lack of empowerment, funding constraints, and funding breaks as discussed in Sec. 13.2. This leads to a number of additional recommendations for reducing cost and schedule overruns [Deloitte Consulting, 2008]:

- Defense acquisition authorities need to understand and guard against "low bid" scenarios, where due to immature requirements specifications or lack of skill and talent, source selection awards turn out to be "change order" problems
- Establishing clear performance goals prior to program startup and applying appropriate monitoring processes to report effectiveness and efficiency
- Establishing an enterprise-wide definition of risk. Designing, implementing and maintaining an effective risk management program. Top executives set the tone, design, direction, and metrics; however, risk management should permeate all layers of the organization
- Defining clear roles and responsibilities, accountability, and authority for managing program costs and schedules. Inside the organization, establishing close coordination between multiple supporting functions, executive management, and the board
- Providing management and governing bodies with improved transparency into the organization's risk management practices. Executives and the Board should keep risk on the agenda and require timely information from operations and other supporting functions for critical decisions
- Ensuring the overall risk program has adequate support. Certain functions (e.g., legal, IT, HR, finance) should not just own risk, but also help other parts of the business manage risk effectively
- Budgets and schedules need to contain and be certified as "risk tolerant;" i.e., enough slack and contingency time is included to mitigate financial, operational, funding and human resource risks

Note that the first bullet above means that any attempts to dramatically reduce cost will be systematically and forcefully eliminated, which means that it may prove counterproductive. Similarly, there are a number of other traditional approaches that are more likely to make the problem worse rather than better. One of these is called "Back-to-Basics" in which the general idea is to take smaller steps in order to reduce the potential for overruns. This is primarily a bureaucratic approach to slowing down and stretching out procurement programs.

What's the problem with a logical progression of (a) develop technology and then (b) build a system? The first problem is that it inherently stretches the schedule and unfortunately, the government works on a 1-year budget cycle and a 4-year (or shorter) major review cycle. Typically, the government stops a program while it thinks, and it thinks very slowly. No manager likes to be told that stopping a program almost guarantees significant increases in cost and schedule, and nobody wants to take "credit" for these increases. The second problem is that good mission engineering requires working the technology and the mission simultaneously. (See Chap. 3 to 5.) To do good mission engineering we need to trade among the requirements, and, hopefully, between requirements and cost, and the only way to do that is if they are all moving forward together. It seems very unlikely that Apollo would have been faster, better, or cheaper if we had first developed the Saturn V to a largely arbitrary set of requirements and then thought about how to use it to get to the Moon.

13.6.2 An Alternative View of Causes and Solutions

Because I don't entirely agree with the more traditional approaches to reduce cost and schedule overruns, the list below provides what I believe are the major causes and some recommended solutions.

C1. Decision-Making Issues. There is no incentive for the Government to make decisions promptly, particularly if there is a possible risk. As we have discussed above, natural funding and decision cycles are at 1-year and 4-year intervals and many programs now extend over multiple cycles. This means they will be reviewed, re-evaluated, re-assessed, and most likely re-engineered many times from concept to implementation. This adds cost and delay, and delay adds more cost. Everybody can come up with a new thing to test, but nobody has the power to say "No, we don't need that test." As a practical matter, it is virtually impossible for the US to do a 6-month, $1 million program. Our decision making process simply wouldn't support that time frame or that cost.

C2. Contracting Issues. Contracting delays at every phase cause multiple breaks in execution that, in turn, create both cost and schedule overruns for the reasons we have discussed. Another problem is that cost margin isn't allowed in the contracting process and will nearly always be removed by the contract negotiation. This builds in the probability of cost overruns. The third principal contracting issue is that contracting is designed as an adversarial process. Many authors have pointed out the need for the government and industry to work together as a team (see, for example, Nowinski and Kohler [2006]), but the contracting process, and often the culture within both government and industry, strongly discourages that.

C3. Mission Design Issues. Unfortunately, mission and system engineering is often short changed on space programs, frequently because of the need to create requirements and then buy a system that meets those requirements at minimum cost. This means that trades are rarely done between major cost elements (Sec. 5.3) and Figures of Merit are rarely computed or used (Sec. 5.4). System design teams typically won't trade on cost as a parameter, relying on the idea that "It costs what it costs."

As an example of this, different orbits have a cost—but often not to the mission design community. Sec. 10.3.2 creates and evaluates an "Orbit Cost Function," but orbit cost is almost never considered as an element of mission design. (See also Sec. 12.3.2 of Wertz [2009].) Two examples of poor choices in this arena are the use of highly elliptical orbits for communications (See Sec. 10.4.2.3) or Sun synchronous orbits to avoid eclipses.

C4. Programmatic Issues. Perhaps the most substantial issue here is that there is no advantage to under-running a contract in either cost or schedule. As discussed in Sec. 13.5.2, there should be some positive reward for achieving what you would like to get done and this is rarely done in government contracting. External reviewers with "no skin in the game" have no motivation to reduce cost or schedule, but might be blamed if something goes wrong. Therefore, there is no recognition of "reasonable risk," and the push is always toward reducing technical risk, even at the expense of schedule or cost risk, for which the external reviewer won't get blamed. Finally, forcing risk onto the contractor, while not necessarily causing cost and schedule overruns, forces out small, low-cost contractors, which leads to an environment of high cost and long schedules.

C5. Cultural Issues. As discussed in Sec. 13.2, the biggest impediments to both reducing cost and schedule and constraining cost and schedule overruns are typically cultural issues. People don't like to talk about cost or reducing cost and discussing it is often discouraged, both within the government and industry. In addition, it is often the case that the issue isn't cost, but cost overruns, so this encourages the contractor to bid high. That may help the overrun issue, but doesn't help in our long-term goal of trying to reduce cost and schedule. Also, the government and others have a strong inclination to not believe people who say they can do things more economically and are afraid they will simply introduce cost overruns.

Often the introduction of TRLs (Sec. 1.3.4) will cause more harm than good. There is a tendency to spend lots of time deciding whether something can be used in space based on heritage (i.e., TRL), rather than either engineering analysis or common sense. Also, there is a general understanding in the space community that both cost and schedule overruns are acceptable, so long as the system performs well when it's on orbit. Unfortunately, few people think about the other program that was canceled to cover that cost overrun, the disaster monitoring data that missed because the mission was late, or the soldier that died because the system wasn't yet in place.

In summary, today's space program is too often driven more by fear of unknown or adverse consequences, rather than by a desire to get the job done quickly, and at low cost. We have lost in many respects the sense of urgency and the professional engineering judgment that goes with it.

Associated with the causes listed above, I believe there is a commensurate set of solutions that can mitigate, though not entirely eliminate the problem of cost and schedule overruns. These are:

S1. Tiered Expectations. The key here is to have different expectations, and a different set of responses to cost and schedule overruns in a multi-billion dollar operational program than in a multi-million dollar R&D program. There should be FFP contracts for GEO communications satellites or other well-established technologies. (This is in place today.) Here, cost and schedule overruns should be a major problem area. On the other hand, there should be CPFF contracts for programs that include R&D or first unit development with large margins for small programs, new technology, or programs aimed at dramatically reducing cost. The key is how much we are trying to save and what the projected cost would be relative to traditional cost models. This is the example described at the opening of this section. If a program would traditionally cost $100M and we are trying to do it for $10M, an overrun of $10M, while not desirable, is still good performance and a major benefit. On the other hand, a cost overrun of $5B on a $5B operational system should not be acceptable.

S2. Create a Risk Mitigation Plan. The goal here is to identify and attack key risk areas in advance of their becoming major cost or schedule overruns. We would like to monitor progress closely in areas of perceived risk and have back-ups available—**including being willing to back off on performance requirements in order to contain cost and schedule.** This is the fundamental characteristic of trading on requirements. This implies having a goal-oriented team, not one that is process-oriented.

S3. Cultural Approaches. Perhaps the most important element here is to make cost data known and make cost and schedule matter. We want to create a true team activity where we work together for the common good, including cost and schedule. We want to create a plan of attack—design how to attack the problem of excessive cost and schedule and work together toward reducing them. We want to think about the opportunities that are missed—not because the system wasn't perfect, but because we didn't get it there when it was needed or couldn't afford it because of excessive cost overruns.

S4. Programmatic Approaches. The most important approach here is to avoid schedule breaks. Schedule breaks may well be the single largest cause of cost and schedule overruns. There are a number of approaches for avoiding them and it's very important to do so. If schedule breaks can't be avoided, then the next best approach is to recognize that cost and schedule will both increase significantly and make the revised values the new baseline. Also avoid the tyranny of TRLs and the need to do technology development in series. It is much better to develop processes and equipment in parallel with the system because this allows for trades on what the process or equipment needs to do and allows us to either reassign requirements to other parts of the system or, reduce the requirements to be consistent with the capabilities. During this development, we should also have back-ups and alternative approaches. We need better systems and mission engineering throughout the program, including the creation of large margins so that the system is less susceptible to small variations in performance.

Another programmatic approach is to reward cost and schedule underruns. On the whole, rewards are much more effective than punishment. For example, if a contractor is able to drive down cost, we might choose to split the cost savings by using 40% of the savings to reduce the government's cost, 25% to new cost reduction studies or technology, 25% to the contractor, and 10% to the individuals who made it happen. Of course, rewards don't need to be money. We could give preference points toward future programs and contracts or a "thank you meeting" with the Administrator of NASA or the Secretary of the Air Force.

S5. Contracting Approaches. The major method here to use a "should cost" approach based on traditional cost models. Set the budget based on splitting "should cost" from the cost model and "bid cost" from the contractor and provide a tiered reward based on how much cost can be reduced. Similarly, a design-to-cost approach can be used that provides the best capability available for the assigned cost. Allow and reward creativity by specifying **what** and not **how**. For example, it is much better to award a contract for a system to achieve attitude determination to 0.01 deg, 3 sigma, rather than for a blue star sensor with an 8 deg square FOV and sensitivity to magnitude 4.5 in visible light.

We should encourage creativity in contracting by using methods such as the Cassini Resource Exchange in cost, mass, and power developed by Wessen, Porter, and others at JPL [Wessen and Porter, 1998]. Planetary missions are particularly susceptible to cost overruns, in part because there is no motivation for PIs to not go back and ask the program office for more money, more mass, or more power. The basic idea of the resource exchange is to create a "stock market" in cost, mass, and power. At experiment selection, the program office divided all the cost, mass, and power among the PIs, with no margin. If one of the PIs needed more mass, they get it by trading cost or power to one of the other PIs; similarly for cost and power. The program office tracked (and posted on their website), the value of mass and power. The decision-making process was now in the hands of the PIs to determine the best way to use the limited resources available to accomplish the best mission they could within the constrains of power, mass, and cost. The bottom line—the program came in on budget in cost, mass, and power. As this end result became apparent, the value of mass and power went down—i.e., you got more for your excess power (or mass) if you traded early.

S6. Use Multiple SmallSats. Sets of small satellites can do many of the things that larger satellites are more traditionally used for. Smallsats have inherently much shorter schedules, which implies far fewer schedule breaks. It also reduces the cost of individual failures. Cost and schedule overruns are likely to be much smaller dollar values, although, of course, this may not matter to the rule-oriented bureaucracy. Teamwork is easier in small programs and individual responsibility is greater. There are two approaches for using sets of smallsats. The satellites can each be individual missions that work together for better coverage or timeliness, such as the SSTL Disaster Monitoring Constellation. Alternatively, the mission functions can be broken down and split among multiple satellites, as in the DARPA F6 program.

In summary, there are many potential solutions. What they all have in common is that cost and schedule have to matter from the outset.

If our specific goal is to reduce, or contain the schedule, then the answer is to determine the value of doing so and reward that behavior. Make it worthwhile to come in ahead of schedule. The classic example of this is the Northridge earthquake in Los Angeles on Jan. 17, 1994, which caused freeway overpasses to collapse on the I10, at the time the single most heavily used highway in the US. Unfortunately, the freeway doesn't work as well when the bridges have collapsed. The state of California offered a bonus of $250,000/day for every day ahead of schedule that the bridge reopened. The I10 reopened 88 days after the earthquake, 66 days ahead of schedule, the contractor earned a bonus of $16 million, and millions of commuters got back on the freeway 2 months earlier than they otherwise would have, and probably years ahead of what would be the case with normal bidding and contracting. Returning to space missions, if we can constrain the schedule for both decision-making and contracting, we will have gone a long way toward constraining the cost as well.

As with nearly all aspects of space mission engineering, it's a matter of finding the right balance. Some cost and schedule overruns are acceptable in R&D or development programs that are pushing dramatic improvements. Continuing overruns on operational programs are dramatically bad. The hard part is being able to appreciate the difference in a rule-based system.

It seems clear that the right answer is returning to some of the approaches used at the beginning of the space program—being aggressive in what we attempt;

forcing rapid, parallel decisions making; and doing good up-front mission engineering, but doing it quickly. We need dramatic reductions in both mission cost and schedule. The most certain way to fail is not to make an attempt by concentrating only on overruns and not on what has been attempted or achieved. We need to use what we have learned over 50 years of space exploration along with modern technology to change the way we do business in space. We need to Reinvent Space.

References

For annotated bibliography of reducing space mission cost and schedule, see the book website.

Bloomquist, C. 1984. "Spacecraft Anomalies & Lifetimes." Proceedings of the Annual Reliability and Maintainability Symposium, Jan. 24–26.

Caceres, Marco. 2004. "Satellite & Launches Trend Down," *Aerospace America.*, Jan.

Chang, I-Shih. 2001, "Space Launch Vehicle Reliability." *Crosslink*, Systems Engineering, vol. 2, no. 1.

Conger, Robert, Gwynne Gurevich, and James R. Wertz. 2002. "Autonomous On-Board Orbit Control." 20th AIAA ICSSC Conference. AIAA 2002-1976. Montreal, Canada. May 13–15.

Cooper, Lawrence A. 1992. "Assured Access to Space: The Dilemma of Reconstitution and Launch-on-Demand." *Airpower Journal*, Summer 1992, pp. 47–57.

Davidoff, Martin. 1998. *The Radio Amateur's Satellite Handbook.* Newington, CT: The American Radio Relay League.

Deloitte Consulting. 2008. "Can we Afford Our Own Future? Why A&D Programs Are Late and Over-Budget—and What Can Be Done to Fix the Problem." Deloitte LLP.

DoD. 1991. *Reliability Prediction of Electronic Equipment.* MIL-HDBK-217F. Dec. 2.

Finley, James I. 2008. "Small Business Innovation Research (SBIR) Program Phase III Guidance." Memorandum for Secretaries of the Military Departments and Directors of Defense Agencies. Dec. 8.

Fleeter, Rick. 2000. *The Logic of Microspace.* El Segundo, CA: Microcosm Press.

Fleeter, Rick. 1996. "Reducing Spacecraft Cost." In Wertz, James R. and Wiley J. Larson. *Reducing Space Mission Cost*, Chap. 5. El Segundo, CA: Microcosm Press.

Ford, Steve. 2010. *The ARRL Satellite Handbook.* Newington, CT: American Radio Relay League.

Foust, Jeff, D. Vaccaro, C. Frappier, and D. Kaiser. 2008. "If You Build It, Who Will Come? Identifying Markets for Low-Cost Small Satellites." Paper No. SSC08-I-1, 22nd AIAA/USU Conference on Small Satellites. Logan, UT. Aug. 11–14.

Harland, D.M. and R.D. Lorenz. 2005. *Space Systems Failures: Disasters and Rescues of Satellites, Rockets and Space Probes*. New York: Springer.

London, John R. 1994. *LEO on the Cheap: Methods for Achieving Drastic Reductions in Space Launch Costs*. Maxwell AFB, AL: Air University Press.

London, John R. 1996. "Reducing Launch Cost." In Wertz, James R. and Wiley J. Larson. *Reducing Space Mission Cost*, Chap. 4. El Segundo, CA: Microcosm Press.

Marshall, M.H., J.A. Landshof, and J.C. van der Ha. 1996. "Reducing Mission Operation Cost." In Wertz, James R. and Wiley J. Larson. *Reducing Space Mission Cost,* Chap. 6. El Segundo, CA: Microcosm Press.

Maly, J. R., V. M. Stavast, G. E. Sanford, and M. E. Evert. 2009. "Adapter Ring for Small Satellites on Responsive Launch Vehicles." 7th Responsive Space Conf., RS7-2009-1006: Los Angeles, CA. Apr. 27–30.

NASA. 1998. *Planning, Developing and Managing an Effective Reliability and Maintainability (R&M) Program*. Technical Standard, NASA-STD-8729. Dec. 1.

Nowinski, Edmundo H. and Robert J. Kohler. 2006. "The Lost Art of Program Management in the Intelligence Community: A View of How We Manage." *Studies in Intelligence*, vol. 50, no. 2.

Office of the Secretary of Defense. 2007. "Military Power of the People's Republic of China," Annual Report to Congress.

Plam, Yegor, Richard E. Van Allen, James R. Wertz, and Thomas Bauer. 2008. "Autonomous Orbit Control Experience on TacSat-2 using Microcosm's Orbit Control Kit (OCK)." 31st Annual AAS Guidance and Control Conference. Breckenridge, CO. Feb. 1–6.

Reinventing Space Conference. 2011. Website.

Robertson, B. and E. Stoneking. 2003. "Satellite GN&C Anomaly Trends", Proceedings of 26th annual AAS Guidance and Control Conference, AAS 03-071. Breckenridge, CO. Feb. 5–9.

Sarsfield, Liam P. 1998. *The Cosmos on a Shoestring*. Santa Monica, CA: RAND.

Tafazoli, Mak. 2008. "A Study of On-Orbit Spacecraft Failures." *Acta Astronautica*, vol. 64, issues 2-3, Jan.–Feb.

Van Allen, R. E., J. R. Wertz, and T. Barcley. 2010. "NanoEye—Military Relevant Surveillance for Less Than $5 Million Total Recurring Mission Cost." 8th Responsive Space Conference. Los Angeles, CA. Mar. 8–11.

Wertz, James R. 1999. "Architecture for Developing an Economically Viable International, Large-Scale Lunar Colony." IAF Specialists Symposium on Novel Concepts for Smaller, Faster, Better Space Missions. Redondo Beach, CA. Apr. 19–21.

Wertz, James R. 2000. "Economic Model of Reusable vs. Expendable Launch Vehicles." IAF Congress, Rio de Janeiro, Brazil. Oct. 2–6.

Wertz, James R. 2003. "Autonomous Navigation and Autonomous Orbit Control in Planetary Orbits as a Means of Reducing Operations Cost." 5th International Symposium on Reducing the Cost of Spacecraft Ground Systems and Operations, Pasadena, CA. Jul. 8–11.

Wertz, James R. 2004. "Responsive Launch Vehicle Cost Model." 2nd Responsive Space Conference, RS2-2004-2004. Los Angeles, CA. Apr. 19–22.

Wertz, James R. 2005. "Coverage, Responsiveness, and Accessibility for Various Responsive Orbits." Presented at the 3rd Responsive Space Conference, RS3-2005-2001. Los Angeles, CA. Apr. 25–28.

Wertz, James R. 2007. "Circular vs. Elliptical Orbits for Persistent Communications." 5th Responsive Space Conference, RS5-2007-2005. Los Angeles, CA. Apr. 23–26.

Wertz, James R. 2009. *Orbit & Constellation Design and Management: Spacecraft Orbit and Attitude Systems*. Hawthorne, CA: Microcosm Press.

Wertz, James R. 2010. "Assessment of SmallSat Utility and the Need for Dedicated, Low-Cost, Responsive Small Satellite Launch." 8th Responsive Space Conference. Los Angeles, CA. Mar. 8–11.

Wertz, James R. and Simon D. Dawson. 1996. "What's the Price of Low Cost?" 10th Annual AIAA/USU Conference on Small Satellites. Logan, UT. Sept.

Wertz, James R. and Simon D. Dawson. 1997. *1997 Microcosm Directory of Space Technology Data Sources*. Torrance, CA: Microcosm Press. Out of print.

Wertz, James R. and Wiley J. Larson, eds. 1999. *Space Mission Analysis and Design, 3rd ed.* Hawthorne, CA and New York: Microcosm Press and Springer.

Wertz, James R. and Wiley J. Larson. 1996. *Reducing Space Mission Cost*. El Segundo, CA: Microcosm Press.

Wertz, James R., Robert C. Conger, Richard E. Van Allen, Markus Rufer, and Nicola Sarzi-Amade. 2011. "Methods for Achieving Dramatic Reductions in Space Mission Cost." Reinventing Space Conference 2011. Los Angeles, CA. May 2–6.

Wessen, Randii R. and David Porter. 1998. "Market-Based Approaches for Controlling Space Mission Costs: The Cassini Resource Exchange." *Journal of Reducing Space Mission Cost*, vol. 1, p. 9-25, no. 1.

14 Overview of Spacecraft Design

David F. Everett, ***NASA Goddard Space Flight Center***

14.1 The Spacecraft Design Process

Having defined the overall mission objectives and instrumentation, it is now time to develop the initial spacecraft bus design. The spacecraft bus's purpose is the support of the payloads. The mass, power consumption, data rate, pointing requirements, and other aspect of the payloads will directly impact the overall configuration of the spacecraft. The bus must take care of final orbit adjustments; orbit maintenance; pointing; commanding; data storage and downlink; power generation, storage, and delivery; structural support; and thermal control. Exactly how these functions are accomplished will greatly impact the overall cost of the space mission.

In Chap. 3, you learned about establishing the requirements and constraints for the overall mission through discussions with your customer. As you go through this chapter, you may find the design running into trouble with some of those early decisions. Do not be afraid to discuss these issues with your customer—you may find some flexibility you did not anticipate. The Conops from Chap. 4, the environments from Chap. 7, and the orbit as described in Chaps. 8–10 will all drive the basic configuration of the spacecraft, as you will see in Sec. 14.3. This chapter is the next step toward refining your mission architecture that you started in Chap. 5. Sec. 14.7 will expand on the FireSat II and SCS examples of Sec. 5.6. Throughout this chapter, you will need to use the techniques of Chap. 6 as you capture many spacecraft and subsystem requirements and refine your mission requirements. Depending on your mission, you will usually improve your payload definition by working through Chaps. 15–17 first, but you may want to work through the spacecraft design in this chapter to figure out the resources available for the payload. The FireSat II mission takes the first approach and SCS takes the second. To complete your spacecraft design, you will need to iterate with the subsystem designs as described in Chaps. 18–22.

It cannot be said too often: Space Mission Engineering is a complex process with many intertwined steps. You need to hold the big picture objectives in your head while you delve down into the details. You will need to use good engineering judgment as you move back and forth between levels, iterating the design. There is no single, correct solution and "optimum" is a matter of opinion (with your customer's opinion being the most important). Decisions you make will involve millions of dollars, and a single mistake can end a mission. Section 14.6 describes the challenges of three real missions as they moved from preliminary design through operations. As you will see, the space business is one of incremental gain punctuated by catastrophic failures. This isn't a business for the timid, so let's quit wasting time and get started.

Table 14-1 describes the basic steps used to design a spacecraft. The items in Table 14-2 impact the system configuration and must be well understood by everyone working on the design. Note that payload configuration, including its mass, power, data rate, and pointing requirements are key drivers. Chapters 15–17 will guide you through establishing payload parameters. Docu-

Table 14-1. Spacecraft Design Steps.

Step	Reference
1. Document design drivers and requirements, including payload parameters	Sec. 14.2, Chaps. 15–17
2. Determine overall configuration and key trades	Sec. 14.3
3. Partition into subsystems	Sec. 14.4
4. Establish budgets and subsystem requirements	Sec. 14.5
5. Develop subsystem designs	Chaps. 18–22
6. Evaluate overall system configuration against requirements and constraints	Chap. 5
7. Explore options	Perspective of Others
8. Document and Iterate	Steps 1 to 7

menting the drivers creates a clear agreement between the builders and the stakeholders, so the design proceeds in the correct direction. The design drivers will lead to an approximate size and general layout for the system, with the attitude control technique, the propulsion configuration, and the solar array configuration (or other power generation method) defined through some key trade studies. We can then partition the spacecraft into subsystems and establish budgets and requirements for each of those subsystems. With the top-level subsystem requirements in place, we can now hand off pieces of the system to discipline experts who will further define details. As the subsystem designs begin to take shape, we must track the mass and power totals and ensure that the overall system continues to fulfill the mission requirements and constraints. Our team must document their design decisions along the way, leaving a clear path for later reviewers to follow. Inevitably, details of the subsystems will conflict with each other or the mass or power will exceed the original allocations. The systems engineer must remain constantly vigilant for these issues. Sometimes subsystem leads simply misunderstand the requirements, and sometimes the requirements just cannot be met within the budget; but when these obstacles show up, the systems engineer must quickly resolve the issue so effort is not being wasted on the wrong direction. Be sure to talk with other experts and get different perspectives. Ask your subsystem leads for options, not just one solution. Sometimes you will need to revisit the original spacecraft system drivers, and the builders must renegotiate the agreement with the stakeholders. There is no cookbook formula for this process other than simply "iterate."

14.2 Spacecraft System Design Drivers

Table 14-2 summarizes the primary drivers of spacecraft design. These drivers are covered in the rest of this section.

Table 14-2. Spacecraft Design Drivers. The key parameters that drive a spacecraft design come from mission-level decisions and the payload configuration.

Spacecraft Design Drivers	Mission Source	Impact	Thresholds	Ref
Mass	Payload mass	Launch vehicle	<250 kg, <1,000 kg, <7,000 kg	Sec. 14.2.1
Power Consumption	Payload design	Power sys, solar array config	beyond Mars or < 2 weeks	Sec. 14.2.1
Cost	Funding organization	Ripples throughout system	<\$5M, <\$100M, <\$500 M	Sec. 14.2.1
Schedule	Funding organization	Development process	<3 yrs, <5 yrs, >5 yrs	Sec. 14.2.1
Lifetime	Mission design	Redundancy, quality of parts	<1 yr, <3 yrs, <5 yrs, >5 yrs	Sec. 14.2.2
Reliability	Mission design	Redundancy, quality of parts, margin	Experimental, operational, human rated	Sec. 14.2.2, Chap. 24
Delta V	Mission design	Propellant load	0, 100, 1,000, 2,000	Sec. 14.2.3, Sec. 10.3
Orbit	Mission design	Solar array, thermal, radiation reg, launch vehicle	<1,000 km, high-Earth, planetary	Sec. 14.2.4, Ch. 8–10
Payload Accommodation				
— Data Rate, Vol, Latency	Mission purpose	Comm, data storage, ground	Thresholds changing fast	Sec. 14.2.5
— Pointing Requirements	Res or antenna beam	Attitude control system	<5 deg, <0.5 deg, <20 arcsec	Sec. 14.2.5
— Mass, Volume, FOVs	Payload constraints	Mechanical design	Diameter: <1 m, <5 m	Sec. 14.2.5
— Other	Timing accuracy, contamination sensitivity	Data system, master oscillator, cost of ground processing	Mission specific	Sec. 14.2.5

14.2.1 Mass, Power, Cost, and Schedule

Mass is the fundamental resource for the spacecraft designer. The cost of space missions is ultimately driven by the high cost of delivery to orbit. Because the launch vehicle is expensive, and because the spacecraft cannot be retrieved without the cost of a second launch, developers spend significant effort (and money), in the form of extensive analysis and testing, ensuring that the spacecraft will meet the mission objectives. The more it costs to get to orbit, the more the stakeholders are willing to spend to analyze and test the system before launch. Launch vehicles are expensive because it requires a tremendous amount of energy to get to orbit. A 1,000 kg spacecraft in a 600 km circular orbit has a total energy of 34 GJ (kinetic and potential energy) relative to the Earth's surface! That's 9,570 kWhr—enough energy to operate a house for almost half a year. To put this much energy into a spacecraft requires what amounts to a controlled explosion, with all of the force of the chemical energy going out the nozzle of the rocket. This is a very difficult problem, with little margin for error, resulting in an expensive system. More spacecraft mass means a larger and more expensive rocket, so mass is a fundamental cost driver in space systems, with distinct breakpoints when the mass reaches the limit of a particular vehicle.

Because it is the major cost driver, system mass must be estimated early, and the designer must keep careful track of the mass throughout the development. Mass estimation comes in 3 steps:

1. A rough order of magnitude based on payload mass (details in this section)
2. An estimate based on functions and configuration (details in Sec. 14.5)
3. A bottoms-up budget (using Sec. 14.5 guidelines combined with Chaps. 18–22).

Based on historical data and the type of mission (see App. A and Table 14-18), the spacecraft dry mass (including payload) will be between 2.5 and 6.5 times the payload mass. This dry mass, along with the propellant mass (see Sec. 14.5.2) will establish the total mass for the system. From this mass and the target orbit, the spacecraft designer can quickly determine what class launch vehicle is required (see Table 26-7) and, from that, determine the order of magnitude for the cost of the system.

We will further refine this mass estimate in Sec. 14.5, followed by a more detailed estimate based on subsystem conceptual designs. The subsystem roll-up should get the mass estimate within about 30% of the final number at launch (see Sec. 14.6).

The other key resource for the spacecraft designer is power. The power consumption of the electronic components in the system must be generated and delivered to the loads. We establish the power generating capability early in the design process, because power systems considerations, such as solar array size and configuration, will ripple throughout the system design (see Sec. 14.3.3). Once the power system is sized, it becomes another constraint on the design of the rest of the system. Large payload power demands, for payloads such as RF communications or radar, will result in large power systems, with power being a major driver of the overall system design.

Besides mass, power, and cost, schedule tends to be the other dominating constraint driving all other decisions in the development of a spacecraft. The people funding the spacecraft expect a return from the system within a certain amount of time in order to make the funding worthwhile. The spacecraft designer only has a limited time to consider options and choose solutions. The builders have a limited time to assemble the system and check it out. If the time available is unusually short, it can drive all aspects of the system development and potentially jeopardize mission success (see Sec. 14.6.1). If the time is long, it gives the designers time to optimize the system and develop new technologies to reduce the overall mass. But generally, time is money; so a longer development time will cost more money. When establishing the top-level architecture, the system designer should work with the stakeholders to establish a schedule that strikes a balance between driving cost and driving technical decisions and performance.

14.2.2 Lifetime and Reliability

Spacecraft lifetime and the probability that the mission achieves that lifetime will drive decisions about redundancy (duplicate components) and reliability of components (see Table 14-3). The importance of the system will also drive reliability, with experimental, operational, and human-rated providing general classes of increasing reliability (see Table 14-4). Redundant components add to the overall mass and cost of the system. Without a failure, these components are, as the name indicates, unnecessary. Short missions will generally be *single-string*, with only a single copy of each component. Any failure in a single-string spacecraft will generally lead to the loss of the mission; although some areas of the design may lend themselves to *graceful degradation*, where a failure leads to loss of performance but not loss of the entire mission. With thorough testing and careful part selection, single-string spacecraft can be very reliable, as demonstrated by NASA's Small Explorers and by AMSAT spacecraft which continue to operate 10 to 20 years after launch. Testing is easier without the need to verify redundant paths, so testers are more likely to find design flaws, but single-string spacecraft are vulnerable to the failure of a single part or the error in assembly of a single component.

As the desired mission lifetime is increased beyond one year, the designer should start to consider adding redundancy for key components. Various analytic techniques are available to help identify weak links in the design (see Chap. 24). Items that cannot be easily tested (such as components associated with deployments, actu-

Table 14-3. Conservative Redundancy Strategy for Different Lifetimes. This table is based on common practice for NASA missions. It is intended primarily to demonstrate that longer lifetimes will tend to drive more back-up hardware into the design. The actual application of redundancy for your mission should be based on your mission objectives and tolerance for failure.

Lifetime	Redundancy
<1 year	Single-string
1–3 years	Selected redundancy
3–5 years	Block redundancy
>5 years	Fully-cross strapped

Table 14-4. Classes of Reliability.

Class	Description
Experimental	Generally short mission to demonstrate capability or gather data to answer a specific question. Missions in this class are often secondary payloads on a launch vehicle
Operational	Mission to gather critical data or to provide critical services
Human-Rated	Vehicles that must support humans

ators for solar arrays and antennas, and propulsion valves and thrusters) should be the first items considered for redundancy. Complex circuits involving analog circuitry (such as power converters) are the next areas which reliability analysis will generally identify. Beyond 3 years, the spacecraft will frequently carry a second copy of each critical component in a *block-redundant* configuration, where use of a redundant component requires switching all components to the alternate side. In a fully *cross-strapped* system, each redundant component can be separately switched into operation, without changing the state of the other components. We use this configuration for long duration missions or missions where reliability is particularly important (such as human space flight). See Fig. 14-1.

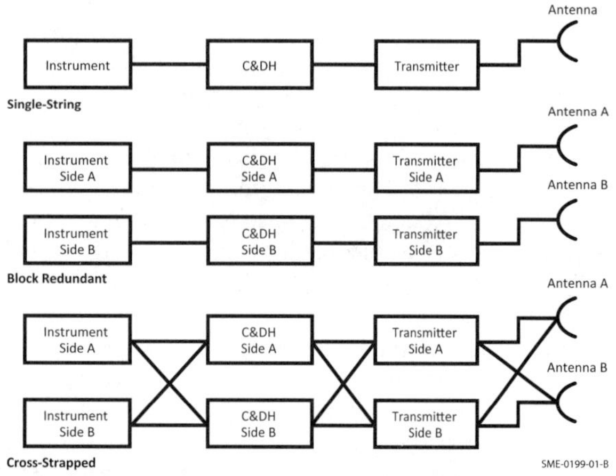

Fig. 14-1. Different Types of Redundancy.

One thing to keep in mind with redundancy is that it will not protect you from design flaws—if side A fails because of a poor circuit design, side B will probably experience the same failure. Consider extra testing, better parts, and more thorough analysis of your single-string design before you add the expensive mass of redundant components. Also consider *functional redundancy*, where completely different components provide the same function, in order to eliminate risks associated with design and manufacturing flaws. Watch carefully the circuitry involved with switching between redundant components. I worked on a spacecraft that included two power-control boxes with a relay to switch between them. It turned out that the relay was less reliable than the box, so we eliminated the relay and one of the boxes and ended up with a **more** reliable system.

Hurley and Purdy [2010] points out that the full reliability of a system includes delays in deploying the system. If you need the system operating but it is still on the ground, then your reliability is zero during that period. One of the biggest challenges in the space business is balancing the costs and delays associated with ensuring reliable performance against the costs and delays associated with a failure after launch. Dealing with rare, catastrophic events is challenging—there are not enough samples for reliable statistics, and our intuition frequently steers us in the wrong direction. Chapter 24 contains a more thorough discussion of risk and reliability.

14.2.3 Total Delta V

The total change in velocity, or *delta V*, required throughout the lifetime of a mission will drive propulsion requirements (see Sec. 14.3.2) and propellant mass. Section 10.3 covers the development of a delta V budget for a mission. The total delta V combined with the *specific impulse* of the thrusters will define the overall mass of propellant required. Specific impulse, I_{sp}, is a measure of thruster efficiency related to the exit velocity of the propellant, with typical units of seconds (see Sec. 18.1). As a first cut at total propellant mass, use the rocket equation with an I_{sp} of 220 sec for a mono-propellant hydrazine system, 300 sec for a bi-propellant system, or whatever I_{sp} is appropriate for the design's propulsion system. For example, a spacecraft with dry mass of 1,000 kg, requiring 1,300 m/s of delta V from a mono-propellant hydrazine system, uses this form of the *rocket equation*:

$$\begin{aligned} M_p &= M_f\left(e^{\Delta V/(I_{sp} g_0)} - 1\right) \\ &= 1000 \cdot \left(e^{1300/(9.8 \cdot 220)} - 1\right) = 828 \text{ kg} \end{aligned} \tag{14-1}$$

where M_f is the dry mass of the spacecraft and g is the acceleration due to Earth's gravity. With a bi-propellant system, the total propellant mass is only 556 kg (replace 220 sec with 300 sec). This method will provide a rough estimate of required propellant, with Sec. 14.5.2 describing the details of a propellant budget.

Different types of propulsion system are commonly used for different delta V totals. If a system has no delta V requirements, propulsion is probably not needed (the exception may be for attitude control). For a small delta V, cold gas is usually a good choice, since pressurized nitrogen is non-toxic and non-flammable and so requires no extra valves for safety. As the delta V gets above about 100 m/s, mono-propellant hydrazine becomes the fuel of choice, since it does not require the complexity of a separate oxidizer. Above 1,000 m/s, the higher efficiency of a bi-propellant system will compensate for the expense of a heavier and more complex propulsion system. For extremely high delta V's, above 2,000 m/s, an ion engine, with its very high I_{sp}, is the only practical choice at this time. These thresholds, based on mass efficiency, are only general rules of thumb, so you should take a careful look at the specifics of your system, including a consideration of solid rockets, before choosing a propulsion system. Section 14.3.2 and Chap. 18 provide more information on the selection of a propulsion system.

14.2.4 Orbit

The mission orbit design, described in Chap. 10, drives many aspects of the spacecraft. The space environment will vary based on where the spacecraft goes (see Chap. 7). The orbit and the mission targets will define where the Sun will be with respect to the spacecraft body, impacting the solar array design (see Sec. 14.3.3) and the thermal design. Spacecraft will frequently keep one part of the body away from the Sun, where radiators are placed to dump heat. The altitude of the orbit will impact the thermal influence of the orbited body on the spacecraft. For low-Earth orbit, the Earth fills almost half the sky, with a temperature near 300 K. For a low lunar orbit, the Moon will fill almost half the sky, but its temperature varies from 150 to 400 K! For a geosynchronous orbit, the Earth is only 17 deg wide, so its thermal influence is minimal, and the spacecraft sees mostly deep space at 3 K. The orbit defines how far away the ground stations will be, impacting the radio link design (see Sec. 21.1). Gravity gradient and atmospheric drag are altitude dependent (see Sec. 19.1.2). These effects, along with Sun location and obstruction of stars by the orbited body will impact the attitude control design.

14.2.5 Payload Accommodation

Spacecraft design is all about payload accommodation. The spacecraft exists to provide for all of the payload's needs. The payload command and data generation requirements will impact the data system design. The instantaneous data rate of the payload interface will impact exactly how data is transferred to the spacecraft bus, including not only the electrical data standards but also the software involved with the transfer. The average data rate over time combined with the frequency of downlinks will impact data storage requirements (see Sec. 14.5.5). The latency requirements of the mission will determine how often the spacecraft must transmit data, impacting the communications system and the overall power consumption. The payloads define how accurately the spacecraft must point, driving the design of the attitude control system. Structurally, the spacecraft must support the payload through launch, and it must provide a stable platform for measurements. Fields of view of multiple instruments can be a challenge, with each instrument needing to stay out of the view of the others, while all mounting to a small panel facing in the same direction. Some payloads are physically large, such as payloads with large antennas or optical apertures. Optical payloads will require a clean environment to protect the optics, and ultra-violet instruments are particularly sensitive to organic contamination. Contamination control considerations can drive the selection of materials and the handling of flight equipment, causing ripple effects throughout the design. Precise timing of measurements can drive onboard clock requirements, resulting in significant mass and power impacts in order to maintain a thermally stable oscillator. The system designer must look carefully at the payload, paying particular attention to unique features, in order to fully understand impacts across the system.

Pointing accuracy typically drives sensor accuracy. For pointing requirements on the order of several degrees, a set of coarse Sun sensors and a magnetometer can provide sufficient pointing accuracy. Horizon sensors and fine Sun sensors provide accuracies around a half a degree or so. Below a half a degree down to tens of arcseconds, a star tracker combined with an inertial measurement unit (gyro) will provide sufficient knowledge. Below this level, special equipment (both sensors and actuators) and extra care in the mounting of components will be necessary. See Sec. 14.3.1 and Sec. 19.1 for more details on attitude control techniques.

14.3 Spacecraft Configuration Alternatives

Having defined the key drivers of the system, it is now time to look at major architectural decisions that will affect all other aspects of the spacecraft design. These key decisions include choosing an attitude control technique, determining whether propulsion is needed and, if so, how it will be implemented, determining the solar array and antenna configurations, and determining an overall autonomy approach. Figure 14-2 provides some examples of spacecraft configurations to give you a feel for the options and decisions ahead.

The overall size of the spacecraft will tend to push aspects of the design in particular directions. Table 14-5 provides some general rules of thumb to help you scale up or scale down from previous designs. These general trends will always have exceptions. Connectors, fittings for propulsion or cryogenics, electronics parts, and other standard products come in fixed sizes, independent of the size of the rest of the system. If you are trying to scale significantly smaller, these items can cause your mass estimates to be unrealistically low.

FAST: No Propulsion; Spinner

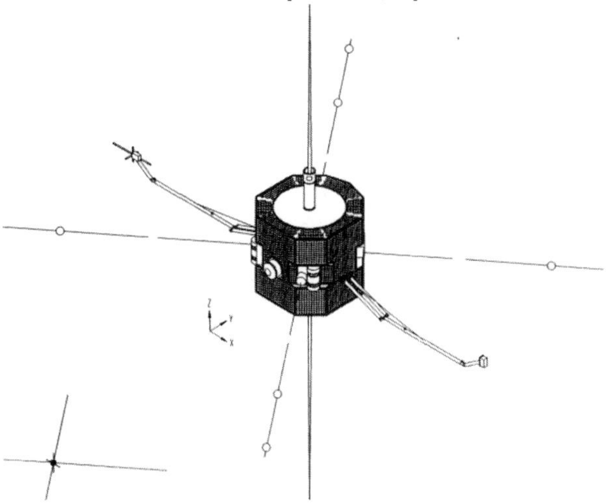

Mission: Particle and field measurements in Earth's auroral acceleration region

Orbit: 350 × 4,200 km, 83 deg

Payload: Electron and ion instruments, magnetometers, electric-field instruments

Configuration Features:

- ***Unique features:*** Single deck for avionics in spin plane, with solar array substrate and a top panel providing radiation shielding
- ***Solar array:*** Wrap-around with conductive surface (minimize impact on measurements) and thick (1.3 mm) coverglass (radiation protection)
- ***Appendage:*** 30 m wire booms, 3 m axial booms, 1 m magnetometer booms
- ***Attitude control:*** 5 RPM orbit-normal spinner, 1 deg pointing accuracy; wire coils used for magnetic torquing; Sun and horizon sensors
- ***Redundancy:*** Single-string

Mass: 191 kg

Average Power: 52 W

WISE: No Propulsion; 3-Axis; Fixed Array

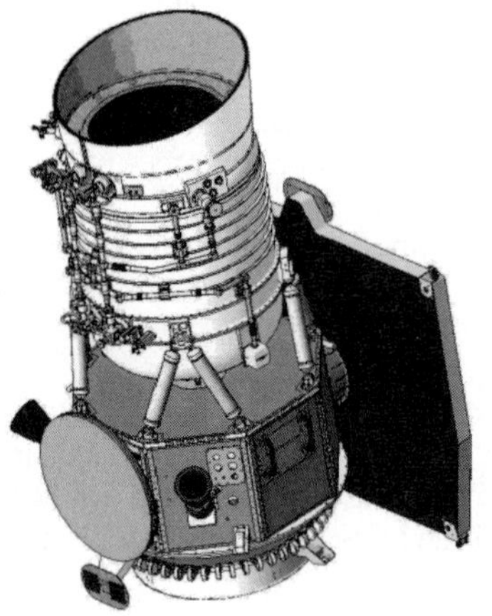

Mission: All-sky infrared survey

Orbit: 525 km, 97.5 deg, 6 pm ascending node

Payload: Solid-hydrogen cryostat cooling infrared telescope

Configuration Features:

- ***Unique features:*** Fixed, passive, phased-array Ku-band antenna (circular, on anti-sun side); struts support and thermally isolate cryostat from spacecraft bus; load isolation system near separation ring; zenith pointing and dawn/dusk orbit allow fixed array
- ***Solar array:*** 3 m^2, fixed
- ***Appendage:*** None
- ***Attitude control:*** 3-axis, constant slew rate for sky survey, 75 arcsec pointing accuracy, 4 wheels; 3 torque bars
- ***Redundancy:*** Single-string

Mass: 661 kg

Average Power: 301 W

TERRA: LEO with Propulsion; Nadir Pointer

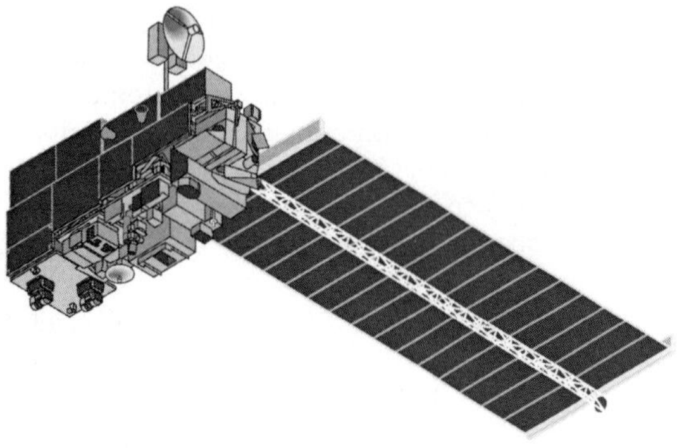

Mission: Earth observation

Orbit: 705 km circular, 98.2 deg, 10:30 pm ascending node

Payload: IR radiometer, high-resolution imager, visible and IR spectrometers

Configuration Features:

- ***Unique features:*** Radiators on anti-sun side; numerous ground-observing apertures
- ***Solar array:*** 45 m^2, single-axis gimbal
- ***Appendage:*** High-gain antenna (HGA)
- ***Attitude control:*** 3-axis, nadir pointer, 2.5 arcminute pointing accuracy
- ***Propulsion:*** 65 kg hydrazine and pressurant
- ***Redundancy:*** Redundant and cross-strapped

Mass: 4,761 kg wet, 4,396 kg dry

Average Power: 2,159 W

Fig. 14-2. Spacecraft Configuration.

Table 14-4◀, Fig. 14-2, Eq. 14-1◀

TRMM: LEO with Propulsion; Nadir Pointer

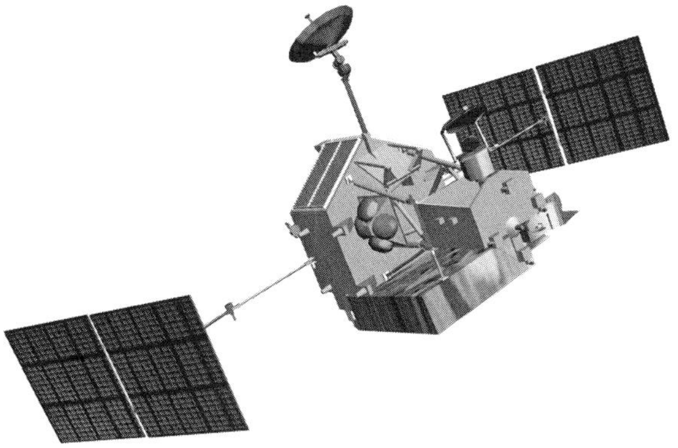

Mission: Tropical rainfall measurement

Orbit: 350 km circular, 35 deg

Payload: Precipitation radar, microwave radiometer, visible and IR radiometers, and lightning imager

Configuration Features:

- ***Unique features:*** Low orbit to support radar measurements; symmetric arrays to balance drag torques; wheels in tetrahedron; large flat-panel radar antenna; yaw flip to keep Sun on same side
- ***Solar array:*** 2 deployed panels, single-axis gimbal; >3,000 W beginning of life
- ***Appendage:*** HGA for communication with TDRSS; antenna for spinning microwave radiometer
- ***Attitude control:*** 3-axis, nadir pointer, 0.2 deg pointing accuracy, reaction wheels
- ***Propulsion:*** 899 kg hydrazine and pressurant; large propellant load to compensate for drag at low altitude
- ***Redundancy:*** Fully redundant and cross-strapped

Mass: 3,504 kg wet, 2,605 kg dry

Average Power: 1,019 W

MAP: High Earth (L2)

Mission: Measure variations in microwave background radiation

Orbit: Earth Libration, L2

Payload: Microwave receivers

Configuration Features:

- ***Unique features:*** Sun shield shadows spacecraft avionics and instruments; instrument antennas perpendicular to sun line
- ***Solar array:*** Deployed in petal arrangement (hidden by Sun shield in this view)
- ***Appendage:*** Sun shield
- ***Attitude control:*** 3-axis, scanning at 2.8 deg/s, 0.25 deg pointing accuracy, 3 wheels, thrusters
- ***Propulsion:*** 194 kg of hydrazine and pressurant
- ***Redundancy:*** Selective redundancy

Mass: 812 kg wet, 724 kg dry

Average Power: 371 W

STEREO: High Earth (Fly Away)

Mission: Solar Observation from 2 spacecraft

Orbit: Solar orbit, Earth fly away

Payload: Extreme UV imager, coronographs, visible imagers, particle and field instruments

Configuration Features:

- ***Unique features:*** Booms keep sensitive instruments away from the influence of the spacecraft electronics
- ***Solar array:*** 2 deployed and stationary wings of 2 panels each
- ***Appendage:*** Particle and field instruments, HGA
- ***Attitude control:*** 3-axis, 7 arcsec pointing accuracy, wheels, thrusters
- ***Propulsion:*** 61 kg of hydrazine and pressurant
- ***Redundancy:*** Selective redundancy

Mass: 619 kg wet, 558 kg dry

Average Power: 514 W

Fig. 14-2. Spacecraft Configuration. (Continued)

TDRS: High Earth (GEO)

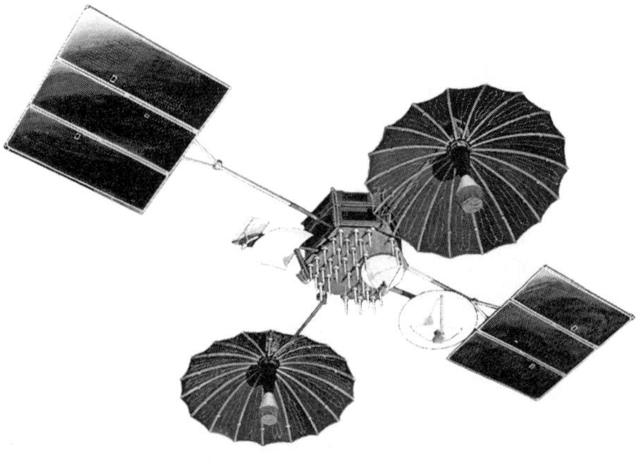

Mission: Communications relay for spacecraft
Orbit: Geosynchronous
Payload: S- and K_u-band radio relays
Configuration Features:

- ***Unique features:*** 2 high-gain antennas for single-access users, S-band phased array for multiple-access users
- ***Solar array:*** 30 m^2 across 2 deployed, single-axis-gimbal wings
- ***Appendage:*** Solar arrays and antennas
- ***Attitude control:*** 3-axis, nadir pointer, 0.2 deg pointing accuracy
- ***Propulsion:*** 552 kg hydrazine and pressurant
- ***Redundancy:*** Fully redundant and cross-strapped

Mass: 2,197 kg wet, 1,523 kg dry
Average Power: 1,621 W

LRO: Planetary (Moon)

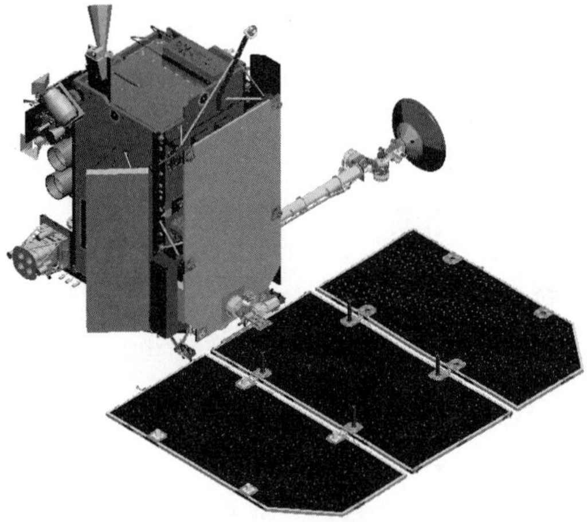

Mission: Lunar mapping
Orbit: Lunar, 50 km circular, 90 deg inclination
Payload: Wide- and narrow-angle cameras, laser altimeter, UV spectrometer, IR sensor, radiation monitor, neutron detector, synthetic aperture radar
Configuration Features:

- ***Unique features:*** Avionics on honeycomb deck with heat pipes; modular assembly
- ***Solar array:*** 10 m^2, 2-axis gimbaled
- ***Appendage:*** 2-axis gimbaled HGA
- ***Attitude control:*** 3-axis using 4 wheels, nadir pointer
- ***Propulsion:*** 897 kg hydrazine and He pressurant
- ***Redundancy:*** Single-string

Mass: 1,915 kg
Average Power: 620 W

New Horizons*: Planetary (Pluto)

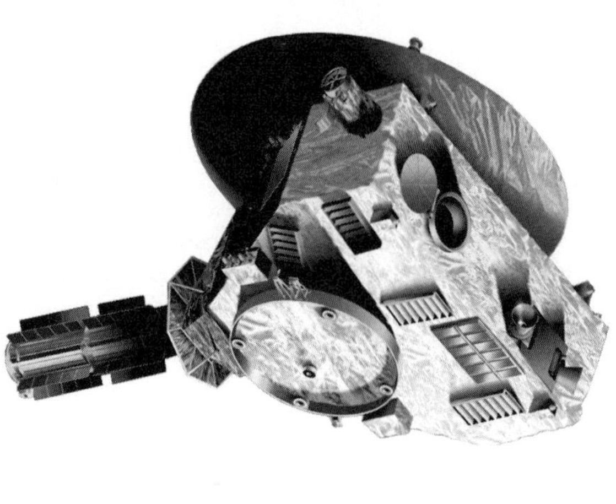

Mission: Pluto exploration
Orbit: Fly-by
Payload: UV spectrometer, IR imaging spectrometer, visible camera, solar wind monitor, particle spectrometer, dust counter, radio science instrument
Configuration Features:

- ***Unique features:*** large high-gain antenna (HGA) for communicating over long distance; small spacecraft to achieve high velocity
- ***Power source:*** Radioisotope thermoelectric generator (RTG)
- ***Appendage:*** RTG cooling fins
- ***Attitude control:*** 3-axis using thrusters for encounter, 5 RPM spin stabilized about HGA axis for cruise
- ***Propulsion:*** 77 kg of hydrazine and He pressurant
- ***Redundancy:*** redundant and cross-strapped

Mass: 478 kg wet, 401 kg dry
Average Power: 200 W

*Fountain et. al. [2008]

Fig. 14-2. Spacecraft Configuration. (Continued)

Table 14-4◀, Fig. 14-2, Eq. 14-1◀

Table 14-5. Scaling of Spacecraft Features. These are general trends assuming relative proportions stay the same (all dimensions grow or shrink equally). Any one dimension is considered *r*. The lateral frequency is important for launch. Place heavier (denser) items closer to the launch vehicle interface to keep the height down and the frequency up (see Sec. 22.1.3 for more details).

Feature	Scaling
Surface Area	Increases slower than volume (r^2 vs. r^3)
Mass	Increases with volume
Power	Increases with volume (more components)
Thermal Control	Surface area for radiators becomes more scarce on larger spacecraft, since power goes with volume
Solar arrays	Small spacecraft, with lower power, are more likely to have enough surface area for body-mounted arrays
Stability	Torque required to rotate a spacecraft goes up with moment of inertial. MOI is proportional product of mass and r^2 so torque goes as r^5. Larger spacecraft are much more stable.
Lateral Frequency	Larger structures tend to have lower frequencies, with an interplay among MOI of base, height, and mass—goes as $1/r$ for proportional growth, $1/(\text{c.m. height})^{1.5}$ for constant base and mass, as center of mass (c.m.) moves.

14.3.1 Attitude Control Technique

Depending on the pointing requirements of the system, various options exist for stabilizing and pointing a spacecraft. All spacecraft must have a method to counteract external torques (see Sec. 19.1.2 for more on external torques) and orient the system in order to keep the instruments pointed in the correct direction. Many early spacecraft were spin stabilized, using the momentum of the entire system to maintain the needed pointing accuracy. But the spinning can add complexity to the instrumentation if accurate measurements are required in all three directions. With modern computational power, three-axis stabilized spacecraft have become the norm, with only special circumstances driving the design toward a spinner.

Spinner

Spin stabilization is an ancient technique. A good discus throw relies on spin stabilization, as does a modern plastic disc thrown in a game of ultimate, and rifling in guns spins projectiles to improve accuracy. Older launch vehicles, like the Scout and the Delta II, used spinning upper stages to ensure the thrust went in the desired direction. Spin stabilization is still used today for some kick motors and certain special spacecraft applications.

A spin stabilized system intentionally puts momentum in the spacecraft body. The body's momentum vector will stay oriented in inertial space, reacting at right angles to any torque, just as a tilted, spinning top on a table will turn the force of gravity trying to tip it over into a slow precession of the spin axis. In the near-zero friction environment of space, a spacecraft set to spinning will maintain that spin for a very long time. The system is passively stable, requiring no power to maintain orientation.

But a system is only unconditionally stable if it is spinning around its maximum moment of inertia, like the flying disc. A system can spin for a short period of time around its minimum moment of inertia, but any energy damping in the system will tend to re-orient the spin axis so that the body is spinning around its maximum moment of inertia. A pencil-shaped object can spin around its long axis, but eventually it will settle into a flat spin. Spacecraft designers take advantage of this property by intentionally spinning around the maximum moment of inertia and installing a *nutation damper*. The nutation damper is generally a fluid-filled structure, where any asymmetry in the spin of the system will cause the fluid to flow, with the viscosity of the fluid dissipating energy.

Practical spinning spacecraft will need some method to control the spin rate and some method to adjust the orientation of the spin axis (spin precession control). The spin rate can generally be set once and left for a long time, but an orbit-normal spinner in low-Earth orbit will need to keep its spin axis moving at the rate the orbit is precessing around the Earth (see Secs. 9.5.2 and 9.5.3 for an explanation of orbit nodal regression). Both the spin rate and the precession can be managed from the ground, without a sophisticated control system on board the spacecraft. Spin rate can be measured with a sensor that produces a blip as its field of view crosses the horizon or moves past the Sun, or with a sensor (magnetometer) that measures the changing magnetic field (for a low-Earth orbiter). Sun sensors and magnetometers can also be used to measure the spin axis orientation.

Spin-stabilized spacecraft sometimes have a *de-spun platform*, in which part of the spacecraft remains inertially fixed while the rest of the system spins. A motor rotates between the spun and de-spun sections at the spacecraft spin rate, and slip rings carry signals across the interface. The Geostationary Earth Observing Satellites (GOES) monitored weather in the United States from de-spun platforms for many years.

Instead of spinning the entire spacecraft, some systems utilize a *momentum wheel*, which is a motor-driven wheel which spins at a constant rate, putting a fixed momentum into the system, but leaving the rest of the system unspinning—a configuration known as *momentum bias*. This configuration requires some method of external torquing to counteract environmental torques. One example is a *B-dot algorithm*, where a spacecraft in low-Earth orbit uses the rate of change of the measured magnetic field to set the current in an electromagnet, and that magnet torques the spacecraft opposite to the body's spin rate. This stabilization technique, with a momentum bias, B-dot for rate damping, and a bang-bang controller to precess the momentum axis toward the Sun, was used by the early Small Explorer missions as an analog *safe hold*. A safe hold mode provides a very simple contingency control mode when the spacecraft processor is unavailable due to some fault condition.

Spinning spacecraft frequently utilize body-mounted solar arrays for power generation (see Sec. 14.3.3). Because of the constantly-changing orientation, more solar cells must be carried to generate the same amount of power. Spinning spacecraft tend to be power limited. The 191 kg FAST spacecraft shown in Fig. 14-3 operated on less than 60 W orbit average power.

Fig. 14-3. Fast Auroral Snapshot Explorer (FAST) was a Spin-stabilized Spacecraft. (Photo courtesy of NASA GSFC)

If the upper stage of the launch vehicle or a kick stage spins for stability, the spacecraft will often need to despin after the burn. Thrusters can provide the torque necessary to stop the spin, but another option is a *yo-yo despin*. A yo-yo de-spin uses weights which release from the spacecraft and unwind a cable, similar to a toy yo-yo. As the weights move out, they reduce the spin rate of the system by increasing the moment of inertia, just like a figure skater extending her arms to reduce her spin rate. The spin momentum of the spacecraft body is transferred to the weights, and then the weights are released when the cable is fully unwound. Unfortunately, this leaves at least two weights with cables free-flying, creating a collision hazard for other spacecraft, so this technique is not used near operational orbits anymore. The SAMPEX spacecraft used a yo-yo despin after launching in 1992 (see Fig. 14-4).

Fig. 14-4. SAMPEX Spacecraft. SAMPEX Launched on a Scout Rocket, with a Spinning Upper Stage. The yo-yo mechanism for the despin wrapped around the spacecraft when the arrays were folded. You can see the attach band going horizontally across the middle of the spacecraft. (Photo courtesy of NASA GSFC)

Three-Axis Stabilized

Most modern spacecraft utilize three-axis stabilization. Attitude sensors provide feedback to a control system where actuators such as reaction wheels or thrusters rotate the system to its proper orientation. Processors now have enough computational capability to perform the necessary calculations to operate a 3-axis control algorithm while simultaneously handling the instrument commanding and data collection. Although the control algorithm is more complicated, other aspects of the system become less complex with 3-axis control. There is none of the complexity associated with a de-spun platform, the solar arrays can generate more power with a fixed orientation to the Sun, and the instruments do not need to compensate for spin motion in their measurements.

The highest precision pointing control is achieved on spacecraft using *reaction wheels* for attitude control. The spacecraft controls the speed of spinning wheels in order to adjust the torque applied to the body. External torques on the spacecraft are counteracted by torquing the reaction wheels, with the net result being a gradual increase in the wheel speed without changing the attitude of the spacecraft. Eventually, the system must use some external force, such as that introduced by thrusters or electromagnetic torquers, to remove the momentum from the system. Low-Earth orbiting spacecraft which do not otherwise require propulsion typically will use *electromagnetic torquers* for momentum unloading, using the torque produced by the electromagnets attempting to align with the Earth's magnetic field.

Three-axis stabilization takes on different appearances depending on where the spacecraft is pointed. Systems typically operate in an inertial reference frame, but the target is not always inertial. Many systems look at the body that is being orbited, and some systems use the Sun as the orienting target.

Inertial Pointer—Inertially-pointed spacecraft typically use the stars as reference. This configuration is most convenient for spacecraft observing the sky. The solar array configuration of an inertial pointer will vary, depending on the orientation of the orbit with respect to the Sun and any precession of the orbit. Engineers typically talk about X, Y, and Z axes for an inertially-pointed spacecraft.

Nadir Pointer—Nadir pointing is most useful for a spacecraft observing the body being orbited. As in an aircraft, axes are frequently described as roll, pitch, and yaw; with *roll axis* oriented about the direction of travel, *pitch axis* oriented normal to the orbit plane, and *yaw axis* oriented around the nadir vector. In order to remain nadir pointing, the spacecraft must rotate once per orbit around the pitch axis. This rotation rate must vary if the orbit is not perfectly circular.

Although horizon sensors were frequently used in the past to control pointing with a nadir pointer, modern systems usually use star sensors and on-board computation to calculate the correct direction to point in order to maintain a nadir orientation. Momentum bias in the pitch axis can help stabilize the spacecraft—in one quarter of an orbit, the roll axis direction rotates about the pitch axis by 90 deg, assuming the alignment that the yaw axis had in inertial space. So errors about the yaw axis become errors about roll, and the spacecraft can operate with sensors and actuators in only two axes.

Nadir-pointed spacecraft will generally keep one side of the pitch axis oriented away from the Sun so that radiators can dump heat from the electronics into space. As the Sun moves with respect to the orbit plane, the spacecraft may need to perform a *yaw flip*. In a yaw flip, the spacecraft is rotated 180 deg about the yaw axis, usually when the Sun is near the plane of the orbit.

Solar Pointer—Solar pointing is frequently used as a safe attitude, since spacecraft frequently use solar power and simple sensors and algorithms can quickly find the Sun. Also, any mission observing the Sun will be a Sun pointer. A sun sensor will define two of the three axes, and some other sensor (like a star sensor or magnetometer) must determine the orientation about the Sun vector.

Other

A small set of simple spacecraft require no active control. They are naturally stable by design. Most common in this category are *gravity-gradient* spacecraft, which use the gradient of the gravitational field in orbit to align the minimum moment of inertia axis (usually the longest axis) with the nadir vector (remember that the MOI is calculated around the axis). Spacecraft have been designed with *passive magnetic dampers*, where the Earth's magnetic field induces currents in the rotating spacecraft, and those currents dissipate power through resistive losses, reducing the tumble rate. A low-altitude spacecraft can use the atmosphere to provide orientation by placing the center of mass ahead of the center of pressure from the atmospheric drag—like a weathervane. Spacecraft which use *aerobraking*, where atmospheric drag intentionally changes the orbit instead of using thrusters, typically use this technique.

14.3.2 Need for Propulsion and Its Impact

Propulsion configuration is another major architectural decision that must be made early in the spacecraft design. Propulsion systems can be used to move the spacecraft to its final orbit, maintain that orbit or change it as necessary, maintain attitude control, and perform a final change of orbit for disposal of the system. The spacecraft designer should first consider whether propulsion is needed at all. Is there enough capability in the launch vehicle to put the spacecraft in its final orbit? Can the system operate with the imperfect performance of a real launch vehicle, where the final orbit is slightly different from the optimal? Can the system tolerate the change in orbit due to atmospheric drag? Is there any need for propulsion to dispose of the system? Can magnetic torquers or some passive system such as gravity gradient be used to counter environmental forces and dump accumulated momentum? If the answer to any of these questions is "no," then propulsion of some type is required. Any system going beyond low-Earth orbit will need some sort of propulsion system.

Achieving Final Orbit

If the launch vehicle does not take the spacecraft to its final orbit, the spacecraft designer can include a kick stage which is jettisoned at the end of the orbit adjust. A *kick stage* provides a large delta V over a short period of time in order to make a large change to the orbit of a spacecraft. A kick stage is generally a solid rocket motor. Jettisoning the stage eliminates the mass of the spent motor from the system, reducing the amount of fuel that is needed for later orbit adjusts and maintenance. As an example of a kick stage, geosynchronous spacecraft frequently use an *apogee kick motor* fired at the apogee of a geosynchronous transfer orbit (see Sec. 9.6.1) to raise the perigee of the orbit to near geosynchronous altitude. The designer must trade the fuel mass saved in later maneuvers if the stage is jettisoned against the mass and complexity associated with separating part of the spacecraft. Integral propulsion systems enable the builders to concentrate on a single system, with all margin carried in one set of fuel tanks. Any unused margin from the orbit adjustment can be used for orbit maintenance. For orbit adjustments requiring high precision, such as those used for planetary trajectory maneuvers or for the final orbit adjustments, the precision of a liquid system is generally

Table 14-5◀, Fig. 14-4◀, Eq. 14-1◀

preferred over a solid kick stage. A liquid propulsion system can be shut off when the appropriate delta V has been achieved, but a solid burns until the fuel is expended. The integral propulsion system also allows the operators to change the orbit of the spacecraft multiple times, perhaps adjusting to changing mission demands. A final consideration with staging is the disposal of the spent stage—does the kick stage end up in an orbit that can jeopardize operational assets?

The high thrust of a large delta V maneuver will require either spin stabilization or active thruster control to maintain the proper attitude during the burn. Spin stabilization requires precision balancing of the system, and it frequently requires some sort of nutation control system to keep the spin straight while the mass properties of the system change with expulsion of the propellant. Active thruster control may require a gimbaled nozzle on the main rocket or simply sufficient torque authority from the attitude control thrusters. For a liquid burn using multiple thrusters, the delta V thrusters can sometimes be individually turned off briefly (known as *off-pulsing* or *off-modulation*) to maintain control. Alternatively, attitude thrusters can be on-pulsed briefly while the main engines burn continuously.

Station Keeping

Once in the final orbit, many missions must maintain that orbit to a high precision. *Station-keeping maneuvers* are small adjustments to the velocity of the spacecraft in order to keep the system within some orbit tolerance. Perturbations to the orbit can be caused by atmospheric drag or gravity effects. Adjustments are generally a few meters per second or less. Most spacecraft use a liquid propulsion system for these high-precision maneuvers, but geostationary communication spacecraft, which have large power generation capability, frequently use electric thrusters. Electric thrusters have a much larger specific impulse, resulting in less fuel required for a long operational life. Because the maneuvers are small, liquid systems generally use smaller thrusters for station keeping. These smaller thrusters can also be used for attitude control and momentum management.

Attitude Control and Momentum Management

Many spacecraft use reaction wheels (see Sec. 19.1.4) for attitude control. These wheels can provide very high precision pointing, and they can temporarily compensate for external torques, but eventually an external force is needed to compensate for the momentum which builds up in the system (the wheels cannot keep spinning faster forever; they become *saturated*, or spinning at their maximum rate). In the absence of the Earth's magnetic field, or for systems which already have propulsion for orbit adjustment, a propulsion system provides a good method to provide an external torque on the system. Controllers will perform a *delta H maneuver*, changing the momentum (mathematical symbol of H) of the system without changing the attitude or the orbit. The wheels are commanded to a new speed and the thrusters fire to hold the attitude, or the thrusters fire and the wheels hold attitude by spinning down.

Some spacecraft utilize propulsion exclusively for attitude control. Any time the attitude drifts outside a *deadband*, a thruster will fire, pushing the attitude back into its control box. This technique works well for systems that do not require precision pointing and can handle the fuel mass used. Since fuel is expended for every excursion outside the deadband, the system cannot take advantage of long-term averaging of external torques, so attitude control using thrusters will generally consume more fuel than attitude control with wheels and thrusters for momentum dumping. Any errors in the control algorithm (such as an overly tight deadband) can quickly consume the mission's fuel budget. The system designer must trade the mass, complexity, and precision of the wheels against the extra fuel mass and risk of a propulsion-only system.

Disposal

Spacecraft designers must consider the final disposition of the system, to prevent damage to other spacecraft and loss of life on the ground. Chapter 30 provides a full discussion of disposal. If the spacecraft will be moved to a different orbit at the end of the mission, then the propulsion system must include this capability. A controlled de-orbit of the spacecraft, where the impact point is targeted for an unpopulated part of the ocean, will require significant delta V. For a mono-propellant hydrazine system, the mass of the fuel required for a controlled de-orbit from low-Earth orbit is about 7% of the total mass of the system.

14.3.3 Solar Array Configuration

Most spacecraft use photovoltaic solar arrays for generating power. The solar array configuration will constrain the overall structural design and impact the orientation of the spacecraft in flight. Large solar arrays must be folded and firmly locked for launch. Deployed arrays can impact the stability of the spacecraft and interfere with instrument fields of view. The arrays must be positioned to control shadowing (see Sec. 21.2.2).

After determining the solar array area required (see Table 21-12), we must determine a suitable layout for the array. The array design must operate over the full range of the solar *beta angle*, the angle between the Sun and the plane of the orbit. For an Earth-orbiting spacecraft, the beta angle varies as the orbit precesses and as the Earth goes around the Sun (see Fig. 14-5). Depending on where the spacecraft points and how the Sun moves with respect to that pointing, the solar array configuration can be body-mounted, deployed and fixed, or deployed and articulated.

Body-mounted arrays provide limited power, since their area is constrained by the surface area of the spacecraft, which is constrained by the launch vehicle fairing volume. This may not be an issue for small spacecraft, which have limited volume available for power-consuming components. For spinning spacecraft (see Sec. 14.3.1), wrap-around body-mounted solar arrays are generally the required configuration in order to generate power throughout the spin. Spin-stabilized spacecraft tend to be

Table 14-5◀, Fig. 14-4◀, Eq. 14-1◀

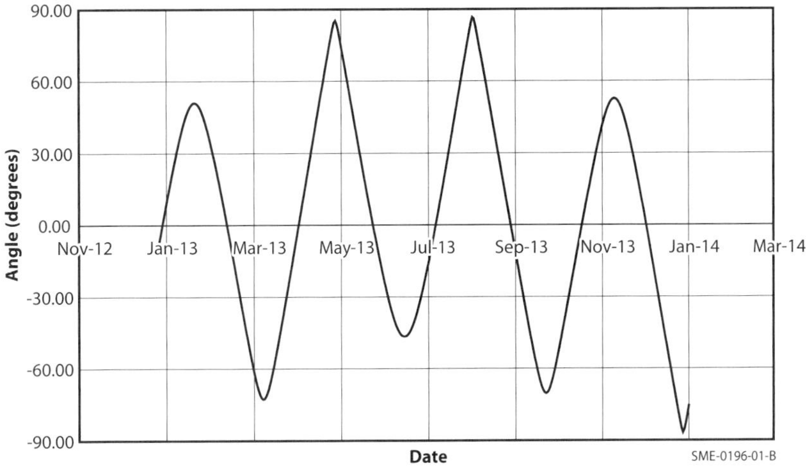

Live Calc

Fig. 14-5. Beta Angle Over a Year for a 400 km, 70 deg Inclination Orbit.

power constrained, although the simple attitude control system helps reduce the power demands of the bus. The COBE spacecraft used an alternate configuration for additional power, with deployed, double-sided arrays placed 120 deg apart and radial to the spin axis (see Fig. 14-6). This configuration doubles the number of solar cells, and it requires deployment mechanisms, but it generated for COBE over 2 times more power for the same size spacecraft with body-mounted arrays. Special circumstances may allow a fixed solar array on a non-spinning spacecraft. The Wide-Field Infrared Survey Explorer (WISE) was a zenith pointer flying in a Sun-synchronous orbit, with significant room in the launch-vehicle fairing. WISE flew a panel array that was fixed to the body, with no deployment necessary (see Fig. 14-2). Body mounted arrays on multiple spacecraft faces can provide an economical solution, eliminating the need for array pointing or even spacecraft pointing.

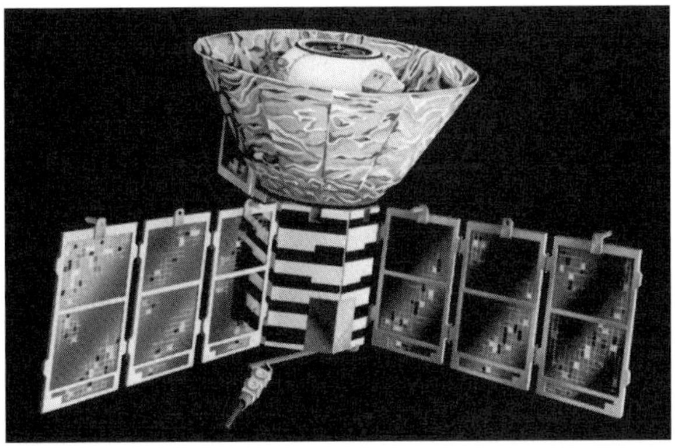

Fig. 14-6. COBE.

Most non-spinning spacecraft use deployed solar panels. If you can design the mission to constrain the Sun to within about 30 deg of a particular body vector, the array can probably remain rigidly fixed to the spacecraft body after deployment. If the direction to the Sun cannot be this constrained, then the spacecraft will need articulated arrays. For low inclination orbits, the Sun will remain near the plane of the orbit. A single axis of rotation (on the pitch axis for a nadir pointer) will probably be sufficient to keep the arrays pointed toward the Sun. Higher inclination orbits will have a large variation in beta angle, resulting in the need for two-axis gimbals on the array. A significant exception to this rule is the *Sun-synchronous orbit*, where the orbit precesses at the same rate that the Earth orbits the Sun. In this case, the beta angle variation is again small. Gimbals on solar arrays add significant complexity to the system, so the designer should avoid them if possible. In addition to the complexity of a mechanism in space which must operate over thousands of cycles, gimbals are a source of jitter, they require significant hardware and software for control, they complicate safe mode, and the thermal design, including blankets on moving parts, is challenging. The problems have certainly been solved many times, but it does add to the overall cost of the system.

The final aspect of solar array design involves deciding whether to place arrays on one side of the spacecraft or symmetrically on two sides. At first glance, it would appear that a single panel would always be the way to go—fewer mechanisms and deployments to worry about and no shadowing from the spacecraft body for high beta angles. But as a panel gets longer, the moments of inertia (MOI) go as the length **squared**, requiring more torque from the attitude control system. Balancing the array on two sides of the spacecraft cuts the contribution from the array to the MOI in half. Longer arrays will also be less stiff, so they will be more likely to create jitter and couple into the control bandwidth of the attitude control system (see Sec. 19.1.5). In low-Earth orbit, solar arrays produce significant drag area, so symmetric arrays will keep the center of pressure of the system near the center of mass. An offset of the two centers will produce a torque on the spacecraft which must be overcome by the control system (see Sec. 19.1.2). Away from the drag of an atmosphere, asymmetric arrays still create torque in the system due to solar pressure.

14.3.4 Communication Antenna Placement

Depending on the type of mission, the placement of communication antennas may affect the overall spacecraft configuration (see TDRSS and New Horizons in Fig. 14-2). For low-Earth orbit science missions communicating with the ground, omni antennas will generally support the needed data rates. You can usually place two antennas, each viewing half the sky, without much difficulty, although solar arrays may get in the way. For more distant missions, medium or high-gain antennas are generally required (see Sec. 21.1.5). If your mission design can afford to stop collecting measurements while downlinking data, you can fix a high-gain antenna to the spacecraft body and use the spacecraft to point it at the ground station. For continuous operation, the antenna will mount on gimbals, and a boom will keep the antenna from striking the spacecraft body. A dual-axis-gimbaled antenna hanging out on a boom will affect your attitude control stability, although not as much as a gimbaled solar array, since the solar array mass is generally much greater than the mass of even a large high-gain antenna.

14.3.5 Spacecraft Autonomy

Although it does not have a large impact on the general shape of the spacecraft, the level of autonomy in the system can greatly impact the mission costs and the system design. All spacecraft must perform some functions without interaction from the ground, but the amount of autonomy designed into the system will vary greatly with application. More autonomous spacecraft will require more complex software, faster processors, and more memory. The hardware resources will demand more power and mass, and the entire system will require more testing. There are three main reasons for autonomy:

1. Reduce the operations costs
2. Execute mission critical functions when the ground is unavailable
3. Protect the spacecraft from unexpected events or failures

Early in the design process, the mission designer should decide the general approach for operation of the spacecraft. For a short mission (a few months), it probably makes sense for the ground operators to monitor the spacecraft continuously, with very little action taking place without explicit commands from the ground. It is generally prudent to have the spacecraft builders present for the early check-out of the spacecraft, so having them stick around for another month or two will not add much more to the cost, certainly less than adding a bunch of autonomous functions. For more extended missions, the designers trade complexity on board against manpower and autonomy on the ground to control the system. For instance, operators can work reduced hours if the spacecraft can store a time-tagged command sequence and execute that sequence over the course of a day or two. This is very simple autonomy, still requiring the operators to determine every command that the spacecraft will execute, but allowing a single uplink where the operators send all of the commands at once. More sophisticated autonomy can enable the spacecraft to respond to incoming data, changing configurations in order to maximize the information gathered. Modern flight computers have enough capability to enable spacecraft to autonomously select targets based on some pre-programmed criteria, or to autonomously rendezvous with another spacecraft and perform docking operations. These sorts of algorithms require extensive modeling and testing on the ground to ensure proper operation on orbit. It is up to the mission designer to work with the spacecraft and ground system teams to determine the optimum balance between autonomy and operators.

Some missions, especially planetary missions, must execute critical functions, such as an orbit insertion burn, without contact from the ground. In planetary missions, the time delay in radio signal from the ground to the spacecraft does not allow operators to send real-time commands in reaction to events. The timing of most orbit maneuvers is such that on-board time-tagged commands must be used to ensure proper execution.

The long communications delays in planetary missions also require the spacecraft to autonomously recover from failures during critical events. If the spacecraft only has one opportunity to perform a burn in order to achieve orbit, on-board autonomy must handle failures and switch over to redundant components—the spacecraft must be *fail operational*. But even for missions that do not have critical maneuvers, system designers usually add autonomy to preserve the spacecraft after failures or unexpected anomalies. In these situations, it is simpler to design the spacecraft to *fail safe*, going to a mode which preserves the system until the ground can diagnose the situation and hopefully correct it. A spacecraft *safe mode* is the safe state to which the spacecraft transitions when a failure is detected. Safe is generally defined as:

1. *Power Positive*—more power being generated by the solar arrays than being consumed by the system, so that the battery recharges. If the battery becomes fully discharged, there is no longer any way to communicate with the spacecraft, and the attitude control system will no longer function, preventing a change in attitude that would allow recharging of the battery. In other words, a spacecraft with a dead battery is dead.
2. *Thermally Benign*—all temperatures must stay within survival limits
3. *Commandable*—the orientation of antennas and the configuration of the receiver must be such that

the ground can send commands in order to correct problems. The transmitter is frequently off in safe mode to save power, but the mode must support output of housekeeping telemetry when the ground commands transmit, to enable troubleshooting.

Safe mode generally requires some control of the attitude of the spacecraft. Safe mode considerations can drive antenna placement and avionics hardware features. Many spacecraft have hardware-decoded commands to allow resets and transitions to redundant hardware even when the software is not functioning (see Sec. 29.1 Step 6 for more discussion of autonomy).

14.4 Partitioning Spacecraft into Subsystems

After completing the top-level configuration trades, it is time to go to the next level of detail in the spacecraft design. This extra level of detail will require partitioning the spacecraft into subsystems, with a different subsystem expert responsible for each of the partitions. Significant work can then occur in parallel, with the systems engineer ensuring that each subsystem lead stays connected with the overall system concept. By dividing the system in a way that minimizes interfaces between subsystems, the systems engineer can minimize the effort required to coordinate among the subsystem engineers. Ideally, each spacecraft would have a unique subsystem partitioning designed for that particular mission. Practically, our spacecraft development organizations are already divided into particular disciplines (see Table 14-6), so the subsystems we use for spacecraft development are generally the same for each spacecraft, reducing the required coordination between organizations. So we may end up with the attitude determination and control group designing a box that communicates with each of the attitude sensors and actuators, separate from the command and data handling (C&DH) box. Then the C&DH group only has to worry about a single interface with the ADC, instead of each of the sensor and actuator interfaces. We may face a small increase in mass in order to provide clear lines of responsibility, but the overall cost of the system will be less if the organization operates more efficiently. Over the long term, we may see re-organizations within the industry, as software takes over many functions, digital logic operates at higher speeds, and the distinctions between TT&C, C&DH, ADC, and Power electronics blur.

A classic partitioning of functionality in a spacecraft is the hardware vs. software trade. Functions performed in hardware are deterministic and static, and they can be done independently of other tasks on the spacecraft. If you have a simple function that must always operate the same way, a hardware solution will ensure that ground operators cannot disturb the critical functionality (such as a hardware-decoded command for resetting the system to a known state). If you have a function which requires significant computation, hardware can remove that burden from the flight processor (encoding of downlink telemetry is an example). Software provides the flexibility to finish the details of a function late in the development, or even change functionality after launch. Software does not add to the mass of the spacecraft, but

Table 14-6. List of Common Spacecraft Subsystems.

Subsystem Name	Function	Reference
Propulsion	Spacecraft thrust, including fuel storage and plumbing	Chap. 18
Attitude Determination and Control (ADC) or Attitude Control System (ACS)	Sensors, actuators, and software necessary to control the spacecraft pointing	Sec. 19.1
Position and Orbit Determination and Control	Sensors and software necessary to control the spacecraft orbit	Sec. 19.2
On Board Processing or Command and Data Handling (C&DH)	Electronics and software used to receive and distribute commands and to store and forward payload data and spacecraft telemetry	Chap. 20
Telemetry, Tracking, and Command (TT&C) or RF Communications	Radio and associated hardware, such as cabling and antennas, used to communicate with the ground or other spacecraft	Sec. 21.1
Power	Electronics, power generation, and power storage devices, as well as harnessing for power distribution	Sec. 21.2
Structures and Mechanisms	All the hardware that supports the spacecraft, including the primary structural components, brackets, fasteners, and the actuators and mechanisms associated with deployed or movable structures	Sec. 22.1
Thermal Control	All of the hardware necessary to control the temperature of the spacecraft	Sec. 22.2

it is not always cheaper than hardware, because more complex code requires more complex testing. How much can be done in software is generally limited by the speed of the processors available. As flight processors have become faster, more functionality has moved to software, and this has generally made our spacecraft smaller, more capable, and more adaptable. Programmable logic, such as Field-Programmable Gate Arrays (FPGA's), blur the lines between hardware and software, since the logic can be treated as a piece of hardware, but it can have its functionality changed via programming late in the design cycle. Some programmable logic includes embedded micro-controllers, with the ability to change the code on the fly, further blurring the distinction.

The rest of the section will discuss the subsystems most frequently encountered in the spacecraft industry, include driving requirements for each subsystem and an introduction to the perspective of each—what do the subsystem leads worry about, and what does the systems engineer need to know to communicate with each. The tables of driving requirements are based on the experience of dozens of preliminary mission designs; they provide a good starting point, but each mission will have some unique features.

14.4.1 Propulsion

The propulsion subsystem provides the necessary thrust to change the orbit of the spacecraft and dump momentum. The total change in velocity (delta V) dominates the propellant budget. The three parameters in Table 14-7, combined with the configuration selected through the trades discussed in Sec. 14.3.2 will define the overall propulsion configuration. The propulsion lead must work with the attitude control and orbit control leads to ensure proper thruster sizing; with the mechanical lead to ensure proper support of the tank mass and proper placement of thrusters; and with the thermal lead to ensure proper temperature control (hydrazine has a freezing point near that of water). Electronics to operate the propulsion can either be part of the propulsion subsystem or part of the attitude control system. The mass summaries in App. A place the control electronics for propulsion in the attitude control system.

Table 14-7. Propulsion Design Drivers.

Major Design Drivers	Driven By	Impact
Delta V	Mission design	Fuel required
Spacecraft Dry Mass	Spacecraft design	Fuel required
Thrust for Maneuvers and Control	Trajectory and ADC design	Thruster sizing

14.4.2 Attitude Determination and Control

The attitude determination and control (ADC) subsystem, also known as the attitude control system (ACS), determines the orientation of the spacecraft in space, it re-orients the spacecraft toward commanded or pre-programmed targets, and it holds that attitude. It takes four parameters to describe the attitude of the spacecraft—three define a vector in inertial space and a fourth describes the rotation about that vector. Attitude is frequently represented using *quaternions*, which are an extension to the complex number system. Quaternions are easily manipulated with matrix mathematics and are well suited for computer computation. For a 3-axis-controlled spacecraft, the ADC is a major piece of the overall spacecraft bus. The sensors and actuators add significant mass to the system, and the software required to control a spacecraft's attitude can consume a major portion of the total processor bandwidth. Table 14-8 shows the major drivers of the ADC design.

The fundamental driving requirement for ADC is the pointing control, typically driven by how accurately the payload must be pointed. Observational payloads around the Earth or any other body typically need position information relative to the body in addition to attitude information in order to locate the observation with respect to a map of the body. Communications payloads and outward looking payloads generally do not need high-precision position information. Communications payloads and space weather instrumentation (measuring electrons, ions, and fields) generally have looser pointing requirements than other payloads.

How accurately the spacecraft must point will impact the accuracy of the sensors and the precision of the actuators. Typically, more accurate sensors are heavier and more expensive, consume more power, and have lower reliability—more complexity is required for more accuracy. The on-board knowledge is typically better than the pointing because of the errors introduced by the actuators. The ground knowledge of pointing is generally better than the on-board solution. Errors introduced by predicted orbit position (rather than definitive orbit solutions after the fact) and by less accurate on-board algorithms (as compared with what can be done on the ground) will reduce the spacecraft's instantaneous estimate of attitude. The stability of the payload pointing will be affected by imbalance of reaction wheels and motion of spacecraft appendages as well as structural stiffness and stability over temperature, both for the payload mounting and the ADC sensor and actuator mounting. The stiffness of appendages must typically put the first resonance at a frequency that is at least a factor of 10 above the controller bandwidth to prevent amplification of oscillations. If this is not practical, a structural filter can be incorporated in the control system, but this approach requires significant testing and analysis (see Sec. 19.1.5).

The actuators provide the torque to re-point the spacecraft. The actuators must provide more torque for faster attitude changes or larger spacecraft moments of inertia. Reaction wheel systems also provide momentum storage, so that external torques from effects such as solar pressure, atmospheric drag, and gravity gradient can be temporarily compensated without thrusters or electromagnetic torquers. (See Sec. 19.1.2 for more details on external torques.) The wheels will spin faster and faster as the torques are

Table 14-8. Attitude Determination and Control Design Drivers.

Major Design Drivers	Driven By	Impact
Pointing Control Accuracy	Payload requirements	Sensors and actuators
Pointing Knowledge	Payload requirements	Sensors
Stability	Payload requirements	Actuators, appendages
Maneuvers	Payload requirements	Actuators
Max Slew Rate	Payload requirements	Actuators
Spacecraft Moment of Inertia	Spacecraft config	Actuators
Time Between Momentum Unloads	Operational availability	Momentum storage
External Torques	Spacecraft config, orbit	Momentum storage
Sun, Earth, Moon Avoidance	Payload requirements	Algorithms, sensors
Safing Requirements	Reliability, lifetime	Algorithms, sens & act
Solar Array Configuration	Orbit	Stability, external torq
Antenna Pointing Requirements	Data system design	Pointing ctrl, algorithm

reacted, storing momentum, until the spacecraft uses thrusters or electromagnets to remove the excess momentum. The dumping of momentum will typically add some instability into the system, so we would like to go as long as possible without dumping momentum.

For many payloads, such as those with sensitive or cold detectors, pointing at the Sun can be fatal. Some payloads must avoid the Earth or even the Moon. These considerations, along with the safing considerations described in Sec. 14.3.5, will impact the required sensors and on-board algorithms. For instance, most spacecraft carry coarse Sun sensors which face in all directions on the system, allowing it to autonomously determine where to find the Sun.

The other major function of the ADC subsystem is the control of solar array and antenna pointing. The ADC subsystem has the on-board knowledge of attitude, so it is fairly easy to add information about where to find the Earth and where to find the Sun, then generate the proper commands to the hardware to point the antenna and solar panel. The ground typically uploads an *ephemeris table* which describes in inertial coordinates the direction of the Sun or the direction of the Earth vs. time from the expected position of the spacecraft. Alternatively, the spacecraft can use an on-board algorithm to calculate the Sun and Earth directions, with a modest increase in processing power. For Earth-orbiting missions, a Global Positioning Satellite (GPS) receiver can provide very accurate orbit information, possibly eliminating the need for additional position determination algorithms.

14.4.3 Position and Orbit Determination and Control

Historically, spacecraft orbit determination was a function of the ground system, with the spacecraft providing some hardware to enable the necessary measurements. During ground contacts, coherent transponders would provide range and range-rate information, which the operators then processed to determine the spacecraft orbit. The controllers would then send the appropriate command to the propulsion system to adjust the orbit as necessary. While this method is still quite common, modern computational capability has enabled autonomous orbit control by spacecraft. An on-board GPS receiver determines the spacecraft position and velocity, and then the spacecraft processor can compute an orbit for the system. This orbit is refined over multiple measurements, with algorithmic filtering ensuring that a bad sample will not cause a bad final solution. The spacecraft can then compare this orbit solution to the desired orbit and calculate and execute the propulsive maneuvers necessary to adjust the orbit. This technique will allow one spacecraft to get close enough to another spacecraft so that more specialized sensors, such as a scanning lidar or optical sensors with image processing, can calculate the maneuvers necessary for autonomous rendezvous and even docking between spacecraft. More information about orbit determination and control is in Sec. 19.2.

14.4.4 On-board Processing

The On-board Processing subsystem is frequently known as the Command and Data Handling subsystem (C&DH). It receives commands from the ground via the communications system, passes them to the appropriate components and payloads, collects telemetry from across the system, stores that telemetry, collects and stores science data, and forwards the real-time and stored data to the ground via the communications system. The C&DH contains the flight processor, where the software runs, and it contains the non-volatile memory where the software is stored. The primary drivers for the C&DH are in Table 14-9.

The C&DH is the primary point of contact for the system's interaction with the payloads. The hardware and software interfaces for commanding the payloads and reading the data impact the complexity of the C&DH. For data rates below 100 kbps, a slower-speed serial interface like the MIL-STD-1553 can be used for communication with the payloads. Using a common, robust data standard will improve reliability and reduce integration and testing costs. Higher data rates demand more complex interfaces, such as Spacewire (standard ECSS-E-ST-50-12C based on IEEE 1355) or custom solutions. As the data rates increase, more work must be done by the C&DH hardware, with less data handling being done in software.

Table 14-9. On-board Processing Design Drivers.

Major Design Drivers	Driven By	Impact
Instrument Data interface	Payload requirements	Hardware design
Processing requirements	Ops concept, algorithms	Processor, power
Data Storage volume	Payload, ops concept	Hardware design
Timing accuracy	Payload	Oscillator, hardware design

Table 14-10. Processor Utilization vs. Processor Type and Speed.

Year	Mission	Processor	ACS Rate	Utilization	
				ACS	C&DH
1995	SWAS/ WIRE	386/387 @ 16 MHz	10 Hz	23%	55%
2000	Triana	Rad6000 @ 20 MHz	10 Hz	28%	63%
2007	LRO	Rad750 @ 132 MHz	5 Hz	1.7%	48%

Hardware solutions must be fixed earlier in the build cycle, since software can generally be changed after the hardware is complete, through reprogrammable memory. The designer should pay particular attention to the *handshaking*, the interaction between the payload and the C&DH, on the data interface which regulates the data flow. For most applications, it is critical that the handshaking allows the C&DH to pause, with data held on the instrument side of the interface, during high-speed transfers. This allows time for the C&DH to execute other critical functions without dropping payload data.

The processing requirements define the speed of the processor, the dynamic memory (typically Random Access Memory or RAM), and the non-volatile memory (usually Programmable Read Only Memory, PROM, or Electrically Erasable Programmable Read Only Memory, EEPROM). Table 14-10 provides a reference level of processor utilization for different speed processors. All three missions used a 3-axis attitude control system, and all three had a similar level of autonomy. The instrument managing software in the flight computer is part of the C&DH total. The increase in ACS utilization with the Rad6000 processor was due to an increase in complexity which outpaced the increase in speed—Triana ran extra filters and produced more telemetry. Also, the Rad6000 is a Reduced Instruction Set Computer (RISC) processor, so it did not have the floating point math built in like the 386/387 combination used on SWAS and WIRE. With LRO, the large increase in processor speed allowed substantially more instrument support on the C&DH side, with the ACS code approaching "insignificant." LRO could handle a lower ACS cycle due to its much larger size (larger spacecraft change pointing much slower). You can use this table as a starting point to estimate, for your processor, how much processing bandwidth will be required for these functions. Assuming about 25% utilization at 20 MHz and 10 Hz ACS cycle, increasing the speed to 132 MHz is a factor of 6.6, which cuts utilization to 3.8%, and running at 5 Hz instead of 10 Hz cuts utilization in half again, resulting in 1.9%—very close to the LRO measured value of 1.7%. For lower processing demands, consider operating the processor at a slower speed to save power. Faster processors generally consume more power.

The non-volatile memory stores the software code, with PROM used for code that is unchangeable in flight and EEPROM used for code that can be altered during flight. The *boot code* copies the software from non-volatile memory into RAM where it executes (the software pulls itself up by the bootstraps). The RAM is used for temporary storage during software execution, and it can also be used for storage of some key telemetry information. The C&DH also contains a larger bank of RAM or perhaps even hard disks for storage of payload data. The volume of data generated between ground contacts determines how much memory the C&DH must carry. The LRO Rad750 processor card, selected in 2005, contained 64 kbytes of PROM, 4 Mbytes of EEPROM, and 36 Mbytes of radiation-hard RAM for the processor and another 8 Mbytes of RAM for the high-speed data interface. The larger data storage on LRO used 1800 Mbytes of Dynamic RAM on each of 4 cards. This RAM memory included 600 Mbytes for coding to correct errors caused by radiation.

The C&DH generally maintains the master clock for the spacecraft. An oscillator provides the reference, with a counter, called the *mission elapsed timer* (MET), keeping track of the number of cycles in the oscillator since applying power to the system. The count represents seconds and subseconds. The software then adds an offset to the MET to determine the seconds and subseconds since some *epoch*. The epoch is the reference date and time to which all spacecraft time is referenced. A typical epoch is midnight starting January 1, 2001. The sum of the MET and offset is the number of seconds and fractional seconds since that epoch. The required time-tagging accuracy of the payload determines the precision and accuracy of the onboard oscillator and the frequency and methodology of maintaining the clock. A high-precision oscillator will have a built-in oven to maintain the temperature of the oscillator. Without an oven, over the typical temperature range of a spacecraft, the system will be able to maintain the clock to within 0.5 seconds over a day. The absolute accuracy of an oscillator's frequency is usually poorer than its precision (its variation from the initial value). This means that the clock will generally drift somewhat from the ideal, but the drift will be about the same every day. More C&DH details can be found in Chap. 20.

14.4.5 Telemetry, Tracking, and Command

The Telemetry, Tracking, and Command (TT&C) subsystem provides the radio link between the spacecraft and the ground, and it provides signaling necessary to determine the spacecraft's distance and velocity over time. The distance, or *ranging*, information is determined by measuring the delay of ranging signals that are sent from the ground to the spacecraft, received by the TT&C, then retransmitted to the ground. The velocity information is determined by the ground measuring the *Doppler shift* of the spacecraft's signal at the station over time. Because of the fixed velocity of radio waves, the frequency of the signal will shift up with an approaching spacecraft and down with a receding spacecraft as the waves either bunch up or spread out. The equation for the shifted frequency is:

$$f = f_{xmit} \cdot \left(1 - \frac{V_{rel}}{c}\right) \tag{14-2}$$

Where f_{xmit} is the transmit frequency on board the spacecraft, V_{rel} is the relative velocity receeding along the line of sight, ($V_{rel} < 0$ for an approaching spacecraft) and c is the speed of light. This same shift occurs for the signal sent from the ground to the spacecraft. Most Doppler tracking is done with a TT&C system that transmits at a frequency which is proportional to the received frequency, called a *coherent transponder*, so that the ground knows exactly what frequency to expect from the spacecraft. The difference between the expected frequency and the actual frequency is the *two-way Doppler shift*, since the signal is shifted on the way both to and from the spacecraft. If the spacecraft does not transmit a coherent signal, then its frequency is set by an internal oscillator, and the ground will only expect a *one-way Doppler shift* from the oscillator-derived frequency. Table 14-11 contains the major drivers for the TT&C design.

Table 14-11. TT&C Design Drivers.

Major Design Drivers	Driven By	Impact
Data Rate & Distance	Payload, ops concept	RF power, antenna
Frequency	Data rate, regulations	Hardware design
Ground Station EIRP	Ops concept	Recvr sensitivity, ant
Ground Station G/T	Ops concept	Xmit pwr, antenna
Duty Cycle	Ops concept	Orbit-average power

Radio Frequency (RF) engineers use link budgets to describe the performance of the radio links in the TT&C. A full discussion of link budgets is in Sec. 21.1.4. The most important things for the systems engineer to know about link budgets are:

- Links are generally described in decibels (dB). This is a logarithmic scale, so an increase in 3 dB means a doubling of the power
- RF power required is proportional to the data rate, so a doubling of the data rate will require a doubling of the transmitted power
- RF power is inversely proportional to the distance squared. So a doubling of the distance results four times more transmitter power
- Antennas can provide significant gain, meaning that you can reduce the transmitted power by orders of magnitude if you use a high-gain antenna
- The gain of an antenna is inversely proportional to its beamwidth. If the antenna focuses all of its power in a narrow beam, the link is more efficient, so the antenna gain is much greater than 1. But the spacecraft must then point that beam
- The gain of a high-gain antenna is proportional to the area of the antenna, so doubling the diameter of an antenna increases the gain by roughly 6 dB
- The antenna size is proportional to the frequency
- It is generally a good idea to maintain 3 dB of margin in the link. This covers unexpected factors and later degradation

The frequency selection is usually dictated by international regulations and planned data rates. See Table 21-3 for more information.

The main performance parameters for a ground station are the *Effective Isotropic Radiated Power (EIRP)*, which is a combination of the transmitter power and the antenna gain, and the *G/T ratio*, which is the antenna gain divided by the noise temperature of the receiver. The G/T is a convenient figure of merit which comes out of the link equation (see Eq. (21-4)). With a higher EIRP from the ground, the spacecraft antenna gain can be reduced. With a higher G/T on the ground, the spacecraft transmitter power or antenna gain can be reduced.

The spacecraft power consumed by the TT&C transmitter is substantially greater than the RF power transmitted. A 5 W transmitter will consume about 30–35 W. For higher transmitter powers (>20 W), alternate amplifier technology is used, so transmitters become more efficient. A 50 W transmitter will consume about 120–160 W. The receiver in the TT&C should be continuously powered, so that the ground can always get a command to the spacecraft. The transmitter can be turned off when not in view of a ground station, reducing the average power consumption of the TT&C.

Some general rules of thumb for omni-directional antennas and a typical S-band TT&C:

- For spacecraft in low-Earth orbit, omni antennas will support about 2 kbps command link from TDRSS
- Those same omni antennas will support about 8 kbps link to TDRSS and 4,000 kbps to a 13 m ground station using a 5 W transmitter

More details on the TT&C system can be found in Sec. 21.1.

The international community has developed standards for spacecraft communications. The Consultative Committee for Space Data Systems (CCSDS) maintains the standards documents. These standards include coding on the radio links as well as command and telemetry packet and transfer frame formats.

14.4.6 Power

The power subsystem provides all of the power generation, storage, and distribution for the spacecraft. The design drivers are in Table 14-12.

Table 14-12. Power Subsystem Design Drivers.

Major Design Drivers	Driven By	Impact
Power Consumption	Payload Req	Solar array, battery
Power Distribution	Spacecraft design	Power electronics, wiring
Eclipse Duration	Orbit	Battery
Bus Voltage	Spacecraft design	Power electronics, wiring
Payload Duty Cycle	Ops concept	Solar array, battery

The needs of the payload will drive the overall power consumption of the spacecraft. Something will need to generate the power—usually a photovoltaic solar array, although deep-space or high-power missions may use other techniques as described in Sec. 21.2.6. Very short missions may simply use stored energy from a battery. When array power is not available, a battery will keep the system operating. The power electronics controls the charging of the battery, and it controls the switching of power to the spacecraft loads. Lithium ion batteries are becoming the first choice for most spacecraft today.

Most spacecraft use a 28 V bus. Since there is power lost in the conversion of 28 V to the lower voltages typically used by electronics, very small spacecraft use lower-voltage buses. If the spacecraft has large power demands and long harness runs, it may make sense to use a larger voltage. The International Space Station operates around 160 V on its power bus. The total power consumed by a component is:

$$P_{comp} = V \times I \tag{14-3}$$

where P_{comp} is the component power and I is the current into the component. Higher voltages will reduce the current used by components, and it will therefore reduce the power lost in harnessing, since the power dissipation is:

$$P_{dis} = I^2 \times R \tag{14-4}$$

where P_{dis} is the power dissipation, I is the current in the harness, and R is the resistance of the harness. Most components on a 28 V bus will draw constant power, because of the design of the internal electronics. This means that a **drop** in bus voltage will cause components to draw **more** current. Be careful during the testing of such components, because laboratory power supplies typically reduce their voltage if a component's current exceeds the supply's current limit—if the supply goes into current limiting mode, the supply voltage drops, causing the component under test to draw even more current, eventually taking the voltage down below the normal operating range. For this reason, you should require all components on the spacecraft bus to survive indefinitely without damage any voltage below the operating range all the way to 0 V.

Transistors have largely replaced relays for spacecraft power switching. Modern circuitry allows for resettable circuit-breaker functionality to protect harnessing and the power bus, rather than using fuses for over-current conditions. Latching relays are still used in cases where a system must maintain a switch in a given configuration even after a power outage. Relays also find some application in safety circuits, since they completely isolate the source voltage from the potentially hazardous actuator.

The solar arrays typically require a long development cycle. The systems engineer must define the power requirements early, so that the power engineer can size the array. The mechanical team then must design and fabricate the array substrate, before the array manufacturer can populate the array. The systems engineer must then carefully monitor the power consumption of the spacecraft to prevent exceeding the array's capability.

One way to delay the sizing of the array without delaying the delivery of the array is through the use of a *modular design* for the solar array. In this approach many individual solar array modules are assembled onto a frame to create the full-sized array. The solar array builder can assemble each of the modules while the spacecraft team is still sizing the power system, with the exact array configuration coming later. The spacecraft builder can keep an inventory of modules for rapid solar array development. The WIRE spacecraft solar array was a modular design. The mass impact of this approach was small [Everett, et al. 2000]. Figure 14-7 shows the WIRE engineering unit solar array structure, with one frame populated with modules and the other unpopulated. Section 21.2 provides more details on power systems.

14.4.7 Structures and Mechanisms

The spacecraft structure supports all the spacecraft components and payloads throughout the launch, and it provides a stable platform for on-orbit operations. Table 14-13 describes the design drivers for the structure.

The acceleration of the launch vehicle is the dominant load for the structure, with the maximum load generally occurring near the end of a stage, since the mass of the fuel is almost gone but the rocket still has the same thrust as it did early in the flight. Some liquid launch systems can reduce the thrust toward the end of the burn to limit this effect. Expect loads of about 6 to 10 g's, depending

Table 14-13. Mechanical Subsystem Design Drivers.

Major Design Drivers	Driven By	Impact
Launch Vehicle	Launch mass	Structure strength, stiffness
Payload Accommodation	Payload config	Structure shape
Solar Array Area	Power system design	Appendage, overall shape
Structural Stability	Pointing requirements	Stiffness, joint design, material selection
Center of Mass Offset	Launch vehicle, ACS design	Layout, balance mass
Thermal Radiator Area	Power dissipation	Structure layout

Fig. 14-7. WIRE Modular Solar Array. (Photo courtesy of NASA GSFC)

on the rocket, with smaller systems creating higher loads. Lateral loads, although generally smaller, can also have significant impact on the design. Most vehicles produce less than 3 g's laterally, but the drop transient of the Pegasus can be significantly more, especially near the end of the spacecraft, since there is a rotational component to the transient. Some vehicles have a sine transient during motor ignition, especially as one stage burns out and the next starts. The spacecraft's natural frequencies must stay away from the launch vehicle driving frequencies in order to avoid coupling excessive energy into the system. *Load isolation systems* have become more common in recent years. Composed of flexures and dampers and functioning like the springs and shock absorbers on a car, a load isolation system reduces the high-frequency components of loads transmitted from the launch vehicle into the spacecraft. Launch vehicles typically impose requirements on spacecraft frequency and the position of the center of mass.

In addition to the static and transient loads, a launch vehicle produces vibro-acoustic loads. The noise from the launch vehicle couples into the spacecraft through the air around the vehicle during the early part of the flight. Blankets inside the fairing can help reduce this environment. Large structures, like the solar array panels, will absorb energy from the acoustic environment and couple it into the structure. Additionally, the launch vehicle will transmit vibration directly through the mounting to the spacecraft. The vibration loads tend to dominate the structural design of smaller components.

Any devices in the system which release energy suddenly will produce a shock load. The separation interface with the launch vehicle is generally the biggest source of shock, but other releases, such as the deployment of a solar array, can produce a shock transient. Shock loads tend to cover a large frequency range, with much of the higher frequencies attenuating rapidly across interfaces.

Mechanical engineers must take all of the above-described loads into consideration when designing a structure that will also provide the necessary views for all of the payloads and spacecraft components. Additionally we ask them to minimize the mass, so we can maximize the payload. Structural modeling is an important aspect of the design process, with modern computer modeling providing accurate predictions of the structural frequency and the stress on individual items. Despite the success of structural modeling, it is still important to conduct some tests to confirm the validity of assumptions built into the model.

Payloads which require high-precision pointing place additional demands on the spacecraft structure. We need to ensure that the movement of the structure, as it expands and contracts with temperature changes, does not excessively move the payload or spacecraft attitude sensors. *Flexures* bend in one direction while remaining stiff in another, preventing the buildup of stress which can distort a surface. We can use materials like graphite-composite, which do not change size much over temperature. An effective optical bench structure uses graphite-composite face-sheets over an aluminum honeycomb core. This arrangement produces a very stiff plate that is extremely light weight and does not change much in size over temperature. Section 22.1 provides more details on spacecraft structures, including some strategies for estimating mass.

Spacecraft mechanisms, which must operate in the micro-gravity environment of orbit, can be difficult to test on the ground in a 1 g environment. A motor with plenty of torque margin to move a solar array around in space may not have any hope of moving that array when it is loaded by gravity. During the design phase, it is important to carefully consider the need for each mechanism on the spacecraft, since each will require detailed analysis and each will be potentially difficult to test, creating a risk that it will not operate correctly on orbit. Simple springs and hinges generally provide a more reliable one-time operation, such as a solar-array deployment, than a motor. Any deployment must have a method to hold the component in place during launch, generally under compression, then release it at the appropriate time. Release mechanisms are generally electrically

Table 14-14. Thermal Subsystem Design Drivers.

Major Design Drivers	Driven By	Impact
Thermal Environment	Orbit	Entire thermal design
Power Dissipation	Spacecraft design	Radiator area
Op and Survival Temps	Payload, components	Entire thermal design
Structural Configuration	Mechanical drivers	Restricted radiators
Structural Stability	Pointing requirements	Tight temperature limits

actuated. *Electrically-actuated explosive devices* (EED) can cut a cable or bolt, release the threads on a bolt, or provide some other such release by detonating a small explosive charge with heat generated by electrical current. EED's generally create a large shock, since they release suddenly. Other types of non-explosive actuators are available today, some of which can be reset, allowing multiple tests with the device that will actually fly.

Kick-off springs generally get a structure moving after its release, overcoming any static friction that might be present. Section 22.1.5 provides more details on mechanisms.

14.4.8 Thermal Control

The thermal subsystem keeps all components and payloads within operating temperature ranges during normal operations and it keeps everything within survival limits under all circumstances. Table 14-14 lists the design drivers for the thermal subsystem.

The power dissipation of the system combined with the orbit's thermal environment will drive the thermal design. The system must conduct internally-generated heat to the outside of the spacecraft where it can be radiated to space. Ideally, the radiators will face deep space, with its 3 K background temperature. For low-Earth orbit, the Earth is about 300 K and fills half the sky, making it more difficult to find room on the spacecraft for radiators that need to run below this temperature. Since the Sun is only a half-degree across from Earth distance and it is surrounded by deep space, radiators can face it, but they need white or shiny coatings which reflect optical energies and still radiate in the infrared. Smaller spacecraft generally have plenty of surface area to radiate the heat that can be generated by the few components that fit in their small volume. On larger spacecraft, it can be a challenge to move heat from its source out to a radiator. *Heat pipes* provide an effective means to transport heat within a spacecraft. Heat pipes use the evaporation and condensation of a working fluid like ammonia to transport the heat. The pipes can be designed to take advantage of capillary action in the micro-gravity environment to move the fluid to the source of the heat while the vapor moves to the radiator.

The biggest thermal challenges come when temperatures must be kept within a very narrow temperature range. The thermal engineer can solve temperature range issues by adding more radiator area, enabling the system to dissipate more heat. But that extra heat dissipation will be a liability during cold cases, resulting in additional heater power. In the extreme, we can run the radiator so cold that we always need some level of heater power to maintain the desired temperature. One of the biggest system-level trades related to the thermal system involves this tradeoff between thermal system performance, radiator area, and power consumption.

Section 22.2 contains more information about the thermal subsystem.

14.4.9 Other Specialties (Cross-cutting Disciplines)

The topics below; contamination control, risk & reliability, parts control, mission assurance, and safety; are typically handled by discipline experts who operate at the spacecraft system level. These are not subsystems, but they are part of the partitioning of work necessary to build a spacecraft. These considerations will impact the cost of the system.

Contamination Control

We have all seen the dust that accumulates on surfaces over time. Many of us have also experienced the film that forms on the inside of car windshields—a hard-to-remove scum that requires window cleaner or vinegar to remove, leaving the rag black. There are many sources for the dust, not the least of which is the surface layer of our skin flaking off as new layers grow below. The film on the windshield is due to *outgassing* of the plastics in the car—molecules in the plastic escape the material, float around in the car, and then deposit on the glass. The "new car smell" is actually your nose detecting those molecules floating around in the car's air. Clearly, we do not want to cover spacecraft optics with dust or a film of molecules, so we must be very careful about the environment in which we assemble the spacecraft, and we must choose materials for the spacecraft that will not excessively outgas. Controlling these contaminants is a specialty in the spacecraft business, with engineers focusing on processes and procedures for maintaining cleanliness levels.

There are some general principles and rules of thumb that the systems engineer needs to know. The spacecraft requires some top-level requirements for particles and molecular contamination. Typically, different surfaces will require different cleanliness levels. The top-level contamination requirements will also drive the selection of materials for use in the spacecraft. Those material requirements flow out to everything installed on the spacecraft. Some materials are never flown in space, because they will simply evaporate in a vacuum, leaving a film over everything. The payload is the chief driver of top-level contamination requirements, although star trackers, solar arrays, and sensitive thermal surfaces (where we don't want a change in optical properties, since we are rejecting heat in the sunlight) can also be drivers. Ultraviolet instruments are particularly susceptible to molecular contamination, since the molecules generally have resonances at ultraviolet wavelengths, absorbing a significant portion of incoming photons. Molecular contamination will tend to discolor at optical wavelengths as ultraviolet radiation from the sunlight changes chemical bonds. These changes also make it difficult to remove the contaminants through heating.

IEST-STD-1246 is the standard for surface cleanliness, replacing FED-STD-1246 in the United States. A number and a letter, such as 450 A, are used to represent the particle and molecular contamination levels, respectively. The number corresponds to the largest single particle in microns allowed within a square foot, although there are also limits on the number of smaller particles. The letter is simply a non-volatile residue limit as defined in the standard.

Outgassing products tend to accumulate on cold surfaces. For surfaces below freezing, any water that evaporates out of the spacecraft, such as out of graphite epoxy structure, will accumulate. Critical components, such as telescopes, will typically use *decontamination heaters*, which keep critical surfaces warmer than the surrounding area, driving contaminants away. These decontamination heaters are powered during the early part of the mission, when the spacecraft is first experiencing the hard vacuum of space and components are outgassing at the highest rate. Sometimes decontamination heaters are operated after propulsive maneuvers, since thrusters may leave products behind. On top of the material and assembly constraints described above, the spacecraft designer must account for the power loads associated with these heaters.

Based on the cleanliness requirements, the contamination control plan will call out the *clean room* environment in which the spacecraft and its components must be assembled. A clean room is a facility where filters and air motion maintain particle count and organic and aromatic molecules below a certain level. ISO 14644 is the international standard for clean rooms and it replaces FED-STD-209 in the United States. The FED-STD-209 designations referred to the maximum number of particles greater than 0.5 μm in a cubic foot of air. The ISO 14644 standard uses 1 cubic meter as the standard volume with 0.1 μm as the standard particle for class 6 and cleaner and 0.5 μm still used for the dirtier classes. Table 14-15 describes common practices for the most common clean room classifications. The cleaner the room, the more care and monitoring required in order to maintain the classification, driving the cost up.

Risk and Reliability

Once a spacecraft is launched, it generally cannot be retrieved (the Space Shuttle provided some limited exceptions). A single failure in the wrong place can end a mission. The designers perform analyses to investigate what failures might be fatal and how likely it is that they might occur. A *risk* is a bad event that might occur. The criticality of the risk is the combination of likelihood that the bad event occurs and the consequences of that occurrence. The reliability of components is the likelihood that the components will fail. Designers can add redundancy or use more reliable parts to increase the reliability of the overall system. The system architecture will affect the criticality of each part. The designer must be careful to avoid an architecture that, despite redundancy, has *single points of failure*, where one failure can take out all of the redundancy. A full description of reliability and risk management is covered in Chap. 24.

Parts Control

The space industry has developed a set of processes and procedures to ensure that electronic parts will operate over the life of the mission. Modern electronic parts include features smaller than 1 μm! These features are susceptible to manufacturing flaws, particles, packaging issues, moisture, electrostatic discharge (during ground handling or in flight), and even individual protons ejected by the Sun. Screening procedures test the potential flight parts and destructively test parts made in the same batch or *lot*, before they are considered qualified for flight. This screening detects flaws in individual parts, flaws in the manufacturing process, and weaknesses induced by a radiation environment. Obviously, the more screening, the more expensive the parts will be. Good quality parts are expensive, but they reduce the expense of failures later in the development or in flight. Modern part manufacturing techniques have greatly improved the consistency and reliability of commercial electronic parts, but some level of screening, such as a 500-hour high-temperature burn in, perhaps conducted at the circuit-card level, is prudent even for the most inexpensive of space missions. Do not underestimate the impact of the radiation environment. Part response due to single-event effects and total ionizing dose is not always predictable (see Sec. 7.3 for more details). NASA's Electronic Parts and Packaging Program provides information on electronic parts on their website, including the Instructions for EEE Parts Selection, Screening, Qualification, and Derating (EEE-INST-002). Although these instructions are intended to provide direction to NASA developers, they provide good general information about a variety of parts and part qualities. See Sec. 24.1.3 for more information on parts.

Mission Assurance

Mission assurance, which includes *quality assurance*, refers to the discipline that monitors the spacecraft build and ensures that the builders follow proper processes and procedures. The mission assurance team reviews the plans for the assembly during the design phase. During build, they review and approve procedures, monitor the execution of those procedures, and inspect the flight hardware after build steps. Quality assurance typically refers to the monitoring and inspections. For any spacecraft development, it is essential that everyone involved with the

Table 14-15. Most Common Cleanroom Classes.

ISO 14644 Designation	FED-STD-209 Designation	Typical Practices
Class 6	*Class 1000*	Full-cover garments with clear plastic face masks; clean garments for each use; daily surface cleaning; precision cleaning of new items; items carefully restricted
Class 7	*Class 10,000*	Full-cover garments with cloth face masks; weekly cleaning of garments; weekly cleaning of surfaces; precision cleaning of new items; items restricted
Class 8	*Class 100,000*	Smocks, shoe covers, gloves and hair nets; regular cleaning of surfaces; wipe-down cleaning of new items; some items restricted

system pay attention to quality (since a single failure can take down a mission), but mission assurance provides that extra set of eyes to help spot those unavoidable human errors that are bound to happen. It is important to get the mission assurance team on board early in the development, to work with the builders so that everyone has the same expectations for later processes and procedures.

Safety

Spacecraft and especially launch vehicles store large amounts of energy. It is essential that the spacecraft designer consider what might happen to that energy if something goes wrong. The spacecraft manufacturer, the customer, and the launch site range will all have safety requirements that will impact the spacecraft design and handling. Table 14-16 shows some examples of the common safety considerations.

The propulsion hazard is pretty obvious. Once a spacecraft is fueled, the flammable and toxic fuel is generally under pressure. The tanks and lines are critical safety items. Any heaters on the system must be monitored to prevent a runaway heater from building pressure to the burst point or damaging insulation on wires. (The Apollo 13 mishap was caused by a runaway heater which melted insulation during ground testing. During flight, the exposed wiring caused a spark which started a fire, which heated the oxygen tank until it exploded, taking out the redundant oxygen tank.) The general strategy for safety of people is to ensure that no two failures or individual operations will cause a hazardous event. So the propulsion system generally has three valves in series, and any electrical operations require three switches in series, with each switch separately controlled. This strategy, with three *inhibits* (independent features that stop an event), is known as *two-fault tolerant.*

Batteries store a large amount of energy in a small volume. Overcharging can cause an explosion. A rapid discharge can lead to overheating and a fire or explosion. Batteries are generally designed to prevent some hazards, such as thermal switches in each cell to prevent thermal runaway. Other hazards must be controlled through procedures and protective circuits on the spacecraft. Frequently, the voltage of each individual cell must be monitored during charging or discharging before launch. The wiring for this monitoring must be within the spacecraft's mass budget, even if the monitoring circuits stay on the ground.

Deployables, such as fold-up solar arrays, generally use some electrically-activated device to release. That device may be hazardous in itself, like an EED, which uses a small explosive charge to cut a cable or bolt, or it may simply release the energy needed to unfold the deployable. Either way, three inhibits are needed to prevent electrical actuation. Transmitters on the spacecraft may also require three inhibits if the signal levels exceed the levels to which the launch vehicle has been designed. Cryogenic solids and liquids also require special care, since the simple warming of the system will result in an explosive buildup of pressure if it is not allowed to vent.

Table 14-16. Safety Impacts on Spacecraft Design.

Component	Hazard	Design impact
Propulsion System	Fire, explosion, toxic gas	Pressure vessel design guidelines, extra valves, extra electrical switches
Battery	Fire, explosion, toxic materials	Battery design rules, charging restrictions, cell monitoring
Deployables	Impact with personnel, interference with launch vehicle operation	Extra electrical switches
Transmitters	Interference with launch vehicle operation	Extra electrical switches
Cryogenics	Explosion	Relief valves, burst disks

14.5 Creating Preliminary Spacecraft Budgets

After determining what subsystems are appropriate for the particular design, the next step is the allocation of resources and requirements to those subsystems. In other words, we must decide exactly what we expect each subsystem to do (the requirements), and we must decide how much of the spacecraft resources will be necessary to do that job. Obviously, this will be an iterative process. We start off knowing pretty well the subsystem driving requirements, and we discussed those requirements in the previous section, but our initial estimates of the resources to achieve those requirements is merely an educated guess based on experience. But we need to give our subsystem designers a starting point, so we make those guesses.

The fundamental resource of a spacecraft is mass. Because of the high cost of launch vehicles and the step function in cost when you outgrow a vehicle, the system design must stay within established mass limits. Power becomes another limited resource once you choose the solar array size—a choice that must generally occur early in the development. The long, multi-step assembly process for an array, combined with the array's impact on the attitude control and thermal systems will drive you to decide early the array configuration and size (see Sec. 14.3.3). Table 14-17 lists technical resource budgets that are typically tracked by spacecraft systems engineers. You may not need to track all of them for your system, and some of them may be tracked at the subsystem level, but it is a good idea to think through your resources early and decide what is important. The subsections below will walk you through some of the key budgets.

In order to ensure that the system stays within the mass capability of the launch vehicle, we set aside *margin*, which is extra mass that is not assigned to any particular subsystem. We also carry margin for all the other spacecraft resources, like power, signal levels on the radio link, fuel, processor utilization, and memory. One of the biggest challenges for a spacecraft systems engineer is properly managing margin. If you hold too much margin, the subsystem designs become overly constrained and the cost of the system rises, or you lose out on capability you could have had in your system. If you hold too little margin, you will find yourself with an assembled spacecraft that doesn't work—it is too heavy for the launch vehicle, its solar arrays don't generate enough power to support its function, there is insufficient fuel, or some other such crisis. The consequence of exceeding capability is severe—you don't want to get to the end and have something that doesn't work. Margin covers the uncertainty of the design, so you can reduce it as the design matures.

Figure 14-8 shows the typical management of margin for resources like mass and power. We allocate to a subsystem a mass total that includes the *current best estimate* and a *contingency* related to the maturity of the subsystem design. We want every subsystem designer to be able to meet their requirements within the total we have allocated, but we also want that designer to have some flexibility in the exact implementation. The contingency gives them the room to adjust, without impacting the rest of the system. On top of the allocation, we, as systems designers, carry additional *system margin* to handle unforeseen situations. Perhaps we need to add another function to our design after exploring the details—for instance, on LRO we added an extra box late in the design phase to provide launch-pad lightning suppression. Or perhaps a subsystem cannot achieve their requirements within the resource allocations. Or perhaps a design error requires compensation elsewhere in the system. The WISE mission added a load-isolation system to compensate for an undersized support within an already-built instrument. These sorts of problems are part of the normal design process, so we carry system margin to handle them. Our *total resource margin* is the sum of the contingencies for each subsystem plus the system margin. A *lien* is a potential impact to the system margin. We carry a lien when there is a significant risk that a subsystem will exceed an allocation (see Sec. 24.2 for more on risk management). The lien is still system margin, but it is margin that is only available for solving a specific problem. If we later retire the risk without it becoming a problem, we can release the lien back into the general pool of system margin.

Table 14-17. Typical Budgets Tracked by the Spacecraft Systems Engineer.

Parameter	Reference
Mass	Sec. 14.5.1
Power	Sec. 14.5.3
Pointing and Alignment	Sec. 14.5.4
Propellant or Delta V	Secs.14.5.2, 10.3
TT&C Link	Sec. 21.1.4
Data System	Secs. 14.5.5, 20.1, 20.2, 28.2
• ***CPU utilization***	
• ***Non-volatile memory***	
• ***Volatile processor memory***	
• ***Processor data bus utilization***	
• ***Peripheral data bus (i.e., 1553)***	
• ***Timing***	
• ***Data latency***	
• ***Operational availability***	

A final note on margin: it is appropriate to launch with performance margin. Cutting the design to the edge may seem the most efficient, but some events are **unforeseeable**. Having extra processor capability at launch will allow you to add additional processing after launch. To do that, you will need more memory for code space. Extra power can solve mistakes in the thermal design that you couldn't properly test on the ground, or it can allow you to run the transmitter longer to downlink more data or compensate for a failed high-gain antenna. Fuel

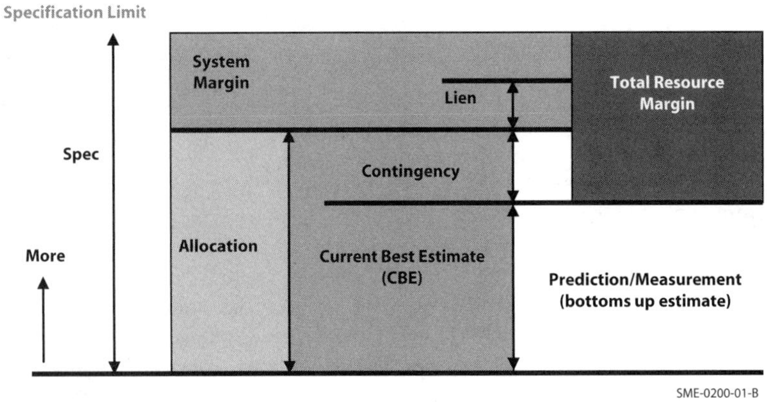

Fig. 14-8. Graphical Presentation of Margin.

margin will give you options to salvage a mission after a failed maneuver. Spacecraft are generally irretrievable for repair, so margin is your insurance. The systems engineer's biggest hope on launch day is that there is enough margin to cover the things we have forgotten. Buy your insurance wisely, though. The best margin can be consumed to increase return from your system if everything goes well. Extra fuel will extend the life of a spacecraft that requires orbit maintenance. Extra power can be used to boost communications bandwidth beyond requirements early in the mission or run extra instruments, with the system dropping back to required performance as the arrays degrade toward the end of life.

14.5.1 Mass

Appendix A and Table 14-18 will help you make a first cut at a mass budget. Start with your target launch mass, then subtract your propellant mass (see Sec. 14.5.2). Using App. A and Chaps. 15–17, determine a reasonable allocation for the payload. Remember that this allocation includes contingency above your current best estimate. For a new payload design, this contingency should be on the order of 30% of the CBE (see Sec. 14.6). Then set aside system margin. A good starting point is 25% of the remaining mass, based on historical trends. Use App. A and Table 14-18 and some judgment about subsystem complexity to take a first stab at the target CBE's for the subsystems. For some applications, this cut may be enough. The next iteration of mass requires quite a bit more work, with the details of Chaps. 18–22 getting you a better estimate of the mass for each subsystem. With those better estimates in hand, take a look at your total mass margin, including the payload contingency, and decide whether your initial cut at payload mass allocation was good. Adjust as appropriate, take some of your system margin and allocate it as contingency, and document your allocations. If you run into trouble with this iterative process, go back and revisit your starting assumptions. Perhaps your target mass is too low. The SCS example in Sec. 14.7.1 will walk you through this process.

Table 14-18. Average Mass by Subsystem as a Percentage of Dry Mass for 4 Types of Spacecraft. Types include those with no propulsion, those in Low-Earth Orbit with propulsion, those in high-Earth orbit, and planetary missions. See App. A for more information.

Subsystem (% of Dry Mass)	No Prop	LEO with Prop	High Earth	Planetary
Payload	41%	31%	32%	15%
Structure and Mechanisms	20%	27%	24%	25%
Thermal Control	2%	2%	4%	6%
Power (incl. harness)	19%	21%	17%	21%
TT&C	2%	2%	4%	7%
On-Board Processing	5%	5%	3%	4%
Attitude Determination and Control	8%	6%	6%	6%
Propulsion	0%	3%	7%	13%
Other (balance + launch)	3%	3%	3%	3%
Total	100%	100%	100%	100%
Propellant	0%	27%	72%	110%

14.5.2 Propellant

The propellant budget follows directly from the delta V budget. Sec.14.2.3 shows how you use the rocket Eq. (14-1), to determine mass of the fuel. In reality, there is not a single I_{sp} for all maneuvers. A large orbital maneuver may use a more efficient engine than smaller housekeeping maneuvers. You need to itemize each of the maneuvers, keeping track of the fuel mass used and the remaining mass of the system after each. That remaining mass is then used with the next maneuver's delta V and I_{sp} to calculate the fuel use.

Table 14-19 shows the Lunar Reconnaissance Orbiter fuel budget at launch. The total launch mass is the system dry mass (1,017.7 kg) plus: *residuals* (5.2 kg), which is fuel that cannot be expelled from the system; the *pressurant* (3.2 kg), which is a gas used to pressurize the system (helium in this case); and usable propellant (889.2 kg). The table itemizes specific uses for the fuel: the mid-course correction (MCC), thruster checks, lunar-orbit insertion (LOI), mission orbit insertion (MOI), regular station keeping, momentum unloading, extended mission, and additional margin. The critical MCC and LOI-1 burns were preceded by engineering burns to confirm the performance of the attitude control system during thruster maneuvers. The MCC burns were done in a *blow-down* configuration, without the pressurant valve open, resulting in a lower I_{sp} than later maneuvers. All other maneuvers were done in a *regulated* configuration, with the pressurant flowing through a regulator and providing constant pressure to the fuel. The LOI-1 maneuver used large thrusters with higher efficiency, while all other maneuvers used smaller thrusters for more accuracy. The station keeping maneuvers have a somewhat lower efficiency than MOI-1 to account for the fact that short maneuvers don't give the thrusters enough time to get to full efficiency. Finally, there is a fuel mass associated with delta H, which are momentum dumping maneuvers. LRO had a requirement to carry fuel for an extended mission. The final, as-built system came in a bit under the target mass, which translated to additional margin.

Built into this budget are some conservative assumptions about the delta V required and the I_{sp} performance—we used the worst-case predictions, but our actual performance ended up somewhat better. It is important for the systems engineer to be aware of this hidden margin so that we don't add margin on top of the margin.

14.5.3 Power

The initial estimate for the solar array size should be based on an estimate of the power consumed by the spacecraft. Just like with mass, you should itemize the subsystems and eventually the individual components in a subsystem and add up the total power. Table 14-20 provides some general guidance on power consumption based on type of spacecraft, based on historical data. Some rules of thumb on power consumption:

- The faster a data system operates, the more power it will consume. The digital logic circuits that run our flight computers consume drastically more power when they are switching than when they are at a steady state. So faster processors consume more power.

Live Calc

Table 14-19. LRO Fuel Budget at Launch. (Courtesy of Charles Zakrzwski)

Total Launch Mass (kg)	1915.27					
Maneuvers	**Delta V (m/s)**	**Effective I_{SP} (s)**	**Total Propellant Used for Maneuver (kg)**	**Delta H Propellant (kg)**	**Total Propellant Used (kg)**	**S/C Mass at End of Burn (kg)**
MCC Eng	2	202	1.93	0	1.93	1,913
MCC Burn(s)	28	202	26.85	0	26.85	1,886
Thruster Check Out				0	0.23	1,886
LOI Eng	8	223.6	6.87	0	6.87	1,879
LOI – 1	583	223.6	438.64	0	438.64	1,441
LOI – 2-5	362	220	222.48	0	222.48	1,218
MOI – 1	48	220	26.80	0	26.80	1,191
MOI – Others	8	217	4.47	0	4.47	1,187
Station Keeping	162	217	86.98	0	86.98	1,100
Momentum Unloading		N/A		17	17.00	1,083
Extended Mission	69	217	34.54		34.54	1,048
Additional Margin	46	217	22.41	0	22.41	1,026
Totals	1316				889.20	

Table 14-19, Fig. 14-8◀, Eq. 14-4◀

Table 14-20. Average Power by Subsystem for 4 Types of Spacecraft. Types include those with no propulsion, those in Low-Earth Orbit with propulsion, those in high-Earth orbit, and planetary missions. See App. A for more information.

Subsystem (% of Total Power)	No Prop	LEO Prop	High Earth	Planetary
Payload	43%	46%	35%	22%
Structure and Mechanisms	0%	1%	0%	1%
Thermal Control	5%	10%	14%	15%
Power (incl. harness)	10%	9%	7%	10%
TT&C	11%	12%	16%	18%
On-board Processing	13%	12%	10%	11%
Attitude Determination and Control	18%	10%	16%	12%
Propulsion	0%	0%	2%	11%
Average Power (W)	299	794	691	749

- Communications systems trade power for antenna size. This is an important system-level trade. You may be trading a smaller antenna for a larger solar array.
- You will generally need more heater power if the spacecraft environment has large variations. There are ways around this problem, but generally you will need radiator area for the hot case and you will need heater power to make up for the heat lost by the radiator area during the cold case. Extra heater power available makes the thermal design easier.
- Power consumption estimates tend to peak around the time of Preliminary Design Review. The major uncertainty at this point is heater power consumption. Estimates for other components are generally pretty good by this point.

After you have determined the spacecraft power consumption, you need to size the solar array as described in Sec. 21.2.2. The solar array size will impact the attitude control system (primarily the system moment of inertia) and the structural design.

You need to think a bit about the safe mode power configuration. You want the spacecraft to consume as little power as possible in safe mode, so you can give the control system time to acquire the Sun on the solar array before depleting the battery. One of the power budgets to track will be the safe mode power consumption. Depending on your design, you may have several other driving cases, where you will have to track the power consumption for each of those modes.

14.5.4 Pointing and Alignment

The pointing and alignment budget encompasses not only the attitude control system pointing budget, but also structural effects on pointing. For payloads that demand accurate pointing, you will need to account for the alignment errors such as:

- Internal alignments within the payload
- The alignment of the payload to the structure
- The alignment of the attitude control sensors to the structure
- The movement of the sensors and payload with respect to each other due to temperature changes, one-time changes from the launch environment, and changes due to the structure no longer experiencing its own weight (also known as *1 g release*).

For the highest accuracy pointing, you should locate attitude sensors on the same structural support as the payload. On LRO, our instrument module supported the three instruments with tight pointing requirements along with our two star trackers. We made this module with graphite-composite facesheets to minimize changes due to thermal expansion, since graphite-composite has a much lower coefficient of thermal expansion than aluminum.

In addition to alignments, actuator performance will also affect pointing. Reaction wheels will provide continuously variable torque for smooth control, but imbalances in the wheels can create jitter. Thrusters and torque bars generally provide on-off, or *bang-bang*, control, so your pointing budget will need to account for a *dead-band*—angles over which the control system will allow an error before activating the actuator. You can improve pointing performance with control algorithms which include filtering, such as a Kalman filter. You can also include structural filtering within the algorithm to reduce interaction with flexible modes.

Since the errors associated with pointing and alignment are generally random and uncorrelated, we can combine terms as a root-sum-square rather than as an arithmetic sum. For high-performance pointing, you should plan to perform a *structural-thermal-optical performance* (*STOP*) analysis around the time of the preliminary design review, with updates as you finalize the design. A STOP analysis

Table 14-21. System-Level LRO Pointing Budget for Narrow Angle Camera. Each axis is allocated separately. The Attitude Determination and Control (ADC) errors are allocated to the knowledge (based on the sensors' performance and their alignment) and control (based on the algorithm and wheel performance). The jitter of solar array motion causes high-frequency errors that cannot be corrected. The thermal distortion is movement of the star trackers due to changing structural dimensions over temperature. The static bias accounts for errors that are fixed over time. The three separate items of static bias are uncorrelated, so they can be combined as a root sum of the squares. The budget also accounts for errors within the instrument itself.

		Arc-Sec		
		Rx	Ry	Rz
ADC	ADC Knowledge	30	30	30
	ADC Controller	15	15	15
Jitter	Jitter	30	30	30
Thermal	Thermal Distortion	60	60	60
Static Bias Contributors	1-g Release	75	75	75
	Launch Shift	20	20	20
	Ground Alignment Accuracy	300	300	300
Static Bias RSS		310	310	310
Instrument		21	21	21
	Total	**466**	**466**	**466**
	Requirement	**516**	**516**	**516**
	Unallocated Margin	**50**	**50**	**50**

uses a structural model along with temperature predictions to determine how much optical alignments will change during the course of mission operations. This analysis will highlight changes that might be necessary to meet pointing requirements. On LRO after performing the STOP analysis, we added flexures under the star tracker mount to prevent tracker alignment shifts caused by the mismatch between the tracker's aluminum base and the graphite-composite instrument module. Table 14-21 is an example pointing budget.

14.5.5 Data System

The data system includes several different budgets which are tracked by various engineers on the team. The interaction among processing capability, on-board data links, data storage, data latency, downlink data rate, RF link budgets, contact time, and ground station availability affects the overall architecture of the system. For the conceptual design of a spacecraft, you need to look for key drivers: is the collection rate high? Are there limited contact opportunities? Does the on-board data require a lot of processing before downlink? Based on your Concept of Operations (see Sec. 4.3), you will have a target number of passes and a duration for those passes. Taking the total data collected, divided by the contact time, you get your required downlink data rate. From there, use Sec. 21.1.4 to calculate your RF link budget. System-level considerations related to RF link budgets can be found in Sec. 14.4.5. You will size your data storage based on your data collection rate and the maximum time between passes. As your design matures, you will need to account not only for data collected by the payload, but also for system performance data that is generated by each component, called *housekeeping data.*

Table 14-22. LRO Data Volume Budget. LRO used a file system to collect data. The total files per day was used to determine ground handling overhead associated with number of files.

Type	Data per Orbit (Mbits)	Data per Day (Gbits)	Files per Orbit	File per Day
CRaTER Instrument	610.20	7.78	2.00	25.49
Diviner Instrument	180.52	2.30	22.60	288.00
LAMP Instrument	168.22	2.14	2.00	25.49
LEND Instrument	20.52	0.26	2.00	25.49
LOLA Instrument	225.96	2.88	2.00	25.49
LROC Instrument	34,659.16	441.67	28.00	356.81
Spacecraft Housekeeping	1,242.30	15.83	2.00	25.49
Total (Gbits):	37.11	472.87	61	772

Table 14-22 and Table 14-23 provide examples from LRO. We allocated to each instrument a certain amount of data collection per orbit based on the operations concept for that instrument. That allocation set the total data volume per day. Then we sized the recorder based on how much of that data would accumulate before we could start downlinking. LRO downlinked science data from the Moon to a single ground station, so transmission only occurred when the Moon was visible and high enough in the sky at that ground station. Gaps between transmissions could be as much as 1,101 minutes (18.35 hours) when we accounted for a possible missed contact. The 412 Gbit recorder was sized to store the mission data over this period with margin. LRO's 100 Mbps downlink data rate enabled the transfer of all of this data within two 45-minute contacts (see Sec. 28.3 for more information on recorder sizing).

Table 14-23. LRO Recorder Usage Budget. The recorder was divided into partitions for ease of data management. The data collection was dominated by the LRO Camera (LROC) images. The current storage is based on the orbit data collection rate from Table 14-22 times the orbits between supports.

Max Time Between Supports:	1,101	Minutes	
Max Orbits Between Supports:	9.74		
Recorder Size:	412	Gbits	
	Partition 1 LROC	**Partition 2 Other Science**	**Partition 3 Spacecraft House-keeping**
Partition Size (Gbits):	376.32	14.00	22.00
Current Storage CBE (Gbits):	337.70	11.74	12.10
Remaining Space (Gbits):	38.62	2.26	9.90
Remaining Margin (%):	10.26%	16.11%	44.98%
Partition Usage (%):	89.74%	83.89%	55.02%
Additional Images/Orbits:	30.57	1.87	7.97

14.6 Design Evolution

This section describes how some real spacecraft evolved from the initial concept to the final product. The intent of the section is to provide some real-life lessons about where the design can go wrong. Each new design is unique, and it is impossible to forecast what problems will occur along the way, but you can be sure that there will be problems! Go into the design looking for places where problems can be mission ending. Be prepared for the unexpected. Tackle problems, or potential problems, as soon as you spot them. With all of that effort, and a little luck, you may have enough margin to overcome anything you have missed.

Figure 14-9 shows the growth in payload mass for 9 different NASA missions. Except for two outliers, all of the mass growth is between 20% and 37% of the value at the System Requirements Review. All of these payloads were based on some previous designs, but various mission-unique challenges led to similar growth. Despite this pattern in the payloads, Fig. 14-10 shows drastically different growths in the total system dry mass. It seems that the dry mass growth tends to be driven more by the available margin (see Fig. 14-11)—spacecraft designers will tend to expend mass margin to solve problems. On missions that had tight mass margin, like WIRE, the designers limited mass growth or even reduced mass in the system. On missions with large margin, the designers consumed much of the margin. Also notice in these graphs that the increase after the Critical Design Review (CDR) is limited to the 10–15% range, and even WIRE, which decreased after the Preliminary Design Review (PDR), still grew after CDR. (Milestones such as PDR and CDR are described in Sec. 3.4.2.)

Figure 14-12 shows the power trend for the payloads of 6 of the above missions (data from the other 3 missions was not readily available). Power does not show the same trend as mass. In fact, power frequently trends downward, especially after CDR. Fig. 14-13 and Fig. 14-14 shows a similar pattern for the overall power of the spacecraft. One of the main factors affecting the final drop in power consumption is the final update of the thermal model after vacuum testing. Spacecraft builders can frequently adjust blankets on radiators, based on actual performance, and reduce the overall heater power consumption. Margins also tend to trend upward at the end, with the solar array performance coming in a bit better than specification and the overall system power consumption dropping a bit. Because the solar array size must be fixed early in the process, it is important to be conservative with power estimates. As a spacecraft designer, you can keep this trend in mind, designing your mission to be able to take advantage of extra power margin to enhance performance—perhaps with more transmitter time or more payload operation. But don't cut the margin too tightly, or you will have no room to fix any late problems with the thermal design (larger radiators means more heater power) or other subsystem.

14.6.1 LRO

Launched on June 18, 2009, the Lunar Reconnaissance Orbiter (LRO), shown in Figs. 14-15 and 14-16, provided detailed mapping of the Moon, particularly in the polar regions. Because of the need to capture into and maintain a low (50 km), polar, lunar orbit, this 1916 kg spacecraft was almost half fuel. The conceptual design placed the system on a Delta II launch vehicle, with a spinning upper stage. A Presidential mandate tightly constrained the development schedule for LRO. The spacecraft preliminary design to support the 7 payloads included a custom fuel tank to carry the mono-propellant hydrazine. As the preliminary design review approached, the propulsion lead realized that the spinning upper stage of the Delta II would cause motion in the fuel that would interact with the Delta's guidance system. He could not guarantee that we would be able to achieve the nutation time constant that the launch vehicle required. Rather than continue with a design that might not work, the systems team considered other architectures, including a solid rocket motor kick stage for lunar orbit insertion (see Sec. 14.3.2). In the end, the customer decided to switch

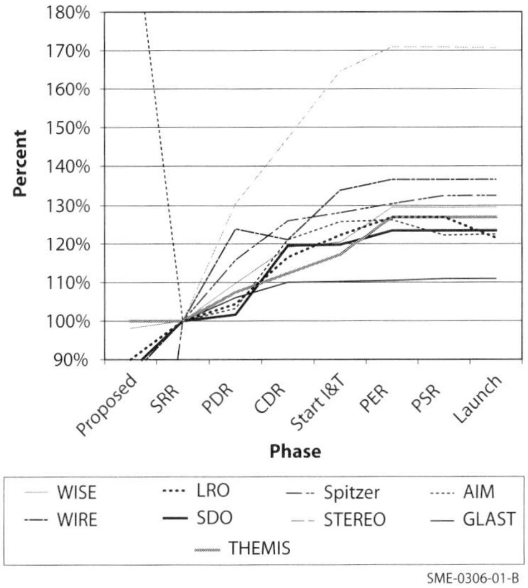

Fig. 14-9. Growth of Payload Mass for Various Spacecraft.

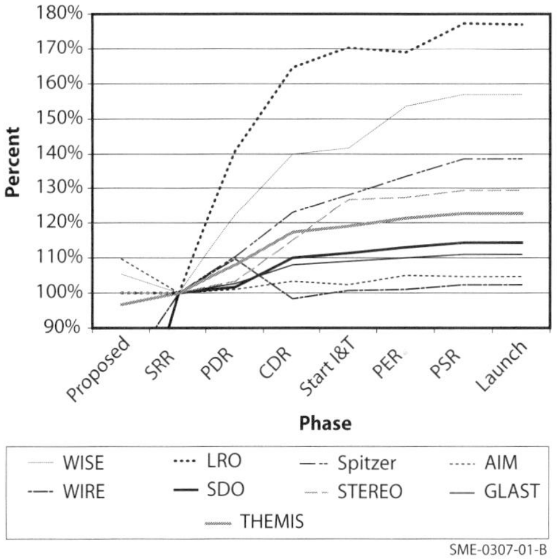

Fig. 14-10. Growth of System Mass for Various Spacecraft.

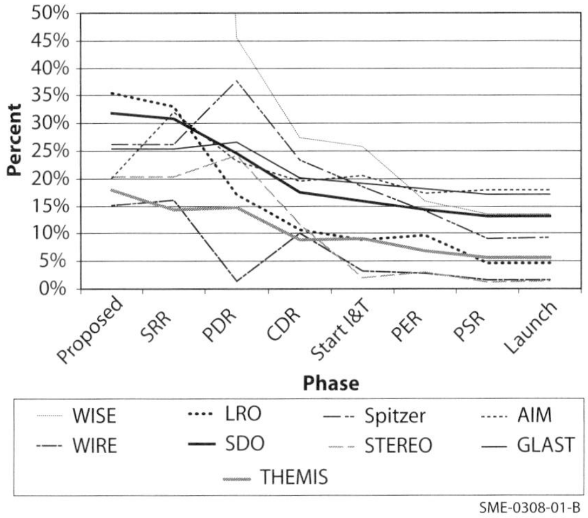

Fig. 14-11. Dry Mass Margin Depletion for Various Spacecraft.

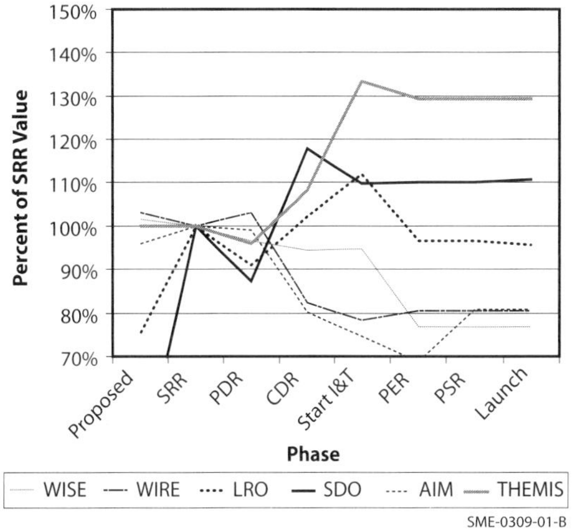

Fig. 14-12. Growth of Payload for Various Spacecraft.

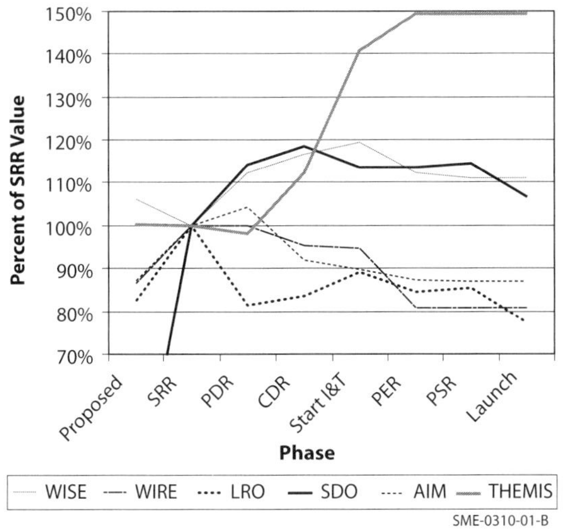

Fig. 14-13. Growth of System Power for Various Spacecraft.

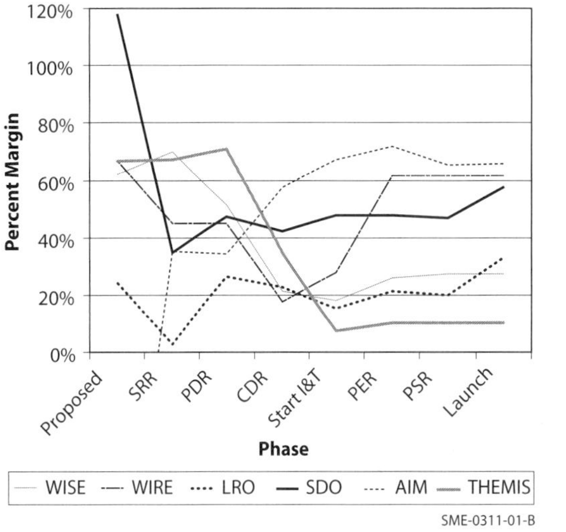

Fig. 14-14. Power Margin Depletion for Various Spacecraft.

Fig. 14-15. Lunar Reconnaissance Orbiter Showing Solar Array, High-gain Antenna, and Thermal Radiator. (Photo courtesy of NASA GSFC)

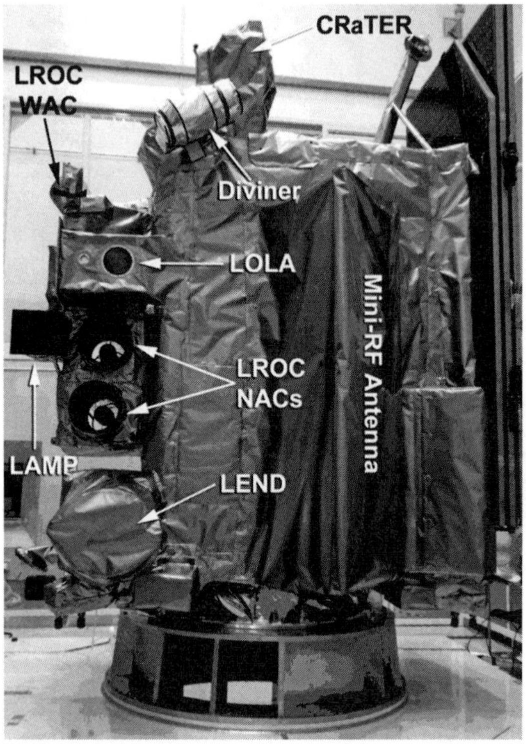

Fig. 14-16. Lunar Reconnaissance Orbiter with Instruments Labeled. (Photo courtesy of NASA GSFC)

LRO to a different launch vehicle. The non-spinning upper stage of the Atlas V eliminated issues related to nutation time constants, and the extra mass capability allowed the customer to fly an extra payload. The extra mass capability also allowed the LRO team to use existing fuel tanks instead of designing a new tank, reducing the risk of not meeting schedule. This change is the major reason for the increase in Fig. 14-9 between SRR and CDR.

The new vehicle and new tanks required the team to redesign the structure and, with it, the thermal system. Flying at 50 km above the Moon's surface presents a difficult thermal environment (see Sec. 14.2.4). When the Sun is in the plane of the orbit, the spacecraft travels from solar noon to midnight in less than an hour. At solar noon, the Moon's surface temperature is around 140 C. At midnight, it is –140 C. The Moon takes up half the sky as seen by the spacecraft, so the heat load goes from about 1300 W/m^2 of infrared energy from the Moon and 1300 W/m^2 from the Sun to almost zero from each in less than an hour. The thermal engineer had to couple the mass of the system together thermally, so that the electronics would not experience wild swings in temperature. All of the avionics were placed on a single panel, with heat pipes conducting all of the heat out to a zenith-facing radiator. This arrangement had the added benefit of allowing table-top integration of the avionics on the isothermal panel.

The mechanical team worked with the integration lead and other engineers to design a structure that enabled parallel processing (see Fig. 14-17). The propulsion team began assembly of the propulsion module almost a year before it was integrated with the rest of the system. At one point during integration, blanket technicians completed work on the propulsion module in one clean room while technicians installed heaters on the instrument module and the avionics were electrically tested in another clean room. Without these parallel operations, the LRO development would have taken at least another 4 to 6 months.

The launch vehicle change put the mechanical and thermal teams behind, and it delayed the PDR by 3 months. But the team continued to press forward to a Critical Design Review (CDR) just 10 months after PDR, by which time the mechanical and thermal teams had caught up. After CDR should theoretically be a calm time for the systems engineer—the design is complete and the vendors are all building the components to specification. In reality, this is the time when the real problems start to occur. As lead systems engineer, I was involved with the resolution of over 50 problems during this period—problems such as failed parts or components not meeting specification. In some cases, the team worked with NASA experts on parts or other specialties, and in some cases, I adjusted requirements across subsystems to maintain system integrity. For example, we changed the idle pattern in the ground system because the transponder sometimes did not lock properly to the baseline pattern. The transponder vendor was able to isolate the problem to a software design flaw, and he could

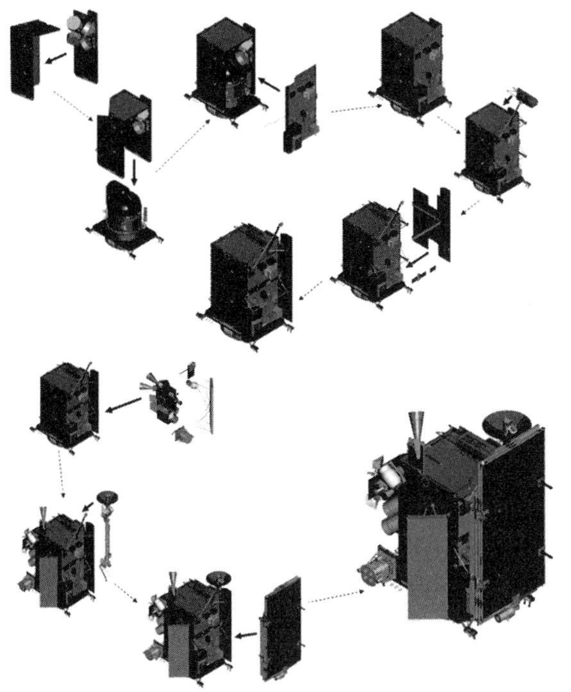

Fig. 14-17. LRO Modular Assembly.

prove that only our baseline pattern was a problem, so we changed the baseline rather than updating the transponder software.

Because of the interface tests we conducted during development, the team encountered very few issues during system integration. At our Pre-Environmental Review (PER), a member of the review team identified that we had missed running a test during the thermal vacuum testing of the solar array gimbal—we had not sent full solar array power through the system. We redesigned our system-level test to include this power-flow path. Within hours of the start of system-level thermal balance, we discovered a serious error in the gimbal thermal design—we were off by a factor of 14 in our estimate of power dissipation. The team came up with a simple design for an extended radiator and opened up some blankets, alleviating most of the problem. Had we not conducted this test, the spacecraft would have been seriously crippled in flight by overheating solar array gimbals. We encountered several other relatively minor problems during thermal vacuum as well as one major issue with an instrument. We were able to correct the problem with the instrument on the flight spare unit, and we installed the spare just before going to the launch site.

The mass chart (Fig. 14-9) shows how the mass settled out pretty well at CDR, except for the final 5% bump during assembly. Despite efforts to account for everything added to LRO, the final sum of components is still about 40 kg less than the actual measured mass. This extra mass is probably due to extra blanketing, tape, harnessing, harness shielding, brackets, and other such items. The lesson is clear—some bump up in mass after CDR is inevitable, despite our best efforts—there are always things we don't think of. Power consumption, on the other hand, dropped. The actual measured power of each component generally came in under specification. The thermal team, using actual power dissipation numbers, could reduce the size of the radiator, which reduced the heater loads under all conditions.

The mandated schedule was a driving factor throughout the spacecraft development. The team needed to make decisions quickly, always based on engineering judgment and experience and frequently with little analysis, and then we moved forward with the design. We had to decide what shortcuts to take to speed the development. But throughout the process, we were very aware of the possibility that a mistake could lead to mission failure. We fostered an environment where engineers were comfortable raising concerns with the project, and we explored those concerns. We cut corners and took risks, if the problems would manifest before launch. We relied on a solid test program to wring out any errors we may have made along the way. The lesson here actually came to the team in the form of a fortune cookie, "People forget how fast you did a job—but they remember how well you did it."

LRO achieved lunar orbit on June 23, 2009. All systems operated as planned (high praise for a spacecraft!), except for the laser altimeter, which experienced some mis-alignment when targeting the cold surfaces of the Moon. We eventually attributed this mis-alignment to a blanket that was a bit too tight, shrinking when cold and pulling on the instrument structure. This problem reduced some data from the instrument, but overall we were able to meet payload and mission objectives. We finished commissioning in mid-September 2009. As of this writing, LRO continues to operate successfully in lunar orbit, producing detailed images like Fig. 14-18 with enough resolution to spot trails left behind by the Apollo astronauts.

14.6.2 WISE

The Wide-field Infrared Survey Explorer (WISE), launched December 14, 2009, and shown in Fig. 14-19, used frozen hydrogen to cool infrared detectors so that it could produce an all-sky survey at 23, 12, 4.6, and 3.6 μm greater than 500 times more sensitive than IRAS. This mission built on the instrument developed for WIRE (see Sec. 14.6.3). It was competitively selected into the Explorer program in 2003, which limits the total mission cost. The target launch vehicle was initially a Taurus 2210. By the time of the System Requirements Review in December 2004, NASA was considering a dual manifest on the Delta II, but did not decide until March 2005. WISE became a sole payload on the Delta II when its co-manifested payload was cancelled.

The budget environment at NASA during the WISE development restricted the funds available, so the project delayed some parts of the build, such as the spacecraft bus. These delays are not unusual with NASA missions

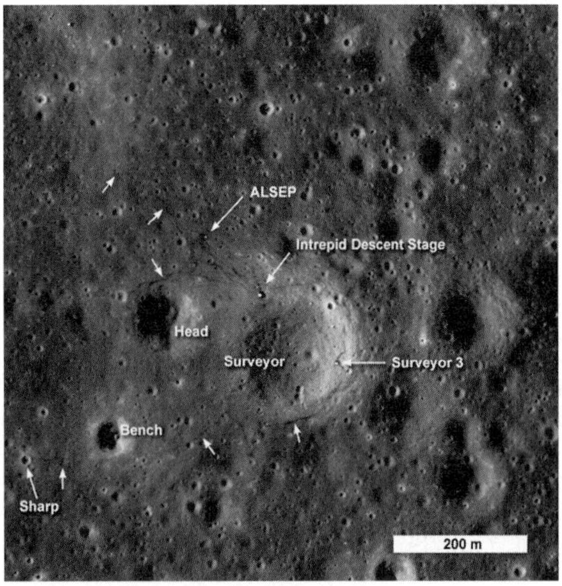

Fig. 14-18. Apollo 12 Landing Site as Seen by LRO. (Photo courtesy of NASA GSFC and ASU)

because of the political nature of the funding, but the project management was able to successfully schedule work to stay within each year's available funding and launch within a year and a half of the originally-targeted date. These types of constraints can be frustrating to spacecraft designers, but it is part of the business. As a designer, you must be aware of your constraints, and you must be flexible to handle delays. For instance, if you design for a low orbit, taking advantage of the smaller atmosphere at solar minimum (see Sec. 9.4.4), you may have a broken design if the launch is delayed.

The biggest challenge for WISE came when an instrument engineering unit failed during mechanical testing. The team discovered a mistake in the design of the structure that supported the telescope inside the *cryostat*. (The cryostat is an insulated container that stores the frozen hydrogen and uses it to cool the telescope and detectors below 20 K.) By this time, the cryostat assembly had already begun, and it was going to be a significant cost and schedule impact to replace the structure. The team considered a number of options, finally selecting incorporation of a *load-isolation system* into the design. A load isolation system functions like the suspension system in a car, reducing the higher frequency loads from the launch vehicle—smoothing the bumps in the road with springs and dampers. This load isolation system was able to reduce the dynamic environment enough to keep the cryostat support structure within the limits it could support. The extra mass margin of the Delta II enabled this decision.

The other major challenge to WISE was detector performance. The long-wavelength detectors did not have quite the sensitivity originally expected. The team tracked this performance measure throughout development, and concentrated extra effort on the detectors and the optical elements in the path when the potential problem was spotted. This effort did improve the situation, but in the end, the performance did not quite meet the original requirements. Upon consulting with the customer and the science team, everyone agreed that the mission objectives would still be achieved with slightly less performance at one wavelength, so they changed the requirement. The lesson here is to not be afraid to talk with your customer if your system is having trouble achieving a requirement.

Early images from WISE show excellent performance (see Fig. 14-20). The final all-sky survey is a new standard reference for astronomers. And the mission provided a big advance in asteroid science.

Fig. 14-19. WISE During Final Preparations for Launch. (Photo courtesy of NASA/JPL-Caltech)

14.6.3 WIRE

NASA selected the Wide-Field Infrared Explorer (WIRE) as the fifth Small Explorer mission in 1993. WIRE, shown in Fig. 14-21, used frozen hydrogen to cool infrared detectors to 7.5 K in order to study galaxies with high rates of star formation. The original proposal called for a 25 cm aperture telescope, but this aperture grew during the preliminary design phase to 30 cm. Although this growth greatly increased the science potential of the instrument, it also increased the size and mass of the instrument, but the team appeared to have sufficient mass margin to handle the change. As the detailed design of the system began, the cryostat team

Fig. 14-20. IC342, also Known as the Hidden Galaxy, as Seen by WISE. (Photo courtesy of NASA/JPL-Caltech/UCLA)

realized that they were overly optimistic when scaling the mass from a much larger mission. Even though the mass of the overall structure reduced proportionally, the valves and fittings on the cryostat did not scale with size. With the small WIRE cryostat, the valves and fittings were a significant contributor to the total mass. The other big impact to mass margin at this time was a change in mission orbit. The preliminary designers did not take into consideration the dispersions in launch vehicle performance. The final, solid-rocket stage of the Pegasus vehicle might underperform enough to leave one apse of the orbit 90 km low (see "Achieving Final Orbit" in Sec. 14.3.2 for more information about solid vs. liquid propellant). The original baseline orbit was 400 km, but the mission could not meet its 4-month lifetime with a perigee at 310 km altitude. The orbit baseline was changed to be no lower than 450 km after launch vehicle dispersions, allowing for a launch at solar maximum, but cutting into the mass margin significantly.

WIRE had the advantage of well-established mass for the avionics, since the spacecraft bus was based on the already-built SWAS. The one area where mass could be reduced was the spacecraft structure. The mechanical team decided to use a fully-bonded graphite-composite structure in order to reduce mass. Major brackets, such as those supporting the reaction wheels and star tracker, were built into the structure, further reducing the mass. The mechanical team produced a structure that was only 11% of the total system mass, allowing the system design to absorb more instrument mass growth instead of implementing costly mass reduction of the payload.

The WIRE avionics were built immediately after the avionics for the fourth SMEX mission, Transition Region and Coronal Explorer (TRACE). The WIRE team made deliberate design decisions in the system so that the avionics would remain **identical** to TRACE's avionics. Boxes for one mission were tested back-to-back with the other. Much of the software was identical, except for the attitude control software. Overall, this combined-build strategy reduced the cost of the spacecraft bus for both TRACE and WIRE by about 20% over the originally anticipated cost.

Fig. 14-21. WIRE During Testing. (Photo courtesy of NASA GSFC)

Throughout the entire mission development, the cryostat remained a major concern. There are layers and layers of insulation, there are multiple support structures to produce a thermally-isolated path, there is a labyrinth of plumbing, and the entire structure was bonded together, making rework difficult if not impossible. Besides the normal safety considerations of cryogenics (see "Safety" in Sec. 14.4.9), the cryogen is highly flammable in air. Launching on a Pegasus requires dropping it from an aircraft with people aboard, so the launch system included a safety vent for the cryogen to handle the case of the cryostat suddenly warming. Launch site operations of a cryostat requires around-the-clock monitoring and delicate close-out procedures (no small feat on a runway with 20+ MPH winds blowing, see Fig. 14-22 for a picture of the runway operations).

The WIRE team got everything right, except for one little glitch, lasting about 12 ms. A flaw in the pyro electronics box (a mundane part of the instrument electronics design), resulted in a start-up transient that prematurely released the instrument cover. The heat from the Earth caused cryogen to vent at an abnormally high rate. That venting caused the spacecraft to tumble faster, resulting in more exposure to the heat of the Earth. Within 24 hours, all of the mission cryogen was vented and WIRE was spinning at 60 revolutions per minute. It took us a week to use the magnetic torquers to despin the spacecraft. Although the instrument was useless, we did manage to get a little science out of our star tracker, but the primary mission was a total loss. There are a few lessons from the WIRE failure:

Fig. 14-22. WIRE Servicing While on Pegasus Under Carrier Aircraft. Dewars contain liquid helium. Access to the spacecraft is through a fairing door inside the tent to the left of the dewars. The safety vent is visible running up the side of the aircraft. (Photo courtesy of NASA GSFC)

- The space business is very unforgiving. A single tiny flaw can take down the whole mission, so the team must be constantly vigilant even with the routine parts of the design.
- Peer reviews of detailed designs are critical. Because of a combination of scheduling and poor judgment, no one outside the electronics designer's organization took a detailed look at the pyro electronics box circuit design. The flaw in the design was due to a feature of the programmable logic that was unknown to the designer. An outside reviewer may have caught the problem.
- The systems engineer must always consider the coupling of spacecraft mass loss to attitude control capability. I had considered scenarios with high cryogen vent rates from the perspective of instrument life, and I had considered the torques on the system from nominal vent rates, but I never put the two together. The placement of the hydrogen vent caused torques in the worst-case scenario that were only a factor of 2 greater than the torque authority of the magnetic torquers. Had we considered this, we may have placed the vent closer to the spacecraft center of mass and had enough authority.
- Spacecraft testing needs to continually look for unexpected events. We were continuously monitoring the pyro electronics for spurious signals, but the test equipment was overly sensitive to tiny glitches, and we had no way to capture the waveform of those glitches. When we first integrated the electronics, we connected an oscilloscope to capture the waveforms of the transients, but all we saw were tiny glitches. It turns out that the electronics only put out a large glitch, big enough to fire pyros, when it had been off for over 1.5 hours! We never actually captured a waveform after leaving the box off for a long time. With modern equipment, it should be standard procedure to continuously monitor waveforms, enabling engineers to review the signals after test equipment raises an alarm.
- It is generally a series of events that lead to a spacecraft failure—bad design, mistake during build, inadequate test, and a failure to anticipate something. The industry uses checks and balances along the way to try to catch flaws—design reviews, testing, mission assurance, etc. It is impossible to be perfect, and we cannot afford to be excessively conservative. There are plenty of examples where costs can be reduced, by cutting out some redundancy within the process, but the system designer should only deviate from standard practice with his eyes wide open.

14.7 Examples

14.7.1 SCS Example

Picking up the Supplemental Communications System design from Sec. 5.6, we are targeting 200 kg for each spacecraft, and we are assuming that all three spacecraft are launched on a single rocket, with the rocket taking all three to the 20,500 km altitude. (Note that this assumption implies a 6-hour mission for the launch vehicle—an assumption that should be revisited with a launch-vehicle expert, since this is much longer than a typical mission.) Based on the total delta V budget in Table 10-7, the fuel budget is in Table 14-24. The 2 kg for momentum management is an allocation without much analysis. Use Chap. 19 to estimate the external torques, and determine

Table 14-24. SCS Fuel Budget.

	delta V (m/s)	Effective I_{sp} (s)	Propellant for Maneuver (kg)	S/C Mass after Burn (kg)
1st burn	18	220	1.7	198.3
2nd burn	17	220	1.6	196.8
Rephasing	5	220	0.5	196.3
Momentum Management	0		2.0	194.3
Disposal	20	220	1.8	192.5
Residuals (kg)			0.5	
Total	60		8.0	
Total Launch Mass: 200 kg				

Table 14-24, Fig. 14-22, Eq. 14-4◀

Table 14-25. Driving Requirements for SCS and FireSat II Missions.

Parameter	SCS Value	FireSat II Value
Mass	Maximum of 200 kg	To be determined by first iteration
Power Consumption	To be determined by first iteration	To be determined by first iteration
Cost	Low-cost	Low-cost
Schedule	Not a major driver	Not a major driver
Lifetime	10 yrs	8 years
Reliability	Assume this is not a driver, since it provides supplemental support	Want high reliability, can rely on multiple spacecraft for redundancy
Delta V	60 m/s + ADC	764 m/s
Orbit	21,000 km circular, 0 deg inclination	700 km circular, 55 deg inclination
Payload Accommodation — ***Data Rate, Volume, and Latency*** — ***Pointing Requirements*** — ***Mass, Volume, Fields of View*** — ***Other***	Maximize data rate through payload, which translates to maximizing power. Pointing of 1 degree accuracy to support cross-links. See text for more info.	10 Mbps, 48 × 22 × 18 cm^3, 90 minute latency 0.1 pixel, 3 sigma; pixel is 500 m: 15 arcsec 20 kg, 50 W without contingency 0.65 deg along track, 58 deg cross track Sun avoidance; Sun can dwell no more than 30 seconds within 1 degree of instrument boresight

if this number overly constrains the offset between center of mass and center of solar pressure. The residuals round the total to an even 8 kg.

Since the primary design objective is the maximization of communications bandwidth, we don't know exactly what the size of the payload will be. We know the final mass of the system, and we know the delta V, so we will use the design process to determine the power and mass available for the payload. Going down the list of drivers from Table 14-2 we create Table 14-25.

As you can see, "maximizing bandwidth" doesn't tell us much about the payload until we do some additional work. Chapter 16 explains how to design a communications payload. Since the antenna for our payload must cover 26.8 deg (horizon to horizon), we cannot drastically improve the gain of the payload antenna in order to improve data rate—all we can do is maximize the power available for the payload transmitters. Our first objective is estimation of the power available for the payload, so our payload designer can move forward. Our first cut at this won't be very accurate, so we will need to iterate. We can reduce the power required for cross links by increasing the gain on the cross-link antennas, which requires an increase in pointing accuracy. But these antennas can remain fixed to the spacecraft body, since the relative geometry between spacecraft remains fixed. In order to keep the system within the category of a "coarse" pointer (see Sec. 14.2.5), we will assume a 1 deg accuracy for pointing of the cross-link antennas.

Because this is a small, low-cost, supplemental system, we will assume a single-string system, even though the lifetime is 10 years. For this multi-spacecraft system, it probably makes more sense to carry extra spacecraft in the constellation to provide redundancy, rather than adding extra components to a single spacecraft. We will look for options of graceful degradation as appropriate.

The next step is defining the overall configuration of the spacecraft. We know we need to point one antenna at the Earth and point two cross-link antennas at two other spacecraft, so we must have a 3-axis-stabilized nadir pointing spacecraft, with 3 fixed payload antennas. The spacecraft flies too high for use of a magnetometer for attitude determination, and it will be in eclipse for part of the orbit, so Sun sensors won't always give a solution. The pointing requirement is loose enough to allow the use of a horizon sensor, but a low-cost star tracker could work if the ground regularly sends up orbit ephemeris information. Another possibility is the use of the cross-links themselves to provide pointing feedback to the spacecraft, adjusting the attitude to maximize the signal. This option will need further investigation on a later iteration. We will need some sort of gyro for measuring rate during attitude maneuvers, since star trackers generally cannot perform this function. The gyro-sun sensor combination can provide enough information for safe mode. Assume 4 reaction wheels in order to provide graceful degradation in the event that a wheel is lost during the 10 year lifetime.

We know we need a propulsion system. Based on the delta V, assume a hydrazine system. If we were to use cold gas, the 220 I_{sp} becomes 50 sec, resulting in a fuel mass of 25 kg. The practical considerations of a hydrazine system (see Sec. 18.8), will make its dry mass heavier than cold gas, but probably not 17 kg heavier. The 8 kg in the fuel budget leaves us with 192 kg for the dry mass of the spacecraft, including the payload.

Since the spacecraft operates with a 0 deg inclination, we know that the beta angle of the Sun will vary between 23.5 deg and –23.5 deg over the year. If we only use a single-axis gimbal on our solar array, tracking the pitch-axis motion, then the solar array output may drop as much as cos(23.5 deg) or 92% of its peak. Since the variation is small, a second gimbal on the array is not necessary. In order to minimize the solar pressure disturbance on attitude, we will put a solar array on each side of the spacecraft.

Table 14-26. SCS Initial Mass Estimates. The second column follows directly from Table 14-18 with a dry mass of 192 kg. The target mass is based on engineering judgment as described in the rationale column. Note that the propellant mass for this mission (4%) is a much lower percentage than the high-Earth mission average (72%), justifying a reduction in propulsion system dry mass. This lower percentage also reduced the target for the structure mass, since the structure does not need to support a large propellant load. The low propellant load followed directly from our assumption that the launch vehicle will take the spacecraft to nearly the mission orbit; this is frequently not the case for high Earth missions.

Subsystem	Mass Based on Table 14-18 (kg)	Target Mass (kg)	Rationale
Payload	61	47	Allows 30% growth contingency for new instrument
Structure	46	40	10% contingency, assuming straightforward structure design, 2 kg reduction for light propulsion
Thermal	8	7	15% contingency
Power	33	28	15% contingency
Communications	8	7	10% contingency, available parts
C&DH	6	5	10% contingency, available parts
Attitude Control	12	10	15% contingency to handle uncertainty in strategy
Propulsion Dry Mass	13	9	20% contingency for unique design, reduced by 2 kg because of small propellant load
Other/Margin	5	39	Total margin set at 25%
Total Dry Mass	**192**	**192**	
Propellant	8	8	Fuel budget
Launch Mass	200	200	

We will want the spacecraft to require little interaction with controllers most of the time, but during peak loading, we can expect controllers to be available continuously. Commands to the spacecraft will primarily be occasional configurations of the payload, even during peak loading. Other commands will be necessary to control the thruster firings associated with orbit adjustment and momentum dumping. The spacecraft must only store housekeeping data, since the payload is only acting as a bent pipe.

We will partition the system into the standard set of subsystems, but for a spacecraft this small, we should be able to combine some of the power electronics with the C&DH. Based on Table 14-18 and some guidance from App. A, we will start with estimates associated with a spacecraft in high-Earth orbit and apply some engineering judgment to come up with target masses for each subsystem. These estimates are shown in Table 14-26. The second column shows the mass derived by multiplying the percentages in the high-Earth column of Table 14-18 by the dry mass. We'll use the "other" total as margin. As described in Sec. 14.5.1, we should carry about 25% total mass margin at this point, so we assume some growth contingencies and reduce our target masses accordingly. The spacecraft's communication system is separate from the payload, providing the simple housekeeping and control functions using a single transponder and an omni antenna system.

Focusing on the power system, we need to know the maximum eclipse period. From Table 9-4, we know that we have a 12 hour orbit. Figure 14-23 shows that we have a maximum eclipse of 58 minutes every orbit, and two eclipse seasons of 80 days each per year, giving a total of 320 cycles per year, or 1,600 cycles in 5 years. These eclipses and the system power draw will define the size of the battery. The solar arrays will need to generate about 12/11 of the average usage since they will be in sunlight for only about 11 of the 12 hours. Using Fig. 21-6, the mass of the array will be about 34% of the 28 kg target or 9.5 kg. Using Table 21-15 and the GaAs improved MJ cells, we get 195 W/m^2 EOL and 2.8 kg/m^2, for a power output of 70 W/kg from the array, or about 665 W from the array. At a beta angle of 23.5 deg, we will get 92% of this, or about 612 W. During the maximum eclipse, the Sun angle is minimum, so the average power available is 11/12 of 665 W or about 610 W. Using Table 14-20, the power available for the payload is 35% of the total, or about 214 W. Assuming a 50% depth-of-discharge for the battery, we will need about 1,330 Whr for the hour-long eclipse. Based on

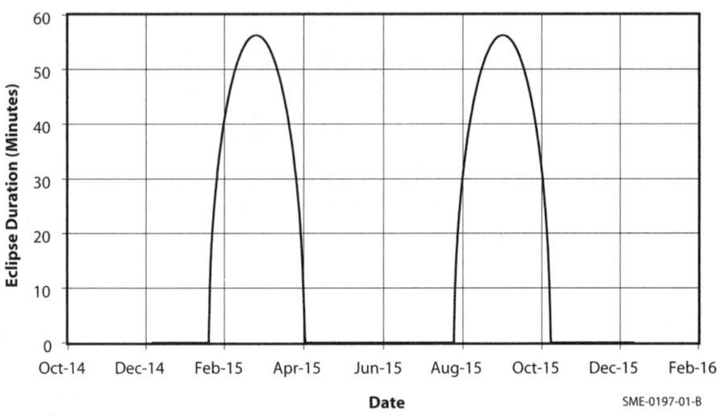

Live Calc **Fig. 14-23. Eclipse Duration vs. Date for SCS Spacecraft Over One Year.**

Table 21-18 with a lithium-ion battery at 125 Whr/kg, we need about 10.6 kg for the battery. Assuming 4.8 kg for electronics and harnessing (from Fig. 21-6, 17% of 28 kg power system), we have only consumed about 9.5 + 10.6 + 4.8 = 25 kg, which is reasonably close to the 28 kg target, given the roughness of the calculations. We will allocate 214 W to the payload as a starting point.

We now have a 47 kg, 214 W estimate for the SCS payload. This is our target design point at this time. We are carrying 30% margin, or 14.1 kg at the system level for our payload, so we need to make sure the payload designer does not carry excess margin on top of this. We need a power system that supports 610 W orbit-average. This starting point will be used in Chap. 16 to calculate a reasonable payload configuration, then we will feed the results of that back into an updated set of allocations and requirements.

14.7.2 FireSat II Example

In the SCS example, we started with a target mass for the entire system, and we determined the mass and power available for the payload. In this example, we will start with the FireSat II payload and determine the mass and overall configuration for the spacecraft. The flow ends up looking a bit different, since we have some flexibility in our final system mass. Following the process defined in Sec. 14.1, we need to first document the design drivers and requirements for this system. Table 14-25 lists the requirements we know at this time. Since we need multiple spacecraft to achieve the coverage, we will plan to launch two spacecraft on a single vehicle, utilizing on-board fuel for the orbit adjusts.

The FireSat II constellation needs to reliably deliver the fire images, but it is important to get the system launched so that it can start to deliver the data. In order to achieve this balance, we will go with a single-string spacecraft bus, with back-ups coming through multiple spacecraft. Then we end up with an overall system that exhibits graceful degradation—we get very good coverage from multiple spacecraft, but if one fails, we still get coverage, just less frequently. We do not want to overly rush the build of the spacecraft, though, since we are building multiple copies—a single mistake will get multiplied.

The FireSat II instrument requires a nadir-pointing spacecraft. The orbit has a period of 99 minutes, with a maximum eclipse time of 35 minutes. Figure 14-24 shows the beta angle across a year of operations. The Sun gets as far as about 75 deg from the plane of the orbit, and it crosses to both sides of the plane. Since the instrument detectors must run cold, we will plan to yaw-flip the spacecraft at 0 deg beta angle, about 10 times per year, in order to keep the instrument radiator on the shaded side of the spacecraft. This yaw flip could be performed with reaction wheels, but it may take too long. We will assume a thruster assist as described in Sec. 19.1.4. Table 19-12 shows 49 g per maneuver, for a total of 3.9 kg over the 8 year mission.

With the large variation in Sun angle, we will need to conduct a trade on the solar array configuration.

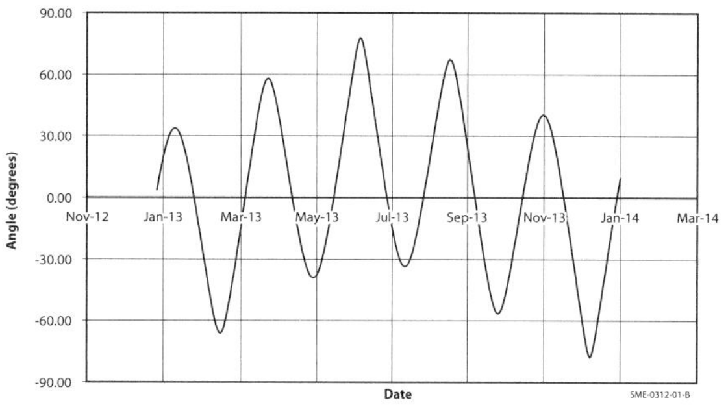

Fig. 14-24. FireSat II Solar Beta Angle Over a Year of Operations.

Table 14-27 shows the options for the solar array trade, with advantages and disadvantages. A two-axis gimbal provides the smallest array area, but it is the most expensive gimbal. For 141 W orbit-average power consumption (see Table 14-28) and a 98% efficient lithium-ion battery (from Table 21-18), the power needed from the array is 220 W. Using Table 21-15 and the GaAs improved MJ cells, we get 197 W/m^2 EOL, so the required array area using a 2-axis gimbal is 1.1 m^2. With a single-axis gimbal, we arrange the array so it splits the 75 deg angle in half, and the total area is increased to compensate for the cosine loss. With a body-mounted array, the average projected area of the array must be at least 1.1 m^2. (When laying out body-mounted arrays, the designer needs to avoid very shallow angles, since the sunlight will tend to skip off the coverglass, despite anti-reflective coatings.) With a body-mounted array, the volume of the spacecraft will need to provide enough surface area for the array. With the yaw flip, we can limit the solar array covering to 4 sides of the spacecraft. With a cylindrical fairing on the launch vehicle, the smallest possible fairing that will provide 1.1 m^2 of surface area on the ends is 1.18 m in diameter, and that diameter requires a minimum length of 1.07 m. These dimensions are close to the Pegasus fairing dimensions, with other vehicles providing more room. Note also that a body-mounted solar array on a non-spinning spacecraft will generally run hotter than a deployed array, since it cannot radiate out the back.

For our initial conceptual design, we will choose the body-mounted array. We can avoid the cost of a deployment system, a gimbal system, and the software to drive the array. Our customer is very interested in simplicity. As we get into a more detailed design phase, we should re-visit this trade. We may be able to package a gimbaled array in a way that allows two spacecraft to fit in a smaller launch vehicle, or perhaps the mass of the gimbal and drive electronics will be less than the mass of solar cells on multiple faces. The detailed trade will require some drawings of the spacecraft and some careful subsystem analysis.

FireSat II will need a propulsion system. With a delta V as high as 764 m/s, we should compare the mass

Table 14-26◀, Fig. 14-24, Eq. 14-4◀

Table 14-27. FireSat II Solar Array Trade.

Array Configuration	Array Area	Rationale	Advantages	Disadvantages
2-Axis Gimbal	1.1 m^2	197 W/m^2 from Table 21-15	Smallest total array area	Expensive powered mechanism Deployment mechanism needed Software needed to drive gimbals
1-Axis Gimbal	1.4 m^2	Based on 37.5 deg cosine loss	Significantly less expensive that 2-axis gimbal	Expensive powered mechanism Deployment mechanism needed Larger array area Software needed to drive gimbals
Body Mounted	Avg projected area, >1.1 m^2	Higher temperature due to mounting	No expensive mechanisms	Very large total array area May increase volume of spacecraft Array will tend to run hotter, requiring more array area

of a mono-propellant system to a bi-propellant system. We should carry 30% margin on the payload estimate of 20 kg, resulting in 26 kg allocation. Using Table 14-18, LEO with propulsion, the payload is 31% of the dry mass, so dry mass is 84 kg. With an I_{sp} of 220 sec, the propellant mass is 36 kg for a monopropellant system. A bi-prop system with 300 sec I_{sp} requires 25 kg of propellant, so there is only an 11 kg savings, which will be eaten up by the extra complexity. We will go with a mono-propellant propulsion system, even if the dry mass grows some.

From LEO, we are in view of ground stations for about 10 minutes out of the 99 minute orbit. With a 10 Mbps continuous data collection rate, we will need to downlink every orbit at 100 Mbps to get all of the data down. We should investigate data compression and on-board processing to reduce the total data volume. If the on-board algorithm can identify fires, we can limit our downlinks to data immediately surrounding a fire, which will drastically reduce the total volume. At a 100 Mbps downlink rate, we will need an X-band transmitter, but reducing the data rate to 5 Mbps would allow us to use a less expensive S-band system (see Table 21-3).

Using typical subsystems and Tables 14-18 and 14-20, the mass and power allocations are shown in Table 14-28. Contingency of 30% has been added to both the mass and power numbers to allow for growth during development. This contingency has been added before applying the Sec. 14.5 tables, so the 30% has effectively been added to all of the subsystems. Given that this is a very small spacecraft, not all subsystems may scale per the table averages, so we should carry additional mass at the system level. We will assume a target launch mass of 150 kg for each spacecraft, leaving us some margin. This assumes that one spacecraft will support the other for launch. The 150 kg number will be used by mechanical, propulsion, and ADC engineers in their subsystem analysis. Table 14-29 shows the fuel budget for this wet mass.

As a sanity check on our power system mass, we can take a look at the weight of our body-mounted array. Assuming an octagonal spacecraft 1.2 m across the octagon and 1.1 m tall, with array on both ends and 5 of the side panels, the total surface area is about 4.6 m^2. At 2.8 kg/m^2 (from Table 21-15), the total array mass is 12.9 kg. 141 W for 35 minutes with a 30% depth of discharge requires 274 Whr. At 125 Whr/kg, per Table 21-18, the battery will be 2.2 kg. That only leaves 2.9 kg for the power electronics and the spacecraft harness. Our body-mounted array will probably drive our power allocation a bit above 18 kg, but we will wait for our detailed subsystem analysis to reallocate, using some of our 14 kg of system-level margin if necessary.

Table 14-28. FireSat II Mass and Power Using Tables from Sec. 14.5. Payload mass and power numbers include 30% contingency to allow for growth during development.

	Mass Based on Table 14-18 (kg)	Power Based on Table 14-20 (W)
Payload Total	26	65
Structure	23	1
Thermal	2	14
Power (incl. harness)	18	13
TT&C	2	17
On-Board Processing	4	17
ADC	5	14
Propulsion	3	0
Other	3	
Total Dry	86	141
Propellant mass (kg)	50	
Total Wet Mass (kg)	136	
Target Launch Mass (kg)	150	
System-level Margin (kg)	14	

At this point, we need to go into more detailed analysis of each of the subsystems, which will be covered in later chapters. To complete the conceptual design, we will need to rack up the mass and power totals from the

Table 14-29. FireSat II Fuel Budget.

	delta V (m/s)	Effective I_{sp} (s)	Propellant for Maneuver (kg)	S/C Mass after Burn (kg)
1st Burn	141	220	18.3	131.7
2nd Burn	139	220	16.0	115.7
Maintenance	21	215	1.1	114.5
Rephasing	0	220	0.0	114.4
Momentum Management	0		3.9	110.6
Disposal	183	220	9.0	101.6
Residuals, Margin (kg)			1.6	100.0
Total	484		50.0	
Total Launch Mass: 150 kg				

subsystem analyses and compare that to the analysis we have done here, reconciling any discrepancies by considering options and performing trades. Once we have a consistent design, including mass and power totals that accommodate uncertainty in the development, we will document our design and deliver it to our customer.

14.8 Future of Spacecraft Design

Over the last 20 years, there have been some clear trends in spacecraft design. The most prominent change is the increasing role of software. With more powerful radiation-hard processors has come the ability to put more functionality into those processors. Functions in software can be changed after launch, improving the flexibility and versatility of today's spacecraft. With the increased software complexity has also come increased difficulty with software during development. Today's software subsystem lead is really a spacecraft systems engineer, working across all of the subsystems except structure. The industry is starting to realize this fact and incorporate within the systems team engineers who are familiar with the details of software design. Software is becoming more abstract, isolating most developers from the details of the hardware. Efficiency of the code itself is being traded for efficiency in the writing of the code—as we get faster processors and larger memory, we can afford code that requires more steps and more memory to perform the same task. Features such as file systems allow manipulation of large volumes of payload data with few steps on the part of the programmer and the operations team, while underneath the top-level code resides a very complex operating system which utilizes complex device drivers. As we look ahead at the next generation of spacecraft, we can expect to see very sophisticated software, with complex attitude control algorithms and filters; autonomous orbit adjustments and maintenance; file system transfers with the ground that allow autonomous, reliable transfer; sophisticated on-board signal processing; and autonomous target selection. In short, our spacecraft will be more capable of taking care of themselves, with a reduction in operations costs. Software development costs will go up because of the increasing complexity, but the functionality will increase faster than the costs, saving money in other areas. The biggest challenge with software, which will only get worse, is ensuring that the inevitable flaws in the code do not prematurely end the mission.

Along with improved software capability has come an increased use of data standards. Spacecraft can now afford the overhead associated with packaging data inside standard headers, which allow easier handling of the data on-board and on the ground. The work of the Consultative Committee for Space Data Systems [CCSDS, 2011] since the 1980s has taken spacecraft toward standard data interfaces, but the explosion of the Internet over the last 15 years has accelerated work on commercial data standards. Billions of dollars spent by commercial industry on Internet Protocol (IP), mobile IP, IP Security (IPsec), Ethernet, and Universal Serial Bus (USB) will enable the space industry to simplify spacecraft interfaces, spacecraft testing, and flight operations. Over the last 20 years, the MIL-STD-1553 [DoD, 1978] data bus has replaced more custom serial interfaces. Many spacecraft components now use this standard, greatly reducing the documentation and errors associated with the development of signaling between two electronics boxes. Over the last 10 years, Spacewire (standard ECSS-E-ST-50-12C [ESA, 2003] based on IEEE 1355) has started to claim the high-speed serial interfaces. But, over the same time, the commercial industry has solved many of the issues spacecraft face, using IP, Ethernet, and USB. The challenges of mobile IP, where users have limited power in hand-held devices, is very similar to the challenges of a spacecraft in Earth orbit with limited power. Command link security is becoming a bigger issue as electronics needed for spacecraft communication become cheaper, so the advantages of IPsec will become greater. Protocols used for bank transactions will be used to ensure command link security, rather than the current practice of custom hardware.

Field-Programmable Gate Arrays (FPGA) have drastically changed digital design over the last 25 years. Most digital circuits are now FPGA's with some support parts around them. These parts reduce the design cycle time, since mistakes or changes during development can be implemented by altering the programming of the FPGA, rather than changing physical wiring on the circuit boards. Radiation-hard versions of these parts are available for flight. FPGA's can even include simple microprocessors, and some FPGA's can initialize using external memory, so the ground can re-program circuit functionality. FPGA's blur the line between software and hardware, making the hardware much more flexible.

On the payload side, detectors used in imagers continue to grow. Larger detectors mean higher resolution and more data collected. Spacecraft will need to support higher data rates from the payloads and to the ground. Data storage requirements will grow. High data rate communication is already moving to higher frequency radio bands, such as the K_a*-band* which covers 26.5–40 GHz, because of crowding and bandwidth limitations at the lower frequencies. On-board processing is already used to compress measurement data; future missions will also use software to perform other processing on the data. For instance, with a mission like FireSat II, the on-board processing will identify regions in an image which contain fires, then downlink those portions of the image with higher resolution. Our society in general is demanding higher bandwidths, so there will be constant pressure on communications payloads, too, with similar impacts on the spacecraft design—higher power, larger antennas, and higher frequencies. Some applications, especially space-to-space links, will use optical communication.

Significant reductions in the cost of space transportation could drastically change the industry. It doesn't really make sense to launch a $20 million spacecraft on a $200 million rocket, but if the cost to lift a spacecraft into space came down by an order of magnitude, then it would make sense to reduce analysis and testing and risk additional failures. This cost reduction will require either a drastic increase in the number of launches, creating more of an assembly-line operation, with simpler rockets; or we will need some completely new technology to overcome the basic-physics challenge of accelerating mass to more than 7.5 km/s. There are some commercial companies experimenting with simpler rockets, so perhaps there will be some decrease in launch costs. The change should increase opportunities to fly spacecraft, but it will probably not be enough to drastically change how we design, build, and test space systems.

The design process itself has been changing with the increased capability of our computers. For over 20 years, we have been using computers for mechanical drafting and electrical schematic drawing. The process of going from computer to hardware has become more and more automated. The ongoing revolution now is in the integration of computer models, using standard data formats like those in ISO 10303. We will soon be able to create a model of the entire spacecraft, with mechanical, thermal, electrical, and dynamic properties, all shared across the team. Preliminary designs will come together faster, with designers analyzing more options. Rather than configuration management with text documents, we will use the data model representation of the spacecraft to capture the current configuration. But we will still need the creativity and common sense of human designers. We will still need designers who understand the basics of spacecraft and who can exercise good judgment, quickly disregarding the absurd or foolish solutions and exploring the possibilities of what can go wrong. These creative and knowledgeable individuals are essential for our continued exploration and utilization of space.

References

For annotated bibliography of overview of spacecraft design, see the book website.

CCSDS. 2011. Website

DoD. 1978. Mechanical Electrical and Functional Characteristics of a Serial Data Bus. MIL-STD-1553.

ESA. 2003. Space Engineering, Data and Networks. ECSS-E-50-12C.

Everett, David F., T. Correll, S. Schick, and K. Brown. 2000. "Recovery of the Wide-Field Infrared Explorer Spacecraft." 14th Annual USU Conference on Small Satellites. Logan, Utah. Aug. 21–24.

Fountain, Glen H., et al. 2008. "The New Horizons Spacecraft," *Space Science Reviews*, vol. 140, issue 1-4, pp. 23–47.

Hurley, Mike and Bill Purdy. 2010. "Designing and Managing for a Reliability of Zero." ESA 4S Symposium, Funchal, Portugal, Paper No. 1885505, May 31–Jun. 4.

15 Overview of Payload Design

Jeffery J. Puschell, *Raytheon*

The *Payload* is defined as the total complement of equipment carried by a spacecraft that interacts with the *subject* in performance of a particular mission. The subject of the mission is what exists outside the spacecraft that is sensed by or interacts with the payload, as discussed in Sec. 4.1 and Sec. 14.2. *Passive subjects* are ones that the mission design cannot control, for example, the fire used in the FireSat II example. *Active subjects* are ones which the design and basic parameters can be controlled by mission design, such as a GPS receiver on the Earth. Mission subjects will fall into at least one, and sometimes both of these types. Although typically unique to each mission, payloads are the main reason missions fly, and what drives the mission size, cost and risk. So, consequently, a critical part of mission analysis and design is to understand and recognize what drives a particular set of space payloads so that those elements can become an integral part of the overall system trade process designed to meet *mission objectives* at minimum cost and risk.

In this chapter, we will summarize the overall process of payload design and sizing, in Sec. 15.1 and Sec. 15.2 we discuss the different types of payloads, select the subject and discuss undertaking subject trades (i.e., how to best go about achieving the mission objective). Section 15.3 lays out the details of the payload design process, using the background information on the electromagnetic spectrum provided in Sec. 15.4, which is the primary way of observing and communicating from space. Finally, we will review some examples of this process in Sec. 15.5. *Communication Payloads* (Chap. 16) and *Observation Payloads* (discussed in Chap. 17) are the two most common types.

15.1 Types of Space Payloads

As shown in Table 2-1, there are many space communities with various objectives and goals, and Table 1-15 lists over 70 space mission applications. These communities and applications focus on **what** we are trying to achieve and **why** we are trying to achieve it. In contrast, the mission payload focuses on **how** to achieve it. Putting the payload in space and obtaining results is what the mission is all about. How the design meets the needs of the end users (or the people that pay for the mission) determines the why.

Mission payloads may be unique in the details of their implementation and objectives, but share many of the same design characteristics. There are, in fact, only a few broad types of payloads (defined in Table 15-1), however, each can be used for a wide variety of applications. For example, the Hubble Space Telescope is used for astronomical observation, but basically the same instrument, turned upside down, can be used for military reconnaissance or surveillance, and in GEO may be used for continuous environmental monitoring.

If the subject or payload is active, it will involve a more complex (and therefore, likely more expensive) design process, but also adds flexibility that can greatly improve performance. For example, in a communications system where the subject is active, we can put more performance on the spacecraft and make the ground system simpler (such as direct broadcast radio or TV), or we can ask the ground unit to perform much of the work or have the relevant data. (The GPS receiver in your car calculates where it is based on the relatively simple signals from the GPS satellites. The ground system also contains all of the maps on which the information is displayed.)

A similar relationship holds for the payload. A *passive payload* is one that is just observing, watching, or taking in data, such as a space telescope. While these payloads can be complex and expensive, they are simply dealing with what the outside world provides. In contrast, an *active payload* is one that interacts directly with the subject, such as a radar that provides its own illumination, essentially the equivalent of a flash photograph in visible light. This gives us a great deal of flexibility because we can control the illumination to provide just the characteristics that we need. Because we have brought our own illumination, the space radar works equally well

Table 15-1. Types of Space Payloads.

Payload Type	Sample Function	Active or Passive Payload	Active or Passive Subject	Examples	References
Observation	Remote sensing Space-based Earth-based Space weather	Passive or Active	Passive	Hubble Telescope LandSat Active: TerraSar X Weather Doppler Meteorology Wind Lidar	Chap. 17
Communications/ Navigation	One Way comm. 2-way comm. Navigation Tracking	Active	Active	Direct Broadcast TV Telephone GPS/GLONASS/GNSS Galileo Navstar Wireless Internet (WiFi)	Chap. 16
In-Situ	Rovers Space manufacturing In-situ measurements Exploration	Active	Passive	Mars or Lunar rovers Viking Mars lander Magnetic field meas. Gravity measurements	Squyres, et al. [2003] Gabriel [2007] Young [2007] Ball et al. [2007]
Action at a Distance	Space weapons Power transmission National security Spacecraft tracking	Active	Passive or Active	Space-based laser Space-based radar Satellite solar power Guidance Military data	Zachen [2007] Glaser et al. [1997] Klein [2006] Aviv [2006] Pillai et al. [2008]
People (Human spaceflight)	Exploration Space tourism Construction and repair Space experiments	Passive or Active	Passive	Apollo Space tourism Lunar colony ISS	Eckart [2006] Seedhouse [2008] Harland and Harvey [2008] Pelton and Marshall [2009]

at night and, because we also control the wavelength, we can pick one that allows us to penetrate clouds or light foliage. The demerit is that we need a really big "flashlight" for this task and both the power required and the thermal control to get rid of lots of excess heat are major problems and a big expense.

Payloads meeting these different objectives will be different in many of their details (such as exposure time or wavelength band), but will share many of the same design characteristics.

Communications Payloads. By far the largest and most "popular" group of spacecraft, the main goal of communication payloads is to transfer information. Communications missions, traditionally dominated by large geosynchronous spacecraft, range from one-way broadcast of television signals to wideband full-duplex telecommunication connectivity. The advances of technologies in these payloads have been astounding, from smaller spacecraft in LEO used as alternative architectures for global coverage to CubeSats as discussed in Sec. 25.4. In fact, there have been so many advances, that we have devoted all of Chap. 16 to a detailed discussion of this type of payload.

Observation Payloads. Observation payloads cover a wide and diverse range of missions and applications using remote sensing. Any observation that a spacecraft makes without directly contacting the object in question is considered remote sensing. Imaging the Earth's surface, sounding the Earth's atmosphere, providing early warning of a ballistic missile launch, tsunami, or hurricane, or seeking out new worlds by observing the chemical spectra of distant galaxies, are all remote sensing missions. We focus mostly on the electromagnetic spectrum to determine the nature, state, or features of physical objects or phenomenon.

As shown in Fig. 15-4, we can evaluate different aspects of the electromagnetic radiation to exploit different characteristics, with respect to spatial, spectral, and intensity information content, depending on the particular mission. We can also evaluate this information in the temporal context that supports comparisons and cause-and-effect relationships. Depending on the source of the electromagnetic radiation being sensed, we can establish the activity of the sensor. If the instrument measures direct or reflected solar radiation in the environment, we distinguish that it is a passive sensor. Active sensors, such as *radar* and *lidar*, emit radiation that generate a reflected return which the instrument measures. The physical principles of remote sensing and the categories of the sensors are the same, regardless of whether the payload is studying space weather, mapping the topography of Earth, or observing electromagnetic phenomena elsewhere in the universe.

One of the best known observation systems, the Hubble Space Telescope, has been repaired and kept up to date with the latest available remote sensing technology by a series of five servicing missions between 1993 and 2008. This remarkable capability and the unprecedented legacy of scientific discovery that it enabled was made possible by the skill of designers of the instruments and the US Space Shuttle astronauts. With the imminent retirement of the US Space Shuttle, future payload and spacecraft servicing may occur with remotely controlled or automated robotic systems. For the extended version of observation payloads, see Chap. 17.

Navigation. GPS, GLONASS, Galileo, and other international navigation systems have demonstrated a wealth of applications for military, civilian, academic, and recreational users. GPS provides information for real-time position, velocity, and time determination. It is available worldwide on a broad range of platforms, including pedestrians, cars, ships, commercial and military aircraft, and spacecraft. The heart of GPS is a spread-spectrum broadcast communication message that can be exploited using relatively low-cost receivers.

In Situ Science. Sample collection and evaluation serves an important role in planetary and space science. Perhaps the most elaborate instance of sample collection took place in the Apollo missions when approximately 300 kg of samples from the Moon were returned to Earth for analysis. Other examples of sample collection and analysis include planetary landers (such as Viking and Mars Exploration Rovers, Spirit and Opportunity).

Action at a Distance. While communication, navigation and remote sensing applications are quite mature and dominate the use of space, action-at-a-distance concepts such as space-based lasers, space-based radar and space-based solar power still occupy a relatively small niche in the realm of space mission design. In particular, concepts for weapons in space became a topic of intense study and debate as part of the Strategic Defense Initiative and space-based strategic missile defense. Development of certain operational space weapons has been prohibited under the Anti-Ballistic Missile Treaty of 1972. Although some experts view widespread weaponization of space as inevitable, it has not become a stated objective of US national policy. Of course, space has been used to support military objectives since the dawn of artificial spacecraft, but the vast majority of military space applications fall into the categories of remote sensing and communications. Extensive studies have been done on satellite solar power, i.e., generating solar power in space for use on Earth. Several commercial ventures in the US, Japan, and Europe have announced plans to develop space-based solar power systems.

Human Spaceflight. Human spaceflight involves a human payload consisting of a flight crew and possibly passengers. Human spaceflight has been an ongoing international activity by the US, Russia, and more recently, China since 1961 with the first human spaceflight by the Soviet cosmonaut Yuri Gagarin. Human spaceflight occurs through the Russian Soyuz program, the US Space Shuttle program, and the Chinese Shenzhou program. However, the US government is expected to lose human spaceflight launch capability [Kraemer, 2006] with retirement of the Space Shuttle. Recently, to help fill the gap between the Space Shuttle Program and a possible next US government human spaceflight program, there has been a growing trend in the US toward commercial human spaceflight to help supply the International Space Station and to stimulate commercial spaceflight and other applications through the Commercial Crew Development (CCDev) and Commercial Orbital Transportation Services programs. The 21st century will see Space Tourism become a reality, with pioneers like Sir Richard Branson of Virgin Galactic and John Carmack of Armadillo Aerospace leading the way; already they are building space ports in New Mexico and pre-selling seats on their upcoming launches due to begin in 2012.

Exploitation of physical resources in space, either from the Moon or asteroids, has sparked innovative and imaginative concepts for augmenting Earth's limited resources or enabling human exploration of the solar system. Many authors (e.g., Eckart [2006]) have created designs for lunar bases, but all require a dramatic reduction in launch cost. In the nearer term, however, space-based materials processing and manufacturing are more likely to mature and exploit the characteristics of the microgravity environment (see Chap. 7).

15.2 Mission System Concept or Subject Trade—What Is the System Measuring or Working With?

Space mission requirements and constraints have been defined in Sec. 3.5. Mission requirements dictate the technical performance of the payload while operational implementation is determined by the mission concepts and constraints. Frequently, the technical specification and operations concept for payloads are interrelated. For example, increasing temporal resolution, that is, reducing revisit time, may reduce the requirement for spatial resolution in an optical sensor system. We must ensure the mission requirements capture fundamental needs of the users without constraining the designer's ability to satisfy these requirements through alternative technical means.

As an example, the FireSat II overall mission requirements are to detect, locate, and identify forest fires, then define the level of detail needed to satisfy the overall mission. Based on sensor data, several questions need to be answered and decisions need to be made:

- What is the timeframe for detecting a fire? 20 minutes? 1 hour?
- What is the geographic extent of the fire?
- What are the primary combustibles?
- In what direction is the fire spreading? How quickly?
- Where is the fire burning hottest?

- Can flaming fires be distinguished from smoldering fires?
- Can a distinction be made between petroleum, chemical, and organic material-fueled fires?
- Where to strategically place firefighting efforts to contain and suppress the fire most effectively.
- How much smoke and ash is the fire generating?
- Are any other sources of information available that might also be used (e.g., air, ground, or space-based)?

Mission priorities and objectives addressed by these questions will determine the specific observables linking payload performance with mission performance. To choose a remote sensing payload, the key steps to a disciplined and repeatable design begin with determining the elements of information that we need to address the problem. We must specify the physically observable quantities that contribute to elements of information about the problem in sufficient detail to ensure they can be detected by a spacecraft payload with sufficient resolution to provide meaningful insight into the subject.

Establishing different performance levels provides a framework for trading off performance across a number of different design features. For all missions, payload performance evaluation categories include physical performance constraints and operational constraints. Examples of physical performance constraints include limits on spatial, spectral, radiometric, and temporal resolution. Operational constraints include sensor duty cycle limits, tasking and scheduling limits on sensor time, and resource contention such as inability of the sensor to view two targets of interest simultaneously.

Within each sensor constraint category, we should establish an absolute minimum threshold such that any performance that does not meet this capability is unacceptable. At the other extreme, we should specify the performance goal in order to establish the performance that will fully satisfy the requirement. Table 15-2 illustrates a sample of performance levels for the FireSat II mission payload across the functional areas of resolution, quantity, timeliness, periodicity, geolocation accuracy, and completeness. These distinctions can be critical in determining the viability of a mission concept. In commercial remote sensing, for example, the range of performance requirements from threshold to goal is typically determined through market analysis and business development case studies. These studies frequently identify a minimum resolution (or other performance parameter) below which a remote sensing spacecraft concept will not be profitable. Some of the payload constraints identified in Table 15-2 could be used to constrain the payload or the higher level FireSat II satellite constellation or both. For example, based on the understanding of astrodynamics and satellite constellation design we developed in Chaps. 9 and 10, respectively, we know the timeliness threshold of 2 hours and the revisit interval threshold of 90 min cannot be achieved with a single payload in low Earth orbit unless that payload is on board a highly maneuverable satellite. On the other hand, if we were able to relax the completeness requirement to encompass only one specific part of the world such as the continental US, then this mission could be carried out with a payload on board a single geosynchronous satellite and the timeliness and revisit rate requirements would drive a variety of payload characteristics such as Earth scan rate and detector array size.

Mission parameters, such as identifying and locating forest fires, need to be established in such a way that we can evaluate, size, and design candidate sensors. This parameterization involves a process of requirements analysis that focuses on matching the tasks involved in the mission with categories of discipline capabilities. If we match mission requirements with existing or probable capabilities, the result is a set of potential information requirements. We then try to identify the characteristics of the subject (i.e., signatures) that correspond to information requirements through a set of rules. For example, for FireSat II, these rules yield a set of mission observables necessary to detect fires, such as specific wavelength bands and spectral sensitivities that our sensor needs. These observables provide the basis for the payload characteristics that comprise the baseline design to satisfy the mission. The basic sensor types and corresponding infor-

Table 15-2. Sample Threshold and Performance Goal Requirements for the FireSat II Payload. Performance goal represents the maximum meaningful level of performance across all design features. Surpassing performance goal does not increase the value of the system. Likewise, performance falling below threshold prevents the system from meeting mission requirements, which would likely lead to program termination.

	Acceptable	Desired
Subject Characteristics	Identify, locate, and track progress of fires	Determine thermal conditions within fires and products of combustion
Quantity	Simultaneously measure and track 7 fires	Simultaneously measure and track 20 fires
Timeliness	Report detection of fire within 2 hours	Report detection of fire within 20 min
Revisit Interval	Update status of fire every 90 min	Update status of fire every 45 min
Geolocation Accuracy	Determine location and extent of fire within ±1 km	Determine location and extent of fire within ±100 m
Completeness	Map fires in North America and one other selectable region (e.g., Persian Gulf)	Map fires globally

Table 15-2, Fig. 15-0, Eq. 15-0

mation that might satisfy the FireSat II mission are shown in Table 15-3. It may also be possible to satisfy mission requirements by observing different phenomenologies, such as visible signatures associated with flame and smoke, thermal infrared signatures from fire, spectral analysis of the products of combustion, or an algorithm combining all of these.

The selection of a spacecraft payload represents the fundamental leap in determining how to satisfy mission requirements with a space sensor. In the previous section we introduced a top-down framework for considering the general problem of spacecraft design. Here we turn our attention to the payload; in particular, a methodology for determining the type of payload to employ and the physical quantities to measure.

Table 15-3. Simplified Subject Trades for FireSat II Mission. The information type allows for subject trades to be made among the different signatures that can be exploited to satisfy FireSat II mission requirements.

Sensor Type	Information Type
Electro-optical Imager	Visible return from light or smoke cloud produced by the fire
Spectrometer	Spectral signatures from products of combustion
Radiometer	Thermal intensity

The process for linking mission requirements to payload design, begins with a task (or mission requirement) and ends with a spacecraft payload design. Figure 15-1 divides this process into intermediate steps to focus on the requirements analysis, subject trades and payload analysis. In this section, we will focus on describing this process. Section 17.2 provides some of the specific techniques that are employed in this process for visible and IR systems. This process can be extended to consider cost as an independent variable (CAIV) and evaluate performance of different payload designs with respect to threshold and goal requirements as a function of cost to try to determine the best value for specific missions.

For the FireSat II mission design, we need to identify specific signatures that would allow candidate sensors to provide viable solutions to the mission requirement. We observe physical phenomena through signatures, and we must choose which signature will provide the desired information. The specific signatures that a payload senses must be evaluated in light of the particular focus of the mission. For example, a spectrometer that is sensitive enough to detect all fires, but which cannot be used to differentiate campfires from forest fires could generate a large false alarm rate and render it operationally useless. Defining the key signatures and observables that support the information content needed to satisfy the mission determines the performance limits for the payload design.

15.2.1 Subject Trades

The objective of a space mission is typically to detect, communicate, or interact. The subject, as an element of the space mission, is the specific thing that the spacecraft will detect, communicate, or interact with. For GPS, the subject is the GPS receiver. For FireSat II, we could assume that the subject is the heat generated by the forest fire, but other subjects are possible: light, smoke, or changes in atmospheric composition.

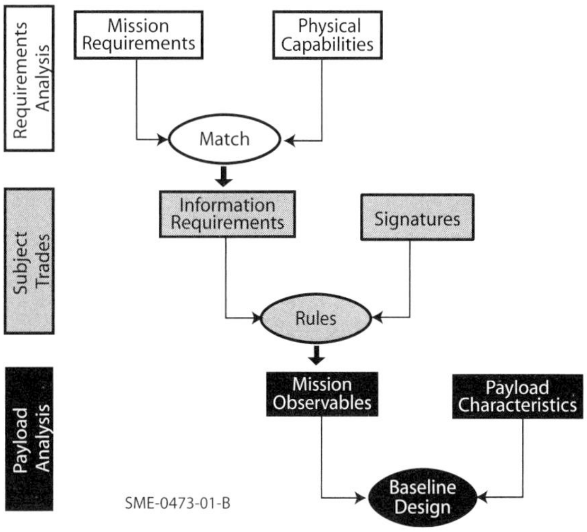

Fig. 15-1. Process for Linking Mission Requirements to Payload Design. The process moves from mission requirements to a payload design in three steps: requirements analysis, subject trades, and payload analysis.

What we choose as the subject will dramatically affect performance, cost, and the mission concept. Thus, we must do this trade carefully and review it from time to time to ensure it is consistent with mission objectives and our goal of minimizing cost and risk.

Table 15-4 summarizes the subject-trade process. We begin by looking at the basic mission objectives and then ask what subjects could meet these objectives. To do this, we should look at what we are trying to achieve, the properties of space we intend to exploit, and the characteristics of what we are looking at or interacting with. Table 15-5 shows examples of subject trades for four representative missions. As the missions change, the nature of the subject trades will also change. For FireSat II, we are looking for a well-defined subject (the forest fire), and we want to do this at minimum cost and risk. With the Space Telescope, we must ask, "What am I looking for? What am I trying to detect and how can I detect it?" For any of the science missions, we would ask, "Is the subject some distant and unknown object, and is it detectable in the part of the electromagnetic spectrum I am able to explore?"

For a space system intended to detect airplanes, the main subject trades would concern mission goals. Are the targets cooperative or noncooperative? Do we need to track over the poles? Should we track in high-density areas around airports or over the open oceans? The answers to these questions will determine the nature of the subject trades.

Table 15-4. Subject Trade Process. See discussion earlier in this section.

Step	FireSat II Example	Where Discussed
*1. **Determine fundamental mission objectives***	Detect and monitor forest fires	Sec. 3.3
*2. **Determine what possible subjects could be used to meet these objectives (i.e., what could the system detect or interact with to meet the objectives)***	Heat, fire, smoke, atmospheric composition	Sec. 15.2
*3. **Determine broad class of ways that the spacecraft can detect or interact with the possible subjects***	Heat –> IR flame, smoke –> visual atmospheric composition –> lidar	Sec. 15.2
*4. **Determine if subject is passive or controllable***	Initially assume passive fire detection	Secs 4.1, 15.2
*5a. **For controllable subjects, do trade of putting functionality at the subject, in the space system, or in the ground system***	N/A	Secs. 5.3, 15.2
*5b. **For passive subjects, determine general characteristics that can be detected***	Forest fire temperature range and total heat output	Sec. 15.2
*6. **Determine whether multiple subjects and payloads should be used***	Not initially	Sec. 15.2
*7. **Define and document initial subject selection***	IR detection of heat	Sec. 4.3
*8. **Review selection frequently for alternative methods and possible use of ancillary subjects***		Sec. 15.2

Table 15-5. Subject Trades Examples.

Mission	Property of Spacecraft Used	General Object of Study or Interaction	Alternative Mission Subjects	Key Subject Trades	Comments
FireSat II	Global perspective	Forest fires	Fire (visible or IR) Smoke (visible or IR) Increased CO_2 Decreased vegetation	None—IR detection probably best choice	See low-cost alternative in Chap. 13
Airplane Detection	Global perspective	Airplanes	Skin (radar, visible) Plume (IR) Radio emissions (RF)	Radar vs. IR vs. active RF	Need to examine goals; cooperative vs. noncooperative targets; high density vs. ocean tracking
Truck Communications System	Global perspective	Portable telecommunication centers	Current radio Current CB Standard TV New telecommunication center Cellular relay	Complexity of truck element vs. complexity of space & ground station	
Space Telescope	Above the atmosphere	Distant galaxies unknown phenomena	Quasars Galaxies Planets Visible spectrum Unknown objects	Is the subject known or unknown?	

Perhaps the easiest subject trades are those in which the system will be interacting with a ground element that is a part of the system, such as direct broadcast television or a truck communication system. In this case, the subject trade becomes simply an issue of how much capacity should go on the spacecraft vs. how much should go in the unit on the ground.

Determining whether a subject is active or passive is our next task. Active subjects can be controlled by the designer, such as ground stations, antennas, or receivers; transmitters used for ground communications, direct broadcast television, or data sources would qualify as well. Because we can control the subject, we can add more or less capability to it. Thus, we might choose to have a simple receiver on the ground with a high power, accurately pointed, narrow-beam transmitter on the spacecraft. Or we could place a sophisticated, sensitive receiver on the ground with a small, lower-cost system in space. Usually, the solution will depend on the number of ground stations we wish to interact with. If there are many ground stations, as in direct-broadcast television, we will put as much capability as possible into the satellite to drive down the cost and complexity of the ground stations. On the other hand, if there are only a few ground stations, we can save money by giving these stations substantial processing and pointing capability and using a simpler, lighter-weight, and lower-cost satellite.

Passive subjects are those in which the characteristics may be known but cannot be altered. This includes phenomena such as weather, quasars, or forest fires. Even though we cannot control the object under examination, we can choose the subject from various characteristics. We could detect forest fires by observing either the fire itself or the smoke in the visible or infrared spectrum. We could detect atmospheric composition changes or, in principle, reductions in vegetation. Thus, even for passive subjects, the subject is part of the system trades.

We do not always know whether a given mission has passive or active subjects; in some cases, we can choose either type. For example, we could detect airplanes passively with an IR sensor or radar, or actively by listening for or interrogating a transponder on the airplane. Satellites that monitor the weather or environment could do complex observations or simply collect and relay data from sensors on the ground.

Using *multiple subjects* to meet our mission objectives can be advantageous, providing much more information than a single subject and can eliminate ambiguities that can occur with observing only one aspect. However, multiple subjects usually require *multiple payloads*, which will invariably, drive up the space mission cost and complexity. Thus, a *principal trade* is between a low-cost mission with a single subject and single payload vs. a more expensive mission that achieves higher performance by using several payloads to sense several different subjects related to the same objective.

For FireSat II, we tentatively select the heat of the forest fire as the subject of the mission, keeping in mind that this may change as the design evolves. Of course, we should make these trades as rapidly as possible because they strongly affect how the mission is done.

We should then document the subject selection and review it frequently during the program's early stages, looking for other possible methods and subjects. Looking for *alternative subjects* is perhaps the single most important way to drive down the cost of space missions.

15.3 Payload Design

Payload definition and sizing determine many of the capabilities, as well as, the limitations of the mission. The payload determines what the mission can achieve, while the size of the payload, along with any special structural, thermal, control, communications, or pointing restrictions, influence the design of the remainder of the spacecraft support systems [Pillet et al. 2005].

Let's start by assuming that the mission objectives are defined and the critical requirements are understood. This section will concentrate on the trade space of possible payloads and making an informed selection among them. This process is a useful guide for moving from a blank piece of paper to a preliminary set of payloads. Iterating on the process produces a more detailed definition and more useful set of payloads that can meet the mission objectives at minimum cost and risk.

As shown in Table 15-6, the process begins with an understanding of mission requirements described in Secs. 3.5, 4.4, 5.5, and Chap. 6. The mission requirements have a major effect on all aspects of space vehicle design, but it is frequently necessary to treat the components and subsystems separately for preliminary design and sizing. We begin with the payload because it is the critical mission element bounding spacecraft performance. Chapters 14 and 18 through 22 treat the remainder of the spacecraft systems and trade-offs involved in the overall spacecraft design.

Once the mission requirements are understood, we must determine the level of detail required to satisfy different aspects of the mission. For FireSat II, varying levels of detail are required if the task is to identify the existence of a fire, assess the damage caused by fires, or characterize the combustibles in a fire. Additionally, the timeliness demands placed on the mission could be vastly different depending on whether the data is to support long-term scientific analysis or real-time ground activity.

We summarize the basic steps in this process below and discuss them in more detail in Chap. 16 for Communications Payloads, and Chap. 17 for Observation Payloads.

1. Select Payload Objectives. These objectives will, of course, be strongly related to the mission objectives defined in Sec. 3.3 and will also depend on the overall mission concept, requirements, and constraints from Chaps. 3 through 6. However, unlike the mission objectives which are a broad statement of what the mission must do to be useful, the payload objectives are more specific statements of what the payload must do (i.e., what is its output or fundamental function). For FireSat II, this is specific performance objectives in terms of identifying fires. For the space manufacturing example in Table 15-6, called WaferSat, the payload objective is a definition of the end product to be manufactured.

2. Conduct Subject Trades. The subject is what the payload interacts with or observes. As discussed in detail in Sec. 15.2, a key part of the subject trade is determining what the subject is or should be. For a mobile communications system, it is the handheld user receivers. In that case, the subject trade is to determine how much capability to put in the user unit and how much to put on the satellite. For FireSat II, we may get very different results if we define the subject as the IR radiation produced by the fire or as the smoke or visible flickering which the fire produces. In addition to defining the subject, we need to determine the performance thresholds to which the system must operate. For FireSat II, what temperature dif-

Table 15-6. Process for Defining Space Payloads. See text for discussion. See Chap. 16 for a discussion of communications payloads, including SCS.

Process Step	Product	FireSat II (Remote Sensing) Example	Space Manufacturing Example	Where Discussed
1. Use mission objectives, concept, requirements, and constraints to select payload objectives	Payload performance objectives	Identify smoldering and flaming fires	Manufacture ultra-pure silicon wafers	Secs. 3.3, 3.5, 4.4, 5.5 and Chap. 6
2. Conduct subject trades	Subject definition and performance thresholds	Distinguish smoldering fires that are 3 K warmer than the background from flaming fires that are 10 K warmer than the background	Less than 1 ppb impurities over 50 cm square wafers	Sec. 15.2
3. Develop the payload operations concept	End-to-end concept for all mission phases and operating modes	Determine how end users will receive and act on fire detection data	Define user method to specify product needs, recover and use materials	Secs. 4.2, 15.3 Chap. 29
4. Determine required payload capability to meet mission objectives [identify key characteristics of interest]	Required payload capability	12-bit quantization of radiometric intensity in the 3–5 mm wavelength	Throughput of 5,000 wafers/day on orbit	Sec. 15.3
5. Identify candidate payloads	Initial list of potential payloads	Specifications for Sensors #1 and #2	Specifications for Factories #1 and #2	Sec. 15.3
6. Estimate candidate payload capabilities and characteristics [mission output, performance, size, mass, and power]	Assessment of each candidate payload	Sensor #1 meets the sensitivity requirement but requires a data rate of 10 Mbps. Sensor #2 can only identify flaming fires that are 10 K warmer than the background but requires a data rate of only 1.5 Mbps	Factory #1 produces 6,000 wafers/day, weighs 80 kg, and uses 2 kW Factory #2 produces 4,000 wafers/day (some of which will have >1 ppb impurities), weighs 100 kg, and uses 500 W	Sec. 15.3
7. Evaluate candidate payloads and select a baseline	Preliminary payload definition	Spacecraft and ground architecture based on 1.5 Mbps data rate. Adjust mission requirement to identify flaming fires only (not smoldering)	Select #1 with 1,000 wafers/day margin to be sold to reduce cost	Sec. 15.3 Chaps. 16, 17
8. Assess life-cycle cost and operability of the payload and mission	Revised payload performance requirements constrained by cost or architecture limitations	FireSat II spacecraft with acceptable mission performance and cost	Payload repackaging to accommodate launch as an Ariane secondary payload on ASAP ring	Sec. 15.3 Chaps. 5, 11
9. Identify and negotiate payload-derived requirements	Derived requirements for related subsystems	Data handling subsystem requirement to accommodate payload data rate of 1.5 Mbps	ACS system to provide 140 continuous min of jitter less than ± 1 nm	Sec. 15.3
10. Document and iterate	Baseline payload design	Baseline FireSat II payload	Baseline WaferSat payload	

ferences must we detect? For WaferSat, how pure must the resulting material be? For mobile communications, how much rain attenuation must we be able to accommodate? These will be iterative trades as we begin to define the payload instruments and can intelligently evaluate cost vs. performance.

3. Develop the Payload Operations Concept. Ultimately, the data or product produced by the payload must get to the user in an appropriate form or format. How will the end user of FireSat II data receive and act on the satellite data? How will the manufacturer recover the WaferSat materials and define what is to be done on the next flight? Payload operations will have a major impact on the cost of both the spacecraft and mission operations. As discussed in Chap. 29, payload operations may be done by the same facility and personnel that handle the spacecraft or, as with the Space Telescope, payload operations may be an entirely different operations activity.

4. Determine the Required Payload Capability. What is the throughput and performance required of the payload equipment to meet the performance thresholds defined in Step 2? For FireSat II, what are the specifications on the equipment needed to meet the temperature, resolution, or geolocation requirements? For WaferSat, how many wafers of what size will it produce? For mobile communications, how many phone calls or television channels must it handle simultaneously?

5. Identify Candidate Payloads. Here we identify the possible payloads and their specifications. For simple missions there will be a single payload instrument. For most missions, there will be multiple instruments or units which frequently must work together to meet mission requirements. Different complements of equipment may break the tasks down in different ways and may even work with different aspects of the subject. Thus, a system designed to identify the source of solar storms may have an imager and a spectrometer or a magnetometer and an instrument to map small temperature fluctuations on the photosphere or in the solar wind.

6. Estimate Candidate Payload Characteristics. Here we need to determine the performance characteristics, the cost, and the impact on the spacecraft bus and ground system so that we can understand the cost vs. performance for each of the viable candidate systems. Payloads will differ in their performance and cost, but also in weight, power, pointing, data rate, thermal, structural support, orbit, commanding, and processing requirements. We must know all of these impacts to conduct meaningful trades.

7. Evaluate Candidates and Select a Baseline. We examine the alternatives and make a preliminary selection of the payload combination that will best meet our cost and performance objectives. In selecting a baseline, we must decide which elements of performance are worth how much money. The payload baseline is strongly related to the mission baseline and cannot be defined in isolation of the rest of the parts of the mission and what it will be able do for the end user.

8. Assess Life-cycle Cost and Operability. Ultimately, we want to determine mission utility as a function of cost. This process was described in detail in Chap. 5. Typically it will not be a simple cost vs. level of performance characterization. Rather, it is a complex trade that requires substantial interaction with potential users and with whatever organization is funding the activity. It may become necessary at this point to relax or prioritize some of the mission requirements in order to meet cost and schedule objectives. For FireSat II, we may decide that only one type of fire or one geographic region will be addressed. For WaferSat, we may reduce the purity, the size of the wafers, or the throughput.

9. Define Payload-derived Requirements. In this step we provide a detailed definition of the impact of the selected payloads on the requirements for the rest of the system (i.e., the spacecraft bus, the ground segment, and mission operations). FireSat II will have power, pointing, geolocation, and data rate requirements. WaferSat may care very little about pointing and geolocation, but will have requirements on the spacecraft cleanliness levels and jitter control. These, in turn, may levy secondary requirements such as storage for on-board commands or thermal stability for pointing and jitter control.

10. Document and Iterate. Although this point is emphasized throughout the book, we stress again the need to document what we have decided, and why. The "why" is critical to allowing the system trades to proceed at a future time. We can make preliminary decisions for a wide variety of reasons, but we must understand these reasons in order to intelligently continue to do payload and system trades. Like all of the space mission analysis and design processes, payload definition is iterative. We will come back to the process many times as we learn more about the consequences of preliminary choices.

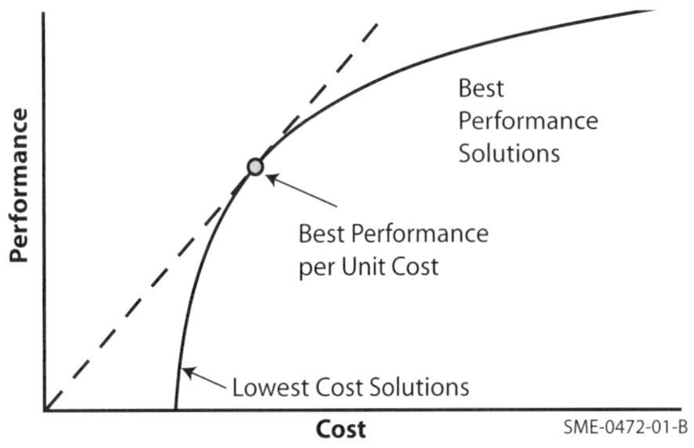

Fig. 15-2. Performance vs. Cost. The tangent point is the highest performance per unit cost.

Figure 15-2 illustrates the conceptual process of payload sizing. At the bottom end of the curve, we need to spend a minimum amount of money to achieve any performance at all. Near minimum performance, a small amount of additional expense will substantially increase performance. At the top end of the curve, we can spend a lot of money for very small improvement. The overall payload performance per unit cost follows a straight line through the origin and whatever point on the performance vs. cost curve we are working at. Therefore, the maximum performance per unit cost occurs where a straight line through the origin is tangent to the curve. There are good reasons for operating at any region along the curve in Fig. 15-2. To design a good payload, we must decide where along the curve our particular mission should be. At the high end, we obtain the best available performance. This would be appropriate for some military or science missions, such as the Space Telescope or Chandra X-Ray Observatory. Very small satellites such as CubeSats are at the bottom end of the curve. They perform modestly at very low cost. They may also be appropriate for multi-satellite, distributed architecture systems. Large commercial activities such as communications satellites, need the best performance per unit cost.

The key to deciding how to size our payload is to look carefully at the mission objectives, particularly the tacit rules which often imply how well we want to do. Do we need the best performance regardless of cost? Can the mission proceed only on a minimum budget? Is this a long-term, continuing and potentially competitive activity in which performance per unit cost is critical? The answers to these questions will let us correctly size the payload and the mission to meet our mission objectives.

15.4 The Electromagnetic Spectrum

As Fig. 15-4 illustrates, the *electromagnetic spectrum* extends across a very broad range that spans at least sixteen orders of magnitude in wavelength or frequency. It includes *gamma rays* and *X-rays*, with extremely short wavelengths measured in angstroms (Å = 10^{-10} m), as well as *visible* and *infrared* (IR) wavelengths of 10^{-7} to 10^{-3} m and the *microwave* region from 0.1 to 30 cm. Finally, it ranges into the *radio* spectrum, with wavelengths as long as kilometers. As the figure shows, satellite systems operate over the entire spectral range. Normal wavelengths for comsats, radars, and microwave radiometers range from approximately 1 m to 1 mm, whereas visual and IR systems operate from around 0.35 to 100 mm (1 micron 10^{-6} m = 1 μm).

For all electromagnetic radiation in a vacuum, the relation between the wavelength, λ, and the frequency, υ, is

$$c = \lambda\, \upsilon = 2.997\,924\,58 \times 10^8 \text{ m/s} \qquad (15\text{-}1)$$

where c is the speed of light. Thus, in terms of frequency, the usable electromagnetic spectrum ranges from radio waves measured in kilohertz (kHz) to gamma rays with frequencies in the tens of exahertz (EHz). (1 kilohertz = 1,000 cycles/s ≈ 300 km wavelength; 1 exahertz = 10^9 GHz = 10^{18} cycles/s ≈ wavelength of 3 Å or 3 × 10^{-10} m).

At any temperature above absolute zero (0 K), all matter continuously emits electromagnetic radiation. This is called *thermal radiation* or *blackbody radiation*. For a *perfect blackbody*, the rate of total energy emission and the energy distribution by wavelength or frequency is a function only of the temperature, *T*. The spectrum of emitted radiation by a real body is related to the perfect blackbody by a radiation efficiency factor called *emissivity*, which is the ratio at every wavelength of the emission of a real body to that of the ideal or blackbody under identical conditions. For solid opaque objects without extended atmospheres like spacecraft or asteroids, emissivity depends largely on surface characteristics. For planets or stars that have atmospheres, emissivity is determined by how light propagates through the atmosphere of these objects. Even though the emissivity of real objects can be much less than one, in practice, the blackbody energy distribution is a good starting point for analysis. The spectral energy distribution of a blackbody is given by *Planck's Law:*

$$E_\lambda = \frac{2\pi h c^2 \varepsilon}{\lambda^5} \frac{1}{e^{ch/kT\lambda} - 1} \qquad (15\text{-}2)$$

where E_λ is the emitted power density per unit wavelength (also called the spectral irradiance and typically measured in $Wm^{-2}\ \mu m^{-1}$), λ is the wavelength, h is Planck's constant (6.6260755 × 10^{-34} Ws^2), *T* is the temperature in K, c is the speed of light, ε is the emissivity and k is Boltzmann's constant (1.380658 × 10^{-23} Ws/K). Figure 15-3 shows typical energy distribution curves for various blackbody temperatures. When E_λ is divided by the solid angle (in steradians) for an extended source emitting in a given direction, the result is L_λ which is called the *spectral radiance* (typical units, $Wm^{-2}\mu m^{-1}sr^{-1}$).

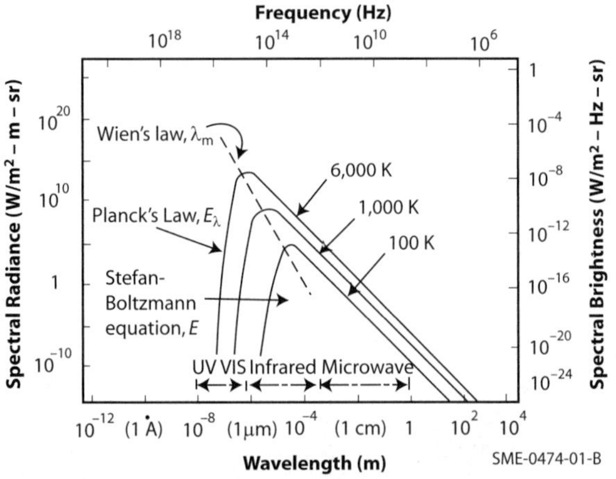

Live Calc

Fig. 15-3. Planck's Blackbody Radiation Curves as a Function of Wavelength and Frequency [Chen, 1985]. Planck's Law defines the shape of the curve over all frequencies, the Stefan-Boltzmann's Law defines the area under the curve (the total energy emitted over all wavelengths), and Wien's displacement law defines the wavelength of maximum radiance.

From Planck's Law we can derive two other important relations. First, we obtain the *Stefan-Boltzmann's Law* by integrating Eq. (15-2) over the complete spectrum, which results in the total *radiant emittance*, W_b:

$$W_b = \varepsilon\, \sigma\, T^4 \qquad (15\text{-}3)$$

where σ is the Stefan-Boltzmann constant, 5.67051 × 10^{-8} $Wm^{-2}\ K^{-4}$, and W_b is in Wm^{-2}.

Next, we derive *Wien's Displacement Law* by differentiating Eq. (15-2) and setting the result equal to zero. The straight-line result defines the locus of peak spectral radiance vs. temperature, as shown on Fig. 15-4 and defined by

$$\lambda_{max} = 2.898/T \qquad (15\text{-}4)$$

where λ_{max} is in μm and *T* is in K.

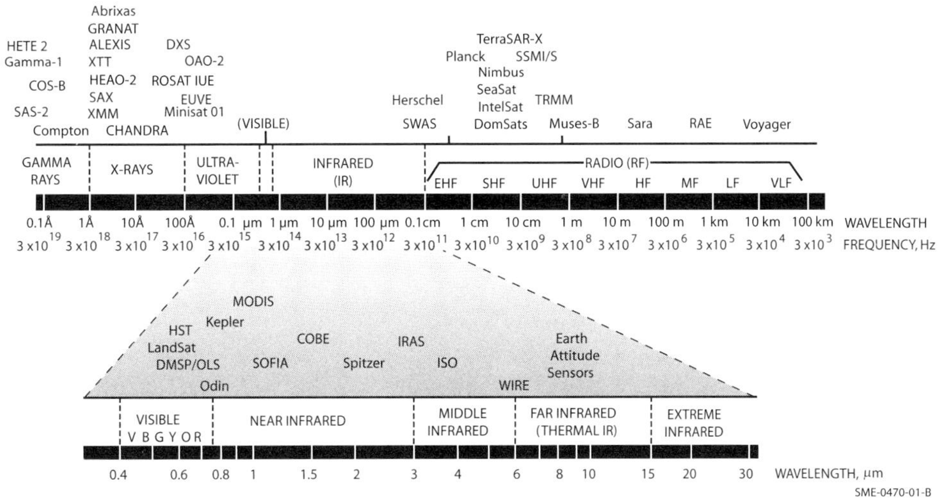

Fig. 15-4. The Electromagnetic Spectrum. The expanded view highlights visible and infrared wavelengths frequently exploited by satellites. Sample space missions across the entire spectrum are listed above the band region.

Remote-sensing instruments are aimed at a target on the Earth's surface or in space. Radars measure the characteristics of reflected, self-generated signals. For other sensors, an object's spectral radiance, or brightness, depends on its equivalent blackbody temperature or brightness temperature. This is the temperature of a perfect radiating body which has the same radiance. Visible wavelength systems can take advantage of the Sun's reflected energy, based on its brightness temperature of about 6,000 K. Of course, without sunlight, visible wavelength images are much less distinct. Laser-based sources of illumination can improve image quality for visible wavelength systems operating with low levels of natural illumination. On the other hand, systems using infrared and passive microwave radiometry measure the thermal emission from the Earth or other objects or scenes of interest. Thus, they can operate day or night, and for long enough wavelengths these systems can operate through clouds and other atmospheric disturbances. Note, however, as shown in Fig. 15-3, that thermal emission in the RF is much weaker than in the infrared spectral region. Well known sources of thermal radiation include the cosmic background radiation with brightness temperature of 2.7 K, room temperature objects at about 300 K and the hottest known stars with brightness temperatures close to 40,000 K. A typical Earth surface temperature is about 300 K, depending on location and season. Noctilucent clouds in the Earth's mesosphere at altitudes of about 80 km can be as cold as 150 K.

As Fig. 15-5 shows, the electromagnetic spectrum has many frequency bands for which the Earth's atmosphere is nearly opaque. We must avoid these bands if we wish to observe ground scenes or communicate to the surface of the Earth. This phenomenon also allows us to sound the atmosphere and measure such interesting data as the thickness and location of cloud layers, water vapor contained in clouds, and other upper-atmospheric phenomena using the opaque bands. Clouds, rain, and snow tend to produce noise and thus attenuate signals for both communication and remote-sensing, even in the window bands. However, as the figure shows, for long wavelengths, atmospheric effects are relatively weak, which is one of the important reasons why almost all communication systems operate in the RF and why RF imaging techniques such as Synthetic Aperture Radar (SAR) discussed in Sec. 17.2 are so valuable in providing nearly all weather imaging capability.

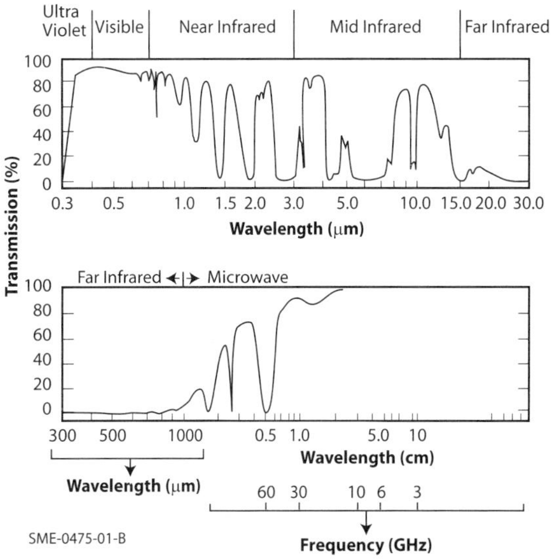

Fig. 15-5. Transmission Characteristics of the Earth's Atmosphere. Transparent regions are referred to as *windows* in the atmosphere.

When a sensor views an area in space, the radiation that reaches the sensor could come from a number of sources. The energy reflected directly from the target is usually the dominant feature of interest for optical re-

Table 15-7. Sources of Radiation. Radiation that reaches the sensor can come from a number of different sources. This table shows all direct and single-scatter radiation that reaches a space sensor.

Source	Path to Sensor	Spectral Band
Sunlight	Scattered by the atmosphere	Visible
	Scattered by the atmosphere, then reflected off the Earth	Visible
	Reflected off the Earth	Visible
	Reflected off the Earth, then scattered by the atmosphere	Visible
Ground	Emission (including fires, volcanos, and man made lighting)	IR & Visible
	Emission scattered by the atmosphere	IR
Atmosphere	Emission	IR
	Emission reflected by the Earth's surface	IR
	Emission scattered by the atmosphere	IR

mote sensing, but other emitted, reflected and scattered energy can complicate the picture (Table 15-7).

The sources of radiation in Table 15-7 give rise to a number of different strategies for distinguishing different phenomena within the atmosphere or on the surface. For a given application, any of the sources of radiation will either be the subject being analyzed or noise to be minimized. Radiative measurements include the full complexity of all the effects on that radiation such as reflection, refraction, absorption, transmission, and scattering by material substances in solid, liquid, and gaseous phases. Distinguishing and identifying features using remote sensing techniques must take all of these variables into account. As Miller and Friedman [1996] advise, "when modeling the real world, allow for some slack to represent reality."

15.5 Examples

Space mission payloads span a remarkably broad range of subject, function, size, mass, power and other characteristics, depending on what is needed to respond to mission requirements. This final section of the chapter examines three very different payloads: the Hubble Space Telescope, the TerreStar-1 communication satellite, and QuakeSat. Both Hubble Space Telescope and TerreStar-1 were designed to put significant capability into space, to provide a unique astronomical observation capability in the case of Hubble and, in the case of TerreStar-1, to enable use of small handheld communication transceivers from the surface of the Earth to geosynchronous orbit. QuakeSat was constrained by cost to simplify the space segment to the greatest degree possible and to build system capability through post processing of data in the ground segment.

Hubble Space Telescope. The Hubble Space Telescope (HST) is one of the most important astronomical observatories in history, because of the breathtaking range of discoveries made by scientists using this unprecedented research tool. Scientific discoveries made with HST range from imaging the first planet outside the solar system to discovering the source of relatively long duration gamma ray bursts first noticed in the 1960s by the DoD Vela satellites. Perhaps, the most fundamental scientific research made with HST involves measuring the expansion rate of the Universe so accurately that the rate of change of that expansion can be assessed with much higher confidence. This work shows the expansion rate of the universe is actually increasing rather than decreasing as had been previously thought and may require a form of energy called dark energy to explain.

The idea of putting a telescope into space was first suggested by Oberth [1923]. The first steps toward the HST began in 1946, when the American astronomer Lyman Spitzer wrote a seminal paper describing the advantages of a space-based astronomical observatory. The two main advantages of an extraterrestrial observatory include: angular resolution limited only by diffraction, rather than by local atmospheric turbulence, as occurs on the surface of the Earth and the capability to observe entire electromagnetic spectrum including portions of infrared and ultraviolet strongly absorbed by atmosphere (Fig. 15-5). Professor Spitzer and others pursued the idea of a large space telescope for decades, until it was finally approved for development in 1978. HST was launched into orbit by the space shuttle in 1990.

HST's mission is to enable scientific discovery and study of astronomical objects from space in ways that cannot be achieved from the Earth's surface. The passive subjects of this mission are every astronomical object ranging from the moon to the most distant known objects, with some emphasis and priority given to the most distant objects. Unlike virtually every other space payload developed and launched to date, HST was designed to be serviceable, so that its suite of scientific instruments could be repaired and updated with the latest technology over a period of decades. Five servicing missions have occurred to date, with the most recent one completed in 2009. Clearly, HST's mission would benefit from the largest and highest quality telescope that could be launched into space within budget and other constraints. Early design thinking pointed to a 3 m aperture telescope. However, in the end, due to budget constraints and the need to fit HST within the space shuttle cargo bay, the HST ended up as a 2.4 m diameter telescope. Likewise, a higher orbit would have benefitted the mis-

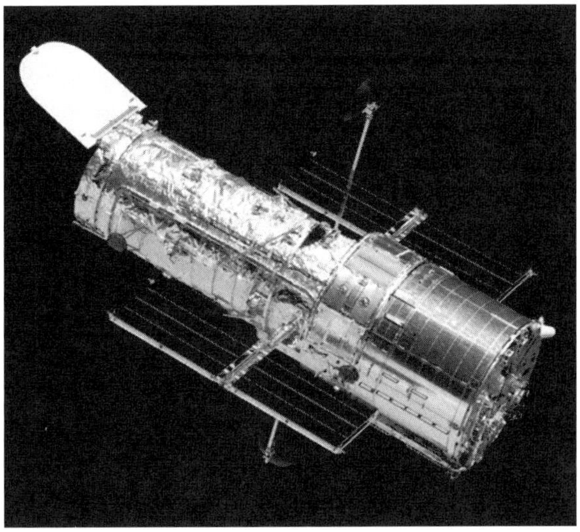

Fig. 15-6. Photograph of Hubble Space Telescope Taken from the Space Shuttle Atlantis at the End of the Final Servicing Mission (STS-125). (Photo courtesy of NASA)

sion objectives by being more distant from the Earth thereby increasing the solid angle available for astronomical observations at any given time and by reducing thermal and scattered light effects of the Earth on the system. However, the important need for astronauts to service the observatory required the HST be within range of the space shuttle.

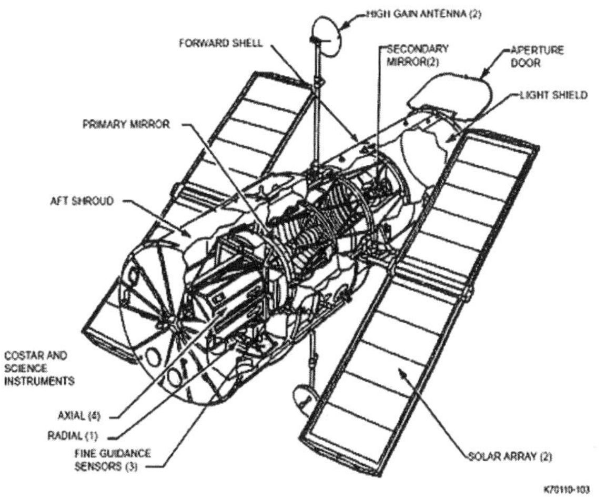

Fig. 15-7. Cutaway View of the Hubble Space Telescope. (Photo courtesy of NASA)

HST orbits at an altitude of slightly less than 600 km. The telescope is a 2.4 m Ritchey-Chretien reflector. Figure 15-6 shows a photograph of the HST captured by the space shuttle Atlantis, at the end of the fifth and almost certainly final servicing mission (STS-125). Key characteristics of the system are summarized in Table 15-8. Figure 15-7 shows a cutaway view of the HST and its instruments.

Table 15-8. Hubble Space Telescope Characteristics.

Launch Date	1990 April 24
Orbit	569 km altitude, 28.5 deg inclination
Primary Mirror Diameter	2.4 m
Telescope Focal Length	57.6 m
Length	13.2 m
Maximum Diameter	4.2 m
Mass	11,110 kg
Required Power	2.8 kW
Current Instrument Suite	NICMOS: near infrared camera/spectrometer COS: Cosmic Origins Spectrograph ACS: optical survey camera WFC3: wide field optical camera STIS: optical spectrometer/camera FGS: three fine guidance sensors
Line of Sight Stability	34 nrad over 24 hours
Cost at Launch	$1.5B (1990$)
Expected Mission End of Life	2014

HST was launched with a flawed primary mirror. Shortly after launch, HST images revealed a serious problem with the optical system. Images appeared sharper than ground-based images, but the best image quality obtained was much lower than the expected diffraction limited performance. Point sources spread out over more than one arcsec, instead of the specified and expected 0.1 arcsec. Analysis showed the primary mirror had been ground to a wrong shape resulting in a large halo in the point spread function (PSF), despite a detailed and extended pre-launch test program. The mirror was ground very precisely to the wrong shape, because a key piece of test equipment had been assembled incorrectly. This piece of equipment called a null corrector is intended to make a non-spherical mirror like the HST primary look spherical in testing. This fabrication flaw reduced effectiveness of the telescope for observations of very faint objects and for high contrast imaging. Spectroscopy and observations of bright objects were not seriously affected. Following a detailed investigation, a "Corrective Optics Space Telescope Axial Replacement" (COSTAR), essentially two mirrors in the light path with one figured to correct the spherical aberration, was designed and installed in the HST during the first servicing mission with Endeavor (STS-61) in 1993. COSTAR fixed the problem and enabled many of the key discoveries made by HST. However, to fit COSTAR into HST, one instrument had to be removed. Astronomers selected the High Speed Photometer. Subsequent HST instruments were designed to compensate for the distortion caused by the primary mirror so that COSTAR was no longer needed. It was returned to Earth on May 24, 2009 at the end of the last servicing mission.

The intended serviceability of HST along with highly skilled work by the engineers and astronauts who designed and implemented the COSTAR repair made it possible to rescue the HST mission. Normally, space mission hardware is not repairable in flight, although software fixes are frequently implemented to improve performance in-flight. (Some would argue that it would have been less expensive to build a better, more modern replacement telescope and launch it on a less expensive expendable.) Recent trends with development of fractionated spacecraft with replaceable modules and robotic servicing spacecraft to increase mission lifetime of large communication satellites suggest the lessons learned by HST may find more widespread implementation in future space missions.

TerreStar-1. At the time of its launch in 2009, TerreStar-1 was the largest satellite ever put into geosynchronous transfer orbit and the largest commercial communications satellite ever built. TerreStar-1 carries S-band (~2 GHz carrier frequency) transponders for providing mobile voice and data communications across North America. An interesting feature of this system is that it is enhanced by an Ancillary Terrestrial Component (ATC) to improve coverage performance in areas where the satellite signal could be blocked by buildings, dense forests or other surface features. One of the defining characteristics of the satellite is an 18 m reflector that was unfurled after launch. The reflector is used to generate hundreds of spot beams across the coverage area to enable use of small handheld phones for two-way communication. Since its launch, Terrestar-1 has been surpassed in size by the SkyTerra satellite, launched in 2010. Table 15-9 summarizes key characteristics of TerreStar-1.

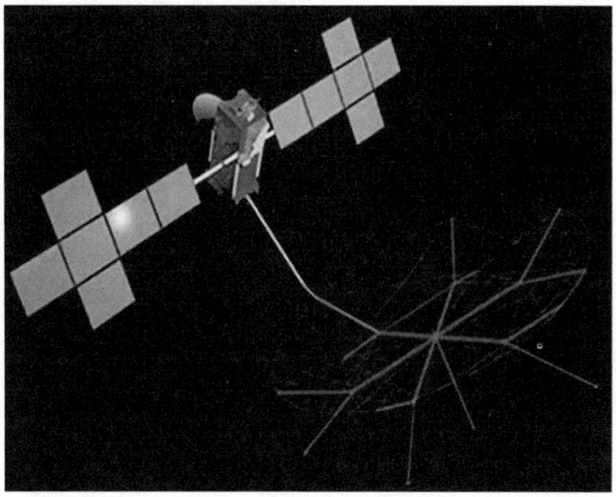

Fig. 15-8. TerreStar-1 Satellite Showing the Unfurled 18m Reflector. (Graphic courtesy of Space Systems/Loral)

TerreStar-1's mission is to provide two-way communication across a broad region for small handheld phones that will operate seamlessly with a ground-based 2G/3G cellular phone network or with the satellite in remote areas and during times of natural disaster or other interruptions in ground-based network service. The active subject in this mission is small, highly mobile communication terminals with users that aren't terribly concerned with whether their needs are being met by a ground-based network or a satellite-based network. The mission need to maintain communication in remote areas and during times of crisis, drove the design to include a highly reliable space segment. The need to make the ground-based communication terminals small and relatively low power, drove the space payload design to include a large aperture reflector on board to generate the large number of spot beams. From Eq. (17-6), we can estimate the size of each spot as being ~700 km in diameter at nadir, assuming diffraction limited performance for the reflector. By steering these spots actively throughout the coverage area, the system can minimize the total amount of power required to maintain contact between the satellite and the ground-based terminals while maintaining the relatively low data rate communication required for this system. The satellite generates hundreds of spot beams covering the Continental US, Canada, Alaska, Hawaii, Puerto Rico, and the US Virgin Islands.

Table 15-9. TerreStar-1 Characteristics.

Launch Date	2009 July 1
Orbit	Geostationary (35,786 km altitude) at 111 W longitude
Deployable Reflector Diameter	18 m
Communication Band	S-band (~2 GHz)
Size	7.6 × 3.6 × 2.8 m^3 (32.44 m span in orbit)
Mass	6,910 kg
Required Power at End of Life	14.2 kW
Number of Beams	~500
Expected Mission End of Life	2024

QuakeSat. QuakeSat (flown 2003–2010) was a triple Cubesat system developed by QuakeFinder/Stellar Solutions, Stanford University and Lockheed Martin in 2002–2003. Its mission was to detect, record and report ELF radio emission by seismic activity occurring in conjunction with earthquakes and to help establish whether such signals could be used to predict earthquakes. The intent, as described by Long et al. [2002] was to follow up previous reports of ELF detection by the Russian satellite, Cosmos 1809, which detected ELF signals immediately after a magnitude 6+ earthquake in Spitak, Armenia in 1989 and a French satellite, Aureol 3, that also reported similar results in a worldwide survey of ELF frequencies over active earthquake regions. Early trade studies showed that this mission could be implemented at very low cost using a Cubesat-based approach.

The key element in the QuakeSat payload was an AC magnetometer sensitive to low frequency magnetic field variations in the 0.5–1,000 Hz frequency range. The magnetometer was mounted at the end of a 70 cm long boom, as shown in Fig. 15-9. To provide an indication of spacecraft orientation, an infrared sensor was pointed along the direction of the boom to detect either the bright thermal emission from Earth or the cold darkness of deep space.

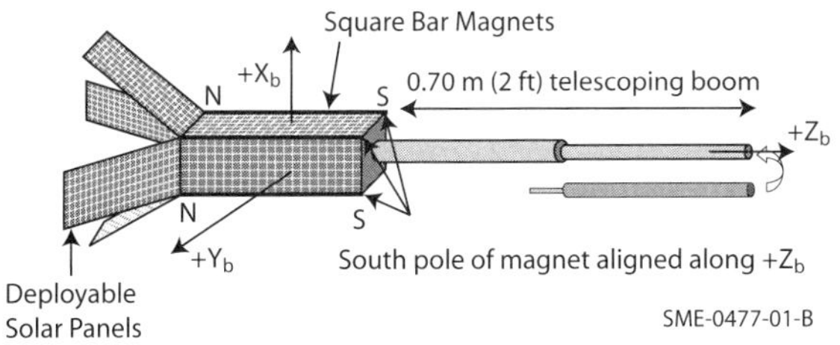

Fig. 15-9. QuakeSat Satellite Showing ELF Sensor on Deployable Boom. (Graphic courtesy of QuakeFinder/Stellar Solutions, Stanford University, and Lockheed Martin)

Table 15-10. QuakeSat Characteristics.

Launch Date	2003 June 30
Orbit	840 km altitude, polar sun synchronous orbit at terminator
Size	36 × 11 cm^2 (stowed) and 152 × 81 cm^2 (deployed)
Mass	4.5 kg
Required Power at Beginning of Life	14 W
Key Payload Element	AC magnetometer
Spacecraft Attitude Alignment	Within ~10 deg of local magnetic field line
Cost at Launch	~$1M
Expected Mission End of Life	6 months after launch (operated successfully for at least 11 months)

Flagg et al. [2004] reported that QuakeSat detected the type of signals expected for the mission within about 2 months after launch. Interpretation of the data was complicated by the complex propagation path taken by the signal along Earth magnetic field lines and by being in a terminator orbit, whose crossing time coincides with turbulent activity in the ionosphere. In parallel with this space-based measurement system, the QuakeSat team made similar measurements using a ground-based network. Results from these measurements found that the signals of interest appear to be short duration pulses lasting only 1–10 sec that occur with a duty cycle of approximately 5–10%. Thus, a LEO satellite like a single QuakeSat would be within measurement range of specific earthquake areas for only about 2–15 minutes per day, so chances of being at the right place when pulsations occur are relatively small. Nevertheless, an advantage of a low cost Cubesat approach (Sec. 25.4) is that it would be relatively inexpensive to deploy a large constellation of these satellites, if the mission appears promising. Work continues in this area.

References

For annotated bibliography of overview of payload design, see the book website.

Aviv, David G. 2006. *Laser Space Communications.* Norwood, MA: Artech House, Inc.

Ball, A. J., J. R. C. Garry, R. D. Lorene, and V. V. Kerzhanovich. 2007. *Planetary Landers and Entry Probes.* New York, NY: Cambridge University Press.

Chen, H.S. 1985. *Space Remote Sensing Systems: An Introduction.* Orlando, FL: Academic Press.

Eckart, Peter. 2006. *The Lunar Base Handbook, 2nd ed.* Space Technology Series New York, NY: McGraw Hill Companies.

Flagg et al. 2004. "Using Nanosats as a Proof of Concept for Space Science Missions: Quakesat as an Operational Example." SSC04-1X-4. 18th USU Conference on Small Satellites. Aug.

Gabriel, Kamiel. 2007. *Microgravity Two-Phase Flow and Heat Transfer.* Space Technology Library. El Segundo, CA: Microcosm Press and Springer, NY.

Glaser, Peter E., F. P. Davidson, and Katnka Csigi. 1997. *Solar Power Satellites.* Chichester, UK: Praxis Publishing and Springer.

Harland, David M. and Brian Harvey. 2008. *Space Exploration 2008.* New York, NY: Springer.

Klein, John. 2006. *Space Warfare.* New York, NY: Routledge.

Kraemer, Robert S. 2006. *Rocketdyne: Powering Humans Into Space.* Reston, VA: AIAA.

Long, et al. 2002. "A Cubesat Derived Design For a Unique Academic Research Mission in Earthquake Signature Detection." SSC02-1X-6. 16th USU Conference on Small Satellites.

Miller, John L. and Edward Friedman. 1996. *Photonics Rules of Thumb: Optics, Electro-optics, Fiber Optics, and Lasers.* New York, NY: McGraw Hill Companies.

Oberth, Hermann. 1923. *Die Rakete zu den Planetenräumen* (By Rocket into Planetary Space) (in German) München, Germany: R. Oldenbourg.

Pelton, Joseph and Peter Marshall. 2009. *License to Orbit: The Future of Commercial Space Travel.* Burlington, ON, Canada: Apogee Books.

Pillai, S. Unnikrishna, K. Y. Li, and B. Himed. 2008. *Space Based Radar: Theory & Applications.* New York, NY: McGraw Hill Companies.

Pillet, V. Martinez, and A. Aparicio, and F. Sanchez. 2005. *Payload and Mission Definition in Space Sciences.* Cambridge, UK: Cambridge University Press.

Seedhouse, Eric. 2008. *Tourists in Space: A Practical Guide.* Chichester, UK: Praxis Publishing and Springer

Squyres, S.W., et al. 2003. "Athena Mars Rover Science Investigation." *Journal of Geophysical Research.* Vol. 108, Issue E12.

Young, Anthony. 2007. *Lunar and Planetary Rovers.* Chichester, UK: Praxis Publishing and Springer.

Zarchan, Paul. 2007. *Tactical and Strategic Missile Guidance, 5th ed.* Progress in Astronautics and Aeronautics. Reston, VA: AIAA.

16 Communications Payloads

Rabindra Singh, Ed Pentaleri, and Kent M. Price,
Space Systems/Loral

16.1 Space Mission Communications Architectures

All spacecraft must include a communications function, whether associated with telemetry, tracking, and control (TT&C) in support of satellite operations (Chap. 21), transmission of data generated by observation and scientific payloads (Chap. 17), or as a primary mission objective (Chap. 16). By any measure, communications applications are dominant among all satellite missions, with support for terrestrial communications being most significant. This chapter discusses architecture and key design concepts and considerations for RF communications payloads dedicated to support terrestrial communications. Table 16-1 describes the process flow for developing space mission communications architectures and detailed designs.

Before a design team can begin to develop a communications payload architecture, there must exist a higher-level *space mission communications architecture* to define the context within which the communications payload architecture must function, and to define connectivity, interfaces, and requirements associated with other elements of the overall communications system. Since these higher-level connectivities, interfaces, and requirements determine the feasibility of communications payload architectures and guide their optimization, we begin with a brief overview of space mission communications missions and associated architectures.

We then follow with the *communications payload architecture* which describes the configuration of payload elements that is used to receive transmitted RF signals, and to filter, amplify, direct, and re-transmit them to other receivers.

The *communications link design* is the detailed link assessment, where we incorporate the ground and satellite terminal characteristics, with propagation details to establish a solution which provides an acceptable positive

Table 16-1. The Communications Payload Design and Sizing Process. The link budget (Step 3) is a deterministic process that allows us to determine that each communications link will work successfully under the assigned conditions.

Step	Comment	Where Discussed
1. Define Space Mission Communications Architecture	Defines mission objectives and requirements	Sec. 16.1.1
2. Define Communications Payload Architecture	Defines the configuration of payload elements	Sec. 16.1.6
3. Perform Link Analyses	Required for all links	Sec. 16.2
4. Define Communications Payload Design	This is the hardware implementation of each link	Sec. 16.3
5. Estimate Payload Mass, Power, and Thermal Demands	Key sizing parameters	Sec. 16.3
6. Document and Iterate	Throughout the Architecture and Design Process	Secs. 16.1, 16.2, 16.3

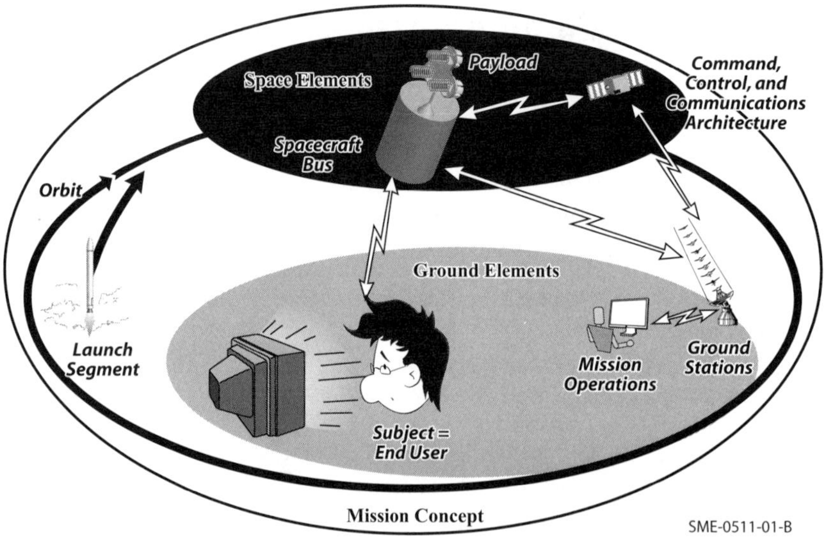

Fig. 16-1. Space Mission Communications Architectures Are Typically Divided Into Space Elements and Ground Elements. Although there is no universally accepted definition for the boundary between the space and ground elements, the full system architecture comprises a network of one or more satellites, ground terminals, control facilities, and user terminals (in some applications) that are interconnected by communications links.

margin to the link performance and thereby consistent with the architectural description. The *communications payload design* is the detailed implementation of the architecture, comprising the specification of components and the detailed description of the way that those components are integrated on the satellite to satisfy system performance requirements, again in a manner that is consistent with the architectural description.

Following a sequence analogous to that developed in Chap. 4 for the overall *space mission architecture*, this section describes a systems engineering process flow for synthesizing and refining *communications payload architectures*. Development of the corresponding *communications link design* is presented in Sec. 16.2 and *communication payload design* is presented in Sec. 16.3.

16.1.1 Space Mission Communications Architectures

Space mission communications architectures are typically divided into two segments, a space segment and a ground segment, as illustrated in Fig. 16-1, that between them comprise a network of satellites, ground terminals, control facilities, and user terminals (in some applications) that are interconnected by communications links.

Table 16-2 describes the elements of the space mission communications architecture that the communications payload architecture and design must support. (See Chap. 15.) In short, the space mission communications architecture defines the topology for the overall communications network and the data rates and protocols in each direction on the communications link between each node in the network of system elements (nodes being

Table 16-2. Space Mission Communications Architecture Elements. These elements differ somewhat from those in Table 4-13 because for communications payloads the "subject" often is the end user.

	Element	Description/Comment	Where Discussed
1	***Constellation Definition and Network Topology***	Includes orbit type and the number of satellites that operate together within the system as well as physical-layer connections between nodes of the satellite communications system, satellite to ground-terminal links, satellite to end-user links, and satellite-to-satellite links (cross-links)	Chap. 10, Sec. 16.1.2
2	***User terminal characteristics and the number and distribution of user terminals***	Individual user terminals and ground terminals User terminals are not present in all space mission architectures or even in all space communications system architectures. Where they do exist, the user-terminal characteristics and distribution are often abbreviated in terms of a description of the coverage areas, and the corresponding *G/T* and *EIRP* contours (*G/T* and *EIRP* are discussed in Sec. 16.3). Ground terminals typically used as principal interfaces to terrestrial wide-area networks	Secs. 16.1.3, 16.3
3	***Spectrum Allocation and Reuse***	Operating bands (typically RF) of the electromagnetic spectrum used in each direction of each communications link in the system, including any spectral reuse that may be required to satisfy capacity and geographic coverage requirements	Sec. 16.1.4
4	***Traffic Characteristics***	Data rates in each direction for each link or type of link, and any switching that may be required between different nodes of the communications network. FSS, MSS, and BSS for example, exhibit very different traffic characteristics	Sec. 16.1.7

defined as satellites, user terminals, and ground terminals). That is, the space mission communications architecture provides all of the information that is needed to understand the number of communications links that each satellite's communications payload must support, the characteristics of those links, whether switching may be required between different beams, and whether the satellite beams that support the communications links can be fixed or whether it may be necessary to modify either the shape or the direction of satellite beams while on-orbit.

16.1.2 Constellation Definition and Network Topology

The orbit type and the number of satellites in the constellation have a fundamental impact on the design of any space mission. For a communications mission, orbit type and constellation size are interrelated. As an example, whereas a single satellite (free flyer) in *geosynchronous* (or *geostationary*) orbit can provide continuous availability to a fixed region of the earth, multiple satellites must be used in a coordinated manner to provide continuous availability for systems based on constellations that employ other orbit types. (See Chap. 10.)

Orbit type also plays an important role in the definition of the satellite communications payload. Orbit diameter plays a principal role (in combination with user-terminal and ground-terminal characteristics and the geographic distribution of user terminals and ground terminals that must be served) in determining the power and sensitivity that will be required for the communications payload to maintain terrestrial communications links, for example. And whereas satellites in geosynchronous orbit may be able to use fixed antennas for terrestrial communications links and satellite cross-links, systems based on satellites in other types of orbit must either use tracking antennas or lower-gain antennas that have more limited communications capacity.

The network topology of the space communications network is defined by the number and locations of the various nodes: satellites, user terminals, and ground terminals and by the flexibility that is required for establishing connections between nodes. Like the orbit type, this topology, combined with the required traffic characteristics plays a fundamental role in shaping the requirements for the communications payload architecture. In fact, just as satellite constellations are classified according to orbit type (LEO, MEO, GEO, polar, or inclined), they too are classified according to the topology and flexibility of the network required for a given communications mission. Table 16-3 describes several examples of orbit-type and space communications network topology, and summarizes key advantages and disadvantages associated with each.

Table 16-3. Comparison of Five Sample Space Mission Communications Architectures, with Focus on the Relationship Between Orbit Type and the Space Communications Network Topology.

	Orbit Type	Advantages	Disadvantages
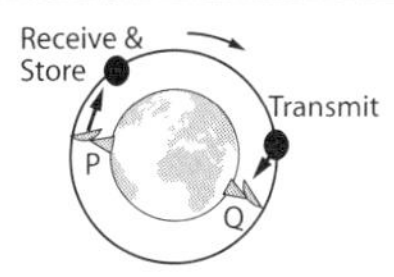	*A. Low-Altitude Single Satellite, Store & Forward*	• Low-cost launch • Low-cost satellite • Polar coverage with inclined orbit	• Long message access time and transmission delay (up to several hours)
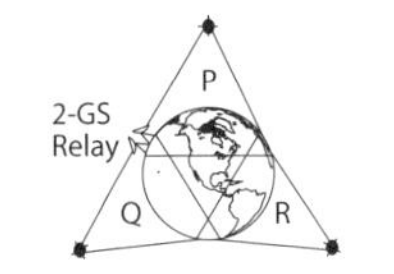	*B. Geostationary Orbit*	• No switching between satellites • Ground station antenna tracking often not required	• High-cost launch • High-cost satellite • Need for stationkeeping • Propagation delay • No coverage of polar regions
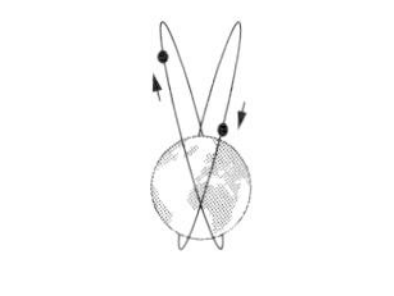	*C. Molniya Orbit*	• Provides coverage of polar region • Low-cost launch per satellite	• Requires several satellites for continuous coverage of one hemisphere • Need for ground station antenna pointing and satellite handover • Network control more complex • Need for stationkeeping
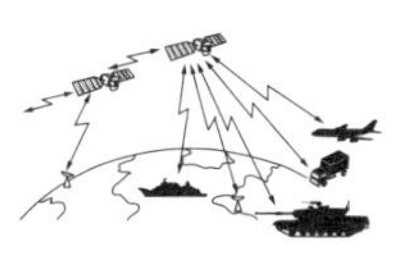	*D. Geostationary Orbit with Crosslink*	• Communication over greater distance without intermediate ground-station relay • Reduced propagation delay • No ground stations in foreign territory: – Increased security – Reduced cost	• Higher satellite complexity and cost • Need for stationkeeping • Relay satellite and launch costs • No coverage of polar regions
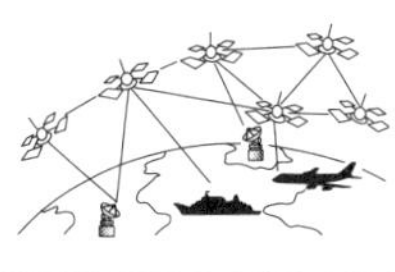	*E. Low-Altitude Multiple Satellites with Crosslinks*	• Highly survivable—multiple paths • Reduced jamming susceptibility due to limited Earth view area • Reduced transmitter power due to low altitude • Low-cost launch per satellite • Polar coverage with inclined orbit	• Complex link acquisition ground station (antenna pointing, frequency, time) • Complex dynamic network control • Many satellite required for high link availability

16.1.3 Terrestrial Terminals

In this context, the term *ground terminal* is equivalent to Earth station, ground station, gateway, and Earth terminal, and is used in connection with the principal terrestrial nodes within the communications system. Ground terminals are distinguished from user terminals by virtue of their typically much larger RF sensitivity and much greater peak radiated power flux density, and in their frequent role as trunk-line interfaces to land-line or terrestrial RF wide-area networks [Elbert, 2000].

In contrast, user terminals, which may be land mobile, airborne, or ship borne, typically have much lower sensitivity than ground terminals, operate at much lower power, and serve a single user or a relatively small number of users on a local-area network. Both ground terminals and *user terminals* share in common the fact that they each include one or more antennas, a transmitter, a receiver, and control equipment required to communicate with the satellite.

16.1.4 Spectrum Allocation

To ensure that all users of the RF spectrum can operate without interfering with or being interfered by other users, *spectral allocation* is governed both by national and international regulatory bodies. To ensure the interoperability of both terrestrial and space-based systems, including commercial, scientific, military, and personal uses, these regulatory bodies have defined very detailed specifications that control the *frequency ranges* (bands) and maximum *power flux densities* that must be used for each application, as well as coordination that is required to take place between users in overlapping or adjacent geospatial domains. Because these regulatory requirements and coordination with other users place strict limits on the operating bands and radiated power flux density, spectral allocation has a direct impact on the architecture of satellite communications payloads.

Within the US, for example, the Federal Communications Commission (FCC) regulates spectrum allocation for commercial applications, while the National Telecommunications and Information Administration (NTIA) coordinates and regulates government users, including military, intelligence, meteorological, scientific, and other missions. International standards, including regulations that govern spectrum allocation*, power flux density limits, and coordination requirements, are defined by the Radio Regulations (RR) of the International Telecommunications Union (ITU), an agency chartered by the United Nations to standardize and coordinate the operation of telecommunications systems and services.

Although cognizant regulatory authorities define permitted uses for each portion of the RF spectrum, coordination with existing users often imposes further restrictions on the operating bands available for a new application. And while the *operating band* specified for new applications must clearly be compatible with other parts of the space mission *communications architecture* (e.g., existing user terminals), further constraints must usually be observed in order to maintain interference within prescribed limits near the boundaries between operating bands, and at geospatial boundaries that are reserved for existing users or are governed by other regulatory entities. Given the complexity of regulatory compliance and coordination with other users, spectral allocation can be one of the fundamental factors that determines whether a satellite communications architecture will be designed to operate at L, S, C, X, K_u, or K_a band, and the feasibility of specific constellation types, orbits, and other factors that are fundamental to both system and satellite payload architectures.

Figure 16-2 shows how the NTIA allocates the RF spectrum across various applications. As a specific example of the way that these allocations can affect the architecture of a satellite communications payload, Fig. 16-2 highlights the 500 MHz wide K_u-band transmit and receive operating bands (11.7 to 12.2 GHz and 14.0 to 14.5 GHz, respectively) that are typical for many commercial communications satellite applications. The NTIA defines non-commercial uses of these bands as including communications satellites and Earth stations operated by both Federal civilian and military agencies for voice, data, and video signals using commercial geostationary satellites, and for radio astronomy research conducted by the National Science Foundation.

Spectrum Reuse

The *capacity* of a *communications link* is directly related to the *spectral bandwidth* available to support the link. Given the tremendous constraints to bandwidth allocation presented by regulatory prescriptions and coordination with other users, the total bandwidth available to a new application is frequently far smaller than what is necessary to support the traffic capacities required with a single beam for each geographic coverage area that must be served. This limitation can be overcome, however, by dividing the allocated spectrum into non-overlapping bands and designing the satellite communications payload so that each service area is covered by an array of beams, each of which occupies a band that is different than the bands occupied by adjacent beams, as illustrated in Fig. 16-3. This strategy for satisfying capacity needs within limits of spectral constraints is known as *frequency reuse*, because each of the spectral sub-bands can be reused many times, provided that beams operating at the same frequency are sufficiently isolated from one another by virtue of the shape (or roll-off) and direction of each beam.

Using this technique, the effective bandwidth available can be multiplied to achieve a reuse factor that is given by the ratio of the number of beams to the number of unique frequency bands (also referred to as "colors").

* It should be noted that the ITU is also charged with allocating satellite orbits (orbital slots).

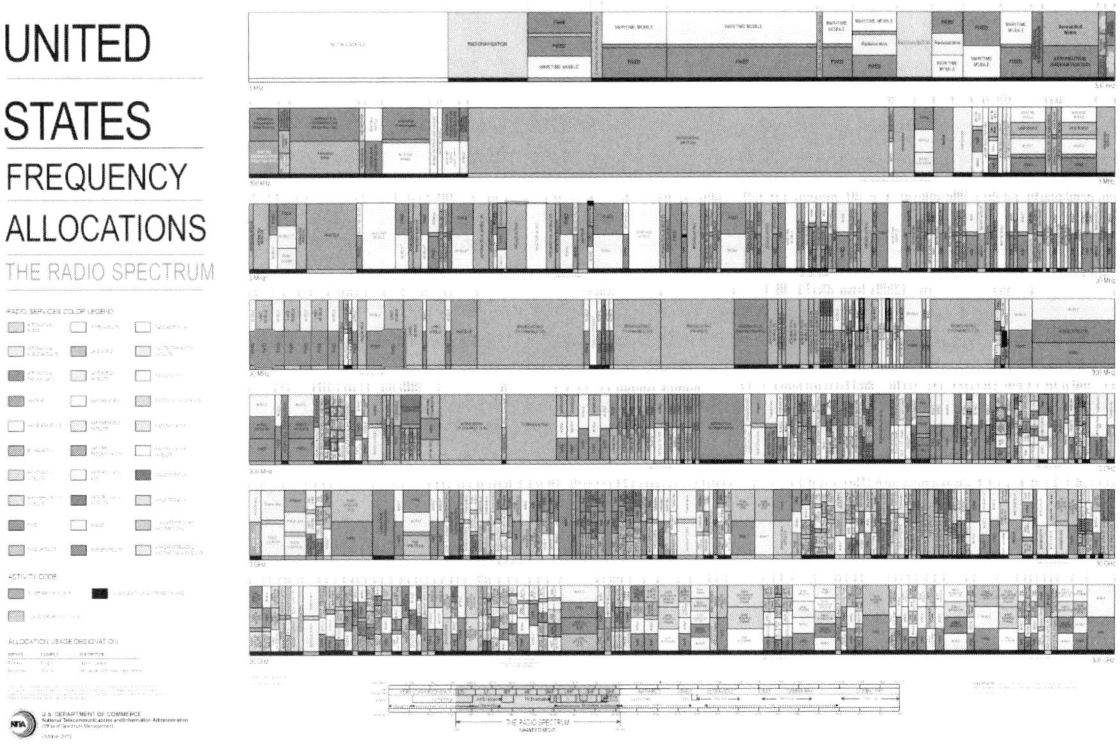

Fig. 16-2. Radio Spectrum Frequency Allocations, as Defined by the United States National Telecommunications and Information Administration (NTIA), Showing the Detailed and Complex Assignments of Bandwidth Across Applications [NTIA, 2010].

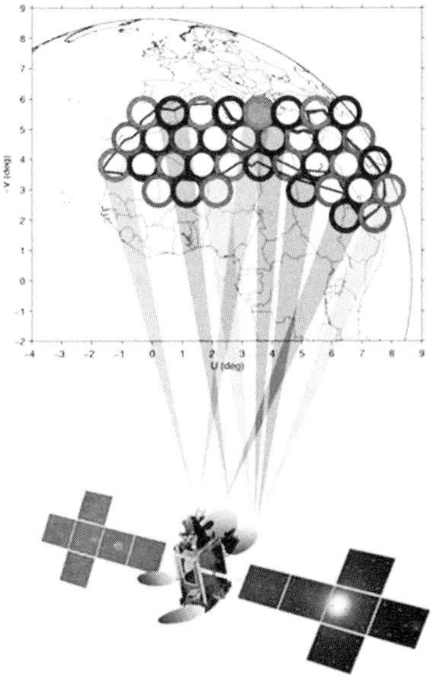

Fig. 16-3. By Dividing Available Bandwidth into Non-overlapping Sub-bands, Each Sub-band Can be "Reused" Over Non-adjacent Geographic Areas.

Likewise, *polarization reuse* can be used to further multiply the total usable bandwidth by taking advantage of the isolation (typically in the range of about 30 dB) that can be achieved between orthogonal polarizations (whether linear or circular).

In Fig. 16-3 we can see the benefit of polarization and frequency reuse. If there was only polarization reuse with *linear horizontal* and *vertical polarization* applied to one single ubiquitous coverage area, then the effective bandwidth would be 2 × 500 MHz = 1 GHz divided into a total of 24 (36 MHz) transponders. If however, we also employ frequency reuse, with 4 color spot beam coverage as shown in Fig. 16-3, we achieve sufficient isolation between beams of the same color. Then the effective bandwidth for $n = 36$, $m = 4$ is $2 \times 500 \times 36/4 = 9$ GHz or an equivalent of 225 36 MHz transponders. In other words, we have achieved an order of magnitude improvement in capacity. The drawback to this is the increased architecture complexity of the communications payload.

Although frequency and polarization reuse can be used effectively to increase the capacity of space mission communications systems, these system-level architectural elements drive fundamental aspects of the corresponding communications payload architectures by requiring the implementation of multi-beam arrays or phased arrays. Defining channelization, bandwidth allocations, decisions as to the use of analog vs. digital payload alternatives, are also among the many attributes that can be driven by the decision to implement frequency and polarization reuse.

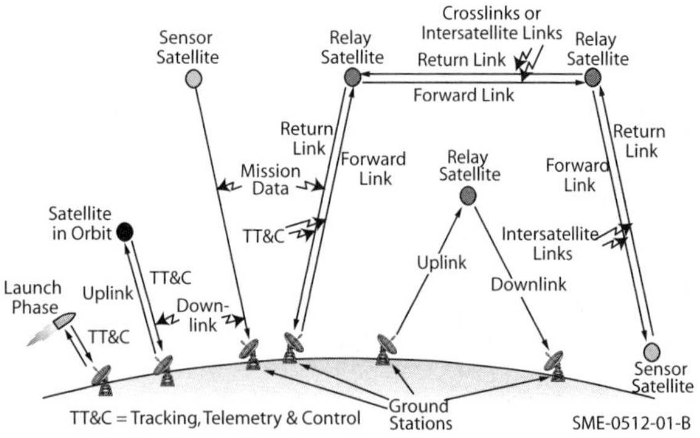

Fig. 16-4. Communications Links Carry Telemetry, Tracking, and Command (TT&C) Data or Mission Data Between Nodes of the Space Mission Communications System.

16.1.5 Communications Links

Communications links allow a satellite system to function by carrying *telemetry, tracking and command* (TT&C) data (Chap. 21) or mission data between nodes of the space mission communications system. In many cases, this involves transmission of the sensor data that are collected by a separate observation payload (Chap. 17). In other cases, however, the entire purpose of the space mission is to provide satellite-based communications, where the data on the communications links and the mission data are one and the same. (Fig. 16-4).

In this chapter, we focus on the architecture and design of spacecraft communications payloads that support the exchange of mission data between system elements via *radio frequency* (RF) communications links. *Link analysis* is fundamental to the development of both communications payload architectures and detailed designs. A detailed discussion of link analysis is presented in Sec. 16.2.

16.1.6 Communications Payload Architecture Development

Following a sequence analogous to that developed in Chap. 4 for the overall space mission architecture, this section describes a systems engineering process flow for synthesizing and refining communications payloads architectures. The corresponding process for developing a communications payload design is described in Sec. 16.3.

Table 16-4 describes the process for developing a *communications payload architecture*. The process comprises five steps: defining the architectural requirements, identifying the architectural elements subject to trade and identifying the main alternatives that are available for each tradable element, synthesizing candidate architectures, assessing performance, and down-selecting and iterating concepts until a final architecture emerges.

Definition of Requirements

Like any development effort, the process for developing a communications payload architecture begins with defining an appropriate set of requirements. The specific set of requirements that is flowed down to the satellite communications payload will differ from one development to the next, depending on a number of factors, including technical and regulatory considerations, program risk, business considerations, and other factors. An important example of a regulatory factor is in the specification of the specific operating bands that must be used for each coverage area (Sec. 16.1.1). While it is common for the operating bands for each beam to be specified on the basis of existing ground segment hardware that is to be used or on the basis of licenses that have been applied for or already received, there are cases in which payload architectures may be developed with little or no practical limit as to specific operating bands. This may occur, for example, in the development of new satellite communications systems that do not require the use of specific existing user terminals. In the absence of such constraints, it may be possible to better optimize overall system architecture and performance. Rather than having ground segment or regulatory considerations impose an *a-priori* constraint on system and payload architectures, payload driven requirements might guide specifications that are flowed to gateway and user terminal developers and spectrum license applications.

Table 16-4. Communications Payload Architecture Development Process

	Step	Description/Comment
1	***Define architectural requirements***	Specify the attributes that must be exhibited in order for the communications payload architecture to be viable and how candidate architectures will be assessed to rank alternatives
2	***Identify elements subject to trade and identify the main alternatives for each tradable element***	List those payload elements that can be supported by more than one alternative. Identify the design degrees of freedom, focusing on the alternatives that have the greatest potential to materially affect measures of effectiveness
3	***Synthesize candidate architectures***	Identify element alternatives and combinations of element alternatives that work well and that do not work well
4	***Assess compliance***	Evaluate the performance of each candidate architecture in terms of the requirements
5	***Ranking, selecting, iterating, and finalizing architectural concepts***	Rank candidate architectures based on measures of effectiveness, assess sensitivity of highest-rated alternatives, and iterate architectural concepts until a final architecture can be selected

Table 16-5. Partial Listing of Typical Requirements Flowed Down From the Communications System to the Communications Payload Architecture.

	Requirement	Representative Requirements
1	*Coverage*	Definition of uplink and downlink coverage areas and gateway locations Specification *G/T* and *EIRP* required for each coverage, including gateways
2	*Coverage Flexibility*	Description of coverage areas and gateway locations that are to be fixed, gateway locations and user beam coverages that may be moved after launch, and user-beam coverages whose shape must be capable of being changed while on-orbit
3	*Connectivity*	Definition of the mapping required between uplink beams/channels and downlink beams/channels
4	*Connectivity Flexibility*	Specification of switching and routing that the communications payload must accommodate
5	*Operating Bands*	Intended uplink and downlink operating bands for both communications signals and for bus and payload telemetry, tracking, and control Approximate channel sizes and counts (in some cases)
6	*Size, Mass, Power, and Thermal Budgets*	Aperture suite must be compatible with a specific bus configuration and launch fairing Maximum allowable mass, DC power, and thermal dissipation
7	*Lead Time (Development Risk)*	Target date or calendar months from contract to launch or on-orbit delivery
8	*Payload Cost/Price*	Target cost or price for payload development, production, integration, and test

Table 16-5 provides a list of requirements that are typically involved in the definition of a communications payload architecture. Because these requirements will be used to assess compliance and rank performance in steps 4 and 5 of the process, it is important that requirements are stated in a way that allows them to be objectively evaluated for each of the candidate architectures.

Identification of Tradable Elements and Principal Alternatives

Once the payload architectural requirements have been defined, the next step in the architecture development process involves identifying the elements of the communications payload that are subject to trade, and the main alternatives for each *tradable element*. The satellite communications payload architecture comprises the four elements described in Table 16-6: antennas, spectrum allocation, repeater type, and payload topology. In most instances, antennas, repeater type, and payload topology will be tradable, though there is sometimes at least some flexibility with respect to spectrum allocation. For each of the tradable elements, many alternatives are available. Note that although some of these alternatives are represented at a very high level in Table 16-6, the actual array of alternatives from which the design team has to choose spans many dimensions within each architectural element, and cannot possibly be represented in such a simple tabulation. Of the universe of alternatives within each tradable architectural element, only a subset will have potential applicability for a particular payload, and these are the building blocks from which the payload architecture will be constructed.

Synthesis of Candidate Architectures

Based on the main alternatives that have been identified for each tradable element, synthesis of the communications payload architecture begins by considering the alternatives (a) in different combinations, and (b) with different connectivity between components. As will be true for the detailed design, synthesis of candidate architectures typically begins by considering the orbital slot that the satellite will occupy, the geographic areas that must be serviced, the operating bands for uplinks from and downlinks to each coverage area, the characteristics of the ground terminals and user terminals with which the satellite must establish RF connections (frequently referred to as communications or *Comm links*), and the data rates that must be supported on each link.

Ordinarily, the *orbital slot* and the required bandwidth allocations will have been specified as part of the space mission communications architecture, as will the characteristics of the ground terminals and user terminals. In these cases, it is common for the terminal characteristics to have been translated into (A) the power flux density at the spacecraft that will be received from terrestrial terminals and (B) corresponding power flux density that must be transmitted by the communications payload (expressed as *equivalent isotropic radiated power,* or *EIRP* (Sec. 16.2).

Based on an understanding of the alternatives available in terms of *Low-Noise Amplifiers* and typical input signal losses, *link analyses* (Sec. 16.2) are performed to obtain an initial estimate as to the *antenna directivity* that will be required to reliably detect and distinguish uplinked signals that reach the satellite from thermal noise and other sources of interference. A similar link analysis is performed for each downlink from the satellite, as well, but in this case with the objective of estimating the characteristics of the transmit antennas that will be required for each beam.

The link analyses yield estimates of the directivity that will be required for both receive and transmit antennas. Another outcome of the link analysis is an initial estimate of the bandwidth that will be required for each link. From the directivity, the design team can estimate the size that will be required for each antenna. The bandwidth requirements give insight as to whether the spectral allocations are sufficient to avoid the cost and complexity of *frequency reuse*. While the required con-

Table 16-6. Tradable Elements of the Communications Payload Architecture and Principal Alternatives for Each.

	Element Types	Description	Principal Alternatives
1	*Antennas*	Both transmit and receive antennas for both user links, gateways, and inter-satellite cross-links	• Single element vs. array • Element Geometry (e.g., horn, reflector, helix) • Antenna geometry (e.g., direct radiating, Newtonian, Gregorian, Cassegrain) • Physical vs. electronic beam forming • Fixed vs. mechanical steering vs. electronic steering • Articulation for antennas stowed during launch
2	*Spectrum Allocation*	Spectrum allocated for the communications mission within each beam or coverage area	• L, S, C, X, K_u, K_a • Specific operating bands to be used for each transmit and each receive beam.
3	*Repeater Type*	The subsystem that performs the following functions: receiving, frequency conversion, filtering, analog-to-digital (A/D) and digital-to-analog (D/A) conversion, switching/routing, and amplification	• Transponder: Receives, filters, routes, amplifies, and retransmits analog RF signals • Analog Processor: Supports flexible bandwidth reallocation by filtering received signals into channels and using switch matrices for routing • Digital Channelizer: Filters received analog signal into narrow channels that are digitized to allow highly flexible, reconfigurable bandwidth routing before being converted back to high-power analog RF signals suitable for re-transmission • Router: Performs A/D conversion on received analog signal to support extraction of routing information for demodulated signals. Regenerates and remodulates high-power analog signals for re-transmission. • Digital Processor: Uses information extracted from demodulated signals to control payload configuration or information handling, as, for example, in providing automated phase and amplitude control for phased array bandwidth and spatial coverage adjustments
4	*Payload Topology*	Highest-level concept describing (a) the signal-processing sequence, and (b) the overall strategy for directing the flow of analog and digital signals through the repeater	• Few-to-few (typical for fixed coverages linking gateways and VSATs that serve geographically dispersed terrestrial WANs and LANs) • Many-to-few/Concentrating (typical for broadband satellite services (BSS) and mobile satellite service (MSS) applications) • Few-to-many/Diverging (typical for digital audio radio services (DARS) • Many-to-many (typical for satellite-based broadband IP access) • Intersatellite links

nectivity and connection flexibility between beams determine the nature of switching that will be required, the question of whether beam steering (either mechanical or electrical) needs to be part of the communications payload architecture dictates whether beam forming is necessary. In this manner, by taking consideration of each of the requirements, as well as each of the alternatives available for tradable elements of the architecture, the design team synthesizes one or more candidate architectures to be considered.

Assessment of Compliance

Once candidate architectures have been developed, an assessment must be performed against each. This assessment is performed with respect to the requirements that were identified or flowed down as the first step of Table 16-4. Despite the fact that many requirements will have been identified, even at this early stage of development, assessment of compliance at the first several iterations is ordinarily quite fast because some aspects of the candidate architectures (e.g., switching flexibility) will be compliant by design. While others, such as *EIRP,* can be readily determined on the basis of relatively simple link budget calculations, there are some (such as the ability of available satellite buses to accommodate the number and sizes of apertures) that are likely to yield to the initial judgments of members of the design team, based on experience in previous development efforts.

Ranking, Selecting, Iterating and Finalizing Candidate Architectures

Like the design process, development of architectures is an intrinsically iterative process. At each iteration, candidate architectures are ranked according to their compliance assessment. Equally important as the selection process, the *compliance assessment* also provides insight into the sensitivity of each alternative architecture with respect to pertinent measures of performance. This insight provides valuable guidance as to refinements, optimizations, and elaborations that should be considered, identifying requirements that cannot be satisfied, for additional information that is needed in order for a final architecture to be selected. In this manner, the design team proceeds through successive iterations until a final architecture is identified or it becomes clear that compliance to the requirements cannot be achieved. In the latter case, the design team may solicit or propose relaxation of one or more requirements, at which point the process may resume.

To complete its work in the case that a preferred architecture does emerge the design team must elaborate the preferred architecture at a level sufficient to (A) obtain the concurrence of the program sponsor, and (B) ensure that the documentation of the preferred architecture is sufficiently detailed and unambiguous as to provide a basis for the detailed design.

System-Level Architecture Trades: Partitioning of Performance and Functionality Between Space and Ground Segments

The satellite communications payload is a classic example of an *active* or *controllable subject* (Chap. 4), in the sense that system architects have broad flexibility in partitioning performance and functionality between ground-based and space-based elements. One of the most fundamental examples of this is found in the partitioning of power and aperture sizes between the satellite and ground segment terminals (gateways and user terminals).

Although it might be technically feasible to design a system that uses essentially the same amplifiers and antennas on the satellite, gateways, and user terminals, this never happens in practice. The reason for this is that launch vehicle constraints on mass and size create tremendous incentive to minimize the size, mass, and total power consumed by the satellite payload. On the other hand, in comparison with the satellite, gateways are virtually unconstrained in any of these dimensions. Likewise, user terminals (which may be as small as a mobile phone or a pager), frequently have even more severe size, mass, and power constraints than the satellite communications payload. As a result, the design of satellite communications systems always biases amplifier power and aperture size allocations away from the satellite and toward the gateway, while the nature of the mission will determine the direction and the degree to which aperture size and power are partitioned between the satellite and ground terminals.

In a similar sense, system architectures allow certain functional elements of the satellite communications system to be moved between the space and ground segments. Whereas routing of bit streams is typically performed within the ground segment, some military missions in particular may lead to the development of space-based routing capabilities, such as in applications like command and control of remotely controlled weapons systems, for example, that can have severe latency constraints. Likewise, for satellites that use antenna arrays with electronic steering or beam forming, there are potential advantages in moving beam forming hardware and electronics from the satellite (where these functions have typically been implemented) to ground-based systems where these subsystems can be both implemented at lower cost and more readily maintained over the course of mission life.

This partitioning of performance and functionality typically takes place at the system level. Although these types of trades are not typically open to trade at the level of the communications payload architecture, it is nevertheless worthwhile for payload designers to recognize that such trades exist so that alternatives can be presented when initially stated requirements cannot be satisfied.

Table 16-7. Comparison of Principal Types of Commercial Space Communications Missions.

	Fixed Satellite Service (FSS)	Broadcast Satellite Service (BSS)	Mobile Satellite Service (MSS)
Coverage Areas	Typically large, geographically separated	May be large, but often subdivided into smaller regional coverages, depending on market-driven differences in required capacity and content	Service typically provided over large coverage areas by patterns of overlapping spot beams
Terminals	Usually gateway ground terminals or VSATs	Satellite uplinks from ground terminals and broadcasts directly to small fixed or mobile user terminals	Vehicle-mounted terminals (e.g., providing voice/internet access to aircraft or train passengers), and small hand-held terminals (e.g., satellite-enabled mobile phones) or laptop computers
Traffic	Typically symmetric voice and data flows between coverage areas Supports broadcast to VSATs	Asymmetric, with low to moderate data rates to individual user terminals, and little or no data returning from users	Nominally symmetric low bandwidth voice and data to and from individual user terminals

16.1.7 Satellite Communications Missions

Space Mission applications are dominated by satellite communications missions. This section describes the *principal classifications* used for commercial space communications missions, and key ways in which differences between these missions affect the payload communications architectures. Table 16-7 summarizes key attributes that differentiate the three principal categories of commercial satellite communications missions.

Fixed Satellite Services (FSS)

For many years, *Fixed Satellite Service* (FSS) missions have been the backbone of the commercial satellite industry. Although many permutations exist, FSS satellite communications are ideal for providing fixed-bandwidth, broadcast or telephonic connectivity between large geographically separated coverage areas. And while it is increasingly common for FSS satellites to incorporate a limited amount of beam switching capability, the coverage areas served by FSS systems are typically fixed throughout the mission lifetime of each satellite in the system. Because they provide essentially fixed connectivity and capacity, FSS satellite payloads can be implemented by relatively simple, low cost satellite designs that incorporate fixed, dedicated antennas, and analog repeaters built from very mature component technology, including dedicated high-power amplifiers, analog signal filtering, and mechanical switching. Although business considerations continually push toward larger, more powerful, and higher capacity solutions, most FSS satellite payloads can ordinarily be packaged on low to moderate power satellite buses.

Table 16-7, Fig. 16-4◀, Eq. 16-0

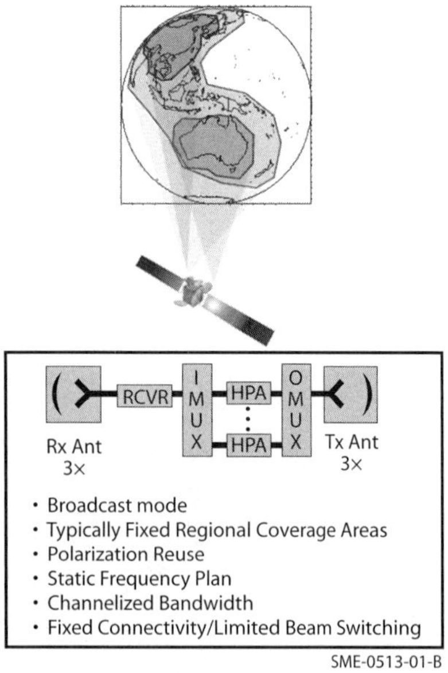

Fig. 16-5. An FSS Satellite Providing Fixed Connectivity Between Ground Terminals in Large Coverage Areas. Depending upon mission requirements, the communications payload may be configured to provide connectivity between terminals within any single coverage area or between any coverage area and one or both of the others. The communications payload architecture, as described in the simplified payload block diagram, is directly related to the FSS mission through the number and type of antennas, the absence of beam switching, and the very straightforward filtering and amplification chain.

FSS systems are capable of supporting broad beam coverage of large geographic areas, providing point-to-point, point-to-multipoint (broadcast), and multipoint-to-point connectivity to ground terminals ranging from very small aperture terminals (VSATs with apertures less than 1 m in diameter) to large gateways with aperture sizes of 10 m or more.

Figure 16-5 illustrates a hypothetical FSS satellite and the kernel of the corresponding payload architecture, as described by a highly simplified "payload block diagram." While the FSS satellite depicted in the figure may be a free-flyer, or may be part of a broader constellation of satellites, this particular satellite provides service to three coverage areas whose operating frequencies are coordinated such that the two smaller coverage areas are able to overlap with the largest. Depending upon mission requirements, the communications payload may be configured to provide connectivity between terminals within single coverage areas or (more commonly) between any coverage area and one or both of the others. Communication may be asymmetric or unidirectional (as in broadcast applications), or may be highly symmetric (as in telephony). A heterogeneous mixture of ground terminals may be served within each region.*

The payload architecture, as described by the simplified payload block diagram, is directly related to the key elements of this FSS payload through the inclusion of three fixed (non-steering) *transmit (Tx)* and three fixed *receive (Rx) antennas*†, each with shaping appropriate to support the required coverage areas, a very straightforward filtering and amplification chain, and fixed connectivity between coverage areas (no switching).

Broadcast Satellite Services (BSS)

Although the FSS satellite communications systems can support broadcast mission elements and functionality, another category of satellite communications systems is more highly optimized specifically for particular broadcast applications. As a category, *broadcast satellite services* (BSS) are growing in commercial significance, and include specialized variants: *direct-to-home* (DTH) video broadcasts to small fixed user terminals, digital audio radio service to small fixed and mobile user terminals (digital radio receivers), and *digital mobile broadcast* (DMB) of video and voice to handheld or vehicle-mount terminals.

Whereas the data flows in FSS networks are typically symmetric, with similar amounts of traffic flowing in each direction between coverage areas, the data flows in BSS systems are highly asymmetric by definition, with large capacity in the "forward" direction (toward end users), and little or no capacity in the "return" direction (from end users). This difference alone drives a fundamental difference in satellite architecture in terms of payload topology. And whereas the terrestrial terminals in FSS systems tend to be collectors that serve as aggregators of data from networks of data generators and consumers, BSS systems are designed to broadcast directly to individual users. This difference has direct implications for payload architecture because user terminals are invariably smaller and less sensitive than the gateway and VSATs that are the basis for FSS systems. As a result, the BSS satellites must transmit substantially greater power flux densities in order to communicate at a given rate with its user terminals than an FSS satellite must transmit to communicate at the same rate with a VSAT or gateway ground terminal. This transmit power differential drives BSS satellites toward the use of large, high-gain antennas and super high-power amplifier combining networks, integrated on a high-power satellite bus, as is illustrated in Fig. 16-6.

Mobile Satellite Services (MSS)

The last main category of commercial satellite communications mission is referred to as *mobile satellite services* (MSS). As in the case of the BSS mission, MSS

* It should be noted that whereas the example provided in Fig. 16-5 represents a mission in which data originating from terrestrial users is transmitted to the satellite, and filtered, amplified, and retransmitted to other terrestrial users, most observation satellites include a communications payload designed to provide similar functionality. In this case, however, the observation payload and associated signal-processing electronics generate the signals that are to be transmitted to Earth; typically to fixed ground terminals, instead of receiving communications uplinks from the Earth.

† These will often be combined into single antennas that support both transmit and receive functions.

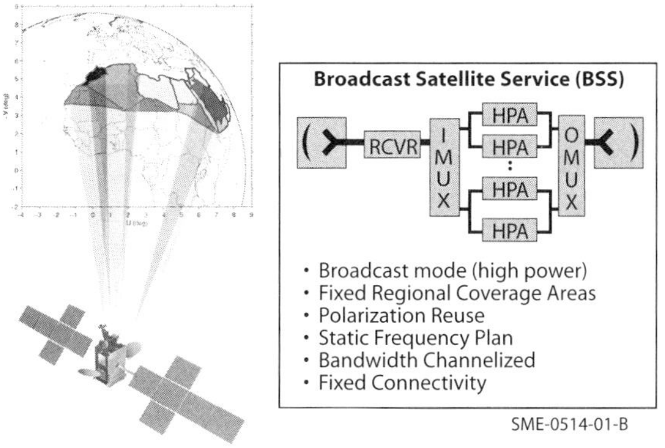

Fig. 16-6. A BSS Satellite Providing Fixed Broadcast Communication Directly to Small Fixed and Mobile User Terminals Within Regional-beam Coverage Areas Tailored for Market-driven Capacity and Content. Asymmetric capacity requirements and service to disadvantaged terminals tend to drive payload architectures for these missions toward asymmetric topologies and high-power combining networks.

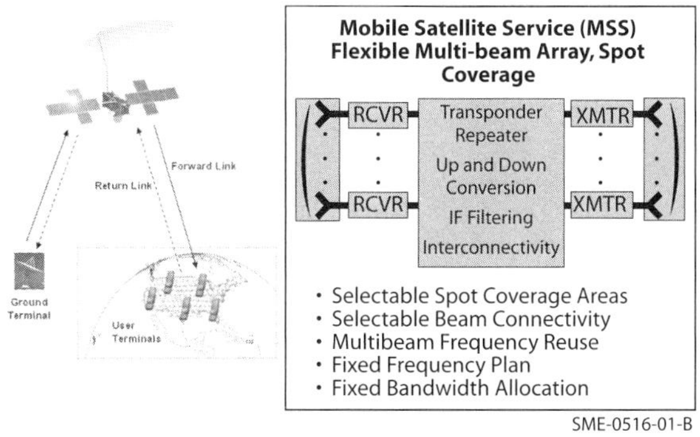

Fig. 16-7. An MSS Satellite Providing Two-way Communication Directly to Disadvantaged Mobile User Terminals Over a Wide Geographic Area. Service to disadvantaged terminals requires very high gain, which is achieved by overlapping highly directive beams where adjacent beam spots occupy different frequency bands. Corresponding military applications (COTM) may also require beam steering, beam forming, and reallocation of bandwidth between different beams. All of these mission requirements result in communications payload architectures that differ dramatically from those used to support FSS and BSS missions.

missions are optimized for direct communications with small individual user terminals. In contrast, MSS missions are optimized for individualized low data-rate user links rather than broadcast of common data at higher rates to many users, and typically require the ability to accommodate similar forward and return traffic flows to each user terminal. As a result, a typical MSS mission therefore involves two-way (full duplexed) communication between the satellite communications payload and mobile phones or laptop computers equipped with the appropriate antennas and electronics. Given these form factors, user terminals are limited in both their sensitivity to signals transmitted from orbiting satellites, and in the signals that they are able to transmit back to the satellite.

Both the need for nominally symmetric two-way traffic, and the transmit/receive limitations of the user terminals drive the communications payload architectures for MSS missions in dramatically different directions than those that are typical for FSS and BSS missions. As a consequence, MSS satellites are designed to have high sensitivity for uplinked return-direction signals from the mobile user terminals, and must also be able to radiate with high power flux density in the forward direction toward the mobile user terminals. For MSS systems based on geosynchronous orbits, these considerations typically drive satellite communications payload designs toward the use of multiple high-gain spot beams whenever the service areas that must be covered are larger than a few hundred miles in diameter.

Although uncommon in purely commercial MSS applications, it is increasingly common for corresponding military missions (referred to as *Comm on the Move*, or COTM) to also require additional capabilities and flexibility beyond those described above for commercial MSS systems. Among these are the ability to support flexible bandwidth allocation between beams, and various processing functions, such as those related to electronic beam forming and the detection and suppression of jamming threats. Figure 16-7 illustrates how both typical commercial MSS requirements and corresponding requirements for military COTM applications can result in the development of payload architectures that are dramatically different than those for FSS and BSS communications systems.

Military Satellite Communications Systems

Although this chapter is presented mainly in the context of commercial communications applications, it should be noted that similar principles apply to non-commercial satellite communications missions, as well. In particular, while military satellite communications systems share important similarities with those of their commercial counterparts, there are important differences between the two that frequently result in fundamentally different architectures and designs. Table 16-8 provides a high level comparison between typical commercial and military satellite communications mission requirements, and how these differences may influence system or payload architectures, despite similar core FSS-like or MSS-like missions.

16.1.8 Concluding Remarks

This section describes the principal classifications used for commercial space communications missions, and key ways in which differences between these missions affect the payload communications architectures. Table 16-7 summarizes key attributes that differentiate the three principal categories of commercial satellite communications missions.

Section 16.1.6 described the process by which communications payload architectures are developed, including the way that the space communications architecture and

Table 16-8. Qualitative Comparison Between Key Factors that Differentiate Commercial and Military Satellite Communications Missions, and Corresponding Consequences for Satellite Communications Architectures.

	Commercial	Military	Typical Consequence to Satellite Communications Architecture
Coverage Areas	May be large or small, but typically stable over extended time horizons that can be predicted at the time initial architectures are being conceived, years in advance of launch	• Global or nearly global access may be required for a small number of users at small to moderate data rates • System may be required to provide large capacity (many users at high data rates) to theaters of operation on short notice (days to months) • Premium is placed upon flexibility, availability, and robustness over maximizing total capacity	Whereas commercial communications satellite payloads are usually able to make extensive use of fixed apertures and fixed bandwidth allocation, with limited beam switching and beam shape flexibility, military satellite communications payloads must often be designed to support steering or tracking to allow beams to be moved, or beamforming to allow beam shapes to be changed
Capacity	• Required capacity tends to be stable or slowly changing over mission lifetime • Often strong incentives to maximize total payload capacity (Gbps), with little or no need for coverage flexibility	• May require only low capacity in most places at most times, but the ability to augment communications capacity to much higher levels on short notice (hours/days) • Peak capacity is typically far below the peak capacity delivered by commercial satellite systems	Commercial satellite applications tend to be optimized for maximum capacity, while corresponding military applications tend to be optimized to robustly provide lower capacity on short notice as theaters of operation are defined and evolve
Reliability, Availability, and Robustness	• Business considerations motivate maximum reliability and availability to maximize return on investment • Operating environment is typically assumed to be permissive/ uncontested	• Maximum reliability and availability are motivated by the desire to maximize military readiness and speed • Contested operating environment must often be assumed	Commercial and military satellite communications missions may be driven to similarly high levels of reliability and availability, but may achieve those objectives based on different motivations, through different solutions, and in response to dramatically different threat and risk assessments. For example, whereas commercial satellite communications systems may emphasize component-level redundancy and ground terminal diversity to minimize weather-related availability reduction, military systems may add component protection/hardening, satellite level redundancy, and ground terminal diversity to provide additional protection against adversarial threats

the requirements of the overall space communications mission affect the communications payload architecture. Section 16.1.7 described how fundamental differences between different types of communcation missions can drive differences in communications payload architectures and designs.

Communications payload design, the subject of Sec. 16.3, is the process of defining the specific and detailed implementation of the communications architecture. Communications links were defined in Sec. 16.1.5. Although a certain amount of link analysis is required in support of communications payload architecture development, communications payload design can not even begin without link analysis, and link analyses remain as a core element of the entire communications payload design process. For this reason, Sec. 16.2 provides a detailed discussion of link analyses and link budgets, which are tools used to systematically perform link analyses.

Although the discussions in both 16.2 and 16.3 are generic, concepts are illustrated through examples based on FSS applications. Additional sample missions are provided in web-based supplements (Sec. 16.4) in which examples are provided for both the SCS and FireSat II missions, with the SCS examples illustrating analysis of alternative missions and solutions for situations in which the original mission requirements could not be satisfied by currently available technology.

A further web supplement covers special topics (Sec. 16.5), including extensions of the concepts described here to other payload types and topologies, including regenerative payloads, processing payloads, routing payloads, ground-based beam forming, hosted payloads, and non-commercial payloads.

16.2 Communication Link Analysis

An RF communication link consists of a transmitter and receiver separated by a free space distance. The transmitter antenna radiates an electromagnetic wave into free space, and the receiver antenna collects the portion of radiated energy which falls on it.

Figure 16-8 shows a satellite communications system which transmits information from a single ground terminal to a number of users, and receives information at the ground terminal from a number of users. The system includes uplink from Earth to satellite, and downlinks

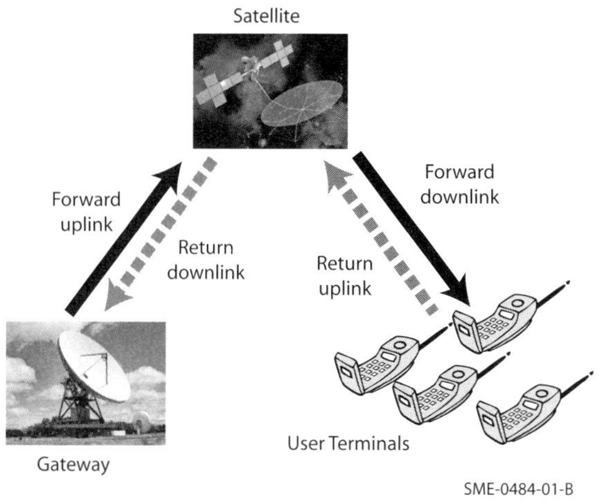

Fig. 16-8. Space Mission Communications System Uplinks and Downlinks. Forward communications links carry information toward user terminals, while Return communications links carry information away from user terminals. Both Forward and Return links include uplinks and downlinks.

from satellite to Earth. In addition to differentiating uplinks from downlinks, a further distinction is made between transmissions that are directed toward end users *(forward links)* and those that are directed away from end users *(return links)*. A space mission communications system may also contain *intersatellite links* (ISLs) that transmit information from one satellite to another, a feature that is used to relax signals between user and/or ground terminals that are beyond the line-of-sight perspective from one another from a single satellite.

The link consists of three parts: transmitter, the propagating electromagnetic signal, and a receiver. The link equation is expressed in terms of received power, transmitted power, the factor by which the transmit and receive antennas amplify signals (gain), and total losses:

$$P_{Rx} = P_{Tx} + G_{Tx} + G_{Rx} - L_{Tx+Rx} \tag{16-1}$$

where P_{Rx} is the power at the receiver, after being collected by the receive antenna and passing through the input section of the receiver; P_{Tx} is the power radiated from the transmitter amplifier; G_{Tx} is the gain of the transmit antenna; G_{Rx} is the gain of the receive antenna; and L_{Tx+Rx} represents all losses, including those associated with the transmitter, the receiver, free space dispersion, and other losses, including atmospheric effects.

Losses include antenna pointing loss, propagation losses in the atmosphere, free space loss, and line losses at the transmitter and receiver.

Regardless of whether the link under consideration is a forward or a return link, link analysis must be performed on an end-to-end link between user terminal and ground terminal that represents the combination of two individual links: the uplink to the satellite and the downlink from the satellite. The principal result of the calculation is the ratio of received power to noise. To interpret the result, this ratio is compared to detection thresholds that are tabulated for appropriately selected operating parameters (Sec. 16.2.1.5). The difference between the power-to-noise ratio and the tabulated detection threshbold is a parameter referred to as the *link margin*. When this value is positive, the received signal can be detected, and the link is said to "close." When it is negative, however, the signal cannot be detected, and the link does not close. To ensure the robustness of a given link, the design team typically designs to a link margin greater than zero, with the magnitude of the positive margin usually being dependent upon the mission criticality of the link.

The *link equation* and the *link analyses* that use it are fundamental to the design of communications system of all types. Despite the simple appearance of Eq. (16-1), however, many physical processes and concepts are represented by each term of the equation. Before the details of the link equation can be adequately described or understood, it is therefore necessary to develop a basic foundation in regard to the following topics:

- Sec. 16.2.1.1 Electromagnetic Waves
- Sec. 16.2.1.2 Polarization
- Sec. 16.2.1.3 Decibels
- Sec. 16.2.1.4 Antennas
- Sec. 16.2.1.5 Modulation, Coding, and Spectral Efficiency
- Sec. 16.2.1.6 Bit Energy to Noise Ratio (E_b/N_o) and Coding Gain
- Sec. 16.2.1.7 Atmospheric Effects

Once these topics have been introduced, we will be prepared to examine in Sec. 16.2.2, the details of the link equation and link analysis in greater detail, and to introduce the *link budget* (step 3 of Table 16-1), a tool for performing link analyses that allows us to optimize design parameters and verify that each communications link will work successfully under the required conditions. Because of the importance of link analyses to the design of communications systems, this section closes with a detailed example of a link analysis and corresponding link budget in the context of an FSS communications link (Sec. 16.2.3).

16.2.1 Overview of Physical Principles of Satellite Communications Links

Fundamental to satellite communications is the propagation and use of electromagnetic waves in establishing a communication link. This section examines the fundamentals of electromagnetic waves and their characteristics for communications.

16.2.1.1 Electromagnetic Waves

The communications links used in space mission communications systems are based on the propagation of electromagnetic radiation through the Earth's atmosphere and the space beyond the atmosphere. Although the vast majority of satellite communications links are based on radio frequency (RF) electromagnetic waves, a small but important and growing fraction is based on signals that are generated in other parts of the electromagnetic spectrum. The discussion in this chapter is presented in the context of RF communications links.

Electromagnetic radiation is generated by accelerating electric charges and by changing electric currents. A current oscillating at a frequency, f, generates electromagnetic radiation in the form of propagating waves whose frequency match that of the source. For the purposes of this chapter, we can consider only the electric component of these waves, which can be described by the following relations.

$$e = |\mathbf{E}|\sin(\omega t) \qquad (16\text{-}2)$$
$$\omega = 2\pi f$$
$$\phi = \omega t$$
$$\lambda = v/f = c/f$$

where

e ≡ instantaneous magnitude of the electric field vector, **E** (V/m),

E ≡ amplitude of the electric field vector

ω ≡ angular rotation of **E** (rad/s)

ϕ ≡ phase angle of **E** (rad)

t ≡ time (s)

f ≡ frequency of the electromagnetic oscillations (Hz)

λ ≡ wavelength (m)

c = speed of light (2.99792458×10^8 m/s)

Figure 16-9 illustrates an electromagnetic wave with the electric and magnetic field vectors orthogonal both to one another and to the direction of propagation.

By convention, the portion of the electromagnetic spectrum used for satellite communications is divided into a number of ranges (or bands). Letter designations for these bands are listed in Table 16-9.

As was discussed in Sec. 16.1.1, regulatory contraints governing satellite operating bands impose a significant constraint on both the architecture and design of communications satellite payloads, with regulatory authority for these assignments being shared between a combination of national and international regulatory bodies.

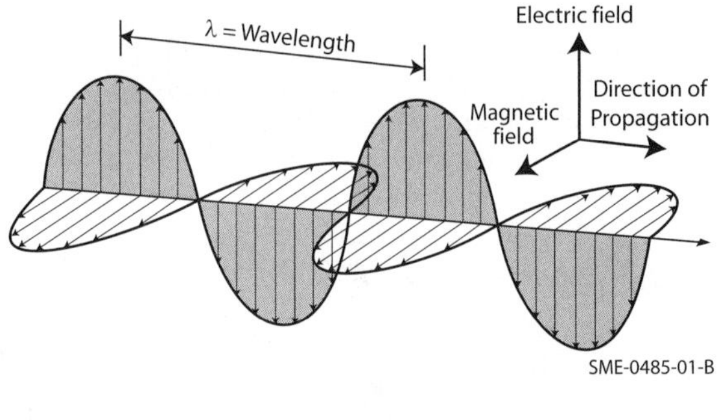

Fig. 16-9. Electromagnetic Wave.

Table 16-9. Satellite Band in the Electromagnetic Spectrum.

Band	Frequency (GHz)
V-band (intersatellite links)	40 to 75
Q-Band	30 to 40
K_a-band	18 to 30
K_u-band	11 to 18
X-band	7 to 11
C-band	4 to 7
S-band	2 to 4
L-band	1 to 2

16.2.1.2 Polarization

The term "polarization" refers to the spatial alignment of the electric field vector, with a single electromagnetic wave being referred to as either "vertically" (V) or "horizontally" (H) polarized. Although the designation is ultimately at the discretion of the user, polarization assignment is typically based on the orientation of the electric field with respect to the Earth's surface.

Circular or elliptical polarization can be obtained through the superposition of two electromagnetic waves having the same frequency that propagate in the same direction and have electric fields that are perpendicular to one another. In this case, the linearly polarized constituent waves combine through vector addition to form a single resultant wave, whose direction of propagation is the same as that of the constituent waves, but whose electric field rotates in a manner that is dependent upon the phase relationship between them. So-called "circular" polarization results if the constituent waves are of equal amplitude, while unequal amplitudes result in "elliptical" polarization. In each case, the polarization sense is *right-handed* (RHCP) if the electric field vector rotates clockwise as viewed in the direction of propagation, and *left-handed* (LHCP) otherwise.

The concept of "polarization" is important because antennas can be designed to respond with high specificity to electromagnetic radiation of one polarization sense, while strongly rejecting orthogonally polarized signals. As a result, by designating both frequency and polarization, polarization becomes a tool that communications engineers can use to effectively double the spectrum available for use. Therefore, the process of bandwidth allocation discussed in Sec. 16.1 takes both frequency and polarization into account.

16.2.1.3 Decibels

Communications engineering is a discipline that involves physical processes (such as amplification and attenuation) and physical quantities (such as power) that typically change by many orders of magnitude within even a small part of the physical system. As an example, the power flux density at a point 100 meters from a ground terminal aperture radiating information toward a geosynchronous satellite may be more than one hundred billion (100,000,000,000) times greater than the portion of the signal that ultimately reaches the receive antenna of the satellite. Although it often appears to be a significant and unnecessary complication to those who are first introduced to the technique, communications engineers use logarithms to both compactly express values that might otherwise extend to many, many digits, and to quickly and efficiently perform many of the calculations that are routinely required.

The decibel (dB) is a base ten logarithmic unit that describes the ratio of a physical quantity (such as the power of an electromagnetic wave) relative to a specified or implied reference level. The decibel value of a number, P is computed as

$$P(\text{dB}) = 10\ \log(P/P_{ref}) \qquad (16\text{-}3)$$

where P_{Ref} is the value to which the decibel expressed quantity is referenced. Note that because decibels express the value of interest in terms of a ratio to a reference level or value, the reference value is critical to interpreting a value that is expressed in decibels.

As an example, 2 Watts (2,000 mW), can be expressed in decibel form as either

$$10\log_{10}(2\ \text{W}/1\ \text{W}) = 3\ \text{dBW} \qquad (16\text{-}4)$$

or as

$$10\log_{10}(2{,}000\ \text{mW}/1\ \text{mW}) = 33\ \text{dBmW} \qquad (16\text{-}5)$$

Although 3 dBW and 33 dBmW refer to the same physical quantity, the notation "dBW" tells the engineer that the value "3" is to be referenced to 1 W, whereas the notation "dBmW" indicates that the value "33" is to be referenced to 1 mW. The only time that a reference value is *not* provided is when the value being expressed represents a pure ratio (which is dimensionless) because pure ratios are obtained by dividing two values that each have the same units. Thus in our earlier comparison of the power received at a geosynchronous satellite, as compared with the power near a terrestrial transmitter, we would express the pure ratio as $1/10^{11}$. Thus, if the power near the transmitter were 10 μW, we might express the ratio in decibel form as

$$10\log_{10}(10^{-11}\ \mu\text{W}/1\ \mu\text{W}) = -110\ \text{dB} \qquad (16\text{-}6)$$

In addition to the advantages of compact notation, certain calculations are simplified once values have been expressed in decibels by virtue of the fact that the values being manipulated are proportional to the base-ten logarithms of the quantities they represent. As a result, we can multiply two quantities by adding their decibel equivalent. Likewise, once two numbers are expressed as decibels, relative to the same reference, we can find their ratio to one another by subtracting the denominator from the numerator. Similarly, exponentiation is replaced by multiplication (positive exponents) and division (negative exponents). Because communications engineering involves large amplification and attenuation factors, and frequently involves calculations with numbers that may differ by many orders of magnitude, decibel math can be simpler, faster, and less error prone, allowing simple addition and subtraction of small numbers to replace multiplication and division of numbers that extend to many digits. Once one becomes accustomed to this type of arithmetic, remembering the decibel equivalents of several common factors listed in Table 16-10 allows rapid calculations and unit conversions.

As examples, the decibel equivalent of a 134.9 W amplifier output power relative to a 1 W reference is 21.3 dBW. If this value needs to be used in a calculation in which other values are expressed in mW, we can express the amplifier's output power as either 134,900 mW, or as 21.3 dBW + 30 = 51.3 dBmW. Likewise, if we are interested in using an amplifier that has only half this power, we can compute that power as either 67.45 W or as 21.3 dBW – 3 db = 18.3 dBW. If the output of the original 139 W amplifier is attenuated by a factor of 40, we can use paper and pencil to find that the attenuated signal will be 134.9 W / 40 ≈ 3.37 W, or we can compute the value quickly by subtracting 16 dB (the decibel equivalents of two factors of two and one factor of ten) from 21.3 dBW to find the attenuated power level of 5.3 dBW.

Table 16-10. Decibel Equivalents Useful for Frequently Used Multiplication and Division, Including Unit Conversions.

Factor	Multiply by Adding/Divide by Subtracting Decibel Values
1	0
2	3
10	10
20	13
100	20
1,000	30

16.2.1.4 Antennas

Antennas are used to launch an electromagnetic wave into space or receive an electromagnetic wave, and to amplify the transmitted or received signals that travel in particular directions relative to the antenna. There are many types of antennas, including simple dipoles, direct radiating horns, reflector antennas, and direct radiating or reflected arrays. Many factors, including the operating frequency, coverage/pattern requirements, and the amplification factor delivered by the antenna determine which antennas are likely to be useful for a given application.

Antenna Gain

Although antennas may be as simple as a single dipole, they frequently include a number of components that operate together as precise mechanical assemblies of feeds, reflectors, and subreflectors. The total amplification factor of an antenna is given by its *gain*, G, a value that includes both the focusing effect of the antenna (directivity, D), which is a measure of the antenna's ability to concentrate energy in a given direction, and various losses (including ohmic transmission-line losses, L for example).

$$G = D - L \qquad (16\text{-}7)$$

Table 16-10, Fig. 16-9◀, Eq. 16-7

Gain is commonly calculated from the frequency, physical size of the antenna aperture, and the antenna efficiency, according to the formula:

$$G = \eta\left(\frac{4\pi}{\lambda^2}\right)A \qquad (16\text{-}8)$$

where G is the gain, η is the dimensionless antenna efficiency, as a function of all losses, including ohmic losses, aperture efficiency, and spillover losses, A is the antenna area (m^2), and λ is the signal wavelength (m).

For an antenna with a circularly symmetric radiating aperture, such as a parabolic reflector antenna of diameter, D, this can be expressed in terms of the signal wavelength or frequency, f, as

$$G = \eta\left(\frac{\pi D}{\lambda}\right)^2 = \eta\left(\pi D\frac{f}{\mathrm{c}}\right)^2 \qquad (16\text{-}9)$$

where, c denotes the speed of light.

Using the decibel-based arithmetic described in the last section, we can express the gain (dB) in terms of aperture size, antenna efficiency, and signal frequency as

$$G = 20.4 + 20\log(f) + 20\log(D) + 10\log(\eta) \qquad (16\text{-}10)$$

where, here, we have expressed f in GHz, combining this conversion with the constants π and c in to the constant 20.4. The relationships given in Eqs. (16-7) through (16-10) can be applied to antennas in a variety of contexts that are pertinent to satellite communications payload architecture and design, including calculations involving point-to-point links between ground terminals and the satellite, and highly directive user terminals. They cannot be applied to antennas whose shaping has been defined to yield irregular coverage contours.

Figure 16-10 illustrates the variation of antenna gain as a function of signal frequency and aperture size, assuming an antenna efficiency of 55%, and with the dBi notation indicating that the directivity in this instance has been normalized to that of an isotropic radiator.

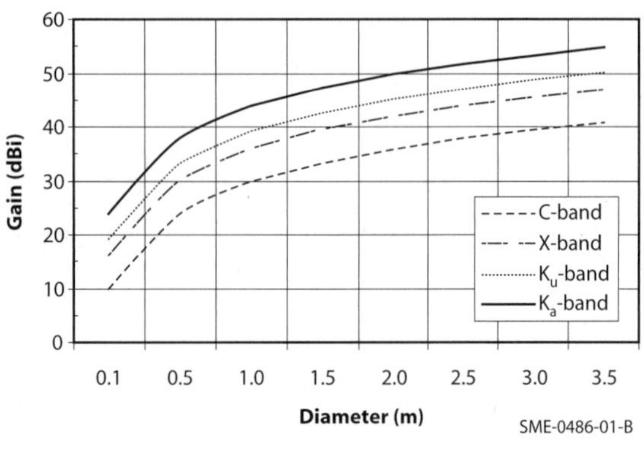

Fig. 16-10. Gain vs. Aperture Diameter, Plotted for Operating Frequencies Common to Satellite Communications Systems.

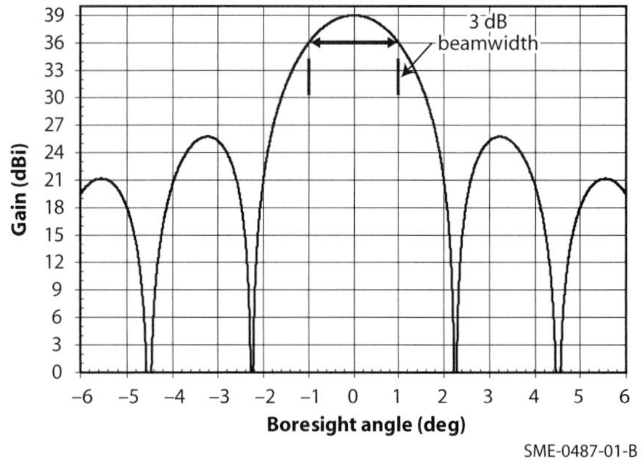

Fig. 16-11. Antenna Pattern for a Hypothetical 0.75 m Parabolic Reflector with Uniform Illumination, and Operated at 14 GHz.

The pattern of antenna gain as a function of angle is usually described in relationship to its peak, or *boresight* value. The half-power beamwidth is the angle with respect to boresight, within which the gain is within 3 dB (50%) of the peak. An antenna having a circularly symmetric aperture is approximated by the formula

$$\Theta = 21/(fD) \qquad (16\text{-}11)$$

where Θ is the half-power beamwidth (deg), f is the frequency (GHz), and D is the antenna diameter (m).

Figure 16-11 shows the variation, or *pattern*, of such an antenna's gain as a function of the angle from boresight for a uniformly illuminated, 0.75 m diameter paraboloid operating at 14 GHz with 65% efficiency and 39 dBi peak gain. 72% of the total power from this antenna is radiated in directions that fall within the 2 deg half-power beamwidth, while 90% is radiated into the main lobe at angles between boresight and the first null, which appears at ~2.2 deg from the boresight.

Pointing Errors

All antennas have pointing errors. These errors may be relatively static, as in the case of fixed misalignment, or variable, as in the case of wind driven pointing errors that can often be significant for large ground terminal apertures. One of the most important sources of pointing error in satellite antennas is related to thermal distortion that results from variable heating of different antenna and spacecraft structures, which changes as the orientation of the satellite and its antennas change with respect to the Sun, Earth, and other satellite structures, like solar panels and other antennas. When analyzing a communications link, it is important to recognize that the antennas on both ends of the link contribute to pointing errors.

Figure 16-12 illustrates the beam peak pointing loss (rolloff in gain) as a function of pointing error, expressed as a fraction of the 3 dB beamwidth of an antenna with a uniformly illuminated circular aperture. Though wide variations are possible, typical design points allow for a maximum pointing error that is 10% of the half-power beamwidth (e.g., 0.2 deg for 2 deg beam). Figure 16-12

Table 16-10◀, Fig. 16-11, Eq. 16-11

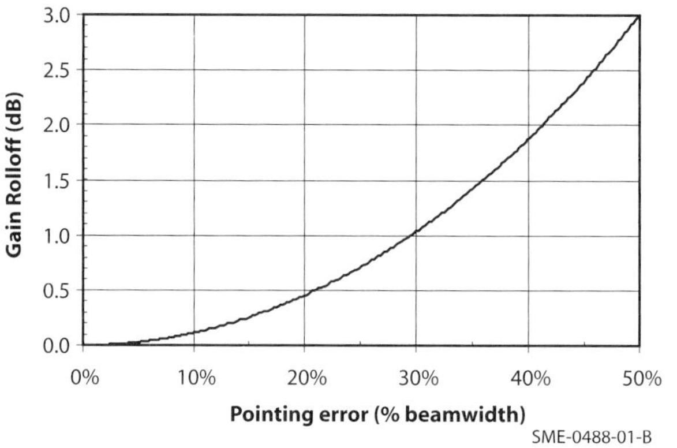

Fig. 16-12. Reduction in Gain Resulting from Pointing Loss, Expressed as a Function of 3 dB beamwidth.

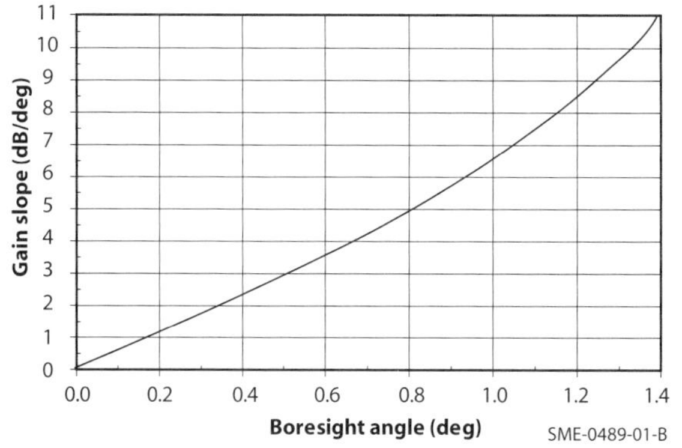

Fig. 16-13. Absolute Value of Gain Slope vs. Boresight Angle for the Antenna Whose Pattern is Presented in Fig. 16-11.

shows that at this limit, losses on the link associated with this aperture alone will amount to approximately 0.12 dB. At 20% of the beamwidth, pointing losses will grow to 0.45 dB.

In general, pointing loss is computed as the product of the *pointing error*, measured in deg, and the *gain slope*, measured in dB/deg. Because beam antenna patterns are typically flattest near the peak, pointing induced losses are usually smallest near the peak. In practice, it is therefore most important to consider pointing errors near the *edge of coverage* (EOC), where the gain is reduced and where gain slopes can be greatest. Figure 16-13 shows the gain slope corresponding to the pattern shown in Fig. 16-11. If for this antenna, the EOC point were taken to be 3 dB down from the peak, then the corresponding EOC gain slope would be 6.5 dB per deg, yielding a 1.3 dB EOC pointing loss for a 0.2 deg pointing error. One conventional practice for addressing pointing error is to use reflector shaping to design antennas in a manner that minimizes the variation in directivity across a coverage area. This has two effects: (A) making more efficient use of power, by reducing peak gains and increasing EOC gains, and (B) reducing gain slope within the coverage area. By designing antennas to have EOC gain margin that is greater than or equal to the predicted pointing losses, requirements will be satisfied as long as actual pointing is within the tolerances that have been predicted.

Shaped Beams

In many space communications missions, satellite antennas are required to cover an irregular area, such as the continental United States (CONUS), which subtends an angle approximately 5 deg × 3 deg as viewed from geosynchronous orbit. At 14 GHz, the antenna required to produce such a beam would be about 0.3 m × 0.5 m. If such an area were to be covered by a simple parabolic reflector, it would be necessary to adjust the pointing and the operating point of the system so that the gain at the edges of the specified coverage, and about 3 dB below the peak of the beam, would be compliant to the minimum requirements of the application. As a result, the gain over most of the coverage area would be greatly in excess of the requirements, while coverage would also be provided in areas where it is not likely to be useful (ocean areas) or may be either unwanted or even prohibited (Canada, Mexico, and Caribbean islands). Shaped reflector antennas allow the limited transmitted power and receiver sensitive resource of the spacecraft to be used more optimally by producing flatter patterns that conform more closely to the contours of the desired coverage area. In so doing, these antennas also maximize opportunities to coordinate the operations of new satellite communications systems with existing systems.

The directivity of an antenna whose shaping has been tailored can be estimated by considering the solid angle subtended within the coverage area. Given that the directivity of an antenna represents its ability to concentrate energy, and is often referenced to the directivity of an isotropic antenna, we can estimate the directivity of a shaped antenna by comparing the solid angle subtended within the coverage to the solid angle of an isotropic antenna (4π steradians = 41,253 deg^2). Because the directivity of an isotropic radiator is, by definition, 0 dBi, the maximum directivity achievable for an antenna that covers a smaller solid angle is given by

$$D_{Ideal} = 10 \log_{10} (41{,}253/A_\theta) \qquad (16\text{-}12)$$

where D_{Ideal} is in dB and coverage area, A_θ is measured in deg^2. Using the decibel-based arithmetic described earlier in this chapter, Eq. 16-12 can be recast as

$$D_{Ideal} = 46.15 - 10 \log(A_\theta) \qquad (16\text{-}13)$$

This provides a first level approximation for the link equation, the subject of Sec. 16.2.2. As an example, an ideal antenna that concentrates all of its radiated power into a spot beam whose area is 1.0 deg^2 would have directivity of 46.15 dBi.

For a satellite in geosynchronous orbit at 35,786 km altitude above mean sea level, the Earth has an apparent diameter of 17.2 deg, corresponding to a solid angle of about 232 deg^2. Using Eq. (16-13), we find that an ideal Earth coverage antenna would have a directivity of 22.5 dB.

Table 16-10◀, Fig. 16-13, Eq. 16-13

To estimate the directivity of an aperture designed to provide coverage over CONUS, one would substitute the 13.3 deg^2 CONUS land area into Eq. (16-13) to obtain an estimate of the ideal directivity for such an antenna as approximately 34.9 dBi.

The ideal directivity calculations do not include antenna radiated efficiency, which is a measure of the power being radiated outside the desired coverage area. Antenna efficiencies typically range between 55% to 75%, corresponding to a –2.6 to –1.25 dB adjustment to the ideal directivity estimated from Eq. (16-13). Equation (16-14) modifies Eq. (16-13) to account correctly for antenna efficiency, where D_{Ideal} is in dBi. Equation (16-14) is plotted in Fig. 16-14 for several values of η.

$$D_{Ideal} = 10\log(41{,}253/A_\theta) + 10\log(\eta) \qquad (16\text{-}14)$$

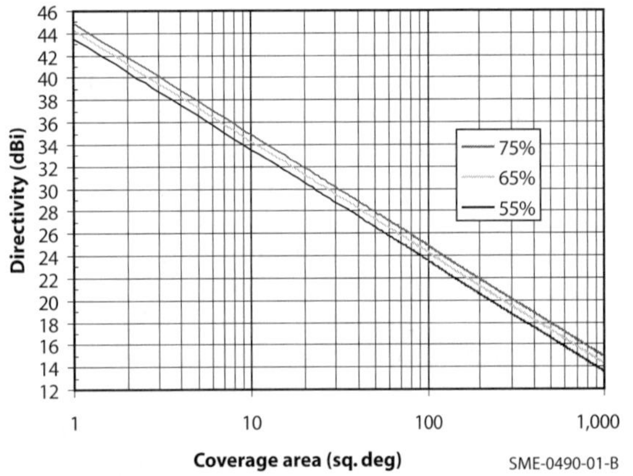

Live Calc **Fig. 16-14. Directivity Estimated on the Basis of Coverage Area for Several Values of Antenna Efficiency.**

Antenna Noise Temperature and Noise from Feed Losses

Equally important as accounting for signal power, the link analysis must also account for all significant sources of noise. In the broadest sense, noise includes all in-band sources of electromagnetic energy received other than those that are desired to support the communications mission. These include *black body thermal noise* radiated from the environment, noise generated from within the link, and non-thermal sources of interference from outside the system, including other RF transmitters that are not part of the space mission communications system being designed. Although they represent very different processes, the first two of these are usually considered together, while outside sources of interference are accounted for separately.

The first noise component that we consider is thermal radiation that originates from objects within the field of view of the receive antenna. Although perfect black bodies do not exist in nature, each object within the antenna's field of view radiates electromagnetic radiation with power spectral density that is approximated by that of a black body.

$$N_o = kT \qquad (16\text{-}15)$$

where N_o is in W/Hz, k = 1.3806504×10^{-23} J/K = –228.6 dBJ/K is the Boltzmann constant, and T is the object's effective *brightness temperature* (K), the temperature that would be required of a black body in equilibrium with its environment to exhibit a similar radiation spectrum.

Despite the apparent simplicity of Eq. (16-15), generating a detailed and accurate prediction of the noise power received by an antenna is complicated by the fact that the noise power received must be weighted by both the solid angle of the objects within its field of view and by the antenna's pattern of directivity, yielding a value of the *antenna noise temperature*, T_A, given by

$$T_A = \frac{1}{4\pi}\iint T(\theta,\varphi) D(\theta,\varphi)\sin(\theta)\,d\theta\, d\varphi \qquad (16\text{-}16)$$

where $T(\theta, \varphi)$ is the brightness temperature of each point within the antenna's field of view, and $D(\theta, \varphi)$ is the antenna's directivity pattern.

In practice, although Eq. (16-16) is likely to be used in support of the detailed design to predict the *noise spectral density* for the specific antenna patterns, satellite location, and orientation, early link analyses for satellite receive antennas are likely to be based on more subjective estimates of the antenna noise temperature, based on a general understanding of the antenna's intended coverage and simpler models of the Earth's brightness temperature, such as that shown in Fig. 16-15.

Likewise, initial downlink analyses, which involve terrestrial receivers will be estimated, based on typical brightness temperature for the sky that ranges from approximately 5 K at zenith to about 150 K near the horizon at K_u band, and brightness temperature of approximately 300 K for ground that may occupy a portion of an antenna's field of view (including side lobes) under some circumstances.

The concept of *noise temperature* is used to characterize the noise performance of RF components. For antennas, the noise temperature comprises two components: (A) noise that originates from the thermally radiated energy of objects that appear within the antenna's field of view, and (B) noise that originates from the temperature of the antenna feed structure and transmission losses within the antenna and feed assembly itself.

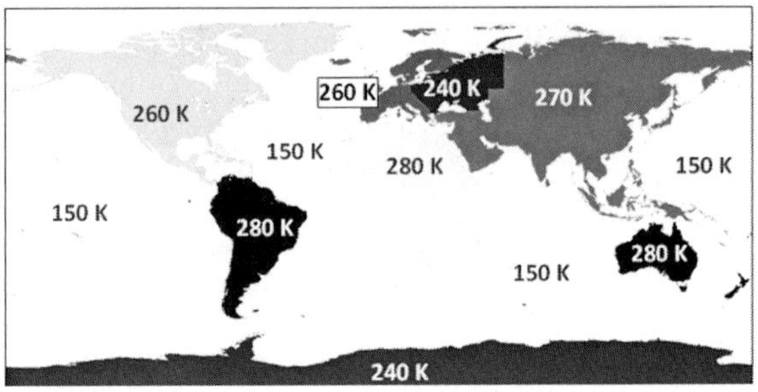

Fig. 16-15. ESA/EUTELSAT K_u-band Brightness Model of the Earth.

Table 16-10◄, Fig. 16-15, Eq. 16-16

The second component of noise received by the antenna is associated with RF losses from within the antenna feed network itself, as well as losses in other passive components between the antenna feed and the receiver. While these losses will eventually be determined either by computer simulation or by direct measurement, estimates are used to support initial link analyses. In either case, it is typical for the noise power associated with antenna feed and other input losses to be represented as a simple resistive element that injects a constant *noise power spectral density*, $N_o = kT_L$, where T_L is the effective thermodynamic temperature of the modeled resistance. In Sec. 16.2.2.4, this noise source and thermally radiated noise received from objects within the field of view of the antenna will be combined with receiver noise to define an effective *system temperature*, T_S, that can be used to compactly represent the noise received from all three of these sources.

16.2.1.5 Modulation, Coding, and Spectral Efficiency

To carry information content between transmitter and receiver, the *electromagnetic waves* that comprise the operating bands of the communications system (carriers) are modified to encode data. Carrier *modulation* is performed by varying the carriers' frequency, amplitude, or phase. *Demodulation* is the process by which signals are recovered from modulated carriers. The modulation scheme and commonly used error-correction coding schemes play an important role in determining the power required to transmit a given amount of information on a communications link, and together with the characteristics of the filters used to minimize interference between adjacent carriers, determine the *spectral efficiency* (expressed in bps/Hz) with which information can be transmitted on that link. Both of these factors are fundamentally important parts of the link analyses that must be performed in support of both the communications architecture development and the detailed communications payload design.

Signals in modern communications systems are typically transmitted in digital format, at data rates measured in *bits/second* (b/s or bps). Modulators and demodulators operate on *symbols*, with the modulation scheme determining the number of bits that are encoded per symbol. Modulation techniques that function by varying carrier phase, known as *phase-shift keying* techniques [Ford, 2007], have distinct advantages over amplitude and frequency modulation techniques, both in terms of *bit energy* (E_b) and spectral efficiency (bps/Hz), and are therefore virtually ubiquitous in modern satellite communications applications. The most basic of these modulation schemes, *binary phase-shift keying*, (BPSK), encodes information onto carriers through the use of two phase states per symbol, thereby encoding 1 bit of information per symbol. Higher order modulations are also possible and in use, with *quadrature phase-shift keying* (QPSK), 8-PSK, and 16-PSK using 4, 8, and 16 phase states per symbol, respectively, corresponding to 2, 3, and 4 bits per symbol.

Although higher order modulation schemes improve spectral efficiency by encoding more bits per symbol than lower order schemes, this efficiency comes at a cost. With m representing the number of bits per symbol, the phase difference between allowable symbol states is inversely proportional to 2^m. As a consequence, implementing higher order modulation schemes increases the susceptibility of communications links to phase-noise-induced errors. In addition to requiring more careful attention to phase noise and phase stability in the communications payload, implementation of higher order modulation schemes requires signals to be transmitted with higher values of bit energy. Based on this, the tradeoff between spectral efficiency and total payload power consumption is an important factor for designers and operators of satellite communications systems.

Despite the fact that digital encoding is used on a communications link, a series of analog processes are involved in the formation of the digital bit stream. While the desire to maximize the total information carrying capacity motivates the designer to minimize bit energy, the *bit error rate* (BER) increases as bit energy becomes closer to that of the noise associated with these processes. *Forward Error Correction* (FEC) is used to mitigate the effects of increasing BER without requiring the implementation of more complicated communications channels and handshaking between transmitter and receiver. By encoding redundant bits onto the communications link, FEC algorithms allow the receiver a limited ability to detect and correct errors without the need for a return-channel to confirm that data have been successfully transmitted. The *code rate* of an FEC algorithm is defined as

$$\rho = n/(n+r) \tag{16-17}$$

where r represents the number of redundant bits added by the FEC algorithm for every n unique information bits transmitted on the link. Although increasing the coding rate improves the ability of the receiver to correct bit errors, thereby allowing bit energy to be reduced below the level that could otherwise be used to achieve a given BER, bandwidth use per information bit increases in direct proportion to the ratio r/n. Selection of the code rate for a particular application involves a balance between considerations for power consumption and spectral efficiency, with typical code-rate values ranging between approximately ½ and 9/10.

In practice, filters are used to minimize interference between carriers that occupy adjacent frequency bands. To optimize overall performance, a *rolloff factor* is specified for these filters, with the rolloff factor having the effect of creating small unused spectral bands between channels. Together, the modulation scheme, code rate, and rolloff factor determine the spectral efficiency, Γ, of a communications link as

$$\Gamma = m/[\rho(1+\alpha)] \tag{16-18}$$

where m represents the number of bits per symbol for the encoding scheme, ρ is the FEC code rate, and α is the filter rolloff factor. Table 16-11 gives examples of spectral efficiency (exclusive of filter rolloff) for several combinations of modulation and code rate.

Table 16-10◀, Fig. 16-15◀, Eq. 16-18

Table 16-11. Spectral Efficiency (exclusive of filter rolloff) for Several Combinations of Modulation and Code Rate.

Modulation Method	Bits per Symbol	Code Rate	Spectral Efficiency
BPSK	1	0.5	0.5
QPSK	2	0.5	1.0
QPSK	2	0.8	1.6
8-PSK	3	0.8	2.4
16-PSK	4	0.8	3.2

16.2.1.6 Bit Energy to Noise Ratio (E_b/N_o) and Coding Gain

The figure of merit used in link budgets is the bit error rate (BER), the principal performance metric that is a measure of quantization error in digital communications links. As was discussed qualitatively in Sec. 16.2.1.5, the probability of quantization errors increases as bit energy is reduced and becomes closer to the noise level that characterizes the communications link. In particular, provided that the noise source itself can be appropriately characterized, it is possible to predict the *BER* of a communications link as a function of the bit-energy to noise-spectral-density ratio, denoted as E_b/N_o, for a given modulation scheme and code rate. BER can be approximated by

$$BER \approx \frac{1}{m}\operatorname{erfc}\left(\sqrt{\frac{mE_b}{N_o}}\sin\left(\frac{\pi}{M}\right)\right) \tag{16-19}$$

where N_o is the noise power spectral density, and the M-ary PSK modulation scheme encodes m bits per symbol, where $M = 2^m$. Figure 16-16 plots this relationship for BPSK/QPSK (same curve), 8-PSK, and 16-PSK modulation.

Figure 16-16 shows that for fixed bit energy, quantization error increases as the number of bits per symbol increases, and that to maintain a constant BER as the symbol rate increases, it is necessary to increase bit energy.

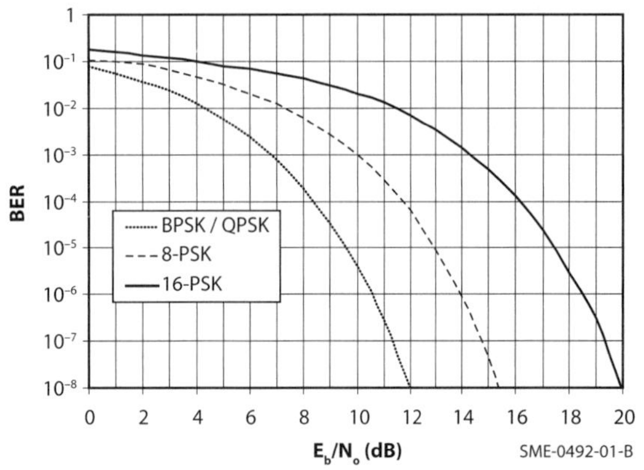

Fig. 16-16. Predicted BER Curves as a Function of E_b/N_o

Table 16-11, Fig. 16-17, Eq. 16-19

The effect of FEC coding upon BER is illustrated in Fig. 16-17 for QPSK modulation with three code rates: $\rho = 1$ (no forward error correction), 0.86 (6/7), and 0.80 (4/5). *Coding gain* is the reduction in E_b/N_o from the value required for an uncoded link to the values that can be achieved by increasing redundancy (decreasing ρ). As was described in Sec. 16.2.1.5, for a fixed bandwidth allocation, this comes at the cost of reduced throughput on the communications link.

In the example illustrated in Fig. 16-17, an uncoded QPSK signal requires $E_b/N_o = 9.6$ dB to achieve a BER of 10^{-5}. With $\rho = 0.86$, E_b/N_o can be reduced to 4.4 dB, and with $\rho = 0.80$, it can be further reduced to 3.4 dB, for coding gains of 5.2 and 6.2 dB, respectively. Bit error rates vary widely with application, with voice applications allowing BER values in the range of 10^{-3}, and data links often requiring values in the range of 10^{-11}.

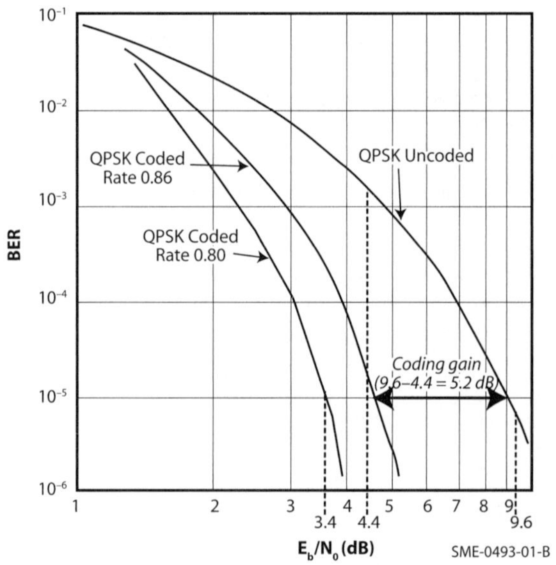

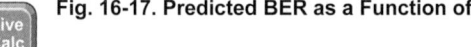

Fig. 16-17. Predicted BER as a Function of E_b/N_o

16.2.1.7 Atmospheric Effects

Gases and rain in the atmosphere attenuate electromagnetic radiation. Iononospheric effects are not significant at frequencies above 1 GHz.

Attenuation by Atmospheric Gases

Figure 16-18 depicts the total attenuation resulting from atmospheric gases as a function of frequency corresponding to the ITU "mean annual global reference atmosphere," with attenuation corresponding to a vertical path from sea level to the top of the atmosphere [ITU, 2011]. For elevation angles between 5 deg and 90 deg, attenuation increases by the cosecant of the elevation angle.

Also shown in Fig. 16-18 are contribution to total atmospheric attenuation due to dry air alone, and due to water vapor in the atmosphere. These curves clearly

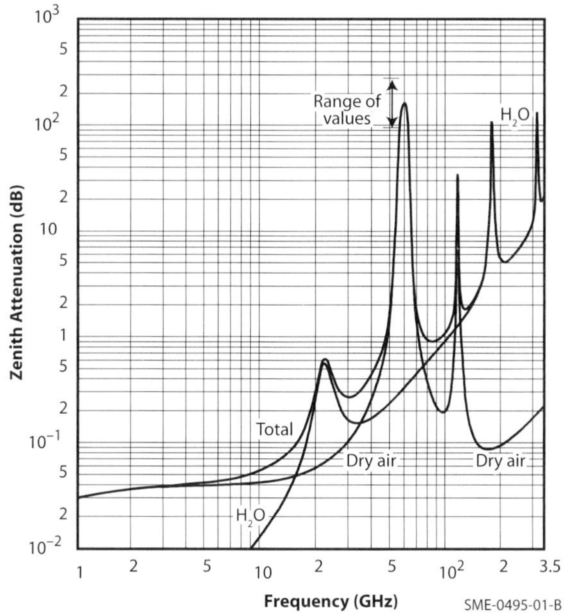

Fig. 16-18. Total Attenuation of Electromagnetic Radiation Versus Frequency due to Atmospheric Gases, for a Vertical Path from Sea Level to the Top of the Atmosphere (approximately 15 to 17 km at the equator)

show peaks due to water vapor at 22 GHz, and molecular oxygen at approximately 60 GHz. One interesting consequence of the enormous attenuation due to molecular oxygen is that terrestrial transmitters and sources operating near 60 GHz are very effectively isolated from those in orbit. Both the ITU and the US FCC have exploited this by designating bands in the range of 60 GHz for use as intersatellite links.

Precipitation Losses

Precipitation in the form of rain and wet snow attenuates RF signals through both absorption and scattering (depolarization). Precipitation-induced losses are dependent upon the product of a rate-dependent attenuation coefficient and the path length that the RF signals are required to traverse through rainfall regions within the atmosphere.

Because losses are a function of the concentration of water in the atmosphere, precipitation-induced losses are heavily dependent upon geographic and seasonal variations in weather. To provide a means for predicting rain precipitation effects upon satellite communications, the ITU [2002] has created a geographic database of rainfall rates, as well as algorithms for determining the frequency with which rainfall rates in excess of a user-specified value are likely to be exceeded. Using these resources, link analyses are often performed on the basis of availability objectives for the link being analyzed.

For a specific transmitter/receiver geometry (satellite and terrestrial terminal location), this is done by using the ITU model "*PROPA*" to determine a precipitation rate that will not be exceeded with frequency greater than the target availability. With this precipitation rate known, the attenuation due to precipitation can be computed. By accounting for this attenuation throughout the course of the link analysis, precipitation-driven link availability can be achieved so long as the overall link budget closes.

Scintillation

Scintillation refers to variations in signal amplitude, phase, and angle-of-arrival result from refractive index variations within the troposphere and the ionosphere, and occur over short time frames; typically less than a second. Within the troposphere, refractive index changes are driven by weather, and are frequency independent. Ionospheric refractive index changes are frequency dependent, and result from localized variations in charged particle densities, which can vary rapidly in the various layers of plasma that comprise the ionosphere.

Although a budget is allocated in link budgets to accommodate signal variations due to scintillation, scintillation does not ordinarily represent significant constraint to the design of satellite communication links above 1 GHz. For example, though peak-to-peak variations as large as 1 dB were very infrequently observed in association with heavy rainfall events, K_a-band data from the 20.2 and 27.5 GHz beacons of the ACTS satellite at K_a-band showed scintillation values typically below 0.2 dB. Although scintillation amplitudes may be as much as 5 dB or more at frequencies below about 1 GHz, they are typically no more than a few tenths of a dB for L-band signals, and smaller still at higher frequencies.

16.2.2 Link Equations and Link Budgets

As was mentioned earlier, link analyses are fundamentally important during both the synthesis and assessment of architectural alternatives, and during the development of the detailed communications payload design. Using Eq. (16-1) as a starting point, the analysis proceeds by accounting for increases and decreases in power through each part of the link from the transmitter and its antenna, and through space to the receiver antenna and electronics where the signal is measured and decoded. In this manner, the link analysis is treated much as a budget, in which positive allocations are required from specific identified sources, and negative allocations are made to accommodate expected losses. Because of the high cost and complexity associated with launching and operating a communications satellite, there are enormous pressures to ensure that the communications payload is highly optimized to deliver the best possible combination of performance and reliability. Given this, each component of the *link budget* is scrutinized to ensure that it is realistic and achievable, without being overly conservative [Gordon and Morgan, 1993]. In the end, positive allocations (power, and power amplification) must balance with negative allocations (attenuation, other losses, and margin) for the budget to close.

Table 16-11◀, Fig. 16-18, Eq. 16-19◀

Because noise is added at various stages through both the uplink and the downlink on payloads, link budgets must be computed for these payloads in both the uplink to the satellite and the downlink to a terrestrial terminal, and for both forward and return links. The principal metric in this budget is the margin, or excess above the minimum threshold requirement for the composite link, in received signal-to-noise power ratio at the receiver, E_b/N_o. The link is said to "close" if the margin to the requirements is ≥ 0. These requirements are determined and widely tabulated according to the modulation scheme and code rate that are to be used for the link. In practice, it is common to design to a positive margin target, referred to as implementation margin, whose specific value will vary depending upon various elements of perceived risk, as a means of accommodating normal variations in unit performance and unforeseen factors associated with production, integration, and test.

In the subsections that follow, we first consider budget entries that account for signal power (Secs. 16.2.2.1 through 16.2.2.3), after which we describe how noise factors into the link budget (Secs. 16.2.2.4 and 16.2.2.5). We conclude the discussion of the link budget by showing how signal power and noise factors are combined to compute the carrier-to-noise ratio (Sec. 16.2.2.6), and how margin is computed for the overall link that comprises both uplink and downlink. We end in Sec. 16.2.2.7 with a sample budget computed for an FSS satellite communications link.

16.2.2.1 Transmitted Power and Transmitter Output Losses

A transmitter receives baseband data, modulates it onto a higher-frequency carrier, amplifies it, and broadcasts it via an antenna. So far as the link analysis is concerned, the principal product of the transmitter is a measure of the power radiated in the direction of the peak of the transmit antenna directivity pattern: *equivalent isotropic radiated power*, *EIRP*. The *EIRP* (dBW), is equal to the power of the transmitter (dBW) minus losses associated with output transmission lines and other hardware between the transmitter and antenna (dB), plus the gain of the transmit antenna (dBi). The result corresponds to the power that an isotropic radiator with no output losses would be required to have in order to radiate with power flux density equivalent to that at the beam peak of the transmit antenna.

$$EIRP = P_{Tx} + G_{Tx} - L_{output+Tx\ antenna} \tag{16-20}$$

Two things are worth noting at this point:

- The value of the transmitter power used in Eq. 16-20 is the *RF output power of the high-power amplifier*, which is related to the *DC bus power* required to operate the high-power amplifier through the amplifier's efficiency factor, which varies from amplifier to amplifier, and as a function of the amplifier's operating parameters
- It is common to carry the nominal maximum RF output power (or "nameplate" power) in the link budget, even though the amplifier might not be operated at that power in practice. To account for the intended operating point, the *output backoff* (OBO) value is carried as an additional loss term to represent the factor by which output power is reduced below nominal

16.2.2.2 Free-Space and Atmospheric Losses

The signal that reaches the receive antenna is reduced by a combination of free-space losses and atmospheric scattering and attenuation losses. So-called propagation or *free-space loss* (L_S) is by far the largest loss factor, and simply represents the reduction in power flux density that results from geometric dispersion of the electromagnetic radiation as it travels through space. Free-space loss, L_S, can be expressed in decibels as

$$L_S = \left(\frac{4\pi r}{\lambda}\right)^2 \tag{16-21}$$

where r is distance between the transmit and receive antennas, and λ is the wavelength of the RF carrier. Free space loss L_S (dB) can be be expressed as

$$L_S = 92.45 + 20\log_{10}(r) + 20\log_{10}(f) \tag{16-22}$$

where r is the distance (km), and f is the carrier frequency (GHz).

The signal that reaches the receive antenna is further reduced by atmospheric losses. In practice, these are best estimated either by using geographic databases and models of precipitation rates and attenuation factors published by the ITU, or corresponding rain-rate maps and tabulations, each of which is provided with detailed use instructions and guidelines.

16.2.2.3 Received Power

The accounting for changes in power that occur at the receiver is similar and complementary to that described in Sec. 16.2.2.1 for changes in power that occur within the signal path of the transmitter. In this case, however, the signal is first increased by the gain of the receive antenna, then reduced by losses (principally transmission-line) before the signal reaches the receive amplifier.

One final factor that must be accounted for in predicting the power available at the receiver is pointing loss, which is the result of pointing errors at both the transmit and the receive antennas. Pointing loss can be estimated based on a bottoms-up estimate of maximum pointing errors for both transmit and receive antennas, combined with knowledge of the predicted antenna patterns, or by setting a loss budget that is consistent with previous experience. If estimated on the basis of estimated pointing errors, pointing loss is determined by finding the directivity of the transmit or receive antenna at the boresight angle corresponding to the maximum predicted pointing error, and subtracting this from the antenna's peak directivity.

Table 16-11◀, Fig. 16-18◀, Eq. 16-22

The total power at the receive amplifier can therefore be expressed as

$$C = EIRP + G_r - L_S - L_{atm+prec} - L_{in} - L_{Tx+Rx} \quad (16\text{-}23)$$

where $EIRP$ and L_S have the meanings and units described previously, $L_{atm+prec}$ represents atmospheric and precipitation losses (dB), G_r is the gain of the receive antenna (dBi), L_{in} represents input losses to the receiver (dB), and L_{Tx+Rx} is the sum of transmitter and receiver pointing losses (dB).

16.2.2.4 Noise

The link budget must account for all significant sources of noise in the link. In Sec. 16.2.1.4, we described the *noise-power spectral density* and absolute noise power that originate from thermal radiation of objects within the receive antenna's field of view, and from RF losses within the antenna feed and passive components between the feed and the receiver.

In addition, the link budget must also account for noise that is generated within the receiver itself. For purposes of link analysis, this noise can be adequately characterized in terms of the *noise figure*, which is defined for a cascaded chain of one or more units as the ratio of the signal-to-noise at the input of the device or chain to the signal-to-noise at the output.

Noise figures are specified for all active units in the payload, and representative values are therefore readily available for link analyses that may be performed at any stage of the development process. It is important to note that **noise figures are always quoted at a reference temperature of T_0 = 290K.**

For the receiver's input signal chain, we can determine the *effective system noise temperature*, T_S, as a composite of the antenna and input-loss noise temperatures as

$$T_S = T_A(L) + (1-L)T_L + (F-1)T_o \quad (16\text{-}24)$$

where T_A and T_L are the antenna noise temperature and the effective temperature of the feed and other passive input components, respectively, L is the loss through the antenna feed and passive components upstream of the receiver, expressed as a ratio of the output power to input power, and F is the receiver noise figure. [Note that F is usually quoted in dB, and must be converted to its non-logarithmic representation for use in Eq. (16-24).]

Using the effective system noise temperature given by Eq. (16-24), we can compactly represent all three of the significant sources of noise within the link other than RF interferers, which are accounted for separately. Thus, the noise power spectral density at the receiver is simply computed as $N_o = kT_S$ [W/Hz]. Likewise, by multiplying this by the *noise bandwidth**, B_N, of the receiver or the receiver prefilter we can determine the expected value of the measurable in-band noise

$$N = kT_S B_N \quad (16\text{-}25)$$

which can be expressed in terms of decibel values as

$$N = -228.6 + T_S + B_N \quad (16\text{-}26)$$

where N is in dBW, –228.6 is the Boltzman constant in dBJ/K, T_S is in dBK and B_N is in dB-Hz.

16.2.2.5 Receiver G/T

The ratio of the receive-antenna gain to the noise temperature of the receiver, T_S, obtained from Eq. (16-24) is referred to as *G/T*, and is used in link analyses to compute the signal-to-noise ratio. As such, *G/T* is also the principal figure of merit used to characterize receiver sensitivity, just as *EIRP* is the principal figure of merit used to characterize the transmitter. Like *EIRP*, *G/T* is typically expressed in decibels, and is computed as

$$\frac{G}{T} = G_R - T \quad (16\text{-}27)$$

where *G/T* has units of dB/K, and G_R and T have already been expressed in dBi and dBK, respectively.

16.2.2.6 Receiver C/No

The received signal power, C, from Eq. (16-23), and the noise power, N, from Eq. (16-26) come together in the *carrier-to-noise* ratio, which can be computed by combining these equations to obtain the result

$$C/N = (EIRP + G_R - L_{Comb.}) - (-228.6 + T_S + B_N) \quad (16\text{-}28)$$

where all losses have been combined into the single term, $L_{Comb.}$.

Combining with Eq. (16-27), this reduces to

$$C/N = EIRP + G/T - L_{Comb.} - B_N + 228.6 \quad (16\text{-}29)$$

To obtain the bandwidth-independent ratio of carrier power to noise power spectral density, we multiply the carrier-to-noise ratio by the bandwidth (equivalent to adding B_N to Eq. (16-29), which has all terms expressed in decibels):

$$C/N_o = EIRP + G/T - L_{Comb.} + 228.6 \quad (16\text{-}30)$$

16.2.2.7 Available E_b/N_o and Composite Link Performance

The final step of the link analysis, which involves determining and interpreting the values of E_b/N_o for both the uplink and the downlink, varies slightly, depending upon whether the communications payload is to be implemented as a *transponder* or as a *regenerative* payload. The reason for this is that whereas *transponding payloads* amplify and re-transmit both the signal and the noise that are uplinked to them, regenerative payloads demodulate the signals carried on the uplink, stripping away uplinked noise before remodulating and transmitting signals onto the downlink.

* Note that the *noise bandwidth* of a component may be different from the nominal (typically 3 dB) bandwidth quoted or measured for a device because of noise that is admitted to the link within the rolloff region of the applicable filter

Table 16-11◀, Fig. 16-18◀, Eq. 16-30

Because the transponding payload includes signal-to-noise contributions from both the uplink and downlink beams, the last step of the link analysis requires the uplink and downlink to be treated as a single combined link. For regenerative payloads the analysis is performed independently for uplink and downlink beams. Once E_b/N_o has been computed for the appropriate link, this value is compared against the value required for the modulation scheme and code rate to be used. The difference between the predicted and required values of E_b/N_o is the *link margin*, the principal metric of link quality. This same analysis must be completed for each link that the satellite must support, including both forward (toward end users) and return (originating from end users) links.

Because C represents the total RF power required to carry all of the information in the signal that is to be transmitted, E_b/N_o is obtained from C/N_o by simply dividing by the data rate, R_b, that the carrier is required to support. Performing the calculation with each of the terms expressed in decibels, we compute R_b (dB-Hz) = $10 \log_{10}(R_b \text{ (bps)})$, with which we find

$$E_b/N_o = C/N_o - R_b \qquad (16\text{-}31)$$

For regenerative payloads, we can interpret this result separately for each uplink and downlink by comparing these results with the threshold value required to close the link for the modulation scheme and code rate to be implemented.

For transponding payloads, however, we must first determine a composite value for E_b/N_o by expressing E_b/N_o non-logarithmically for both uplink and downlink, adding these intermediate results, and re-expressing the combined result in decibels so that

$$\left(\frac{E_b}{N_o}\right)_{Composite} = 10\log_{10}\left(10^{-(E_b/N_o)_{uplink}/10} + 10^{-(E_b/N_o)_{downlink}/10}\right) \qquad (16\text{-}32)$$

Because satellite communications payloads always have lower gain antennas than those used at ground terminals, and because ground terminals often are able to implement higher-power amplifiers than those that can be used on the satellite payloads with which they are linked, the composite value of E_b/N_o for forward communications links is always dominated by the downlink component that represents the satellite-to-user-terminal portion of the overall link. Likewise, even if the return-link *EIRP* from user terminals to the satellite is greater than the *EIRP* for the downlink to the ground terminal, the ground terminal receiver will always have much greater sensitivity (as reflected in its *G/T*) than the corresponding satellite receiver. The composite value of E_b/N_o for return links is therefore dominated by the uplink, which again represents the user terminal-to-satellite portion of the overall link. Thus in each direction, it is the combined performance limits of the satellite and user terminals that constrain link performance most.

To interpret the value of E_b/N_o for each link that has been analyzed, these results must be compared with the threshold value required for the coding scheme that is to be implemented. Table 16-12 lists key parameters for a variety of modulation and code-rate combinations that are supported by the Digital Video Broadcasting-Satellite, Second Generation (DVB-S2) standard.

Link margin, M_L is given by

$$M_L = (E_b/N_o)_{\text{Predicted}} - (E_b/N_o)_{\text{Required}} \qquad (16\text{-}33)$$

The link closes when the link margin is zero, which from Eq. 16-33 is clearly the condition for which $(E_b/N_o)_{\text{Predicted}}$ is precisely equal to $(E_b/N_o)_{\text{Required}}$. The link does not close if link margin is negative. To ensure that the system will function as intended despite risk factors such as adverse stackup of normal variations in unit performance and unforeseen factors associated with production, integration, and testing, the design team typically designs to a link margin greater than zero, with the magnitude of the positive margin usually being dependent upon the mission criticality of the link.

16.2.3 Communications Satellite Link Budget Example

We conclude by providing a detailed description of the link budget for a representative transponder-based FSS satellite to be placed in geosynchronous orbit and operated at K_u-band to provide service to users in the continental United States (CONUS). The spectrum allocation for this example is 14.0 to 14.5 GHz for uplinks and 11.7 to 12.2 GHz for downlinks. The communications payload will have 24 channels, with 12 on each polarization. Each channel has a 36 MHz bandwidth, and adjacent channels are separated by 5 MHz guard bands so that all channels fit within the 500 MHz band that has been allocated for this satellite. Table 16-13 shows the link budget in the forward direction for this communications link for two user terminal profiles:

1. "Small Terminal": 0.50 Mbps data rate and 1.3 m user terminal aperture
2. "Large Terminal": 44 Mbps data rate and 2.5 m user terminal aperture

Wherever applicable, Table 16-13 provides references to equation numbers and data sources from earlier in the chapter. Entries that are annotated as "Given" are those that are subject to regulatory constraints, requirements of the design, or constraints dictated by components likely to be selected in the design, and are assumed to be outside the control of the link designer. These include:

- Uplink and downlink frequencies (specified by ITU and national authorities, such as the US Federal Communications Commission)
- Channel bandwidth (design requirement, in this case to provide compatibility with existing services)
- Ground-terminal output losses (typical for existing facilities)

Table 16-12. Symbol Rate, Spectral Efficiency, and E_b/N_o Required for Link Closure for Various Combinations of Modulation and Code Rate that are Supported by the Digital Video Broadcasting-Satellite, Second Generation (DVB-S2) Standard.

Modulation	Bits/ Symbol	Code Rate	Spectral Efficiency	E_b/N_o
QPSK	2	1/4	0.49	0.75
QPSK	2	1/3	0.66	0.59
QPSK	2	2/5	0.79	0.73
QPSK	2	1/2	0.99	1.05
QPSK	2	3/5	1.19	1.48
QPSK	2	2/3	1.32	1.89
QPSK	2	3/4	1.49	2.31
QPSK	2	4/5	1.59	2.67
QPSK	2	5/6	1.65	2.99
QPSK	2	8/9	1.77	3.73
QPSK	2	9/10	1.79	3.89
8PSK	3	3/5	1.8	3.00
8PSK	3	2/3	2.0	3.65
8PSK	3	3/4	2.2	4.43
8PSK	3	5/6	2.5	5.41
8PSK	3	8/9	2.6	6.46
8PSK	3	9/10	2.7	6.7
16APSK	4	2/3	2.6	4.76
16APSK	4	3/4	3.0	5.49
16APSK	4	4/5	3.2	6.03
16APSK	4	5/6	3.3	6.42
16APSK	4	8/9	3.5	7.42
16APSK	4	9/10	3.6	7.61

- Satellite line loss (typical value for satellite payloads of this type)
- System noise temperature (defined by coverage area, input losses and likely component selection)
- Implementation Margin = 3 dB (conservative for initial scoping analyses)

Entries labeled as "Inputs" are parameters that can be optimized and traded by the link designer to achieve link closure with the required margin. These include:

- User data rate (not common for this to be a tradable parameter)
- Modulation and coding (tradeoff of bandwidth and capacity)
- Ground-terminal aperture size and power
- Satellite antenna directivity (subject to satisfying coverage requirements)
- Satellite power per channel
- User terminal size and power (often not subject to trade because of requirements to support terminals that are already deployed)

Entries that are designated as "Assume" represent initial estimates, and will be validated and optimized as the payload design evolves and becomes more mature. These include:

- Amplifier backoff
- Input section losses between the satellite antenna and receiver
- Antenna efficiency

The user-terminal size and the data rata, modulation, and coding are adjusted so that the end-to-end links close with the required link margin Satellite *EIRP* and *G/T* requirements are computed for the coverage areas that have been specified by the customer, based on ground-terminal *EIRP*, user-terminal *G/T*, and desired data rate, modulation and coding, and 3 dB margin.

With support from antenna design engineers a single antenna with a 3.5 m × 2.4 m shaped reflector and a 0.7 m diameter subreflector is defined to support both receive (up) and transmit (down) links on orthogonal linear polarizations.

Forward Uplink Sample Link Budget Description

After considering several alternative trades between free design parameters, the budget closes with a set of parameters that appear to be realistic and achievable. In the final configuration, the ground-terminal is specified to have a 10 m antenna and one 200 W high-power-amplifier for each 36 MHz uplink channel.

In the case of the "Small Terminal" scenario, the uplink *EIRP* for each ground-terminal channel is shared among multiple users, whereas the uplink *EIRP* is dedicated to single terminals in the "Large Terminal" scenario.

The ground terminal backoff is 4 dB for the small terminal, multiple carrier case and 2 dB for the large terminal, single carrier case. Ground-terminal output losses are fixed at 2 dB.

At 14 GHz, the free-space loss (L_S) between the ground terminal and the geosynchronous satellite at the 38,000 km gateway-to-satellite range is 207 dB. Atmospheric loss for the specified ground terminal location and required link availability is calculated to be 10 dB. The satellite receive antenna meets the customer specified *G/T* requirement of 6 dB/K. The predicted value of E_b/N_o on this link is approximately 20 dB, a value that is sufficiently large as to contribute very little to the value of E_b/N_o for the overall link.

Forward Downlink Sample Link Budget Description

The *EIRP* is calculated for each scenario based on the 34.1 dBi *edge-of-coverage* (EOC) transmit gain for the antenna described above, assuming that each channel will be served by a 150 W high power amplifier.

At 11.7 GHz, the space loss for the GEO satellite at the maximum satellite-to-user range of 39,000 km is 205.9 dB*. Atmospheric loss for the user-terminal location considered in this case is 7 dB.

Table 16-12, Fig. 16-18◄, Eq. 16-33◄

Table 16-13. Sample FSS Link Budget, Forward Direction. Note that equation numbers and data sources are referenced in the right-hand column.

FSS Forward Link Cases	Units	Small user	Large user	Comments and References	
Uplink frequency	GHz	14.00	14.00	K_u-band uplink	Given
Gateway terminal type		Tracking	Tracking		
Diameter	m	10	10		Input
Beamwidth	deg	0.15	0.15		Eq. 16-11
Gain	dBi	60.7	60.7	55% efficiency	Eq. 16-10
Transmit power	W	200	200		Input
Backoff and line loss	dB	–6.0	–4.0	2 dB line loss + backoff	Assume
***EIRP*, gateway**	dBW	77.7	79.7	Gateway	Eq. 16-20
EIRP per user		62.3	79.7	*EIRP* / no. users	Calculation
Propagation range	km	38,000	38,000	Gateway to satellite	Given
Space loss	dB	–207.0	–207.0		Eq. 16-22
Atmospheric losses	dB	–10.0	–10.0	99.97% availability	
Net path loss	dB	–217.0	–217.0		Calculation
Satellite antenna, type		3.5 × 2.4 m, shaped		Gregorian	
Coverage area	deg^2	**13.30**	13.30	CONUS	Given
Antenna efficiency	%	70%	70%		Assume
Gain	dBi	33.4	33.4	Derived from coverage	Eq. 16-14
Line loss on satellite	dB	–2.0	–2.0		Assume
Received carrier power, *C*	dBW	–123.3	–105.9		Eq. 16-23
Sys. noise temp	dB-K	27.2	27.2		Derive
G/T	dB/K	6.2	6.2		Eq. 16-27
Receiver C/N_o	dB-Hz	78.1	95.5	k = –228.6	Eq. 16-30
Data rate per user	dB-Hz	57.0	76.4	Single user data rate	Calculation
Available E_b/N_o, uplink	dB	21.1	19.1		Eq. 16-31
Downlink frequency	GHz	11.70	11.70	K_u-band downlink	Given
Satellite antenna, type		3.5 × 2.4-m, shaped		Gregorian	
Coverage area	deg^2	13.30	13.30	CONUS	Given
Antenna efficiency	%	70%	70%		Assume
Antenna gain	dBi	33.4	33.4	Derived from coverage	Eq. 16-14
Satellite *TX* power	W	150	150	Per channel	Input
Backoff and line loss	dB	–5.5	–4.5	2.5 dB line loss	Assume
EIRP per channel	dBW	49.6	50.6		Eq. 16-20
EIRP per user	dBW	34.2	50.6	*EIRP* / no. users	Calculation
Propagation range	km	39,000	39,000	Satellite to users	Given
Space Loss	dB	–205.6	–205.6		Eq. 16-22
Atmospheric losses	dB	–7.0	–7.0	99.97% availability	
Net path loss	dB	–212.6	–212.6		Calculation
User terminal type		Small user	Large user		
Diameter	m	**1.2**	**2.3**		Input
Beamwidth	deg	1.5	0.8		Eq. 16-11
Gain, *G*	dBi	40.8	46.4	55% efficiency	Eq. 16-10
Line loss	dB	–2	–2		Assume
Receive carrier power, *C*	dBW	–139.7	–117.6	Single carrier	Eq. 16-23
System noise temperature, *T*	dB-K	27.0	27.0		Derive
G/T	dB/K	13.8	19.4		Eq. 16-27
Receiver C/N_o	dB-Hz	61.9	84.0	k = –228.6	Eq. 16-30
Data rate per user	dB-Hz	57.0	76.4	Single user data rate	Calculation
Available Eb/No, downlink	dB	4.9	7.6		Eq. 16-31
End-to-end E_b/N_o	dB	4.8	7.3	Uplink plus downlink	Eq. 16-32
Modem implementation loss	dB	–1.2	–1.2	QPSK	Table 16-11
Required E_b/N_o	dB	0.6	3.0	DVB-S2 waveform	Table 16-12
Link Margin	dB	**3.0**	**3.1**		Given
Channel bandwidth	MHz	36	36		Given
Number of channels		24	24	500 MHz, 2 polarizations	Sec. 16.2.1.5
No of users/ channel		35	1		Input
Single user data rate	Mbps	0.500	44		Input
Code rate		0.33	0.83	DVB-S2 waveform	Table 16-12
Single user bandwidth	MHz	1.015	35.52	QPSK, factor 1.34×	Sec.16.2.1.5
Bandwidth used / channel	MHz	35.5	35.5		Sec. 16.2.1.5
Total capacity	**Mbps**	**420**	**1,056**		

Table 16-13, Fig. 16-18◀, Eq. 16-33◀

For the "Small Terminal" scenario, QPSK modulation and code rate 1/3 are assumed. From Table 16-13, we see that this set of operating parameters will require $E_b/N_o \geq 0.6$ dB for closure on the combined link. For the "Large Terminal" scenario, QPSK modulation and code rate 5/6 are assumed, requiring $E_b/N_o \geq 3.0$ dB for closure on the combined link. In each case the tradable parameters have been varied so that these links close with the required implementation margin.

Link Capacity

The *link capacity* shown at the bottom of Table 16-13 for each scenario is calculated as the number of channels (24) multiplied by the number of user terminals and the maximum required single user data rate. Link capacities of 420 and 1,056 megabits per second (Mbps) are computed for the "Small Terminal" and "Large Terminal" scenarios, respectively.

* Note that the free-space loss for the downlink in this example is smaller than that for the uplink, despite the larger propagation range for the downlink. This is the result of the frequency dependence of the free-space loss, as described by Eqs. (16-21) and (16-22).

16.3 Communications Payload Design

Communications payload design is the process of developing a specific and detailed description as to how the communications payload architecture (Sec. 16.1) is to be implemented. Link analysis (Sec. 16.2) is used in the development of the communications payload architecture, but assumes an even more significant role in the payload design process. Link budgets are maintained and updated throughout the design process to continually refine predicted performance, verify compliance to system-level requirements, and to support analyses for troubleshooting and optimization of subsystems and lower-level assemblies.

Table 16-14 describes the typical process flow for the design of space mission communications payloads. As

Table 16-14. Typical Process Flow for Communication Payload Design.

	Step	Description	Principal Assumptions/Inputs	Outcome
3.1	***Communication Payload Connectivity and Aperture Design***	Define payload connectivity and detailed antenna implementation to meet the initial mission/link requirements, and also the spacecraft/mission constraints	• Payload connectivity requirements, orbital nodes, beam to beam connectivity • Aperture sizing, link characteristics, and frequency reuse requirements • To meet the mission and link requirements • To meet the spacecraft constraints for size, mass, power, thermal	• Payload implementation and subsystem definition • Antenna implementation and subsystem definition
3.2	***Communication Payload Block Diagram Design***	Define detailed frequency channelization and corresponding amplification, filtering, frequency conversion, switching, routing between receive and transmit apertures	• Understanding of typical unit performance specification ranges and limits • Connectivity, connectivity flexibility, and reliability from top-level requirements flow-down	• Detailed frequency channelization • Payload block diagram illustrating component functions, counts, and reference designation, connectivity between components, channel numbering, switching, and redundancy provisions
3.3	***Communications Payload Sizing, with Detail Equipment List, Size, Mass, Power, Thermal***	Estimate the payload size, mass, power, and thermal requirements, and verify that they are within bus and launch-vehicle allocated budgets	• Aperture specifications from previous step • Link parameters for all other beams: Operating bands, terminal *G/T* and *EIRP* values, modulation, coding, data rates, availability, and expected receiver noise and interferences • Required connectivity flexibility (beam-to-beam routing/switching) • Bus and launch vehicle constraints: payload size, mass, power, and thermal	• Total aperture count and configuration concept • Total payload power requirement • Payload switching / routing concept • Redundancy concept for critical units • Total payload mass and volume • Verification that payload can be accommodated by bus and launch vehicle
3.4	***Communication Payload Detail Design and Requirements Flowdown***	Determine component specifications and select components Finalize and document the design	• Detailed frequency plan • Payload block diagram • Payload equipment list • Provides a component capabilities driven feedback into the design for iterative optimization • Redundancy requirements • Environmental requirements • Update to size, mass, power, thermal, within risk/uncertainty margin allocated	• Detailed specification for all components and parts to be used in the communications payload, with detail sufficient to support both procurement and performance assessments • Finalized frequency plan and payload block diagram • Specifications for all parts, units, and higher-level assemblies • Mechanical drawings • Final design approval / design freeze

was described in Sec. 16.1, customer mission requirements flow into the communications payload architecture. By describing interfaces to other parts of the space communications system (links and aperture counts) and an overall concept for the types of payload elements that are to be used (e.g., a transparent payload with fixed antennas having shaped reflectors) and the way that those components are to be configured (e.g., specification of uplink and downlink switching), the architecture imposes constraints on the design that can be translated into specific requirements that will both bound and guide the direction of the detailed design process, as described in Table 16-14.

The communications payload design process begins with the development of preliminary antenna designs, a process that begins with link analyses for each beam to define the *G/T* and *EIRP* that each antenna is required to deliver. With fundamental aspects of the antenna concepts having been defined as part of the architecture, computer simulations are used to develop preliminary design concepts and performance predictions. The key objectives of the first step of the process are to develop preliminary antenna designs to a level of maturity required to (A) understand the approximate size, weight, and mechanical configuration of each antenna, including attachment to the bus and any articulation that may be required, (B) predict key measures of antenna performance with high fidelity so that the payload design can be developed in parallel with development of more detailed antenna designs, and (C) demonstrate that the preliminary mechanical designs and RF performance predictions are compatible with mission requirements.

In the second step of the process, payload block diagrams are developed, building on the topology described by the payload architecture to elaborate all details of the channelization and routing of RF signals between the receive and transmit apertures, including amplification, filtering, frequency conversion, and switching. The payload block diagram specifies not only the types of components that will be required, but also describes the number of each component required for the complete payload. The way that the components are connected to one another, and key characteristics about the components, (such as part identification codes, nominal power, operating band, and channel assignments of certain active and passive components), will be useful throughout the remainder of the design process and into later testing and troubleshooting. Development of the payload block diagram requires initial budgets to be created for numerous aspects of payload performance. These budgets, analogous in many respects to the link budgets described in Sec. 16.2, are used to determine initial component specifications, evaluate design alternatives as each aspect of the design matures, and as the basis for testing that must be performed throughout the process of satellite payload integration.

From the payload block diagram, the design team has sufficient information in component counts and top level component specifications to estimate the total mass, power requirements, and thermal dissipation requirements that will be required for the payload, confirm that these are within the design envelope of the satellite bus, and begin developing concepts as to mechanical layouts and configurations. With this third step of the process, the detailed physical configuration of both the communications payload and the satellite begin to emerge on a large scale, as do challenges that inevitably force certain aspects of the design to be iterated.

The final step in the communications payload design process, comprises finalizing and documenting component specifications and detailed designs. Outputs from this step include finalized versions of the payload block diagram, equipment lists, specifications for individual parts, units, and higher level assemblies, mechanical and electrical drawings and assembly instructions, and end-user documentation that describes all aspects of routine payload operations, operating constraints, and procedures for diagnosing and recovering from faults and performance anomalies.

16.3.1 Preliminary Antenna Design

The architecture includes a definition of the payload antennas that are to be implemented in terms of the basic geometry, whether frequency reuse is required, and whether beam forming or beam steering are required. Table 16-15 describes the principal degrees of freedom in the aperture selection process, gives examples of some of the main alternatives that are available, and describes which types of application requirements typically play a role in identifying candidates from among the available alternatives. From this, it is clear that the details of the antenna design process can vary dramatically from one application to the next.

The preliminary antenna design is further complicated because it involves optimization in multiple dimensions, and is subject to combinations of constraints that can be traded against one another. For example, while receiver sensitivity and the output power from high power amplifiers can each be traded against antenna gain to achieve link closure, geographic coverage is reduced as gain increases. Likewise, although the wide separation between uplink and downlink frequencies means that the optimal design for transmit and receive antennas that serve the same coverage area should be very different from one another, size and mass limitations create a strong motivation to use single apertures to support both transmit and receive functions whenever possible. The preliminary antenna design process must work through these trades at a level sufficient to allow the approximate size, weight, and mechanical configuration of each antenna to be understood, and at a level sufficient that key measures of antenna performance can be predicted with high fidelity so that the payload design can be developed while detailed antenna designs are being completed. In order for the preliminary antenna design to be accepted, the design team must be able to demonstrate that the preliminary mechanical designs and RF performance predictions are compatible with mission requirements.

Table 16-15. Principal Antenna-Specification Degrees of Freedom, and Typical Alternatives and Associated Requirements or Considerations.

Antenna Attribute	Available Alternatives	Related or Relevant Requirements
Antenna Geometry	• Direct radiating (dipole, horn, spiral) • Reflector (aligned/offset, Gregorian, Cassegrain) – Non-parabolic reflector shaping – Multiple reflectors • Lens	Coverage area and directivity, frequency plan vs. capacity (need for frequency reuse), frequency reuse beam-to-beam isolation, coverage keep-out zones, bus/launch vehicle packaging, mass, size, electronic beam forming/steering, thermal distortion, pointing accuracy and precision
Feed	• Feed/element type • Single vs. multiple elements • Transmit only, receive only, or transmit/receive • Polarization (linear, circular)	Operating band and bandwidth, aperture efficiency, electronic beam forming/steering, frequency reuse), bus/launch vehicle packaging, beam-to-beam isolation, transmit receive isolation, ground terminal polarization
Coverage Flexibility	• Mechanical steering (gimbaled assembly, steerable feeds, steerable or selectable reflectors) • Electronic steering and beam forming (amplitude or phase)	Coverage flexibility, reconfiguration/tracking speed, bus/launch vehicle packaging, reliability, intended service life, cost/complexity, discrete vs. continuously variable coverage specification, required pointing/tracking accuracy and precision
Articulation for Apertures Stowed During Launch	• Deployable rigid reflectors • Unfurlable reflectors	Bus/launch vehicle packaging, pointing accuracy, precision, and stability, reliability, coverage flexibility

Regardless of the antenna definition specified by the payload architecture, the preliminary antenna design process begins with link analyses for each link that the communications payload must support, using information flowed down from mission requirements and the architecture definition. The information flowed down into the initial link analyses includes details of link geometry (satellite locations, coverage areas), RF band allocations, key characteristics of the user and ground terminals with which the communications payload must establish RF links, required data rates, and link availability. With these inputs, link budgets are developed that define minimum *G/T* values that the payload receivers must achieve, and *EIRP* that must be delivered at the *payload transmit antennas*. From the initial link analysis results and the antenna concept defined by the payload architecture, combined with an understanding of available alternatives and key performance parameters for receivers and high power amplifiers, the design team assesses the appropriate partition between receiver sensitivity and receive antenna gain, and between amplifier power and transmit antenna gain.

Although it is routine for apertures to be optimized in some way for the requirements of many, if not all of a satellite payload user beams, there is always a strong motivation to reuse successful, flight-proven designs to the greatest extent possible. Once the design team has identified the antenna configuration, detailed and typically intensive, computer-based numerical simulations are conducted to predict all aspects of antenna performance required to support the development of payload budgets, and to demonstrate compliance to system-level requirements. These simulations will typically yield very accurate and precise pattern predictions, which will be useful for higher fidelity modeling of link performance, and will serve as the basis for subsequent steps in the payload design process.

Parabolic reflector antennas were used for the high-gain applications discussed in Sec. 16.2. Such antennas are best suited for applications that require peak gain greater than 20 dB, and beamwidth less than 15 deg, requirements that are typical for satellite ground terminals and satellite reflectors.

Lighter and simpler antennas [Ford, 2009] tend to be appropriate for lower gain, wider beam applications. For example, an Earth-coverage antenna for a geosynchronous satellite might be designed with a beamwidth of about 18 deg. For this requirement, a simple direct radiating horn antenna would likely be selected for virtually any operating band, whether C-band, X-band, K_u-band, or K_a-band.

Figure 16-19 illustrates the configuration of a typical communications satellite that incorporates both high-gain parabolic reflectors and low gain direct radiating Earth-coverage horn antennas.

Mission applications that require beam scanning may be supported with either mechanically or electrically steered beams, with important trades to be made between beam agility (scan rate), and payload cost, weight, and size. *Phased-array* antennas offer significant potential performance advantages over mechanically steered arrays, offering virtually instantaneous repointing and beam forming, but at considerable penalties in terms of cost and complexity.

As Table 16-15 suggests, the range of antenna alternatives available to the communications payload design team is enormous, and it is only possible here to convey a sense of the key trades and considerations that are made in the communications payload design process. Table 16-16 summarizes the attributes of several antenna types that can provide additional insight into these trades.

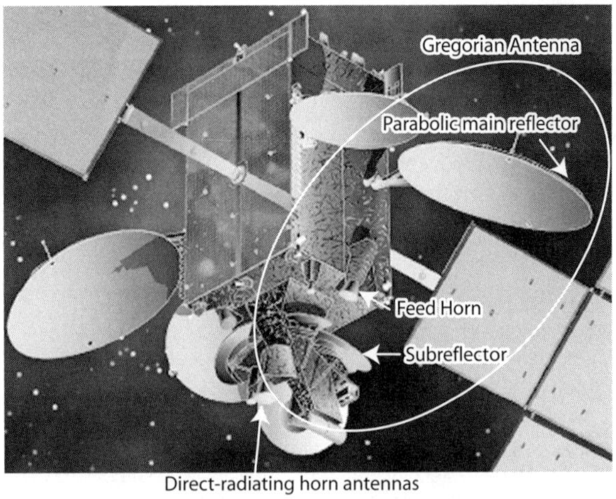

Fig. 16-19. Modern Geosynchronous Satellite that uses both and Direct-radiating Earth-coverage Horn Antennas and High-gain Gregorian Antennas with Parabolic Main Reflectors and Offset Subreflectors.

16.3.2 Communications Payload Block Diagram Design

Once preliminary antenna designs and performance predictions are available, the communications payload design team has sufficient information to begin designing the heart of the communications payload. The *payload block diagram* details all of the components and component connectivity required to implement the channelization and the corresponding amplification, filtering, frequency conversion, switching, and routing that takes place between payload receive and transmit apertures. The payload block diagram specifies not only the types of components that will be required, but also describes the number of each component required for the complete payload, the way that the components are connected to one another, and key characteristics about the components, such as part identification codes, nominal power, operating band, and channel assignments of certain active and passive components will be useful throughout the remainder of the design process and into later testing and troubleshooting.

Developing the payload block diagram requires a variety of initial payload budgets to be completed. Like the link analysis discussed in Sec. 16.2, these budgets track various aspects of payload performance, and compliance to performance specifications. In addition, they are invaluable tools for defining unit specifications, supporting trades during the design process, and supporting troubleshooting during integration and test phases. Like the link budgets, many of these payload budgets are maintained and updated throughout the design, integration, and test process, with initial performance estimates being replaced with improved performance predictions as the design matures, and with measured data as it becomes available.

Table 16-16. Antenna Types for Satellite Systems. (Formulas from Jasik [1961]) In these equations, C, D, L, and λ are in meters and f is in GHz.

Antenna Type	***Parabolic Reflector*** 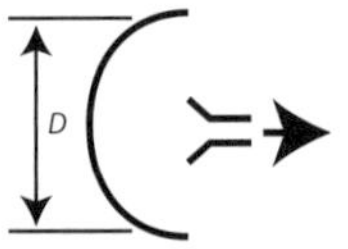	***Helix*** 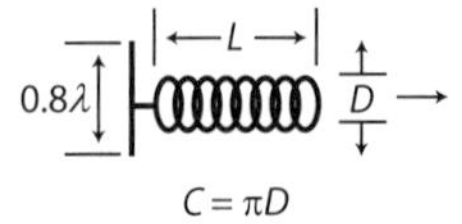	***Horn*** 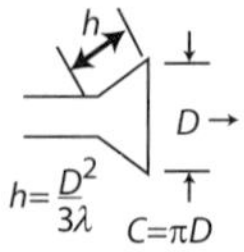	***Array*** 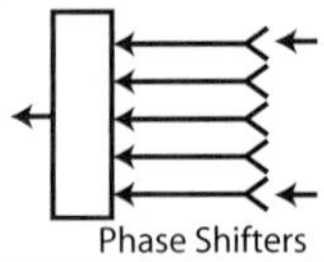
Beam Shape	Conical	Conical	Conical	Conical (scanning)
Typical Max Gain (dBI)	15–65	5–20	5–20	5–20
Peak Gain (dBI)	$17.8 + 20 \log D + 20 \log f$ ($\eta = 0.55$)	$10.3 + 10 \log (C^2L/\lambda^3)$ $0.8 \le C/\lambda \le 1.2$ ($\eta = 0.70$)	$20 \log (C/\lambda) - 2.8$ ($\eta = 0.52$)	$10 \log (A/\lambda^2) + 8$
Half-Power Beamwidth (degs)	$\dfrac{21}{fD}$	$\dfrac{52}{\sqrt{C^2L/\lambda^3}}$	$\approx \dfrac{225}{(C/\lambda)}$	
Size, m	D	DL	D	A
Mass, kg	10–30	10–15	1–2	20–40
Features	• Folded Optics, parabolic offset feed typically employed for satellite application • Mechanical steering • Simple lightweight structure • High *EIRP*	• Lower frequency applications • Deployed helix, increased complexity	• Ideal for global coverage, low gain applications with broad coverage area	• Flat packaging • Electronic beam steering • High aperture efficiency • Multiple independent steerable beams • High losses in feed distribution • High *EIRP* • High cost and weight

Figure 16-20 illustrates how the link budget is used to represent the allocation of *EIRP* contributions between elements in the output section of the power-amplification chain and transmit-antenna contribution. Similar allocations are made in a variety of ways with other link budgets listed in Table 16-17, providing a basis for the development of key components of unit-performance specifications, unit, and higher level testing, and for troubleshooting and understanding various measures of payload performance sensitivity.

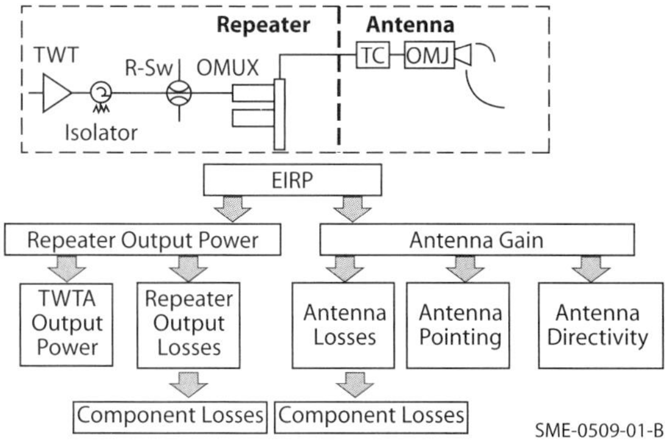

Fig. 16-20. Allocation of *EIRP* Contributions Between the Power-amplification Chain and Transmit-antenna Contributions.

Table 16-17. Payload Budgets Required as Part of the Communications Payload Design Process

EIRP and G/T	**Phase Shift**
Gain/Loss	**AM/PM Transfer and Conversion**
Noise Figure	**Overdrive**
Input Losses	**Amplitude Linearity**
G/T Stability	***G/T* Degradation**
SFD Variation over Frequency	**Coherent Self Interference**
Output Power and Losses	**Transmit Power Loading**
EIRP Stability	**General Spurs**
Frequency Response and Rejection	**Specific Spurs**
Gain Slope	**Passive Intermodulation**
Group Delay	**Peak Power for Multipactor**
Group Delay Ripple	**RF Susceptibility**
Group Delay Stability	**Antenna Isolations**

Because of their great cost, designers and manufacturers of satellite communications payloads are constantly challenged to maximize the performance, and hence the potential revenue generating capacity of each communications payload. As a result, satellite communications payloads are highly optimized to support the unique mission requirements of each application. Payload budgets provide a structured way of predicting, tracking, balancing, and allocating many aspects of communications payload performance between different parts of the system.

The most common communications mission today are for geosynchronous FSS and BSS satellite communications applications [Elbert, 2008]. To facilitate the description of key components that are used to build and populate the payload block diagram, we will refer to the highly simplified description of the key FSS payload functional blocks illustrated in Fig. 16-21.

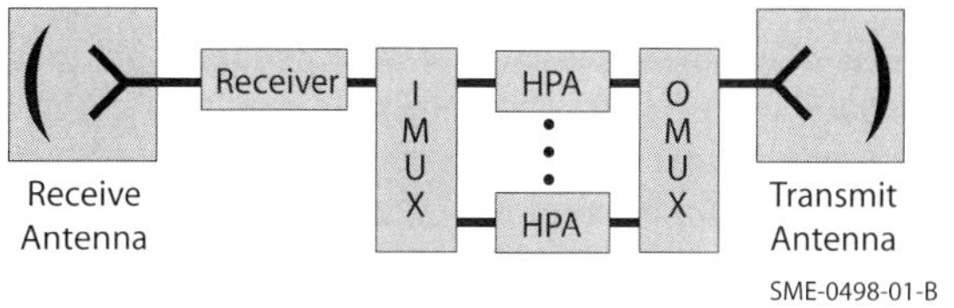

Fig. 16-21. Highly Simplified Schematic Illustrating Key Functional Blocks of a Typical FSS Payload.

Receive Antenna: Uplinked signals (and noise) are captured by the receive antenna, which is designed to efficiently couple energy from free space into coaxial transmission lines, where they pass through prefilters to remove out-of-band signals before reaching the receiver. The receive antenna plays a pivotal role in determining the sensitivity of the satellite to uplinked signals, as well as the geographic distribution of users that can be served. **Receiver**: The receiver amplifies the uplinked signal and converts it to the downlink frequency. The receiver comprises a *low noise amplifier* (LNA), a *down converter* (D/C), a *local oscillator* (LO) and a *power supply*, and may be realized either as individual components, or an integrated assembly. Receivers are typically required to have low noise generation, high gain, high linearity, and zero to low spurious signal generation. The noise figure of the LNA is the primary contributor to the payload *G/T* performance, and is a function of frequency, bandwidth, and operating temperature. Figure 16-22 includes a simple block diagram that illustrates how the components of a receiver relate to one another and to the receiver inputs and outputs. A photograph of a satellite communications payload receiver is also shown in Fig. 16-22.

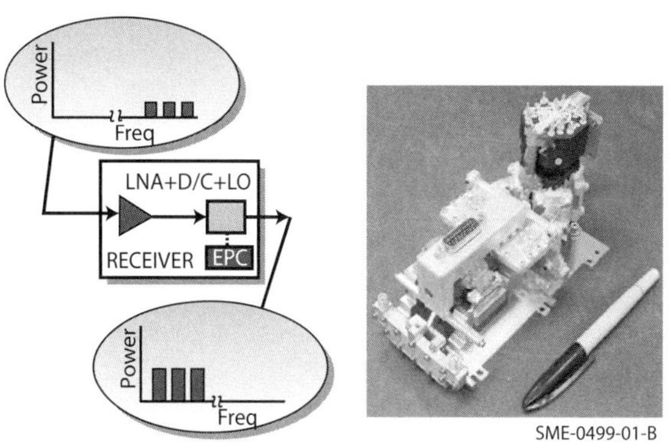

Fig. 16-22. Schematic Diagram of Receiver Functionality and an Image of an Integrated Receiver Unit. High-frequency, low-power signals at the receiver input are amplified and converted to lower frequency.

HPA: The *high-power amplifier* (HPA) provides commandable amplification on the downlink signal path within the communications payload in a compact form factor, using very mature technology that offers high reliability. The HPA usually consists of a *channel amplifier* (CAMP), a *traveling wave tube* (TWT) amplifier, and an *electronic power conditioner* (EPC) power supply. The channel amplifier provides medium-power amplification (typically between 40 and 60 dB) and gain control. A linearizer is sometimes needed to improve transponder linearity when the HPA is operated near maximum (or *saturated*) power, where its output becomes non-linear. A final stage of amplification (typically in the range of 40 to 60 dB) is usually provided by a high-efficiency *traveling wave tube amplifier* (TWTA), which comprises a TWT and an EPC. In a travelling wave tube, an electron beam interacts with an RF signal, and energy transferred from the electron beam increases the energy of the RF signal, typically providing RF output power between 60 and 150W. The principal metrics of TWTA performance are the RF power output, and the overall efficiency (typically in the range of 50 to 65%) for converting DC bus current into RF output power. Figure 16-23 illustrates the relationship between the HPA and HPA inputs and outputs, and also shows a photograph of a flight-qualified HPA.

Solid State Power Amplifiers (SSPAs) are sometimes used in place of TWTAs at lower L-band and S-band frequencies, serving the same function as TWTs, but without need for high-voltage power supplies. This component savings translates directly to reducing payload mass, but does so at the expense of reduced RF output power and lower efficiency (25–55%). Where SSPAs are a viable alternative, the specifics of the application requirements determine which choice is most appropriate [Brown, 2002].

The HPA is the main contributor to payload nonlinearity (an important metric of communications payload performance), and is therefore the principal source of signal distortion when operated in its non-linear range, near saturation. Non-linearity is characterized by the ratio of the carrier power to the power in the third-order intermodulation product, an interfering signal that is generated in the amplifier at a frequency that is offset from that of the carrier. Figure 16-24 depicts the non-linear input-output characteristic of a TWTA operated near saturation, AM-PM signal modulation, and variation in the generation of third-order intermodulation products at low power and high power operating points.

The increased production of intermodulation products at TWTA operating points near saturation, will cause interfence to adjacent-channel operation, and can be mitigated in one of two ways: (A) by using higher-power amplifiers capable of delivering the desired output power when operated within their linear range, or (B) increase channelization of the payload, so that the bandwidth and the power required for each signal path is reduced. The latter strategy has the potential to dramatically increase the number of payload channels, cost, and mass.

IMUX: The *input multiplexer* (IMUX) assembly separates the broadband signals into individual channel frequencies. This function may also be realized through the use of hybrid splitting or channel dropping through integrated circulators (as shown). An IMUX is necessary to minimize unwanted intermodulation products generated by subsequent high power amplifiers operated in their non-linear region. IMUX passband response is typically a contributor to linear impairment, such as amplitude and group delay distortion. Figure 16-25 (Left) depicts the function of an IMUX, and includes a photograph of an IMUX representative of those that might be part of a satellite communications payload.

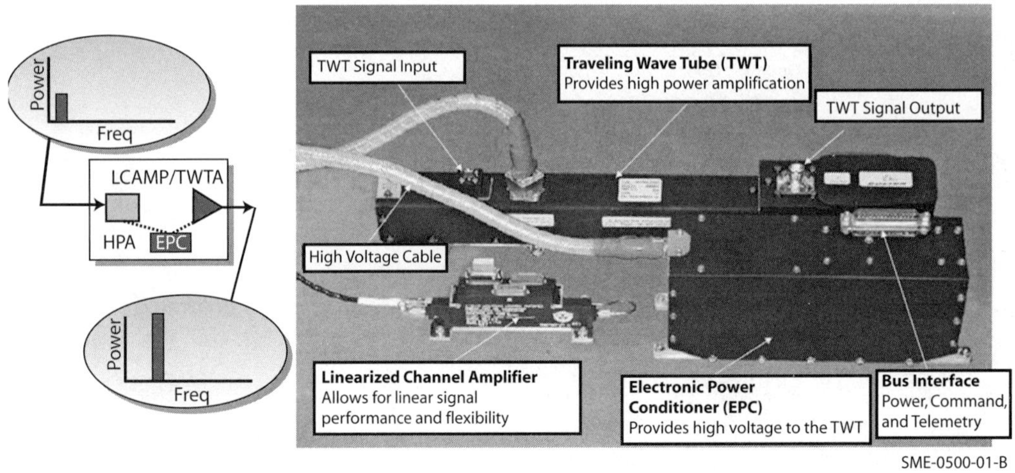

Fig. 16-23. Schematic Diagram of High-power Amplifier Functionality, and an Image of a High-Power Amplifier Comprising a Linearized Channel Amplifier (LCAMP), a Traveling Wave Tube (TWT) Amplifier, and an Electronic Power Conditioner (EPC).

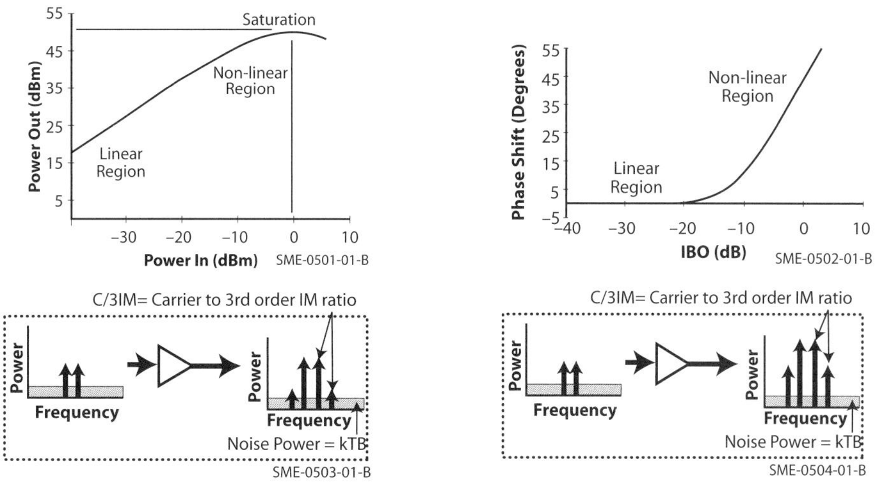

Fig. 16-24. Non-linearity C/3IM Levels Operated in Backoff vs. Close to Saturation.

OMUX: The *output multiplexer* (OMUX) assembly combines narrow-band signals from individual amplifier chains onto a single common broadband signal. An OMUX is necessary for minimizing the number of ports that are required on the transmit antenna. OMUX passband response is typically a contributor to linear impairment such as amplitude and group delay distortion. High power-handling capability is a critical requirement in OMUX design. Figure 16-25 (Right) depicts the function of an OMUX, and includes a photograph of an 8-channel OMUX.

Transmit Antenna: The *transmit antenna* efficiently couples energy from waveguide (or coaxial, in some instances) transmission lines to free space. The transmit antenna determines the coverage area that can be supported by the communications payload downlink, and in conjunction with the HPAs, determines the *EIRP* of the communications payload.

Reflector Surface Reuse: Although transmit and receive antennas are shown separately in Fig. 16-17, transmit and receive functions are frequently supported on *orthogonal polarizations* of a single antenna, allowing overall payload mass to be reduced, and space to be made available for adding antennas to serve other payloads or functions, or for other components. As a result, it is common for transmit and receive functions to be combined in a single antenna when uplink and downlink frequencies are within about 30% of one another. Because they operate at different frequencies, combining transmit and receive functions into a single antenna generally prevents either from being fully optimized, with performance being degraded further as the frequency difference grows. In most applications where transmit and receive functions are combined and performance degradation is split evenly between the transmit and receive functions, gain is degraded approximately 0.2 dB, as compared with the performance that might have been obtained for separately optimized antennas.

Payload Reliability and Robustness: Many factors contribute to the overall *reliability* of a system design. The reliability of the payload is strongly influenced by both the required mission life, and by failure rates for components used in the design. Failure rate is often expressed as either the *failure in time* (FIT) rate, which expresses the number of failures per billion operating hours, or in terms of the *mean time between failures* (MTBF), which is the measure used in the overall *probability of success (Ps)* analyses of the payload design over the mission life.

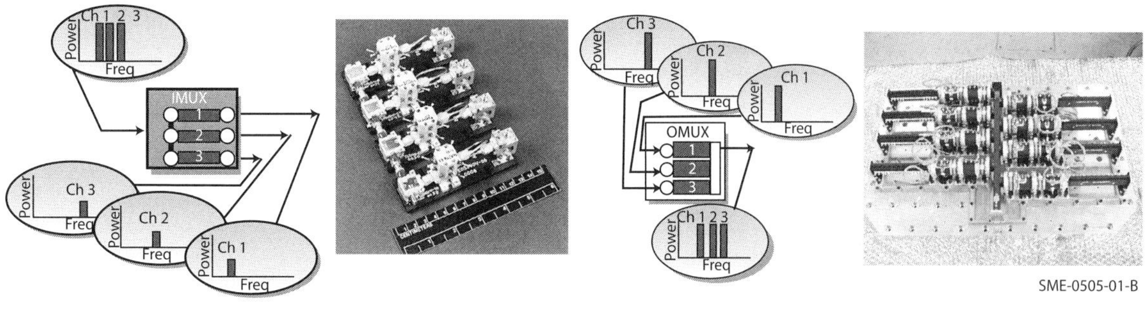

Fig. 16-25. IMUX Input Multiplexer (left 2 images) and OMUX Output Multiplexer (right 2 images).

Table 16-17◀, Fig. 16-25, Eq. 16-33◀

The communications payload *Ps* performance is affected most by the FIT rates for active components and their electronics, and high voltage supplies. To mitigate against these types of failures and potential loss of service, switching circuits are implemented at several points in the payload block diagram to allow failed units to be replaced with redundant units (Fig. 16-26). To provide the most appropriate balance between cost, complexity, and reliability, these switching circuits are often implemented as *switch rings,* which afford a high degree of flexibility in terms of the choice of which redundant units can be used in place of a given unit that has failed. Payload block diagrams typically incorporate redundancy switch rings and redundant units in Receiver (LNA plus downconverter) and HPA (CAMP+TWTA) blocks.

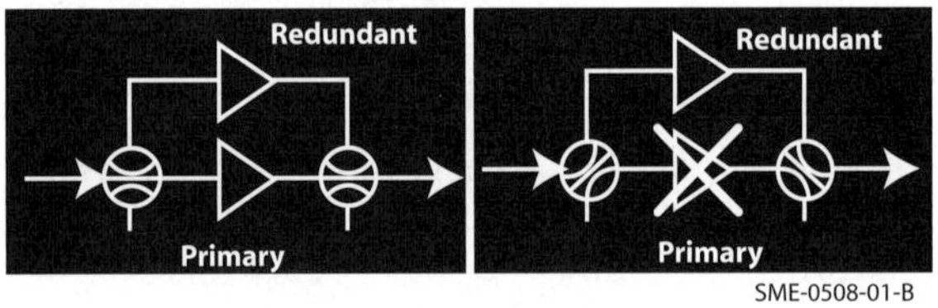

Fig. 16-26. Redundancy Switch Rings.

This detailed payload block diagram also describes *ancillary units* and hardware, including *passive devices* such as isolators, loads, hybrids, and even barrel connectors, which depicts the communication payload architecture for each beam or coverage area defined by the mission need. In this example, we have identified the major components of the payload, the ancillary components have not been defined at this stage of the block diagram, but would be at subsequent stages of more detailed block diagram release. The next level detailed block diagram would include spur filters, isolators, splitters, test couplers, detailed redundancy ring topology, and defined interconnect coax, transitions, waveguide.

Figure 16-27 shows the channelized frequency plan and payload block diagram for a typical FSS payload. Though more detailed than the diagram shown in Fig. 16-21, which reduced the diagram to its most fundamental functional blocks, the payload block diagram shown here is still greatly simplified in comparison with working block diagrams for even the simplest of modern communications payloads, which provide identifying information for each individual unit, including passive hardware such as isolators, loads, hybrids, waveguide and cable segments, and even barrel connectors.

The details of the payload's channelization begin to emerge early in the development of the payload block diagram and associated budgets, and from this comes a detailed picture of the channelized frequency plan that will be used by the communications payload. Like the payload block diagram and the payload budgets, the channelized frequency plan will be a key reference throughout the remainder of the design development, through payload integration, test, and on-orbit operations

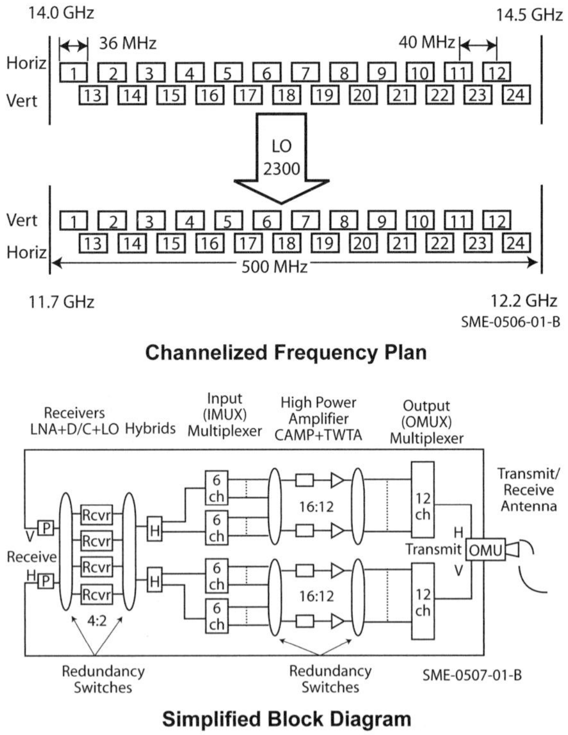

Fig. 16-27. A Representative FSS Payload Channelized Frequency Plan and Simplified Block Diagram.

Figure 16-27 shows a representative FSS payload channelized frequency plan and simplified payload block diagram.

The frequency plan shows the local oscillator frequency that defines the frequency conversion, as well as channel spacing that is staggered between polarizations to minimize cross-talk interference. The frequency plan and the payload block diagram shows that the design has been developed to include a total of 24 channels. The block diagram indicates that transmit and receive functions are supported on orthogonal polarizations by a single antenna, as well as redundancy for critical units. For example, the notation 4:2 under the receiver block means that 4 receivers are provided at launch to support 2 active receivers corresponding to "four-for-two" redundancy.

16.3.3 Communications Payload Sizing

Parts databases for modern communications satellites catalog hundreds of thousands of individual parts that must be procured, integrated into successively higher-level assemblies, and tested. The payload block diagram is a critically important tool that is used by design, integration, and test personnel alike to understand the hardware requirements for the communications payload and how they are intended to relate to one another and operate together. Despite the enormous parts count, the satellite bus engineers are expected to predict and track the satellite's total size, mass, power, thermal dissipation requirements, and center of gravity to within very tight

Table 16-18. Mass, Power, and Thermal Dissipation (MPT) Budget Table, Based on Build History for Multiple Satellites.

	Payload MPT		Quantities			Unit			Total		
			Unit	Total	Active	Mass (kg)	Power (W)	Thermal (W)	Mass (kg)	Power (W)	Thermal (W)
1	Input Ancilliary (Test Coupler, Preselect Filter)	waveguide	# uplinks	4		0.30			1.20		
2	RCVR Input Red Ring Switches	waveguide	#RCVRs	8		0.20			1.60		
3	RCVR, LNA+D/C+LO	waveguide	#RCVRs	8	4	1.20	10.0	10.0	9.60	40.0	40.0
4	RCVR Output Red Ring Switches	coax	#RCVRs	8		0.10			0.80		
									0.00		
5	Input Ancilliary (Hybrid, SatPads, ...)	coax	#RCVRs	8		0.15			1.20		
6	IMUX, single channel	coax	#channels	48		0.26			12.48		
7	TWTA Input Red Ring	coax	#TWTs	64		0.10			6.40		
8	**LCAMP**		#TWTs	64	48	0.20	3.4		12.80	163.2	
9	**TWT RAD**	**150.0 65% 92%**	#TWTs	64	48	1.00	230.8	40.4	64.00	11076.9	1938.5
10	**EPC SINGLE**	OBO: **0.0**	#TWTs	64	48	2.00	24.3	24.3	128.00	1167.2	1167.2
11	TWTA Output Red Ring	waveguide	#TWTs	64		0.30			19.20		
12	Termination Loads	waveguide	#TWTs	64							
13	OMUX, single channel	waveguide	#channels	48		0.90			43.20		
14	Output Ancilliary (Harmonic Filter, Test Coupler)	waveguide	#downlinks	4		1.00			4.00		
15	Output Loss	**2.0**			48						2657.1
16	Interconnects (coax, waveguide, brackets,harness ...)	**40%**							121.8		
17	Antenna Subsystem (feed, subreflector, main reflector)	waveguide	# up/downlinks	2		20.00			40.00		
18	**Total**								**466.3**	**12447.3**	**5802.8**

tolerances, and to refine those estimates and retire their small contingency margins as the satellite design matures, and further still as integration proceeds.

Because of its role in specifying components and component counts, completion of the payload block diagram represents a major milestone toward developing precise predictions of the payload mass, power, and thermal dissipation requirements. Once the payload block diagram has been defined, the payload equipment list can be generated, allowing the satellite bus engineering team to assess the communication payload and overall satellite *mass, power, and thermal dissipation* (MPT) requirements. Whereas early MPT estimates are top-down estimates that are based on previous satellite-build experience, the first reasonably precise estimates are only possible when a bottoms-up accounting can be performed.

Likewise, with the component specifications and connections described by the payload block diagram, bus and payload engineers can work together to define and optimize mechanical layouts. This is the first step toward verifying that all components can be physically accommodated within the satellite bus with the connectivity that is required, and the first step toward predicting the satellite center of mass.

In Table 16-18 we see the MPT budget for a typical FSS satellite communications payload, showing allocations that have been made to each type of payload component. Allocations for any given satellite can be compared with final allocations that were made on earlier satellites as a means of judging whether allocations are realistic, or whether further review or design optimizations may be required.

Lines 1 through 14 of the table contain entries that correspond with functional blocks of the payload block diagram. The mass allocation for these items is derived from historical data, and provided for reference. The unit column under quantity provides a guideline for interpreting each value listed in the table. For many units, component size is proportional to the signal wavelength so that mass values vary as a function of operating frequency, with greater mass allocations being required as the operating frequency decreases. Allocations for interconnects, such as coaxial and waveguide connectors, are made on line 16. This mass is not trivial, and generally exhibits a dependence on operating frequency.

DC power consumption occurs only in active units (Receiver and HPA), and is captured on line 3 and on lines 8 through 10. Power consumption for active units increases as operating frequency increases, with the largest differences occurring in TWTs (line 9). This systematic effect is mainly associated with a decrease in efficiency as units progress toward higher-frequency operation. Note that in certain applications, it is worthwhile to consider the trade between efficiency and the increased risk of single point failure vs. the advantage of improved power use efficiency that may be achieved through the use of power supplies that support multiple units (such as dual EPCs, that may supply two TWTs, or master converters that may power multiple LNAs).

Thermal dissipation is also dominated by TWT power levels, and increase with operating frequency for the very same reasons as described above for DC power consumption. An important factor that offsets this pattern is the availability of radiation-cooled TWT configurations for K_u-band and K_a-band applications, which offer greater efficiency than the conduction-cooled tubes available for C-band applications. Radiation-cooled tubes are able to dissipate approximately 50% less heat to the satellite bus than their conduction-cooled counterparts, radiating the difference directly to space.

Like the link and payload budgets, the MPT budget provides a systematic way to estimate and track the communications payload MPT requirements, and to verify

Table 16-18, Fig. 16-27◀, Eq. 16-33◀

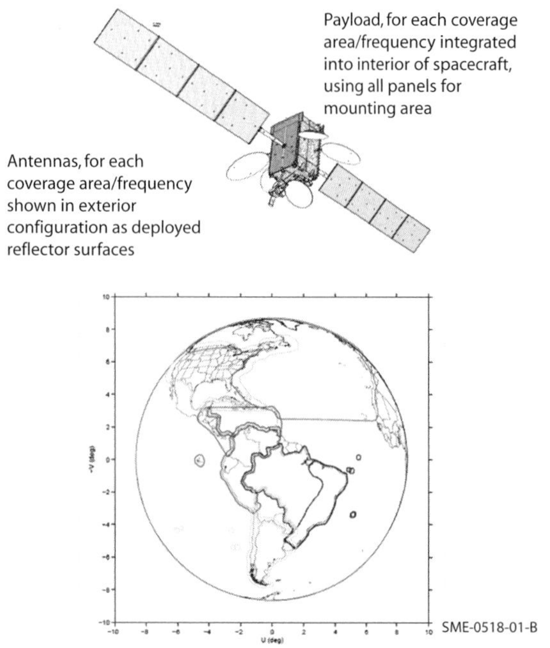

Fig. 16-28. FSS C/K_u-Band Satellite Concept and Coverage Requirement.

compatibility of the payload with both the satellite bus and the launch vehicle.

Sample MPT Budget for an FSS Payload

Here we consider a hybrid C/K_u-band FSS payload, rather than the pure K_u-band payloads that have been used as examples earlier in this section, with 24-channel coverage being divided between two polarizations for one C-band coverage area (South America) and for a second non-overlapping K_u-band service area (CONUS), as illustrated in Fig. 16-28. In this example, both receive and transmit antennas use 2.8 m shaped parabolic reflectors to optimize coverage contours and average link margins within the regions to be served. Because the uplink and downlink frequencies are within 16% of one another for the C-band payload, and within 30% for the K_u-band payload, transmit and receive functions are supported by single antennas for both payloads. As in the previous examples, channelizaton is achieved with 12 36 MHz wide channels on each polarization, with channels spaced at 40 MHz intervals so that 500 MHz spectrum allocated for this mission is almost completely used (Fig. 16-29). The payload design yields a block diagram four times that of the detailed block diagrams shown in Fig. 16-30. The communications payload MPT budget for this communications satellite is shown in Table 16-19.

The MPT budget for this communications payload predicts a total payload mass of 756 kg, a DC power requirement of 17 kW, and a thermal dissipation requirement of 8.4 kW, each of which is within the limits that can be accommodated by modern satellite buses routinely placed in geosynchronous orbit.

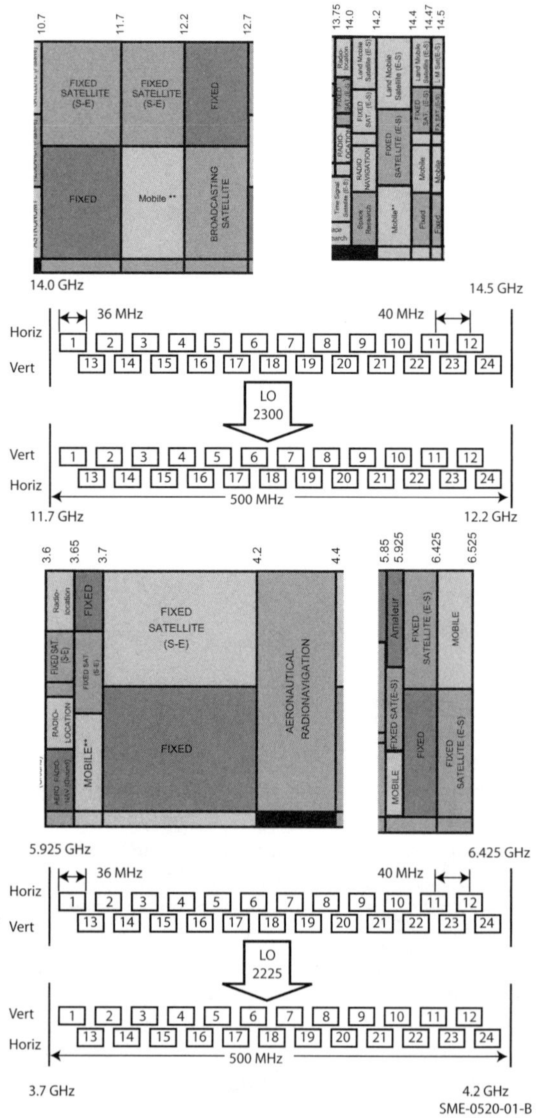

Fig. 16-29. FSS C/K_u-Band Satellite Concept and Coverage Requirement.

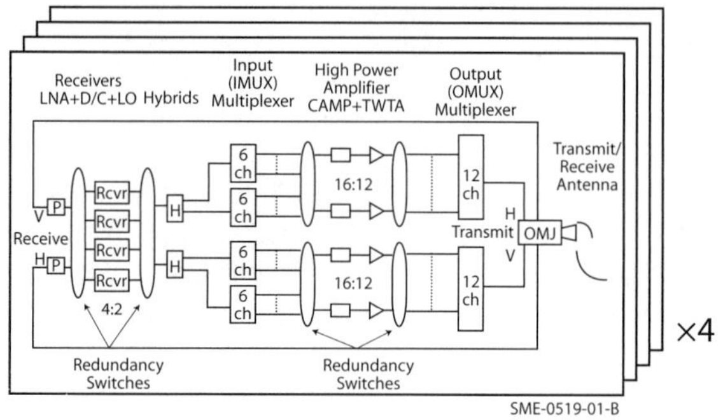

Fig. 16-30. FSS C/K_u-Band Satellite Payload Block Diagram (2 coverage areas and 2 frequencies payloads scaled from Fig. 16-27.

Table 16-18◀, Fig. 16-30, Eq. 16-33◀

Table 16-19. FSS C-Band and K_u-Band Mass, Power, and Thermal Dissipation (MPT) Budget Table.

C-Band MPT				Quantities			Unit			Total		
				Unit	Total	Active	Mass (kg)	Power (W)	Thermal (W)	Mass (kg)	Power (W)	Thermal (W)
1 Input Ancilliary (Test Coupler, Preselect Filter)		C-Band	WR137	# uplinks	4		0.70			2.80		
2 RCVR Input Red Ring Switches		C-Band	Coax	#RCVRs	8		0.15			1.20		
3 RCVR, LNA+D/C+LO		C-Band	Coax	#RCVRs	8	4	1.00	12.0	12.0	8.00	48.0	48.0
4 RCVR Output Red Ring Switches		C-Band	Coax	#RCVRs	8		0.15			1.20		
										0.00		
5 Input Ancilliary (Hybrid, SatPads, ...)		C-Band	Coax	#RCVRs	8		0.15			1.20		
6 IMUX, single channel		C-Band	Coax	#channels	48		0.35			16.80		
7 TWTA Input Red Ring		C-Band	Coax	#TWTs	64		0.15			9.60		
8 **LCAMP**				#TWTs	64	48	0.30	3.4		19.20	163.2	
9 **TWT CC**	**65.0**	**65%**	**91%**	#TWTs	64	48	0.80	100.0	35.0	51.20	4800.0	1680.0
10 **EPC Single**		OBO:	**0.0**	#TWTs	64	48	1.30	14.1	14.1	83.20	678.7	678.7
11 TWTA Output Red Ring		C-Band	Coax	#TWTs	64		0.30			19.20		
12 Termination Loads		C-Band	Coax	#TWTs	64							
13 OMUX, single channel		C-Band	WR229	#channels	48		0.90			43.20		
14 Output Ancilliary (Harmonic Filter, Test Coupler)		C-Band	WR229	#downlinks	4		1.00			4.00		
15 Output Loss			**1.5**			48						911.2
16 Interconnects (coax, waveguide, brackets, …)		C-Band	**30%**							78.2		
17 Antenna Subsystem (feed, subreflector, main reflector)			waveguide	# up/downlinks	2		20.00			40.00		
18 **Total**										379.0	5689.9	3317.9

K_u-Band MPT				Quantities			Unit			Total		
				Unit	Total	Active	Mass (kg)	Power (W)	Thermal (W)	Mass (kg)	Power (W)	Thermal (W)
1 Input Ancilliary (Test Coupler, Preselect Filter)		K_u-Band	WR75	# uplinks	4		0.30			1.20		
2 RCVR Input Red Ring Switches		K_u-Band	WR75	#RCVRs	8		0.20			1.60		
3 RCVR, LNA+D/C+LO		K_u-Band	WR75	#RCVRs	8	4	1.20	10.0	10.0	9.60	40.0	40.0
4 RCVR Output Red Ring Switches		K_u-Band	Coax	#RCVRs	8		0.10			0.80		
										0.00		
5 Input Ancilliary (Hybrid, SatPads, ...)		K_u-Band	Coax	#RCVRs	8		0.15			1.20		
6 IMUX, single channel		K_u-Band	Coax	#channels	48		0.26			12.48		
7 TWTA Input Red Ring		K_u-Band	Coax	#TWTs	64		0.10			6.40		
8 **LCAMP**				#TWTs	64	48	0.20	3.4		12.80	163.2	
9 **TWT RAD**	**136.0**	**65%**	**92%**	#TWTs	64	48	1.00	209.2	36.6	64.00	10043.1	1757.5
10 **EPC DUAL**		OBO:	**0.0**	#TWTs	32	24	2.00	44.9	44.9	64.00	1077.3	1077.3
11 TWTA Output Red Ring		K_u-Band	WR75	#TWTs	64		0.30			19.20		
12 Termination Loads		K_u-Band	WR75	#TWTs	64							
13 OMUX, single channel		K_u-Band	WR75	#channels	48		0.90			43.20		
14 Output Ancilliary (Harmonic Filter, Test Coupler)		K_u-Band	WR75	#downlinks	4		1.00			4.00		
15 Output Loss			**1.8**			48						2215.0
16 Interconnects (coax, waveguide, brackets, …)		K_u-Band	**40%**							96.2		
17 Antenna Subsystem (feed, subreflector, main reflector)			waveguide	# up/downlinks	2		20.00			40.00		
18 **Total**										376.7	11323.6	5089.8

16.4 Sample Missions

Get More

We can now apply this approach to the SCS and FireSat II missions. See the book website for this expanded discussion along with additional MPT tables for each mission.

References

Get Ref

For annotated bibliography of communications payloads, see the book website.

Brown, Charles D. 2002. *Elements of Spacecraft Design, AIAA Education Series*. Reston, VA AIAA.

Elbert, Bruce R. 2000. *The Satellite Communication Ground Segment and Earth Station Handbook*. Norwood, MA: Artech House.

Elbert, Bruce R. 2008. *The Satellite Communications Applications Handbook, 3rd. ed.* Norwood, MA: Artech House Inc.

Gordon, Gary D. and Walter L. Morgan. 1993. *Principles of Communications Satellites*. Hoboken, NJ: John Wiley and Sons.

Ford, Steve. 2007. *HF Digital Handbook, 4th ed.* Newington, CT: American Radio Relay League.

Ford, Steve. 2009. *The ARRL Satellite Handbook.* Newington, CT: American Radio Relay League.

ITU. 2002. *ITU Handbook on Satellite Communications*. International Telecommunications Union. Hoboken, NJ: John Wiley and Sons.

ITU. 2011. International Telecommunications Union. Website.

Jasik, Henry. 1961. *Antenna Engineering Handbook*. New York, NY: The McGraw-Hill Companies.

NTIA. 2010. *National Telecommunications and Information Administration*. Website.

17 Observation Payloads

Jeffery J. Puschell, *Raytheon*

Space-based observation payload missions have dramatically changed our perception of the world by delivering vitally important imagery and remote sensing data on life-threatening hurricanes and other severe weather, surveillance and reconnaissance data of critical importance to military planners, national decision makers, stunning imagery, and measurements of distant astrophysical objects at wavelengths not accessible from the Earth's surface. Future space-based observation missions are expected to provide continuous video surveillance of the Earth, improve weather forecasting by constraining forecast models with more accurate and detailed measurements, contribute to more complete understanding of climate change, and help resolve some of the deepest cosmological mysteries of our time related to dark matter and dark energy.

Observation payloads can be divided into two broad categories defined by whether the observed light is from active illumination of the scene by the payload itself or a cooperative illumination source, or from passive illumination by the Sun or by other uncooperative sources including the scene itself. Radars and laser-based sensors like DLR's TerraSAR-X and NASA's ICESAT are examples of active systems. Passive sensor examples include visible wavelength imagers like the commercial GeoEye and DigitalGlobe imagers that rely on reflected sunlight along with infrared remote sensors like NASA's Atmospheric InfraRed Sounder (AIRS) and passive microwave radiometers like the US DOD Special Sensor Microwave Imager Sounder (SSMIS) that detect thermal emission from the scene.

Earth observations by both active and passive payloads occur in three primary spectral regions known as solar reflectance, thermal infrared and microwave or radio frequency (RF). Space astronomy payloads like NASA's Chandrasekhar X-Ray Observatory and Compton Gamma Ray Observatory have observed objects at X-ray and gamma ray wavelengths, in addition to these four primary spectral regions. Schowengerdt [2006] and Schott [2007] are excellent sources for detailed discussion of solar reflectance and thermal infrared systems. Sharkov [2003] presents a comprehensive treatment of passive microwave observation systems. Cantafio [1989] provides extended discussions of active space-based RF systems.

Solar reflectance systems operate from the near ultraviolet (~0.35 μm) to the shortwave infrared (~2.5 μm) by observing reflected sunlight. These systems offer the potential for higher spatial resolution than other spectral regions because of their relatively short wavelengths, but can only operate in daylight, unless a laser or other source of active scene illumination is used [Nischan, et al. 2003].

Thermal infrared or emissive systems operate in the spectral region dominated by thermal emission from commonly observed objects on Earth (~3–300 μm). Objects of interest include the surface of the Earth (~300 K), the upper atmosphere (~220 K), biomass fires (~600–1,200 K), and missile launches (~300–1,600 K). The thermal infrared region is affected by absorption of light by molecules in the atmosphere. Observations of the Earth's surface are possible only within certain wavelength ranges known as atmospheric windows, which occur in between strong molecular absorption bands. These strong absorption bands provide a means for probing temperature structure of the atmosphere along with the 3-D distribution of trace gases such as water vapor and ozone. Thermal infrared sensors can operate both day and night because the detected signal is from thermal emission by the scene itself and does not rely on reflected sunlight.

Microwave/RF systems operate at millimeter and centimeter wavelengths. Passive microwave radiometers operate chiefly at millimeter wavelengths (20–200 GHz). Spatial resolution of these systems is three to five orders of magnitude worse than for visible wavelength sensors with the same aperture size, but they are capable of collecting unique information over large areas. Active RF

Table 17-1. Advantages of Various Observation Paylod Types.

Observation Payload Type	Advantages
Passive EO—Solar Reflectance Spectral Region	Mature technology enabling high sensitivity measurements, high spatial resolution even with relatively small wavelengths, rich phenomenology
Passive EO—Emissive	Mature technology enabling high sensitivity measurements, high spatial resolution even with relatively small wavelengths, rich phenomenology, effective day or night
Passive Microwave	Mature technology enabling high sensitivity measurements, rich phenomenology, effective day or night and through virtually all weather conditions
Passive X-Ray and Gamma-Ray	Enables detection of high energy events on Earth and throughout the universe
Active EO	Day/night operation even at Solar reflectance wavelengths
Active RF—Real Aperture Radar	Day/night, all weather capability for detecting precipitation, mapping clouds, characterizing large scale features and altimetry
Active RF—Synthetic Aperture Radar	Day/night, all weather performance with spatial resolutions comparable to much shorter wavelength systems because of the large synthetic aperture

systems also known as radars provide their own illumination of the scene in the centimeter to millimeter bands. The reflected signals can be processed to identify physical features in the scene. Radar systems can be designed to penetrate most atmospheric disturbances, such as clouds, because only larger features can reflect signals at radar wavelengths.

Regardless of spectral region or mode of operation, sensitivity of an observational payload depends on the observation geometry, effective sensor aperture size, integration time, detector sensitivity, spectral bandwidth, transmission through the atmosphere, spatial sample size and the spectral radiance from the scene itself. Sections 17.1 and 17.2 discuss these design considerations in detail.

17.1 Observation Payload Design

Observation payloads collect data (e.g., imagery, spectral radiance, distance) on remote objects such as the surface of the Earth, relatively nearby objects such as another satellite or distant astrophysical objects that can be processed into information (e.g., temperature, reflectance, chemical composition, topography) to provide insight into physical characteristics of these remote objects for scientific, weather forecasting, military and policy making purposes—just to name a few. Observation payloads operate across the entire electromagnetic spectrum from gamma rays and X-rays to RF frequencies. In addition, observation payloads include cosmic ray and other directional particle sensors used to probe the Sun, supernovae, active galactic nuclei, and other unknown astrophysical objects. Table 17-1 lists the advantages of various observation payload types. For specific mission applications for observation payloads missions, e.g., missile warning, environmental, and remote sensing, see the book website.

Two basic types of observation payloads exist: so-called passive payloads such as visible-infrared and microwave imagers that observe intrinsic emission from the scene, whether it be reflected sunlight, thermal emission or gamma rays and active payloads such as lidars and radars that supply their own source of light to enable specific types of measurement such as ranging or to enhance signal-to-noise ratio and spatial resolution.

Space-based observation payloads include the following major categories.

Passive solar reflectance systems observe that part of the electromagnetic spectrum dominated by reflected sunlight—the ultraviolet (~0.3 μm) through the short-wave infrared (SWIR) at ~2.5 μm. These systems offer the potential for relatively high spatial resolution from space, because their shorter operating wavelengths diffract less than longer wavelengths. However, because they rely on reflected sunlight for Earth observations, most of these systems operate effectively only during daytime. Observation payloads in this category include:

- Largely panchromatic imagers like GeoEye and DigitalGlobe
- Commercial imagers that specialize in collecting high special resolution imagery, multispectral (~10 spectral band with wavelength, λ, and spectral bandwidth, $\delta\lambda$, such that $\lambda/\delta\lambda \sim 10$ typically)
- Synoptic imagers like the GEOS imager
- Polar orbiting environmental imagers like MODIS that provide routine global-scale observations
- Hyperspectral (~100 spectral band with $\lambda/\delta\lambda \sim 100$ across a broad contiguous spectral region) imagers, such as Hyperion that provide more detailed spectral measurements over limited spatial regions.
- Low light level imagers like the OLS onboard the DMSP satellite that provide panchromatic imagery of moonlit or airglow lit scenes on Earth at night
- Polarimeters such as POLDER that provide measurements of linear polarization of spectral radiance in different spectral bands across the entire solar reflectance spectral region

See the book website for more color photos from various types of observation payloads.

Emissive or thermal infrared systems observe that part of the electromagnetic spectrum dominated by thermal emission from the scene itself in atmospheric transmission windows from ~3 μm to ~300 μm in wavelength. In some cases, these systems operate outside atmospheric transmission windows to enable less cluttered observations high above the surface of the Earth. These systems operate effectively day or night, because they do not rely on sunlight to create an observable signal. Like solar reflectance systems, emissive systems include:

- Multispectral imagers like the GOES imager and MODIS
- Hyperspectral systems like the Thermal Emission Spectrometer (TES) that flew on the Mars Global Surveyor to map mineralogy on Mars and search for evidence of water
- Ultraspectral (~1,000 spectral bands with $\lambda/\delta\lambda$ ~1,000 across a broad contiguous spectral region)
- Systems like the AIRS sensor on board the NASA Aqua satellite and the IASI on board the Eumetsat MetOp satellite that provide detailed spectra of the Earth's atmosphere and surface to enable 3-D instantaneous maps of temperature distribution on the surface and in the atmosphere along with the maps of water vapor and other trace gases

Passive microwave systems observe thermal emission at much longer wavelengths than emissive infrared systems. The microwave part of the electromagnetic spectrum extends from ~1 mm to ~1 m in wavelength. Normally, microwave radiation is referenced to frequency rather than wavelength. In frequency, the microwave spectral region ranges from ~0.3 GHz to ~300 GHz. Like emissive infrared systems, passive microwave systems operate effectively day or night. At frequencies less than 10 GHz, microwave radiation is relatively unaffected by clouds, so that these longer wavelength systems can operate under virtually all weather conditions. For higher frequency microwave systems, clouds and fog along with absorption by water and oxygen molecules in the atmosphere can influence the signal from the surface. Well known passive microwave systems include:

- AMSU is used primarily for mapping temperature and water vapor structure in the atmosphere. The system flying today is the most recent version of systems that have operated on board the TIROS/POES satellites since 1978. AMSU is divided into two parts called A (used mostly for temperature sounding) and B (used mostly for water vapor sounding), which together operate in 20 spectral channels ranging from 23.8 GHz to 183.3 GHz in frequency and with different spectral resolutions for some frequencies. AMSU-A has a spatial sample size at nadir of about 45 km. The higher frequency AMSU-B has a spatial sample size of about 15 km at nadir
- SSM/I is used primarily for near-surface wind speed, total column water vapor, total column cloud liquid water and precipitation. It has been on board DMSP satellites since 1987, but has heritage back to the Nimbus 7 and Seasat missions launched in 1978. SSM/I operates in seven channels ranging from 19 GHz to 89 GHz in frequency. SSM/I operates with spatial resolutions ranging from 13 km to 69 km, depending on frequency
- The SSMI/S instrument is the follow-on instrument to SSM/I and measures microwave energy at 24 discrete frequencies from 19 to 183 GHz with a swath width of 1,700 km at 12.5 km to 75 km spatial resolution at nadir. The synoptic solar reflectance and emissive infrared systems used in conjunction with these passive microwave systems operate with ~1 km spatial resolution using much smaller aperture sizes, because of the diffraction performance advantage of shorter wavelengths

X-ray imagers observe thermal and non-thermal emission from astrophysical objects including the Sun, neutron stars, supernovae, the center of our Galaxy and distant unknown objects at wavelengths ranging from less than 3 pm to 10 nm, corresponding to frequencies ranging from above 10 EHz (1 EHz is 10^{18} Hz) down to 30 PHz (1 PHz is 10^{15} Hz). X-rays are often referenced in units of electron Volts (eV) rather than wavelength or frequency. In eV, the X-ray spectral region extends from about 0.1 KeV to 400 KeV. The first X-ray observations from space were made with geiger counters that flew on board converted V-2 rockets starting in 1949. UHURU also known as SAS-1 launched in 1970 was the first satellite with an X-ray observation payload. The Chandra X-ray observatory, launched in 1999, observes the 0.1 KeV to 10 KeV spectral region, with 2.4 μrad (0.5 arcsec) angular resolution using a 1.2 m diameter X-ray telescope. The satellite is in a highly elliptical orbit that enables the observatory to make X-ray measurements from well out the Earth's Van Allen belts. The effective collection area for the Chandra observatory is only 0.04 m^2 at 1 KeV, despite the much larger telescope diameter. Conventional optical approaches are not effective at X-ray wavelengths, because no suitable refractive material is available to build X-ray lenses and standard reflector telescopes do not work because X-rays are either absorbed or transmitted at near normal incidence to reflecting mirrors. Therefore, X-ray instruments use either a coded aperture method or a grazing incidence telescope, also known as a Wolter telescope, to collect and focus X-rays. In Wolter telescopes, the angle of reflection from the mirror is very low—typically 10 arc-minutes to 2 deg. Chandra uses a Wolter telescope that consists of nested cylindrical paraboloid and hyperboloid surfaces coated with iridium or gold. Chandra uses four pairs of nested mirrors. The relatively thick substrate (2 cm) and very careful polishing allowed a very precise optical surface, which is largely responsible for Chandra's unprecedented and unmatched angular resolution. However, thickness of the substrates limits the fill factor of the aperture, leading to the low effective collection area.

Gamma ray payloads observe emission of the highest energy photons from astrophysical objects including the Sun, supernovae, the center of our Galaxy and distant unknown objects. Gamma rays do not penetrate Earth's atmosphere very well so direct astronomical observations of gamma rays must occur from high in the atmosphere or from space. Wavelengths for gamma rays are shorter than 3 pm, corresponding to frequencies greater than 10 EHz (1 EHz is 10^{18} Hz). The first gamma ray observations of the Sun and distant galactic and extragalactic objects were made by OSO-3 launched in 1967. Shortly thereafter, mysterious gamma ray bursts from very distant, but still only partially identified objects were discovered by the Vela satellites designed to detect gamma rays from nuclear explosions on Earth. Recent gamma ray observation payloads include the instruments on board the Fermi Gamma Ray Telescope, a successor to the Compton Gamma Ray Observatory. These instruments detect gamma rays in two broad spectral ranges using scintillation detectors that detect small flashes of light created by gamma rays passing through a crystal and pair production techniques at the highest energies that create electron-positron pairs created by incoming gamma rays.

Active electro-optical systems like lidars, ladars and altimeters use active illumination of the scene by a laser to create a measurable signal that can be read out rapidly over time to remotely sense backscattered light from water droplets, aerosols and trace gases in the atmosphere as a function of distance from the system and for range measurements and altimetry, when looking at the Earth, Moon, and other space objects.

- The first lidar in space was the Lidar In-space Technology Experiment (LITE) carried onboard the Space Shuttle in 1994. LITE measured clouds with a backscatter lidar based on a Nd:YAG laser operating at three different wavelengths: 1,064 nm, 532 nm (second harmonic) and 355 nm (third harmonic)

- CALIPSO, launched as part of the A-train of Earth Science satellites in 2006, is also a backscatter lidar based on a Nd:YAG laser. CALIPSO transmits both the fundamental (1,064 nm) and second harmonic (532 nm) of the Nd:YAG laser in a nadir beam. The vertical resolution is 30 m and horizontal resolution 333 km

- ICESAT launched in 2003 carried a Nd:YAG based laser altimeter used primarily for measuring thickness of Arctic ice sheets, but also for providing global topography and vegetation data. The main challenge for building a laser-based observational space payload is producing a reliable laser for extended duration use in space—previous instruments like ICESAT experienced failure of some laser modules after only a few months of operation

Lessons learned from ICESAT benefit future missions such as the upcoming AEOLUS mission with the ALADIN lidar, planned for the Atmospheric Dynamics Mission (ADM). ALADIN is a wind-measuring lidar, based on the third harmonic of a Nd:YAG laser. ALADIN will measure wind speed along the lidar line of sight by measuring the Doppler shift of the backscattered light using two methods: coherent (heterodyne) detection by mixing the return signal with a local oscillator and a direct direction method using a narrowband etalon. These techniques will be applied to measuring Doppler shifts of light returned to a receiver from Mie (aerosol) and Rayleigh (molecular) scattering respectively. While useful as a pathfinder for future winds lidar missions by providing information not available to today to numerical weather forecast models, AEOLUS will only measure a single component of the 3-D wind vector.

Active RF systems like radars and synthetic aperture radars (SARs) use active illumination of the scene by a coherent RF transmitter to create a signal that can be detected and read out rapidly in time to produce detailed range resolved RF imagery of precipitation in clouds, surface wakes on the ocean and detailed topography of Earth and other planetary solid surfaces. Like passive microwave systems, active RF systems operate at much longer wavelengths than visible and infrared systems that are routinely used for imagery—typically at centimeter wavelengths. Consequently, for practical payload sizes, active RF systems tend to operate at much coarser spatial resolution than visible and infrared systems—but they can operate through almost any possible weather condition. For example:

- Precipitation radar (PR) onboard the TRMM satellite. The TRMM PR launched in 1997 was the first spaceborne radar designed to measure vertical structure of rainfall precipitation in the lower atmosphere. It operated at 13.8 GHz (2 cm in wavelength) using a 128-element electronically scanned array to allow fast and complex cross-track scanning over a swath width of 215 km with a cross-range spatial resolution of about 4.3 km and a range resolution of 250 m. As shown in Fig. 17-1, the TRMM PR operated in conjunction with other observational payload systems—a passive microwave imager and a visible-infrared imager

- Systems (like TRMM PR) are very useful, but they cannot provide spatial resolution approaching visible-infrared systems with feasible collector sizes. A different type of radar takes advantage of

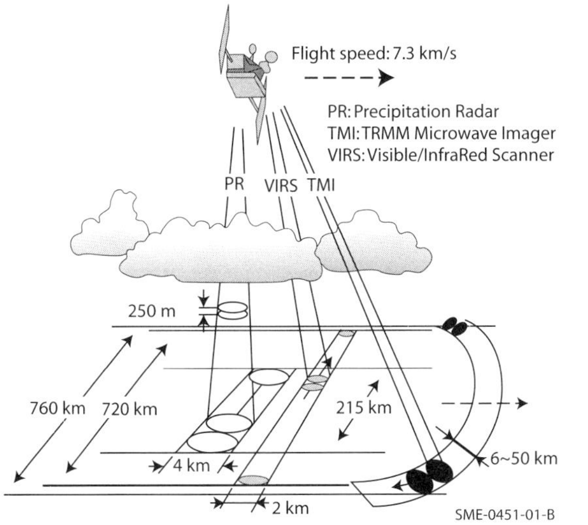

Fig. 17-1. The TRMM PR observed rainfall observation in conjunction with a passive microwave imager, the TMI, and a visible-infrared imager called VIRS. While the PR and VIRS made cross-track scans, the TMI made a conical scan, similar to the SSM/I and SSMI/S.

the relatively relaxed tolerances at these long RF wavelengths for coherent phase and Doppler shift measurements of a radar return signal

- Synthetic Aperture Radar (SAR) processes coherent measurements of phase and Doppler shift across the wide beamwidth of a RF system to synthesize a virtual aperture with a size equivalent to the distance the physical antenna moves while the scene location remains illuminated by the beam. The corresponding spatial resolution in the along spacecraft track direction approaches resolutions achievable with visible and infrared systems.
- SEASAT launched in 1978 was the first known SAR in space. It operated in L-band at a frequency of 1.275 GHz or 23.5 cm in wavelength. SEASAT operated for only about 105 days, failing when a short circuit in the satellite's electrical system ended the mission. Nevertheless, the mission was very successful and laid the processing foundation for following systems
- Since SEASAT, SARs have been developed and flown by Canada, Japan, Europe, and Russia. TerraSAR-X, an X-band (9.65 GHz) SAR developed by the German Aerospace Center (DLR) and launched in 2007 has produced remarkable imagery that is especially useful for urban landscapes. Along with its partner satellite, TanDEM-X, launched in 2010, high resolution digital elevation maps are being produced for flood plain maps and traffic monitoring among many other applications

To determine the radiometric performance of an optical instrument, we must consider the observation geometry, effective aperture, integration time, detector sensitivity, spectral bandwidth, ground pixel size, and the transmission through the atmosphere. For passive Earth observations, we define three basic categories, depending on the spectral range

Wavelengths covered in the first case range from 0.3 to 2.5 μm, and they include the ultraviolet, visible, near and short wavelength infrared. The instrument receives radiation reflected from the atmosphere, as well as from the surface of the Earth, when illuminated by the Sun. We will normally neglect thermal radiation emitted by the Earth in this case

The second case applies to wavelengths ranging from the long infrared region (8–14 μm) through the microwave and RF. In these wavelengths, instruments receive thermal radiation emitted from the atmosphere and the surface of the Earth when reflected radiation from the Sun is negligible

The mid-wavelength infrared spectral region (3–8 μm) is our final case, where contributions from both emissive and reflected sources must be considered. The radiance from emissive and reflected sources is shown in Fig. 17-2. It can be seen that the thermal emitted radiance of the Earth increases with wavelength, corresponding to Planck's law, and that the reflected radiance from the Earth's surface decreases with wavelength

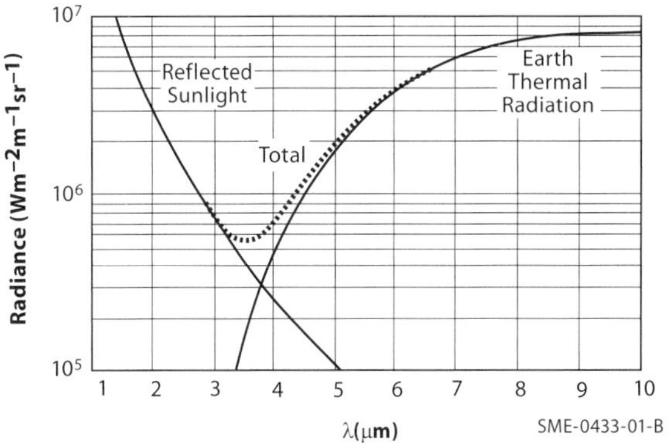

Fig. 17-2. Radiance from Direct and Reflected Sources. Radiance contribution in Watts per square meter per meter (wavelength) per unit solid angle of reflected sunlight from the Earth and emitted radiation from the Earth as a function of wavelength. The sum is shown as a dashed line. The Sun is modeled as a blackbody with a temperature of 6,000 K, the reflection coefficient of the Earth's surface and the transmission of the atmosphere are modeled as constants for clarity.

In the ultraviolet through SWIR bands, we resolve images produced by energy (chiefly from the Sun) reflected from the target scene rather than energy from the relatively low self-emission that occurs in the reflectance bands. But in the infrared, we see things almost entirely by their self-emission, with very little energy being reflected, particularly at night

We may use the same optical train elements —lenses, prisms, mirrors, and filters—to collect infrared energy as for visible and UV, but we must apply them differently. For example, ordinary glass is opaque to IR beyond 3 μm, whereas germanium, which is opaque in the visible band, is transparent in the 1.8 to 25 μm region

We must consider atmospheric scattering caused by molecules, aerosols and other particles in the air. The amount of scattered radiation from atmospheric molecules is a function of the inverse fourth power of the wavelength

For haze, the situation is more complex, but the scattering extinction coefficient goes roughly as the inverse first to second power of the wavelength. Thus, IR penetrates haze and dust much better than visible radiation because the IR wavelengths are four or more times those in the visible spectrum. The same phenomena explain the reddish color of the sky near dawn and sunset. At these times, shorter green, blue, indigo, and violet wavelength signals are greatly attenuated as they travel farther through the atmosphere than when the Sun is overhead

The following sections provide more detailed information on the best known observation payloads— those that use electro-optical techniques in the solar reflectance and emissive spectral regions to observe and measure physical properties of scenes in the ultraviolet through submillimeter spectral region, and those that use radio frequency technology.

17.1.1 Electro-optical Observation Payloads

Electro-optical imagers and remote sensors scan a scene using mechanical or electrical means. Geostationary Earth Orbit (GEO) spacecraft appear to be almost stationary relative to the Earth, so that an optical instrument operating in GEO needs to scan in two dimensions to collect an image frame. The original approach for geostationary environmental imaging spacecraft, still used today in the European Meteosat Second Generation (MSG) system, involves spinning the entire spacecraft about a north-south axis to enable the east-west scan, while moving a relatively large elliptical mirror (~80 cm along the major axis) in front of the imager optics to perform the north-south scan. Three axis stabilized spacecraft in geosynchronous orbit like the US GOES environmental satellite system have imagers that use a two axis scanner in front of the imager collection optics to scan the scene in two dimensions. Alternatively, large format two dimensional focal plane array and optical technologies for advanced missile warning sensors have been used to create a full-Earth staring imager that requires no mechanical scanner to sample the entire Earth scene.

The sub-satellite point for a spacecraft in low Earth orbit (LEO) moves with respect to the scene on the ground at a speed of approximately 7 km/s (See Chap. 8). In most LEO systems, the motion of the spacecraft is used to eliminate scanning in the *ground track* direction (except for spacecraft motion and image rotation corrections), so that the scanning system of the optical instrument need move only in the *cross-track* direction. Several methods for doing so are described below. Illustrated in Fig. 17-3A, *whiskbroom sensors* scan a single detector element on the ground in the cross-track direction, thereby creating a single scanline of pixels in the final image or other data product. Whiskbroom scanners can also use multiple detectors, to create multiple scanlines of pixels simultaneously (Fig. 17-3B). This technique reduces the required scan rate compared to a system with a single detector. The required scan rate is reduced so that the dwell time per detector sample is multiplied by the number of detector elements used. *Push broom scanners* cover a full swath width using a linear arrangement of detector elements called a linear array, line array, or scanning array. As illustrated in Fig. 17-3C, the read-out process delivers one line after another in the ground track direction, like pushing a broom, hence the name. The integration time is defined by the velocity of the sub-satellite point and the size of the pixels on the ground. To improve signal-to-noise ratio of the image, at the expense of area coverage rate, push broom imagers or their host spacecraft can compensate for motion of the sub-spacecraft point along the Earth's surface to increase effective dwell time.

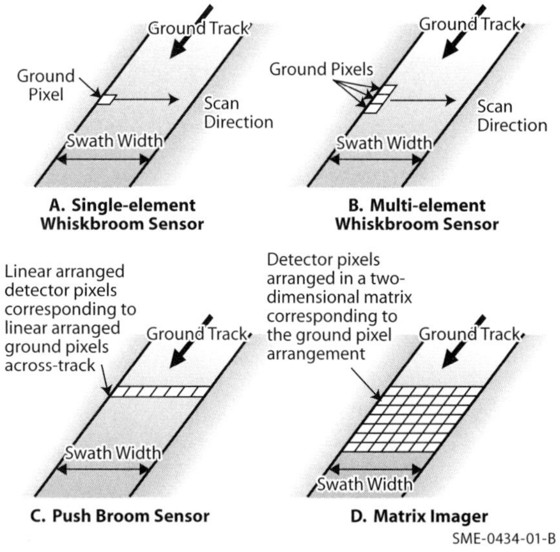

Fig. 17-3. Scanning Techniques for Electro-Optical Instruments. See text for discussion.

Step-and-stare scanners use a 2-dimensional array of detector elements to collect data over an entire region of interest by staring at part of the scene and then stepping to another location in the scene in a predetermined pattern of steps and staring again, until the region is completely covered. Each detector element corresponds to a spatial resolution element on the ground. These systems operate in two basic modes in LEO. In the first mode, integration times are determined by velocity of the sub-satellite point and size of the ground pixel, as in the pushbroom sensor. No advantage is achieved with

Table 17-2. Comparison of Optical Sensor Scanning Methods. We list relative advantages and disadvantages of different scanning mechanisms

Scanning Technique	Advantages	Disadvantages
Whiskbroom Scanner—Single Detector Element	High uniformity of the response function over the scene Relatively simple optics	Short dwell time per pixel High bandwidth requirement and time response of the detector
Whiskbroom Scanner—Multiple Detector Elements	Uniformity of the response function over the swath Relatively simple optics	Relatively high bandwidth and time response of the detector
Push Broom Sensor	Uniform response function in the along-track direction No mechanical scanner required Relatively long dwell time (equal to integration time)	High number of pixels per line imager required Relatively complex optics
Step-and-Stare Imager with Detector Array	Well defined geometry within the image Long integration time (if motion compensation is performed)	High number of pixels per array imager required Complex optics required to cover the full image size Calibration of fixed pattern noise for each pixel Highly complex scanner required if motion compensation is performed

respect to the integration time in the simplest case. A short integration time is needed to avoid image smear during read-out. The second mode allows a longer integration time. If we shift the image array in the focal plane or move the line of sight of the instrument, the image motion can be compensated to very low speeds relative to the ground. The instrument line of sight can be adjusted by moving a scan mirror or by tilting the spacecraft itself to compensate for the movement of the sub-spacecraft point. Step-and-stare sensors require relatively complex scanner optics or spacecraft operations to cover large areas at high signal to noise ratio from low Earth orbit, especially. The fixed pattern noise must be removed from the image because each pixel has a somewhat different responsiveness and dark signal, creating additional complexity. Table 17-2 summarizes the distinguishing features of optical scanning methods.

In GEO and other high altitude orbits, another approach to capturing a 2 dimensional scene can be used that involves positioning the scene with respect to the instrument. In this case, the instrument moves to the next part of the scene between integration periods either along-track or across track to image the entire scene. This scan motion can be continuous across a large swath, as in the geosynchronous GOES and MTSAT imagers. If this shift occurs in a series of discrete steps, this approach is referred to as a step-and-stare imager. This technique is used in geosynchronous orbit in the GOES Sounder, for example. If the instrument field of view only covers a part of the required scene, then moderately complex (and also moderately sized) optics are required. We can use highly agile and accurate pointing mirrors in front of the instrument's optics to adjust the line of sight.

For space missions, optical instruments often rely on existing designs. Custom tailoring of current optical and detector design approaches are common in optimizing the performance and cost of the instrument. Let's follow a scene photon through an observational payload by considering first the optical subsystem involving a telescope and a spectral separation approach and then the detectors.

Telescopes. This discussion considers the telescope optics used to collect and transform light from the scene onto a focal plane along with approaches used to separate the incoming light into different wavelength bands.

We treat reflective telescopes (telescopes using mirrors) and refractive telescopes (telescopes using lenses) together. There are advantages and disadvantages to both these telescopes that will be discussed in detail later.

There are several ways to describe a telescope. Parallel rays of light falling on a perfect lens will all converge at the focal point, whose distance from the lens is called the *focal length, f*. The focal length largely determines the length of the optical collection system and, for a single lens, it is related to the lens surface's radius of curvature. The focal length of a spherical reflecting surface is one-half its radius. For a parabolic reflector whose y-z surface is defined by the equation $z^2 = 4fy$, the quantity f is the focal length; it equals the distance from the focus to the nearest point on the reflecting surface.

In design practice, we normally determine the required focal length based on instantaneous field of view or angular spatial sampling size and the physical size of detector elements in the image plane. The plate scale, s, or length per field-of-view angle is given by:

Table 17-2, Fig. 17-3◀, Eq. 17-0

$$
\begin{aligned}
s &= f \text{ (unit length/rad)} \\
&= \left(\frac{\pi}{180}\right) f \\
&\approx 0.01745 f \text{ (unit length/rad)}
\end{aligned} \tag{17-1}
$$

where s and f are in the same units. The image size is a function of s and the size of the detector— ranging from a single element to a large array—employed at the focal plane. As Fig. 17-4 shows, the focal length needed to record an object or scene of radius R, is given by the magnification, M,

$$
M = \frac{f}{h} = \frac{r_d}{R} \tag{17-2}
$$

where h is the distance from the spacecraft to the object, r_d is the radius of the detector array in the image plane, and R is the radius of the object, with the image and object measured perpendicular to the line of sight. The magnification or scale, r_d/R, is the ratio of the image size to the object size. It is ordinarily a very small number for space-based observation payloads. We express the scale on the image plane as "1 μm equals × km on the ground."

We can also describe an optical element or system by its so-called infinity F-number or F-stop, often written as f/, F, F No., or F#. It is defined as f/D, where D is the effective entrance aperture, which is the effective diameter of the lens or primary telescope mirror. Image brightness is proportional to F^{-2}, so an *f*/4 lens gives an image four times brighter than an *f*/8 lens.

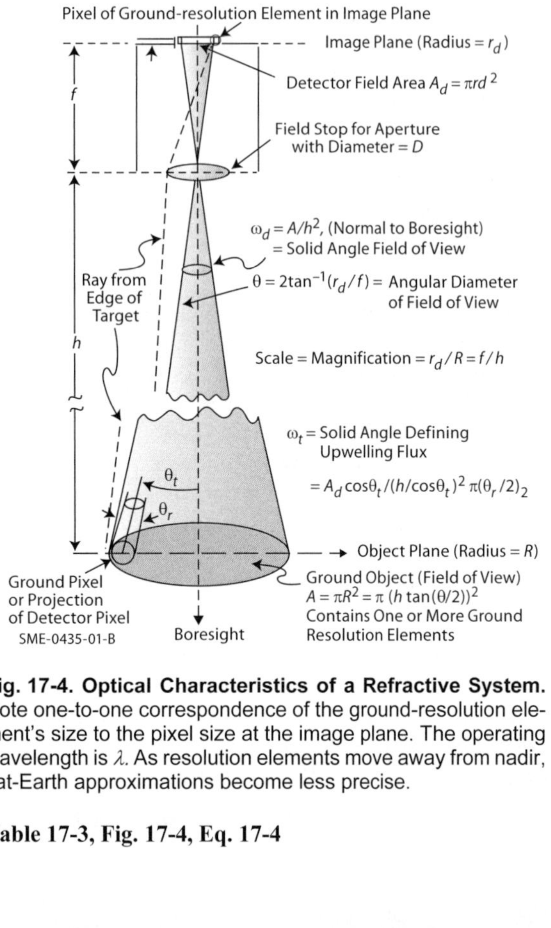

Fig. 17-4. Optical Characteristics of a Refractive System. Note one-to-one correspondence of the ground-resolution element's size to the pixel size at the image plane. The operating wavelength is λ. As resolution elements move away from nadir, flat-Earth approximations become less precise.

The numerical aperture, NA, gives the same information in another way:

$$
NA \equiv \frac{1}{2F\#} = \frac{D}{2f} \tag{17-3}
$$

or

$$
F\# = \frac{1}{2NA} = \frac{f}{D} \tag{17-4}
$$

The largest numerical aperture for optics used in air is 1. Thus, the smallest F# is 0.5.

Table 17-3. Principal Aberrations in Optical Systems. See Table 17-4 for which of these are mitigated in various optical systems.

Chromatic Aberration is dispersion of the light due to the refractive index of a lens being a function of the wavelength. Causes different colors to focus at different distances.

Spherical Aberration is dispersion in which light from the periphery of a spherical lens or mirror is focused nearer the element than light from the center. Can be eliminated by making the optical surface parabolic, rather than spherical.

Coma is dispersion of off-axis portions of the image. (So named because in a telescope, off-axis star images look liketear drops, or the coma of a comet pointing toward the center of the image.)

Astigmatism is aberration in which the distorted image is asymmetric such as when light in a horizontal plane comes to a slightly different focus than light in a vertical plane. A common problem in human vision.

Distortion is when an otherwise sharp image is distorted in shape, such as when straight light on the surface being viewed appear curved on the focal plane. An uncorrectable distortion occurs when trying to image the celestial sphere onto a flat focal plane. (See Sec. 8.1.)

Curvature of Field is when a sharp image is formed on a focal surface which isn't flat. Can be corrected in film systems by using a slightly curved focal plane.

All telescopes experience *aberrations*, or imperfections in the quality of the image, in addition to diffraction which limits system resolution as discussed below. Principal optical aberrations are listed in Table 17-3. *Chromatic aberration* is wavelength or color dependent. This imperfection is due to various wavelengths being bent by different amounts when passing through the lens. As a result, only systems with at least one refractive element will suffer chromatic aberration. This is due to the fact that reflective surfaces treat all wavelengths the same, which is not absolutely true since some surfaces will reflect visible light, for example, but not X-rays. However, when reflection does occur, it is independent of wavelength to the first order.

Three basic types of telescopes are shown in Fig. 17-5. In each of these telescope approaches, there is a corresponding refractive and reflective design. Table 17-4 shows the aberrations that can be corrected in these telescopes. The lens doublet is the classic refractive telescope lens and can be designed to elimi-

Table 17-4. Aberrations that can be Corrected by the Three Basic Optical Systems. Checks indicate errors that are fully correctable and parenthetical checks indicates that corrections are possible only for dedicated design parameters. (See Table 17-3 for definitions.)

Image Error	Doublet/ Schmidt	TeleOptic/ Cassegrain	Triplet/ TMA
Lateral Chromatic Aberration	✓	✓	✓
Length Chromatic Aberration	✓	✓	✓
Spherical Aberration	✓	✓	✓
Coma	✓	✓	✓
Astigmatism		(✓)	✓
Distortion	(✓)	(✓)	✓
Curvature of Field		(✓)	✓

nate spherical aberrations, coma, distortion and chromatic aberrations. In tele-optic lens systems, the distance between the optical element and the focal plane is shorter than the focal length. Spherical aberrations, coma, astigmatism, curvature of field effects, and even chromatic aberrations can all be eliminated by tele-optic lenses. The simplest refractive (spherical) optical system that theoretically allows for correction of all distortions is the lens triplet. While this approach offers many important advantages, it can be relatively challenging to implement because each of the optical elements is highly sensitive to displacement or tilt. The ray traces in Fig. 17-5 show different locations of the image in the focal plane relating to various viewing angles. All five of the third-order aberrations as compensated by the lens triplet include: spherical aberrations, coma, astigmatism, curvature of field, and distortion. Similar to tele-optics, it is also free from chromatic aberrations. The same behaviors exist in the corresponding reflective systems as well. The Cassegrain telescope is a reflective implementation of a tele-optic lens, and the Schmidt Mirror System is an all-reflective doublet. The Three-Mirror Anastigmatic system is similar to the lens triplet with respect to all the aberration corrections, but with an all-reflective design. Generally, reflective optical systems are free from chromatic aberrations. However, reflective systems typically have a much smaller field of view than their refractive counterparts.

Space remote sensing telescopes tend to be more complex than ones used on the ground. This is due in part to effects such as thermal distortions and radiation which can alter performance of instruments and cause space-based telescopes to fall short of meeting performance requirements over the intended lifetime of the instrument. These environmental effects and the challenging image quality and spectral coverage requirements for many systems limit the technologies for manufacturing the lenses and mirrors. Even if operating temperature ranges are controlled to within a few deg, thermal distortions can still limit the performance of the optical system. Cosmic radiation effects can degrade the transparency of most optical glass over time. Figure 17-6 shows the cross sectional view of the high resolution optical lens system, a German-built Modular Optoelectronic Multispectral Scanner (MOMS 2P) designed to achieve a resolution of 6 meters on the ground.

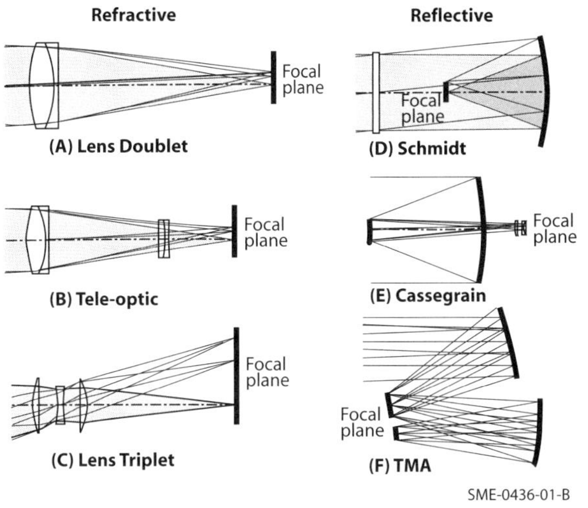

Fig. 17-5. Basic Configurations for Refractive and Reflective Optical Systems. Each of the reflective systems on the right is analogous to the corresponding refractive system on the left. TMA = Three-mirror anastigmatic.

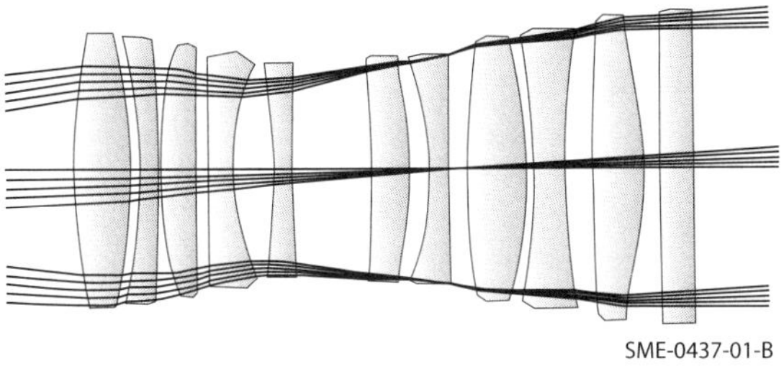

Fig. 17-6. Lens Cross Section of the Panchromatic Objective of the MOMS 2P Instrument. The sensor has a focal length of 0.66 m and an aperture size of 0.15 m. The complexity of this optical system is representative of sophisticated remote sensing payloads.

The angular resolution of an optical system determines its ability to enable recognition of fine spatial detail in Earth observation data. A telescope that can just barely resolve two close stars is said to have a resolving power equal to the angular separation of those two stars. We are more interested in the ability to distinguish fine detail on the surface for Earth observing systems. Thus, for these systems, spatial resolution is normally expressed as the smallest physical separation of two objects on the surface that can be resolved by the instrument.

Table 17-5. Diffraction-Limited Resolution. Note that the Synthetic Aperture Radar provides resolutions similar to visual or IR systems, independent of range and wavelength for ranges up to the maximum signal-to-noise limit by synthesizing the required aperture.

	Ground Resolution = $h\lambda/D$			
	Aperture Size, D	**Visible (λ = 0.5 μm)**	**IR (λ = 3 μm)**	**Passive Microwave (f = 10 GHz; λ =3 cm)**
From an orbiting spacecraft (h = 900 km)	1 m	0.45 m	2.70 m	27.0 km
	3 m	0.15 m	0.9 m	9 km
From a synchronous spacecraft (h = ~35,800 km)	1 m	17.9 m	107 m	1,074 km
	3 m	6.0 m	35.8 m	358 km
From SR-71 (h = 20 km or 70,000 ft)	0.3 m	0.033 m	0.200 m	2.00 km

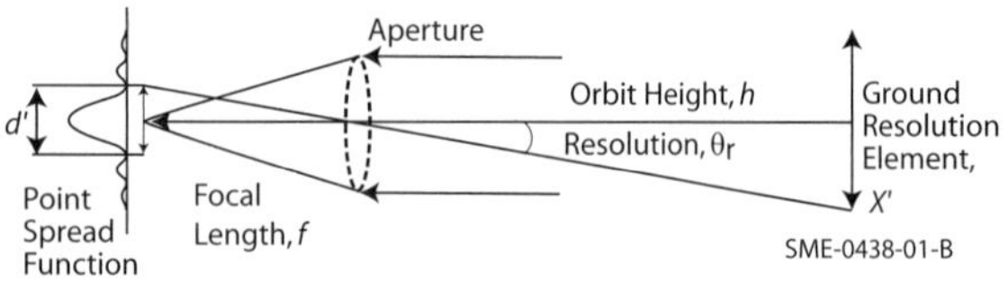

Fig. 17-7. Point Spread Function for Imaging System with Diffraction. The optical wave front from an ideal point source on the ground is imaged as the point spread function by the optical system. The diameter of the aperture and the wavelength determine the extent of the point spread function measured by the diameter, d', of the first intensity minimum.

For a perfectly designed and fabricated optical system, the theoretical limit to angular resolution performance is determined by diffraction, which is the apparent bending of light occurring whenever light encounters an obstacle, such as an element in a telescope or other optical system. Diffraction blurs the image of a point source of light, such as a distant star, into a pattern with elements that get progressively fainter away from the center, as shown in Fig. 17-7. The shape of the diffraction pattern is determined by the shape of the optical element causing the diffraction, so that a circular mirror or lens produces circular rings, whereas a square aperture produces a pattern with 2-D series of rectangular shapes. The diffraction pattern is also known as the diffraction disk, the Airy disk (for a circular aperture) or the point spread function. For a circular aperture, the angular distance, θ_r, from the maximum at the center of a point source image to the first dark interference ring, is called the Rayleigh limit and is given by

$$\theta_r = \frac{1.22\lambda}{D} = \frac{1.22}{f\ F_{cutoff}} \tag{17-5}$$

where λ is the wavelength, D is the aperture diameter of the optical instrument, f remains the focal length, and F_{cutoff} is the optical cutoff spatial frequency in units of inverse length (say m^{-1}) that limits the resolution of the image in the focal plane. θ_r is expressed in radians. The bright lobe at the center of this Airy disk diffraction pattern contains 84% of the total energy arriving at the focal plane from a point source, from its center out to the first minimum. For a satellite at altitude, h, the linear resolution or ground resolution limit, X', at nadir as defined by the cutoff frequency is

$$X' = \frac{h\lambda}{D} \tag{17-6}$$

A more general expression is to replace h with the slant range, R_S, from Eq. (8-31), to determine the resolution away from nadir (R_S here = D in Chap. 8). Keep in mind that this is the resolution perpendicular to the observation system line of sight and that actual spatial resolution on the surface of the Earth is degraded by the effect of geometric projection or $1/\sin\varepsilon$, where ε is the elevation angle at the specific spacecraft and Earth locations of interest, obtained from Eq. (8-28). Ground resolution at nadir for several representative system configurations is given in Table 17-5. Most space-based optical systems have the ability to produce images with angular resolution as good as the theoretical limit and are therefore described as being diffraction limited.

When we implement an optical system using a detector array, we add an additional design parameter, the quality factor, Q, defined as the ratio of the physical size in the focal plane corresponding to the spatial frequency cutoff to the detector element size, d, that is

$$Q = \frac{d'}{d} = \frac{X'}{X} \tag{17-7}$$

where d' is given by

$$d' = \frac{\lambda f}{D} \tag{17-8}$$

X is the ground pixel size, and X' is the ground resolution corresponding to d' in the focal plane (See Fig. 17-8). Q typically ranges from 0.4 to 2. For $Q > 1$, the detectors are smaller than the cutoff and resolution is limited by diffraction in the optics. This gives the best possible image resolution for a given aperture. For $Q < 1$, the resolution is limited by detector size. This design point may be chosen if image quality is less important than aperture size, as would be the case, for example, when increased light gathering power is required. A good starting point is $Q = 1$, which allows good image quality.

Table 17-5, Fig. 17-7, Eq. 17-8

From the definition of the magnification, Eq. (17-2), we have:

$$\frac{d}{X} = \frac{d'}{X'} = \frac{f}{h} \tag{17-9}$$

Combining Eqs. (17-7) to (17-9), we obtain expressions for the detector size, d, in terms of the other basic system parameters:

$$d = \frac{d'X}{X'} = \frac{d'}{Q} = \frac{\left(\frac{\lambda f}{D}\right)}{Q} \tag{17-10}$$

where the parameters are defined above and, as usual, λ is the wavelength, f is the focal length, and D is the aperture diameter.

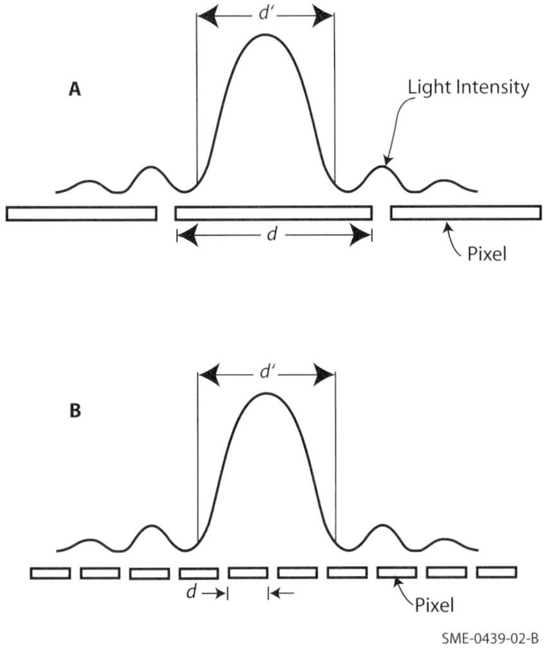

Fig. 17-8. Effect of Varying Quality Factor. Different sizing of the detector pixel with respect to the point spread function is shown by varying the Quality Factor, Q. A low quality factor results in the relative sizing in diagram (A) on top and a large quality factor results in the relative sizing in diagram (B) on bottom.

Spectral separation approaches. As noted above, space-based observation payloads operate with different spectral sampling approaches, depending on intended mission. These spectral sampling approaches fall into four broad categories summarized below called panchromatic, multispectral, hyperspectral and ultraspectral.

Panchromatic or PAN spectral sampling involves one band per broad spectral region (e.g., one band covering the entire visible part of the spectrum). PAN imaging is useful for collecting high SNR, high spatial resolution imagery where spectral content of a scene is considered less important than image sharpness and clarity. Well known systems using PAN imaging include the commercial imaging GeoEye and DigitalGlobe systems.

Multispectral Imaging (MSI) uses ~3–50 relatively wide ($\lambda/\delta\lambda$~10 typically) spectral bands to identify major features of a scene (rocks, trees, crops, water). Well known MSI examples include Landsat, AVHRR, GOES imager and sounder and MODIS.

Hyperspectral Imaging (HSI) systems collect ~30–300 moderately high spectral resolution ($\lambda/\delta\lambda$~100) spectral bands over a contiguous spectral region. HSI systems provide more detailed physical information on a scene than PAN and MSI system and are used to identify components within major scene features (e.g., types of minerals, trees, crops and health, bathymetry, composition) based on spectral signatures. Well known examples of space-based hyperspectral systems include, Hyperion and the TES instrument that mapped Mars at thermal infrared wavelengths.

Ultraspectral Imaging systems collect ~300–3,000 spectral bands with very high spectral resolution ($\lambda/\delta\lambda$~1,000) across a broad contiguous spectral region. Ultraspectral systems are used primarily in the infrared to collect detailed spectra of the Earth's atmosphere and surface for physical analysis of gas absorption features for trace gas detection and mapping and retrieval of vertical temperature structure and distribution of water vapor in the atmosphere. Well known ultraspectral systems include AIRS, MIPAS and IASI.

Spectral separation occurs in a device called a spectrometer that can use filters, dispersive elements or interferometers to isolate spectral ranges of light for remote sensing and imaging. PAN and MSI systems most often use filters to separate out desired ranges of wavelength for measurement whereas HSI and ultraspectral systems almost always use dispersive or interferometric approaches but can use filter spectrometers. Some systems sample the Earth with a hyperspectral approach and then process data onboard the spacecraft to MSI bands for transmission to Earth, as illustrated in Fig. 17-9.

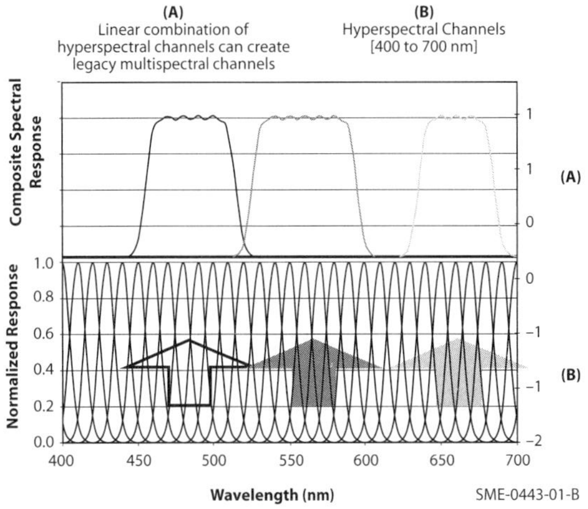

Fig. 17-9. Data from Hyperspectral Imagers Used to Create Virtual Multispectral Channels. (Courtesy of NASA)

Table 17-5◀, Fig. 17-9, Eq. 17-10

Filter spectrometers use optical bandpass filters to transmit narrow wavelength bands from the scene spectrum to an individual detector, or a 1-D or 2-D focal plane detector array. Early optical filters were based on stacks of colored glass that defined spectral bandpasses. Virtually all optical filters used today are based on an interferometric device called an etalon to define high tailored spectral responses precisely. Multispectral filter spectrometers can use discrete filters (one or more per focal plane), filter wheel mechanisms to rotate different filters into a detector line of sight or integrated spectral filter assemblies also known as butcher block assemblies (Fig. 17-10) to cover ~10 spectral bands in a single focal plane. Hyperspectral filter spectrometer approaches include tunable filters and spatially variable filters such as the wedge filter that can collect data as a pushbroom imager. Advantages of filter spectrometers include relatively high optical throughput and relatively easy implementation for multispectral applications, especially. One of the disadvantages of filter spectrometers is that high spectral resolution filters with predictable characteristics can be very expensive and difficult to produce consistently. Filter spectrometer examples include all of the best known MSI systems (e.g., MODIS, GOES, AVHRR) and the hyperspectral Linear Etalon Imaging Spectral Array (LEISA) on the New Horizons to Pluto.

Fig. 17-10. Integrated Spectral Filter Assembly also Known as a Butcher Block Filter Assembly for the Multispectral THEMIS Imager On-board Mars Odyssey 2001. (Photo Courtesy of Raytheon)

Dispersive spectrometers use a grating or prism to separate light at different wavelengths into distinct angles. The spectrum of a single ground sample is dispersed and then focused onto different detectors along one dimension of a 2-D detector array. The spectrum is typically sampled at Nyquist rate so that number of detectors along the spectral axis is twice the number of points in reported spectrum. Advantages of dispersive spectrometers relative to Michelson interferometer approaches discussed in the next paragraph include superior performance in the SWIR and in that part of the MWIR where noise is photon limited and no moving parts in the spectrometer except possibly for a mechanical cooler. Disadvantages include sensitivity to temperature changes that can affect the focal length and therefore spectral calibration and radiometric accuracy and a tendency toward relatively large complex instruments especially for missions requiring high spectral resolution and wide field of view Earth coverage. Well known examples of space-based dispersive spectrometers include Galileo-NIMS, AIRS, and Hyperion.

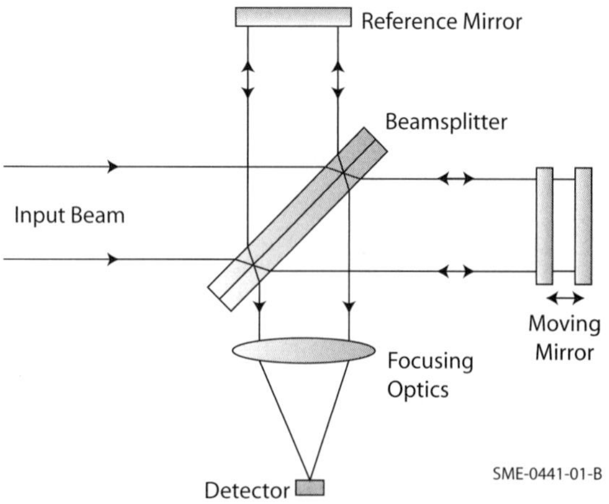

Fig. 17-11. Michelson Interferometer, the Most Widely Used Form for a Temporally Modulated Fourier Transform Spectrometer.

Interferometers achieve spectral separation using constructive and destructive interference of light from the same part of a scene. Two broad classes of interferometers flown in space include Fourier transform spectrometers (FTS) in which the optical path difference between two interfering beams varies in time or space and multibeam interferometers like the Fabry-Perot interferometer in which multiple beams from the same scene element interfere to select a series of narrowband transmission ranges from which one is selected using another etalon or blocking filter. Nearly all optical filters used in MSI systems are based on a special type of Fabry-Perot interferometer (FPI) called an etalon. The best known interferometer used in space is the temporally modulated FTS (TFTS) implemented frequently with a design approach similar to what is shown in Fig. 17-11. In principle, a temporally modulated FTS can measure all optical frequencies simultaneously. In reality, practical limits such as detector sensitivity cutoffs, optical coatings and electronics frequency ranges restrict spectral range. The moving element in the TFTS and the resulting variation in optical path difference modulates intensity of optical frequencies across a broad spectral range in front of a single detector for each pixel that converts received optical signal into an electrical signal. The resulting plot of detected irradiance versus time (corresponding to changes in optical path difference) is called an interferogram. The interferogram is converted to an optical spectrum using a Fourier transform. General advantages of interferometer approaches include simplest and most compact instrument approach for high spectral resolution and coverage applications (especially for the FPI) and superior performance for detector noise limited TFTS instruments, because detector noise is multiplexed across the spectrum. Disadvantages for the TFTS include reliability concerns because of the moving elements in the interferometer and the so-called multiplex disadvantage for photon noise limited instruments in which photon noise from the broad spectral band observed by the TFTS in every interferogram sample is multiplexed into each spectral channel by the Fourier transform. FPI disadvantages include relatively low optical throughput, especially at high spectral resolution, which leads to larger collection optics than other spectrometers and limited spectral range for each etalon which can lead to requirements for many etalons in a system, to cover the broad spectral range required for some missions. Space-based interferometer examples include TFTS instruments like IASI, TE,S MIPAS, and FPI-based instruments like HRDI.

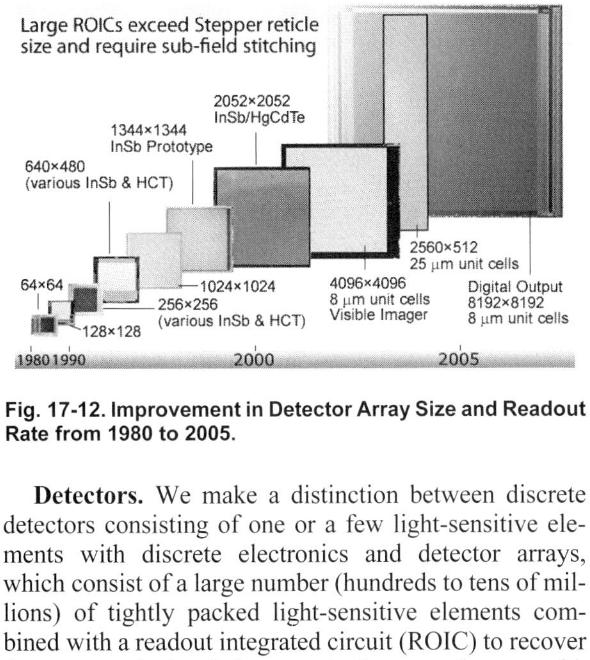

Fig. 17-12. Improvement in Detector Array Size and Readout Rate from 1980 to 2005.

Detectors. We make a distinction between discrete detectors consisting of one or a few light-sensitive elements with discrete electronics and detector arrays, which consist of a large number (hundreds to tens of millions) of tightly packed light-sensitive elements combined with a readout integrated circuit (ROIC) to recover the measured signal from each detector element with minimum complexity. As shown in Fig. 17-12, since the 1980s, detector technology has taken advantage of improvements in integrated circuit design and fabrication capabilities and advanced rapidly from relatively small format ~64 × 64 detector array designs to much larger format (~8,192 × 8,192) digital output approaches.

We must select the materials used for detector elements depending on the spectral range of the instrument being designed. The ability of photon detector elements to absorb photons relates directly to the energy of the incident photons (and consequently to the wavelength of the radiation as well) and the effective band gap of the material. Detector material generates random noise that reduces sensitivity of the instrument. This noise increases with operating temperature of the detector. Therefore, frequently, we must lower the temperature of the detector elements so that the self-generated noise does not degrade the signal-to-noise ratio of the instrument. This requirement becomes more stringent as the wavelength of the radiation being detected increases. With few exceptions, detectors have to be cooled for wavelengths in the short wave infrared (SWIR) and longer. All matter, at temperatures greater than absolute zero, generates thermal photons. Thus, frequently, for infrared imagers, the optics and interior structures of the instrument have to be cooled to reduce interference from light radiated by the instrument itself.

For the spectral range between 400 nm and 1,100 nm, silicon detectors and imagers are used most frequently. Silicon is attractive because it is possible to combine the detector elements and read-out electronics in a single monolithic chip. Furthermore, silicon substrates are available in larger size than other materials, which enables larger format devices. We can produce 1-dimensional line arrays or 2-D area arrays with a very large number of elements (e.g., 10,000 × 10,000 and greater) with silicon. Incident photons are converted to an electrical output signal in the array. For charge-coupled device (CCD) arrays with read-out electronics, the process begins when incident photons are converted by each detector element into electrons according to a conversion efficiency dictated by the characteristic spectral response. The electrons are then collected for the entire integration time for each detector element. The read-out of the charge generated—up to millions of electrons per detector element—is performed via an analog shift register across the arrays into a serial output port. 2-D CCDs may have more image smear relative to 1-D arrays during frame transfer. Also, in 2-D monolithic array designs, detector fill factor is generally lower than in 1-D arrays or in so-called hybrid arrays in which a detector array is bonded to a separate ROIC. Figure 17-13 shows a typical spectral response function for a silicon imager.

When radiometric performance of the optical instrument is paramount, we use time delay integration (TDI) methods. TDI describes an imaging principle that uses the image motion along the rows of a 2-D detector array to extend the integration time. Integration time is extended by electronically shifting the integrating pixel cell synchronously to the movement along the row. The signal-to-noise ratio of this concept is improved by the square root of the number of TDI stages. The primary advantage of TDI imager systems compared to line imagers is the improved signal-to-noise ratio. The disadvantage is the increased requirement for spacecraft attitude and orbit stability (due to the required synchronization of the shifting pixel). Some TDI sys-

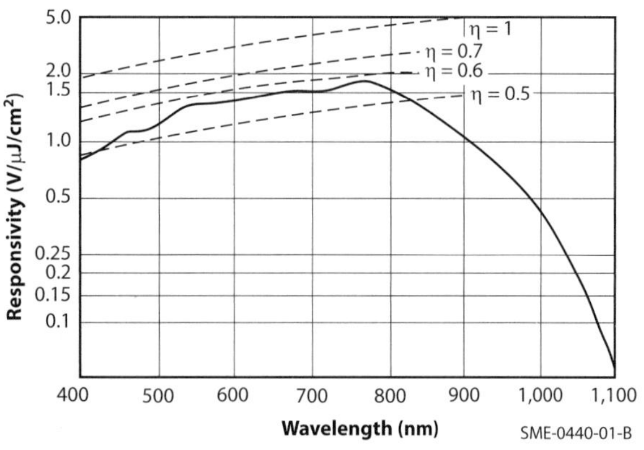

Fig. 17-13. Spectral Response Function of a Silicon Line Imager. The spectral response is shown in terms of the output voltage resulting from illumination by energy density vs. the wavelength from 400 to 1,100 nm. The imager reaches a quantum efficiency (generated electrons per incident photon), denoted by η, above 50% between 400–800 nm. Outside this wavelength region the quantum efficiency drops to small values making the imager less suitable above 900 nm.

tems perform the integration in software by adding together measurements from the different detectors that view the same part of the scene.

We classify and select infrared detectors according to their spectral band of operation and a figure of merit called specific detectivity for photon detectors. The operating temperature of the detector dictates the cooling requirements for the sensor focal plane. Infrared sensors often have non negligible time constants for response with respect to integration time. The size of infrared detector arrays is ultimately limited by the size of substrate material on which the detectors can be grown. Recent work at Raytheon has produced infrared arrays with format sizes up to 4,096 × 4,096. We detect infrared wavelengths with thermal detectors or photon detectors. Thermal detectors exploit the fact that absorbed heat raises the temperature of the detector, which changes its electrical characteristics. The advantage of thermal detectors is relatively uniform response with respect to wavelength. Thermal detectors can also be operated at ambient temperatures, although they have lower sensitivity and much slower response times, which can limit their applicability in whiskbroom scanners, for example. Photon detectors use absorbed photons to generate charge carriers. These systems offer the advantages of higher sensitivity and shorter time response, but they must be operated at low temperatures.

Infrared detectors are often rated by the specific detectivity, D^*, given by

$$D^* = \frac{\sqrt{A \Delta f}}{NEP} \tag{17-11}$$

where A is the detector area, Δf is the noise equivalent bandwidth, and NEP is the noise equivalent power of the detector. The factor D^* is strongly wavelength dependent showing its peak value at the cut-off frequency. See the book website for a list of IR FPA manufacturers.

The selection of a detector or detector array is driven by several factors. The primary design issues center on maximizing detectivity in the spectral band of interest while operating at the highest possible temperature and a sufficiently small time constant. In addition, we must consider the geometry of the detector and the array as well as associated calibration issues.

17.1.2 Radio Frequency Observational Payloads

Radio frequency observation payloads can scan the Earth in ways that are analogous to electro-optical payloads. Likewise, systems for collecting or transmitting optical and RF signals operate exactly the same in theory with collecting, reflecting and focusing light—only the physical hardware is different. Thus, the primary mirror in a visible and infrared system and the large reflector of a dish antenna in passive microwave radiometry and radar, for example, are equivalent.

However, because of the much longer wavelengths at which RF systems operate compared with optical systems, the equations shown in the previous section for diffraction limited angular resolution and corresponding horizontal resolution on the surface lead to RF system apertures that are orders of magnitude larger than corresponding optical systems for the same surface resolution. Likewise, for the same real aperture diameter, a passive microwave or radar system will provide much coarser surface resolution than an optical system with the same aperture diameter.

Nearly all RF systems detect collected irradiance coherent using the superheterodyne method. Superheterodyne detection, invented in the early 20th century, involves mixing an incoming RF signal collected by an antenna with a coherent, phase stable and low noise local oscillator to produce sum and difference frequencies called intermediate frequencies (IFs) that are much lower in frequency than the incoming signal and therefore easier to process. The IF signals contain the same amplitude and phase information as the RF signal. The amplitude is scaled by a constant, measureable amount and the phase difference is a constant that can also be measured.

This ability of RF systems to measure both amplitude and phase of the received signal with a relatively high degree of accuracy enables a technique called synthetic aperture radar (SAR) that can provide radar imagery with spatial resolution in one dimension that is comparable to spatial resolutions obtained with high performance optical systems.

To understand the importance of SAR, consider first how real aperture radar works. Radar illuminates an area with pulses of microwave radiation. These pulses are reflected from the illuminated scene and collected and processed by a receiver. Radar determines the distance of the reflecting object by precisely measuring the time difference between transmission time of the outgoing pulse and time the return pulse is received. This distance or range is the time difference times the speed of light divided by two. Spatial resolution along the radar line of sight is not range or directly wavelength dependent, as it is for horizontal resolution perpendicular to the line of sight. Instead, it is determined by the effective pulse-width, δt multiplied by the speed of light, c, divided by two, which is equivalent to the reciprocal of the effective pulse bandwidth, B times the speed of light. That is

$$\text{Range Resolution} = \frac{c\delta t}{2} = \frac{c}{B} \tag{17-12}$$

Pulse bandwidth and therefore data rate inside the instrument grow, as the range resolution improves. Many radars, including SARs, transmit a pulse using a linear frequency modulated (FM) "chirp" in which the frequency of the transmitted radar pulse varies linearly over a selected frequency range. This variation in frequency determines the RF bandwidth of the system. Chirp length and slope are constrained by range resolution for a system and depend on RF pulse power, pulse repetition frequency (PRF) and analog-to-digital converter (ADC) sampling rate and dynamic range. For example, the German TerraSAR-X system launched in 2007 and described by Werninghaus and Buckreuss, [2010], operates with a transmit bandwidth ranging from 5 to 300 MHz (with 300 MHz being used in an experimental mode). Consequently, TerraSAR-X is capable of operating with range resolutions extending from 1 m to 60 m.

In the direction perpendicular to the radar beam, the so-called cross range or azimuthal direction, spatial resolution of real aperture radar is limited by its physical size, just like a passive optical system. In this case, cross range spatial resolution is given by 1.22 $\lambda R_s/D$. From space, good range resolution can be achieved, but poor cross range horizontal spatial resolution, typically on the order of a kilometer even for practical but very large systems, cannot be avoided by real aperture radar at frequencies low enough to penetrate all weather conditions.

Interestingly enough, this significant disadvantage for radar, of large beam width or angular field of view, can be turned into an advantage, if the system has the ability to measure precisely, record and process the phase and Doppler shift of the radar return signal. A radar pointing toward the Earth's surface with a wide beam illuminates a scene location for an extended period of time (possibly up to seconds in duration) as the satellite passes overhead. If, during this time, the radar measures the phase and Doppler shift for each return, an aperture can be synthesized that is equivalent to the distance the real aperture antenna moves while the scene location is in the beam. This synthesized aperture can be orders of magnitude larger than the real radar antenna, which makes it possible to produce radar imagery with a meter of resolution. Longer wavelengths and smaller aperture diameters result in wider beam divergences, which can illuminate a scene location longer and therefore provide a longer baseline for creating a synthetic aperture.

Figure 17-14 illustrates a typical space-based SAR with co-located transmitter and receiver. This transmitter-receiver configuration is known as a monostatic configuration. As the satellite passes by a target location of interest, it maps out a strip along the Earth's surface. The dots in the figure represent a series of positions at which the SAR transmitter emitted a pulse. Each pulse travels to the Earth's surface and illuminates a scene location. A small fraction of that outgoing pulse returns to the receiver and is collected by the same antenna. The SAR records the phase histories of the responses at each scene location as the transmitter beam moves across the scene and then phase shifts and adds them together with appropriate weighting to minimize sidelobes in the synthesized beam to determine the range and scene brightness of one spatial resolution element at a time until the complete scene is described. SAR achieves a very high signal processing gain because this summation of the range correlated radar responses is done coherently with both amplitude and phase. In many cases, thousands of pulses are summed for each spatial resolution element, resulting in a signal processing gain of up to 10,000 or more for the TerraSAR-X compared with a single pulse.

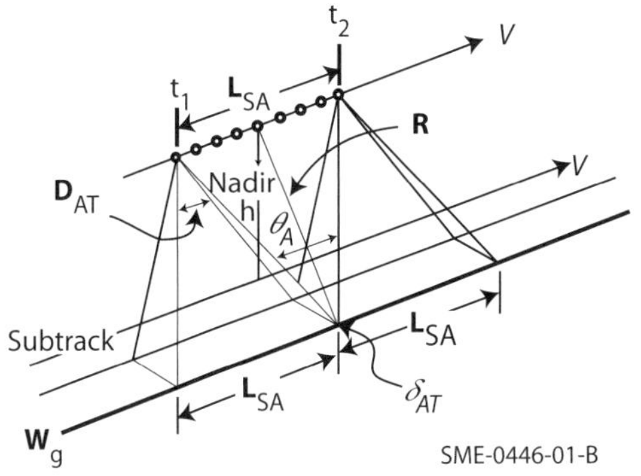

Fig. 17-14. Basic Principles of Synthetic Aperture Radar.

SAR performance is constrained by ambiguity relationships associated with the 2-D scene sampling that limit PRF and real aperture collector size. The basic idea is to collect data in the along track and in the range direction that can be processed into a unique image. In Fig. 17-14, L_{SA} is synthetic aperture length, and is the distance the satellite moves to illuminate the target. V is the satellite velocity, R is the target range, θ_A and D_{AT} are respectively the aperture azimuth beamwidth and the along-track antenna length of the real SAR antenna, δ_{AT} is the Earth target resolution element along-track dimension, and W_g is the satellite ground swath. The dwell or integration time, t_I, is given by:

$$t_I = \frac{L_{SA}}{V} = \frac{\lambda R}{VD_{AT}} \tag{17-13}$$

The aperture azimuth beamwidth is given by:

$$\theta_A = \frac{\lambda}{D_{AT}} \tag{17-14}$$

Additionally, the following relations apply:

$$\mathbf{L_{SA}} = \theta_A \mathbf{R} = \frac{\lambda \mathbf{R}}{D_{AT}} \tag{17-15}$$

$$\delta_{AT} = \frac{\lambda}{2\mathbf{L_{SA}}}\mathbf{R} = \frac{\lambda \mathbf{R}}{2\lambda \mathbf{R}/\mathbf{D_{AT}}} = \frac{\mathbf{D_{AT}}}{2} \tag{17-16}$$

The achievable azimuthal (i.e., along track) resolution of a SAR is approximately one half the along track radar antenna size and this resolution is independent of radar frequency and range to first order and improves with smaller real antenna aperture. Based on that one equation alone, it appears that along track resolution could be improved simply by making physical size of the antenna length very small. However, achieving a given along track resolution also requires that the radar send out a pulse every time the radar moves half of the along track antenna size. That is

$$2 \times \frac{V}{D_{AT}} < \text{PRF} \tag{17-17}$$

or

$$\text{PRF} > \frac{V}{R_A} \tag{17-18}$$

where V is the satellite velocity, D_{AT} is the antenna length, and R_A is the azimuthal resolution. Better azimuthal resolution requires a higher transmitter PRF. This means that less time is available between pulses to collect data. Only one pulse can be in the target space at a time to avoid ambiguities in range that would prevent construction of a unique image solution. This condition sets another limit on PRF which is a function of swath width ($S = R_f - R_n$) as shown in Fig. 17-15 for the SEASAT SAR imaging geometry, and the pulse duration, T, resulting in

$$\text{PRF} < \left(2T + \frac{2S}{c}\right)^{-1} \tag{17-19}$$

Not surprisingly, more spacing between pulses is required as the swath width or nadir angle increase. Thus, ultimately, a trade must be made in the design or specific system configuration between increased spatial coverage and improved along track spatial resolution, δ_{AT}. All of this reduces to a relationship between swath width, S, and along track spatial resolution for the single look case [Raney, 1998].

$$2 \times \frac{S}{\delta_{AT}} < \frac{c}{V} \tag{17-20}$$

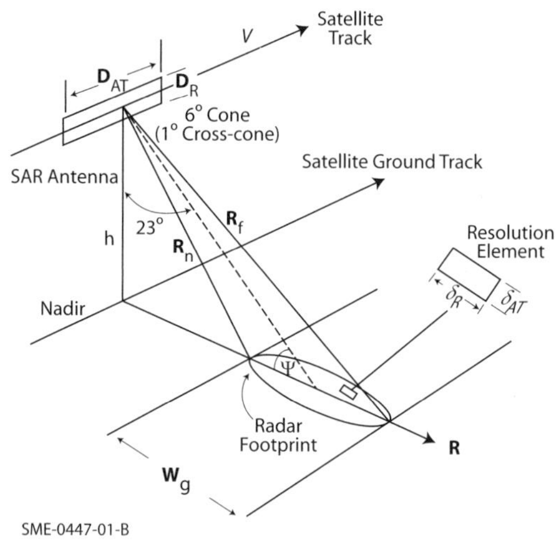

Fig. 17-15. SEASAT SAR Imaging Geometry.

In Fig. 17-15, the velocity, V is 7,450 m/s, the altitude, h is 800 km, and the ground swath, W_g is 100 km. **R** is the cross-track or range direction, Ψ is the grazing angle, and the satellite ground track is in the along track (AT) or azimuth direction. The following relations apply:

$$\delta_{AT} \geq \frac{\mathbf{D_{AT}}}{2} \tag{17-21}$$

$$\delta_R \geq \frac{c}{2\beta} \tag{17-22}$$

$$\mathbf{W_g} = \frac{\mathbf{R_f} - \mathbf{R_n}}{\cos\Psi} = \frac{\lambda \mathbf{R}}{\mathbf{D_R}\sin\Psi} \tag{17-23}$$

Where c is the speed of light, and β is the transmitted pulse bandwidth.

17.2 Observation Payload Sizing

The sizing of an observational payload is an iterative process that involves trading and optimizing different payload approaches, frequently across a large trade space of candidate possibilities. In the early stages of this process, it is important to be able to examine different options without designing each one in detail. Initial assessment of design alternatives requires estimates of size, mass, power, data rate and constraints on spacecraft pointing control and stability among other interface characteristics to narrow down the possibilities for more thorough consideration. These assessments flow from detailed description and understanding of the mission to the operations concept and initial specifications for the observation payload that determine payload size, mass, and power, as illustrated in Table 17-6.

High-resolution wide field-of-view optical instruments, especially those with hyperspectral capability across a broad spectral region, typically generate data

Table 17-6. The Observation Payload Sizing Process. Note that Steps 2 and 3 are highly iterative and may well drive both the mission and payload design.

Step	Where Discussed
1. Define Mission Requirements and Objectives	Chaps. 3, 4, 6
2. Determine Mission Geometry and Orbit Parameters	Chaps. 8, 10
3. Define Payload Requirements (ITERATE WITH STEP 2)	Sec. 17.2.2
4. Define Payload Operations Concept	Sec. 17.2.1
5. Determine Spatial Sampling	Sec. 17.2.3
6. Determine On-board Signal Processing	Sec. 17.2.4
7. Determine Radiometric Sensitivity Performance	Sec. 17.2.5
8. Estimate Payload Size, Mass, and Power	Sec. 17.2.6
9. Determine Payload Figures of Merit	Sec. 17.2.7
10. Document and Iterate	

rates on the order of several hundred Mbps and above. To send this data stream to a ground station in real time, the system may need several parallel channels with capacities up to 300 Mbps each. If data collection is short compared to the available downlink time, the data can be stored on-board and transmitted to the ground over time to reduce the required downlink data rate.

Trends for future systems indicate a growing tendency toward more on-board processing to decrease downlink data rate requirements and to enable broadcast of information derived from observational payload data directly to users. Continuing improvements in powerful processing hardware and associated algorithms enable sophisticated on-board processing capability comparable to ground-based processing. Given the significant impact that high speed processing systems can have on payload size, mass, and power, selection of an on-board data processing approach is becoming an ever more important element in the observation payload design trade space. To maintain the flexibility required for continuous improvements in system performance, software uploads to the hardware must be possible to update and modify operational algorithms from the user community. The need to upload large quantities of software relatively quickly must be considered, when specifying uplink data rate requirements for an observation system.

This section discusses each of the steps in the observation payload sizing process. In addition, figures of merit for comparing different design approaches are considered along with the description of an observation payload that fulfills requirements for the FireSat II mission.

17.2.1 Payload Operations Concepts

The operations concept for using the observation payload must be considered early in the preliminary design process. The end-to-end mission need must be understood along with the physics, associated engineering and phenomenology of the collection and interpretation of data. The payload operations approach as driven by end data user requirements needs to be a realistic and cost-effective way to achieve mission objectives.

Specific collection operations involving tasking and scheduling of the sensor, processing of the mission data, and distribution of the data can dramatically increase complexity of the systems engineering challenge and decrease the final accuracy of the system, if not selected carefully and within context of quantitative figures of merit. Not only can physical effects such as atmospheric correction, calibration, and rectification degrade system performance, but technical effects such as quantization and data compression errors can decrease the resolution of the system from the perspective of the end user. For additional information about technical aspects of the end-to-end throughput or image chain problem for remote sensing and imagery collected from space, see Schott [2007].

The operations concept for a system like FireSat II must consider all aspects of the operational mission, including different mission phases and alternative operating modes (See Chap. 29). In preliminary mission planning, we should be aware of the expected sequence of events during each mission phase. For normal FireSat II mission operations, a sample timeline includes the following steps:

1. Fire starts somewhere on the Earth
2. Sensor field-of-view passes over the fire and collects data, as part of a global fire reconnaissance mission
3. Measurements of the fire are transmitted through the sensor data stream
4. Data is analyzed at the mission ground station or processed on board
5. Fire detection algorithm determines the probability of a fire at the analyzed location—this could be a multistep process with a rapid, but crude fire detection algorithm that triggers a more accurate algorithm or set of measurements
6. If fire is detected, system generates appropriate messages to Customer that indicates presence of fire at specific location
7. Customer organization reports fire and notifies responsible authorities and appropriate researchers
8. System continues to monitor the fire and region near the fire, in conjunction with its global reconnaissance mission to track progress of the detected fire and monitor nearby areas for new fires

To ensure mission success, an operations concept for each mission phase and each spacecraft operating mode—including contingency and failure modes—must be created within operating environment limitations (See Chap. 29).

Table 17-7. Characteristics of Typical Payloads.

Purpose	Instrument Name	Size L × W × D (m)	Mass (kg)	Avg. Pwr. at 28 V (W)	Data Rate (Mbps)	Aperture (m)	Pointing Accuracy (deg)
Solar Physics	Lyman—Alpha Coronograph	2.8 × 0.88 × 0.73	250	87	13.5	—	0.003
	X-ray Telescope Spectrom.	2.7 × 1 dia.	465	30	0.4	—	0.003
	Solar Optical Telescope	7.3 × 3.8 dia.	6,600	2,000	50+	1.25	—
	Solar Magnetic Velocity Field	2 × 0.4 × 0.4	183	322	2+	—	0.003
	100 m Pinhole Camera	1 × 1 × 2	1,000	500	0.5	—	—
	Extreme UV Telescope	2.75 × 0.86 × 0.254	128	164	1.28	—	—
	Solar Gamma Ray Spectrom.	1 × 1 × 13	2,000	500	0.1	140 cm^2	0.003
Space Plasma Physics	Ion Mass Spectrometer	0.5 × 0.5 × 0.4	80	334	0.01	—	1
	Beam Plasma	0.6 × 0.7 × 0.7+	17	38	0.016	—	5
		two 0.7 dia. ant.				—	—
	Plasma Diagnostics	—	2,000	250	50	—	—
	Doppler Imaging Interferom.	(0.25)^3	100	620	0.2	—	—
	Proton (Ion) Accelerators	6.7 × 3.4 × 3.10	500	1,500	0.256 (4.2 TV)	—	1
High Energy Astrophysics	Gamma Ray Burst	2 × 4 dia.	1,000	120	0.01	3	—
	Cosmic Ray Transition	3.7 × 2.7 dia.	1,500	230	0.1	2.7	—
	X-ray Spectrom./Polarimeter	1.6 × 1.6 × 3	2,000	300	0.03	—	0.1
	Short X-ray	1 × 1 × 3	1,000	300	0.025	1 × 3	0.1
	Hi Energy Gamma Ray Tele.	3 dia. × 4	10,000	100	0.003	3	0.1
Resources	Gravity Gradiometer	0.23 m sphere	10	1			1–2
	Synthetic Aperture Radar	2.8 × 3.7 × 1.4	808	3,000	120	8 × 2.8	2.5
	Multi-Spectral Mid-IR	1.4 × 1.5 × 0.9	270	170	8	0.18	0.1
	Enhanced Thematic Mapper	2 × 0.7 × 1.1	400	600	75	0.406	0.005
Materials Processing	Materials Experiment Assem.	1 × 1 × 2	900	500	0	—	—
	Solidification Experiment		1,100	3,000	0.02	—	—
Environmental	Limb Scanning Radiometer	4.8 × 1.9 dia.	~800	125	0.52	—	—
	Microwave Radiometer	4 × 4 × 4	325	470	0.20	4	±0.1
	Dual Frequency Scatterom.	4.6 × 1.5 × 0.3	150	200	0.01	4.6 × 0.3	1
	Ocean SAR	20 × 2 × 0.2	250	300	120	20 × 2	0.1
	Solar Spectrum	0.4 × 0.3 × 0.6	16	60	Low	—	±3
	Doppler Imager	1.25 × 0.6 × 0.8	191	165	20	—	±3
	Imaging Spectoral	1.0 × 1.6 × 1.0	250	225	11	0.18	0.04
Planetary Science	Multi-Spectral Imager	0.54 × 0.37 × 0.29	13	12	2	0.12	—

17.2.2 Required Payload Capability

Often, mission requirements can be met in a number of different ways. It's not always obvious how to go through the various candidate approaches and select the best one for any given mission. The general approach outlined here is a simple, repeatable method for selecting a payload to satisfy an observation mission. After we select a physical phenomenology (for example, measuring thermal infrared radiance to detect the high brightness temperature that is characteristic of forest fires), three system characteristics need to be determined. The first is the spatial sampling approach needed to satisfy the mission information need, followed by the radiometric sensitivity levels needed to achieve fire detection and false alarm requirements. The third and frequently most important system characteristic from a mission implementation and cost perspective are the implications of spatial sampling and radiometric sensitivity characteristic on payload size, mass, and power.

Table 17-7 provides a small sampling of remote sensing payloads and corresponding spacecraft missions. Categorizing remote sensing missions is complicated by the fact that sensors usually have multiple uses, and they can be categorized according to any number of different aspects, such as measurement technique (active or passive), event measured (such as fire or deforestation), and measurement resolution (spatial, spectral, radiometric, temporal). Frequently, these multiple uses lead to conflicting requirements that further complicate payload design and development. Remote sensing payload examples include imaging spectroradiometers that passively measure the intensity of scene spectral radiance across a broad range in wavelength and polarimeters that measure polarization state of a transmitted, scattered or reflected wave. Scatterometers are active RF instruments (radars) that measure surface roughness of the ocean by measuring radar return signals that depend on wind speed and direction.

Table 17-7, Fig. 17-15◀, Eq. 17-23◀

Measurement procedures used in observation payloads and associated processing algorithms are customized to deliver information that can be retrieved from the measurements to understand the subject. We describe the fundamental measurement content provided by passive Earth observation instruments in terms of spatial and spectral resolution and radiometric sensitivity. We continue by discussing the basic types of detectors and collection techniques that are available in the design of a remote sensing instrument.

We frequently use imaging sensors, based on electro-optical devices, to measure and analyze spatial features. Visible wavelength imaging is a common approach for providing data needed for topographic mapping and photogrammetry. Altimeters are also especially valuable in providing fundamental spatial measurements. Kramer [2001] lists examples of these types of sensors.

As noted above, spatial resolution depends on the range from the sensor to the target, the aperture and focal length of the collection optics, detector element size, signal processing approach and the wavelength of the incident energy. We can characterize the spatial resolution by the smallest angular distance the sensor can resolve or directly as the ground range in units of length for the size of the smallest object that can be discriminated. Effective spatial resolution is a function of these many different design parameters in a remote sensing system and more, including the scene itself. Optical system and focal plane array characteristics determine theoretical limits to spatial resolution for any system geometry. In addition, these same characteristics define the ground sample distance (GSD), the distance on the ground (usually referenced to the sub-spacecraft point) at which the sensor samples the scene. Frequently, the effective spatial resolution is different from the GSD. Normally, the effective spatial resolution is about twice the GSD. However, for low contrast targets or target detections with low signal-to-noise ratio, effective spatial resolution can be coarser than twice the GSD. The smallest physical features that can be discriminated for specific target characteristics using any candidate sensor measurement approach determine the limits of spatial resolution in a remote sensing system. Information from spectral content of scenes can be used within context of plausible assumptions to derive spatial information that has finer resolution than the GSD.

Spectral content is provided by spectrometers that collect data that can be used to identify different components in a scene (e.g., rocks, trees, and water) and sometimes chemical composition of objects being measured. The spectral radiance received by a sensor is a composite of the spectral radiances emitted by all objects in the instantaneous field-of-view. The radiance reaching a possible multispectral FireSat II imager, for example, will include spectra from soil, vegetation, and cities in addition to any fire that might be there. The combined spectrum of all these scene elements may be very different from the spectrum of a forest fire by itself. Combining information from different spectral bands has been used often and successfully to isolate key scene elements from each other and improve the usefulness of a sensor.

Space-based spectrometers are frequently grouped into one of three categories: multispectral, hyperspectral and ultraspectral. Multispectral systems typically have tens of discrete spectral bands with relatively low ($\lambda/d\lambda$~10) spectral resolution. Hyperspectral and ultraspectral systems employ hundreds and thousands of spectral bands, respectively, across a contiguous spectral range with spectral resolutions that are typically moderate ($\lambda/d\lambda$~100) for hyperspectral systems and high ($\lambda/d\lambda$~1,000) for ultraspectral systems. Following Slater [1980], we consider a multispectral image of a scene with concrete, asphalt, soil, and grass. Figure 17-16 shows typical spectral reflectance for these four scene elements. If a candidate imager has only three bits of radiometric sensitivity (low, medium, and high), for example, then no single image, whether panchromatic or filtered to a particular band region could distinguish these four scene features. However, even a simple, but well calibrated two-band multispectral system can uniquely resolve these four scene elements using bands in the 600–700 nm and 700–900 nm wavelengths. Returns for each of these materials are shown in Table 17-8.

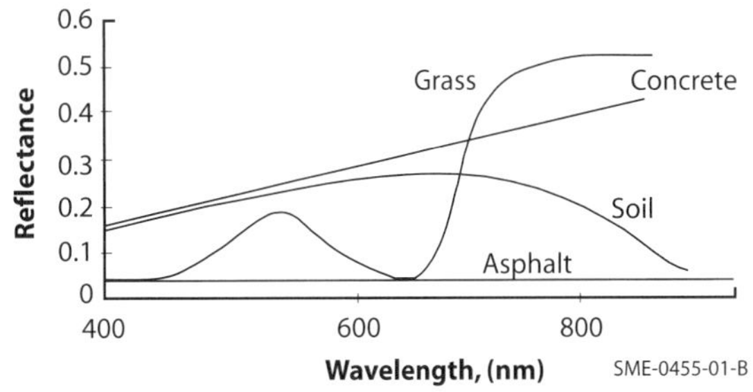

Fig. 17-16. Typical Spectral Reflectance Curves for Grass, Concrete, Soil, and Asphalt. A single-band low-resolution sensor can not distinguish all 4 types, but a 2-band, low-resolution sensor can, as shown in Table 17-8 [Slater, 1980].

Table 17-8. Spectral Resolution for Sample Two-Band Sensor. Combining low-resolution sensor returns for the two-band sensor can uniquely identify the four materials from Fig. 17-16.

Material	Sensor Reading 600–700 nm	Sensor Reading 700–900 nm
Concrete	Medium	High
Asphalt	Low	Low
Soil	Medium	Low
Grass	Low	High

Multispectral data with more spectral bands and especially hyperspectral and ultraspectral data contain much more physically meaningful detail, which can be used to recognize and quantify characteristics of complex scenes. However, the higher spectral resolution of hyperspectral and ultraspectral systems, especially, reduces measured signal-to-noise ratio (SNR)—all other system characteristics being equal—which can impact system design in many ways ranging from reducing spatial resolution to recover SNR to increasing aperture size to improve light gathering capability.

We can also use the measured spectral radiance level to extract useful information. For example, if we have an imager with four or more bits of sensitivity operating in the 700–900 nm wavelength, then a single spectral radiance measurement could be used to distinguish among all four candidate scene types, if we assume a pixel contains only one scene type and we understand the details of the solar illumination and viewing geometry precisely. The ability to measure spectral radiance precisely goes beyond detecting either the presence or absence of energy at a given wavelength. For example, if a FireSat II sensor were designed to detect fires based on measuring brightness temperatures of Earth's thermal emission, then a high enough brightness temperature would indicate presence of fire. But, the radiometric resolution of the instrument needs to be good enough to allow the system to discriminate between a forest fire and a campfire.

Thus, merely detecting the presence of thermal energy in a spectral band characteristic of burning biomass does not satisfy FireSat II mission needs. The number of bits needed to describe the intensity or brightness temperature information for a FireSat II instrument will be determined by two practical limits [Slater, 1980]: (1) the expected signal-to-noise ratio, and (2) the level of confidence needed to discriminate between different threshold signal levels. Consequently, signal-to-noise ratio (SNR) or equivalent parameters such as difference in scene brightness temperature equivalent to the system noise or noise equivalent delta temperature (NEDT) are performance discriminators for candidate observation payload designs.

17.2.3 Spatial Sampling

The spatial sampling of a scene by an optical instrument is determined by the scanning method used as described in Table 17-2, and by spacing of the detector elements in the focal plane, which can be constrained by optical system design characteristics such as operating wavelength, aperture diameter, and focal length. If the spatial sampling method is not selected with care, obvious image artifacts and not so obvious radiometric errors may be introduced into the data. Figure 17-17 shows the effect of sampling by a detector array observing three scenes with different spatial frequency structures. The response of the detectors to each scene pattern is shown as a gray level intensity in the three diagrams. Spatial frequency is defined as the inverse of the width of a black-and-white line pair, and is expressed in line pairs per meter or simply in units of inverse meters. The same detector array, shown to the right of each arrow, samples

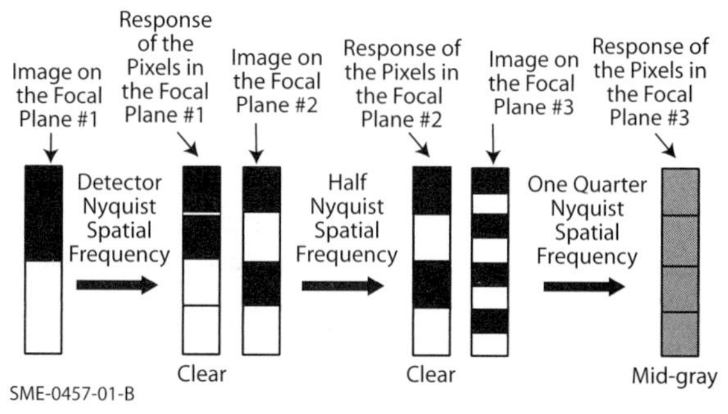

Fig. 17-17. Effect of Sampling Frequency on Image Quality. The three diagrams show illumination patterns having different spatial frequencies present in the scene (left of the arrows) sampled at the same sampling frequency, that is, the same detector array (right of the arrows). The response of the pixels is shown as intensity (gray level) in the three diagrams. From left to right: Sampling an illumination pattern with Nyquist frequency (the highest possible frequency that can be reconstructed without error). Sampling an illumination pattern with half the Nyquist frequency. Sampling an illumination pattern with one quarter the Nyquist frequency.

the scene in all three cases. That is, in these simple examples, the different scene structures are sampled at the same spatial sampling frequency, defined as the inverse of the distance between centers of the sampling detectors. The maximum spatial frequency which can be reconstructed without error after the sampling/restoration process is half of the sampling frequency or twice the sample distance in the focal plane. The left diagram in Fig. 17-17 illustrates this so-called detector Nyquist sampling case, where the scene feature as seen in the focal plane is twice the size of the detector. In the center, sampling of an illumination pattern occurs at half the Nyquist frequency of the scene structure, showing that reconstruction of the original illumination pattern is feasible without error even at half the Nyquist rate. However, if the sampling pattern is shifted by half a pixel with respect to the illumination pattern, then reconstruction fails. And on the right, sampling an illumination pattern with one quarter the Nyquist frequency of the scene structure results in a pixel response of mid-gray since every detector pixel is illuminated over half its area in the example. All samples in the third case show the same constant value which corresponds to a spatial frequency of zero, which was not present in the original scene. This creation of signal power at new frequencies is known as aliasing. Such frequency components cannot be removed by additional processing of the reconstructed image. To avoid these errors completely in an actual system, the scene must be sampled at twice the optical cutoff frequency described in Eq. (17-5). This Nyquist sampling of the optical cutoff frequency defines the lowest rate at which this band limited data must be sampled to avoid errors in scene reconstruction. Many systems do not sample the scene at the Nyquist rate of the cutoff frequency, because normally, very little power exists in the higher frequencies being aliased into the measurements and because radiometric sensitivity requirements typically determine aperture diameter and spatial sampling needs. Furthermore, it is not usually cost effective to sample an optical system at the Nyquist rate of the optical cutoff frequency because this approach results in a much larger number of detectors than would otherwise be required by alternative approaches, such as sampling at twice the Rayleigh criterion or at the spatial resolution required by the mission, which can significantly increase system cost relative to other approaches. The result is that we usually have a certain amount of unavoidable aliasing which degrades image quality and radiometric accuracy of such systems.

The Modulation Transfer Function (MTF) is the ratio of the measured contrast variation in the image to the actual contrast variation in the ground scene as a function of spatial frequency. MTF is zero at the optical cutoff frequency described in Eq. (17-5). Figure 17-18 shows the theoretical MTF of an optical system with and without a central obscuration such as an on-axis secondary mirror and support structure. The theoretical MTF can be approximated by a line starting at 1 when the spatial frequency is 0 and falling to 0 at the cut-off frequency, $F_{cut\text{-}off} = D/\lambda f$, where D is the aperture diameter, λ is the wavelength, and f is the focal length of the optical system. The MTF of a telescope is the autocorrelation function of the entrance pupil function. In optical terms, the MTF is the absolute value of the complex Optical Transfer Function (OTF) which describes how the complex amplitudes of the optical wave front are transferred by an optical system at different spatial frequencies.

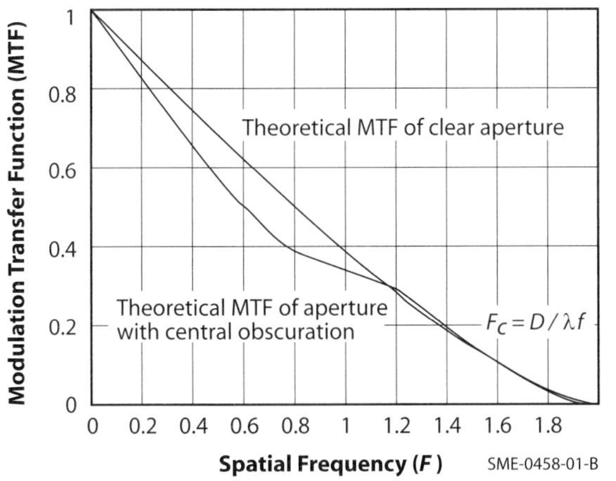

Fig. 17-18. Modulation Transfer Function of Circular Diffraction-Limited Optical System vs. Spatial Frequency. MTF curves for a clear circular optical system is compared with one having a central obscuration (as found in on-axis reflective telescopes). The MTF can be thought of as a function dependent on the spatial frequency, *F*, which describes the modulation (contrast) function through the optical system (analogous to the frequency dependent gain of an electrical transmission block). The MTF starts at 1 for spatial frequencies near 0 and drops to 0 at the cutoff frequency, $F_C = D/\lambda f$.

The MTF describes the ability of an imaging system to transfer contrast from a scene to an image in the focal plane as function of spatial frequency. It is a measure of the quality of an optical system. The point-spread function illustrated in Fig. 17-8 describes exactly the same properties by showing the two-dimensional intensity distribution in the focus of the optical system. The two functions are related by Fourier transform. System level MTF is also affected by spatial sampling in the focal plane by detector arrays and by signal processing of data collected with 2-D imaging detector arrays.

17.2.4 Signal Processing

Analog signal processing for visible wavelength detector arrays based on CCDs or Si:PIN diode arrays is very similar to processing used in infrared detector arrays with an integrated multiplexer. In all cases, weak analog signals need to be amplified and conditioned, maintaining high dynamic range and high processing speed. High speed electronic signal processing with high accuracy can become a cost and schedule driver in development of high-resolution wide field of view instruments. Concerns about electrical noise and other electromagnetic interference dictate that this processing be conducted as close to the focal plane assembly as possible—frequently on the chip itself. Simultaneously, careful thermal isolation between the detector arrays and the heat dissipating electronics must maintain a stable minimum operating temperature for the detector arrays.

For infrared detector arrays, the dark current increases with operating temperature. The exact rate depends on detector material, bias voltage and fabrication methods. However, across a wide range of designs, the dark noise typically goes up by a factor of 10 with each rise in temperature of 10 K. Infrared imagers are usually cooled to low temperatures; therefore, we must minimize each heat leak to their cryostat to keep the cooling power low. Frequently, the cooling requirement becomes more stringent as the wavelength of the radiation to be measured becomes longer. For wavelengths in the 100 μm range, detectors are typically cooled to 4 K. Even small heat leaks, such as those from the necessary electrical wiring and mechanical connection to the spacecraft, transport excess heat that increase required cooling power.

Figure 17-19 shows the typical functional blocks found in the electronics of an optical instrument. The signal flow through the electronics begins with a detector in the focal plane of the instrument. This detector converts photons to analog electrical signals, which are then amplified, conditioned and converted to a digital signal stream. Any additional signal processing is performed in the digital data processing block. The analog and digital signal processing blocks operate synchronously with the readout of the detector arrays. In most observation systems, a central timing subsystem supplies appropriate timing signals to all relevant electronic blocks to guarantee synchronous operation. Given electrical signals processed in the instrument electronics are weak, special attention to power conditioning and

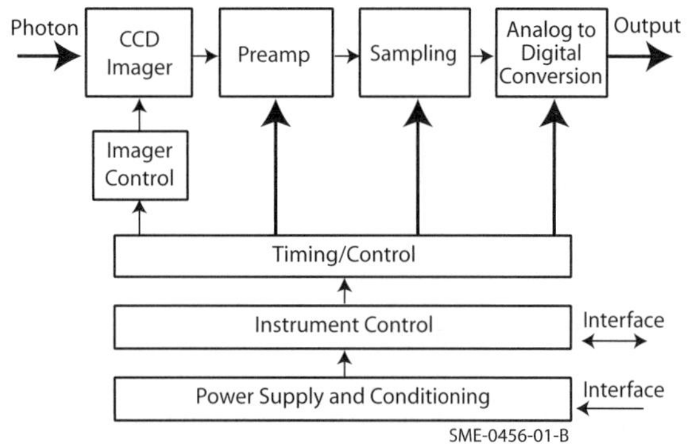

Fig. 17-19. Block Diagram of an Optical Instrument. Photons are collected by the Detector Array, then amplified and processed. The primary supporting functions of power and control are also depicted. The sampling process for charge coupled device signal processing typically uses correlated double sampling to eliminate reset noise.

grounding is required. Careful filtering and clean electrical grounding across a wide electrical bandwidth must be implemented to decouple digital and analog signals.

The instrument control processor manages the signal processing and timing functions performed by the instrument and it interfaces to the main spacecraft processor. Depending on the design, the spacecraft processor may transmit time-tagged commands that are executed by the instrument processor.

Analog signal processing for detector arrays frequently involves correlated double sampling. This technique takes two slightly time-shifted samples of the analog signal and subtracts one from the other to extract their image-related video signal. The adaptation of this video signal to the input range of the analog-to-digital converter requires setting gain and offset parameters for every detector in the system. Any non-uniformity in photo response and dark signal must be removed from each pixel. This task is frequently conducted on board the spacecraft because some of the most straightforward data compression algorithms become invalid if the detector samples are not normalized in this way. Furthermore, normalizing detector samples is required for most effective use of on-board calibration methods in the sensor.

The process of normalizing pixels is based on characteristics of the detector arrays. For arrays with a highly linear response, one-or two-point correction is generally sufficient. Highly nonlinear detectors, like some infrared detectors, require n-point correction techniques. Figure 17-20 illustrates an example of two-point correction. The offset (dark signal) and gain factor (response) are corrected by first subtracting the individual offset value and then by dividing by the individual response for each detector.

High-resolution wide field of view optical instruments typically generate data rates on the order of several hundred Mbps and above. To send this data stream to a ground station in real time, the system may need several parallel channels with capacities up to 300 Mbps each. If data collection is short compared to the available downlink time, a buffer memory can reduce the downlink data rate over a longer transmission time.

Trends for future systems indicate a growing tendency toward more on-board information processing to decrease communication requirements. Continuing improvements in powerful processing hardware and associated algorithms enable sophisticated on-board processing capability comparable to ground-based processing. To maintain the flexibility required for continuous improvements in system performance, software uploads to the hardware must be possible to update and modify operational algorithms from the user community. The need to upload relatively large quantities of software must be considered, when specifying uplink data rate requirements for an observation system.

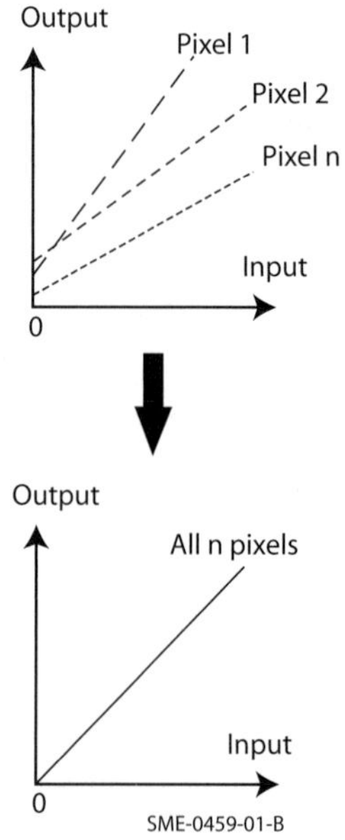

Fig. 17-20. Two-point Normalization of Pixel Response. The top diagram shows the original response functions of individual pixels. The bottom diagram shows the normalized response function of the same pixels, where the effects of the variations in offset values and responsivity values have been removed from the individual pixels.

17.2.5 Radiometric Sensitivity Performance

In order to describe the radiometric sensitivity performance of an observation payload, we must follow a scene photon through the entire end-to-end system. For a solar reflective system operating in the visible or near infrared, that means we start with the source of the reflected light, the Sun. Figure 17-21 shows the radiance distribution of the Sun versus wavelength.

The measured power density in a spectral band of interest is given by integration of the different components of spectral radiance input at the scene over solid angle and across the spectral bandwidth of the sensor. To first-order we assume that lambertian (ideal or dif-

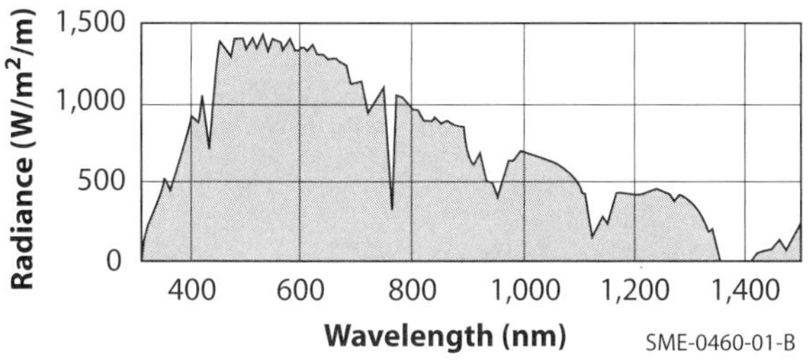

Fig. 17-21. Solar Radiance. Radiance of the Sun at sea level as a function of the wavelength.

fuse) reflection with a constant reflection coefficient occurs at the target scene (reasonably good approximation for small spectral bandwidth). The area of the ground sample radiating power to the instrument determines the power density per solid angle. The atmosphere attenuates this radiation by a constant transmission factor (again, invoking an approximation for small spectral bandwidth). Scattered light in the atmosphere contributes significantly to upwelling signal levels, especially over relatively low reflectance areas like the ocean. The entrance aperture of the payload at orbital altitude collects a very small fraction of the total power radiated by the scene. The collected signal power is attenuated further by transmission through the optics, during the integration time some amount of energy (power times integration time) is collected by each detector in the array. This collected energy divided by the photon energy (which is wavelength dependent, of course) leads to the number of available signal photons per detector. These signal photons are converted into electrons or pairs of electrons and holes inside the detector, depending on the detector material. The quantum efficiency of the detector multiplied by the number of photons is equal to the number of available electrons or electron/hole pairs. These charge carriers are collected by the detector junction and correspond to the output signal of the detector. This signal is expressed in units of electrons, whether electrons or holes are collected by the junction. For convenience, all noise components in the signal measurement process such as dark current, readout noise or instrument background for emissive infrared systems are stated in electrons.

Radiometric performance of an instrument is determined by the signal-to-noise ratio and dynamic range. The signal-to-noise ratio describes the image quality for any given set of measurement conditions, including sensor aperture diameter and instantaneous field of view and scene intensity. The number of noise electrons associated with the signal follows Poisson statistics and equals the square root of the number of signal electrons. Readout of the detector arrays results in additional noise electrons. The signal noise is added to the readout noise since they are statistically independent values, resulting in a total number of noise electrons in the denominator of the signal-to-noise ratio. For emissive infrared systems especially, background from structures inside the instrument that radiate spurious thermal photons create additional noise in the detector that has to be considered in the total number of noise electrons, too.

The required maximum dynamic range of the instrument is the ratio of the sum of the signal, instrument background, dark noise, and readout noise electrons the sensor sees between maximum possible brightness and completely dark scenes. In the solar reflectance part of the spectrum, the brightest scene is typically reflection from thick clouds or snow, and the darkest scene is deep space.

In order to estimate radiometric performance of instruments operating in the mid and long-wavelength emissive infrared spectral region, spectral emission of the surface and atmosphere of the Earth must be modeled. A reasonable approximation for much of the Earth's surface is a blackbody with an equivalent temperature of 290 K. The atmospheric transmission as a function of the wavelength is well understood for any given path orientation and set of atmospheric characteristics up to high zenith angles from the surface. The multiplication of the spectral radiance with the atmospheric transmission results in the upwelling radiance from the surface measured at the sensor. The atmosphere emits significant amounts of thermal radiation and can be the largest single source of emission, depending on wavelength. The integration of upwelling spectral radiance over the selected bandwidth and area of the spatial resolution element results in the power per solid angle. Input power at the sensor's entrance aperture is calculated, based on sensor instantaneous field of view and effective aperture of the receiving optics. This power is converted via the optical transmission factor to input power at detector (usually in the picoWatt range). As with the solar reflective sensors, during the integration time, a certain amount of energy is accumulated per detector. The division of that energy by the energy of one photon gives the number of photons available per detector which is converted by the quantum efficiency to the available number of electrons or electron/hole pairs per detector which corresponds to its output signal.

To characterize the radiometric performance of an instrument that measures thermal emission, a more commonly used figure of merit for radiometric sensitivity is the noise-equivalent delta temperature (NEDT) for the instrument at a given scene temperature. NEDT is given by the temperature difference at a specified scene temperature that is normally relevant to the mission, which generates a signal equivalent to the total number of noise electrons at that scene temperature. NEDT characterizes the instrument's ability to resolve temperature variations for a specified scene temperature.

17.2.6 Payload Size, Mass and Power

We need to be able to estimate the size, mass, power and other system level characteristics of an observation payload before completing a detailed design. We want to be able to compare system options without necessarily designing each in detail. This section describes methods to estimate the overall size and key parameters, including data rates. In Sec. 17.2.8, we will apply these methods to FireSat II.

Regardless of the nature of any particular payload, we would like to estimate its size, weight, and power even before we have done a detailed design. To do so, we can use three basic methods:

- Analogy with existing systems
- Scaling from existing systems
- Budgeting by components

The most straightforward approach is to use an analogy with existing systems. To do this, we turn to the list of existing payloads in Table 17-7 or other payloads that we may be aware of which have characteristics matching the mission we have in mind. Kramer [2001] offers a very thorough list of existing sensors. We look for payloads whose performance and complexity match what we are trying to achieve and make a first order estimate that our payload will have characteristics comparable to the previously designed, existing payload. While this approach is rough, it does provide a first estimate and some bounds to decide whether the approach we have in mind is reasonable.

A second approach, described in more detail below, is scaling the payload estimate from existing systems. This can provide moderately accurate estimates of reasonable accuracy if the scale of the proposed payload does not differ too greatly from current payloads. In addition, scaling provides an excellent check. Most existing payloads have been carefully designed and optimized. If our new payload is either too large or too small relative to prior ones, there should be some reason for this change in characteristics. If more detailed estimates based on detailed budgets don't scale from existing systems, we must understand why.

The most accurate process for first-order payload sizing is budgeting by components. Here, we develop a list of payload components such as detectors, optics, optical bench, and electronics. We then estimate the weight, power, and number of each. This is the best and most accurate approach but may be very difficult to apply at early mission stages because we simply don't have enough initial information. Ultimately, we will size the payload with budgeting by components. We will develop budgets as outlined in Chap. 14 for each payload instrument for weight, power, and any critical payload parameters. These budgets will then help us monitor the ongoing payload development. However, even with a detailed budget estimate, it is valuable to use scaling as a check on component budgeting. Again, we wish to understand whether the components scale from existing payloads and, if not, why not.

Scaling from Existing Systems

An excellent approach for early design concept work is to adjust the parameters in Table 17-7 to match the instrument we are designing. We will scale the instruments based on aperture—a main design parameter that we can determine from preliminary mission requirements. To scale, we compute the aperture ratio, R, defined by

$$R = \frac{A_i}{A_o} \tag{17-24}$$

where A_i is the required aperture of our new instrument, and A_o is the aperture of a similar instrument (Table 17-7). We then estimate the size, weight, and power based on ratios with the selected instrument from Table 17-7, using the following:

$$L_i \sim RL_o \qquad L = \text{linear dimensions} \tag{17-25}$$

$$S_i \sim L_i^2 \qquad S = \text{surface area} \tag{17-26}$$

$$V_i \sim L_i^3 \qquad V = \text{volume} \tag{17-27}$$

$$W_i \sim KR^3 W_o \qquad W = \text{weight} \tag{17-28}$$

$$P_i \sim KR^3 P_o \qquad P = \text{power} \tag{17-29}$$

The factor K should be 2 when R is in the range of 0.5 or less and 1 otherwise. This reflects an additional factor of 2 in weight and power for increased margin when scaling the system down by a factor of more than 2. When the system grows, the R^3 term will directly add a level of margin. For instruments more than a factor of five smaller than those listed in Table 17-7, scaling becomes unreliable. We recommend assuming a mass density of 1 gm/cm^3 and power density of 0.005 W/m^3 for small instruments. An example of these computations for FireSat II is in Sec. 17.3.8.

17.2.7 Figures of Merit for Evaluating Candidate Payloads

Multi-parameter performance indices can be defined for comparing optical instruments with similar performance characteristics. For high spatial resolution imagers three basic figures of merit describe the quality or expected information content in the image. The three defining figures of merit are signal-to-noise ratio at zero spatial frequency, MTF of an instrument at the detector Nyquist frequency (corresponding to the leftmost diagram in Fig. 17-17), and the ground sample distance, GSD. We define a relative quality index (RQI) to allow relatively straightforward quantitative comparisons with a reference instrument denoted by the subscript ref.

$$\text{RQI} = \frac{\text{SNR}}{\text{SNR}_{ref}} \times \frac{\text{MTF}}{\text{SNR}_{ref}} \times \frac{\text{GSD}_{ref}}{\text{GSD}} \tag{17-30}$$

This relative quality index allows the designer to trade requirements with respect to each other. For example, a higher SNR can compensate for a lower MTF at the detector Nyquist frequency for a given GSD. Such comparisons enable first-order insights into the relationships between complexity, performance, and cost of candidate imagers. For example, suppose we consider a well understood reference instrument with SNR of 512, MTF of 0.5 and GSD of 25 m. If we then compute design parameters for some specific mission, we can calculate a relative quality index, for this candidate design with respect to the known reference instrument. For instance, if our design choices lead to an instrument with SNR of 705.2, MTF of 0.47 and GSD of 30 m, then the RQI for this system will be 108%, suggesting the candidate instrument is slightly better than the reference instrument. This type of index offers a straightforward method for comparing several competing sensors across three (or potentially more) key performance figures of merit.

17.2.8 Example of Observation Payload Sizing

To illustrate the preliminary design process for payloads, we will estimate the basic parameters for the FireSat II payload developed throughout Chaps. 1–10. We cannot expect to carry out a detailed design without substantial input from an IR payload designer. Still, we would at least like to know whether the FireSat II payload is the size of a shoebox or the size of a truck.

Table 17-9 contains the details of the design analysis process for visible and infrared systems. We start with basic system parameters such as the orbital height, minimum observation angle and ground resolution. We then calculate quantities that describe instrument performance. In particular, we determine the image processing parameters and system data rate, size of the optics for a given spatial resolution, and the radiometric sensitivity performance of the sensor. Sample computations for the FireSat II imager are presented in the third column.

The FireSat II altitude trade led to a preliminary altitude, h = 700 km. From this, we can determine the apparent angular radius of the Earth, ρ:

$$\rho = \sin^{-1}\left(\frac{R_E}{R_E + h}\right) = 64.3 \text{ deg} \tag{17-31}$$

A key parameter in the system design is the minimum elevation angle, ε, at which the system can work. We do not have an estimate of that yet, but we do know that IR payloads do not work well at small elevation angles. Therefore, we will tentatively assume a minimum elevation angle of 20 deg, recognizing that this may be a very critical trade at a later stage. With this assumption, we can compute the nadir angle range, η, the maximum ground-track angle or swath width, λ, and the maximum range to the target, D, from the formulas in Sec. 8.3:

$$\sin\eta = \cos\varepsilon \sin\rho = 57.9 \text{ deg} \tag{17-32}$$

$$\pi = 90 - \eta - \varepsilon = 12.1 \text{ deg} \tag{17-33}$$

$$D = R_E\left(\frac{\sin\lambda}{\sin\eta}\right) = 1{,}578 \text{ km} \tag{17-34}$$

These equations imply that the sensor on board the spacecraft will have to swing back and forth through an angle of ±57.9 deg to cover the swath. The swath width on the ground will be 2 × 12.1 = 24.2 deg wide in Earth-central angle, with a maximum distance to the far edge of the swath of 1,578 km. Had we been able to work all the way to the true horizon ($\varepsilon = 0$), the maximum Earth central angle would be $90 - \rho = 27.5$ deg, and the swath width would be 55 deg. Increasing the minimum elevation angle to 20 deg has very dramatically reduced the size of the available swath.

We next find the orbit period, P, and longitude shift per orbit, ΔL, (Secs. 10.2.1 and 10.2.1.6 web):

$$P = 1.659 \times 10^{-4} \times (6{,}378 + h)^{3/2} = 98.8 \text{ min} \tag{17-35}$$

$$\Delta L = 98.8 \times (360/1440) = 24.7 \text{ deg} \tag{17-36}$$

Therefore, at the equator, successive node crossings are 24.7 deg apart. Notice that this is slightly larger but very close to the 24.2 deg swath width which we computed above. This is an important characteristic for FireSat II. It would be extremely valuable to have the swaths overlap so that every FireSat II spacecraft can cover all locations on the Earth twice per day. Therefore, in designing the payload, we should work hard to maintain either the altitude or the minimum elevation angle to provide some swath overlap. Doing so could dramatically reduce the number of spacecraft required and therefore the cost of the system.

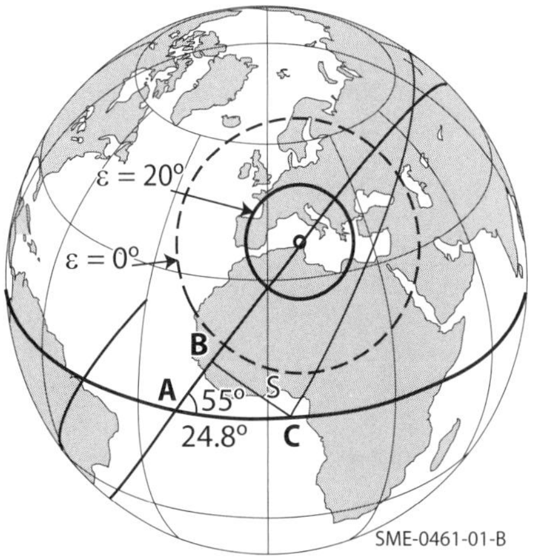

Fig. 17-22. Computation of FireSat II Ground-Track Parameters.

As Fig. 17-22 shows, the swath width does not need to be quite as large as the spacing between nodes along the equator. Even at the equator, it is enough to have a swath width equal to S, the perpendicular separation between the ground tracks. In Chap. 10, we selected an inclination for FireSat II of 55 deg to cover up to 65 deg latitude. Consequently, we can use the spherical triangle ABC shown in the figure to compute S as follows:

Table 17-8◀, Fig. 17-22, Eq. 17-36

Live Calc

Table 17-9. Parameter Calculations for a Passive Optical Sensor. IRC = Inside Rear cover

Step	Calculation	FireSat II	Comments
	A. Orbit and Viewing Geometry		
Select altitude, h, and eccentricity, e	Table 10-1; Sec. 10.4	h =700 km, e = 0	See Sec. 10.6 for constellations
Compute orbit period, P	Tables 8-11, 8-12, IRC	P = 98.8 min	
Compute ground track velocity, V_g		V_g = 6.76 km/s	Varies with true anomaly
Compute node shift per orbit, ΔL	IRC	ΔL = 24.7 deg	= longitude shift at all latitudes
Compute Earth angular radius, ρ	Tables 8-11, 8-12, IRC	ρ = 64.3 deg	
Determine min working elevation angle, ε_{min}		ε_{min}= 20 deg	Major system trade; small elev angle provides more coverage, but makes it harder for payload
Compute max nadir angle, η_{max}	Tables 8-11, 8-12, IRC	η_{max} = 57.9 deg	Only slightly less than Earth ang. radius
Compute max Earth central angle, λ_{max}	Tables 8-11, 8-12, IRC	λ_{max} = 12.1 deg	
Compute slant range, R_s	Tables 8-11, 8-12, IRC	R_s = 1,584 km	min distance = altitude
Compute swath width, SW	= 2 λ_{max}	SW = 24.3 deg	
	B. Pixel Parameters and Data Rate		
Specify maximum along-track ground sampling distance, Y_{max}	Design parameter	Y_{max} = 1.12 km	Based on spatial resolution requirements at λ_{max}
Determine along-track instantaneous field of view, IFOV	$IFOV_Y = \frac{Y_{max}}{R_s} \cdot \frac{180\text{deg}}{\pi}$	$IFOV_Y$ = 0.041 deg	One pixel width in along-track direction
Specify max cross-track ground sampling distance, X_{max}	Design parameter	X_{max} = 1.12 km	Based on spatial resolution requirements at λ_{max}
Specify number of cross-track detector samples at nadir in one pixel	Design parameter	N_{samp} = 3	Makes pixel same size in along-track and cross-track directions
Determine cross-track IFOV	$IFOV_X = \frac{X_{max}}{R_s} \cdot \frac{180\text{deg}}{\pi N_{samp}}$	$IFOV_X$ = 0.014 deg	
Determine cross-track ground pixel resolution, X, at nadir	$X = IFOV_X \cdot N_{samp} \cdot h\left(\frac{\pi}{180\text{deg}}\right)$	X = 495 m	Best cross-track resolution for this instrument
Determine along-track pixel resolution, Y, at nadir	$Y = IFOV_Y \cdot h\left(\frac{\pi}{180\text{deg}}\right)$	Y = 495 m	Best along-track resolution for this instrument
Determine number of cross-track pixels, Z_c	$Z_c = \left(\frac{2 \cdot \eta_{max}}{IFOV_X}\right)$	Z_c = 8,569	Ground pixel size varies along the swath
Find number of swaths recorded along-track in 1 sec, Z_a	$Z_a = \frac{V_g \cdot 1\text{ sec}}{Y}$	Z_a = 13.7	Number of successive swaths without gaps at nadir
Find number of pixels recorded in 1 sec, Z	$Z = Z_c \cdot Z_a$	$Z = 1.12 \times 10^5$	
Specify number of bits used to encode each pixel, B	Design parameter	B = 14 bits	Based on radiometric resolution requirement and dynamic range
Specify number of spectral bands, N_{bands}	Design parameter	N_{bands} = 5	
Estimate data rate, DR	$DR = Z \cdot B \cdot N_{bands}$	DR = 8.2 Mbps	Large number may challenge downlink capacity
	C. Define Sensor Integration Parameters		
Specify number of pixels for whiskbroom inst. N_m	Design parameter	N_m = 16	Must be large enough to allow sufficient integration time
Specify swath overlap, O	Design parameter	O = 1.185	
Find pixel integration period, T_i	$T_i = \frac{Y}{V_g} \cdot \frac{N_m}{O} \cdot \frac{X}{2\pi h}$	T_i = 111 μs	Integration time of each detector pixel at nadir
Find resulting pixel read-out frequency, F_p	$F_p = 1/\ T_i$	F_p = 9 kHz	

Table 17-9, Fig. 17-22◀, Eq. 17-36◀

Table 17-9. Parameter Calculations for a Passive Optical Sensor. (Continued) IRC = Inside Rear cover

Step	Calculation	FireSat II	Comments
	D. Define Sensor Optics		
Specify width for cross-track detectors, d_x	Design parameter	$d_x = 50\ \mu m$	Typical for available infrared detectors
Specify quality factor for imaging, Q	Design parameter	$Q = 0.4$	$0.4 < Q < 2$ ($Q = 1.1$ for good image quality)
Specify operating wavelength, λ	Design parameter	$\lambda = 10.8\ \mu m$	Based on subject trades
Define focal length, f	$f = \frac{h \cdot d_x}{(X/N_{samp})}$	$f = 0.2$ m	Use altitude and Eq. (17-8)
Find diffraction-limited aperture, D	$D = \frac{\lambda f}{Q d_x}$	$D = 0.12$ m	Eq. 17-10
Compute F-number of optics, F#	$F\# = f/D$	$F\# = 1.85$	Typical range = 4–6
Compute along-track field of view of optical system, FOV	$FOV = IFOV_Y \cdot N_m$	$FOV = 0.65$ deg	*FOV* for the array of pixels
Determine cut-off frequency, F_c	$F_c = D/(\lambda f)$	$F_c = 51{,}000$/m	Referred to nadir
Determine cross-track Nyquist frequency, F_{nc}	$F_{nc} = 1/(2d_x)$	$F_{nc} = 10{,}000$/m	Referred to ground sample resolution at nadir
Determine along-track Nyquist frequency, F_{na}	$F_{na} = 1/(2d_x N_{samp})$	$F_{na} = 3{,}333$/m	Referred to ground sample resolution at nadir
Compute relative Nyquist frequencies, F_{qc} and F_{qa}	$F_{qc} = \frac{F_{nc}}{F_c};\ F_{qa} = \frac{F_{na}}{F_c}$	$F_{qc} = 20\%$ $F_{qa} = 6.7\%$	% of the cutoff frequency used for this case
Find optics PSF as a function of distance, r, from center of detector	$PSF(r) = [\lambda J_1(Z) / Z]^2$ $Z \equiv \pi r D/\lambda f$		Use $-2d < r < 2d$ J_1 is the Bessel function of order 1
Find optical modulation transfer function (MTF_0) for clear circular optics	$MTF_0(F) =$ $\frac{2C}{\pi}\left[\frac{\pi}{2} - \frac{C}{F_c\sqrt{1-C^2}} - a\sin C\right]$		Use $0 < F < F_c$ $C \equiv F / F_c$
Compute detector MTF cross-track, MTF_X, and along-track, MTF_Y	$MTF_X = [\sin(F_X)/F_X]^2$ $MTF_Y = \lvert\sin(F_Y)/F_Y\rvert$		Use $0 < F < F_c$ $F_X \equiv \pi X F$ $F_Y \equiv \pi Y F$
Compute system MTF cross-track, MTF_S	$MTF_S(F) =$ $MTF_0(F) \cdot MTF_x(F)$		Let *F range:* $0 < F < F_c$
	E. Estimate Sensor Radiometry (for Nadir Viewing)		
Define equivalent blackbody temperature, T	Design parameter	$T = 290$ K	Blackbody temperature of the Earth
Define the operating bandwidth, $\Delta\lambda$	Design parameter	$\Delta\lambda = 0.4\ \mu m$	Based on subject trades
Determine blackbody spectral radiance, L_λ	$L_\lambda = E(\lambda)/\pi$ $E(\lambda)$ from Eq. (15-2)		Use range $\lambda \pm \Delta\lambda/2$
Look up transmissivity, $\tau(\lambda)$ of the atmosphere	See Fig. 15-5	See Fig 15.5	Evaluate operating bandwidth
Compute upwelling radiance, L_{upi}	$L_{upi}(\lambda) = L_\lambda\, \tau(\lambda)$		Total input radiance as a function of wavelength
Compute integrated upwelling radiance, L_{int}	$L_{int} = \sum L_{upi}(\lambda_i - \lambda_{i+1})$	$L_{int} = 3.31$ W/m^2/sr	Evaluate over operating bandwidth
Compute radiated power, L, from a single detector sample at nadir	$L = L_{int} \cdot X \cdot Y/N_{samp}$	$L = 2.7 \times 10^5$ W/sr	Total power from the ground scene that arrives at the instrument
Compute input power, P_{in}, at sensor	$P_{in} = \frac{L}{h^2} \cdot \left(\frac{D}{2}\right)^2 \cdot \pi$	$P_{in} = 5.7 \times 10^{-9}$	P_{in} is power at the entrance to the optics
Define optical transmission factor τ_o	Design parameter	$\tau_0 = 0.80$	Typical value for optical systems
Find input power, P_D, at the detector pixel	$P_D = P_{in} \cdot \tau_0$	$P_D = 4.5 \times 10^{-9}$ W	Very little power arrives at each pixel
Determine available energy, E, after integration time at nadir	$E = P_D \cdot T_i / N_{samp}$	$E = 1.7 \times 10^{-13}$ J	Radiometric design challenge for FireSat II

Table 17-9. Parameter Calculations for a Passive Optical Sensor. (Continued) IRC = Inside Rear cover

Step	Calculation	FireSat II	Comments
E. Estimate Sensor Radiometry (for Nadir Viewing) (Continued)			
Find number of available photons, N_p	$N_P = E\lambda / hc$	$N_P = 9.2 \times 10^6$	*h* is Planck's constant, *c* is speed of light
Define quantum efficiency, QE, of detector at λ	Design parameter	$QE = 0.80$	Typical physical property of detector material
Compute number of photocarriers available, N_e	$N_e = N_p \cdot QE$	$N_e = 7.3 \times 10^6$	Evaluate for an ideal detector
Determine number of noise electrons, N_n	$N_n = \sqrt{N_e}$	$N_n = 2{,}708$	Considers only Shott noise
Determine number of read-out noise electrons, N_r	Design parameter	$N_r = 5{,}000$	Typical value
Determine total number of noise electrons, N_t	$N_t = \sqrt{N_e + N_r}$	$N_t = 2{,}709$	Assumes uncorrelated noise processes
Find signal-to-noise ratio of the image, SNR	$\text{SNR} = N_e / N_t$	SNR = 2,707	Assuming signal dominates background
Determine sensor dynamic range, DR	$DR = N_e / N_r$	$DR = 1{,}467$	With respect to cold space
F. Find the Noise-Equivalent Temperature Difference			
Compute noise-equivalent temperature difference, $NE\Delta T$	$NE\Delta T = \frac{\lambda T^2}{W\,\text{SNR}}\left[1-\exp\left(\frac{W\Delta\lambda}{\lambda^2}\right)\right]$	$NE\Delta T = 0.02$ K	Temperature limit the instrument can resolve $W = 1.4388 \times 10^{-2}$

$$S = \sin^{-1}[\sin(24.8 \text{ deg})\sin(55 \text{ deg})] = 20.1 \text{ deg} \quad (17\text{-}37)$$

The perpendicular separation between the orbits at the equator is 20.1 deg. Because the swath width is 24.2 deg, we now have some overlap margin even at the equator and substantial margin at higher latitudes, which are the primary areas of interest. We could, therefore, increase the minimum elevation angle to 25 deg. This would be a reasonable option. At present, we instead choose to hold ε at 20 deg and to provide some margin on altitude and elevation angle for later payload trades. We next compute the required resolution and data rates for FireSat II. From Table 3-4, we initially estimated the needed ground resolution as 500 m. Thus, the required resolution at nadir, θ_r, from an altitude of 700 km is:

$$\theta_r = 0.500/700 = 7.1 \times 10^{-5} \text{ rad} = 0.041 \text{ deg} \quad (17\text{-}38)$$

However, as shown in Fig. 17-23, the projected IFOV or Ground IFOV (GIFOV) at end of scan for a maximum slant range of 1,580 km grows to about 3.0 km in the cross track direction and 1.1 km in the along track dimension. This growth in GIFOV would cause the sensor to fall a factor of six short of the needed 500 m ground resolution in the worst case direction, and would probably prevent any further development of this system. We could mitigate this effect by designing in zoom optics that would reduce the IFOV with scan angle. However, we seek to develop a reliable, low cost system and introducing a complex zoom optics system would likely increase system cost while also reducing its reliability. A lower cost approach is to increase the format size of the focal plane assembly to sample at a higher spatial frequency to enable better ground resolution at end of scan. For example, increasing the spatial sampling rate by a factor of three in the cross track direction leads to the ground resolution versus nadir angle curve shown in the lower part of Fig. 17-23. In this case, GIFOV grows from 500 m × 500 m at nadir to 1.1 km × 1.1 km at end of scan. The price we pay in system performance for this approach is reduced sensitivity at end of scan. In the 3.8 μm band, NEDT at 300 K for this single +0.041deg^2 IFOV is close to 0.5 K. However, this is a fire detection and mapping system and while it might be useful to have better sensitivity at end of scan at room temperature, we are most interested in performance for fire signatures at temperatures close to 450 K and above. NEDT at 450 K for this system concept is about 0.2 K, which is more than adequate for distinguishing fire from other scene features.

Using this resolution, we can follow the procedure outlined in Table 17-9 to compute the data rate for FireSat II as 8 Mbps. This data rate is relatively high, but well within capabilities of existing technology. Nevertheless, to reduce cost, we should look at ways to reduce the downlink data rate. One approach is to process the data on board or more simply, turn off the imager over the oceans or other areas where fire detection is of limited utility or use well known and well understood data compression techniques such as Rice compression to reduce data rate by roughly a factor of two. For now, we will leave the value as computed, recognizing that this may need to be reduced later in the system design.

We next compute mapping and pointing budgets for FireSat II. We do not have a firm mapping requirement, but we do have some broad sense of what is needed. We begin, therefore, with a rough estimate of performance

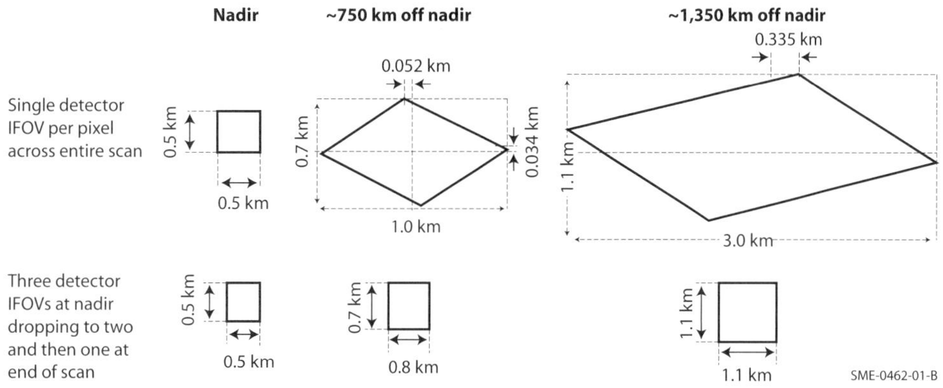

Fig. 17-23. Selected FireSat II Spatial Sampling Approach Results in Much Better Ground Resolution at End of Scan than a Single Detector IFOV per Pixel.

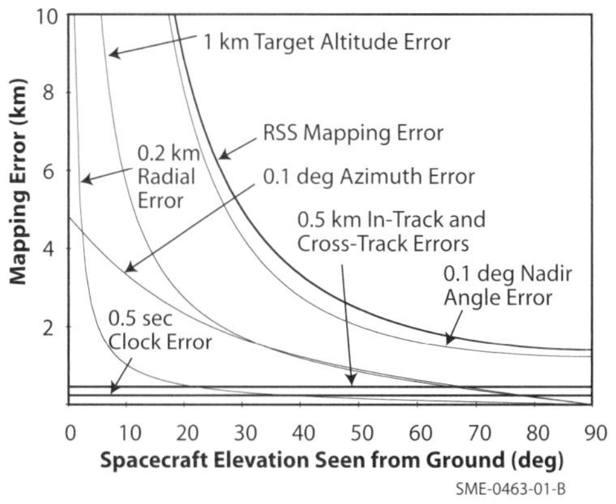

A. 0.1 deg Nadir Angle Error

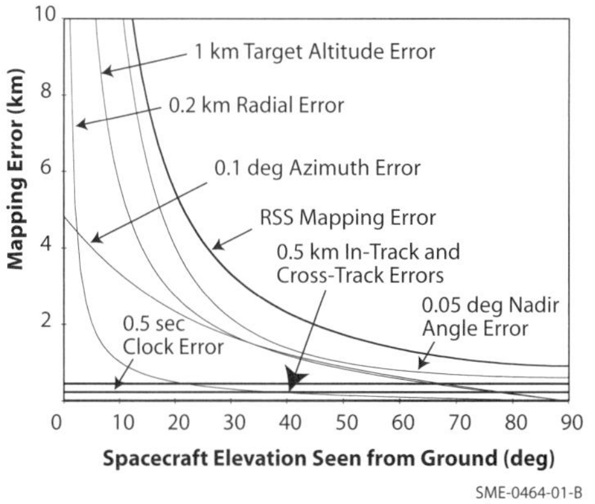

B. 0.05 deg Nadir Angle Error

Fig. 17-24. FireSat II Mapping Budget. Reducing the nadir angle error below 0.05 deg will have relatively little impact on the overall mapping error because of the 1 km target altitude error. Compare with Fig. 8-50.

parameters and create the mapping error as a function of the elevation angle shown in Fig. 17-24. In this figure, we have used a 0.1 deg nadir angle and azimuth errors corresponding to a relatively inexpensive pointing system based on an Earth sensor. We know we can go to a more expensive system if necessary. In looking at Fig. 17-24A, we see that the mapping error at our chosen minimum elevation angle of 20 deg is between 6 and 8 km. While we are not certain what our mapping requirement is, we are reasonably sure that it is smaller than 6 km. We need to locate fires more accurately than this. Note also that the accuracy has been set almost entirely by our crude attitude number of 0.1 deg.

The next most critical parameter is the 1 km error in target altitude. This means that we assume we can determine the altitude of the fire above the Earth to 1 km—a reasonable accuracy with an oblate Earth model. But significantly improving this accuracy would require carrying a map of the altitudes of all of the regions of interest. That could be very difficult, particularly in mountainous areas, and would cost a lot more money. Therefore, it is of little value to drive the error in nadir angle down below approximately 0.05 deg because it would no longer be the dominant error source. Fig. 17-24B shows the curves that we would achieve with the error in nadir angle reduced to 0.05 deg and all of the other error sources remaining the same. Now the contribution of the errors in nadir angle and target altitude are comparable, so we will use this budget to establish a preliminary mapping requirement of 5.5 km at a 20 deg elevation angle, and 3.5 km at a 30 deg elevation angle. This may still be considerably cruder than we would like, so we may need to revisit this issue.

Now that we understand the mission geometry, we evaluate the optical, signal processing, and radiometric performance of the instrument using the process described in Table 17-9. The third column in that table summarizes results of computations for a whiskbroom sensor design for the FireSat II mission.

The example FireSat II design considers only initial feasibility of the instrument. Several challenges remain with this design and additional iterations are required within context of mission requirements and constraints to optimize the instrument design. For example, the computed data rate of 25.5 Mbps will present some design challenge for a very low cost system. A second challenge with the design is the relatively poor SNR for some of the bands at end of scan for lower temperature scenes in the range of 300 K or colder. We're prepared to accept this performance limitation, however, because our mission is to detect fire, not measure sea surface temperature or cloud top temperature with high spatial resolution across a wide swath.

We now select a "similar instrument" from Table 17-7 for our FireSat II example. We appear to have two options: the Planetary Multispectral Visible-Infrared Imager or the Multispectral Mid-IR instrument. We tentatively select the Multispectral Mid-IR as our similar instrument and will scale from its fundamental parameters of 1.4 m × 1.5 m × 0.9 m size, 270 kg weight, and 170 W power, for its 0.18 m aperture. We first compute the aperture ratio, R

$$R = 0.11/0.18 = 0.61 \tag{17-39}$$

The value 0.61 is close enough to 0.5 that we select K to be 2 to reflect our assessment that we are dealing with a significantly scaled down system that requires increased margin. With this fundamental ratio, we now estimate the FireSat II payload parameters as

$$\text{Size} = 0.9 \text{ m} \times 0.9 \text{ m} \times 0.5 \text{ m} \tag{17-40}$$

$$\text{Weight} = 2 \times 270 \times 0.61^3 = 123 \text{ kg} \tag{17-41}$$

$$\text{Power} = 2 \times 170 \times 0.61^3 = 77 \text{ W} \tag{17-42}$$

If we now scale from the Planetary Multispectral Visible-Infrared Imager, we derive a very different estimate for the FireSat II payload parameters. In this case,

$$R = 0.11/0.12 = 0.92 \tag{17-43}$$

We now estimate the FireSat II payload parameters as

$$\text{Size} = 0.50 \text{ m} \times 0.34 \text{ m} \times 0.27 \text{ m} \tag{17-44}$$

$$\text{Weight} = 12.8 \times 1.00^3 = 10.0 \text{ kg} \tag{17-45}$$

$$\text{Power} = 12 \times 1.00^3 = 9.3 \text{ W} \tag{17-46}$$

As described in Sec. 17.2.6, we have incorporated a factor of 2 to provide margin against scaling down the payload size for the Multispectral Mid-IR instrument significantly. The aperture diameter for the planetary instrument is the same as for this FireSat II payload. Therefore, we have not built margin into this scaling calculation.

Clearly, we find that simple scaling laws can give widely divergent estimates for size, mass, and power for concept payloads, depending on the reference payload. To resolve this difference, we need to look in more detail at the closest reference instrument, namely the Planetary Multispectral Visible-Infrared instrument and use a combination of the other methods described in Sec. 17.2.5, analogy with existing systems and budgeting by components to derive a higher confidence estimate.

The planetary instrument, while identical in aperture size with the FireSat II payload, is different at the next level of detail. It has two focal planes, versus the single focal plane for FireSat II. That difference allows us to reduce the dimensions of the instrument by a few centimeters in width and depth. Likewise, the planetary instrument has a long sunshield that is not needed for FireSat II, which further reduces the instrument length by tens of centimeters. However, FireSat II requires a scanner that adds back most of that length. A rough estimate of the scanner size is that it would be a few centimeters shorter than the sunshield so that a small reduction in instrument size is expected. Another difference is FireSat II requires active cooling, which adds to the power and mass of the instrument. Likewise, the higher data rate for the FireSat II instrument adds a substantial amount of power to the nominal instrument description. The size, mass, and power values in Table 17-10 account for all of these differences, based on existing hardware. Thus, as summarized in Table 17-10, our first guess is that the FireSat II payload is a simple, moderately sized instrument that would fit well on a small to medium-sized spacecraft with high data rate capability.

Table 17-10. Space Summary of FireSat II Initial Parameter Estimates.

Parameter	Nominal Value	Comments
Altitude, h	700 km	Range = 600 to 800 km
Inclination, i	55 deg	Coverage to 65 deg latitude
Swath width, $2\lambda_{max}$	24.2 deg	20.1 deg required
Nadir angle range, η	±57.9 deg	
Instrument	mid-range IR scanner	Payload needs expert input
Ground resolution	501 m at nadir (along track)	Key parameter—needs trade study
Instrument resolution	2.714 mrad	0.00409 deg
Aperture, A	0.11 m	
Size	0.48 × 0.22 × 0.18 cm^3	
Weight, W	20 kg	
Power, P	50 W	
Data rate, DR	8 Mbps/sec	May be limiting feature
Mapping	3.5 km @ ε=30 deg 5.5 km @ ε=20 deg	

Our initial analysis of a small, lightweight FireSat II payload shows that the mission is feasible but challenging. Several refinements and iterations on the design have the potential to improve the viability and cost-effectiveness of the payload concept. To illustrate the end point of a more complete and detailed design process, in Sec. 17.3, we turn our attention to VIIRS, a large instrument and a mature design with a fire detection mission among many other missions.

17.2.9 Life-cycle Cost and Operability of the Payload

Spacecraft designs are heavily driven by the need to minimize cost, while simultaneously meeting an acceptable level of performance. Over the years, a number of approaches have been proposed and implemented to treat cost as an independent variable. For systems where cost and performance may be traded, it is no longer sufficient to simply state mission requirements clearly and realistically. Rather, mission requirements may now become involved in the iterative process of design

Table 17-11. Impact of Remote Sensing Payloads on the Spacecraft Design.

Impact Area	Typical Requirements to Support Payload	Additional Considerations
Structure	Mount the optical instruments isostatically to the spacecraft bus Do not apply excessive forces or torques to the payload instrument Make the mounting structure or base plate for optical components stiff enough to prevent any misalignment when subjected to the forces and vibrations of launch	Carefully analyze aging of material (e.g., stress release in metal parts), humidity release, transition to microgravity, and acceleration forces Typical stability requirements at critical locations within the optical instrument housing are in the μm and mdeg range
Thermal	Make large opto-mechanical assemblies temperature stabilized or isothermal Operate refractive optical systems typically within a specific temperature range to achieve required performance (frequently they employ semi-active temperature control) Make reflective systems entirely from the same material which leads to a compensation of thermal effects (typically done for cryogenic optical systems)	Large reflective systems (which use Zerodur, Aluminum, or Beryllium or newly developed materials such as SiC or CsiC as materials for the mirrors) and mounting structures (which use composite materials) are temperature sensitive and may require semi-active temperature control of structure and mirrors Temperature gradients in optical components can severely degrade performance
External Alignment	Align the optical axis of the instrument and the line of sight of the pointing device with an external reference on the spacecraft. External alignments may need to be on the order of 1 arc sec	User reference cubes to achieve alignment External alignment requires a calibrated optical bench
Pointing	For monocular optical instruments, make the pointing requirements on the order of 0.1 to 0.01 of the swath width, typically For stereoscopic instruments, automated digital terrain mapping requires pointing knowledge of 1/5 of a pixel	Mount attitude determination sensors (e.g., star sensors) to the instrument (not the bus) to minimize the effects of thermoelasticity Do pointing by maneuvering the spacecraft or by pointing devices (such as pointing mirrors for the front of the instrument or gimbals for the entire instrument)
Assembly Integration and Verification	Optical instruments require clean rooms and clean laminar air flow benches for all integration and verification activities Clean room requirements typically range from 100 to 100,000 ppm	Cleaning optical surfaces is generally not possible During exposure to the environment, use cleanliness samples to verify the level of contamination
System Accommodation	Sensor must have an unobstructed field-of-view Sensor must have a guard cone to prevent performance degradation due to stray light Avoid pointing toward the Sun	Orient radiators and passive coolers for infrared systems to prevent interference with optical devices Calibration devices impose geometric constraints with respect to the optics of the system and the orbit

[Fleeter, 2000]. Several excellent examples of how to include cost as a system parameter rather than a given are described by Shishko, et al. [1996].

Working through trade-offs associated with cost, performance, and requirements in early stages of payload definition keeps payload designers focused on the best sensor characteristics to maximize mission performance and minimize cost. Designers sometimes want to perform a purely analytical evaluation of the costs and benefits of various design options. Unfortunately, relative benefits of different design features are difficult if not impossible to quantify in a clear and universally accepted way. Well understood and clearly stated analysis methods can be useful for providing a common framework for evaluating different designs. Ultimately, however, judgments about meeting mission goals within cost and schedule limitations rely on the insight of experienced designers and other analysts, adding to the challenges and significance of this portion of the payload definition process.

After we establish the final payload type and basic payload performance requirements, final design of the payload can begin. The final payload design could be as simple as an evaluation of existing payloads that are available or it could involve detailed design, fabrication, and testing of an entirely new instrument. The final step in the payload definition and sizing process is the decision by the responsible organization to buy or build the payload.

Integrating a payload into a spacecraft introduces a number of practical considerations for the spacecraft and other payload subsystems. These derived requirements can have a significant impact on other parts of the spacecraft. Table 17-11 contains an overview of some of the spacecraft accommodation considerations for a payload. Resolving the impact of these requirements on the spacecraft and other parts of the payload means we must assess the performance, cost, and technical risk for each subsystem to accommodate the payload.

17.3 Sample Mission—VIIRS

Spaceflight instruments that can automatically detect fires already exist. The remarkably versatile MODIS (Moderate-resolution Imaging Spectroradiometer), has been flying on board NASA Earth Observing System satellites since 1999. MODIS has provided an abundance of data in support of scientific investigations into Earth's atmosphere, oceans and land use that goes well beyond

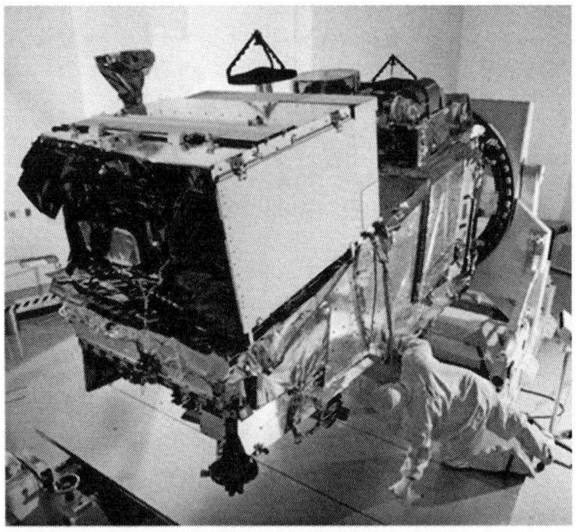

Fig. 17-25. Photograph of FU1 Integrated onto the NPP Spacecraft at Ball Aerospace. (Photo courtesy of Ball Aerospace)

fundamental needs for the FireSat II mission. MODIS is being replaced by the Visible/Infrared Imager Radiometer Suite (VIIRS), the next-generation imaging spectroradiometer for the NOAA/NASA Joint Polar Satellite System (JPSS) and the US Department of Defense Weather Satellite System (DWSS). VIIRS, described in Fig. 17-25, replaces and improves upon three different operational and research sensors with a single instrument. These three sensors are the MODIS, the Advanced Very High Resolution Radiometer (AVHRR) operating on board NOAA POES and EUMETSAT Polar System Metop since 1978 and the Operational Line Scanner (OLS) on board DMSP since 1976.

VIIRS is a whiskbroom scanner that monitors Earth from a 833 km polar Sun-synchronous orbits at visible-infrared wavelengths (0.4–12 μm) and provides well calibrated moderate (~km) spatial resolution measurements of light upwelling from Earth in support of a large number of high priority applications ranging from weather prediction for civilian and military needs to climate change monitoring, land usage, public health alerts and predictions of electrical power usage. Figure 17-26 shows that VIIRS offers significant improvements over the systems it replaces by providing 22 spectral bands with 4 times better spectral coverage than AVHRR, thereby enabling new agricultural, climate, disaster monitoring, public health and weather data products, 3 times better spatial resolution than AVHRR and MODIS at end of scan enabling sharper imagery over a much greater area and a fully calibrated Day/Night Band (DNB) that improves nighttime weather forecasting and military applications compared with OLS. VIIRS benefits from substantial US R&D investment in MODIS and other NASA Earth observing systems that led to a wide range of new environmental data products, including fire products, from well characterized instruments in polar sun synchronous orbits.

A key to the VIIRS architecture shown in Fig. 17-27 is a rotating telescope assembly that enables a flexible design needed to meet a remarkably diverse set of requirements for multispectral imaging spectroradiometry and low light level day/night imaging. Advantages of the rotating telescope design relative to scan mirror based systems like AVHRR and MODIS include better control of straylight, smaller range in angle of incidence of light on the fore optics to reduce striping and polarization sensitivity and better protection from contamination and degradation over time because all of the optical elements are placed deep inside the instrument housing,

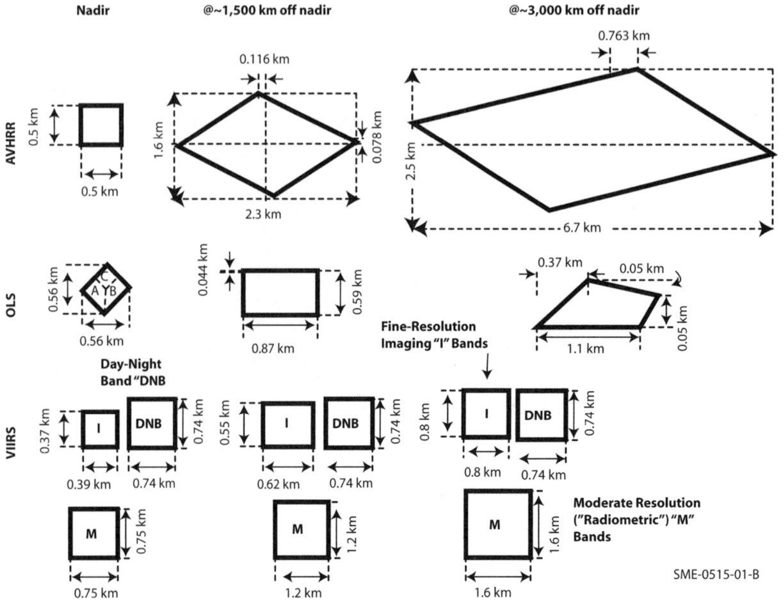

Fig. 17-26. VIIRS Spatial Sampling Approach Compared with the Legacy AVHRR and OLS Sensors. (Graphic courtesy of NASA)

Table 17-11◀, Fig. 17-26, Eq. 17-46◀

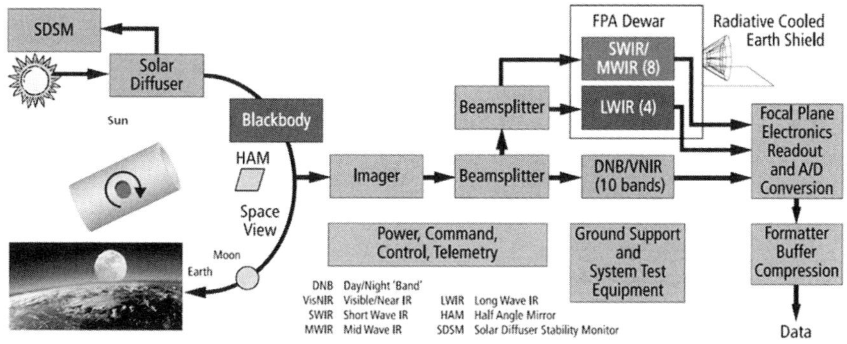

Fig. 17-27. VIIRS Design Architecture.

Many challenges were overcome in design and fabrication of the rotating telescope assembly to produce a well understood high performance subsystem. Significant US investment in the VIIRS architecture has resulted in an excellent imager that is ready to provide high fidelity data for the international science, weather and other environmental data product communities with unprecedented spatial resolution at end of scan.

The VIIRS fire detection algorithm is derived from the MODIS algorithm described by Kaufman and Justice [1998] and Giglio, et al. [2003]. The algorithm uses calibrated and geolocated data from five VIIRS spectral bands: M5 (0.672 μm), M7 (0.865 μm), M11 (2.25 μm), M13 (4.05 μm), M15 (10.763 μm), M16 (12.013 μm). In addition, the algorithm makes use of solar zenith and azimuth angles along with a global database describing whether a pixel is land, water or sometimes water. The algorithm follows these steps.

Identify potential fire pixels. The algorithm prescreens pixels by selecting only those clear sky pixels on land that have valid measurements. Then, the algorithm selects potential fire pixels by identifying pixels with spectral characteristics consistent with fire, based on temperature thresholds and differences in apparent brightness temperature between bands.

Generate statistics on pixel characteristics near potential fire pixels and separate potential fire pixels from the background. In this part of the process, the algorithm uses neighboring pixels to estimate the radiometric signal of a potential fire pixel in the absence of fire. Then, a series of threshold tests are used to perform relative fire detection. These tests look for the characteristic signature of an active fire in which both the M13 brightness and the M13 and M15 brightness temperature difference depart substantially from that of the non-fire background.

Make tentative fire detection based on absolute brightness temperature in M13. If the M13 brightness temperature is greater than 320 K at night, then fire detection is confirmed. During the day, the M13 brightness temperature in a pixel must be greater than 360 K for tentative fire detection.

Reject false alarms. Tentative fire detections made during the day are susceptible to false alarms because brightness temperature measurement can be contaminated with sunglint and other false signals resulting from background characterization errors in regions with abrupt boundaries between land and water or along the boundaries of deserts. These false alarms can be rejected with good reliability by using information derived from the solar reflective M5, M7 and M11 bands.

Export fire pixel locations with quality control information.

The VIIRS sensor and algorithm system illustrates many of the features of an automated fire detection system. In the context of the FireSat II mission, this example provides a point design with finalized tradeoffs in size, mass, power, resolution, and data processing that has already been built and tested.

17.4 The Evolution of Observation Payloads

In less than 60 years, space-based observation payloads have evolved from simple 35-mm film movie cameras on board converted World War II missiles providing imagery for just a few minutes to aggregations of widely different instruments covering much of the electromagnetic spectrum simultaneously from Earth orbit for more than 10 years. The very first space-based observation payload flew on board a German V-2 rocket captured by the United States near the end of World War II. This rocket was launched from White Sands Missile Range on October 24, 1946 and produced the image shown in Fig. 17-28. Clyde Holliday from Johns Hopkins University/Applied Physics Laboratory, developer of this first space-based imager, wrote: "Results of these tests now are pointing to a time when cameras may be mounted on guided missiles for scouting enemy territory in war, mapping inaccessible regions of the earth in peacetime, and even photographing cloud formations, storm fronts, and overcast areas over an entire continent in a few hours…the entire land area of the globe might be mapped in this way" [Holliday and Hamilton, 1950]. See the book website for a more extended discussion of how these payloads have evolved.

As new observational payloads are developed with ever increasing data collection rates, the driving technology for these systems is expected to shift from focal

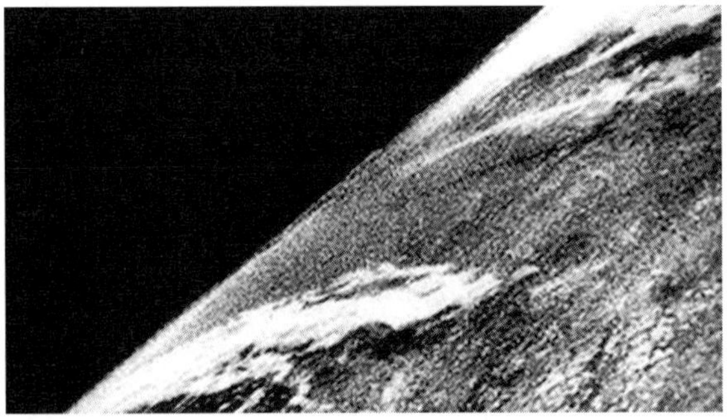

Fig. 17-28. The First Observational Payload to Collect Images from Space (>100 km alt.). Did So Using a V-2 Rocket Launched from White Sands Missile Range on October 24, 1946.

plane technology for visible-infrared systems toward on board and ground processing to handle the vast amounts of data generated by ever more capable systems. Future systems based on distributed architectures that are refreshed routinely may be able to keep pace with availability of improved technology better than today's systems which are refreshed on decade time scales.

Space-based observation systems are most valuable when they're effective, ubiquitous, affordable, reliable, flexible and rapidly replaceable. Readers should not confuse low system cost with low performance. The original Iridium system proved that it is possible to achieve both low cost and unprecedented performance. Unfortunately, the failure of the original Iridium business model prevented this production approach from being sustained in near term upgrades and in the building of similar expected systems. Any future observation system must meet its operational or research performance requirements. For instance, regardless of satellite constellation, space imagers must meet operational performance requirements for parameters such as spatial resolution, spectral coverage, area coverage rate, sensitivity and geolocation. Likewise, systems in any architecture must meet system level hardness, reliability and operational lifetime needed to fulfill customer mission needs. System-level trade studies early in program development need to be broadened to consider alternative system architectures that might be built at lower overall cost using highly engineered and reliable systems designed for affordable, efficient manufacturing and operationally effective performance and built using well understood and continuously improving processes. These early studies would trade satellite design life, technology improvement schedule, constellation refresh rate, survivability, and cost within context of firm system performance parameters.

References

Get Ref **For annotated bibliography of observation payloads, see the book website.**

Cantafio, Leonard J. 1989. *Space-Based Radar Handbook.* Norwood, MA: Artech House, Inc.

Davis, Gary. 2007. Report to the 35th Meeting of the CGMS. Darmstadt, Germany. Nov. 5–9.

de Weck, Olivier, et al. 2003. "Technical Success and Economic Failure." MIT Industry Systems Study. ESLC. Unit 1, version 1. Massachusetts Institute of Technology, MA.

Fleeter, Rick. 2000. *The Logic of Microspace.* El Segundo, CA: Microcosm Press and Kluwer Academic Publishers.

Giglio, L., Descloitres, J., Justice, C.O., Kaufman, Y. 2003. "An Enhanced Contextual Fire Detection Algorithm for MODIS." *Remote Sensing of Environment.* 87:273-282.

Holliday, Clyde and A. Hamilton. 1950. Micrometer. US Patent #2521917.

Johnson, Torrence. 2008. COSPAR Scientific Structure. Website.

Kaufman, Y. J. and C. O. Justice, et al. 1998. "Potential Global Fire Monitoring from EOS-MODIS." *Journal of Geophysical Research-Atmospheres, 103(D24), 32215-32238.*

Kramer, Herbert J. 2001. *Observation of the Earth and the Environment.* New York, NY: Springer-Verlag.

Minsky, Marvin. 1990. Semantic Information Processing. MIT Press.

Nischan, Melissa L., Rose M. Joseph, Justin C. Libby, and John P. Kerekes 2003. Active Spectral Imaging. SPIE Proceedings.

Raney, R. K. 1998. "Radar Fundamentals: Technical Perspective, Principles and Applications of Imaging Radar." *Manual of Remote Sensing,* vol. 2. pp. 9–130.

Reichhardt, Tony. 2008. "Satellite Smashers." *Air and Space Magazine*. Mar. 1.

Rogers, Everett. 1986. *Communication Technology.* Tampa, FL: Free Press Publishing.

Schott. 2007. Optical Glass. Description of Properties and Information. Website.

Schowengerdt, Robert. 2006. *Remote Sensing: Models and Methods for Image Processing, 3rd ed.* Burlington, MA: Elsevier/Academic Press.

Sharkov, Eugene. 2003. *Passive Microwave Remote Sensing of the Earth.* New York, NY: Springer.

Shishko, R. and E. J. Jorgensen. 1996. "Design-to-Cost for Space Missions" in Wertz and Larson, Reducing Space Mission Costs. Torrance, CA: Microcosm Press and Kluwer Academic Publishers.

Sladen, Rod. 2008. "Iridium 28 Replacement by Iridium 95." Website.

Slater, Phillip. 1980. *Spectroradiometric Considerations for Advanced Land Observing Systems.* NASA Report via University of Arizona Grant. Tempe, AZ.

Space. 2009. Website.

Taverney, Thomas. 2011. "An Answer to Affordability of Space Systems." *Space News*. Jan 31. pp 19–20.

Werninghouse, R. and S. Bukreuss. 2010. "Transactions on Geoscience and Remote Sensing." *IEEE*, vol. 48. pp. 606–614.

18 Spacecraft Subsystems I—Propulsion

Ivett A. Leyva, *Air Force Research Laboratory*

This chapter starts with a review of the basic rocket performance parameters, the rocket equation and staging. Different classes of chemical rockets used for space propulsion are then examined in Sec. 18.3. A brief description of plumes is given in Sec. 18.4. Section 18.5 guides the reader on how to size common components for a conventional chemical propulsion system. Electric propulsion and other potential new systems are presented in Secs. 18.6. and 18.7. Section 18.8 concludes with two examples of preliminary designs for a propulsion system. Commonly used references in the field of rocket propulsion are: Sutton and Biblarz [2010], Turner [2009], Hill and Peterson [1992], Jahn [1968], Micci and Ketsdever [2000], Brown [1996, 2002], and Humble, et al. [1995].

The first task of a propulsion system is to propel a spacecraft from the Earth's surface to an initial or parking orbit using one of the launch vehicles discussed in Chap. 26. Depending on the desired final orbit, an onboard propulsion system or an upper stage might be needed to provide the final boost. Chapters 9 and 10 offer a detailed description of orbits. As the spacecraft performs its mission, when its orbit needs to be closely controlled, an on-board propulsion system also accomplishes orbit maintenance (Chap. 9), de-orbit (Chap. 30) and re-entry operations. Beside translational movements, rotational movements are needed as well to keep a satellite pointing in the right direction. This is achieved through what is called attitude control (Sec. 19.1). An on-board propulsion system can either perform attitude control maneuvers, or it can be used to unload momentum from on board equipment, such as reaction wheels.

Propulsion systems distinguish themselves by their energy source and how they produce thrust. With the exception of a few cases, the propulsion systems discussed in this chapter produce thrust by accelerating and ejecting a fluid through a converging-diverging nozzle. The oldest and most common type of propulsion system is a *chemical rocket* in which propellants combust, producing high temperature products that are then expanded through a nozzle. The historic rockets that propelled the Apollo missions, those most commonly used on launch vehicles and missiles, and even the rockets that the Chinese used nearly 1,000 years ago all fall under this category. Other types of propulsion systems are nuclear and solar. In *nuclear rockets,* propellants are heated through nuclear fission of certain materials like uranium. In *solar propulsion,* energy from the Sun is collected and used to produce thrust. Some designs use solar energy directly to heat a propellant which can then be expanded through a nozzle to produce thrust. Alternatively, in solar sails, discussed in Sec. 18.7, the pressure from solar photon bombardment pushes against a sail to produce low levels of thrust. In *electric propulsion*, discussed in detail in Sec. 18.6, solar or nuclear energy is converted to electrical energy to either heat and then accelerate a propellant, or directly accelerate a propellant through electric and magnetic body forces. Finally, missions with minimal propulsive needs can use a *cold gas thruster*, where a non-reacting high-pressure gas is accelerated through a nozzle. Because of their similarities with chemical propulsion systems, cold gas thrusters are presented in Sec. 18.3.

Table 18-1. Propulsion Subsystem Selection and Sizing Process.

Step	References
1. Determine All the Functions the Propulsion System Must Accomplish Such As • Orbit insertion • Orbit maintenance • Attitude control • Controlled de-orbit or re-entry • Establish the life expectancy of the mission.	Table 18-2
2. Determine the Required ΔV and Thrust for Orbit Insertion and Orbit Maintenance	Table 18-2, Secs. 18.1, 14.2, 14.5
3. Determine the Required Total Impulse, Thrust Level for Control Authority, and Duty Cycles for Attitude Control	Table 18-2
4. List Propulsion System Options • Chemical (solid, liquid [monopropellant, bipropellant], hybrid, cold gas) vs. electric propulsion or other. • Single or separate propulsion systems for orbit maintenance and attitude control (if needed)	Secs. 18.3, 18.6, Table 18-3
5. Estimate Key Parameters for Each Option (some will be quantitative as below but others might be qualitative, consider both)	
• I_{sp}	Sec. 18.1
• Thrust	Sec. 18.1
• Total mass (including propellant mass)	Sec. 14.5, Table 10-7
• Power requirements	Sec. 14.5.3
• System volume including tankage, thrust chamber, feedlines, valves	Sec. 18.5
• "ilities" such as reliability (if system has been tried before, what has been the success rate), manufacturability, storability, scalability, vulnerability	
• Cost, schedule, acceptable risk for program	
• Toxicity of propellants and character of plume (especially if it can interact with critical instruments or parts of the spacecraft and generate inadvertent torque)	Sec. 18.4
6. Conduct Trade Studies • Choose a baseline propulsion system • Document trade results and the reasons for those results. Iterate the process as necessary	Sec. 5.3

In designing a propulsion system, the first step is to determine the objectives of the mission. Is it an interplanetary mission? Is the spacecraft to be placed in LEO or GEO? How long will the spacecraft be functional? What are the top level constraints on cost, schedule, and what is the risk allowed to try a new propulsion technology? Are there any political angles to the mission that need to be taken into consideration? For example, are international partners available? Does the nature of the payload bias the choice for a propulsion system? For example, having very sensitive instruments might put a constraint on what kind of exhaust you can have from a propulsion system. The orbit of the spacecraft needs to be determined at this stage as well.

Designing a propulsion system is, by nature, a multidisciplinary effort. Once the top-level objectives for the mission are set, the lower level requirements for the propulsion system can be addressed. For a detailed discussion of this process see Humble, et al. [1995]. Table 18-1 lists a series of considerations for determining the propulsion system for a given mission. In Step 1, list all the functions the propulsion system will have to fulfill for the duration of the mission, i.e., from orbit insertion to de-orbit. In Steps 2 and 3, get quantitative details on performance requirements like ΔV, thrust, and total impulse needed from the propulsion system. In Step 4, list the available propulsion systems to meet the above requirements. Don't try to select a system at this point, just list the available options. In Step 5, list all the quantifiable figures of merit for the propulsion system, such as thrust, I_{sp}, propellant mass, propellant mass fraction, and volume. Qualitative factors also have a big play on ranking different propulsion systems. For example, a system which has been successfully used before and can meet the requirements could directly provide a design solution. Also, if the people in the team have experience with a particular rocket type, this might play into the decision of which one to choose. In Step 6, reach consensus with the team on what factors matter the most. Once the weight factors are determined for each quantitative requirement, proceed to rank the different options and choose a baseline. Document your decisions and how you arrived to them. More often than not as the design matures, the requirements change necessitates reconsideration of the choices for propulsion systems. Keep flexibility in mind and be prepared for the design to change over time.

18.1 Basic Rocket Equations

The thrust of rocket engines is most often measured in stationary thrust stands. *Load cells* are typically used to measure the force that the engine imparts on the supporting structure. Note that we can measure thrust without much knowledge of how it is produced. Following the analysis of Hill and Peterson [1992], we use a control volume (CV) to understand the relationship between thrust and flow conditions (Fig. 18-1). In this case, the CV encloses the rocket and cuts through the structure holding it in place. By inspection, we can see that the rocket does not produce forces in the y-direction, so we are only interested in the forces in the x-direction.

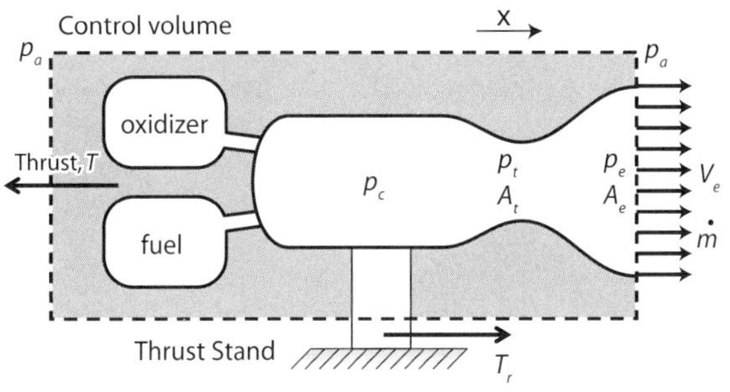

Fig. 18-1. Control Volume Depicting Thrust Developed in a Rocket.

Applying Newton's second law in the x-direction results in

$$\sum F_x = \frac{d}{dt}\int_{CV} \rho V_x \, dVOL + \int_{CS} \rho V_x^2 \, dA \tag{18-1}$$

where ρ is the density and V_x is the x-velocity of the fluid in the control volume. The first term on the right hand side is the time rate of change of the integral of the momentum per unit volume over the control volume (CV). The second term is the flux of momentum through the control surface (CS). The left side of the equation represents the sum of forces, F_x, acting **on** the control volume in the x-direction. These are the pressure forces and the force from the support on the control volume *(T_r)*, which has the same magnitude as the thrust but opposite direction (Newton's 3rd law). Let's assume T_r is in the positive x-direction since the support has to exert a force to the right to counteract the rocket thrust.

Evaluating the terms on the left and right hand sides of Eq. (18-1) and for the case of steady operation, we have,

$$T_r + p_a A_e - p_e A_e = \dot{m} V_e \tag{18-2}$$

$$T_r = \dot{m} V_e + A_e (p_e - p_a) \tag{18-3}$$

(T_r acts in the positive x-direction)

where A_e is the exit area of the rocket nozzle, $\dot{m}$ is the *mass flow rate* being expelled through the nozzle (mass the rocket is losing per unit time), p_e and p_a are the nozzle exit plane and ambient pressures respectively, and V_e is the nozzle exhaust velocity. Since $\dot{m} V_e$ is positive and dominates over the second term for practical operating conditions, the reaction force T_r will be in the positive x-direction.

The thrust, T, and the reaction force T_r have the same magnitude but act in opposite directions as required by Newton's 3rd law. The resulting expression for thrust is then:

$$T = \dot{m} V_e + A_e (p_e - p_a) \tag{18-4}$$

(T acts in the negative x-direction)

Examining Eq. (18-4) we see from the first term that thrust depends on how much mass you eject from the engine and the velocity it attains as it leaves the nozzle. The second term represents a mismatch between the nozzle exit plane and the ambient pressures. As the rocket travels through the atmosphere and p_a changes, this force changes and it can add to or subtract from the thrust. For upper stage engines and in-space propulsion systems, p_a is close to or practically zero.

To increase thrust, we could increase V_e by using a larger nozzle exit area, A_e, while keeping the same chamber temperature and pressure, chemical composition, and throat area, A_t. However, this would result in a lower p_e, which could have adverse effects if p_e drops below p_a. This is why large area ratios (A_e / A_t) are preferred in upper stage engines where the rocket is fired at very low values of atmospheric pressure or at vacuum. However, we must make a trade-off between the extra thrust produced and the additional weight and length of a larger nozzle.

For a fixed area ratio and mass flow rate, we can increase V_e and thrust by increasing the chamber temperature and pressure, which can be accomplished by changing the fuel/oxidizer mixture ratio or the propellants used. Increasing the chamber temperature would require more cooling (which degrades performance) or more expensive materials. Increasing the chamber pressure would require thicker (heavier) walls. Finally, we can augment thrust by increasing $\dot{m}$, for example by using a bigger throat area. However, this would imply a shorter burn time for a given amount of propellants or larger and heavier tanks to carry more propellant.

If we divide the thrust from Eq. (18-4) by the mass flow rate exhausting from the nozzle, we obtain the *equivalent or effective exhaust velocity,* which is a measure of how efficiently the engine produces thrust. Some authors denote this velocity as c.

$$V_{eq} = \frac{T}{\dot{m}} = V_e + \left(\frac{p_e - p_a}{\dot{m}}\right) A_e \qquad (18\text{-}5)$$

Note that when p_e equals p_a, V_e equals V_{eq}.

A relatively easy way to measure the performance of a rocket in a static stand is by measuring c^*, (pronounced c star) which is the *characteristic exhaust velocity,*

$$c^* = \frac{p_c A_t}{\dot{m}} \qquad (18\text{-}6)$$

where p_c is the chamber pressure and A_t is the throat area. This is a measure of the efficiency of the combustion. Note that it is independent of the nozzle design. Values for c^* range from 1333 m/s for hydrazine (N_2H_4), 1640 m/s for hypergolic systems of nitrogen tetroxide (N_2O_4) and monomethylhydrazine (MMH), and up to 2360 m/s for liquid oxygen (LOX)-liquid hydrogen (LH_2) systems. Experimental results, though, are usually given in terms of c^* efficiency against the theoretical values computed from thermochemistry. Efficiency values (c^*_{exper}/c^*_{theor}) are usually in the range of 90–98%.

Rocket Equation and Specific Impulse. To derive the famous rocket equation, let's start with a free body diagram (Fig. 18-2) showing the forces acting on a rocket as it flies through the atmosphere. T is the thrust produced by the rocket (assumed to act along the longitudinal axis of the vehicle); V is the velocity of the rocket; D is the drag force, which is opposite to the direction of flight; L is the lift force, which is perpendicular to the direction of flight; Mg is the weight of the rocket; V_e is the velocity of the exhaust from the rocket nozzle, and $\dot{m}$ is the mass ejected through the nozzle per unit time. Please note that due to gravity and the aerodynamic forces (D and L), the direction of flight, γ, does not coincide with the direction of thrust, θ. Also note that to keep accelerating upward, the thrust produced by the rocket has to overcome both the drag and the weight of the vehicle. In practice, at launch we want the thrust-to-weight ratio, T/Mg, to be on the order of 1.3 to have acceptable accelerations.

For convenience of analysis, let's apply Newton's 2nd law in the direction of flight (γ),

$$\sum F_\gamma = M\frac{dV}{dt} = T\cos(\theta - \gamma) - D - Mg\sin\gamma \qquad (18\text{-}7)$$

As time passes, the terms in Eq. (18-7) change (e.g., the mass of the rocket, M, decreases as a function of time, winds affect the aerodynamic forces), and the direction of flight can change as well. If the direction of flight changes, it means our x_γ-y_γ coordinate system has

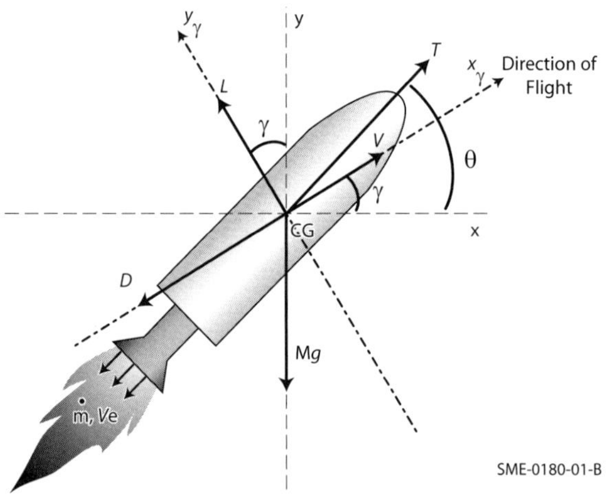

Fig. 18-2. Forces Acting on a Rocket as it Flies.

rotated with respect to the fixed x-y coordinate system. Remember, by definition we are choosing x_γ to be aligned with the direction of flight. Thus, accounting for the possible rotation of the axes, the acceleration in the direction perpendicular to flight is given by

$$\sum F_{\perp\gamma} = MV\frac{d\gamma}{dt} = T\sin(\theta - \gamma) + L - Mg\cos\gamma \qquad (18\text{-}8)$$

To calculate the velocity attained by a rocket after a certain time, we integrate Eq. (18-7), from an initial time, t_o, to a final time, t_f:

$$\frac{dV}{dt} = \frac{T}{M} - \frac{T}{M}[1 - \cos(\theta - \gamma)] - \frac{D}{M} - g\sin\gamma \qquad (18\text{-}9)$$

$$\int_{Vo}^{Vf} dV = \int_{t_o}^{t_f} \frac{T}{M}dt - \int_{t_o}^{t_f} \frac{T}{M}[1 - \cos(\theta - \gamma)]dt$$
$$- \int_{t_o}^{t_f} \frac{D}{M}dt - \int_{t_o}^{t_f} g\sin\gamma dt \qquad (18\text{-}10)$$

$$\Delta V = \Delta V_{prop} - \Delta V_{steering} - \Delta V_{drag} - \Delta V_{gravity} \qquad (18\text{-}11)$$

Equation 18-11 shows how the drag, weight, and the fact that the thrust is not in the direction of flight, subtract from the thrust force produced by the rocket. The combined losses due to gravity and drag are about 1,300–1,700 m/s for LEO.

If we substitute the expression for V_{eq} from Eq. (18-5) into Eq. (18-10) realizing that $\dot{m} = -dM/dt$ and neglecting drag and gravity (resulting in $\theta = \gamma$), we obtain

$$\Delta V = \int_{t_o}^{t_f} \frac{T}{M}dt = V_{eq}\int_{t_o}^{t_f} \frac{\dot{m}}{M}dt = -V_{eq}\int_{M_o}^{M_f} \frac{dM}{M} \qquad (18\text{-}12)$$

$$\Delta V = -V_{eq} \ln\left(\frac{M_f}{M_o}\right) = V_{eq} \ln\left(\frac{M_o}{M_f}\right) \quad (18\text{-}13)$$
$$= V_{eq} \ln\left(\frac{M_o}{M_o - M_p}\right)$$

Eq. (18-13) is the *ideal rocket equation* first introduced by Russian schoolteacher Konstantin Tsiolkovsky (1857–1935) in 1903, where M_o is the initial mass, M_f is the mass after the burnout time, and M_p is the propellant mass defined as,

$$M_p = M_o - M_f \quad (18\text{-}14)$$

The *mass ratio* has been defined by different authors as either M_f/M_o or M_o/M_f.

For solid rocket motors in particular, the *total impulse*, I, is an important performance parameter defined as the integral of thrust, T, over the burn time, t,

$$I = \int_0^t T(t)dt \quad (18\text{-}15)$$

This quantity is proportional to the energy provided by the propulsion system. If the thrust is constant over the burn time, the total impulse is simply the product of the thrust times the burn time.

The *specific impulse*, is usually defined as the total impulse normalized by the weight of the propellants. For constant thrust and uniform propellant mass flow rate, the specific impulse reduces to

$$I_{sp} = \frac{T}{\dot{m} g_o} = \frac{V_{eq}}{g_o} \quad (18\text{-}16)$$

where T is the thrust, $\dot{m}$ is the mass flow rate, and g_0 is the gravitational constant at the Earth's surface, 9.80665 m/s^2, which gives a value of I_{sp} expressed in seconds in SI units. The expression in terms of V_{eq} comes from using Eq. (18-5). The use of the constant g_0 is in fact arbitrary, depending on whether the total impulse is normalized by the mass or the weight of the propellants. It can be thought of as a conversion factor and does not change where the gravitational acceleration is different. If omitted, I_{sp} is expressed in m/s and becomes the effective exhaust velocity of Eq. (18-5). Whether one uses g_0 or not to compute I_{sp} has been a matter of confusion in the rocket community, so keep good track of units when dealing with I_{sp} values.

Specific impulse is a measure of how efficiently we produce thrust. In a sense, it is similar to the specific fuel consumption for a gas turbine or miles per gallon for a car. Analyzing the expression for I_{sp} in Eq. (18-16) we can see that higher values of I_{sp} reduce the propellant rate needed to achieve a given thrust magnitude. For launch propulsion systems, thrust is more important than I_{sp} because we must have enough force to get off the ground and through the atmosphere. For upper stage engines and in-space propulsion, I_{sp} is more important because the weight has been significantly reduced and we want to minimize the propellant carried.

A simplified relationship between specific impulse, I_{sp}, chamber temperature, T_c, and exhaust species molecular weight, MW, is given by,

$$I_{sp} = \sqrt{\frac{R_u T_c}{MW}\frac{2k}{k-1}\left[1-\left(\frac{p_e}{p_c}\right)^{\frac{k-1}{k}}\right]} + \frac{p_e - p_a}{p_c} c^* \varepsilon \quad (18\text{-}17)$$

where k is the ratio of the specific heats, c_p/c_v (assumed constant for reactants and products). Usually this ratio is denoted by γ but to avoid confusion with γ from Eqs. (18-7) to (18-10), it is denoted k in this formula. R_u is the universal gas constant (8.314472 J/mol K), p_e is the nozzle exhaust pressure, p_c is the combustion chamber pressure, p_a is the ambient pressure, ε is the nozzle area expansion ratio; namely the nozzle exit area divided by the throat area, A_e/A_t, and c^* is the characteristic exhaust velocity defined in Eq. (18-6). From this expression we see why it is preferred to have exhaust gases with low molecular weight such as the water vapor or unburned hydrogen produced from H_2 and O_2. Also, we see why a higher chamber temperature results in a higher specific impulse.

Substituting Eq. (18-16) into the ideal rocket Eq. (18-13) we obtain an expression in terms of I_{sp},

$$\Delta V = I_{sp} g_o \ln\left(\frac{M_o}{M_f}\right) \quad (18\text{-}18)$$

where we can see that ΔV is linear with I_{sp} so any improvements on the specific impulse will have a big effect on ΔV. Because the rocket equation is so widely used, the following alternate forms in terms of the propellant mass can be very useful for preliminary design calculations as we will see in the examples at the end of this chapter.

$$M_p = M_f\left(e^{\Delta V/V_{eq}} - 1\right) = M_f\left[e^{\Delta V/\left(I_{sp} g_o\right)} - 1\right] \quad (18\text{-}19)$$

$$M_p = M_o\left(1 - e^{-\Delta V/V_{eq}}\right) = M_o\left[1 - e^{-\Delta V/\left(I_{sp} g_o\right)}\right] \quad (18\text{-}20)$$

Figure 18-3 shows the effect of I_{sp} on ΔV as a function of M_p/M_f. For launch vehicles, this ratio approaches 5–10, but for in-space propulsion, it ranges from 0.2 to 1, showing how hard it is to achieve the required ΔV to at least reach LEO (~9.5 km/s with losses). In ascending order, the values of I_{sp} selected are representative of cold gas thrusters, monopropellant, solid and high performing liquid rockets, as we will see later. We can see that the higher the I_{sp} the higher the ΔV achieved for a given M_p/M_f. Also, for a given I_{sp}, we want to maximize M_p/M_f to achieve larger ΔV values.

Table 18-1◀, Fig. 18-2◀, Eq. 18-20

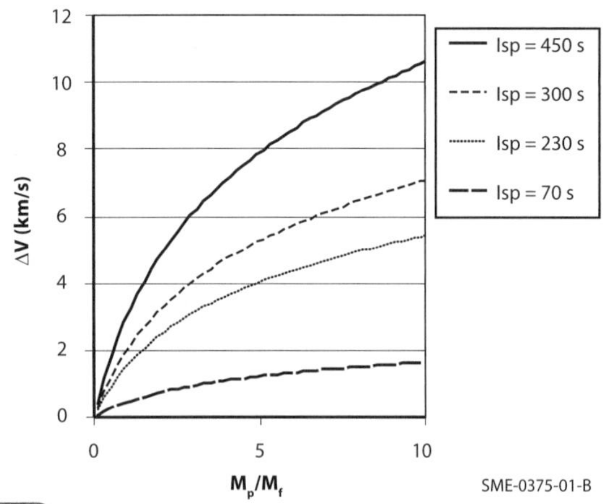

Fig. 18-3. ΔV as a Function of M_p/M_f and I_{sp}.

As a common practice, the requirements for a propulsion system are listed in terms of ΔV, thrust, total impulse, number of pulses, and duration of the pulses. Table 18-2 shows typical requirements for different functions a propulsion system has to execute. Beware that the specific requirements will be dependent on the spacecraft design and its mission. Table 18-3 serves as an overview of how different propulsions systems, to be studied in the rest of this chapter, can be used for different applications along with their typical I_{sp} ranges.

18.2 Staging

There is no launch vehicle today that can place a payload to at least LEO with a single stage. Therefore, the question is not whether a vehicle will have stages but rather how many. The answer usually lies between 2 and 6 depending on the particular mission [Sutton and Biblarz, 2010]. Having more than 1 stage is advantageous because we dispose of the mass of the expended stage (e.g., rocket engines, tanks, remaining propellant) and don't waste energy propelling empty tanks or unusable engines throughout the mission. Also, with more than 1 stage, the propellant tanks, and the overall vehicle, can be smaller since they carry less mass. With each added stage though, we add complexity to the vehicle design such as more inter-stage structure, joints, separation mechanisms, and separate engines and tanks. Therefore, it is recommended to use as few stages as needed to achieve the mission objectives.

Table 18-2. Typical Functions and Requirements for Upper Stages and In-Space Propulsion. [Wertz and Larson, 2003]

Propulsion Function	Typical ΔV and Other Requirements
Orbit Transfer to GEO (orbit insertion)	
Perigee Burn	2,400 m/s
Apogee Burn	1,500 (low inclination) to 1800 m/s (high inclination)
Initial Spin Up	1–60 rpm
LEO to Higher Orbit Raising ΔV	
Drag makeup ΔV	60–500 m/s
Controlled Re-entry	120–150 m/s
Acceleration to Escape Velocity from LEO Parking Orbit	3,600–4,000 m/s into a heliocentric orbit
Orbit Maintenance	
Despin	60 to 0 rpm
Spin control	± 1 to ±5 rpm
Orbit correction ΔV	15 to 75 m/s per year
East-West stationkeeping ΔV at GEO	3 to 6 m/s per year
North-South stationkeeping ΔV at GEO	45 to 55 m/s per year
Survivability or evasive maneuvers (highly variable) ΔV	150 to 4,600 m/s
Attitude Control	3–10% of total propellant mass
Acquisition of Sun, Earth, Star	low total impulse, typically <5,000 N-s, 1K to 10K pulses, 0.01 to 5.0 sec pulse width
On-orbit normal mode control with 3-axis stabilization, limit cycle	100K to 200K pulses, minimum impulse bit of 0.01 N-s, 0.01 to 0.25 sec pulse width
Precession control (spinners only)	low total impulse, typically <7,000 N-s, 1K to 10K pulses, 0.02 to 0.2 sec pulse width
Momentum management (wheel unloading)	5 to 10 pulse trains every few days, 0.02 to 0.10 s pulse width
3-axis control during ΔV	on-off pulsing, 10K to 100K pulses, 0.05 to 0.20 s pulse width

Table 18-3. Overview of Common Applications for Different Propulsion Systems.

Propulsion System	Orbit Insertion		Orbit Maintenance and Maneuvering	Attitude Control	Typical Range of I_{sp} (s)
	Perigee	Apogee			
Cold Gas			X	X	45–73
Solid	X	X			290–304
Liquid					
Monopropellant			X	X	200–235
Bipropellant	X	X	X	X	274–467
Electric		X	X	X	500–3,000

To analyze the performance of multiple stages, we use the same equations used for a single stage. The ΔV for each stage is

$$\Delta V_i = V_{eqi} \ln(\frac{M_{oi}}{M_{fi}}) \tag{18-21}$$

Where i refers to the stage in question, V_{eqi} is the effective exhaust velocity of stage i, M_{oi} is the total mass of the vehicle before the stage i ignites (including all subsequent stages and payload), M_{fi} is the final mass of the vehicle after stage i is expended but before it separates. The total gain in velocity for all the stages is the sum of the individual gains:

$$\Delta V_t = V_{eq1} \ln(\frac{M_{o1}}{M_{f1}}) + V_{eq2} \ln(\frac{M_{o2}}{M_{f2}}) + V_{eq3} \ln(\frac{M_{o3}}{M_{f3}}) + \ldots \tag{18-22}$$

Sutton and Biblarz [2010] show that for a 2-stage vehicle, with similar effective exhaust velocities and I_{sp}, a greater payload mass is achieved when the two stages have the same mass ratio M_{oi}/M_{fi} rather than the same mass. In that case, the stages are said to be similar and it follows that ΔV is the same for each stage. This result extends to more than 2 stages. However, as we go to more stages, the gains on payload mass become smaller and smaller: about 8–10% for a third stage and 3–5% for a fourth stage [Sutton and Biblarz, 2010]. In practice, the performance (e.g., I_{sp}, thrust, M_p/M_o) of the propulsion systems for the different stages is different so the partition of ΔV needs to be optimized to get the largest *payload fraction*, defined as

$$\lambda = M_{payload} / M_o \tag{18-23}$$

Hill and Peterson [1992] show an analytical method to optimize the ΔV distribution. Ideally, once we have assigned ΔV's to the different stages, we start sizing the vehicle from the top down, sizing the final stage first. For a given ΔV needed, the maximum payload fraction is achieved if (1) stages with higher I_{sp} are above those with lower I_{sp}; (2) the higher the I_{sp} of a stage, the more ΔV it should contribute [Wertz and Larson, 2003]; (3) a small increase in I_{sp} is more effective in upper than in lower stages, hence LOX/H_2 is usually chosen for upper stage systems [Sutton and Biblarz, 2010].

18.3 Chemical Propulsion Systems

18.3.1 Cold Gas Thrusters

As mentioned in the introduction, cold gas thrusters don't rely on combustion to produce thrust, but there are enough similarities with chemical propulsion systems to cover them here. Like in chemical rockets, the thrust from cold gas thrusters originates from expanding high pressure gases through a converging-diverging nozzle and the thrust Eq. (18-4) applies. However, the chamber pressure is only as high as the reservoir tank, and there is no temperature rise due to chemical reactions. Cold gas thrusters are used in cases when the thrust and I_{sp} requirements are low and a small impulse bit is important. Table 18-4 shows some examples of available cold gas thrusters. Generally they are used for total impulse up to about 22,000 N-s [Sutton and Biblarz, 2010]. Their main use is for attitude control and small ΔV applications. The I_{sp} of the commonly used gases like He, N_2, and Freon-14 are 165 sec, 73 sec, and 45 sec respectively [Micci and Ketsdever, 2000]. Hydrogen could also be used (I_{sp}~ 272 sec) but both H_2 and He have the worst risk of leaks because of the small size of the molecules. The main advantage of cold gas systems is their simplicity. In a typical cold gas thruster system, there are only valves, filters, regulators and relief valves connecting the storage high pressure tank to the thruster (Fig. 18-8). Historic examples of systems using cold gas propulsion systems include (1) the Viking Orbiter using N_2 thrusters (I_{sp} = 68 sec) on its reaction control system [Brown, 1996; Holmberg, Faust, and Holt, 1980], (2) the Landsat 3 using Freon-14 thrusters for attitude control [Brown, 1996; Landsat 1978] and (3) the manned maneuvering unit used by shuttle astronauts for extra vehicular activities in 1984, which was powered by N_2 cold gas thrusters [Bergonz, 1982].

Table 18-4. Example of Cold Gas Thrusters.

Engine	Manu.	Status	Engine Mass (kg)	Length (m)	Prop.	Nominal Thrust (N)	Specific Impulse (s)	Operating Pressure (kPa)
SVT01 Solenoid Valve Thruster[1]	AMPAC	Flown on SNAP-1, DMC Alsat, UK	0.051	0.021	Butane, GN2, Xe, CF4	0.01–0.05	70 GN2, 45 CF4	150 to 1,000
Proportional MicroNewton Thruster[1]	AMPAC	Qualification Test Demonstrated on Engineering Model	0.281*	0.10*	GHe, GN2, Dry air	Up to 0.001	70 GN2	100 to 500
Solenoid Actuated 58E142A Thruster[2, 3]	Moog	Flown on SIRTF/SPITZER	Up to 0.016	~0.032	GN2	0.12 at 690 kPa	>57	340 to 2,070
Solenoid Actuated 58-118 Thruster[2, 3]	Moog	Flown on SAFER (Shuttle EVA)	0.022	~0.0254	GN2	3.5	>70 (71.5–73)	1,482

References: [1] Courtesy of AMPAC In-Space Propulsion and Schappell, et al. [2005], [2] Bzibziak [2000], [3] Bzibziak [2010]. * Includes feedback sensor, Isolation valve and nozzle heater.

18.3.2 Liquid Rocket Engines (LREs)*

Liquid rocket engines (LREs) can be used throughout a mission. They can be used as first and upper stage engines to propel a payload into its initial orbit. LREs can also be used for orbit insertion, maintenance, maneuvering, and attitude control. Some launch vehicles, like the Saturn 5, utilized all LREs for the first stage. Others like Ariane 5, Atlas 5, Delta 4, and the Space Shuttle (to retire circa 2011), utilize a combination of liquid and solid rockets for liftoff (see Chap. 26 for more details on launch vehicles). For attitude control especially, liquid rockets are a good choice because of their capability for multiple restarts [Brown, 1996]

LREs can be classified in several ways. One way is to classify LREs depending on whether turbopumps are used to pressurize the propellants before they enter the combustion chamber or whether high pressure tanks are used instead. The simplicity of the pressure-fed configuration needs to be traded with the additional weight of the heavier, thick-wall tanks needed to hold the propellants at high pressure. Pump-fed LREs are also classified according to their work cycle; that is how they ultimately produce thrust. Common types of cycles are gas generators, expanders, and oxygen-rich staged combustion. See Sutton and Biblarz [2010] for a detailed explanation on these cycles. Finally, LREs are also classified according to the type of propellants they use. Thus, there are monopropellant and bipropellant engines.

18.3.2.1 Monopropellants

In a monopropellant system, as the name suggests, there is one propellant which decomposes exothermically as it passes through a catalytic bed. This results in heated, high-pressure gases which are expanded through a converging-diverging nozzle to produce thrust. One advantage of a monopropellant system is that it avoids the mixing step of a two-propellant system which could lead to combustion roughness or even instabilities. A typical system consists of a pressurization system, a propellant tank, a propellant valve, a catalyst bed (including a heater for the catalyst material) and a converging-diverging nozzle. Table 18-5 shows some examples of monopropellant thrusters, some of which are shown in Fig. 18-4. In general, monopropellant systems have an I_{sp} range from 165–244 sec and they are used for ΔV requirements of 1,000 m/s or less [Micci and Ketsdever, 2000]. The propellants of choice today are hydrazine (N_2H_4) and hydrazine blends. Hydrazine first decomposes into hydrogen and ammonia (T_{flame} ~1,700 K) when it comes into contact with the catalyst bed. Subsequently, the ammonia decomposes into nitrogen and hydrogen in an endothermic reaction lowering the flame temperature to about 1,394 K. Therefore, one aspect of the design of hydrazine monopropellant systems is how to limit further dissociation of ammonia to achieve the best I_{sp} [Brown, 1996]. The main advantages of hydrazine are its relatively high I_{sp} [230 sec], system simplicity, long term storability, clean exhaust, stability, restart capability, and low flame temperature [Brown, 1996]. The main disadvantages are its lower I_{sp} compared to bipropellants, its toxicity, and high freezing point at 274K [Thompson, 2001]. Therefore, research is being conducted to find alternative monopropellants which are safer to handle and have lower freezing points, such as amine azides [Thompson, 2001]. Today, granular alumina coated with iridium is commonly used for catalyst beds (e.g., Shell 405 catalyst bed). The size of the catalyst bed is in part driven by the time the propellant needs to be in contact with the catalyst. One of the main concerns with the operation of monopropellant systems is the degradation of the catalyst bed over the mission life. Degradation is a function of the total amount of propellant used, mass flow rate or operating pressure, number and size of thermal cycles, and number of pulses.† Catalyst bed heat-

* Historically, rockets using liquid propellants are denoted as liquid rocket engines while rockets using solid propellants are denoted as solid rocket motors.

† As a note, because of the smaller mass flow rates, microsatellites (10–100 kg) will likely incur less degradation [Ketsdever, 2000].

Table 18-5. Representative Monopropellant Systems.

Engine	Manufacturer	Status	Engine Mass (kg)	Length (m)	Propellants	Nominal Thrust (N)	Specific Impulse (s)	Total Impulse (N-s)
Liq AOCS thrusters[1]	SEP	D5a, spot, geos, exosat, geos, exosat, ERS, Helios, Envisat	0.320/0.355	0.108/0.145	Hydrazine	3.5-16.5 (v) at max p	230/232 (v)	5.2E+05–6.15E+05
MONARC-5[2]	AMPAC In-Space Propulsion	Flight qualified	0.49	0.203	Hydrazine	4.5	233	4.60E+05
MONARC-90[2]	AMPAC In-Space Propulsion	Flight qualified	1	0.3	Hydrazine	90	235	3.50E+06
MONARC-445[2]	AMPAC In-Space Propulsion	Flight qualified	1.6	0.41	Hydrazine	445	235	5.60E+06
MRE-0.1[3]	Northrop Grumman Space Technology (NGST)	Chandra X-ray Observatory, DSP, STEP 4	0.5 (STM) 0.9 (DTM)	0.175	Hydrazine	1 at 2.41 MPa inlet p 0.8 at 1.90 Mpa inlet p	216 at 1.90 MPa inlet p	
MRE-1.0[3]	NGST	Pioneer, HEAO, TDRSS, FLTSATCOM, EOS, SSTI, STEP4	0.5 (STM) 1.0 (DTM)	0.188	Hydrazine	5 at 2.76 MPa inlet p 3.4 at 1.90 MPa inlet p	218 at 1.90 MPa inlet p	
MRE-5.0[3]	NGST	GRO	1.5 (DTM)	0.264	Hydrazine	36 at 2.76 Mpa inlet p 28 at 1.90 MPa inlet p	232 at 1.90 MPa inlet p	
DOT-5[1]	KB Khimmash	Spacecraft thruster	0.9		Hydrazine	5	230	
MR-103G[4]	Aerojet	Flight proven	0.33	0.173	Hydrazine	0.19-1.13	202-224	97,078
MR-111C[5]	Aerojet	Flight proven	0.33	0.169	Hydrazine	1.3-5.3	215-229	
MR-107N[6]	Aerojet	Flight proven	0.74	0.213	Hydrazine	109-296	229-232	2.6E+05
MR-80B[7]	Aerojet	Flight qualified	8.51	0.411	Hydrazine	31-3,780	200-225	
CHT-1[8]	EADS Astrium	>500 units flown	0.29	0.172	Hydrazine	0.32-1.1 (v)	200-223	1.12E+05
CHT-20[8]	EADS Astrium	Flight proven	0.395	0.195	Hydrazine	7.9-24.6 (v)	224-230	5.17E+05
CHT-400[8]	EADS Astrium	Flight proven	2.7	0.325	Hydrazine	130-455 (v)	214-224	>5e5

References: [1] Sweetman [2006], [2] Courtesy of AMPAC In-Space Propulsion, [3] Northrop [2010a], [4] McRight, et al. [2005], [5] Swink, et al. [1999], [6] Frei [2001], [7] Morrisey [1992] and Dawson, et al. [2007], [8] Astrium [2010b]. (v)= vacuum

ers are almost always used to preheat the bed prior to operation in order to increase bed life and to also decrease the ignition delay. Monopropellant systems used for attitude control need to restart multiple times. How quickly thrust can be generated is also important. Other factors to consider when designing a monopropellant system are how fast the valves respond, how fast the catalyst heats up so that it can promote decomposition of the propellant, and how fast the pressure rises [Brown, 1996].

18.3.2.2 Bipropellants

In a bipropellant system, a fuel and an oxidizer combust either spontaneously after they contact each other (hypergolic systems), or as a result of an ignition source. Table 18-6 shows many examples of bipropellant engines and Fig. 18-5 shows representative engines. This type of system is much more complex than cold gas or monopropellant systems (Fig. 18-8). They are used for high ΔV requirements (>1,000 m/s) [Micci and Ketsdever, 2000] and their I_{sp} ranges from about 270 to 466 sec.

Both propellants undergo a series of processes from the moment they are injected into the combustion chamber to when they leave the nozzle. The propellants can be injected as liquids, gases, or supercritical fluids (mostly the case in recent engines). Depending on what thermodynamic state they are in when they are injected, and what type of injector is used, the mixing process can be very different. In cryogenic engines, for example, a shear coaxial injector is commonly used, which consists of a center tube carrying liquid oxygen and an annular tube carrying H_2. If a propellant is liquid, it has to break into droplets first, vaporize, and then mix and combust with the other propellant. If the propellants are in the super-

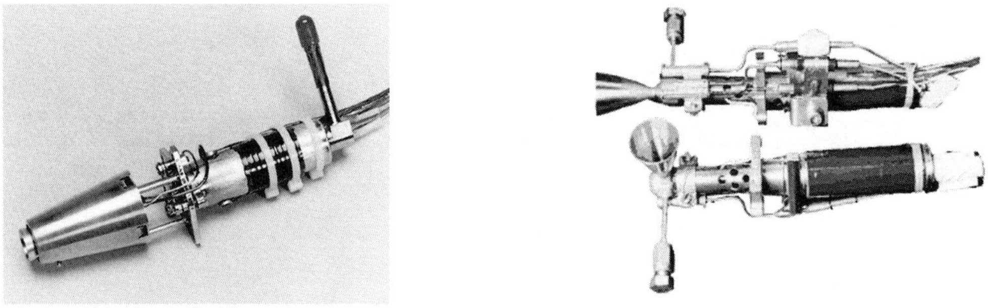

Fig. 18-4. Typical Hydrazine (N2H4) Monopropellant Engines. (Pictures courtesy of GenCorp Aerojet and AMPAC In-Space Propulsion respectively.)

critical phase (*P* >critical pressure, T >critical temperature), no droplets are formed and the fluids mix more in the fashion of two dense gases.

There are two choices to pressurize the propellants; the simpler one is to pressurize the propellants in their storage tank by means of a high pressure inert fluid. The high pressure propellant then discharges into the combustion chamber. In this case, the storage tanks have to be designed to withstand high pressures, which requires thicker and heavier tanks. Such pressurized feed systems are usually preferred when the total impulse needed is relatively low, short periods of operation are required, and the thrust to weight ratio is low. This design is the common choice for in-space propulsion systems. Alternatively, *turbopumps* (pumps driven by turbines) can be used to pressurize the propellants, so storage tanks don't need to withstand such high pressures. However, the pressurization system as a whole increases in complexity. Turbopumps are usually not used for in-space applications, but rather they are used for higher pressure, higher performing systems. Virtually all major boost liquid rocket engines flying today use turbopumps.

There are many different ways to configure a working cycle for a bipropellant rocket engine. For a detailed description including diagrams see Sutton and Biblarz [2010]. The cycle most used for cryogenic upper stage engines is the *expander cycle*. In this cycle, one propellant (usually hydrogen) is first used to cool the combustion chamber, and then the heated H_2 is used to run the turbine or turbines which run the pumps. After the warm hydrogen leaves the turbine, it is injected into the combustion chamber. Some of the hydrogen goes directly from the cooling jacket to the combustion chamber. At that point, liquid oxygen and warm hydrogen mix and combust. One limitation of this cycle is how much heat can be transferred from the combustion chamber walls to the H_2; hence an active area of research for expander cycles is heat transfer enhancement techniques. Some of the advantages of expander engines are their simplicity and the fact that no propellant is thrown overboard. This last feature makes this a closed or *topping cycle*. The RL-10 is the premier example of an expander cycle (Fig. 18-5). Derivatives from this engine are used on both the Atlas V and Delta IV launch vehicles. Hydrogen is particularly well suited for this application since it absorbs heat efficiently and it does not decompose chemically like heavier hydrocarbons do. As a note, for heavy hydrocarbons like RP-1 or RP-2, we have to carefully study the thermal decomposition characteristics of the fuels as they heat up while cooling a combustion chamber. If these hydrocarbons are heated beyond a certain temperature they can produce carbonaceous deposits, which can clog cooling channels and modify the heat transfer process by coating the walls with deposits.

A second cycle to consider is the gas generator cycle. In this case, some of the propellants are combusted in what is generally called a 'gas generator', a little misleading since it is, in fact, another smaller combustion chamber. The hot products from the gas generator drive the turbine and generally they are exhausted overboard after that, which makes this an open cycle. Dumping hot gases overboard decreases the I_{sp} by about 2–5% for a given chamber pressure [Humble, et al. 1995]. The rest of the propellants combust in the main chamber. Since the turbine is driven with combustion products, the temperature can be higher than that achieved on an expander cycle. The F-1 rocket engine which powered the Saturn V used a gas generator.

The last and most complicated cycle is *staged combustion*. This is similar to the gas generator cycle except that the hot products which drive the turbine are injected into the main chamber instead of being thrown overboard. Also, the gas generator usually consists of either very rich or very lean mixtures. That is, there is usually much less or much more oxidizer than needed to burn all the fuel present in the mixture, respectively. This cycle promises the highest I_{sp} and is used on the Russian RD-180 engine powering the Atlas V today.

Closely coupled to the cycle we choose are the cooling techniques for the combustion chambers. Regenerative cooling is where one propellant (usually the fuel) is passed around the nozzle to cool it, as in the expander cycle. In ablative cooling, the combustion chamber walls are made of ablative materials which decompose into gases as they heat up, and these gases act as cooling for the walls. In radiation cooling, mostly used for engines operating at vacuum, the heat produced by combustion and conducted through the chamber walls is rejected

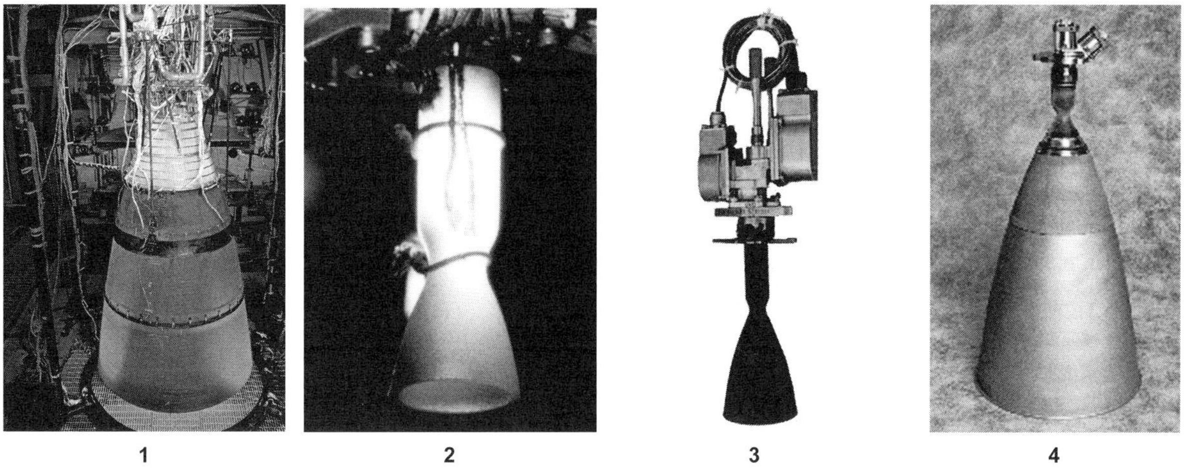

Fig. 18-5. Representative Liquid Rocket Engines. Photos courtesy of [1] RL10B-2, Pratt & Whitney Rocketdyne, [2] KEW-7, Pratt & Whitney Rocketdyne, [3] LEROS LTT, AMPAC In-Space Propulsion, [4] HiPAT™, GenCorp Aerojet.

through radiation. Finally, in film cooling some of the propellant is injected along the walls of the chamber, usually close to the injector exit plane and/or at the throat, and the thin film covering the wall acts as insulation. Eventually the propellant used as coolant will mix and burn but the flame temperature will be lower than that attained toward the center of the chamber since the mixture ratio will be much greater than stoichiometric.

18.3.2.3 Dual-Mode Systems

In a dual-mode propulsion system, hydrazine is used for both bipropellant and monopropellant thrusters. The hydrazine tank is shared by both classes of thrusters, potentially simplifying the overall spacecraft propulsion system. Dual-mode systems also have the advantage of using the bipropellant engine for high-thrust, high ΔV maneuvers (e.g. orbit insertion, apogee circularization) and the monopropellant thrusters for attitude control. The Mars Global Surveyor, launched in 1996, used a dual-mode propulsion system [Brown, 2002] and they are still used today (see Table 18-6).

18.3.3 Solid Rockets

Solid rockets pose a major advantage over liquid rockets: simplicity. In a solid motor, there are few or no moving parts (the only movable parts may be nozzles for thrust vectoring). In contrast, many liquid rocket engines have complex turbopumps and feed systems. The other advantage is that solid propellants have higher density than liquid propellants needing less volume for storage given the same mass. The propellant mixture can be stored for years inside the solid motor (like in tactical and strategic missiles). Table 18-7 shows examples of solid rocket motors. They can be scaled up or down in thrust relatively easily; thus, their range varies from a few Newtons (N) to more than 1 MN. Solid motors are used when the total impulse required is known. They can provide from a few hundred to 10^9 N-s [Brown, 2002]. In exchange for the above advantages, solid motors have lower I_{sp}, than LOX/LH_2 engines and comparable or less I_{sp} than storable and LOX/hydrocarbon engines. Unlike liquid engines, where the propellants are admitted to the combustion chambers through valves which can be controlled, the fuel and the oxidizer in solid rockets are mixed together in what is called the propellant grain. Once combustion is established there is no mechanism to stop it. Because of this, we can neither check a solid motor performance before firing it, nor can we use one for a mission requiring multiple starts.

The main components of a solid motor (Fig. 18-6) are the case which houses the propellants and contains the pressure, the igniter which starts the combustion process,

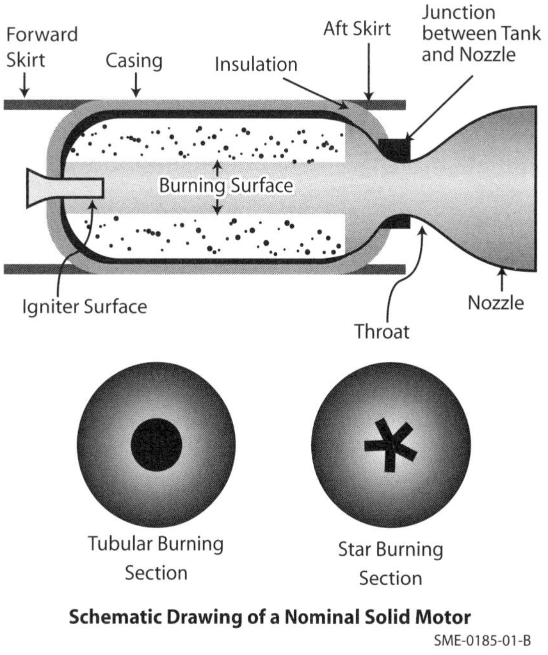

Fig. 18-6. Schematic Drawing of a Nominal Solid Rocket Motor.

Table 18-6. Representative Bipropellant Rocket Systems.

Engine	Manufacturer	Status	Engine Mass (kg)	Length (m)	Propellants	Nominal Thrust (kN)	Specific Impulse (s)
YF-73[1]	CALT	H-8 3rd stage CZ-3 delivery of payloads to GTO	236	1.44	LOX/LH2	44.15 (v)	420 (v)
Aestus[2]	EADS Astrium	Ariane 5 upper stage	111	2.20	NTO/MMH	29.4	324 (v)
S400-12 (-15)[3]	EADS Astrium	>60 missions flown	3.6 (4.3)	0.503 (0.669)	NTO, MON-1, MON-3 and MMH	0.42 (0.425)	318 (321)
10 N Bipropellant Thruster[4]	EADS Astrium	> 90 spacecraft have these thrusters	0.35 to 0.65	0.126–0.159	NTO, MON-1, MON-3 and MMH	0.010	291
Unified Propulsion System—Apogee Kick Engine [1]	Japan IHI company ltd	provides GEO insertion and attitude/orbit control for 2t-class satellites	15.7	1.03	NTO/hydrazine	1.7	321.4
LE-5B[1]	Mitsubishi	H-IIA Stage 2	285	2.63	LOX/LH2	137.3/82.4 (throttled) (v)	447/448
R2.2000[1]	Russian Federation	Used on Phobos spacecraft as main engines	74	1.03	NTO/UDMH	13.73-19.61	316-325
Orbital Maneuvering System[1]	Aerojet	Shuttle: orbit insertion, maneuvering, and reentry initiation	118	1.96	NTO/MMH	26.7 (v)	316 (v)
R-40[5]	Aerojet	Flight proven (Space Shuttle)	6.8	0.554–1.04	NTO (MON-3)/MMH	3.87	281
HiPAT™ [6]	Aerojet	Apogee thruster Flight Proven	5.2-5.44	0.628–0.726	NTO (MON-3)/ MMH	0.445	320-323
R-1E [7]	Aerojet	Flight proven (Space Shuttle)	2	0.312	NTO (MON-3)/ MMH	0.111	280
5lb Cb[8]	AMPAC In-Space Propulsion	Flight qualified	0.82-0.91	0.216–0.270	NTO/MMH	0.022	293-295
LEROS LTT[8]	AMPAC In-Space Propulsion	Flight qualified	0.6	0.27	NTO/MMH	0.009	274
XLR-132[1]	Rocketdyne	Applicable for kick stages, deep space, space transfer vehicle	54	1.2	NTO/N2H4	16.7 (v)	340 (v)
TR-308[9] ***Dual Mode Liquid Apogee Engine***	Northrop Grumman Space Technology	Flown on Chandra X-ray Observatory	4.76	0.706	NTO/N2H4	0.472	322
TR-312-100MN Dual Mode Liquid Apogee Engine[9]	Northrop Grumman Space Technology	Pre-Qualification Testing	6.03	0.71	NTO/MMH	0.503	325
RL10B-2[10]	United Technologies Pratt and Whitney	Delta 3 Stage 2, Delta IV Stage 2	301.2	4.15	LOX/LH2	110.1	465.5
RL 10A-4[1] ***RL-10A-4-2***[11]	United Technologies Pratt and Whitney	Atlas 2A/2As Atlas V	168	2.29	LOX/LH2	99.2 (v)	451 (v)

v = vacuum
References: [1] Sweetman [2006], [2] Astrium [2010c], [3] Astrium [2010d], [4] Astrium [2010e], [5] Stechman [1985], Hill [1980], Sund and Hill [1979], Drenning, et al. [1978], [6] Wu, et al. [2001], Stechman [2001], [7] Stechman [1990], [8] Courtesy of AMPAC In-Space Propulsion, [9] Northrop [2010b], [10] United Technologies Pratt & Whitney (UTPW), [2009a], [11] UTPW [2009b].

Table 18-6, Fig. 18-6, Eq. 18-23◀

the thrust skirt to connect the motor to the rest of the vehicle, the nozzle, and a mechanism to transfer the loads from the nozzle to the rest of the motor body, usually a polar boss [Humble, et al. 1995]. The case is lined with an insulation layer so that the case material does not see the high combustion temperatures. The cases themselves can be metallic (e.g., aluminum, titanium), fully composite (e.g., carbon fiber with an epoxy resin) or composite with metal liners [Humble, et al. 1995]. Aluminum is the most commonly used fuel today. Other potential fuels are magnesium (considered a 'clean' fuel) and beryllium (with toxic exhaust products). For oxidizers, Ammonium perchlorate (AP) is the most common, used on the Space Shuttle Solid Rocket Motors. Ammonium nitrate is the second most used oxidizer. The fuel and oxidizer are held together by a 'binder', which gives structural integrity to the fuel/oxidizer mixture (<20% of the total propellant mass) and also acts as a fuel. The binders are usually long-chain polymers [Humble, et al. 1995]. Two common binders are hydroxyl-terminated polybutadiene (HTPB) and polybutadiene acrylonitrile (PBAN). From the data that Humble, et al. [1995] gathered, typical ranges for percentage of total mass of the different components are: 82–94% for the propellant mass, 1–6% for the insulation, 3–8% for the case, and 1–6% for the nozzle.

Solid motors are commonly used in the first stage of launch vehicles like the Atlas V, Delta IV, Ariane 5, H-2 and the Space Shuttle. They provide extra thrust needed during take-off and may be jettisoned after their firing, refurbished, and reused. They are also used for kick stages (i.e., apogee kick motors, AKM) to GEO orbits, orbit insertion for planetary missions, and in ballistic and tactical missile systems. Table 18-7 shows applicable examples of solid motors. For example, the Inertial Upper Stage (IUS), used from 1982 to 2004 [Isakowitz, Hopkins, and Hopkins Jr., 2004], consisted of a two-stage solid rocket motor system. An Orbus 21 motor (186 kN thrust) and an Orbus 6 motor (76.5 kN) were used for the first and second stages respectively. The IUS placed payloads into GEO. In 1989, the IUS placed the Magellan and Galileo missions into their initial interplanetary orbits to Venus and Jupiter, respectively.

A very important consideration for choosing a solid motor is its total impulse capability shown in Eq. (18-15). Most qualified solid designs can be tailored to the specific total impulse requirements for the mission by "off-loading" propellant. As a rule of thumb, solid motors are typically capable of offloading up to about 20% for a given design. To choose the right motor for the application at hand, we also should know how the thrust will vary as the motor fires. The burning rate of the propellants and how the combustion proceeds and the propellants get consumed falls into the realm of internal ballistics. The burning rate, r_b, denotes how much of the burning surface recedes as a function of time, usually in the order of 0.1–8 cm/s [Humble, et al. 1995; Sutton and Biblarz 2010]. It is measured perpendicular to the burning surface. The burning rate is usually described as

$$r_b = a p_c^n e^{\sigma_p \Delta T} \tag{18-24}$$

where p_c is the chamber pressure, the pressure exponent n falls between 0.2 and 0.6, a is a constant dependant on the ambient grain temperature and the units used in the above equation. For r_b in cm/s and p_c in MPa, a ranges from 0.4 to 0.6 for typical motors [Sutton and Biblarz, 2010]. ΔT is the difference between the temperature at which the constant, a, is evaluated and the actual propellant temperature [Humble, et al. 1995]. σ_p denotes temperature sensitivity, and it ranges from 0.001 to 0.009 1/K [Sutton and Biblarz, 2010]. From Eq. (18-24) we see that to double the burning rate we would need to increase p_c by four times if the exponent n were 0.5. The mass being consumed by the combustion is:

$$\dot{m} = A_b r_b \rho_b \tag{18-25}$$

where A_b is the burning area, r_b is the burning rate and ρ_b is the density of the combustion products. As the pres-

Table 18-7. Representative Solid Rockets. [Sweetman, 2006; ATK, 2008]

Engine	Manufacturer	Status	Engine Mass (kg)	Length (m)	Propellants	Burn Time Avg. Thrust (kN)	Specific Impulse (s)
Star 27 (TE-M-616)	ATK	AKM for Canada's CTS, Japan's GMS/Bs and several USAF GPS and NOAA GOES satellites	361.2	1.24	AP/HTPB/Al	25.44 (v)	287.9 (v)
Star 37FM (TE-M-783)	ATK	AKM, GPS Block IIR, NASA ACTS	1,148	1.69	AP/HTPB/Al	47.3 (v)	289.8 (v)
Orbus 6/6E	UTC Chemical Systems Division (historic)	IUS 2nd stage	3018	1.98	86% solids HTPB (UTP 19360A)	81 (v)	303.5 (v)
Orbus 1	ATK	upper stages and space motor; starbird stages 3/4	470.4	1.25	90% solids HTPB	30.4 (v)	293.3
Star 30bp (TE-M-700-20)	ATK	AKM has flown from Shuttle, Delta and Ariane	542.8	1.51	89% solids HTPB	26.62 (v)	293.3 (v)

v = vacuum

sure increases, the burning rate increases and so does the mass being burned per second and, by consequence, the thrust as well, see Eq. (18-4). Because of this tight relation between thrust, burning rate, and burning mass, we have to be careful not to develop large cracks that propagate on the propellant grain. An unintentional or uncontrollable growth in burning area and burning rate can result in unmanageable chamber pressure rise and failure of the case.

System considerations when choosing a solid motor are (1) the need to spin stabilize the spacecraft during the solid burn (most spacecraft applications which are not upper or transfer stages) since the burning rate increases with acceleration perpendicular to its surface, (2) the thermal constraints for solid motors, paying attention to the soak back for motors which are embedded with spacecraft structures and (3) how the thrust level may affect deployables.

18.3.4 Hybrid Rockets

Hybrid rockets aim to combine some of the best traits from liquid and solid rockets. Its origins go back to Russia in the late 1930s. In a typical hybrid engine, the oxidizer is liquid but the fuel is solid. A reverse configuration is also possible. See Chiaverini and Kuo [2007] for a recent, very detailed description of hybrid rockets. Figure 18-7 shows a schematic description of a typical hybrid rocket. A very common fuel used for hybrid rockets is HTPB which can be used with LOX, N_2O or N_2O_4. The I_{sp} for these propellant combinations at chamber pressures of 3.45 MPa and exit pressure of 0.1 MPa are 280 sec, 247 sec, and 258 sec respectively. If paraffin, another very common propellant, is used as fuel instead, the I_{sp} increases by 1 s for the oxidizers considered above [Chiaverini and Kuo, 2007]. The potential applications of hybrid rockets span from upper stage orbital control to tactical missiles to launch systems. Some of the advantages of hybrid rockets typically mentioned [Chiaverini and Kuo, 2007; Humble et al., 1995] are: (1) safety from fabrication to transportation to storage—unlike solid rockets, the fuel and oxidizer are stored separately so there is very little risk of a detonation or explosion; (2) higher I_{sp} than solid rockets; (3) higher density impulse than liquid rockets (but lower than that of solids); (4) ability to throttle by controlling the flow rate of the liquid propellant which also results in greater maneuverability; (5) restart capability; (6) can idle the engine to check system operation prior to launch; (7) when the grain is not aluminized, it avoids the hydrochloric acid or aluminum oxide exhaust from typical solid rockets minimizing the environmental impact during launch; (8) potentially lower propulsion cost than solid and liquid rockets; (9) higher reliability (due to less parts in the system) than liquid rockets; and (10) stronger than solid-propellant grains because they are less sensitive to cracks and debonds.

Even though the first hybrid rockets can be traced to the 1930s, why don't we see them occupying a prominent place in mainstream launch or spacecraft propulsion systems? Chiaverini and Kuo [2007] remark that hybrid rockets don't have the same launch readiness as solid rockets and they have lower I_{sp} than liquid rocket engines. In hybrid rockets not all the fuel is consumed, when used with liquid oxidizers, so the effective mass fraction of the hybrid is less than that for a solid rocket. Because the mixture ratio varies during operation, the specific impulse varies as a function of time. Regression rates of commonly used hybrid propellants are low in comparison to solid propellants (except potentially for paraffin) and this is an active area of research. Finally, analytical and numerical models are not as mature as those for liquid and solid rockets

In the 1980s there was a growth in commercial satellites which gave a new boost to hybrid rocket technology as an alternative for a low-cost and safe way to launch those payloads. AMROC and Thiokol had partial success with hybrid rockets but their plans to use high-thrust hybrids (1.1 MN thrust) ended, in part, due to combustion instability problems. A lesson learned from those experiences is that the LOX has to be completely vaporized before coming into contact with the fuel [Chiaverini and Kuo, 2007]. In 2004, SpaceshipOne won the Ansari X Prize [Dornheim, 2003a] using a rocket propulsion system consisting of a 74 kN hybrid rocket powered with N_2O as the liquid oxidizer and HTPB as the solid fuel. A hybrid motor is scheduled to be also used for SpaceShipTwo [Norris, 2009]. Lockheed Martin launched a 267 kN hybrid rocket from Wallops, Virginia with a projected I_{sp} of 290 sec in 2003 [Morring, 2003] and tested a hybrid rocket on a DARPA program in 2005 [Lockheed, 2005]. In terms of smaller hybrid rocket development, most of it is happening at the university level at places like Purdue [Tsohas et al., 2009], Penn State [Evans, 2009] and Stanford [Dyer et al., 2007].

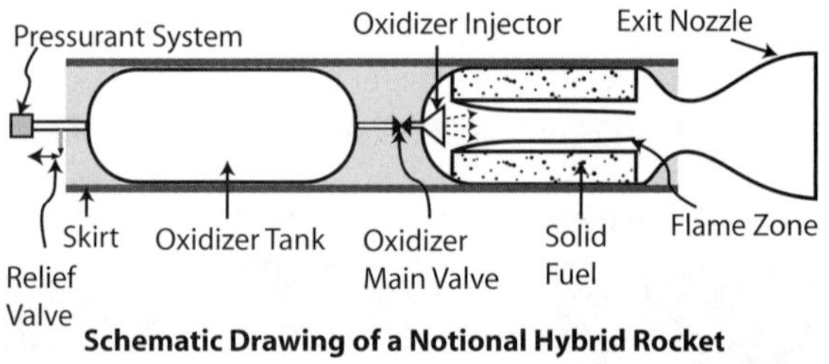

Fig. 18-7. Schematic Drawing of a Nominal Solid Rocket Motor.

18.4 Plume Considerations

The plume or exhaust from a rocket is made up of combustion products, such as water vapor from LOX/H_2 engines, and sometimes also unburned propellants which can react with ambient air outside the rocket. For example, the ambient air can complete the oxidation of partially oxidized elements like CO, NO, H_2, which then go to CO_2, NO_2, and H_2O respectively. Sometimes the exhaust plume can contain toxic gases like hydrogen chloride (HCl) from the solid boosters of the shuttle. Along with HCl, nitrogen dioxide (NO_2), and nitric acid (HNO_3) make up the three major toxic emissions from common rockets [National Research Council, 1998]. An assessment of the emissions from rocket exhaust into the stratosphere is presented in Jackman, et al. [1996]. Plumes also contain solid particles like carbon soot from hydrocarbon liquid rocket engines, or aluminum oxide particles (Al_2O_3) and alkali metal impurities from solid rockets. Al_2O_3 particles are in fact an orbital debris issue if they stay in orbit. For a detailed treatment of plumes see Simmons [2000]. For a good introduction, see Sutton and Biblarz [2010].

Depending on the altitude at which the vehicle is flying (ambient pressure, p_a) and the combustion conditions of the rocket, the plume takes on different shapes. Since the area ratio and the chamber pressure usually don't change as the rocket is fired, then there is only one value of ambient pressure for which the rocket exit pressure, p_e, will match the ambient pressure. This exit pressure or altitude is a design parameter. For upper stage engines, which operate at or near vacuum conditions, the bell nozzles have much greater exit-to-throat area ratios than booster engines.

As an example, if we were to test the full nozzle of an upper stage engine exhausting to atmosphere, then for $p_a > \sim 2.5 p_e$ [Sutton and Biblarz, 2010], the flow would separate, creating recirculation zones inside the nozzle. Even if the flow does not separate, creating additional losses, when $p_a > p_e$ we have a loss in thrust as seen in Eq. (18-4). In this situation, the nozzle is said to be overexpanded because the nozzle was "expanded" to a value of exit pressure lower than the value of the ambient pressure (see Thompson [1972] for a nice explanation of supersonic nozzle flow regimes). A system of oblique shocks will be created to bring the pressure up to the ambient value. The initial slope of this plume is contracting. In actual flight, the plume of an upper stage engine would look very different when expanded to vacuum. At high altitudes when the exit pressure is more than the ambient pressure, the nozzle is said to be underexpanded because it did not expand down to the ambient pressure. A series of Prandtl-Meyer expansions will be set up to bring the exhaust pressure down to ambient. In this case, the plume will be expanding. When the nozzle exit and the ambient pressures match, the plume has more of a cylindrical shape.

When designing the propulsion system for a spacecraft, consider where the exhaust of the plume will go. Will it impinge on critical instruments, such as cameras or other optical instruments which can be contaminated, or solar panels where it can alter the effective thrust direction? Unintended torque results if the axis of the thrust force associated with the plume is misaligned with the primary vehicle or spacecraft axes. For example, if the plume impinges on a solar panel, a force is developed (integration of the plume pressure over the impinging surface), which, when multiplied by the moment arm of the thruster to the center of mass of the spacecraft or applicable control axis, results on a torque. If such torques exist, they represent an added burden to the attitude control propulsion system which has to correct them. It is a complicated matter to predict the force the plume exerts on a surface. The analyses vary from quick estimates [Genovese, 1978] to very complicated computational fluid dynamic simulations and direct simulation Monte Carlo methods [Markelov, 2007]. The objective is to understand, among others, the spread of the plume, the chemical composition, and the velocity of the gases as they impinge a surface. In the initial design stages, a rule of thumb for thruster placement is to use a 60 deg half angle cone as a keep-out zone with the origin at the midpoint of the thruster's nozzle throat. The cone half angle is measured from the centerline of the nozzle.

Plumes can transfer significant heat to the spacecraft even if they are directed away from it. High temperature blankets or metallic heat shields are often employed to protect spacecraft surfaces from heating due to thruster radiation and plume impingement. We must consider cases in which thrusters in close proximity fire simultaneously, as well as cases in which operating thrusters thermally affect non-operating thrusters.

The plumes are also very closely studied as identifiers for defense purposes. The emissions are mostly in the infrared range with some in the visible and ultraviolet. The specific wavelengths depend on the propellants used. For example for LH_2/LOX engines, the major plume component is water vapor which has emissions in the infrared at 2.7 and 6.3 μm [Sutton and Biblarz, 2010]. As a note, when a stage event happens and the plume from the starting stage impinges on the discarded stage, a stagnation region will be created between the two stages, and this will create a region of very high temperature which will increase the emission signal of the plume in the infrared. The plume can also attenuate radio and radar signals, so we must consider if the plume is on the communication line between an antenna on the vehicle and an antenna on the ground. The exhaust from solid rockets attenuates communication more than that from liquids. Finally, plumes produce a lot of noise. The level of noise is highest close to the exit plane [Sutton and Biblarz, 2010]. We need to estimate the noise produced by the propulsion system if noise regulations need to be met.

18.5 System Design Elements

Charles M. Zakrzwski,
NASA Goddard Space Flight Center

This section will cover more detailed aspects of spacecraft liquid propulsion design. Figures 18-8 A-C gives a system schematic of representative cold gas, monopropellant, and hypergolic bipropellant systems. One can see the simplicity of a typical cold gas thruster, which consists only of a tank, a couple of valves, a filter,

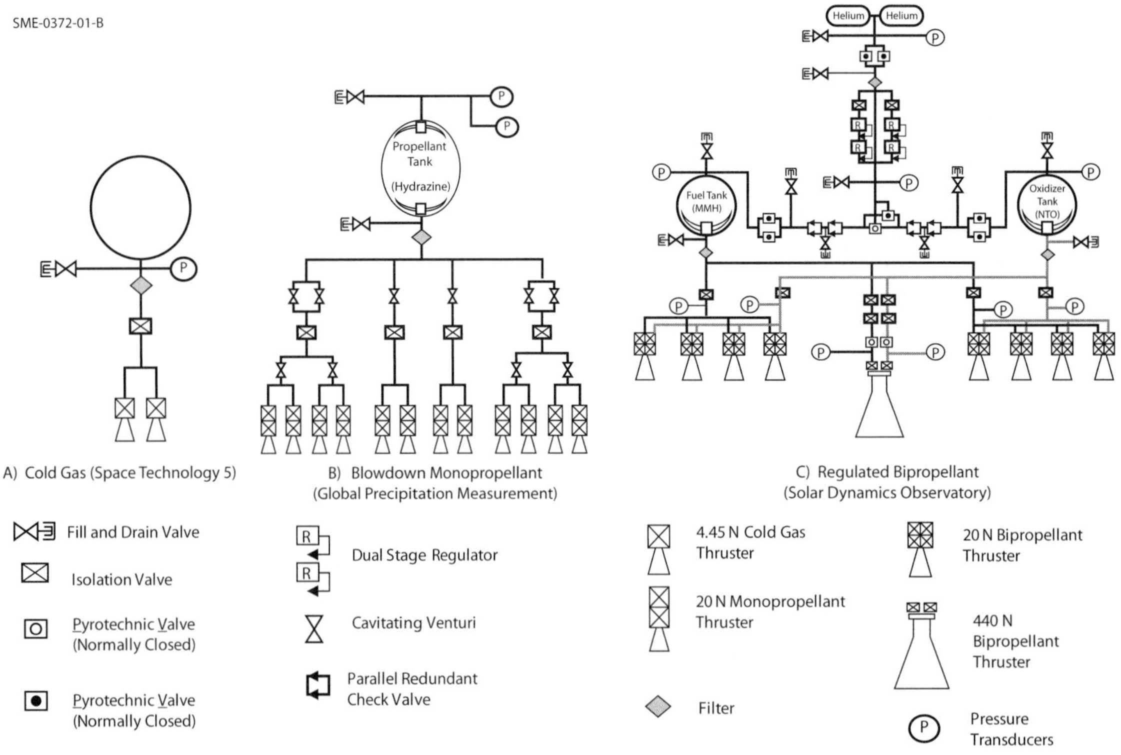

Fig. 18-8. Fluid Schematics of Spacecraft Propulsion Systems.

a pressure transducer and a nozzle. In what follows, we will focus on options for propellant storage and manifolding, pressurization systems, and other miscellaneous elements.

18.5.1 Propellant Storage

Besides thrusters, the tanks required to hold liquid are usually the most important part of a propulsion system. An ideally designed tank would have the lowest possible mass to hold and expel the required amount of propellant at the required pressure while being able to satisfy the volume and mounting constraints of the spacecraft. Because propellant tanks are pressure vessels, for mass efficiency reasons, they commonly are cylindrical or spherical in shape, although ellipsoidal, tear-drop, toroidal, and other shapes have been used.

Most spacecraft propellant tanks are either all metallic, Composite Overwrapped Pressure Vessel (COPV) tanks with metallic liners, or a hybrid of the two in which only cylindrical tank sections are overwrapped. The majority of the qualified and flown metallic tanks have been constructed of titanium, though stainless steel tanks are common and aluminum tanks have also been used in a limited number of cases. The COPV propellant tanks typically have a titanium liner (although stainless steel and aluminum have also been used) with a carbon fiber winding overwrap. Aluminum lined COPV propellant tanks with aluminum Propellant Management Devices (PMD) are being developed specifically to demise upon reentry into the Earth's atmosphere.

Integral to the choice of tanks and overall spacecraft design is the tank mounting provision. Tanks can be mounted in a variety of ways, but the most common methods are boss end mounts, hemispherical ring mounts, or circumferential skirts or tabs. Attention should be given to the most efficient way to mount the tanks so that the combined mass of the tank and spacecraft support structure are minimized. The change in tank size as it is pressurized can be significant. Usually tank mounting designs must make provisions to allow for the expansion and contraction of the tank during pressure cycles. Flexures are often used for this purpose.

Because of the amount of stored energy in both propellant and pressurant tanks, tanks are often the most safety critical component on a spacecraft, and their design, testing, and implementation are governed by several standards [AIAA, 1999; AIAA, 2006; Air Force Space Command, 2004].

Propellant Tank Internal Devices. Devices internal to propellant tanks are used to ensure that only propellant (and not pressurant gas) is expelled from the tanks. If significant pressurant gas is sent through the thrusters, the system can lose its ability to maintain the required pressure, and thruster performance and life can be compromised. Internal fluid management devices can also act as controls on the location and movement of propellant (*slosh*) which can affect attitude control and act as an energy dissipation mechanism for spin-stabilized spacecraft. For spin-stabilized spacecraft or spacecraft using launch vehicles with spin-stabilized stages, it is important to develop an early understanding of how the onboard propellant configuration affects what is known as the nutation time constant. The nutation time constant is the exponential constant, k, in an equation of the form: $\theta = e^{kt}$, where t is time and θ represents the nutation angle, which is the angle between the momentum vector and the coning angle. If θ grows faster than the vehicle control system can compensate, the system will be headed in the wrong direction. Baffles, vanes, screens, bladders, diaphragms, and other internal devices can be added to tanks to help control internal propellant motion, but testing is often required to prove the effectiveness of a particular design. (See discussion of LRO's nutation time constant issue in Sec. 14.6.1). Propellant slosh can also be a concern for 3-axis stabilized spacecraft. Slosh can cause pointing disturbances, and has the potential of being magnified during thruster maneuvers if the periodic thruster force is in resonance with the fluid motion.

To separate liquid propellant from pressurant gas, tanks use either physical barriers or devices that depend on surface tension. *Positive expulsion devices* include diaphragm tanks (both metallic and elastomeric), bladder tanks, bellows tanks, and piston tanks. Elastomeric diaphragms, which are internally attached around the hemisphere of the tank, are perhaps the most common positive expulsion devices because of their large cycle capability and minimal operational constraints. Disadvantages of diaphragms tanks include their higher mass and material incompatibilities with common oxidizers.

Surface tension devices internal to tanks, often referred to as *Propellant Management Devices* (PMD's), come in a variety of designs and levels of complexity. They are typically lighter than positive expulsion devices and are compatible with most fuels and oxidizers. PMD's use surface tension forces to keep fluids separate from gases as fluid is depleted from the tank. The design of PMD's is a specialized field and can be very complicated depending on mission requirements. PMD design relies on empirical and analytical approaches. End-to-end testing of a PMD in zero gravity environments is almost always cost prohibited. Detailed design depends on the detailed mission profile.

Sizing Propellant Tanks. The tank volume required can be found from the density of propellants at the maximum expected operating temperature. The National Institute of Standards and Technology [NIST, 2010]. Table 18-8 lists the density for some common propellants.

Table 18-8. Propellant Densities as a Function of Temperature.

Density (g/cm³)	283 K	293 K	303 K	313 K	323 K
GN₂ @ 27.6 MPa	0.300	0.284	0.273	0.264	0.255
Hydrazine	1.02	1.01	0.999	0.990	0.982
MMH	0.884	0.875	0.866	0.856	0.847
NTO	1.47	1.44	1.42	1.40	1.38

Knowing the propellant mass (M_p) and the density of the propellant (ρ_p) at temperature, the required propellant tank volume (V_p) can be found from the density definition:

$$V_p = \frac{M_p}{\rho_p} \tag{18-26}$$

It is common practice to have a 20% margin on propellant volume at the conceptual study phase to allow for growth in ΔV requirements, spacecraft mass growth, or other factors. As a minimum, it is wise to use at least a 5% margin to allow for the expansion of propellant due to propellant density variations as a function of temperature. For initial trade studies, the mass of a propellant tank can be estimated using empirical data from qualified tank designs. Figures 18-9 and 18-10 show graphs of qualified tank design masses as a function of volume for tanks with PMD and diaphragm operating pressures between 1.4 and 3.1 MPa. These graphs can be used to estimate propellant tank mass. Note that this does not account for differences in propellant expulsion devices or mounting requirements.

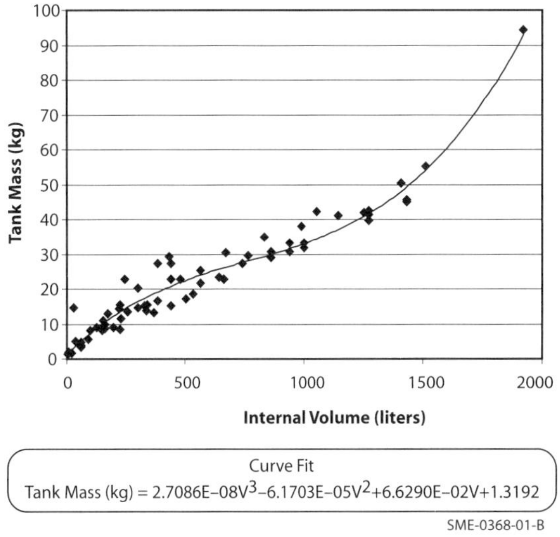

Fig. 18-9. Typical PMD Propellant Tank Mass.

18.5.2 Propellant Manifold

The propellant manifold (or propellant feed system) consists of all the hardware that is required between the propellant tank and the thrusters. Valves integral to thrusters are sometimes considered part of the manifold system because they are relied upon as mechanical inhibiters to thruster firing. For this reason, many thrusters incorporate series redundant valves for fault tolerance. Referring to Fig. 18-8 the various components will be discussed.

Lines and Fittings. The two most common tube and fitting materials are titanium and stainless steel. Titanium tubing is lighter and compatible with oxidizers. Stainless steel is less expensive, more readily available,

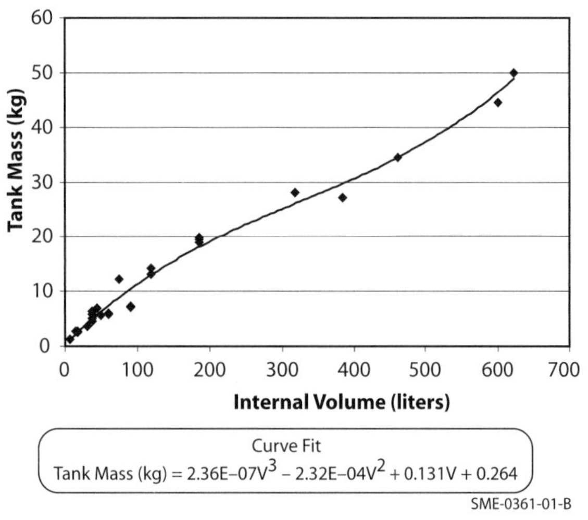

Fig. 18-10. Typical Diaphragm Propellant Tank Mass.

and easier to weld. Fabrication of lines involves the bending, precision cleaning, and chemical passivation of the lines. Integration of manifolds and components is performed in clean rooms to prevent any internal contamination of the propulsion systems.

Isolation Valves. Isolation valves (or latch valves) are valves that can be commanded to an open or closed position and remain in that position without continuous power. They serve several functions like providing a required mechanical inhibit between the tank and the thruster outlet, isolating groups or banks of thrusters in the event of system failures; and isolating individual tanks in a multi-tank system in order to control spacecraft mass properties.

Pyro Valves. Pyro valves are pyrotechnically actuated, one-time-use valves. They can be either normally open (allowing flow until fired closed) or normally closed (preventing flow until fired open). They can serve the same function as isolation valves with the exception that they can only be operated once. The advantages they have over isolation valves include lower leak rates, smaller steady state pressure drop, and smaller mass. Pyro valves are often used to isolate components for safety and reliability concerns during the ground operations and launch phase, or to isolate system components after they have completed their function during the mission. System implementation of pyro valves must include consideration of shock induced from activation.

Filters. The standard practice is to have propellant filters immediately downstream of propellant tanks and any fill and drain valve servicing the tank, since the majority of particulates are likely to come from the tank or fuel itself. The size of the filter is dependent on the amount of propellant required to pass through the filter, the size of particulate filtration, and the allowable steady state pressure drop. In addition to these stand-alone filters, other individual components such as isolation valves, regulators, and thruster can have integral filters. The inclusion of filters in the system does not alleviate the need to maintain strict cleanliness of the propulsion system. Particulate contamination can cause valve leakage or flow blockage that can be mission ending. Chemical contamination can lead to catalyst bed poisoning for monopropellant systems or degradation of material properties in high temperature coatings for bipropellant systems.

Fill and Drain Valves. Some fill and drain valves are used solely for functional testing of components once the system is fully integrated. It is a standard requirement to have access to the fill and drain valves once the spacecraft is in the launch vehicle fairing to allow for emergency offloading of propellants.

Pressure Transducers. Pressure monitoring is required for propellant loading, pressurization, and ground operations. Pressure monitoring on orbit is also used to evaluate the performance of the system, to indicate possible failures, and to estimate parameters such as thrust, specific impulse, and propellant mass consumption.

Flow Control Orifices. They are typically simple, machined fittings welded in line with the system manifold. Flow control orifices are sometimes used to equalize any difference in pressure drops between fuel and oxidizer feed lines so that the ideal thruster mixture ratio is maintained. Flow control orifices are also used to minimize the transient flow in propulsion systems that can cause damaging internal pressure spikes. Pressure spikes of this nature, called *water-hammer* events are common in the plumbing and piping industry. Water-hammer events occur in liquid propulsion systems when valves command to change state. (You may have experienced water hammer in your home plumbing system if you suddenly turn a faucet on or off.)

18.5.3 Aspects of Pressurization Systems

Blow-Down Systems. A blow-down system is one in which an initial gas volume (or ullage) in a propellant tank system is pressurized to a beginning-of-life pressure and then allowed to expand and decrease in pressure as propellant is consumed. This simple pressurization scheme can save on the cost and complexity of a regulated pressurization system. To use this type of system the mission must allow for the required tank volume and accommodate decreasing thrust levels as the mission proceeds. Blow-down systems are more common on cold gas and monopropellant systems since monopropellant thrusters are typically qualified over a wide range of thruster inlet operating pressures (5.5–2.4 MPa). Bipropellant systems often have a limitation on the allowable inlet pressure range because of the need to have an acceptable fuel to oxidizer mixture ratio. Because of this, the blow-down pressure range for bipropellants is limited. It is common to have bipropellant systems start off in a pressure regulated mode, and then transition to a blow-down mode once the ullage in the propellant tank is sufficiently large to allow for blow-down operation.

Regulated Systems. Pressure regulated systems are, as the term implies, systems in which the propellant tank pressure is regulated at a fixed pressure over part or all of the mission life. The advantages of pressure regulated

Table 18-8◀, Fig. 18-10, Eq. 18-26◀

Table 18-9. Pressurant Gas Density as a Function of Temperature and Pressure.

	Nitrogen Gas Density (kg/m³)				Helium Gas Density (kg/m³)			
	293 K	303 K	313 K	323 K	293 K	303 K	313 K	323 K
13.8 MPa	156.2	150.0	144.3	139.1	21.26	20.61	19.99	19.41
20.7 MPa	224.9	216.1	208.0	200.6	30.94	30.02	29.15	28.33
27.6 MPa	284.0	273.4	263.6	254.6	40.06	38.90	37.81	36.78
34.4 MPa	333.8	322.2	311.4	301.4	48.68	47.31	46.02	44.79

systems include; maximizing the propellant that can be carried in a given tank volume, providing for consistent thrust and impulse levels, and providing consistent mixture ratios for bipropellant systems. The pressurant gas, most often He or N_2, is stored in high pressure tanks (typically at 13.8 to 41.4 MPa) and regulated to the operational pressure of the propellant tanks or thrusters. Regulation is performed by a mechanical regulator or, in some cases, a series of high-pressure valves commanded open and closed by a pressure feedback control loop.

Pressurant Mass Determination. To obtain a first order estimate of the mass of pressurant gas and the size and mass of the high pressure tank, you can work backwards from the end-of-life pressure required and total propellant tank volume. (For a detailed determination of pressurant gas mass you must consider the effects of the pressurant gas dissolving into the propellant, which is a function of pressure, temperature, and the type of fluids being used.) For a pressure regulated system, the following steps can be taken as a first approximation.

1. Estimate a maximum beginning of life operating pressure and temperature of the high pressure tank. This would be the operational design requirements for the pressurant tank. Choose 27.6 MPa at 323 K as a starting point if you have no other inputs.
2. Determine the density of the pressurant gas at this state using a lookup table.
3. Assuming the ideal gas law, $PV = nRT$, for the end of life condition we can write:

$$V_{total} = \frac{M_{gas} R_{gas} T}{P} \tag{18-27}$$

where P is the end-of-life (EOL) tank pressure, which is often assumed to be the lowest acceptable thruster inlet pressure. The pressurant gas mass, M_{gas}, is unknown. R_{gas} is the specific gas constant of the pressurant gas and is found by dividing the universal gas constant by the molecular weight of the pressurant gas. T is the gas temperature at end of life and can be assumed to be the lowest operating temperature of the tanks. V_{total} is the total gas volume of both the propellant tank and pressurant tank as shown in Eq. (18-28).

$$V_{total} = V_p + V_{pres} \tag{18-28}$$

V_p is the propellant tank volume which was found above in Sec. 18.5.1., V_{pres} is the pressurant tank volume which is unknown. Assuming all of the pressurant gas is held within the high-pressure tank at the beginning of life (BOL) we have from the density equation

$$V_{pres} = \frac{M_{gas}}{\rho} \tag{18-29}$$

Here ρ is the density of the pressurant gas at maximum pressure and temperature found in Step 2. Substituting Eqs. (18-27) and (18-29) into Eq. (18-28) we get the following equation for the pressurant gas mass.

$$M_{gas} = \frac{PV_p}{\left(R_{gas}T - P/\rho\right)} \tag{18-30}$$

Solve for the pressurant mass with the assumed EOL tank pressure and EOL tank temperature. As an initial estimate, 689 kPa at 293 K for these EOL values can be used.

4. Determine the pressurant tank volume from the gas density and mass (Eq. 18-29).
5. With the assumed beginning-of-life maximum operating pressure of the pressurant tank from step 1 and derived pressurant tank volume from step 4, the graph in Fig. 18-11 can be used to estimate the pressurant tank mass. Figure 18-11 uses this maximum operating pressure multiplied by the volume as a way to indicate the pressurant gas mass capability of tanks. The plotted points corresponds to flight tank data with all metallic tanks represented by the x's and composite overwrapped tanks represented by the o's. A curve fit for each tank type is given to estimate the tanks mass for a given pressure-volume parameter.

Both all-metallic and COPV tanks are included on this graph. The transition from all-metallic to COPV obviously occurs around a PV of 1.2 MPa × m³.

Regulators. Mechanical regulators are commonly used, although as mentioned previously, electronically controlled valves in a pressure feedback system have also been used. The selection of a regulator is a function of such parameters as; the desired operating pressure, the range of flow rates required, the regulator *lock-up pres-*

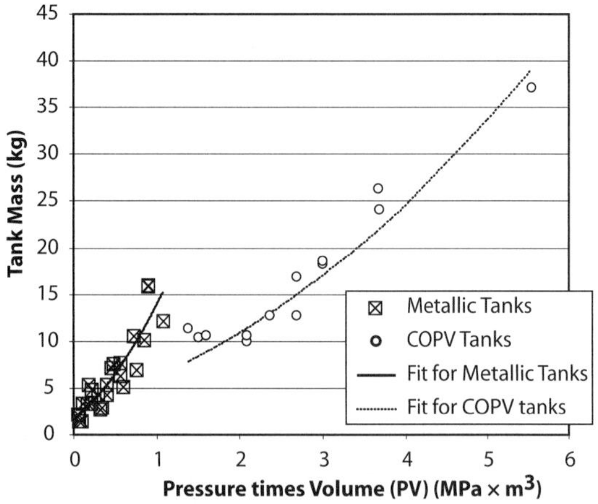

Metallic Tank Mass (kg) = 5.4548 × $(PV)^2$ + 6.6092 × (PV) + 1.862
COPV Tank Mass= 0.7266 × $(PV)^2$ + 2.5119 × (PV) + 2.9826

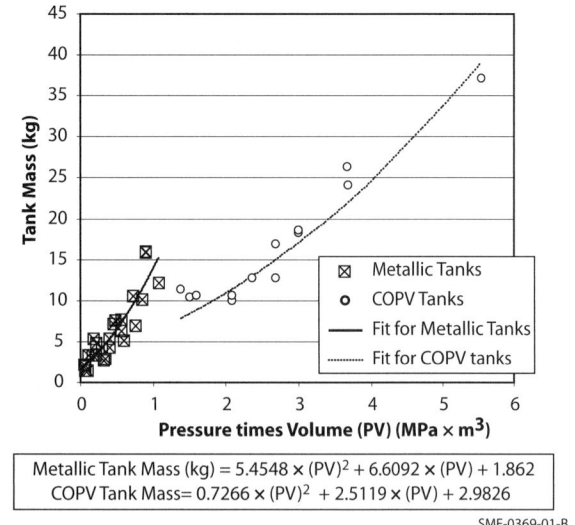

SME-0369-01-B

Fig. 18-11. Pressurant Tank Mass as a Function of Operating Pressure Times Volume.

sure (the minimum downstream pressure at which the regulator closes completely), the maximum upstream pressure, and the minimum opening pressure. Another common consideration is the ability of the regulator to handle a "*slam start*" event. Slam start occurs when a sudden high-pressure surge is initiated by an upstream pyro valve or isolation valve being opened. Regulators will take time to react and the system will have a limit on the amount of gas allowed to pass downstream before the regulator reaches its normal operating condition. Also, it is a good practice not to rely on regulators to isolate high-pressure sources from low-pressure tanks over long durations (several months or greater) because of the potential for leakage. Isolation valves or pyro valves are often used instead.

Check Valves. Check valves are used to allow gas flow in one direction but prevent gas from flowing in the opposite direction. They are commonly used to prevent fuel and oxidizer vapors from migrating from the gas side of the propellant tanks and mixing with one another in shared pressurization systems. Most bipropellants pressurize both fuel and oxidizer from a common regulated gas source in order to have a reliable mixture ratio at the thrusters. If fuel and oxidizer vapor mix, there is a strong potential for combustion which will cause catastrophic system failure.

18.5.4 Other System Considerations

Thermal Integration. Although temperature limits can vary slightly, typical hydrazine and non-cryogenic bipropellants have temperatures ranging from 281 to 323 K. Many spacecraft configurations will require that part or all of the propellant lines be wrapped with heaters to keep the propellant above a minimum temperature. Individual flow components may have heaters placed directly on them or on mounting brackets or plates. These heaters are typically etched foil elements enclosed on both sides by Kapton® film. Propellant tanks are typically covered with heaters attached to the outside of the tanks. The poor thermal conductivity of titanium, stainless steel, and carbon windings drives the thermal design such that relatively low power heaters cover a large portion of the components. Often, aluminum or even copper tape is used to distribute the heat from the heaters to the rest of the components. In most situations the propellant lines, components, and tanks have individual blankets. These heaters, tape, wiring, and blankets can add significant mass.

Hydrazine thrusters typically require preheating of the catalyst bed prior to operation of the thruster. Catalyst bed heaters are usually heated for a predetermined time prior to thruster operation instead of relying on temperature monitoring. This power is usually book kept under the thruster's operating power instead of thermal system power.

Another thermal concern is the temperature drop due to pressurant gas expansion as propellant is consumed. This is primarily a concern for long or high thrust burns in which the pressurant gas is expanded at a rate that does not allow for relative thermal equilibrium between the tank and gas. It is possible for the temperature in the pressurant tanks to decrease dramatically (for example a change of over 50 K may be possible). To accommodate large burns you can start with a high initial gas temperature before the start of the burn, or you can heat the pressurant gas through a heat exchanger before it reaches critical components.

Electrical Interfaces. Electronics are required to operate propulsion systems. Drive electronics for propulsion valves (thruster valves, isolation valves, and pyro valves) supply the appropriate power to actuate valves and account for effects such as the back EMF (Electro-Magnetic Field) seen with solenoids. Valve drive electronics are often part of the attitude control subsystem because they must work in union with the rest of the spacecraft control system. Sometimes pyro valve drivers are placed on a separate pyro valve bus with other pyrotechnic components. Power to the propulsion survival heaters often comes directly from the spacecraft power supply subsystem. Power for catalyst bed heaters and pressure transducers may also come directly from the power subsystem or from an attitude control box. Propulsion telemetry, which is primarily pressure, temperature, and valve position readings, is sometimes handled directly by the spacecraft command and data handling subsystem.

18.6 Electric Propulsion

William Hargus,
Air Force Research Laboratory

Electric propulsion traces its roots to Robert Goddard and others who independently determined that, unlike chemical propulsion, which is limited to intrinsic molecular bond energy, electric propulsion has the capability to increase specific impulse to values of 20,000 sec or more [Jahn, 1968; Goddard and Penray, 1970; Choueriri, 2004]. Despite this early recognition of the potential benefits of electric propulsion, routine electric propulsion flight did not occur until the early 1990s. Although confined to low thrust applications due to limited on-board power generation and storage, electric propulsion is presently one of the more dynamic and inventive propulsion fields.

18.6.1 Classification by Acceleration Mechanism

Although there are a multitude of thruster concepts, electric propulsion may be divided into three general classes by the mechanism by which the propellant is accelerated [Jahn, 1968].

18.6.1.1 Electrothermal

In electrothermal electric propulsion, propellants are electrically heated and then expanded through a nozzle. There are several energy deposition methods by which electrothermal acceleration of propellants may be realized. These vary from relatively simple resistive heaters *(resistojets)* and slightly more complex electrical arc heaters *(arcjets)*, both of which accelerate their heated propellant through a supersonic converging-diverging nozzle [Jahn, 1968], to more exotic laser ablative thrusters, which have demonstrated that a nozzle is not necessary due to the two dimensional isentropic expansion of the superheated ablation products from a surface [Phipps, 2006].

For electrothermal thrusters, the rocket Eqs. (18-13 and 18-18) hold and light propellants will yield the highest specific impulse. The use of propellants containing carbon and oxygen is generally avoided due to carbon deposits shorting across electrodes and oxidation of refractory metal nozzles. However, various electrodeless thruster concepts utilizing inductively coupled, or microwave resonance cavity, plasmas have been developed in the laboratory to overcome this limitation [Hruby et al., 1997; Balaam and Micci, 1995; Sullivan et al., 2004].

18.6.1.2 Electrostatic

In electrostatic propulsion, electric fields are used to accelerate charged particles. The force acting on a charged particle in the presence of electric and magnetic fields is described by the Lorentz equation [Jahn, 1968; Wangsness, 1986].

$$\boldsymbol{F} = q(\boldsymbol{E} + \boldsymbol{v} \times \boldsymbol{B}) \tag{18-31}$$

where $\boldsymbol{F}$ is the force on a charged particle of charge q and velocity $\boldsymbol{v}$ produced by electric field $\boldsymbol{E}$ and magnetic field $\boldsymbol{B}$. For electrostatic electric propulsion, where there is no magnetic field or it does not contribute substantially to the propellant acceleration, Eq. (18-31) reduces to $\boldsymbol{F} = q\boldsymbol{E}$.

An interesting system level issue for electrostatic electric propulsion is that heavy propellants are preferred to light propellants. This preference stems from limited spacecraft electrical power. Using the definition of I_{sp} and defining the thruster efficiency η as the quotient of the output directed kinetic energy flux

$$\frac{1}{2}\dot{m}V_e^2 = \frac{1}{2}Tg_o I_{sp} \tag{18-32}$$

and the input electrical power P_{elec}, Eq. (18-33) illustrates the limiting relationship between P_{elec}, T, and I_{sp} [Jahn, 1968].

$$T = \frac{2P_{elec}\eta}{g_o I_{sp}} \tag{18-33}$$

where g_o = 9.80665 m/s, is the Earth's gravitational constant, and I_{sp} is the thruster's specific impulse. Since electrical potentials of several hundred volts are required to accelerate ion beams, light ions produce very high specific impulses, but correspondingly low thrust levels at constant thruster power. High mass ions have long been used to increase thrust levels but consequently the I_{sp} is lowered. This is strongly preferred in Earth orbit where customer demand often dictates shorter orbit transfer times. For interplanetary missions, high specific impulse may alternatively be the mission enabler.

The original propellants of interest for electrostatic thrusters during early development efforts in the 1960s and 1970s were cesium and mercury, but owing to their toxicity, modern thrusters generally use xenon, although krypton and bismuth have received recent attention [Jahn, 1968; Goebel and Katz, 2008]. Electrostatic thrusters must also neutralize the accelerated ion beam to ensure the spacecraft is not charged negative by the emitted positive ion beam. Due to charge separation during acceleration by electric fields, neutralization of the ion beam is required of all electrostatic thrusters. The use of dedicated neutralizers, particularly hollow cathode electron sources, generally requires very high propellant purity (less than 10 ppm oxygen or water) in order to avoid oxidation, and subsequent failure, of the sensitive, easily poisoned electron sources.

Electrostatic thrusters may be subdivided into two categories. The first includes *gridded* and *Hall effect thrusters*. Gridded thrusters (I_{sp} = 1,500–10,000 sec), often referred to as *ion engines* or *Kaufmann thrusters*, and Hall effect thrusters (I_{sp} = 1,000–3,000 sec) both produce a plasma and then accelerate the positive ions which are subsequently externally neutralized. The primary difference between the two types is that the gridded ion engines produce their electric field between two, or more, very precisely aligned perforated screens, while the Hall effect thrusters magnetize the electrons in order to produce a similar, but less focused, potential difference. A more subtle difference is that ion engines produce and confine their ions non-neutrally, while the Hall effect thrusters retain a net neutral plasma during propellant production and acceleration. Ion thrusters are therefore limited in their specific thrust due to their need to contain substantial charge densities. The second subcategory of electrostatic thruster is the *electrospray* [Zeimer, 2009]. Here, ions, or in some cases charged clusters or droplets, are electrostatically extracted from an electrically conductive liquid and accelerated. Specific impulses ranging from 100 sec to over 20,000 sec have been demonstrated with liquids including doped glycerin, liquid metals, and various ionic liquids (molten salts). It is possible to operate these devices in a bipolar mode where the ion accelerator alternatively extracts positive and then negative ions thus eliminating the need for a dedicated neutralizer. The primary technical barrier to more widespread application of this technology has been the difficulty in scaling from microscopic single emitters to large parallelized ion extraction arrays.

18.6.1.3 Electromagnetic

Electromagnetic electric propulsion can also be described by Eq. (18-31). However, the force on the charged particles is produced by the interaction of the charged particle velocity, and the magnetic field. Since the electric field does not play a significant role in the acceleration of the plasma, Eq. (18-31) reduces to $\boldsymbol{F} = q\boldsymbol{v} \times \boldsymbol{B}$.

Electromagnetic thrusters are not as extensively developed as the other electric propulsion classes. This is due to their need for either a strong magnetic field (oftentimes heavy and complex), or high pulsed power for pulsed operation (unsteady operation). These requirements have been more difficult to accommodate on current spacecraft flown, but the electromagnetic thrusters hold promise for future high power spacecraft. On the other hand, electromagnetic thrusters can use more readily storable propellants. Light propellants, some of which are condensable and therefore more easily stored, can produce good efficiencies (>50%) as well as high specific impulses (2,000–5,000 sec). Since both positive and negative particles are accelerated, neutralizers are not necessary for electromagnetic thrusters.

The two major subcategories of electromagnetic electric propulsion consist of applied magnetic field and self-induced magnetic field devices [Jahn, 1968]. However, most development has focused on self-field devices. This is due to the limited spacecraft power and mass available for propulsion that precludes heavy permanent or electromagnets. As a result, electromagnetic thruster development has, for the most part, concentrated on pulsed low-power devices with high instantaneous powers so that the requisite magnetic fields are self-generated as in the case of the *pulsed plasma thruster* (PPT) [Burton and Turchi, 1998].

One significant drawback of pulsed systems is that pulse-forming networks usually rely on large capacitors. This short-term energy storage requirement makes many electromagnetic thrusters relatively high mass devices. However, scaling studies show that in electromagnetic electric propulsion, specific impulse and efficiency both increase with power. As a result, there is continuing interest in the development of high power electromagnetic thrusters with the assumption that electrical power levels on spacecraft will routinely reach several hundred kW in the coming decades.

18.6.2 Thruster Selection and Critical Subsystems

Selection of an appropriate electric propulsion thruster for any particular mission must take into account a number of important engineering constraints, including available power, mass, and volume. Furthermore, the use of electric propulsion, at present, constrains the mission planner to low thrust trajectories. Once all these constraints are identified and understood, a chart such as the one in Fig. 18-12 can be used to select an appropriate thruster.

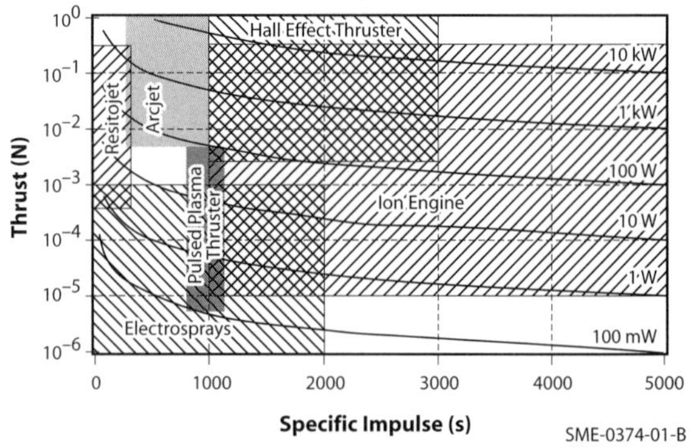

Fig. 18-12. Thruster Operational Envelopes with Respect to Thrust and Specific Impulse. Constant power lines assuming 100% conversion efficiency are included to illustrate electric propulsion thruster electrical power requirements.

It is important to note that there is considerable variability in the operating parameters (namely power) of nearly all electric propulsion thrusters. Thruster performance is usually quoted for an optimal so called *nominal condition*. Usually this condition exhibits peak electrical conversion efficiency, maximum lifetime, most stable operation, or some such combination. However, many steady state electric thrusters may be operated between 25% and 200% of their nominal power. With special regard to electrostatic thrusters, the specific impulse can also be raised and lowered somewhat arbitrarily by varying the applied acceleration potential. It must be stressed that operation at off nominal operating parameters will likely be detrimental to the thruster electrical conversion efficiency in the short term, and lifetime in the long term. The loss of efficiency can generally be discerned from available test data, but the effect of off-nominal operation on lifetime is difficult to predict without ground test verification.

Electric propulsion systems are themselves composed of a number of subsystems. These include the thruster itself, power processing, propellant distribution, tankage, and thruster mounts (sometimes including gimbals). The most complex electric propulsion subsystem is nearly always the *power processing unit (PPU)* subsystem. The PPU regulates the spacecraft bus power and converts it into thruster required electrical potentials and currents. PPU's vary from relatively simple current sources for resistojet heating elements, several independent high voltage DC power supplies for ion engines and Hall thrusters, and extend even to high current, negative impedance arcjet power supplies coupled with pulsed arc initiation start circuits. The PPU subsystem also generally includes valve drivers for the propellant management subsystem and the digital control interface to spacecraft-based command and control.

PPU subsystems required to produce and regulate suitable electrical power for electric thrusters have finite efficiencies that strongly depend on the spacecraft bus voltage since higher bus voltages tend to increase processing efficiency. PPUs can be single set point, multiple set point, or continuously variable over some range. The addition of flexible power operation may decrease efficiencies from above 95% to below 90%. The resulting waste heat must be rejected without adversely affecting the operation of the host spacecraft. Thermal design of electric propulsion systems must be accounted for early in spacecraft design. As an example, consider the difficulties involved in safely rejecting 1 kW of heat from a 10 kW, 90% efficient PPU subsystem mounted within a spacecraft.

Although often viewed as the products of conventional electrical engineering, PPUs are usually the most expensive and massive component of an electric propulsion system. Space rated precision control of electrical power (typically 1–5 kW, but modules of 30 kW have been flown [Cassidy, 2002]) is expensive. The regular obsolescence of space-rated analog and digital electronic components require constant minor redesign, and discourages low rate production of power processing subsystems as prohibitively expensive for commercial spaceflight activities.

There are a number of additional subsystems usually required for an electric propulsion thruster system. The *propellant management* subsystem transfers and regulates the flow of propellant from the propellant storage tank to the thruster. For gas-fed systems, the assembly minimally consists of a pressure regulator to lower the propellant pressure to a working pressure, followed by a flow regulator with appropriate feedback. Liquid electrothermal systems using monopropellants will add a catalyst bed to convert the storable liquid into a suitable gas.

Propellant storage is generally critical for electric propulsion, particularly electrostatic thrusters that use xenon propellant. These thrusters have high propellant purity requirements, and up to now, require metal-lined tanks capable of withstanding approximately 15 MPa, yielding a storage specific gravity of greater than 1. For most electrothermal systems, propellant storage is a modified version of that used for hydrazine monopropellant systems. Although gimbals add complexity, electric propulsion is well suited to complex gimbal mechanisms. The low thrust levels, and the need to reduce the possibility of high energy plumes interacting with the spacecraft surfaces can make the added complexity worthwhile on the system level [Pidgeon et al., 2006].

18.6.3 Existing Systems

The following are electric propulsion thrusters (organized by thruster technology) that have spaceflight experience, or substantial preparation for flight. These systems represent the bulk of flight capable electric propulsion at present. It should be cautiously noted that there are always developers with new electric propulsion concepts. While the propellant acceleration mechanism often engenders substantial research interest (and sometimes passion), the critical support subsystems (e.g., propellant management and storage, power processing) are unfortunately often viewed as small issues to be resolved later. This is poor engineering practice and the complete propulsion system must always be considered *in toto*.

While most rocket propulsion texts have introductory sections dealing with electric propulsion, the content is often times not up-to-date [Hill and Peterson, 1992; Sutton and Biblarz, 2010]. While dated, Jahn's text on electric propulsion [1968] remains the most complete source on the subject. Several recent texts with updated electric propulsion descriptions are available [Tajmar 2003; Micci and Ketsdever, 2000; Goebel and Katz, 2008]. However, due to the strong academic research in the field, the most recent advances are best documented in the technical literature, most notably proceedings from AIAA and ERPS (Electric Rocket Propulsions Society) conferences, as well as peer-reviewed journals.

18.6.3.1 Electrothermal Systems

Electrothermal propulsion represents the vast majority of spacecraft electric propulsion heritage. Most are resistojets, but there are also a significant number of arcjets. The propellant for nearly all is hydrazine, but there are a few cases where ammonia has been used for its higher specific impulse. The common use of hydrazine is due to flight heritage and the ease of reliable exothermic gasification through catalyst beds. Although capable of higher specific impulses (800 sec versus 600 sec for hydrazine), ammonia has much more limited flight experience and requires auxiliary heaters for reliable gasification. Table 18-10 presents available resistojets. Similarly, Table 18-11 presents available arcjets. In most cases, the thrusters have flight heritage, or substantial flight preparation. With only one exception, power levels for flight proven electrothermal thrusters are below 2 kW. The sole exception is the 26 kW ESEX arcjet that flew on an experimental demonstration in 1999 [Cassidy, 2002].

Resistojets, due to their simplicity, only offer approximately an 80 s increase in specific impulse over hydrazine monopropellants. Yet, since they also use hydrazine propellant, resistojets can utilize existing qualified propellant management systems. This ease of transition coupled with their low power levels (<1 kW) have allowed this technology to proliferate widely. Arcjets have extended the electric propulsion inroads of resistojets by substantially increasing specific impulse at the expense of more complex power processing and increased power consumption. The adoption of arcjets for north-south GEO station keeping reduces fully fueled propulsion

Table 18-10. Resistojet Nominal Operating Parameters. [Aerojet, 2003a; Surrey, 2007; Smith, 2006]

Manufacturer	Name	Power (W)	Propellant	I_{sp} (s)	Thrust (mN)	Thruster Mass (kg)
Aerojet	MR-502A	750	N_2H_4	300	395	0.9
Aerojet	MR-502B	500	N_2H_4	300	235	0.9
SSTL	LPR	15-30	Butane/Xe/N_2	55-100	100	0.2

Table 18-11. Arcjet Thruster Nominal Operating Parameters. [Messerschimd et al., 1996; Aerojet, 2003b; Aerojet, 2003c; Lichon et al., 1996; Cassidy, 2002]

Manufacturer	Name	Power (kW)	Propellant	I_{sp} (s)	Thrust (mN)	Thruster and PPU Mass (kg)
Univ. Stuttgart	ATOS	0.75	NH_3	480	115	5.0
Aerojet	MR-509	1.8	N_2H_4	502	254	5.5
Aerojet	MR-510	1.8	N_2H_4	600	258	5.6
Aerojet	LPATS	0.5	N_2H_4	475	85	4.3
Aerojet	ESEX	26	NH_3	815	2,000	55

system mass to approximately 35% that of the hydrazine system it replaces. It should also be noted that alternative propellants, such as hydrogen or helium, can offer substantial improvements in specific impulse, but are not yet practical since they require cryogenic storage.

18.6.3.2 Electrostatic Systems

Goebel and Katz [2008] present the most up to date discussion on flight-qualified ion engine and Hall effect thruster propulsion systems. Table 18-12 provides a listing of currently available commercial ion engines from a variety of American, European, and Asian suppliers. At present, flight proven electrostatic thrusters operate at power levels below 5 kW; however, several thrusters under development may exceed this by a factor of 4, and ground demonstrations have shown that thrusters can be easily clustered.

For these ion engine systems, system level mass can be approximated as follows. Thruster mass will scale 7 kg/kW with higher values for lower nominal thruster power levels. Propellant power management mass can be estimated to be 5–6 kg/kW for high power systems (>5 kW), and slightly higher for lower power ion thruster systems. An additional 5–10 kg must be allocated for propellant management. The propellant of all systems presented in Table 18-12 is xenon, which can be stored at pressures of approximately 13 MPa with a specific gravity near 1. Despite the high pressures, the tankage fraction is approximately 10%. These values represent reasonable estimates at the time of this publication and may be reduced as more specialized and integrated systems are constructed. It should also be noted that a number of small ion engines (200 W, or less) have been and continue to be developed, primarily by universities [Takao et al., 2006; Loeb, Feili, and Meyer, 2004]. These

Table 18-12. Nominal Operating Parameters of Available Ion Engines. [Goebel and Katz, 2008; Astrium EADS, 2010; QinetiQ, 2004]

Manufacturer	Name	Grid Diameter (cm)	Power (kW)	I_{sp} (s)	Thrust (mN)	Efficiency (%)
L3	XIPS-13	13	0.42	2,500	17.2	50
L3	XIPS-25	25	2.0–4.3	3,500	80–166	68
L3/NASA	NSTAR	29	0.5–2.3	<3,100	<92	<61
JPL	NEXIS	65	15–25	<8,500	<500	<81
Aerojet/NASA	NEXT	36	0.5–6.9	<4,200	<236	<70
Qinetiq	T-5	10	0.48	3,200	18	55
Qinetiq	T-6	30	5.0	4,700	145	NA
Astrium	RIT-10	10	0.46	3,400	15	52
Astrium	RIT-XT	21	5.0	4,500	150	NA
Mitsubishi	μ10	10	0.34	3,100	8.1	36
Mitsubishi	ETS-8	12	0.57	2,500	22	48

Table 18-12, Fig. 18-12◄, Eq. 18-33◄

Table 18-13. Nominal Operating Parameters of Available Hall Effect Thrusters. [Goebel and Katz, 2008; Pidgeon et al., 2006; Semenkin, 1999; Aerojet, 2003c; Busek, 2007a; Busek, 2007b]

Manufacturer	Name	Power (kW)	I_{sp} (s)	Thrust (mN)	Efficiency (%)
Fakel EDB	SPT-50	0.35	1,100	20	35
Fakel EDB	SPT-70	0.70	1,500	40	45
Fakel EDB	SPT-100	1.35	1,600	80	50
Fakel EDB	SPT-140	4.5	1,750	300	55
SNECMA	PPS-1350	1,500	1,650	88	55
Busek	BHT-200	0.200	1,390	13	44
Busek	BHT-600	0.600	1,650	42	55
Busek	BHT-8000	8.0	1,900	512	60
Busek	BHT-20K	20.3	2,750	1,080	70
Aerojet	BPT-4000	4.5	1,770	290	55
TsNIIMASH	D-55	1.3	1,730	77	53
TsNIIMASH	D-110	3.0	2,000	1,777	60

are not included in Table 18-12 due to their large number and lack of flight experience. However, these thrusters may also be of interest to the spacecraft designer, particularly for small satellites.

Table 18-13 provides a listing of representative Hall effect thrusters from a variety of American and European suppliers. Of these thrusters, the SPT-100 constructed by the Russian Fakel Engineering Design Bureau (EDB) is the most widely flown and emulated. This thruster has been exported to a number of nations and is at present the most popular Hall effect thruster in orbit. Hall effect thrusters from other nations have seen more limited flight activity.

As is the case for ion engines, there is also a number of smaller Hall effect thrusters under development [Ito et al., 2007; Warner et al., 2006]. Again, these are primarily efforts of universities and other research labs. As such, they do not have support subsystems such as power processing systems or propellant management assemblies readily available. Hall effect thruster system masses may be approximated using nearly identical specific powers as for ion engine systems. Figure 18-13 shows a pair of SPT-100 on a spacecraft during assembly. Note that only the thrusters are visible and the ancillary subsystems are generally placed within the visible structure.

18.6.3.3 Electromagnetic Systems

Flight electromagnetic thrusters have, with one notable exception, been limited to pulsed-plasma thrusters (PPT). PPTs generally function by using a pulsed electric discharge across the face of a solid block of propellant. The instantaneous current is sufficiently large that a strong magnetic field is induced. Combined, the electric field and induced magnetic field electromagnetically accelerate ionized propellant with specific impulses ranging from 300 sec to 50,000 sec and efficiencies starting at 10% and rising substantially with specific impulse up to greater than 50% [Burton and Turchi, 1998].

Table 18-14 presents a summary of US flown PPT systems. These are listed by their spacecraft name as they have generally been single point designs for the past 35 years. The reader will notice that rather than thrust, T, impulse bit ($I_{bit} = \int T dt$) is presented as the momentum flux performance parameter. Since these thrusters are by their very nature, pulsed, their time-integrated momentum flux (i.e., time-integrated thrust) through a single electromagnetic propellant acceleration event constitutes a single impulse bit, I_{bit}. The solid propellant for all systems in Table 18-14 is polytetrafluoroethylene (PTFE, C_nF_{2n+2}) better known by the DuPont brand name Teflon. Other polymers have been examined in the laboratory, but have not proved viable.

Fig. 18-13. Photograph Showing a Fakel EDB SPT-100 Mounted on a Space Systems Loral Spacecraft Under Construction. Note the two Hall effect thrusters on this side of the spacecraft, one with a safety cover. (Photo courtesy of Space Systems Loral.)

The attraction of PPT technology to spacecraft designers has been and remains the simplicity of integration of these thrusters onto a spacecraft. The thruster does not require a propellant feed system or tankage. The only connections required to the spacecraft are bus

Table 18-14. Pulsed Plasma Thruster Nominal Operating Characteristics. [Burton and Turchi, 1998; Arrington and Haag, 1999; Busek, 2007c]

Thruster Designation	Discharge Energy (J)	I_{sp} (s)	I_{bit} (mN-s)	I_{bit}/Discharge (mN-s/J)	Specific Energy (mg/J)
LES-6	1.85	300	26	14	4.8
SMS	8.4	450	133	15	3.4
LES-8/9	20	1,000	297	15	1.5
TIP-II(NOVA)	20	850	375	19	2.3
MIPD-3	100	1,130	2,250	23	2.0
Millipound	750	1,210	22,300	30	2.5
EO-1	43	1,136	737	60	10.0
MPACS	1.96	827	80	41	10.0

power and rudimentary control. In the case of the MPACS PPT on the FalconSat-3 spacecraft, switching thruster power on and off is the control strategy [Busek, 2007c]. For a particular thruster, the impulse bit is linear with discharge energy. Another advantage of PPT technology is the very precise impulse bits achievable. As a result, the primary usage of PPTs has been very accurate propulsive attitude control. In fact, the Earth Observer 1 (EO-1) spacecraft reported that the jitter of using their PPT was approximately 10 times less than using momentum wheels [Arrington and Haag, 1999].

The system level mass of these thrusters can be typified by using the LES-8/9 PPT as an example [Burton, 1998]. This thruster has a total mass of 6.6 kg of which only 750 g was polytetrafluoroethylene propellant. The capacitor mass consumes an additional 1.93 kg, while the controls and structure represent the remaining 3.92 kg. Almost certainly, the non-propellant mass can be reduced with recent advances in capacitor technology and electronics, as well as in the optimization of the structural mass; however, the use of solid propellant makes the propellant feed difficult to arbitrarily expand to increase total impulse capability.

Magnetoplasmadynamic (MPD) thrusters superficially resemble the arcjets from which they were originally derived; however, they accelerate their propellant at much lower densities and to much higher exit velocities via the Lorentz force [Jahn, 1968]. MPD thrusters offer a number of potential advantages, especially at high power. They are capable of operating with large thrust densities at high power, are mechanically and electrically relatively simple, may operate on a variety of propellants (hydrazine to noble gases), and are capable of variable specific impulse. Unfortunately, MPD thruster application has been stymied by low thrust efficiencies at low power.

One experimental MPD has been flown by the Japanese space agency in 1996 [Toki et al., 2000]. This 43 kg demonstration MPD thruster system used hydrazine propellant and pulsed self-field configuration with a 120 μs pulse with a peak instantaneous power of approximately 720 kW and a peak current of 6 kA at a potential of 120 V (average power of 480 W). It produced impulse bits of 3.6 mN-s with an I_{sp} of 1,000 sec at a firing frequency of 0.5–1.8 Hz. Although a low-power flight demonstration, this experiment demonstrated the on-orbit use of pulsed electromagnetic propulsion.

18.6.4 Future Technologies

A number of electric propulsion technologies are on the cusp of flight development. Several thrusters, such as very large Hall effect thrusters, ion engines, or full sized MPD thrusters, have already been extensively developed in the laboratory and await adequate spacecraft power levels. Many other electric propulsion concepts also have a substantial pedigree, but due to various factors, these technologies have not yet been fully implemented. The amount of development to be realized for each future electric thruster depends on the tractability of the underlying physics as well as the willingness of the spacecraft community to underwrite the expense of a complete propulsion system. For successful fielding of an electric thruster, the systems must include such mundane subsystems as propellant feed and storage as well as the critical PPU system that are all too often ignored in the laboratory.

Despite having relatively low specific impulse, electrothermal propulsion remains a field of active development. Concepts being pursued include very small resistojets for use on miniature spacecraft [Ferguson and Sovey, 1967; Smith, 2006]. Other technologies of interest include electrodeless thrusters, most notably propellant heating using microwave resonance cavities [Sullivan, 2004], inductive coupling [Gesto, 2006], or laser ablation [Phipps et al., 2004]. The goal of these new electrothermal thrusters is to be able to use propellants with oxygen, and/or carbon that are more storable, exhibit higher performance, and are less toxic than hydrazine. There is also some discussion of multimode propulsion where a single propellant is used for both onboard chemical and electric propulsion systems, thereby providing considerably increased mission flexibility.

In addition to the scaling up of electrostatic thrusters [Jacobson et al., 2003], several programs are investigating the boosting of specific impulse of Hall effect thrusters above 3,000 sec for interplanetary missions, primarily to take advantage of commercial Hall effect thruster system-level investments [Vial, 2009; Peterson et al., 2005; Hofer and Gallimore, 2006]. Hall effect thruster developers are also examining alternative propellants such as krypton [Linnell et al., 2006], bismuth [Tverdokhlebov et al., 2002], and iodine [Dressler, 2000].

Probably the most exciting ongoing research in electrostatic thrusters is the development of massively parallel arrays of electrosprays [Smith et al., 2009; Legge et al., 2007; Zeimer, 2009]. If the efficiencies demonstrated for single emitters can be maintained over thousands, or millions, of microscopic emitters, it may be possible to develop electrostatic thrusters of very large power levels with greater than 80% electrical efficiency over wide ranges of specific impulse, using condensed phase propellant storage. Progress in this technology lies not in improving on the physics of the propellant acceleration, but in the engineering of the parallel arrays and requisite propellant distribution system.

High power electromagnetic thruster development has long focused on MPD thrusters, which scale best for power levels above 100 kW. Metallic propellants such as lithium have been proposed [Tikhonov, 1997], but lifetimes are expensive to verify and spacecraft interactions with condensable metallic propellants are worrisome. Other devices such as pulsed inductive thrusters (PIT) [Mikellides and Neilly, 2007], the field reversed configurations (FRC) [Martin and Eskridge, 2005], the variable specific impulse magneto-plasma rocket (VASIMR) [Chang-Diaz, 2000], and several other plasmoid accelerators [Choueriri, 2006; Poehlmann et al., 2007] are also currently being investigated as potential high power thruster technologies (Sec. 18.7.4). These systems scale well for very high power systems and are not limited by propellant selection.

18.7 Alternative Propulsion Systems for In-Space Use

Marcus Young,
Air Force Research Laboratory

Research and development is very active in the space propulsion field in general: flight-qualified propulsion systems are continuously being improved; steady research is being conducted on alternative, but not yet adopted, propulsion systems, and entirely new types of propulsion systems are being investigated. It is useful to stay up-to-date on propulsion research because significant developments in either space access or in-space propulsion systems may enable entirely new classes of space missions. This section summarizes the state of development of in-space propulsion systems as of 2010.

The state of development of emerging propulsion technologies is commonly measured relative to the DoD or NASA (TRL) defined in Sec. 1.3.4. We will focus primarily on the most fundamental characteristics of propulsion technologies with intermediate TRLs, 3–6.

In-space propulsion systems are, in general, physically smaller than space access systems and are applied to a much broader range of applications which leads to a much wider range of useful technologies. A primary difference is the inclusion of electric propulsion systems which have significantly higher specific impulses at significantly lower thrust levels. Development continues on the entire range of systems and only a very brief review can be given here.

It is reasonable to assume that the current state-of-the-art for in-space propulsion systems will continue to improve through improvements in available materials, wider operating ranges, increased lifetimes, and new propellants. This section focuses on new ways of propelling moderately sized spacecraft (m = 500 kg–10,000 kg) and summarizes leading candidates for both small spacecraft (m < 500 kg) propulsion systems and large spacecraft (m > 10,000 kg) propulsion systems.

18.7.1 New Propulsion Systems for Moderately Sized Spacecraft

A variety of high performance chemical and electric propulsion systems for moderate-scale satellites have been developed. Chemical propulsion systems with ever higher energy densities are being investigated. Existing moderate-scale electric propulsion systems provide a nearly complete set of consistent high performance devices except, perhaps, at a specific impulse of around 1,000 sec where both electrothermal and electrostatic/electromagnetic systems typically have unacceptably low efficiencies.

Solar Thermal Propulsion. One potential method of achieving high thrust efficiency at specific impulses around 1,000 sec is *solar thermal propulsion* [Henshall and Palmer, 2006]. Solar thermal propulsion absorbs direct solar energy with a heat exchanger. A propellant gas, typically hydrogen, flows over the heat exchanger and is expelled out of a nozzle to produce thrust. The technology has been under development for decades and may also find use in small satellite propulsion systems. Designs for solar thermal propulsion typically yield specific impulses between 400 sec (ammonia) and 1,000 sec (hydrogen) and operate at heat exchanger temperatures of 2,000 K to 3,000 K. Long term hydrogen storage is still a problem that requires addressing for many systems. Dual mode systems (both power and propulsion) using significant thermal energy storage may bypass the need for photovoltaic cells and electrochemical batteries entirely. The basic technology for solar thermal propulsion systems is proven and could be employed in the near-term.

Momentum Exchange. Traditional propulsion systems generate thrust by accelerating propellant and ejecting it from the spacecraft. The useful lifetime of the propulsion system is completed once the store of propellant has been exhausted. For a limited class of missions (certain formation flying missions with satellite spacing of 10s of meters to over 1 km) it is conceptually possible to either bounce the propellant (in the case of light) [Bae, 2008] or collect the ejected propellant and reuse it (in the case of droplets) [Joslyn, et al. 2010] between multiple satellites. In GEO the required thrust forces for such applications are typically between 20 and 100 mN (1 km), while in LEO it is 100 to 1,000 mN.

Liquid droplet propulsion systems send a stream of liquid droplets between two spacecraft to maintain a separation force between them. One recently investigated concept uses a stream of low vapor pressure silicone oil droplets between two satellites to produce thrust [Joslyn, et al. 2010]. The droplet propulsion system requires an order of magnitude less mass than traditional electric propulsion systems and two orders of magnitude less power to accomplish this limited role. The liquid droplets typically have diameters < 1.5 mm, speeds of about 5 m/s, and are fired at a frequency of about 0.5 Hz.

The highest achievable specific impulse is produced by photon emission: 3×10^7 seconds. Photons are not regularly used for propulsion because the power/thrust is prohibitively high. A *photonic laser thruster* investigated by Bae [2007], however, bounces the laser multiple times between the emitting craft and a reflector on the satellite that is being accelerated. The laser gain media is in between two mirrors (one on each satellite) effectively creating a laser cavity in the entire gap between the two satellites. Proof-of-concept experiments using mirrors with a reflectance of 0.99967 achieved a thrust amplification factor of approximately 3,000×, achieving a thrust per unit power of approximately 20 mN/kW. Using a higher reflectance mirror (R = 0.99995) a total thrust of 1.34 mN could be generated with 10W (134 mN/kW). The maximum separation that can be maintained between the two surfaces is estimated to be 1,000 km.

Both classes of momentum exchange propulsion systems are at a relatively low level of development and would require significant developmental efforts to yield flight ready systems. It is unlikely that the technology could be ready for application in the near-term.

18.7.2 Solar Sail

Richard E. Van Allen, *Microcosm, Inc.*

The concept of utilizing light pressure as a means of space propulsion is attributed to Konstantine Tsiolkovskii [1921], 5 years before Robert Goddard launched the first liquid-fueled rocket. Tsander [1924] coined the term "solar sailing" in the first technical publication on this topic. In that paper, Tsander calculated several interplanetary trajectories for solar sail spacecraft and identified several useful configurations. It wasn't until the 1950s that additional papers were published [Wiley, 1951; Garwin, 1958]. Leap forward 20 years to the 1970s before the possibility of rendezvousing with Halley's Comet triggered more analyses of solar sail applications [Wright, 1974, 1976; Friedman et al., 1978].

About the same time that the US dropped trying to advance solar sail technology, a non-profit organization called the World Space Foundation was formed to promote a range of space related areas, among them advancing solar sail technology. During the period from 1977 to 1986, organization volunteers built 2 square solar sails, 225 m^2 and 900 m^2, respectively, and performed a ground deployment demonstration of the 225 m^2 sail in 1981 ["Solar Sail Unfurled," 1981]. A serious effort was initiated to perform a Space Shuttle deployment demonstration of the 900 m^2 sail, but it was shut down as a result of the loss of the Space Shuttle Challenger in 1986.

The Russians actually succeeded in deploying a 20-meter diameter spinning mirror from a Progress resupply spacecraft in 1993 that was called Znamya 2 (intended as an experiment to beam solar power to the ground, but unfurled in a way similar to how a solar sail would unfurl). However, a follow-on 25-meter diameter mirror failed to deploy in 1999 [Caltech, 2002]. The Planetary Society continued the hardware efforts begun by the World Space Foundation and with private funding built and attempted to launch Cosmos 1 in 2001. Unfortunately, the suborbital demonstration flight failed due to a launch vehicle failure [Cosmos 1, 2012]. A second attempt, this time for an orbital demonstration, also was unsuccessful because of another launch vehicle failure. In 2010, after nearly 90 years, the Japanese launched a solar sail spacecraft (Ikaros) as a secondary payload on an interplanetary mission to Mercury that validated what until then had been the theoretical ability of a solar sail to change its attitude in a controlled fashion and to change its acceleration. Now that the theory behind solar sailing has been validated, there are exciting and practical applications for solar sails that can become reality in the next 10 years. These missions include levitating payloads above and below the equatorial plane at geosynchronous altitude to make more efficient use of that crowded region and positioning payloads in "stationary" orbits above the poles for other interesting missions.

Technical Basis and Solar Sail Designs

Solar sailing **does not** involve the conversion of light into electrical energy (via solar cells), and **does not** utilize the transfer of momentum from solar wind (ionized particles ejected from the Sun)—due to the low density of the ionized particles, whose effect is < 0.1% that due to light pressure. Solar sailing **does** utilize the energy and momentum from light. The reflection of sunlight on a mirrored surface causes a change of momentum that is continuous, and the amount of "propellant" is limitless. Effectiveness falls off as the square of the distance from the Sun, so solar sails are most effective for missions out to about the orbit of Mars.

Light generated thrust can be used to raise or lower an orbit altitude relative to any celestial object (e.g., Sun, planet, Moon, asteroid, comet), by inclining the sail to direct the component of thrust parallel to the orbit velocity vector. If the thrust is in the direction of the orbit velocity vector, posigrade thrust raises the orbit; if the thrust is in the opposite direction, the retrograde thrust lowers the orbit. Figure 18-14 provides an overview of the geometrical relationship of solar sail orientation relative to the incoming light (shown orbiting the Sun, but the vector relationship also applies to a solar sail orbiting a planet), and Fig. 18-15 is an expanded view of Fig. 18-14 that provides the details associated with the defining solar sailing Eq. (18-34a).

The thrust, F, on a flat solar sail is perpendicular to the surface of the sail with a magnitude given by:

$$F = (2RSA/c)\sin^2\theta \qquad (18\text{-}34a)$$

$$= 9.113\times10^{-6}\left(RA/D^2\right)\sin^2\theta \qquad (18\text{-}34b)$$

where, in the second form, F is in Newtons, R is the fraction of incident light reflected by the sail (maximum of 1), D is the distance from the Sun to the solar sail in AU, S is the solar flux in W/m^2, A is the sail area in m^2, c is the speed of light, and θ is the sail tilt angle—the angle between the Sun-Earth line and the sail. Equation (18-34a) doesn't take into account all the factors that translate into the force resulting from light pressure because solar sail performance involves more than the single reflectance factor. Forward [1989b, 1990b] analyzed the effects of various optical properties on realistic "grey" solar sails that have finite transmittance and absorptance and non-perfect reflectance, which was further broken down into specular, diffuse, and back reflectance.

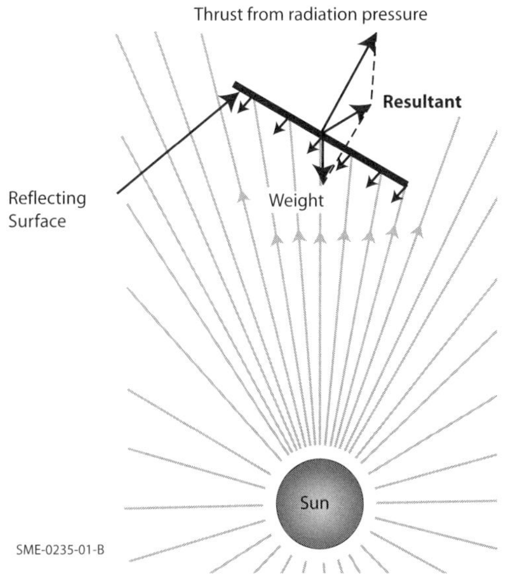

Fig. 18-14. General Depiction of How Solar Sails Maneuver.

There are several factors to consider when designing a solar sail, starting with the decision on the sail material, including reflectivity, fragility, and lifetime. Aluminum is the best material because of a combination of its high reflectivity (86% – 97% for wavelengths from about 0.2 to 1.5 μm) and low density (2.70 g/cm^3) compared to gold (reflectivity 20% – ~100%, 19.32 g/cm^3), silver (reflectivity ~0% – ~100%, 10.49 g/cm^3), and copper (8.96 g/cm^3). At the thicknesses involved, all candidate materials are fragile, but rip stops can be incorporated to mitigate tearing, which is most likely to occur during

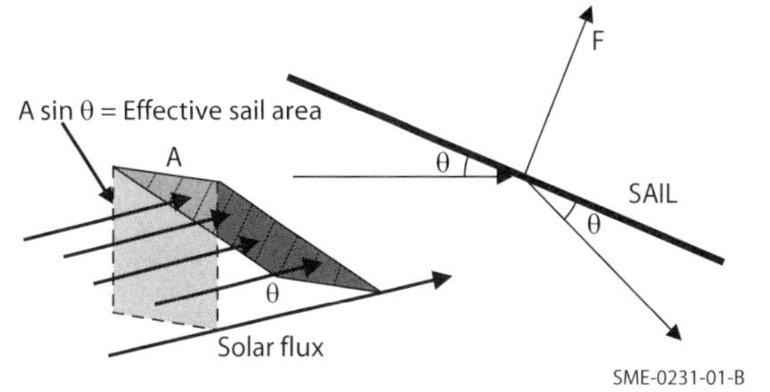

Fig. 18-15. Defining Solar Sail Equation Geometrical Relationships.

deployment. Typically, the aluminum would be coated onto a backing material. Two candidate backing materials are Mylar® and Kapton®, but Mylar® degrades when exposed to ultraviolet light, so Kapton® currently is the better material.

Because solar sails for practical multi-hundred kilogram payloads could have dimensions of several kilometers, saving mass is a critical factor, even for such thin material. One option would be to coat the aluminum film on a polymer substrate that breaks down in ultraviolet light, leaving just the aluminum film (so Mylar® might actually be better than Kapton® in this case). Another interesting option for mass reduction that would make sense for very large solar sails, in the square kilometer range and larger, would be to perforate the sails with holes that are smaller than the wavelength of light ($< \approx 650$ nm), which could reduce the solar sail mass by a factor of about 8 [Forward, 1984]. A third option to consider would be aluminum coated carbon fibers.

There are 3 fundamental solar sail designs: square (3-axis stabilized), circular, and heliogyro (multiple "helicopter blades"). For the 3-axis stabilized configuration, booms are required to support the sail material. Boom material options include composite, open truss, and inflatable structures. The 4-boom version is the most structurally efficient, but there are significant mass and deployment reliability implications associated with this configuration. For attitude control, a combination of tip vanes that are essentially miniature solar sails and a moveable center of mass can be used. The circular configuration requires movement of the center of mass relative to center of pressure to maintain control and may have lower mass than the heliogyro. The heliogyro configuration requires substantial edge tendons along the blades to withstand centrifugal forces. The deployment is simpler than for the square sail configuration, but this configuration is not as mass efficient as a square sail. Relative to control, the heliogyro requires rotation to maintain stability, and the blades can be changed in pitch to control the rotation rate and attitude.

Solar Sail Applications

Independent of the particular design of a solar sail, Table 18-15 lists their advantages and disadvantages.

Table 18-15. Solar Sail Advantages and Disadvantages.

ADVANTAGES
Not propellant limited, as is the case for chemical, electric, and nuclear
Can achieve orbits not achievable by any other means or achievable only to a limited extent (e.g., cylindrical orbits, retrograde solar orbits)
Permits efficient use of geosynchronous altitude by allowing stacking of multiple satellites at the same longitude
Can perform dual roles [applies to, for example, transfers associated with going to and from geosynchronous Earth orbit (GEO) or transfers to and from another planet]
• Boost payload to desired orbit and maintain orbit
• Boost payload to desired orbit, drop it off, and return for another payload
Minimal to no orbit debris
• Can return payloads for repair
• Can place payload on a trajectory to burn up in the atmosphere or boost it into a safe orbit
Very large, thus very visible
For comparable missions, fewer spacecraft required (e.g., GEO communications satellite, see Fig. 18-16—levitated orbit allows cross pole communications with 2 spacecraft instead of 3 needed to send signals "around" the geosynchronous belt)
DISADVANTAGES
Very little operational experience when compared to chemical or electric propulsion
Complex deployment, independent of configuration
Requires continuous control to maintain desired orientation
Main benefit for inner planet missions (similar to solar electric)
Vulnerable
• To attack
• From orbital debris
• From micrometeorites
Long time required to spiral out to desired orbit when compared to other propulsion technologies, such as chemical and nuclear (for interplanetary missions, an option is to use chemical propulsion for Earth escape)
Very large, thus very visible
Higher performance versions require space fabrication

There's a wide range of missions that can benefit from the use of solar sails, as indicated by Table 18-16. Included are Earth-oriented missions, missions to the moon and planets, and supply/resupply missions in support of human missions to the Moon and Mars.

Regarding the disadvantage listed in Table 18-15 associated with chemical and nuclear propulsion, this one needs some amplification and expansion because the disadvantage is not necessarily a true disadvantage. Regarding flight time, as solar sail technology improves, and assuming for interplanetary missions that chemical propulsion is used to achieve Earth escape, absolute flight times can approach achievable flight times possible from chemical propulsion. McInnes [2004] in a figure originally created by NASA/JPL provides data on flight times to Mars as a function of solar sail acceleration. From that figure, the minimum flight time to Mars for a solar sail capable of achieving an acceleration of 1 mm/s^2 is 370 days (+ about 100 days for capture and spiral down to a useful altitude). The corresponding minimum energy (chemical propulsion) coplanar Hohmann Transfer time to Mars is approximately 259 days. (The characteristic Hohmann Transfer is representative of a flight time to Mars, but is not what realistically would be implemented.) However, if the launch date is missed (as was the case for the Mars Science Laboratory mission), the impact will be a wait of 780 days for Earth and Mars to be aligned for another Hohmann Transfer trajectory flight opportunity.

There are 2 Earth oriented missions that are particularly fascinating, are extremely challenging technologically, and demonstrate the unique capabilities of solar sails. One will be discussed in the paragraphs that follow, while the other will be contained in a more complete discussion of solar sails that will be available on the web. They were chosen also because of the increased focus on the utilization of space to better understand the Earth's environment that is certain to be an area of continuously increasing interest over time. Both of them were devised by Forward [1989a, 1990b]. In the first instance, solar sails can use light pressure to *levitate* a payload (e.g., communications) above or below the geosynchronous plane and maintain it there indefinitely **at a fixed longitude,** in what is called a *cylindrical orbit* [Forward, 1989a, 1990b]. More specifically, a levitated orbit allows continuous communications with and/or observation of latitudes not possible with equatorial geosynchronous satellites or with high inclination low altitude satellites. Even more intriguing, but technologically extremely challenging, for levitation distances > 1 Earth radius, only 2 satellites are required for cross-Earth communications (180 deg separation), rather than the three minimum required for geosynchronous equatorial communications satellites (120 deg separation).

Table 18-16. Solar Sail Mission Candidates.

EARTH ORIENTED	*SPACE EXPLORATION*
Commercial/Scientific • Weather • Communications • Miscellaneous – Solar storm warning – Payload repair/replacement *Government/Military* • Weather • Communications • Surveillance, especially at high latitudes—optical, signals • Satellite Inspection/Negation (i.e., anti-satellite) • Orbit transfer vehicle—transport payloads to/from desired orbits	• Solar—especially very high latitude • Retrograde orbit missions (e.g., Halley comet rendezvous) • Inner planets—Venus, Mercury, Earth, Mars • Human mission supply/resupply—Moon, Mars • Outer planets—combine sail capabilities with gravity assist • Interstellar missions—use gravity assist from close flyby of the Sun to accelerate sail to solar system escape velocity; replace solar light source with laser source to push sail

In the second instance, a solar sail maintains its position over a pole and can provide continuous service (e.g., broadcast, data transmission, weather services, and various types of observation) to any region on the Earth, including polar regions, with only 1 spacecraft, called a *statite* orbit—[Forward, 1989a, 1991, 1993]. See the website for a more extended discussion and sample calculations.

Looking at levitated orbits using non-perforated sails (i.e., sails whose sail material does not have perforations that are smaller than the wavelength of light, but which has a significant impact on reducing the mass of the sail), levitation distances of practical payloads are limited by total sail and payload mass. However, performance is still sufficient to allow stacking of communications satellites with separations sufficient to avoid signal interference and essentially eliminates the problem of crowding of the equatorial plane. Perforated sails significantly alleviate the limitations of non-perforated sails so that practical payloads become possible and also permit additional stacking.

Figure 18-16 illustrates the overall levitated orbit geometry. The maximum altitude achievable, Z (m), is provided in Eq. (18-35a) and is a function of the tilt angle, θ, that results in the maximum force normal to the equatorial plane, F_P; and is inversely proportional to the ratio of sail mass, m (kg), to sail area, A. The tilt angle defined in Eq. (18-36), is the angle between the Sun-Earth line and the sail as a function of φ, the angle between the Sun-Earth line and Earth's equatorial plane, both angles measured in radians. The other parameters shown are considered to be constants. Besides R, S, A, and c, already defined, there are the constants r, the geosynchronous radius in m; G, the universal gravitational constant (m^3/kgs^2); and the mass of the Earth, M (kg).

$$Z = \{[(2RSr^3)/(GMc)]\sin^2\theta\cos(\theta - \varphi)\}[1/(m/A)] \quad (18\text{-}35a)$$

$$= [1.715 \times 10^3 \sin^2\theta\cos(\theta - \varphi)][1/(m/A)] \quad (18\text{-}35b)$$

$$\theta = \operatorname{atan}\left(\frac{3}{2}\tan\varphi + \frac{1}{2}\sqrt{9\tan^2\varphi + 8}\right) \quad (18\text{-}36)$$

Note that there is an equatorial component to the force (not shown in Fig. 18-16, but parallel to the Earth's equatorial plane). It is much less than the gravitational attraction of the Earth, but it does have the effect of displacing the near-circular orbit to the side of the Earth away from the Sun. As is the case with current GEO satellites, it will be necessary to separate solar sail spacecraft that will be stacked at the same longitude, which means that Z for each will have to be held relatively constant throughout the year. To maintain a constant Z, the tilt angle, θ, will have to vary from the value that results in the maximum force normal to the equatorial plane, which means that the sail angle will have to be trimmed over time.

If the above equations are applied to a sail whose mass is assumed to be equal to its payload/bus mass, levitation distances vary between 50 km and 11,000 km as the sail thickness varies from 1 μm to less than 0.01 μm. (0.5 μm translates into a levitation distance of 150 km, and 0.02 μm represents the practical limit to sail thickness.) Note that the minimum physical satellite separation at GEO is about 0.2 deg or 150 km, and in a few cases even 0.01 deg [Hudgins, 2002; Union of Concerned Scientists (UCS) Satellite Database, 2010]. The payload mass is assumed to be the same as the total spacecraft mass for a GEO satellite, since the Sail/Payload/Bus will still require such subsystems as solar cells for power and a communications subsystem. Launch masses for GEO satellites range from about 1,000 kg to

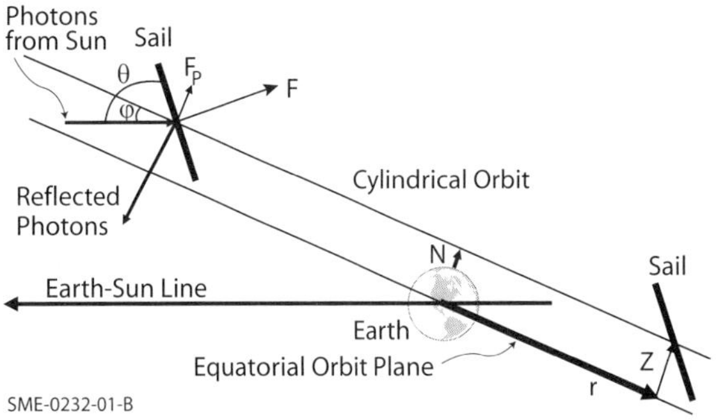

Fig. 18-16. Levitated Geosynchronous Orbit Overview and Detailed Geometry.

6,500 kg [UCS Satellite Database, 2010]. Assuming no change in launch capability would imply a maximum bus/payload mass of 3,250 kg, which is what has been chosen. Clearly, very large sails are required.

There are some interesting general operational issues/challenges associated with solar sails in general and with each of these orbit types in particular. In the general category, reflection from the sails is not specular since the sail material is not a perfect reflector. Hence some light is absorbed and some light is transmitted through the sail material. Also, the sail is not perfectly flat. In the case of the levitated orbits, 2 times/day the sail is approximately edge-on to the Earth so that there is potential communications impairment due to the physical blockage of the spacecraft antenna by the sail itself. Candidate solutions to this situation include a cutout in the sail to permit an unobstructed communications path and putting the antennas on the tip vanes (at least for square sail configurations). Additionally, 1 or 2 times/year the sail is shadowed by the Earth once/day at all levitated altitudes that are less than about 4 Earth radii. The worst case time in the shadow is about 70 minutes, during which the levitated altitude decreases by about 5%, which is not a major impact. Besides the long round trip light time of several seconds, another operational issue for stationary polar orbits is the need for a clock drive for the ground station antennas. However, the electronics is still relatively simple because the spacecraft remains at almost the same range.

Finally, there are some regulatory issues to consider, in particular for the levitated orbits. Since multiple satellites can be stacked at the same longitude, some regulation will be required relative to stacking separation distances. Related to the stacking issue is who will control the physical separation of the satellites at a particular longitudinal location to ensure that separation distances are maintained. Finally, as is already the case, care will be needed to avoid communications interference.

A number of enabling technologies required to field a functionally useful solar sail are listed in Table 18-17.

Solar sails can perform unique scientific, commercial, and military missions, and the stage is set for near-term space missions to validate deployment and control methodologies. Enabling technologies are still required to permit high performance missions (e.g., levitated geosynchronous, stationary polar).

Table 18-17. Enabling Technologies and Related Events for Solar Sails.

SPACE FABRICATION
• Sail material
• Supporting structure/deployment methods
CAPABILITY TO REPAIR/UPGRADE SPACECRAFT
• Periodically replace part or all of the sail
• Perforated substituted for part or all of the non-perforated sail material
• Carbon fiber replacement for aluminized Kapton
UPGRADE/REPLACE PAYLOADS
• Change of mission
• Take advantage of technology improvements—continued advances in electronics will cause payload components to shrink in mass/volume, while capabilities increase

18.7.3 Propulsion Systems for Small Satellites

Satellites with practical functionality are being constructed with ever decreasing dimensions. The classes of small satellites are discussed in Sec. 2.1.8 and smallsats and cubesats are discussed in Secs. 25.3 and 25.4, respectively, so only relevant propulsion systems will be discussed in this section. Propulsion systems are advantageous at all size scales and propulsion systems are being investigated for the entire range of smallsats. Microsatellite propulsion requirements vary significantly, but often times require very low impulse bits, high thrust levels, high thrust-to-noise levels, and significant Delta Vs.

Solid and liquid chemical propulsion systems are being developed along with electrothermal, electrostatic, and electromagnetic electric propulsion systems. The following discussion will focus primarily on propulsion for microsatellites, or *micropropulsion.* Microsatellites represent the transition: at 100 kg propulsion systems can be shrunken down versions of traditional propulsion systems while by 10 kg they are likely to be very different systems. The general rule of thumb for microsatellites is that they have 1 W/kg of power available for propulsion. A total wet mass of the propulsion system itself is typically 10–20% of the total mass of the satellite. In general, the smaller the satellite the more integrated (sharing components with other subsystems) the propulsion system must be and the more MEMS fabrication will be used. All of the support hardware must also be shrunk. Issues arising from scaling propulsion systems to small dimensions produce a wide variety of concerns across the entire range of micropropulsion systems as shown in Table 18-18.

Propulsion systems from all classifications of full-scale propulsion have been successfully shrunk to the scale relevant for microsatellites. Additional new types of propulsion systems, such as solid propellant digital microthrusters, have also been developed, primarily for application at the smaller size scales (near 10 kg). Table 18-19 lists typical performance numbers for micropropulsion systems that have been demonstrated in the laboratory environment, but have typically not been flight qualified (TRL 3–6). Positions left blank lack sufficient published information to draw conclusions. With a sufficient developmental effort, the majority of technologies listed in Table 18-19 could be flight ready in the next 10–20 years. Research is being conducted in the fields of nanopropulsion and picopropulsion, but in general the technologies are not sufficiently developed to warrant inclusion in the table.

18.7.4 Propulsion Systems for Very Large Satellites

In contrast with smallsats, however, some categories of satellites continue to increase in size. GEO communications satellites, for example, have steadily increased in

Table 18-17, Fig. 18-16◀, Eq. 18-36◀

Table 18-18. Common Micropropulsion Concerns.

Scaling Issue	Concern	Affected Thrusters
Small Length Scale	High Heat Transfer	Chemical
	Passage Clogging	Chemical
	High Field Strengths	Electric
	Rarefied Flows	Chemical
	High Magnetic Fields	Electromagnetic
	Valve Leakage	All
	Voltage Limited	Electric
High Surface-to-Volume Ratio	Increase Heat Transfer	Chemical
	Increase Wall Losses	Electric
Short Residence Times	Limited Mixing Time	Bipropellant
	Frozen Flow Losses	Chemical
	Limited Vaporization Time	Chemical
Reynold's Number 10^2–10^4	High Viscous Losses	Chemical
	Limited Mixing	Chemical
Limited Materials/Manufacturing	Relative Surface Roughness	Chemical
	Compatibility Limitations	Chemical
	Nonuniform Properties	All

Table 18-19. Representative Relatively Mature Micropropulsion Systems [Scharfe, 2009]

Thruster Type	Thrust [N]	I_{sp} [s]	Power [W]	Thruster Mass [kg]
Cold Gas	5×10^{-4} – 3	40–80	—	0.01–1
Laser (Ignition)	1×10^{-3}– 1×10^{-2}	37–100	—	—
Monopropellant	1×10^{-6} – 1.5	100–230	≤ 6	0.01–0.5
Decomposing Solid	—	230	—	—
Electrothermal	≤ 0.22	50–250	3–300	0.1–1
Laser (Ablation)	1×10^{-6}	100–300	2	—
Bipropellant	1×10^{-6} – 45	100–320	≤ 6	0.01–0.5
Laser (Plasma)	1×10^{-4} – 1×10^{-3}	500–1,000	2	≤ 1
Solar Thermal	5.6×10^{-2} – 1	200–1,100	—	≤ 10
Hollow Cathode	1×10^{-6} – 1×10^{-2}	50–1,200	5–1,000	—
Hall/Ion	4×10^{-4} – 2×10^{-2}	300–3,700	14–300	≤ 1
Electromagnetic	3×10^{-5} – 2×10^{-3}	200–4,000	≤ 10	0.06–0.5
FEEP/Colloid	1×10^{-7} – 1.5×10^{-3}	450–9,000	1–100	0.1–1

size from approximately 35 kg with 28 Watts in 1963 (Syncom 2) to approximately 6,910 kg (Terrestar-1) with up to 25 kW in total power in 2009 (Space Systems Loral 1300 series). It is assumed that there are no technical limitations to scaling chemical propulsion systems to the larger sizes relevant for this range of satellites. High performance electric propulsion systems at power levels of 100–200 kW, however, must be further developed. Several candidate technologies have already been demonstrated in the lab and are sufficiently well characterized to begin to make comparisons.

As mentioned in Sec. 18.6.3., a *magnetoplasmadynamic* (MPD) thruster is similar to an arcjet in physical geometry, but it accelerates the propellant using the Lorentz force as the ionized propellant passes through a high intensity arc. Two classifications of the MPD thruster exist depending on whether the magnetic field is self generated (self field MPD) or externally applied (applied field MPD). Applied field MPDs are typically a more attractive option at lower power levels as of 2009.

Hall thrusters for moderately sized spacecraft are a flight-qualified technology as described in Sec. 18.6.3.

Table 18-20. Performance of High-Power Electric Propulsion at 200 kW [Brown, 2010].

	NASA-457M Cluster (4 thrusters)	High I_{sp} NHT (2 channels)	Moscow Aviation Institute 200kW AF-MPD	VASIMR VX-200 (design goals)	ELF-375 (design goals)
Input Power (kW)	200 (4 × 50)	200	123–186	200	200
Specific Impulse (s)	1,800–3,500	4,000–5,000	2,760–4,240	4,000–5,000	1,500–5,000
Thrust (N)	7.6–9.5	5.3–6.1	4.5	5	7–18
Mass Flow Rate (mg/s)	220–540 (Xe)	100–160 (Kr)	92–128 (Li)	100–125 (Ar)	140–1,200 (Xe)
Efficiency	42%–65%	60%–65%	35%–50%	48%–60%	65%–85%
Specific Mass (kg/kW)					
Thruster	2.2	0.5	—	1.5	0.25
Thruster + PPU	3.1	1.4	—	—	0.70
Major Dimensions (m)	1.1 by 1.1 0.15 length	0.69 diam. 0.10 length	— —	1.5 diam. 3.0 length	0.38 diam. 0.50 length

Traditional single channel Hall thrusters can become quite heavy at high-power levels, but it is conceivable that an array of small thrusters could be assembled to achieve power levels of hundreds of kW at acceptable mass levels. The *NASA-457M* is chosen to represent the possibility of clustering existing systems [Manzella et al., 2002]. One way to overcome this limitation is to use a Hall thruster with multiple concentric channels. This allows the thruster channels to share the magnetic circuit and significantly reduce the thruster footprint. *Nested channel Hall (NHT)* thrusters are under development.

The *Variable Specific Impulse Magnetoplasma Rocket (VASIMR)* was designed as a high-power electric propulsion system so it has both high specific impulse (4,000–5,000 sec) and high thrust (5 N). VASIMR has three different stages: a helicon radiofrequency (RF) section to ionize the plasma, a second RF section that uses ion cyclotron resonance frequency (ICRF) to further heat the plasma, and a superconducting electromagnetic nozzle as the final stage. Ground testing of a laboratory model (*VX-200*) has validated the expected performance levels of the device (η_t = 60%, I_{sp} = 5,000 sec, P = 200 kW). A VASIMR device (*VF-200*) will be tested on the international space station sometime around 2014 to demonstrate space-based performance.

A *plasmoid* is a coherent structure of plasma and its self-generated magnetic field. *Field reverse configuration* (FRC) is a particular method of generating a plasmoid where an axial bias field is rapidly reversed producing closed field lines that confine the plasmoid against its thermal pressure. The plasmoid can then be accelerated using various methods. The *ELF-375* thruster being developed at MSNW uses a rotating magnetic field acceleration scheme to accelerate the plasmoid [Slough et al., 2009]. Inductive techniques do not require electrodes and could theoretically have longer lifetimes.

Table 18-20 shows a comparison of the performance of various high power electric propulsion devices, scaled to 200 kW to allow a direct comparison. Several of the more developed technologies (clustered Hall thrusters, nested Hall thrusters, and VASIMR) could be flight ready in the next 10 years, while MPD thrusters and the ELF thruster would likely take longer to be fully developed. The primary limitation for all of the technologies is the inability to test any of them on the ground for significant periods.

18.8 Examples

Get More See the book website for a discussion of the SCS and FireSat II propulsion system design.

References

Get Ref **For annotated bibliography of propulsion, see the book website.**

Aerojet. 2003a. *MR-502A Improved Electrothermal Hydrazine Thruster (IMPEHT) Datasheet.*

Aerojet. 2003b. *MR-509 Low Power Arcjet System Data Sheet.*

Aerojet. 2003c. *MR-510 Arcjet Thruster and Cable Assembly Data Sheet.*

AIAA. 2006. *Composite Overwrapped Pressure Vessels (COPVs).* AIAA Standard for Space Systems. S-081A-2006e. Rev.

AIAA. 1999. *Metallic Pressure Vessels, Pressurized Structures, and Pressure Components.* AIAA Standard for Space Systems. S-080-1998e.

AFSC. 2004. *Range Safety User Requirements Manual —Volume 2 Flight Safety Requirements.* Manual 91-710, vol. 2, AFSPCMAN 91-710 V2. Jul. 1.

Arrington, L. A. and T. W. Haag. 1999. "Multi-Axis Thrust Measurements of the EO-1 Pulsed Plasma Thruster." 35th Joint Propulsion Conference. AIAA-99-2290. Los Angeles, CA. Jun. 20–24.

Astrium EADS. 2010a–2010e. Website

Bae, Y. K. 2007. "Photonic Laser Propulsion: Photon Propulsion Using and Active Resonant Optical Cavity." Space 2007 Conference. AIAA-2007-6131. Long Beach, CA. Sept. 18–20.

Bae, Y. 2008. "Photonic Laser Propulsion: Proof-of-Concept Demonstration." *Journal of Spacecraft and Rockets,* vol 45, no. 1. pp.153–155.

Balaam, P. and M. M. Micci. 1995. "Investigation of Stabilized Resonant Cavity Microwave Plasmas for Propulsion." 1995. *Journal of Propulsion and Power*, vol. 11, no. 5. Sept–Oct. pp. 1021–1027.

Bergonz, F. 1982. *Manned Maneuvering Unit*. NASA Johnson Space Center Satellite Serv. Workshop, vol. 1, pp. 32–43 (SEE N83-11175 02-16).

Brown, C. D. 1996. *Spacecraft Propulsion*. Reston, VA: AIAA.

Brown, C. D. 2002. *Elements of Spacecraft Design*. Reston, VA: AIAA.

Brown, D. L. 2010. *Personal Communication.*

Burton, R. L., and P. J. Turchi. 1998. "Pulsed Plasma Thruster." *Journal of Propulsion and Power*, vol. 14, no. 5. Sept.–Oct. pp. 716–735.

Busek Company. 2007a. *Low Power Hall Effect Thruster Systems Data Sheet, 2nd ed.* Natik, MA: Busket Company.

Busek Company. 2007b. *High Power Hall Effect Thruster Systems Data Sheet.* Natik, MA: Busek Company.

Busek Company. 2007c. *Micro Pulsed Plasma Thruster Data Sheet*. Natik, MA: Busek Company.

Bzibziak, R. 2000. "Update of Cold Gas Propulsion at Moog." 36th Joint Propulsion Conf. AIAA 2000-3718. Huntsville, AL. Jul. 11–19.

Bzibziak, R. 2010. *Personal Communication*.

Caltech. 2002. "Projects, Organizations, and Missions." Website.

Cassidy, R. J. 2002. "Development and Flight Qualification of a 26-Kilowatt Arcjet Propulsion Subsystem." *Journal of Propulsion and Power*, vol. 18.

Chang-Diaz, F. R. 2000. "The VASIMR Rocket." *Scientific American Inc.*, vol. 283, no. 5. Nov.

Chiaverini, M. J. and K. K. Kuo. 2007. *Fundamentals of Hybrid Rocket Combustion and Propulsion*. Reston, VA: AIAA.

Choueriri, E. Y. 2004. "A Critical History of Electric Propulsion: The First 50 Years (1906-1956)." *Journal of Propulsion & Power,* vol. 20, no. 2. Mar–Apr.

Choueriri, E. Y. and K. Polzin. 2006. "Faraday Acceleration with Radio-Frequency Assisted Discharge." *Journal of Propulsion and Power*, vol. 22, no. 3. May–Jun. pp. 611–619.

"Cosmos 1: The First Solar Sail." 2012. Jul. 5. Website.

Dawson, M., G. Brewster, C. Conrad, M. Kilwine, B. Chenevert, and O. Morgan. 2007. "Monopropellant Hydrazine 700 lbf Throttling Terminal Descent Engine for Mars Science Laboratory." 43rd Joint Propulsion Conf. AIAA 2007-5481. Cincinnati, OH. Jul. 8–11.

Dornheim, M. A. 2003. "Ideal Hybrid Fuel is … Wax?" *Aviation Week & Space Technology*. Feb. 3. pp. 52–54.

Dressler, R. 2000. "Propellant Alternatives for Ion and Hall Effect Thrusters." 38th Aerospace Sciences Meeting. AIAA-2000-0602. Reno, NV. Jan. 10–13.

Drenning, C. K., R. J. Phillips, R.V. Loustau, and F. L. Falconer. 1978. "Design and Fabrication of Space Shuttle Reaction Control Thruster Insulated Scarf Nozzles." 14th Joint Propulsion Conference. AIAA 1978-1006. Las Vegas, NV. Jul 25–27.

Dyer, J., G. Zilliac, E. Doran, Z. Dunn, K. Lohner, C. Bayard, A Sadhwani, G. Zilliac, B. Cantwell , and A. Karabeyoglu. 2007. "Design and Development of a 100 km Nitrous Oxide/Paraffin Hybrid Rocket Vehicle." 43rd Joint Propulsion Conference. AIAA 2007-5362. Cincinnati, OH. Jul. 8–11.

Evans, B. 2009. "Hybrid Rocket Investigations at Penn State University's High Pressure Combustion Laboratory: Overview and Recent Results." 45th Joint Propulsion Conference.AIAA-2009-5349. Denver, CO. Aug. 2–5.

Ferguson, H. and J. Sovey. 1967. *Performance Tests of a 1/2-Millipound (2.2 mN) Ammonia Resistojet Thruster System.* NASA TN D-4249. Nov.

Forward, R. L. 1984. "Light-Levitated Geostationary Cylindrical Orbits Using Perforated Light Sails." Technical Note. *The Journal of the Astronautical Sciences*, vol. 32, no. 2. Apr–Jun. pp. 221–226.

Forward, R. L. 1989a. "The Statite: A Non-Orbiting Spacecraft." 25th Joint Propulsion Conference, AIAA-1989-2546, Monterey, CA. Jul. 10–12.

Forward, R. L. 1989b. "Grey Solar Sails." 25th Joint Propulsion Conference. AIAA-1989-2343. Monterey, CA. Jul. 10–14.

Forward, R. L. 1990a. "Light-Levitated Geostationary Cylindrical Orbits: Correction and Expansion." *The Journal of the Astronautical Sciences*, vol. 38, no. 3. Jul–Sep. pp. 335–353.

Forward, R. L. 1990b. "Grey Solar Sails." *The Journal of the Astronautical Sciences*, vol. 38, no. 2. Apr–Jun. pp. 161–185.

Forward, R. L. 1991. "Statite: A Spacecraft That Does Not Orbit." *Journal of Spacecraft*, vol. 28, no. 5. Sep–Oct. pp. 606–611.

Forward, R. L. 1993. "Statite: Spacecraft That Utilizes Light Pressure and Method of Use." U.S. Patent 5,183,225. Feb. 2.

Frei, T. 2001. "Mars Polar Lander Thruster Cold Start Validation Testing." 37th Joint Propulsion Conf. AIAA-2001-3261. Salt Lake City, UT. Jul. 8–11.

Friedman, L., et al. 1978. "Solar Sailing—The Concept Made Realistic." AIAA 16th Aerospace Sciences Meeting. Jan.

Garwin, R. L. 1958. "Solar Sailing—A Practical Method of Propulsion within the Solar System." *Jet Propulsion*, vol. 28. Mar. pp. 188–190.

Genovese, J. E. 1978. "Rapid Estimation of Hydrazine Exhaust Plume Interaction." 14th Joint Propulsion Conference. AIAA-78-1091. Jul.

Gesto, F. 2006. "Ion Detachment in the Helicon Double-Layer Thruster Exhaust Beam." *Journal of Prop. & Power*, vol. 22, no 1. Jan–Feb. pp. 24–30.

Goddard, E. C. and G. E. Penray. 1970. *The Papers of Robert H. Goddard.* New York, NY: The McGraw-Hill Companies.

Goebel, D. M. and I. Katz. 2008. *Fundamentals of Electric Propulsion: Ion and Hall Thrusters.* Hoboken, NJ: John Wiley and Sons.

Henshall, P. and P. Palmer. 2006. "Solar Thermal Propulsion Augmented with Fiber Optics: Technology Development." 42nd Joint Propulsion Conference. AIAA-2006-4874. Sacramento, CA. Jul. 9–12.

Hill, P. and C. Peterson. 1992. *Mechanics and Thermodynamics of Propulsion, 2nd ed.* Reading, MA: Addison-Wesley Publishing Company.

Hill, C. S. 1980. "SSRCS First Flight Certification Testing." 16th Joint Propulsion Conference. AIAA 1980-1130. Hartford, CT. Jun. 30–Jul. 2.

Hofer, R. R. and A. D. Gallimore. 2006. "High Specific Impulse Hall Thrusters, Part 2: Efficiency Analysis." *Journal of Propulsion and Power*, vol. 22, no. 4, pp. 732–740. Jul–Aug.

Holmberg, N. A., R. P. Faust, and H.M. Holt. 1980. Viking'75 Spacecraft Design and Test Summary. *NASA Reference Publication 1027.*

Hruby, V., J. Kolenicik, K. D. Annen, R. C. Brown. 1997. "Methane Arcjet Experiments." 28th AIAA Plasma Dynamics and Lasers Conf. AIAA-1997-2427. Atlanta, GA. Jun. 23–25.

Hudgins, E. L. 2002. *Space: The Free-Market Frontier.* Cato Institute, p. 230.

Humble, R. W., G. N. Henry, and W. J. Larson. 1995. *Space Propulsion Analysis and Design*. McGraw-Hill
Isakowitz S. J., J. B. Hopkins, and J. P. Hopkins Jr. 2004. *International Reference Guide to Space Launch Systems, 4th ed.* Reston, *VA:* AIAA.

Ito, T., N. Gascon, S. Crawford, and M. A. Cappelli. 2007. "Experimental Characterization of a Micro-Hall Thruster." *Journal of Propulsion and Power*, vol. 23, no. 5. Sep–Oct. pp. 1069–1074.

Jackman C. H., D. B. Considine, and E. L. Fleming. 1996. "Space Shuttle's Impact on the Stratosphere: An Update." *Journal of Geophysical Research*, vol. 101, no. D7.

Jacobson, D. and D. Manzella. 2003. "50 kW Class Krypton Hall Thruster Performance." 39th Joint Propulsion Conf. AIAA-2003-4550. Huntsville, AL. Jul. 20–23.

Jahn, R. 1968. *Physics of Electric Propulsion.* New York: McGraw-Hill

Joslyn, T. B. and A. K. Ketsdever. 2010. "Constant Momentum Exchange between Microspacecraft Using Liquid Droplet Thrusters." 46th Joint Propulsion Conf. AIAA-2010-6966. Nashville, TN. Jul. 25–28.

Legge, R. S., P. Lozano, and M. Martinez-Sanchez. 2007. "Fabrication and Characterization of Porous Metal Emitters for Electrospray Thrusters." 43rd Joint Propulsion Conference. IEPC-2007-145. Florence, Italy. Sept. 17–20.

Lichon, P. G., and J. M. Sankovic. 1996. "Development and Demonstration of a 600-Second Mission-Average Isp Arcjet." *Journal of Propulsion and Power*, vol. 12, no. 6. Nov–Dec. pp. 1018–1025.

Linnell, J. A. and A. D. Gallimore. 2006. "Efficiency Analysis of a Hall Thruster Operating with Krypton and Xenon." *Journal of Propulsion and Power*, vol. 22, no. 6. Nov–Dec. pp. 1402–1418.

Lockheed Martin Corp. 2005. Press Release. Feb. 2.

Loeb, H. W., D. Feili, and B. K. Meyer. 2004. "Development of RIT Microthrusters." The 55th IAC. IAC-04-S.4.04. Vancouver, BC. Oct.

Manzella, D., R. Jankovsky, and R. Hofer. 2002. "Laboratory Model 50 kW Hall Thruster." The 38th Joint Propulsion Conference. AIAA-2002-3676. Indianapolis, IN. Jul. 7–10.

Markelov G. N. 2007. "Plume Impingement Analysis for Aeolus Spacecraft and Gas/Surface Interaction Models." *Journal of Spacecraft and Rockets*, vol. 44, no. 3, pp. 607–618.

Martin, A., and R. Eskridge. 2005. "Electrical Coupling Efficiency of Inductive Plasma Accelerators." *Journal of Physics*, vol. 38. Nov. pp. 4168–4179.

McInnes, C. R. 2004. *Solar Sailing—Technology, Dynamics and Mission Applications.* Chichester, UK: Springer-Praxis Publishing.

McRight, P., C. Popp, C. Pierce, A. Turpin, and W. Urbanchock. 2005. "Confidence Testing of Shell-405 Catalysts in a Monopropellant Hydrazine Thruster." 41st Joint Propulsion Conference. AIAA-2005-3952. Tucson, AZ. Jul. 10–13.

Messerschimd, E.W., D. M. Zube, K. Meinzer, and H. L. Kurtz. 1996. "Arcjet Development for Amateur Radio Satellite." *Journal of Spacecraft and Rockets*, vol.33, no.1. Jan–Feb.

Micci, M. and A. Ketsdever. 2000. "*Micropropulsion for Small Spacecraft*." Progress in Aeronautics and Astronautics, Vol. 187. Reston, VA: AIAA.

Mikellides P. G. and C. Neilly. 2007. "Modeling and Performance Analysis of the Pulsed Inductive Thruster." *Journal of Propulsion and Power*, vol. 23.

Morrisey, D. C. 1992. "Historical Perspective—Viking Mars Lander Propulsion." *Journal of Propulsion and Power*, vol. 8, no.2. pp. 320–331.

Morring, Jr., F. 2003. "Test Puts Hybrid Rockets Back on the Table." *Aviation Week & Space Technology*. Feb. 3. p. 50.

NIST Chemistry WebBook. 2011. Website.

NRC. 1998. *Assessment of Exposure-Response Functions for Rocket-Emission Toxicants.* Life Sciences. Wash., D.C: Nat. Acad. Press.

Norris, G. 2009. "Virgin Galactic's SpaceShip Two Revealed in Desert Rollout." *Aviation Week & Space Technology*. Dec. 14. p. 37.

Northrop Grumman Space Technology. 2010a & 2010b Propulsion Systems.

Peterson, P., D. Jacobson, D. Manzella, and J. John. 2005. "The Performance and Wear Characterization of a High-Power High-Isp NASA Hall Thruster." 41st Joint Propulsion Conference. AIAA-2005-4243, Tucson, AZ. Jul. 10–13.

Phipps, C., J. Luke, T. Lippert, M. Hauer, and A. Wokum. 2004. "Micropropulsion Using a Laser Ablation Jet." *Journal of Propulsion and Power*, vol. 20, no. 6. Nov–Dec. pp. 1000–1011

Phipps, C. R. 2006. *Laser Ablation and Its Applications*. NY: Springer

Pidgeon, D. J., R. L. Corey, B. Sauer, and M. L. Day. 2006. "Two Years On-Orbit Performance of SPT-100 Electric Propulsion." 24th International Comm. Satellite Systems Conference. AIAA-2006-5353. San Diego, CA. Jun. 11–14.

Poehlmann, F., N. Gascon, and M. A. Cappelli. 2007. "The Deflagration-Detonation Transition in Gas-Fed Pulsed Plasma Accelerators." The 43rd Joint Propulsion Conf. AIAA-2007-5263. Cincinnati, OH. Jul. 8–11.

QinetiQ. 2004. *GOCE T5 Based Electric Propulsion System Data Sheet.*

Schapell, D. T., E. Scarduffa, P. Smith, and N. Solway. 2005. "Advances in Marotta Electric and Small Satellite Propulsion Fluid Control Activities." The 41st Joint Propulsion Conference. AIAA-2005-4055.Tucson, AZ. Jul.10–13.

Scharfe, D. B. 2009. 45th Joint Propulsion Conference. AIAA 2009-4824. Denver, CO. Aug. 2–5.

Semenkin, A. 1999. "Development Program and Preliminary Results of the TAL-110 Thruster." Joint Propulsion Conf. AIAA-1999-2279. LA, CA. Jun.

Simmons, F. S. 2000. *Rocket Exhaust Plume Phenomenology*. AIAA.

Slough, J., D. E. Kirtley, and T. Weber. 2009. "Pulsed Plasmoid Propulsion: The ELF Thruster." The International Electric Propulsion Conference. IEPC-2009-265. Ann Arbor, MI. Sept. 20–24.

Smith, P. 2006. "Resistojet Thruster Design and Development Programme." 42nd Joint Propulsion Conf. AIAA-2006-5210. Sacramento, CA. Jul. 9–11.

Smith, K. L., M. S. Alexander, M. D. Paine, and J. P. W. Stark. 2009. "Scaling of a Colloid Thruster System for MicroNewton to MilliNewton Thrust Levels." The 30th International Electric Propulsion Conference. IEPC-2009-112. Ann Arbor, MI. Sept. 20–24.

"Solar Sail Unfurled." 1981. Bulletin—Quarterly Report of the Solar Sail Project, vol. 2, no. 3, Jul–Sept.

Stechman R. C. 1985. "Modification of the Space Shuttle Primary Thruster (870 lbf) for Apogee and Perigee Kick Stages." 21st Joint Propulsion Conference. AIAA-1985-1222. Monterey, CA. Jul. 8–10.

Table 18-20◀, Fig. 18-16◀, Eq. 18-36◀

Stechman R. C. 1990. "Development History of the 25 lbf (110 Newton) Space Shuttle Vernier Thruster." 26th Joint Propulsion Conference. AIAA 1990-1837. Orlando, FL. Jul. 16–18.

Sullivan, D. J., J. F. Kline, R. B. Miles, and S. H. Zaidi. 2004. "A 300 W Microwave Thruster Design and Performance Testing." 40th Joint Propulsion Conf. AIAA-2004-4122. Ft. Lauderdale, FL. Jul. 11–14.

Sund, D. C., and C. S. Hill. 1979. "Reaction Control System Thrusters for Space Shuttle Orbiter." 15th Joint Propulsion Conference. AIAA-1979-1144. Las Vegas, NV. Jun.18–20.

Sutton, G. P., and O. Biblarz. 2010. *Rocket Propulsion Elements, 8th ed.* Hoboken, NJ: John Wiley and Sons.

Sweetman B. 2006. *Jane's Space Directory*. Jane's Information Group.

Swink, D. G., O. M. Morgan, and J. C. Robinson. 1999. "Design and Analysis of a Low-cost Reaction Control System for GPS IIF." 35th Joint Propulsion Conf. AIAA-1999-2469. Los Angeles, CA. Jun. 20–24.

Tajmar, M. 2003. *Advanced Space Propulsion Systems*. NY: Springer.

Takao, Y., H. Kataharada, T. Miyamoto, H. Masui, N. Yamamoto, and H. Nakashima. 2006. "Performance Test of Micro Ion Thruster Using Microwave Discharge." *Vacuum*, vol. 80, no. 11-12. Sept. pp. 1239–1243

Thompson, D. 2001. "Amine Azides Used as Monopropellants." US Patent 6,299,654 B1.

Thompson P. 1972. *Compressible Fluid Dynamics*. New York: McGraw-Hill.

Tikhonov, V., S. Semenikhin, J. Brophy, and J. Polk. 1997. "Performance of 130-kW MPD Thruster with an External Applied Field and Lithium as Propellant," IEPC-97-117, 25th International Electric Propulsion Conference, Cleveland, OH.

Toki, K., Y. Shimizu, and K. Kurki. 2000. "On-Orbit Demonstration of a Pulsed Self-Field Magnetoplasmadynamic Thruster System." *Journal of Propulsion and Power,* vol. 16, no. 5. Sept–Oct. pp. 880–886.

Tsander, F. A. 1967. *From A Scientific Heritage*. NASA TTF-541, Quoting from author 1924 report.

Tsiolkovskii, K. E., 1921. *Extension of Man Into Outer Space*.

Table 18-20◀, Fig. 18-16◀, Eq. 18-36◀

Tsohas, J., B. Appel, A. Rettenmaier, M. Walker, and S. Heister. 2009. "Development and Launch of the Purdue Hybrid Rocket Technology Demonstrator." 45th Joint Propulsion Conference. AIAA-2009-4842. Denver, CO. Aug. 2–5.

Turner, M. J. L. 2009. *Rocket and Spacecraft Propulsion, 3rd ed.* Springer.

Tverdokhlebov, S. O., A. V. Semenkin, J. E. Polk. 2002. "Bismuth Propellant Option for Very High Power TAL Thruster." The 40th Aerospace Sciences. AIAA-2002-0348. Reno, NV. Jan. 14–17.

Union of Concerned Scientists. 2010. "Satellite Database." Jul. Website.

Vial, V., and O. Duchemin. 2009. "Optimization of the PPS®x000-Technological Demonstrator for High ISP Operation." The 45th Joint Propulsion Conf. AIAA-2009-5283. Denver, CO. Aug. 2–5.

Wangsness, R. K. 1986. *Electromagnetic Fields, 2nd ed.* Hoboken, NJ: John Wiley and Sons.

Warner, N. Z. and M. Martinez-Sanchez. 2006. "Design and Preliminary Testing of a Miniaturized TAL Hall Thruster." The 42nd Joint Propulsion Conf. AIAA-2006-4994. Sacramento, CA. Jul. 9–12.

Wertz, J. and W. Larson. 1999. *Space Mission Analysis and Design, 3rd ed.* Hawthorne, CA: Microcosm Press and Springer.

Wiley, C. 1951. "Clipper Ships of Space." Astounding Science Fiction. May.

Wright, J. L. 1974. "Solar Sailing: Evaluation of Concept and Potential." Battelle Memorial Institute Report, BMI-NLVP-TM-74-3. Nov.

Wright, J. L. and J. Warmke. 1976. "Solar Sailing Mission Applications." AIAA/AAS Astrodynamics Conference, 2001.

Wu, P. K., P. Woll, C. Stechman, B. McLemore, J. Neiderman, and C. Crone. 2001. "Qualification Testing of a 2nd Generation High Performance Apogee Thruster." The 37th Joint Propulsion Conference. AIAA 2001-3253. Salt Lake City, UT. Jul. 8–11.

Zeimer, J. K. 2009. "Performance of Electrospray Thrusters." The 30th International Electric Propulsion Conf. IEPC-2009-242. Ann Arbor, MI. Sept.

19 Spacecraft Subsystems II—Control Systems

19.1 Spacecraft Attitude Determination and Control Systems

Scott R. Starin,
NASA Goddard Space Flight Center

John Eterno, *Southwest Research Institute*

In the year 1900, Galveston, Texas, was a bustling community of approximately 40,000 people. The former capital of the Republic of Texas remained a trade center for the state and was one of the largest cotton ports in the United States. On September 8 of that year, however, a powerful hurricane struck Galveston island, tearing the Weather Bureau wind gauge away as the winds exceeded 100 mph and bringing a storm surge that flooded the entire city. The worst natural disaster in United States' history—even today—the hurricane caused the deaths of between 6,000 and 8,000 people. Critical in the events that led to such a terrible loss of life was the lack of precise knowledge of the strength of the storm before it hit.

In 2008, Hurricane Ike, the third costliest hurricane ever to hit the United States' coast, traveled through the Gulf of Mexico. Ike was gigantic, and the devastation in its path included the Turk and Caicos Islands, Haiti, and huge swaths of the coast of the Gulf of Mexico. Once again, Galveston, now a city of nearly 60,000, took the direct hit as Ike came ashore. Almost 200 people in the Caribbean and the United States lost their lives; a tragedy to be sure, but far less deadly than the 1900 storm. This time, people were prepared, having received excellent warning from the GOES satellite network (Fig. 19-6). The GOES satellites have been a continuous monitor of the world's weather since 1975, and they have since been joined by other Earth-observing satellites. This weather surveillance, to which so many now owe their lives, is possible in part because of the ability to point accurately and steadily at the Earth below. The importance of accurately pointing spacecraft to our daily lives is pervasive, yet somehow escapes the notice of most people. But the example of the lives saved from Hurricane Ike as compared to the 1900 storm is something no one should ignore. In this section, we will summarize the processes and technologies used in designing and operating spacecraft pointing (i.e., attitude) systems.

Attitude is the three-dimensional orientation of a vehicle with respect to a specified reference frame. *Attitude systems* include the sensors, actuators, avionics, algorithms, software, and ground support equipment used to determine and control the attitude of a vehicle. Attitude

Fig. 19-1. Satellite Image of Hurricane Ike. (Photo courtesy of NASA)

systems can have a variety of names, such as attitude determination and control system (ADCS), attitude ground system (AGS), attitude and orbit control system (AOCS), guidance, navigation and control (GNC), or whatever other term describes the designers' focus in achieving the attitude needs of a particular mission. When we use an acronym in this section, we will use ADCS, but any given specialist may be more familiar with other terms.

Spacecraft attitude changes according to the fundamental equations of motion for rotational dynamics, the Euler equations, here expressed in vector form in the spacecraft's reference frame:

$$\dot{\mathbf{H}} = \mathbf{T} - \omega \times \mathbf{H} \tag{19-1}$$

This vector Eq. (19-1) represents the conservation equations for the *angular momentum*, which is denoted by **H**. Recall that linear momentum is the translational motion of a body that will remain constant unless a force acts to change it, and it is calculated (in Newtonian physics anyway) as mass times velocity. Analogously, angular momentum is the rotational motion of a body that will continue unless changed by a *torque*, and it is calculated as the body's *moment of inertia* times its angular velocity (or rotation rate). The moment of inertia is a 3-by-3 matrix of values that describe the distribution of mass in a body. There is always a coordinate frame, called the principal axis frame, for which the moment of inertia matrix is diagonal. The difference between the geometric and principal axis frames is of great interest to ADCS designers, as we will see later in this section.

Note that in the form above, the Euler equation makes it clear that the magnitude of angular momentum in a system can only be changed by applying external torques, T, because the change due to the term $\omega \times$ H can only change the direction of H, not the magnitude. The magnitude of a body's angular momentum will remain constant in the absence of external torques upon it, even when parts of the body can move with respect to other parts, such as a gyroscope spinning in its housing. If part of the body starts to spin in one direction in the absence of external torques, the rest of the body will have to spin in the opposite direction so that total angular momentum is conserved. With this in mind, we can relate the angular velocity of the spacecraft, ω, to H by the equation:

$$\mathbf{H} = \mathbf{I}\omega + \mathbf{h} \tag{19-2}$$

where I is the moment of inertia and h is the angular momentum stored by any rotating objects that are part of the spacecraft, such as momentum wheels or gyroscopes. So, by the product rule of calculus, the Euler equations can be rewritten as a matrix equation:

$$\dot{\mathbf{I}}\omega + \mathbf{I}\dot{\omega} + \dot{\mathbf{h}} = \mathbf{T} - \omega \times \mathbf{H} \tag{19-3}$$

or, after moving some terms around:

$$\mathbf{I}\dot{\omega} = \mathbf{T} - \dot{\mathbf{h}} - \dot{\mathbf{I}}\omega - \omega \times \mathbf{H} \tag{19-4}$$

The form of Eq. (19-4) allows us to understand how attitude can change due to a variety of causes. The first term on the right-hand side represents the external torque's direct contribution to attitude dynamics; this term includes how some actuators can be used to control spacecraft attitude by creating external torques. The second term gives the relationship between changes in on-board rotating objects' speeds and changes in the spacecraft's rotational velocity; this term is where certain other control actuators enter into the dynamics as so-called internal torques. The third term shows how changes in the spacecraft moment of inertia (representing how mass is distributed in the spacecraft), such as by solar array articulation, can affect attitude dynamics; in the absence of changes in mass properties, the third term disappears. The fourth term is called the *gyroscopic torque*, and it shows how the angular momentum appears to change direction, but not magnitude, in the spacecraft's frame of reference when the spacecraft is rotating. All these effects combine to determine the rate of change of the angular velocity on the left-hand side.

Attitude determination is the process of combining available sensor inputs with knowledge of the spacecraft dynamics to provide an accurate and unique solution for the attitude state as a function of time, either onboard for immediate use, or after the fact (i.e., post-processing). With the powerful microprocessors now available for spaceflight, most attitude algorithms that formerly were performed as post-processing can now be programmed as onboard calculations. Therefore, though there are still good engineering reasons for certain processes to be performed only by ground-based attitude systems (see Chap. 28), it will be sufficient to focus our attitude determination discussions in this chapter on the design and implementation of onboard systems.

The product of attitude determination, the attitude *estimate* or *solution*, is attained by using sensors to relate information about external references, such as the stars, the Sun, the Earth, or other celestial bodies, to the orientation of the spacecraft. Frequently, any single sensor has a noise level or (see Sec. 16.3) other drawback that prevents it from providing a fully satisfactory attitude solution at all times. Therefore, more than one sensor is often required to meet all mission requirements for a given mission.

The combination of information from multiple sensors is a complex field of study. The possibilities for any given mission range from simple logical combination of sensors, depending on mode, to modern information filtering methods, such as Kalman filtering. Many methods require some prediction of a future attitude from current conditions. Because all spacecraft sensors must use the spacecraft's reference frame as a basis for attitude determination, the development of angular momentum according to the spacecraft's frame of reference can be important for some attitude determination algorithms. This is the reason for the spacecraft-referenced aspect of the Euler equations.

Attitude control is the combination of the prediction of and reaction to a vehicle's rotational dynamics. As

Table 19-1. Steps in Attitude System Design. An iterative process is used for designing the ADCS.

Step	Inputs	Outputs
1a) Define Control Modes ***1b) Define or Derive System-Level Requirements by Control Mode***	Mission requirements, mission profile, type of insertion for launch vehicle	List of different control modes during mission. Requirements and constraints.
2) Quantify Disturbance Environment	Spacecraft geometry, orbit, solar/magnetic models, mission profile	Values for torques from external and internal sources
3) Select Type of Spacecraft Control by Attitude Control Mode	Payload, thermal & power needs Orbit, pointing direction Disturbance environment Accuracy requirements	Method for stabilization & control: 3-axis, spinning, gravity gradient, etc.
4) Select and Size ADCS Hardware	Spacecraft geometry and mass properties, required accuracy, orbit geometry, mission lifetime, space environment, pointing direction, slew rates. Failure detection and redundancy	Sensor suite: Earth, Sun, inertial, or other sensing devices. Control actuators: reaction wheels, thrusters, magnetic torquers, etc. Data processing avionics, if any, or processing requirements for other subsystems or ground computer.
5) Define Determination and Control Algorithms	Performance considerations (stabilization method(s), attitude knowledge & control accuracy, slew rates) balanced against system-level limitations (power and thermal needs, lifetime, jitter sensitivity, spacecraft processor capability)	Algorithms and parameters for each determination and control mode, and logic for changing from one mode to another.
6) Iterate and Document	All of above	Refined mission and subsystem requirements. More detailed ADCS design. Subsystem and component specifications.

discussed in Secs. 7.3 and 7.4, spacecraft exist in an environment of small and often highly predictable disturbances. Therefore, in certain cases they may be passively controlled. That is, a spacecraft may be designed in such a way that the environmental disturbances cause the spacecraft attitude to stabilize in the orientation needed to meet mission goals. Alternately, a spacecraft may include actuators that can be used to actively control the spacecraft orientation. These two general types of attitude control are not mutually exclusive. A spacecraft may be mostly or usually passively controlled and yet include actuators to adjust the attitude in small ways or to make attitude maneuvers (i.e., slews) to meet other objectives, such as targets of opportunity or communication needs.

As seen earlier, external torques change the total angular momentum, and internal torques exchange momentum between different rotating parts of the spacecraft. In this way *reaction wheels* or *control moment gyroscopes* may be used to change spacecraft pointing without affecting total angular momentum. Because environmental disturbances create external torques on the spacecraft, they also create angular momentum that must be either stored or removed by the attitude system. Small external torques that vary over the course of an orbit but have a mean of zero may be managed just through storage, but those torques that have a non-zero mean (secular torques) will cause a gradual increase in angular momentum, and this momentum build-up must eventually be removed with actuators that create external torques. Thrusters, magnetic torquers, or even solar trim tabs can be used to create controlled external torques on the spacecraft, thus controlling the total angular momentum.

Attitude system design is an iterative process. Table 19-1 lists typical steps in a design process and what inputs and outputs would be expected for each step. Figure 19-2 presents all the processes involved in attitude systems. The FireSat II spacecraft, shown in Fig. 19-3, and the Supplemental Communications System (SCS) constellation of spacecraft, shown in Fig. 19-4, will be used to illustrate this process.

19.1.1 Control Modes and Requirements

The first step of the attitude system design process is the definition of guiding requirements based ultimately on mission goals (Sec. 3.3). Since mission goals often require more than one mode of operating a spacecraft, the guiding requirements generally begin with a description of the control modes the ADCS is expected to execute to meet those goals. Tables 19-2 and 19-3 describe typical spacecraft control modes and requirements.

The final form of ADCS requirements and control modes will be the result of iteration; control modes are designed to achieve certain sets of requirements, and better understanding of the actual needs of the mission often results from having these modes of controlling the spacecraft well defined. This iteration takes place in a trade space where a single set of ADCS hardware must be used in different ways to meet different sets of requirements.

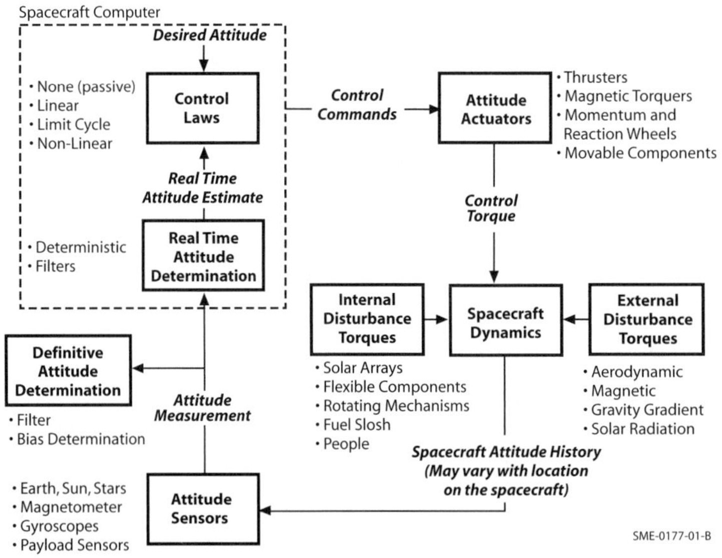

Fig. 19-2. Diagram of a Complete Attitude Determination and Control System. Definitive attitude determination usually occurs in ground processing of telemetry, whereas onboard, real-time determination design focuses on being extremely reliable and deterministic in its operation.

The ADCS will also be dependent on certain other subsystems, such as the power (Sec. 21.2) and structural (Sec. 22.1) subsystem. Attitude needs will also impose requirements on other subsystems, such as propulsion, thermal control, and structural stability. Figure 19-5 shows many of the complex interactions needed to bring the ADCS design in line with the needs of the whole mission (see Sec. 3.1).

Different mission needs may impose different requirements on the ADCS. One such critical need for many missions is orbit control. For many spacecraft the ADCS must control vehicle attitude during the firing of large liquid or solid rocket motors for orbit insertion or management. Large motors can create large disturbance torques, which can drive the design to larger actuators than may be needed for the rest of the mission.

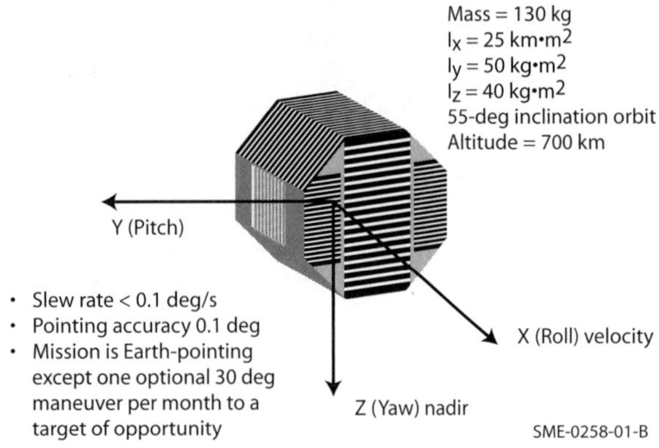

Fig. 19-3. Hypothetical FireSat II Spacecraft. We use this simplified example of a low-Earth orbiting satellite to discuss key concepts throughout the section.

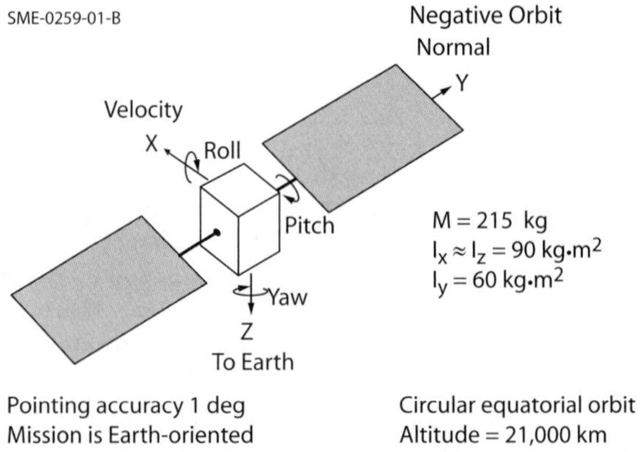

Fig. 19-4. One Member of the Hypothetical Supplemental Communications System (SCS) Constellation. We will also use this collection of three spacecraft in medium Earth orbit to illustrate attitude system design practices.

Once the spacecraft is on station, the payload pointing requirements usually dominate (see Sec. 8.6). These may require planet-relative or inertial attitudes and fixed or spinning fields of view. There is usually also a need for attitude slew maneuvers, and the frequency and speed of those maneuvers must be defined. Reasons for slews can include:

- Acquiring the desired spacecraft attitude initially or after a failure
- Repointing the payload's sensing systems to targets of opportunity or for calibration purposes
- Tracking stationary or moving targets, including communication stations
- Directing the vehicle's strongest motor to the proper direction relative to orbital motion

Table 19-1◄, Fig. 19-4, Eq. 19-4◄

Table 19-2. Typical Attitude Control Modes. Performance requirements are frequently tailored to these different control operation modes.

Mode	Description
Acquisition	Initial determination of attitude and stabilization of vehicle for communication with ground and power generation just after launch. Also may be used to recover from power upsets or emergencies.
Orbit Insertion	Period during and after boost while spacecraft is brought to final orbit. Options include no spacecraft control, simple spin stabilization of solid rocket motor, and full spacecraft control using liquid propulsion system. May drive certain aspects of ADCS design.
Normal Mission, On-Station	Used for the vast majority of the mission. Requirements for this mode should drive system design.
Slew	Reorienting the vehicle when required.
Contingency or Safe	Used in emergencies if regular mode fails or is disabled. Will generally use less power or fewer components to meet minimal power and thermal needs.
Special	Requirements may be different for special targets or time periods, such as when the satellite passes through a celestial body's shadow, or *umbra*.

Table 19-3. Typical Attitude Determination and Control Performance Requirements. Requirements need to be specified for each mode. The following lists the performance criteria frequently specified.

Criterion	Definition*	Examples/Comments
Accuracy	Knowledge of and control over a vehicle's attitude relative to a target attitude as defined relative to an absolute reference	0.25 deg, 3σ, often includes determination errors along with control errors, or there may be separate requirements for determination and control, and even for different axes
Range	Range of angular motion over which determination & control performance must be met	Any attitude within 30 deg of nadir. Whenever rotational rates are less than 2 deg/sec.
Jitter	Specified bound on high-frequency angular motion	0.1 deg over 60 sec, 1 deg/s, 1 to 20 Hz; prevents excessive blurring of sensor data
Drift	Limit on slow, low-frequency angular motion	0.01 deg over 20 min, 0.05 deg max; used when vehicle may drift off target with infrequent command inputs
Transient Response	Allowed settling time or max attitude overshoot when acquiring new targets or recover from upsets	10% max overshoot, decaying to <0.1 deg in 1 min; may also limit excursions from a set path between targets

* Definitions vary with procuring and designing agencies, especially in details (e.g., 1σ or 3σ, amount of averaging or filtering allowed). It is always best to define exactly what is required.

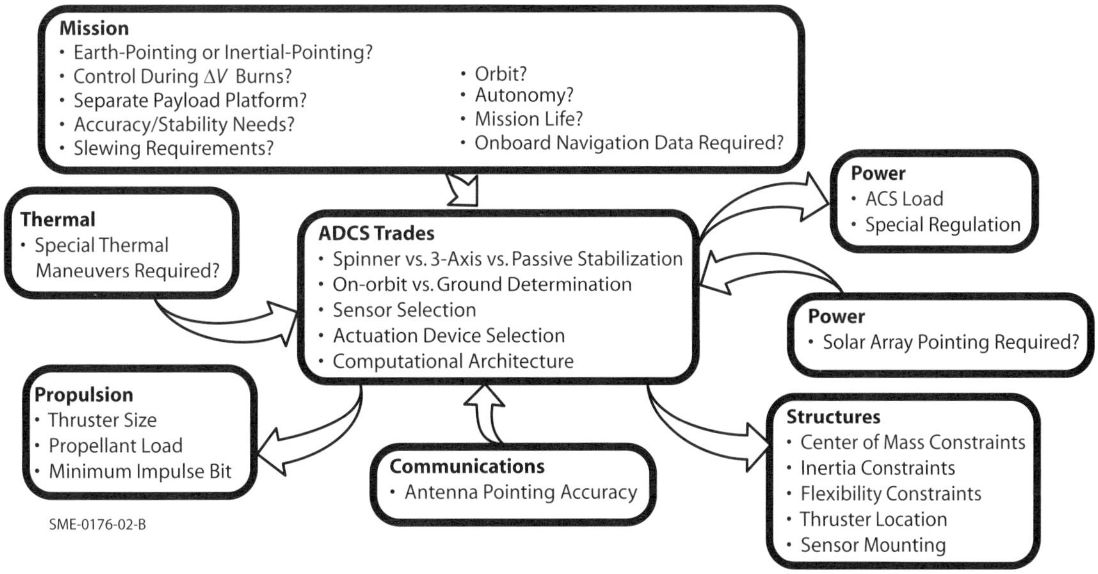

Fig. 19-5. The Impact of Mission Requirements and Other Subsystems on the ADCS. Direction of arrows shows requirements flow from one subsystem to another.

19.1.2 Quantify the Disturbance Environment

The environment in which the spacecraft will operate constrains what types of control methods will be effective. For example, the relatively strong magnetic fields that occur in low Earth orbit (LEO) can create disturbance torques that need to be managed, but they also allow the use of magnetic torquers, a means of attitude control not available at much higher altitudes like geosynchronous orbit (GEO). Here, we will focus on the torque disturbance environment as the primary driver for control mode and hardware selection, but the sensitivity of the ADCS designer must be to more than just the external torque disturbances of the operational orbit. For example, some attitude sensors, such as star cameras that use charge-coupled devices (CCDs) for imaging, can be highly sensitive to the intense radiation in the Van Allen belts of the Earth's magnetosphere (see Sec. 7.3). Active Pixel Sensor (APS) cameras may be more robust. Depending on the specific model, the star camera may underperform or even provide no information at all when the spacecraft occupies these regions.

Only three or four sources of torque matter for the typical Earth-orbiting spacecraft: gravity-gradient effects, magnetic field torques on a magnetized vehicle (as most spacecraft will be), impingement by solar-radiation, and aerodynamic torques for LEO satellites. Figure 19-6 summarizes the relative effects of these disturbances for different flight regimes. Chapter 7 describes the Earth environment in detail, and Hughes [2004] provides a thorough treatment of disturbances.

Other external disturbances to the spacecraft are either small relative to the four main external disturbances, such as infrared emission pressure, or they are limited in time, such as outgassing. Occasionally, what is normally negligible can become surprisingly large, even exceeding the usual disturbance torque sources, but this is one of the reasons for maintenance of healthy engineering margins and operational plans that are adaptable to unforeseen events.

Centroids. Estimation of environmental torques often requires the use of geometrical averaging. Anyone with a technical education will be familiar with the centroid of an area, but it may have been some time since the reader encountered this concept. The centroid is the point in an area through which any line drawn in any direction will evenly divide moments about the line (or any point along the line). To express it another way, the sum of all area elements multiplied by their distances from a line will be zero for any line passing through the centroid. In a sense, it is the average point for the area. If a source of pressure were applied evenly over the area, the total solar pressure force could be represented as being applied entirely at the centroid for the purposes of determining moments, and therefore disturbance torques. A solid body can also have centroids. The *center of mass* (cm or CoM) is the point (usually inside) the body through which any plane will divide the mass moment evenly. By applying a force at or along the center of mass, no torques are created. This is why freely rotating bodies rotate about their centers of mass.

As a practical example, the point that may be regarded as the location of a body for purposes of gravitational forces is called the *center of gravity* (cg); i.e., all effects of gravity on the body can be considered to act at the cg. In the essentially uniform gravity that we humans occupy, the center of mass is usually indistinguishable from the center of gravity, but in the free-fall of a space orbit, the absence of direct gravitational forces and torques means that the change, or *gravity-gradient*, over the extent of a body can be important. For elongated or flattened objects in orbit, the cm may be offset from the cg, so that the gravitational force is effectively applied with an offset from the cm, creating a torque—this is the gravity gradient torque. Note that the cg is a function of the current attitude of the spacecraft, not just its mass configuration, which is critical in attitude analysis.

Other environmental effects can be understood in terms of offsets between centroids of different effects on a body. When the aerodynamic force centroid, which is at the centroid of the *ram area* (the area presented to the velocity direction), is not aligned with the cm, a torque is created. Solar radiation pressure is more intense on certain surfaces (reflective) than others (absorptive). The total pressure force over the Sun-pointing surface of a spacecraft can be considered to act through a *center of pressure* (cp) with an average reflectance, and the offset of that point from the cm results in solar radiation pressure torque. The location of this cp is a function of attitude as well as surface properties. Some modern surfaces can have their reflectance change with a change in applied voltage, usually for thermal reasons, but which results in a controlled change in cp location. So, in detailed modeling of spacecraft, the determination of the weighted averages of various forces is important to a good understanding of the torque environment.

Modeling Major Disturbances. Now, we will present the equations used to model major disturbances with some explanation and demonstration of how they can be used to design attitude systems. After the explanations, Table 19-4 will show disturbance calculations for the FireSat II and SCS examples.

Solar Radiation Pressure. As discussed in Sec. 18.5, sunlight has momentum, and therefore it exerts pressure on those objects it strikes. If an object absorbs all the sunlight falling on it, then it absorbs all of its momentum and experiences a certain pressure force because of it. If the sunlight is instead reflected exactly back along its path, such as by a mirror, the pressure force felt is twice as much.

If a sunlit flat plate were mirrored on one half and painted black on the other, the pressure distribution across the plate would be uneven and a torque would result. Alternately, if the plate were all black, but a weight were attached to one end in the plate's shadow, a torque would also result because the center of pressure would be in the center of the plate, but the center of mass would be closer to the weighted end. These phenomena are called *solar radiation pressure* (SRP) torques.

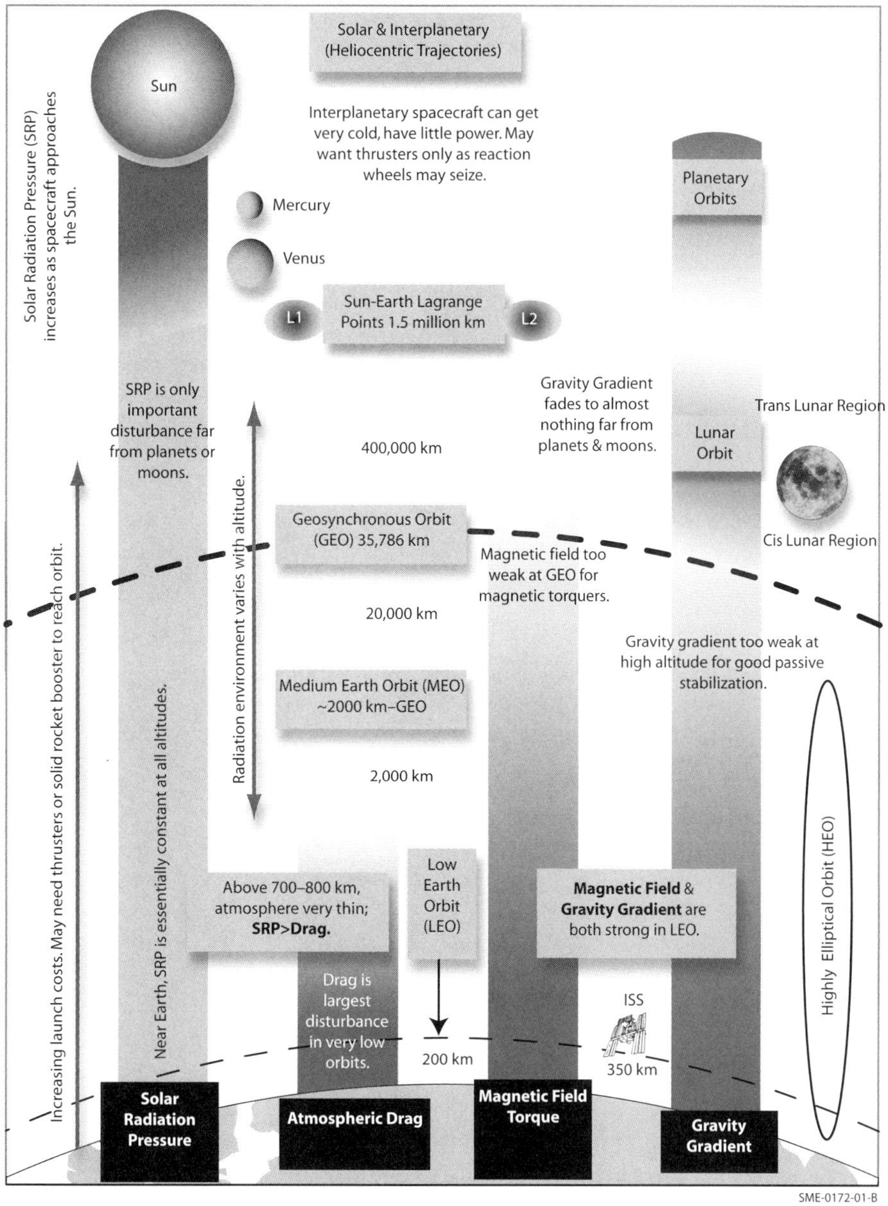

Fig. 19-6. Effects of Major Environmental Disturbances on Spacecraft Attitude System Design. The diagram has a roughly logarithmic scale of altitude. The columns represent the four major disturbance sources, with the intensity of color for each column indicating the strength of that disturbance in the various flight regimes.

Now imagine a spacecraft like FireSat II in sunlight. Some parts of the spacecraft stick out further from the center of mass than others. Some surfaces are more reflective than others; solar arrays would absorb more light than reflective metallic surfaces would. Also, surfaces that are angled with respect to the Sun would have less pressure on them than similar surfaces directly facing the Sun. All this goes to demonstrate that accurately predicting SRP torques is very tricky. That said, a good starting estimate can be gleaned by assuming a uniform reflectance and using the following equation:

$$T_S = \frac{\Phi}{c} A_S (1+q)(cp_S - cm)\cos\varphi \qquad (19\text{-}5)$$

where T_S is the SRP torque, Φ is the solar constant adjusted for actual distance from the Sun (average value: 1,366 W/m^2 at 1 AU), c is the speed of light (3×10^8 m/s), A_S is the sunlit surface area in m^2, q is the unitless reflectance factor (ranging from 0 for perfect absorption to 1 for perfect reflection), φ is the angle of incidence of the Sun, and cp_S and cm are the centers of solar radiation pressure and mass.

Table 19-4. Disturbance Torque Summary and Sample Calculations. See text for detailed discussion and definition of symbols. FireSat II is mainly affected by magnetic torques, with the 30-degree offset attitude also affected by gravity gradient torques. SCS satellites are mainly affected by solar radiation pressure torques.

Disturbance	Type	FireSat II	SCS
Solar Radiation	Cyclic for Earth-oriented; constant for Sun-oriented	FireSat II is very small and Earth-oriented (though not Earth-pointing), and has body-mounted arrays. Therefore, its surface area is small and its cp_s is close to its cm. A_s = 1.2 m × 1.1 m = 1.3 m^2; q = 0.6 φ = 0 deg; $cp_s - cm$ = 0.1 m T_s = (1,367)(1.3)(1 + 0.6)(0.1)/(3 × 10^8) = 9.6 × 10^{-7} N·m	SCS is small and Earth-pointing, so the surface area will be fairly small, However, the need to balance the masses of three stowed satellites on the launch vehicle may reduce our control over mass placement and may cause the center of pressure to be considerably offset from the cm with respect to the Sun. A_s = 2 m × 1.5 m = 3 m^2; q = 0.6 φ = 0 deg; $cp_s - cm$ = 0.3 m T_s = (1,367)(3.0)(1 + 0.6)(0.3)/(3 × 10^8) = 6.6 × 10^{-6} N·m
Atmospheric Drag	Constant for Earth-oriented; variable for inertially oriented	Similar to SRP. The ram face will always be the same, so the cp and cm locations can be designed a bit better in this direction. A_r = 1.3 m^2; $cp_a - cm$ = 0.05 m; C_d = 2.0 For 700 km orbit: $\rho \approx$ 10^{-13} kg/m^3; V = 7,504 m/s T_a=(0.5)(10^{-13})(2.0)(1.3)(7504)^2(0.05) = 3.7 × 10^{-7} N·m	Similar assumptions as for SRP, except that being Earth-pointing, the same face will be presented to the ram direction all the time, so we can expect a little more control over the cp and cm locations. A_r = 3 m^2; $cp_a - cm$ = 0.2 m; C_d = 2.0 For 21,000 km orbit: $\rho \approx$ 10^{-18} kg/m^3; V = 3,816 m/s T_a = (0.5)(10^{-18})(2.0)(3)(3,816)^2(0.2) = 8.7 × 10^{-12} N·m
Magnetic Field	Cyclic	55 deg inclination orbit; assume 0.5 A·m^2 for a very small, uncompensated vehicle. R = (6,378 + 700) km = 7,078 km D = 0.5 A·m^2; λ = 1.9 for 55 deg B = (7.8 × 10^{15})(1.9)/(7.078 × 10^6)^3 = 4.2 × 10^{-5} T T_m = (0.5)B = 2.1 × 10^{-5} N·m	Equatorial orbit; assume 1 A·m^2 for a small, uncompensated vehicle. R = (6,378 + 21,000) km = 27,378 km D = 1 A·m^2; $\lambda \approx$ 1.2 for equatorial orbit B = (1)(7.8 × 10^{15})(1.2)/(2.7378 × 10^7)^3 = 4.6 × 10^{-7} T T_m = 1(B) = 4.6 × 10^{-7} N·m
Gravity Gradient	Constant for Earth-oriented; cyclic for inertially oriented	With body-mounted arrays, FireSat II is fairly symmetric and small, so the moment of inertia can be balanced very well: We'll set θ=1 deg. R = 7,078 km I = 25 kg·m^2; I_y = 50 kg·m^2 Normal mode: θ = 1 deg T_g = (3)(3.986 × 10^{14})|25–50|sin(2 deg) / (2)(7.078 × 10^6)^3 = 1.5 × 10^{-6} N·m Target-of-opportunity: θ = 30 deg T_g = 3.7 × 10^{-5} N·m	Deployed solar arrays dominate moment of inertia, so $I_x = I_z > I_y$. However, the ability to balance mass may be limited by the need to fit 3 satellites on the same launch vehicle, so we'll assume a large difference between the geometric and principal axes: θ = 10 deg. R = 27,378 km I_z = 90 kg·m^2; I_y = 60 kg·m^2 T_g = (3)(3.986 × 10^{14})|90–60|sin(20 deg) / (2)(2.7378 × 10^7)^3 = 3.0 × 10^{-7} N·m

Atmospheric Drag. In much the same way photons striking a spacecraft can exert pressure, so too can the rarified atmosphere that clings to Earth (and certain other planets) at the edge of space. The atmospheric density is roughly an exponentially decaying function of altitude, so that generally only spacecraft in low Earth orbit (LEO) encounter enough particles to cause noticeable disturbances. Those that do experience a pressure force known as *atmospheric* (or *aerodynamic*) *drag.* The atmospheric drag force itself is an important consideration for orbit planning (Chap. 9) and orbit prediction and tracking (Sec. 19.2). When the center of atmospheric pressure, determined by the spacecraft area exposed to the atmosphere in the direction of the orbital velocity (i.e., ram direction), is not aligned with the center of mass, a torque results. The atmospheric (or aerodynamic) torque can be estimated as

$$T_a = \frac{1}{2}\rho C_d A_r V^2 \left(cp_a - cm\right) \tag{19-6}$$

where T_a is the atmospheric drag torque, ρ is the atmospheric density in kg/m^3, C_d is the drag coefficient (usually between 2.0 and 2.5 for spacecraft), A_r is the ram area in m^2, V is the spacecraft's orbital velocity in m/s, and cp_a and cm are the centers of aerodynamic pressure and mass in m. Average atmospheric density and orbital velocity as functions of altitude are tabulated in App. I.

Magnetic Field. The Earth's liquid core is a dynamo that generates a magnetic field powerful enough to have important effects on the space surrounding the planet (see Sec. 7.3). Most spacecraft have some level of residual *magnetic moment*, meaning they have a weak magnetic field of their own. These residual moments can range anywhere from 0.1–20 A·m^2, or even more depending on the spacecraft's size and whether any onboard compensation is provided.

When a spacecraft's residual moment is not aligned with a local magnetic field, it experiences a *magnetic torque* that attempts to align the magnet to the local field, much like a compass needle. The Earth's magnetic field is complex, asymmetric, not aligned with the Earth's spin axis, and varies with both geographical movement of the dipole and changes in solar particle flux. However, for use in the ADCS design process, it is usually sufficient to model the Earth's magnetic field as a dipole and to determine the maximum possible value of the magnetic torque for a spacecraft's altitude. The following equation yields this maximum torque:

$$T_m = DB = D\left(\frac{M}{R^3}\lambda\right) \tag{19-7}$$

where T_m is the magnetic torque, D is the spacecraft's residual dipole moment in A·m^2, and B is the magnetic field strength in tesla (T). The magnetic field strength in turn is calculated from M, the magnetic moment of the Earth multiplied by the magnetic constant ($M = 7.8 \times 10^{15}$ tesla·m^3); R, the distance between the spacecraft and the Earth's center in m, and λ, which is a unitless function of the magnetic latitude that ranges from 1 at the magnetic equator to 2 at the magnetic poles. So, a polar orbit will see roughly twice the maximum magnetic torque of an equatorial orbit.

Gravity-Gradient. As described in the earlier subsection on centroids, *gravity-gradient* torques are caused when a spacecraft's center of gravity is not aligned with its center of mass with respect to the local vertical. Without getting into the math of the matter, the center of gravity of a spacecraft in orbit is dependent on its attitude relative to Earth (or whatever body the spacecraft is orbiting), and that cg is not, in general, the same as the center of mass. However, when one of the spacecraft's principal axes is aligned with the local vertical, the cg is always on that principal axis, and therefore there is no gravity-gradient torque. The gravity-gradient torque increases with the angle between the local vertical and the spacecraft's principal axes, always trying to align the minimum principal axis with the local vertical.

A simplified expression for the gravity-gradient torque for a spacecraft with the minimum principal axis in its Z direction is

$$T_g = \frac{3\mu}{2R^3}\left|I_z - I_y\right|\sin(2\theta) \tag{19-8}$$

Where T_g is the gravity-gradient torque about the X principal axis, μ is the Earth's gravitational constant (3.986 $\times 10^{14}$ m^3/s^2), R is the distance from the center of the Earth in meters, θ is the angle between the local vertical and the Z principal axis, and I_y and I_z are the moments of inertia about Y and Z in kg·m^2.

Remaining significant disturbances on the control system are internal to the spacecraft. Fortunately, we have some control over them. If we find that one is much larger than the rest, we can specify tighter values for that item. This change would reduce its significance but most likely add to its cost or weight. Table 19-5 summarizes the common internal disturbances. Misalignments in the center of gravity and in thrusters will show up during thrusting only and are corrected in a closed-loop control system and through on-orbit calibration of the thrusters.

Likewise, momentum wheel friction torques can be compensated in either a closed-loop or a compensatory fashion; some reaction wheels are designed with friction compensation included in some commanding modes. Liquid slosh and operating machinery torques are of greater concern but depend on specific hardware. If a spacecraft component has fluid tanks or rotating machinery, the system designer should investigate disturbance effects and ways to compensate for the disturbance, if required. Standard techniques include propellant management devices (e.g., slosh baffles) or counter-rotating elements.

19.1.3 Selection of Spacecraft Control Methods

Now that we understand the requirements on the control system and the environment in which it will operate, we can select one or more methods of controlling the spacecraft. Multiple methods may be indicated when different modes of operating the spacecraft have significantly different requirements or result in different disturbance profiles (as we will see in our FireSat II example). Table 19-6 lists several methods of control, along with typical characteristics of each. European Standard ECSS-E-60A, [ESA, 2004] for Spacecraft Control Engineering outlines their design and verification process.

Passive Control Techniques. *Gravity-gradient control* uses the inertial properties of a vehicle to keep it pointed toward the Earth. This relies on the fact that an

Table 19-5. Principal Internal Disturbance Torques. Spacecraft designers can minimize internal disturbances through careful planning and precise manufacturing, which may increase cost.

Disturbances	Effect on Vehicle	Typical Values
Uncertainty in Center of Gravity (cg)	Unbalanced torques during firing of couples thrusters Unwanted torques during translation thrusting	1–3 cm
Thruster Misalignment	Same as cg uncertainty	0.1–0.5 deg
Mismatch of Thruster Outputs	Similar to cg uncertainty	±5%
Reaction Wheel Friction and Electromotive Force (i.e., back EMF)	Resistance that opposes control torque effort. These torques are the limiting mechanism for wheels speed.	Roughly proportional to wheel speed, depending on model. At top speed, 100% of control torque (i.e., saturation)
Rotating Machinery (pumps, filter wheels)	Torques that perturb both stability and accuracy	Dependent on spacecraft design; may be compensated by counter-rotating elements
Liquid Slosh	Torques due to liquid dynamic pressure on tank walls, as well as changes in cg location.	Dependent on specific design; may be mitigated by bladders or baffles
Dynamics of Flexible Bodies	Oscillatory resonance at bending/twisting frequencies, limiting control bandwidth	Depends on spacecraft structure; flexible frequencies within the control bandwidth must be phase-stabilized, which may be undesirable.
Thermal Shocks ("snap") on Flexible Appendages	Attitude disturbances when entering/leaving umbra	Depends on spacecraft structure. Long inertia booms and large solar arrays can cause large disturbances.

Table 19-6. Attitude Control Methods and Their Capabilities. As requirements become tighter, more complex control systems become necessary.

Type	Pointing Options	Attitude Maneuverability	Typical Accuracy	Lifetime Limits
Gravity-Gradient	Earth local vertical only	Very limited	±5 deg (2 axes)	None
Gravity-Gradient + Momentum Bias	Earth local vertical only	Very limited	±5 deg (3 axes)	Life of wheel bearings
Passive Magnetic	North/South only	Very limited	±5 deg (2 axes)	None
Rate-Damping + Target Vector Acquisition	Usually Sun (power) or Earth (communication)	Generally used as robust safe mode.	±5–15 deg (2 axes)	None
Pure Spin Stabilization	Inertially fixed any direction	Repoint with precession maneuvers; very slow with torquers, faster with thrusters	±0.1 deg to ±1 deg in 2 axes (proportional to spin rate)	Thruster propellant (if applies)*
Dual-Spin Stabilization	Limited only by articulation on despun platform	Same as above	Same as above for spun section. Despun dictated by payload reference and pointing	Thruster propellant (if applies)* Despun section bearings
Bias Momentum (1 wheel)	Local vertical pointing or inertial targets	Fast maneuvers possible around momentum vector Repoint of momentum vector as with spin stabilized	±0.1 deg to ±1 deg	Propellant (if applies)* Life of sensor and wheel bearings
Active Magnetic with Filtering	Any, but may drift over short periods	Slow (several orbits to slew); faster at lower altitudes	±1 deg to ±5 deg (depends on sensors)	Life of sensors
Zero Momentum (thruster only)	No constraints	No constraints High rates possible	±0.1 deg to 5 deg	Propellant
Zero momentum (3 wheels)	No constraints	No constraints	±0.0001 deg to ±1 deg (determined by sensors and processor)	Propellant (if applies)* Life of sensors and wheel bearing
Zero Momentum (CMG)	No constraints Short CMG life may require high redundancy	No constraints High rates possible	±0.001 deg to ±1 deg	Propellant (if applies)* Life sensors and CMG bearings

* Thrusters may be used for slewing and momentum dumping at all altitudes, but propellant usage may be high. Magnetic torquers may be used from LEO to GEO.

Table 19-6, Fig. 19-6◀, Eq. 19-8◀

elongated object in a gravity field tends to align its longitudinal axis through the Earth's center. The torques that cause this alignment decrease with the cube of the orbit radius and are symmetric around the nadir vector. Thus, the yaw of a spacecraft around the nadir vector is not controllable by this method. This technique is used on simple spacecraft in near-Earth orbits without yaw orientation requirements, often with deployable booms to achieve the desired inertias. Satellite geometry is shown in Fig. 19-4 and discussed in Sec. 8.1.2.

Frequently, we add dampers to gravity gradient satellites to reduce libration—small oscillations off of the nadir vector caused by other environmental disturbances. For example, long deployed booms are particularly susceptible to thermal shocks when entering or leaving umbra. These spacecraft also need a method of ensuring attitude capture with the correct end pointed at nadir—the gravity-gradient torques stabilize either end of the minimum inertia axis equally.

In the simplest gravity-gradient spacecraft, only two orientation axes are controlled; the orientation around the nadir vector is unconstrained. To control this third degree of freedom, a small constant-speed momentum wheel is sometimes added along the intended pitch axis. The momentum-biased wheel will be most stable when perpendicular to the nadir and velocity vectors, and therefore parallel to the orbital momentum vector. The stable state of the gravity-gradient plus momentum bias wheel establishes the desired attitude through small energy dissipations onboard without the need for active control.

A third type of purely passive control uses permanent magnets onboard to force alignment along the Earth's magnetic field. This is most effective in near-equatorial orbits where the North-South field orientation is reasonably constant for an Earth-referenced satellite.

Spin Control Techniques. *Spin stabilization* is a passive control technique in which the entire spacecraft rotates so that its angular momentum vector remains approximately fixed in inertial space. Spin-stabilized spacecraft (or *spinners*), employ the gyroscopic stability discussed earlier to passively resist disturbance torques about two axes. Additionally, spinners are generally designed to be either insensitive to disturbances around the third axis (the spin axis) or else have active means of correcting these disturbances.

The vehicle is stable (in its minimum energy state) if it is spinning about the principal axis with the largest moment of inertia. Energy dissipation mechanisms onboard, such as propellant slosh, structural damping, or electrical harness movement, will cause any vehicle to progress toward this state if uncontrolled. So, disk-shaped vehicles are passively stable whereas pencil-shaped vehicles are not. See Fig. 19-7. Spinners can be simple, survive for long periods without attention, provide a thermally benign environment for components (because of even heating), and provide a scanning or sweeping motion for sensors. The principal disadvantages of spin stabilization are that the vehicle mass properties must be carefully managed during vehicle design and assembly to ensure the desired spin direction and stability, and that the angular momentum vector that provides stability also limits maneuverability. More fuel is required to reorient the vehicle than a vehicle with no net angular momentum, making this technique less useful for payloads that must be repointed frequently.

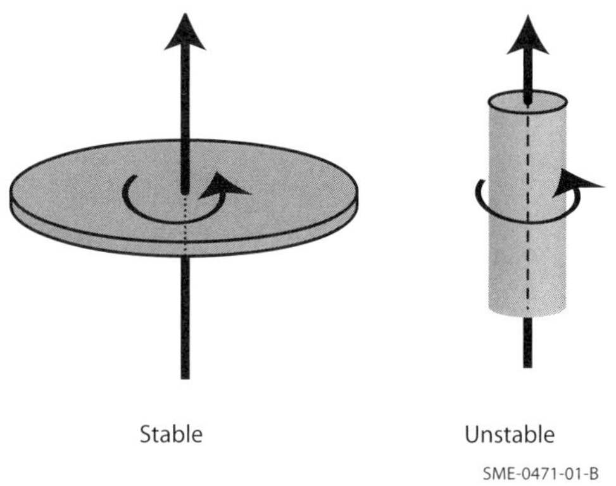

Fig. 19-7. Stable and Unstable Spinners.

A spinner requires extra fuel to reorient because of the gyroscopic stiffness, which also helps it resist disturbances. In reorienting a spinning body with angular momentum, **H**, a constant torque, **T**, will produce an angular velocity, ω, perpendicular to the applied torque and angular momentum vector, of magnitude $\omega = \mathbf{T}/\mathbf{H}$. (This follows from the earlier-introduced Euler equations.) Thus, the greater the stored momentum, the more torque must be applied for a given ω. For a maneuver through an angle θ, the torque-time product—an indication of fuel required for the maneuver—is a constant equal to $\mathbf{H}\cdot\theta$. Alternately, for a vehicle with no initial angular momentum, a small torque can be applied to start it rotating, with an opposite small torque to stop it when it has reached its new target. The fuel used for any angle maneuver can be arbitrarily small if a slow maneuver is acceptable. (Note that the spinner can only be maneuvered relatively slowly; a fast slew is usually not an option.)

A useful variation on spin control is called *dual-spin stabilization*, in which the spacecraft has two sections spinning at different rates about the same axis; this kind of spinner is also known as a *gyrostat*. Normally one section, the rotor, spins rapidly to provide gyroscopic stiffness, while the second section, the stator or platform, is despun to keep one axis pointed toward the Earth or Sun. By combining inertially fixed and rotating sections on the same vehicle, dual spinners can accommodate a variety of payloads in a simple vehicle. Also, by adding energy dissipation devices to the platform, a dual spinner can be passively stable spinning about the axis with the smallest moment of inertia, as long as the rotor is spinning about its own maximum moment of inertia. This permits more pencil-shaped spacecraft, which fit better in launch vehicle fairings and would not normally be stable spinning about their long axes. The disadvantage of dual-spin stabilization is the added complexity of the platform bearing and slip rings between the sections. (Slip rings permit power and electrical signals to flow between the two sections.) This complexity can increase cost and reduce reliability compared to simple spin stabilization.

Spinning spacecraft, both simple and dual, exhibit several distinct types of motion that are often confused. *Precession* is the motion of the angular momentum vector caused by external torques, including thruster firings used to correct environmental disturbances. *Coning* (or *wobbling*) is the apparent motion of the body when it is spinning about a principal axis of inertia that is not aligned with a body reference axis or axis of symmetry—for example, the intended spin axis. Coning looks like motion of the intended spin axis around the angular momentum vector at the spin rate. Figure 19-8 shows various natural rotations.

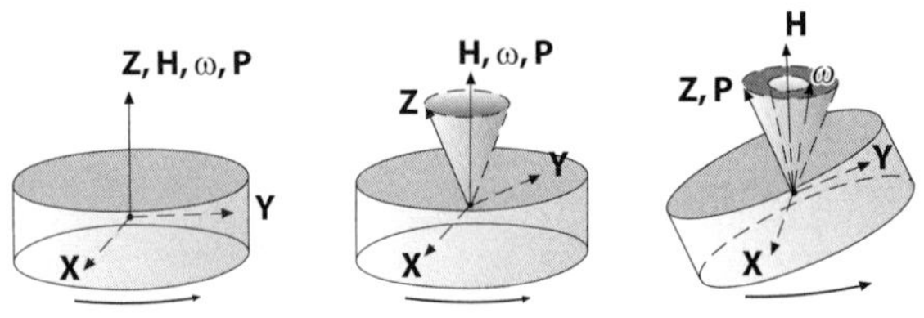

Fig. 19-8. Types of Rotational Motion. H = angular momentum vector; **P** = principal axis; *ω* = instantaneous rotation axis; **Z** = geometrical axis.

Nutation is the torque-free motion of a simple rigid body when the angular momentum vector is not perfectly aligned with a principal axis of inertia. For rod-shaped objects, this motion is a slow rotation (compared to spin rate) of the spin axis around the angular momentum vector. For these objects spinning about a minimum inertia axis, additional energy dissipation will cause increased nutation. For disk-shaped objects, spinning around a maximum inertia axis, nutation appears as a tumbling rotation faster than spin rate. Energy dissipation for these objects reduces nutation, resulting eventually in a clean spin. For these reasons, minimum-axis (or minor-axis) spinners are often concerned with minimizing energy dissipation, whereas maximum-axis (or major-axis) may actually include mechanisms, such as a passive nutation damper, to dissipate energy quickly.

Nutation is caused by disturbances such as thruster impulses, and can be seen as varying signals in body-mounted inertial and external sensors. Wobble is caused by imbalances and appears as constant offsets in body-mounted sensors. Such constant offsets are rarely discernible unless multiple sensors are available.

Spin stability normally requires active control, such as cold-gas thrusters or magnetic torquers, to periodically adjust the spacecraft's angular momentum vector to counteract disturbance torques. In addition, we may need to damp the nutation caused by disturbances or precession commands. Aggravating this nutation is the effect of energy dissipating phenomena like structural flexure and flexible harness or fluid motion, which are present in any spacecraft to some degree. Once the excitation stops, nutation decreases as these same factors dissipate the kinetic energy added by the control effort. However, this natural damping can take hours. We can neutralize this error source in minutes with nutation dampers. We can also reduce the amount of nutation from these sources by increasing the spin rate and thus the stiffness of the spinning vehicle. If the spin rate is 20 rpm and the nutation angle from a given disturbance is 3 deg, then nutation from the same disturbance would be reduced to 1 deg if the spin rate were 60 rpm. We seldom use spin rates above 90 rpm because of the large centripetal forces demanded of the structure and the consequent effects on design and weight. In thrusting and pointing applications, spin rates under 20 rpm may not be advisable as they may allow excessive nutation. However, applications unrelated to attitude control, such as thermal control or specialized payload requirements, are frequently less sensitive to nutation and may employ very low spin rates.

3-Axis Control Techniques. Spacecraft stabilized in all three axes are much more common today than those using spin or gravity-gradient stabilization. They can maneuver relatively easily and can be more stable and accurate, depending on their sensors and actuators, than more passive stabilization techniques. They are, however, more expensive and often more complex. Recent processor improvements have led to comparable or better total reliability, see Chap. 24.*

The control torques about the axes of 3-axis systems come from combinations of momentum wheels, reaction wheels, control moment gyros, thrusters, solar or aerodynamic control surfaces (e.g., tabs), or magnetic torquers. Broadly, however, these systems take two forms: one uses momentum bias by placing a momentum wheel along the pitch axis; the other is called *zero momentum* and does not use momentum bias at all—any momentum bias effects are generally regarded as disturbances. Either option usually needs some method of angular momentum management, such as thrusters or magnetic torquers, in addition to the primary attitude actuators.

In a *zero-momentum* system, actuators such as reaction wheels or thrusters respond to disturbances on the vehicle. For example, an attitude error in the vehicle results in a control signal that torques the wheel, creating a reaction torque in the vehicle that corrects the error. The torque on the wheel either speeds it up or slows it down; the aggregate effect is that all disturbance torques are absorbed over time by the reaction wheels, sometimes requiring the collected angular momentum to be removed. This momentum removal—called *desaturation*, *momentum dumping*, or *momentum management* —can be accomplished by thrusters or magnetic torquers acting automatically or by command from the ground.

When high torque is required for large vehicles or fast slews, a variation of 3-axis control using control

* For critical space applications, there is no replacement for thorough risk and reliability assessment.

moment gyros, or CMGs, is available. These devices work like momentum wheels on gimbals. The control of CMGs is complex and their lifespan is limited, but their available torque for a given weight and power can make them attractive.

A very specialized form of zero momentum control, here called *active magnetic control*, can be attained from a combination of a magnetometer, a Global Positioning System (GPS) receiver (or other form or orbit information), and computationally intensive software filtering. The GPS feeds the spacecraft location to the onboard processor, which then determines the local magnetic field based on onboard models. The magnetometer data is filtered using the Euler equations to determine the attitude, and magnetic torquers make corrections in the two available directions at any given moment—corrections about the magnetic field vector are not possible. Active magnetic control can be an inexpensive backup control mode for a LEO satellite, or it can be a primary control mode for a satellite in a highly inclined orbit. (The highly inclined orbit has large changes in magnetic field direction, allowing the filtering algorithm to better determine a 3-axis attitude solution.) This attitude knowledge can also be combined with other sensors, such as Sun sensors, for more accuracy. Active magnetic control is an increasingly common control method, and we include it here as an example of how increased onboard computational power and the presence of new resources, such as the GPS constellation, have allowed completely new methods of attitude determination and control.

As a final demonstration of zero momentum 3-axis control, simple all-thruster systems are used for short durations when high torque is needed, such as during orbit insertion maneuvers or other orbit adjustments (delta V) from large motors discussed in Sec. 9.6. These thrusters then may be used for different purposes such as momentum dumping or provision of small delta Vs during other mission phases.

Momentum bias systems often have just one wheel with its spin axis mounted along the pitch axis, ideally normal to the orbit plane. The wheel is run at a nearly constant, high speed to provide gyroscopic stiffness to the vehicle, just as in spin stabilization, with similar nutation dynamics. Around the pitch axis, however, the spacecraft can control attitude by torquing the wheel, slightly increasing or decreasing its speed. Periodically, the momentum in the pitch wheel must be managed (i.e., brought back to its nominal speed), as in zero-momentum systems, using thrusters, magnets, or other means.

The dynamics of nadir-oriented momentum-bias vehicles exhibit a phenomenon known as *roll-yaw coupling*. To understand this coupling, consider an inertially fixed angular momentum vector at some error angle with respect to the orbit plane. If the angle is initially a positive roll error, then a quarter-orbit later it appears as a negative yaw error with no roll component remaining. As the vehicle continues around the orbit, the angle goes through negative roll and positive yaw before regaining its positive roll character. This coupling (or commutation) is due to the apparent motion of the Earth-fixed coordinate frame as seen from the spacecraft, and it can be exploited to control roll and yaw over a quarter orbit using only a roll (or only a yaw) sensor, instead of needing one sensor for each of the roll and yaw axes.

Effects of Requirements on Control Type. With the above knowledge of control techniques, we can proceed to select a control type that will best meet mission requirements in the expected operational environment. Tables 19-7 and 19-8 describe the effects of orbit insertion and payload slew requirements on the selection process. It is also useful here to once again reference Fig. 19-6 for information on how altitude can affect the space environment. Certain control types, such as gravity-gradient stabilization or active magnetic damping, are better in some orbits than in others.

A common control approach during orbit insertion is to use the short-term spin stability of the combination of spacecraft and orbit-insertion motor. Once on station the motor may be jettisoned, the spacecraft despun using thrusters or a yo-yo device, and a different control technique used from that point on.

Payload pointing will influence the attitude control method, the class of sensors, and the number and kind of actuation devices. Occasionally, pointing accuracies are so stringent that a separate, articulated platform is

Table 19-7. Orbit Transition Maneuvers and Their Effects. Using thrusters to change orbits creates special challenges for the ADCS.

Requirement	Effect on Spacecraft	Effect on ADCS
Large Impulse to Complete Orbit Insertion (thousands of m/s)	Solid motor or large bipropellant stage. Large thrusters or a gimbaled engine or spin stabilization for attitude control during burns.	Inertial measurement unit for accurate reference and velocity measurement. Different actuators, sensors, and control laws for burn vs. coasting phases. Need for navigation or guidance.
On-Orbit Plane Changes to Meet Payload Needs or Vehicle Operations (hundreds of m/s)	Large thrusters needed, but these thrusters may be needed for other reasons also, such as orbit insertion, coasting phase, or stationkeeping.	Separate control law for thrusting. Actuators sized for thrusting disturbances (possibly two sizes of thruster). Onboard attitude reference for thrusting phase.
Orbit Maintenance/Trim Maneuvers (<100 m/s)	One set of thrusters	Thrusting control law. Onboard attitude reference.

Table 19-8. Slewing Requirements That Affect Control Actuator Selection. Spacecraft slew agility can demand larger actuators for intermittent use.

Slewing	Effect on Spacecraft	Effect on ADCS
None or Time-Unconstrained	Spacecraft constrained to one attitude (highly improbable), or reorientations can take many hours.	Reaction wheels, if planned, can be smaller If magnetic torquers can dump momentum, reaction control thrusters may not be needed
Low Rates ***From 0.05 deg/s (orbital rate) to 0.5 deg/s***	Minimal	Depending on spacecraft size, reaction wheels may be fully capable for slews If reaction wheels not capable, thrusters will be necessary Thrusters may be needed for other reasons; i.e., stationkeeping
High Rates ***>0.5 deg/s***	– Structural impact on appendages – Weight and cost increase	– Control moment gyros or thrusters needed. If thrusters needed for other reasons, two thrust levels may be needed.

Table 19-9. Effects of Control Accuracy Requirements on Sensor Selection and ADCS Design. More accurate pointing requires better and more expensive sensors and actuators.

Required Accuracy (3σ)	Effect on Spacecraft	Effect on ADCS
>5 deg	• Permits major cost savings • Permits gravity-gradient (GG) stabilization	• Without attitude determination • No sensors required for GG stabilization • Boom motor, GG damper, and a bias momentum wheel are only required actuators • With attitude determination • Sun sensors and magnetometer adequate for attitude determination at ≥ 2 deg • Higher accuracies may require star trackers or horizon sensors
1 deg to 5 deg	• GG not feasible • Spin stabilization feasible if stiff, inertially fixed attitude is acceptable • Payload needs may require despun platform on spinner • 3-axis stabilization will work	• Sun sensors and horizon sensors may be adequate for sensors, especially a spinner • Accuracy for 3-axis stabilization can be met with RCS deadband control but reaction wheels will save propellant for long missions • Thrusters and damper adequate for spinner actuators • Magnetic torquers (and magnetometer) useful
0.1 deg to 1 deg	• 3-axis and momentum-bias stabilization feasible • Dual-spin stabilization also feasible	• Need for accurate attitude reference leads to star tracker or horizon sensors and possibly gyros • Reaction wheels typical with thrusters for momentum unloading and coarse control • Magnetic torquers feasible on light vehicles (magnetometer also required)
< 0.1 deg	• 3-axis stabilization is necessary • May require articulated and vibration-isolated payload platform with separate sensors	• Same as above for 0.1 deg to 1 deg but needs star sensor and better class of gyros • Control laws and computational needs are more complex • Flexible body performance very important

necessary. An articulated platform can perform scanning operations much more easily than the host vehicle and with better accuracy and stability. Trade studies on pointing requirements must consider accuracy in attitude determination and control, and the most stringent requirements will ultimately drive ADCS component selection. Table 19-9 summarizes the effects of accuracy requirements on the ADCS approach for the spacecraft. Section 14.5 discusses how to develop pointing budgets.

FireSat II Control Selection. For FireSat II, we consider two options for orbit insertion control. First, the launch vehicle may directly inject the spacecraft into its mission orbit. This common option simplifies the spacecraft design since no special insertion mode is needed. An alternate approach, useful for small spacecraft such as FireSat II, is to use a monopropellant propulsion system onboard the spacecraft to fly itself up from a low parking orbit to its final altitude (see Sec. 9.6). For small insertion motors, reaction wheel torque or momentum bias stabilization may be sufficient to control the vehicle during this burn. For larger motors, delta-V thruster modulation or dedicated attitude control thrusters become attractive.

Once on station the spacecraft must point its sensors at nadir most of the time and slightly off-nadir for brief periods. Since the payload needs to be despun and the spacecraft frequently reoriented, spin stabilization is not the best choice. Gravity-gradient and passive magnetic control cannot meet the 0.1 deg pointing requirement or the 30 deg slews. This leaves 3-axis control and momentum-bias stabilization as viable options for the on-station control.

The periodic 180 deg yaw slews (i.e., slews around the nadir vector) would have to overcome any momentum bias in the Y axis (perpendicular to the orbit normal). When we do the example momentum bias sizing in Table 19-11 later, we will see that a bias of approximately 20 N·m·s would be required to maintain the required 0.1 deg accuracy. The magnetic torquers could not perform this slew in 45 minutes because of the bias to be overcome. Instead, we will use the propulsion system to perform the yaw slew.

For the optional off-nadir pointing requirement, 3-axis control with reaction wheels might be more appropriate. Mass and power will be especially precious for this very small satellite, so carrying and running 3 reaction wheels simultaneously may be more than the system budgets can handle. Since the SCS will provide an example of 3-axis control with reaction wheels, we will use the magnetic torque and momentum wheel combination for FireSat II, and for actuator sizing (Table 19-11) we will assume the 30 degree offset pointing is done about the pitch axis, so that the momentum wheel performs that slew also. If offset pointing is needed about roll, thrusters will have to be used; the thruster force sizing example in Table 19-12 shows how this might work with the momentum wheel stopped.

SCS Control Selection. For the Supplemental Communication System, we will focus on taking advantage of the gentle disturbance environment and 1 deg accuracy requirement to design a light, inexpensive attitude system that can be installed in all 3 satellites. At the SCS altitude of 21,000 km, with the configuration we've assumed, there are no good passive stabilization methods available to us. Reaction wheels will be needed to reject the disturbances, which are dominated by the solar radiation pressure torques (see Table 19-4). So, as long as the reaction wheels are there anyway, we might as well use them for 3-axis stabilization.

While the greater part of the SRP torques will be cyclic, some small part will be secular. Therefore, the momentum stored in the reaction wheels will gradually increase and will need to be removed periodically by thrusters. The use of 100 A·m^2 magnetic torquers for momentum removal is feasible from the point of view of the available magnetic field. However, the propulsion system has to be included anyway to separate the 3 satellites and establish the constellation, and constantly running torquers would be an additional power drain. Since power is a major challenge for this mission, we will use the thrusters for momentum unloading.

19.1.4 Selection and Sizing of ADCS Hardware

We are now ready to evaluate and select the individual ADCS components. For all ADCS hardware, we will determine the minimum performance level needed to meet requirements. Then, standard components available from manufacturers will be selected if possible, sometimes resulting in better performance than the minimum required. If standard components are not available, specialized components may be designed and built, but this can often be prohibitively costly for most customers, and so a revision of the requirements is more likely to be more in line with available hardware.

Actuators. Options for actuator selection are summarized in Table 19-10. First, we will discuss momentum-exchange devices, which conserve angular momentum in the spacecraft: reaction wheels, momentum wheels, and control moment gyros. Then, we will move on to external torque actuators, which change the angular momentum of the spacecraft when they are activated: magnetic torquers and thrusters (cold-gas, hot-gas and electric) are the most commonly used in this category.

Wheel control provides smooth changes in torque, allowing very accurate pointing of spacecraft. Some wheels can cause vibrations, or jitter, at high speeds, but this can often be mitigated with vibration isolators or changes in structural design. *Reaction wheels* are essentially torque motors with high-inertia rotors. They can spin in either direction and provide one axis of control for each wheel. *Momentum wheels* are reaction wheels with a nominal spin rate above zero to provide a nearly constant angular momentum. This momentum provides gyroscopic stiffness to two axes, and the motor torque may be controlled to change pointing around the spin axis. In sizing wheels we must always consider two performance quantities: angular momentum capacity, and torque authority.

To determine the necessary momentum capacity, we must distinguish between cyclic and secular disturbances in the spacecraft's environment. We typically size reac-

Table 19-10. Typical Attitude Actuators. Actuator weight and power usually scale with performance.

Actuator	Performance Range	Mass (kg)	Power (W)
Thrusters ***Hot Gas (Hydrazine)*** ***Cold Gas***	Thrusters produce force; multiply by moment arm for torque 0.5 to 9,000 N < 5 N	Mass and power vary (See Chap. 18 for details on propulsion systems)	
Reaction and Momentum Wheels	Maximum torques: 0.01 to 1 N·m Practical momentum storage capacity: 0.4 to 3000 N·m·s	2 to 20	Varies with speed: 10 to 100
Control Moment Gyros (CMG)	Max. torques: 25 to 500 N·m	> 10	90 to 150
Magnetic Torquers	1 to 4,000 A·m^2 (See Table 19-4 for torque examples)	0.4 to 50	0.6 to 16

tion wheels to be able to store the full cyclic component of momentum without the need for frequent momentum dumping. Therefore, the average disturbance torque for ¼ or ½ an orbit determines the minimum capacity of the wheels. The secular component of momentum will also need to be stored for the amount of time the spacecraft must be operational without a momentum dump being performed. This time may be determined by requirements on payload observation continuity, or it may be the amount of time the spacecraft must survive without ground intervention.

The necessary torque authority of the reaction wheels is defined either by slew requirements or the need for control authority to be well above the peak disturbance torque. If the peak disturbance is too close to the torque authority available, pointing accuracy may suffer.

For 3-axis control, at least three wheels with non-coplanar spin axes are required. Often, a fourth wheel is carried in case one of the primary wheels fails. If the wheels are not orthogonal (and a redundant wheel never is), additional torque authority or momentum capacity may be necessary to compensate for non-optimal geometry. However, the redundancy of the fourth wheel can have additional benefits, such as being able to avoid any wheel speed passing through zero (which can cause attitude error transients) or even as power storage, as driving a spinning wheel toward zero speed will provide power to the spacecraft.

For spin-stabilized or momentum-bias systems, the cyclic torques will cause cyclic variations of the attitude, whereas the secular torques cause gradual divergence of the attitude away from the ideal target. We typically design the stored angular momentum, determined by spin rate and inertia of the spinning body, to be large enough to keep the cyclic motion within accuracy requirements without active control. Periodic torquing will still be needed to counteract secular disturbances, and the cost of this torquing in propellant, if performed by thrusters, will constrain the maximum stored momentum.

For high-torque applications in which fine control is still needed, *control moment gyros* (CMG) may be used instead of reaction wheels. CMGs are single- or double-gimbaled wheels spinning at constant speed (and therefore providing momentum bias stiffness when not actuating). By turning the gimbal axis, we can obtain a high-output torque whose size depends on the speed of the rotor and the gimbal rate of rotation. Control systems with two or more CMGs can produce large torques about all three of the spacecraft's orthogonal axes, so we most often use them where agile (i.e., high angular rate) maneuvers are required. The use of CMGs requires complex control laws and careful momentum management to avoid wheel saturation. Also, because the CMG torque is created by twisting what is essentially a stiff gyroscope perpendicular to its spin axis, the bearings of the wheel suffer a great deal of wear and tear, causing most CMGs to have shorter lifetimes than other actuators. Because CMGs combine a short life with high cost, weight, and power needs, they are generally used only on very large spacecraft and only when absolutely necessary to achieve the mission goals.

Spacecraft also use *magnetic torquers* as actuation devices. These torquers are magnetic coils (electromagnets) designed to generate magnetic dipole moments of commanded magnitude. When three orthogonal torquers are mounted to a spacecraft, they can create a magnetic dipole of any direction and magnitude up to the strength of the torquers. Magnetic torquers can compensate for a spacecraft's residual magnetic field or attitude drift from minor disturbance torques. They also can be used to desaturate momentum-exchange systems, though they usually require much more time than thrusters. A magnetic torquer produces a torque proportional and perpendicular to the Earth's varying magnetic field; therefore, at any given moment, no torque can be provided about the Earth's magnetic field vector. However, as a spacecraft changes in latitude or altitude while following its orbit, different directions of the field become available.

Electromagnets have the advantage of no moving parts, requiring only a magnetometer for sensing and wire coiled around a metallic rod in each axis. (Some torquers are even internally redundant, as they have two coils around the same metallic core.) Because they use the Earth's natural magnetic field, and this field reduces in strength with the cube of distance from the Earth's center, magnetic torquers are less effective at higher orbits. We can specify the torquer's dipole strength in $A{\cdot}m^2$ and tailor it to any application. Table 19-11 describes sizing rules of thumb for wheels and magnetic torquers, and works through those rules for the FireSat II and SCS examples. SCS has no slewing requirements, so we size its reaction wheels based only on momentum storage needs.

Thrusters (i.e., rocket engines) are possibly the most frequently flown attitude actuator because of their dual use in adjusting orbital parameters. Almost every spacecraft that needs to perform orbital maneuvers (Sec. 9.6) will use thrusters to achieve that goal, and in many cases, some subset of the thrusters used is for attitude control. Thrusters produce a force on the spacecraft by expelling material, called propellant, at high velocity from their exit nozzles. Hot-gas propulsion systems include thrusters that chemically alter the propellant to extract the energy needed for rapid mass expulsion. These systems may be monopropellant, in which the propellant is catalyzed to break down chemically, or bipropellant, in which a fuel is mixed with an oxidizer to achieve combustion just prior to expulsion. Cold-gas systems include thrusters whose propellant is not altered chemically during propulsion. In a cold-gas system, the energy may come from phase change of the propellant, or simply from pre-pressurizing the propellant in its tank. A third type of thruster is electrical, which, due to the usually small forces involved, is only used for attitude control in special circumstances. Electrical propulsion (Sec. 18.4) is accomplished by using magnetic or electrostatic fields to eject plasma or magnetic fluid to achieve a reaction force on the spacecraft. Propulsion is discussed in detail in Chap. 18.

Table 19-10◀, Fig. 19-8◀, Eq. 19-8◀

Table 19-11. Simplified Equations for Sizing Reaction Wheels, Momentum Wheels, and Magnetic Torquers. The FireSat II momentum wheel is sized for the baseline pointing requirements and for the optional design with 30 deg slew requirements. SCS reaction wheels are sized for momentum storage capacity.

Parameter	Simplified Equations	Application to FireSat II and SCS Examples
Torque from Reaction Wheel for Disturbance Rejection	Control torque, whether from reaction wheels or magnetic torquers, must equal worst-case anticipated disturbance torque plus some margin: $T_C = (T_D)$(Margin Factor)	For the FireSat II spacecraft, magnetic torque dominates during regular observations: $T_D \approx T_m = 2.1 \times 10^{-5}$ N·m (see Table 19.4). This torque is manageable by most reaction wheels and magnetic torquers. Momentum requirements or slew torque, not disturbance rejection, will be used for actuator sizing.
Slew Torque for Reaction Wheels	For max-acceleration slews with no resisting momentum (½ distance in ½ time): $\theta/2 = ½\,(T/I)(t/2)^2$ $T = 4\theta I/t^2$	FireSat II needs to make a 30-deg slew about the Y axis (50 kg·m^2) in 10 minutes using its momentum wheel: T = (4)(30 deg)(π/180 deg)(50 kg·m^2)/(600 sec)^2 = 2.9×10^{-4} N·m (This is a small value.) The total momentum change for the wheel during the slew is $T \cdot t/2$ = 0.087 N·m·s.
Momentum Storage in Reaction Wheel	One approach to estimating wheel momentum, h, is to integrate the worst-case disturbance torque, T_D, over a full orbit, with period P. For gravity gradient, the maximum momentum accumulates in 1/4 of an orbit. A simplified expression for such a sinusoidal disturbance is: $h = T_D \cdot P \cdot (0.707)/4$ where 0.707 is the rms average of a sinusoidal function. For the SCS solar pressure torques, the torque buildup depends heavily on attitude and orbit geometry, but to keep this simple we will assume the maximum also accumulates in ¼ orbit.	For FireSat II, the maximum gravity gradient torque (during 30-deg off-pointing) is estimated at: $T_D = 3.7 \times 10^{-5}$ N·m (Table 19-4) and the 700 km orbital period is 5,926 sec: h = (3.7×10^{-5} N·m)(5,926 sec)(0.707/4) = 0.039 N·m·s If the magnetic torquers were not capable of handling this momentum, a small reaction wheel with storage of 0.4 N·m·s would be sufficient even if 30-deg off-pointing were held for an entire quarter-orbit. For SCS, $T_D = 6.6 \times 10^{-6}$ and P = 45,083 sec. SCS storage: $h = (6.6 \times 10^{-6})(45{,}083)(0.707/4) = 0.06$ N·m·s We will size 1.0 N·m·s wheels to minimize thruster burns and potential jitter from high wheel speeds.
Momentum Storage in Momentum Wheel	For momentum-wheel stabilization, roll and yaw accuracy depend on the wheel's momentum and the external disturbance torque. A simplified expression for the required momentum storage is: $h = (T/\theta_a) \cdot (P/4)$ where θ_a = allowable motion.	The value of h for the FireSat II yaw accuracy requirement of 0.1 deg (0.0017 rad) would be h = (2.1×10^{-5} N·m/0.0017 rad)·(5,926/4 sec) = 18.4 N·m·s For 1 deg accuracy, we would need only 1.8 N·m·s. The same results would hold for a spinner. Note that this capacity would need to be added to the momentum change needed for the 30 deg slews, which for FireSat II is less than 0.1 N·m·s.
Torque from Magnetic Torquers	Magnetic torquers use electrical current through the torquer to create a magnetic dipole *(D)*. The Earth's magnetic field, *B*, acts on *D*, resulting in torque *(T)* on the vehicle: $D = T/B$ Magnets used for momentum dumping must equal the peak disturbance + margin to compensate for the lack of complete directional control. (Note that if magnetic torque is the dominant disturbance, the torquers need mainly to cancel the spacecraft's residual dipole.)	Table 19-4 estimates the maximum Earth field, *B*, for FireSat II to be 4.2×10^{-5} tesla. We calculate the torque rod's magnetic torquing ability (dipole) to counteract the worst-case gravity gradient disturbance, T_D, of 2.1×10^{-5} N·m·s as D = (2.1×10^{-5} N·m)/(4.2×10^{-5} tesla) = 0.5 A·m^2 which is a small actuator. The Earth's field is cyclic at twice orbital frequency; thus, maximum torque is available only twice per orbit. A torquer of 3 to 10 A·m^2 capability should provide sufficient margin, which also gives enough capacity to remove increased gravity gradient torques during offset pointing.

Note: For actuator sizing, the magnitude and direction of the disturbance torques must be considered. In particular, momentum accumulation in inertial coordinates must be mapped to body-fixed actuator axes.

Thrusters provide torque proportional to their moment arm, which is the amount that their line of force is offset from the vehicle's center of mass. When thrusters apply their force along a line that intersects the center of mass of the vehicle, there is no torque. So, while the amount of force available from a thruster may be large, the torque available is limited by the physical extent of the vehicle and how the thrusters are mounted on the vehicle. When mounted to maximize torque authority, thrusters have the advantage of being able to provide large, instantaneous control torques at any time in the orbit. The disadvantages of thrusters are that they use expendable propellant, they can disrupt orbit determination activities, and the plumes of expelled matter can impinge on the surface of the spacecraft, possibly heating or contaminating surfaces.

Attitude functions to which thrusters can be applied include controlling attitude, controlling nutation and spin rate, performing large, rapid slews, and managing angular momentum. In all of these functions, large torque authority can be helpful. To some extent, the ability to change angular momentum by relatively small amounts is also necessary. Another consideration in selection of thrusters is how fine and how precise the delivered torque impulse needs to be. Torque applied over a period of time creates a change in angular momentum, which has a corresponding change in the rotational rate of the spacecraft. As attitude changes with non-zero rate, attitude control accuracy is directly determined by the minimum thruster impulse available. If a 50 N thruster with a 1 meter moment arm must provide a change in angular momentum accurate to within 1 N·m·s, then it will be necessary to fire the thruster for a period of time no greater than 20 ms. The thruster valves must be capable of opening and closing that rapidly and precisely, and of propellant actually flowing into the thruster and out the nozzle, which takes a finite amount of time. This need for speed and precision in engine valve control also has implications in the design of the avionics that drive the thruster valves; often, special electronics cards must be developed for a given mission to meet thruster-based attitude control requirements.

FireSat II Actuators. The baseline FireSat II spacecraft will use magnetic torquers for momentum dumping, but thrusters will be needed for the 180 degree slews that must be done periodically to keep the Sun off the radiator. Because the slew must be about the yaw axis, the momentum bias in the wheel would resist the thruster torque, complicating the control design. Instead, we will use the thrusters to remove the momentum bias, rotate the spacecraft, and then re-establish the momentum bias. One way to remove the wheel momentum is to use thrusters for 3-axis control while driving the wheel to zero speed. As the wheel slows down, it causes the spacecraft to rotate, and the thrusters are fired to counteract the rotation; the same thing happens when the wheel is once again sped up to re-establish the momentum bias. The thrusters must provide much more torque than the wheel, but generally the attitude control accuracy requirements are loosened for this kind of maneuver to avoid firing the thrusters more than is necessary. Good accuracy is less important here because science data would not be collected anyway during the slew. The total fuel mass needed for the momentum changes and the slew depends on the specific impulse, I_{sp}, of the selected thruster/propellant combination; we will assume the I_{sp} is 218 sec.

SCS Actuators. The SCS satellites will need to use thrusters for orbit maintenance and momentum dumping. We will want to minimize the number and size of thrusters, since the spacecraft are so small. However, the lower limit will most likely come from the orbital maneuvering needs, and not the attitude control needs. We will suppose 4 1-lb thrusters are needed for orbital maneuvering and steering, and in Table 19-12, we will present and work through procedures and simplified equations for sizing thrusters using SCS as an example. SCS has no stated slew requirement, but for the purposes of the example, a slew requirement of 30 deg in 60 sec will be supposed. A thorough discussion on the topic of propulsion systems, including estimating propellant needs, can be found in Chap. 18.

Sensors. We complete this hardware unit by selecting the sensors needed for attitude determination. Consult Table 19-13 for a summary of typical devices as well as their performance and physical characteristics. Note, however, that sensor technology is changing rapidly, promising ever more accurate and lighter-weight sensors for future missions.

Sun sensors are visible-light or infrared detectors that measure one or two angles between their mounting base and incident sunlight. They are popular, accurate, and very reliable, but they require clear fields of view. They can be used as part of the normal attitude determination system, part of the initial acquisition or failure recovery system, or part of an independent solar array orientation system. Since most low-Earth orbits include eclipse periods, Sun-sensor-based attitude determination systems must provide some way of tolerating the regular loss of this data without violating pointing constraints (see Chap. 16).

Sun sensors can be quite accurate (<0.01 deg), but it is not always possible to take advantage of that feature. We usually mount Sun sensors near the ends of vehicles to obtain an unobstructed field view, so the Sun sensor accuracy can be limited by structural bending on large spacecraft. Spinning satellites use specially designed Sun sensors that measure the angle of the Sun with respect to the spin axis of the vehicle, and they issue a pulse correlated to the time the Sun crosses the sensor to provide spin-phase information. Also popular are coarse Sun sensors, which are simply small solar cells (see Sec. 21.2) that issue a current roughly proportional to the cosine of the Sun angle. These sensors are so small and inexpensive that it is often feasible to put several in many directions on a spacecraft, and then to estimate the Sun direction by solving the linear system equations that results. Because coarse Sun sensors use no power and almost never fail, they are often used in low-power acquisition and fault recovery modes.

Table 19-12. Simplified Equations for Preliminary Sizing of Thruster Systems. SCS thruster requirements are small for this low-disturbance, minimal slew application. It is likely that the thrusters needed for orbit maintenance can also serve for momentum dumping. FireSat II thrusters are needed for 180 degree slews and for orbit insertion and maintenance.

Simplified Equations	Application to Examples
Thruster force level sizing for external disturbances: $F = T_D / L$ **where** **F is thruster force** **T_D is worst-case disturbance torque** **L is the thruster's moment arm**	For the SCS worst case T_D of 6.6×10^{-6} N·m (Table 19-4) and a thruster moment arm of 0.5 m $F = (6.6 \times 10^{-6}\text{ N·m})/(0.5\text{ m}) = 3.3 \times 10^{-6}\text{ N}$ This small value indicates orbit maintenance and momentum dumping requirements, not disturbance torques, will determine thruster size. Also, using thrusters to fight cyclic disturbances uses precious propellant; it is generally better to store the momentum in wheels.
Sizing force level to meet slew rates: **Determine fastest slew rate, ω, required in the mission profile.** **Develop a slew profile that accelerates the vehicle quickly, coasts at that rate, and then decelerates quickly. The acceleration required, α, comes from equating these two torque definitions:** $T = F \cdot L = I \cdot \alpha$	Assume FireSat II does a 30-deg slew in less than 1 min (60 sec), accelerating for 5% of that time, coasting for 90%, and decelerating for 5%. $\omega = 30\text{ deg} / 60\text{ sec} = 0.5\text{ deg/sec}$ To reach 0.5 deg/sec in 5% of 1 min, which is 3 sec, requires an acceleration $\alpha = \omega/t = (0.5\text{ deg/sec})/(3\text{ sec}) = 0.167\text{ deg/sec}^2 = 0.003\text{ rad/sec}^2$ $F = I\alpha/L = (25\text{ kg·m}^2)(0.003\text{ rad/sec}^2)/(0.5\text{ m}) = 0.15\text{ N}$ This is very small. It is certainly within the 5 N of thrust that the propulsion design selected. However, it is so much smaller that specialized circuitry would be needed to fire the thrusters for very brief amounts of time, which may impact thruster efficiency.
Determining fuel needed to complete FireSat II yaw slew: **Thrusters will need to remove the momentum bias from the wheel, rotate the satellite 180 deg, and then re-establish the momentum. Fuel mass, m, is estimated as:** $m = F \cdot t/(g \cdot I_{sp})$ **where** **t is the on-time of one thruster**	Changing momentum bias: The minimum thruster on-time needed to remove or create a given momentum, h, is $t = h/T = h/(F \cdot L)$. For FireSat II: $t_{bias} = (18.4\text{ N·m·s})/(5\text{ N} \cdot 0.5\text{ m}) = 7.4\text{ sec}$ We will bring this up to 10 seconds to account for any additional attitude correction firings needed during wheel torquing. Yaw slew: We'll plan on a slew rate of 1 deg/sec to finish the slew itself in under 5 minutes, leaving plenty of time for wheel stopping and starting. 1 deg/sec amounts to an angular momentum of: $h = (40\text{ kg·m}^2)(1\text{ deg/sec})(\pi\text{ rad}/180\text{ deg}) = 0.7\text{ N·m·s}$ and therefore an on-time for both starting and stopping the slew of: $t_{accel} = t_{decel} = (0.7\text{ N·m·s})/(5\text{ N} \cdot 0.5\text{ m}) = 0.3\text{ sec}$ Total thruster on-time per slew: $t_{total} = 10 + 0.3 + 0.3 + 10 = 21$ seconds Fuel required per 180-degree slew: $m = (5\text{ N})(21\text{ s})/(9.8\text{ m/s}^2 \cdot 218\text{ s}) = 49\text{ g fuel}$
Sizing force level for momentum dumping: $F = h/(Lt)$ **where** **h is the stored wheel momentum** **L is the thruster moment arm** **t is the burn time**	For SCS with 1.0 N·m·s wheels and 1-sec burns, $F = (1.0\text{ N·m·s})/(0.5\text{ m} \times 1\text{ sec})$ $= 2.0\text{ N}$ This is still well within the range of 1-lb thrusters, which are commonly used for orbit maintenance on small spacecraft. Reaction wheels with even larger capacity might be desirable if it would further reduce the number of times the thrusters must be used.

Table 19-13. Typical ADCS Sensors. Sensors have continued to improve in performance while getting smaller and sometimes less expensive.

Sensor	Typical Performance Range	Mass (kg)	Power (W)
Gyroscopes	Drift Rate = 0.003 deg/hr to 1 deg/hr Drift rate stability varies widely	< 0.1 to 15	< 1 to 200
Sun Sensors	Accuracy = 0.005 deg to 3 deg	0.1 to 2	0 to 3
Star Sensors (Scanners & Cameras)	Accuracy = 1 arcsecond to 1 arcminute = 0.0003 deg to 0.01 deg	2 to 5	5 to 20
Horizon Sensors	Accuracy:		
Scanner/Pipper	0.05 deg to 1 deg (0.1 deg is best for LEO)	1 to 4	5 to 10
Fixed Head (Static)	< 0.1 deg to 0.25 deg	0.5 to 3.5	0.3 to 5
Magnetometer	Accuracy = 0.5 deg to 3 deg	0.3 to 1.2	< 1

Star sensors have improved rapidly in the past few years and represent the most common sensor for high-accuracy missions. Star sensors can be scanners or trackers. *Scanners* are used on spinning spacecraft. Light from different stars passes through multiple slits in the scanner's field of view. After several star crossings, we can derive the vehicle's attitude. We use *star trackers* on 3-axis stabilized spacecraft to track one or more stars to derive two- or 3-axis attitude information. The majority of star trackers used today work much like digital cameras (and many of these are increasingly called *star cameras*, rather than trackers), allowing starlight to fall on a CCD or an APS, to create an image of the star field. Then, internal processing determines a 3-axis attitude based on a star catalog. Many units are able to determine a very accurate attitude within seconds of being turned on.

While star sensors excel in accuracy, care is required in their specification and use. The most accurate star cameras are unable to determine attitude at all if the spacecraft is rotating too fast, and other star sensors must know roughly where they are pointing to make their data useful. Therefore, the vehicle must be stabilized to some extent before the trackers can operate effectively. This stabilization may require alternate sensors, which can increase total system cost. Also, old star sensors are susceptible to being blinded by the Sun, Moon, planets, or even high radiation levels, such as in the Van Allen belts, which is a disadvantage that must be accommodated in their application. Where the mission requires the highest accuracy and justifies a high cost, we often use a combination of star trackers and gyroscopes. The combination of these sensors is very effective: the gyros can be used for initial stabilization and during periods of inference in the star trackers, while the trackers can be used to provide a high-accuracy external reference unavailable to the gyros. As APS star trackers rapidly improve, an increasing number of spacecraft include the technology. They are often more robust than comparable CCD trackers and are able to ignore the moon and certain other celestial objects in the field of view. Some APS trackers are even able to track at full performance at rotational rates, much higher than that of a CCD.

Horizon sensors (often known as *Earth sensors*) are infrared devices that detect the contrast between the cold of deep space and the heat of the Earth's atmosphere (about 40 km above the surface in the sensed band). Simple narrow field-of-view fixed-head types (called *pippers* or *horizon crossing indicators*) are used on spinning spacecraft to measure Earth phase and chord angles, which, together with orbit and mounting geometry, define two angles to the Earth (nadir) vector. *Scanning horizon sensors* use a rotating mirror or lens to replace (or augment) the spinning spacecraft body. They are often used in pairs for improved performance and redundancy. Some nadir-pointing spacecraft use *staring sensors*, which view the entire Earth disk (from GEO) or a portion of the limb (from LEO). The sensor fields of view stay fixed with respect to the spacecraft. This type works best for circular orbits, as they are often tuned for a tight range of altitudes.

Horizon sensors provide Earth-relative information directly for Earth-pointing spacecraft, which may simplify onboard processing. The scanning types require clear fields of view for their scan cones (typically 45, 60, or 90 deg half-angle). Typical accuracies for systems using horizon sensors are 0.1 to 0.25 deg, with some applications approaching 0.03 deg. For the highest accuracy in low-Earth orbit, it is necessary to correct the data for Earth oblateness and seasonal horizon variations.

Magnetometers are simple, reliable, lightweight sensors that measure both the direction and magnitude of the Earth's magnetic field. Magnetometer output helps us establish the spacecraft's attitude relative to the local magnetic field, which information then can be combined with magnetic field models and orbit information to determine attitude relative to the Earth and inertial reference frames. However, their accuracy is not as good as that of star or horizon sensors. The Earth's magnetic field can shift with time and is not known precisely in the first place. To improve accuracy, we often combine magnetometer data with data from Sun or horizon sensors. As a vehicle using magnetic torquers passes through changing magnetic fields during each orbit, we use a magnetometer to control the magnitude and direction of the torquers' output relative to the present magnetic field. In earlier spacecraft the torquers usually needed to be inactive while the magnetometer was sampled to avoid corrupting the measurement. However, improvements in onboard computing capability mean that coupling matrices can be used to extract the torquer inputs from the field measurement, allowing constant sampling even while torquing. Finally, good spacecraft ephemeris and magnetic field models can be used in place of magnetometers for some missions, but magnetometers will generally be more accurate.

GPS receivers are well known as high-accuracy navigation devices, but they can also be used for attitude determination. If a spacecraft is large enough to place multiple antennas with sufficient separation, attitude can be determined by employing the differential signals from the separate antennas. Such sensors offer the promise of low cost and weight for LEO missions. They can provide attitude knowledge accurate to 0.25–0.5 deg for antenna baselines on the order of 1 meter [Cohen 1996], and so are being used in low accuracy applications or as back-up sensors. Development continues to improve their accuracy, which is limited by the separation of the antennas, the ability to resolve small phase differences, the relatively long wavelength of the GPS signal, and multipath effects due to reflections off spacecraft components.

Gyroscopes are inertial sensors that measure the speed or angle of rotation from an initial reference, but without any knowledge of an external, absolute reference. We use gyros in spacecraft for precision attitude determination when combined with external references such as star or Sun sensors, or, for brief periods, for nutation damping, or attitude control during thruster firing. Manufacturers use a variety of physical phenomena, from simple spinning rotors to *ring lasers*, *hemispherical resonating surfaces*, and *laser fiber optic bundles*. Gyros based on spinning rotors are called *mechanical gyros*, and they may be large *iron gyros* using ball or gas bearings, or may reach very small proportions in so-called *MEMS gyros*. (MEMS stands for *microelectromechanical systems*.) The gyro manufacturers, driven largely by aircraft markets, steadily improve accuracy while reducing size and mass.

Error models for gyroscopes vary with the technology, but characterize the deterioration of attitude knowledge with time. Some examples of model parameters are *drift bias*, which is simply an additional, false rate the sensor effectively adds to all rate measurements, and *drift bias stability*, which is a measure of how quickly the drift bias changes. When used with an accurate external reference, such as a star tracker, gyros can provide smoothing (filling in the gaps between tracker measurements) and higher frequency information (tens to hundreds of hertz), while the tracker provides lower frequency, absolutely referenced information whenever its field of view is clear. Individual gyros provide one or two axes of information and are often grouped together as an *inertial reference unit* (IRU) for three full axes and, sometimes, full redundancy. IRUs with accelerometers added for position and velocity sensing are called *inertial measurement units* (IMU).

Sensor Selection. Sensor selection is most directly influenced by the required orientation of the spacecraft (e.g., Earth-, Sun- or inertial-pointing) and its accuracy. Other influences include redundancy, fault tolerance, field of view requirements, and available data rates. Typically, we identify candidate sensor suites and conduct a trade study to determine the most cost-effective approach that meets the needs of the mission. In such studies the existence of off-the-shelf components and software can strongly affect the outcome. In this section we will only briefly describe some selection guidelines.

Full 3-axis knowledge requires at least two external, non-parallel vector measurements, although we use IRUs or spacecraft angular momentum (in spinners or momentum-biased systems) to hold or propagate the attitude between external measurements. In some cases, if attitude knowledge can be held for a fraction of an orbit, the external vectors (e.g., Earth or magnetic) will have moved enough to provide the necessary information. In 3-axis star trackers, each identified star acts as a reference vector, which allows a single piece of hardware to generate a full 3-axis attitude solution.

For Earth-pointing spacecraft, horizon sensors provide a direct measurement of pitch and roll axes, but require augmentation for yaw measurements. Depending on the accuracy required, we use Sun sensors, magnetometers, or momentum-bias control with its roll-yaw coupling for the third degree of freedom. For inertially pointing spacecraft, star and Sun sensors provide the most direct measurements, and IRUs are ideally suited. Frequently, only one measurement is made in the ideal coordinate frame (Earth or inertial), and the spacecraft orbit parameters are required to convert a second measurement or as an input to a magnetic field model. Either the orbit parameters are uplinked to the spacecraft from ground tracking and propagated by onboard processing, or they are obtained from onboard GPS antennas.

FireSat II Sensors. The external sensors for FireSat II could consist of any of the types identified. For the 0.1 deg Earth pointing requirement, however, horizon sensors are the most obvious choice since they directly measure the two axes we most need to control. The accuracy requirement makes a star sensor a strong candidate as well; its information would need to be transformed, probably using an onboard orbit ephemeris calculation, to Earth-relative for our use. The 0.1 deg accuracy is at the low end of horizon sensors' typical performance, so we need to be careful to get the most out of their data. We assume we also need a yaw sensor capable of 0.1 deg, and this choice is less obvious. Often, it is useful to question a tight yaw requirement. Many payloads, e.g., antennas, some cameras, and radars, are not sensitive to rotations around their pointing axis. For this discussion, we will assume this requirement is firm. We could use Sun sensors, but their data needs to be replaced during eclipses. Magnetometers don't have the necessary accuracy alone, but with our momentum-bias system, roll-yaw coupling, and some yaw data filtering, a magnetometer-Sun sensor system could work for normal operations. The magnetometers would also improve the control effectiveness of the magnetic torquers.

At this point we consider the value of an inertial reference package. Such packages, although heavy and expensive for high-accuracy equipment, provide a short-term attitude reference that would permit the Earth vector data to be used for full 3-axis knowledge over an orbit. A gyro package would also reduce the single measurement accuracy required of the horizon sensors, simplifying their selection and processing. Such packages are also useful to the control system if fast slews are required, and here is where FireSat II demands a gyro. We need to perform the 180 degree slews as quickly as we can, to avoid losing too much data. So, we will include a MEMS-based inertial package for FireSat II. They will be arranged perpendicular to one another, in a pyramid around the Z axis. This arrangement gives 3 axes of information with maximal redundancy around the slewing axis. Now that we have decided to include gyros, a careful trade study should be done to determine whether an inexpensive MEMS gyro package combined with just the Earth sensors eliminates our need to include Sun sensors and magnetometers. Leaving out some of these other sensors could give better reliability or lower total cost. We may also choose a slightly different arrangement of the sensors to improve accuracy in one direction at the expense of accuracy in another direction. We would need to do these kinds of detailed trade studies in later iterations of the design process.

Finally, we will want a simple, coarse control mode to initially point the arrays at the Sun and to protect the spacecraft in the event of an anomaly. By using 6 coarse Sun sensors pointing along the positive and negative of

Table 19-13◀, Fig. 19-8◀, Eq. 19-8◀

each axis, the spacecraft can derive the location of the Sun from any attitude and use magnetic torquers to rotate the spacecraft so the arrays are lit. Then, since the attitude relative to nadir will change as FireSat II follows its polar orbit, we can be sure to get a good communication signal at some point, so that we can receive telemetry and send commands.

SCS Sensors. For SCS attitude determination, low-power gyros can provide rate information. Accurate gyros can be heavy and often use a lot of power; we have neither high accuracy needs nor an excess of power or mass in our budgets. Therefore, we will use light and inexpensive MEMS gyros. We need a minimum of 3 MEMS gyros—one for each axis—but by employing 4–6 gyros we can cross-compare the gyro data and remove the larger bias errors that MEMS gyros normally have.

With rate information onboard, we only need an occasional update from an attitude sensor. If the magnetic field were stronger, we might be able to filter magnetometer data to get to 1 deg of accuracy, but it is doubtful at this high altitude. Star cameras are small and very accurate, but they are expensive. One useful rule of thumb is: If at all possible, sense the thing you need to point at. Sun pointers should have Sun sensors and Earth pointers should have Earth sensors. Because the satellites will have the same direction pointing toward the Earth throughout their mission, the best option appears to be an Earth sensor. We would need to select a sensor designed for high altitudes. However, we still have no yaw data, and since the satellites must point accurately at multiple targets simultaneously, yaw accuracy is critical.

Because the satellites will be communicating with each other, it is conceivable that the communication signal strength could be used as an attitude determination data source for yaw control. That is, a feedback loop would close around the communication system's own measure of its link margin; maximizing the link margin would provide the attitude goal we want. For this exercise we will not assume such an option is available. Instead, we will choose the star camera after all; a simple onboard ephemeris calculation will tell the spacecraft where its target satellite is in inertial space. There may be clever tricks that we could use with ground-based methods to avoid using star cameras, such as combining orbit tracking and attitude data. However, the complexity of operating three separate satellites that have to work together will likely prove more expensive in software development and operating costs than just buying three star cameras. At least we save money by not including horizon sensors. As for our rule of thumb of sensing what you're pointing at, we now see there can be situations for which this rule cannot be followed. Still, it's always a good place to start.

We will propose the same plan for an initial acquisition and safe control mode as for FireSat II. However, SCS will use reaction wheels for control, and will have the benefit of accurate rate sensors to improve performance. This is a good thing, since SCS satellites need more power than FireSat II, and so will probably not have as much time to acquire the Sun (i.e., get the solar arrays lit). Table 19-14 summarizes our FireSat II and SCS hardware selections.

Once the hardware selection is complete, as discussed in Sec. 6.4, it must be documented for use by other system and subsystem designers as follows.

- Specify the power levels and weights required for each assembly
- Establish the electrical interface to the rest of the spacecraft
- Describe requirements for mounting, alignment, or thermal control
- Determine what telemetry data we must process
- Document how much software we need to develop or purchase to support onboard calculation of attitude solutions

Specific numbers depend on the vendors selected. A typical list for FireSat II might look like Table 19-15, but the numbers could vary considerably with only slight changes in subsystem accuracies or slewing requirements.

19.1.5 Define the Determination and Control Algorithms

Finally, we must tie all of the control components together into a cohesive system. Generally, we begin with a single-axis control system design (See Fig. 19-2). As we refine the design, we add or modify feedback loops for rate and attitude data, define gains and constants, and enhance our representation of the system to include three axes of motion (though we may still treat these as decoupled for early design iterations). To confirm that our design will meet requirements, we need good mathematical simulations of the entire system, including sensor error models and internal and external disturbances. Usually, linear differential equations with constant coefficients describe the dynamics of a control system well enough to allow us to analyze its performance with the highly developed tools of linear servomechanism theory. With these same tools, we can easily design linear compensation to satisfy specifications for performance.

We typically apply linear theory only to preliminary analysis and design. We also maintain engineering margin against performance targets when using linear theory because, as the design matures, so does our understanding of the nonlinear effects in the system. Nonlinear effects may be inherent or intentionally introduced to improve the system's performance.

Another reason to maintain margin, especially in actuator sizing, is that while systems engineers always carefully budget mass, they cannot usually track the moment of inertia matrix as well. Moment of inertia is the most important quantity to ADCS designers, and a given mass may have a wide range of moment of inertia values depending on how the mass is distributed.

Table 19-13◀, Fig. 19-8◀, Eq. 19-8◀

Table 19-14. FireSat II and SCS Spacecraft Control Component Selection.

Mission & Type	Components	Rationale
FireSat II Actuators	Momentum Wheel (1)	• Pitch axis torquing • Roll and yaw axis passive stability
	Magnetic Torquers (3)	• Roll and yaw control • Pitch wheel desaturation
	Thrusters (4)	• Rapid changes in pitch wheel momentum • 180-deg yaw slew maneuvers
FireSat II Sensors	Horizon Sensor (1)	• Provide basic pitch and roll reference • Can meet 0.1 deg accuracy • Lower mass and cost than star sensors
	Sun Sensors (6)	• Initially acquire vehicle attitude from unknown orientation • Coarse attitude data • Fine data for yaw • Coarse yaw data
	Magnetometer (1)	• Needed for more precise magnetic torquing
	MEMS Gyros (3)	• Needed for rotational rate data during thruster operations
SCS Actuators (for each satellite)	Reaction Wheels (3)	• 3-axis stabilization • Storing momentum from solar radiation torques
	Thrusters (4)	• Thrusting and steering during orbit maneuvers • Removing momentum from reaction wheels
SCS Sensors (for each satellite)	Star Camera (1)	• Determining absolute attitude
	MEMS Gyros (4)	• Determining rotational rates; having 4 gyros allows large biases to be canceled out • Propagating attitude solution when star sensor data unavailable
	Sun Sensors (6)	• Initially acquire vehicle attitude relative to Sun to get power quickly

Table 19-15. FireSat II Spacecraft Control Subsystem Summary. The baseline ADCS components satisfy all mission requirements, with thrusters required for orbit injection and 180 degree slews.

Components	Type	Weight (kg)	Power (W)	Mounting Considerations
Momentum Wheel	Mid-size, 20 N·m·s momentum	< 5 total, with drive electronics	10 to 20	Momentum vector on pitch axis
Electromagnets	3, 10 A·m^2	2, including current drive electronics	5 to 10	Orthogonal configuration best to reduce cross-coupling
Sun Sensors	6 wide-angle coarse Sun sensors providing 4π steradian coverage; 5-10 deg accuracy	< 1 total	0.0	Free of viewing obstructions and reflections
Horizon Sensors	Scanning type (2) plus electronics; 0.1 deg accuracy	5 total	10	Unobstructed view of Earth's horizon
Gyroscopes	MEMS (3) only low accuracy needed	< 1 total	0.1	Mounted perpendicular to each other, in a pyramid around Z axis
Thrusters	Hydrazine; 5 N thrust	Propellant weight depends on mission	N/A	Alignments and moment arm to center of gravity are critical
Magnetometer	3-axis	< 1	5	Need to isolate magnetometer from electromagnets, either physically or by duty-cycling the magnets

Feedback control systems are of two kinds based on the flow of their control signals. They are *continuous-data* systems when sensor data is electrically transformed directly into continuously flowing, uninterrupted control signals to the actuators. By contrast, *sampled-data* systems have sensor sampling at set intervals, and control signals are issued or updated at those intervals. Most modern spacecraft process data through digital computers and therefore use sampled-data control systems.

Although it is beyond the scope of this book to provide detailed design guidance on feedback control systems, the system designer should recognize the interacting effects of attitude control system loop gain, capability of the attitude control system to compensate for disturbances, accuracy of attitude control, and control system bandwidth.

3-Axis Stabilization. Different types of active control systems have different key parameters and algorithms. For systems in which spacecraft rates will be kept small, 3-axis control can frequently be decoupled into three independent axes. In this simplest form, each axis of a spacecraft attitude control system can be represented as a double-integrator plant (i.e., $1/Is^2$ in the s-domain) and may be controlled by a *proportional-derivative (PD) controller*, which has control torque

$$T_C = K_P \theta_E + K_D \omega_E \tag{19-9}$$

Here, θ_E is the attitude error angle, and ω_E is the attitude rate error. The most basic design parameter in each axis is its *proportional gain*, K_P. (K_P is also often called a *position gain.*) This gain represents the amount of control torque we want to result from a unit of attitude error, and so it has units of torque divided by angle, e.g., newton-meters per radian. The proportional gain is selected by the designer and must be high enough to provide the required control accuracy in the presence of disturbances, which can be guaranteed by setting $K_P > T_D/\theta_{E,max}$, where T_D is the peak disturbance torque, and $\theta_{E,max}$ is the allowable attitude error. Note that this error will remain for as long as the disturbance torque remains; the error that remains in the presence of disturbances is called *steady-state error.*

The value of K_P also largely determines the attitude control system bandwidth, which is a measure of the range of errors the system can correct. The mathematical definition of *bandwidth* requires a bit more explanation than we want to go into here, but it can be approximated as

$$\omega_n \approx \left(K_P / I\right)^{1/2} \tag{19-10}$$

where I is the spacecraft moment of inertia. The bandwidth defines the frequency of disturbances and of commanded motions at which control authority begins to diminish. Attitude control and disturbance rejection are effective from 0 frequency (i.e., constant or d.c. inputs) up to the bandwidth. *Speed of response* is approximately the reciprocal of bandwidth. Note from Chap. 16, proportional gain is inversely proportional to allowable error, and bandwidth is proportional to the square root of the proportional gain. Therefore, high accuracy implies high K_P and high bandwidth. However, there are practical limits on bandwidth. If the bandwidth is high enough that it includes bending frequencies for the spacecraft structure, then control-structure interactions must be carefully considered. If the bandwidth is higher than the maximum sampling rate of critical attitude sensors, some care must be taken to avoid excessive attitude responses to the slow updates. Finally, high bandwidth control systems may be more likely to have adverse reactions to inaccurate or lagging system inputs; this condition is referred to as having insufficient stability margin.

There are design techniques to address these concerns. One such technique is to modify the system response to increase stability while keeping the same attitude accuracy by increasing attitude rate *damping*, which is controlled by the *derivative gain*, or *rate gain*, K_D. For a given value of K_P, increasing K_D will slow down the response of the control system, but it will not diminish the accuracy in the end, provided the disturbance environment or slewing requirements do not require very high speed of response. This technique is often used to improve stability margins in systems where the final accuracy is more important than the amount of time it takes to achieve that accuracy. Note that, though there are multiple methods for selecting K_P and K_D, such as linear-quadratic regulation (LQR) and other state-space methods, the system response generally must still be understood in terms of bandwidth and damping to achieve confidence that the control gains will provide both stability and adequate performance.

Sometimes the problem facing a designer is that stability margin requirements are not difficult to meet, but accuracy requirements are very difficult. A common technique for improving on the performance of a PD is to add an integrator to the feedback loop; this is called a *proportional-integral-derivative controller (PID).* Recall that in a regular PD controller, a steady-state error of some kind will remain as long as there are disturbance torques to create it. The integrator causes the correcting control torque to gradually increase over time to remove that steady-state error completely. If the disturbance torque changes magnitude or direction, the PID controller will take some time to adjust, but it will track with no steady-state error. This improved performance generally comes at the price of reduced stability margins, so the stability and performance requirements must always be carefully balanced.

In addressing control-structure interactions, the control designer must keep in mind that, if bending causes apparent attitude errors, the control system may aggravate the bending motion, eventually affecting control stability and perhaps damaging the bending structures. Though there are control design techniques to deal with these potential problems, the control designer will often start by recommending a minimum frequency for structural bending modes that would allow flexible effects to be neglected. This minimum frequency is generally an order of magnitude greater than the bandwidth needed to achieve required accuracy. Then, structural engineers will attempt to honor this restriction in their design. For further discussion of how structural flexibility interacts with feedback control systems, see Sec. 3.12 of Agrawal [1986].

Spin Stabilization and Momentum Bias. The fundamental concept in spin stabilization is the nutation frequency of the vehicle. For a spinning body, the inertial nutation frequency, ω_{ni} is

$$\omega_{ni} = \omega_S I_S / I_T \quad (19\text{-}11)$$

where ω_S is the spin frequency, I_S is the spin axis of inertia, and I_T is the transverse axis inertia. For a momentum-bias vehicle with a non-rotating body and a momentum wheel (or a dual-spin vehicle with a non-rotating platform), the nutation frequency is

$$\omega_{ni} = h / I_T \quad (19\text{-}12)$$

where h is the angular momentum of the spinning body (or bodies). (Note that this is really the same equation as for a spinning body, for which $h = \omega_S I_S$.) Thus, spacecraft with large inertias and small wheels have small nutation frequencies (i.e., long periods).

Attempting to control the vehicle with a bandwidth faster than the nutation frequency causes it to act more like a 3-axis stabilized vehicle, that is, the stiffness of the spin is effectively reduced. In general, we attempt to control near the nutation frequency or slower, with correspondingly small torques for given attitude errors. Because we generally wish to avoid changing the spin rate with control torques, the torque is applied perpendicularly to the spin. We can then relate the achieved angular rate, ω, to the applied torque by simplifying Euler's equations to only the gyroscopic torque component:

$$\mathbf{T} = \omega \times \mathbf{H} = \omega\mathbf{H} \quad (19\text{-}13)$$

where $\mathbf{H}$ is the system angular momentum. A lower limit on control bandwidth is usually provided by the orbit rate ω_O, which for a circular orbit, is

$$\omega_O = (\mu/r^3)^2 \quad (19\text{-}14)$$

where $\mu = 3.986 \times 10^{14} \mathrm{m}^3/\mathrm{s}^2$ for Earth orbits and r is the orbit radius.

Example of Magnetic Momentum Management. Managing the long-term buildup of angular momentum in the orbiting spacecraft often drives the ADCS requirements. As would be expected for an element so central to ADCS design, there are many different methods for keeping momentum to levels that do not degrade data or equipment. We present here a simple, common, and relatively inexpensive algorithm for commanding magnetic torquers using only magnetometer data. It functions as an excellent active rate damping controller, and after the spacecraft's rate becomes very low, it keeps the angular momentum at manageable levels by canceling it out on an orbit-averaged basis. Often called B-dot, this algorithm is based on back-differencing magnetometer data to estimate the time derivative of the magnetic field (or "Bdot"). For rate damping purposes, we assume the B-field is changing in the body due only to spacecraft rotation, which is true for all but rotation rates on the order of orbital rate. Specifically,

$$\mathbf{Bdot} = \mathbf{B_{k+1}} - \mathbf{B_k} = -\omega \times \mathbf{B} \quad (19\text{-}15)$$

The spacecraft dipole vector, $\mathbf{D}$, is set equal to a gain multiplied by the magnetic field:

$$\mathbf{D} = -k\,\mathbf{Bdot} = k\omega \times \mathbf{B} \quad (19\text{-}16)$$

Then, when the magnetic field acts on that vector, it produces a control torque

$$\mathbf{T_c} = \mathbf{D} \times \mathbf{B} \quad (19\text{-}17)$$

that is always in a direction that slows down the spacecraft rotation except when ω is aligned with $\mathbf{B}$ (in vector terminology, $\omega \cdot \mathbf{T_c} \le 0$). Once the spacecraft is slowed down, the algorithm will attempt to follow the magnetic field vector, its success determined by the strength of the gain, k, that is chosen. However, whether it follows the field doesn't matter: The goal of slowing the spacecraft and then maintaining a slow momentum has been achieved. Flatley, Morgenstern, Reth and Bauer [1997] did not invent the B-dot controller, but their paper nicely explains in clear English and equations how something so simple works so well.

Algorithms for Attitude Determination. A full discussion of attitude determination algorithms requires a dedicated reference such as Wertz [1978]. We will highlight only some of the basic concepts.

The basic algorithms for determination depend on the coordinate frames of interest and the geometry and parameterization of the measurements. Useful coordinate frames can include the individual sensor frames, the local vertical frame, and an inertial frame, such as Earth-centered inertial (ECI). The geometry of the measurements is different for different sensors, as discussed in Sec. 19.1.4, and they are generally parameterized as sequential rotations about the axes of a frame, called *Euler angles* (e.g., roll, pitch, yaw), or as attitude *quaternions*, which are unit vectors with four elements that define a rotational axis in a frame, called the eigenaxis, and the amount of rotation about the eigenaxis. Inertial reference units (with their supporting software) and star sensors are well suited to quaternions, whereas Earth-pointing vehicles often use a local-vertical set of Euler angles, much like aircraft.

Simple spacecraft may use the sensor output directly for control, whereas more complex vehicles or those with higher accuracy requirements employ some form of averaging, smoothing or Kalman filtering of the data. The exact algorithms depend on the vehicle properties, orbit, and sensors used.

FireSat II Algorithms. For our momentum-bias FireSat II example, control separates into pitch-axis control using torque commands to the momentum wheel and roll-yaw control using current commands to the magnetic torquers. The pitch-wheel desaturation commands must also be fed (at a slower rate) to the torquers. The pitch-wheel control is straightforward, using PD control and, optionally, *integral control*, in which commands are augmented by a small torque proportional to the integral of the attitude error. The roll-yaw control design starts by using the linearized nutation dynamics of the system, and is complicated by the directional limitations of electromagnetic torque (the achievable torque is perpendicular to the instantaneous Earth magnetic field).

Table 19-15◀, Fig. 19-8◀, Eq. 19-17

Get More

Table 19-16. ADCS Vendors. Typical suppliers for ADCS components. An up-to-date version of this table can be found on the book website.

Company	Sun Sensors	Earth (horizon) Sensors	Magnetometers	Star Sensors	Gyro/IMU	GPS	Momentum/ Reaction Wheels	CMG	Magnetic Torquers	Thrusters
Adcole Corporation	X									
Aerojet										X
Ball Aerospace and Technologies Corp.				X						
Billingsley Aerospace and Defense			X							
Bradford Engineering	X						X			X
Comtech AeroAstro	X			X						
EADS Astrium					X	X		X		X
EADS SODERN		X		X						
EMS Technologies, Inc.				X						
Finmeccanica (incl. SELEX Galileo)	X	X		X	X					
ITT Aerospace						X				
General Dynamics						X				
Goodrich (incl. Ithaco)			X		X		X		X	
Honeywell Space Systems (incl. Allied)							X	X		
Jena Optronik	X			X						
L-3 Space & Navigation					X		X	X		
Kearfott Guidance and Navigation Corp.					X	X				
MEDA			X							
Micro Aerospace Solutions					X					X
Microcosm, Inc.									X	
NASA Goddard Space Flight Center						X	X			
Northrop Grumman (incl Litton)					X					X
Øersted—DTU				X						
Optical Energy Technologies	X	X								
Rockwell Collins Deutschland (incl. Teldix)							X			
Servo Corp. of America		X								
StarVision Technologies				X						
Surrey Satellite Technologies—US LLC	X		X	X	X	X	X	X	X	X
Systron Donner Inertial					X					
Terma				X						
Watson Industries, Inc.			X		X					

The nadir-oriented control system may use an Earth-referenced, aircraft-like Euler angle set (i.e., roll, pitch, and yaw), although quaternions may simplify calculations during off-nominal pointing; quaternion calculations generally require fewer arithmetic steps, they simplify tracking commands, and they have no singularities. The horizon sensors directly read two of the angles of interest, pitch and roll. Yaw needs to be measured directly from Sun position (during orbit day) or from the magnetometer readings (using a stored model of the Earth's field plus an orbit ephemeris), or inferred from the roll-yaw coupling described earlier. MEMS gyro data can be used to enhance the attitude estimate, but they can have large biases that change with temperature, so it may be best not to have to rely on them for our accuracy requirements. The magnetic field and Sun information require an uplinked set of orbit parameters, and increase the computational requirements of the subsystem. Overall, meeting the 0.1 deg yaw requirement when the Sun is not visible will be the toughest challenge facing the ADCS designer, and planning to coast through the dark periods without direct yaw control may be most appropriate.

SCS Algorithms. A 3-axis PD controller will be sufficient for our control accuracy needs. In this control algorithm, an error angle and error rate is calculated for each axis, and a control torque calculated based on those. That calculation done for the three axes gives a control torque vector, which is then distributed among the reaction wheels. If one of the wheels is asked to issue a control torque that exceeds its capability, then the spacecraft would have a total torque vector that is not in the same direction as the requested vector. For our mission, that is not too much of a danger, since we don't have any elements that would be damaged by Sun exposure or the like. Still, it is a simple matter to scale all 3 vector components by the same factor that would make the largest of them equal to its limit while preserving the direction of the torque vector. Note that this is safe for a PD controller, but that stability problems can result if the same tactic is used for a PID controller without taking some care to prevent problems.

The data from the star camera and the rate gyros in each SCS satellite can be combined in any of a number of ways. We will simply trust the star camera attitude as accurate whenever it gives us data it indicates is valid, and we will use the gyros to provide direct rate measurements and to propagate the attitude solution by integrating the rate over the sampling time if the star camera fails to provide a valid attitude. This method is not the most accurate, but generally, more accuracy comes at the expense of more complexity, which then costs money and time in flight software development and testing. This is a good lesson to wrap up this section: Though it can be tempting to always reach for your best, most expensive tool, it is better engineering to try to get by with the cheapest system that will meet your requirements with appropriate margin, as discussed in Chap. 13.

19.2 Spacecraft Trajectory Navigation and Control Systems

Karl D. Bilimoria, *NASA Ames Research Center*

The previous section covered various aspects regarding the determination and control of a spacecraft's rotational motion. This section covers the corresponding aspects of a spacecraft's translational motion, utilizing the terminology defined below.

Trajectory refers to the path traveled by a spacecraft. *Orbit* refers to a special type of trajectory that forms a closed circular or elliptical path. Trajectories that do not fall under the classification of an orbit have open paths, e.g., a hyperbolic path of a planetary fly-by, or a launch/reentry path that intersects the surface of the Earth or other celestial body. Although a distinction is made here in the context of navigation and translational control, the terms orbit and trajectory are sometimes used interchangeably, as in Chap. 9. *Navigation* is the determination of the spacecraft's current translational states (position and velocity), relative to a specified reference frame, as a function of time. *Trajectory control* is the determination and execution of the translational commands (thruster firings) required to drive the current states towards the desired states which may be determined by a guidance system.

The purpose of this section is to help answer the following questions: As a function of the system used, how accurately can the user know the spacecraft's translational states (position and velocity)? Similarly, how accurately can the user control the spacecraft's trajectory? What are the mass and power requirements of the navigation and control systems to achieve the corresponding functions? Section 19.2.1 outlines the system definition process. Section 19.2.2 then discusses the various options available for navigation systems, and Sec. 19.2.3 describes the control options for orbit maintenance and making changes to trajectory parameters. Some design considerations for trajectory navigation and control systems are presented in Sec. 19.2.4.

19.2.1 System Definition Process

Table 19-17 summarizes the process for defining the trajectory navigation and control functions. Each of the steps is described below.

Step 1. Define top-level functions. The first step is to determine the key mission objectives that require navigation data or trajectory control. Examples include a repeating ground track orbit, a geostationary slot, or interplanetary flight.

Step 2. Estimate navigation accuracy requirements. Mapping and pointing trades (see Sec. 8.6) typically provide preliminary estimates of the required navigation accuracy. In most cases, the pointing and mapping requirements are satisfied by trading between position and attitude accuracy, so navigation accuracy requirements are generally performed in conjunction with attitude accuracy requirements.

Step 3. Determine where navigation data is needed. A data flow analysis helps determine where the data comes from and where it is needed. For a simple low-cost satellite mission where a single ground station performs all of the data evaluation, system control, and mission planning, the best solution is probably to do the navigation at the ground station. At the other extreme would be a satellite communicating with many distributed users, each of whom needs to know the satellite position or derivative information such as the ground look-point location. In this case, the navigation data is probably needed on the spacecraft, although we could also navigate from the primary ground station and distribute the results to other users. In some cases, navigation data may be needed by the spacecraft itself for payload functions such as target selection and/or for control functions such as orbit maintenance.

Table 19-17. Process for Defining the Trajectory Navigation and Control Functions.

Step	Principal Issues	Discussed
Define top-level functions and requirements for trajectory navigation and control	How do the key mission objectives depend on trajectory navigation and control functions?	Secs. 3.5, 4.4, 6.1, 10.1
Estimate navigation (position) accuracy requirements	What are the pointing/mapping trades?	Sec. 8.6
Determine where navigation data is needed	Is it needed only at ground station or at multiple user sites, for mission planning and execution? Is it needed on board the spacecraft for payload and/or control functions?	Sec. 4.2.1
Conduct trade for autonomous vs. ground-based navigation	Is there a need for real-time navigation data? Do the potential operational benefits justify the risk associated with a non-traditional approach?	Secs. 4.2.1, 19.2.4
Select navigation method	Which method best satisfies the mission requirements?	Sec. 19.2.2
Determine whether trajectory control is needed	What are the mission requirements for orbit maintenance and/or change?	Chap. 10, Sec. 19.2.3
If yes, conduct trade for autonomous vs. ground-based trajectory control	Do the potential operational benefits justify the risk associated with a non-traditional approach?	Secs. 4.2.2, 19.2.3
Define requirements for trajectory navigation and control systems	State requirements in terms of **what** is needed rather than **how** it is done	Sec. 19.2.1

Step 4. Conduct autonomous navigation trade. Ground-based navigation is the traditional approach. Decide if the potential operational benefits justify the risk (technical and/or programmatic) associated with a non-traditional approach. Autonomous navigation may be preferred if real-time navigation data is needed, either on board the satellite or by the end user.

Step 5. Select navigation method. Section 19.2.2 summarizes the various options available for spacecraft navigation, along with advantages and disadvantages. Based on the mission objectives, typical navigation methods can be ground-based, space-based, semi-autonomous, or fully autonomous.

Step 6. Determine need for trajectory control. At the system design level, decide if there is a need to maintain or change the orbit. If trajectory control is not needed, eliminating the propulsion subsystem can save some weight/cost. On the other hand, maintaining the orbit may significantly extend mission life and thereby reduce the cost per year.

Step 7. Conduct autonomous control trade. If trajectory control is required, decide whether to do so from the ground or autonomously on board the spacecraft. Ground-based trajectory control is the traditional approach. Decide if the potential operational benefits justify the risk (technical and/or programmatic) associated with a non-traditional approach. A key question is the complexity and frequency of the trajectory control actions that need to be performed. For example, ground-based control may be preferred if the mission calls for infrequent but complex maneuvers.

Step 8. Define system requirements. Top-level system requirements are defined in terms of what capability is needed rather than how it is implemented. Detailed trade studies, done later in the design cycle, will help select the best trajectory navigation and control systems that meet these requirements.

19.2.2 Navigation

Spacecraft navigation pertains to the knowledge of the vehicle's translational states: components of position and velocity. For closed trajectories, i.e., orbits, the 6 translational states can also be expressed in terms of the 6 orbital elements. In principle, knowledge of the state vector at any one time allows us to predict the position and velocity of the spacecraft at other times.

Spacecraft navigation data can be obtained from onboard sensors such as accelerometers and star trackers, or from external tracking/surveillance sensors such as radar or optical devices. *Tracking* is the process of updating an object's location by first predicting where it will be and then observing it. Tracking sensors are used when high-precision data are needed about a specific object. *Surveillance* is the process of searching for objects whose location may or may not be known. These sensors typically "stare" across an area of the sky and register objects passing through their field of view. They can observe multiple objects simultaneously, and continually add to the quality of the tracking catalog by ensuring that the data are accurate and up-to-date.

Radar sensors provide range and range-rate measurements, and may additionally provide azimuth and elevation angles. Rates of azimuth and elevation angles may also be available but can be quite noisy and hence may not be useful. Range, azimuth, and elevation data provide position vectors. Velocity vectors can be determined from position-vector rates (directly measured or computed from successive position measurements) or by other means such as Doppler shifts.

Optical sensors, unlike radar sensors, cannot provide range information. Hence the state vector has to be determined from angles-only observations of right ascension and declination from time-tagged images of the satellite's star background by comparing with star catalogs. Iteration or additional processing are required to compensate for the lack of direct range information. Navigation data can be obtained from three pairs of right ascension and declination angles using various techniques [Vallado, 2007].

When a radar/optical sensor detects an object, it makes a series of observations as the object moves along its trajectory. Most modern sensors make hundreds or thousands of observations during each pass of the space object. A typical pass interval is ~15 min for low Earth orbit (LEO) and ~10 hrs for deep space orbits. Using dense measurements (~100 observations per pass) from a small number of sensors often provides higher quality navigation data than using sparse measurements from many sensors.

There are many techniques available for determining position and velocity vectors using various types of measurements: range and range-rate (three simultaneous observations from three separate sensors); range-only (six independent time-tagged observations); three time-tagged position vectors (range, elevation, and azimuth); two position vectors and time-of-flight [Vallado, 2007]. The sensor-relative position and velocity data are then transformed to the Earth-centered inertial (ECI) frame. The transformation requires that the sensor site location and velocity be known accurately, and this requirement poses some challenges for satellite-based sensors. Combining multiple data types/sources can reduce the error in the estimated state vectors. Range data is preferred, but angular data can be useful too.

State vector (position and velocity) data forms the basis of orbit determination, which involves estimating the spacecraft's orbital elements and accounting for perturbations to its natural orbit. The overall process of orbit determination requires estimation (which is linked with initial orbit determination), prediction, and uncertainty estimates. The process of orbit determination iteratively solves for a description of a satellite's orbit in terms of a state vector at an epoch, based upon observations and measurements.

The observation update interval for a spacecraft should be timed so that the next observation occurs before trajectory propagation theory would introduce enough error to keep the next sensor from re-acquiring the target, or when the most stringent navigation accuracy requirement for the satellite would not be met. Satellite state vector update rates are typically once per day for LEO to once per week for geosynchronous Earth orbits (GEO).

19.2.2.1 Ground-based Navigation Systems

Ground-based navigation systems have sensors at one or more locations on the surface of the Earth. It is the traditional way to obtain navigation data. These systems can be categorized as active or passive.

Active ground-based navigation systems interact with the spacecraft being tracked via telemetry signals. A ranging signal is sent to the spacecraft on the uplink, and a response signal from an on-board transponder is received on the downlink. The signal transit time and Doppler shift are used to compute position and velocity relative to the ground station. This type of navigation data is generally collected at the spacecraft operator's ground station.

Passive ground-based navigation systems utilize sensors that do not interact with the object being tracked. They simply use reflected energy: radio waves for radar sensors and visible-spectrum light waves for optical sensors.

Satellite position accuracies from ground-based navigation systems depend on sensor accuracy, amount of data, and the spacecraft's altitude. However, position accuracies typically range from a few kilometers in LEO (much better for laser ranging) to tens of kilometers in GEO. The principal ground-based navigation systems are described below.

Space Surveillance Network (SSN). Operated by the US military, this is the world's most comprehensive space surveillance system. The SSN is a network of radars and optical sensors located at 25+ sites around the northern hemisphere. It can track space objects as small as 10 cm in low Earth orbit. SSN sensors take a combined total of roughly 500,000 observations in a day. Data from the SSN, fused with data from some other sources, is used to maintain the active space catalog that in 2010 contained around 15,000 objects of which only about 1,000 were operational satellites. A key function of the SSN is to catalog and track space debris to support analyses of close approaches (conjunctions) that may pose a threat to operational spacecraft. Spacecraft operators can exchange space situational awareness data with the SSN operator through the Commercial and Foreign Entities (CFE) program.

There are three types of radars in the SSN, the most common being phased-array radars that can track objects up to an altitude of a few thousand kilometers. There are also conventional dish-type radars that can track objects as small as ~25 cm out to the GEO belt (about 40,000 km). Finally, there is the Space Fence which is a system of multi-static radars (3 transmitter sites and 6 receiving stations) spread out across the continental US at a latitude of roughly 33 deg north. This component of the SSN performs surveillance in the strict sense of the word because it does not need to be tasked. The existing VHF space fence tracks objects that pass through its sensor field out to an altitude of about 30,000 km. The new S-band space fence, planned for initial operational capability in 2015 and full capability in 2020, will be able to track even smaller objects. It will use multiple globally positioned radars which will allow for the detection of much smaller space objects than the current system due to their geographic separation and higher radio frequency. With the capability to perform 750,000 observations per day and track over 100,000 objects, the new Space Fence will significantly reduce coverage gaps and significantly improve space situational awareness in low and medium-altitude Earth orbits [James, 2010].

The SSN also has optical telescopes that passively collect light reflected off space objects and can track very distant objects, up to a few hundred thousand kilometers away. The Ground-based Electro-Optical Deep Space Surveillance (GEODSS) one-meter telescopes use low-light-level TV cameras to track basketball-sized deep-space objects from about 5,000 km out to GEO altitudes. There are 4 GEODSS sites located in the vicinity of Socorro, New Mexico; Maui, Hawaii; Diego Garcia, British Indian Ocean Territories; and Morón, Spain.

The SSN includes some space-based assets, which will be described later in Sec. 19.2.2.2.

Deep Space Network (DSN). NASA operates an international network of antennas to support interplanetary spacecraft missions. DSN has provided navigation data derived from spacecraft radio signals since the early 1960s for lunar and interplanetary space exploration. With its current sensors, DSN can provide a geocentric angular accuracy on the order of 1 nrad which corresponds to a position accuracy of 150 m at a distance of one astronomical unit (AU).

The DSN currently consists of 3 deep-space communications facilities placed approximately 120 degrees apart in longitude around the world, located in the vicinity of Los Angeles, California (known as the Goldstone site), Madrid, Spain, and Canberra, Australia. This geographic distribution permits constant observation of spacecraft as the Earth rotates, and helps to make the DSN the largest and most sensitive scientific telecommunications system in the world. Each complex consists of 4 or more deep space stations equipped with ultrasensitive receiving systems and large parabolic dish antennas. All DSN antennas are steerable, high-gain, parabolic reflector antennas. The smallest are 26 m diameter antennas used for tracking LEO spacecraft. The 70 m diameter antenna is the largest and most sensitive DSN antenna, and is capable of tracking spacecraft traveling more than 16 billion kilometers from Earth.

Russian Space Surveillance System. This system is operated by a space-surveillance division of the Russian military [Podwig, 2010]. To monitor objects in low Earth orbits the system uses the Russian early-warning radar network which currently includes 9 stations. The space surveillance network includes the Krona system at Zelenchukskaya in the North Caucasus which has dedicated X-band space surveillance radars. Another system of this type is being deployed near Nakhodka in the fareastern part of Russia. To monitor objects in high-altitude orbits, the space surveillance system uses optical sensors. The main optical observation station, Okno, located in Nurek, Tajikistan, began operations in 1999. Its telescopes allow detection of objects in all orbital regimes up to altitudes of about 40,000 km. However, this optical sensor network lacks coverage outside the borders of the former Soviet Union and thus does not have global radar coverage of the GEO belt.

International Scientific Optical Network (ISON). This system is a network of optical telescopes around the world, managed by the Russian Academy of Sciences. ISON is a partnership of many academic and scientific institutions, currently including 30 telescopes in 20 observatories in 10 countries [Weeden et al., 2010]. ISON is a heterogeneous mix of telescopes of various sizes and capabilities, but as a network it can track a wide range of object sizes throughout deep space (GEO belt) and provide a significant number of observations.

European Space Surveillance and Tracking System. The role of this planned system is to detect, catalog, and predict the movement of objects orbiting the Earth. The Space Surveillance Test and Validation Centre is located in Spain. A precursor system utilizes existing radar and optical sensors; dedicated sensors are planned to developed and deployed after 2011.

There are some individual radar sites currently operational in Europe [Weeden et al., 2010]. They include the French GRAVES bi-static radar fence, the German tracking and imaging radar (TIRA) system that tracks and images LEO objects, and the Norwegian GLOBUS II tracking radar that tracks and images GEO objects.

Indian Deep Space Network (IDSN). The IDSN complex located about 100 km from Bangalore has 3 antennas. The technical facilities in IDSN include a 32 m Deep Space Antenna, an 18 m Antenna Terminal, an 11 m Antenna Terminal, the Indian Space Science Data Centre, and a technical services complex. Operational since 2008, the ISDN was used during the Chandrayaan-1 lunar mission for tracking, orbit control, and housekeeping operations.

Chinese Space Surveillance System. China is believed to have a network of phased array radars at various locations within its borders, each likely to have 3,000 km range and 120 degree of azimuth coverage [Weeden et al., 2010]. It is also believed to have longrange precision mechanical tracking radar. China's main optical sensor capabilities are coordinated by the Purple Mountain Observatory, which operates multiple telescopes in 4 separate locations that can track satellites throughout all orbital regimes. However, China lacks coverage outside of its borders and thus does not have global coverage of the GEO belt.

19.2.2.2 Space-based Navigation Systems

Space-based navigation systems have sensors on one or more spacecraft orbiting the Earth; the overall system may include ground stations to receive/process data from the satellites. Space-based sensors can detect debris, spacecraft or other distant space objects without interference from weather, atmosphere, or lighting conditions. The principal systems are described below.

Tracking Data Relay Satellite System (TDRSS). NASA established this system in the early 1980s to replace its worldwide network of ground tracking stations. The TDRSS space segment currently has 8 operational satellites (including spares) located in geosynchronous orbit. This constellation provides 100% visibility to user spacecraft operating at altitudes from 10,000 km down to 1,200 km, decreasing to 85% visibility at 300 km altitude [Teles et al., 1995] due to line-of-sight limitations. The TDRSS ground segment is located near Las Cruces, New Mexico, and consists of two functionally identical ground terminals collectively known as the White Sands Complex. An additional ground terminal complex in Guam communicates with the satellites not visible from New Mexico.

The user spacecraft needs an onboard TDRSS transponder. High-precision range and range-rate tracking of the user spacecraft relative to the tracking data relay satellites is performed according to a resource schedule. Highly accurate estimates of the tracking data relay satellites' position and velocity are also available, enabling the TDRSS ground segment to determine the user spacecraft's position with a 3-sigma accuracy of about 50 m. This navigation data is relayed from the TDRSS ground segment to the user's ground station.

Space-Based Surveillance System. The US military's Midcourse Space Experiment (MSX) missile defense test satellite, launched in 1996, carried the first dedicated space-based optical device (a visible-band electro-optical camera) for space situational awareness. Until its end-of-life in 2008, the MSX satellite used its space-based visible (SBV) sensor to augment the US Space Surveillance Network's ground-based sensors by expanding surveillance and tracking of objects in the GEO belt. MSX is being replaced by a more advanced constellation of orbiting sensors (and supporting ground infrastructure) known as the Space-Based Surveillance System (SBSS). The first "pathfinder" satellite of this system was successfully placed into a 630 km Sun-synchronous orbit in 2010. It has a 30 cm telescope on a two axis gimbal with a 2.4 megapixel image sensor. Today, many GEO objects go days without being tracked. The SBSS will provide the ability for uninterrupted scanning of the entire GEO belt every 24 hours.

19.2.2.3 Autonomous Navigation Systems

Autonomous navigation systems utilize sensors onboard the spacecraft to determine navigation states in real time. These instruments may need signals transmitted from other satellites and/or ground stations (semi-autonomous), or not need any transmitted signals at all (fully autonomous).

Global Navigation Satellite Systems (GNSS). These satellite constellations provide geo-spatial positioning data with global coverage. An overview of operational and some planned GNSS constellations is provided below. Position (e.g., latitude, longitude, altitude) of receivers are determined using time signals transmitted along a line-of-sight by radio from the satellites. Signals from 4 or more satellites are used to compute the receiver's horizontal and vertical position vector components. Receivers using civilian signals typically provide position data with an accuracy on the order of 10 m [Hofmann-Wellenhof et al., 2008].

GNSS satellites have an orbital altitude of about 20,000 km (exact value depends on the constellation), and their antennas are designed to provide signals only in a cone covering the Earth's surface. Hence global coverage is not assured at altitudes well above LEO, but it is possible to use the signals for navigation at altitudes up to and beyond GEO by using the spillover of the beam beyond the edge of the Earth's disk.

US Navstar Global Positioning System. Commonly known as GPS, this military-operated system has been globally available since 1994. There are 24 satellites (plus spares) in 6 orbital planes with a period of about 12 hours (2 revolutions per day) at about 20,200 km altitude. The orbital planes are evenly spaced by 60 deg in right ascension, with an inclination of 55 deg [Logsdon, 1992]. There should always be 6 satellites within line-of-sight from almost any point on Earth; this requires uneven spacing in mean anomaly along an orbit. Each satellite repeats its ground track on a 1-day cycle and hence will pass the same Earth location every day. Commercial GPS receivers are available for spacecraft, and they are commonly used in LEO. For example, the EO-1 mission used GPS for orbit determination.

Russian GLONASS. This military-operated system is nearly complete and is planned to become globally available in 2011. The full constellation provides 24 satellites in 3 orbital planes with a period of 11.3 hours at 19,100 km altitude. The orbital planes are evenly spaced by 120 deg in right ascension, with an inclination of 65 deg. There is even spacing in mean anomaly within each orbital plane, and an argument-of-latitude displacement of 15 deg between successive orbital planes. Each satellite repeats its ground track on an 8-day cycle; since there are 8 satellites in each orbit, a satellite will pass the same Earth location every day.

European Galileo. This civilian-operated global navigation system is under development by the European Commission and the European Space Agency. Initial operational capability is anticipated around 2015, with full capability expected sometime after 2020. The full constellation design calls for 27 satellites (plus 3 spares) in 3 orbital planes with a period of 14 hours at 23,222 km altitude. The satellites will be spread evenly around each orbital plane with an inclination of 56 deg.

Other Systems. The Chinese Beidou-1 regional navigation system is operational. There are 3 satellites (plus 1 backup) in GEO providing coverage over a substantial portion of eastern and southern Asia. Beidou-2, commonly known as Compass, is a system of 35 satellites that is planned to provide global coverage by 2020. Eight Beidou-2 satellites had been deployed by April 2011.

The Indian Regional Navigational Satellite System (IRNSS) is currently in development. It consists of 3 geostationary satellites and 4 geosynchronous satellites at 29 deg inclination that are anticipated to provide coverage over the Indian sub-continent by 2014.

TDRSS On-board Navigation System (TONS). This NASA system, developed in the early 1990s, utilizes the space segment of the TDRSS described earlier in Sec. 19.2.2.2. TONS works by forwarding the ground communication signal from the TDRSS to the user satellite, measuring the Doppler effect on that signal, and processing it using an onboard extended Kalman filter to accurately estimate the user satellite's state vector.

TONS provides position data with a 1-sigma accuracy of 10 m [Gramling and Long, 1995]. Navigation using TONS requires the user satellite to carry more onboard equipment than is required for navigation using the basic TDRSS, but the advantages are autonomy and increased accuracy of navigation data.

Doppler Orbitography and Radiopositioning Integrated by Satellite (DORIS). Operated by the French space agency, DORIS is a world-wide network of about 60 ground beacons that emit radio signals. The signals' frequency shift caused by the movement of the user satellite (Doppler effect) is measured by a receiving antenna on board the satellite to generate its own navigation data. DORIS has been used by several satellites, including TOPEX/Poseidon and Envisat, for precise orbit determination on the order of a few centimeters.

Optical Stellar Navigation. Imaging devices are used to observe a local celestial body against a known background star field. Navigation states are calculated using optical measurements: the angle formed by a star and the horizon of a celestial body, and the apparent angular diameter of the celestial body. In some cases, the observation tasking request is planned by the ground station and uplinked to the spacecraft well in advance; the images acquired by the spacecraft are then downlinked to the ground station for processing to determine the navigation states. In other cases, onboard systems command image acquisition and perform the calculations to determine the navigation states.

Throughout the primary mission of Deep Space 1, about once per week, its automatic navigation system (AutoNav) was invoked by the operating sequence to acquire optical navigation images. It turned the spacecraft and the integrated camera and imaging spectrometer to record images of asteroids and stars, and then used on-board image analysis for navigation. The apparent position of an asteroid relative to the much more distant stars enabled AutoNav to calculate the location of the spacecraft in the solar system.

Optical Landmark Navigation. Image-based on board navigation is accomplished by tracking landmarks such as craters. Tracking individual craters enables orbit determination accuracies on the order of the camera resolution, e.g., several meters for small bodies such as asteroids.

Navigation relative to the celestial body is accomplished by comparing the current image against a reference map stored on the spacecraft; spacecraft attitude information is also required. Generating the reference map in advance of onboard use requires a substantial effort at the ground station. For example, the Near Earth Asteroid Rendezvous (NEAR) mission used an on-board landmark-tracking navigation system during its rendezvous with the asteroid Eros in 2000–01. In preparation for this event, ground crew manually extracted and identified craters from thousands of optical images—about 10,000 craters were identified on Eros' 32-kilometer long and 16-kilometer wide body. Feature recognition software could be used to assist this process in future missions.

In 2005, the Hayabusa spacecraft mission to the asteroid Ikotawa used optical navigation (with some ground assistance) for proximity operations within a few kilometers of the asteroid's surface. Additionally, a target marker was released from the spacecraft to provide a visual target for the landing site. Hayabusa's navigation sensors included a lidar and laser range finder.

Horizon Scanner Navigation. These systems feature spinning sensors that move along the surface of a cone. Each scan generates horizon entry/exit points on the edge of the celestial body disc seen by the satellite. These points are used to determine the spacecraft's distance and direction relative to the celestial body. For example, the Microcosm Autonomous Navigation System (MANS) system uses two spinning sensors that provide Earth/Sun/Moon position measurements to determine satellite position and attitude. For most low-Earth orbit conditions, the position accuracy is 500 m with one sensor and 100 m with two sensors. Other horizon scanner systems include Honeywell's Earth Reference Attitude Determination System (ERADS) and the Compact Autonomous Navigation System (CANS) developed by the Chinese.

19.2.3 Trajectory Control

Trajectory control utilizes the spacecraft's propulsion system to alter the magnitude and/or direction of the vehicle's velocity vector. This requires a thruster burn of a specific duration, and often requires a prior attitude change maneuver to properly orient the thruster(s) used for trajectory control.

Most small spacecraft do not have onboard propulsive systems; this has the advantage of reducing spacecraft complexity, weight, and cost. However, no trajectory control is possible after the spacecraft has been placed into orbit, and hence the orbital parameters will drift significantly over time due to the cumulative effect of secular gravitational-field perturbations. LEO satellites will also experience a continuous decay of orbital altitude due to atmospheric drag. An uncontrolled trajectory may be acceptable for some satellites with a mission life of 1 to 3 years. Other spacecraft will generally require some type of trajectory control.

In some cases, the propulsive force for trajectory change may be provided by another spacecraft. The Space Shuttle has boosted the Hubble Space Telescope's orbit during servicing missions. The International Space Station (ISS) periodically has its orbit raised by a few kilometers by visiting spacecraft such as Progress supply ships, Space Shuttles, and Jules Verne automated transfer vehicles. In an emergency, the ISS can use the thrusters on its own Zvezda service module for orbital maneuvering.

This section provides basic information about various types of trajectory changes from a controls perspective. Some typical values for the frequency and magnitude (ΔV) of the required control are also presented. Section 9.6 covers orbital maneuvers from an astrodynamics perspective.

19.2.3.1 Orbit Maintenance

After a spacecraft has been placed into the desired orbit, minor adjustments are generally required to compensate for disturbances so that the orbital parameters remain within mission tolerances. The disturbances can arise from a non-uniform gravity field of the central body, atmospheric drag (at lower altitudes), solar radiation pressure, and gravity effects of celestial bodies other than the central body. Orbit maintenance maneuvers typically require a small ΔV, but are performed numerous (~100) times over the mission life of the spacecraft.

For Earth orbits, the equatorial bulge creates significant secular perturbations as well as long-period (order of days or weeks) and short-period (order of minutes or hours) cyclic perturbations. Solar radiation pressure produces a small force that can affect the orbital trajectory over long periods of time; this force depends in part on the spacecraft structure and its orientation with respect to the Sun. High altitude orbits are affected by the gravitational forces of the Moon and Sun. Orbits below 1,000 km altitude are significantly affected by atmospheric drag that varies over time according to the solar cycle which has a period of about 11 years.

A commonly used maintenance maneuver for LEO satellites is orbit raising to compensate for altitude decay due to atmospheric drag. The frequency of performing this maneuver depends on the nominal orbital altitude (more frequent at lower altitudes) and the tolerance within which the altitude must be maintained (depends on mission performance requirements). A spacecraft adjusts altitude by firing its thrusters to provide an in-plane ΔV at the appropriate point(s) along the orbit. The ΔV required for altitude maintenance is quite small; for example a 1 km adjustment at 1,000 km altitude requires a ΔV of 0.5 m/s. Orbit raising maneuvers for LEO satellites are typically performed at intervals of a few weeks. For example, Envisat maintains its orbital altitude within tens of meters on a cycle of roughly 15 days to maintain its nominal altitude of 800 km.

Satellites in Sun-synchronous orbit (SSO) need to perform periodic corrections in inclination to maintain the SSO precession rate of the orbital plane, and in longitude of ascending node to maintain the desired mean solar time at the ascending/descending node. This is accomplished by firing thrusters to provide an out-of-plane ΔV at the appropriate point(s) along the orbit. Satellites with repeating ground track orbits (SSO or otherwise) also need to perform maintenance maneuvers to adjust their orbital parameters. For example Envisat maintains its ground track to within 1 km, its mean solar time to within 5 minutes, and makes small corrections to its inclination every few months.

GEO satellites are assigned slots to avoid possible radio interference and to maintain adequate physical separation from neighboring satellites. These slots are distributed along the Equator approximately 2 deg apart in longitude (about 220 km distance), and the associated station-keeping box is ±75 km in each of the three spatial dimensions. GEO satellites experience a resonance effect due to the Earth's non-uniform gravity field, which causes perturbations along the orbital path, resulting in East-West drift. Hence they need to perform phasing adjustments to remain within the along-track boundaries of their station-keeping box. GEO satellites also experience out-of-plane perturbations due to Sun-Moon effects, which cause North-South drift. Hence they need to perform inclination adjustments to remain within the cross-track boundaries of their station-keeping box. See Sec. 9.5.1 for coverage of orbital perturbations experienced by GEO satellites.

19.2.3.2 Moderate Orbit Changes

Moderate orbit changes are sometimes required in response to planned or opportunistic modifications of mission objectives. They typically require a moderate ΔV, and are performed only a few times over the mission life of the spacecraft. Some applications of moderate orbit changes are described below.

A change in mission objectives of a SSO satellite may require a modification of the mean solar time, which in turn requires a change in longitude of ascending node. This can be done by making a small change in altitude which changes the nodal rotation rate caused by Earth oblateness; see Eq. (9-54). After the ascending node has reached the desired longitude, the altitude is changed back to the original value. Another approach is to first determine the two points at which the initial and final orbits intersect. A single burn that applies a ΔV normal to the orbital plane at either of these intersection points provides a change in longitude of ascending node.

GEO satellites are moved into their (original or new) longitude slot with a phasing maneuver. This is typically done by placing the spacecraft in a drift orbit by making a small change in altitude which modifies the along-track velocity. After the spacecraft has drifted to the desired position along the orbital track, the altitude is changed back to the original value. For example, the process of moving a GEO satellite by 1 deg of equatorial longitude (about 110 km distance) over 1 day requires a total ΔV of 5.7 m/s; see Eq. (9-81).

All GEO satellites are required to raise their altitude by ~300 km for end-of-life disposal to a graveyard orbit; this requires a ΔV burn of ~11 m/s which corresponds to roughly 3 months of station-keeping propellant. Some LEO spacecraft are deorbited according to the 25-year disposal rule [NASA, 2009]. The spacecraft performs a deorbit burn that results in an initially slow altitude-decay rate that subsequently becomes faster as atmospheric density increases at lower altitudes. The intent is to complete the deorbit within 25 years after end-of-life, based on a conservative estimate of the solar cycle. From Table 9-21, a spacecraft in a 600 km circular orbit needs to perform a ΔV burn of about 107 m/s to lower its perigee to 216 km so that it will complete its deorbit in approximately 25 years. For more information on spacecraft disposal, see Sec. 9.6.4 and Chap. 30.

19.2.3.3 Major Orbit Changes

Major orbit changes correspond to substantial changes in one or more orbital parameters. They typically require a large ΔV, but are performed very few times (usually just once) over the mission life of the spacecraft.

A common type of major orbital maneuver is a large change in semi-major axis. A Hohmann trajectory provides the minimum-energy transfer between two coplanar circular orbits; see Sec. 9.6.1 for more information. For example, a Hohmann transfer from a 191 km parking orbit to geosynchronous altitude (35,781 km) requires a ΔV of 3.9 km/s with a flight time of 5.26 hours [Vallado, 2007]. In practice, most orbit transfers are relatively close to a Hohmann transfer, although high-energy transfers are sometimes used when transfer time is critical. If the spacecraft design trade-offs do not permit the use of large rocket engines to provide the impulsive (short-duration) burns required for a Hohmann transfer, then low-thrust chemical or electric propulsion systems can be used to achieve orbit transfers over much larger periods of time than a Hohmann transfer. For orbit transfer maneuvers, the propulsive force is applied in the orbital plane. Hohmann transfers require that the thrust be tangential to the orbital path.

Another common type of major orbital maneuver involves a substantial change in orbital plane inclination, e.g., a satellite launched from a high-latitude site that needs to be placed into a low-inclination orbit. A spacecraft changes the inclination of its orbit by firing its thrusters to provide a propulsive force normal to the orbital plane at the ascending or descending node; Eq. (9-78) provides the ΔV relationship for circular orbits. For example, a 10 deg change in inclination requires a ΔV equal to almost 18% of the orbital velocity; at 1,000 km altitude this translates to a ΔV of 1,283 m/s. For an elliptical orbit, the thruster burn should be performed at the node where the satellite has the smaller velocity because this requires a smaller ΔV.

Some maneuvers require a major change in both semi-major axis and inclination, e.g., transfer from an inclined low-altitude parking orbit to GEO. In such cases, performing a combined orbit-raising and inclination-change maneuver requires less ΔV than performing two separate maneuvers. The thrust direction for such combination maneuvers has both in-plane and out-of-plane components. The first burn of the combination maneuver typically provides only a small fraction of the inclination change; most of the velocity vector change is devoted to orbit raising. This burn puts the spacecraft on a highly elliptical geosynchronous transfer orbit (GTO) with inclination slightly less than that of the parking orbit. The GTO perigee is equal to the parking orbit altitude, and the apogee is equal to GEO altitude. The second burn of the combination maneuver occurs at GTO apogee; it provides most of the inclination change and also circularizes the orbit by raising the GTO perigee to GEO altitude.

Occasionally, a major orbit change is made in response to large-scale revisions of mission objectives. For example, after the International Sun/Earth Explorer 3 (ISEE-3) completed its original mission at the Sun-Earth L1 Lagrange point, it was repurposed and renamed the International Cometary Explorer (ICE). Three years later, ICE passed through the tail of Comet Giacobini-Zinner.

19.2.3.4 General Trajectory Changes

The above categories of trajectory change maneuvers involved closed orbital paths. Some other types of trajectories are covered below.

Interplanetary Flight. During long-duration interplanetary missions, some trajectory errors build up over time. To correct such errors in the spacecraft's solar or planetary orbital parameters, a Trajectory Correction Maneuver (TCM) is planned and executed. This adjustment involves computing the direction and magnitude of the velocity vector required to get back on the desired trajectory; this is known as guidance. An appropriate time is determined for making the change. The spacecraft is commanded to rotate to the appropriate attitude and its thrusters are fired for a pre-calculated time interval. TCMs generally involve a ΔV on the order of 1–10 m/s, using control thrusters that provide a thrust force on the order of 10 N. The velocity change magnitude is necessarily small due to the limited amount of propellant mass available on interplanetary spacecraft. Information on interplanetary orbits can be found in Sec. 10.7.

The Cassini spacecraft provides an example of the accuracy achieved in TCM burns. Burn durations were executed within about 0.1% of the planned value, and the pre-burn pointing maneuvers were executed within about 0.4 deg. Over the course of 7 years from launch to arrival at Saturn, the Cassini spacecraft executed only 17 such planned, small-velocity adjustments.

Flybys or gravity-assist trajectories can save much energy (ΔV) in interplanetary flight, albeit at the expense of increased transit time. For example, the MESSENGER spacecraft arrived at Mercury after performing flybys past Earth and Venus. Between flybys, trajectory control was accomplished using 4 monopropellant thrusters (22 N each) and "solar sailing" by rotating the spacecraft and tilting its solar panels to use the very small solar radiation pressure to gradually alter the spacecraft's trajectory. For more information on planetary assist trajectories, see Sec. 9.6.3.

Atmospheric Entry and Descent. This phase of flight begins when the spacecraft enters the atmosphere shortly after a deorbit burn. The subsequent trajectory of the spacecraft is governed by gravitational and aerodynamic forces—there are no propulsive forces. The aerodynamic force acting on the spacecraft can be adjusted by reorienting the vehicle in the atmosphere. Capsule spacecraft (e.g., Apollo and Soyuz) use reaction control system (RCS) jets to perform these attitude-change maneuvers; winged spacecraft (e.g., Space Shuttle) transition from RCS jets to aerodynamic control surfaces at higher dynamic pressures. In both capsule and winged spacecraft, trajectory control is accomplished by changing the vehicle bank angle (orientation of the lift vector relative to the horizontal) to steer the vehicle toward the desired landing/splashdown site.

Using aerodynamic control surfaces on a winged spacecraft provides very precise trajectory control; the Space Shuttle has made over 130 successful landings on different runways. Capsule spacecraft lack the high-precision trajectory control available to winged spacecraft at low altitudes, but they are generally within 10 kilometers horizontal distance from their touch/splash down target at parachute deployment.

Powered Descent and Landing. This is a good option if the atmosphere of the planet/moon is too thin for aerobraking and parachute landing. Trajectory control in the vertical axis can be accomplished by a throttled descent engine that provides the desired descent-rate profile. Trajectory control in the horizontal axes is accomplished by tilting the thrust vector of the descent engine, with an appropriate throttle increase to compensate for the reduction in vertical component of thrust. The thrust vector can be tilted by rolling/pitching the vehicle to the appropriate attitude using RCS jets; this approach was used by the Apollo lunar landers. The Phoenix Mars Lander used a system of multiple descent thrusters for a powered descent from 570 m altitude to touchdown.

19.2.4 Design Considerations

This section presents some general guidelines for the selection of navigation and trajectory control systems during the design cycle of a spacecraft.

A key decision is the choice of autonomous vs. traditional navigation and trajectory control. Another high-level decision is the choice of combined vs. separate systems for attitude and trajectory control. There are pros and cons for each of these options and the final choice depends on the interplay between mission requirements such as performance, reliability, and cost. These choices in turn affect the options available for subsystem selection and design.

19.2.4.1 Navigation Systems

Ground-station tracking performed by the spacecraft operator requires transponder and telemetry equipment on board the spacecraft. Note that this type of navigation data is available only when the spacecraft is visible to the operator's ground tracking station. Even if the tracking stations are geographically distributed, like the SSN or DSN, resource sharing/allocation constraints will limit the update rate of navigation data. It is possible for a satellite operator to acquire navigation data without any on-board equipage by accessing publicly available tracking data from the US Space Surveillance Network. Two-line element sets are available to users at no cost, but they are updated only twice a day and the accuracy of the data will likely be less than that achievable by transponder signals. However, this may be acceptable for some low-cost nanosatellites.

A space-based tracking system such as TDRSS can provide high-accuracy navigation data to the spacecraft operator; this requires a specific type of transponder on board the user spacecraft. With some additional on-board equipage, the TONS system can use TRDSS signals to provide autonomous navigation capability. Another autonomous navigation option for spacecraft in LEO is to install commercially available GPS receivers on board the spacecraft. For interplanetary flight, autonomous navigation is available with optical stellar navigation. Autonomous navigation relative to a celestial body such as an asteroid can be performed using optical landmark navigation. Space-based and autonomous systems can generally provide navigation data at any desired update rate, whereas ground-based systems can provide navigation data only at times when the spacecraft is visible to the ground tracking station(s).

Note that all navigation systems requiring on-board equipment have varying amounts of direct (acquisition) costs as well as indirect costs associated with mass and power usage.

Get More Table 19web-1 provides some data on mass, power, and accuracy for flight-qualified navigation systems.

19.2.4.2 Control Systems

Propulsion options for trajectory control include cold gas, liquid (monopropellant, bipropellant, dual mode, hybrid), and electric; see Chap. 18 for details. Cold gas propulsion systems are inexpensive, low performance systems that are rarely used unless there is an overriding requirement to avoid the hot gases and safety concerns of liquid propulsion systems. A widely used type of propulsion for spacecraft control is monopropellant hydrazine which decomposes explosively when brought into contact with an electrically heated metallic catalyst in the decomposition chamber of a control thruster. Although its efficiency is lower than that of many other options, propulsion using monopropellant hydrazine is popular because of its simplicity and reliability. Some spacecraft produce control thrust using bipropellants: a fuel such as hydrazine and an oxidizer such as nitrogen peroxide. This bipropellant combination is hypergolic and ignites spontaneously upon being mixed in the combustion chamber of a control thruster. The Hayabusa spacecraft used/tested ion propulsion engines during its deep-space mission to the asteroid Ikotawa. Deep Space 1 also demonstrated ion propulsion during its mission.

The size and number of thrusters depend on the ΔV requirements of the various maneuvers that need to be performed over the life of the spacecraft. The total number of control thrusters on a spacecraft can range from a few to as many as 30. Note that in some cases, the same thrusters may be used for attitude (rotational) control as well as trajectory (translational) control. In general, long steady burns are used for trajectory control while short-pulse (~10 ms) firings are used for attitude control.

The spacecraft's flight control computer selects the appropriate control thruster(s) and commands a burn duration by utilizing on-board control laws (autonomous control system) or simply executing commands uplinked from mission control. The thruster burn profile varies widely, depending on the specific parameters of the desired trajectory change maneuver. The flight computer controls thruster burns by sending commands to open/close the appropriate valves that regulate the flow of propellant to the combustion chamber.

Several types of thrusters are available for trajectory control. For example, a small thruster (mass of 0.1 kg) can provide a propulsive force of 0.1 N, while a large thruster (mass of 10 kg) can provide a propulsive force of 3,000 N. Note that limits on payload acceleration may set an upper limit on propulsive forces. The specific impulse of control thrusters typically lies in the range of 200–300 sec.

As an example, orbit control (and backup momentum unloading) on Landsat 7 was provided through a blowdown monopropellant hydrazine control system with 12 jets that each provided 4.4 N of thrust. A single tank contained 122.5 kg of hydrazine, corresponding to roughly 6% of the total spacecraft mass.

Table 18-6 lists flight-qualified thrusters available for trajectory control. Performance, mass, and power data can be found in Table 18-5 (cold gas thrusters) and Table 18-8 (bipropellant thrusters).

References

For annotated bibliography of control systems, see the book website.

Agrawal, B. N. 1986. *Design of Geosynchronous Spacecraft*. Englewood Cliffs, NF: Prentice-Hall, Inc.

Cohen, C. E. 1996. *Global Positioning System: Theory and Applications, Vol. II*, B. Parkinson, J. Spilker, P. Axelrad, and P. Enge (Eds.), American Institute of Aeronautics and Astronautics.

European Space Agency. 2004. "Space Engineering: Control Engineering." ECSS-E-60A. The Netherlands. 14 Sept.

Flatley, T. W., W. Morgenstern, A. Reth, and R. Bauer. 1997. "A B-Dot Controller for the RADARSAT Spacecraft," NASA GSFC Flight Mechanics/Estimation Theory Symposium, Greenbelt, MD.

Gramling, C. J. and A. C. Long. 1995. "Autonomous Navigation Using the TDRSS Onboard Navigation System (TONS)." *Advances in Space Research* 16:(12)77–(12)80.

Hofmann-Wellenhof, B., H. Lictenegger and E. Wasle. 2008. *GNSS: Global Navigation Satellite Systems.* Wein, Austria: Springer-Verral-Wien.

Hughes, P. C. 2004. *Spacecraft Attitude Dynamics*, Mineola, NY: Dover Publications, Inc.

James, L. 2009. "Keeping the Space Environment Safe for Civil and Commercial Users," Statement to the Subcommittee on Space and Aeronautics, House COmmittee on Science and Technology.

Logsdon, T. 1992. *The Navstar Global Positioning System.* New York: Springer.

NASA. 2009. "NASA Technical Standard: Process for Limiting Orbital Debris," NASA–STD–8719.14 (with Change 4). Washington, D.C.: NASA Office of Safety and Mission Assurance.

Podwig, P. 2010. "Early Warning: Russian Strategic Nuclear Forces." Dec. 8. Website.

Teles, J., M. V. Samii, and C.E. Doll. 1995. "Overview of TDRSS." *Advances in Space Research* 16:(12)67–(12)76.

Vallado, D.A. 2007. *Fundamentals of Astrodynamics and Applications* (3rd ed). Hawthorne, CA and New York: Microcosm Press and Springer.

Weeden, B., P. Cefola, and J. Sankaran. 2010. "Global Space Situational Awareness Sensors," *Advanced Maui Optical and Space Surveillance Technologies Conference*, Maui, Hawaii.

Wertz, James R. ed. 1978. *Spacecraft Attitude Determination and Control.* Dordrecht, The Netherlands: D. Reidel Publishing Company.

20 Spacecraft Subsystems III—On-Board Processing

L. Jane Hansen, *HRP Systems, Inc.*

Mission-supporting computer systems include the computers on board the spacecraft, as well as those on the ground, as illustrated in Fig. 20-1. On board the spacecraft, both large computing systems and microcontrollers have become an integral part of the overall system, as well as being part of most spacecraft subsystems. A key feature of on-board flight software (FSW) is the hard, real-time and deterministic nature of the execution. Ground based computer systems are often used to test the on-board systems, prior to launch, and then again, after launch they are used to support daily operations. The post-launch systems are often derived from systems originally used for developing and testing space-based elements.

Computer systems often cross traditional subsystem and organizational boundaries. In previous chapters, we have described some of the spacecraft subsystems that are implemented by specific disciplines, such as sensors and actuators, for *attitude determination and control* (ADCS). While the sensors and actuators, as well as the control law algorithms, are specified by an ADCS specialist, we often include the processing associated with each as part of the on-board processing. This means that in most cases, the task of defining computer system requirements and associated costs takes on a scope that includes many, potentially integrated disciplines. When subsystem functionality is migrated to a centralized processor, the computer system resource estimation process takes on a larger scope than when each functional subsystem contains its own processing element. This is primarily due to the fact that domain experts from different disciplines, with different implementation styles and processes, will be required to integrate their parts of the system into a single processing product. When we create this single product, we must attempt to integrate the development approach and styles of the different organizations by creating a programming standard and style guide. We can achieve some synergy in the final product by developing a standard set of "utilities" such as mathematical functions that can be used by all discipline specific software. In smaller spacecraft, many of the functional software components are co-resident on a limited number of processing elements with limited resources which may require additional management to assure there are no duplications and utilities are properly defined. However, when the management overhead is traded against the potential for each discipline carrying their own computing resources, the weight and power associated with processing is often prohibitive. Thus, when designing spacecraft software it is important that we include both flight software experts and the subsystem domain experts who are familiar with the various disciplines.

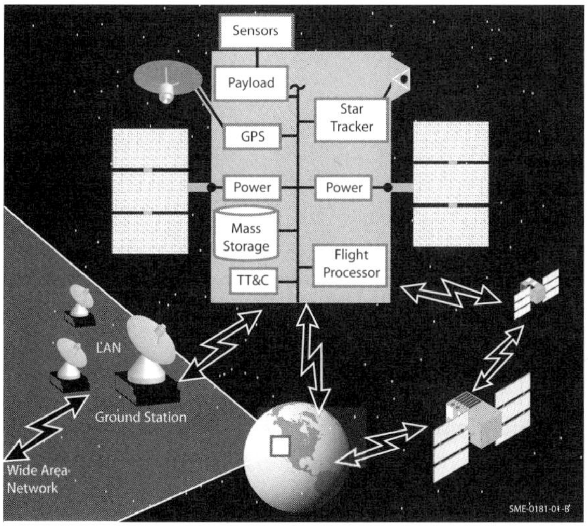

Fig. 20-1. Mission Computer Systems. Notice that there are many interfaces and managing their compatibility is critical to reducing cost and risk. Also, notice that the development tools and environment required to build, integrate, and test the computer hardware and software are included as part of the mission computer system

In this chapter we discuss how to refine the computer system requirements, generate computer system resource estimates, evaluate the implementation effort, and define the tasks associated with developing computer systems on board a spacecraft. Additionally, we will briefly examine the interactions between the on-board computer systems and the ground-based computer

Table 20-1. Computer Systems Development Process. This iterative process defines top-level requirements during a program's concept through development phases.

Define Requirements • Evaluate Mission Objectives for direct implications to computer systems • Evaluate derived requirements from all disciplines to find synergy and define utilities • Develop Top-Level Computer Requirements
Allocate Top-Level Computer Requirements • Evaluate Candidate Architectures and Interfaces • Perform Functional Partitioning • Evaluate Reliability Requirements • Establish System Baseline
Define Computer System Requirements • Define Processing Tasks • Establish Software Size and Timing Requirements • Establish Computer Size, Weight, Power and Throughput Requirements • Identify Target Hardware
Define Development and Deployment Strategy • Identify Operating System and Development Environment • Identify Required Support Tools • Detail a Configuration Control Process • Document Test and Integration Approach • System Deployment and Long-term Support

systems, with an emphasis on deployment through on-orbit operations. In most cases, given a reasonable set of requirements, we can create multiple approaches for implementation that will all meet the mission needs. It is important to understand the prioritization of the mission requirements and the specifics of the flow-down requirements, as well as the often unspoken implementation requirements such as keeping employees involved on the projects or using specific subsystem elements. In this chapter we will discuss how these overlapping requirements influence the baseline computer system design. Finally, we will examine various approaches to modular processing that may be incorporated to facilitate rapid assembly, integration, and test (AI&T) and reduce the timeline associated with early on-orbit checkout.

As outlined in Table 20-1, we discuss the iterative process used to estimate computer resources, based on mission requirements and operational needs, flowed into processing requirements and software development approaches, continuing with deployment and operational constraints. We will also explore alternative approaches and constraints being put on on-board computer systems such as *reusable flight software* (FSW) modules, the use of *plug-and-play* (PnP) technologies, and other modular implementation concepts. We will accomplish this by first discussing the computer system elements and the process of specifying the requirements, we will move on to the task of creating a baseline computer system architecture from top level requirements. Next, we will evaluate the resources required to achieve the baseline system. This includes hardware and software, in addition to development and on-orbit support. We will use the FireSat II example to clarify some of the key components and concepts of the estimation process. In the final section we will address modular approaches to processing which can be used for rapid integration and rapid response missions, to reduce inventory on a constellation or fractionated space system, or as a means of standardizing interfaces to increase the potential market for subsystems functionality. Table 20-2 provides definitions for terms frequently used in estimating computer system resource requirements.

20.1 Computer System Baseline

Chapter 6 discusses the requirements definition process while Chap. 14 discusses the top-level spacecraft design process, identifies key design drivers, and looks at the evolution of the design of the mission lifecycle.

Table 20-2. Definitions Associated with Computer Systems. Often when discussing computer system design and development we use terms which have a specific meaning to those involved in the discipline.

Embedded Systems	A built-in processor or microprocessor, providing real-time control as a component of a larger system, often with no direct user interface.
Real-Time Processing	Handling or processing information at the time events occur or when the information is first created. Typically, embedded or on board processing is real-time.
Hard Real-Time	Requiring precise timing to achieve their results, where missing the time boundary has severe consequences. Examples include attitude control software and telemetry downlink. [Stankovic and Ramamritham, 1988].
Soft Real-Time	Requiring only that the tasks are performed in a timely manner, the consequences of missing a time boundary are often degraded, but continuous, performance. Examples include orbit control software and general status or housekeeping.
Operating System Software	Manages the computer's resources such as input/output devices, memory, and scheduling of application software.
Application Flight Software (FSW)	Mission specific software which does work required by the user or the mission rather than in support of the computer.

Through the design process, we determine system requirements and allocate them to subsystems, identify operational modes for the spacecraft bus and payload, allocate top-level requirements to the computer system (among other spacecraft elements), define the subsystem interfaces in a broad sense, and identify peripheral system requirements. Defining requirements for the computer system begins with these results. Figure 20-2 illustrates that the computer system baseline must include hardware and software, as well as the associated documentation. Documentation is critical to the success of any program, whether it is small or large, short timeline or long, inexpensive or very costly. Documentation often starts at the system level and flows down to the components. We often use different documents for processing hardware and software. Because software is often hard to manage, we create additional management documents, such as the software development plan (SDP) for software configuration items (CI). A list of necessary documentation, by type, is shown in Table 20-3. Not all of the documents listed in Table 20-3 are created for every program.

For a software product the four most important documents, in order of importance are the Software Requirements Document (SRS), the Software Design Document (SDD), the Software Test Plan (STP), and the Software Test Descriptions (STD). In addition, a Software Development Plan (SDP), a Software Standards and Practices (SSP), and an Algorithm Design Document (ADD) are often needed. There are guidelines for developing software documentation in terms of military and NASA standards, data item descriptions (DIDs), as well as templates that are provided by IEEE, AIAA, SAE, and other professional organizations. For smaller, shorter programs we can tailor the documentation to meet the needs of the program. However, when tailoring occurs, it is imperative that documents of different types are not merged together. For example, a requirements document will outline the functional capabilities of the system, without regard to the implementation. A design document will delineate the implementation, providing traceability back to the requirements that generated the need. A design document, such as an Algorithm Design Document (ADD), cannot be included in a requirements specification because this mixes two different types of documentation that have different purposes in the development life-cycle.

For computer hardware, documentation is developed to describe the actual hardware design, including the instruction set architecture (ISA), form factor (size), weight and power. Additionally, because we use the processing hardware to execute the software, we require documentation that describes how the software developer will use the hardware, often defined as a hardware-software Interface Control Document (ICD). This includes information about the number of bits per word and the speed, as well as memory type, access speed, and scrubbing mechanisms (discussed in more detail later in this chapter). Other hardware design features that we need to have documented include the use of specialized processing chips such as digital signal processors (DSPs), the implementation of mathematical functions — those that are supported in hardware versus software (a hardware implementation is faster than those implemented using software), fixed versus floating point processing availability, the number and types of input/output (I/O) lines—digital and analog, power requirements and interface, and available operating system support packages. For computer systems that meet military standards, we consult documentation that describes testing requirements such as MIL-STD-883H

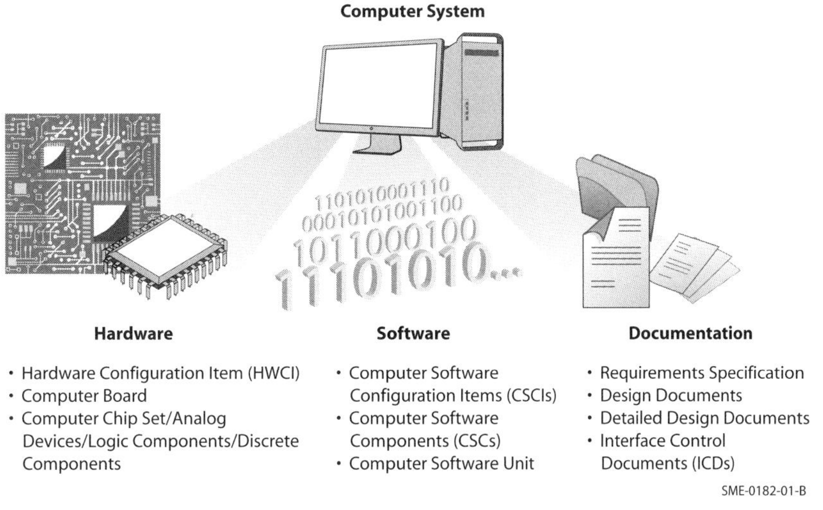

Fig. 20-2. Hierarchy of Elements in a Computer System. Computer systems consist of hardware, software, and their interface definitions. Hardware and software components are in a hierarchy, building to the final configuration item. Documentation provides a mechanism to transfer pertinent information about each element and how they interact. Documentation also has a hierarchy, but it starts with top-level requirements and leads to increased implementation detail.

Table 20-3. Documentation for Computer Systems. Computer systems documentation address all aspects of the software development life-cycle. Documentation may be tailored for specific programs but it is important that tailoring does not combine documentation from different types.

Document	Type	Description
System Segment Specification (SSS)	Requirements	Defines the top level requirements derived from the mission objectives for the spacecraft bus components
Configuration Item (CI) Functional Product Specification (FPS)	Hardware Requirements	Defines the requirements, performance, design, test, manufacture, and acceptance test requirements for hardware elements
Hardware Interface Control Document (ICD)	Requirements	Defines the physical interface requirements for the component
Hardware-Software ICD	Requirements	Defines how the processing hardware is used to implement software
Software Requirements Specification (SRS)	Software Requirements	Defines the requirements for the software flowed down from the SSS and how to meet requirements
Interface Requirements Specification (IRS)	Requirements	Defines the internal and external data interface requirements for the software system
Critical Item Product Fabrication Specification	Program Management	Establish requirements for manufacturing and acceptance of critical end items
Software Development Plan (SDP)	Program Management	Outlines software development policies, standards, and procedures
Software Resource Document (SRD)	Program Management	Describes necessary resources for software development
Software Standards and Practice (SSP)	Program Management	Identifies policy and styles for standardized software development
Hardware Detailed Design Document	Design	Defines hardware design
PCB Layout / Schematic	Design	Details printed circuit board (PCB) layout and design via schematics
Enclosure / Power / Connectors	Design	Defines hardware enclosure, power supply, connectors, and other physical device requirements
Software Design Document (SDD)	Design	Defines software design
Interface Design Document (IDD)	Design	Details Software internal and external interfaces
Algorithms Design Document (ADD)	Design	Provides mathematical description of algorithms to be implemented
Engineering Support Log	Implementation	Documents all aspects of use during hardware development and subsequent laboratory utilization
Unit Development File (UDF)	Implementation	Documents software development process and decisions
Hardware Test Plan	Test	Describes hardware test approach
Hardware Test Procedures	Test	Describes how to perform tests
Hardware Test Report	Test	Documents test results
Software Test Plan (STP)	Test	Describes software test approach
Software Test Procedures	Test	Describes how to perform tests
Software Test Report	Test	Documents test results
Hardware User's Guide	Deployment	Describes how to operate and utilize hardware
Software User's Guide	Deployment	Describes how to install, initialize, and operate software
System User's Guide	Deployment	Describes how to communicate with and operate processing system

Get Stnd [DoD, 2010a] test method standard for microcircuits, or MIL-STD-202G [DoD, 2003] test methods for electronic and electrical parts. Finally, when we develop computer hardware for use in spacecraft applications we also review and comply with the applicable documentation that outlines the required environmental testing (MIL-STD-810G [DoD, 2008] test methods for determining the environmental effects on equipment) and power distribution and loading requirements (MIL-STD-461F [DoD, 2007] requirements for the control of electromagnetic interface characteristics of subsystems and equipment, [AIAA, 2007], Electrical Power Systems for Unmanned Spacecraft Standard).

To arrive at a baseline computer system, we:

1. Allocate mission and system requirements to functional on-board processing components
2. Partition and allocate the computational requirements to space or ground, payload or

spacecraft, individual subsystems, and to hardware or software

3. Define the computer system requirements, detailing the type of processing (e.g., mathematical, database) and associated data storage requirements
4. Develop computer system operational modes and states, based on the computer system requirements
5. Evaluate the internal and external interfaces of the processing system (analyze data flow and throughput requirements), while establishing the candidate architectures and topologies iteratively
6. Select a baseline architecture
7. Form a baseline computer system specification from the architecture, modes and states, and system level requirements and create the appropriate documentation
8. Establish an implementation approach with associated processes
9. Determine a product deployment and operational use strategy

The first six steps are associated with requirements definition and typically occur before the System Requirements Review (SRR). These general activities are discussed in more detail in Sec. 20.1. We usually complete steps 7 through 9 by the Preliminary Design Review (PDR) although iterations on the products from the first six steps are shown again as part of the PDR. These preliminary design activities are discussed in more detail in Sec. 20.2. Revisiting and iterating between steps occurs frequently because requirements are often contradictory or not complete, especially in the early design stages. Requirements can also be unreasonable or too narrow in scope. For example, if we determine that the star tracker must have a specified level of accuracy on its own to meet pointing or mapping requirements, without synergy that might come from other available attitude determination sensors such as Earth sensor or gyro; we might over-specify the star tracker. By using an iterative process, we can refine contradictory computer requirements and question the validity of others. An assumption made for one subsystem to reduce its complexity may increase the complexity and cost for another subsystem dramatically. Often, a compromise solution is needed and can be achieved by using an iterative design process between the various disciplines.

20.1.1 Requirements Definition

When designing computer systems for space applications, we want to optimize the availability, capability, flexibility, and reliability of the system while minimizing cost and risk, yet meeting size, weight, and power constraints. Additionally, the reduction of schedule time, from mission need to space vehicle implementation, may also be important. This leads to the use of the phrase "faster, better, cheaper" and current experience shows that achieving two out of the three will result in the optimal solution. Often achieving one is a lofty goal. Our objective is to meet the system and mission requirements, whether the resulting system is implemented on the ground, in space, or distributed between the two. With the onset of more powerful space qualified computer systems, we can implement more of the requirements in a space-based system which makes the spacecraft more autonomous and often reduces the volume of data that is transmitted to the ground station. Because there is always a desire for more data to be downloaded, we use data compression techniques to reduce the size of the downloaded data. However, the compressed data must be "re-created" on the ground so we need to assure that time critical functions can be completed with minimal delay whether on the spacecraft or on the ground.

As mission objectives evolve, we blend complex hardware and software to meet them and we continue to evaluate the location of their implementation. As we increase complexity in the systems, particularly the space based systems, there is an exponential increase in the associated testing that is required because when we implement requirements in space based assets we must be certain that they have been implemented accurately. In particular, the portion of the on-board system that is responsible for preservation of the spacecraft must be guaranteed to work. Thus, we make the critical implementation as simple as possible and assure that if a failure occurs, the system will fail safe. In general, we strive to keep the on-board processing systems simple, implementing requirements at the lowest level, then building up the capabilities needed to meet evolving mission requirements. Additionally, the size, weight, and power consumption of the on-board assets is often closely scrutinized and thus we must continue to make trade-offs between space based implementations and ground based implementation. It is important that we maintain margin in space-based assets so that we can use the resources to enhance system capability post launch or fix problems that occur on orbit. We often can mitigate problems such as subsystem failures or malfunctions by changing their usage in the flight software implementation. This has some inherent risks and so we must make these enhancements carefully.

The primary design drivers used to measure our success in optimizing the computer system design are shown in Table 20-4. Mission requirements, shown on the left, typically dictate the system-level drivers, shown in the next column. These flow down to the subsystems where we establish driving requirements for computation assets. Finally, logistics support personnel set down the requirements which we feed back against the computer and system level drivers, helping to manage the overall design process. We weigh each of the design drivers based on mission objectives and constraints. Again, this iterative process requires multi-discipline participation and often crosses traditional subsystem and organizational boundaries.

Table 20-4. Design Drivers for Computer Systems. These are factors that we evaluate throughout the design process. When flowing down mission requirements, including system level processing requirements, we must be careful to design hardware and software with the "ilities" in the fourth column in mind.

Mission Requirements	System Level Processing Requirements	Computer Level Requirements	Additional Requirements "ilities"
• Customer Needs • Expected Availability – Weeks – Months – Year or More • Number of Satellites • Number and Location of Ground Stations • Level of Autonomy • Security Requirements • Programmatic Issues – Cost – Schedule – Risk	• Functional Capabilities • Processing Partitioning – Payload vs. Spacecraft – Onboard vs. Ground • Physical Characteristics – Size – Weight – Power – Radiation • Communication Protocol – Commercial Digital Standards – Commercial Analog Standards – Protection / Encryption	• Throughput • Memory • Radiation Hardness • Development Tools • COTS Software availability • Emulator / Engineering Model availability	• Testability • Feasibility • Usability • Reusability • Reliability • Flexibility • Maintainability • Interchangeability • Replaceability

As with all systems and subsystems, poor computer system requirements definition results in an inferior product and erroneous requirements are very expensive to correct. Requirements volatility is often the primary cause of program development failures. Thus, requirements have high leverage, meaning that a small improvement early in the process helps to avoid many problems later. Next, in the process of defining top level requirements, we overlay the mission timeline and mission modes onto the mission needs and requirements. For example, we need to evaluate when the mission must be executed, at what frequency or interval the spacecraft functions are supposed to occur, where, when, and how the mission data will be utilized, and how the system will be deployed. Some of these issues are discussed in Chaps. 3, 4, and 5. It is with all of this information that a mission timeline is developed as described in Sec. 4.2.3 and simplified for illustration in Fig. 20-3. For spacecraft, one key element of the timeline will be the availability of a launch system. Once a potential launch system is identified, we add the launch system requirements (environmental, location, time frame, and data interfaces) into the mix of mission requirements and needs. Flowing mission needs into system and subsystem requirements is difficult, subjective, and time consuming. One approach to doing this is to study a set of questions, such as those shown in Table 20-5, which will motivate needed trade studies and identify areas of negotiation for the overall requirement development process.

20.1.2 Requirements Flow-Down

The requirements that are documented in the System Segment Specification are split between the hardware and software implementation. We document the requirements for software, in terms of processing tasks and system interfaces, in Software Requirements Specifications (SRS) and

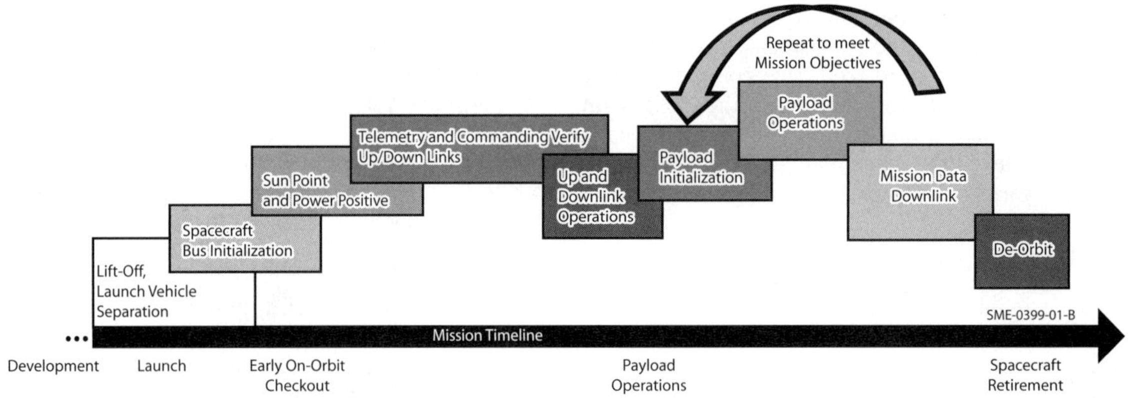

Fig. 20-3. Simplified Mission Timeline. The time phasing of a mission helps to identify top level mission modes which evolve as the requirements definition process matures and all of the on-board processing requirements are established.

Table 20-5. An Approach to System Requirements Definition. General questions which we ask in all aspects of life can be directly applied to computer system requirements derivation by evaluating the specific parameters listed below. (R. Holmes, S. Jacobs, and R. Lane of TRW.)

Questions to Ask	Parameters to Review
What Must The System Do?	Evaluate and establish basic functional requirements.
Why Must It Be Done?	Establish traceability from functions to mission objectives. Be sure to challenge the requirements and assess their validity.
How Can We Achieve it and What are The Alternatives?	Evaluate candidate architectures including network topology, data flow, control flow, and UML diagrams to understand the implications of various approaches on the final design. Investigate emerging technologies and perform trade studies as needed to assure a robust solution. A combination of traditional architectures is an acceptable "hybrid" solution.
What Functions Can We Allocate to Which Parts of the System?	Perform functional partitioning to development block diagrams of ground station and vehicle, as well as spacecraft and payload.
Are all Functions Technically Feasible?	Determine if the value of state-of-the-art technology outweighs the risk. Evaluate the potential use of off-the-shelf hardware and software. Look for data flow bottlenecks and reallocate functions to evenly distribute the data flow. Review baseline block diagrams for potential holes.
Is the System Testable?	Develop nonintrusive test plan and procedures that ensure the system will meet mission objectives. Are test points available outside the system for easy "black-box" testing.

Interface Requirements Specifications (IRS). We define the Computer Software Components (CSCs) and the lower level Computer Software Units (CSUs) which are integrated together to create the Computer Software Configuration Items (CSCIs). We document the hardware requirements in the Hardware Requirements Specification (HRS) and establish the necessary Interface Control Document (ICD) based on the system topology and network specification. The detailed design for hardware includes Printed Circuit Board (PCB) layout, the chips and components that are used to populate the PCB, the power subsystem, I/O transceivers, and the enclosure interconnect structure and form factor. We use traceability analysis to make sure the requirements are complete as depicted in Figure 20-5. We must trace the computer system's requirements to parent requirements, which come from various sources. For example, we may derive computer system requirements from top-level requirements, operational concepts, or launch-vehicle interfaces. We must also trace the flow of requirements to the components to reduce excessive capabilities. Whenever a top-level requirement changes, good traceability allows us to examine the effect of this change on lower-level requirements and how we will meet the new requirements. Often, we re-evaluate a top level change in requirements when we see its effects at the lower level implementation. In any case, traceability allows us to identify all areas where we must evaluate the design to incorporate changes. If we flow the requirements properly during conceptual design, we can accurately run tests at each level during development.

We use the baseline requirements that are generated at the top level, to flow down requirements to specific subsystems and implementations. To define requirements for a computer system, it is convenient to develop a system *state diagram*. The state diagram shows valid states of the system (such as "off" or "initialized") and the conditions required to achieve them, based on mission requirements as they overlay on mission modes via the mission timeline. For each mission mode, such as sun point, safe mode, or navigate, we might want to construct different state diagrams. The computer system states and state transitions must be consistent with the allocated requirements and the mission concept of operation (See Chap. 4). Figure 20-4 is an example of a simple state diagram for a computer system, showing the general states and the source of their transitions. On and off are the obvious first choices for system states. Even when a system must be on at all times, we should consider having an off state to allow graceful degradation if the system were to fail or shut down for some reason. This is where we consider the fail-safe concept discussed earlier. Other states relate to what the system must do and include related state transitions or causes for change of state. For a specific mission and mission requirements we might have several substates in place of one state shown in Fig. 20-5. Or we might not have a state shown in the figure if it's not applicable to our mission. For example, several fail-safe conditions will be associated with the error contingency state shown. However, we may implement the contingency concepts differently for each specific spacecraft based on mission requirements and mission phase.

When developing the state diagram for a spacecraft computer system, we must keep in mind implications for the ground system. Complex state transitions influence ground station software that deals with the spacecraft's limitations and constraints. Other domain experts that help define the spacecraft and the engineers that specify the ground station are also needed to review the spacecraft computer system state diagram to assure that the complexity and risk of the resulting implementation is balanced between the various subsystems or domains, and whether the requirements are implemented on the spacecraft or as part of a ground-based system.

Functional partitioning is a structured methodology which begins with decomposing requirements into their

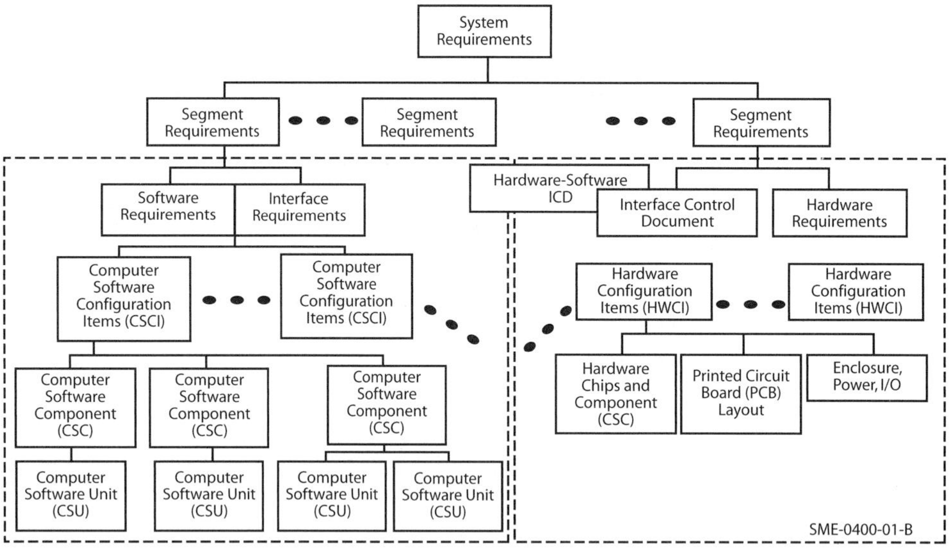

Fig. 20-4. Traceability Analysis Helps Understand How Top Level Changes in Requirements Affect Implementation.

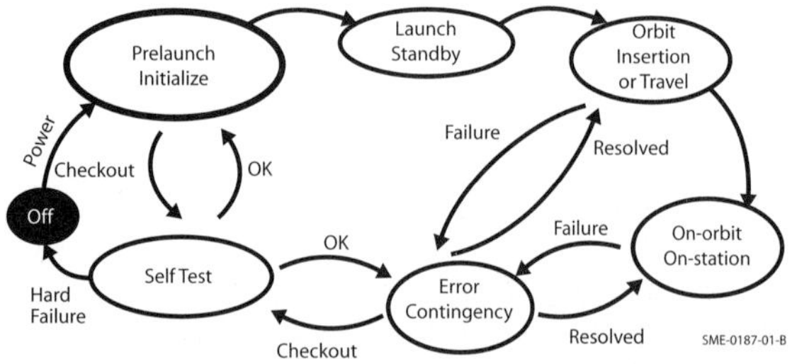

Fig. 20-5. Typical State Transition Diagram for an On-board Computer System. The state diagram shows the valid states of the system and the conditions needed to achieve each state.

lowest functional component and ends in the creation of multiple candidate architectures. This method allows us to group similar functions in subsystem definitions without unnecessary influence from traditional subsystem or organizational boundaries. The processing for a spacecraft system is usually partitioned between various processors in the vehicle and on the ground. The top-level considerations determine where the processing will be performed to meet the system performance requirements (both technical and programmatic) Table 20-6. This allocation of processing or functional partitioning is performed after the major processes have been determined and estimates of the processing timelines, or at least the time dependencies, are available.

If the initial analyses call for on-board processing, we further partition functions between self-contained components, a silicon based implementation, firmware, or software. Self-contained components perform a complete function with the implementation being transparent to the end user. Silicon based implementation includes field programmable gate arrays (FPGAs) where specific functional elements are committed to hardware via a single approach. *Firmware* is the software which resides permanently in non-volatile memory but is not intrinsically part of the computer itself. Silicon implementations and firmware both reduce the susceptibility to upset, but we cannot modify the implementation after launch. Certain elements of the system are clearly hardware: space-qualified computers and processors, the data bus, and so on. Software is often used for state transitions via evaluation of state data, and processing complex mathematical algorithms for attitude and orbit determination and control. Software typically executes out of random access memory (RAM) where read/write functions can occur nearly an infinite number of times. We store data elements that are generated as part of the processing in either Dynamic RAM (DRAM) or Static RAM (SRAM) depending on whether the data is changing frequently or relatively static. DRAM requires periodic refreshing due to the implementation approach while SRAM uses bistable latching circuitry to assure the data is electrically maintained. However, all RAM is only maintained when power is applied, and because RAM is susceptible to single-event upsets (Chap. 7), firmware is often the answer for critical processes such as initialization or contingency operations. Firmware often executes out of read only memory (ROM) or programmable ROM (PROM) where we can write a finite number of times. Direct memory access (DMA) allows access of the memory without utilizing the central processing unit (CPU) which makes reading and writing to memory faster and does not impact other ongoing processing tasks. This is particularly important for command and data handling (C&DH) functions or payloads that produce large quantities of data that need to be stored for upcoming downlink opportunities.

We next evaluate the *Instruction Set Architecture* (ISA). This is the machine code format used by a specific processor, such as the Intel X86 family of processors, 68040, RAD6000, RAD7000, RH3000, and MIL-STD-1750A [DoD, 2010b]. The ISA defines

Table 20-6. Functional Partitioning Requirements for Spacecraft Computer Processing. We partition functions in a general sense using mission timelines as the starting point. We must partition functions to various processors and subsystems so that each element of the system maintains an acceptable level of complexity. A large increase in the complexity of any element will greatly impact our test requirements.

Perform Processing in Space	Perform Processing on Ground
• When processing delays would be intolerable • When data can be fused or reduced to provide a more coherent solution to the ground when downlink bandwidth is limited	• When human interaction with processing is necessary • When the downlink bandwidth from vehicle to ground is satisfactory
Perform Processing in Hardware	**Perform Processing in Software**
• When very high performance is needed • When processing is highly mathematical • When well-defined, inexpensive hardware for the process is available • When a function will be required for multiple vehicles and a cost-effective hardware component can be created	• When processing complexity exceeds that available in hardware • When changes in processing need to be made after hardware is acquired • When expensive, custom hardware can be replaced by software • When there is considerable unused computer capacity
Allocate Processing Between Spacecraft Bus and Payloads	**Do Not Allocate Processing Between Spacecraft Bus and Payloads**
• When payload processing is distinctly different from spacecraft bus processing or developed by completely different organizations • When payload performance accountability is critical	• When payload processing is minimal • When synergy exists between standard bus process and payload processing
Allocate Processing Along Organizational Lines	**Do Not Allocate Processing Along Organizational Lines**
• When there are geographical, contractual, or other impediments to effective inter-organizational communication • When there are standard subsystems and accurate interface control documents which are typically managed within a defined organization	• When the project is small enough that there is a single organization with strong top-down authority • When subsystems are so complex that specific disciplines and experienced organization personnel are required

the software developer's interface to the processor at the lowest level. To evaluate hardware architectures, we examine instruction sets, recognizing advantages and disadvantages of the two basic types: *general-purpose* and *custom ISA*. General purpose ISA's support all kinds of processing but with only moderate performance. They allow us to modify algorithms more easily, but they slow down processing because they are not designed for a specific algorithm. Custom ISAs, such as *Digital Signal Processors* (DSPs) or *Application Specific Integrated Circuits* (ASICs) support specific algorithms or classes of functions very well but often require additional engineering support to optimize the performance of the software functions in the hardware implementation. We can then define our computer systems as a "black box" that we load flight software into, or we can build up our processing capability using single board computers (SBCs) or microcontrollers that are resident in a single enclosure or distributed throughout the spacecraft. For larger spacecraft, with extensive processing requirements and long on-orbit life time requirements, we typically use an integrated flight computer, while smaller spacecraft, such as CubeSats, as well as those with limited lifetime requirements of 5 or less years, we often use stand alone SBCs and microcontrollers.

Additionally, we look at computer system attributes such as error detection and correction (EDAC) mechanisms, network protocol, data up and down link capabilities, to determine if there is a viable hardware implementation or if the feature must be implemented in software. We typically prefer hardware implementations of these lower level capabilities as they operate more efficiently. The term EDAC can include errors in memory due to environmental issues (i.e., Single Event Upsets, or SEUs) or errors in processing due primarily to undiscovered software features. Memory errors often occur at the bit level due to cosmic rays or alpha particle emissions. It is important that we check each memory location periodically for errors which we call *memory scrubbing*. Memory scrubbing is often performed as a background function but should not require more than 5–10% of the overall processing capability at any time. We can find errors in processing using a software error handling utility that understands typical processing errors, such as divide by zero, and performs a work-around to assure that the error does not halt the processing unnecessarily. Finally, we can implement a *watch-dog timer*, in either hardware of software, which causes a hard reset (re-boot) of the computer or other corrective action, if it is not serviced at a predetermined frequency. Thus, if there is an error in processing that causes the software to hang, the watch-dog is not serviced and the system will reset.

20.1.3 Architecture Evaluation

An *architecture* is a framework for developing a system that will guide the development of that system, but at a gross level. We mold the architecture to meet mission requirements and operational needs, creating a baseline system. The architecture shows us the system's parts and how they interact, often through a block diagram. The computer system architecture shows the system structure (topology), the data network and system interactions (data architecture and protocol), the hardware, and software architectures. Architecture studies for computer systems must also address the data, hardware, and software architectures. *Topology* is the form taken by interconnecting the various subsystems and components. *Data architecture* addresses the physical structure of the data network or bus, as well as the protocol or logical interaction across the bus. A *protocol* is a set of rules for sending data between computers, or between computers and peripherals. The *hardware architecture* defines the *instruction set architecture* (ISA) and the functional elements that are available in hardware. Finally, the *software architecture* defines how the processing instructions execute. Software processing can function as a single thread, executing from top to bottom, repetitively, or as scheduled modules, where processing order is based on major and minor frames organized by system states. Alternatively, software processing can be event driven, where interrupt service routines preempt normal execution in a deterministic way when hardware interrupts occur, or as multi-thread where varying functions execute concurrently within a processor.

After partitioning functions, performing trades, creating state diagrams with state transitions, evaluating the data architectures, and analyzing data flow, we can develop a block diagram for our specific computer system implementation. The system *block diagram* illustrates how we implement an architecture, showing types and numbers of processors and networks, including topology and protocol when reasonable. It provides a point of departure for developing more detailed software, hardware, and interface requirements. An initial block diagram, such as the one shown in Fig. 20-6, shows the basic topology of the system indicating the type of subsystems that we might need and the fact that each will interact with the central processor. Figure 20-6 implies a point-to-point connection between each of the subsystems and the central processor.

We next analyze the flow of data to determine how to manage interfaces between components. We want clean, simple interfaces—a data path is inefficient and slows down the flow if it calls for data to pass through a component without being examined or used. We might have the data flow in a circular path, known as a ring configuration, which is shown in Fig. 20-7. We might incorporate a multi-drop data bus, such as the ones shown in Fig. 20-8, with either a dedicated processing resource or distributed processing resources. This data bus topology allows point to point data transmissions across a common network with interconnections to the various components integrated into the bus structure.

Once we have considered various topologies and their applicability to our system requirements, we create a baseline system architecture. The architecture will highlight the topology and the necessary subsystems that we need to meet the system objectives. This block diagram drawing, in conjunction with the state and state transition diagram will provide the foundation for the baseline architecture. As a baseline we typically select a hybrid system architecture, where we combine the positive attributes of several of the topologies while eliminating or reducing the risk associated with the negative attributes. Iteratively, we now evaluate the impact of mission requirements on the baseline computer system. Information regarding the selected orbit, expected period of operation, and any high performance requirements such as large field of view with continuous coverage or tight pointing and mapping criteria will affect the fidelity of the hardware and software needed for the specific mission.

Next we look at specific hardware implementation for the processing resources identified in the system block diagram. Several mission parameters drive the hardware selection. For example, the orbit we select will define the radiation environment. When we increase the required level of fidelity or include a requirement for autonomous operations, we often require a more capable computer

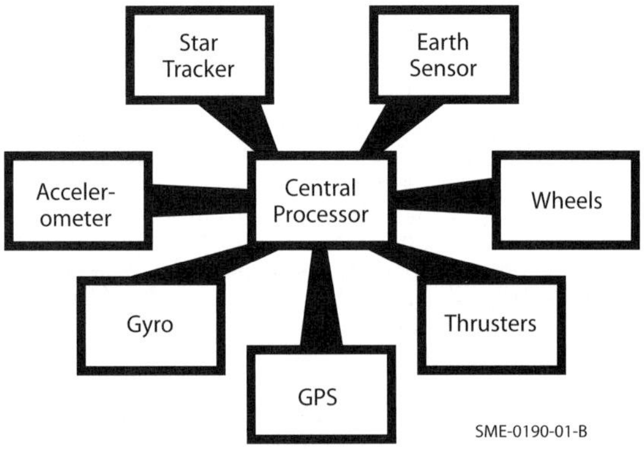

Fig. 20-6. Initial Block Diagram Showing a Centralized Topology. This drawing depicts a *Centralized Topology* which has point-to-point interfaces between processing units and a single management computer, or central node, or hub. This is a highly reliable topology that works best with a few, well-defined subsystems. The negative attributes of the topology include large and distributed wiring harnesses as well as the need for new wiring and interface software if a new component is desired.

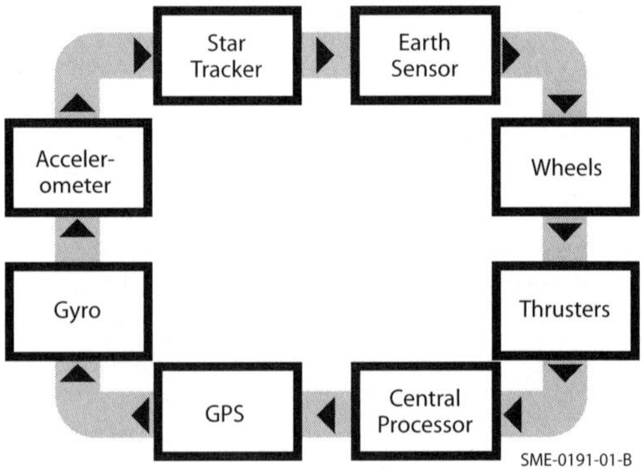

Fig. 20-7. Block Diagram Showing Ring Topology. This drawing depicts a *Ring Topology* which allows data to traverse the ring, providing identical information to multiple nodes. In the configuration the wiring harnesses are relatively small and can be distributed about the spacecraft. However, the negative attributes of the ring topology include the fact that each data transmission is dependent on the previous node to reach its destination.

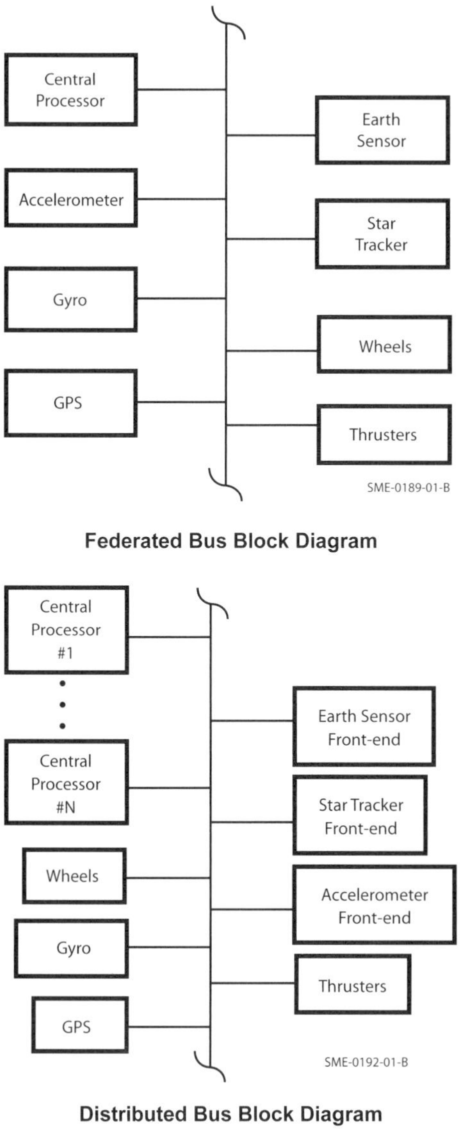

Fig. 20-8. Block Diagram Showing Bus Network Topology. A *federated bus architecture* uses a common data bus with all processors sharing the bus. This encourages the use of standard - protocols and communication schemes for all nodes and results in deterministic message transfer across the network. A *distributed architecture* uses multiple "like" processors to execute all software on an as-needed basis. This results in a highly reliable system that can implement fault tolerance and redundancy with limited impact to physical constraints such as size, weight, and power.

system with additional redundancy. Either of these conditions can develop if we have to perform rapid transitions between differing orbits, or travel to distant targets. These mission requirements may impact software development. More complex requirements lead to more complex software implementation, which requires a more robust design and more test cases to accomplish a desired level of preflight validation. Inadequate requirements definition may cause cost and schedule risk for both hardware and software, as modifications and last minute changes may be required.

When the mission environment is not as demanding or multiple copies of a satellite will perform the same tasks, we can select computer hardware for the mission based on less stringent environmental consideration. Often we can use commercial rather than space-qualified parts. Additionally, as the possibility for achieving unknown states goes down, we may reduce the software complexity and the level of pre-flight testing. As we increase the expected mission life or mission criticality, we should specify the use of more robust hardware, specifically space-qualified components and systems. We also increase the risk that software will operate in a manner that was not predetermined, and thus we should do more thorough pre-flight testing and system validation.

When we impose high performance requirements on the spacecraft computer systems we also increase the performance requirements of both the hardware and the software. High-data rate payloads such as imaging devices or communication subsystems impose the need for higher bandwidth data busses and often increase the processing performance requirements. When we require tight attitude knowledge and control, we not only impose a requirement for increased accuracy on the sensors, we also increase the computational complexity of the software, which in turn affects the processing performance requirements.

20.2 Preliminary Design

During the preliminary design phase of the software development process, we add detail to the baseline architecture by developing the SRS, IRS, STP, and SDP. Using these requirements specifications we estimate the size of the software to be developed as well the processing throughput. From these estimates and an understanding of the overall project, we can select a target computer system for implementation of the embedded flight software. We also establish a software development approach, documented in the SDP, that includes the level of automation and reuse that will be used in the development, the software development environment including cross compiler if necessary, other types of tools that will be utilized, and the build process that will be executed, as well as the product deployment and *concept of operations* (ConOps) that will be employed. The general test philosophy that will be implemented and the type of testing that will be performed are documented in the STP.

20.2.1 Defining Processing Tasks

While establishing requirements for the spacecraft, we define processing tasks by classifying what the spacecraft must do. It is important that we identify all the potential processing tasks early, including adequate margin, to eliminate or accommodate surprises later in the development cycle. Software for on-board processing falls into five principal classes.

Operating system (OS) software directly manages computer resources and controls their allocation to spacecraft and mission tasks. This includes basic executive functions such as scheduling tasks for execution, time management, interrupt handlers, input/output device handlers and managing other peripheral drivers, carrying out diagnostics and built-in tests, and memory fault management. All computer systems must manage these processes. We often consider software for the operating system as overhead to application software.

System management software includes such items as fault detection and correction, long duration event schedulers (such as reconfiguring the power system during eclipses), and payload system management. Software in this class manages control flow and is therefore logic intensive. Simple instruction sets are sufficient for this class because it requires few floating-point computations.

Control system software, such as attitude or orbit determination and control, requires an input stimulus and responds by changing the state of the system. This software is often mathematically intensive—requiring high accuracy and strict timeliness.

Command and data handling (C&DH) software typically collects state of health (SoH) data for downlink to the ground station, is also manipulates and compacts large quantities of data as they are collected and readied for transmission. This function often demands special computer architectures, such as signal processors, as well as large storage capacity for collected data.

Payload management software includes functions such as monitoring the payload status, managing multiple payloads, and interfacing with the payload to mode it and to assure the spacecraft is providing adequate support (i.e., pointing), as well as collecting data, preparing it for downlink to the ground station, and potentially compacting large quantities of data as they are collected. This function may be integrated with the System management software and the C&DH software.

As we refine the list of processing tasks to be developed, we need to decide if we can use existing software components or must develop new ones. When using existing software components it is important to understand its pedigree and have continued contact with the original developer as well as any other organizations or projects that are reusing the component. In general, we want to use established, proven algorithms because new ones involve technical risk, added costs, and a longer implementation schedule. However, if much tailoring is needed to make the algorithm fit to need, it may be better to start fresh so that risk associated with unknown attributes can be avoided. Early emphasis on risk assessment and reduction is part of defining processing tasks.

There are many different types of operating systems that can be implemented for a spacecraft computer system. They are often characterized by proprietary versus non-proprietary, free versus cost, as well as footprint and overhead when compared with the application software modules. When looking for a spacecraft implementation, the most likely candidates are those that have a moderate cost and are highly reliable with a moderate footprint and many associated tools or those that are free, with a small footprint and open source, shareware type tools. These include the operating systems listed in Table 20-7, along with many others that are included in the Wikipedia listing.

Table 20-7. Operating Systems for Spacecraft Computer Processing. When selecting an operating system for a spacecraft application it is important to research the reliability of the product, the footprint or size consumed in memory, the throughput or overhead added to the processing load, and if the product is free or requires licensing as well as the development tools that are associated with the operating system.

For Cost	Supplier	Operating System
	Wind River	VxWorks
	Green Hills	Integrity
	QNX	QNX Posix microkernel OS; usually a real time embedded OS
For Free	**Supplier**	**Operating System**
	GNU (free software foundation)	UNIX based
	Linux	UNIX based
	BSD (Berkley Software Distribution)	UNIX based
	OAR Corporation	RTEMS (real-time executive for Multi-processor systems)

Run-time kernel software normally supports higher-order languages. For example, it may represent, store, optimize, and pack data; drive input or output; handle exceptions or errors; and interact or interface with other programs, other devices, or even other mixed-language programs. The *I/O handler* controls data movement to and from the processor, as well as packing data for any specific interface. Likewise, the *device handler* or device driver software manages interfaces and data between the processor and any peripheral devices.

Utilities are software routines which several functions use. For example, different components of application software in a single processor might access a set of mathematical operations called *math utilities*. Their size and complexity vary directly with the application and its mathematical requirements. If the processor provides such utilities implemented in hardware, they are referred to as *built-in functions* (BIFs), and the hardware specification will often define these functional elements.

Built-in test software provides initial, periodic, or continuous testing for computer elements under the control of software or firmware. Diagnostic software not only identifies faults or failures but also isolates them. We can make it sophisticated enough to recover from some of them. For built-in testing and diagnostics, we can write the software as firmware. The computer vendor

Table 20-8. Software Estimation Process. The *estimation-by-similarity* technique uses existing, well characterized functions and their relationship to functions under development to estimate processor memory and throughput needs for the new functions. The *bottoms-up estimation* process forces the estimator to break the functions into the smallest components, which are then evaluated based on experience.

Step	Notes
1. List all application functions allocated to the given computer.	Document any assumptions.
2. Break down the functions from step 1 into basic elements.	This often requires several iterative steps. We should continue to break down the functions until we have reached the lowest level we can identify. Group functions back into utilities if they are used by multiple states or modes and unique software elements if they are only used in one instance.
3. Define the real-time execution frequency for each of the basic elements.	We only need to perform this step for those functions which are time critical. Execution frequency is not required for utility or background functions.
4. Estimate the source lines of code (SLOC) and memory needed for each function by: A. **Similarity:** Find a function with similar processing characteristics and known size. Compare the complexity of the known function with the new one and adjust the code size directly. Adjust the code estimate for differences in development language, such as assembly versus higher order language. Determine the SLOC from the memory used.	**Similarity**—Requires knowledge of both the existing functions and the new functions in terms of specific requirements, complexity, and general implementation. Some rules of thumb are: • A 25% increase in complexity implies a 25% increase in code • If the known function is in assembly code, increase the code size by 25% for a higher order language. • If the known function is in a higher order language, decrease the code size by 20% for assembly code.
B. **Bottoms-Up:** Identify the SLOC for executable elements of the lowest level functions as well as the data structures and one time only initialization software. Sum the SLOC for all executable and nonexecutable functions separately. Determine the memory requirements, based on SLOC.	**Bottoms-Up**—Requires knowledge of general elements of each function and how to implement the capability.
5. Estimate throughput requirements based on: A. **Similarity:** Find a function with similar processing characteristics and known throughput requirements. Compare the complexity of the known function with the new one and adjust the throughput value for differences in complexity directly. Based on the frequency of execution from step 3 above, compute the total throughput requirements for the new function.	Throughput should be expressed as instructions per second.
B. **Bottoms-Up:** Based on an average number of computer instructions executed per SLOC for a specific compiler and processor, multiply the number of instructions by the execution frequency. Define a "loop factor" for executable SLOC to represent internal loops within the function.	The internal loop factor for an ACS function associated with a three axis stabilized spacecraft will be 3—each function will be repeated for each axis. In order to estimate throughput from SLOC, the lines of code related to initialization and data must be separated from the executable lines of code. The loop factor is applied only to the executable SLOC.
6. Determine the operating system and overhead requirements by similarity to other implementations. Compare the complexity of the known operating system and overhead functions to the new and adjust accordingly.	You must identify all application code prior to this step. Complexity for operating system functions is based on number of tasks scheduled per second, the number of interrupts to be handled, and the amount of I/O data.
7. Determine the margins for growth and on-orbit spare based on where you are in the development cycle and Fig. 20–10 that outlines the margin at each milestone.	Growth and spare requirements are important and should be strictly calculated.

may even supply them. If not, we would have to decide whether we need this added reliability, despite the processing and cost overhead.

We measure software size by words of memory, and processing time by *throughput*, usually expressed in thousands or millions of instructions per second (*KIPS* or *MIPS*, respectively). We estimate the size and throughput of on-board software for several reasons. When we begin defining a computer system, we use the software estimates in conjunction with requirements for spare processing to determine how much computing power we need to perform the mission. During system development, we revise the estimates to make sure hardware capacity is not exceeded. We can also use software size estimates to estimate cost.

Processor throughput is a function of the instruction set and the clock speed. With only one instruction, a computer's throughput is proportional to clock speed. If it has two instructions, one (A) requiring two clock cycles and the other (B) requiring seven cycles, the computer's throughput also depends on the instruction mix. The *instruction mix* is the proportion in which the software uses the instructions. For example, if the software is 60% type A instructions and 40% type B, the throughput available with a 10 MHz clock is $(10/[(0.6 \times 2) + (0.4 \times 7)])$ = 2.5 MIPS. If the mix is reversed, the throughput available is 2.0 MIPS. Table 20-8 shows the basic steps used to estimate the software processing throughput. Both an estimation based on similarity and a bottoms-up evaluation of each element will yield a potential throughput estimate. These two approaches are often used as they bound the problem, with the similarity technique leading to a smaller throughput estimate than the bottoms-up approach.

System Requirements Review is the milestone when we formally identify computer resource requirements. A good rule of thumb is to set the amount of computer memory and throughput at the System Requirements Review at four times the estimate of what has been estimated to date for software size and throughput. Empirically, initial software size and throughput estimates double from this review to launch because early requirements are uncertain, and changes in software are easier to make than changes in hardware during late stages of spacecraft development. We also want spare memory and throughput at launch to correct anomalies or to increase performance after system calibration. Thus, we need to establish reserve capacity when initially defining requirements. A reasonable value for post-launch reserve is 100% spare (equivalent to 50% of machine capacity).

Most on-board flight software is executed under a *real-time operating system (RTOS)* which provides the timing and system services for the processing resource. The size and functionality of the RTOS should be tailored for each mission, based on mission needs. The RTOS software is typically quite small (<1K SLOCs) and is not included in the estimate of source lines of code (SLOCs) for costing purposes. This is primarily because we typically purchase the RTOS and then tailor the run-time version of the software based on the system services used by the specific software implementation. RTOS procurement usually includes the tools needed to create the embedded flight software and there is often a small fee ($100–$1,000) for each time the RTOS is embedded in a processor and flown. Table 20-9 lists general categories of application software and estimates for size and execution frequency. In some cases, the actual code size may not be significant, however, the size of the storage required may be more extensive. For example, with command processing, each of the potential ground commands must be stored with the associated command sequence for execution. In general, typical spacecraft of moderate size (~450 kg) will contain less than 100K SLOC in total. Not only do the number of SLOCs drive the cost but the amount and type of testing that we require is based on the SLOCs as well. The more complex we make the vehicle processing, the more we must test to be sure all possible paths within the software have been tested and the software not only does what we require, but also does not do anything that is undesirable.

An *Executive* is often used to manage states and state transitions, which are developed based on the mission timeline and the state diagram and make the embedded flight software custom for the specific mission. This software is usually quite concise and often tailored from a previous version of state machine software. This element

Table 20-9. Estimating Source Lines of Code (SLOC) for Typical Spacecraft Functions. These are SLOCs for typical spacecraft functions with nominal performance. As performance requirements increase, the complexity of processing often increases as well which ultimately leads to an increase in the SLOC estimates. NtH= Nice to Have

Computer Software Component (CSC)	Source Lines of Code (SLOC)	FireSat II
Executive	1,000	Req.
Communication		
Command Processing	1,000	Req.
Telemetry Processing (standard)	1,000	Req.
Telemetry Processing (with compression)	3,500	
Attitude / Orbit Sensor Processing		
Rate Gyro	800	Req.
Sun Sensor	500	NtH
Earth Sensor	1,200	
Magnetometer	200	Req.
Star Tracker (without star id)	400	
Star Tracker (output quaternion)	2,000	Req.
GPS (output position/velocity)	300	Req.
GPS (output with pseudo ranges)	2,500	
Attitude Determination and Control		
Kinematic Integration	2,000	Req.
Kalman Filter	6,000–10,000	
Error Determination	800	
Precession Control	3,500	
Ephemeris Propagation	2,000	Req.
Complex ephemeris	4,000	
Orbit Propagation (linear models)	3,000	
Orbit Propagation (complex environment)	8,500	Req.
Attitude Actuator Processing		
Magnetic Control (torque)	600	Req.
Thruster Control	600–1,200 (catalyst bed)	Req.
Reaction Wheel Control	1,200	Req.
CMG Control	1,500	
Fault Detection		
Monitor	4,000	Req.
Fault Identification	2,500	Req.
Fault Correction	5,000	
Utilities		
Basic mathematics	800	Req.
Transcendental mathematics	1,500	Req.
Matrix mathematics	1,200–2,300	Req.
Time Management and conversion	700	Req.
Coordinate conversion	1,500–3,500	Req.
Other Functions		
Momentum Management	3,000	Req.
Power Management	1,200	Req.
Thermal Control	800	Req.

of the FSW will not be a cost driver for the software development effort, but will add the structure needed to make testing more straight forward.

Communications software includes processing external commands and collecting internal data for transmission to an external source. The information in Table 20-9 assumes a modest number of ground commands (~100) and collection of data for telemetry to the ground. It does not include inter-processor commanding, but we can allow for this commanding by similarity of function. The actual code used to de-commutate commands is relatively straight forward but as the number of commands increases, the storage space required to maintain the command lists and associated command sequences will increase. Similarly, to pack information into digital data packets for distribution in the telemetry stream is a relatively small function. However, if extensive compression is used or if decisions are being made on-board the vehicle based on the data that is collected, then the processing complexity will increase and thus the SLOCs and the associated cost will increase as well.

Attitude-sensor software handles data from various sensors, compensates for sensor misalignments and biases, and transforms data from sensor to spacecraft body coordinates. Processing for gyros, accelerometers, Sun and Earth sensors, and magnetometers involves decoding and calibrating sensed data. Processing for star trackers involves identifying stars against a star catalog, which can require extensive data and memory resources. It is also possible that the star tracker will provide an attitude quaternion as the output which greatly reduces the I/O handling and associated processing but makes fault tolerance when the star tracker fails potentially more cumbersome.

The *Attitude Determination and Control* category covers various control methods that make use of the data processed by the attitude sensor software. In *kinematic integration*, we estimate current attitude by integrating sensed body rates using gyros. Using *error determination*, we find how far the spacecraft's orientation is from that desired. For spin-stabilized spacecraft, we maintain attitude control using precession control. The precession-control size and throughput numbers reflect those of a thruster-based system and account for the processing that determines how much torque is needed on the vehicle to achieve the desired attitude. The thruster control function listed in the table is for a 3-axis stabilized control system using thrusters. This element of the software is responsible for assigning the specific thrust to each thruster, based on the mounting location of the thruster and the total vehicle torque that is desired. Table 20-9 also lists control algorithms using reaction wheels, control moment gyros, and magnetic torquers. Also in this category are object ephemerides, which we can maintain using crude table look-ups and curve fits, or very complex algorithms with increasingly complex environmental models. The orbit propagator integrates the spacecraft's position and velocity information.

Fault detection is closely tied with autonomy. Monitors exist to identify failures or adverse conditions in on-board equipment and we typically down-link these failures to the ground for diagnosis and commanding. Size and throughput vary widely depending on the system. Processing for corrective actions usually depends on tables of pre-stored procedures and, therefore, requires considerable data but not many actual lines of code. The more autonomous the fault detection becomes, the more complex and thus larger the embedded flight software becomes.

Momentum management monitors the reaction wheels looking for saturation and then unloads or shed momentum using magnetic torquers or other non-saturating mechanisms for attitude control. *Power management* and *thermal control* are support functions that often reside in on-board computers. Through power management, the computer controls battery charge and discharge and monitors the power bus. Active thermal control involves monitoring and controlling temperatures throughout the spacecraft.

We should not attempt to use all of the available memory or throughput. Asynchronous processing, such as interrupt handlers, introduces a level of uncertainty in throughput. Costs also rise dramatically as we shoe-horn the software into existing memory [Boehm, 1981]. As a rule of thumb, we should use 70% or less of available throughput. After System Requirements Review, we continuously update estimates for software size and throughput as requirements solidify. We plot them as *reaction curves* to ensure we can detect whether the software is growing too much. Figure 20-9 shows a typical reaction curve for software development, measured as a percentage of maximum use. As long as the estimates fall below the curve, no extraordinary action is required. When they exceed it, we must pare down the requirements, relax the restriction on reserve capacity, or increase the resources available.

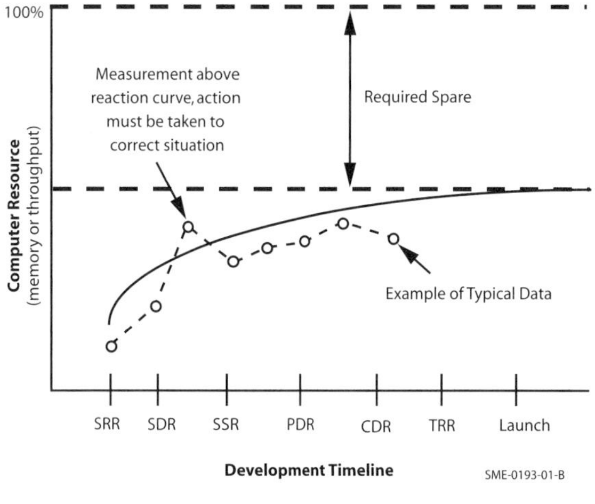

Fig. 20-9. Reaction Curve for Using Computer Resources. Reaction curves mitigate risk. They discipline our management of onboard computer resources. Whenever an estimate exceeds the reaction curve, we correct the situation.

20.2.2 Computer Selection Guidelines

After examining what the computer system must do, based on the software requirements, we assess the size and throughput requirements for the software. Based on this initial sizing estimate, we can determine our hardware resource requirements. We must find a computer system which meets all of our basic needs, as well as the spare allocation, and has the required support environment. Each computer considered must have suitable system software (operating system or kernel and built-in functions such as mathematics). Additionally, we must determine if radiation susceptibility is an issue for our mission. This is based on the mission life-time and the orbit selected for the mission. In almost all cases, processors should be purchased rather than developed to avoid paying the nonrecurring development costs, and incurring schedule risks. The alternative to purchasing a black box processor includes the integration of a single board computer (SBC) with other computer boards to create a custom processor box, or developing a custom microcontroller from Commercial off-the-shelf (COTS) parts such as an FPGA and various soft core ISA implementations.

Hardware processing architectures for spacecraft on-board processing have followed the commercial market, albeit with slower general acceptance due to the space-based environment. As commercial processing resources improve exponentially, so do space-based processing resources. While resources continue to increase, the basic functional elements of a typical spacecraft have remained relatively stagnant. Thus, we find that on-board processing resources are usually more than sufficient for baseline processing tasks. However, as the processing resources become more capable, we find ways to continue to enhance our processing performance by making the error checking more intricate or incorporating higher fidelity models on-board the vehicle. When pairing on-board processing resources with on-board processing requirements, it is important to have a quantitative mechanism for evaluating performance. We evaluate hardware architectures to determine their ability to meet our processing needs. We use a *benchmark program* that contains a specified instruction mix so that various computers can be compared to a standard measure of performance. Typical benchmarks used for evaluating computer resources in space applications are shown in Table 20-10.

Table 20-10. Benchmark Programs Used to Evaluate Computer Performance. Listed below is a set of traditional benchmark programs highlighting their strength in measuring the performance of a computer system.

Benchmark	Measures
Dhrystone	A test designed primarily to measure a CPU's integer performance. An outcome of the Dhrystone test is the MIPS rating.
Khornerstone	A suite of 21 tests developed in 1987 by SRS/Workstation Laboratories to measure the overall performance of a computer's CPU, floating-point capabilities, and disk I/O.
Linpack	This test measures a CPU's floating-point performance. Results reported in mflops (millions of floating point ops per sec).
MIPS	Millions of instructions per second. Refers to a CPU's ability to process integer operations.
Whetstone	This test, written in Fortran in the late 1960s at the National Physical Lab in Whetstone, England, measures floating-point performance. An optimized compiler can improve Whetstone performance, thus making the test somewhat misleading.

When we select a benchmark it is important that we use one that has a similar instruction mix to the one we expect in our operational flight software. For example, if our flight software will be mathematically intensive we could use Khornerstone, Linpack, or Whetstone. However, if our flight software focuses on integer math, the Dhrystone benchmark is a good match. Additionally, when we are evaluating the type of mathematics that will be performed by the on-board processor, we should also consider the type of functions the processor is to support. If the processor will be performing significant commutation or multiplexing at the bit level (I/O handling and manipulation) we should find a suitable hardware ISA that supports this type of processing. If the primary purpose of the on-board processor will be to perform command and data handling (C&DH), we should consider a processor that supports bulk data moves such as *Direct Memory Access (DMA)* command or a block move command. This allows the hardware to traverse the data, moving larger portions of data without software intervention.

In many cases, the processor performance for any candidate hardware component will far exceed the requirements for traditional spacecraft processing needs or the processing required for a single processor is so diverse that focusing on point solutions such as DMA is not suitable. Often in the case of smaller spacecraft, we even consider incorporating payload management as well as payload data processing, refinement, and/or compression functions into a single on-board processor. In this case, the trade off is to reduce size, weight and power (SWaP) by using a single, multi-purpose processor, rather than optimizing multiple processors' performance for various aspects of the spacecraft functionality.

If we determine that several hardware solutions can meet the performance needs we outlined in the software resource estimation process, a computer's heritage can be a major selection criterion. We often select a computer previously used in space by NASA, ESA, the DoD, or a major commercial space venture if we are supporting a long-life, high radiation environment, or national security mission. By starting with computers which have prior use in space, the major development, qualification testing, and documentation risks and costs will have been borne by the prior programs. However, while older space computers are often highly reliable, they are typically more expensive and less capable. Thus, if the mission has a reduced life-time (less than 3 to 5 years), will be in a low-earth orbit (LEO), and can be quickly and easily replaced if failed, COTS processors and SBC integrated boxes are often the better solution.

Table 20-11. COTS Processors Used with Either ADCS and C&DH Functional Focus. Listed below are several COTS processors and their associated mission, along with the focus of the embedded flight software and rate of execution for the ADCS which is typically the driving factor in terms of execution speed.

Year	Mission	Processor	ADCS Rate	% ADCS	% C&DH
1995	SWAS/ WIRE	386/387 @16Mhz	10 Hz	23%	55%
2000	Triana	Rad6000 @20 Mhz	10 Hz	28%	63%
2007	LRO	Rad750 @132 Mhz	5 Hz	1.7%	48%

Building an operational system depends on the development philosophy and environment we select. Procuring COTS hardware and software is the easiest way we can build a capability. Table 20-11 shows several COTS processors that were used in real missions along with the focus of the embedded flight software, either ADCS or C&DH. However, off-the-shelf items often don't meet our needs exactly. Thus, we must tailor the COTS products or adjust the need to match what is available. The break-even point is different for each program depending on the number and types of requirements, individual skills, our knowledge of the product, and whether the COTS products are maintainable and of high quality. If we opt for custom development, we must also consider the development and test tools we will need to create the operational unit. We may need special hardware, software, or integrated systems. For single-unit or unique systems, developing support tools can cost as much as developing the operational units. We must evaluate these support tools during conceptual design, and include their cost in the overall development cost. As with the cost of other developmental tools, we may be able to amortize these costs over multiple products or projects.

20.2.3 Software Development

Many issues associated with the development cycle affect conceptual design and long-term life-cycle cost. For example, we select hardware and software design concepts during requirements definition but we draw on implementation and development experience to do so. Because we often have to cost activities for developing a computer system before a complete design is available, we must take into account the many aspects of software and hardware development, testing, and integration. Software-based tools and standards such as MIL-STDs, IEEE and SAE Specification Guide, and ANSI or ISO standards help us structure our methods and give us more management and technical controls. The Software Engineering Institute (SEI) as well as the International Standards organization (ISO) have established a rating system for the software development process. Companies can apply to SEI for increasing levels of performance ratings and can become certified with ISO as being ISO compliant. The SEI also supports Capability Maturity Model Integration (CMMI) as process improvement approach that increases an organizations performance. According to the Software Engineering Institute, CMMI helps "integrate traditionally separate organizational functions, set process improvement goals and priorities, provide guidance for quality processes, and provide a point reference for appraising current processes."

In addition to the development process, long-term issues, such as life-cycle costs, require attention during conceptual design. The complete life-cycle costs include conceptual design, detailed design, implementation, system integration, test, and on orbit maintenance as well as the tools associated with each life-cycle phase. There are many software development life-cycle models we can use. However, the key for developing costs estimates for software development is to ensure that life-cycle issues such as launch and early check-out, on-orbit maintenance, and potential development, test, and uploading of new software components are taken into account.

Additionally, we must consider the availability of tools, their maturity and availability, based on the processing and processors selected. This includes such tools as cross-compilers, linkers, assemblers, and the host processors on which they reside. A *host machine* is the computer where the development activity is to take place. The *target machine* is the embedded microprocessor or ground-based computer where the code will perform throughout its lifetime. A *cross-compiler* executes on the host, compiling software for the target processor. For both assembly language and higher order languages, the loaders and debuggers allow us to store software in the target processor and evaluate its performance based on either symbolic or physical information. Sometimes the host computer and the target computer have the same ISA. In this case the compiler is not the issue but library and other functions' availability on the target should be explored. Table 20-12 summarizes the various life-cycle issues which we must address during the early phases of program development.

Modeling tools are another set of tools that need to be evaluated and considered as we create spacecraft on-board processing system. The *unified modeling language* (UML) for software intensive programs is used to specify, visualize, modify, construct and document the artifacts of an object-oriented software-intensive system under development while the system modeling language (SysML) is a general-purpose modeling language for systems engineering applications. It supports the specification, analysis, design, verification and validation of a broad range of systems and systems-of-systems. UML and SysML are implemented in many tools to combine techniques for architecting software and systems in terms of stakeholder use cases and requirements to diagram functional, performance, and interface requirements. Additionally, the tools provide a standardized mechanism for us to visualize the system implementation and maintain traceability to the requirements.

Table 20-12. Summary of Life-Cycle Cost Issues. Through the use of development and protocol standards, auto-code generation, and re-use of common software and hardware modules, as well as increasingly capable development tools we create a means of controlling and streamlining the costs associated with computer system development [Boehm, 1989].

	Standards	Automation and Re-Use	Development Tools
Example	• DoD Standards • IEEE Standards • ANSI Standards • AIAA Standards • SAE Standards • ISO Standards • MIL-Specification • Data Item Description (DID) • Structured Development • Object Oriented Development	• Commercial Off-the Shelf (COTS) Software • Computer Aided Software Engineering (CASE) • Automated Code Generation	• Compiler, Assembler, and Linker • Cross Compiler • Loader and Debugger • Code Analyzers and Optimizers • Test Case Generator • Code Management Software • Simulators and Emulators
Benefits	• Adds structure to development activities • Standardizes documentation between and among programs	• Reduces development time which implies lower costs	• Allows for more generic software to be developed and then compiled specifically for target hardware • Aids in configuration management • Simulation and emulation increase testing efficiency effectiveness
Notes	• Tailoring is critical • Must balance required amount of documentation with associated costs	• Documentation must accurately reflect the implementation • MUST continue to test at the same level for all sources of software	• Be sure that a development environment is available for the hardware selected for the project

Many of the major aerospace organizations participated in developing the SysML standard including Northrop Grumman Corporation, Lockheed Martin Corporation, The Boeing Company, NASA, BAE Systems, Thales, EADS Astrium GmbH, and the Israel Aircraft Industries. Additionally, component manufacturers such as Raytheon Corporation, IBM, and Motorola, software development support suppliers such as Gentleware AG, Pivot Point Technology Company, Telelogic AB, Artisan Software Tools, Ceira Technologies, Deere & Company, EmbeddedPlus Engineering, Eurostep Group AB, I-Logix Inc, and oose.de Dienstleistungen für innovative Informatik GmbH participated in the standardization of SysML. Finally, organizations such as the Georgia Institute of Technology and INCOSE (International Council on Systems Engineering) participated in the standards process. Several tools are COTS products that support the UML/SysML visualization for the requirements and development process. These are shown in Table 20-13.

It is important that we manage the software development activities throughout the program life cycle. There are many tools that help in this effort. The UML and SysML tools described above, as well as compilers and debuggers associated with a particular software development environment can be licensed for the equivalent of several full-time equivalent (FTE) software engineers. However, there are also tools available for free that provide some aspects of the more expensive licensed tools. An important part of planning for a software development project is determining which tools will be needed to improve development efficiency and provide continued traceability between requirements and implementation.

Table 20-13. UML Based Software Development Tools. UML based design and CASE (computer aided software engineering) tools are designed to aid in the software development process by reducing the complexity of dynamic systems through the use of visualization and modeling schemas.

Supplier	Tool Name
Atego (Merger of Artisan Software and Aonix)	Artisan Studio
Visual Paradigm	Simulacian
Telelogic (owned by IBM)	TAU Generation 2 Rhapsody (rational rose, doors)
Embedded Plus	Sys. Modeling and Sim Toolkit
Microsoft	Visio
Sparx	Enterprise Architect

Finally, the use of configuration management tools allows us to maintain control of code revisions, providing traceability between major and minor software releases, as well as assuring that various software releases can be recreated. Again, we can license configuration management tools, or there are tools available that provide the basic capabilities for free. A critical aspect of software development is that we maintain management control throughout the life-cycle of the product.

20.2.4 Integration and Test

As Fig. 20-10 shows, testing usually begins at the lowest level and builds incrementally. By building our test scenarios from the bottom up, we can reduce the complexity and thus the risk. Testing must be rigorous at all stages from the unit level to the system level [Kaner et al., 1999]. Software and hardware testing follow the same general path, with the subsystem resulting when we integrate the hardware and software. At this level, we test the entire computer system. We perform path testing, functional testing, and performance testing. We must document each test thoroughly using test procedures that trace back to the original test plan, and thus the requirements, and outputting a test report that notes the details of the test execution. The test report can become crucial to identifying anomalous behavior prior to launch or on-orbit. It is more important that we document behavior, even if off-nominal, than that we justify why test outcomes are acceptable.

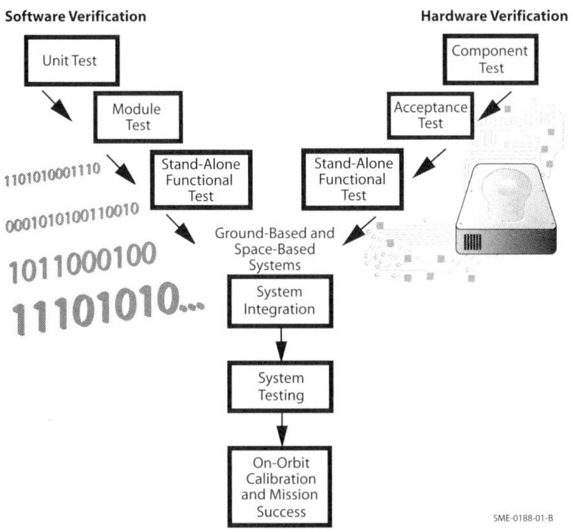

Fig. 20-10. Levels of Testing. Testing builds incrementally as the product develops from component to system. It begins at the lowest level building up into system and mission requirements verification as the elements are integrated.

Finally, we test the whole spacecraft, both in terms of functional performance through "day-in-the-life" test scenarios, and through environmental testing such as thermal, vacuum, and vibration testing. Unfortunately, we cannot completely determine whether the processing system performs properly until it is in orbit. Once operational, the system needs general testing to ensure it continues to perform as required following launch and environmental exposure. Just as acceptance test procedures or inspections check systems for damage on delivery, retesting on-orbit checks for damage during launch. This testing is often referred to as *on-orbit check-out and calibration.*

In general, integration and test pulls disciplines and subsystems into a configuration that meets top-level, system requirements. In this sense, integration and test is much the same as systems engineering. System testing includes all activities that increase confidence in the system's performance. It ensures that we have met requirements and that anything happening beyond these requirements does no harm to the system, while preserving specified functions. Testing for these "extras" is the most difficult because we do not always know what we are looking for. Testing, especially for the software-intensive computer resources associated with space systems, is a complex undertaking. It can consume up to half of the development cost and a significant percentage of support costs over the life-cycle.

20.3 FireSat II Example

Using the FireSat II example from the previous chapters, we will examine the actual flow down process from mission requirements to derived requirements for on-board processing. We will also develop a baseline architecture for a possible on-board processing or avionics implementation to meet the requirements and walk through the software sizing and processor selection process. Subsystem requirements that will directly impact the on-board processing as well as those that will be affected by the on-board processing implementation will be discussed. It is important to note that with the traditional subsystems so highly integrated in this digital processing implementation, we must coordinate and iterate on-board processing requirements with those generated by other subsystems (such as attitude determination and control systems (ADCS), telemetry, tracking, and command (TT&C), and power/thermal management) to assure that all derived requirements are met at each level of design.

We will use Table 20-1 Computer Systems Development Process as the roadmap for performing the FireSat II example. First, we define requirements. These requirements are based on mission objectives and their direct implication to computer systems. We evaluate derived requirements from other system areas to determine if they will impact the on-board processing requirements. Specifically, when we determine processing specific requirements from mission level objectives, we partition the information we have into traditional subsystem requirements as outlined in Table 20-14.

For the FireSat II example, we begin with Table 3-5, finding all of the requirements that may affect on-board processing. Table 20-15 shows the requirements that we identified as discussed in other chapters, but, where the outcome of decisions made will affect the on-board processing; however, as was stated before, it is imperative that we work other disciplines.

Next, we define the top-level computer or on-board processing requirements. All launch and early operations will be handled by the launch vehicle provider. As the spacecraft on-board processing component, including the telemetry tracking and command (TT&C) we will provide a fixed set of go/no-go functional tests and results to be used on the launch pad and at power up following launch vehicle separation.

This step also includes functional partitioning of requirements to implementation and the development of a candidate architecture and the associated interfaces. Because of the number of requirements that can be

Table 20-14. Flow Down of Mission Objectives into Potential On-board Processing Requirements.

System Attribute	Typical Trade Space	Baseline System Implications
System Timing	Event or data driven system versus a systematic scheduled data delivery system.	Usually payload centric processing is event of data driven and maintenance of the spacecraft functions are then secondary.
Asset Preservation	Hard Real-time data delivery and network determination versus Dependable Performance in terms of fault detection and system safe mode protection.	A hard real-time system typically focuses on performance of the ADCS to achieve performance while an expensive asset that must be maintained might allow for data to be less precise.
Communications	Type of ground contact, often based on orbit (i.e., LEO implies infrequent contact while GEO implies continuous contact) or amount of data to be stored, compressed, parsed, and forwarded.	These elements will drive the on-board storage and antenna design. It is often very difficult to download a lot of raw data in LEO with limited ground contact.
Data Storage	Acceptable data reduction or maintenance of complete raw data sets.	Extensive data storage often requires high radiation tolerance which is often expensive.
Growth	Is the mission partially defined and might there be on-orbit enhancements or mission growth?	This affects the system design in terms of maintainability and ease of enhancement, which directly affects processing margins, need for software uploading, and ground testing.

Table 20-15. Derived On-board Processing Requirements Based on Mission Level Requirements Established by Other Disciplines. Requirements from Table 3-5. (See Sec. 3.5)

Requirement	Description	Implication to On-Board Processing
Performance	Identify emerging fire within 8 hours of start and with less than 10% false positive	• LEO (~450 km) provides for recurrence within 2.5 hours/less radiation than high elevations/orbit inclination may still be an issue • Payload responsible for false positives reliability
Interpretation	Interpreted data to end user within 5 minutes	• On-board processing of information/autonomous evaluation of potential fire (autonomous rules for fire id. must be well-wrung out) • Additional testing for additional autonomy (funding and schedule)
Timeliness	Commandable within 3 minutes of events, stored coverage areas executed on-board	• Must have continuous up-link capability, potentially via multiple ground stations OR when location is identified and notification occurs, immediate response of stored command sequence (storage)
Mission Design Life	8 years	• Long-Life parts with reasonable radiation tolerance
System Availability	95% excluding weather and 24 hour maximum down time	• Potential redundancy to assure limited down time
Data Distribution	Up to 500 fire-monitoring offices and 2,000 ranges worldwide (maximum of 100 simultaneous users)	• Bandwidth and frequencies covered by communications discipline, on-board processing must be able to handle up to 500 event driven sequences with different downlink data files (Storage)
Data Content, Form, and Format	Location and extent in lat/long for local plotting, avg. temp. for each $40 m^2$ grid	• High fidelity mapping / knowledge to identify ground location. • Temperature from what sensor and correlated to ground how
Cost	Non-Recurring <$50M Recurring <$10M /year	• Processing components and RTOS, with Software Development costs limited to 7.5% ($3.75M) • Schedule Requirement—increase costs by <10% ($4.2M)
Schedule	Operational within 3 years	• Increase cost for rapid test and integration, quicker delivery of subsystem components
Risk	Probability of success >90%	• Autonomy must be tested, upload capability for enhancements and potential feature fixes
Regulations	Orbital debris and civil regulations	• Must have end-of-life retirement—deorbit
Interfaces	Interoperable through NOAA ground stations	• Antenna issue but orbit and pointing must be maintained for NOAA locations

directly traced to the potential payload and payload management, we will determine that payload processing will be separate from the spacecraft general processing and it will be the responsibility of the payload supplier. Thus, the autonomy functions needed for identification (within 10%) will be implemented and tested by the payload supplier. Additionally, fault monitoring and identification will be part of the baseline on-board processing functions but the ability to work-around a fault or provide graceful degradation will be done on the ground and uploaded since there is ample time within the 24 hour window for multiple passes.

The standard "rules" used to determine stored command sequences based on fire identification will be provided by the payload supplier but implemented within the C&DH functional elements of the spacecraft bus processing. Storage required for this function based on the potential identification of up to 500 fires at one time will be provided by on-board processing. Additionally, storage for the potential up-linked stored sequences based on the 3 minute commandability to the vehicle following a fire identification will also be provided by on-board processing. Control will require thrusters that must have enough propellant to perform de-orbit functions following the 8 year nominal life of the vehicle. Fine attitude control will be provided via reaction wheels and the associated momentum management will be provided by torquers and an associated magnetometer for direction identification. A sun sensor has been identified as nice-to-have for maintaining power, and since the associated processing is not significant, this will be part of the system baseline. A star tracker with quaternion output, a gyro with delta-V and acceleration, as well as a high resolution GPS receiver will be part of the baseline system configuration for attitude (star tracker/gyro) and orbit (GPS) determination. On-board orbit control will assure that a recurring path is created during each orbital pass but service will only be provided to those stations that are in the up/down-link performance of the system. Other data distribution can be handled by ground-station to ground-station data transfers.

Interoperability with NOAA ground stations will drive antenna size and frequency allocation which we will assign to the communication discipline but antenna pointing will impact on-board processing. To achieve this level of interoperability with NOAA ground stations, we will focus on coarse pointing resolution with a larger antenna. We make this selection from the on-board processing perspective because the knowledge requirement for the fire identification is higher than the control requirement and we don't want to implement a costly function in the main processing, if we don't need to. However, on-board storage in terms of C&DH and stored command sequences will be supplied by the on-board processing. Basic utility functions, math and coordinate transformations, as well as power and thermal control will be part of the baseline on-board processing. It is assumed that the thermal control will be passive and the power will maintain a 20% margin throughout operations.

The total SLOC count for the baseline spacecraft processing associated with the FireSat II mission is 38,900 SLOC as detailed in Table 20-16. This value, with 100% margin since we are well before SRR, will be used to determine the size and throughput requirements for the on-board processing and a mass storage device will be added to the system to assure that the data and stored sequences/commands can be accommodated. The ADCS is approximately 40% of the available processing (15,700/38,900) and the C&DH is only 5% (2,000/38,900) so the best processor, with past mission history shown in Table 20-11 is the RAD600 or the RAD750 whichever is available in the most radiation tolerant configuration for a reasonable amount of money.

Table 20-16. Estimating Source Lines of Code (SLOC) for FireSat II Spacecraft Functions. Items selected as Required and Nice-to-Have are shown in Table 20-9. Since the Nice-to-Have items are relatively small, we will include them in the baseline. Payload functions (including pointing) will be done within a payload processor that is outside the responsibility of the on-board processing organization.

Computer Software Component (CSC)	Source Lines of Code (SLOC)
Executive	1,000
Communication	2,000
Attitude/Orbit Sensor Processing	3,800
Attitude Determination and Control	12,500
Attitude Actuator Processing	2,400
Fault Detection	6,500
Utilities	5,700
Other Functions	5,000
Total	**38,900**

The Wind River VxWorks RTOS will be used as the baseline operating system and associated development environment because the board support package (BSP) for necessary RTOS functions is quite mature for the RAD600 /750 series of processors. A baseline system architecture is shown in Fig. 20-11 based on the need for a reasonable amount of throughput on the spacecraft bus as well as the payload side and the decision to reduce risk associated with on-board processing, by partitioning the payload functioning and processing from the on-board spacecraft bus functions.

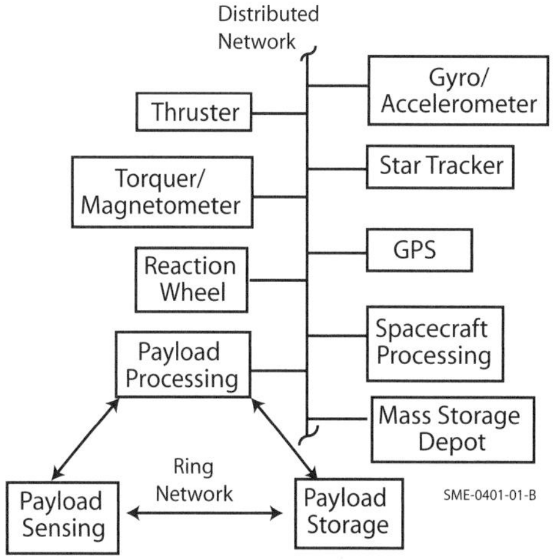

Fig. 20-11. FireSat II Spacecraft Baseline On-board Processing Architecture.

This architecture takes into consideration a distributed network for the primary spacecraft bus functions. The network protocol is a nominal command response system ([DoD, 1996]/ARINC 667 part 4) and provides deterministic timing with standardized interfaces. The payload on-board processing system has been baselined as a ring architecture since there are a limited number of items that need to interact with each other. The ring provides a certain level of redundancy and fault tolerance. This baseline will be iterated with the various other subsystem domain experts until a final configuration is selected to best meet the needs of all of the stakeholders.

Next, we select a tailored set of documentation to be provided as part of the FireSat II effort. This will include an SRS/IRS integrated document and a hardware PFS with integrated ICD. Test plans and procedures will be developed for the flight software and then for the spacecraft bus avionics as a stand-alone system. The User's Guide will be developed at the system level implying that some of the development staff may be required for long-term support. With the high reliability requirement and 24 hour down minimum, this is probably a good trade (personnel for documentation) in the long run. Finally, we evaluate reliability based on the mission objectives and data that might be provided by the supplier of various components. Again, the baseline system design is iterated based on the reliability, availability, and cost/schedule requirements and the functional performance needs.

20.4 Modular Approaches to Processing

L. Jane Hansen, *HRP Systems, Inc.*
Paul Graven, *Microcosm, Inc.*

Spacecraft development has become excessively and increasingly expensive in terms of cost and time, which has led to intolerance for failure, further driving higher costs and longer schedules driving ever more intolerance for failure. This spiral has led to very complex processing systems, one's that are highly reliable and custom built, as well as being expensive to create and replace. With an emphasis on processing systems and FSW, we will examine an alternative approach where we use modularity and software reuse to create components that are essentially "off-the-shelf". These components can be rapidly assembled to create a spacecraft or we can create a number of less expensive spacecraft that can be quickly and inexpensively replaced. We will first examine an approach to create modular processing and potentially less expensive spacecraft and later we will address issues associated with software reuse.

"Modularity is a general systems concept: it is a continuum describing the degree to which a system's components can be separated and recombined, and it refers to both the tightness of coupling between components and the degree to which the "rules" of the system architecture enable (or prohibit) the mixing and matching of components."[Schilling, 2000]. In this context we see that space systems offer numerous potential opportunities for application of modularity. However, the conventional wisdom is that space systems are so unique, and typically so customized, that there would be little benefit from the introduction of modular architectures. Historically, we have viewed spacecraft as tightly integrated, non-modular, custom designs that are driven by the desire for maximizing the performance in a specific mission scenario. Until a decade or so ago we believe that this was essential to meet many mission needs. Currently, we see that component, computer, and digital network performance capabilities have dramatically increased such that they are more than adequate to support modular approaches without sacrificing mission capabilities. Certainly there is overhead in terms of mass, processing and time that can be reduced by tight integration, but in most cases the increased costs will not be offset by improved mission performance.

The inclusion of modular designs and modular components has become prevalent across numerous high-technology industries and markets, and the reasons are fundamentally economic. We know that modular architectures reduce the cost of offering variety and of the introduction of new technologies into products. We have seen that innovations and improvements can be rapidly introduced at the module level without the need for broader design changes. Modularity can also enable supplier competition, which drives cost reductions, by allowing easy substitution of alternative components based on performance, price, or availability. These benefits have been clearly demonstrated in the computer industry.

The first significant foray into modularity in the computer industry was the development of the IBM System/360 which was announced in 1964 and reviewed by Baldwin and Clark [1997]. Prior to the development of the System/360 architecture, offerings from every computer manufacturer and even new designs from a given producer were wholly incompatible requiring custom hardware and software and "upgrades" required costly and risky migration efforts. Development of a robust modular architecture turned out to be more challenging than anticipated, however, the rewards were remarkable. By 1969, IBM stock accounted for more than 70% of the total market value of the computer industry.

One attempt at change in the spacecraft industry is the incarnation of Operationally Responsive Space (ORS). ORS is rooted in the concepts that if spacecraft were available off-the-shelf (OTS) or if many smaller and cheaper, potentially expendable spacecraft, could be assembled quickly, with system performance that is "good enough," rather than optimal, then cost and schedule would become more manageable. In the ORS paradigm we have a quick turn-around from identifying a mission need, to designing and implementing a solution, then deploying that solution for a reasonable, if not limited, on-orbit life-time. The *CubeSat* (Sec. 25-4) is a standardized 10 × 10 × 10 cm (1U or 1 unit) spacecraft that performs a very specific function over a limited lifetime. The CubeSat originated at Stanford University and the early specifications and standards for CubeSats were developed at Cal Poly, San Luis Obispo. CubeSats evolution was originally due to university experimentation and the 1U CubeSat was scaled to include multiple units (e.g., "2U" is 20 × 10 × 10 cm, a "3U" CubeSat 30 × 10 × 10 cm). As we see these more complex CubeSats evolve and become operational, we also see their application expanding beyond universities, including commercial, military and ORS applications.

We see another mechanism for meeting the ORS concept of rapid response in the development of spacecraft busses that are built to inventory so that we can quickly pair the bus with a COTS payload to meet a range of ORS mission requirements with "good enough" functionality, rather than optimal performance. Alternatively, spacecraft can be built quickly either with "existing," fully tested, building blocks or modular components that are capable of flexible configuration to meet a diverse range of mission requirements. We see that there are differing opinions as to the granularity of the built-to-inventory components:

1. Complete, ready-to-fly spacecraft
2. Spacecraft busses and payloads held separately in inventory
3. Functional subsystem elements combined to create functional services, then stocked on shelves and snapped together to create a complete spacecraft, or
4. Lower-level components being rapidly assembled with the aid of a configuration wizard that determines the parts that are needed to create a spacecraft that will meet specific mission requirements.

Fig. 20-12. A Fractionated Spacecraft Each of a Subset of the Overall Functionality that is Desired. (Courtesy of DARPA)

We have also seen that there are several implementation concepts or approaches that are associated with creating modularity for spacecraft and spacecraft processing architectures. First, there is *fractionated spacecraft* where we create several individual spacecraft, each with a subset of the desired functional capabilities as shown in Fig. 20-12. Figure 20-13 shows how the fractionated spacecraft operate together as a cluster or constellation to have all the functions needed to meet the desired mission objectives [Brown and Eremenko, 2006]. In a second approach, we create a few types of *modular buses* that meet different mission performance parameters yet maintain a standard interface to the launch vehicle and to the payload. This concept is shown is shown in Fig. 20-14. In this implementation we might have a

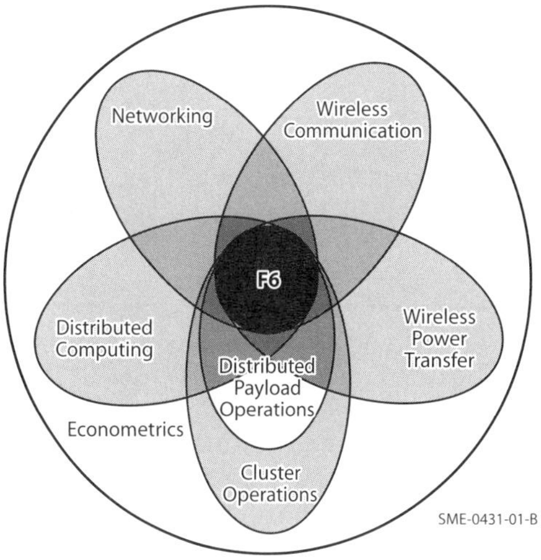

Fig. 20-13. Sample Functional Elements of the Fractionated Spacecraft.

spacecraft bus that has a high-performance ADACS (attitude determination and control system) but moderate radiation tolerance (suitable for LEO imaging spacecraft), and another with moderate ADACS capabilities but high radiation tolerance (suitable for MEO communication spacecraft). In a third approach to modularity, we develop *Plug-and-Play components*, (PnP) at the subsystem and down to the individual device, so that a specific mission can be met by rapidly assembling the necessary components or devices to an equipment manifest that is generated by a design tool, given the specific mission requirements and objectives. Figure 20-15 shows a car-

Fig. 20-14. In the NRL/ORS ISET Approach Several Modular Spacecraft Busses are Created to Mate with Standard, Off-the-shelf Payloads to Meet Specific Mission Needs. (Courtesy of NRL)

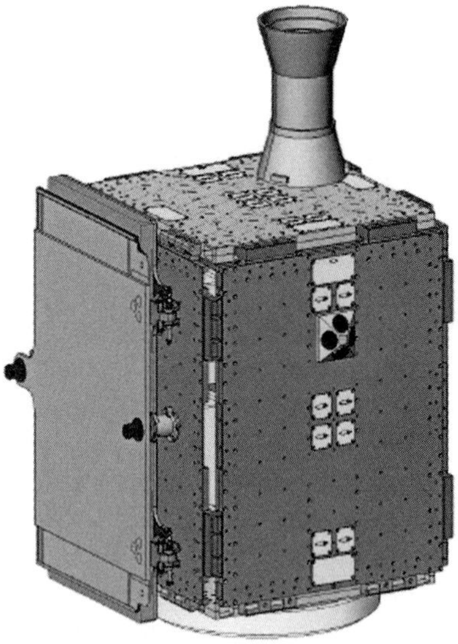

Fig. 20-15. Cartoon of the Plug-and-Play (PnP) Satellite (PnPSat) with Modular Panels and Embedded Wiring Harnesses.

toon of the AFRL PnPSat. An interesting attribute we find with the AFRL PnP vehicle is that modular panels have been created with standard grid pattern for easy assembly of components onto the bus structure. Additionally, within each modular panel is embedded wiring and routers creating the PnP data network.

The fractionated spacecraft was introduced by DARPA in the early 2000s. The basic concept is that we would implement different functional elements on each of a small number of spacecraft that we operate as a complete functional system. For example, downlink capabilities on one spacecraft, high bandwidth processing on another, and imaging on yet another. If we were to implement the fractionated spacecraft, we would create a cluster of fairly specific functional elements that are straightforward to replace individually if failure occurs. However, we must assure that all the elements of the cluster can communicate with each other (perhaps through an intermediary) and we must maintain precision control of both the attitude and orbit of each of the spacecraft and the integrity of the formation. (Sec. 23.2)

The concept of modular spacecraft has been explored by numerous organizations and companies over the last 25 years. Recently, the Integrated Systems Engineering Team (ISET) project, established by the Naval Research Laboratory (NRL) and the Office of the Secretary of Defense/Office of Force Transformation (OSD/OFT), developed specific requirements for "what" a spacecraft bus must do to meet the needs of various mission categories (i.e., imaging, communications), including a description of the various elements that are required to create a "system". For each type of spacecraft bus we would implement a standardized interface from the bus to the launch vehicle and from the bus to the payload making them virtually interchangeable. The general concept is that once we identify the mission requirements, we select the appropriate spacecraft bus from a list of available units and then integrate the payload. After a few instances of integration with this standardized interface, we hope that the integration time and effort is reduced, thus reducing the overall cost of the spacecraft. Also, because the spacecraft was ready to go, we have significantly reduced the time to launch. (Sec. 23.6).

Another mechanism for reducing the time to launch is by creating PnP spacecraft components that can be rapidly assembled into a spacecraft. In thinking about plug-and-play (PnP) for spacecraft we borrow terminology and even concepts from the commercial implementation of PnP. Specifically, we look at the PC-based concept of PnP, where the user plugs a mouse into a PC resident USB socket and invokes the operating system to find the correct driver, configures the system parameters, and then seamlessly allows the user to begin operations. In this example, and in general, PnP attempts to hide interface complexity from the user by establishing standard interfaces. The issue here is that the standards must be agreed to by all parties that would use or develop the components, and there must be a reasonable return on investment (ROI) for the spacecraft community to adhere to them.

ESA has also published a draft standard for a PnP SpaceWire Protocol Definition (SpW-PnP-PD). This draft standard was created by the University of Dundee and focuses on the data transfer protocol, the plug aspect of PnP, without specifically addressing the play element. With help from the AIAA, a group of people from the spacecraft community are working to create a complete set of standards for a Spacecraft PnP Architecture (SPA). The standards focus on the interface definition, based on the Open System Interconnection Reference Model (OSI Reference Model or OSI Model) which includes seven layers. The OSI seven layer model begins at the lowest level with the physical medium, moves to the data-link, network and transport layer, then adds the session, presentation and application layers. It is the middle layers, the data-link, network, and transportation layers that provide the functional and procedural means to effectively transfer data from a source to a destination. We can define the data source as individual devices, subassemblies, subsystems, or the spacecraft bus itself. When we are discussing FSW, we can consider a data source as functional services, such as navigation and attitude determination services.

For PnP, as defined by SPA, we would create individual spacecraft components that are PnP compatible which would include implementing a standard physical interface as well as a data protocol that allows the component to describe its function, command and control, and data output using a machine negotiated mechanism. The Transducer Electronic Data Sheets (TEDS) used by the automotive industry (IEEE 1451) has been augmented for use with spacecraft components creating an extended TEDS or xTEDS. This machine negotiated interface is based on extensible mark-up language (XML) and includes information about the component that a subscriber or controller would need to

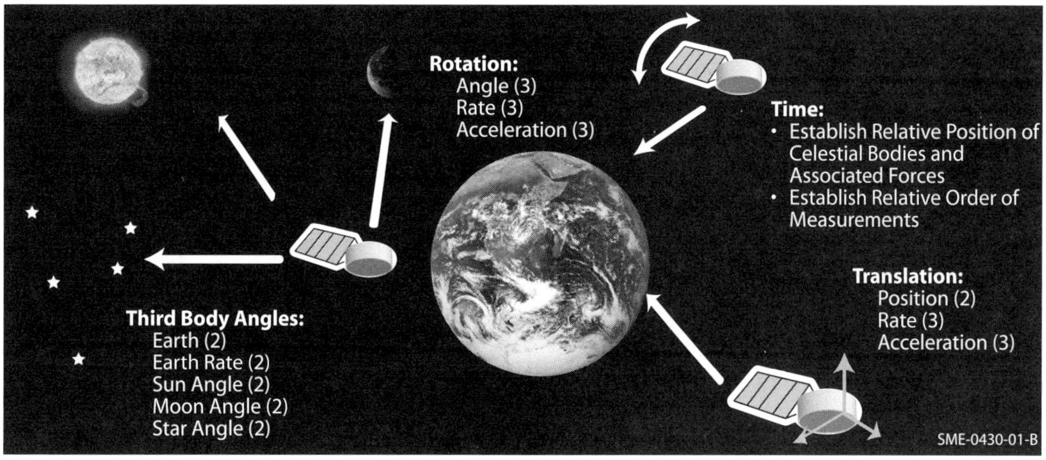

Fig. 20-16. "Atomic-level" Data Elements are Based on Physics and Geometry Rather than Specific Devices/Equipment Within a Platform.

know to make full use of that component. Specifically, the xTEDS provide a "service description" for components, such that functions not detailed in the xTEDS are effectively invisible to SPA. In terms of PnP hardware, the AFRL PnPSat team is making great strides toward acceptance of traditional commercial PnP practices as viable in the spacecraft industry. Through the implementation of appliqué sensor interface modules (ASIMs) we can augment existing, legacy hardware to meet the SPA standards. AFRL and the ORS Office have supported several activities to develop ASIM technology and PnP enabled components.

To fully achieve the concept of PnP spacecraft, we find that innovation in development of FSW is required. This innovation can range from process oriented enhancements to actual software implementations that facilitate new missions, including operationally responsive space. Specifically, the reuse of off-the-shelf software modules is highly desirable. As discussed earlier in this chapter, software costs are traditionally based on the number of source lines of code we develop for each specific discipline. If we can reuse software modules, much in the same way that we might make use of an off-the-shelf modular spacecraft bus, the only recurring cost is the cost of integration and system level test.

If we are to support software reuse we must develop an architecture that is data-centric such that the resulting FSW implementation can be implemented, tested, and ready off-the-shelf. To achieve this, we need to partition software and data at the lowest levels, using terminology that originates in the physics of the device rather than the manufacturer. Much like atomic elements in chemistry, we call those low level data elements *atomic data elements* to imply that they are the smallest elements that can be observed. Additionally, to achieve software reuse the core algorithms must be designed to be generic and the software must be developed and tested, before the specifics of the mission may have been identified. Thus, we will define specific mission parameters associated with the vehicle configuration and characteristics in a way that will facilitate the reuse of the generic core algorithms we have developed and tested. To create reusable FSW we must define data elements at the *atomic data level*. Figure 20-17 shows atomic data for an attitude determination and control system (ADCS) application. Here we define data as they are measured or sensed such that there is a direct tie to physics and geometry (e.g., spacecraft motion, rates, expressed in body coordinates), rather than subsystem or component implementation specific parameters. By having all of the components that supply spacecraft rotation present their data interface using atomic data definitions, sensors can be interchanged based on availability without impacting the primary algorithms.

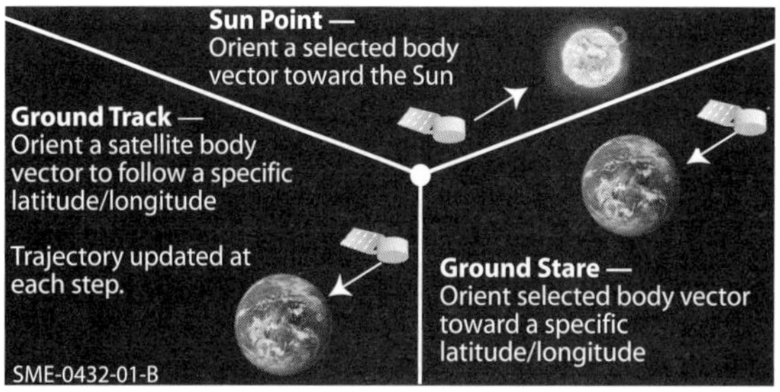

Fig. 20-17. Atomic Level Moding Facilitates One Control Law Designed to Reduce the Error Between Sensed and Desired State.

The control algorithms remain abstracted from the data sets and data is resolved to the atomic level. Additionally, we can create the command and control aspect of a PnP ADCS system with its elements reduced to the atomic level. By using atomic level command we allow a user to build-up any capability that is required, without necessarily being aware of the capability when the FSW is created. Traditional modes such as sun point, ground track, and ground stare, are all achieved using atomic level mode commands. These modes include the following:

- SLEW—Slew to a vector (time, position, velocity)
- TRACK—Maintain pointing to a vector (time, position, velocity)
- RATE—set body rates to a vector (de-tumble, spin-up)
- STANDBY—transitional or cruise (minimum power consumption)
- MOMENTUM-DUMP—reduce stored momentum

By using this atomic level moding, there may be varying modes of operation that will be performed with respect to varying objects. As shown in Fig. 20-16, the objects or pointing directions are defined to include celestial objects (e.g. Sun, Moon), nadir, and zenith. Additionally, the ability to point to a vector (position) or target (state vector including rates) can be accommodated. This leads to an additional concept for the reuse of the PnP ADCS FSW. Since the inputs, processing, and outputs are the same for any of the traditional modes, there can also be a single control law. While this may not allow for optimal gains in each of the ADCS modes, we have created responsive FSW that is modular and OTS.

If we standardized the input and output (I/O) mechanisms of all components, for any vehicle whether spacecraft, Unmanned Aerial Vehicle (UAV), Autonomous land vehicle or sea vehicle, the hardware components and even the application FSW can be similar which provides many benefits to the all autonomous vehicle industries. First, this level of interface transparency facilitates reuse at the algorithm, component, and subsystem level. As electronics become smaller, and micro-electromechanical systems (MEMS) are used to implement GN&C sensing, sensors and potentially actuation/propulsion devices, could be shared between the various vehicle types. The environmental concerns will differ, but as the electronics become more and more capable, it is possible that other methods of accommodating the environment, such as radiation hardening (rad-hard) by design, may help to make devices reusable for different vehicle types.

If more advanced PnP techniques are applied to the standardization process, we can create a resulting system that will be able to support self-discovery and configuration. This will further facilitate rapid assembly and test, while providing for a robust, fault-tolerant performance with graceful degradation in the event of device or subsystem failures. Moreover, this approach will greatly improve the interoperability of the various types of vehicles, helping with economies of scale for the smaller market vehicles such as spacecraft and submarines by leveraging the larger market vehicle products such as those developed in support of aircraft and UAVs. And finally, with the development of vehicle agnostic components with PnP interfaces, we will create a completely modular spacecraft, as well as other autonomous vehicles, which provides a natural transition into an integrated system of systems from underwater to land and air, and into space.

References

For annotated bibliography of on-board processing, see the book website.

AIAA. 2007. *Electrical Power Systems for Unmanned Spacecraft.* Standard #S-122-2007.

Baldwin, C. Y. and K. B. Clark. 1997. "Managing in an Age of Modularity." *Harvard Business Review.* Sept-Oct.

Boehm, Barry W. 1981. *Software Engineering Economics.* Englewood Cliffs, NJ: Prentice-Hall.

Brown, O. and P. Ermenko. 2006. "The Value Proposition for Fractionated Space Architectures." AIAA-2006-7506, Sept. 19–21.

DoD. 1996. *Aircraft Internal Time Division Comand/Response Multiplex Data Bus.* MIL-STD-1553B, Jan. 15.

DoD. 2003. *Electronic and Electrical Component Parts.* Test Methods Standard. MIL-STD-202G. Jul. 18.

DoD. 2007. *Requirements for the Control of Electromagnetic Interference Characteristics of Subsystems and Equipment.* Interface Standards. MIL-STD-461F. Dec. 10.

DoD. 2008. *Environmental Engineering Considerations and Laboratory Test.* Test Method Standard. MIL-STD-810G. Oct. 31.

DoD. 2010a. *Microcircuits.* Test Method Standard. MIL-STD-883H. Feb. 26.

DoD. 2010b. *Sixteen-Bit Computer Instruction Set Architecture.* MIL-STD-1750A. Apr. 12.

Kaner, Cem, J. Falk, and H. Nguyen. 1999. *Testing Computer Software, 2nd Ed.* Hoboken, NJ: John Wiley and Sons.

Schilling, M. A. 2000. "Towards a General Modular Systems Theory and Its Application to Interfirm Product Modularity. *Academy of Management Review*, vol 25, pp. 312-334.

Stankovic, J. A., and K. Ramamritham. 1988. *Hard Real-Time Systems.* IEEE Computer Society Press, Washington DC.

21 Spacecraft Subsystems IV—Communications and Power

21.1 Telemetry, Tracking, and Command (TT&C) Subsystem

Robert S. Bokulic and **Christopher C. DeBoy**
Johns Hopkins University/Applied Physics Laboratory

The *telemetry, tracking, and command (TT&C) subsystem* provides for communications and radiometric tracking between the spacecraft and ground stations. These functions are accomplished through the transmission of electromagnetic signals, typically at radio frequencies (RF). The TT&C subsystem provides the spacecraft with an uplink (or forward link) for commands, a downlink (or return link) for mission data, and radiometric links (i.e., Doppler shift and ranging signals) that enable the velocity and distance to the spacecraft relative to the ground station to be measured for the purpose of determining the spacecraft orbit. The mission data includes both the spacecraft engineering data (sometimes referred to as *housekeeping data*) and the sensor/instrument data generated by the spacecraft payload. The latter data may be integrated with the engineering data on the same link or returned to Earth via a separate wideband downlink.

This section will provide us with a solid understanding of the typical requirements on the TT&C subsystem and how these requirements can be implemented in a basic design. We will learn to perform a link analysis and use the results to make top-level system decisions, including subsystem transmitter power and antenna size requirements. We will learn the architecture of a TT&C subsystem and be able to create a block diagram design and perform tradeoffs that lead to sizing of the elements in the subsystem based on spacecraft mass and power requirements. Finally, we will gain familiarity with the various technologies currently available to implement the subsystem and the emerging technologies that hold promise for the future. An emphasis will be placed on high bit rate communications, and the challenges associated with bandwidth.

21.1.1 Preliminary Design Process

The TT&C preliminary design process begins with the definition of top-level requirements and constraints as flowed down from the mission-level requirements. A preliminary RF link analysis is typically performed early-on to "size" the subsystem, particularly the spacecraft power amplifier and high gain antenna. A hardware block diagram is then developed, followed by various tradeoff studies to refine the equipment selection. A point design can then be generated to determine bus power, mass, data return, and link margins. The frequency assignment process can then be initiated through the National Telecommunications and Information Administration (NTIA). Table 21-1 presents an outline of the preliminary design process for a typical TT&C subsystem.

21.1.2 TT&C Requirements

Many requirements levied onto the TT&C subsystem are determined by various aspects of the mission itself. For instance, the range between the spacecraft and the ground station is set by the nature of the mission. The spacecraft attitude control system (spinning, 3-axis, or pointing control accuracy) is typically determined by bus power and concept of operations (CONOPs) considerations. The ground station antenna sizes and capabilities are often dictated by mission type (near-Earth, NASA, military, deep-space, or commercial). There may be limits on the size, placement, and number of spacecraft antennas. While the TT&C system engineer can of course influence these requirements and is an important player in the overall spacecraft system design, these types of requirements are often considered drivers for the TT&C design. The TT&C system engineer typically has more flexibility in defining downlink data rate, an important, first-order requirement in sizing the TT&C system that also determines (or is determined by) data volume and number of passes. The downlink data rate is set to balance the achievable RF output power with antenna size and placement constraints for the mission. This calculation can be relatively straightforward for some missions, yet require substantial analysis for other missions. For example, consider a mission in low-Earth orbit with a daily science return requirement of 10 Gbits. If the satellite is in view of the ground station four times per day with 10-minute pass durations, then the required downlink data rate is calculated rather easily to be 4.2 Mbps. In

Table 21-1. TT&C Subsystem Preliminary Design Process.

Step	Details	Where Discussed
Define Top-Level Requirements and Constraints	• Redundancy • Ground network/ground station compatibilities • Distance to ground station (orbit geometry) for normal, mission-critical, and emergency operations • Data rate/data volume and associated data quality (bit error rate, frame error rate) • Frequency band and emission constraints • Radiometric tracking accuracy (Doppler, ranging) • Antenna coverage • Standards (CCSDS, SGLS, other) • Power, mass constraints • High-level electrical interfaces with other subsystems such as MIL-STD-1553, RS-422, and low voltage differential signaling (LVDS). • Environmental (especially temperature and radiation)	Sec. 21.1.2 Sec. 21.1.3
Perform Preliminary Link Analysis to Size the Subsystem	• Determine antenna characteristics (gain, beamwidth, size) and RF output power based on (1) mission data return and (2) emergency mode communications. • Determine driving requirements for fixed-pattern (low and medium gain) antenna coverage: LEOP, emergency mode, maneuvers, Doppler tracking	Sec. 21.1.4
Develop Subsystem Block Diagram	• Major hardware components including transponders, power amplifiers, diplexers, RF switching assemblies, and antennas • Top-level subsystem electrical interfaces • Preliminary cost estimate is often generated at this stage.	Sec. 21.1.5
Perform Tradeoff Studies to Refine Equipment Selection	• Transponder vs transceiver technologies • Antenna technologies (reflector, waveguide, wire, patches, others) • Solid-state vs traveling wave tube power amplifier technologies • Passive network technologies (waveguide vs coaxial diplexers, RF switches, transmission lines)	Sec. 21.1.5
Develop Point Design Based on Tradeoff Selections	• Balance performance vs cost and power/mass constraints. Outputs of this step are: – Detailed subsystem block diagram – Power, mass, and volume table – Refined link analysis, link margins – Data return projections – Refined cost estimate	Sec. 21.1.6
Initiate Frequency Assignment Process	• Application via government sponsor to the NTIA for specific frequency of operation assignments	Sec. 21.1.3
Documentation	• Internal memoranda, design review presentations, requirements document.	—

contrast, a mission in a highly elliptical Earth orbit experiences substantial variations in ground station distance and viewing time. A fixed downlink data rate would be inefficient in this case. Calculation of a variable downlink data rate schedule and associated average daily science return requires a combination of link analysis, orbital analysis, and on-board recorder utilization analysis.

Table 21-2 presents a summary of the typical TT&C subsystem requirements for near-Earth and deep-space missions.

21.1.3 Frequency Bands of Operation

The TT&C subsystem operating frequency band is selected based on several considerations. The nature of the mission (science, military, commercial) may dictate the use of specific ground stations with dedicated bands of operation. In selecting from the available bands, the primary consideration is meeting downlink data rate requirements (the downlink is usually the driver because of the limited transmit power on the spacecraft, compared to the transmit power available at a ground station). A close review of the Friis link, Eq. (21-1) through Eq. (21-3) reveals that the operating frequency of a communications link can be optimized to a first order by considering the nature of the antennas used in the link. Three basic cases exist:

1. **Low Gain/Low Gain:** Links with low gain antennas on both ends (driven by pattern coverage requirements) favor operation at lower RF frequencies such as VHF and UHF (ex: proximity operations).

Table 21-2. Typical TT&C Subsystem-Level Requirements.

Parameter	Typical Requirement Near-Earth Mission	Deep-Space Mission
Ground Network Compatibility ***(see also Chap. 28)***	**Near Earth Network** (NEN) for NASA Category A missions (within 2 × 10^6 km from Earth) **Space Network** (SN) for near-Earth missions that have a requirement for nearly continuous contact with Earth. Also known as the Tracking and Data Relay Satellite System (TDRSS). **Air Force Satellite Control Network** (AFSCN) for military missions **European Space Agency (ESA)** **Indigenous National Networks** (Japanese Aerospace Exploration Agency JAXA, Indian Space Research Organization ISRO) **Independent Ground Station Assets** (Universal Space Network, or dedicated mission antennas)	**Deep Space Network** (DSN) for NASA Category B missions (beyond 2 × 10^6 km from Earth) **ESA** Deep Space Stations
Earth-Spacecraft Distance	Worst-case links are typically calculated at the maximum slant range distance (lowest ground antenna elevation angle)	Worst-case links are typically calculated at the maximum distance from Earth in the spacecraft trajectory
Data Rates	**Uplink:** 125 to 1 kbps emergency mode 1 to 2 kbps normal mode 1 Mbps memory reload **Downlink:** Up to 10 kbps engineering data & emergency mode Up to ~5 Mbps mission data on same link with engineering data Greater than 5 Mbps mission data on separate wideband downlink May be variable depending on mission geometry and dynamics.	**Uplink:** 7.8 bps emergency mode 15.6 to 2000 kbps other modes 1 Mbps memory reload (future) **Downlink:** 5 to 10 bps emergency mode Up to 10 kbps engineering data Up to 10's Mbps science data (100's of Mbps future) Usually variable due to widely varying geometry of a deep space mission.
Frequency Band ***(B_N= necessary band-width as defined by the NTIA; see Table 21-3)***	S-band for uplink S-band for downlink B_N up to 6 MHz X-band for downlink B_N up to 400 MHz K_a-band for downlink B_N > 400 MHz	X-band for uplink X-band for downlink up to several Mbps K_a-band for downlink > several Mbps
Radiometric Tracking Accuracy	**Doppler:** < 5 cm/sec over 1 to 10 sec (1σ) **Ranging:** < 10 m over 1 to 10 sec (1σ)	**Doppler:** 0.1 mm/s over 60 sec (1σ) **Ranging:** 1–10 m over 60 to 600 sec (1σ)
Antenna Coverage	Narrow or moderate beam coverage for mission data return is dependent on attitude control requirements and CONOPs Omni-directional pattern usually required for launch and early operations (LEOPs) and emergency mode	Narrow beam (high gain) antenna usually required for science return Moderate beam (medium gain) antenna may be needed depending on CONOPs Omni-directional pattern usually required for LEOPs and emergency mode
Standards	CCSDS (NASA and military) SGLS (military)	CCSDS
Data Quality	**Uplink:** Bit error rate ≤ 10^{-5} to 10^{-6} (typically uncoded data) **Downlink:** Frame error rate ≤ 10^{-4} (typically w/ forward error correction coding)	
Redundancy	Highly dependent on high-level mission cost/mass/reliability tradeoffs. Usually flowed down directly from mission requirements.	
Power and Mass	Highly mission dependent and managed through an iterative process between the spacecraft systems engineer and TT&C system engineer.	
Electrical Interfaces	RS-422 (complementary digital) (simple, low-power) Low voltage differential signaling (LVDS) (simple, very low-power) Universal asynchronous receiver-transmitter (UART) (simple, low-power) MIL-1553 bus (for inter-box interfaces) I^2C bus (for telemetry status signals)	
Special Environmental Conditions	Radiation, temperature, shock	

2. **High Gain/Low Gain:** Links with a high gain antenna on the ground and a low gain antenna (driven by pattern coverage requirements) on the spacecraft are RF frequency independent to a first order. Constraints such as component availability, cost, size, and passive losses often drive the designer to choose a lower microwave frequency such as S-band. Many near Earth links fall in this category.

3. **High Gain/High Gain:** Links with high gain antennas on both ends (driven by maximum antenna size constraints) favor operation at higher RF frequencies such as X, K_u, and K_a-band. X-band is commonly used for space-to-Earth links for near-Earth and deep space missions. K_u-band is currently used for spacecraft-to-spacecraft links via TDRSS but is being phased out. K_a-band is rapidly gaining prominence for spacecraft-to-Earth and spacecraft-to-spacecraft links for near Earth and deep space. Pointing requirements, atmospheric loss, and atmospheric noise must be carefully accounted for at K_a-band.

Communications links operating at frequencies 10 GHz and above can experience severe degradation due to rain attenuation (fades of 10 dB or more). Link parameters such as transmit power and antenna gain are sized to overcome a selected amount of rain loss; this determines the expected availability of the system and drives cost. Below 10 GHz, and especially at S-band and below, rain loss is a relatively minor consideration.

The use of lower frequencies also results in less expensive hardware on the spacecraft. There are multiple commercial providers of L-band and S-band TT&C communications equipment, with generally increasing cost as one moves to X-band and above. However, spectral crowding in the heavily-used S-band from terrestrial cellular communications is creating pressure to move all satellite links to higher frequency bands. Additionally, limitations are set on the *necessary bandwidth*, B_N, of the transmitted signal in certain bands. These limitations could drive a system to a higher frequency band if a wide bandwidth is required. The National Telecommunications and Information Administration (NTIA) defines necessary bandwidth as the minimum emission bandwidth necessary that allows an acceptable quality of performance, and provides guidance on calculating B_N for various emission classes. Refer to Annex J of the NTIA Redbook [NTIA, 2010]. Table 21-3 provides guidance on frequency band selection and the necessary bandwidth recommendations set forth by the Space Frequency Coordination Group (SFCG) [SFCG, 2011].

Once the operational frequency band and bandwidths are selected, the frequency approval process can begin. For US government NASA or military missions, this is a 4-stage process with the NTIA that results in authority to operate in the desired bands. This process is also used to coordinate with other agencies around the world via the International Telecommunications Union (ITU) to ensure that the mission will operate without interference with the spacecraft and ground systems of other countries and vice-versa. Depending on the type of mission, not all stages need to be completed. For an operational space mission, only stages 2 (Experimental, or Preliminary) and 4 (Operational) are typically required (see Fig. 21-1). Stages 1 (Conceptual) and 3 (Developmental) may be skipped as less-evolved versions of the Stages 2 and 4 submittals, respectively.

Commercial missions typically provide their TT&C links within their payload service allocation, often at the band edges. Licenses are sought from the FCC through a similar process to the NTIA, and the FCC also coordinates submittals to the ITU for international assignment. Frequency approval within other countries follows their domestic approval authority process.

21.1.4 Preliminary Link Analysis and Modulation/Coding Tradeoffs

Initial sizing of the TT&C subsystem is done by calculating the required combination of RF transmit power and downlink antenna size. Both the RF transmit power and antenna aperture area are proportionally related to the downlink bit rate, which becomes the driver for this analysis. We will review the basic link equations needed to perform the sizing and discuss the various tradeoffs involved. The link equations can also be applied to the uplink and emergency downlink scenarios. In some cases, the emergency mode downlink will drive the transmit power requirement because a broader beam (lower gain) antenna is used for emergencies. This section will present an overview of the link analysis process and provide examples that will allow a systems engineer to make basic tradeoffs in sizing the TT&C subsystem and verifying the robustness of the links. A wealth of detailed information on RF link analysis and design can be found in the CCSDS standards documents, particularly CCSDS 401.0-B-20 [CCSDS, 2011], and the DSN Telecommunications Link Design Handbook [DSN, 2011].

Get Stnd

A communications link with a transmitter system located a distance d from the receiver system can be described mathematically by a relatively simple equation. Assuming *free space propagation* where the transmitted power P_t spreads isotropically (uniformly) in space as it propagates but does not suffer other propagation effects such as weather, diffraction, or multipath loss, the power density at the receiver system can be described as $P_t/(4\pi d^2)$ where $4\pi d^2$ is the surface area of a sphere of radius d. The transmit antenna will often be designed to focus the radiated power density in the direction of the receiver system. This focusing effect is quantified by the *gain* of the antenna, described mathematically as the power density radiated in a given direction relative to the power density that would have been radiated in that direction by an isotropic radiator. If the transmitter system incorporates an antenna with gain G_t, then the power

Table 21-3. RF Channel Allocations for Space Missions. Note: necessary bandwidth (B_N) limitations are given as guidance where applicable

Frequency Band	Channel Allocations (GHz)		Examples
	Near Earth	Deep Space	
VHF/UHF	0.144 to 0.146 (amateur) 0.435 to 0.438 (amateur)	0.435 to 0.450 (forward) 0.390 to 0.405 (return)	Microsats, amateur radio satellites, Mars/Electra relay link
S-Band Military	1.7 to 1.9 (up) 2.2 to 2.3 (down) $B_N \leq 6$ *MHz*	N/A	Many missions
S-Band NASA	2.025 to 2.12 (up) 2.2 to 2.3 (down) $B_N \leq 6$ *MHz*	2.0 to 2.1 (up) 2.2 to 2.3 (down)	Many near-Earth and deep-space TT&C links and TDRSS multiple access links. Note: S-band not supported for future deep space missions
C-Band Commercial	3.7 to 4.2 (down) 5.925 to 6.425 (up)	N/A	Communications satellites
X-Band Earth Science	8.0 to 8.4 (down) $B_N \leq 400$ *MHz*	N/A	Landsat, RADARSAT
X-Band Space Science	8.4 to 8.45 (down) $B_N \leq 10$ MHz	8.45 to 8.5 (down)	Many near Earth and deep space missions.
K_u-Band Commercial	~11 (down) ~14 (up)	N/A	Direct broadcast. Specific frequencies vary by region.
K_u-Band TDRSS	13.9 (forward) 15.0 (return)	N/A	Shuttle and Space Station links to TDRSS. Note: frequency band being phased out for space missions.
K_a-Band Commercial	17.7 to 20.2 (down) 27.5 to 30.0 (up)	N/A	Direct broadcast. Fixed Satellite Service.
K_a-Band TDRSS and Lunar	22.6 to 23.6 (forward) 25.2 to 27.2 (return) 40 to 40.5 (forward) 37 to 38 (return)	N/A	High data rate links through TDRSS. Lunar trunk link.
K_a-Band Deep Space	N/A	34.2 to 34.7 (up) 31.8 to 32.3 (down) 37 to 38 (return) 40 to 40.5 (forward)	Mars Reconnaissance Orbiter (MRO) high data rate planetary science link. Deep space trunk link.

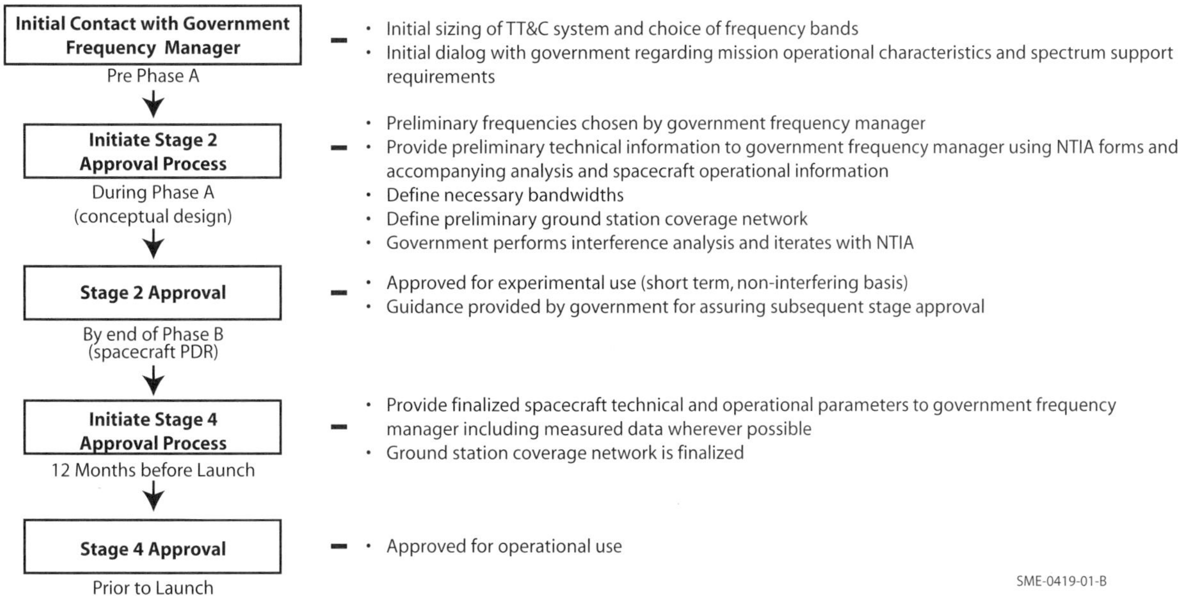

Fig. 21-1. Example Flow of NTIA Approval Process for an Operational Space Mission.

density at the receiver system becomes $P_tG_t/(4\pi d^2)$. The receiver system will have an antenna with an *effective aperture area* A_{er} that intercepts the power density at that location and converts it into a received power level at the output port of the antenna. The received power, P_r is:

$$P_r = \frac{P_tG_t}{4\pi d^2}A_{er} \tag{21-1}$$

This equation is intuitive for large aperture antennas where one can envision the physical aperture of the antenna to be intercepting the power density present at its surface (in practice the effective aperture area is less than the physical aperture area by a factor of η which represents the overall efficiency of the antenna). Antenna theory can be used to relate the effective aperture area of any antenna to its gain, resulting in the expression $A_e=(G\lambda^2/4\pi)$ where G is the gain of the antenna (either transmit or receive) and λ is the wavelength of the RF signal. Using this expression, the received power of the communications link can now be expressed as either:

$$P_r = \frac{P_tA_{et}A_{er}}{d^2\lambda^2} \tag{21-2}$$

$$P_r = \frac{P_tG_tG_r}{(4\pi d/\lambda)^2} \tag{21-3}$$

where A_{et} is the transmit antenna effective area and G_r is the receive antenna gain. Equations (21-1) through Eq. (21-3) are three forms of the Friis link equation. The equations can be modified to include the effect of thermal noise in the receiver system by dividing the total received power by the total system noise power. Using Eq. (21-3), the received signal-to-noise ratio (SNR) is:

$$SNR = \frac{P_r}{N} = \frac{P_tG_tG_r}{(4\pi d/\lambda)^2 \mathrm{k}T_sB} \tag{21-4}$$

where N is the receiver system noise power in Watts, k is Boltzmann's constant (1.38×10^{-23} W/K·Hz), T_s is the system noise temperature in Kelvin, and B is the noise bandwidth of the receiver system in Hz. Additional losses in the link are accounted for by reducing the SNR proportionally. A closer examination of Eq. (21-4) reveals several parameters of interest. First, P_tG_t is numerically equal to the power that would be transmitted by an equivalent system with an isotropic radiator instead of a real antenna, and is referred to as the *effective isotropic radiated power* (EIRP). Second, $(4\pi d/\lambda)^2$ is referred to as the *space loss* (a unitless parameter), sometimes also called the *path loss* or *spreading loss*. Finally, $N_o=\mathrm{k}T_s$ is the *noise power density* of the receiver system in W/Hz. Equation (21-4) is general and may be modified to represent the *SNR* of the received data stream, commonly referred to as the *energy per bit-to-noise density ratio* (E_b/N_o). Before doing so, however, it is important to review two of the most common forms of data modulation for spacecraft: residual carrier phase modulation (PM) and suppressed carrier phase modulation.

Modulation Techniques

Residual Carrier Phase Modulation (PM) is the most commonly used TT&C modulation technique for both military and civilian space applications. It apportions part of the transmitted power into the data and part into a discrete carrier component to enable precise phase tracking of the carrier by the ground station for demodulation and Doppler tracking purposes. In the absence of ranging and assuming rectangular (unfiltered) data bits, the proportions of transmitted power in the data and carrier are $P_t\sin^2(\beta)$ and $P_t\cos^2(\beta)$, respectively, where β is the *phase modulation index*. Each data bit (after any forward error correction coding) is typically split in time with the polarity reversed for the second half of the bit time to produce a spectrum that lacks energy around 0 Hz to minimize interference with phase tracking of the carrier. This type of data formatting is often referred to as bi-phase or Manchester line coding. Figure 21-2a illustrates the resulting modulated RF spectrum of residual carrier PM. Note that the "main lobe" of the spectrum (defined as the portion between first nulls on each side of the carrier) is 4 times the coded bit rate, resulting in a relatively inefficient transmitted spectrum. Residual carrier PM is often used for uplinks and for downlinks with low-to-moderate bit rates where the transmitted bandwidth is not a driver. It can also be used in the absence of Manchester line coding to conserve spectrum width if suitable measures are taken to ensure that long strings of 1s or 0s in the data are broken up. Pseudo-randomization of the data before modulation is a common way to accomplish that objective. The transmitted spectrum will then appear as shown in Fig. 21-2b except with the residual carrier component at center frequency still present. A derandomizer must be used in the ground receiver system to recover the original data pattern.

The phase modulation index, β is set by the designer usually between 45 deg and 90 deg. The modulation technique approaches the theoretical best efficiency possible as β approaches 90 deg. Values of 60 deg and higher are typically used for normal-mode downlink bit rates to maximize the received data power. Lower values are typically used for very low bit rate (10s of bps) emergency mode links to ensure adequate carrier component power for maintaining lock in the ground receiver. A subcarrier is typically used for low bit rate data to reduce interference with the carrier tracking loop. The presence of a sinusoidal subcarrier and/or a ranging waveform changes the simple equations presented here. A full explanation of modulation modes and the corresponding equations can be found in the CCSDS standards.

Suppressed Carrier Phase Modulation, which places all of the power into the data, is also popular for spacecraft communication systems. *Binary phase-shift keying (BPSK)* corresponds to β = 90 deg (phase symbols spaced 180 deg apart) and maximizes the power in the data. It is popular because it has the best power efficiency theoretically possible and is relatively simple to implement on the spacecraft. Each data bit (after any forward error correction coding) is modulated directly onto the carrier resulting in the spectrum illustrated in Fig. 21-2b. The main lobe width is 2× the coded bit rate, or half the width of the residual carrier PM spectrum because the data bits are modulated directly (not split in polarity) onto the carrier. BPSK is considered for higher bit rate uplinks (i.e., memory uploads) and moderate bit rate downlinks. *Quadrature phase-shift keying (QPSK)* encodes pairs of coded bits into phase symbols spaced 90° apart to reduce the transmitted main lobe width by a factor of two compared to BPSK (Fig. 21-2c). It is popular for high data rate communications because its power efficiency is also the best theoretically possible (same as BPSK) but in half the transmitted bandwidth. A filter is often included in the transmitter to ensure that the QPSK spectrum rolls off at the NTIA-required rate of –12 dB per octave beyond the necessary bandwidth points. Care must be taken in designing the filter to prevent substantial spectrum "re-growth" once the signal passes through a non-linear power amplifier.

Recovery of either BPSK or QPSK must be done in the ground receiver using a nonlinear operation to regenerate a coherent carrier reference signal for demodulation. This operation introduces ambiguities in the absolute phase of the coherent carrier reference signal. Compensation for this ambiguity must be incorporated into the spacecraft design and might be accomplished through differentially encoded data, transmission of a known pattern, or error correction coding. Other downsides of using BPSK or QPSK are their sensitivity to phase noise and additional "squaring" or "quadrupling" noise generated in the nonlinear carrier recovery tracking loop. Nevertheless, these modulation techniques are very popular due to their relatively simple implementation on the spacecraft, high power efficiency, and, in the case of QPSK, relatively narrow main lobe width.

Further reduction of the transmitted spectrum width and sidelobe levels can be achieved through more advanced modulation techniques. Techniques that encode more bits into each transmitted symbol, such as 8-PSK and 16-PSK, can be used to reduce the width of the main lobe of the spectrum at the expense of substantially reduced power efficiency relative to QPSK. *Gaussian Minimum-Shift Keying (GMSK)* applies special filtering and encoding of the data to generate symbols with gradual phase transitions between them, thereby substantially reducing the sidelobe levels at the expense of a slightly wider main lobe bandwidth compared to QPSK. GMSK has been used widely for cell phone applications and is gaining popularity in the space community for high data rate transmissions. The downside is its reduced power efficiency relative to QPSK and increased complexity on both the spacecraft and ground ends of the link. Generally speaking, bandwidth-efficient modulation techniques, whether seeking to reduce the width of the main lobe or reduce the level of the sidelobes, will increase the complexity of the implementation and reduce the power efficiency of the link relative to basic modulation techniques. Nevertheless, bandwidth-efficient techniques are gaining popularity as data rate requirements increase and implementation becomes easier as a result of advanced digital processing technologies [Deutsch, 2008], [Wesdock, 2008].

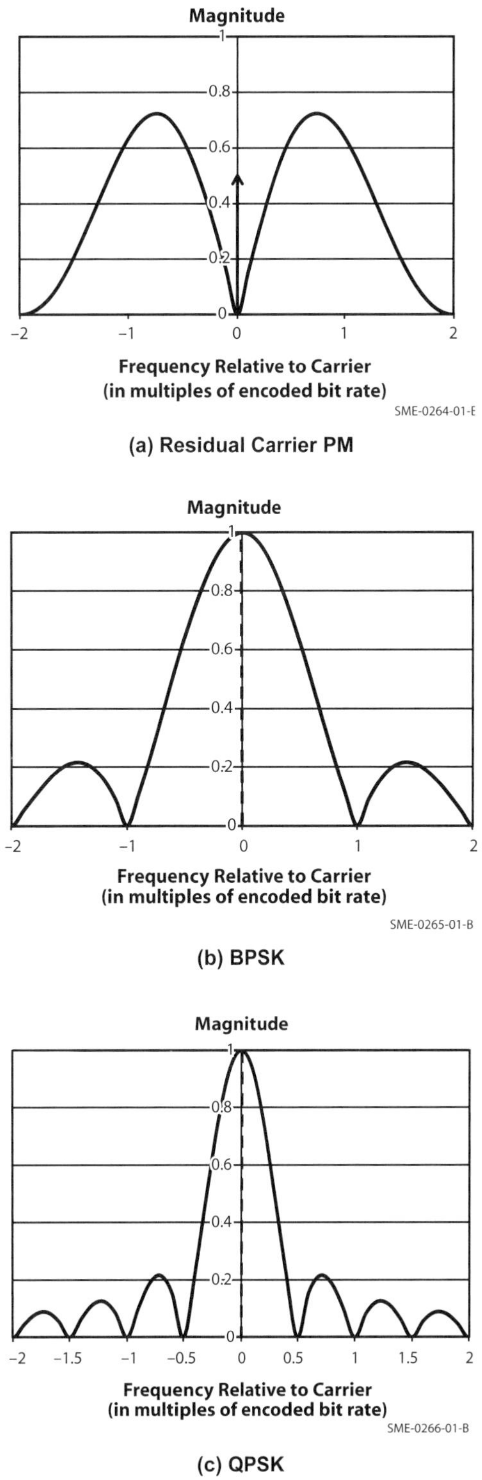

Fig. 21-2. Normalized Magnitude Spectra of Commonly Used Spacecraft Modulation Techniques.

Returning now to our discussion of link analysis, Eq. (21-3) can be modified for residual carrier PM modulation by recognizing that the energy in each transmitted bit (E_b) is equal to $(P_r/R)\sin^2(\beta)$ where R is the bit rate (substituted for bandwidth) and $P_r\sin^2(\beta)$ is the fraction of total received power contained in the data. See Eq. (21-5). The remaining received RF power, represented by $P_r\cos^2(\beta)$, is the fraction of total received power contained in the discrete carrier component and is used by the ground receiving system as a coherent reference for demodulation.

$$\frac{E_b}{N_o} = \frac{P_t G_t G_r}{(4\pi d/\lambda)^2 \mathrm{k} T_s R}\sin^2(\beta) \qquad (21\text{-}5)$$

Forward error correction coding adds symbols to the data stream, thereby increasing the transmitted symbol rate relative to uncoded data. Common examples include rate-1/2 convolutional coding that doubles the symbol rate and rate-1/6 Turbo coding that multiplies the symbol rate by a factor of six. Generally speaking, codes that incorporate a higher number of additional symbols perform better in noise but increase the transmitted bandwidth, resulting in a classic tradeoff.

Table 21-4 provides downlink analysis examples for the FireSat II and SCS missions operating at S-band, and a deep space mission operating at X and K_a-bands. The unit of power is expressed in dBm (decibels relative to 1 milliwatt). The FireSat II and SCS missions incorporate a low gain antenna that must provide coverage over an entire hemisphere, resulting in a worst-case gain of –4 dBic (dB relative to an isotropic antenna that is circularly polarized). The main differences between the links for these two missions are the distance and associated data rates. Additionally, the FireSat II mission incorporates QPSK modulation to minimize the transmitted spectrum width. The cost of the FireSat II hardware might be minimized through the use of a single-string architecture, radiation resistant (instead of hardened) hardware, and an appropriate tradeoff of risk versus parts reliability. The deep space mission is fairly aggressively sized to achieve a high data rate return, including 100 W transmitters and a 3 m diameter dish antenna. Note the substantial increase in data rate when going from X to K_a-band operation. On the downside, the K_a-band system will cost more, require tighter antenna pointing control, and be more susceptible to weather effects. Atmospheric loss and other weather effects at K_a-band can be mitigated to some extent through ground site diversity and by varying the downlink data rate as a function of ground antenna pointing elevation angle. Weather effects would not be an issue for crosslinks with other spacecraft such as TDRSS.

Downlink margin requirements are typically determined by uncertainties in the link analysis, sponsor requirements, and company policy. Typical values for planning purposes might be 6 dB for a near Earth mission (where more uncertainty in the spacecraft antenna patterns and ground station performance exist) and 3 dB for a deep space link (where the ground station performance is highly characterized). Lower operational link margins can be used, especially when the data rate is adjustable or retransmission of erroneous frames is automatically done. In the latter case the use of the CCSDS File Transfer Protocol (CFTP) provides the capability of automatically retransmitting files, thereby allowing for lower operational link margin and a higher frame error rate. Uplink margins are treated in the same manner but are often set to be substantially higher than the downlink margins to ensure mission robustness in the event of unforeseen attitude control problems. Generally speaking, higher link margins on both the downlink and uplink, especially for emergency modes, result in additional mission robustness but can be expensive and hard to justify because of the difficulty in quantifying unforeseen problems at the design phase stage.

The Decibel

A bel is simply the base-10 logarithm of a unitless power ratio: 2 converts to 0.3 bel, 100 to 2.0 bel. It is more convenient to work with tenths of bel's, so the decibel (abbreviated dB) is used in practice (2 converts to 3 dB, 100 converts to 20 dB). The satellite communications link equation is multiplicative, with more than a dozen terms depending on the complexity of the link. Some terms differ by 30 orders of magnitude (Boltzmann's constant is on the order of 10^{-23} W/Hz-K, and satellite distances may be millions of km, or 10^9 m). Converting all terms in the link equation to decibel form allows for easier manipulation, because multiplying two numbers is equivalent to adding their logarithms. Many elements in a link equation have units related to absolute power. These elements can be converted to dB-form by comparing them to a reference value and appending a suitable identifier. For example, transmit powers are frequently listed in units of dBW (power relative to 1 W) or dBm (power relative to 1 mW). In this way, a 2 kW transmit power can be represented as 33 dBW (= $10\log_{10}(2000)$). Other factors like bandwidth and noise temperature are proportional to noise power, and the same conversion applies. The term dB-Hz refers to a bandwidth relative to 1 Hz, and dB-K to an absolute temperature relative to 1 K. Antenna gain is commonly denoted in dBic (gain relative to an isotropic, circularly polarized antenna).

21.1.5 Hardware Design and Key Technologies

Figure 21-3 shows a representative block diagram of a redundant TT&C subsystem. The subsystem typically consists of five basic hardware elements: transponder, power amplifier, diplexer, RF switching/combining network, and antennas. A wideband transmitter might be in-

Table 21-4. Downlink Analysis Examples.

Parameter	Sym	Near Earth Links FireSat II	SCS	Deep Space Links Mars	Mars	Notes
RF Frequency **(GHz)**	f_c	2.2	2.2	8.4	32	
Distance to Ground Station	d	2,560 km	26,000 km	2.5 AU	2.5 AU	Antenna ground elevation angle =5 deg
Information Bit Rate	R	5 Mbps	50 kbps	500 kbps	2.1 Mbps	Before any error correction coding
Phase Modulation Index **(rad pk)**	β	QPSK	1.2	1.2	1.2	Typical for non-emergency data rates
Transmit Power **(dBm)**	P_t	36	36	50	50	4 W SSPA for FireSat II and SCS; 100 W TWTA for deep space
Transmit Passive Loss **(dB)**	L_p	–2	–2	–2	–2	Between the transmitter and antenna
Transmit Antenna Gain **(dBic)**	G_t	–4 (Hemi)	–4 (Hemi)	46 (3-m dish)	58 (3-m dish)	Includes pointing loss
EIRP **(dBm)**	$P_tG_tL_p$	30	30	94	106	
Path Loss **(dB)**	$(4\pi d/\lambda)^2$	–167.5	–187.6	–282.4	–294.0	
Atmospheric Loss		~0	~0	–0.3	–1.0	No rain
Ground Antenna Gain **(dBic)**	G_r	45.0	45.0	68.2	79.0	10-m dish for FireSat II and SCS; 34-m dish for deep space
Total Received Power **(dBm)**	P_r	–92.4	–112.6	–120.5	–110.0	
Data-to-Total Power **(dB)**	$\sin^2(\beta)$	0	–0.6	–0.6	–0.6	
System Noise Density **(dBm/Hz)**	$N_o = kT_s$	–174.6 (T_s=250 K)	–174.6 (T_s=250 K)	–183.8 (T_s=30 K)	–179.6 (T_s= 80 K)	
Received E_b/N_o **(dB)**	$\frac{P_r \sin^2(\beta)}{N_o R}$	15.2	14.5	5.7	5.7	
Required E_b/N_o **(dB)**		5.5	5.5	1	1	Rate ½ convolutional coding for FireSat II and SCS; Rate 1/6 Turbo coding for deep space
Receiver System Loss **(dB)**		–3	–3	–1	–1	Relative to theory
Link Margin **(dB)**		6.7	6.0	3.7	3.7	

Note: losses are represented by negative decibels. Other small losses not included in example.

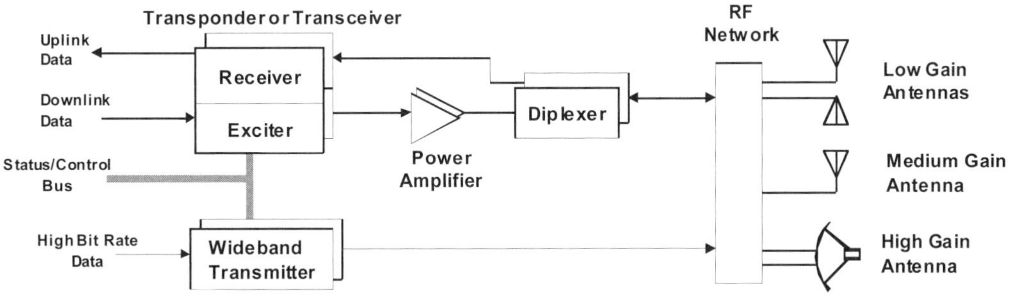

Fig. 21-3. TT&C Subsystem Block Diagram.

cluded depending on the data return requirements of the mission. The power amplifier is often built into the transponder and wideband transmitter when the RF output power is relatively low (≤ 5W) but may be a separate standalone component for higher power levels. Cross-strapping between redundant systems is not shown but can be added at the cost of greater complexity.

Transponders/Transceivers: the transponder or transceiver is the heart of the subsystem because it provides for modulation and demodulation and controls the modes of operation of the subsystem. The transponder incorporates receive, transmit, two-way Doppler tracking, and ranging functions. It generates the downlink signal by phase-locking to the uplink signal and deriving the downlink signal in phase coherence with the uplink signal. This process results in a fixed "turnaround ratio" for the transponder that enables accurate orbit determination from observation of the two-way Doppler shift as a function of time. Standard downlink/uplink turnaround ratios are 256/205 for SGLS, 240/221 for NASA S-band and 880/749 for NASA deep space X-band transponders, although other turnaround ratios are possible for special applications. A basic transponder will incorporate serial data and clock signals for the downlink telemetry and uplink command data. Transfer of the downlink data can also be done via spacecraft bus (i.e., MIL-STD-1553) [DoD, 1978] at the expense of additional power and cost. A trend for the future is to incorporate a packetized data interface for the downlink telemetry to enable the use of commercial standards (i.e., USB) and increase the flexibility of the transponder in selecting bit rates and coding modes. Mode controls and status telemetry for the transponder can be implemented in several ways including discrete signal lines, universal asynchronous receiver/transmitters (UARTs), or the spacecraft bus (i.e., MIL-STD-1553). The transponder often includes a "pass-through" channel that enables uplink ranging modulation to be turned around and modulated onto the downlink signal, thereby enabling accurate range measurements to be made by the ground station for orbit determination. Most ranging systems today are simply "elbows" or "bent-pipes", where the uplink modulation and associated noise are passed through to the downlink. A trend for the future is to incorporate regenerative ranging where the transponder locks to the uplink ranging signal and regenerates it for modulation onto the downlink, as in a digital repeater. This technique results in less power wasted in the downlink on turnaround ranging noise and more power available for data return and ranging.

A simpler and lower-cost alternative to the transponder is a *transceiver system* that provides separate receive and transmit functions without phase coherence between the signals. The downlink signal frequency will be dependent on the stability of the on-board oscillator, which will limit the accuracy of Doppler shift measurements. The transceiver alternative is viable for missions that rely on alternate means for orbit determination such as an on-board GPS receiver or radar skin tracking.

The transponder/transceiver technology area is poised for substantial improvements in the future as modern analog and digital signal processing technology becomes available for spacecraft use. Great strides have been made in the past 20 years on the reliability of plastic encapsulated microcircuits (PEMs), making them candidates for use in spacecraft instead of hermetically sealed parts. This trend enables the designer to take advantage of low-power, highly integrated parts available in the commercial sector such as frequency synthesizers, upconverters/downconverters, direct digital synthesizers (DDS), and vector modulators. Digital signal processing technology is already incorporated into most modern transponders, and the potential for greatly improved performance in the near future exists. Current designs make use of application-specific integrated circuits (ASICs) to achieve a combination of small size, low power, and radiation hardness. The ASIC design cycle, however, can be relatively expensive resulting in a tendency to resist changes after the circuits are fabricated. Future transponder designs will make increasing use of radiation-resistant field programmable gate arrays (FPGAs) to provide the designer with more flexibility for incorporating custom signal processing functions and making late design changes. These FPGAs are currently available with millions of gates. Open-source processors are available for downloading into the FPGAs and custom digital signal processing functions can be designed into them. Firmware design tools are relatively mature at this point. As the digital technology continues to improve, software-defined radios (SDRs) will become increasingly viable for spacecraft use. These radios have great functionality and flexibility but typically have high power and mass relative to conventional TT&C transponders. Improvements in technology, particularly the availability of low-power general-purpose processors, will make SDRs a more attractive choice for some missions in the future. Improvements in on-board digital processing will naturally enable more functionality and reconfigurability of the TT&C transponder; for example, increasing use of uplink forward error correction coding, reconfigurable receiver loop bandwidths, downlink low density parity-check coding (LDPC), FFT-based uplink signal acquisition, and bandwidth-efficient modulation techniques such as Gaussian minimum-shift keying (GMSK).

Power Amplifiers: power amplification of the downlink signal is accomplished either with a solid-state power amplifier (SSPA) or traveling wave tube amplifier (TWTA). The SSPA is relatively low mass and size compared to the TWTA, simple to implement, and power efficient at RF power levels of 15 W and less operating at RF frequencies of X-band and below. The TWTA becomes an attractive choice at RF power levels of approximately 15 W and above because of its superb power efficiency at those levels. Table 21-5 illustrates typical mass and efficiency performance achieved with current spaceborne power amplifiers. The overall efficiency is defined as the RF output power divided by the spacecraft bus input power. A substantial drop in solid-state power amplifier efficiency occurs when going from X-band to K_a-band operation. This performance may represent a problem for some missions that require K_a-band operation but have very limited bus power available. Improvements in K_a-band solid-state efficiency and the development of K_a-band TWTAs operating at lower RF power levels are potential areas for technology development in the future.

The choice of power amplifier technology is often a fairly straightforward one. Near-Earth missions operating at S-band or lower in frequency benefit most often by the small size and relative low cost of a solid state amplifier built into the transponder or transceiver. Missions that require high EIRP due to a high data rate requirement or large Earth distance may benefit from the high RF power and efficiency of a TWTA that is purchased separately from the transponder or transceiver. Some special requirements, such as high shock, rapid power cycling, or the need for an active phased array antenna, will drive a mission to solid-state technology at any of the frequency bands.

Diplexers: the diplexer is a filtering component that couples the receiver and transmitter signals together onto a single RF cable or waveguide. It provides filtering for the receiver input to prevent interference and overload

Table 21-5. Power Efficiency and Mass for Spaceborne Power Amplifiers.

	SSPA		TWTA	
Frequency Band	**Overall Efficiency**	**Mass**	**Overall Efficiency**	**Mass**
S-band	30–40%	0.5 to 1.5 kg, depending on RF output power, including power converter	60%	~2.5 kg including power converter
X-band	20–28%		50–60%	
K_a-band	11–17%		50–60%	

from the transmit signal and other signals including those on the spacecraft and those present during launch and flight operations. It provides filtering at the transmitter output to reduce output noise at the receive frequency and reduce harmonics. Because of its highly resonant nature, the diplexer must be carefully specified and designed to prevent a high vacuum breakdown phenomenon called *multipactor discharge*. This phenomenon can occur at RF power levels as low as a few watts at S-band. Many missions have suffered schedule delays late in the development cycle because of a multipactor discharge problem. Multipactor discharge is of particular concern in filters but can occur anywhere that high RF power levels exist including the power amplifier, RF cables, the RF switching/combining network, and antennas.

RF Network: the RF network design can vary greatly depending on the redundancy and operational requirements on the TT&C subsystem. In its simplest form, the network is simply an RF power divider that splits the RF signal between two hemispherical coverage antennas. This type of network is often used on missions that require omni-directional antenna coverage. The actual coverage pattern is relatively constant over the main lobe area of each antenna but becomes highly variable where the two antenna patterns meet because of interferometry nulls. Alternatively, the network could consist of an RF switch that selects between two hemispherical coverage antennas. This arrangement creates higher overall antenna gain (the signal is not split) than the omni-directional pattern but the spacecraft must select which antenna to use. Some missions incorporate a combination of low gain antennas, a medium gain antenna, and a high gain antenna, thereby driving the RF network to a more complex combination of switches. Care must be taken to mitigate potential single point failures when designing the RF network.

Antennas: the design of the spacecraft antenna system is tailored to accommodate the mission coverage requirements, orbital parameters, spacecraft attitude control characteristics, and bit rate requirements. Antennas are usually custom-designed, although some might be purchased as "off-the-shelf" items. The antenna directs the radiated power into the appropriate regions of space to maximize the efficiency of the RF transmission through free space. A key metric for an antenna is its *gain*, defined as the power density radiated in a given direction relative to that of an isotropic (uniform) radiator. The antenna gain includes inefficiencies in the design such as spillover and resistive losses and is usually expressed in dBi for a linearly polarized antenna and dBic for a circularly polarized antenna. Most civilian and military space missions incorporate circularly polarized antennas to prevent mismatches in physical orientation between the spacecraft and ground station antennas as a function of orbit location. In contrast, some commercial geosynchronous satellites with a fixed orientation will incorporate linearly polarized antennas.

Key tradeoffs when specifying antennas are between beamwidth, gain, and effective aperture area (size). The beamwidth is inversely related to both the gain and effective aperture area. A narrow-beam antenna will have relatively high gain and large size because the radiated power is focused in a given direction. It is typically used for high rate mission payload data return. Conversely, a broad-beam antenna will have relatively low gain and small size because the radiated power is spread over many directions. It is often used as the primary antenna for near-Earth missions with modest downlink bit rate requirements. It is also used whenever the spacecraft attitude is not precisely controlled or known, for example, launch and early operations, emergency mode recovery, thrusting maneuvers, and Doppler tracking during science acquisition periods. A conical or fan beam antenna, often termed "medium gain", is useful on some missions with special requirements. For example, they can be used on deep space missions with limited RF transmit power that cannot establish an emergency downlink using a low gain antenna. For initial design purposes, one can use the information and rules-of-thumb in Table 21-6 to determine the characteristics and applications of various antenna types.

Shaping the beam pattern of an antenna can be used to provide advantages to missions. For example, in the common LEO case of a nadir-pointed broad-beam antenna, the edges of the beam pattern can be increased in gain compared to the boresight to account for the extra path loss to the ground station at these look angles. This technique provides a more constant receive power at the ground station, and increases the link data rates that are typically sized for the worst-case path loss/look angle. The fan beam antenna has a narrower beamwidth in one axis than the conical-beam antenna. If the spacecraft can rotate in one dimension, then the fan beam can be used to apply more gain to TT&C links, particularly useful in deep space missions.

Antenna placement can be challenging, and should be addressed early in the design phase. Integrating broad-beam, omni-directional antennas onto a spacecraft with large extended structure or solar arrays can substantially perturb the beam pattern. The beam pattern will be affected by any protrusion into or near its field of view, or by reflective surfaces in the back-lobe of the antenna. Achieving a perfectly clear field of view is not always possible. Gain measurements should be taken with the antenna on a representative satellite mock-up at an antenna range to check for destructive interference in the antenna gain pattern.

Spin-stabilized missions present a particularly challenging problem to the antenna designer. The antenna pattern must often be co-aligned with the axis of rotation, resulting in the need to keep the spin axis pointed at Earth or to use a relatively broad antenna pattern to cover the Earth direction as the geometry varies. A "pancake" or "donut" antenna pattern with constant gain about the equator of the spacecraft can be used on missions that keep the spin axis aligned in a direction perpendicular to the Earth orbit plane. Electronically despun antennas, which switch between radiating elements as the spacecraft rotates, can be used to keep a relatively narrow beam pointed in the Earth direction. These antennas incorporate complex feed and switching networks and depend on accurate knowledge of the Earth direction as the spacecraft rotates.

A few words should be said about electronically steered phased-array antenna technology. This technology can simplify spacecraft packaging and operations by eliminating the need for a mechanical gimbal to point the antenna. Its use in spacecraft designs to date, however, has been relatively limited because of the high cost and mass of the antenna, especially when two-dimensional scanning is required. Two notable accomplishments are the X-band one-dimensional scanned antenna flown on the MESSENGER mission to Mercury and the X-band two-dimensional scanned antenna flown on the Earth Orbiting-1 (EO-1) mission. Both of these antennas operated

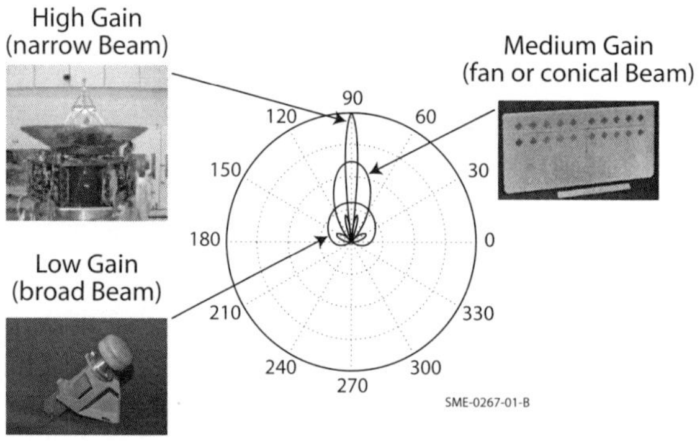

Fig. 21-4. Representative Antenna Technologies and Associated Beam Patterns.

in transmit-only mode and had distributed solid-state power amplifiers to maximize transmit efficiency. Hopefully, further applications for electronic scanning will drive the technology developments in packaging and electronics necessary to enable low-cost, low-mass electronically steered antennas in the future.

Wideband Transmitters: the wideband transmitter is an optional element depending on the data return requirements of the mission. Moderate or low data rate requirements (up to, say, 6 Mbps) can often be handled by the TT&C transponders assuming that the transmitted spectrum is consistent with NTIA limits. Additional wideband transmitters, typically operating at X-, K_u-, or K_a-band, can be added to the subsystem for higher data rate operations. These transmitters may have an integral power amplifier depending on RF output power requirements and are typically connected directly to the high gain antenna to minimize loss.

Table 21-6. Antenna Characteristics and Applications.

Antenna Type	Full 3 dB Beamwidth	Gain	Applications	Notes
High Gain Parabolic Reflector Antenna	$BW_{3db} = 66\lambda/D$ λ = wavelength D = diameter The beamwidth is typically in the single-digit degrees.	$G = 10\log(4\pi A_e/\lambda^2)$ $= 10\log(\pi^2 D^2/\lambda^2)\ \eta$ A_e = effective aperture area λ =wavelength η= overall efficiency	High data rate downlink/return link.	Effective aperture area is equal to the physical aperture area times the overall efficiency, typically between 55 and 65%.
High Gain Phased Array Antenna	Dependent on element and array pattern design. Basic tradeoffs between beamwidth, gain, and size still apply.		Flat packaging requirement. Electronic beam steering requirement.	Electronically steering antenna can be used to eliminate mechanical gimbals.
Medium Gain Antenna	Typically between 10 deg and 90 deg Can be conical beam or fan beam.	6 to 25 dBic	Deep space missions for emergency mode or to fill coverage gap at large Earth distances.	Might be used to reduce transmitter power required to support emergency mode communications. Examples include a small patch antenna array, waveguide horn, small dish reflector.
Low Gain Antenna	90 deg to 180 deg	0 to 6 dBic	Normal mode communications for Earth orbiters. LEOP coverage. Emergency mode coverage. Extended Doppler tracking for deep space missions.	Examples include single patches, quadrifilar helix, open-ended waveguide.

21.1.6 Subsystem Design Examples

Tables 21-7 and 21-8 present TT&C subsystem design examples for representative near-Earth and deep-space missions, respectively. Included are component quantities, bus power consumption, and masses for representative redundant systems. These examples correspond to the traditional "box and harness" approach to spacecraft design where the major hardware functions (transponder, power amplifier, diplexer) are implemented as standalone electronics boxes that are integrated together at the subsystem and spacecraft levels. This approach provides for a structured, systematic approach to the spacecraft bus design. However, the box and harness approach may result in excessive mass and power consumption for extremely small spacecraft designs such as microsats and nanosats. In these cases, the TT&C hardware could be implemented as board-level products that are carefully integrated with the other subsystems within the spacecraft structure. Such a highly integrated approach dictates the need for a small team environment and careful attention to interface and electromagnetic compatibility details. The approach can dramatically reduce total TT&C mass to the 500 g region. Single-board UHF radios are available with receive-only DC power consumption in the 100 to 200 mW range, and RF transmit powers around 5 W (40% overall efficiency).

Table 21-7. Representative Power and Mass Summary for a Near-Earth TT&C System.

Unit	Qty	DC Bus Power (W)	Total Power (W)	Unit Mass (kg)	Total Mass (kg)	Notes
S-Band Transponder	2	4 (Rx) 40 (Rx & Tx)	8 (2Rx) 44 (2Rx & Tx)	3.5	7	Built-in 5 W SSPA
S-Band Diplexer	2	0	0	0.2	0.4	
S-Band Cables	All	0	0	3	3	Approximately 10 RF cables
S-Band Antennas (low gain)	2	0	0	0.4	0.8	Forward and aft combined to form omni pattern
X-Band Wideband Transmitter	2	60	60	3.5	7	For wideband payload data return. Built-in 5 W SSPA.
X-Band Cables	All	0	0	0.5	1	2 RF cables, typically
X-Band Antenna (high gain)	1	0	0	1.5	1.5	0.5 m diameter parabolic reflector. Gimbal is separate.
TOTAL:			44 W (S only) 104 W (S and X)		20.7	

Table 21-8. Representative Power and Mass Summary for a Deep Space TT&C System.

Unit	Qty	DC Bus Power (W)	Total Power (W)	Unit Mass (kg)	Total Mass (kg)	Notes
X-Band Transponder	2	12 (Rx only) 14 (Rx and Tx)	24 (2Rx) 26 (2Rx & Tx)	3	6	Low-power exciter output (no built-in SSPA)
X-Band TWTA	2	50	50	2.5	5	RF output power= 25 W
X-Band Diplexer	2	0	0	0.6	1.2	
X-Band Switching Network	2	0	0	0.5 to 1.0	1 to 2	Dependent on number of switches. Includes interface plate.
X-Band Cables	All	0	0	5	5	18 RF cables (with SMA connectors)
X-Band Low Gain Antennas	2	0	0	0.7	1.4	Switched waveguide horns with 70 deg. Beamwidth (3 dB)
X-Band Medium Gain Antenna	1	0	0	1.5	1.5	0.3 m waveguide horn with 5 deg beamwidth (3 dB)
X-Band High Gain Antenna	1	0	0	6	6	1.5 m diameter parabolic reflector
K_a-Band Exciter (Modulator)	2	3	3	0.3	0.6	incremental increases to X-band transponder
K_a-Band TWTA	2	81	81	2.8	5.6	RF output power= 40 W
K_a-Band Waveguide	All			3	3	
K_a-Band Antenna (High Gain)	1			2.5	2.5	Additional feed and structure added to existing 1.5 m diameter parabolic reflector. Gimbal is separate.
Ultrastable oscillator	2	2.5	5	1.3	2.6	
TOTAL:			81 W (X Tx/Rx) 165 W (X Tx/Rx & K_a Tx)		41.4 to 42.4	

Table 21-8, Fig. 21-4◀, Eq. 21-5◀

21.1.7 Special Topics

Very High Bit Rate Communications

For almost all missions, significant data return is critical to mission success. Data rates have increased with technology, and the restricted bandwidths in the S- and X-bands are pushing missions to utilize K_a-band frequencies for data rates in excess of 10's of Mbps.

The move to higher frequencies (even to optical bands) comes with substantial challenges that require significant investments in advanced technology. Atmospheric losses and outages at K_a-band and optical frequencies are much higher, especially losses due to rain, which may require spatial diversity on the ground and the use of transmission protocols to overcome. Higher operating frequencies demand a tighter surface accuracy specification on the antennas and more accurate pointing from the attitude control system. Though the TT&C functions can be included in the high bit rate links, concerns regarding communications during spacecraft emergencies, such as attitude control anomalies, require that a lower rate, lower frequency capability is retained for robustness.

Emergency Mode Recovery

The design of the TT&C subsystem will frequently be driven by how the system must support the spacecraft during emergencies. The spacecraft may experience problems that cause it to lose knowledge or control of its attitude. With unknown or anomalous attitude, maintaining communications is critically important in reestablishing control before batteries drain too low or faults progress further, ending in mission failure. It is the unfortunate lot of the TT&C subsystem engineer that many emergencies on the spacecraft manifest themselves first as a loss in communications.

The brute force approach to providing emergency mode TT&C capability is to design the antenna system to provide continuous uplink and downlink coverage over the entire sphere about the spacecraft. Typically two low gain antennas are oriented towards opposite hemispheres on the spacecraft, and a power splitter connects them to the rest of the RF system. Commands can be transmitted successfully to the spacecraft and telemetry received no matter what attitude the satellite exhibits. The drawback to this approach lies in the use of the splitter. Where the two hemispherical antenna patterns meet, the resultant sum pattern will experience significant nulls when the patterns of the two LGAs combine destructively. Additionally, half the RF power is transmitted through the opposite antenna. This scheme works best in LEO missions with robust link margins. Alternatively, a switch may be used instead of a power splitter, which removes the nulling effect and focuses all of the RF power into one hemisphere but requires the satellite to autonomously switch hemispheres over time to guarantee that a link can be established.

For missions at longer ranges, a hemispherical coverage antenna may not provide sufficient gain to establish a low rate emergency link, and a higher gain TT&C antenna must be used. Most spacecraft are able to robustly point in the direction of the Sun, even in emergency situations. If the maximum angular separation of the Earth from the Sun is known, a medium gain antenna might be used to provide coverage. One solution is to point a conical-beam antenna at the Sun and wobble the rotation axis of the spacecraft to cause the antenna beam to sweep out a wider volume of space than its actual beam pattern. Another solution is to use a fanbeam antenna with a rotating spacecraft. The spacecraft rotates slowly about the spacecraft-Sun line, and the RF power received from the spacecraft is monitored on the ground. When the fanbeam antenna sweeps through the Earth direction, the increase in received RF power is seen on the ground. The spacecraft can then be commanded to stop rotating at precisely the correct time to leave the fanbeam antenna pointed directly at Earth, reestablishing communications. This approach was used successfully on the NEAR and MESSENGER deep-space missions.

Ultrastable Oscillators

Ultrastable oscillators (USOs) are precision, temperature-compensated, oven-controlled crystal oscillators that exhibit extraordinary short-term frequency stability, with Allan deviations* of approximately $\Delta F/F = 3 \times 10^{-13}$ measured in time intervals of 1 to 100 seconds and excellent phase noise. This performance is achieved for relatively low mass and power compared to an atomic clock which provides better long term stability. USOs consume approximately 2.5 W or less with about 1 kg mass, and are trending lower in both categories.

USOs can be used to the advantage of the TT&C subsystem and satellite design in several ways. They permit precise timekeeping on the satellite over large time intervals. One-way Doppler tracking becomes feasible using a USO, permitting autonomous satellite navigation for landing assists. Precision ranging between tandem spacecraft is enabled for gravity field mapping. As a reference source for the TT&C radio's downlink signal, USOs can provide such a stable signal that the received signal on the ground can be used to deduce properties of planetary atmospheres as the planet occults the satellite when viewed from Earth.

21.1.8 Future Trends

Spaceflight TT&C technology tends to lag commercial, terrestrial RF communications technology due to the difficulties and expense involved in qualifying parts for space, particularly due to high-reliability, packaging, and radiation constraints. The gap is closing, as indicated earlier, with the increased use of qualified PEMs and highly integrated RF parts. With advances in space-qualified digital technology, the conversion from RF (analog) to digital is migrating closer to the antenna. Similarly,

* Allan deviation is a measure of the fractional change in oscillator frequency due to noise processes. It excludes systematic changes such as frequency drift and temperature effects.

software-defined radios (SDRs) are becoming more prevalent with improvements in digital processors and FPGAs. SDRs promise increased in-flight flexibility, reduced hardware assembly costs for subsequent missions (since potentially only the software settings need to be changed), and ease of technology insertion (via software or firmware, without changing the hardware). Mission data rate requirements generally increase with time, requiring wider bandwidths, more power, or more efficient transmitters or coding. The drive to higher data rates and the squeeze at lower frequency bands due to competition from cellular systems and wireless applications (especially at S-band) serve to impel TT&C frequencies to higher bands such as K_a-band. The ultimate limiting factor for the use of higher frequencies is weather effects, which drives complexity in operating the link efficiently.

21.2 Power

Joseph K. McDermott, Jeremiah P. Schneider, and Scott W. Enger
Lockheed Martin Space Systems Company

This section describes the *Electrical Power System* (EPS), which provides, stores, regulates, and distributes electrical power to payloads/instruments, and other flight subsystems (i.e., thermal, communication, guidance, and navigation). Nothing on the spacecraft can function without electrical power. The need for more power is growing as power begets powerful machines and enables missions that will change the world. The challenges for space power systems focus around maximizing efficiency, safety, reliability, and radiation harness; while minimizing mass, volume, thermal requirements, and costs (development, procurement, integration, and operational).

The power systems defined in this section are mostly applicable for today's LEO, GEO, planetary, and deep space spacecraft missions and emerging high altitude air ships. In this section we focus on the fundamentals of space electrical power systems, including their mission and requirement drivers, with an emphasis on the processes and methodologies for determination of the power system architectures. The 4 basic components of an EPS, shown in Fig. 21-5, are independently addressed in Secs. 21.2.2 through 21.2.5, along with a mission (FireSat II) sizing example, to provide a basic understanding of these subsystems and the processes used to size and optimize the EPS.

A GEO communications spacecraft power system mass comprises ~30% of the spacecraft dry mass, with percentages to the 4 basic EPS components as shown in Fig. 21-6. Figure 21-6 also depicts the typical cost distribution for the 4 main EPS components. The EPS mass and cost distributions may vary from mission to mission, although one can typically expect the energy source and energy storage systems to be the main players for both EPS mass and cost. The large mass and cost allocations for the power source and energy storage components dictate early trade studies, usually focused around selection and optimization of the solar arrays and batteries. Sections 21.2.2 and 21.2.3 go into detail for the power source (solar array) and energy storage (battery) systems to help identify the key early EPS trade studies.

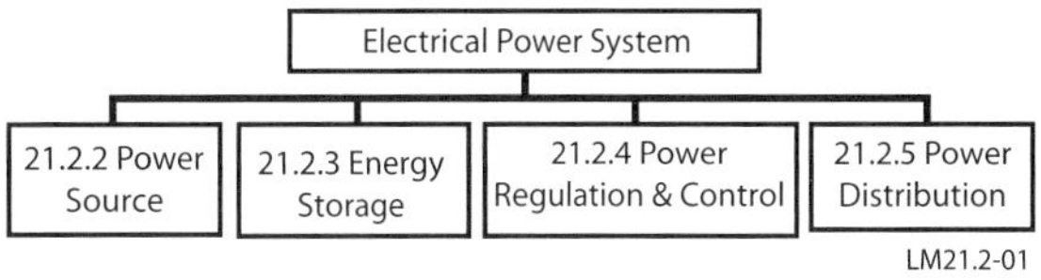

Fig. 21-5. Functional Breakdown for the Spacecraft's Power Subsystem. We start with these 4 basic functions and must determine requirements for the hardware, software, and interfaces for each.

Section 21.2.6 summarizes where investments and research are focused for future power systems that may offer new and improved power system architectures and topologies to further support and enable future missions. Based upon the power source and energy storage mass and cost allocations shown in Fig. 21-6, advancements in power generation technologies and energy storage systems are the focus of Sec. 21.2.6.

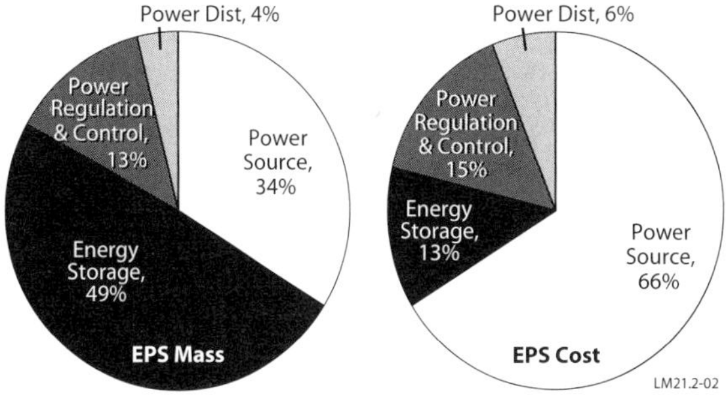

Fig. 21-6. Mass and Cost Breakdown for the Spacecraft's Power Subsystem. The large mass and cost allocations for the energy source (solar array) and the energy storage system (batteries) result in power system trade studies focused around these EPS components prior to design and manufacture.

21.2.1 Mission and Design Requirements

Systems engineering and power system design must begin with an understanding and definition of requirements. Table 21-9 lists typical functions performed by the EPS. The 3 most important EPS sizing requirements are the demands for average and peak electrical power; the orbital profile (inclination and altitude); and mission life. We must identify the average and peak electrical power loads for mission operations during the transfer orbit where there may be limited power generated from the solar array; for operations at beginning-of-life (BOL); and operations at end-of-life (EOL). For many missions, the EOL power demands must be reduced to compensate for power source (e.g., solar array) perfor-

Table 21-9. Typical Top-Level Power Subsystem Functions. Each of these functions consists of sub-functions with myriad design characteristics which we must develop to define and meet mission requirements.

- Supply a continuous source of electrical power to spacecraft/vehicle loads during the mission life.
- Control and distribute electrical power to the spacecraft / vehicle.
- Support power requirements for average and peak electrical loads.
- Provide converters for AC and regulated DC power buses, if required.
- Provide command and telemetry capability for EPS health and status, as well as control by ground station or an autonomous system.
- Protect the spacecraft payload against failures within the EPS.
- Suppress transient bus voltages and protect against bus faults.
- Provide ability to fire ordnance, if required.

mance degradation. The average electrical power needed at EOL determines the size of the power source. For any mission, the identification and tracking of spacecraft component average and peak power loads as a function of mission phase are critical to proper requirements definition. Section 14.5.3 shows a sample power budget with typical input data that we may use to begin the sizing process. If peak power requirements are not fully defined, a first-estimate is to multiply average power by 2 or 3 to obtain peak power requirements for attitude control, payload, thermal, and EPS (when charging the batteries). Fortunately, all the systems do not require peak power at the same time during the mission. Table 21-10 summarizes the power subsystem design process, which we discuss further in the following subsections.

Table 21-11 shows the principal effects of mission requirements on the power system design. The definition and tracking of power system requirements are critical for any mission. Requirements will change as the program matures from concept to flight, and we must fully understand requirement changes to properly assess spacecraft/vehicle impacts. The power budget table in Sec. 14.5.3 provides an example template for tracking subsystem electrical power requirements. The key to ensuring a spacecraft power system is properly sized is in the detail and tracking of a power system budget via a mission-specific power budget profile.

With proper requirements definition, we are now ready to examine and select the best power system architecture (Sec. 21.2.2), and then we can work through the design process beginning with the power source.

21.2.2 Power Generation/Sources

A *photovoltaic cell* or *solar cell* is a device that converts sunlight into electricity. Solar cells are connected in series to form a *string*; the number of cells in a string determines the string voltage. A *solar array* is made up of one or more strings in parallel. Earth-orbiting spacecraft at low-Earth to geosynchronous orbits have usually employed photovoltaics as their power source. Often, photovoltaics were the only real candidate for these low-power missions (less than 15 kW) because solar cells were well-known and reliable. Photovoltaic sources are not attractive for interplanetary missions to the outer planets because solar radiation decreases with the square of the distance, thus rapidly reducing the available energy from a solar array. To configure and size a solar array, we must understand cell types and characteristics; solar-

Table 21-10. The Preliminary Design Process for the Power Subsystem. All of these design steps must link back to mission requirements to satisfy the owner and users. Note that derived requirements may impact previous design decisions and force designers to iterate the design process.

Step	Information Required	Derived Requirements	References
1. Identify Requirements	Top-level requirements, mission type (LEO, GEO), spacecraft configuration, mission life, payload definition	Design requirements, spacecraft electrical power profile (average and peak)	Secs. 10.1, 10.2
2. Select and Size Power Source	Mission type, spacecraft configuration, average load requirements for electrical power	EOL power requirement, type of solar cell, mass and area of solar array, solar array configuration (2-axis tracking panel, body-mounted)	Secs. 10.1, 10.2, 14.3.3, 21.2.2, Table 14-20
3. Select and Size Energy Storage	Mission orbital parameters, average and peak load requirements for electrical power	Eclipse and load-leveling energy storage requirement (battery capacity requirement), battery mass and volume, battery type	Sec. 21.2.3
4. Identify Power Regulation and Control and Distribution	Power-source selection, mission life, requirements for regulating mission load and thermal-control requirements	Peak-power tracker or direct-energy-transfer system, thermal-control requirements, bus-voltage quality, power control algorithms	Secs. 21.2.4, 21.2.5
5. Estimate the Mass, Average Power and Peak Power Requirements	Power profile budget from systems engineering that combines all payload and spacecraft housekeeping loads. Mass largely driven by power generation and energy storage.	Average and peak power (W)	Secs. 21.2.1, 21.2.3

Table 21-11. Effects of System-Level Parameters on the Power Subsystem. Most aspects of the mission affect the power subsystem because so many other subsystems require specific power attributes.

Parameter	Effects on Design
Average Electrical Power Requirement	Sizes the power-generation system (e.g., number of solar cells, primary battery size) and possibly the energy-storage system given the eclipse period and depth of discharge
Peak Electrical Power Required	Sizes the energy-storage system (e.g., number of batteries, capacitor bank size) and the power-processing and distribution equipment
Mission Life	Longer mission life (> 7 yr) implies extra redundancy design, independent battery charging, larger capacity batteries, and larger arrays
Orbital Parameters	Defines incident Solar energy, eclipse/Sun periods, and radiation environment
Spacecraft Configuration	Spinner typically implies body-mounted solar cells; 3-axis stabilized typically implies body-fixed and deployable solar panels

array design issues, sizing calculations, configurations, regulation; and radiation and thermal environments. Key design issues for solar arrays include spacecraft configuration, required power level (peak and average), operating temperatures, shadowing, radiation environment, illumination or orientation, mission life, mass and area, cost, and risk. Table 21-12 shows the solar array design process.

Step 1. Mission life and the average power requirement are the two key design considerations in sizing the solar array for most spacecraft. We size a photovoltaic system to meet power requirements at EOL, with the resulting solar array often oversized for power requirements at BOL. This excess power at BOL requires coordinated systems engineering to avoid thermal problems. The longer the mission life, the larger is the difference between power requirements at EOL and BOL. We usually consider photovoltaics a poor power source for missions lasting more than 10 years because of natural degradation in the solar array. Section 21.2.4 (Power Regulation and Control), discusses how we manage excess power from the solar array. The average power requirement can be obtained from Sec. 10.1 and 10.2.

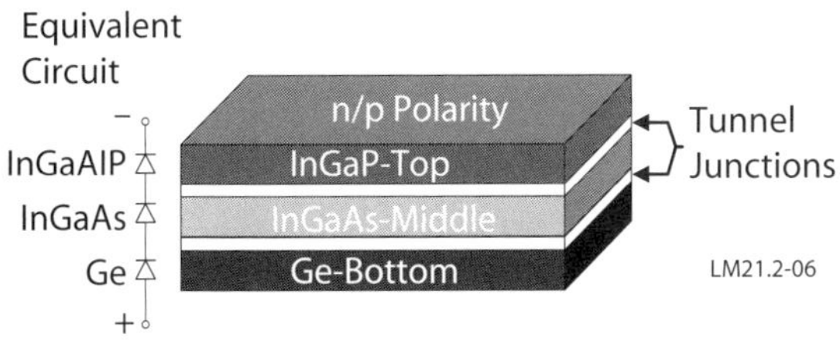

Fig. 21-7. Typical Triple Junction Cell Schematic. Each junction collects energy over a different range of the Solar spectrum.

In designing a solar array, we trade off mass, area, cost, and risk. Silicon cells cost the least but with lower efficiency, so when the total array cost, area, mass and environmental effects are considered, it may not be a better choice than the more costly gallium-arsenide (GaAs) cells. Triple junction GaAs cells have become the standard for most space applications, due to their higher collection efficiency and suitability for use in the higher radiation environment of most space missions. Due to their extensive use, many thousands of hours of on-orbit data is available to predict performance, reducing program risk. In the US, these cells are produced by Emcore and Spectrolab. Figure 21-7 shows a typical triple junction solar cell structure.

A solar array's illumination intensity depends on orbital parameters such as the Sun incidence angles, eclipse periods, solar distance, and concentration of solar energy. Tracking and pointing mechanisms on the solar array often adjust for these influences. If we mount the cells on the body of the spacecraft, we must orient them so they will generate adequate power throughout the mission.

Step 2. To estimate the solar array area required for a spacecraft, we first determine how much power, P_{sa}, the solar array must provide during daylight to power the spacecraft for the entire orbit

$$P_{sa} = \frac{\left(\frac{P_e T_e}{X_e} + \frac{P_d T_d}{X_d}\right)}{T_d} \tag{21-6}$$

where P_e and P_d are the spacecraft's power requirements (excluding regulation and battery charging losses) during eclipse and daylight, respectively, and T_e and T_d are the lengths of these periods per orbit. The terms X_e and X_d represent the efficiency of the paths from the solar arrays through the batteries to the individual loads and the path directly from the arrays to the loads, respectively. The efficiency values for eclipse and daylight depend on the type of power regulation: direct energy transfer or peak-power tracking. (A description of these methods follows in Sec. 21.2.4. For direct energy transfer, the efficiencies are about $X_e = 0.65$ and $X_d = 0.85$; for peak-power tracking they are $X_e = 0.60$ and $X_d = 0.80$. The efficiencies of the former are about 5% to 7% greater than the latter because peak-power tracking requires a power converter between the arrays and the loads.

Step 3. Table 21-13 shows the efficiencies and radiation-degradation sensitivities of typical solar cells. Triple

Table 21-12. Solar Array Design Process. In the FireSat II example column, I_d represents inherent degradation, θ is the Sun incidence angle, L_d is life degradation, and X_e and X_d represent the efficiencies of the power distribution paths. The material following the table further explains these quantities

Step	Reference	FireSat II Example
1. Determine requirements & constraints for power subsystem solar array design		
• ***Average power required during daylight and eclipse***	Input parameter, Secs. 3.5, 10.1, 14.1, 14.3	110 W during daylight and eclipse
• ***Orbit altitude & eclipse duration***	Input parameter	700 km 35.3 min
• ***Design lifetime***	Chaps. 2, 3	5 yr
2. Calculate amount of power that must be produced by the solar arrays, P_{sa}	Step 1 (Orbit period – T_e) Eq. (21-6)	$P_e = P_d = 110$ W $T_e = 35.3$ min $T_d = 63.5$ min Assume a peak power tracking regulation scheme with $X_e = 0.6$ and $X_d = 0.8$ $P_{sa} = 239.4$ W
3. Select type of solar cell and estimate power output, P_o, with the Sun normal to the surface of the cells	*Si: $P_o = 0.148 \times 1{,}368$ W/m^2 = 202 W/m^2 *GaAs: $P_o = 0.185 \times 1{,}368$ W/m^2 = 253 W/m^2 *Multijunction: $P_o = 0.28 \times 1{,}368$ W/m^2 = 383 W/m^2	Si solar cells $P_o = 202$ W/m^2
4. Determine the beginning-of-life (BOL) power production capability, P_{BOL}, per unit area of the array	Tables 21-13, 21-15 Eq. (21-7)	$I_d = 0.77$ $\theta = 23.5$ deg (worst case) $P_{BOL} = 143$ W/m^2
5. Determine the end-of-life (EOL) power production capability, P_{EOL}, for the solar array	Performance degradation Si: 3.75% per yr, GaAs: 2.75% per yr, Triple Junction: 0.5% per yr Eq. (21-8) Eq. (21-9)	Performance degradation is 3.75% per year $L_d = 0.826$ for 5 yr mission $P_{EOL} = 118.1$ W/m^2
6. Estimate the solar array area, A_{sa}, required to produce the necessary power, P_{sa}, based on P_{EOL} an alternate approach	Eq. (21-10)	$A_{sa} = 2.0$ m^2 $A_{sa} = 2.5$ m^2
7. Estimate the mass of the solar array		$M_a = 9.6$ kg
8. Document assumptions		

junction GaAs cells have become the standard for most space applications due to their high efficiency and radiation resistance, but at a high cost. Silicon solar cell technology is mature and can be lower cost for some applications where radiation is not a concern. Single junction GaAs and InP cells are shown here for reference, but are not widely available commercially.

To complete this step, we identify the type of solar cells and how their performance will degrade during the mission. The *energy conversion efficiency* of a solar cell is defined as the power output divided by the power input. The power input value for a planar solar array is the 1,368 W/m^2 or the *solar constant* (the amount of energy received at the top of the Earth's atmosphere on a surface oriented perpendicular to the Sun's rays). Ideally, silicon and gallium arsenide and triple junction GaAs solar cells have efficiencies of about 24.7%, 21.8%, and 33.8%, respectively. These solar cell efficiencies give us ideal solar cell output performance per unit area, P_o, of 338 W/m^2, 298 W/m^2 and, 462 W/m^2. We also need to note that these efficiency values often refer to laboratory cells and not production cells, which have lower average efficiencies. In the next step, we will identify losses inherent to panel assembly (diodes, interconnect cabling, transmission losses) to size the array adequately.

Table 21-12, Fig. 21-7◀, Eq. 21-6◀

Table 21-13. Performance Comparison for Photovoltaic Solar Cells. Note that the stated efficiencies are for single solar cells, not solar arrays.

Cell Type	Silicon	Thin Film Amorphous Si	Gallium Arsenide	Indium Phosphide	Triple Junction GaAs
Planar Cell Theoretical Efficiency	29%	12.0%	23.5%	22.8%	40+%
Achieved Efficiency:					
Production	22%	8.0%	18.5%	18%	30.0%
Best Laboratory	24.7%	11%	21.8%	19.9%	33.8%
Equivalent Time in Geosynchronous Orbit for 15% Degradation					
– 1 MeV electrons	10 yr	10 yr	33 yr	155 yr	33 yr
– 10 MeV protons	4 yr	4 yr	6 yr	89 yr	6 yr

Step 4. Next, we must determine the realistic power production capability of the manufactured solar array. As shown in Table 21-14, an assembled solar array is less efficient than single cells due to design inefficiencies, shadowing and temperature variations, collectively referred to as *inherent degradation*, I_d. Solar cells are applied to a substrate, usually honeycomb aluminum, and interconnected, resulting in losses of 10% of the solar array's substrate area. This accounts for the design and assembly losses. If we configure the spacecraft well, its appendages will shadow few cells, and shadowing losses should be slight. The temperature of a typical flat solar panel receiving normal incident radiation ranges from about 67 C in LEO to 53 C in GEO. The reference temperature for silicon solar cells is 28 C, with performance falling off 0.5% per degree above 28 C. Body-mounted arrays on nonspinning spacecraft are typically about 5 C warmer than deployed solar arrays because they can't radiate heat into deep space as efficiently.

Table 21-14. Elements of Inherent Solar Array Degradation. Although individual solar cells may have adequate efficiency, after we manufacture the solar array, these elements cause some degradation in the cumulative efficiency by the amounts indicated.

Elements of Inherent Degradation	Nominal	Range
Design and Assembly	0.85	0.77–0.90
Temperature of Array	0.85	0.80–0.98
Shadowing of Cells	1.00	0.80–1.00
Total Inherent Degradation, I_d	0.72	0.49–0.88

We commonly refer to the current-voltage characteristics of a solar cell as the I-V curves. Figure 21-8 depicts a first-quadrant I-V curve for a planar array in LEO. This curve characterizes BOL and EOL performance. As the figure illustrates, the three significant points for solar-array design are:

- *Short-circuit current*, I_{sc}, where voltage = 0
- *Peak-power point*, where voltage times current is maximized
- *Open-circuit voltage*, V_{oc}, where current = 0

We must also consider how temperature affects the I-V characteristics. While a LEO spacecraft is in eclipse, the solar-array temperature can get as low as –80 C. The highest operating temperature for an LEO spacecraft solar array is 100 C, occurring near the end of a full Sun period during an orbit.

The operating temperature of the array is a key issue because the solar cell's performance depends on temperature. A *current-voltage*, or *I-V plot*, illustrates the performance of a solar array (see Fig. 21-8). A change in the operating temperature of the solar cell or array causes 3 changes in the I-V curve:

- A scaling of the I-V curve along the current axis
- A translation or shifting of the I-V curve along the voltage axis
- A change in the I-V curve shape affecting the roundness of the knee region

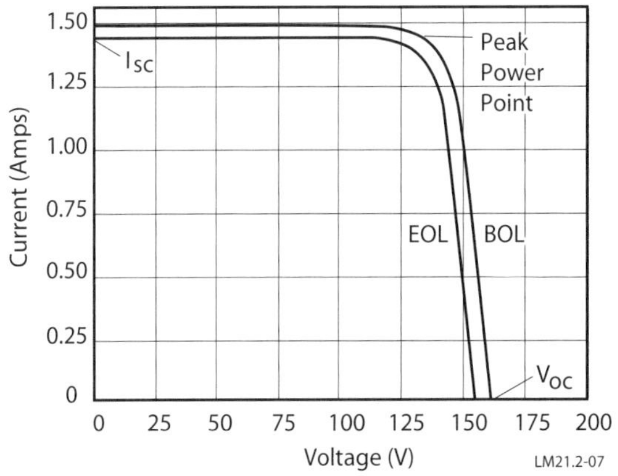

Fig. 21-8. I-V Plot for a Planar Array. The power available is simply the area under the curve.

The *temperature coefficient* or percent degradation of performance with increasing temperature, for any solar cell, depends on factors such as the type of cell and its output-power characteristics, actual operating temperature, and radiation environment. Gallium arsenide and indium phosphide have lower temperature coefficients, but higher temperature still means reduced performance. Solar arrays using gallium arsenide and indium phosphide also resist radiation better than silicon and provide greater EOL power for a given area. We must establish a profile for operating temperatures during a mission, so the photovoltaic system can generate adequate power throughout.

The peak-power point depends on the array's operating temperature at BOL and EOL. Thus, an array often provides maximum power exiting an eclipse period because it is at its coldest operating temperature. Transient voltage excursions often occur when leaving eclipse, so we may need to clamp voltages to protect spacecraft loads. By understanding how the array's performance relates to these variables, we can get the highest output power from the array.

Usually, solar cells in series-parallel combinations make up a *solar array*. The number of series-connected solar cells in one string establishes the bus voltage available at EOL at the operating temperature; the number of parallel strings depends on the required current output. Isolation (bypass) diodes mounted within the solar array typically minimize the effects of shadowing and reversed-biased solar cells.

Solar-array configurations are either planar or concentrator, and either type can be body- or panel-mounted. Most photovoltaic applications to date have employed a *planar array* in which solar cells are mounted onto a surface (typically a composite panel with either insulated aluminum or carbon facesheets) with an adhesive. A Kapton®, Kevlar®, or fiberglass sheet usually insulates the solar cell from the support structure. Figure 21-9 shows a planar array on the Genesis program, while Fig. 21-10 illustrates an A2100 rigid panel. Figure 21-11 shows a large flexible solar array wing for the International Space Station.

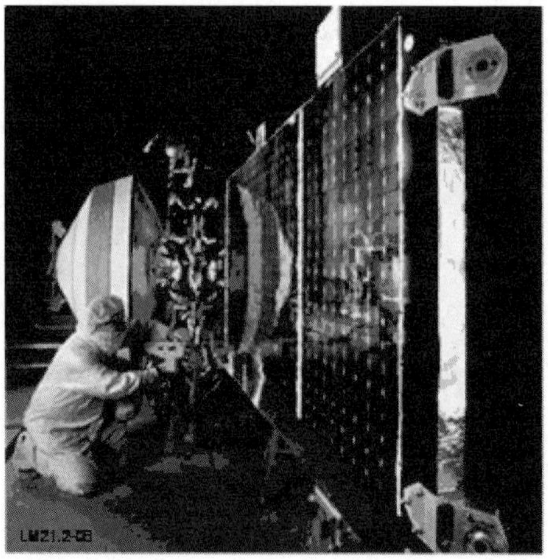

Fig. 21-9. Deep Space Planar Solar Array During Testing with the Satellite.

Concentrator solar arrays increase the solar cell's output by using mirrors or lenses to focus more solar radiation on the cells but can add significant complexity to the array design. For example, depending on the design

Fig. 21-10. Geostationary Spacecraft Rigid Panel Solar Array. Each panel is approximately 7.1 m^3 and produces 1.4 kW.

Fig. 21-11. Space Station Flexible Solar Array. The Space Station array is made up of 8 wings, each wing produces 32 kW, for a total of 256 kW.

of the concentrator, collection may occur over a narrower angle of offset from the Sun, meaning that more accurate pointing of the solar array would be required to take advantage of the concentrating affect. Also, the thermal design is an important consideration in concentrating systems, to ensure that no components will exceed acceptable operating temperatures.

Panel-mounted solar arrays usually apply only to 3-axis stabilized spacecraft. The panel-mounted approach tracks and points the solar array to get the best Sun incidence angle. The body-mounted approach reduces the requirements for tracking and pointing on any spacecraft (spinning or stabilized). But the less effective Sun incidence angle and increased array temperature of body-mounted cells produce a lower efficiency in orbit. Panel-mounted solar arrays are usually mounted on a boom. Deployable panel arrays are either flexible or rigid, according to the type of substrate material employed for mounting. For most spacecraft, we try to place the solar array away from the payload and other spacecraft subsystems because of the variable and often high temperature of the solar cells.

Body-mounted planar cells are typical on spinning spacecraft, which tend to even out the environmental heating of the spacecraft by exposing all areas to Sun and space as the craft rotates. In general, this raises the operating temperature of the body mounted solar cells, but helps to avoid hot spots on the spacecraft. Since body mounted solar cells tend to operate at a higher temperature than deployed solar cells, they operate less efficiently. However, the fact that not all the cells are collecting solar energy at the same time creates a larger impact on the power output of body mounted solar arrays. The decrease in power depends on the spacecraft's configuration and the drive mechanisms of the solar array (if any). For example, a stabilized array using Sun-tracking and pointing on two axes would fully use the solar array's surface area. But the array's reduction in output power per total surface area would be approximately π for body-mounted cells on a cylindrical, spinning spacecraft and 4 for body-mounted cells on a cubic-shaped spacecraft that does not employ active tracking. The output power decreases because not all cells are illuminated. The solar array impacts must be considered as part of a system level trade study, which includes the cost and design for the solar array's total surface area against the cost and complexity of stabilizing the spacecraft and using a drive system for the solar array. If the spacecraft is planned to spin for other reasons not related to the solar array, then it generally makes sense to use body mounted cells, avoiding the complexity of a deployed solar array. However, if the spacecraft will be 3-axis stabilized, the additional energy collection per square meter of solar cells provided by a deployed array that orients to the Sun may well be worth the additional complexity and expense to the overall system.

Shadowing considerations are important because a solar cell will go into open circuit (become high resistance) when not illuminated. In a simple series-connected string of solar cells, the shadowing of one cell results in the loss of the entire string. Shadowing may be caused by spacecraft components such as transmitting or receiving antennas, deployment mechanisms, or structures such as the solar array. We can reduce shadowing effects by actively pointing and tracking solar arrays on 3-axis stabilized spacecraft, using diodes, or designing series-parallel arrays. On spinning spacecraft, we must lay out solar cells so all solar cells within a string are illuminated. Diodes, which bypass groups or single solar cells in a string, help prevent damage to reduce the effects of shadowed solar cells.

We can improve solar cell performance with coverslides, coatings, and back-surface reflectors. Coverslides provide a hermetic seal yet allow the cell to receive sunlight and reject heat. They are textured or smooth. A textured coverslide is used for body-mounted solar cells that do not actively point toward the Sun. It reflects incident solar energy back onto the solar cell, improving the overall efficiency. Smooth coverslides are used for spacecraft whose arrays actively track and point. By decreasing reflective losses on solar cells, coatings allow cells to use more of the incident energy. Back-surface reflectors direct incident solar radiation that passes through the solar cell back through the cell again to improve overall efficiency. By reducing solar absorptance, they help the solar array manage thermal energy. Solar-cell vendors are continually improving the mechanical and thermal characteristics of coverslides, coatings, and back-surface reflectors. Thus, we must coordinate mechanical and thermal characteristics of these cells with the vendors.

At beginning-of-life, the array's power per unit area is Eq. (21-7)

$$P_{BOL} = P_o \, I_d \cos\theta \qquad (21\text{-}7)$$

where P_o was calculated in step 3 is I_d inherent degradation from step 4, and $\cos\theta$ is referred to as the cosine loss. We measure the Sun incidence angle, θ between the vector normal to the surface of the array and the Sun line. So if the Sun's rays are perpendicular to the solar array's surface, we get maximum power. Obviously, the geometry between the array and the Sun changes throughout the mission and different solar array panels will have different geometry. We configure the solar array to minimize this cosine loss. For example, in GEO with a flat, silicon solar array and a worst-case Sun angle of $\theta = 23.5$ deg angle between equatorial and ecliptic planes and the nominal value of I_d, the power output at beginning-of-life is 143 W/m^2, calculated using the values in Table 21-12.

Step 5. Radiation damage severely reduces a solar array's output voltage and current. At geosynchronous altitude, we must guard against solar-flare protons on-station, trapped electrons on-station, and trapped electrons and protons during transfer orbits. (Chapter 7 explains these terms.) Electrons and protons trapped in the Earth's magnetic field cause most degradation of solar cells. Silicon solar cells protected by coverslides lose 15% of their voltage and current (shielding assumed) when exposed to a total fluence of 10^{16} of 1-MeV equivalent electrons (4 to 5 years for a LEO spacecraft). As mission planners, we should coordinate degradation characteristics with the solar-cell manufacturer, based on the radiation environment the spacecraft will encounter. Degradation of a solar cell also depends on its design. More modern technologies, such as triple junction GaAs cells are more radiation hardened. They lose 11% of their power when exposed to 1-MeV, 5×10^{14} electrons/cm^2 fluence.

Next, we must consider the factors that degrade the solar array's performance during the mission. *Life degradation*, L_d, occurs because of thermal cycling in and out of eclipses, micrometeoroid strikes, plume impingement from thrusters, and material outgassing for the duration of the mission as well as material property degradation, such as darkening of solar cell cover glass. In general, for a silicon solar array in LEO, power production can decrease by as much as 3.75% per year, of which up to 2.5% per year is due to radiation. For gallium-arsenide cells in LEO, the degradation is about 2.75% per year, of which radiation causes 1.5% per year. The actual lifetime degradation can be estimated using Eq. (21-8).

Table 21-14◀, Fig. 21-11◀, Eq. 21-7

Table 21-15. Typical Solar Array Design Parameters. Most commonly used cell technologies. Note: Power values assume a 0 degree inclined GEO orbit.

Technology	Typical BOL Efficiency	Typical Size (cm)	Cell Watts/sq meter SS BOL (approx)	Array Watts/sq meter SS BOL/15 Yr EOL (approx)	kg/sq meter BOL SS (approx)	$/Watt BOL SS (Approx)
Si	14%	4 × 6	191	116/92.6	2.3	378
GaAs (SJ)	18.5%	4 × 6	252	158/132	2.7	852
GaAs (MJ)	22.6%	4 × 6	308	194/163	2.8	695
GaAs (improved MJ)	26%	4 × 6	354	202/188	2.8	617
GaAs (ultra MJ)	28	32.3 cm^2	382	245/210	2.8	617
SPL: Spectrolab, SS: Summer Solstice	—	—	—	—	—	—

$$L_d = (1 - D)^L \tag{21-8}$$

where D is the degradation per year and L is the satellite lifetime in years.

Step 6 The array's performance per unit area at end-of-life is Eq. (21-9).

$$P_{EOL} = P_{BOL} \, L_d \tag{21-9}$$

Using the FireSat II example array in Table 21-12 for a 5-year mission, L_d is 82.6%, resulting in a P_{EOL} of 118.1 W/m^2. The solar-array area, A_{sa}, required to support the spacecraft's power requirement, P_{sa}, is

$$A_{sa} = P_{sa} / P_{EOL} \tag{21-10}$$

The resulting solar-array area for the example spacecraft is about 2.0 m^2. If we had used a perfectly pointed array, the BOL power would have been 155 W/m^2, resulting in an EOL power of 128 W/m^2 and an array area of 1.9 m^2. So, having to account for the cosine loss costs us 0.1 m^2 in array size and the equivalent mass.

Solar-array sizing is more difficult than it appears from the above discussion. Typically, we must consider several arrays with varying geometry. Also, the angle of incidence on the array surface is constantly changing. We must predict that angle continuously or at least determine the worst-case angle to develop an estimate of P_{EOL}. Table 21-15 shows a comparison of solar performance at the cell level, as well as at the array level for BOL and EOL.

The power source generates electrical power within the spacecraft. Launch vehicles such as Atlas or Delta use primary batteries (discussed in Sec. 21.2.3) as the power source for electrical loads because the batteries usually need to last less than an hour. But batteries alone are too massive for missions that last from weeks to years. These missions need a source that can generate power over many orbital cycles to support electrical loads and recharge the batteries.

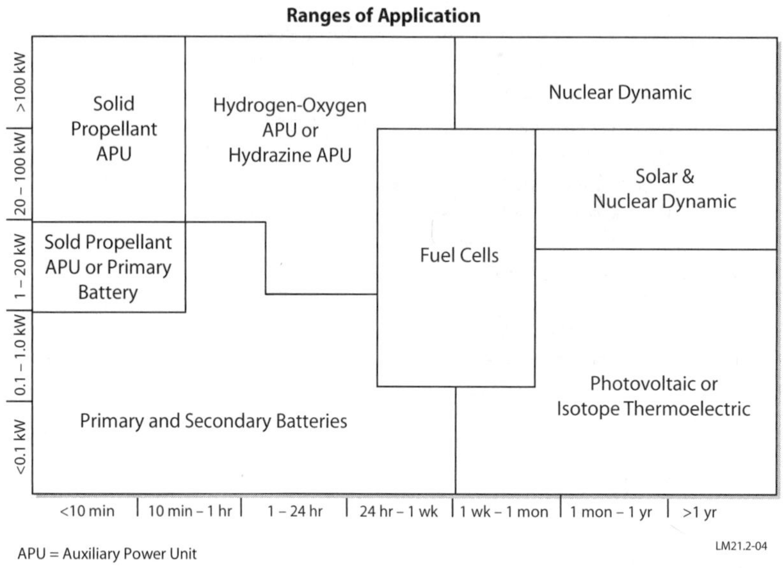

Fig. 21-12. Ranges of Application for Various Power Generation Technologies.

Table 21-15, Fig. 21-12, Eq. 21-10

Typically, we use 4 types of power sources for spacecraft as shown in Fig. 21-12. Photovoltaic solar cells, the most common power source for Earth-orbiting spacecraft, convert incident solar radiation directly to electrical energy. Static power sources use a heat source—typically plutonium-238 or uranium-235 (nuclear reactor), for direct thermal-to-electric conversion. Dynamic power sources also use a heat source—typically concentrated solar radiation, plutonium-238, or enriched uranium—to produce electrical power using the Brayton, Stirling, or Rankine cycles. The fourth power source is fuel cells, used on manned space missions such as Gemini, Apollo, SkyLab, and the Space Shuttle. These will be covered in more detail in Sec. 21.2.6.

Advanced Technologies

There are several promising areas of new technology, or new applications of technology. For example, NASA's Phoenix Lander, shown in Fig. 21-13 used circular fold up solar arrays to successfully operate on Mars.

The large circular objects on either side of the spacecraft are solar array wings, showing that solar arrays do not have to be square or rectangular. This design uses typical space cells, but mounts them on flexible gores that make up fan-like structures that fold up for launch, and unfold after the satellite has been deployed. This is an example of a creative way to maximize use of the volume and mass available for the spacecraft within the launch vehicle fairing.

Fig. 21-13. Phoenix Lander Photo Applied to Picture of Mars Estimating Actual Landing Conditions. The round solar array wings fold up like a fan for storage in the launch configuration, then deploy for operations.

21.2.3 Energy Storage

Energy storage is an integral part of the spacecraft's electrical-power subsystem providing all the power for short missions (<1 week) or back-up power for longer missions (>1 week). Any spacecraft that uses photovoltaics or solar thermal dynamics as a power source requires a system to store energy for eclipse periods and peak-power demands. High energy density storage technologies include batteries, super-capacitors, fuel cells, and fly wheels. This section will focus on batteries for energy storage, recognizing that research and development of super-capacitors, flywheels and fuel cells may result in promising energy storage systems for future missions. Figure 21-14 lists the main battery chemistries/types that are available today along with expected performance for both *primary* (non-rechargeable) and *secondary* (rechargeable) energy storage applications. The secondary batteries shown in Fig. 21-14 are capable of thousands of charge/discharge cycles for most space applications. The silver zinc (AgO/Zn) battery shown in Fig. 21-14 is typically a primary battery, although it may be applicable for recharge for applications that require limited (<100 charge/discharge cycles) recharge capability.

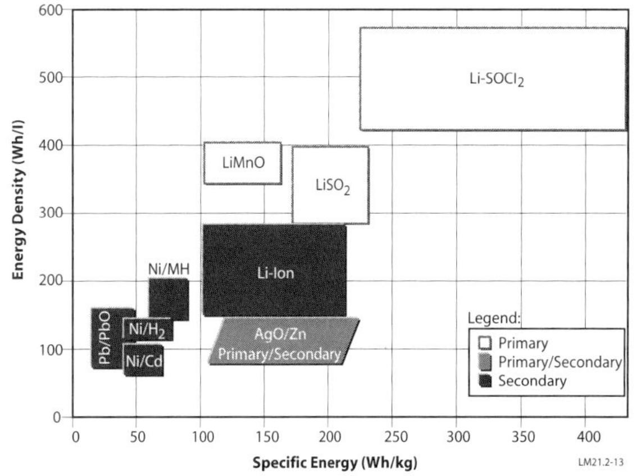

Fig. 21-14. Aerospace Battery Types. Energy density and the specific energy characteristics are the key parameters for battery selection to support energy storage for a mission. Note the performance characteristics shown above are at the cell level, and the packaging associated with a battery can reduce these values by ~10–25%. Technology advances for the shown battery types, along with chemistries under development, should be monitored to properly assess trade studies for battery type selection..

A *battery* consists of individual cells connected in series. The number of cells required is determined by the bus voltage requirements. The amount of energy stored within the battery is the *ampere-hour capacity* or watt-hour (ampere-hour, Ah, at times operating voltage) capacity. Batteries can be connected in series to increase the voltage or in parallel to increase the current output, with the net result being an increase in watt-hour capacity.

Table 21-16 lists battery issues to consider early in the conceptual phase of any program. Most of all, we try to provide a stable voltage for all operating conditions during the mission life because load users prefer a semi-regulated bus voltage. The difference in energy storage voltage between end-of-charge and end-of-discharge often determines the range of this bus voltage.

Table 21-15◀, Fig. 21-14, Eq. 21-10◀

Table 21-16. Issues in Designing the Energy Storage Capability. Energy storage usually means large batteries and we must consider all their characteristics when designing this subsystem.

Physical	Size, weight, configuration, operating position, static and dynamic environments
Electrical	Voltage, current loading, duty cycles, number of duty cycles, activation time and storage time, limits on depth-of-discharge, and short-circuit (fault) recovery
Programmatic	Cost, shelf and cycle life, mission, reliability, maintainability, produceability and safety

Figure 21-15 highlights the charge-discharge characteristics of a typical battery system. At the left edge, the voltage is low because the spacecraft just came out of eclipse where it used battery power. During the charge phase, there is positive current from the power regulator, so the battery voltage rises. In the discharge phase (in eclipse again), there is a negative current, so the battery voltage decreases. Discharge phase may also occur when the spacecraft is not in eclipse if peak power demands exceed the output power capability of the power source (i.e., solar arrays). We want a flat discharge curve that extends through most of the capacity, yet we need to avoid the knee of the discharge curve for bus voltage regulation and to avoid battery cell damage due to reverse voltages. Overcharging quickly degrades most batteries, and a key to long battery life is to minimize battery overcharge. We also need to match the electrical characteristics of the battery cells as charge imbalances stress and degrade the batteries, resulting in a shorter life for the EPS.

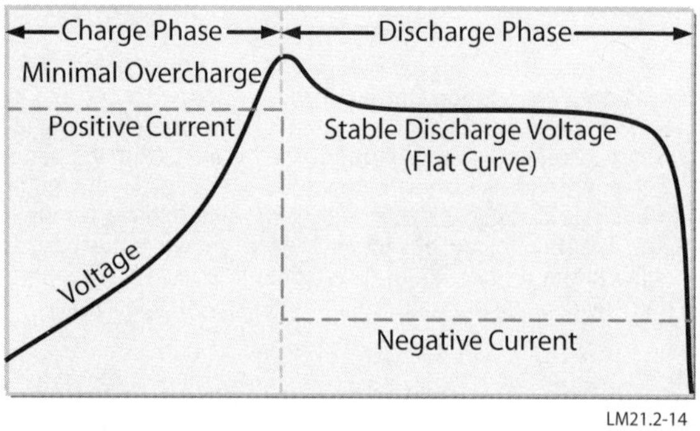

Fig. 21-15. Battery Charge/Discharge Voltage Profile. Secondary batteries may cycle through this type of profile hundreds or thousands of times during their mission life. At the left edge, the voltage is low because the spacecraft just came out of eclipse where it used battery power. Battery charge power is available when the solar array output is greater than all mission critical power loads, which will increase the battery voltage. In the discharge phase (eclipse again), the battery is supplying spacecraft power (negative current), resulting in decreasing battery voltage.

All battery cells are either primary or secondary. *Primary battery cells* convert chemical energy into electrical energy but cannot reverse this conversion, so they cannot be recharged. Primary batteries typically apply to short missions (less than one day) or to long-term tasks such as memory backup, which use very little power. The most common primary batteries are highlighted in Table 21-17, and one can see the wide ranges in each couple's specific-energy density. We cannot specify a value for specific energy density because cells vary in design and depend on mission requirements. We must coordinate mission requirements with the battery manufacturer to specify battery performance. The typical application comments for Table 21-17 are important factors for launch vehicles, the most predominant user for space qualified primary batteries.

Table 21-17. Characteristics of Selected Primary Batteries. Primary battery manufacturers can meet power requirements within these ranges of specific energy density. We must tradeoff cost and mass with capacity while ensuring mission accomplishment.

Primary Battery Types	Specific Energy (WHr/kg)	Typical Application
Silver Zinc	60–130	High rate, short life (minutes)
Lithium Thionyl Chloride	175–440	Medium rate, moderate life (<4 hours)
Lithium Sulfur Dioxide	130–350	Low/medium rate, long life (days)
Lithium Carbon Monoflouride	500–800	Low rate, long life (months)
Thermal	30–60	High rate, very short life (minutes)

A *secondary battery cell* can convert chemical energy into electrical energy during discharge and electrical energy into chemical energy during charge. It can repeat this process for thousands of cycles. A secondary battery provides power during eclipse periods on spacecraft that employ photovoltaics and can also level loads. Secondary batteries recharge in sunlight and discharge during eclipse. The spacecraft's orbital parameters, especially altitude, determine the number of charge/discharge cycles the batteries have to support during the mission life. A geosynchronous satellite needs to store energy for two 45-day eclipse periods per year with eclipses lasting no more than 72 min each day. The geosynchronous orbit demands few charge/discharge cycles during eclipse periods, thus allowing a fairly high (> 60%) depth-of-discharge. On the other hand, LEO spacecraft encounter at most one eclipse period each orbit or about 15 eclipse periods per day, with maximum shadowing of approximately 36 min. Therefore, the batteries must charge and discharge about 5,000 times each year, so the average depth-of-discharge is limited to ~30%, much lower than for geosynchronous spacecraft. Table 21-18 highlights performance characteristics and system impacts for today's most common secondary aerospace batteries.

Depth-of-Discharge (DOD) is simply the percent of total battery capacity removed during a discharge period. *State-of-Charge (SOC)* is the amount of total battery capacity at any given time. For example, if a 10 Ah battery has 1 Ah of capacity removed, the DOD was 10%

Table 21-18. Characteristics of Selected Secondary Batteries. Though secondary batteries have much lower specific energy densities than primary batteries, their ability to be recharged makes them ideal for backup power on solar powered spacecraft.

Performance Characteristics for Rechargeable Batteries	Ni-Cd	$Ni\text{-}H_2$	Li-Ion	System Impact
Energy Density (W-hr/kg)	30	60	125	Mass savings and vehicle center of gravity
Energy Efficiency (%)	72	70	98	Reduction of charge power reduces solar panel mass & size
Thermal Power (scale 1–10)	8	10	1	Reduction of radiators, heat pipes sizes
Self Discharge (% per day)	1	10	0.3	Simple management at launch pad & more margin during transfer
Temperature Range (°C)	0 to 40	–20 to 30	10 to 25	Management at ambient and thermal control reqs
Memory Effect	Yes	Yes	No	No reconditioning management
Energy Gauge	No	Pressure	Voltage	Easier state of charge assessment
Trickle Charge	Yes	Yes	No	Balancing need prior to eclipse. Li-Ion typically requires cell equalization circuitry.
Modularity	No	No	Yes	One cell design
Heritage	Yes	Yes	Yes	Risk Assessment. Continued Li-Ion LEO testing and missions establishing heritage.

(1 Ah/10 Ah), while the SOC is now 90% (9 Ah remaining/10 Ah total). Figure 21-16 illustrates that the higher the depth-of-discharge (DOD) then the shorter the cycle life for Nickel Cadmium (Ni-Cd), Nickel Hydrogen ($Ni\text{-}H_2$), and Lithium Ion (Li-Ion) secondary batteries. The cycle life versus DOD characteristics depicted in Fig. 21-16 is based upon extensive flight and test data for both Ni-Cd and $Ni\text{-}H_2$. Li-Ion data is just becoming available that will mature and further qualify its cycle life characteristics as a function of DOD. Once we work with the cell/battery supplier to fully understand the batteries' cycle life versus DOD characteristics, we can determine the total capacity of the batteries based upon the mission power budget profile.

The Nickel-Cadmium (Ni-Cd) battery was the most common space battery type prior to the 1980s. A 28 V_{dc} aerospace Ni-Cd battery usually consists of 22–23 series-connected cells. Ni-Cd battery cells for aerospace missions had nominal capacities of 5 to 100 Ah. Today, Ni-Cd batteries are selected for spacecraft based upon an extensive, mission-specific Ni-Cd data base that results in very low mission risk relative for the energy storage system.

The Nickel-Hydrogen ($Ni\text{-}H_2$) battery became the common energy storage system of choice for aerospace applications during the 1980s and 1990s. The three space-qualified design configurations for $Ni\text{-}H_2$ are individual pressure vessel, common pressure vessel, and single pressure vessel. The individual pressure vessel was the first $Ni\text{-}H_2$ technology used for aerospace application. Here, a single electrochemical cell is contained within a single pressure vessel. It has a working terminal voltage of 1.2 to 1.5 V_{dc} depending upon discharge loads. The typical individual pressure vessel battery design consists of multiple cells/pressure vessels connected in series to obtain the desired battery voltage. Cell diameters are typically 9 to 12 cm, with capacity ranges from 20 to over 300 Ah. Figure 21-17 shows a $Ni\text{-}H_2$ battery module for a geostationary spacecraft.

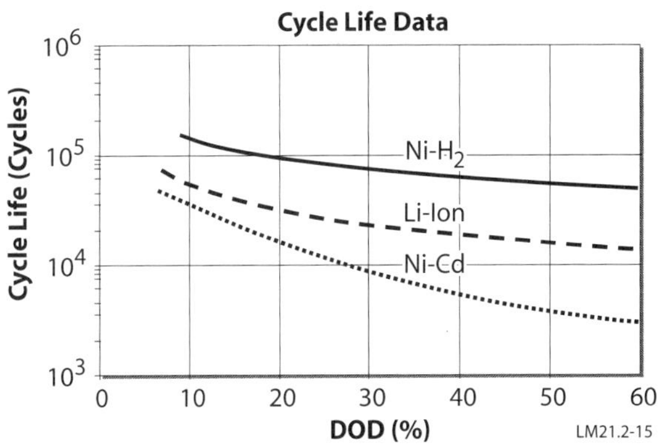

Fig. 21-16. Depth-of-Discharge vs. Cycle Life for Secondary Batteries. Increased cycle life reduces the amount of energy available from the batteries during each cycle — DOD decreases with cycle life.

The common pressure vessel $Ni\text{-}H_2$ battery is very similar to individual pressure vessel technology, with the primary difference in the wiring connection of the internal electrode stacks. In the individual pressure vessel, the electrode stacks are all connected in parallel. In a common pressure vessel, there are two sets of electrode stacks within the pressure vessel that are series connected, yielding a working minimal terminal voltage of 2.4 to 3.0 V_{dc} depending upon discharge loads. This design has a higher specific energy at the battery level since there are half as many pressure vessels and a significant reduc-

Fig. 21-17. $Ni\text{-}H_2$ vs Li-Ion Battery Comparison. The above geostationary spacecraft utilizes 4 batteries for energy storage. The relative volume required for these 4 batteries is shown in the lower schematics. The Li-Ion battery has obvious volumetric advantages and offers ~82 kg mass savings along with significant cost savings. However, its main disadvantage is a higher risk assessment due to a maturing data base and a tighter temperature operating range.

tion in cell piece-parts. Common pressure vessel $Ni\text{-}H_2$ technology has been space qualified in the 6 cm and 9 cm cell diameter configuration for capacities in the 12 to 20 Ah ranges.

The single pressure vessel $Ni\text{-}H_2$ battery is designed such that a common hydrogen supply is used by three or more series connected cells with a single pressure vessel. Each cell stack contains its own electrolyte supply which is isolated within individual cell stack containers. The key operating characteristic of this design is to allow the free movement of hydrogen within the cell stacks while maintaining cell stack electrolyte isolation. These batteries are presently available in a 12.5 cm or 25 cm diameter design.

Lithium Ion (Li-Ion) battery technology offers a significant volumetric and energy density advantages over Ni-Cd and $Ni\text{-}H_2$ battery types. In addition, the higher recharge efficiency of Li-Ion require a less complex and less costly thermal control system and Li-Ion have a very low self discharge rate on the order of 5% per year. The nominal operating voltage for a Li-Ion cell is 3.6 to 3.9 V_{dc}, which allows us to reduce the number of cells by approximately two-thirds when compared to Ni-Cd or $Ni\text{-}H_2$ cells resulting in significant battery volume and mass reductions. The Li-Ion secondary battery system offers a 65% volume advantage and a 50% mass advantage for most present day aerospace battery applications. Figure 21-17 shows a Li-Ion battery module designed and under qualification for the same A2100 spacecraft as the $Ni\text{-}H_2$ battery module. The advantages of a Li-Ion battery are easily seen for these two battery types on the same spacecraft. Li-Ion batteries have been qualified for numerous GEO and LEO missions. Aerospace Lithium batteries typically require cell equalization/conditioning and bypass circuitry to meet mission life requirements, and Range Safety requires individual cell voltage monitors for Lithium batteries prior to launch. Thermal control requirements for a Li-Ion battery are tighter due primarily to the fact that the design and emerging life cycle database for Li-Ion batteries has been focused around operation and performance in the 10–25 C temperature range. As the test database expands over the next several years resulting in lower overall mission risk, Li-Ion will likely become the preferred rechargeable battery for most, if not all, spacecraft missions.

To size a secondary battery, we must identify the parameters and apply the equation in Table 21-19. The parameter values used in the equation can vary significantly with battery type. The ideal battery capacity is the average eclipse load, P_e, times the eclipse duration, T_e. This ideal capacity must be increased to include the battery-to-load transmission efficiency, n, and the depth-of-discharge constraints. For LEO, we limit the battery's DOD to be 40–60% for $Ni\text{-}H_2$, 20–40% for Li-Ion, and 10–20% for Ni-Cd batteries. We base these expectations on the average DOD over 24 hours and assume the batteries are fully recharged at least once during this period. The number of batteries, N, may be equal to one for this calculation if you simply require battery capacity. Two to five batteries are typical for most spacecraft. We must have at least two (unless the battery uses redundant cells) because the spacecraft needs redundant operation with one unit failed. But more than five batteries require complex components for recharging. Battery capacity may also be required to help meet peak power loads during full Sun conditions. For some missions, the peak power loads may drive the required battery capacity rather than the average load resulting from an eclipse period.

Table 21-19. Steps in the Energy Storage Subsystem Design. To obtain the required battery capacity in Amp-hr, divide by the required satellite bus voltage.

Step	Consider	FireSat II Example
1. Determine the Energy Storage Requirements	• Mission length • Primary or secondary power storage • Orbital parameters – Eclipse frequency – Eclipse length • Power use profile – Voltage and current – Depth of discharge – Duty cycles • Battery charge/discharge cycle limits	• 5 yrs • Secondary power storage • 16 eclipses per day • 35.3 min per eclipse (T_e) • Eclipse load 110 W (P_e) – 26.4 V, 4.2 Amp (max) • 20% (upper limit)
2. Select the Type of Secondary Batteries	• Ni-Cd (space qualified) • NiH_2 (space qualified) • Li-Ion (space qualified)	• Ni-Cd, Ni-H_2 or Li-Ion. Selection based upon trade studies and program risk assessment
3. Determine the Size of the Batteries (Battery Capacity)	• Number of batteries • Transmission efficiency between the battery and the load	• N = 3 batteries (non redundant) • n = 0.90 • Cr = 119 W-hr • Cr = 4.5 Ah (26.4 V bus)
Battery Capacity: $C = (P_e T_e/(\text{DOD})Nn)$ W-hr (for battery capacity in Ah, divide by bus voltage)		

21.2.4 Power Regulation and Control

Many loads within a spacecraft require a voltage at a different level than that provided by the voltage source. When this is the case, DC-DC voltage converters are generally used. A DC-DC converter can also keep the load voltage within a range specified by the load. To know what voltage levels are acceptable to specific loads we start with the load requirements. Input power requirements we look for in a load are: voltage range, current, acceptable normal/abnormal transient time duration, and voltage ripple. Table 21-20 shows an example of a load's input power requirements. If a voltage regulator can provide the load with the specified input power then the supplier of the load is guaranteeing their product will operate as specified.

Table 21-20. Example of a Load's Input Power Requirements.

Condition	Range
Normal Steady State Voltage Range	25 to 31 V DC
Normal Transients	20 to 36 V DC*
Abnormal Transients	0 to 40 V DC*
Nominal Ripple	1 V peak to peak
Max Current	15 Amp
Inrush Current	25 Amp*
* Note: Include time duration and wave shape of transients as applicable.	

Many techniques are used to regulate and control power going into a load. When charging, a battery acts as a load on the spacecraft's power bus. Because the energy source output voltage does not always meet the requirements specified by the battery, we must, at a minimum, control the source's output power so that the battery input power requirements are met. The energy source determines how we regulate a spacecraft's power. Since most aerospace applications use solar photovoltaics, we will examine power regulation emphasizing that viewpoint. Power regulation at the main power bus divides into 3 main categories: controlling the solar array, regulating bus voltage, and charging the battery.

We must control electrical power generated at the array to prevent battery overcharging and undesired spacecraft heating. The two main power bus control techniques, illustrated in Fig. 21-18 are a *peak-power tracker (PPT)* and a *direct-energy-transfer (DET)* subsystem. The main difference between these two approaches is how they deal with the input power from the solar array. A DET system directly transfers the power from the solar array to the power bus. This implies that the solar array must operate at the same voltage as the rest of the power bus (ignoring line loss). With a PPT, the solar array and bus can operate at different voltages, and the peak power tracker is functionally between the solar array and the bus, processing all the solar array power.

When a power bus is dominated by the battery voltage, such as in a DET system, the solar array also operates at that voltage and cannot deliver the full power it is capable of at all times. Since the solar array is designed to never exceed a voltage past the peak power point seen in Fig. 21-8 it will reach its full power producing capability only when the battery is at its highest voltage which occurs when the battery is fully charged. When the battery is at its minimum voltage, at the beginning of its charge cycle, the solar array operates well below the peak power point.

A solution to this issue is the PPT which is a DC-DC converter operating in series with the solar array. The objective of the DC-DC converter is to keep the voltage of

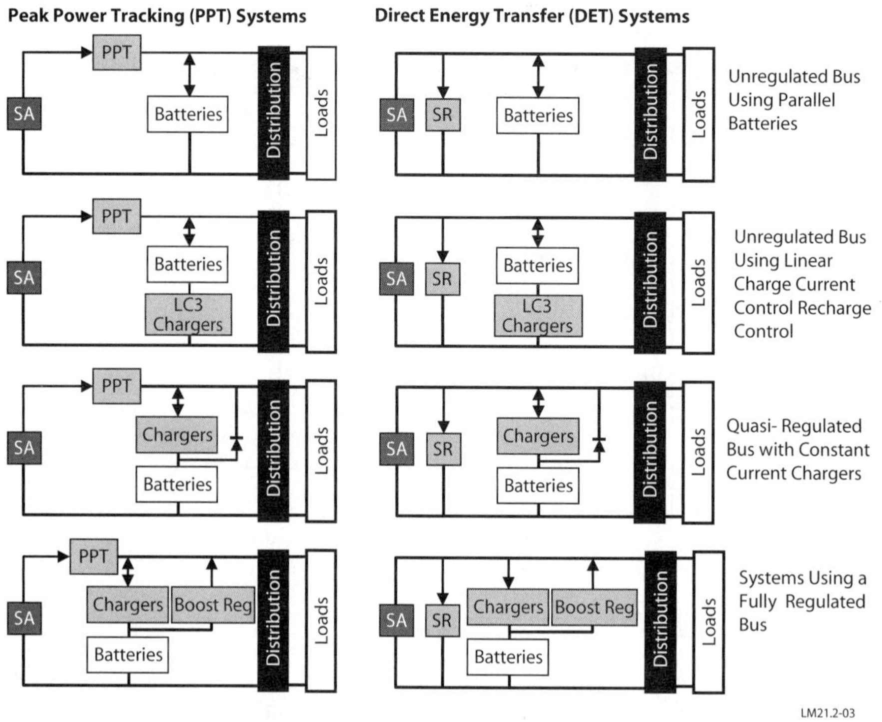

Fig. 21-18. Techniques for Power Regulation. The basic approaches are *Peak Power Tracking (PPT)*, which places a regulator in series with the solar arrays and the load, and *Direct Energy Transfer (DET)*, which uses a regulator in parallel with the solar arrays and load.

the solar array at a value slightly below, for stability reasons, the maximum power point. When the solar array is at this value it is utilizing its full power producing capability. In order for the DC-DC converter to achieve its goal, it uses a buck or boost converter to track the battery voltage then will adjust the duty cycle of the converter to bring the solar array voltage to the desired max power point. The buck and boost converter will be discussed later in this section. A disadvantage of the PPT is the additional weight, complexity and cost it adds to the system. PPTs also have a 3–8% power loss to contend with and are a significant noise source to the rest of the system.

For direct energy transfer systems, a *shunt regulator* operates in parallel to the array and shunts the array current away from the subsystem when the loads or battery charging do not need power. Power subsystems with shunt regulation are extremely efficient. A shunt-regulated subsystem has the advantages of fewer parts, lower mass, and higher total efficiency at EOL. The main disadvantage of the shunt-regulated subsystem is that the full power potential of the solar array cannot be utilized.

Batteries can be charged individually or in parallel. A parallel charging system is simpler and lower cost, but does not allow flexibility in vehicle integration. It can also stress batteries so they degrade faster. When batteries are charged in parallel, the voltage is the same but the current and temperature are not. Because current is not rigidly controlled, one battery could receive all the available charge current, and a thermal runaway condition could result if the bus voltage of the hottest battery is not controlled. Parallel batteries eventually end up balancing out, so we could use them for missions under five years. Individual charging optimizes the battery use by charging all the batteries to their own unique limits. It also forgives battery deviations in systems with several batteries. Unfortunately, individual chargers add impedance, electronic piece parts, and thermal dissipation not present in a parallel system.

When charging the battery a control loop must be implemented to prevent overcharging. There are several different methodologies used to determine when a battery is at its maximum capacity; voltage, current and pressure are three of the parameters commonly used as a capacity gauge. When one of these parameters reaches a predetermined level a control algorithm will usually go into a trickle charge mode or stop charging the battery all together. The fully charged mode depends on the battery chemistry used. A configuration comparison of the EPS topologies shown in Fig. 21-18 is provided in Table 21-21.

Power Regulators

A power regulator is an electrical device used to bring an unregulated bus to within the specifications required by the various loads throughout the system. Here we will consider two regulator topologies; linear regulators and switch-mode regulators. (See Tables 21-23 and 21-24.)

Linear regulators were once widely used in all spacecraft power subsystems for both small and large loads but have lost favor for utilization on large loads due to the development of the more efficient switch-mode reg-

Table 21-21. Configuration Comparison.

System	Pros	Cons	Best Application
Unregulated Direct-Energy Transfer (U-DET)	High solar array and battery to load efficiency Fewer EPS components	More complex load converters Potential "lockup" problems and large solar array	Small load variations Small power source variation for most of sunlight period
Regulated Direct-Energy Transfer (R-DET)	Tightly regulated input to spacecraft component Simpler, lighter, more efficient load converters	Additional EPS converters Series power loss between battery and load	Heritage spacecraft loads requiring tight regulation Large solar array power/voltage variations
Maximum Power Tracking	Shunt regulator or battery charge regulator not required Can make maximum use of solar array energy in some cases	Less efficient than DET at EOL in many cases More dissipation inside spacecraft	Large variations in solar array input throughout mission

ulators in the 1970s. Some newer devices such as the low drop out regulator (LDO) have improved the efficiency of linear regulators and are used for local voltage regulation and to provide low frequency noise rejection. Increased efficiency of the linear regulator is achieved by reducing the input-to-output voltage differential.

A series regulator is seen in Fig. 21-19. The basic operating principle of the series regulator is to measure the voltage at the load then make adjustments on the series resistor to maintain a desired voltage at the load. The series resistor is the main cause of inefficiency in this system. As can be seen in Table 21-22 efficiency of the series regulator is dependent on both the line (input) voltage and the voltage at the load. As the line voltage further deviates from the load voltage the efficiency decreases.

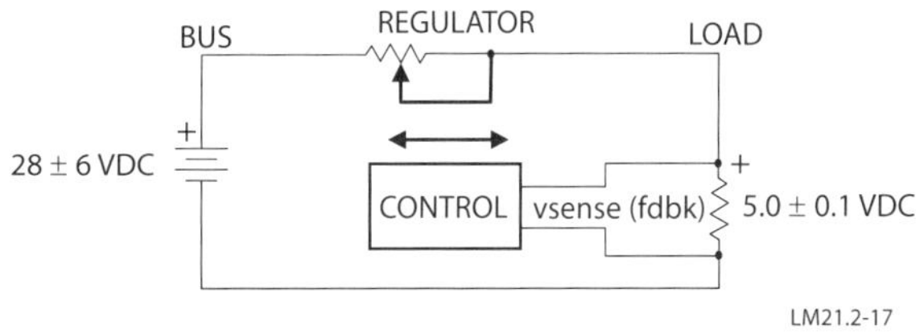

Fig. 21-19. Series Regulator. Constant voltage load efficiencies are shown in Table 21-22.

In response to the poor efficiencies achieved by most linear regulators, switch-mode regulators were developed. Today these are the most commonly used regulator topologies. They regulate power using active electronics, switching semiconductors, transformers, inductors and capacitors which conserve energy rather than simply bleeding it off the way a linear regulator would. The advantage of switch-mode regulators is high efficiency which means low power losses and low heat dissipation. Figure 21-20 shows a block diagram of the basic operating principal of switch-mode regulators.

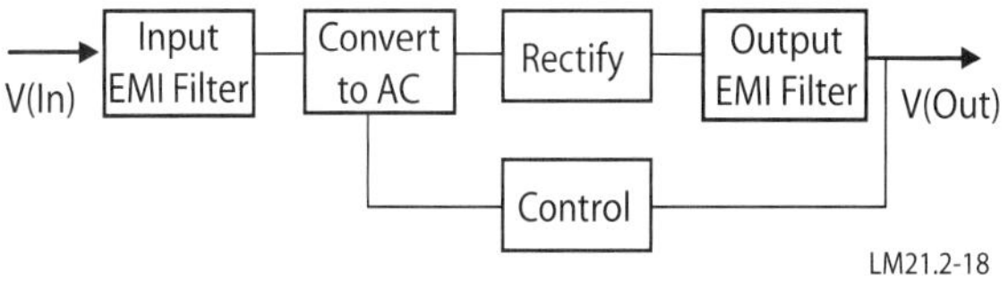

Fig. 21-20. Basic Operating Principle of Switch-Mode Regulators.

The most common regulator topologies are the Buck and Boost regulators which either reduce (buck) or increase (boost) the voltage at the output of the regulator. A buck-boost regulator can increase or decrease the input voltage. By adding more components, and thus complexity, to these basic topologies, greater efficiencies can be achieved. Common buck or boost derived regulators, from least complex to most complex, are the flyback, single switch forward, two switch forward, push-pull, and full bridge regulators. As complexity increases in the above list, so does each regulator's ability to process more power, ranging from 20 W to greater than 600 W. Further increases in efficiency can be achieved by implementing resonant mode switching within one of the above regulators. This technique saves power by turning on solid-state switches when the sine-wave voltage across the transistor is at zero, thus eliminating switching losses; of course further complexity is added when implementing resonant mode switching.

Table 21-22. Series Regulator Efficiency. Efficiency of the series regulator is dependent on the line voltage and load voltage.

V (BUS) =	Load Power =	R (Reg) =	Reg. Loss	Total Source	Efficiency
22 V	5 W	17 Ω	17 W	22 W	22.7%
28 V	5 W	23 Ω	23 W	28 W	17.9%
34 V	5 W	29 Ω	29 W	34 W	14.7%

Table 21-22, Fig. 21-20, Eq. 21-10◀

Table 21-23. Linear Regulator Advantages/Disadvantages.

Advantages	Disadvantages
• Wide gain-bandwidth and excellent transient response • Excellent ripple rejection below 1 MHz • No spectral line noise added to the output • No-load operation possible • Simple single pole transfer function	• Efficiency is dependent on input to output voltage differential and output current • High dissipation concentrated in single device, cooling may be a problem

Table 21-24. Switch-Mode Regulators Advantages/Disadvantages.

Advantages	Disadvantages
• Most commonly used topology • Usable at switching frequencies from 20 KHz to 2 MHz • Mature topology, developed in 1970's, supported and predictable reliability, parts available • Efficiencies greater than 95 percent are possible	• Ripple and Noise generated at the switching frequency and integral modules. • Transient requirements forces most buck PWM circuits to be operated at low duty cycle and with high voltage and current stresses • More complex than linear regulators • Harder to analyze and simulate than linear regulator • Stability issues can occur if not thoroughly analyzed

When choosing a switching frequency for a switch mode regulator several factors to be considered are packaging, efficiency, performance, and cost. As the frequency increases, the magnetic components and filter capacitors reduce in size. However, the switching losses are higher and gate drive circuitry consume more power as frequency increases. To compensate for lower efficiencies at higher frequencies a soft-switching topology can be considered to eliminate switching losses. Correct shielding and grounding becomes more critical as frequency and noise emissions increase.

When constant (non-varying) power is required by a load, the converter supplying the power can be modeled by negative impedance, meaning that as voltage decreases at the input, the current into the converter increases in order to maintain constant power. Negative impedance can cause stability issues when thorough analysis has not taken place. To maintain stability, it is necessary that the magnitude of the equivalent load impedance be higher than the magnitude of source impedance.

To design the power regulation and control subsystem, follow the steps in Table 21-25.

Table 21-25. Steps in the Power Regulation and Control Subsystem Design.

Step	Consider	Possibilities
1. Determine Load Requirements	Voltage Range Current Transients Ripple	
2. Determine the Power Source	All spacecraft loads, their duty cycles, and special operating modes	Primary batteries Photovoltaic Static power Dynamic power
3. Design the Electrical Control Subsystem	Power source Battery charging Spacecraft heating	Peak-power tracker Direct-energy transfer
4. Develop the Electrical Bus Voltage Control	How much control does each load require? Battery voltage variation from charge to discharge Battery recharge subsystem Battery cycle life Total system mass	Unregulated Quasi-regulated Fully regulated Parallel or individual charging < 5 yrs—parallel charge > 5 yrs—independent charge

21.2.5 Power Distribution

A spacecraft's power distribution system consists of cabling, fault protection, and switching gear to turn power on and off to the spacecraft loads. It also includes command decoders to command specific load switches on or off. The power distribution system is a unique feature of the electrical power subsystem and often reflects individual spacecraft loads and power-switching requirements. Power distribution designs for various power systems depend on source characteristics, load requirements, and subsystem functions. In selecting a type of power distribution, we focus on keeping power losses and mass at a minimum while attending to survivability, cost, reliability, and power quality. An equivalent circuit of a distribution system is shown in Fig. 21-21. The DC source is represented by a battery and a series resistance. Elements for consideration in the distribution line are lumped inductance, noise pickup, capacitance from parallel lines and resistance from line copper, fuse and switching elements. Solid state relays have surpassed mechanical relays for power switching because of increased flight history, reliability, and low power dissipation. It is usually necessary to add a decoupling capacitor at the load to minimize the effects of transient caused by varying loads. The capacitor is represented by a capacitor in series with an inductor and a resistor. Since distribution systems are made up of long wires, they act as an antenna to pickup noise and to radiate out noise to the rest of the system. Cable length is normally dictated by mechanical considerations and is therefore beyond the control of the electrical designer. Wire inductance is approximately 0.36 μH per foot, don't forget to count both the power and return wires when determining the cable's total inductance. For example: A 10-foot power cable, run as a pair, will be found to have an inductance of around 7.2 μH. If the cable is twisted, the inductance will be reduced to approximately one third of the untwisted value, or in this case, 2.4 μH. Even relatively small inductances can become a source of noise.

The *load profile* of a spacecraft is a key determining factor in the design specifications of a power distribution subsystem. Predominant spacecraft loads (radar, communications, motors, computers) may require low to high-voltage anywhere from 1–120 V_{dc} converted from the 28-V_{dc} power bus. Spacecraft power loads often turn on or off or otherwise vary their power consumption. When a load's current varies, voltage spikes are created due to the inductance in the distribution lines. This transient behavior may produce noise that the distribution system translates to other loads, potentially harming working components. With ever-decreasing voltage levels for spacecraft loads, (currently as low as one volt for computer processors) and rising current needs, proper shielding, twisting of pairs and grounding must be considered at the beginning of the power distribution design phase.

High current cables are frequently improperly designed. The distribution cable voltage drop, in the supply and return path, must meet the load voltage regulation requirements. In addition, the cable harness often lacks adequate de-rating for the worst case environment, temperature, and the effects of vacuum. Copper I^2R power loss is the most basic of considerations in power design. High voltage distribution helps reduce the current and thus the I^2R loss. At higher current, the greatest concern is cable power dissipation and insulation damage due to heating. This is especially a problem in cables with large numbers of conductors because, when bundled together, it is harder for a cable to dissipate heat. At lower voltages, loss of regulation due to *IR* drop is the most prevalent problem as discussed earlier. The trend of digital circuits to progressively lower logic voltages and increase current transients has aggravated the problem. The remote sense capability of power converters may be used to reduce the voltage variation associated with cable resistive voltage drop. The remote sense feature moves the converter voltage feedback sense point from the output terminals to the load. The converter then adjusts the duty and output voltage to maintain the required voltage at the load. The remote sense is capable of compensating for a cable drop of around 105–110% of the nominal output. If the load varies over a large range and there is great difficulty associated with additional copper, then remote sense is a good option. If the remote sense feature is not available, additional copper is the simplest and most efficient option to meeting the load regulation requirements.

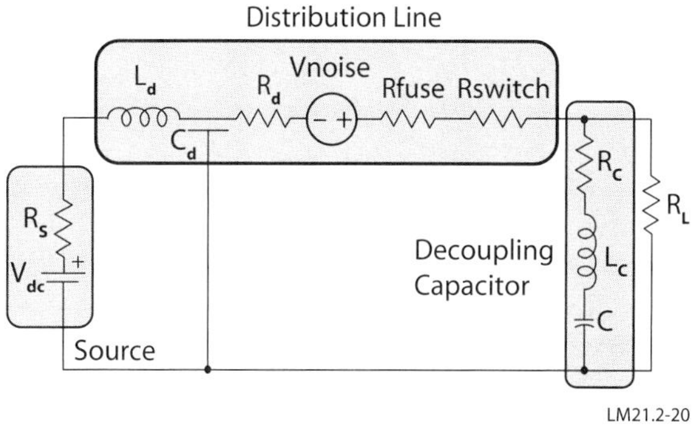

Fig. 21-21. Power Distribution System Equivalent Circuit.

The harness or cabling that interconnects the spacecraft's subsystems is a large part (10–25%) of the electrical-power subsystem's mass. As seen in Fig. 21-22, the harness connected to the power distribution unit (labeled PDDU in this example) takes up a considerable amount of volume inside the spacecraft, and therefore, routing must be considered early in the design phase. To avoid strain on the wiring inside the harness a minimum bend radius of 10 times the diameter of the harness should be used when routing. We must keep harnesses as short as possible to reduce voltage drops, noise and to regulate the bus voltage. A maximum voltage drop across the distribution line of 2% of the minimum source voltage is an industry standard. For example, lets say we have a heater which has a maximum current draw, *I*, of 10 A and 26 V_{dc} is our minimum bus voltage, we must then design the cabling so that the load will see a voltage, V_{min}, no less than:

Table 21-25◀, Fig. 21-21, Eq. 21-10◀

Fig. 21-22. JUNO Flight Harness.

$$V_{min} = 26\ V_{dc} \times 0.98 = 25.48\ V_{dc} \quad (21\text{-}11)$$

Our voltage drop must be less than 0.52 V_{dc}. This means our wire resistance, R_w, needs to be less than

$$R_w = V/I = 0.52\ V_{dc} / 10\ \text{A} = 0.052\ \Omega \quad (21\text{-}12)$$

If the heater is a long way from the source, a large gauge wire would be used or multiple smaller gauge wires in parallel would be used to decrease the wire resistance. Remember to include the return wires when calculating the total length of your wire, so if the heater is six meters from the source the total wire length will be twelve meters.

Figure 21-23 depicts the relationship between current and cable mass.

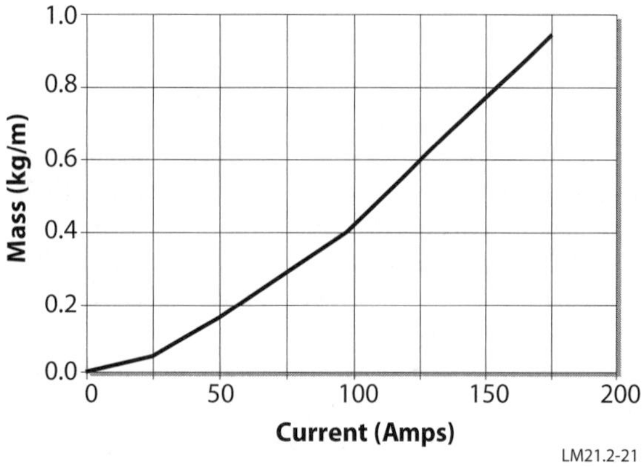

Fig. 21-23. Cable Mass vs. Current. We must account for the cable and harness mass when designing the power subsystem. Operating low current (less than 30 A) devices helps keep this mass low.

Systems for distributing power on spacecraft have been predominantly DC because solar arrays and batteries output a direct current power. Conversion to AC would require more electronics, which would add mass to the EPS.

Power distribution systems are either centralized or decentralized, depending on the location of the converters. The decentralized approach places the converters at each load separately, these are called *point of load (POL)* converters, whereas the centralized approach regulates power to all spacecraft loads within the main bus. The decentralized approach implies an unregulated bus because distributed converters regulate power. A regulated power bus typically has some power converters at the load interface because electronics may require different voltages (+5, ±12 V_{dc}). An advantage of the centralized system is that we do not have to tailor-design the EPS for different applications. Larger spacecraft with high power levels use the decentralized distribution systems, with an unregulated bus, usually.

Fault protection within the EPS focuses on detection, isolation, and correction of faults. Its main purpose is to isolate an electrical short that could eventually degrade or cause loss of the mission. A short circuit will draw excessive current, and if this condition continues, the short may stress cables and drain the energy storage reserve. Typically, we would isolate these faults from the EPS bus with fuses (sometimes resettable). *Fuses* are pieces of wire specially designed to pass a reasonably well defined current, and because current causes the fuse material to heat up, a current higher than that of what the fuse is designed to pass will melt and burn open. Fuses are normally specified to blow in some defined period (e.g., 5 sec) at currents of say 200%. The higher the current through the fuse the faster the fuse will blow (timing is not very reproducible). When sizing a fuse, be conservative. When a fuse in orbit is blown, the function powered off that circuit is lost. A rule of thumb for currents greater than 1 A is to size the fuse to twice the maximum current expected on the circuit when operating normally. At lower currents greater margin is needed. Most spacecraft power loads have some sort of fuse in series with the power bus to isolate faults. If the mission requires us to know where load faults occur, fault-detection circuits can be added.

To design the Power Distribution subsystem, follow the steps in Table 21-26.

21.2.6 Future Power Systems

Future power systems will focus around more power at a lower cost to enable new missions. The enabling factor for future power systems will focus around the power source and the energy storage subsystems. The most common spacecraft power sources with EPS design parameters are shown in Table 21-27. Solar photovoltaics remain the optimum power source selection for most spacecraft missions today. Solar thermal dynamic, RTG, and fuel cell power sources are preferred when solar photovoltaics is no longer a viable candidate. Nuclear reactors will likely be required for manned Lunar or Mars based missions due to power requirements > 100's kW. However, the costs associated with a reactor are not within the projected budget for the majority of US space missions planned for the next decade.

Planetary missions beyond Mars and Jupiter, and Deep Space missions, have an inherent limitation of solar power (solar energy flux) as shown in Fig. 21-24.

Table 21-26. Steps in the Power Distribution Subsystem Design.

Step	Consider	Possibilities
1. *Determine the Electrical Load Profile*	• All spacecraft loads, their duty cycles, and special operating modes • Inverters for AC requirements • Transient behavior within each load • Load-failure isolation	• Low-voltage DC: 5 V • High-voltage DC: 270 V • High-voltage 1-phase AC: 115 Vrms, 60 Hz • High-voltage, 3-phase AC: 120/440 Vrms, 400 Hz
2. *Decide on Centralized or Decentralized Control*	• Individual load requirements • Total system mass	• Converters at each load—for a few special loads • Centralized converters control voltage from the main bus (no specialized power requirements)
3. *Determine the Fault Protection Subsystem*	• Detection (active or passive) • Isolation • Correction (change devices, reset fuses, work around lost subsystem)	• Cable size (length and diameter) and excess current-carrying ability • Size of power storage in case of a short circuit • Location of fuses and their type

Table 21-27. Matrix for Comparing Most Common Spacecraft Power Sources. We may use different factors to select the correct power source but specific power and specific cost are used extensively. Almost all Earth orbiting missions use solar photovoltaic and nearly all missions beyond Mars use radioisotope thermoelectric generator (RTG) based power systems. Solar photovoltaic is the most common power source for spacecraft missions today.

EPS Design Parameters	Solar Photovoltaic	Solar Thermal Dynamic	RTG	Nuclear Reactor	Fuel Cell
Power Range (kW)	0.2–300	5–300	0.2–10	5–300	0.2–50
Specific Power (W/kg)	25–200	9–15	5–20	2–40	275
Specific Cost ($/W)	800–3,000	1,000–2,000	16K–200K	400K–700K	50K–100K
Hardness					
– Natural Radiation	Low–Medium	High	Very high	Very high	High
– Nuclear Threat	Medium	High	Very high	Very high	High
– Laser Threat	Medium	High	Very high	Very high	High
– Pellets	Low	Medium	Very high	Very high	Medium
Stability & Maneuverability	Low	Medium	High	High	High
Low-orbit Drag	High	High	Low	Medium (due to radiator)	Low
Degradation Over Life	Medium	Medium	Low	Low	Low
Storage Required for Solar Eclipse	Yes	Yes	No	No	No
Sensitivity to Sun Angle	Medium	High	None	None	None
Sensitivity to Spacecraft Shadowing	Low (with bypass diodes)	High	None	None	None
Obstruction of Spacecraft Viewing	High	High	Low	Medium (due to radiator)	None
Fuel Availability	Unlimited	Unlimited	Very low	Very low	Medium
Safety Analysis Reporting	Minimal	Minimal	Routine	Extensive	Routine
IR Signature	Low	Medium	Medium	High	Medium
Principal Applications	Earth-orbiting spacecraft	Interplanetary, Earth-orbiting spacecraft	Interplanetary	Interplanetary	Interplanetary

Solar photovoltaics have supported most Earth orbiting missions and planetary missions out to Mars. The large solar arrays on Juno (~60 m^2) combined with low overall power requirements (~ 200 W average) enabled NASA's New Frontiers Juno mission.

Sections 21.2.1 through 21.2.5 primarily focused on power systems based upon solar photovoltaics as the power source with batteries for energy storage for LEO and GEO missions. Research and development continues on photovoltaic power source systems, and Fig. 21-25 shows historical advancements along with the anticipated potential for multi-junction cell efficiencies. Even with the solar cell efficiency advancements shown in Fig. 21-25, there are missions where the "Sun does not Shine." For these missions, one must consider the other power sources shown in Table 21-27.

Table 21-27, Fig. 21-23◀, Eq. 21-12◀

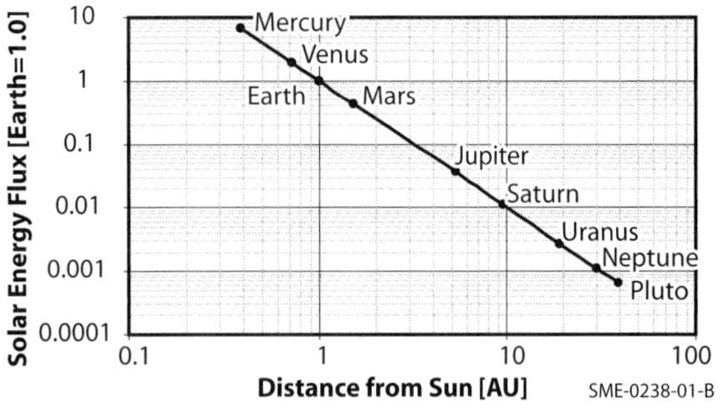

Fig. 21-24. Solar Energy vs. Distance from the Sun. The quick reduction of solar flux past Mars requires very large solar arrays, as shown for NASA's Juno spacecraft and its mission to Jupiter. Missions past Jupiter require a non-solar power source, such as a Radioisotope Thermoelectric Generator (RTG) based power source.

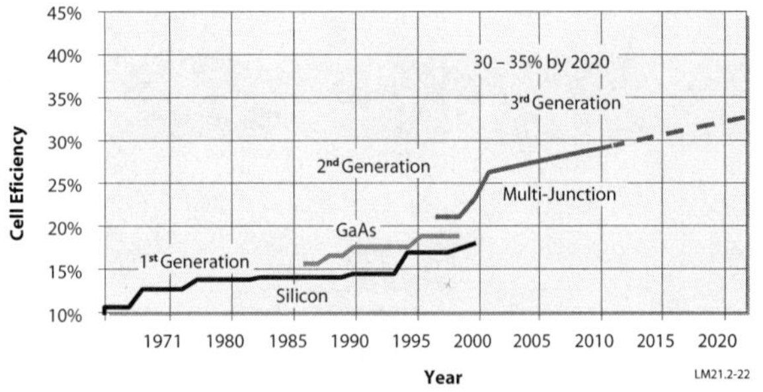

Fig. 21-25. Solar Cell Efficiency Advancements. Multi-Junction solar cells described in Sec. 21.2.3 offer the potential for reduced power generation mass and costs for future missions. Additional work continues on solar cell technologies, especially in areas that promise to reduce the mass or volume of the completed solar array.

For missions that require hundreds of Watts for power where solar energy is no longer viable, the most common power system utilizes heat transport from a reactor (typically fueled with plutonium-238) to drive a power converter based upon the power conversion technologies shown in Fig. 21-26. Static power conversion technologies have no moving parts, while dynamic power conversion technologies utilize a working engine. The most common static power conversion technologies are Thermoelectric and Thermionic. The most common static power source for spacecraft is the thermoelectric couple. This basic converter uses the temperature gradient between the p-n junction of individual thermoelectric cells connected in a series-parallel arrangement to provide the desired DC electrical output from each converter. This temperature gradient comes from slow decay of the radioactive source. The thermal-to-electric conversion efficiency for a thermoelectric source is typically 5–8%.

Thermionic energy conversion produces electricity through a hot electrode (emitter) facing a cooler electrode (collector) inside a sealed enclosure that typically contains an ionized gas. Electrons emitted from the hot emitter flow across the inter-electrode gap to the cooler

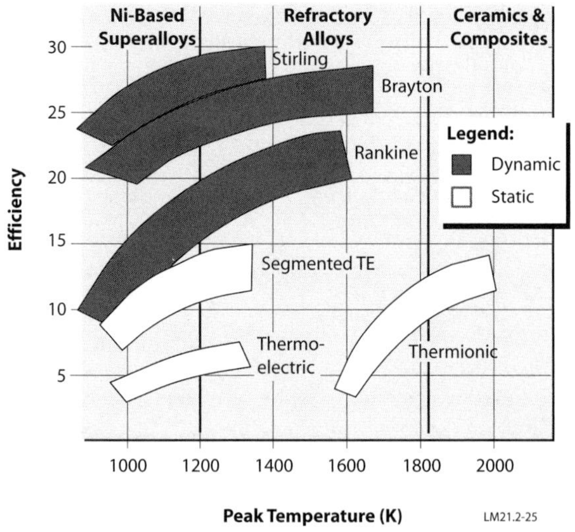

Fig. 21-26. Heat from Reactor to Electric Power Conversion Technologies. Static power conversions technologies have lower efficiencies but high reliability, while dynamic power conversion technologies have high efficiencies with less demonstrated life, thus higher mission risk.

collector. There they condense and return to the emitter through the electrical load connected externally between the collector and the emitter. We choose the collector and emitter temperatures for best overall system performance. In choosing the collector temperature, we try to decrease the weight and size of thermal radiators, and we choose materials based on mission life requirements. Thermionic power sources usually rely on a reactor heat source because of the high temperature required for efficient thermionic conversion. Power efficiencies for a thermionic power conversion are typically 10–20%.

In contrast to static sources, dynamic power sources use a heat source and a heat exchanger to drive an engine in a thermodynamic power cycle. The heat source can be concentrated solar energy, radioisotopes, or a controlled nuclear-fission reaction. Heat from the source transfers to a working fluid, which drives an energy-conversion heat engine. For a dynamic solar-power source, the balance of energy remains as latent and sensible heat in a heat exchanger (molten eutectic salt), which provides continuous-energy to the thermodynamic cycle during eclipse periods. A dynamic power source using a nuclear reactor or plutonium-238 decay does not require thermal-energy storage because the source provides continuous heat. The most common and practical power dynamic technologies are Stirling, Rankine and Brayton. Stirling-cycle engines use a single-phase working fluid as the working medium. The thermodynamic cycle consists of two isothermal processes (compression and expansion) and two constant-volume processes (heating and cooling). Power-conversion efficiencies for Stirling engines are 25–30%. Rankine-cycle engines are dynamic devices that use a 2-phase fluid system employing a boiler, turbine, alternator, condenser, and pump. This power-conversion cycle is essentially the same as that used to generate electricity from fossil and nuclear energy on Earth. Power-conversion efficiencies for Rankine-cycle engines are 15–20%. Brayton-cycle engines are dynamic devices that use a single, compressible working fluid as the working medium. The thermodynamic cycle consists of adiabatic compression and expansion stages separated and coupled by stages that add or reject heat at constant pressure. Placed after the turbine, a recuperator-heat exchanger improves the cycle's efficiency. Power conversion efficiencies for the Brayton cycle are 20–35%. Significant mission risk issues for radioisotope based power sources include the availability of the radioactive element, the costs for the fuel, launch safety requirements, and the generally negative public perception towards nuclear power systems.

Fuel cells are a common power source selection for short-duration missions, such as the Space Shuttle. Fuel cells convert the chemical energy of an oxidation reaction to electricity. They are self-contained generators that operate continuously without sunlight, but must carry their own reactant supply. The hydrogen-oxygen (referred to as "alkaline" because of the potassium hydroxide (KOH) electrolyte) fuel cell is the most popular type today because of its relatively high specific power (275 W/kg on the Space Shuttle), low reactant mass (hydrogen and oxygen), and useful by-product (water). A typical single cell produces a voltage of 0.8 V_{dc}. In combination, a fuel cell unit can create many kilowatts of power (each Shuttle fuel cell produces 16 kW peak or 12 kW continuous). The energy conversion efficiency can run as high as 80% for low current draws, but as current increases, the efficiency drops to 50–60%, due to activation over-potential and electrical resistance in the electrolyte solution between electrodes. However, compared with other power sources shown in Table 21-27, fuel cell efficiencies are high. The three Space Shuttle fuel cells are state-of-the-art power generators that produce all of the Shuttle electricity for the 28 V_{dc} bus. Their high efficiency (70%), low weight (260 kg), and excellent reliability (> 99% available) attest to their quality. Other important factors are their 15-minute start-up time, instantaneous shutdown, and long lifetime (2,400 hours before refurbishment). Besides electricity, these fuel cells produce crew drinking water, at a rate of 0.36 kg/kWh, or about 104 kg a day.

Research is underway to solve the short-mission limit with fuel cells, caused by carrying large reactant masses. Because the fuel cell reaction is reversible, we can use electrolysis to create more reactants from the water by-product. To optimize each process, however, we have to use separate units for generating electricity and separating the water. Any long-duration mission could use this regenerative system if it had some input electricity from solar cells, nuclear generators, or other power system during periods of low electrical load. Figure 21-27 shows an example of a regenerative system utilizing electricity from a solar array to drive the electrolyzer unit. The solar array provides power to the electrolyzer and the rest of the electrical bus during the day. The electrolyzer cracks water from the fuel cell into hydrogen and oxygen which are stored in tanks to be used by the fuel cell at night. The fuel cell powers the electrical bus at night by creating electricity from the hydrogen and oxygen as well as creating water that will used by the Electrolyzer.

Space battery improvements over the next 10 years will be focused around the battery chemistries and types defined in Sec. 21.2.3, with focus around Lithium batteries for primary (non rechargeable) applications; and Lithium batteries and regenerative fuel cells for secondary (rechargeable) applications. Fuel cells should be closely monitored as a viable and enabling energy storage technology for future space missions.

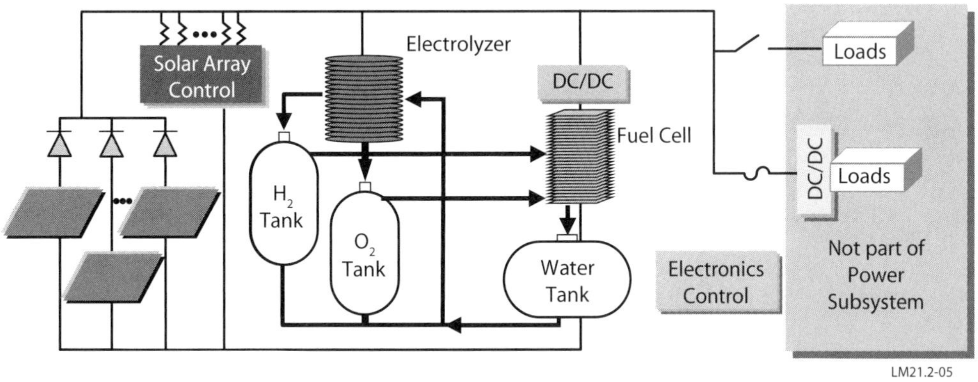

Fig. 21-27. Regenerative Power System. A solar array to power the loads electrolyze water during the day, and a fuel cell to produce electricity and water at night.

Table 21-27◀, Fig. 21-27, Eq. 21-12◀

References

For annotated bibliography of communications and power, see the book website.

American Gear Manufacturer's Association (AGMA). 2005. "Design Manual for Bevel Gears." ANSI/AGMA 2005-D03.

American Gear Manufacturer's Association (AGMA). 2003. "Rating the Pitting Resistance and Bending Strength of Generated Straight Bevel, Zerol Bevel and Spiral Bevel Gear Teeth." ANSI/AGMA 2003-C10.

CCSDS. 2011. Consultative Committee for Space Data Systems Website.

Deutsch, L. 2008. "Selecting Codes, Modulations, Multiple Access Schemes, and Link Protocols for Future NASA Missions." 2008 IEEE Aerospace Conference IEEEAC Paper #1497.

DoD. 1978. *Mechanical Electrical and Functional Characteristics of a Serial Data Bus* MIL-STD-1553.

Jones, A., 1946. "New Departure Engineering Data: Analysis of Stresses and Deflection." General Motors Corporation. Vol. 2. Bristol, Conn.

NASA. 2011. Deep Space Network Telecommunications Link Design Handbook 2011 (810-005). Website.

NTIA. 2010. National Telecommunications and Information Administration. Manual of Regulations and Procedures for Federal Radio Frequency Management, revised Sept. 2010.

Oberg, E., F. Jones, H. Horton, and H. Ryffel. *Machinery's Handbook.* New York, NY: Industrial Press.

Palmgren, Arvid. 1959. Ball and Roller Bearing Engineering, 3rd Ed. SKF Industries.

SFCG. 2011. Space Frequency Coordination Group.

Shigley, Joseph E., and Larry Mitchell. 1993. *Mechanical Engineering Design, 4th Ed.* New York, NY: McGraw Hill.

Spring Manufacturer's Institute (SMI). 1986. Technology & Engineering. Vol. 25–26.

Wahl, A. M. 1963. *Mechanical Springs, 2nd Ed.* New York, NY: McGraw-Hill.

Wesdock, J. 2008. "Formulation of the Modulation Recommendations for Future NASA Space Communications," 2008 IEEE Aerospace Conference. IEEEAC Paper #1575.

22 Spacecraft Subsystems V—Structures and Thermal

22.1 Spacecraft Structures and Mechanisms*

Michael Pryzby, *ATK Space Systems*

Having defined the initial spacecraft bus design, it is now time to develop a more detailed spacecraft bus design and arrive at a bottom up mass estimate. At this point in the process, there should be considerable understanding and documentation of the mission and spacecraft systems level requirements. These spacecraft systems requirements will flow down to the mechanical subsystem and allow the mechanical team to arrive at a detailed concept. Following preliminary analysis and sizing, a bottom up mass estimate can be derived for the subsystem. This section will focus on the critical topics that affect the conceptual layout and sizing of the mechanical subsystem. It is not intended to be an analytical tutorial on how to size the system.

Table 22-1. Spacecraft Structure Design Steps.

Step	Reference
Overview Layout of Section	Sec. 22.1
Define Objectives and Constraints Define Structural Requirements and Constraints	Sec. 22.1.1
Define Concepts / Designs Configuring the Spacecraft Design Modeling Design Options and Trade Studies	Sec. 22.1.2
Preliminary Analysis and Sizing Requirements Analysis	Sec. 22.1.3
Evaluate and Validate Verification Philosophy Mechanical Verification and Testing	Sec. 22.1.4
Mechanisms Overview Mechanisms	Sec. 22.1.5

* The author would like to recognize the following contributors to Sec. 22.1: Ed Devine–ATK Space, Mike McEachen–ATK Space-Goleta, Roger Kraus–ATK Space and Michael Golob–Vantage Systems, Inc. (photo contributions).

Chapter 14 details the process for establishing a preliminary concept for the spacecraft. That chapter should be re-read or scanned prior to reading this chapter. The mechanical structure is the backbone for the spacecraft, and touches every other subsystem. One should have a good understanding of how all the subsystems interrelate prior to delving into the mechanical layout.

Table 22-1 describes the basic process used to design a preliminary structure. Before you start to layout the structure, you have to understand your design space. The mission level requirements and performance requirements provide the outline of that design space. Several key documents provide the key information to begin to shape the design space. The *Mission Requirements* document can provide substantive details on the mission design life, orbit parameters, launch vehicle class, and payloads specifications. They can also provide constraints, like schedule and cost. *The Payload* or *Science Specification* defines how well the flight segment must perform. From here, you can gather constraints like pointing accuracy and knowledge. Payload performance specifications also provide the interface details for the payloads. A preliminary *Concept of Operations* will partition the mission into numerous phases. For each phase, you can derive the mechanical functions required to meet mission goals. You will also get an understanding of the different spacecraft states and configurations for each phase. From all of these documents, you can then generate a top level mechanical subsystem requirements document.

Once you have an idea of the requirements and functions of the mechanical subsystem, you can start to partition them into smaller and smaller segments or subsystems. For a mechanical system, the system usually breaks down into a couple of modules. Typically, the following types of modules apply: primary bus (primary load path to interface with the launch vehicle), propulsion module (if there is a prop system, it consists of tanks, propellant, thrusters, associated control electronics, and support structure), instrument module (can be an optical bench with or without payload electronics: stability typically drives what is mounted on the module), avionics module (structure for the spacecraft bus electronics, faraday cage, radiation shielding) and, if needed, deployables (solar arrays, antenna systems, covers, and/or shields).

As you partition the mechanical subsystem, you can also can start a preliminary concept of the spacecraft. As the concept is fleshed out, the requirements and constraints will become more obvious. The iterative process of collecting requirements and constraints will continue indefinitely or until time or money runs out. One of the great unwritten benefits of major mission reviews is that it forces engineers to have to stop designing, document their work, and move on.

At the end of this process detail, a section was included describing the selection and sizing of mechanisms. Mechanisms can be complex little subsystems on their own. They are often organized in the project structure to be part of the mechanical team or subsystem. However, due to their complexity, spaceflight mechanisms can create major havoc with project costs and schedules and are best elevated on par with other subsystems, not just a subset to the mechanical team.

22.1.1 Structural Requirements and Constraints

Figure 22-1 shows a typical process for technical requirement definition per the NASA Systems Engineering Handbook. As mentioned earlier, the inputs to the process (right hand side) are the top level requirements and a baselined concept of operations. In a typical flow down of requirements, the level 2 documents would flow down a mechanical subsystem (level 3) document.

The mechanical systems lead should work closely with the Mission System team during creation of level 2 documents. During that process, the top level requirements for the subsystem can be initiated and traced to its higher level requirements. The process requires numerous discussions with the key stakeholders for the mission. Five of the key personnel for the mechanical team to work with are Instruments/Payloads, Thermal, GNC, I&T, and Launch Vehicle personnel. Keeping the systems team in the loop will only help minimize finding unknowns later. The system team will help find any other critical drivers that may have been overlooked. This will save you from more design changes and iterations later.

The instrument/payload team is the primary reason the mission is flying. Their needs should be the primary focus of all subsystems. I have yet to meet a *principal investigator* (PI) who did not want more capability from the spacecraft than what was originally proposed. PIs will always be willing to negotiate—typically for more. If you recognize that any procurement or selection process is not perfect, you know that PIs cannot always propose their exact needs or wants. There are many trades the PI must go through to be competitive in the selection process. They have to make assumptions about where to best compromise to win the competition. Therefore, some flexibility by the spacecraft leads early in the design process can yield better mission success and results. Pointing is almost always an area where increased performance is welcome. For example, if a PI proposes extremely tight pointing requirements from a bus, their proposal may be judged as too expensive to accommodate. To meet the extreme pointing they desire, the PI may be attempting herculean efforts on their side of the interface or else they may be required to perform a lot of data post-processing to meet mission (level 1) requirements. In discussing needs, you may find a simple option on the subsystem side that can make a huge difference on the instrument side. Quite possibly, the bus structure might require a composite frame to meet weight and stiffness requirements. The low coefficient of thermal expansion (CTE) or stiffness of the composite could increase stability by an order of magnitude and reduce risk on the PI's side of the mission. These key discoveries

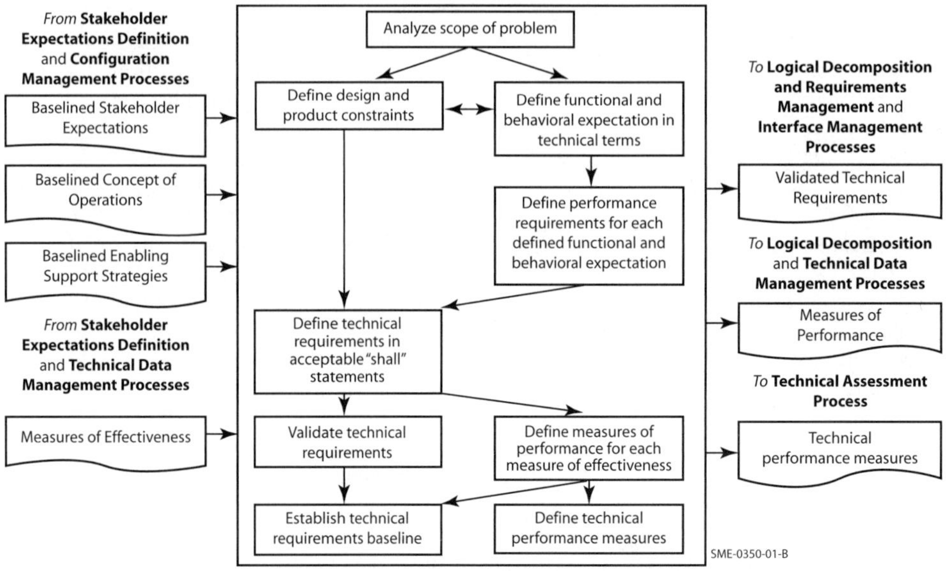

Fig. 22-1. Technical Requirement Definition Process.

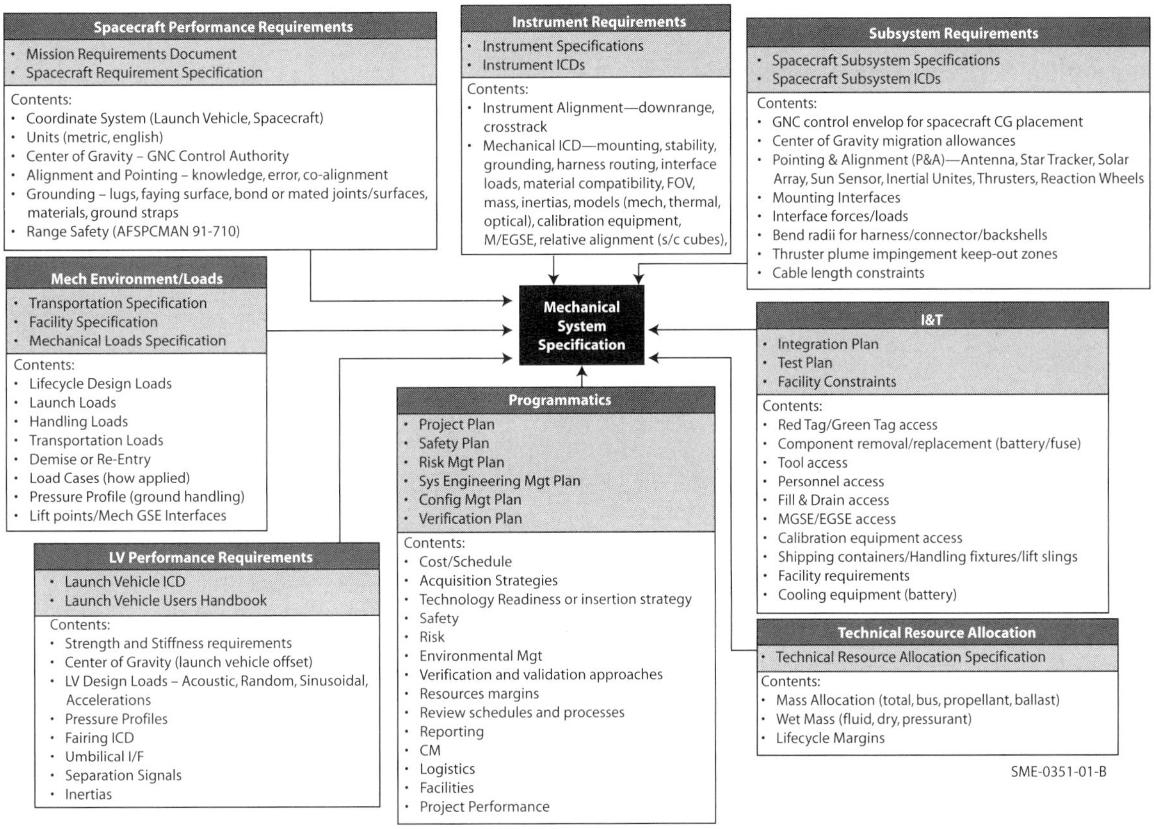

Fig. 22-2. Top Level Document Flowdown to Mechanical Systems.

will be what makes a mission successful. Finding more elegant solutions reduce risk, costs, and schedules by simplifying mission designs, saving resources, and reducing iterations. Unfortunately, for many engineers, the only way to make this happen is to get out and interact with people outside your normal sphere of peers.

> An excerpt from **A Project Manager's Lessons Learned,** [Madden, 2005]
>
> ***Item 75.*** A scientific proposal takes about 9 months to put together. It takes NASA HQ about 9 months to a year to select the winning proposals. Then, it takes 3 to 4 years to sell the program. This means 5 to 6 years after the initial thoughts, the real work starts. Managers, for some strange reason, do not understand why a scientist wants to build something different than proposed. Managers are strange people.

Figure 22-2 lists typical level 1 and 2 documents that will flow requirements down to the mechanical subsystem. Depending upon where you are in the design phase, the state of these documents and requirements can vary quite a bit. The more discussions you can have about these range of requirements and the more questions you can answer, the less chance you will have costly design iterations later.

The following subsections give a quick overview on the types of requirements or constraints the lead mechanical engineer can use to derive the mechanical system specification. This section will list the areas requirements are derived from and a short blurb regarding how the requirement might affect the design.

Performance/Mission

Performance and Mission requirements will provide details and constraints regarding top level items affecting the mechanical subsystem. This will include items like mission life (key for mechanisms to determine number of cycles of the life of the item), pointing and stability requirements, grounding, range identification, launch vehicle class, and orbit parameters.

Environment

Given the mission orbit parameters, numerous environmental requirements can be derived from the influences or concerns highlighted below. See Table 22-2.

Thermal: The thermal environment and mission orbit dictate the size and placement (field of view) of radiators. It also dictates range of temperatures used to analyze thermally induced stresses on the structure or mechanism, including the survival and operational ranges of the hardware. It determines the range of temperatures used to calculate temporal structural stability (how much an optical bench will flex over temperatures, or

Table 22-2. Environmental Concerns by Mission Phase.

Orbit Class or Mission Phase	Environmental Concerns or Influences
Launch	Venting, pressure profile, atomic oxygen, aerodynamic heating, launch loads
LEO	Atomic oxygen, thermal radiation (solar, planetary/albedo, reflected), vacuum, micrometeoroids, magnetic fields
MEO or GEO	Additional cosmic radiation, solar wind
De-Commissioning	Re-entry (loads, thermal) insertion orbit loads

even pointing). It can also dictate the amount of thermal shift from ground test to on-orbit temperatures (key for cryogenic operations). The environment can also constrain component placement options for thermal shielding (mount components internally to the bus (relatively warm/thermally stable) or external to bus (more variability/easier to radiate high power). See Chap. 22.2 for more on thermal design and effects on other subsystems.

Radiation: The radiation environment dictates the amount of radiation shielding required to protect sensitive electronics (more shielding can be provided by adding more metal/material around sensitive components via thicker walls in electronic box packaging or by increasing bus panel thickness), faraday cage shielding (RF shielded/sealed enclosures) grounding paths (faying surface specification, grounding lugs, surface/joint mating materials/designs, materials and coatings).

Launch: The launch vehicle typically drives the design loads (accelerations, acoustic, shock/separation). It provides the spacecraft bus volume constraints (the spacecraft must be packaged within launch vehicle fairing volume), pressure profiles (venting paths of structure and electronics), center of gravity (CG) location (offset from thrust line), umbilical access, propulsion fill and drain access, strength and stiffness requirements of the spacecraft bus, and moment of inertias (affects component placement and packaging). See Chap. 26 for more information on launch vehicle considerations and their affects on other subsystems.

Interfaces/Subsystems

Alignments: There are often requirements that relate the alignment of one item to another. Examples of these types can include Instrument to Instrument (including cross-track, downrange alignments), Instrument to Sensor (Star Tracker, IRU, positional and pointing components relative to an instrument), Antenna to Sensor (ST, IRU to high gain antennas). The requirements can cover one time shifts or deformation usually from a result of launch loads or a system deployment. They can be for on-orbit deflections like from orbit period thermal changes or jitter from an operating mechanism (moving arrays, antenna, optical steering mirrors). There are also longer duration effects, like temporal thermal affects as the spacecraft processes in an orbit over the seasons. See Fig. 22-3 for a sample of a typical alignment budget allocation and flow down. Also see Sec. 6.2 and Sec. 14.5.4.

Mechanical ICD: Many requirements come from just mounting a component. Details like component mounting (area, location, fastener types/size), stability, grounding, interface loads (load specifications can go both ways including high frequency response/jitter, deployments forces, mechanisms forces), material compatibility, field of view (glint, stray light, un-impeded), mass, moment of inertia, models (mechanical, thermal, optical), calibra-

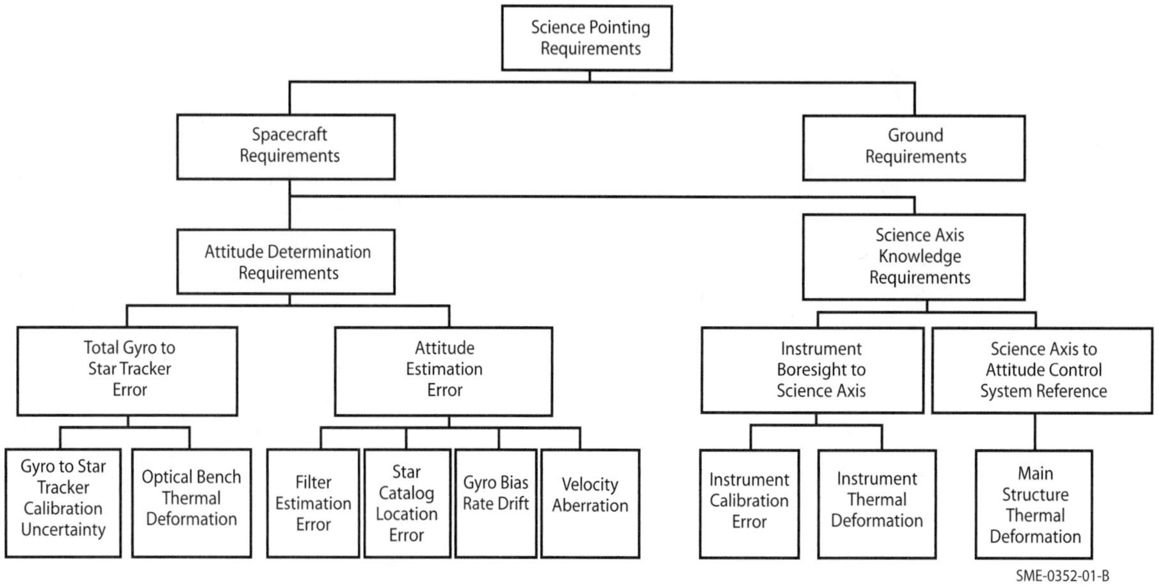

Fig. 22-3. NASA Systems Engineering Handbook—Pointing Requirement Allocation and Flowdown.

tion equipment access, mechanical/electrical GSE access and interfaces, alignment cube positioning and access for ground alignment, harness routing and strain relief for electrical connector backshells.

Center of Gravity: The launch vehicle and the spacecraft ACS will also provide requirements for the spacecraft CG. The net thrust of a system should travel through the system's CG for better control and more efficient use of propellant. The farther the CG is off the thrust line, the more control pulsing the system will need to do to maintain direction. Care should also be taken to account for CG migration controls (depleting propulsion fuel on-orbit, deployed or jettisoned components/systems).

Programmatic

Maybe surprisingly to many, programmatics can affect many areas of the design. These needs should be addressed early. The effects can be the source of numerous iterations.

Programmatics will define how requirements are levied on the project and how the requirements will be managed. They will address cost and schedule constraints. They can determine acquisition strategies (make or buy decision criteria), technology readiness thresholds or insertion strategy (what level of readiness must all technology be to be considered for the mission and how else do you increase the technology readiness level), safety, risk, environmental management (allowed materials, processes and waste), verification and validation approaches, resource margins, review schedules and processes, reporting, configuration management (CM), logistics, facilities, and project performance. All of these items can affect execution of the mission and mechanical subsystem. There should be time dedicated early in the mission to understand these requirements and make sure they are properly flowed down into the mechanical subsystem specification.

22.1.2 Design Concepts

David Watson, ATK Space

Configuring the Spacecraft

Significant program cost and schedule can be saved by efficiently configuring the spacecraft early in the design process. Decisions made on how the spacecraft looks, where both major and minor components are placed, how easily the structure is to design and analyze, and how efficient the load-paths are through the structure, all greatly affect the success or failure over the life of the program. Therefore, considerable time, resources, and experience should be applied during this phase of the program so that early and accurate assessments of mass, strength, and stiffness can be achieved.

An efficient and robust bus module that is able to support all of the payloads, the equipment boxes, the solar arrays, and the propulsion module should be the goal when configuring the spacecraft. Decisions on placement of components should be made with these thoughts in mind:

1. Effect on center of gravity
2. Length of electrical harness required for components
3. Electrical grounding needed for components
4. Amount of support structure required
5. Stiffness required

An example of this packaging effort would be placing as many of the large mass components and subsystems (e.g., main payloads, propulsion module) along the centerline of the Spacecraft. This is important because the launch vehicle interface is typically the center of the structure where all of the load must be reacted. If the major mass items are centered over the launch vehicle interface, then the eccentric loading, and resulting necessary structure to support it, will be minimized. Also, most launch vehicles require a lateral center of gravity to be within 12.5 cm of the centerline. This requirement becomes difficult to achieve if major mass items are offset from the center.

An efficient structure can also be achieved by placing as many large mass items as low as possible on the bus structure. This packaging will reduce the overall bending moment at the launch vehicle interface and, in the process, increase the overall spacecraft launch frequency.

Once the large mass items are conceptually identified, the engineer can estimate the vertical and lateral center of gravity using a simple sketch and spreadsheet. Calculating the $\Sigma(Md)$ divided by the ΣM, where M is the mass of each major component and d is the distance of the same component from each axis, vertical or lateral as applicable, will produce an approximate center of gravity (CG). This calculation can be done with a limited number of major mass components or subsystems, typically the payloads, the propulsion system/tanks, solar arrays, the bus structure (assume 20% of wet mass), batteries, and any other unique heavy spacecraft component. Initially, I like to use a rule of thumb of any component used in this preliminary calculation should be at least 5% of the total mass of the system. (One exception will be for post launch deployed systems. The distance of a deployed system can be large enough to shift the CG, especially if any fuel or propellant has been expended, even for smaller masses.) The center of gravity sensitivity can then be monitored by varying the location of these items within the spreadsheet.

Design simplicity should always be maintained throughout the configuration process. If the primary structure of the spacecraft is difficult and complex to design, then it will be equally hard to analyze and build. If the structure is not robust then the risk of failures during component, subsystem, and system-level testing is increased. Increases in complexity and risk invariably lead to significant cost and schedule pressures on the program.

Design Modeling

All of the spacecraft design concepts and configurations that are generated in the conceptual and preliminary design phases of the program are usually documented and visualized using a *Computer Aided Design* (CAD) tool. The most popular CAD tools in the spacecraft industry are Pro-E, NX (formerly IDEAS and Unigraphics), and Catia. These CAD tools are 3-dimentional modeling suites that spacecraft designers and engineers use from conceptual design through detailed modeling and then ultimately to production models and drawings that will be used to manufacture all of the structural components. ISO 10303, STEP AP-203 provides a standard format for exchanging data between CAD tools.

In the conceptual design phase, it is important to model the major bus, propulsion, and payload modules to determine overall system envelopes and interfaces. This CAD modeling effort includes, but is not limited to, the following tasks:

1. Assembly layout of all major components of the spacecraft to determine required interfaces and envelopes. These mechanical interfaces will need to be managed throughout the program with Mechanical Interface Control Drawings and Documents (MICDs).
2. Placement of assembled model in the launch vehicle fairing to verify static and dynamic clearances or interferences. This launch vehicle check will also be used to design the interface between the bus module and the launch vehicle adapter.
3. Modeling of all component and instrument Fields of View (FOV) to ensure full performance within requirement specifications. Any interferences must be negotiated at a system level early in the program to make the necessary mechanical or performance changes.
4. Modeling of all major bus and payload equipment to ensure adequate volume and access as well as assist in determining mass and center of gravity (CG) limits.
5. Transfer of CAD model to other spacecraft subsystem engineers for concurrent modeling. The structural analysis and thermal analysis engineers will use the CAD model to translate geometry into a system level finite element model and thermal model, respectively. The power engineers will use the CAD model to verify expected solar array area.

When done properly, the CAD model can also be used to help the engineer and program estimate the total mass of the spacecraft. In general, the structural mass of the spacecraft will range between 15% and 20% of the overall wet mass of the spacecraft. This rule of thumb can be used as an early program guideline from which to confirm the validity of the conceptual design. The CAD model and the finite element model can be used to capture the mass of the primary structural elements but the design team should carefully add other items that are often overlooked:

1. Secondary structure such as brackets for antennas, star trackers, and reaction wheels
2. Fasteners and inserts
3. Adhesives
4. Honeycomb panel inserts and fittings
5. Paints and thermal coatings

The program assumed Weight Growth Allowances (WGAs), not intended to account for these excluded items and often are not enough to cover the increases in mass that are produced when all of these are calculated.

Design Options and Trade Studies

Performing trade studies is an important part of the design process. Trade studies are needed early in the program to ensure that the most informed decision can be made by the program with the most available information at that time. The goal of a trade study is to choose the most efficient and cost-effective technical solution that meets all of the necessary requirements. Risk, reliability, producibility, cost, and schedule should all be included and evaluated when performing a trade study and making a decision. Engineers have a tendency to want to make a design optimal, instead of acceptable, for a given set of requirements.

When performing a trade study, be sure to understand customer priorities. For example, over-optimization of mass may lead to expensive materials or complicated structures. Often, cost and schedule benefits can be realized by sacrificing mass.

Simplicity should also be considered when performing a trade study. The simplest design may not be the lightest but it is often the most cost-effective solution. A simple design usually has fewer parts to design, analyze, manufacture, and assemble which results in cost and schedule savings at every stage of the program.

Structural trade studies often involve the general construction of the bus, the component materials, and the method of attachment of the bus structure. Typically, the primary structure is composed of a combination of machined metallic components, composite beams and struts, and honeycomb panels (two facesheets bonded to a core structure). An attempt should be made in the conceptual design phase to decide between a truss structure versus honeycomb panels, primary composite versus metallic components, and whether to bolt the components together or bond them. Each of these decisions will allow the rest of the assembly to be packaged and configured.

A truss design is often a lightweight solution of beams (composite or metallic) that efficiently transfer spacecraft load from one area to another. A truss works well when a large expanse of space needs to be covered without many secondary features needed to be attached in that area. A truss structure beam can be of various cross-sections; rectangular, circular, and I-beams are the most typical. These truss shapes connect at "nodes" that are typically metallic fittings with arms that attach to each truss member. A honeycomb panel will often be a better solution over the truss if structure is required to be available to mount or attach equipment boxes, thermal hardware, or other spacecraft components. The honeycomb panel may weigh more than the truss beam, but often less secondary structure is required. All of the spacecraft components can attach to the honeycomb panels using standard structural inserts.

The material trade is also important. Choosing a composite material or a metallic material affects all aspects of the structure from early design ultimately to assembly and testing. Since composite materials typically require significant development, qualification, and testing, they should only be used when necessary. Composite materials are often required when instrument pointing accuracy is required. Composites typically vary minimally when exposed to temperature changes and, therefore, will remain very stable in many launch and on-orbit spacecraft environments. This thermal stability is important for a structure that is supporting a very accurate and sensitive instrument. When designed properly, composite materials can also show a mass benefit over traditional metallic structures. This mass benefit must be weighed against the potential increased cost and schedule impact. Composites cost more because the raw materials are expensive and the development costs of the tooling and building-block testing are non-trivial. These development costs can often be offset if multiple units are being made or if tooling can be reused.

Even in the early design stages, the method of structural attachment should be considered and baselined. Most structure is either bolted or bonded together. A bolted connection is typically made with a high strength steel bolt and a corresponding nut or other retention device. A bonded connection is made with an adhesive that is applied between the interfaces and cured at the appropriate temperature. In general, the bonded attachment is used with composite connections but the bolted attachment can be achieved with either metallics or composites. The decision to go with bolts or bonds should primarily be made based on the assembly plan. Bonded joints are permanent while bolted joints can be removed. Bonded joints also often require a non-destructive inspection to confirm the structural integrity which can be time-consuming. Bolting and bonding the same components is unnecessary and should be avoided.

22.1.3 Structural Analysis and Sizing

Craig Stevens, *NASA GSFC*

Requirements

Structural analysis is often required to perform preliminary sizing of the primary structure. This allows a more thorough resource estimate to be made. It also allows an assessment of the preliminary design against the mission requirements. These mission requirements are generally defined by the following:

- Loads & Environments
- Stiffness
- Design & Strength Criteria
- Performance (i.e., pointing)
- Accommodations (e.g., Interfaces, Layout)
- Mass Properties (e.g., DNE Mass, CG Location)

The loads and environments are often considered the largest design driver for a structure. These loads and environments come from manufacturing, ground operations, ground testing, launch (landing), and on-orbit.

The launch loads and environments are often the driving case for most spacecraft structures. These loads are often launch vehicle and mission dependent. The landing cases are often only considered for STS payloads, sounding rocket recovered payloads, and interplanetary structures. Preliminary loads and environments are defined in launch vehicle mission planner's guides which are often available to the public. See Chap. 26.

Manufacturing stresses can be significant for brittle parts such as Beryllium and for parts that require high temperature curing such as graphite fiber reinforce plastic (GFRP) parts. Procedures and inspections should be well-planned to mitigate the risk of failure due to manufacturing.

Ground operations such as crane lifts and transportation should also be considered. Lifts load the structure in configurations that are not seen in flight. These lifts often drive the design of large structures. Transportation loads from an air-ride truck or aircraft can also be significant for large spacecraft as well. A shock isolation system is often considered to minimize the exposure of sensitive hardware.

Ground testing such as thermal vacuum testing in 1 g and workmanship screening of avionics boards can drive structural designs as well.

On-orbit environments are usually driven by the thermal design. The thermal environments should be estimated during ascent and operations. The structure should be designed to survive exposure to these environments as well.

Structural stiffness is often driven by the launch vehicle loads and environments. The stiffness is often measured by the natural frequency of the structure. The first natural (fundamental) frequency of the spacecraft is usually required to be greater than a value to prevent dynamic coupling with the launch vehicle fundamental frequency. These values are also defined in launch vehicle mission planner's guides.

The design and strength criteria are often defined at the organizational level. Standards such as NASA-STD-5001 [2008], AIAA-S-110-2005 [AIAA, 2005], and MIL-STD-1540B [DoD, 1989] have been developed for this purpose. Other, more detailed standards have been created at lower organizational levels such as the General Environmental Verification Standard GEVS (GSFC-STD-7000) developed at NASA Goddard Space Flight Center [2005]. These standards define the minimum strength margin required for a structural design. Most implement this through the use of design factors of safety that depend on the material, failure mode, and verification philosophy.

The structural design and analysis is also often driven by mission performance requirements. These requirements such as pointing (bias and stability) require significant engineering and analysis of structure material and interfaces. Interfaces are designed using a kinematic (flexure) mounting scheme to allow the structure to expand and contract during operation thermal excursions. Interfaces are also designed with press-fit shear pins to prevent shifting during launch and operation.

The physical layout of the structural design is most driven by the accommodation of the launch vehicle interface, payloads, and other spacecraft subsystems. The launch vehicles often use standard interfaces (such as marmon bands of pre-defined diameter) that should be used for the design. Interfaces to the launch vehicle and heavier items, such as propellant tanks, are important to define early in development because the primary structural load path is defined using their geometry. Payloads generally have requirements for field of view (regard) that must be met.

Structural Analysis

Analysis of the structure can begin once most of the requirements and preliminary design have been defined. The first step in the analysis procedure is to create a structural model of the preliminary design. Following the creation of a structural model, the model is analyzed to demonstrate compliance of the most driving requirements. This analysis is often divided into the areas of loads and dynamics, and stress analysis.

Finite Element Model

Preliminary sizing analysis typically utilizes a finite element model (FEM) of the primary structure and significant mass items. The spacecraft geometry can be imported into finite element pre-processors in STEP and IGES formats. The primary structure is modeled using a mesh of two-dimensional (e.g., plate, laminate) elements to represent rings and panels. Truss and frame structures are represented using beam and bar elements. Typical spacecraft mesh sizes can easily maintain a node-spacing of approximately 1 inch or less using today's computers. Instruments and components are readily represented with lumped mass elements at the center of mass locations and rigid-body elements (RBEs) connecting the lumped mass node to the interface locations. Rigid-body interpolation elements (such as RBE3s) that provide no artificial stiffness are recommended at this stage to ensure that all structure is sized adequately. Large and flexible subsystems such as solar arrays should be modeled similar to the primary structure if a design has been established. These items often drive the fundamental frequency and the size of the structural members. Instruments and other significant mass items that require specialized (semi-kinematic) mounting should be modeled due to their effect on the stiffness and strength of the structure. Physical models of the mounts should be included if possible or appropriate interface degrees of freedom should be released at a minimum. Nonstructural mass should be added to equipment panels and other structure to account for the mass allocated to other nonstructural items. Finally, the mass of the model should be scaled to maximum mission capability at this early development phase. This should be defined by the mission systems engineer and is usually limited by the launch vehicle or spacecraft propulsion capabilities.

The model is constrained at the launch vehicle interface which is usually the center of the separation plane. The constraints depend on the type of separation system used for the mission. For a standard marmon band, the model is constrained in all degrees of freedom at the nodes around the circumference of the launch vehicle interface ring.

Finally, the model should be verified using the appropriate validity checks before beginning any analysis. The free-free modes check, unit gravity check, and the unit displacement check should be performed at a minimum. These checks demonstrate that there are no numerical or modeling issues and that the model is free of unintended constraints. A thermal stress check should also be performed on models used for any thermal stress and distortion analysis.

Loads and Environments

The first step in the analysis procedure begins with an assessment of the mission loads and environments. The results of the assessment should reveal which loads and environments drive the design. These results will allow the analysis effort to take focus.

The primary structure launch limit loads (load factors) are the best place to start for preliminary sizing of the spacecraft structure. These load factors are usually computed for each significant launch event, such as liftoff and maximum dynamic pressure (max Q). The load cases are typically provided as combination of axial and lateral loading (relative to the launch vehicle coordinate system. See Sec. 26.5.1 for typical loads. It should be noted that smaller launch vehicles often have higher load factors. It is important to note that these preliminary loads are typically only valid for spacecraft of typical mass and stiffness. In other words, spacecraft must meet the launch vehicle mass properties and frequency requirements to ensure that the preliminary loads are adequate and stable. In all cases, these load factors should be verified using mission-specific launch vehicle coupled loads analysis (CLA) as described in Sec. 26. The first CLA cycle is typically performed approximately around the preliminary design review phase of project development.

Sine vibration environments are derived from analysis of the launch vehicle dynamic environments. The sine vibration environments are estimated by computing the shock response spectra of the launch vehicle transient events and sustained sinusoidal environments (such as POGO). See Sec. 26.5.2. These environments are used for analyzing the dynamic response of the spacecraft, estimating the loads at subsystems and components, and testing the spacecraft for sensitivity to the low-frequency dynamic environment. The sine vibration environments are derived at the spacecraft interface for both axial and lateral directions and are typically limited to frequencies between 5 and 100 Hz. The maximum expected flight levels are typically on the order of 1G peak amplitude. Limiting or notching is often required due to differences between the launch vehicle and test/analysis configurations. Limiting the sine vibration responses to not exceed the CLA levels is typical. Therefore, the sine vibration environment does not typically drive the design of the primary structure.

The vibroacoustic environment is induced by high-intensity acoustic noise created during the launch phase. See Sec. 26.5.3 for more details. The term is used because the environment manifests itself throughout the payload in the form of structure-borne random vibration and as transmitted acoustic excitation. Therefore, the common practice is to specifically consider both the acoustic and random vibration environments and test levels [NASA-STD-7001 1996]. This vibroacoustic environment primarily ranges from 20 Hz to 10,000 Hz. Most will find that the spacecraft level random vibration environments are negligible for larger launch vehicles and spacecraft. The acoustic environments often drive the design of large, lightweight panels with area-to-weight ratios greater than 0.15 m^2/kg. Analysis and/or testing of the spacecraft should be used to create vibroacoustic test specifications for components and instruments. This should be done early in the mission development because the random vibration environment is typically the driving case for the design of small (<20 kg) components and instruments. However, for smaller spacecraft, random vibration testing is sometimes performed instead of acoustic testing. Again, test levels from NASA-STD-7001 or random environments specific to the particular launch vehicle will be applied to the base of the spacecraft.

The shock environment is induced by actuation of shock producing devices such as pyros. Section 26.5.2 provides further explanation of this environment. These devices typically produce large high-frequency accelerations that damage small, brittle hardware. The environment at shock sensitive hardware is most often driven by the launch vehicle separation system. The peak values often range from 0.5 kg to 2 kg. Due to difficulty of analysis and screening of workmanship issues, these shock-sensitive items are often verified by testing.

The thermal environment is derived using thermal analysis of the spacecraft in significant ascent trajectories, orbits, and operational modes. Typical spacecraft temperatures range from 200 K to 330 K. A more extreme thermal environment can significantly drive the design to minimize thermal stresses and distortion. It may also require the selection of more exotic materials to maintain adequate material properties, maximize thermal isolation, and minimize outgassing.

Once assessment of the loads and environments is complete, an analysis of the structure under the most stringent loading conditions can begin.

Dynamics

Preliminary sizing of the spacecraft structure for dynamics begins with analysis of the spacecraft stiffness and mass properties. It is important to understand these properties because they largely determine the stresses experienced by the spacecraft during launch. The stiffness and mass properties are best characterized by performing a finite element analysis, (FEA) and normal modes analysis. The normal modes analysis finds the eigensolution to the undamped, harmonic, multiple degree of freedom system equations of motion. The equations of motion include the stiffness and mass matrices created from the FEM described above. The results of the normal modes analysis are both eigenvalues and eigenvectors which correspond to the square natural frequencies and natural mode shape, respectively. Spacecraft fundamental frequencies in launch configuration are typically between 8 Hz and 50 Hz.

The normal modes analysis mode shapes and element strain energy should be reported as well. These plots can be used to better understand the dynamics and troubleshoot any modeling issues. The element strain energy is an important design tool that measures the strain energy in each element for each mode. The natural frequency can be most easily modified by changing the stiffness of the elements with the highest strain energy.

Finally, modal effective mass fractions should be reported for each mode. The modal effective mass fraction measures what fraction of the overall mass is participating in each direction of a mode. The modal effective mass fraction in each direction (degree of freedom) sums to 1.0 over all system modes. This important parameter indicates which modes may be a significant contributor to the loads of the primary structure. Typically, modes with modal effective mass fractions greater than 0.05 (5% of the total mass) are considered significant. The significant mode with the lowest natural frequency (fundamental mode) should be evaluated against the launch vehicle and/or spacecraft frequency requirements described above. Typically, the results should show a margin of 15% over the frequency requirement during preliminary sizing analysis.

Another aspect of dynamics that should be considered is that of appendage deployments. Deployment hinges, particularly the root hinge, as well as hinge interfaces must be evaluated against the potential sudden start/stop loads of deployments, especially at the end of travel. Excessive loads/stresses generated at deployment hinges may lead to the necessity of dampers or other devices to control the deployment motion.

Spacecraft Fundamental Frequency

We can quickly estimate the fundamental frequency of a spacecraft as a sanity check on the configuration. Most spacecraft have a fundamental mode shape similar to beam bending mode when constrained at the launch vehicle interface. Therefore, we can use a cantilever beam assumption and estimate the fundamental frequency using the following equation [Young and Budynas, 2001].

$$f_n = \frac{1}{2\pi}\sqrt{\frac{3EIg}{WL^3}} = \frac{1}{2\pi}\sqrt{\frac{3EI}{ML^3}} \quad (22\text{-}1)$$

where f_n is the fundamental frequency (Hz), E is the modulus of elasticity, I is the area moment of inertia, g is the acceleration due to gravity, W is the weight of the beam, M is the mass of the beam (W/g), and L is the length from beam root to center of mass.

We can also use empirical data to estimate the fundamental frequency of the spacecraft. The plot below shows historical data which plots the spacecraft (Observatory) fundamental frequency versus the launch mass of several missions. The data generally shows that the fundamental frequency decreases with launch mass. However, the data and trending analysis also shows that the fundamental frequency can vary significantly for spacecraft of similar mass. These frequency variations are due to spacecraft design differences such as structural materials, payloads, propellant mass, separation systems, launch vehicle interface, and spacecraft layout. Therefore, care must be taken when applying these results to a particular mission. Alternatively, this data also shows that the systems and structural engineers can have a significant influence on the spacecraft stiffness.

Example: FireSat II

We can apply the above equation to our FireSat II example mission. We first need to address some key assumptions based on our initial understanding of the mission.

Key Assumptions:

- 2 spacecraft stacked in launch configuration
- Octagonal spacecraft 1.2 m across the octagon and 1.1 m tall
- Separation systems have negligible effect on stiffness
- 260 kg total mass
- Center of mass is at the geometric center of the spacecraft launch configuration (1.1 m)

The beam bending stiffness (EI) in Eq. (22-1) is intended to be constant along the entire length. However, this is obviously not the case for any realistic spacecraft manufactured from multiple parts and materials. Therefore, we shall assume the bending stiffness based on the properties at the launch vehicle interface because this will typically be the area of the structure with the largest strain energy. FireSat II is a low-cost mission; therefore, we will first assume a simple, all metallic structure to save cost. Therefore, we will use the modulus of elasticity of Aluminum 6061 equal to 68.2 GPa. We will also assume a ring at the launch vehicle interface with an outer diameter of 1 m and a wall thickness of 1 mm. Therefore, the area moment of inertia for this beam is calculated as follows:

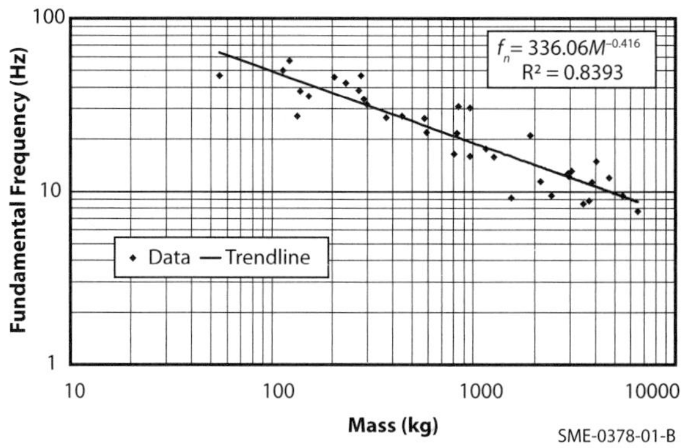

Fig. 22-4. Comparison of Observatory Launch Mass Versus Fundamental Frequency. (Graphic courtesy of NASA)

$$I = \frac{\pi\left(d_o^4 - d_i^4\right)}{64} \quad (22\text{-}2)$$

$$= \frac{\pi\left(1.000^4 - 0.998^4\right)}{64} = 3.92\times10^{-4}\ \text{m}^4$$

where d_o = outer ring diameter, d_i = outer ring diameter. Using the above results in Eq. (22-1), the fundamental frequency is estimated in the following equation

$$f_n = \frac{1}{2\pi}\sqrt{\frac{3\times68.2\times10^9\times3.92\times10^{-4}}{260\times1.1^3}} = 76.6\ \text{Hz} \quad (22\text{-}3)$$

The FireSat II fundamental frequency is estimated at approximately 77 Hz using the given assumptions. Note that this estimate is considered an upper bound because this equation assumes an ideal structural load path and doesn't account for the added flexibilities of the upper separation system.

For FireSat II, we can also estimate the spacecraft fundamental frequency using the empirical data in Fig. 22-4. This data shows that we should expect a fundamental frequency of approximately 35 Hz. In fact, it could be lower because this empirical data does not include many samples of stacked spacecraft connected via separation systems. The separation system compliance often plays a big role in the stack fundamental frequency;

therefore, further analysis may be required if there is a concern about the FireSat II fundamental frequency.

Fundamental Frequency of Deployable Systems

Large deployables often have fundamental frequencies of approximately 1 Hz or less. The deployable fundamental frequency is an important parameter for the ACS engineers to consider during design of the spacecraft attitude control system. We can quickly estimate the fundamental frequency of a deployable such as solar array using simplified equations. One method to estimate the fundamental frequency of a solar array is to assume it is a cantilever beam with its root at the spacecraft interface. Assuming the spacecraft interface is fixed is a reasonable assumption if the spacecraft is significantly heavier than the solar array. We can then apply Eq. (22-1) as follows

$$f_n = \frac{1}{2\pi}\sqrt{\frac{3EI}{ML^3}} \tag{22-4}$$

In this case, we would assume a beam bending stiffness (*EI*) based on the properties of the deployable structure adjacent to the spacecraft interface, such as the boom. We would also apply the mass properties of the deployable.

The deployable fundamental frequency may also be estimated using an alternative method. Due to the relatively low stiffness of the actuators or hinges, these parts often drive the fundamental frequency of the entire solar array. Using this method, the solar panel is assumed to be a rigid body and the fundamental frequency is estimated using the following equation,

$$f_n = \frac{1}{2\pi}\sqrt{\frac{k}{J}} \tag{22-5}$$

where f_n = fundamental frequency (Hz), k = the actuator or hinge torsional stiffness, and J = the mass moment of inertia at the center of rotation of the actuator or hinge. Note that this method requires some knowledge of the deployed actuator or hinge torsional stiffness.

Example: SCS Solar Array

We can use the methods described above to estimate the deployed fundamental frequency of the SCS solar arrays. SCS is a 200 kg, cube-shaped spacecraft carrying two deployable solar arrays. The power system requires that each solar array support 1.7 m^2 of cell area. The total mass of the solar panels is estimated at 9.5 kg (cells and substrate) based on the initial power system estimates. Based on this information, we make the following key assumptions,

- 1m cube-shaped spacecraft
- Solar array mass is 4.75 kg each, including cells and substrate
- Solar array panel is 1 m × 0.7 m
- Center of mass is at the geometric center of the array
- A boom length of 0.5 m is required to accommodate the field of view requirements

It should first be noted that a 1.7 m^2 deployed solar array is a relatively small array and SCS is a low-cost mission. Therefore, we will first assume a simple, all metallic solar array structure to save cost. We will assume the solar array boom is made of Aluminum 6061 and has a modulus of elasticity equal to 68.2 GPa. We will also assume the boom is a tube with an outer diameter of 50 mm and a wall thickness of 0.5 mm at the spacecraft interface. Therefore, the boom area moment of inertia is calculated as follows:

$$\begin{aligned} I &= \frac{\pi\left(d_o^4 - d_i^4\right)}{64} \\ &= \frac{\pi\left(0.050^4 - 0.049^4\right)}{64} = 2.38\times10^{-8}\ \text{m}^4 \end{aligned} \tag{22-6}$$

We then assume that the center of mass is at a distance of 1 m from the spacecraft interface (boom length plus half long dimension of panel). Using these assumptions, we estimate the solar array fundamental frequency using Eq. (22-4),

$$f_n = \frac{1}{2\pi}\sqrt{\frac{3\times68.2\times10^9\times2.38\times10^{-8}}{4.75\times1^3}} = 5.1\ \text{Hz} \tag{22-7}$$

The SCS solar array fundamental frequency is estimated at approximately 5 Hz using the given assumptions. Note that this estimate is considered an upper bound because this equation assumes an ideal structural load path and doesn't account for the added flexibilities of hinges and actuators.

We next estimate the fundamental frequency of the system assuming that the actuator stiffness is known to drive the system stiffness. We will assume an actuator torsional stiffness of 10,000 Nm/radian.

We next need to calculate the mass moment of inertia, *J*, at the center of rotation of the actuator. For simplicity, we will assume the elevation actuator is at the spacecraft interface. We first estimate the solar array panel mass moment of inertia J_{panel} at the center of mass assuming a rectangular, homogenous panel

$$J_{panel} = \frac{m_{panel}\left(a_{panel}^2 + b_{panel}^2\right)}{12} \tag{22-8}$$

where m_{panel} is the mass of the panel, a_{panel} is the length of side 1, and b_{panel} is the length of side 2. Using our assumptions outlined above,

$$J_{panel} = \frac{4.75\left(1^2 + 0.7^2\right)}{12} = 0.59\ \text{kg m}^2 \tag{22-9}$$

Table 22-2◀, Fig. 22-4◀, Eq. 22-9

We can safely assume the boom mass moment of inertia is negligible. However, we must now use the parallel axis theorem to transform the solar array panel mass moment of inertia from the panel center of mass to the actuator center of rotation.

$$J = J_{panel} + m_{panel} d^2 \qquad (22\text{-}10)$$

where d is the length from the solar array panel center of mass to the actuator center of rotation. In this case, d is equivalent to 1 m based on our previous assumptions.

Therefore, the mass moment of inertia is calculated as follows,

$$J = 0.59 + 4.75 \times 1^2 = 5.34 \text{ kg m}^2 \qquad (22\text{-}11)$$

Finally, we calculate the fundamental frequency of the solar array system with actuator from Eq. (22-5)

$$f_n = \frac{1}{2\pi}\sqrt{\frac{10000}{5.34}} = 6.89 \text{ Hz} \qquad (22\text{-}12)$$

Therefore, the solar array panel fundamental frequency is estimated at 6.9 Hz using this method.

These examples show that both the structure and mechanisms can drive the fundamental frequency of a deployable. Therefore, care must be taken during the design and analysis process of both items to ensure that the deployed system meets the ACS frequency requirements.

Stress

Spacecraft stress analysis is often performed using both *Finite Element Analysis* (FEA) and "hand" calculations. Once a *Finite Element Model* (FEM) is created, the stress analysis should be performed using the driving loads and environments uncovered from the assessment described above. As mentioned above, the driving loads for the primary structure are typically the spacecraft launch limit loads. The analysis is performed in multiple load cases by applying the axial load factor and clocking the lateral load factors around in all lateral directions (every 22.5 deg, typically).

The analysis results should provide stresses that should be evaluated against material allowables using a margin of safety calculation and appropriate factors of safety. Material properties are most often found in well-established sources such as MMPDS-01. However, GFRP composites and other non-traditional materials have properties that depend on the manufacturing process and the specific layup. Properties for these items should be attained from material characterization testing of coupons that represent the design materials and manufacturing process.

The specific stress components or combinations required from the analysis depend on the type of material and material properties. Von mises stresses are used to evaluate isotropic and elastic materials, such as aluminum. Brittle and non-isotropic materials require assessment of the margins of safety using the stress components and interaction criteria. GFRP composites often require margins of safety to be evaluated at the ply-level.

Forces are recovered from the FEM to evaluate failures of specific items separate from the FEA. This is because the FEM doesn't have the fidelity to accurately calculate the stresses in those areas. These include inserts/fittings in honeycomb panels, fasteners, and bonded joints. It is wise to compare the recovered forces in primary structure joints to allowables recovered from a detailed joint FEM or previous test data. These joints are often the critical part of the design and can add significant mass.

The stress analysis results should show positive margins of safety for the closing design. All critical margins of safety should be reported. Stress contour plots should also be reported to demonstrate the locations of the critical margins.

Mass Estimate

The mass of the structure should be updated once a preliminary design has been established using the procedure outlined above. The estimate should include all structural entities modeled using physical elements. It should also estimate the mass of fittings, inserts, and other members not represented with physical elements. A maturity factor should also be presented with the estimate.

At this point, there should be two independent mass estimates: one from the CAD model and one from the FEM. In working with the FEM to perform preliminary sizing, we should now have a good approximation for the mass of the mechanical system. As a sanity check, the mechanical system, including the primary structure, secondary structures, and fasteners, should be approximately 15% of the dry mass. Dry mass is the mass of the spacecraft less any propellant (wet or dry) or any gases (expendables) used in the propulsion or attitude control system. An efficient primary structure will be from 8% (very efficient) to 12% (still efficient). The secondary structures will be around 2–5%, and fasteners are usually around 2%. These percentages should include the proper margin at any stage of the mission life. As with any guidelines, these are approximations and should be used as goals, not absolute requirements.

22.1.4 Structural Design Verification Philosophy and Criteria

The number one credo for verification is "Test like you fly, and fly like you test." While this credo has some variations, following this one tenet will give you a fairly high success rate. Having said that, let's try to provide a little more detail and guidance.

Philosophy: Trust but verify. Everything must be verified. There are three typical ways to accomplish this, relative to the mechanical subsystem: by *test*, by *analysis*, or by *inspection*. How a verification method is utilized can depend on the mission phase, the hardware concept, and the management philosophy. In the following section, I will try to provide a high level overview of some philosophies [Sarafin, 1995; Pisacane, 2005].

Analysis: During the mission design phase, analysis will be the primary tool to verify designs and concepts. Analysis is used to determine preliminary loads and environments that will be used in the design and testing phases. FEM are used to assist with preliminary sizing and more detailed analysis for strength and stiffness verifications. CAD models are used to analytically verify mass properties, volumes, interfaces, and possible deployments paths.

Some will argue that one can also verify by similarity. Similarity is a red flag to a lot of review teams and systems engineers. It is becoming widely accepted that there is no such thing as "previously flown" hardware or similarity. See text box below. As most system engineers know, one major technical risk is using existing hardware or designs in a new but similar context. There will be a burden of proof that the projected environment is identical to the previous one. Remember that you will need to look over the product lifecycle, including the manufacturing processes, methods and controls, not just the operational environment. It is rare that an existing design will be able to actually claim similarity. Rarely will it be worth the expense to meet the burden of proof.

> An excerpt from **A Project Manager's Lessons Learned,** [Madden, 2005]
>
> ***Item 1.*** There is no such thing as previously-flown hardware, i.e., the people who build the next unit probably never saw the previous unit; there are probably minor changes; *the operational environment has probably changed*; and the people who check the unit out will in most cases not understand the unit or the test equipment.

Qualification by analysis is just that—analytically verifying a structure that meets its design requirements. I have seen some hardware with large production runs that use statistical analysis for verification. This is a unique case that merits more writing space than we have here. Since your analysis is only as good as your model, you will either have high factors of safety on your analysis to account for uncertainties (this typically results in an over-designed solution), or else you will need some testing to verify your models. The testing is performed to obtain data to correlate model predictions with actual test results. For smaller spacecraft, if you have to test to verify the model and go through the rigors of setting up the test, you may as well just qualify by testing to begin with. The design efficiencies you gain from designing to much lower *design loads* (predicted load times the factor of safety) should pay benefits in the area of overall mass and general risk reduction from a failure in flight. Some large spacecraft may be too large to test as a system, so final verification may need to be done by analysis.

Another time to qualify by analysis can be for small tertiary structures. They are typically low mass, low stress parts where a lack of elegance in the design is a minimal penalty on mass and risk. One should be able to simply and conservatively analyze the parts. Also, any testing of these components would generally be to high test loads (40+ gs') where any instrumentation (accelerometers) of the test article could be of a significant enough mass to influence the test and results.

Test: All flight hardware should see some type of testing. This follows the "test as you fly" mantra. There are four different types of hardware classifications (*development, qualification, proto-flight and flight*) you can use for testing. Those are addressed in the next section. Those types of hardware are used to support three types of testing: *development*, *qualification,* and *acceptance*.

Development testing. This test is not part of the verification process but can be an important part of the design lifecycle. Development testing is used to provide proof of concept or design in areas where we may not be extremely confident in our analysis. Development testing is also used to retire risk on new materials, manufacturing methods or processes and pathfinder operations. In these situations, development testing usually happens early in the design process as we are making trades on concepts.

At this early time in the lifecycle, the final mission design loads will not be accurately known since the mission design will not be that mature. So, extra margin is also carried in the form of a model/load uncertainty factor when determining the testing loads. Development tests are usually to twice the expected mission load and at times, hardware can be tested to failure. The test is used to gather data used to evaluate the design or process. It is not used to qualify a design.

On LRO, we designed a new method for integration of our flight structural panels. The bonded joint between the primary spacecraft deck and the bus walls had never been used before. The integration was planned to take place very late in the integration flow, after hardware was already mated to the flight panels. In a case like this, a development test to retire the risk from using a new process was recommended. Had there been an issue with integration, there would have been a significant set back in cost and schedule if we had been forced to recover an integration issue.

Qualification testing: Qualification testing is a preferred step in the verification process. Qualification testing typically tests primary structures and load bearing components to design loads above the predicted flight loads. See Table 22-3 for nominal test factors of safety. Qualification tests are also taken to destructive levels some times. The tests are usually performed on test articles (known as Qualification or Engineering Units) and not the actual flight components. So, there is the expense of building an extra set of hardware that needs to be accounted for if you decide to use a qualification unit. These tests typically occur when your manufacturing methods and processes are repeatable and there is reasonable proof that subsequent units will perform

Table 22-3. Test Factors and Durations from GEVS.

Test	Protoype Qualification	Proto-Flight Qualification	Acceptance
Structural Loads[1] Level	1.25 × Limit Load	1.25 × Limit Load	1.00 × Limit Load
Duration Centrifuge/Static Load Sine Burst	1 minute 5 cycles @ full level per axis	30 seconds 5 cycles @ full level per axis	30 seconds 5 cycles @ full level per axis
Acoustics Level[2] Duration	Limit Level + 3 dB 2 minutes	Limit Level + 3 dB 1 minute	Limit Level 1 minute
Random Vibration Level[2] Duration	Limit Level + 3 dB 2 minutes/axis	Limit Level + 3 dB 1 minute/axis	Limit Level 1 minute/axis
Sine Vibration[3] Level Sweep Rate	1.25 × Limit Level 2 oct/min	1.25 × Limit Level 4 oct/min	Limit Level 4 oct/min
Mechanical Shock Actual Device Simulated	2 actuations 1.4 × Limit Level 2 × Each Axis	2 actuations 1.4 × Limit Level 1 × Each Axis	1 actuation Limit Level 1 × Each Axis
Thermal-Vacuum	Max./min. predict ±10 C	Max./min. predict ±10 C	Max./min. predict ±5 C
Thermal Cycling[4] Level Duration	Max./min. predict ±25 C	Max./min. predict ±25 C	Max./min. predict ±20 C
EMC & Magnetics	As Specified for Mission	Same	Same

1 If qualified by analysis only, positive margins must be shown for factors of safety of 2.0 on yield and 2.6 on ultimate. Beryllium and composite materials cannot be qualified by an analysis alone.
Note: Test levels for beryllium structure are 1.4 × Limit Level for both qualification and acceptance testing. Also composite structure, including metal matrix, requires acceptance testing to 1.25 × Limit Level.
2 As a minimum, the test level shall be equal to or greater than the workmanship level.
3 The sweep direction should be evaluated and chosen to minimize the risk of damage to the hardware. If a sine sweep is used to satisfy the loads or other requirements, rather than to simulate an oscillatory mission environment, a faster sweep rate may be considered, e.g., 6ª8 oct/min to reduce the potential for over stress.
4 It is recommended that the number of thermal cycles and dwell times be increased by 50% for thermal cycle (ambient pressure) testing.

similarly. *Inspection* plays a vital role in this proof and will be addressed later. Qualification tests are performed at higher than predicted environments and provide design margin as the mission and design matures.

A special type of Qualification testing can be done by using proto-flight hardware. Sometimes, due to schedule, cost, or risk tolerance, there is not adequate resources for a Qualification Unit. The design will still need to be qualified. Proto-flight testing allows you to qualify a design but allows you to do so are lower test levels than Qualification Units. Most important, the unit is still tested to levels that provide design margin. In some cases where material fatigue can be an issue, fewer cycles are used during proto-flight testing to ensure adequate material life remains in the flight article. Proto-flight testing also provides testing to adequate levels to verify *workmanship*, the third test type.

Proto-flight testing is pretty standard in the industry and most often used in areas where risk mitigation is not a priority. Proto-flight is also typically used for composite structures. Composite are unique in that they are heavily susceptible to workmanship issues compared to metallic structures (the brittleness of beryllium makes it another outlier among metallic materials). So even if you test a composite qualification unit to qualification levels, you will still need to perform a qualification-level test on the flight unit when it comes to composite structures. As mentioned above, proto-flight levels can cover both qualification and workmanship verifications.

GEVS, Section

Acceptance testing: So once a design has been qualified, the flight unit would then only need to be tested to acceptance levels, also known as *workmanship testing*. This is the third level of testing used for verification. It is strongly recommended to at least perform some kind of test on all hardware. Testing is a final chance to demonstrate that workmanship was of an acceptable level and that all manufacturing processes were adequately controlled. It does not verify the design is adequate. Only the Qualification or Proto-flight test accomplishes the design verification. Workmanship tests are designed to catch more of the human error in building and integrating spacecraft. Acceptance or workmanship tests are typically tested to

Table 22-4. GEVS Factors of Safety. Flight Hardware Design/Analysis Factors of safety Applied to Limit Loads.[1, 2]

Type	Static	Sine	Random/Acoustic[4]
Metallic Yield	1.25[3]	1.25	1.6
Metallic Ultimate	1.4[3]	1.4	1.8
Stability Ultimate	1.4	1.4	1.8
Beryllium Yield	1.4	1.4	1.8
Beryllium Ultimate	1.6	1.6	2.0
Composite Ultimate	1.5	1.5	1.9
Bonded Inserts/Joints Ultimate	1.5	1.5	1.9

1 Factors of safety for pressurized systems to be compliant with EWR-127 (range safety)
2 Factors of safety for glass and structural glass bonds specified in NASA-STD-5001
3 If qualified by analysis only, positive margin must be shown for factors of safety of 2.0 on yield and 2.6 on ultimate. (See Sec. 22.2.4.)
4 Factors shown should be applied to statistically derived peak response based on RMS level. As a minimum, the peak response shall be calculated as a 3-sigma value.

the design loads. These tests are usually performed at higher levels of assembly (and final assemblies) provided there are adequate facilities.

Inspection: Inspection is typically used in conjunction with other tests to provide verification. Inspection is performed after testing to ensure structural integrity remains. Inspections are also used during manufacturing and integration processes to ensure methods are followed and repeatability can be verified. Inspections can be critical when used with qualification testing to verify there were not deformations, yielding, or any other type of structural integrity violation.

GEVS Factors of Safety Testing

At this point, it is worth discussing test factors, factors of safety, and limit loads. (See Table 22-4.) As mentioned in Sec. 22.1.3, programmatic requirements can affect many areas of the design. GSFC uses GEVS as its guide for general verification. GEVS specifies the test factors and the design factors of safety for a project. It is important to note that different stakeholders (sponsors) can have different guidelines. There are even differences between NASA Centers. It is important to know those guidelines.

At GSFC, structural and mechanical verification testing shall be supported by structural analysis to provide confidence that the hardware will not experience failure or detrimental permanent deformation under test or launch conditions.

Factors of Safety are applied to *limit loads* in order to calculate margins of safety. Factors of Safety include both factors on ultimate strength and yield strength. The yield factor of safety ensures that a prototype or protoflight test can be conducted with low risk of the hardware experiencing detrimental yielding. The ultimate factor of safety provides adequate separation between yield and ultimate failure modes and ensures that the hardware will not experience an ultimate failure under expected loading conditions.

Limit loads is the assumed maximum load the structure will experience. The design load is the limit load multiplied by the factor of safety. The test load is the limit load multiplied by the test factor.

There is also one more factor to keep in mind. In determining the limit load, sometimes the expected loads are derived from models (coupled loads—see Sec. 26.5.1). Depending on the fidelity and accuracy of the models, others factors can be applied to the derived load like a model uncertainty factor (MUF) to determine the limit load.

Hopefully, one can see this is an area where factors can get nested inside other factors and conservatism can get out of hand. Different sponsors have different levels of conservatism and that's how you get different guidelines.

Test Articles

In general, there are four types of test articles or hardware to discuss: development, qualification, proto-flight, and flight. Each type of hardware has specific purposes and associated test criteria. These classifications can range from piece parts all the way up to major assemblies. In general, this test article discussion is for primary structural components or assemblies.

Development Hardware: This type of hardware has many names including development or engineering units. In general, these units are not intended to fly. Engineering or development models are typically rudimentary models (but sufficiently representative) used early in a program development to gather evaluation data. They are used to retire risk and they help verify proof of concepts. The units are typically components and lower level assemblies.

Qualification Hardware: This type of hardware is also known as proto-type hardware. These units typically follow flight manufacturing and handling processes so they are flight-like, but they are never intended to fly. Like development hardware, these units are subject to higher test loads. Qualification hardware is critical to verification of your flight hardware. These units are used to confirm designs are adequate to meet performance requirements (survive predicted flight and ground environments).

Proto-Flight Hardware: Proto-flight hardware is a cross between a qualification unit and a flight unit. Proto-flight units are typically the first article of a production. Unlike Qualification units, Proto-flight units are expected to fly. Proto-flight units are typically used instead of Qualification Units. Testing of these units serves as both a qualification test and it also verifies flight worthiness (workmanship).

Flight Hardware: Flight hardware is just that; hardware that is expected to fly. The testing of these units are more to confirm workmanship. As any material, manufacturing, or integration process is subject to variations, workmanship (or acceptance) tests on flight units intended to verify that all units meet some minimal expected performance level. It is a good practice to test all hardware to at least workmanship (or acceptance) test levels.

The above text is meant as an overview. More details can be found in two books that I constantly reference: Sarafin [1995] and Pisacane [2005].

Mechanical Verification and Environmental Testing

Typically, mechanical tests used for verification are as follows: strength, stiffness, acoustic, shock, articulation/deployment, and mass properties.

Strength: It is recommended to perform at least some kind of strength test on all hardware. Qualification testing is typically performed on qualification units or protoflight units. Test levels are typically above design load levels to provide design margin. Pre-test analysis will determine what areas are critical or have the highest stresses. Testing can be accomplished at any level from component to assembly. Any structural part that is made from a composite material will need to undergo strength testing to at least 1.25 times the design load. Static load testing or sinusoidal burst testing are the norms. For static load testing, actuators or load cells apply loads and displacements and strains are measured with gauges. This test is probably the most effective test, but set-up and execution of numerous configurations can be time consuming. Sine burst tests are performed on a vibration table which imparts high level, low cycle accelerations. Accelerometers measure the responses. Large systems can have issues finding a table that can adequately drive the test article to desired levels.

Fig. 22-5. Static Load Test on LRO.

Table 22-4◀, Fig. 22-5, Eq. 22-12◀

Stiffness: Stiffness tests are typically done via a sinusoidal survey vibration test or modal survey. Accelerometers are used to capture structural responses that are correlated to the input vibration frequencies. The response accelerometers will show resonance occurring in the structure. This data is what is used to correlate predicted responses from FEM. Any discrepancies in the model are tuned to match the test results. Programs will define how accurate the models need to be, relative to the test result (within 2 Hz up to 100 Hz input and assuming a model mass participation of greater than 5–10%). The critical point is to verify that the predicted/measured responses are not near major launch vehicle response frequencies [specified in the Launch Vehicle (LV) Spacecraft Interface Control Document (ICD)]. Spacecraft frequencies that are close to major LV frequencies can easily increase the input loads orders of magnitude above the design load due to *dynamic coupling*. This will end any mission very quickly. Another key area to keep an eye on is the ACS system response. Again, the control frequency of the ACS system should be an octave away from any resultant mode of the spacecraft or deployed appendage. See Sec. 19.1.5 and note box below. This can be tricky sometimes for deployed or articulating antenna systems or solar arrays. However, if the appendage frequency couples with the ACS control system, the resultant responses can overpower the control system and the mission could be lost or severely degraded.

Acoustic: At final assembly, the spacecraft is typically tested for acoustic loads that are generated during launch. The acoustic environment is a random vibration on the spacecraft from noise pressure inside the fairing. Acoustic loading can be amplified within a LV fairing if there is lots of free volume in the fairing. Acoustic loads can only be applied in air. So this issue only applies to the stowed or launch configuration of the spacecraft. LVs can add blankets or use other tricks to minimize acoustic power transmission on a spacecraft in the fairing. Work with the LV representatives if you have any concerns. Special accommodations come at a price. Make sure you really need one before you ask. Typically, one is concerned with acoustic noise when a spacecraft has any large, lightweight, flat surfaces/panels. Imagine a large ship's sail. The bigger the sail, the more wind (or acoustic energy) it will catch. So, large flat surfaces will capture more acoustic energy and probably should be tested. Niche analysts can help analyze acoustic energy imparted on a spacecraft. However, this is an area for specialists. If there is any doubt, test. I think most specialists will tend to err on the side of testing too.

Shock: Shock testing is another area for specialists. Years ago, shock was a large concern due to the pyrotechnics that were used to split bolts or nuts for deployment systems and the high g-loads those pyros created. These days, Non-Explosive Actuators (NEAs) are fairly typical and have flight history. The shock response from NEAs is magnitudes less than previous pyro devices. However, it is still recommended to test and measure responses from explosive device actuations. Remember that the

Transmissibility, T, is the ratio of input to output ($T = x_o/x_i$). It is unitless and is sometimes referred to as the "Q" factor.

Using Newton's second law, the equation of motion, and assuming a sinusoidal input, transmissibility can be derived into

$$T = \left\{ \left[1 - \left(\frac{\omega}{\omega_n} \right)^2 \right]^2 + \left[2\xi \left(\frac{\omega}{\omega_n} \right) \right]^2 \right\}^{-1/2} \qquad (22\text{-}13)$$

Where T is transmissibility, ω is the component frequency, ω_n is the natural frequency, and ξ is the structural damping.

Assuming forcing at resonance $(\omega = \omega_n)$, and $\xi = 0.05$ (a typical structural damping value), then

$$T = \left[(2\xi)^2 \right]^{-1/2} = 1/(2\xi) = 10 \qquad (22\text{-}14)$$

When the component frequency is twice the mounting structure's natural frequency (octave rule) or $\omega/\omega_n = 2$, then

$$T = \left\{ \left[(1-4)^2 + \left[2(0.05)(2) \right]^2 \right] \right\}^{-1/2} \qquad (22\text{-}15)$$

$$= \left[9 + 0.04 \right]^{-1/2} = 0.33$$

Keeping the component frequency an octave above the mounting structure's natural frequency results in a reduction of transmissibility by a factor of 30. This is enough to assume that any input loading will not amplify the component.

shock test is to verify that components near the shock devices are not susceptible to the high impulsive loads from the device. This test should be done at higher or final levels of assembly. Qualifying the shock device is typically performed at low levels of component assembly and is done at temperature extremes. Close scrutiny should take place if the explosive device is near sensitive electronics or RF equipment. As with acoustic testing, the analysis of the shock response and how it is propagated across interfaces is not easily analyzed or quantified (modeling structural damping). Testing and measuring responses are always recommended if there is any concern.

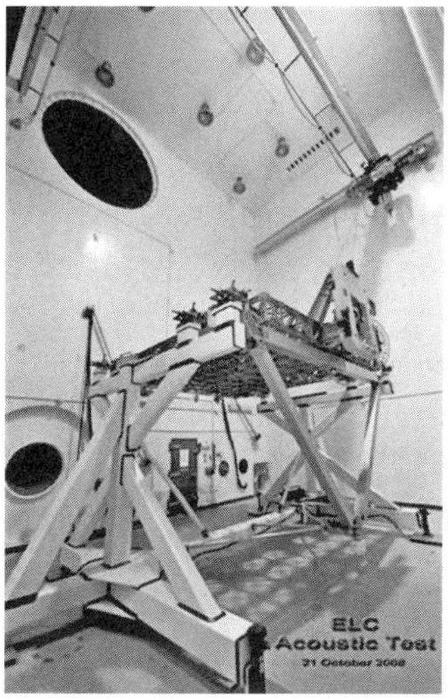

Fig. 22-6. LRO Acoustic Test.

Deployment/Articulation: The next mechanical test we will touch on is related to deployment of a system (e.g., a solar array, high gain antenna, boom or mast) Some of these systems also articulate through a gimbal or equivalent motion system. This is actually a good lead into the next section on mechanisms. However, this section will focus on testing the system at the assembly or spacecraft level. All deployment and articulation systems need to be tested both as a verification (range of motion) and workmanship. In following the "test as you fly" mantra, the test needs to carefully consider two items: temperature and gravity. The final flight assembly needs to be tested to verify range of motion and show

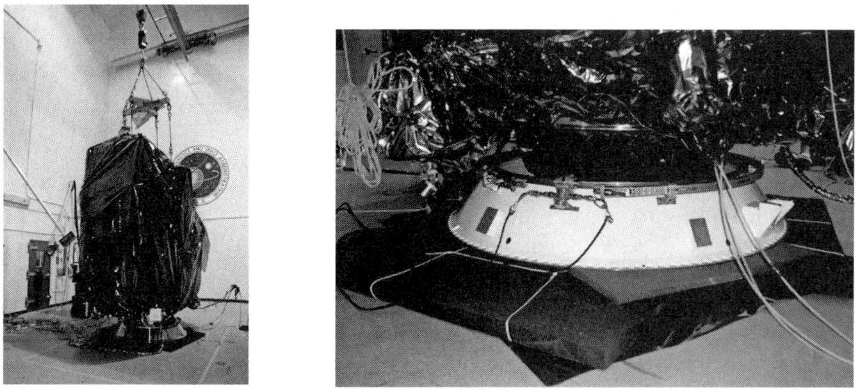

Fig. 22-7. LRO Shock Test/Launch Vehicle Separation Test.

there are no interferences that can bind up the actuation. Pay special attention to blankets, harnesses, launch lock systems or anything else that is near the articulation/deployment path. To assist with the deployment or articulation, you may need to use air tables (simple g-negation test where the article "floats" over the table during a motion in a single plan). More complex systems are needed for multiple plane motions. Simple deployments should verify workmanship test as late as possible. It is recommended to perform a simple "*Pop and Catch*" test at the launch site. The "pop and catch" tests are simply verifying the release mechanisms work. The launch restraint is released and the deployed article is stopped (caught) prior to full deployment. It tests both the final copper connections (electrical configuration and commanding) and the mechanical integration of the release mechanism. Pop and Catch tests are almost always performed if any of the following actions are performed at the launch site: installation of flight pyro or NEAs, integration of appendages like Solar Arrays (sometimes, due to packaging concerns, arrays are shipped separately and integrated at the launch site), blanket installation or adjustments around the mechanisms, any mate/demating of the deployment or mechanism harness.

Fig. 22-8. LRO Mass Properties Test Prior to Environmental Testing.

For all tests, measuring response times and full deployment/articulation times are good ways to verify the system is performing nominally. Trending this data is a recommended practice. It is recommended to track deployment metrics like power, voltage, current, resistance, duration of motion, torque margin, and alignments to name a few. Metrics are unit dependent, but it is rare to keep too much information. These trending/verification tests should be performed prior to each environmental test the unit experiences to ensure the unit entered the test in working order. The units should undergo the same test after each environmental test to verify the deployment system successfully passed the test. It is recommended to perform the deployment test after each environmental test (random, acoustic, thermal vacuum, shock, long transports to the launch site). Depending on project risk tolerance, schedules, and budgets, some projects test only prior to a suite of environmental tests and post-environmental tests. I advise against it because if there are any issues post-testing, it will be extremely difficult in determining the cause of the issue between all the tests the unit experienced. And realistically, you will not be able to prove the mechanism survived any of the environmental test. The project could be required to perform the full suite of tests again. The risk is too high in my opinion and deployment/articulation tests should be added to the comprehensive functional tests used to show post-environmental test acceptance after each environmental test.

Mass Properties: Mass properties are typically measured during a spin balance test. These are crucial for any spacecraft that are spin stabilized either on their own or as part of a spin stabilized launch vehicle. Final mass properties are also critical to attitude control systems to maintain proper control of the spacecraft during the mission. These tests are usually performed just prior to a spacecraft undergoing fine environmental testing and also at the launch site, prior to launch vehicle mating or fairing encapsulation.

The discussion above is a quick overview of environmental testing, more details can be found in two books that I constantly reference: Sarafin [1995] and Pisacane [2005].

22.1.5 Mechanisms and Deployables

Matt Ashmore, *ATK Space*
Chris Lashley, *ATK Space*

By definition, space mechanisms must move to satisfy their required function. Mechanism development includes all the required considerations of structures, such as mass, volume, stiffness, strength and material selection. However, the functional requirements add extra failure modes and another layer of criticality. The high launch vibration environments and harsh thermal/vacuum environments of space, as well as the requirement for high reliability and the impracticality of service and repair add to the difficulty.

Space mechanisms development is governed by the AIAA [2005] Standard S-114-2005. Excellent guidance can also be found in NASA-STD-5017 [NASA, 2006] and GSFC-STD-7000 (GEVS). In response to the relatively high incidence of mechanisms on-orbit failure, the NASA [2011] Glenn Space Mechanisms Project has performed research to capture lessons learned from mechanisms failures and to document best practices.

The process for mechanisms development is shown in Table 22-5. In reality, the process is not as linear as the table implies. Good requirements require some idea of a feasible design solution. The requirements may then be iterated as the design matures and the performance and

Table 22-5. Process for Mechanisms Development. See text for discussion.

Requirements Definition	Identify requirements and document in specification Identify design drivers
Preliminary Design and Analysis	Identify design concepts capable of satisfying requirements Perform trade studies to select "best" design concept Select and size major components. Characterize force/torque margins. Create preliminary design model and functional analysis Ends with PDR
Detailed Design and Analysis	Detailed models and fab/assembly drawings Strength, dynamic, and thermal analysis Final torque margin estimates Assembly and test plans and procedures Ends with CDR
Engineering Testing	Preliminary testing of risky elements in the design Can be components test or full assembly Engineering model Can involve life testing of bearings or gears
Design Qualification	Manufacture and test of a flight like mechanism Tested to qualification levels and durations which exceed flight predictions Can be Qualification Unit which is consumed in testing or Proto-flight Unit which is qualified and then used as the operational unit
Manufacture, Assembly and Test of Operational Units	Final manufacture, assembly and test of operational unit Must be identical or very similar to Qualification Unit Controlled by documented processes and verified by QA

Table 22-6. Examples of the Three Principal Types of Space Mechanisms.

Deployables	Drives	Instrument Mechanisms
• Solar arrays • Deployable antennas (e.g., mesh, linear, quadrifilar, rigid dish) • Deployable booms and trusses • Deployable thermal radiators • Separation systems	• Solar array drives • Antenna pointing gimbals • Reaction and momentum wheels	• Mirror Adjustment mechanisms • Scan/Pointing Mechanisms • Shutter/Selector Mechanisms • Instrument covers

cost constraints become clearer. Requirements should be essentially finalized by the end of the Preliminary Design phase. Verification activities to confirm that the actual performance meets requirements are ongoing throughout the program. Conformance to requirements can be verified by analysis, inspection, demonstration, or test.

22.1.5.1 Classification and Examples

Table 22-6 shows the 3 main types of space mechanisms: deployables, drives, and instrument mechanisms.

Deployables are generally used to create spacecraft on-orbit configurations which are larger than can be packaged in the launch vehicle fairing. These devices generally deploy only once on orbit, but some applications require automatic retraction capability, sometimes for tens or hundreds of cycles. The primary challenge in most deployables' design is to achieve tight packaging efficiency without compromising the strength needed to survive launch or the reliability to successfully deploy on orbit.

Conventional planar solar arrays are typically deployed using lug/clevis hinges and non-explosive release devices. There are also advanced concepts which use motor/cable system to deploy lightweight flexible arrays, such as the Ultraflex design shown in Fig. 22-9. Antenna deployment systems may use rigid tube sections

Fig. 22-9. Ultraflex Solar Array. (Photo courtesy of ATK-Goleta)

and rigid hinges. For applications requiring larger and lighter weight structures, deployable truss booms, shown in Fig. 22-10, can be used. Pyrotechnically actuated marman clampbands, Fig. 22-11, are the classical method of separating spacecraft from launch vehicles.

Drives typically require continuous or frequent operation for the life of the mission. Therefore wear, lubrication and life are critical considerations. Solar array drives

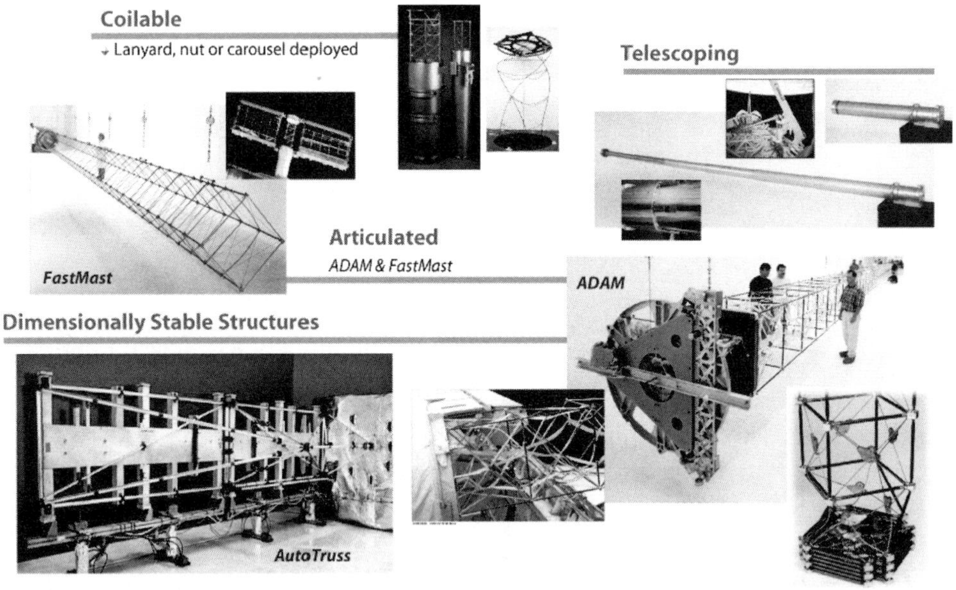

Fig. 22-10. Deployable Structures Examples. (Graphic courtesy of ATK-Goleta)

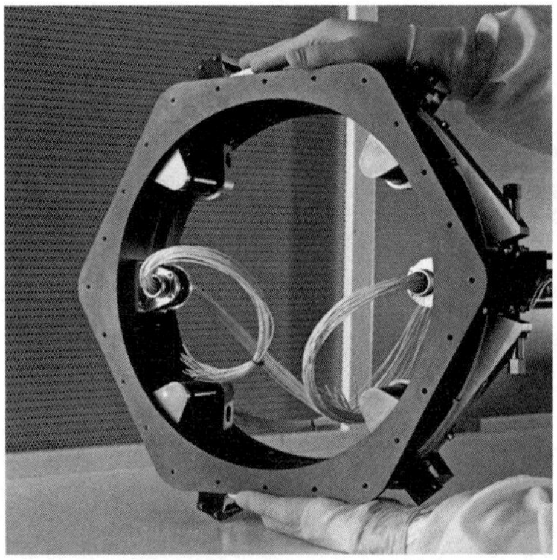

Fig. 22-11. Clamp Band. (Photo courtesy of Sierra Nevada Corporation)

Fig. 22-12. Two-Axis Gimbal. (Photo courtesy of Sierra Nevada Corporation)

and antenna gimbals typically use stepper motors acting through harmonic drive gear reductions to reorient their load as needed. An example of a two axis antenna gimbal is shown in Fig. 22-12.

Reaction wheels (and less common momentum wheels and control moment gyroscopes) are universally employed for spacecraft attitude control. These actuators must function with high reliability over extremely long, high cycle life times. These wheels are typically supported by ball bearings and are driven by brushless DC motors.

Instrument Mechanisms encompass a wide range of devices used to provide optical adjustments for space instruments. High precision and stringent contamination control are drivers here. These mechanisms are highly specialized to meet the requirements and available envelope of the host instrument. Moderate life requirements are typical. Precision adjustment and scanning mechanisms usually incorporate brushless DC motors, precision feedback and closed loop control. Shutter / selector mechanisms are generally simpler and may use open-loop stepper motors. A precision scan mechanism is shown in Fig. 22-13.

22.1.5.2 Requirements

The first step in the mechanisms development process is the definition of requirements. If trade study and design activities proceed too far without well defined requirements, rework and accompanying cost impact usually results. Table 22-7 is a listing of requirements that generally apply to mechanisms.

22.1.5.3 Space Mechanisms Design

To start the preliminary design phase, the development team gets together to brainstorm design approaches

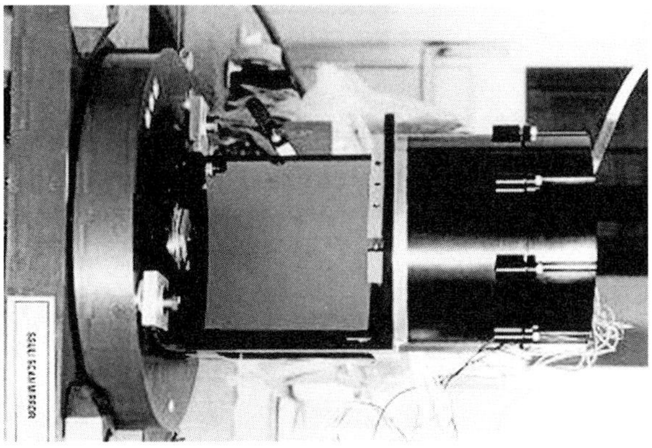

Fig. 22-13. Scan Mechanism. (Photo courtesy of ATK)

that can satisfy the requirements. Trade studies are conducted to rank the design concepts and downselect to one or more superior options. Some general principles are applicable to successful mechanisms design.

The simplest approach possible will usually be the most reliable, lowest cost and easiest to verify. Unnecessary components create more opportunities for failure. Redundancy is a very effective approach to increased reliability. However, 100% mechanical redundancy may lead to a very complex mechanism with extra features, such as differentials and mechanical couplings. In contrast, electrical redundancy with selected mechanical redundancy usually gives the highest overall reliability. Redundant rotation surfaces are an example of selected mechanical redundancy.

Rotary mechanisms are usually more reliable than linear mechanisms. Linear (sliding) mechanisms are prone to cocking and jamming. *Kinematic* techniques should be used for mechanism interfaces and moving parts. A kinematic approach constrains only the *6 degrees of freedom* (DOF) needed to locate a rigid body and produces determinate loads. All 6 DOF are constrained in this approach, but each DOF is constrained no more than once. Additional non-kinematic constraints can produce unpredictable loads and distortions, that can also reduce reliability.

Mechanical parts should be designed and toleranced for efficient manufacture. Some features such as bearing bores and optical alignment features required tight tolerances. Others such as exterior dimensions and structural ribbing can be relaxed to reduce manufacturing cost. Parts should be self jigging to minimize the need for assembly fixtures and designed to be assembled only one way to reduce the risk of assembly error. Reducing parts count also facilitates assembly. Mechanisms should also be designed to be disassembled and refurbished. "I don't anticipate this needing to come apart" are famous last words.

Material should be selected for acceptable outgassing properties in vacuum. NASA [2011] maintains an online database of approved materials and test results. Material combinations in contact should be hard, dissimilar and coated with a suitable surface layer. Hardcoat anodize surfaces impregnated with Teflon are used for aluminum and titanium substrates. Steels may be nitride or carbonized to improve hardness and reduce possibility of galling. Molybdium Disulphide (MoS_2) coatings are also effective in reducing friction and wear. Note: All contacting surfaces that must move in operation must be lubricated. Redundant coatings of dry (MoS_2) and liquid (space-rated) grease are recommended. Dissimilar materials in contact need to be evaluated for corrosion and protected with an appropriate coating if necessary.

Table 22-7. Key Performance Parameters for Mechanisms.

Requirement	Discussion
Performance	Specific description of what the mechanism needs to accomplish
Motion Profile	Position, velocity and/or acceleration requirements Can be simple point-to-point or complex programmable profiles
Accuracy, Resolution and Stability	Allowable errors. Usually stated in deg/arcsec for position
Mass and Power	Allowable assembly mass and peak/average power draw
Life	Operational, ground test and storage life
Reliability and Redundancy	Numerical probability of success for specified life
Temperature Range	Operational, non-op and survival temperatures
Vacuum Environment	All space devices require operation in hard vacuum of space Drives selection of materials for low outgassing
Stiffness	First resonant mode of assembly Must be high enough to avoid resonance with launch vehicle vibration environment Deployed frequency must be high enough not to impact ACS
Design Loads and Random Environment	Quasi-static acceleration loads, random vibration, and shock environments Safety factors used for design & derivation of qualification / acceptance test levels
Interface Definition	Mechanical and electrical interfaces and allowable envelope
Contamination Control	Proximity to sensitive space instruments levies specific requirements on cleaning and assembly controls

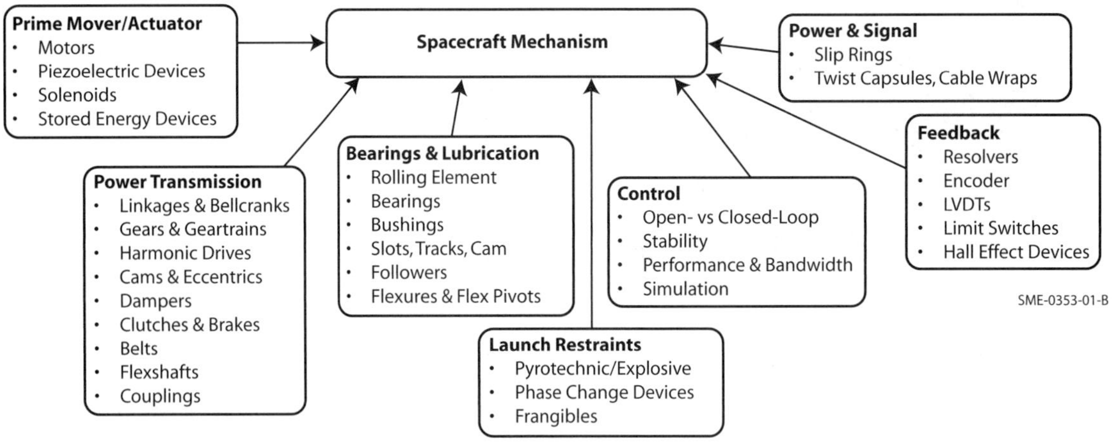

Fig. 22-14. Spacecraft Mechanism Building Blocks.

Most spacecraft mechanisms can be broken into a series of building blocks, drawn from "bins" that can be divided into unique categories. Layout of a mechanism then involves pulling the appropriate building blocks from each bin to create an assembly that meets performance requirements. For preliminary design, the job of the mechanism engineer is to establish a trade space for each bin to determine the best building block (or blocks) to draw, as shown in Fig. 22-14.

The following sections describe these building blocks and how to select and size them in performing a preliminary mechanism layout.

Actuator/Prime Mover Selection

Table 22-8 shows typical primary considerations for actuator selection. Frequently the type of prime mover chosen for the specific mechanism design is greatly narrowed by the nature of the problem itself; (i.e., whether the system must rotate or translate). However, the most obvious actuator may not always end up as the best actuator for certain design scenarios. For example, given proper design, a simple compression spring is just as capable of imparting rotary motion as a torsion spring, and in many circumstances provides a more reliable and space-efficient solution.

Additionally, selection of the prime mover is not necessarily the first step in laying out the mechanism. Factors that influence actuator selection like inertia of the load and mounting provisions are often times unknown until all of the system **ahead** of the actuator has been defined. Smart preliminary design allocates ample real estate within the system structure early on to accommodate unforeseen changes in actuator size, position, and interface needs—a black box with volume margin.

Torque and Force Margins

The objective of any prime mover is to impart motion to a system (the load) by exerting a force, torque, or some combination of the two. In order to assure the motion is imparted under worst-case environmental conditions, a robust mechanism incorporates a prime mover that possesses more available force/torque than is required by the load. This is analogous to a structural factor of safety and ensures that the prime mover will be able to overcome any number of unexpected perturbations to motion, such as stiction, localized cold-welding or galling, or loss of lubrication. Like a structural factor of safety, the torque or force margin accounts for the accretion of "human factors" that may affect mechanism performance, such as buyoffs on mis-toleranced parts, undetected contamination, or cut vs. rolled threads.

Table 22-8. Typical Issues Considered in Actuator Selection.

Type of Motion; Linear or Rotary (or combination)	Total stroke (linear) or angular excursion (rotary)
Type of Load Application; Force or Torque	Whether the actuator must bear launch loads from the remainder of the mechanism
Number of Actuation Cycles	Whether force or torque may vary over mechanism stroke
Duty Cycle	Required positioning accuracy
Required Support Electronics/Power Requirements	Available interface provisions for mounting
Whether There is a Necessity to Return-to-Zero or Reset	Whether there is a necessity to hold position at beginning-of-travel, end-of-travel, & in between

A torque or force margin is a convenient metric by which to demonstrate to an outside reviewer that the selected prime mover is appropriately sized for its intended application. Generally, the margin can be calculated according to the following equations:

Torque Margin:

$$T_{margin} = \left[\frac{T_{avail}}{FS_{known}\left(\Sigma T_{known}\right) + FS_{unknown}\left(\Sigma T_{unknown}\right)} \right]^{-1} \tag{22-16}$$

Force Margin:

$$F_{margin} = \left[\frac{F_{avail}}{FS_{known}\left(\Sigma F_{known}\right) + FS_{unknown}\left(\Sigma F_{unknown}\right)} \right]^{-1} \qquad (22\text{-}17)$$

T_{avail}, F_{avail} represent the available torque/force from the prime mover. T_{known}, F_{known} represent readily quantifiable resistance loads, such as inertial accelerations, position-based-forces from return springs, system running torque. $T_{unknown}$, $F_{unknown}$ represent resistance loads that, though calculable, are difficult to characterize as they be time- and temperature-variant or may not be able to be measured during the test program. This category generally covers all resistances that are frictional in nature, including forces and torques due to thread preload, as well as parasitic drag from grease or shaft seals.

FS_{known}, $FS_{unknown}$ represent the factors of safety over which the available force or torque must demonstrate positive margin. The factors of safety are usually chosen as part of the requirements development process. In general, the "unknown" factor of safety is larger than the "known" in order to account for the uncertainty in determination of "unknown" resistances. Typical values are 1.25–1.5 for FS_{known} and 3.0–4.0 for $FS_{unknown}$.

In some texts, the subscripts "known" and "unknown" are replaced with "fixed" and "variable," respectively.

A robust mechanism will demonstrate a torque or force margin greater than zero. While high margins are desirable, the margin in itself does not equate to a well-designed mechanism. A system which possesses extraordinarily high torque margins must provide adequate protection against being over-driven at high loads. This negatively impacts the ancillary structure around the prime mover—shafts, for example, must be able to withstand the increased drive torque, increasing the system mass. A motor capable of outputting 50 ft-lbf at stall, driving a #10-32 lead screw with a required load of 20 lbf, indeed shows very high Torque Margin, but would not be classified as a well-designed mechanism. As for this design, the motor would consume far more mass, volume, and power than is necessary. **Good mechanism design efficiently balances force and torque margins with mass and size optimization.**

22.1.6 Typical Space Mechanisms

The book website discusses:

Get More

- Motors
- Stored energy devices
- Gearing/power transmission
- Bearings, lubrication, and life.

22.2 Spacecraft Thermal Control*

John E. Oberright,
NASA Goddard Space Flight Center

The Thermal Control subsystem of a spacecraft sets and maintains the temperature range of the spacecraft and the temperatures of all its components. The desired temperatures are achieved by balancing the flow of heat energy across spacecraft interfaces. All Spacecraft components are designed to operate over a defined temperature range. While most components operate at or near room temperatures, others have narrow temperature requirements or are exposed to a wide range of heating environments which demand operation over a wide temperature range.

Therefore, to begin the design process, we need to know the temperature requirements of the components and the heating environment to which the spacecraft will be exposed.

The basic approach to thermal control begins with requirements definition followed by an iterative process of analysis, design and re-analysis and ends with a physical test of the design to verify acceptable performance. In its simplest form the steps are as follows:

- **Define Problem:** Identify temperature requirements and heating environments.
- **Analysis:** Compute maximum and minimum orbit average temperature for the spacecraft using surface property estimates and average power dissipation when subjected to the maximum and minimum heating conditions.
- **Design:** Adjust thermal coatings to see if passive design is possible.
- **Analysis:** Develop multi-node thermal model with individual node power levels, surface properties and network of node connections.
- **Design:** Determine conduction and radiation couplings which combined with external properties and power dissipations will provide acceptable temperatures. If necessary, recommend component relocations and define active thermal control elements.
- **Analysis:** Analytically test the design resiliency by varying couplings, surface properties, power dissipations and environment loads.
- **Test:** Physically perform a thermal balance test to verify design and performance.

See a more complete and detailed process description in Sec. 22.2.4.

---

* This section was prepared with the help and assistance of Wes Ousley, for thermal control hardware information, and Rob Chalmers, for the thermal flux tables.

22.2.1 Requirements

Mission requirements, constraints and boundaries should be set in concert with all other system and subsystem considerations. Thermal considerations must also be included early in the mission concept studies and physical baselines. This leads to a well integrated overall spacecraft system design. Trying to force a rigid physical design to operate at the required temperature is a poor approach to thermal control.

Table 22-9. Typical Temperature Requirements.

Equipment	Operational	Survival
Avionics Baseplates	–20 to 60	–40 to 75
Batteries	10 to 30	0 to 40
Hydrazine Fuel	15 to 40	5 to 50
Solar Arrays	–150 to 110	–200 to 130
Antennas	–100 to 100	–120 to 120
Reaction Wheels	–10 to 40	–20 to 50
Typical Temperature Requirements °C		

Examples of typical spacecraft element operating temperature requirements are shown in Table 22-9. Components that are sensitive to temperature, (e.g., batteries, star trackers) can be located in positions on the spacecraft that provide thermal stability and heaters can be allocated to provide additional control. Components that must be exposed directly to the space environment to perform their functions (antennas, solar arrays) have to be designed to withstand a very wide range of temperatures.

The spacecraft and its elements are required to perform various functions during the mission. These can include pointing instruments, collecting energy from solar arrays, or communicating with ground stations. These functional requirements usually dictate a general configuration and a spacecraft location and orientation in space that will enable the functions. The physical configuration, its location, and orientation will define the radiant energy that falls on the spacecraft surfaces. This energy can be absorbed or reflected as necessary to control the flow of heat into the spacecraft and set the heat balance to achieve the required temperatures. The spacecraft external surfaces become the boundary condition interfaces to control the heat flow between the environment and the spacecraft. The balance of the heat in, out, and through the spacecraft sets temperatures to meet requirements during the mission.

22.2.2 Radiant Energy Heat Balance in Space

The external surfaces of a spacecraft are the boundary conditions which ultimately provide the energy balance with the environment and therefore control the average temperature. The thermal properties of these surfaces are chosen to balance the energy transfer over the required spacecraft temperature range. This is possible because the radiant energy absorbed from the environment is independent of the surface temperature, but the energy radiated from the surface is a strong function of surface temperature (T^4). Figure 22-15 shows how much energy is radiated from a surface with an emissivity of 1 as a function the surface temperature.

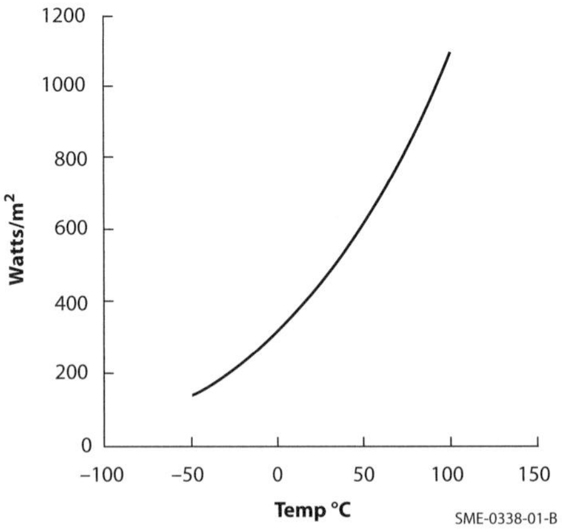

Fig. 22-15. Heat Energy Radiated from a Perfect Emitting Surface (Black Body) as a Function of the Surface Temperature.

Consider a simple flat plate with one side normal to the Sun at 1 AU, and the other side insulated (adiabatic). We can compute the temperature of this object by writing the heat energy balance Eq. (22-18) and solving for T. At equilibrium the heat energy in, Q_{in}, equals the heat energy out, Q_{out}:

$$Q_{in} = Q_{out} \tag{22-18a}$$

$$Q_{in} = SA_p\alpha \tag{22-18b}$$

$$Q_{out} = A_r\varepsilon\sigma T^4 \tag{22-18c}$$

where S is the solar constant (1,366 W/m^2 at 1 AU), A_P is the projected area of the plate toward the Sun, α is the absorptivity of the surface, A_r is the radiating surface area of the plate, ε is the emissivity of the surface, σ is the Stefan-Boltzmann constant (5.67051 × 10^{-8} W/m^{2}K^4, and T is the absolute temperature in Kelvin. Therefore,

$$T = \sqrt[4]{S\left(\frac{\alpha}{\varepsilon}\right)\left(\frac{A_P}{A_r}\right)/\sigma} \tag{22-19}$$

For the insulated flat plate geometry, the projected area, A_p equals the radiating area, A_r and the temperature for the plate becomes a function of the α/ε as shown in Fig. 22-16.

From Eq. (22-19) the ratio of the projected area receiving energy to the radiating area dissipating energy is also an important factor in setting the temperature. Geometric factors determine how the average surface area exposed to heat sources compares to the surface area available to reradiate heat. This area ratio is an important element of heat balance and can be used to adjust the desired temperature of an object in space. Some simple

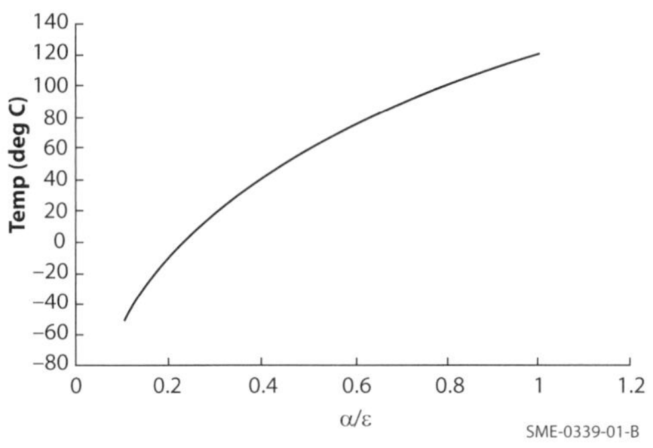

Live Calc

Fig. 22-16. Temperature of a Flat Plate Normal to the Sun at 1 AU with an Insulated Back as a Function of the Surface Properties (α/ε ratio).

geometries with various ratios of absorbing area to reradiating area are shown in Table 22-10. The temperatures are based on surface properties where $\alpha/\varepsilon = 1$ with solar illumination at 1 AU. These six geometries can often be used to estimate average temperatures for various proposed spacecraft configurations or specific surfaces on a spacecraft. They include:

- Flat plate facing Sun with insulated back
- Flat plate facing Sun with radiating back
- Spinning flat plate with both sides active
- Sphere
- Cylinder with insulated ends
- Cube with 1 side facing Sun

Note: A sphere at 1 AU from the Sun with high α and ε will provide an average surface temperature that is close to ideal for life (6 C). If the sphere's surface is coated such that the absorptivity (α) is reduced to 0.2 the temperature drops to –87 C.

Therefore, the average sphere temperature can be controlled if the surface thermal properties can be controlled.

22.2.3 Sources of Radiant Energy in Space

Direct solar energy flux is a function of the distance from the Sun. The radiant energy from the Sun is usually the most significant heat source in spacecraft thermal control. The Sun radiates its energy equally in all directions. However, from the Earth, the Sun appears as a small disc subtending an angle of only ½ deg. This geometry causes the Suns energy to impinge on a surface normal to the Sun as parallel rays. Therefore, one surface can cast a shadow on another and a specular surface can reflect energy to illuminate another surface.

There are two important characteristics of the Sun's radiant energy for spacecraft thermal control. These are

Table 22-10. Temperatures for Various Geometries of Absorbing to Radiating Area ($\alpha = \varepsilon = 1$).

Geometry	Figure	Absorbing Area	Radiating Area	Area Ratio	Resulting Temp.°C Sun (1,366 W/m²) ($\alpha = \varepsilon = 1$)
Plate Facing Sun with Insulated Back	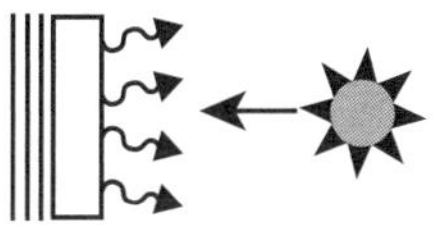	1	1	1	121
Plate Facing Sun with Radiating Back	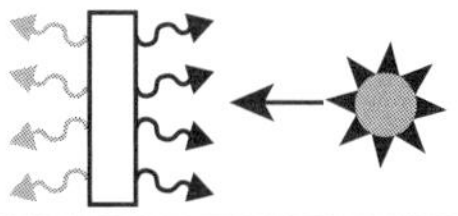	1	2	1/2	58
Plate Rotating in Sun both Sides Active	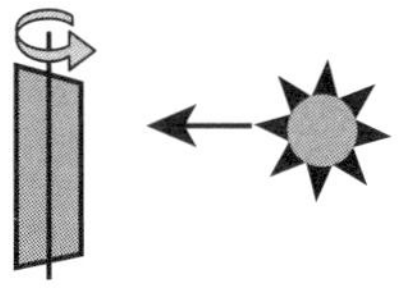	$2/\pi$	2	$1/\pi$	23
Sphere	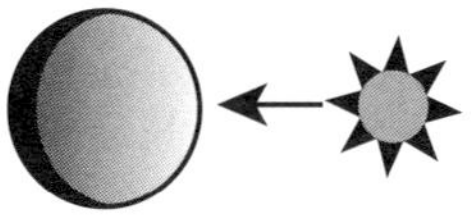	πr^2	$4\pi r^2$	4	6
Cylinder Normal to Sun-Insulated Ends	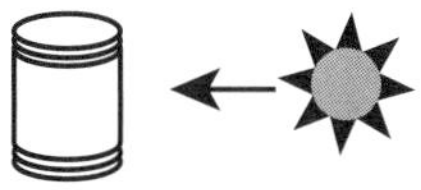	$D \times H$	$\pi \times D \times H$	$1/\pi$	23
Cube (Isothermal) One Side Facing Sun	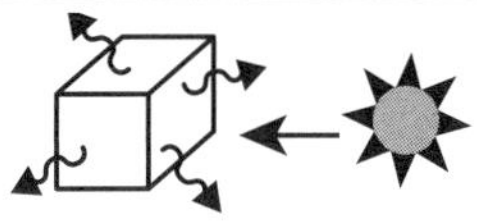	1	6	1/6	–21

Table 22-10, Fig. 22-16, Eq. 22-19◀

Table 22-11. Orbit Average Incident Radiant Fluxes on Surfaces of an Earth-Oriented Cube for Various Circular Orbits. β is the angle of the Sun out of the orbit plane. See Fig. 22-17 for orientation.

Cold Case—W/m²												
500 km	$\beta = 0$			$\beta = 45$			$\beta = 70$			$\beta = 90$		
Surface Orientation	*Solar*	*Albedo*	*Earth IR*	*Solar*	*Albedo*	*Earth IR*	*Solar*	*Albedo*	*Earth IR*	*Solar*	*Albedo*	*Earth IR*
Zenith	418.2			295.8			143.1			1.3		
Nadir	30.4	79.1	186.8	44.7	66.3	186.8	143.1	42.7	186.7	1.3	15.2	186.5
Sun	0.8	24.5	58.3	630.7	23.7	58.1	123.76	19.0	58.1	1,317.0	16.5	58.0
Anti Sun	0.8	24.5	58.2		17.5	58.2		8.3	58.2			58.0
± Ram	287.3	24.6	58.0	226.0	20.6	57.9	143.1	13.3	57.9	1.3	5.3	57.9
700 km	$\beta = 0$			$\beta = 45$			$\beta = 70$			$\beta = 90$		
Surface Orientation	*Solar*	*Albedo*	*Earth IR*	*Solar*	*Albedo*	*Earth IR*	*Solar*	*Albedo*	*Earth IR*	*Solar*	*Albedo*	*Earth IR*
Zenith	418.2			295.8			143.1			1.3		
Nadir	41.3	74.6	176.4	62.0	62.6	176.4	143.1	40.9	176.3	1.3	18.8	176.2
Sun	0.8	21.3	50.8	661.0	21.4	50.6	1,237.6	18.1	50.6	1,317.0	18.2	50.6
Anti Sun	0.8	21.3	50.7		14.6	50.7		6.3	50.7			50.5
± Ram	299.7	21.4	50.5	238.4	18.0	50.5	143.1	11.8	50.5	1.3	5.8	50.5
Hot Case—W/m²												
500 km	$\beta = 0$			$\beta = 45$			$\beta = 70$			$\beta = 90$		
Surface Orientation	*Solar*	*Albedo*	*Earth IR*	*Solar*	*Albedo*	*Earth IR*	*Solar*	*Albedo*	*Earth IR*	*Solar*	*Albedo*	*Earth IR*
Zenith	450.6			318.7			154.2			1.4		
Nadir	32.7	123.9	224.6	48.2	98.9	224.7	154.2	59.6	224.6	1.4	19.7	224.4
Sun	0.9	38.4	70.1	679.5	35.4	69.9	1,333.4	26.5	69.9	1,419.0	21.4	69.8
Anti Sun	0.9	38.5	70.0		26.1	70.0		11.5	70.0			69.8
± Ram	309.5	38.6	69.7	243.5	30.8	69.7	154.2	18.6	69.7	1.4	6.8	69.7
700 km	$\beta = 0$			$\beta = 45$			$\beta = 70$			$\beta = 90$		
Surface Orientation	*Solar*	*Albedo*	*Earth IR*	*Solar*	*Albedo*	*Earth IR*	*Solar*	*Albedo*	*Earth IR*	*Solar*	*Albedo*	*Earth IR*
Zenith	450.6			318.7			154.2			1.4		
Nadir	44.5	116.9	212.2	66.8	93.5	212.2	154.2	57.0	212.1	1.4	24.4	211.9
Sun	0.9	33.3	61.1	712.2	31.9	60.9	1,333.4	25.2	60.9	1,419.0	23.6	60.8
Anti Sun	0.9	33.4	60.9		21.7	61.0		8.7	61.0			60.8
± Ram	322.9	33.5	60.7	256.9	26.8	60.7	154.2	16.4	60.7	1.4	7.5	60.7

	Cold	Hot	Units
Solar Constant	1,317.0	1,419.0	W/m²
Albedo at $\beta = 0$	0.22	0.32	
Albedo at $\beta = 45$	0.26	0.36	
Albedo at $\beta = 70$	0.34	0.44	
Albedo at $\beta = 90$	0.49	0.59	
Earth IR	217.0	261.0	W/m²

the total energy density, or flux, incident on a surface, and the spectral content of that flux. The flux at 1 AU is called the *solar constant* and is calculated at the Earth's average distance from the Sun. As we change distances from the Sun the flux changes as the square of the distance. For deep space missions, or missions to other planets, the solar flux can vary dramatically.

The spectral content of the solar flux emulates the black body (perfect emitter) distribution for a source at 5,780 K. This concentrates the energy in the visible wavelengths with significant amounts near visible in the ultraviolet and infrared wavelengths. This concentration of energy at certain wavelengths allows the selective absorption of the energy (i.e., surface properties).

Reflected Sun (albedo) is a function of orbit and orientation. The solar energy reflected by a planet, albedo, is also a significant source of radiant energy when the spacecraft is near the planet. Think about riding on a spacecraft in near earth orbit and staring down at the Earth directly below. You are only a few hundred miles above the surface but the surface is thousands of miles across and completely fills your view. From higher orbits, the Earth begins to fill less of our view until the albedo at geosynchronous orbits is negligible. The Earth diffusely reflects from 25% to 55% of the incident solar energy depending on the Earth surface properties. Land, sea, clouds, and ice all have different reflectance. So, when on the sunlit side of the Earth, surfaces facing the Earth can have incident energy from 25% to 55% of the direct solar flux. The spectral content of the reflected solar energy is approximately the same as energy directly from the Sun. However, it arrives as diffuse energy and not as parallel rays directly from the Sun.

Computing the albedo incident on the various surfaces requires knowledge of spacecraft orientation and location relative to a sunlit Earth. Surfaces facing away from the Earth will receive no solar energy reflected from the Earth.

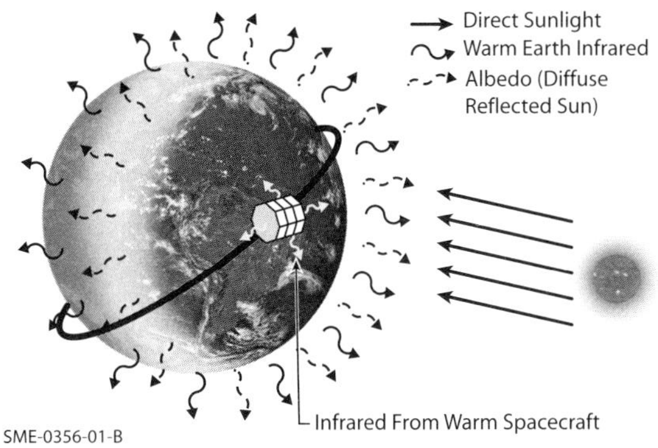

Fig. 22-17. Incident Energy on Spacecraft Surfaces and Radiated Energy from Spacecraft Surfaces.

Planetary infrared energy is a function of the planet's temperature and the spacecraft's orientation to the planet. Planets, moons and other large space bodies can also provide infrared heat sources to spacecraft. These sources are warm compared to space because they have absorbed energy from the Sun and re-radiate it as infrared energy. Most of these sources can be treated as uniform in temperature if they are rotating in the sunlight or have an atmosphere to spread the heat over the surface of the body. The Moon is a notable exception since it does not have an atmosphere and takes 28 Earth days for one revolution. Lunar designs must consider the wide temperature variation on the Moon's surface and resulting wide range of Lunar infrared energy as the spacecraft moves through its orbit. Infrared energy from a warm body in space is transferred just like a warm wall on a cold night or the heat from a fireplace. When you are close to the wall or fireplace, you can easily feel the heat. As you move away from the source the heat flux becomes less and less until it is negligible. The quantity of heat incident on a surface depends on the temperature of the source, and the geometric relationship between the surface and the source. A surface that remains normal to the source throughout its orbit will get a constant infrared flux. A surface pointing away from the source receives none.

Table 22-11 summarizes the incident energy values for several orbit conditions of altitude and β angle considering the accepted range of variation for solar and Earth physical properties, to produce the "hot and cold" range of incident fluxes.

Absorbed Energy; Surface Properties (α/ε)

The incident energy on each surface can be absorbed or reflected by the surface. The surface properties that define the absorbed energy are the, absorptance, (α for solar energy) and emissivity (ε for infrared energy). α is the surface property which defines the percent of incident solar energy that is absorbed by the surface. Solar energy is primarily in the visible part of the electromagnetic spectrum and is absorbed differently from energy in the infrared part of the spectrum. The percent of energy absorbed or emitted at infrared wavelengths is called emissivity. Emissivity is used to determine both the incident infrared energy absorbed and the infrared energy emitted by a surface at the surface temperature. Table 22-14 lists some properties of typical surface finishes and coatings.

22.2.4 Applied Radiant Heat Transfer and Temperature Control in Space

A typical thermal control problem must consider complex geometries and radiant thermal environments. Figure 22-17 shows a spacecraft in orbit, identifies the sources of radiant heating and shows a physical geometry. Following the spacecraft through its orbit and collecting all the radiant energy on each surface for the range of orientations is a task best left to computer programs. However, with a few reference tables (e.g., Table 22-11) and some interpolation, much of the information needed to do thermal analysis and design can be estimated if specific data does not exist. These estimates and assumptions can be "tested" analytically to see if they are critical drivers in meeting requirements. If they are, they can become the high priority items for precision definition, or become requirements placed on the rest of the system. Figure 22-18 shows a flow diagram to illustrate the analysis and design process. Table 22-12 gives an example with numerical values.

Spacecraft and mission information to be collected and computed:

1. A preliminary baseline mission profile is identified. This sets the thermal environment (heat sources for the spacecraft exterior). Variations are expected within the estimated limits. A major change in the mission profile could present a significantly different thermal environment for the flight system and therefore may require a very different design.
2. Location and orientation: (Trajectories, orbits, attitude) are known or baselined; radiant properties of heat sources (solar intensity, planetary reflectance and planetary temperature) are known:
   - Trajectory elements
   - Orbital parameters altitude, eccentricity, inclination
   - Orientation with respect to planet and Sun is known
   - Heat source characteristics are known
3. Power dissipations must be known or estimated for the spacecraft equipment (heat sources for the spacecraft interior)

Table 22-11◀, Fig. 22-17, Eq. 22-19

Table 22-12. Example of a Single Node Thermal Analysis and Calculation. See flow diagram in Fig. 22-18.

INFORMATION: 1. **Mission profile:** circular Earth orbit, inclination 21.5 deg; 2 yr life 2. **Location & orientation:** 500 km alt., spinning cylinder with spin axis always perpendicular to the orbit plane 3. **Internal power dissipation:** 100 W with 200 W spike for 10 min each orbit 4. **Temperature requirements for internal average:** 20 C ± 20 C 5. **Configuration:** cylinder $L = D = 1$ m, ends closed, cylindrical surface 75% covered in solar cells, 25% access panels with very small instrument apertures **ANALYSIS:** 6. **Compute thermal incident energy to the surfaces of a cylinder in the mission orbit:** (Note: the ends of the cylinder are closed and insulated so they will not play a significant part in the energy balance.) The 500 km circular orbit inclined 21.5 deg to the equator will experience a beta angle range of 0 to 45 deg. This translates into a time in sunlight of 62% to 68% out of the 95 minute orbit period. We can use the incident flux values from Table 22-11 if we make some adjustments for spacecraft geometry and surface orientation to Earth and Sun. • ***Direct Sun:*** max and min time in Sun as orbit plane Sun vector changes. • ***Cylinders normal to the orbit plane*** will present a constant area to the Sun that varies as the cos β • ***Albedo:*** reflected solar energy from the sunlit side of the Earth. Nadir surface fluxes can be used, but use surface area = ½ the total surface area • ***Earth IR:*** radiant energy from the warm Earth. Nadir surface fluxes can be used, but use surface area = ½ the total surface area	7. **Compute all absorbed energy:** ***β = 0 (cold)*** $Q_{solar} = SA_{pl}[\%\text{ Sun time}]\alpha_{avg} = 1317\text{ W/m}^2 \cdot 1\text{ m}^2 \cdot 0.62 \cdot (0.85 \cdot 0.75 + 0.9 \cdot 0.25) = 704.3\text{ W}$ $Q_{albedo} = Q_{incident\text{-}albedo} A_{IR}\alpha_{avg} = 79.1\text{ W/m}^2 \cdot \pi/2\text{ m}^2 \cdot (0.85 \cdot 0.75 + 0.9 \cdot 0.25) = 107.2\text{ W}$ $Q_{IR} = Q_{incident\text{-}IR} A_{IR}\varepsilon_{avg} = 186.8\text{ W/m}^2 \cdot \pi/2\text{ m}^2 \cdot 0.9 = 264.1\text{ W}$ ***β = 45 (hot)*** $Q_{solar} = SA_{pl}[\%\text{ Sun time}]\alpha_{avg} = 1419\text{ W/m}^2 \cdot (1\text{ m}^2 \cdot \cos 45^\circ) \cdot 0.68 \cdot (0.85 \cdot 0.75 + 0.9 \cdot 0.25) = 588.4\text{ W}$ $Q_{albedo} = Q_{incident\text{-}albedo}A_{IR}\alpha_{avg} = 98.9\text{ W/m}^2 \cdot \pi/2\text{ m}^2 \cdot (0.85 \cdot 0.75 + 0.9 \cdot 0.25) = 134.0\text{ W}$ $Q_{IR} = Q_{incident\text{-}IR}A_{IR}\varepsilon_{avg} = 224.7\text{ W/m}^2 \cdot \pi/2\text{ m}^2 \cdot 0.9 = 317.7\text{ W}$ **Compute internal power and add to absorbed energy:** 100 W + (10 min/95 min) 100 W = 110.5 W (orbit avg) Total Q_{in} cold = 1,185.5 W Total Q_{in} hot = 1,150.6 W 8. **Compute total Q_{out} :** $Q_{out} = \pi D L \cdot 0.9\sigma T^4 = 16.0 \times 10^{-8}\, T^4$ W 9. **Solve energy balance Eq. (22-22) for T:** Cold avg temperature = 18 C Hot avg temperature = 17.7 C 10. **Meets requirements of 20 C ± 20 C** Note that the changes in the orbit % time have been compensated by the changed projected area for the direct solar absorbed energy and the "cold" orbit average prediction is actually warmer. At this point re-doing the calculations with maximum and minimum surface properties will yield a wider range of possible temperatures. 11. **Change areas and finishes:** The surface of the "access panels" is available to add reflective coatings (low α) or reduce radiation capability (low ε) and result in lower or higher orbit average temperatures

4. Operational and non-operational temperature requirements are established
   - Average temperature limits
   - Allowable temperature gradients
   - Mission unique requirements (e.g., cryogenics)
5. Select simplified geometric shape: cube, sphere, several flat surfaces with an operational orientation representative of the mission flight system (spacecraft)
   - Spinning spacecraft might use a sphere or cylinder
   - Inertial fixed or planet oriented spacecraft, use a cube or flat plates

This is a lot of information to collect, but necessary to perform the analysis. Now we can start thermal analysis and design.

Steps in Doing a Thermal Analysis (Continuing to follow Fig. 22-18)

6. Compute the thermal heating environment: Move the geometric shape through the mission profile with the established orientations relative to the heat sources. For each surface and for each incident heat source, identify the maximum, minimum and average incident heat flux over time, for each mission phase. This involves a lot of averaging over time and area. Programs are available to compute all the geometry and time averages for this step.
   - It is often helpful to imagine yourself on the various surfaces moving through the mission orbit or profile, directed in the expected orientation and visualize the heat source. This can provide an intuitive check on the output of a computer generated set of incident heat sources.
   - Except for special cases (biological or radioactive heat sources), *all energy into a spacecraft arrives by radiant energy.* Even the electrical energy arrives as radiant energy on the solar arrays before being converted to electrical energy and then dissipated as thermal energy.
7. Compute the absorbed environmental heat, Q_{env}, on each object or surface by selecting surface radiant properties (α for a solar source and ε for an infrared source) from the following:

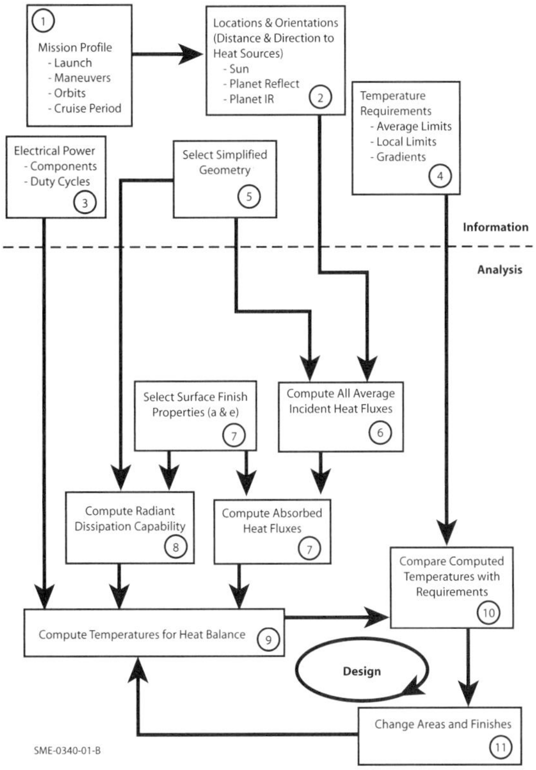

Fig. 22-18. Thermal Analysis and Design Process.

$$Q_{env} = \alpha S\left[A_p + RA_R\right] + \varepsilon IR\, A_{IR} \tag{22-20}$$

where S is the solar irradiance at the planet; R is the percentage of solar irradiance diffusely reflected from the planet; IR is the irradiance of infrared energy from the planet; A_p is the projected area toward the sun; A_R is the area exposed to diffusely reflected solar energy from the planet; and A_{IR} is the area exposed to the infrared energy, emitted from the planet.

8. Compute the total IR dissipation capability of the spacecraft geometry by summing all the external surfaces

$$Q_{out} = \sigma T^4 \sum_1^n \varepsilon_n A_n \tag{22-21}$$

where ε_n is the emissivity at surface n, and A_n is the radiating area at surface n.

9. Use the steady state heat balance equation for an isothermal object, include the electrical power from Step 3 and compute the steady state temperature for the object.

$$Q_{env} + Q_{in} = \sigma T^4 \sum_1^n \varepsilon_n A_n \tag{22-22}$$

where Q_{env} is the heat absorbed from environment loads, and Q_{in}, is the internal power.

10. Compute temperatures for the maximum and minimum heat loads using the maximum and minimum surface properties, and simultaneously using the maximum and minimum internal power dissipation.

11 Solve for T and compare with the requirements.

9a. Compare the temperature results of all these cases and evaluate the adequacy of a passive thermal design.

10a. Adjust the surface properties so the steady state temperature, for the average heat load, is near the middle of the required temperature range.

11a. Iterate results using the available independent variables (e.g., areas, finishes, power dissipation).

Constructing a Multi-node Thermal Model of the Spacecraft

A single, isothermal temperature calculation will rarely be adequate to analyze and design the thermal control subsystem. Even fairly simple spacecraft require the construction of a mathematical thermal model. A thermal model is a collection of isothermal nodes which represent locations in the spacecraft that should each operate as an isothermal unit. For example, a thick structural metal base plate could be a single node since it would readily conduct heat throughout the plate and not support a temperature gradient across the plate. The plate will change temperature over time but the plate will be a uniform temperature at any given time. An avionics box mounted on the structural plate will not necessarily be the same temperature as the plate since it may have electrical power dissipated inside and the conduction path from the box to the plate is finite. Therefore, the avionics box is a separate isothermal node in the thermal model. The collection of nodes in a thermal model can range from one to thousands. The number will be a function of spacecraft size, complexity, and the resolution required of the thermal design. For an unpressurized spacecraft there are only two ways to transfer heat from one node in the model to another node in the model: conduction and radiation. The set of isothermal nodes and all the couplings which interconnect them with heat transfer paths form the "internal" thermal model. See Fig. 22-19.

Conduction Heat Transfer Couplings are calculated by determining the mechanical path that must carry the heat from one node to another and applying the conduction properties of the materials in the path. A collection of series and parallel heat transfer paths can be combined the same way a network of electrical resistors can be combined to represent a single conduction coupling between two nodes in the model.

The heat transferred between the nodes by conduction depends on the temperature difference between the nodes and the coupling from one node to the other. A sample calculation that represents this, shows conduction from a heat dissipation element to an avionics box, to a base plate on which the box is mounted (Fig. 22-19).

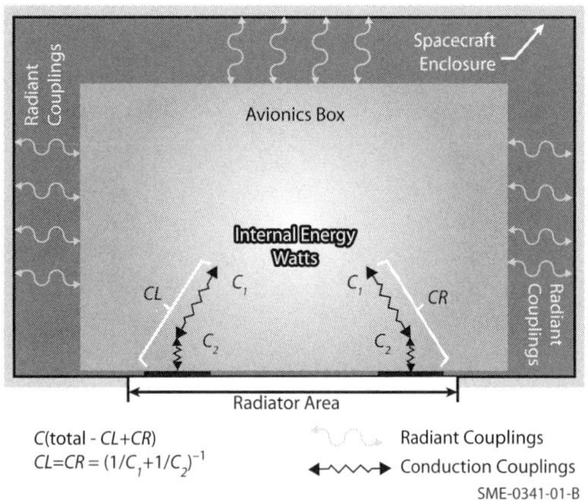

Fig. 22-19. Heat Transfer Inside Spacecraft.

For each leg

$$C_L = C_R = \frac{1}{\frac{1}{C_1} + \frac{1}{C_2}} \quad (22\text{-}23a)$$

$$C_{1,2} = C_L + C_R \quad (22\text{-}23b)$$

Heat transferred from 1 to 2 will be:

$$Q_{1,2} = (C_L + C_R)(T_1 - T_2) \quad (22\text{-}24)$$

Radiant heat transfer couplings between the isothermal nodes are determined by using the geometric view factor relationships between all the node surfaces and the emissivities of each surface. The radiant coupling will be a function of: surface area of each node, geometric view factor of one node surface to another node surface, and the IR emissivity of each surface. The heat transferred will be driven by the difference between the absolute temperature of each node raised to the 4th power. If two 1 m^2 surfaces are close and facing each other, their geometric view factor is 1.0. With a high emissivity on each (0.9) and a temperature difference of 1 deg K near room temperature would transfer 4.6 W from one surface to another. For small temperature differences the heat transferred is roughly linear. The heat transferred from surface 1 to surface 2 can be computed using an approximate radiation coupling as follows:

$$Q_{1,2} = \varepsilon_1 A_1 \times \varepsilon_2 A_2 \times F_{1,2}\sigma(T_1^4 - T_2^4) \quad (22\text{-}25)$$

Where $F_{1,2}$ is the geometric view factor from surface 1 to 2 defined as the percentage of diffuse energy that leaves surface 1 and strikes surface 2.

22.2.5 Thermal Model for Analysis and Design

The thermal model is used as the primary tool for analysis and design of the thermal control subsystem. The "internal" thermal model is radiatively coupled to the environment by connecting all node surfaces that view outside the spacecraft to a thermal sink at 0 K. Now we can apply the thermal loads to the model. These consist of the average absorbed environmental loads (solar and infrared) to the various nodes that have external surfaces and adding the average dissipated electrical power directly into the relevant nodes. Solving the resulting set of simultaneous equations will result in a predicted temperature for each node that balances the total heat transfer matrix for the spacecraft. Transient temperatures can be calculated if we add mass and specific heat properties to each node, and use thermal loads that vary with time.

The surface properties are adjusted to get the predicted temperatures to meet requirements. Known variations and statistical uncertainties in the environmental loads are applied to see the temperature response to the changes in these forcing functions. The conduction couplings can be changed with appropriate mechanical requirements for component attachment. The radiant couplings can be changed by specifying internal surface coatings and radiation shields. Areas that require a narrow operating temperature range can have a dedicated external radiator and a heater controlled by a temperature sensor.

22.2.6 FireSat II Thermal Analysis and Design

The FireSat II thermal design follows the process described in Sec. 22.2.4. The FireSat II mission profile is set by the orbit parameters and the orientation with respect to the Earth. The orbit parameters are: a circular orbit of 700 km, inclined 55 deg to the Earth's equator. The flight dynamics associated with this orbit show that the angle between the solar vector and the orbit plane (β angle) can vary from 0 to ± 78.5 deg (orbit inclination + equatorial tilt). This geometry translates into a range of possible shadow conditions from no shadow over the entire orbit (when β angle exceed ± 60 deg) to the maximum shadow when the solar vector is in the plane of the orbit (β angle = 0 deg.) At the $\beta = 0$ condition, FireSat II will be in the Earth's shadow 35% of the orbit.

FireSat II requires that the surface that contains the instrument aperture be oriented to nadir so that it always points down to Earth. This nadir vector is the yaw axis for the spacecraft. The instrument requires a radiator surface with low environmental loading to provide an efficient way to cool the detector to its operating temperature. Since the Sun is the major environmental heat source, we can designate a surface that will be on the side of the spacecraft which is perpendicular to the orbit plane and shadowed by the spacecraft. The normal to this surface is the pitch axis. When the Sun crosses the plane of the orbit (moves from a positive to a negative β angle) the spacecraft must perform a 180 deg yaw maneuver to keep the instrument radiator on the shady side of the spacecraft. Operationally, this will occur every 45 days. The velocity vector passes through the forward and aft panels of FireSat II and is perpendicular to the yaw and pitch axis, and is therefore also the roll axis. This orientation is shown in Fig. 19-3.

The radiant heat sources that will fall on the spacecraft surfaces in this mission profile will be: the direct Sun, the solar energy diffusely reflected from the sunlit side of the Earth, and the infrared energy emitted from the warm surface of the Earth.

Power dissipation for FireSat II is 200 W total. Of this, 65 W is used by the instrument and 15 W of the instrument power must be dissipated by a radiator, not to exceed 238 K (–35 C). The location and sizing of this radiator is discussed later. Except for the cold radiator, the instrument and the rest of the spacecraft have normal temperature limit requirements of –10 to +40 C.

We now have the geometry and requirements sufficiently defined to perform a simple thermal analysis. The first step is computing the thermal heating environment. Since the diameter and length of FireSat II are nearly identical, it is possible to use a simple cube as a surface representation to collect the relevant heating rates for the analysis. Moving the Earth oriented cubical representation of the spacecraft geometry through the orbit causes the Sun to rise and fall on various surfaces. Also, the surfaces change their geometric relationship to the sunlit portion of the Earth. An Earth oriented spacecraft will usually have constant Earth IR heating over the orbit. Using the orbit average incident fluxes from Table 22-11 we can sum all the orbit average heating for FireSat II keeping the solar and albedo separate from the Earth IR.

For our hot condition, we use the β angle which results in no shadow time combined with the high end of values for the heating sources. For the cold condition, we use the β angle which provides the maximum shadow time for each surface combined with the low end values for the heating sources.

Using Table 22-11, the rate at which energy is absorbed for each surface is:

$$Q = [\alpha(S + S_A) + \varepsilon S_{IR}]A \qquad (22\text{-}26)$$

where S_A is the albedo flux.

With the surfaces mostly covered by solar cells we will assume the effective absorptance is 0.85 (some energy is removed as electrical energy) and an emmisivity of 0.9.

Adding up all the energy for the 6 surfaces on the cube yields: 1,378 W for the cold case 2,173 W for the hot case. When we add the internal power, the total energy into the system varies from 1,578 W to 2,373 W.

The energy leaving the system does so by radiation. Again, assuming solar cell properties gives a total radiation capability from the surface area of all 6 sides:

$$Q = A_S \varepsilon \sigma T^4 \qquad (22\text{-}27)$$

Summing the internal power with the 6 surface heat energy inputs and outputs is equivalent to linking them together with infinite couplings. This gives the thermal average for the spacecraft surface temperatures and the average temperature for an isothermal spacecraft.

The energy balances when the temperature is –5 C for the cold case, and +24 C for the hot case. Table 22-13 shows the details of these calculations.

We can now look at how to tailor the thermal coatings to meet our specific FireSat II requirements. Referring to the average incident flux tables for the β angle limits for FireSat II, we note that the nadir facing surface and the surface which is always on the shaded side of the spacecraft do not have enough incident energy to generate power for the spacecraft. These surfaces are available for thermal control coatings and other spacecraft equipment. This allows us 2 of the 6 sides on our estimating cube for thermal control coatings. These

Table 22-13. FireSat II—Temperature Calculations—First Estimate. From incident energy to temperature at thermal balance.

Cold 700 km β = 0													
Surf. #	**Descrip.**	**Area (m^2)**	**Inc. Solar**	**Inc. Albedo**	**Inc. Earth IR**	**α**	**ε**	**Absorbed Solar + alb**	**Absorbed Earth IR**	**Elec. Power**	**Q_{In}**	**Rad Area/ abs Area**	**Temp (°C)**
1	Zenith-Y	1	418.2			0.85	0.9	355.5	0.0	0.0	355.5	1	16
2	Nadir-Y	1	41.3	74.6	176.4	0.85	0.9	98.5	158.751	0.0	257.3	1	–7
3	Sun-P	1	0.8	21.3	50.8	0.85	0.9	18.8	45.7038	0.0	64.5	1	–84
4	A-Sun-P	1	0.8	21.3	50.7	0.85	0.9	188	45.603	0.0	64.4	1	–85
5	Ram-R	1	299.7	21.4	50.5	0.85	0.9	272.9	45.4509	0.0	318.4	1	8
6	A-Ram-R	1	299.7	21.4	50.5	0.85	0.9	272.9	45.4509	0.0	318.4	1	8
	Total	6	1,060.6	159.9	378.8	0.85	0.9	1,037.4	341.0	200.0	1,578.4	6	–5
Hot 700 km β = 70													
Surf. #	**Descrip.**	**Area (m^2)**	**Inc. Solar**	**Inc. Albedo**	**Inc. Earth IR**	**α**	**ε**	**Absorbed Solar + alb**	**Absorbed Earth IR**	**Elec. Power**	**Q_{In}**	**Rad Area/ abs Area**	**Temp (°C)**
1	Zenith-Y	1	154.2			0.9	0.9	131.0	0.0	0.0	131.0	1	–48
2	Nadir-Y	1	154.2	57.0	212.1	0.9	0.9	179.5	190.8	0.0	370.3	1	19
3	Sun-P	1	1,333.4	25.2	60.9	0.9	0.9	1,154.9	54.8	0.0	1,209.7	1	119
4	A-Sun-P	1		8.7	61.0	0.9	0.9	7.4	54.9	0.0	62.3	1	–86
5	Ram-R	1	154.2	16.4	60.7	0.9	0.9	145.0	54.6	0.0	199.6	1	–23
6	A-Ram-R	1	154.2	16.4	60.7	0.9	0.9	145.0	54.6	0.0	199.6	1	–23
	Total	6	1,950.1	123.8	455.3	0.9	0.9	1,762.8	409.8	200.0	2,372.6	6	24
All surfaces solar cells –200 W internal power; meters, watts, °C, $\sigma = 5.67 \times 10^{-8}$ W/$m^2 \cdot K^4$													

surfaces, not needed for solar cells, are valuable areas. The nadir surface contains the instrument aperture and other spacecraft equipment which may require external mounting, (e.g., communication antennas). Let's assume that of our 2 m^2 available for thermal coatings, 0.5 m^2 is required for other uses. The average spacecraft temperature can be lowered by using coatings to reject as much incident heat as possible while maintaining a high heat radiation capability. With a low α/ε coating on 0.75 m^2 of the nadir and shadowed sides the total energy into the system becomes 1,379 W for the cold case, and 2,034 W for the hot case. The resulting cold and hot orbit average temperatures are –14 C and +12 C. If we cover the available 1.5 m^2 of our working surfaces with insulation to minimize their radiation capability, the average cube temperatures are raised to –3 C and 26 C. Our estimation calculations have shown that we can set the average temperature with passive coatings. The thermal coatings can now be further refined for the specific geometry of the spacecraft using actual surface areas and equipment to set the average temperature.

The requirement for a local cold condition is satisfied as follows. The element to be controlled at a low temperature is isolated from coupling to the spacecraft interior and strongly coupled to an external radiating surface. The external surface location is selected for minimum incident radiant energy loading. For a physical representation of this problem, refer to Fig. 22-22 in Sec. 22.2.8 under "radiators". The cooled element is the "avionics box" which, in this application, is well insulated from thermal coupling with the spacecraft enclosure. It is strongly coupled to a special radiator which is the surface that dissipates the net 15 W of power at a temperature of –35 C.

Start with the location of the radiator to compute its size. The side of the spacecraft that is always shadowed is the only surface that can meet the requirement for a radiator that can dissipate 15 W at –35 C. A surface at –35 C can only dissipate 180 W/m^2. All surfaces on FireSat II, except the shadowed side, have more than that in absorbed environmental energy at one or more β angles. The size of the radiator on the shaded surface is computed as follows. Lower the required temperature to –40 C to allow for some margin. Look up the maximum incident flux on the shadowed surface from Table 22-13. The maximum solar albedo is 34 W/m^2 and the maximum Earth IR is 61 W/m^2. Choose a coating to minimize solar absorption and maximize radiation dissipation. A white paint with $\alpha = 0.2$ and $\varepsilon = 0.9$ is a good choice. The absorbed environmental flux is $34 \times 0.2 + 61 \times 0.9 = 61$ W/m^2. At –40 C, the same surface can dissipate 167 W/m^2. Our net radiator capability is 101 W/m^2, and the required 15 W should therefore need about 0.15 m^2 of radiator area. Typically, the radiator is slightly oversized and has a controlled heater to set the exact temperature.

22.2.7 Thermal Hardware, Tools and Techniques

There are many tools and techniques that can be used to design the thermal subsystem and meet requirements. The art of thermal design lies in choosing and applying the possible solutions while also meeting system level cost and mass constraints. Most common hardware elements used for spacecraft thermal design and control are:

- Coatings (surface finishes)
- Insulation and isolators
- Heaters & their controllers
- Louvers
- Heat pipes

22.2.8 Thermal Control Components

Surface Finishes

In spacecraft thermal designs, wavelength-dependent thermal control coatings are used for various purposes. Solar reflectors such as second-surface mirrors and white paints or silver or aluminum-backed teflon are used to minimize absorbed solar energy, yet emit energy almost like an ideal blackbody. To minimize both the absorbed solar energy and infrared emission, polished metal such as aluminum foil or gold plating is used. On the interior of the vehicle, if it is desired to exchange energy with the compartment or other equipment, black paint is commonly used. Thus, the existing state of the art uses a rather wide variety of coatings which have wavelength dependent thermal properties. The problems of in-space stability, outgassing, and mechanical adhesion to the substrate have been resolved for most coatings. There are many fully qualified coatings, so development and qualification of a new coating for a new design is normally unnecessary.

The two primary surface properties of importance are the IR *emissivity*, ε, and the solar *absorptivity*, α. Table 22-14 shows the range of properties available for some common surface finishes. Two or more coatings are sometimes combined in a checkerboard or striped pattern to obtain the desired combination of average absorptivity and emissivity if it cannot be obtained in a single material.

Thermal control finishes are affected in orbit by charged particles, ultraviolet radiation, high vacuum, and the contaminant films that deposit out on almost all spacecraft surfaces. The general result of these processes is an increase in solar absorptivity with little or no effect on infrared emissivity. This is normally undesirable from a thermal control standpoint because spacecraft radiators must be sized to account for the substantial increase in absorbed solar energy that occurs due to degradation over the mission. These radiators, which are oversized to handle the high solar loads at "end-of-life," cause the spacecraft to run much cooler in the early years of the mission, sometimes necessitating the use of heaters to avoid under-temperatures of electronic components. The degradation is, therefore, a problem not only because of the solar load, but also because of the change in load over the course of the mission. The stability of coating properties is important in order to both limit maximum temperatures and minimize heater-power requirements.

Table 22-13◀, Fig. 22-19◀, Eq. 22-27◀

Table 22-14. Properties of Common Finishes.

Surface Finish	B.O.L. α (Beginning of Life)	ε
Optical Solar Reflectors		
8 mil Quartz Mirrors	0.05 to 0.08	0.80
2 mil Silvered Teflon	0.05 to 0.09	0.66
5 mil Silvered Teflon	0.05 to 0.09	0.78
2 mil Aluminized Teflon	0.10 to 0.16	0.66
5 mil Aluminized Teflon	0.10 to 0.16	0.78
White Paints		
S13G-LO	0.20 to 0.25	0.85
Z93	0.17 to 0.20	0.92
ZOT	0.18 to 0.20	0.91
Chemglaze A276	0.22 to 0.28	0.88
Black Paints		
Chemglaze Z306	0.92 to 0.98	0.89
3M Black Velvet	~0.97	0.84
Aluminized Kapton		
½ mil	0.34	0.55
1 mil	0.38	0.67
2 mil	0.41	0.75
5 mil	0.46	0.86
Metallic		
Vapor Deposited Aluminum	0.08 to 0.17	0.04
Bare Aluminum	0.09 to 0.17	0.03 to 0.10
Vaporized Deposited Gold	0.19 to 0.30	0.03
Anodized Aluminum	0.25 to 0.86*	0.04 to 0.88*
Miscellaneous		
¼ mil Aluminized Mylar,	unstable	0.34
Beta Cloth	0.32	0.86
Astro Quartz	~0.22	0.80
MAXORB	0.9	0.1

* Anodizing and similar surface treatments must be carefully controlled in order to produce repeatable optical properties.

Insulation

Multilayer insulation (MLI) and single-layer radiation shields are among the most common thermal control elements on spacecraft. MLI blankets are used either to prevent excessive heat loss from a component or excessive heating from environmental fluxes or rocket plumes. Most spacecraft are covered with MLI blankets, with cutouts provided for radiator areas to reject internally generated waste heat. MLI blankets are also typically used to protect internal propellant tanks, propellant lines, solid rocket motors, and cryogenic dewars. Single-layer radiation barriers are sometimes used in place of MLI where a lesser degree of thermal isolation is required, since they are lighter and cheaper to manufacture. For applications requiring insulation under atmospheric conditions, foam, batting, and aerogel materials are generally used because MLI is not very effective in the presence of a gas.

Multilayer insulation is composed of multiple layers of low-emittance films with low conductivity between layers, as shown in Fig. 22-20. The simplest construction is a layered blanket assembled from embossed, thin mylar sheets (¼ mil thick) with a vacuum-deposited aluminum finish on one side of each sheet. The embossing results in the sheets touching only at a few points, thereby minimizing conductive heat paths between layers. The layers are aluminized on one side only, so that the mylar can act as a

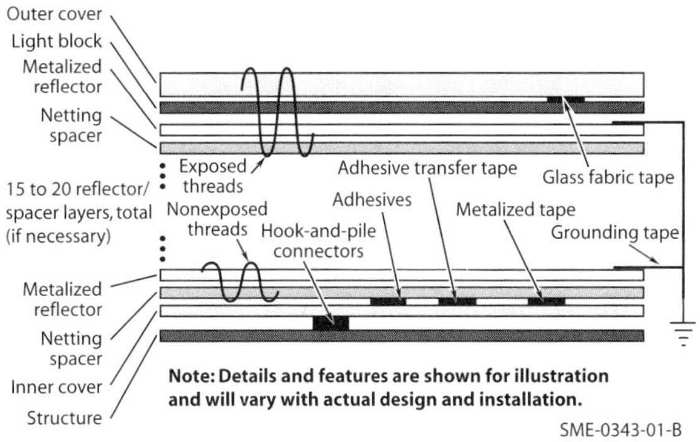

Fig. 22-20. Composition of a Typical MLI Blanket. Mulitlayer insulation blankets are made of fairly sophisticated layers of low-emittance films with low conductivity between layers. (Courtesy of NASA)

low-conductivity spacer. Higher-performance construction uses Mylar film metallized on both surfaces (aluminum or gold) with silk or dacron net, Tissuglas paper, or "Super-Flock" whiskers as the low-conductance spacers.

Figure 22-21 illustrates theoretical and experimental data for embossed aluminized (one surface) Mylar insulation versus number of insulation-blanket layers. The emittance for a multilayer blanket theoretically varies inversely with one over one plus the number of layers. However, in practice, simply increasing the number of layers past a certain value will not improve performance. As the number of layers increases, radiative heat transfer becomes small compared to conductive "shorts" between layers and other losses. Thus, a point of diminishing returns is reached. Considering these trends, about 25 layers are usually sufficient to obtain a minimum overall conductance value.

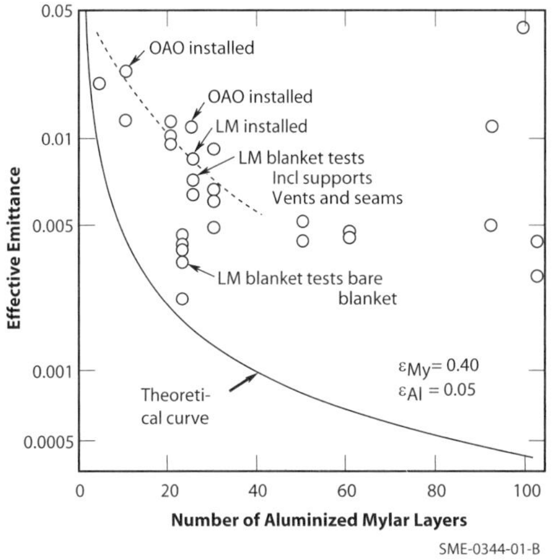

Fig. 22-21. Effective Emittance vs. Number of Aluminized Layers. This figure illustrates theoretical and experimental data for embossed aluminized (one surface) mylar insulation versus number of insulation-blanket layers. Note that the emittance for a multilayer blanket theoretically varies inversely with one over one plus the number of layers.

In well-controlled laboratory tests, it is possible to achieve values of 0.005 or lower for the *effective emittance*, ε^*. However, when a blanket is configured for spacecraft application, experience has shown that an ε^* of 0.015 to 0.030 is typical for medium-sized area applications. As the size of the application increases, the relative performance generally increases. This results from the smaller relative influences of heat leaks due to edge effects, seams, or cable penetrations. For very-large-area applications with minimal penetrations, the ε^* laboratory performance approaches 0.005 at 30 layers. Performance data from cryogenic tankage and controlled calorimeter tests typically show performance of ε^* down to 0.002. Control of discontinuities through the design and fabrication of insulation joints and penetrations is crucial to the problem of reducing the effective emittance of multilayer blankets. Compression of a blanket section dramatically increases heat leakage, as well. Small area blankets show high effective emittance along with considerable manufacturing variation. Very small blankets used to wrap propellant lines typically have effective emittances ranging from 0.05 to 0.30, making low emittance surface finishes a simpler alternative for internal propellant lines. External lines that are exposed to sunlight require MLI blankets to avoid overheating caused by the high absorptance/emittance ratios typical of low emittance surface finishes.

Missions involving planetary landers, rovers, or atmospheric probes usually require insulation that performs well in the presence of an atmosphere. While MLI may still be required to protect the hardware during interplanetary cruise, foam, batting, or aerogel materials are generally added to provide insulation after atmospheric entry and landing in situations where ambient pressure is expected to be high enough to substantially degrade MLI performance. If atmospheric pressure and gravity are low enough, simple trapped gas spaces alone may be sufficient to limit heat loss to the surroundings. The underlying principle behind all of these insulation types is to trap gas within volumes small enough to eliminate convection effects. Total heat transfer is thereby limited to what can conduct through the low conductivity insulation material and gas and radiate across the insulation through a process of multiple absorptions and emissions within the insulation material structure. To complicate MLI design further each layer must be grounded to reduce the chance of electrostatic discharge.

Conduction Isolators

It is usually a good thermal control approach to couple everything together to get an average temperature for the spacecraft internal components. However, there are often local temperature requirements which call for isolation. This can provide very low temperatures or efficient response to the addition of heater power. Radiation isolation is accomplished using MLI. Conduction isolation usually involves custom isolators. These increase in performance as their cross sectional area decreases, their length increases, and the conductivity of the material decreases. For extreme isolation requirements, long slender standoffs made of non-metallic material may be needed. This can be a systems design challenge when also providing adequate mechanical support.

Developments in composite materials have enabled many options in the design of conduction isolation (or enhancement).

Radiators, Thermal

Most spacecraft waste heat is rejected to space by *radiators*. These occur in several different forms, such as spacecraft structural panels, flat-plate radiators mounted to the side of the spacecraft, or panels that are deployed after the spacecraft is on orbit. Whatever the configuration, all radiators reject heat by IR radiation from their surfaces. The radiating power is dependent on the emissivity of the surface and its temperature. The radiator must reject both the satellite waste heat plus any radiant-heat loads from the environment or other spacecraft surfaces that are absorbed by the radiator, as shown in Fig. 22-22. Most radiators are therefore given surface finishes with high IR emissivity (> 0.8) to maximize heat rejection and low solar absorptivity (< 0.2) to limit heat loads from the Sun. Typical finishes include quartz mirrors, silvered or aluminized teflon, and white paint.

The external surface finishes of the radiator couple it to space. Because these surfaces are also exposed to external sources of energy such as sunlight and Earth-emitted IR, their radiative properties must be selected to achieve an energy balance at the desired temperature between spacecraft internal dissipation, external sources of heat, and reradiation to space, as illustrated in Fig. 22-22.

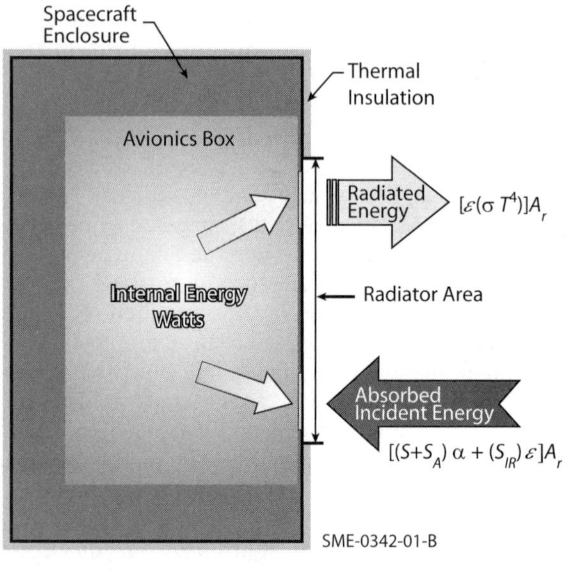

Fig. 22-22. Radiator Energy Balance. Note that we must select radiative properties of the radiator surface to achieve an energy balance among spacecraft internal dissipation, external heat sources and reradiation to space to obtain the desired temperature. A_r is the area of the radiator.

The radiating power of a radiator is a strong function of temperature. The total heat leaving a radiator surface is given by the Stefan-Boltzmann law:

$$Q = A \varepsilon \sigma T^4 \quad (22\text{-}28)$$

where A is the surface area, ε is emissivity, T is the absolute temperature, and σ is the Stefan-Boltzmann constant ($5.670\ 51 \times 10^{-8}$ W/m^2 K^4).

The T^4 term results in a large increase in radiating capability with temperature. Referring back to Fig. 22-15, the radiating power at 50 C is about twice that at 0 C. At cryogenic temperatures the effect is even more pronounced, with a 70 K radiator having only 1/300th the heat rejection capability of a room-temperature radiator. This makes cryogenic radiators extremely sensitive to environmental heating and heat leaks through insulation and supports, and leads to special design considerations.

Most spacecraft radiators reject between 100 and 350 W of spacecraft internally generated electronics waste heat per square meter. The upper end of this range is typical of a radiator that runs at a fairly high temperature (say 40 C), and experiences relatively modest heat backload from the environment or other spacecraft surfaces. The lower end of the range represents a radiator running below room temperature in LEO, where environmental backloads can be substantial. The actual sizing is determined by a thermal analysis that considers the desired operating temperature, worst-case satellite waste heat, environmental heating, and radiative and conductive interactions with other spacecraft surfaces (See Table 22-13).

Heaters

Ideally, thermal control of a satellite or component would be achieved using only passive techniques, such as surface finishes. Unfortunately, orbital and seasonal variations in environment and component heat-generation rates, along with degradations of surface finishes over time, can drive temperature variations in a passive design to ranges larger than some components can withstand. Because of this, heaters are sometimes required to protect components from cold-case environmental conditions or to make up for heat that is not dissipated when an electronic box is turned off. Heaters may also be used with thermostats or solid-state controllers to provide precise temperature control of a particular component. A third common use for heaters is to warm components to their minimum operating temperatures before they are turned on.

The most common type of heater used on spacecraft is the *patch heater*, several of which are shown in Fig. 22-23A. It consists of an electrical resistance element sandwiched between two sheets of flexible electrically insulating material, such as Kapton. The patch may have one circuit, or more than one, depending on whether redundancy is required within the patch. Redundancy is generally required on spacecraft systems since heater circuits can fail. Sometimes the redundancy is provided within the patch and sometimes it is provided by using two separate patches. The patch heaters shown in the figure illustrate the custom shapes to which these heaters may be made. In most instances, however, a simple rectangular patch of some standard dimension is used.

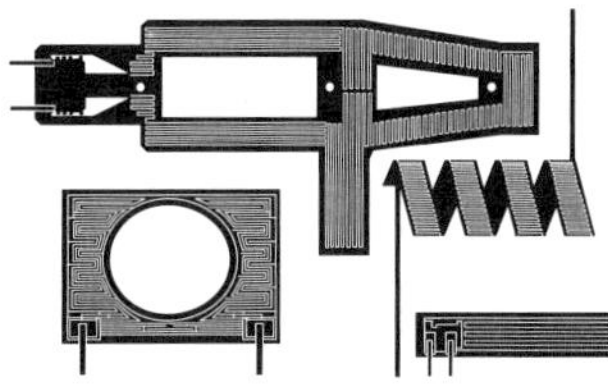

(A) Patch Heaters

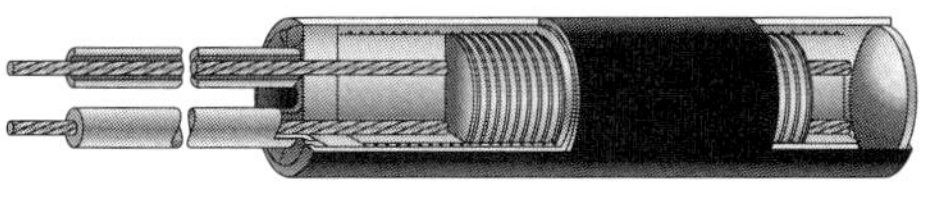

(B) Cartridge Heater

SME-0345-01-B

Fig. 22-23. Types of Heaters. Patch and cartridge heaters are used on many spacecraft to meet the heating needs of different types of equipment. These heaters are very important to the successful operation of key components, so we often use redundancy to increase reliability of these devices.

A *cartridge heater* is another type that is often used to heat blocks of material or high-temperature components such as hydrazine-thruster catalyst beds. Such a heater is shown in Fig. 22-23B and consists of a wound resistor enclosed in a cylindrical metallic case. A hole is typically drilled in the component to be heated and the cartridge potted into the hole. Another attachment technique involves the use of a clamp or small bracket to hold the heater. These heaters are typically a quarter inch in diameter or less, and up to a few inches long.

Almost all heater systems have some sort of switch or control. This typically involves a relay that is commandable from the ground to enable or disable power to the heater, a fuse to protect the spacecraft from a short circuit, and, most commonly, a thermostat or solid-state controller to turn the heater on and off at predetermined-temperatures. More sophisticated satellites sometimes use their on-board computer to monitor temperatures and turn heaters on and off as appropriate, using relays.

The simplest arrangement involves only the heater, a fuse, and a ground commandable relay to turn the heater on and off. This arrangement is typically used for heaters that are activated only for special events, or for heaters that can be left on all the time. A typical application is heating up the catalyst beds on hydrazine thrusters to 100 C before the thruster is fired. (Firing the thruster with a low initial catalyst-bed temperature decreases the catalyst life.) The heater is commanded on, the catalyst-bed is heated, the thruster is fired, and the heater is turned off until the next maneuver, all under ground control.

Historically, the most common control device is a mechanical thermostat, such as the one shown in Fig. 22-24A. These typically consist of a small hermetically sealed can containing a switch driven by a

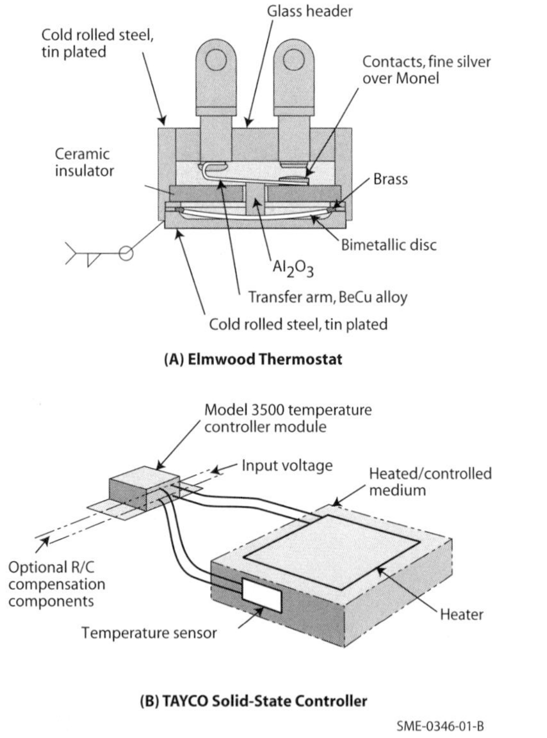

Fig. 22-24. Common Control Device. Mechanical thermostates are typically used to control operation of heaters on a spacecraft.

snap-action bimetallic actuator. The temperature at which the thermostat clicks on, known as its *set point*, is fixed for any given thermostat. The engineer can select from an array of standard thermostats available from the manufacturer to get a set point close to what is desired, or a custom device can be ordered. In addition to the set point, the *dead band*, or the difference between the temperatures at which the thermostat turns on and off, is important. Thermostat dead bands typically range from 5 C to 15 C. A smaller dead band reduces the temperature swing of the device being heated, but increases the number of cycles on the thermostat itself, thus decreasing its reliability. Small dead bands also increase the chance of "dithering," in which the thermostat rapidly cycles on and off. This is a failure condition that can cause the set point to drift lower, resulting in an under-temperature of the component being controlled.

A solid-state controller, an example of which is shown in Fig. 22-24B, replaces the mechanical switch with an electronic device that has a higher reliability and life expectancy. These are used extensively on the DMSP, the Hubble Space Telescope, and the ISS. They employ a temperature sensor that can be located either at the controller or at a remote location, as desired. Another advantage of solid-state controllers is that extremely tight dead bands (<0.1 C) are possible for very precise temperature control, such as required on the Space Telescope. Optical systems, some sensors, and electronic frequency standards often require precise temperature control, which cannot be achieved with a mechanical thermostat.

A number of military and scientific satellites use onboard computers to control heaters. Such systems read the temperatures from telemetry sensors placed throughout the vehicle and send signals to turn relay-controlled heaters on and off as required. This allows enormous flexibility since the control set points and dead bands can be adjusted on orbit by uplinking new tables to the spacecraft computer.

Louvers

Louvers are active thermal control elements that have been used in different forms on numerous spacecraft. While most commonly placed over external radiators, louvers may also be used to modulate radiant heat transfer between internal spacecraft surfaces, or from internal surfaces directly to space through openings in the spacecraft wall. In general, a louver in its fully open state allows the rejection of six times as much heat as it does in the fully closed state, with no power required to operate it. Thus, louvers find applications where internal power dissipation varies widely as a result of equipment duty cycles.

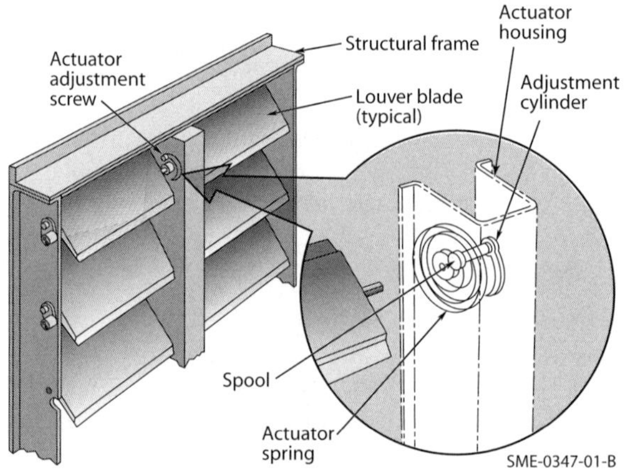

Fig. 22-25. Louver Assembly Schematic. The most commonly used louvers are the "venetian-blind" type that are typically opened to allow heat to radiate away from the spacecraft and closed to keep heat from escaping.

The most commonly used louver assembly is the "venetian-blind" type shown in Fig. 22-25. These louvers consist of four main elements: blades, actuators, sensing elements, and structural elements. The louver is placed over a high emittance, low absorptance spacecraft radiator to modulate the flow of radiant heat from that surface. Blades, which are driven by the actuators, are the louver elements that give variable-radiation characteristics to the radiator surface below. While closed, louvers shield the radiator's view to space, but while open, they allow radiative coupling to space. The radiating characteristics of the radiator can be varied over the range defined by these two extreme positions

The actuators drive the blades according to the perceived radiator temperature. In most louver designs, a bimetallic spiral spring drives each louver blade independently to ensure maximum reliability. Thus a single

Table 22-15. Characteristics of Flight-Qualified Rectangular-Blade Louver Assemblies. Here you can find typical characteristics for three louver assemblies that can be used to estimate mass and size.[a]

	OSC	ATK	Starsys
Blades	3 to 42	Various	1 to 16
Open Set Points (°C)	Various	0 to 40	–20 to 50
Open/Close Differential (°C)	10 or 18	10 or 18	14
Dimensions (cm)			
Length	20 to 110	27 to 80	8 to 43
Width	36 to 61	30 to 60	22 to 40
Height		6.4	6.4
Area (m^2)	0.07 to 0.6	0.08 to 0.5	0.02 to 0.2
Weight/Area (kg/m^2)[b]	3.2 to 5.4	~4.5	5.2 to 11.6
Flight History	Multiple	XTE, Stardust	Multiple

[a] This table contains representative values from past louver designs. Contact manufacturer for additional design possibilities or values for specific designs.
[b] Weight without sunshield.
[c] The Starsys design is a slightly modified version of a JPL louver design that has flown on the indicated spacecraft.

point failure is associated with one blade, not the entire assembly. The actuator spring drives the blade angle as determined by the underlying radiator temperature. A strong conductive path between the actuator and radiator is therefore sought to minimize the temperature gradient between them.

Louver assemblies have been designed for operation in both shadow and sunlight. Two design approaches that have been followed for operation in sunlight are the use of a Sun shield to prevent direct solar illumination of the louver, or the modification of the louver assembly for high temperature operation if it is directly exposed to sunlight. Characteristics of louvers offered by some principal vendors are shown in Table 22-15.

Heat Pipes

A *heat pipe* uses a closed two-phase fluid-flow cycle to transport large quantities of heat from one location to another without the use of electrical power. The heat pipe can be used to create isothermal surfaces or to spread out heat from a localized source uniformly over a larger area. One-way (diode) heat pipes have been tested and flown, as have *variable-conductance heat pipes*, which maintain a constant temperature under varying heat load conditions. Since the driving mechanism is capillary pumping, a relatively weak force, traditional heat pipes may be susceptible to severe performance degradation when operating under gravity or acceleration, so planning is needed to facilitate ground testing. Loop heat pipes and capillary pumped loops are more advanced cousins of the basic heat pipes that can provide constant temperature operation with varying heat loads under gravity or acceleration.

To illustrate how a heat pipe works, consider a simple horizontal heat pipe in equilibrium with an isothermal environment, as shown in Fig. 22-26. The liquid in the wick and the vapor in the vapor space are at saturation. If heat is applied to the evaporator, raising its temperature, liquid in the wick evaporates (removing some of the added heat), which depresses the meniscus in the evaporator since less liquid is present there. This process also raises the local vapor pressure, since it must be in saturation with the heated liquid in the wick.

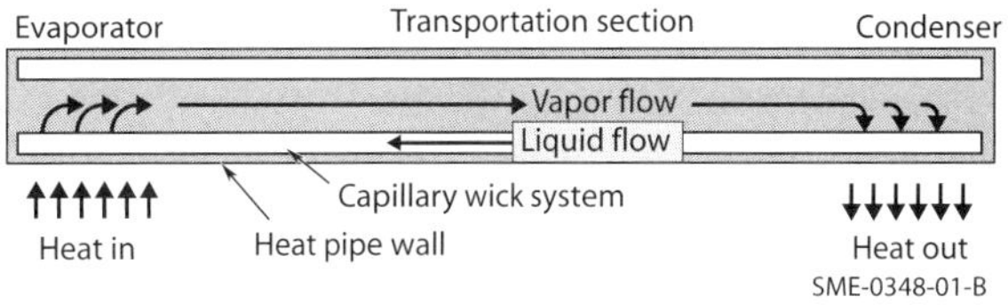

Fig. 22-26. Heat Pipe Schematic. Heat pipes are very efficient in moving heat from one place to another on the spacecraft. See text for a description of operation.

The difference between the increased curvature of the meniscus in the evaporator wick and the unchanged meniscus in the condenser wick causes a difference in capillary pressure sufficient to pull liquid from the condenser wick toward the evaporator. This replenishes the liquid in the evaporator wick. At the same time, heated vapor flows from the evaporator to the condenser, which is at a lower pressure. When this vapor comes in contact with cooler condenser surfaces, it condenses. This cycle is shown schematically in Fig. 22-26.

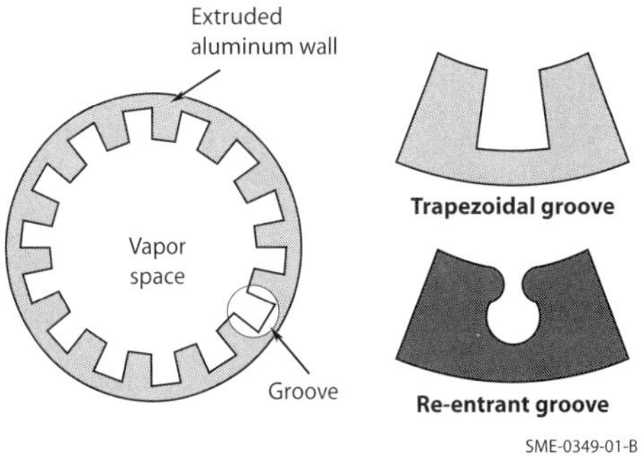

Fig. 22-27. Grooved Heat Pipe. This is an example of the most common wick/envelope design which consists of axial grooves in the wall of extruded aluminum tubing.

Elements of this most basic, constant-conductance, heat pipe consist of a working fluid, a wick structure, and an envelope. The most common wick envelope design consists of axial grooves in the wall of extruded aluminum tubing, as shown in Fig. 22-27. This class of wick is very susceptible to gravity effects during ground testing, but is relatively inexpensive to produce and very consistent. Heat-transfer capability is moderate, but sufficient for many applications. Grooves are typically rectangular or trapezoidal in shape, but more complex shapes such as the "teardrop" or "keyhole" have been extruded with difficulty. Different working fluids can be used depending on the temperature range of interest. In most spacecraft applications, ammonia is the working fluid of choice. Laptop computers, on the other hand, typically use water in heat pipes used to cool high-power chips.

The most obvious application of a heat pipe is one requiring physical separation of the heat source and sink. If a heat pipe is used, it is not necessary to mount all hardware to be cooled directly on radiator panels, or to use relatively inefficient conductive couplings. A closely related class of application is that of the thermal transformer. A small high-powered box can be mounted on one side of a radiator with integral heat pipes; the heat generated will be spread out over a large radiator surface. This approach also permits more efficient use of available "real estate"—the area available for a radiator is seldom centered symmetrically about the heat source, facing the optimal direction.

Heat pipes have also been used to reduce temperature gradients in structures to minimize thermal distortion. The telescope tube of the Orbiting Astronomical Observatory had three ring-shaped heat pipes to minimize circumferential temperature gradients. The ammonia/aluminum heat pipes worked throughout the eight years of mission life.

The diode heat pipe was first proposed as a means of connecting a device to two radiator panels on opposite sides of a spacecraft, with the understanding that at least one of the radiators would be free of any direct solar load at all times during the orbit. The diodes would couple the device to the cold radiator, while preventing heat from leaking back into the system from the radiator in the Sun. This type of thermal design problem—in which heat from a temporarily warm radiator or from a failed refrigerator must be kept from leaking back into the system—is an obvious application for a diode heat pipe.

The variable-conductance heat pipe can be used to control the amount of active radiator area, providing reasonably good temperature control without the use of heaters. This is particularly attractive if electrical power is limited, and this type of design has been flown on a number of satellites. However, if the application requires maintaining a component at virtually a constant temperature, feedback control (at the expense of some heater power) may be employed. A sensor on the baseplate of the device to be controlled can be routed to an onboard computer, and whenever the temperature drops below the desirable range, heaters on the variable conductance heat pipe reservoirs are activated, causing the control gas to expand and block off more of the radiator area. If the temperature rises above the range desired, power to the reservoir heaters is reduced, increasing the active radiator area. This concept usually requires less power than using heaters directly on the box or system to be controlled.

References

For annotated bibliography of structures and thermal, see the book website.

AIAA. 2005. "Moving Mechanic Assemblies for Space Launch Vehicles." S-114-2005. Reston, VA.

DoD. 1989. *Test Requirements for Space Vehicles*. MIL-STD-1540B. Jul. 31.

Madden, J. 2005. "100 Lessons Learned for Project Managers." *NASA Academy Sharing Knowledge*, issue 14, Mar.

NASA. 2011. "Space Mechanisms Project." NASA Glenn Research Center. Website.

NASA. 2006. *Design and Development Requirements for Mechanisms*. NASA-STD-5017. Jun. 6.

NASA. 2005. *General Environmental Verification Standards (GEVS) for GSFC Flight Programs and Projects*. GSFC-STD-7000. Apr.

NASA. 1996. *Payload Vibroacoustic Test Criteria.* NASA-STD-7001. Jun. 21.

NASA. 2008. *Structural Design and Test Factors of Safety for Spaceflight Hardware.* NASA-STD-5001. Jun. 30.

Pisacane, Vincent L and R.C. Moore. 2005. *Fundamentals of Space Systems, 2nd ed.* Cary, NC: Oxford University Press.

Sarafin, Thomas P. 1995. *Spacecraft Structures and Mechanism: From Concept to Launch.* El Segundo, CA: Microcosm Press and Springer, NY.

Young, W. and R. Budynas. 2001. *Roark's Formulas for Stress and Strain. 7th ed.* New York, NY: McGraw-Hill Companies.

23 Space Logistics and Manufacturing

As part of the engineering of a space mission, we need to consider the construction of the system. In Chaps. 9 and 10, we discussed orbits and constellations of spacecraft. Sections 23.1 and 23.2 discuss the trade between a single spacecraft and a constellation of spacecraft in order to meet the same mission objective. The logistics associated with this decision will impact the strategy for manufacturing the spacecraft, launching the system into space, and establishing communication with the ground. Sections 23.3 and 23.4 will cover the standard approach for the manufacturing of flight hardware, including the validation that we have built the right system and the verification that we have built the system right. There is significant effort associated with the integration and test of a spacecraft, and the design must take this process into consideration. Section 23.5 discusses how building a number of spacecraft for a constellation will impact the design and approach to manufacturing, concluding with some interesting details about the construction of the Iridium constellation. Alternate approaches to space manufacturing and how modularity, adaptability, and reconfigurability can be designed into an architecture, leading to significant cost savings are described in Sec. 23.6. Finally, Sec. 23.7 concludes this chapter with a discussion of some less measurable factors, such as culture and motivation, that play into manufacturing, again pointing out that early consideration of assembly, during the design phase, is critical to efficient implementation.

23.1 LEO Communications Constellations

Stuart Eves, *Surrey Satellite Technology*

As will be appreciated from Chaps. 8 to 10, satellites in LEO have relatively limited coverage footprints on the surface of the globe by comparison with their cousins' higher altitude orbits. Bearing in mind this footprint limitation, a system designer wishing to achieve a reasonable level of communications performance is automatically driven towards a constellation involving multiple satellites. Traditionally, both satellites and their launch vehicles have been expensive, and this raises obvious questions about the financial wisdom of constructing multi-satellite communications constellations in LEO—would smaller numbers of satellites in higher orbits not represent a more logical investment? And yet the most prolific satellite series in history, the Russian Strela-1 system, is a communications constellation which over its lifetime saw the launch of some 350 or so relatively short-lived satellites. And in the 1990s, Iridium, Globalstar and Orbcomm all invested large sums in the creation of LEO communications systems. See the book website for a more extended discussion of the historical development of LEO constellation.

The explanation behind the apparent contradiction relates to the user communities that these satellite systems were endeavoring to serve, and the locations of those users on the surface of the Earth. These user communities were either mobile, with small, low-power hand-held receivers, or (in the case of the Strela-1 system), espionage agents who presumably had no desire to advertise their presence by erecting a satellite dish on the roof! In most cases, such terminals will not be "cooperative," (in the sense that the user will not necessarily be able to ensure a clear line of sight to the satellite, or use a highly directional antenna to track the satellite as it moves across the sky). In order to establish a satisfactory link budget to such an uncooperative terminal, it is necessary to ensure that the *Effective Isotropic Radiated Power* (EIRP) from the satellites is sufficient to overcome these limitations. Specifically, the system designer must make certain that the free space path loss (which is dictated by the range between the transmitter and receiver) does not render the system infeasible.

23.1.1 Ground/User Segment Constraints on Design

In order to make valid comparisons between candidate LEO communications systems, it is also necessary to consider the constraints that the user segment places on the design of the satellite. In its simplest terms, this means assuming a common data rate requirement for each system, and ensuring that the satellites deliver an equivalent EIRP at the surface of the Earth, so that the link budget equations can legitimately be compared.

It is for this reason that direct comparisons between systems such as Iridium, Globalstar and Orbcomm are complex, since they were designed with rather differing EIRP and data rate assumptions. (Iridium's power and data rate requirements were higher than either of the other two systems, and debates about their relative merits tend to end up in rather subjective areas, such as the relative voice link quality at 2.4 and 4.8 kbps.)

However, assuming that the constellations **are** being required to provide equivalent levels of service, it is the capabilities and utilization of the user terminals that will ultimately drive the system design. For ease of use, hand-held mobile terminals cannot generally be expected to track the satellites across the sky—satellite engineers tend to assume that users of their systems are "uncooperative" in this regard! This dictates that the terminals are equipped with relatively low gain broad beam antennas, and this usually drives the system towards comparatively low frequencies and more limited data rates than can be achieved through fixed-dish GEO-based systems (despite the physical proximity of the LEO satellites).

It is also reasonable to assume that most users will not be operating in an "open sky" environment. The satellites will thus be expected to make communications links to users in cluttered urban environments, where obscuration by building and trees is likely, and multipath effects are more of an issue. Communication system designs tend to work to assumed elevation angle limits, and these elevation angle limits are frequency dependent. Relatively low frequencies such as UHF can be made to work down to elevation angles of about 5–10 deg elevation, whereas higher frequencies may well require elevation angles as high as 20–25 deg to work successfully. The difference that this makes to the effective size of the coverage footprint of the satellite is significant, and hence frequency choice is one of the most important system design trades that must be performed.

Constraining the elevation angles for a system in LEO obviously shortens the effective communication periods with a given point on the ground. The result is that, as well as requiring more satellites in the constellation to provide continuous coverage, the chances that the system will need to "hand-over" a user from one satellite to another during a communication session is also increased, imposing a greater computational load on the system.

Another obvious constraint on the system design is the RF power that can be emitted by the handset. There is a natural reluctance to avoid "frying" the brains of handset users, and although most of us can think of several people to whom we would happily give such a handset, the health and safety authorities in most countries tend to take a dim view of microwaving the user's neurons. By comparison with modern mobile phones, the original Iridium handsets look uncomfortably large and heavy, and it should be remembered that any communications system will need to conform to user expectations, in terms of size and weight, in order to be a commercial success.

Users are also "uncooperative" in the sense that they tend to cluster into densely populated urban areas. The communications load on the satellites is consequently highly variable around the orbit, and it is clearly necessary to make reliable estimates of traffic loads on the system at peak times before establishing the system capacity, and before sizing crucial parameters such as the orbit average power that the platform will need to supply to the payload. Clearly too, the maximum power consumption will coincide with maximum thermal dissipation requirements of the mission. The thermal control subsystem will thus need to accommodate both the shorter term variations in satellite power usage that occur from orbit to orbit, and also the longer term variations in illumination from the Sun that occur as the orbit planes regress with respect to the Earth.

It will be readily appreciated that, at any given time, the satellites in one plane of a multiple-plane LEO constellation will be experiencing a different pattern of lighting and eclipse conditions than the satellites in another. In a sophisticated system equipped with inter-satellite links, such as Iridium, the possibility exists to route the communications traffic around the network in such a way as to balance the loading on the satellites. More generally, in regions where several coverage footprints overlap, (e.g., over the poles in the case of the

Iridium system), it is possible to route the traffic through the satellite best-placed to handle the traffic.

More specialized users may also impose rather exotic requirements on the system designer. Military special forces and covert agents tend to prefer systems that offer low probability of interception and exploitation. This leads to techniques such as burst transmission, spread-spectrum and frequency hopping, and encryption being employed, and these will all impose constraints on the data rates that can be achieved by the system.

It is not only the user segment that will impose requirements on the satellite design. As discussed earlier, the anchor stations which form the fixed ground segment will need to be able to support the data rates generated by the users in a given region. This may be achieved by a steerable dish antenna, but such an antenna system will clearly only support one satellite at a time, and it is perfectly possible with large constellations, where footprints overlap, to have more than one vehicle in view. This can be solved by appropriate scheduling, which will limit the contact time, (and hence the effective region), that can be serviced by the ground station, or by installing multiple antenna heads. (Satellite to fixed ground station links are typically at higher frequencies than the satellite to user links in order to accommodate the required data rates, with the result that using wide-beam antennas to communicate with more than one satellite simultaneously is not a realistic solution.)

23.1.2 Manufacturing and Testing Processes

Manufacturing and testing of communications satellites clearly has to accommodate real-world constraints, such as time and cost. Particularly in a competitive commercial environment, there is a significant driver to complete satellite construction and testing quickly. A similar pressure potentially exists to maintain the pace of construction especially if you have missions that are intended to be launched on a regular schedule, as was the case with the Russian systems described earlier. In both cases, there is a strong incentive to maintain a common hardware design and establish a "production-line" approach to the satellite construction. In general, this reduces costs through economies of scale, and spreads the non-recurring design costs over a larger number of satellite platforms (See Sec. 23.5).

As the largest constellation constructed in recent times, the Iridium constellation provides an interesting example of the procedures that can be used. Each of the Iridium satellites were constructed on a gimbaled, "island" platform, to which each of the subsystems were delivered for integration. The pace of integration was greatly facilitated by the gimbaled support structure, since a major component of the time-budget for assembly integration and test activities is often the handling time that is necessary to move the satellite into an attitude where a component can safely be added.

For unique, single-satellite production programs, there is often little heritage data on either the design or the expected outputs of the test program. By contrast, the test program for a large constellation can exploit the experience gained with satellites that have already been completed. The test data acquired from early satellites from the production line will clearly need to be compared carefully with the design specifications established by the system engineers to ensure compliance, whereas later satellites can simply be shown to be compliant if they exhibit similar behavior to their predecessors under the same test conditions.

Some pre-launch testing is intended to confirm "workmanship", and these basic functional tests will be required for all satellite systems in the foreseeable future, due to the costs associated with both the satellite hardware and the launch. In the future, mass production of identical satellites for large constellations may permit a "batch-testing" approach, where only some of the satellites are tested before launch. It is also possible that the exigencies of a conflict situation would mean that "responsive space" satellite hardware would be assembled and launched without some of the usual time-consuming tests.

There are, however, some tests, such as mass-properties measurements, where the aim of the test is to establish physical parameters which should not vary significantly from satellite to satellite in a constellation. Measurements of the satellite's moments of inertia and center of mass are made to allow the calibration of momentum wheels, thrusters, and other elements of the Attitude Control System, and any slight variation from one satellite to another (due to slight variations in the wiring harness, for example) should lie well within the performance envelope of the devices used to control the satellite's pointing. It is reasonable to assume, therefore, that for constellation satellite designs, mass-properties testing is only likely to be required on the first vehicle in the series.

Another factor that influences the system design is the availability, of on-orbit spare satellites. As has been mentioned previously, in the case of Iridium, the system design involved a single spare satellite for each of the orbit planes. This offers the opportunity to replace a failed satellite relatively quickly, and without the requirement for a separate launch. It should be noted that the length of time required to achieve this repositioning is dependent on the maneuver capacity of the satellite, and drift times of a couple of weeks would not be unusual, given the likely fuel constraints on the vehicle. Some gaps in coverage are thus likely to persist during this period while the in-plane relocation takes place. In the future, it has been suggested that the advent of responsive launch capabilities would provide the opportunity to insert replacement satellites into a constellation within this sort of time frame. In such a scenario, it might be seen as preferable to keep the spare satellites on the ground, and launch them directly into the slot where they are required. One of the important factors influencing the choice of strategy is the financial cost to the service provider of the downtime in terms of lost revenue and possible contract penalty clauses.

Iridium used an imaginative approach to constellation maintenance when they needed to replenish more than one plane via a single launch. The approach which they adopted was to launch a batch of new satellites into a parking orbit in the same orbital plane as one of those requiring new satellites, but at a lower altitude. Some of the recently launched satellites were then immediately boosted into their operational orbit locations. Due to the higher orbit regression rate resulting from their lower altitude, the remaining satellites in the parking orbit drifted in right ascension relative to the operational constellation. When they were beneath the required plane, they were then boosted to the correct operational altitude.

A word of caution is also appropriate here. The commercial pressure to be "first-to-market" with a satellite-based mobile communication led to a very rapid pace of procurement with all the LEO communications constellations, with the result that much of the satellite production was complete before any significant degree of in-orbit experience had been gained with the hardware. Hence, in contrast to more conventional programs (where lessons learned with earlier satellites in a series can be used to refine the design of the later missions) there was a significant risk of introducing systematic design faults into all the satellites in the series.

23.1.3 Future LEO Communications Constellations

Future LEO communications constellations are likely to follow Iridium's lead and incorporate inter-satellite links. These may be LEO-LEO links, but there are also options to use LEO-GEO links for some of the connections, especially for those regions where the LEO satellites are not in view of a suitable ground station. Such systems could potentially make use of so-called "dark-beams" on the GEO satellites, i.e., those beams with fewer terrestrial users for which the charges are generally lower.

To avoid creating a future debris risk, future LEO communications will follow Iridium's lead and make provision for disposal maneuvers causing the satellite hardware to re-enter the atmosphere within 25 years of the end of the mission.

One innovation which would require regulatory changes would be the merger of terrestrial and space-based mobile systems, allowing users to operate via ground-based infrastructure when suitable hardware is within range, and switching to satellite-based links when in more remote regions. This type of system could also prove beneficial in time of crisis, for example, if any or all of the ground structure became unavailable or overloaded with traffic.

23.2 LEO Monolithic vs Distributed Architectures

Stuart Eves, *Surrey Satellite Technology*

23.2.1 Pros and Cons of Monolithic vs. Distributed Architectures

As the capabilities of small satellites increase, the option to use a constellation of several inexpensive spacecraft as an alternative to a single, large expensive one becomes increasingly attractive.

However, the decision to launch a constellation of satellites rather than one large vehicle impacts all aspects of the system design process, and traditional design processes must change if satellite constellations are to achieve their full potential.

This section will show how areas such as sensor design, platform design, orbit choice, on-orbit operations, communications, redundancy, testing, and launch are all impacted when the baseline objective is to launch multiple satellites.

From a design perspective, it is clearly most cost effective to create a single satellite design, and then vary the concept of operations of the individual spacecraft in the different orbit planes of the constellation. The alternative, (designing bespoke vehicles for each orbital plane) potentially constrains the deployment and replenishment operations, and necessarily involves significantly more expense. But proponents of large satellites would argue that a bespoke design makes the most efficient usage of a satellite's capacity, and that a modified concept of operations, constrained by the satellite's orbit, is also an inefficient concept of operations.

It is the task of the system designer to make an appropriate choice between these two competing views, taking account of changing technical capabilities.

Coverage Requirements

The coverage required from a system is an obvious place to start. If the service is required over a limited area of the globe, and can be satisfied by relatively infrequent passes, there is evidently little incentive to move to a constellation solution.

The applications of LEO satellites are becoming more global in terms of their coverage requirements. As a result of the increasingly globalized economy, systems are used to collect or transfer data over many locations of the globe, rather than simply satisfying an individual governmental focus. This trend is expected to increase as more international and commercial entities enter the market. System design will also need to increase the area coverage rate (or duty cycle) of the satellite system. In the surveillance domain, applications such as monitoring climate change, deforestation, pollution, agricultural productivity, and water resources, all necessitate the collection of large data sets over wide areas. And increasingly, these are applications which benefit from very frequent revisits. Repeat coverage with temporal frequencies of days, rather than weeks or even months, permits a range of change detection products that can be used, for instance, to estimate crop yields, (and hence predict commodity prices), or in cases of extreme climactic conditions (such as droughts), anticipate potential famines and plan disaster prevention operations.

Not all disasters can be predicted in advance, of course, and a high revisit frequency is also clearly a major advantage when a region is affected by a major

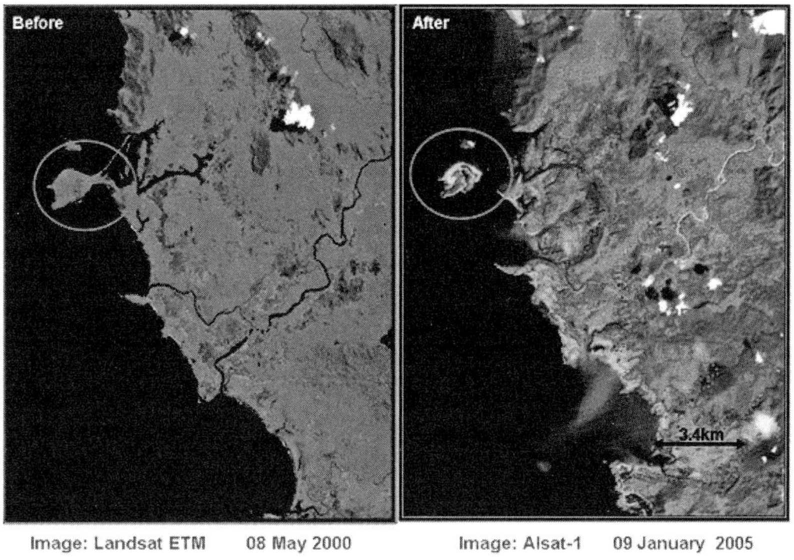

Fig. 23-1. DMC Image of the Indian Ocean Tsunami Shown in Comparison to a Landsat Image of the Same Scene Taken Before the Disaster.

catastrophe such as an earthquake or major tsunami. (An example of the utility of a constellation in this circumstance is illustrated in Fig. 23-1.) The change detection product illustrated was created using timely data over the region affected by the Indian Ocean tsunami from the Disaster Monitoring Constellation (DMC). This imagery was compared with earlier data from the Landsat satellites in order to highlight the areas of greatest change, and hence the regions most in need of disaster relief operations.

Covering such large regions with an individual, monolithic satellite in LEO is potentially problematic and distributed constellations appear increasingly attractive, especially if the temporal requirements call for daily global surveillance coverage from a passive imaging sensor (i.e., one which can only operate on passes when the target region is illuminated).

Clearly, one of the first issues that has to be addressed is how many satellites will be required to meet this coverage requirement. Some estimation techniques are potentially helpful at this point.

The need for adequate spatial or radiometric resolution means that surveillance satellites, especially imaging missions, are rarely deployed above 750 km. At such altitudes (and assuming a fairly "generous" roll capability of around 45 deg) each satellite in a constellation can be "responsible" for a swath of about 600 km on the surface of the Earth.

If it is assumed that the satellites are in near-polar Sun-synchronous orbits (a convenient supposition for many current surveillance systems), then the North-South passes over the equator are close enough to 90 deg for the following approximation to be useful.

Dividing the Earth's circumference (40,074 km), by the assumed swath width (600 km) gives a value of about 67. This is the number of sunlit passes per day required to cover the equatorial region. A satellite in LEO will normally complete between 14 and 15 orbits per day (at an altitude of 750 km, the value is approximately 14.5), and dividing 67 by 14.5 gives a figure of 4.6. Since satellites come in integer amounts, the minimum number of satellites required to provide this coverage pattern is 5. (See Fig. 23-2)

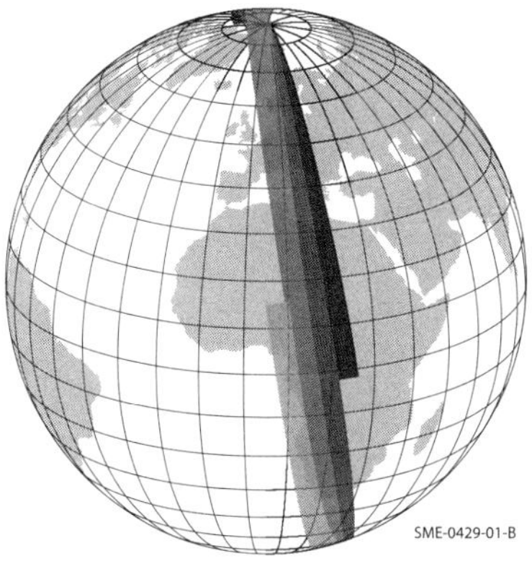

Fig. 23-2. A Five-Satellite, Coplanar, Near-Polar Orbit Coverage Pattern Illustrating How Successive Passes Provide Adjacent Coverage Swaths on the Earth's Surface.

Obviously, though, these swaths must be regularly spaced in order to avoid gaps in the coverage pattern. This can be achieved most simply by spacing the satellites evenly around a single orbital plane, which has the advantage that the coverage is provided at a constant local time of day. In this case, clearly, the Earth-central angle is 360/5 or 72 deg apart, which means that the satellites are not in line-of-sight contact with one-another.

Not only is a shared launch usually the simplest means of achieving the required coverage, it is also potentially the cheapest. All 5 satellites can be launched on a single vehicle, reducing the cost of the constellation, provided they all have propulsion capability and require a common inclination value. We will explore the implications in Sec. 23.2.2.

23.2.2 Satellite and Sensor Design for Distributed Architecture Missions

Sensor

Swath requirements and sensor design are clearly related to the number of satellites in the constellation. For example, in the case of the Disaster Monitoring Constellation (DMC), and the RapidEye commercial remote sensing constellation, the chosen configuration was 5 satellites in a common Sun-synchronous orbit plane, with the satellites at 72 deg separation. The goal in both cases, was to achieve daily global access opportunities delivered in different ways because of the differing area coverage and resolution requirements. In the case of DMC, the need was to monitor large geographic areas, so the satellite platforms were designed to stare at nadir, and their sensors were equipped with a 600 km swath, 32 m resolution, imaging capability. By contrast, RapidEye required higher spatial resolutions of approximately 6 m, so the instantaneous swath of the sensors could only be 80 km. In order to provide the opportunity for global daily revisit with this system, the satellites have a roll capability of up to 45 deg to allow the 80 km swath to be directed anywhere within ±300 km from nadir.

Further beneifts of constellation operations can be derived if satellites are capable of cueing one another. In order to provide the area coverage rates needed to establish effective cueing, a high resolution surveillance sensor is required. Hence many SAR satellites, (and some optical satellites) usually trade off special resolution and area coverage. For example, the SSTL-300 design is equipped with both wide area multispectral sensors capable of delivering swaths of over 200 km at about 15 m resolution, and a high-acuity sensor with a baseline resolution of 1.4 m and a swath of 12 km. In practice, this cueing is most frequently achieved by comparing two images collected on different dates, identifying the regions of change, and then using this information to cue high resolution sensors to identify exactly what these changes are. Clearly, the high revisit frequencies available from constellations allow changes to be identified considerably more quickly, including variations that occur from day to day.

Platform Design

Another area where constellation satellite design is different from that of monolithic satellites is the need to select an appropriate structural configuration for multiple launch scenarios.

In the case of monolithic, large satellites, some designs have made efficient volumetric use of the available space within the launch vehicle shroud. (The Hughes series of cylindrical, spin-stabilized GEO comms satellites provide one example of this, and the Russian Strela LEO missions mentioned in the previous section, are another.)

Since most launch vehicles were designed to carry larger satellites, modern small satellite designs are seldom constrained by mass limits, and rarely fill the available volume on their own.

Multiple launches of small satellites are becoming more common. The "box-body" designs that have routinely been employed, (largely for simplicity), in recent years have not been volumetrically efficient. The challenge for distributed systems is to find a design that both meets the needs of the mission and at the same time fits well inside the launch vehicle shroud, as seen in Fig. 23-3.

Fig. 23-3. An Illustration of a Typical Small Satellite Launch Configuration, Illustrating the Difficulties Involved in Trying to Make Volumetrically Efficient use of the Fairing.

One such design is the SSTL-300 imaging mission, which has a heptagonal cross-sectional design. (As well as providing the opportunity to use a rare word like heptagonal) The rationale behind this design is to provide greater opportunities to launch these missions as part of a constellation. The satellite would be mounted on its zenith-pointing face for launch, with its camera pointing up rather than down. It can be seen from the illustration in Fig. 23-4, that 3 such satellites make a reasonable approximation to a circle, and hence make good use of the space available. The mounted solar cells comprise 4 of the body facets, with others being used as radiator surfaces, or surfaces on which to mount the star cameras (since they point in the anti-Sun direction).

It will be noted that, unlike the earlier designs, (like TopSat) where the optical axis of the missions were oriented "horizontally" at launch, (although, of course, the launch vehicle pitches during flight), the SSTL-300 has its optical axis oriented vertically at launch. The aim of this design change is to minimize the potential loading on the camera optics, since it is clearly possible to exert fairly extreme loads on the very sensitive camera designs during launch. This is especially true of the small satellites that are typically used to build up distributed constellations, since they have comparatively little plat-

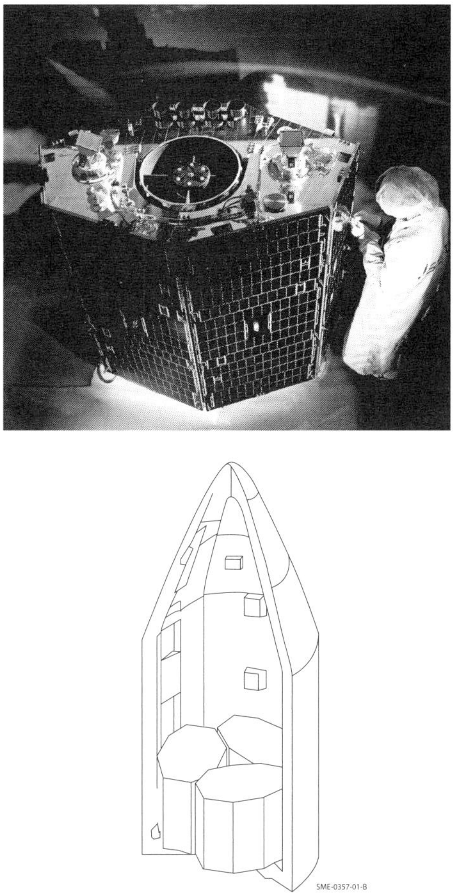

Fig. 23-4. Illustration of the SSTL 300 (Top) and the Envisaged Launch Configuration for 3 Satellites (Bottom).

form structural mass between the launch vehicle and the camera which can absorb some of the vibrational and acoustic loads that are imposed during lift off.

One of the obvious requirements that is likely to be placed on the designer of a distributed system is the ability of the satellites to be launched on more than one launch vehicle. Apart from the obvious commercial advantages of being able to negotiate on price with more than one launch supplier, the likelihood is that a distributed system of satellites is very likely to require multiple launch vehicles in order to reach orbit in an acceptable timeframe, and the turn-around time between launches for a single class of launch vehicle may not be sufficient. This was especially true for the Iridium constellation, where more than 70 satellites were launched on a range of different vehicles.

The technical implication of this approach is the need for a satellite design which avoids structural resonances over the range of frequencies that correspond to the different vibrational modes potentially imposed by the different launch vehicle options. This is obviously something of a challenge, but the situation is helped by the fact that small satellites are comparatively robust, with proportionately fewer resonant modes than their larger cousins.

In those cases where launch vibration concerns remain, (as with the case of TopSat, which had a sophisticated, and potentially vulnerable three-mirror off-axis optical design), the system designer may elect to resort to using a "soft ride" system. Mechanical engineers often like to preserve the mystique of soft-ride systems, describing them as "magic" rubber washers. In practice the "magic" is generally concerned with selecting an appropriate rubber material that will dampen out the vibrations of the launch vehicle, rather than one which will turn the launch platform into a trampoline and make the situation far worse!

Another design consideration for multiple-plane constellations is the fact that, over the system lifetime, a satellite's given plane will have:

A) At any given point in time, a different pattern of activity compared to satellites in other planes of the constellation

B) Over a period of time, differing patterns of activity from month to month

Both these sources of variation arise from the fact that, the satellites in different planes will be oriented differently with respect to the Sun, and that these planes will regress relative to the solar vector. This will affect the times when an optical surveillance system can operate. An active surveillance system, such as a radar or a communications system, will also have differing capacities over time depending on the time-variant illumination conditions of the orbit plane, which will dictate the power generation capacity, and hence the duty cycle of the system. (It should be noted that most active systems will also have a duty cycle limit imposed by the need to cool the payload components. Here too, the ability to radiate waste heat will ultimately be constrained by the angle that the orbit plane makes to the Sun.)

Another area where distributed systems differ from monolithic missions is in terms of their fuel budget allocations. Like all satellites, members of a constellation will need to perform regular station-keeping maneuvers to maintain altitude, but there are additional constraints arising from the need to keep the members of a constellation at the desired relative separation.

In general, satellites in different locations within a constellation will experience differing perturbations, leading to the need to establish a "key" satellite with respect to which the other satellites will maintain station. Obviously, though, this "key" satellite will have to perform fewer maneuvers than the remaining members of the constellation, with the result that their propellant usage will be different over time. For a short-lived mission, this may not matter unduly, but for a longer-lived constellation, a CONOPS which varies the "key" satellite from time to time, in order to distribute the station-keeping requirements more evenly, is a wise policy.

If satellites in a constellation are deployed on a single launch vehicle, then the nominal situation is that they will be deployed around the nominal orbit height, with some satellites moving "prograde" around the orbit plane, and some moving "retrograde" relative to the key satellite, (which is assumed here to be close to the nominal design altitude of the constellation). Clearly those satellites with the greatest drift rates following deployment will have to perform the largest maneuvers in order to establish a common orbit period with the key satellite. Immediately, therefore, the key satellite will be "fuel rich" relative to the satellites that are endeavoring to keep station with it, and hence there is often a case for switching "key" satellite fairly early in the mission.

Indeed, a flexible strategy at this stage is quite likely to be a pre-requisite if the propellant management is to be optimized. Launch vehicles do not always deliver their cargo to exactly the correct altitude and eccentricity. In that case, the initial key satellite may need to be altered in order to minimize the propellant expenditure required to configure the satellites as intended.

A flexible strategy also potentially allows the oldest and most fuel depleted satellites to be "husbanded" toward the end of their missions. A satellite that is almost out of fuel, (save for the de-orbit allocation which is now increasingly viewed as essential), can remain as a useful member of the constellation if the other satellites treat it as the "key" and maneuver with respect to their aged cousin!

Another constellation-related propellant requirement is the potential need to reconfigure the constellation to optimize performance in different potential modes of operation. Hence, satellites in a common orbital plane may be operated relatively close together in a peacetime scenario to collect collocated contemporaneous data of specific locations. In the SAR domain, this could allow the generation of 3-D terrain information products through interferometry, and in the optical domain, could involve the collection of instantaneous stereo pairs, or contemporaneous sampling of the bi-directional reflectance distribution function (BRDF) using hyperspectral sensors. In order to operate in these modes, the satellites clearly need to be relatively close together.

The same co-planar assets could be used at wider separations, (Earth-central angles up to about 40 deg), to cover the same region with a small time interval between the collections. With appropriate rapid processing and cueing, this would allow the first satellite, (possibly operating in a wide-area mode), to cue the second, (possibly operating in a more focused high-resolution mode. Alternatively, the satellites could simply generate two very similar products and then apply change-detection processing to the results to identify the moving targets or other changes in the scene.

Finally, the satellites could be used at maximum separations around the orbit plane, (a mode perhaps most likely in a crisis situation), since this mode of operation would maximize the area coverage rate of the constellation and minimize the "maximum-wait-time" between passes for a user at a given location. Usually, unless the number of satellites in the constellation is large, this mode of operation would result in the satellites being separated by more than 40 deg, which would place them "over the horizon" with respect to the other satellites in the system.

All these modes are viable only if the satellites have been previously designed with mode-changing maneuvers in mind. The total number of such reconfigurations is unlikely to be high, and the propellant expenditure does not have to be excessive if the drift rates, (and hence the propellant usage), are low and the maneuvers are in-plane, but they will not be possible at all if there is insufficient propellant capacity designed into the satellite.

23.2.3 Communications and Inter-Satellite Links (ISL)

Much has been written about constellation design, but an equally important element of a distributed system design is the ground segment. In no small part, this is because the area coverage rates and data volumes associated with multiple satellites require adequate provision in terms of data downlink opportunities.

As noted earlier, a constellation of satellites can be operated in different orbits and in a range of different collection modes. This inevitably means that the satellites will require tasking at different times; will collect data at different rates; and will thus have different data downlink requirements. Inter-satellite links may serve to alleviate some of these issues, while others may be best addressed by the judicious siting of both fixed and mobile elements of the ground segment architecture.

Commanding

The use of a high-altitude asset, (typically in GEO), to relay commands to a LEO satellite in near real time is clearly a far more cost-effective proposition if that LEO satellite is just one of a number of assets that can be serviced by the GEO platform. Previously, GEO data relay has been largely reserved for very high-end platforms, but as the UAV community has demonstrated, the use of high-altitude relay satellites to perform both commanding offers significant benefits. As an example, the Inmarsat satellites are capable of supporting 500 kbps data rates through satellite-borne terminals similar to their terrestrial BGAN system.

It can be demonstrated that a single satellite in GEO can see a LEO surveillance asset at some point on each of its orbits, with the result that for most systems, the longest gap between commanding and having a suitable imaging opportunity, (a sunlit opportunity for optical sensors), is on the order of 45 minutes.

In a comparatively dense constellation, the satellites may be separated by in-plane Earth-central angles of less than 40 deg, and this would provide the opportunity to establish continuously available LEO-LEO command links around the orbit plane. More realistically, the constellation may consist of a more limited number of satellites in several different orbit planes. One approach to improved commanding timeliness in a more sparse constellation is to equip the satellites with a LEO-LEO ISL system which establishes links between the satellites when they come within view of each other close to the poles. This is the approach adopted by the SAR-Lupe constellation of 5 satellites, which operate in three different, near-polar, orbital planes. Clearly some phasing of the satellites is required to ensure that they pass close to the pole at suitable times, and hence periodically come within view of other members of the constellation. This phasing must be conducted without compromising the coverage pattern, and hence will involve changes to both the orbit right ascension and true anomaly.

Data Return

In the future, the timeliness offered by a surveillance constellation will need to be matched by an architecture for the data-return communications that support it. There is little point in offering hourly revisits over the target region if the opportunities to download the data only occur once or twice per day. The most attractive option, if suitable inter-satellite links exist, is to relay the data in near-real-time from the surveillance satellite in LEO. This could be achieved via an indigenous ISL system hosted on the surveillance constellation but the inter-satellite separations in-plane would be constrained if there was a need to maintain continuous long-range ISL links for moving data around the globe, (and the surveillance constellation size would probably have to rival that of the Iridium network to be feasible).

The Iridium network itself represents a possible alternative communications medium, but the data rates that this network support are suitable for voice communications rather than imagery data. Hence, even if equipped with the space-borne equivalent of an Iridium handset, a member of a LEO surveillance constellation would struggle to deliver information in a timely fashion. This conclusion may change with future generations of LEO communications networks, which are likely to support higher data rates. The advent of greater on-board processing capabilities on future surveillance satellites may also help by reducing the size of the image files which need to be transmitted.

In the short-term, therefore, the most appropriate ISL adjunct to a surveillance constellation would appear to be a data relay asset in GEO, focused primarily on the delivery of timely, thin-route commanding information. In part, this is because a satellite in GEO can focus its coverage on the specific region of operational interest, and hence can transfer commands to satellites about to access the region of interest. In the longer term, as ISL capacity improves, it will also be possible to retrieve data from those assets which have just accessed the crisis area in a far more timely fashion.

If an ISL capability is not available, a suitable network of ground stations at varying longitudes and latitudes is the next-best alternative. Ideally these ground stations should be linked either via the internet or via satellite communications to allow them to route commands and return data in the minimum possible time. This sort of architecture has been demonstrated to work successfully with the DMC constellation.

For a military surveillance constellation, there could be a number of different user communities. In practice, the most critical one is the in-theater, war-fighting component, but the strategic intelligence community, the homeland defence community, allies and the system training requirements are all likely to impose additional collection requirements on the system. It should be possible, therefore, to estimate the regions of the globe where the surveillance system will be most active, and then to configure the ground-station network to provide downlink opportunities as soon as possible. Clearly, for the warfighting scenarios, it is somewhat more difficult to plan in advance where the capacity will be most needed. It is suggested that this is the most appropriate role for mobile ground stations, which can be sited in response to a particular crisis, and can therefore ensure that any given satellite in the constellation does not reach its memory capacity and then start to miss imaging opportunities.

23.2.4 Reliability, Redundancy, and Survivability

One of the most subtle aspects of designing at the constellation level concerns the redundancy philosophy. Traditional satellites are typically dual-string redundant in order to guarantee a reasonable probability of meeting the individual satellite's design lifetime. This calculation clearly changes if the satellite assets in question are intended only as a short-term adjunct to a military surveillance capability that is targeted on a particular, short-term conflict or crisis situation, and here the calculations probably favor a single-string approach.

But how is the debate resolved when there could be a mix of in orbit assets and spares on the ground using the same basic design? The answer is to look not at the redundancy of a single satellite, but at the probabilities associated with the constellation as a whole. When multiple satellites are involved, the overall performance degradation resulting from an individual failure is modest, and in a scenario where surge launches are envisaged as a routine part of the system, this would suggest that a far more relaxed approach can be taken to design reliability and the testing procedures.

The debate is complicated by the fact that a military surveillance constellation is likely to be targeted during time of crisis. The failure statistics are less likely to be independent if the cause of failure is hostile enemy action, but again there would appear to be grounds for thinking about satellites as conventional assets where attrition is expected, rather than as grand-strategic assets where failure is to be avoided at all costs. Some mitigation of this *conditional probability problem* may be achieved if the satellites in the constellation are fitted with threat warning systems—essentially the ability to *cry for help* or shout a warning in the event that they come under attack. The advantage of such an approach is that the other members of the constellation can then take precautionary measures, (e.g. rapid maneuvers) intended to reduce their vulnerability and so improve their availability statistics.

Again, the utility of ISL's becomes apparent, but this time for monitoring the platform telemetry and relaying any messages from the threat warning sensors, rather than for interacting with the sensor payload.

Somewhat ironically, one advantage of traditional, large, stove-piped programs is that they typically have bespoke weaknesses and vulnerabilities which do not necessarily read across into other large, stove-piped programs. A potential aggressor is thus presented with the challenge of finding a weakness in several different, separately designed systems. This fact is often overlooked by enthusiasts for "network enabled" capabilities, who tend to overlook the fact that by creating a large number of assets all working to the same standard, they have potentially also created an opportunity for an aggressor to target a significant proportion of their capabilities. (This was arguably one of the principal reasons for the Allies' success in WWII, where the German Enigma machines were cracked, allowing all their most secret communications to be exploited.)

It is strongly recommended, therefore, that one element of constellation spacecraft that **should** be redundant is the command and control subsystem, incorporating a second, "crisis mode" for communicating with the satellites that is only engaged in the event that the primary mechanism is compromised.

Another rather ironic advantage of large monolithic programs arises from their comparatively pedestrian production cycles. If, despite the pre-launch testing, a particular system has a systematic weakness, a traditional monolithic production process is likely to reveal that weakness following the launch of the first satellite in the series, allowing those on the ground to be modified accordingly. By contrast, a rapidly launched distributed system could potentially launch several satellites in a relatively short period of time, with the result that a significant proportion of the satellites in the constellation could be affected by the same design error.

Counter-arguments in favor of distributed systems are the fact that the non-recurring design costs of the system can be spread across multiple missions, and the experience that the builders of the system gain through building multiple copies of the same design. Traditional monolithic systems may take more than a decade to reach fruition, with the result that an engineer in the traditional space industry might only work on two or three satellite designs in an entire career. By contrast, relatively short-lived, and quick-to-build, satellites provide the engineers who work on them valuable experience which helps to avoids errors in both design and assembly. This is, in effect, an example of the traditional commercial advantage of economies of scale being applied in western space industry for the first time. The commercial LEO comms systems mentioned in the previous chapter were some of the first to benefit from these advantages, and the RapidEye constellation of LEO surveillance satellites represents a more recent example.

By comparison, the Russian space industry has been aware of the advantages of mass production for many years. Although comparatively unsophisticated, the Strela communications satellites referred to in the previous chapter are the most populous distributed constellation in the history of space. Over 350 satellites based on this design were launched over a period of more than 20 years before finally being replaced by a more capable system.

For those used to a more rapid pace of technological change, it will be appreciated that maintaining access to the parts required to build a near-identical satellite some 20 years later is an achievement in itself. The driver for doing so is the need to preserve continuity of service, and this is dictated in part by the design and deployment of the ground terminals—which is the subject of the following section. In many cases, however, the desire for data continuity and the re-use of existing technology is outweighed by the desire for data improvement. Here constellations of shorter-lifetime, rapidly replaceable satellites clearly have the edge over large monolithic systems. The later missions in the constellation can employ more up-to-date technologies and thereby deliver better performance. The DARPA F6 concepts envisages a subtly different concept of "distributed" operations, by spreading the functions of a larger monolithic satellite not across a constellation, but across a cluster of co-orbiting sub-satellites equipped with short-range inter-satellite links. In the F6 concept, it is envisaged that new technologies can be introduced to replace elements of the cluster without the requirement to change all of the hardware.

23.2.5 Ground Segment

Many of the advantages that are associated with a distributed space segment also apply to the terrestrial systems which interact with them.

While it is conventional to have a widely dispersed user community consisting of multiple terminals, (especially for satellite communications systems), the command and control segment of many space systems has been largely "monolithic" in character, consisting usually of one or two ground stations invariably in fixed locations.

While this model is generally sufficient for communications systems, (especially traditional ones operating through geostationary satellites which have very large, fixed, communications footprints, allowing continuous contact between the satellite and the ground), it is far less satisfactory for low Earth orbit systems.

In LEO, a satellite's communications footprint is typically only a few thousand km across, and the laws of orbital dynamics dictate that a satellite can only spend a small percentage of its time over a given point on the Earth's surface.

For real time communications services, (and especially safety-critical communications to manned spacecraft), intermittent communications with the ground is either undesirable or unacceptable, and so multiple ground station networks were established to support such systems. These networks involved stations at multiple longitudes, and at a variety of latitudes, in order to facilitate more frequent contact between the space and ground segments. Ideally the aim was to ensure that continuous contact could be maintained, but over unpopulated areas such as the southern oceans and Antarctica, this was not always perceived to be a cost effective solution, and some periods of outage were tolerated by the LEO communications networks.

The precise configuration of the ground station network will depend on the coverage that is required, and the orbital configuration that is selected to best meet that coverage need. But there are some specific advantages to a distributed ground station network that will potentially enhance the performance of all LEO systems that are not equipped with inter-satellite links. These advantages are:

1. More frequent access to the satellites in order to send commands to the on-orbit assets, improving the timeliness of the system
2. More frequent opportunities to download data from the mission, again increasing the end-to-end timeliness of the system
3. Improved speed of checkout of the system, using multiple ground stations. This advantage is of particular utility for the sorts of distributed space systems envisaged by the Operationally Responsive Space community
4. More frequent opportunities to monitor telemetry from the satellites, providing more responsiveness in the event of an anomaly on the satellites
5. Importantly, the increased opportunities to download data from the satellites means that on-board storage capacity can be re-used several times per day, greatly increasing the output from the system and its revenue generating capability
6. In a military context, faster response times for reporting from threat monitoring packages mounted on the satellites

Conclusions

Distributed satellite constellations offer multiple advantages to the system designer, and while they do incorporate certain vulnerabilities, (similar to those encountered in terrestrial computer networks), the advantages appear to significantly outweigh these disbenefits.

Just as today we would find it hard to imagine life without the world wide web, in the future it is anticipated we will be equally reliant on the "space wide web" of distributed satellite systems.

23.3 Spacecraft Manufacturing, Integration and Test

David E. Lee,
Northrop Grumman Aerospace Systems

Much of the focus of *Space Mission Engineering: The New SMAD* is the "what" of space systems—what these systems are able to sense and communicate back to mission operations and end users, quantifying what their reliability will be, and what these systems might cost. This section focuses on the "how"—how individual space qualified hardware components are assembled together, integrated in configured items and then tested as complete spacecraft before being delivered to launch integration (Chap. 27).

An overview of the process of how spacecraft are manufactured from components and then integrated into their final configuration is shown in Table 23-1. This process is fundamental to understanding how space systems are built, as well as the impact of the underlying type testing theory. The methodologies and processes described here apply to space hardware used for both monolithic and distributed/fractionated systems (Secs. 23.2 and 23.5).

In addition, the timeline required for the integration and testing of a spacecraft's flight hardware and flight software can drive the schedule and ultimate cost of space systems. The testing and qualification of flight software is addressed in Chap. 20, and its availability is a critical element of how soon a full up spacecraft can perform its integrated system testing and enter into vehicle-level environmental testing.

23.3.1 Qualification Testing of Space Hardware

Flight hardware for space systems is qualified for space through environmental and operational testing of hardware designed for space applications. The design of this hardware uses materials that will survive in the applicable environments and selecting controlled manufacturing processes to produce this hardware. This regime of qualification testing of space hardware applies to individual piece parts such as electronic components and graphite composite boom structures, to functional components such as reaction wheels and space thruster motors to the individual payloads and spacecraft bus that comprise a flight vehicle.

Qualification of space hardware is critical given, at best, a limited ability to service space hardware on orbit and the environmental stress imposed by launch and relevant space operating regimes and required operating life times of space systems. Unmanned spacecraft are exposed to vibroacoustic launch loads that would kill humans, radiation environments around Jupiter and Saturn many times greater than those in Earth orbit, temperature ranges from +100 C to –100 C transitioning in and out of Earth eclipse and must not only survive but operate reliably and effectively for a decade or two for some missions.

Mission designers and engineers involved in the development of space systems need to understand the interaction between the availability and production of space qualified hardware and feasibility of a given space program. The time and cost required to manufacture and test space flight hardware can and will strongly influence a space program's cost and schedule. These span times and costs are directly driven by the precision manufac-

Table 23-1. An Overview of Spacecraft Manufacturing, Integration, and Test. Delivery of a qualified spacecraft to the launch site involves effective coordination and planning by multiple staffing functions and relies on a global supply chain.

Step	Comments	References
1. Review of Governing Program Documents and Plans	Identify applicable system and lower level tests, verification activities, environmental effects, permissible materials affecting the space segment	Chaps. 6 & 7, Secs. 23.4, 26.5
2. Develop Spacecraft Designs to Implement Required System Functions; Work with Subcontractors and Global Supply Chain	Work within ascribed program budget and schedule to generate required documentation such as drawings, equipment specifications, software development plans, testing plans in coordination with suppliers of space hardware and relevant software; use/adapt space qualified components and units; meet interface requirements with ground and user segments and other supporting systems	Chaps. 14–22, 26–29
3. Manufacture, Assemble and Test Component-level Space Hardware; Develop and Test Unique Test and Support Equipment	Procure subcontracted components and elements; order and purchase space qualified materials and components; develop and perform necessary component qualification tests; procure, develop and validate necessary ground support equipment; produce and signoff flight components; assemble and (qualification/acceptance) test configured items; document and deliver configured items to Integration and Test	Sec. 23.3, Fig. 23-9, Table 23-7
4. Perform Spacecraft-level Integration and Testing	Assemble and interface subsystems and units with flight harnesses; evaluate interface compatibility across subsystems and elements; load core spacecraft executive software and test device drivers; stimulate system with test vectors; perform closed loop testing; execute comprehensive system tests and environmental tests; prepare and package spacecraft for shipment to launch site	Table 23-4, Fig. 23-8

ture of components for flight, specialized technologies required for testing these components and subassemblies and the often unique facilities needed for manufacture, integration and test of space systems.

Given the impact of qualifying hardware for spaceflight, the theory of type testing provides the basis from which space hardware is qualified for space. From the hard won lessons of how to reliably design and build aircraft and launch vehicles from subsystems comprised of multiple components performing individual functions for manned systems, analogous processes are used for manufacturing, integration and test of spacecraft flight hardware. What is unique to space hardware, in comparison to aircraft and launch vehicles, is the time span in which a spacecraft may be initially proposed versus when it actually is launched, a magnitude reduction in production volumes, no on-orbit serviceability, the stress of launch/space environments and required system operation on a 24/7/365 basis for multiple years.

In order to reduce the risks of on-orbit failures and improve flight hardware reliability, we use the theory of type testing. The theory of type testing is the fundamental principle that drives the production of space hardware.

As shown in Table 23-2, type test theory depends on preparing and controlling complete and exact engineering data (drawings, specifications, and procedures). If the engineering data controls the hardware construction completely, all items built to the same data are equivalent and the results of any single-item test are valid for all items that are built using the same data. In particular, if a representative article *(type test article)* passes a sequence of *qualification tests,* all other articles built to the same engineering data should also pass. In other words, the design is *qualified.* Thus, production of space hardware will focus on making sure subsequent articles are identical by directly controlling engineering data (*configuration management*), using material qualified for space and employing the necessary controlled manufacturing processes (under *statistical process control*). Once the design is qualified, subsequent articles built from the same data and controlled manufacturing processes are then subjected to less severe *acceptance tests* that certify the workmanship of these articles.

Table 23-2. Theory of Type Testing. Type test theory is the basis for qualification testing.

Logic	Conditions & Conclusions
Assertions	• Engineering data is complete and exact • Engineering data completely controls manufacture • Manufacturing processes are under process control • Materials used in manufacturing are space qualified and exhibit minimal lot variability • All items manufactured to the same engineering data and using the same materials and with the controlled manufacturing processes are identical
Therefore	Results of a qualification test for one article are valid for all subsequent articles

With the expense, schedule impact and potential risk exposure of qualifying hardware for space, the decision to use new materials, mission-unique components or modified hardware is generally not taken lightly for a space program. Whether because of obsolescence or unavailability of specific components, changes to mission requirements or size/mass/power constraints, a program will need to decide what must be modified or changed with respect to a previously qualified design and actively manage the qualification process for the new article or re-qual (delta qual) of modified designs.

Table 23-3. Space Hardware Qualification Approaches. Depending on the mission type, heritage of a spacecraft's hardware, program cost and schedule constraints, different methods are used to demonstrate that the hardware is qualified for space

Qualification Method	Method Unique Characteristics
Dedicated Qualification Hardware	A specific set of qualification components is constructed and **qualification tests** are performed at the relevant **component qualification levels**. This set of components or a second set of hardware qualification components is assembled into the qualification spacecraft and tested as a spacecraft at **spacecraft qualification levels**. Usually dedicated qual H/W is not approved for flight given cost, risk and schedule constraints. For programs building multiple identical spacecraft, a dedicated qual unit may be cost effective.
Qualify the First Set of Flight Hardware	The first set of flight components is tested at **component protoqualification levels** or **protoflight levels**, then assembled into a S/C which is tested at **spacecraft protoqualification levels/protoflight levels**. This spacecraft is then launched. This is the **protoqual or protoflight concept**.
Qualify by Similarity	Demonstrate that components and the environments they will be subject to are identical to previously qualified hardware. Similarity basis uses type testing, configuration management, conformal material lot sampling, statistical process control. Programs will still expose components, assemblies and S/C to a testing regime but at **acceptance levels**.

An example of a delta qual might be to test an existing thruster motor to run for double its current qualified operation time because of in-stock availability of previously built thrusters versus the cost and schedule associated with developing and qualifying a new thruster (and the expense of building and acceptance testing the new thrusters). In the case of a new qual, using a new processor chip in a qualified Spacecraft Control Processor (SCP) unit because of the on-orbit computation load imposed on the SCP by a new payload or modified mission requirements may trigger not only a qual of the new chip but also a delta qual of the SCP. In either of these cases, a qualification test program must be developed, agreed to and properly funded.

Qualification testing of all flight hardware (and software) is needed to show that a specific spacecraft design is suitable for space [DoD, 2004]. These tests certify that the hardware and software work together properly and that the hardware can and will survive and operate in the prescribed environment. The qualification program for a space system will test each component not already qualified for space as well as the complete spacecraft. The program may also include additional functional and/or environmental testing of selected assemblies or subsystems. Table 23-3 lists three different approaches to qualify hardware for a spacecraft design.

Qualification testing of a component checks how it performs *(functional test)* and testing its ability to survive the anticipated environment (*environmental test*). Functional testing of each component under qualification is powered and exercised by its own special-purpose test set during test. Environmental testing exposes a component to the relevant environmental stresses it will see that can affect its operation. These include vibration loads analogous to in-fairing launch loads, multi-g shock loads similar to launch vehicle separation and thermal vacuum that simulates operation in space. If the component must survive nuclear weapons effects, it may also undergo a flash X-ray test, which simulates a prompt radiation dose. Sometimes, it may be tested to assess its electromagnetic compatibility (EMC) with the rest of the spacecraft to determine its susceptibility (e.g., its sensitivity) to any emitted electromagnetic frequencies from a payload or another part of the spacecraft. Figure 23-5 shows a typical component-level qualification sequence.

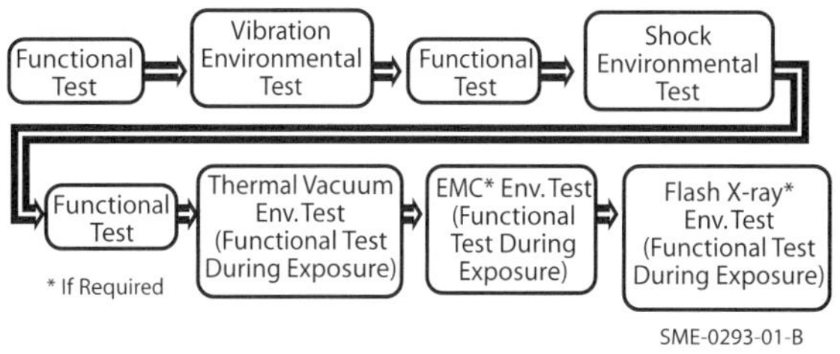

Fig. 23-5. Component-Level Qualification Testing Flow. A component is qualified through a series of functional and relevant environmental tests.

Going back to type test theory, qualification testing focuses on both design and process verification. These qualification tests are conducted to demonstrate that the component design, its manufacturing process and materials selected repeatably produce flight articles (generally identified as hardware configured items or HWCIs) that meet specification requirements. These HWCIs include items such as deployment hinges, solar array assemblies and solid state data recorders—an item, at the assembled level, that has sufficient capability to perform a specific set of functions and that can be tested as a single unit.

After testing has qualified a unit or HWCI for use and operation in space, additional tests, known as acceptance testing, will be performed on any similar/identical articles designated for flight. Acceptance testing is performed on a unit (e.g., software, per batch or lot of manufactured articles) prior to delivery to Spacecraft Integration and Test. Acceptance tests are conducted to demonstrate the acceptability of each HWCI to specification requirements and provide quality-control assurance against any workmanship or material lot deficiencies.

Acceptance testing is applied to stress screened items in order to cause incipient failures due to latent defects that may be in the parts, materials, and workmanship that comprise the unit. Figure 23web-4 (see Sec. 23.4.5.1 on the web) shows the difference between expected temperatures, acceptance test level temperatures and protoqual/qual temperatures for a unit/HWCI.

As an example, Table 23web-1 identifies qualification and acceptance test levels for specific tests applied either at the unit/HWCI level or at the spacecraft/space vehicle levels [DoD, 1999]. These test levels and exposure durations differ because units arrive for vehicle-level assembly having been exposed to and passed their specified component/unit level tests. Engineers should also note that application of these same unit test levels to the integrated space vehicle is not recommended and can involve the very real potential of damaging the fully integrated vehicle.

Figures 23-6 and 23-7 show the magnitude of the typical qualification and acceptance vibration levels and device shock to which components are tested to versus the actual expected load levels imposed by an Atlas-Centaur upper stage on an attached spacecraft. For example, at the spacecraft/launch vehicle interface ring, the expected power density spectrum is equivalent to 2.7 times the force of gravity (2.7 g). Applying an acceptance environment that is 6 dB above this expected load would be ($2.7 \times 4 = 4.3$ dBg + 6 dBg = 10.3 dBg) or an equivalent load of 10.75 g. This is considerably greater than any of the measured vibrational loads imposed on an attached spacecraft and would likely damage the integrated vehicle.

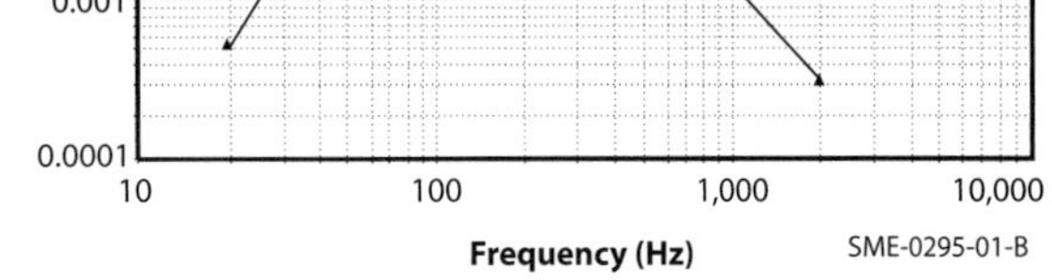

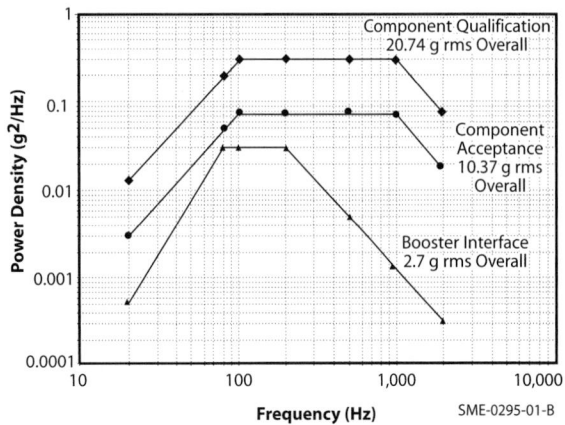

Fig. 23-6. Vibration Levels for Components on the Atlas-Centaur. Component qualification vibration levels are specified by a power density spectrum which is higher than the expected spectrum.

23.3.2 Supply Chain Considerations and Availability of Space Qualified Hardware

Sometimes there is an extended period from when a space mission is initially proposed to the launch and operation of a system in space. As an example, the Chandra X-Ray Observatory (Chandra or CXO), originally referred to as the Advanced X-Ray Astrophysics Facility, was initially proposed to NASA in 1976. Initial work began in 1978 and Chandra was ultimately launched on STS-93 in 1999. In comparison, LCROSS (Lunar Crater Observation and Sensing Satellite) was proposed and selected in early 2006 as a secondary payload to the Lunar Reconnaissance Orbiter, readied for launch in late 2008 and subsequently launched and impacted the Moon in 2009.

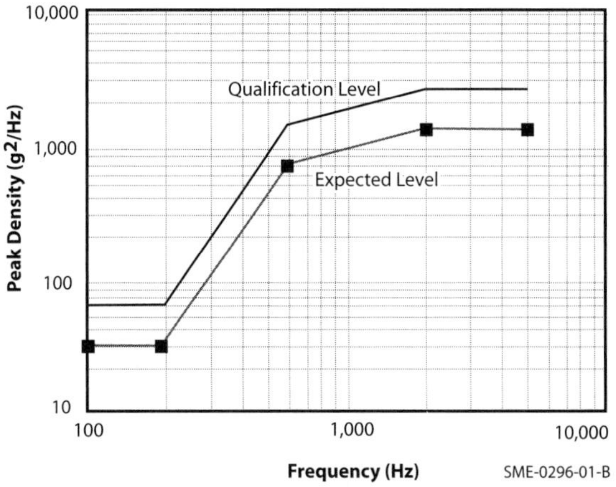

Fig. 23-7. Device Shock Levels for an Atlas-Centaur. Qualification levels are selected to be greater than the expected design levels.

Given the wide variability between the different types and classes of spacecraft as well as their available funding and mission timelines, all space programs are ultimately dependent upon the vendors, suppliers and subcontractors that provide space qualified hardware for flight systems. For some systems such as spacecraft launched into geosynchronous orbit with communication payloads (geocomm sats) or cubesats that are secondary payloads to other missions, a steady demand for production and launch of these systems enables a worldwide supplier base. Here, a geocomm sat may be ordered by a satellite services provider and be ready for launch in less than three years.

In the case of Chandra, multiple design configurations were developed and driven by its launch from the Space Shuttle—initially, the satellite was planned to be operated in LEO and serviced on-orbit similar to the Hubble Space Telescope. Other options considered included robotic servicing and orbit raising and maneuvering by the Orbital Maneuvering Vehicle before a final configuration was selected and built which eventually inserted Chandra into an elliptical orbit of 133,000 km by 16,000 km by use of an Inertial Upper Stage booster rocket once released from the shuttle cargo bay. For Chandra, over two decades passed between when it was originally proposed to when it actually launched.

Whether for a one of a kind spacecraft such as Chandra or Hubble or for production builds of geocomm sats, decisions are made whether to use existing spaceflight qualified hardware or to develop new hardware specific to the mission at hand. Some of these selections may be driven by cost and available schedule—in the case of a commercial geocomm sat derived from platforms such as Boeing's 702 or Lockheed's A2100, designs based on previously flown equipment such as propellant tanks, reaction wheels, and solar array panels can be used and are qualified by similarity.

Other decisions are driven by availability and change —memory chips used and tested in previous flight builds may no longer be produced forcing selection and potentially qualification of different memory chips (change driven by obsolescence) or that chips used in heritage designs may be susceptible to memory upsets in a different orbit regime (change driven by space environment).

Designers and engineers must play a direct role in selecting the appropriate hardware and thus the relevant producers of this hardware when developing a space system. Related to and part of a space program's risk management plan, decisions on which hardware configuration is used in a system need to be documented and potentially tracked if risks are identified in terms of part or component availability, space operational issues or non-technical problems due to regulatory regimes such as ITAR/EAR. Mission designers and system integrators must be aware of the types of problems than can occur related to equipment availability and supply chain issues throughout the development, manufacture, and integration and test of a spacecraft and manage these problems accordingly.

Engineers and supply chain personnel must also verify that vendors supplying spacecraft hardware have satisfactory quality assurance programs. This will involve performing test surveillance, certifying vendors' programs and periodically auditing their performance. Test surveillance includes certifying relevant test equipment and procedures, witnessing tests, approving test records, and reviewing results.

Since test equipment used in the production of flight hardware is in contact and directly affects hardware intended for space, the design, manufacture and calibration of all test equipment used on flight programs must be managed as well. All information used to develop and build the test equipment such as mechanical and electrical assembly drawings, parts lists, wire lists, panel photographs, and calibration test procedures must also be treated as controlled engineering data.

Quality assurance established at both the supplier and system integrator must maintain data records for all formal tests and document and track any testing failures. Often quality assurance personnel keep all failed parts and record failure and anomaly results, so that lessons learned from failures can be used to correct design weaknesses. In addition, while formal procedures govern all tests, troubleshooting may need to deviate from approved procedures. For such troubleshooting operations, quality assurance must approve and maintain records of the exact steps involved.

23.3.3 Space Hardware Manufacture and Assembly

We differentiate between the component and unit level configurations for space hardware versus the integration and testing of a spacecraft bus and overall space vehicle/satellite. At the component/unit level such as processor chips, solar cells, reaction wheels or solid state data recorders, these pieces of a spacecraft perform specific, individual functions (e.g., process data, generate electrical power, spin to control attitude or store collected data in space).

These components must operate in concert with other devices (and relevant software) to provide the necessary spacecraft-level functions and capabilities—generate and distribute power, process and store data on-board, hold operational spacecraft attitudes and handle on-orbit disturbances, communicate to/from ground stations, keep and maintain safe operational temperatures for all components, and perform real-time control of spacecraft operations. Here we focus on the manufacture and assembly of the lower-level hardware and address spacecraft-level integration and test in the following section.

Needless to say, different classes of hardware are manufactured and assembled with different materials and processes. Structural piece parts which are used for the primary load bearing elements of a spacecraft may be machined from metal billets or formed from composite materials on tooling and then assembled together using fasteners and/or bonded together. In contrast, digital electronic units such as the spacecraft processor, payload interface units or solid state recorders are built from discrete electronic chips which are soldered to printed circuit boards which are then assembled together in machined housing frames to form these digital electronic boxes.

For other components such as multi-layer insulation (MLI) blankets, sheets of thermal management material such as aluminized Kapton and scrim are measured, trimmed and assembled together by sewing and/or bonding at the edges. Devices such as space thrusters are constructed from components (e.g., rocket nozzles, titanium tubing, and catalyst beds), assembled with tooling and then subjected processes such as brazing to enable the thrusters to operate for extended periods on-orbit at temperatures over 1,750 C.

Fundamentally, the objective in component/unit level manufacturing and assembly is to produce flight hardware with sufficient functionality that can be tested and measured. In the case of electronic boxes, these are connected to test sets to verify the integrity of signals into and out of the boxes, measure their power demand and thermal dissipation under differing operational conditions and then subject them to flight environmental qualification/acceptance testing. A space thruster would be hot fire tested in a testing chamber to determine its thrust levels and to meet its acceptance performance criteria. Reaction wheels would be connected to wheel control electronics, mounted on lazy susans and then exposed to both test and operational duty cycles to verify

Table 23-4. Design Verification Tests. These tests demonstrate functionality and verify component, subsystem and spacecraft level operation.

Test Category	Example Tests	References
Structural Tests: Verify primary structural members handle flight operational loading conditions	• Static loads test • Modal survey	Sec. 22.1
Deployment Tests: Verify deployment and operation of devices stowed for launch	• First motion • Full extension deployment • Restowage	Secs. 22.1, 25.1, 25.2
Separation Tests: Demonstrate complete separation of components from attachments when released	• Release • Rates of separation	Secs. 22.1 & 22.2, 25.4, 27.8
Antenna Testing: Measure generated electromagnetic fields and actuator/pointing control	• Pattern tests • Closed-loop tracking	Chap.16, Sec. 21.1
Attitude Control Testing: Verify attitude control responses and mode transition behaviors	• Closed-loop testing	Secs. 19.1 & 19.2, 22.1

wheel performance to demonstrate that when a wheel is commanded to rotate counterclockwise, it does so with sufficient accuracy and performance—i.e., it meets spec.

Underlying all of the manufacture and assembly of space hardware is sufficient information from designers in the form of part and assembly drawings, approved part and material documents (PAPLs and PAMPLs), testing procedures, and any relevant test fixtures. These data are the relevant engineering data necessary to move forward with the manufacture of components. For space programs subject to the development phases identified in Chap. 3, close coordination between design and manufacturing is needed to insure a smooth transition from component level design into actual production.

While many of the tables related to the design of individual subsystems in Chaps. 18 through 22 identify a final "iterate and document" step, design changes late into a component's or unit's development can significantly lengthen the overall production of flight hardware. As an example, if a digital processor unit requires a specialized chip such as an ASIC, late design changes can delay the release of the ASIC design to a foundry—where the production cycle time for a custom ASIC may span anywhere from 12 to 24 months. And this delay propagates into a delay of qualification testing of the overall digital processor unit, which, if it is the main spacecraft control processor, may then significantly delay integration of the spacecraft.

For components which are identified as long lead items such as ASICs and control moment gyroscopes, their production cycle times may end up driving the schedule (and thus overall cost) for a whole program. The potential impact of major long lead items will likely be managed as part of the whole program's risk management activity and possibly impact unit design and manufacturing to provide specific steps where risk reduction activities such as early design releases of engineering data may be scheduled and budgeted to check out and possibly test the compatibility of the design with its manufacturing and assembly processes.

At the component and subsystem levels, design verification tests (Table 23-4) can be performed to demonstrate functionality of components and verify operation of both components and subsystems. Structural tests such as static load testing apply a proof load to the flight structure and modal surveys verify the natural frequency, damping factors and mode shapes of the spacecraft. Deployment tests insure the proper deployment of appendages such as solar arrays and booms. Closed loop tests are used to quantify and verify performance of algorithms such as sun tracking on either solar array drive gimbaling or software state transitions due to changes detected such as low battery charge or loss of communication with a simulated ground station.

23.3.4 Spacecraft Integration and Test

Spacecraft bus and space vehicle-level integration and test (I&T) encompass the activities that occur between completion of assembly and testing of unit hardware and software and launch site processing of the spacecraft with the launch vehicle. Fundamentally, this is where the pieces of space hardware are put together and along with the developed flight software, tested as a whole system to make sure that, as an integrated whole, the spacecraft correctly responds to commands and will survive launch to operate as intended in space.

The essential elements that comprise I&T include: the HWCIs and SWCIs that are to provide the basic functions of the spacecraft, all necessary testing apparatus and facilities, relevant documentation (i.e. test & verification plans, approved integration and test procedures, handling documents, and automated test sequences), trained I&T staff and available/on-call support personnel as well as critical I&T management tools (i.e. I&T flow, schedule and budget, test floor and configuration control software). How any and all of these are applied on a given flight program depend directly on the class and type of space system being integrated, prior experience on similar or identical builds and the maturity of the HWCIs and SWCIs under integration.

I&T occupies an unique place in the development and fielding of a space system. Most often, it bears the brunt of delivery delays for both hardware and software and must execute test procedures during early integration with a combination of available EM and flight units that together may generate incorrect telemetry responses to valid spacecraft commands and which have to be tracked down and understood. Specialized test facilities such as acoustic chambers and thermal vacuum chambers may be reserved years in advance by a program as designated in the I&T Plan but conflicts can happen because of schedule slips and end up affecting multiple systems going through I&T. Problems and delays during I&T can be extremely expensive both in terms of time and cost—having a whole I&T crew wait for an essential unit to be reworked can negatively impact a system's schedule and cost.

I&T is also a unique phase in a space system's life cycle because it is usually the first time that all of the "pieces" of the flight part of a system come together to determine how well they operate together and their effectiveness as a total system. Opportunities for the integrated and tested spacecraft to interface with elements of the ground segment (Chaps. 28 and 29) may allow for compatibility testing and validation of many end-to-end system functions. Additionally, I&T is the time and place for execution of the test and verification plans developed during the early phases of a program as discussed in Sec. 23.4 and critically close the link with the system level requirements as developed in Chap. 6.

Planning for Integration and Test

Given the criticality of I&T to a space system, how and where a spacecraft is to be integrated and tested is usually extensively described when a system integrator submits a proposal to develop and deliver the spacecraft. Availability of relevant environmental testing facilities, readily tailorable test procedures, suitability of electronic hardware for system-level test sets may also be called EGSE (electronic ground support equipment)) and prior experience with integrating a given payload or payload suite are all included in the proposal submittal along with the I&T processing flow and schedule. An example of an I&T flow is shown in Fig. 23-8.

The first two steps in the flow define spacecraft bus-level I&T activities. This level of integration and testing is performed prior to integration of the payload. Bus integration normally starts with delivery of an assembled structure or structural frame where the propulsion subsystem may or may not already be integrated into the structure. Liquid propulsion components are assembled to the structure first because the fields used to braze them together are not compatible with electronic components. The spacecraft wiring harness can go on before or after the propulsion components.

Electronic assembly of the spacecraft commonly starts with electric power and command and data handling subsystem components. Integration of the remaining subsystems depends more on the particular spacecraft design. Although the subsystems may have been preassembled and functionally tested, it is common to integrate HWCI one at a time and test subsystems after they are fully integrated together on the spacecraft.

After bus-level integration and testing has completed, integration of the mission payload onto the bus defines vehicle-level integration of the space system. Interface compatibility testing may be performed prior to integrating the payload onto the bus or can be conducted with EM and/or payload simulator hardware and software.

I&T Execution

All operations to be performed on a spacecraft during I&T must be planned and executed under control and quality surveillance. These operation sequences and the data to be collected during each sequence are documented in I&T procedures. Records must be maintained —either or both in hardcopy and electronically—and the results of each integration and test step reviewed before proceeding to the next operation.

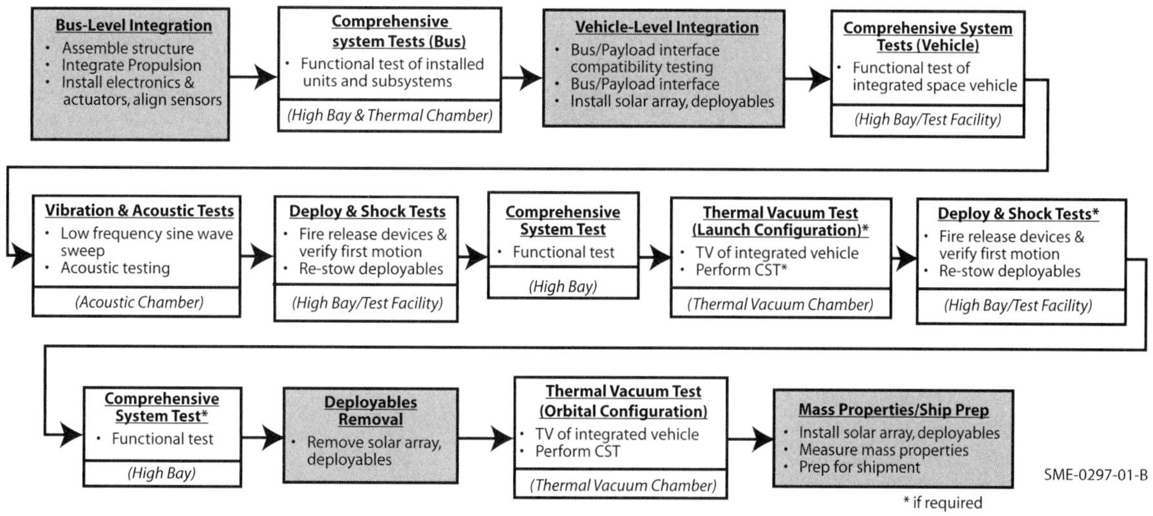

Fig. 23-8. Spacecraft Integration and Testing Flow. Integration and test of a spacecraft brings together for the first time all of the hardware and software required for an operational system and makes sure that everything works correctly as specified.

To functionally test a spacecraft, an I&T crew normally uses a test set comprised of one or more computers with attached information displays for command generation, telemetry decoding and logging, and issuing automated test sequences. The information displays typically consist of an event screen that shows all signal activity and page displays devoted to particular subsystem parameters. The test set also provides stimuli and data-measurement equipment for end-to-end testing of the spacecraft and payload subsystems.

A complete spacecraft functional test may take several days to run and involve subroutines for each subsystem or functional group. Such a test is called an *integrated system test (IST)* or a *comprehensive system test (CST)*. Subroutines are used that test the specific functions of each subsystem, so that only affected subroutines during regression testing need to be run if a subsystem anomaly was detected and subsequently fixed. A reduced version of this functional testing suite may be defined and used at selected points in the integration flow.

During each CST, the test crew records all anomalies or out-of-tolerance measurements and formally resolves each discrepancy. Anomalies which result from operator error or malfunctioning test equipment and which do not damage the spacecraft are easy to resolve. But spacecraft malfunctions demand thorough investigation. If design errors have caused the problems, the design must be corrected and retested. Test rules normally require rerun of an integrated system test (or all affected subroutines) during regression testing or system configuration changes.

A CST timeline normally follows the same operational sequence and transitions involved in going from the launch event to on-orbit operations while also matching the applied test environment: vibration, shock, and thermal vacuum. Similarly, the spacecraft's physical configuration during system-level environmental testing flow is matched to the operational sequence with 1) stowed solar arrays and deployables during vibration testing, 2) performing first motion release/separation tests after vibration testing, 3) deploying and/or physically removing deployables during thermal vacuum testing. Often, test facilities such as thermal vacuum chambers impose physical limits on an articles' size and the ability to perform particular tests at the relevant environment.

First, the mechanically integrated spacecraft goes through temperature cycling to verify proper assembly. A comprehensive system test and performance testing of the payload then take place in a special test facility. (For a communications satellite, this might be an anechoic chamber or screen room.) Separate performance testing of the solar arrays precedes their integration with the spacecraft. *Vibration tests* consist of acoustic testing and vibration by low-frequency sine waves. The system must also pass a *pyroshock test firing* of the deployment ordnance-and a check of the mechanical deployments.

Once the deployables are re-stowed, a thermal vacuum test of this configuration may be conducted. After demonstrating the deployments again, the I&T crew then removes the deployables so the spacecraft will fit into the thermal vacuum (TV) chamber. The spacecraft is then thermal vacuum tested in its orbital configuration. The thermal vacuum cycle activity serves as the final gate to showing readiness for shipment to the launch site. A minimum number of error-free hours (200 is typical) is required of this final run. An ambient comprehensive system test and mechanical verification series may complete the qualification of the integrated space vehicle. *Integrated system tests* (shorter functional tests) supplement this sequence between each environmental exposure and during TV testing. This shortened version of a CST is often used after an environmental test to assure that no failures occurred during the screening activity.

I&T Drivers

As noted earlier, the class and type of space system being integrated, prior experience on similar or identical builds and the maturity of the HWCIs and SWCIs under integration all directly impact the execution of the I&T function on a space program. For Class A programs that require at least single fault tolerance, design life of over 5 years [DoD, 1986], the largest qualification margins are imposed along with additional requirements specific to documentation and at the lowest feasible risk levels. Imposing and managing to these requirements increases the cost and schedule for I&T.

Also, for multi-spacecraft builds as described in Sec. 23.5, the ability to directly influence the vehicle design and developing and verifying the I&T process can greatly reduce the per-unit cost. Use of lean manufacturing methods such as continuous process flow and reducing operation cycle times [Womack et al., 1990] as applied to the production of the Iridium constellation have shown their feasibility and efficacy for space systems (Sec. 23.5). Other approaches to larger volume production, such as modular space vehicle systems where groups of common modules such as spacecraft buses and sensor payloads are built in batches, stored and are subsequently integrated together for a rapid response capability may also foster the ability to leverage lessons learned/knowledge gained from repetition of I&T procedures with block builds.

23.4 Space Mission Verification and Validation

David Parsley*
Northrop Grumman Electronic Systems

This section presents an overview of the space mission verification and validation (V&V) process, and its role in the design of space systems and subsystems. Space pro-

* The author gratefully acknowledges insights and recommendations from Nancy Andreas, Bruce Arnheim, David Berwald, JD Buchanan, Timothy Chin, Simon Dawson, Eric Franco, Elizabeth Guseman, Glenn Horn, Qiong Jackson PhD, Mal Kong PhD, David E. Lee PhD, Leonardo Mendoza, Harvey Moriyama, Robert D. Parker PhD, Dennis Rhoads, Steven Way, Larry Earnest, and Steve Manning.

gram execution and management of cost, schedule, and risk, are guided by definition and implementation of an affordable verification and validation program that incorporates available (or implementable) analysis, simulation, and test methods and facilities. This section gives a step-by-step approach to such a program, particularly as it applies to first article or single article space missions.

An effective V&V program must be an integral part of the up-front planning process and continue through deployment and certification of the on-orbit operational system. It requires a level of planning that spans all levels of the product hierarchy (see Sec. 14.4), demanding coordination among all suppliers and developers in the chain. Responsibility for this coordination lies with the prime integrator, who establishes and enforces general policy and flow of verification events, communicated through formal documentation such as the System Engineering Management Plan (SEMP), System Verification Plan (SVP), Software Development Plan (SDP), Qualification Test Plan (QTP), Acceptance Test Plan (ATP), Software Test Plan, System Safety Plan, EMC Control Plan, and Parts, Materials, and Processes (PM&P) Control Plan. [See Blanchard and Fabycky, 2006; Buede, 2010; EIA, 1994; INCOSE 2007; MITRE, 1998 and AIAA, 2010].

Before proceeding to more specific discussions of the space system verification and validation program, it is important to establish a clear distinction between these two types of activities. *Verification* is a formal process that assures a system or product will meet written requirements, in the specified mission environment. For verification to be considered complete all verification products must pass *sell-off* by the receiving agency. *Verification products* are frequently embodied as Requirement Verification Reports (RVRs) that show compliance to specific requirements in the system or product *compliance documents*: specifications, standards, interface document. Methods of verification, inspection, analysis, test, and similarity are described later in this section. *System validation* is the process for assuring that the system will provide needed services in the mission operational environment.

23.4.1 Space System Verification

Formal connection of verification products to the specification, design, and build of any system can be generally represented by the filled V model as shown in Fig. 23-9. Specific implementation of the scheme is governed by the *System Engineering Management Plan (SEMP)*, which defines tools and products used to generate and capture requirements, design disclosure, error budgets and allocation documents, models, hand-offs to and from manufacturing and Integration and Test (I&T), major simulators, legacy resources, and verification products. It also stipulates rules and protocols to be observed in linking products of the various teams responsible for generating and maintaining them. The SEMP spawns other plans (listed above), including the System Verification Plan (SVP). Initial release is required at System Requirements Review (SRR) and maintained through Test Readiness Review (TRR).

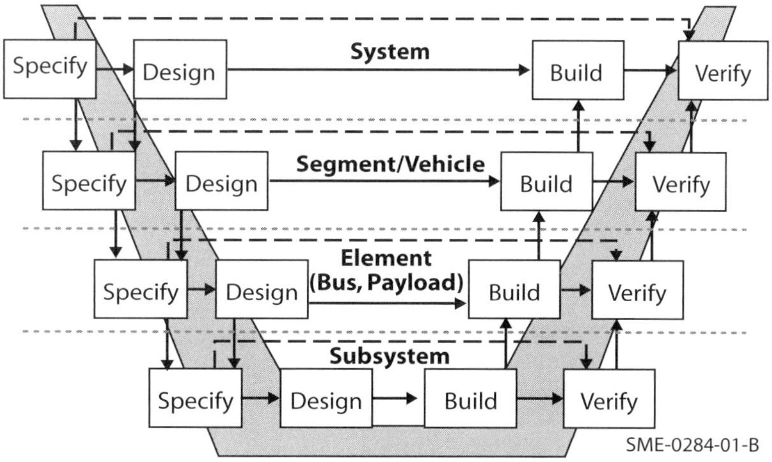

Fig. 23-9. The Filled V Model of System Development. Applicable to a wide variety of systems, the Filled V Model provides a template for architecting the relationships (*schema*) between development products generated over the engineering and manufacturing development phase of a program. It shows how verification depends on the requirements and builds of a specific level of assembly, as well as the relation with verification products above and below in the hierarchy. Requirement trace and decomposition (a design function) are covered in Chapter 6. Note that the hierarchy extends down to lower levels than shown here: component/unit; subassembly; piece-part; wafer; foundry. All must be addressed to achieve a complete space system.

Table 23-5. Steps in Space System Verification Planning.

Step	Comments and Required Information	Ref
1. Capture Requirements in Hierarchical Set of Specifications.	• System spec and SEMP released at SRR • Standards and external interfaces defined • First layer of hierarchy captured in requirement database, schema baselined down to subsystem level	Sec. 6, Chaps. 14, 27, 28, 29
2. Create Verification Cross Reference Matrix (VCRM).	• VCRM preliminary at SRR • System spec VCRM baselined at SDR	Sec. 23.4.2 Table 23-6
3. Map Verification Methods to Available Assets—Assess for Effectiveness, Affordability, and Schedule.	• Draft Verification Plan at SRR • Analysis assets: e.g., heritage simulators and models, program-developed models • Test assets: e.g., thermal vacuum chamber, vibration table, fixtures, acoustic chamber, wind tunnel, optical bench, EMI test facilities, RF ranges	Secs. 20.2.4, 23.3, 23.4.4, 23.4.5
4. Identify Gaps and Update: ***- Requirements baseline*** ***- Verification methods (VCRM)***	• At PDR, preliminary Verification Plan down to unit level, baselined at system level • Trade technical, cost, schedule constraints • Preliminary Integration & Test Plan at PDR	Secs. 11.2, 23.4.3, 23.4.5, 23.5.4, 24.17
5. Plan and Track Closure of Verification Events. Periodically Re-evaluate for Effectiveness in Verifying Requirement Compliance. Hold Test Readiness Reviews (TRRs).	• Verification Plan and I&T Plan baselined down to the unit level well before CDR • Link verification records to requirement database • Test Requirements Document (TRD) with quantitative pass/fail criteria, including measurement error allocation	Secs. 6.3, 23.4.4 Fig. 23-9
6. Conduct Physical and Functional Configuration Audits (PCA and FCA): Unit/Component, Subsystem, Element, Segment. System Sell-off.	• PCA establishes qualified drawings, part list, assembly lines, or suppliers • FCA assures verification of all requirements, archives approved deviations/waivers • Roll up for system sell-off to customer	Sec. 20.1; [MITRE, 1998] [DoD, 1985] Get Stnd

Verification planning is an activity performed at every level of the hierarchy across hardware and software products, and their integrated configurations (See Fig. 20-10 in Sec. 20.2.4). It is important that the *System Verification Plan* (SVP) stipulate a roadmap that takes best advantage of program assets and team capabilities, without over-constraining verification planning at the lower levels of the hierarchy. Another strategy increasingly important in cost constrained environments is that of pushing verification to the lowest practicable level of assembly. Initial release of the SVP is required at *Preliminary Design Review* (PDR). Table 23-5 describes the process for developing a space system verification plan.

23.4.2 Verification Methods

Formal verification is a process by which a product or service (or, *end item*) is evaluated for conformance with written requirements in its compliance documents. It is a rigorous, objective assessment of end item capability to meet each unique requirement, sometimes assessed for groups of related requirements, documented in a *Requirement Verification Report* (RVR). There are at least four widely recognized methods of formal verification:

Inspection: visual inspection of *end item* (EI) and/or its drawings, or possibly an associated *end item data package* (EIDP).

Analysis: definitive qualitative or quantitative pass/fail assessment of a validated mathematical model of the end item, usually at both BOL and EOL.

Test: a regimen exercising the end item, or a validated physical representation thereof, in such a way as to collect data used to directly determine pass or fail.

Similarity: comparison of features of the end item with those of another end item confirmed to be similar, and meeting equal or more stressing requirements.

In addition, some users separately add a special category of test, *demonstration*: a regimen exercising features and functions of the end item, or a validated physical representation thereof, successful completion of which implies compliance for a group of related requirements. Each method is appropriate to the type of requirement being verified, subject to cost constraints and the program's risk posture. Greater certainty in the verification method usually translates into greater expense, hence the desirability of defining methods early in the program to avoid misunderstandings or cost overruns downstream. This definition is typically captured in a *verification cross reference matrix* (VCRM), as shown in Table 23-6.

23.4.3 Real and Virtual Builds

Implicit to the notion of verification is a specific *end item* that is being evaluated for compliance. Since many requirements relate to performance or robustness over mission life, it is not always practical to directly perform an evaluation of the as-built end item prior to delivery and deployment. It is therefore necessary to evaluate a surrogate judged to be similar to the end item, or at least to possess similar characteristics in the area of interest

Table 23-6. Sample Entries for a Verification Cross Reference Matrix (VCRM). There is a unique VCRM for each specification or interface, usually appended at the end of the document.

Unique ID	Para. Number	Text	Analysis	Similarity	Inspect	Test
FIRE1370	3.2.1.8	Space vehicle pointing knowledge shall be ±75 μrad, 1-σ over mission life.	X			
FIRE2040	3.2.2.4	Dimensions of the space vehicle shall not violate launch adapter envelope specified in FIRESAT-ICD-7100.			X	
FIRE2890	3.3.1.5	Materials used to integrate subsystems shall be on the Program Approved Material and Part List.		X		
FIRE3020	3.3.2.2	Radiated emissions shall not exceed 20 dB uV/m between 1MHz and 200MHz.				X

for this particular evaluation. Thus is introduced the generalized concept of build as represented in the Filled V Model (Fig. 23-9).

For the purposes of verification, there are two categories of build: real and so-called "virtual" builds. In the category of *real builds* naturally falls not only the *end item deliverable* (EID) itself, but also qualification units (items built from the same production paper and tooling), mock-ups, prototypes, and others. For software items, it includes code running on emulators embedded in test beds, high level programming language compilations on alternate processors. In most cases, the verification depends on a similarity argument. The greater degree of departure of any real build from the end item, the more uncertainty exists in the verification activity using it.

All type testing, particularly qualification, rests on this concept (Table 23-2). If a type test article passes a sequence of qualification tests, all other articles built to the same engineering data (see Sec. 23.3) would also be expected to pass. In other words, the design is qualified; succeeding builds of this design need only verify proper workmanship [Reeves, 1999]. Alterations to any features of a qualified design must themselves be qualified, since the similarity assessment has been invalidated—a process known as delta qualification. Any of the following changes can require a delta qualification, unless a compelling similarity argument can be made: part or material substitution, change in fabrication tooling or facility, new or revised requirement, change in operating environment or duration, and others.

Virtual build is a more abstract category, including source code listings, logical and arithmetic descriptions (state machines, formal statements, combinatorial expressions, and diagrams the like), closed form mathematical descriptions, and computer models. In this case the build possesses characteristics, similar to the end item, that are specific to a verification type. Table 23-7 describes the application of virtual builds to the four verification methods. (Note that all ground based testing involves a certain amount of simulation and simplification, including environments, interfaces, time spans, and even operational states. The art and science of this discipline will be addressed later in this section.)

Table 23-7. Virtual Builds in End Item Verification. This illustrates several types of virtual builds and their role in different verification activities for end items at various levels of the space system hierarchy.

End Item	Verification Method	Virtual Build	Application
Attitude Control Subsystem	Analysis	MATLAB model	Statistical assessment of performance across parameter variations in tolerance, temperature, radiation, and life
Ground Terminal Software	Similarity	High level programming language code	Variable type compatibility confirmation, based on heritage code
Spacecraft Fault Management	Test	Hardware-in-the-loop test bed	Exercise defined fault scenarios to validate response of chains
Motor Drive Electronics	Inspection	Schematic	Assure proper grounding, isolation, filtering, and shielding as specified in ICD
Motor Drive Electronics	Analysis	SPICE model (net list derived from schematic above)	Statistical assessment of performance and derating across parameter variations in tolerance, temperature, radiation, and life
Thermal Control Subsystem	Analysis	SINDA model	Verify energy balance and temperature limits over life and environments

Table 23-8. Sample of Modeling Methods Commonly Used for Space Mission Verification.

Model Type	Example / tool	Typical Validation Event / Data	Correlation Parameter(s)
Circuit Analysis Model (closed form)	Steady-state analysis	Breadboard	Voltage, current
	Small-signal analysis	Breadboard	Gain vs. frequency
Circuit Analysis Simulator (non-real time)	SPICE	Breadboard	Voltage, current, gain vs. frequency
	VHDL	Brassboard	Timing, logic
Mechanical Stress Analysis	NASTRAN™	Loads test	Stress and strain
Control System Block Diagram	Typically s- or z-domain	Hardware/Software-in-the-loop (HIL/SIL) test bed; mass simulator	Natural frequency, damping ratio, gain, closed loop error
Control System Simulator	MatLab™		
Thermal Model	SINDA™	Thermal balance test	Temperature
Reliability Block Diagram	Lambda Predict™	MIL-HDBK-217 database; life test	Time to failure; accelerating factors
Mass Properties Model	dBMass™	Mass balance test; spin balance test; weighing	Bulk mass, center of gravity, moment of inertia
Dynamic Simulator (non-real-time)	I-DEAS Vibro-Acoustics™; SYSNOISE™	Modal survey; Sinusoidal vibration	Modes, q-factor
Spacecraft Simulator	Custom	Test bed	Demonstration
Link Budget	Tables, graphs, spreadsheet	RF test range; Pointing and alignment test bed	Antenna gain vs frequency, alignment error, temperature, lobes
Error Budget (various)	Monte Carlo Simulator; spreadsheet	Optical bench test; guide-to-hit test; channel characterization	Alignment angle, radiance, in-band noise
Orbit Simulation	STK™	Orbital data from other spacecraft	Altitude vs. time, period, ground track
Phenomenological Model	Custom	Ground truth testing; celestial observation	Radiance, humidity, background noise, absorption

23.4.4 Role of Modeling and Simulation

Model Selection and Management

Modeling is the art and science of creating virtual builds (or, models) of systems of varying complexity and levels of integration. Proper selection and use of models during program development can do much to control cost and risk. In certain instances there is advantage to creating models during concept development for one-time use to support *rapid prototyping*. This can also be effective in other time-critical situations such as trade study and anomaly resolution efforts. But the more frequent application of models is in completing virtual builds in support of design validation and verification of requirements that must be met over the life of the program. In this sense, the methods are predictive, since it is usually impractical to directly confirm compliance with such requirements prior to committing flight assets to service. This is a challenge somewhat peculiar to space missions, demanding extensive ground test programs representing a significant proportion of life cycle cost.

Many requirement categories are common to space mission operations, hardware, and software, and are supported by modeling methods and tools standard in the industry. A few examples are given in Table 23-8. Standardized tools affordably provide a framework within which specific models can be built with manageable risk. These modeling methods have been shown to provide fairly accurate predictions of system response to operational environments and operating conditions, when used in the intended application. As design matures, details are added to reflect the product specifics (e.g., corrections discovered during test). It is important to track versions of the model and the modeling tool used to support various program milestones such as design reviews and sell-off activities.

This discipline is no less important for management of custom models developed by a specific program or organization. Modern space mission programs often manage evolution of model fidelity using a documented *Model Management Plan*.

Models fall into one of several general categories, or combinations thereof:

- ***Physical***—hardware realization of end item configuration to the fidelity necessary to achieve objectives at a particular point in system development
- ***Functional***—rudimentary emulation/simulation responding to commands, time-outs, changes in operating state, transmission mode; may represent a range of degrees of fidelity
- ***Descriptive***—mathematical representation of EID physical features and its external stimuli

- ***Behavioral***—mathematical representation of relationship between EID inputs and outputs, and its external stimuli, usually much less complex than a descriptive model
- ***Empirical***—involves the use of curve fits, look-up tables, and other data-based media to predict excitations and responses (e.g., response of standard structural elements and configurations to shock produced by various pyrotechnic sources along with measured attenuation vs. distance from the source)
- ***Statistical***—statistical representation of EID responses to inputs and external stimuli; also applies to statistical representation of range of values for parameters in descriptive, empirical, and behavioral models (stochastic)
- ***Closed Form***—expressed in a set of equations, state machine description, table, or graph
- ***Finite Methods***—represented by a large number of simple finite entities representing a description of the EID, most commonly a *finite element model* (FEM) grid

More and more, complex systems are being architected through descriptive behavioral models which graphically define, specify, construct, partition and document the functional and physical architectures and designs of systems/software under development. The *Universal Modeling Language* (UML) and its *System Modeling Language* (SysML) extension are the commonly accepted standards to render these models and related system views, such as the *DoD Architectural Frameworks* (DoDAF). These tools are used during V&V to hierarchically capture test cases and standard mission scenarios [INCOSE, 2007].

Model Validation

Significant effort is typically expended on a space program to confirm validity of predictions made by models. *Model validation* (also called *model correlation*) is a formal process of demonstrating the ability of a virtual build to respond to stimuli in a way that imitates what the EID would do, to a quantifiable degree of error. It is important for analyses conducted throughout a space program's life to account for error introduced by the modeling process. This is usually embodied in a term, or set of terms, referred to variously as *model uncertainty factor* (MUF), uncertainty margin, or contingency, depending on the discipline involved. See Akaike [1983]; Blair, et al. [1994], Draper [1995]; Food, et al. [2002]; Kaplan and Bremmer [2010]; Madigan and Raftery [1991]; Raftery [1992]; and Yunis [2008].

As development matures from initial sketches and concepts, through preliminary and detailed design, prototype, integration, and flight build, an explicit objective of the program is to reduce these uncertainty terms in the various budgets maintained on the program. Target values are established in advance, indicating readiness for major program milestones, such as design reviews. These are achieved through a series of dedicated model build cycles and tests of the type given in Table 23-8. A generalized process for evolving model maturity and reducing uncertainty over a space program life cycle is given in Table 23-9. Ultimately, the model and the end item must respond to test case conditions, sequencing, and stimuli with sufficient similarity as to justify use of the model to predict mission performance. These predictions form the basis for many verification products.

Simulators and Emulators

A word should be said about the types of facilities and other resources used for system simulation. The majority of space missions do not include exo-atmospheric human activity (i.e., "unmanned"). Flight equipment prototypes of varying fidelity are integrated and checked out using dedicated *test beds*. In modern systems, extensive software and firmware content obliges designers, systems engineers, and test planners to conduct *software-in-the-loop* (SIL) testing. At the least, this involves exercising interfaces and sequences from pre-defined operational scenarios. SIL and SIL-like tests start early in the development cycle, at low levels of assembly, through the use of breadboards and flight-like prototypes. Embedded software and firmware unit testing is conducted through the use of emulators. An *emulator* is a device that executes instructions in the same way as the flight processor and its core peripherals, usually at a much reduced clock speed.

For systems involving moving assemblies, it will further involve *simulators*, also of varying degrees of fidelity. Development testing uses real-time software simulations connected through test drivers to circuits designed to replicate the hardware interface to the subsystem. Dynamic subsystems dedicated to thrust vector control, spacecraft attitude control, and attitude determination, often extend the simulation to include physical loads, actuators, and sensors, to accomplish highly representative *hardware-in-the-loop* (HIL) testing for purposes of system verification and model validation. Sensor subsystems often employ simulated mission subjects during development and integration, such as point sources, flood sources, black body radiators, and other types of apparatus. Communication systems employ RF ranges, RF signal "hats," and data simulators, to name a few methods.

Today's space systems are designed and deployed in the context of existing surface-based and space-based systems. Interactions within the subject mission and with these existing systems should be exercised early and often, utilizing prototypes and test beds to proof interfaces and operations. As end item deliverables become available, they are substituted for the initial and intermediate prototypes (usually development or articles that have already gone through unit or subsystem qualification). These are also used during crew training and *man-machine interface* validation for ground and operation stations, extending the test regimen to include *man-in-the-loop* methods. Finally, where exo-atmospheric human operations are to be a part of the mission, dedi-

Table 23-9. Steps in Space System Model Generation and Validation.

Step	Comments and Required Information	References
1. Identify Operating Characteristics of System to be Modeled: Performance, Environments, Duration.	Life and environments usually fixed by mission profile defined in CONOPS. Performance parameters are driven by specifications and technical budgets, with an eye to maximizing parameter count per model	Secs. 4.1, 6.2, 29
2. Select Modeling Approach Addressing Selected Characteristics.	Includes physical modeling of system and environments. Simulation limits addressable parameters, but offers flexibility in range and number of test cases, lower material cost and delay, plus ease of upgrade and maintenance. Method selection critiera: sufficiency for defined parameter space, cost, maintenance, reuse, test case accommodation	Secs. 5.4, 23.4.5
3. Define Mission Cases to Meet Modeling Objectives.	Mission cases are typically chosen to represent stressing and nominal conditions from system CONOPS or specification	Secs. 5.5, 29, 30
4. Build Model and Determine Uncertainty Terms.	Tailor model complexity to address parameters of interest within constraints of program resources. Use technical budgets and standards to define uncertainty terms	Secs. 6.3, 11.3
5. Devise Test Cases for Correlating Model to End Item.	Test cases are chosen to optimize correlation of model parameters to those of end item. Approximate mission cases as closely as practical within resource constraints	Chap. 22, Table 23-9
6. Subject Model and End Item (or surrogate) to Test Case Environments and Excitations.	Surrogates (or, prototypes) are commonly used in early to middle phases of system development, when models are often immature. Model objectives are among entry criteria for test case runs	Chap. 22, Table 23-9
7. Correct Model and Reduce Uncertainty Terms.	Divergent responses are reconciled through updates to model. Resultant uncertainty terms are updated using a blend of statistical methods and industry standards	Secs. 6.3, 23.4.4
8. Iterate Until Uncertainty Terms Satisfy Budget Objectives.	Objectives are established by program phase in the SEMP, again based on industry standards and technical budgets	External

cated *vehicle simulators* are used in extensive operational simulations in collaboration with the other system elements and external systems.

23.4.5 Introduction to Space System Testing

23.4.5.1 Environmental Testing and Defect Screening

It is rarely practical to exercise an end item or test article in the full mission environment and duration before committing it to space deployment and fielded service. (One counter-example is the Pioneer Jupiter series, which encountered Jupiter in 1973, path-finding the Solar System grand tour nearly six years before the 1979 launches of Voyagers 1 and 2. Lessons learned were used to modify equipment on the subsequent spacecraft, especially for radiation hardness.) More commonly, proving suitability for deployment and use in the space environment requires subjection of the flight article to ground test conditions that represent stresses of transportation, launch, and space flight. Table 23-10 describes a number of test regimens used to qualify and accept space flight equipment. Practice has shown that these methods can be used to promote timely qualification through accelerated life testing.

Accelerated life testing, as used here, is a quantitative approach to predicting life of a fielded space asset, by subjecting that article and similar ones to stresses exceeding those expected to be experienced during the mission. Traditional methods of reliability testing, qualification, and acceptance, have seen innovations such as test-to-failure and *highly accelerated life testing* (HALT) enter as viable alternatives or supplements [Meeker and Hahn, 1985]. Suitability of these latter methods depends on inherent product robustness, technology maturity, and other considerations [Weibull, 2007].

In addition to demonstrating hardware and software robustness, a primary objective of space hardware environmental testing is to demonstrate ability to perform as required while operated on orbit, after experiencing the rigors of ground processing and transportation, launch, atmospheric flight, and orbital maneuvering and deployment (see Sec. 23.3). It is therefore desirable to subject units, subsystems, payloads, and vehicles to environmental levels, durations, and sequences similar to those expected for the mission. The intuitive construct of this approach is to *Test Like You Fly* (TLYF) [White and Wright, 2005] built on methods usually associated with system validation. Ground testing results are used to characterize, and confirm predictions for, such parameters as post-launch alignment and settling for line of sight (LOS), integrity of moving mechanical assemblies, RF and optical transmission, and thermal control and monitoring. While predictions and measurements are used for final vehicle verification and sell-off, characterization provides data to be used during on-orbit operations. For example, parameter variation under well-chosen temperature conditions will be used to calibrate data for each specific build of the vehicle and payloads during mission life. See the book website for a more extensive discussion of both environmental testing and qualification and acceptance testing, for space and ground systems.

Get More

Table 23-10. Environmental Tests Used for Spaceflight Hardware and Equipment.

Test Name	Description	Assembly Level
Radiation Total Dose	Test characterizes changes in device performance after exposure to total ionizing radiation dose predicted for mission, typically at highly accelerated rate and at elevated temperature	Electronic piece-part
Enhanced Low Dose Rate Sensitivity (ELDRS)	Test characterizes changes in device performance after exposure to total ionizing radiation dose rates more closely approximating that predicted for mission	Electronic piece-part
Radiation Prompt Dose & SEE	Radiation stresses simulating single event phenomena: high-energy protons, neutron bombardment	Electronic piece-part
Electrical Stress Test	Application of electrical stresses above normal use or rating, usually high voltage (Variants: hi-pot test, di-electric withstanding)	Electronic piece-part Cable, printed circuit
Static Load Test	Application of static forces to a UUT, enveloping static and quasi-static acceleration loads predicted to occur in flight	Sub-assembly Subsystem Element
Burn-In	Sustained high temperature operation of UUT over pre-defined time span, watching for failures or unfavorable parametric trends	Electronic piece-part Hybrid micro-circuit
Thermal Shock	UUT exposed to abrupt temperature transitions between extremes	Electronic piece-part Hybrid micro-circuit
Seal Leak	Fill with pressurized gas and immerse in liquid to reveal leaks	Hybrid micro-circuit Unit
Salt Spray	Spray mist of 5% salt solution on UUT in a chamber	Unit
Humidity	UUT exposed to 90 to 95% relative humidity at elevated temperature	Electronic piece-part Unit
Thermal Cycle	Subjects UUT to rapid temperature transitions between defined extremes under normal atmospheric conditions, dwelling at extremes for hours at a time	Unit Element
Thermal Vacuum	Subjects UUT to rapid temperature transitions between defined extremes under near-vacuum conditions, dwelling at extremes and other plateaus for hours at a time. Explicitly simulates on-orbit conditions and operations using conductive and radiative coupling	Unit Element
Random Vibration	Simulates pseudo-random vibration spectrum predicted for launch and atmospheric ascent	Unit Element
Sine Sweep Vibration	Excitation of a UUT structure involving the application of fixed sine wave forces with brief dwell time, stepping through the applicable frequency range to identify resonances and other responses	Unit Element
Acoustic	Subjects UUT to pseudo-random acoustic loads representative of those seen during launch and early ascent	Unit Element
Pyro-Shock	Exposure to transients simulating those resulting from sudden application or release of loads associated with deployment, staging/separation, impact, and release events	Piece-part Unit Subsystem Element
Electromagnetic Interference (EMI)	Encompassing one or more regimens involving: measurement of conducted and radiated emissions from operational UUT; and/or subjection of operational UUT to conducted and radiated noise to assess ability to operate in such environments	Unit Element
Electromagnetic Compatibility (EMC)	Monitoring of critical circuit EMI safety margin (EMISM) during simulated runs in operational configuration	Subsystem Element Segment

23.4.6 Space System Validation and Final Certification

System validation is the process for assuring that the system will provide needed services in the mission operational environment. System validation involves the exercise of simulators, emulators, and development hardware and software, using mission operators, infrastructure, and procedures, through progressive levels of integration and fidelity as the program matures. Activities focus on exposing system elements and subsystems to interfaces (including users and operators), data interchange, available heritage system elements, and event sequences representative of the operational mission and environment. Detailed mission scenarios (or, threads) from system *concept of operations* (CONOPS) are enacted to capture incompatibilities that may have escaped the requirement derivation process. System validation is distinct from both system verification and from model validation described earlier in this section. It is also distinct from the process of requirement validation, shown in Chap. 6, though that process is often incorporated as an early part of the system validation plan. Validation is the final line of defense against previously undiscovered mission hazards related to sneak paths, software bugs, and missed hand-offs.

A commonly used method for planning space system validation testing follows a simple mantra: *First Day, Best Day, Worst Day, Last Day*. Each scenario represents a standard mission operational thread or set of threads, with actual commands and messaging, operator displays, communications links and relays, preferably at projected durations. First Day threads emulate launch day operations, and post-launch deployment and initialization for the spacecraft. This is almost always the most hazardous part of the mission, with success hinging on real-time decisions by ground crews, as well as flight and ground processors. It is essential that fault response scenarios be enacted multiple times in the months leading up to this mission phase (also falls under category of Worst Day).

Best Day scenarios, more often referred to as *day-in-the-life* (or, DITL, pronounced like fiddle), represent the operations for which the mission was desired in the first place. For many missions, this is simply continuous operation, with occasional interruptions for calibration or maintenance activities, such as orbital station keeping. More complex missions involve intricate autonomous or operator-directed orbital rendezvous and docking, real-time tasking, planetary encounter, surface roving, sampling and other *in situ* measurement. In such cases, it is crucial that potentially debilitating phenomena are accounted for, such as celestial body eclipse, communication lag, Doppler effects, solar activity disruptions, and other inherent aspects of the mission. A subset of these scenarios is typically run with on-orbit assets after launch, as a part of final *system certification* for operational use.

Equally critical is the exercise of anomalous scenarios (Worst Day). Here the system equipment and operators conduct normal operations which are interrupted by the occurrence of a fault. This fault can be a hardware failure in space or on the ground, *single event effect* (SEE), or even natural or man-made catastrophe. The aggregate space system must demonstrate ability to respond to and correct the fault, and return to normal (or pre-defined degraded) operations.

Finally, all space missions are required to provide the means for retiring space and ground assets, as part of mission termination (Chap. 30). For space assets in particular, this is critical to preserve availability of orbits and orbital stations that are free of debris or other hazards. Interplanetary missions are required to assure elimination of materials that could harm as-yet-undetected life forms. Exercise of realistic operational scenarios must demonstrate ability to de-orbit or otherwise safe the asset in question, even in the presence of faults. In some cases, mission planners desire the capability to go into dormant or follow-on mission bridging states, and this also will need validation.

Table 23-10◀, Fig. 23-9◀, Eq. 23-0

23.5 Multi-Spacecraft Manufacturing

Wade Molnau, *General Dynamics*
Jean Oliveri, *SpaceX*

Historically, satellite manufacturing, integration, and test has been a crafted and arduous process. Each spacecraft is essentially unique, and is manufactured and tested appropriately. Commercial satellites, while alleviating some of the major impedances to fast and efficient satellite manufacture, have fared only slightly better. The advent of commercial constellations of satellites forces us to seek and develop completely new strategies. We need to incorporate ideas and methods from other industries into satellite supply-chains to meet the cost and cycle-time requirements needed to make space systems compete effectively with their terrestrial counterparts.

This chapter describes a few of the vital changes that need to be addressed to manufacture and test multiple satellites efficiently. These methods and strategies apply to the whole satellite supply chain, and to piece-part, assembly, subsystem, and spacecraft levels. Section 23.3, which details methods used to manufacture and test single satellites, will be augmented here for multiple satellite systems.

Small satellite systems (< 10 spacecraft) may not fully benefit from the methods presented here, but some points will be applicable. Designing manufacturable satellites and associated production systems requires up-front investments in time, money, and capital. Each program needs to trade the benefits of these methods with anticipated investment costs. As the number of satellites grows, the benefits and the usefulness of these methods increases.

We begin with a short description of the goals and challenges of manufacturing, material, test, and launch processing organizations. The majority of the chapter then concentrates on four phases of the manufacturing and test of the spacecraft constellation: (1) creating the manufacturing vision, (2) influencing the design, (3) developing and verifying the process, and (4) producing the spacecraft.

23.5.1 Challenges for Manufacturing, Material, Test, and Launch Processing Teams

The challenges presented to the manufacture of satellite constellations are extremely different from those traditionally conceived for spacecraft. These challenges, however, are not much different from those for other commercial products. Spacecraft for large constellations are designed and built to cost and schedule goals—just like cell phones or cars. Table 23-11 compares a few of the challenges facing the manufacture of a constellation of satellites, while Table 23-12 shows manufacturing issues as they pertain to key metrics—quality, time, and cost.

For instance, time to market often is not only a goal, but a competitive requirement for viability. Time becomes an overriding factor. This drives not only the overall time to market, but the time to complete each system element.

Table 23-11. Typical Constellation Manufacturing Challenges. Note the significant difference between traditional space vehicle manufacture and the newer manufacture process.

Key Metrics	Traditional	Multi-Satellite
Quality	Build, Test, Rebuild, Retest	Build, Verify, Ship, Shoot
Spacecraft Cost	66,000 $/kg	19,800 $/kg
Cycle Time (Integration)	225 days	24 days
Cycle Time (Build to launch)	18 months	2 months

Table 23-12. Constellation Manufacturing Issues. The quality, cycle time, and cost issue relating to the production of a constellation of satellites are different than those encountered while producing single satellites. While quality requirements are different—but still stringent—cycle time and cost issues are now paramount.

- **Six-Sigma Quality is Required**
  - Satellites are not field serviceable!
- **Time is Critical**
  - For Commercial Ventures → First to Market
  - For Government/Military → Leverage the Market
- **Money is a Limited Resource**
  - Fixed Budgets, Commercial Pricing, Continuous Profit Improvement

For manufacturing, this translates to drastically reducing the cycle time required to produce a satellite. We employ lean methodologies to minimize time and cost inefficiencies in the design, build and deployment of our systems.

Quality, as with all spacecraft, is still imperative. Satellites are not field serviceable, and simple defects can render a satellite unusable. The traditional approach places emphasis on high-cost and time-consuming quality assurance methods that check and recheck, test and retest, and verify and re-verify the hardware. Instead, we employ *six sigma* methods to verify that the processes are performing with high-quality results. Robust designs using in-control processes will produce high-quality products—without associated high costs and long cycle times. Six-sigma methods are a cornerstone for lean manufacturing methods (see sidebar).

To meet the additional cycle-time and quality requirements, manufacturing personnel must participate concurrently during the creation of the design. They are responsible for influencing the design and tailoring the design into a final, producible product. Finally, manufacturing must effectively integrate the product during production.

In summary, the challenges presented are to recreate the value-added or useful elements of space hardware design and manufacture while eliminating the non-value-added activities. We must add elements for quick, efficient, and high quality execution. We must drive out non-value-added or superfluous activities and requirements.

Material Challenges

Traditional manufacturing drove spacecraft parts to the costliest and slowest-delivery grade—*S-level*. Unfortunately, these parts are not inherently better than commercial parts—they have just been screened for various properties to improve their overall expected performance or failure rates. The parts are mostly produced on commercial part lines and even from commercial part batches.

Our challenge is to use the *right* parts for the mission—not the highest level parts available. We need to target commercial parts, replacing them only when required. We need to discourage military grade or S-level parts, but allow them in situations where they *must* be used. A simple comparison of part costs, as shown in Fig. 23-10, depicts the drastic difference for S-level, Mil-spec, and commercial parts. Significant cost savings can result from selecting lower-cost parts when applicable. Significant time savings also can result from selecting lower grade parts. Figure 23-10 shows typical lead times for various parts and the significant advantage of using Mil-spec parts over S-level parts. Furthering this comparison, we can receive commercial parts typically even quicker—often in less than a week.

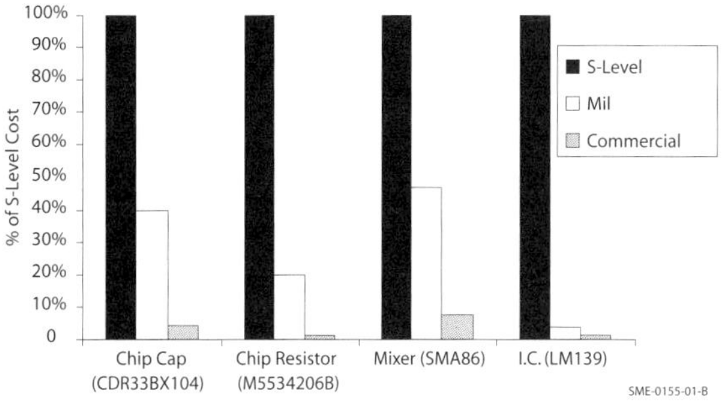

Fig. 23-10. Representative Parts Price Comparison. Commercial parts represent a significant cost savings over Mil-Spec and S-level parts.

Parts selection needs to consider producibility, radiation, out-gassing, and other requirements. We need to strongly consider parts that support efficient manufacturing methods. We should target parts that use the standard process flows—for instance, automated placement and mass reflow for electronic assemblies.

Finally, parts selection needs to be a concurrent engineering activity. All stakeholders—purchasing, production, design engineering—need to have their concerns taken care of. Success in the material area heavily influences overall program cost and schedule performance.

Test Challenges

The test function drives the overall cycle time of spacecraft delivery. This holds true not only for traditional satellites, but for constellations as well. The key is to design test as a process—this includes minimizing

Six Sigma Manufacturing

Six Sigma began at Motorola in 1985 as a means to measure and improve performance in all phases of its business. The ultimate target is virtually perfect execution.
Sigma (σ) is used to designate the distribution or spread about the mean or average of any process or procedure. A simple definition of the *measure* six sigma is 3.4 defects per million opportunities (DPMO), or 99.9997% perfect. Sigma level improvement is not linear. In fact, improvement rates escalate rapidly as the base sigma level slowly increases.

3 Sigma = 66,810 DPMO = 54,000 postal letters lost per day
6 Sigma = 3.4 DPMO = 35 postal letters lost in a year

Six Sigma *methodologies* are a set of tools and procedures to improve processes. Fundamental methods include problem solving, process control and process characterization. They can be applied to any process from engineering to business. Six Sigma *programs* are structures within companies for managing and maintaining continuous improvement. [Harry, 1997 or Harry et al. 2010]

Lean Six Sigma (LSS) began to become popular in 2003 as the marriage of lean and six sigma. What could be better than using lean to drive out waste and non-value producers and six sigma for optimizing value-added processes? [George, 2002]

cycle time, maximizing throughput, and achieving high-quality results.

The purpose of the overall test program is to verify the adequacy of the design and assembly processes. The requirements to verify these two elements—design and processes—are inherently different.

Design verification, more commonly called *qualification testing*, requires detailed and thorough analysis of performance capabilities. This still is a time-consuming process that includes functional test, vibration and shock, thermal vacuum, electromagnetic compatibility, and other tests. This may include multiple iterations, and essentially involves testing the satellite to greater than expected levels. We should cut back and ultimately eliminate these qualification tests after we understand and proof the design. We can achieve significant savings in time and money by relinquishing the need for full-up testing on every unit.

Conversely, *process verification* continues throughout the production of the spacecraft. These tests only verify the performance of the production system and include only simple performance checks. The control of the individual processes throughout the production cycle ensures the high-quality results. Complete testing of the spacecraft would be redundant and non-value added—and not consistent with the principles of lean production. Figure 23-11 shows some key differences between traditional spacecraft production and lean production.

In regards to components, subassemblies, and subsystems, it is critical that they achieve their qualification testing and product testing as early as possible. We need to detect quickly issues with design or process. We can integrate high quality and well-understood components, subassemblies, and subsystems with no additional integration level testing—with high confidence. At integration, we need to verify only incremental processing—usually only shipping and connection.

In summary, test provides possibly the greatest opportunity for significant cost and cycle-time improvements. Intelligent selection of reduced testing, clear distinction between design and process verification, and performance of lowest-level testing greatly enhances the cost-effective, high quality, low cycle-time production of spacecraft without significantly increasing risk.

Launch Processing Challenges

After finishing integration and test, we package and ship the satellites to the launch site for processing and preparation for launch. Traditionally, this has been a complex and time-consuming segment of the satellite delivery process. The requirements for building a multi-satellite constellation include quick and efficient processing of satellites for launch. These requirements may also force the use of multiple launch sites and launch-preparation areas, further driving the need for standardized and simplified launch processing.

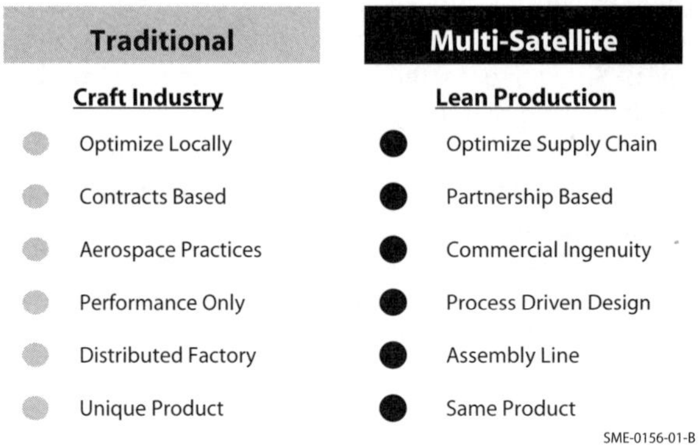

Fig. 23-11. Lean Satellite Production Principles Compared to Traditional Craft Production. Lean production methods originated in the automobile industry. These methods can be applied to the production of satellites as well. See Womack, et al. [1990] for in depth discussion of lean manufacturing.

We need to consider launch-site processing from the start of the program. We should target decisions and trades that support simplified processing. Changes and processing are much easier to handle while at the integration factory. This is where the facilities and skill levels are the most available. Launch-site processing typically takes place at a remote location—often not owned or operated by the satellite manufacturer—that makes processing more difficult.

The spacecraft are transported to the launch-site processing area via protected environment or container. The container environment must provide for temperature, humidity, vibration, and shock protection during the shipping process. In order to support the streamlined processing of the satellites upon their arrival, the shipping process is subject to basic process control. We deem the process to be successful as long as the required parameters—temperature limits, humidity limits, vibration levels, and shock levels—are not exceeded. If these parameters exceed their limits, we need to perform in-depth analysis or additional testing at the launch-site. But, if none of the parameters are exceeded, the satellite can continue with the streamlined process flow that contains little, or preferably no, testing.

Figure 23-12 depicts a streamlined launch-site process flow. The processing includes all the steps needed to prepare the spacecraft from shipping condition to flight condition. Launch team members receive, inspect, load onto the launch dispensers, fuel, package, and transport the space vehicles to the launch vehicle. They charge and monitor the flight batteries, which may be installed at the launch site, when the spacecraft are mounted on the launch vehicle.

We remove all difficult tasks that can be driven to earlier processing. We minimize hazardous operations. For instance, we can replace deployment ordnance with other mechanisms. We should minimize or eliminate test operations. If the shipping process was in control (e.g., no limits exceeded on shipping sensors), we need no test verification of the process. Well-designed tooling and process development can make the remaining processes quick and efficient with little threat of damage to the spacecraft.

23.5.2 Creating the Manufacturing Vision

One of the most important factors relating to a successful production program is the creation of a manufacturing vision. More and more customers today want the "better, cheaper, faster" solutions to their product needs. We should create the manufacturing vision based on the customer's and the market's expectations for the product. The entire project team must embrace this vision. All parties involved with manufacturing must share the manufacturing vision and we must also include everyone else involved with the program from the early design phases through production and test. We must create manufacturing goals to support the vision. Creating manufacturing goals for quality, cycle time and cost must directly relate to the manufacturing vision. For example, if there is a manufacturing vision to produce enough satellites to populate a constellation in a single year then the manufacturing goals must reflect this vision. These goals must be in the form of quantified short cycle times, quantified quality levels and quantified costs. Once the manufacturing goals are in place, the next step is to execute these goals and pursue the manufacturing vision. We must constantly measure the progress towards meeting these goals and share them with the team. We must evaluate progress and make necessary changes to achieve the stated goals. Changes may occur in the design or in the production and test processes. Changing the design and processes to meet the manufacturing goals is an iterative process. It is a give and take scenario where the sum of the changes equals achieving the manufacturing goals.

Establish Goals

We must establish goals in the areas of cycle time, quality and cost. In today's competitive environment, these areas are everything. Many times multiple companies have similar ideas and the only differentiating characteristic between their products is which one makes it to the consumer market first and captures the majority of the market share. Missing the time to market goals will cost a company market share, revenue and brand equity. Therefore we need to know up front when our product must be ready for our customer and then determine our cycle time goals to support this overall schedule.

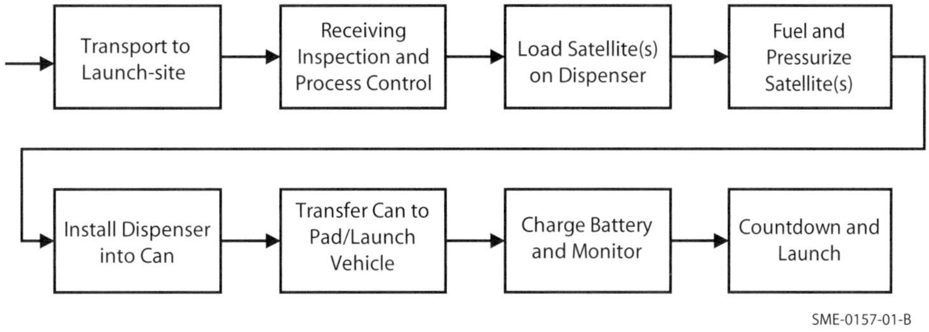

Fig. 23-12. Streamlined Launch-Site Process Flow. Traditional launch-site processing can take several weeks. Streamlined processing can reduce the overall cycle time (transport to launch) to less than two weeks.

As stated previously, one of the unfortunate aspects of building satellites is that they are usually not field serviceable (Hubble Telescope is the most prominent exception). If there is a quality problem after we launch the product into space, we have to live with the degraded performance or, in an extreme case, accept that the product does not meet our mission requirements. We must establish quality goals so that we can design our product accordingly. When we choose components for our product and select processes to build and test our product, we determine our resulting quality levels. As we choose components and processes we need to calculate our cumulative quality predictions and track them to our goals. We will then have the visibility to see what components and processes have a positive or negative impact on the overall product quality. With this data we now make informed trade-off decisions. We can determine which components or processes to change to increase the product quality. Often quality drives cycle time. If a product is designed with low quality levels then we should expect to perform more rework and additional testing. This in turn adds cycle time. Hardware designed around robust processes which exhibit low defect rates result in products with fewer defects which leads to less test time, less rework and lower costs.

Most customers desire low-cost solutions. More and more of the traditional "cost plus" projects are being proposed as fixed price contracts. The days of cost-plus contracts and cost overruns being absorbed by the customer are quickly disappearing. Today the contractor carries the burden of performing to an agreed-upon fixed price. Because of this, the contractor must know the cost goals and understand how they are going to perform to these cost goals. Performance to cost goals directly relates to performance to cycle time goals and quality goals. The addition of unplanned cycle time and of effort required to correct quality problems result in increased cost. In general any unplanned work results in additional cycle time and in additional costs.

Involve Manufacturing Early

Manufacturing early involvement may not always be the accepted way of doing business. Early manufacturing involvement allows the design team to be informed regarding the effects of their choices on downstream manufacturing and test operations. It empowers the design team to make informed decisions and predetermine the expected cycle time, quality and cost performance of the assembly and test operations. It allows management to be aware of what to expect when the product reaches assembly and test.

Getting the design team to accept concurrent engineering can be a difficult task. Many times a company needs a culture change for everyone to embrace the early participation of manufacturing. Management must support concurrent engineering and must pay attention to the analysis results created by the manufacturing representatives. The manufacturing and test participants on the concurrent-engineering team must embrace the manufacturing vision and possess the tools to influence the design to meet this vision. They must show the other members of the design team that their participation is value-added and that early team involvement will save the program time and money in the long run. Everyone on the project team must share the manufacturing vision in order for it to become reality.

Select Parts and Processes Effectively

As was discussed earlier the sum of the project's individual process cycle times (both design and manufacturing/test) must support the overall cycle time goals and the manufacturing vision. Cycle time is inherent in the design. We predetermine the cycle time to assemble and test a product when we choose parts and processes for a particular product. Therefore, during the product design phase we must give appropriate detail to the proper selection of parts and processes. Overall the design team must realize that a design consists of parts and processes. Often the choice of a particular part will dictate the use of a particular process. This relationship is what gave rise to the phrase "pick a part, pick a process." Often design engineers choose parts that meet a limited set of criteria from which the design engineer is searching. They often do this without knowing the downstream impacts that these part choices have in assembly and test.

It's important to have manufacturing and test representatives involved in the part selection process. They can perform analyses to show how certain parts may require additional process steps which have lower process yields leading to more defects, higher cycle times and ultimately higher costs.

An electronic assembly example of this type of analysis is shown in Table 23-13. We can extend this analysis to satellite design and manufacture. Part X and part Y are equivalent in the areas of form, fit and function; therefore, we would assume that the parts are interchangeable. However, the parts vary greatly when we address associated processes, process yields and overall cost. Part X is an 84-lead *ceramic quad flat pack* that must have the leads formed, trimmed, and tinned. The part must then be loaded into a tray for presentation to the part placement (pick and place) equipment. Form, trim, tin and tray placement are non-preferred processes. We must perform these processes in-house, which contributes to increased process time for that part type. The low process yields associated with these non-preferred processes drive this part to contribute 0.273 *defects per unit* (DPU) which leads to increased cycle time and costs associated with rework and potential test failures. Part Y is an 84-lead plastic *quad flat pack* that comes to us formed, trimmed, tinned and loaded on tape and reel to be presented to the pick and place machine. This part uses only preferred processes which leads to lower process cycle times, lower defects per unit and lower rework costs. All of these factors are reflected in the lower total cost of Part Y. Therefore, when selecting a part the design team must look at the downstream impact of their part selection and include the total cost impact of the part in their design tradeoffs.

Table 23-13. Part/Process Cost Relationship.

Part	Package	Part Cost	Processes Used	Process DPU	Process Time (Hr)	Assembly Cost	Rework Cost	Total Cost
Part X	84CQFP	$25.00	1. Lead form/trim 2. Lead tin 3. Pick & place —tray 4. Oven reflow	0.273	0.05	$3.20	$40.95	$69.15
Part Y	84QFP	$17.50	1.Pick & place —tape 2. Oven reflow	0.00306	0.002	$0.128	$0.459	$18.00

By relating parts to processes we can determine the expected time to manufacture and test a product, the associated quality level and the overall cost. Once we make these estimates we can perform "what if" analyses to see if other part/process combinations will make attaining the cycle time, quality and cost goals more realistic. We perform this iterative process early in the design phase, so we can include many design tradeoffs between all of the disciplines.

Parts have many attributes that influence the effectiveness of manufacturing processes. Some of these attributes fall into the categories of cost, interchangeability, availability, reliability and simplicity. Early part-supplier involvement is critical to ensure acceptable levels in all of these categories. The suppliers need to know what our cost goals are for the parts being supplied. The supplier also needs to understand our product design and how the supplier part interacts with our design. The supplier can work with us to determine the appropriate variables to control to ensure that the part is interchangeable and reliable. The supplier also needs to understand our production schedule and our material management philosophy in order to make sure that their parts are available to us when we need them.

Part cost directly impacts product cost. It also has an impact on process development and process execution. Processes used to assemble high-cost parts are usually designed with additional controls and verifications. Typically, this leads to higher stress levels for the people doing the assembly work and more engineering involvement for process verification. Use of higher cost parts drives the desire to perform more rework rather than scrap hardware in the event of unwanted process variations.

Part interchangeability is critical in a product design regardless of the production quantity. The ability to remove and replace a component quickly translates into less non-value-added time. Interchangeable parts have the same form, fit and function for all parts. The supplier of interchangeable parts must use process control to insure that the parts coming into the assembly area are truly interchangeable. If a part is not truly interchangeable, assemblers will have to spend additional time to alter mechanical characteristics of the part to make it fit or perform additional tests to adjust for the varying performance of the part.

Part simplicity directly relates to part cost, interchangeability, availability and reliability. Typically the more simple the part design, the lower the cost. A simple part will have less variables associated with its design, therefore, it will positively impact the component reliability and interchangeability. A simple part will require less production set up time and have fewer variables to cause scrap, and thus, should be more available for use.

Part availability is critical to maintaining product flow in the assembly area. We never want to stop the assembly process due to parts unavailability. Many times the risk of part unavailability is controlled by creating material inventories. However, there can be a great deal of cost associated with carrying part inventories. Typically, we must allocate valuable factory floor space to material storage near its point of use. An alternative to storing material on the factory floor is to store it in a stock room and move the material to the assembly line when we need it. Both of these scenarios result in material being stocked at the assembly location and increase the risk of having large quantities of parts that may become obsolete or require rework/retrofit if there is a design change. The best alternative to either of these scenarios is to have *"just in time (JIT)"* suppliers. Working with JIT suppliers requires less stocking activities and hence less chance of having vast amounts of product that has to be reworked or retrofitted when there is a design change, but can add risk. The supply chain information —especially deliveries, cycle times, and quality—must be well understood to make JIT plausible. If not well understood and reliable, JIT is very risky.

Once material is ready for production it is time to use our manufacturing processes. In the typical aerospace manufacturing environment, processes were developed after the design, so the product could be manufactured and tested to meet the customer's needs. Before the implementation of concurrent engineering this meant that the design was "thrown over the wall" to manufacturing and manufacturing did "whatever it takes" to build, test and deliver the hardware to the customer. Typically, this meant that the processes were highly flexible, required specially skilled workers, lacked good control and were seldom characterized. Today with the advent of *concurrent engineering*, we design in the controlled and repeatable manufacturing processes from the beginning and the manufacturing output is highly predictable.

Concurrent engineering has brought about a change of attitude regarding manufacturing processes in the aerospace industry. No longer do we perform processes just because "that is the way we've always done them." High-quality processes are characterized, controlled and repeatable. Many of these processes have been borrowed from the commercial manufacturing world. The mass reflow of electronic assemblies is an example of this exchange. Mass reflow—the mass soldering of parts on printed circuit boards using a single, controlled thermal cycle—was developed to efficiently produce electronic products for delivery to consumers. Although slow in gaining acceptance, we now use it for spaceflight hardware and other high reliability applications.

The concurrent manufacturing engineer should never be afraid to ask "why" we design or process something the way we do. An example of this is to look at the integration of deployables on a satellite. In the past, certain deployables have always been integrated with the satellite in the vertical position. This was done to minimize the amount of stress that could be preloaded into the deployable mechanisms. Changing the satellite from the horizontal position to the vertical position and back to the horizontal position requires time, space, additional tooling and creates a lot of risk associated with handling the satellite. With today's modern analysis tools much of the stresses associated with preloading the deployable mechanisms in the horizontal position can be modeled and the risks analyzed. If the risks are determined to be low enough then the satellite plane change from horizontal to vertical can be eliminated. This will save time, space, and tooling and also reduce handling risk.

Typically, satellite manufacturing has been a low-volume process. To date, many companies have built or are proposing multi-satellite constellations. These multi-satellite projects drive manufacturing to create production lines for assembling and testing satellites. The "assembly line" concept of these satellite production lines has roots in the automotive industry. Many of the new satellite production lines take mass production assembly line technology one-step further and implement many of the *"lean" manufacturing* principles currently used in the automotive industry. Some of these "lean" manufacturing principles include JIT suppliers, supplier partnering, concurrent engineering, pull production*, and statistically controlled processes.

Manufacturers in other industries have taken the "lean" manufacturing philosophy to the next step—*"agile" manufacturing*. "Agile" manufacturing incorporates all of the principles used in "lean" manufacturing with the addition of flexibility. An "agile" manufacturing line can support multiple product lines on the same assembly line. It also can adapt and respond to product changes which may be directed by changing customer wants and needs. Agile manufacturing is a future possibility for satellite manufacturing.

One of the guiding principles behind lean and agile manufacturing is waste elimination. We must evaluate all of the processes associated with assembly and test in terms of value-added activities and non-value-added activities. During process development and implementation, we should maximize the value-added processes and the non-value-added activities should be minimized. Reduction of the non-value added process steps will drive waste elimination.

Reduction in the number of inspection points is a good example of waste elimination. Satellite production programs have typically had a high content of quality inspection points. Inspection points are examples of non-value-added operations. In the past, multiple inspection points were required because the assembly processes were highly variable and uncontrolled. By institutionalizing concurrent engineering, processes are now designed into the assembly flow that are controlled and repeatable. Because the output of these processes are predictable, we no longer need multiple inspection points. Therefore, we eliminate waste by removing the non-value-added inspection steps.

Another non-value-added recurring process is test. Because test is non-value-added, we need to minimize it to eliminate waste. Although some testing is required, we should minimize redundant testing. One of the benefits of using controlled and repeatable processes is that the output from these processes is predictable. Therefore, we don't have to test something that has been tested earlier if we know that the processes used after the initial test have not injected variability into the product. A good example of this principle is the previously-mentioned minimization of launch-site processing. We test the spacecraft prior to shipping it to the launch site, and don't test it at the launch site unless shipping indicators or sensors show that it exceeded a shipping process limit.

Test is just another process. During the early phases of design, we should view the assembly and test efforts as processes that must be controlled and repeatable. Similar to satellite manufacturing processes, we should establish goals for all test processes. These goals should relate to cycle time, quality (predicted test yields), and cost. We should question any non-value-added steps and, if possible, eliminate them. If a test continually exhibits a 100% yield rate then we need to determine if the test is necessary.

The reality is that test yields are not always 100% and finding defects at higher levels of integration can negatively impact cycle time and cost. The goal of performing a test is to find the defect at the lowest possible level of integration. This reduces the amount of time and effort required to get to the problem area and fix it. Even after tests have been performed there are instances when the quality of the lower level hardware may still be suspect at the higher levels of integration. Therefore, it is important to design in accessibility at the higher levels of integration. We may need this accessibility to repair a defect that has passed undetected through a lower level test operation or to incorporate late design modifications prior to sealing the satellite. Design for accessibility needs to be a goal of the program vision because it doesn't happen without conscious effort. For a detailed discussion of process design and production trends, see Shunk [1992].

*** Pull Production Systems**

Traditional satellite manufacture and mass production in general is based on a push system. In other words, the material and work-in-process is generally pushed or processed through the system. The emphasis is on processing the hardware through the production line as quickly as possible. Unfortunately, this can create pockets of inefficiency and bottlenecks (throughput limiters). These problems require excess factory space for inventory of material and product, and can create excessive defects and cycle times.

Lean production utilizes a pull production methodology. Material and work-in-process is not processed until upstream stations are ready. Downstream processes do not create excess inventory, because the production system will not allow production to continue unnecessarily. The system is tuned for a continuous process flow, with necessary materials being delivered Just In Time in small quantities.

23.5.3 Influencing the Design

Success of production depends on the manufacturing/production disciplines being involved throughout the product design. Through concurrent engineering, we develop the product involving various disciplines of the trade. For satellite design, this includes such expertise as electrical, mechanical, software, test, industrial, and reliability engineering; it also includes other less-technical but equally important functions such as contracts, finance, procurement and scheduling. The manufacturing role, in particular, acts as the main interface between many product teams due to their direct responsibility of ensuring a producible product. All experts must get involved with the design early and continually to the extent they can influence the product to meet their respective goals or to compromise with others. At the very least, if the experts can't reach an acceptable term, they can highlight the issue very early in the program so that they can continually work it into an acceptable term.

To influence the design, the program team must first establish a common vision for the enterprise. This common vision serves to create a working platform that allows the supply chain to collectively communicate. It provides the central theme to which the program will focus regardless of where anyone's portion of the business is located. The common vision creates the need for goals and guidelines in each concurrent design area within the program. Overarching goals must be established to provide incentive for the program; they should be difficult to attain, yet attainable within the program life.

To supplement the goals, the team must establish specifically defined rules and guidelines to bring the goals to fruition. The vision, goals, and guidelines provide the program with a standard, central direction that, in turn, provides the program with the opportunity to be efficient and united. The intention of a common vision is not to strip individual company identity, rather to converge on certain business ideas that alleviate challenges due to diverse mindsets, backgrounds, and corporate cultures.

Designing to goals and guidelines sounds simple but may be difficult in practice; few programs have these clearly outlined at the inception of the program. Implementing goals at the beginning of the program is where they are most effective. DARPA studies have shown that approximately 70% of the cost of the system is fixed by the end of the idea/conceptual design phase (Fig. 23-13).

A concept becomes feasible through refinement and, in turn, producible through other iterations of refinement. If we initiate the guidelines of design at the conceptual level, it is less costly and less painful to iterate to a feasible design. The cost to correct problems occurring from a previous program phase increases by an order of magnitude, approximately (Fig. 23-14). A simple design change during the conceptual design phase will cost 10 times during breadboard phase and 100 times during engineering model phase.

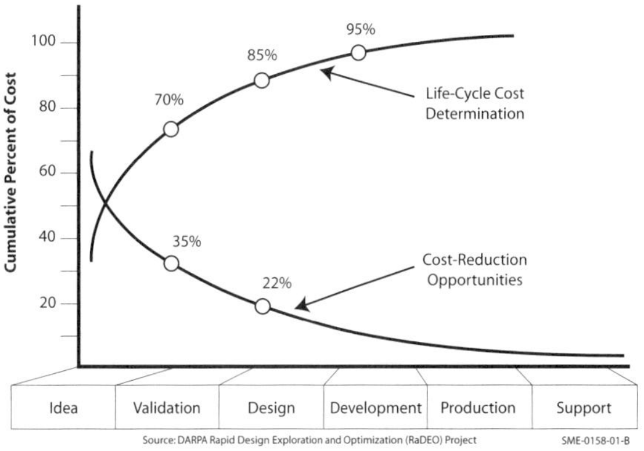

Fig. 23-13. Project Phase/Cost Assignment. The ultimate costs of a system are greatly influenced by decisions made early in the product life cycle. Based on model fit to empirical data.

The feasible design should already be largely configured to the goals and, therefore, iterating to the production level should be relatively smooth. The iteration process is smoother because the team knows what is expected through the long-term goals.

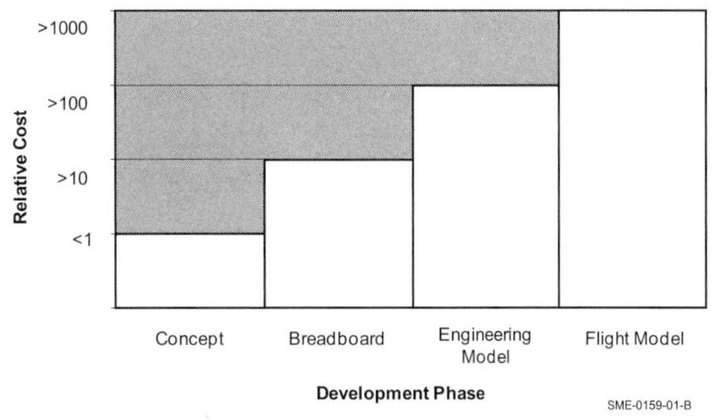

Fig. 23-14. The Relative Cost of Modification / Corrective Action. The relative cost of fixing a design problem escalates rapidly as the design matures.

Production goals and guidelines should include all production-related information for the product. This information encompasses the expectations for both parts and processes as these two ingredients form a product. It also provides structure for the product to grow properly since it addresses quality, capabilities, production rates, facility requirements, procurement, cost, warranty, manufacturability, and testability. For example, The design dictates product quality. If the product has a 2-sigma design, the best we can expect is a 2-sigma product.

Knowing the expectations initially not only assists the product to mature into production, and assists the product team to develop. Having these goals gives the team a purpose to commonly focus their attention. Successful teamwork resolves issues seemingly otherwise unresolvable. Communication becomes clearer and less conflicting because the team uses common terms to explain the common goals. A good team forms to produce a working product without relying upon functional titles and positions. Additionally, trust forms within the team. Yet, trust and competition are not mutually exclusive. Team members may and will form partnerships with competitors for different projects or products, but this practice must not hinder the primary business relationships. Lack of trust causes program inefficiencies.

Initially, the prime contractor must derive the goals and guidelines; however, the suppliers must then work closely with the prime contractor to further develop, understand and modify the expectations as necessary. In any event, if team members don't understand or believe the goals, the team's ability to influence the design is diluted, and the prime contractor must begin to educate them about the goals. Furthermore, it is especially important to derive the goals so they are meaningful. For example, assembly time of a high volume, high complexity product (indicative of the constellation satellite industry) typically comprises less than 35% of the overall cycle time while production test comprises the remaining 65% [Olivieri, 1997]. Using the Pareto Principle* approach we find that the greatest opportunity to influence the design is in production test.

> * **The Pareto Principle**
>
> If we rank order contributors to a problem from greatest influence to least influence, the *Pareto Principle* states that only a few of the contributors will comprise the bulk of the influence. In general, 80% of the contribution comes from 20% of the factors. Pareto analysis is a technique for ranking items according to their contribution and analyzing the top contributors, or the "vital few." The other 80% of the factors that only influence 20% of the contribution are the "trivial many."

Design influence is most effective through mathematical analysis. Personal bias and tradition are not the basis for influence. When we select a part for a product, we inherently select the process as well. This means that predicting behaviors (e.g., quality, reliability, cycle time, assembly process) of the product is possible. We do this by collecting data from suppliers but where data is not available we either run an experiment or locate like-product data. Key predictions include, but are not limited to: *defect per unit*, *defects per million opportunities*, statistical tolerance and variability assessments, *design to unit production cost*, solids modeling, cycle time, process modeling and mapping, design of experiments, and simulations.

Having the data equates to having the knowledge to influence design. The only way we achieve key goals in areas such as quality, manufacturability, and profit is if they are designed in.

Influencing the design is an enterprise challenge. Awareness of our up and down stream product map helps us make smart decisions for the overall program. Locally maximizing cycle time, quality, assembly ease and other areas of importance, does not always provide the same benefit to the overall program. Standardization of analysis tools, metrics, goals, and guidelines help to relate design impacts to the supply chain.

23.5.4 Process Development and Verification

Quality, and the resulting efficiency of manufacturing, is never an accident. It is the result of good design practices and sound process development methods—with the addition of management and execution diligence. Significant process development and verification activities must take place to manufacture high quality products. For satellite manufacturing, we need to apply these methods at all levels—suppliers, sub-tier suppliers, payload assembly and test, space vehicle integration, and launch operations.

In the manufacturing context, we define a process as any activity that changes or touches the product or requires resources. The objective is to use simple, uncomplicated processes that yield high quality results with short cycle times. Very few processes meet these general criteria without development. Therefore, sound development methods are key. The end goal is to have controlled and repeatable high quality processes during the production phase of the program.

Development Methods

We can apply structured development methods to process and product development. Many methods exist, and most have merit. Here, we use a *four-phase process development*, a.k.a. *process characterization*, model. Other useful and powerful models include DMAIC (Define Measure Analyze Improve Control) and DFSS (Design for Six Sigma). We should first apply a development model to critical processes and then extend it to other processes as necessary.

The process characterization model consists of four phases.

Phase 1: *Process Definition*—Map the process to understand the variables and characteristics involved.

Phase 2: *Process Capability*—Establish current level of performance of the process. Does the process perform as needed?

Phase 3: *Process Optimization*—Investigate the variables to determine which variables drive the process output. Determine the best levels for these variables to provide optimal process output.

Phase 4: *Process Control*—Monitor the process and its important variables to determine when its performance has changed or is out of control.

We iterate the cycle to further improve the process as necessary. (See Fig. 23-15.)

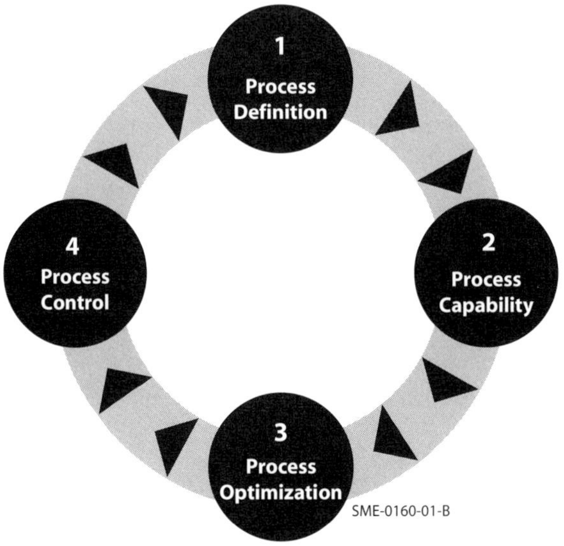

Fig. 23-15. Process Characterization Four Phase Model. We iterate this cycle to continually improve the product or process.

We characterize the process to identify and remove sources of variation. Ultimately, variation is the cause for product quality problems. We use statistical tools, such as *Design of Experiments* and *Statistical Process Control*, to reduce the variation, which improves quality and subsequently reduces cost and cycle time. See Montgomery [2000] for detailed discussions about statistical tools.

Cycles of Learning

In addition to the iterations caused by characterizing the production process, we may need additional cycles of learning when developing satellite constellation production systems. Varying techniques are available, depending on the subject matter.

For instance, we use simulation techniques to model and predict performance. Discrete event simulation packages can model processes, factories, and whole supply chains. We can use these models to determine resource requirements, facility size, inventory schemes, and delivery schedules. We can explore proposed changes to pre-established baselines without risk.

A second source of cycles of learning is the use of prototyping. Prototyping allows for physical evaluation—appearance and dimensional—while changes are easier and less expensive to make. Production changes are extremely costly, and potentially devastating. We can potentially avoid them through early prototyping. The use of *Dynamic Test Models* and *Engineering Development Models* are advanced functional examples of prototypes.

A third source is the use of *pathfinding activities*. The more complex a system and its logistics, the more beneficial pathfinding activities become. They revolve around building a scale representation, usually 1:1, of a product and using it to simulate all handling, manufacturing, and logistical activities. For satellites, this includes practicing and iterating every process, from subsystem receipt to integration processing to launch processing. The resulting benefits of pathfinding include handling streamlining, mechanical checkfit verification, documentation improvement, process development, tooling improvement, facility development, and logistical simplification.

In short, any activity that we can simulate or realize before we create an actual product can have significant payback. These sources of learning are important tools to gain significant process and product knowledge.

23.5.5 Production

All of the previous phases—creating the manufacturing vision, influencing the design, and process development—lead to the final phase—production. All previous goals are to make this phase easy to execute. Failure or lack of attention in the previous phases becomes readily apparent here. They surface as schedule slips, exceeded budgets, and poor quality.

Executing the overall plans and goals established in the earlier phases is paramount. While many production issues are similar for building one satellite or one hundred, some areas are significantly different. These areas include supply chain management and production floor management.

Supply-Chain Management

A supply-chain focus is key to the successfully executing the production phase of a multiple satellite program. The supply chain is defined as all of the suppliers and activities involved with producing a satellite. This involves the major suppliers—bus, payload, and antennas—and the subtier suppliers.

Communicating and coordinating across the supply chain is critical. Fundamentally, all the suppliers need to have a common vision and sense of direction. In effect, the major suppliers become partners. Openly communicating goals, expectations, and problem solving is essential. To facilitate communication, we need to seek a common language and culture through common training and team building. The resulting program culture can be built on the strengths of each partner (Fig. 23-16).

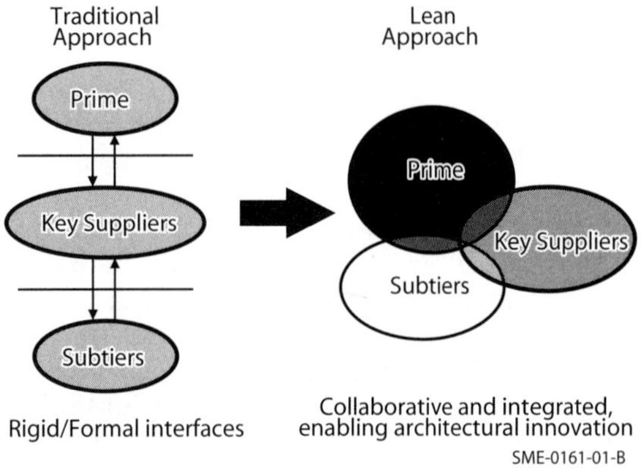

Fig. 23-16. Lean Supply Chain Model. Creating a collaborative and integrated supply chain enables lean performance while traditional approaches create boundaries and limitations.

Concurrent engineering across company lines must occur. All company entities must share the key design rules or characteristics early in the process and maintain them throughout the program. We must carefully define and fully understand the interfaces and handoffs. We should develop and use common tooling and processes. For instance, shipping containers carrying subassemblies to final integration should support integration activities without a tooling transfer. They should seamlessly integrate into the factory. Finally, common metrics across the supply chain allow for meaningful summation of data, so managers can judge the overall system health. These metrics should center around quality, cycle time, and critical parameter performance.

Production Floor Management

Performance and executing the production phase uses principles similar to any production environment. In addition to supply chain management, consistent performance takes lean manufacturing principles of production floor management, including good processes, qualified workers, and timely information.

Short cycle, well understood processes and overall processing is fundamental to lean manufacturing. Simulation or other flow design tools help to determine optimum production flows that reduce the risks of production delays. The flows and processing should include *Just In Time* (JIT) concepts to minimize *Work In Process* (WIP) inventory and improve quality and cycle time. JIT hinges on delivering material items when the flow needs them in a pull fashion. We don't move items until they are ready for processing. Less hardware is in process, thereby reducing the potential for damage and reducing overall floor space requirements.

Qualified workers that understand the processing of space hardware are still required for satellite production. While still required, their roles and specific skills are very different than traditional programs. Highly specialized and narrowly skilled positions now become broader and more generalized. The design attributes resulting from a successful multi-satellite design team will require less intensive processing. In addition to being less difficult, the processing needs to be more repeatable. We can train or certify workers for each repeatable operation, so they can typically monitor their own work. We minimize quality inspections. Instead, the individual or the team is responsible for performing each operation correctly and safely.

The capture and use of timely production data is a third production floor management challenge. Producing multiple satellites with short cycle times requires us to collect, use, and archive data differently from traditional methods. Paper, the traditional documentation medium, is too cumbersome, untimely, and not available to multiple disciplines. Constellations based on a large number of satellites require volumes of data be available to multiple users. We need factory systems for work instruction and process planning; transmittal of product data between suppliers, integrators, and users; and for factory data collection. Factory data collection includes calibration, as-built, WIP tracking, and quality data and/or information. Using common tools for these functions across the supply chain would be an added advantage.

23.5.6 Summary

These methods apply to multiple satellite constellations and were applied to the Iridium program, with outstanding cost and schedule results. Extensive constellation reliability and performance data has been collected on the Iridium system and its satellites. The system is still operating in 2010, even though every satellite has exceeded its 5–8 year design life. Some operational satellites have been in use for over thirteen years at the time of this publication. See the book website for a description of the Iridium Satellite Assembly Process.

Get More

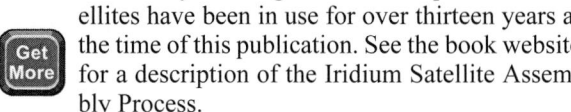

Smaller constellations, non-communication payloads, and high-value missions may use subsets of these practices. In all cases, thoughtful selection of parts and processes and skillful application of concurrent engineering practices are paramount.

23.6 Alternative Approaches to Space Manufacturing

Jaime Esper, *NASA GSFC*

Current NASA space systems are mainly driven by performance and reliability to ensure science requirements are successfully met. Exacting the most performance is necessary, if one is to be assured of only a handful of flights in one's lifetime. Reliability is of course a way to ensure that time wasted is kept at a minimum, and that precious data is acquired (relatively) on schedule. But what if flights were more frequent and opportunities for participation in meaningful science increased? If failure were an option we would not hesitate to take the risks necessary to advance the state of art in supporting the acquisition of volumes of specialized data. If space system costs were reduced, then failure may not be seen as wasteful. Of course, spectacular failures are often the result of launch vehicle or spacecraft malfunctions. So what if both the launch vehicle and the spacecraft were "acceptably" inexpensive? To achieve this, it is necessary to examine the way space systems have been designed, manufactured, assembled, tested, flown, and operated. In other words, we must find alternative approaches to space system manufacturing and implementation. At the same time, we must examine what type of missions may be candidates for this new paradigm, and an architecture developed that clearly establishes some boundary conditions on which to operate. This game-changing application approach also needs to be placed into context with past experiences, to extract what works, and what needs improvement.

23.6.1 Historical References for Alternative Approaches

There are a number of examples of programs and spacecraft that tried to incorporate ideas to reduce the cost of flying space missions, either by providing a multi-mission spacecraft, or by judicious application of programmatic approaches and principles to run a production line. A few examples from the NASA side include the *Multimission Modular Spacecraft* (MMS) and the *Small Explorers Program* (SMEX). Other organizations have also experimented with alternative cost-effective approaches, including Freja, the joint Swedish-German micro-satellite for atmospheric research, and the US Iridium communications production. We will examine each of these in more or less detail, to highlight the areas where the aerospace community has advanced ideas on alternative approaches that attempt to reduce cost, and at the same time advance the state of the art in space manufacturing.

The Multi-Mission Modular Spacecraft (MMS)

The MMS was a standard, 3-axis stabilized spacecraft design conceived to accommodate the largest number of missions, whether in low Earth or in geosynchronous orbits [Bartlett and Cepollina, 1975]. Specifically, 4 design reference missions were envisioned: Sun, Earth, astronomical observations from low-Earth orbits, and Earth observation from geosynchronous orbits. The motivation for developing and implementing the MMS concept was not much different in 1969 than it is today: the desire to get more for less, or at least, to be able to go the extra mile with a constrained budget. The key to the concept was modularity, and the ability to incorporate mission-unique hardware with minimal impact to the established bus design. Cost savings were expected through maximum use of *standard components*, design of a set of *standard subsystem modules* with application to the reference missions, and leveraging the Space Shuttle for "orbit re-supply and retrieval of modular subsystems and instruments," thereby extending the usefulness of a particular mission. Shuttle servicing potential required a clear perspective on interface simplicity. This called for maintaining a minimum number of electrical and mechanical connections at the servicing interface, preservation of thermal interface integrity, one structural and thermal design for all reference missions, and maximum use of previously flown components, including the use of NASA standard components. A basic premise of the MMS design included the use of *interface standards*, permitting module exchange between spacecraft. This would also allow for re-design of internal subsystem configurations in order to implement required performance upgrades. In addition, backward-compatibility would permit the re-fitting of operational spacecraft with subsystems produced at a later date [Falkenhayn, 1988]. The baseline MMS configuration contained three standard modules: attitude control, communications and data handling, and power subsystems. Additional modules were considered mission unique, and included configurations for antenna, solar arrays, and propulsion. The standard subsystem modules were supported by a thrust-axis load bearing structure, outfitted at either end by transition and base adapters. An exploded view of MMS is shown in Fig. 23-17.

The MMS program made important contributions to I&T processes and procedures [Greenwell, 1978]. In the early days at the NASA Goddard Space Flight Center (GSFC), complete prototype spacecraft were produced and tested to environmental levels greater than those expected under operational conditions, in order to demonstrate design margins of safety. After proving hardware so tested would not be degraded, GSFC developed the *protoflight* concept. Instead of building an entire copy for testing alone, protoflight hardware was built and tested to prototype levels but for durations normally used to test flight hardware. This saved the cost of producing hardware intended for testing alone. Protoflight testing was usually applied to the first unit in a series, but not to the production units. Testing at the module level was favored over component or spacecraft system (sans the payload) testing. This was a reasonable approach, as it was envisioned that modules would be produced by different vendors and integrated already

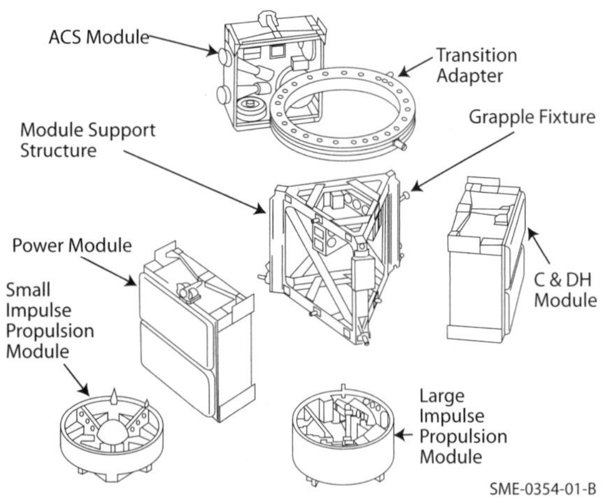

Fig. 23-17. The Multimission Modular Spacecraft. [Bartlett and Cepollina, 1975].

pre-qualified into a flight system on the ground, or as replacement units for orbiting spacecraft. Testing at the payload or observatory level was still executed, but that was the responsibility of the project end-user. Many concepts developed during MMS were incorporated into the defacto standard for spacecraft testing contained in Goddard's *General Environmental Verification Specification* (GEVS) for STS and ELV payloads, subsystems, and components, and applied in spacecraft servicing such as SMM and Hubble Space Telescope (HST).

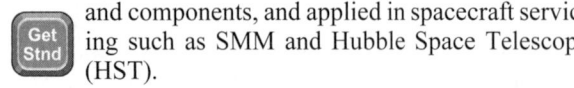

The Small Explorers Program (SMEX)

SMEX was a NASA program started in 1988 to provide frequent flight opportunities for focused and relatively inexpensive space science missions. The program executed at GSFC included a small team that worked across several mission boundaries, with overlapping mission developments. This staggered approach allowed satellite launches once every 12 to 18 months. Structures, thermal designs, and attitude control systems were designed per mission needs, whereas other subsystems were taken from an inventory of spacecraft designs that were developed for the initial 3 SMEX missions (SAMPEX, FAST, and SWAS). The architecture used standardized instrument and operational interfaces including a distributed system (at the subsystem level) with standard hardware and software interfaces. To this end all subsystems/instruments communicated through a MIL-STD 1553/1773 bus [DoD, 1978] (low rate) and RS-422 (high rate) serial port. Initial SMEX spacecraft relied primarily on the GSFC Wallops Flight Facility (WFF) and the Deep Space Network for ground station coverage.

The "SMEX-Lite" architecture was developed to optimize the spacecraft and mission design process in order to shorten development, integration, and test times. Subsystems were broken into functional slices, covering a single basic function. This minimized the rippling effects of changes within the system box. Functional slices had to be easy to interface and transparent to each other, behaving akin to an early implementation of aerospace *plug-and-play* (PnP) components. Most software development activities were planned using a PC representation of each of the functional slices. This concept resulted in the definition of an open architecture for mission design which included the electronics, sensors/actuators, software, solar array, mechanical system, and ground operations system.

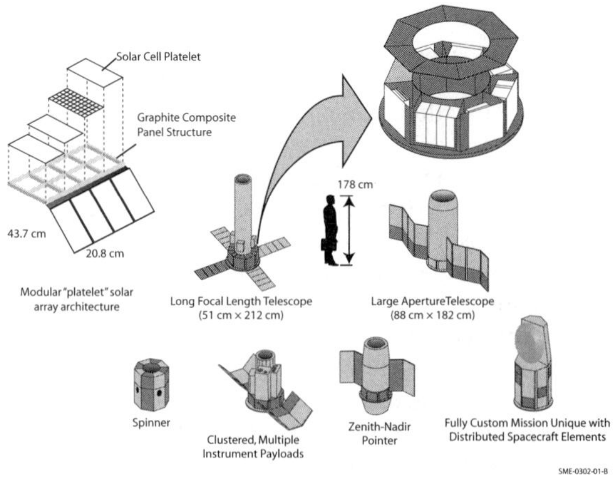

Fig. 23-18. SMEX-Lite Architecture Flexibility.

Industry standards were used for interfacing the functional slices (e.g., PCI bus, MIL-STD 1553). Reliance on programmable devices allowed for rapid prototyping and flexibility of changes to flight circuitry. The use of a standard card size allowed for one mechanical/thermal box design. The solar array design used a modular "platelet" approach, consisting of full string cell configurations mounted on a composite mini-panel. The reduction in spacecraft electronics lead to the adoption of a standard mechanical bus configuration: a monolithic aluminum casting piece, with electronic boxes directly incorporated into it. Ground system testing was to use standard TCP/IP protocols. There was only one SMEX-Lite spacecraft built (TRIANA), and although it was never flown, the SMEX-Lite concepts survived the test of time and have been implemented in numerous NASA and non-NASA spacecraft and flight missions.

The SMEX-Lite modular architecture flexibility, including its structure and modular (sliced) subsystem architecture, promised to enable multiple instrument configurations and mission implementations. Figure 23-18 shows this potential assortment of layout and applications.

Iridium

The Iridium satellite constellation was first placed operational in 1998. This experiment on global communications and data coverage initially found itself in trouble, and not too much later in 1999 its parent company

Iridium LLC went into bankruptcy. With new management, Iridium Satellite LLC is now a viable provider of services to industry and government organizations. The most relevant aspect of this venture for the discussion at hand is that Iridium represents the first mass-production example of commercial satellites in the world.

From a general industry perspective, the production line approach uses similar principles already described: units are assembled concurrently, with standard components that are integrated as the line progresses. In a way, the next project is underway before the previous one is complete. Only the initial units are flight qualified, and the rest are verified by similarity. The one drawback to this approach however, is when it comes time to upgrade the existing system. As the units are identical, all components come together to form a complete system module. Design flexibility may be traded against system flexibility, and the module level of integration. The success of these constellations relies on system-level redundancy, rather than on module-level redundancy, where modules may be interchanged among satellites of different capability, but with standard interfaces. This philosophy is carried into the current thinking behind modular, adaptive, reconfigurable space systems.

The Swedish Small Satellite Program

The Swedish Small Satellite Program has been effective in utilizing tight budgets achieving excellent results to that effect through streamlined project organizations where responsibility is pushed to the lowest possible level, and piggy-back rides [Lundahl, 1998]. The Freja satellite was dedicated to aurora research, and included simple, in-situ instruments and an UV imager. Freja-C was based on its predecessor, and in a sense followed the production-line approach. Astrid, the first Swedish microsatellite, carried instrumentation to study upper atmospheric plasma, with a total mass of 27 kg. Astrid-2 again followed the successful paradigm of limited production run, and was also dedicated to upper atmospheric plasma research. The important point to make here is that the Swedish program started with a basic approach of simple satellites achieving important results, and used serial compatibility with previous mission designs (backward compatible).

23.6.2 A New Architecture for Alternative Space Mission Implementation

Since late 2002 GSFC has been taking a new look at space mission approaches, incorporating experiences from past successful spacecraft and programs. In particular, there are 2 progressively refined, yet common system architectures: the *Modular Reconfigurable Rapid* (MR^2) architecture [Esper et al. 2004], which in many ways remains the same basic approach adopted by the DoD Operationally Responsive Space (ORS) Office today, and a slightly new variation that incorporates adaptive systems into the mix: *Modular Adaptive Reconfigurable Systems* (MARS) [Esper, 2005]. These are the result of government and industry experience and collaboration that extends as far back as the beginning of space flight.

MARS is a system-level architecture that comprises all elements of a space mission life cycle, including ground and space segments. MARS establishes a set of basic guidelines upon which technologies can be developed. Exactly what it means for a technology to be MARS-compatible will be explained. It should be realized however that any static definition of an architecture that has "adaptive" and "reconfigurable" in its term would simply be counterproductive, or at the very least, transient. So this definition is intended to evolve over time.

The defining terms offered for MARS may be thought of as initial, or boundary conditions, in the traditional sense of the term. These boundary conditions, which factor both programmatic and technical concerns, are used to develop a particular solution domain containing a set of technologies. Again, technology evolution and programmatic concerns can necessitate the changing of these initial conditions. This is one key result of the 20/20 hindsight obtained from MMS. There are neither standard boxes nor standard spacecraft. Even standard interfaces, a key element of MARS, are allowed to evolve over time. Insofar as interfaces are known to evolve at a slower rate than technologies though, they qualify here for the term "standard," with a caveat.

So what are the basic premises used to set the stage for development of MARS technologies and systems? They are summarized below. But first, a few definitions are in order.

Modular: MARS systems contain selectable mechanical, electrical, and software components that may be used and re-used in modular or quantized numbers. Modular (or quantum) components used in a system must be capable of evolving to incorporate advances in technology, and they must accept standard interfaces and plug-and-play principles (e.g., Personal Computers). Collectively (and individually) MARS modular components and systems must result in intelligent units, referring to their ability to assemble into larger components or systems on the ground or on-orbit. A module can have varying levels of integration, from the chip to the card, box, subsystem, system, and system of systems. As an extension of the above, a module is capable of carrying a function either by itself, or as a conglomerate system.

True today as it was 40 years ago, plug-and-play interfaces are not yet implemented in space flight systems. The ability to recognize components autonomously as they are added to a modular system is a key in realizing schedule savings and streamlining integration and test. This is important for astronauts on a Moon or Mars base, or for cost-savings on the ground.

Adaptive: This term is used along the lines of the classic control systems definition. In simple terms, an *adaptive control system* is one that is capable of learning from its environment, and acting accordingly. An adaptive MARS system would permit reconfiguration of its mechanical (including thermal), electrical, or software characteristics to changing requirements, whether they are precipitated through an *a priori* definition **("I did not intend for the system to do this, but now that you mention it, by design it can adapt")**, or autonomously required on the field based on previously unanticipated events.

This concept is entirely new, and had not been entertained by the MMS nor the SMEX or other system-level architectures. Rather, due to technological limitations MMS relied more on standard subsystems designed to accommodate the largest number of missions *a priori.* Missions that fell outside of this design envelope were better served by one-of-a-kind approaches.

Reconfigurable: The system must be capable of morphing in order to apply to a host of missions. It also must be easy to produce, integrate, test, and launch. In addition, it must be capable of operating alone or as a collective part, physically detached or attached. Reconfigurable systems are considered at varying scales, from electrical components and MEMS, to whole spacecraft, or pieces of a Moon base. It differs from adaptability in the sense that reconfiguration is expected based on a set of known boundary conditions. A system may be reconfigurable, yet not be capable to adapt to changing requirements in certain cases. However, a system that can adapt is always reconfigurable in that particular instance. MMS can best be described as a reconfigurable-only system, within the limited set of missions for which it was conceived.

***System*:** Normally, one should not have to define what a system is. Yet, there may be as many definitions as there are engineering disciplines. The MARS architecture allows all as it should: a system takes on as many incarnations as there are modules. One could consider an atom as being the most elemental module (true, one could go even smaller), and indeed it is a system composed of protons, electrons, and neutrons (the simple model). For practical purposes, a system is an entity that carries out a specific function, whether it opens and closes tiny MEMS "Venetian blinds" (variable emissivity coating), distributes power over an entire spacecraft, or coordinates construction tasks among multiple robots and humans. The important thing to remember is that the MARS architecture is not limited to small or large systems: it can be as broad or as narrow as required. This broad application of the MARS architecture stands in stark contrast to the MMS design philosophy of only modularizing 3 key subsystems: attitude control, communications and data handling, and power subsystem. **Levels of modularity or integration are then used in MARS to provide the reconfigurability to satisfy a broad range of predefined mission classes, or the adaptability to adjust to unexpected mission requirements**.

The basic design methodology for MARS spacecraft and systems is summarized as follows. Note that these are only broad suggestions in what is hoped to be a reasonable set of principles to follow. However, alternative concepts are not only welcome, but also expected as the space community finds the best implementation approach for the evolving times.

- MARS spacecraft and systems should take advantage of multi-billion dollar commercial standards for manufacturing, computing, and communications technology. This results in sustainable systems, where not only the government is the contributing source of funds to maintain technology relevance.
- The modular design architecture must be capable of advancing along with technology improvements. In other words, the module can contain technology relevant to its time, and is not fictitiously constrained to some standard.
- Standardization is implemented at the interface, not at the subsystem or system level. Electrical interfaces should use commercial standards, such as Ethernet, Firewire, USB, Spacewire, CAN, and other well-established approaches. Of preference would be those electrical interfaces that lend themselves to a plug-and-play implementation. Mechanical and fluid interfaces should also be standard and flexible enough to accommodate various layout configurations. Specialized interfaces can be developed **only** if required for a particular set or sets of applications. Components should electrically attach via standard interfaces much as peripherals attach to a computer. Each peripheral would need to come with its software driver. The driver is either pre-loaded in the operating system, or loaded as needed by the user. Mechanical and fluid interfaces represent a special challenge, since there is currently little use of standards, except in the launch vehicle industry or for space station applications.
- Choice technologies (not standard) may be incorporated, with a list reviewed and **updated** at regular intervals to maintain technological relevance.
- A modular open systems architecture should be encouraged throughout, whether in the software or hardware arena. This would encourage participation by a broad community, and would ensure minimal implementation lock-ins or bottlenecks.
- The flight software should be based on a layered architecture, with maximum re-use of infrastructure and application modules. No doubt, software technology has improved leaps and bounds since the MMS days. Today, software can be developed which is completely independent of the platform or operating system. One of the key factors in the success of the PC platform for instance, is the choice and backwards compatibility afforded between many different types of hardware and software, a concept partly borrowed by MMS and the early SMEX program. This is made possible by the BIOS (Basic Input/Output System) and the soft-

ware layer model. The system BIOS acts as an interface between the hardware and the computer operating system, on top of which the application layer resides. Each layer communicates to the layer below through a standard interface. This way neither the operating system nor the application layers "care" which the hardware host is. The *Open Systems Interconnect* (OSI) Reference Model also defines a modular approach to networking, with each layer (module) responsible for some specific aspect of the networking process. Earlier attempts at software development had more to do with defining standards for High Order Programming Languages [DiNitto, 1978], than concentrating in standard interfaces between highly portable software modules. From an operating system perspective, effort should be spent in ensuring proprietary implementations are kept to a minimum, to stimulate inter-operability among different providers. Whenever a proprietary operating system is used, assurance of compatibility with open code systems should be required.

- As much as possible, communications and information exchange should be done directly from the user to the spacecraft and back, through a distributed internet-like operation. The ensuing architecture calls for the use of spacecraft and space systems as point extensions on the Internet: i.e., each connected through a ground system Ethernet.

Table 23-14 shows a comparison of MMS, SMEX, and MARS concepts and operating principles. Note the similarities, but more importantly, the significant differences that result from 35+ years of technology evolution and hindsight. MMS and the early SMEX were important trailblazers for today's MARS systems and without them we simply could not have evolved to where we are today.

Process Flow

The reduction in design-through-launch life cycle and ensuing cost savings necessitate the existence of a well-established infrastructure. This infrastructure may be based on several approaches: from the pre-built system sitting on a shelf, to the (more desirable) one of having components in a warehouse ready to be integrated to suit. The latter approach lends itself to the greatest degree of flexibility, as modular components may be chosen all the way from the chip level to the box level for a truly unique application every time. Figure 23-19 shows the high-level process behind MR^2 spacecraft [Esper, et al. 2004]. First, a need is identified and a request for action is issued to the MR^2 team. The space system concept is next defined within a virtual design environment, where the mission objectives and the requirements are fine-tuned to develop an operations concept and a spacecraft design. The design also generates an inventory list of required parts and components, which can then be accessed at a *Spacecraft Depot* (SD), in much the same way one would fetch parts to build a project at a "do it

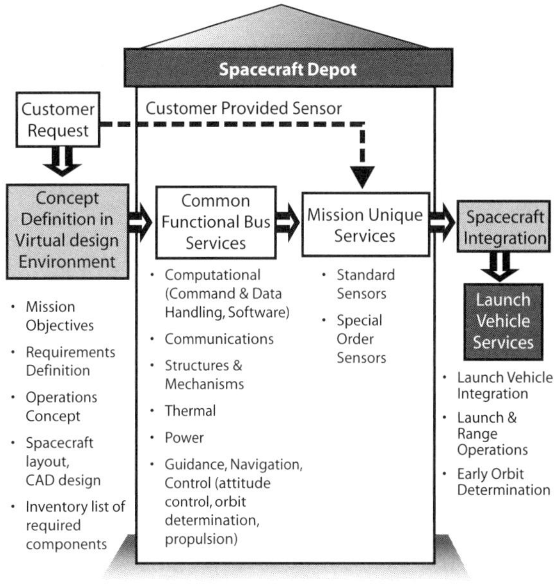

Fig. 23-19. MR^2 Spacecraft Process Flow—The Spacecraft Depot.

yourself" store. In order to be effective, this "store" must contain a variety of select components defined to accommodate multiple mission applications. The length of time for this process depends directly on whether the application sensor (instrument) is sitting on a shelf, is provided by the user, or needs a special order.

The physical location of the SD is a matter of choice and desired objectives. Implementations range from a distributed, virtual SD with components maintained at various manufacturer's sites, to a centralized warehouse. Its final implementation would depend on the need for quick access to all components, versus the market drivers of supply and demand. Clearly, quick-response systems would benefit from a centralized location. This model would not be much different from the one used by individual projects today, which acquire parts in quantities and store them as spare parts. The idea would be to extend this practice to creating a "super project" (in fact a *program*), capable of servicing more than just one mission need.

23.6.3 Boundary Conditions and Mission Applications

Now that several leading approaches to space manufacturing have been identified, and a promising new approach consisting of the sum-value of previous attempts has been defined and placed into historical context, it is important to establish the kinds of missions that can exact benefit from it. Clearly there are legacy approaches for missions that still require the traditional (and expensive) paradigm to space mission implementation. But there are a larger number of possibilities, so far underexploited, that can benefit from current alternatives.

Table 23-14. Comparison of MMS, SMEX, and MARS Concepts and Operating Principles.

Defining Characteristics			
Characteristic	**MMS**	**Early SMEX/SMEX-Lite**	**MARS**
Modularity	Implemented primarily at the subsystem level	Drop-down one level from the "box" to the "functional slice"	Uses **levels of integration**, where a module can be a MEMS device, electronic chip, card, box, subsystem, system, or system-of-systems
Adaptability	Not implemented	Not implemented	System **capable of learning** and acting either *a priori* or real-time from its environment
Reconfigurability	System designed to service a specific class of missions	System designed to service a specific class of missions (small explorers). Drop-down in modularity provides more flexibility than MMS	The system is **entirely morphable** in order to apply to a host of missions. Made possible by modular levels of integration and adaptability
Design Methodology			
Key Area	**MMS**	**SMEX-Lite**	**MARS**
Sustainability, Affordability	The supporting infrastructure did not develop as expected, requiring Shuttle flights, broad spacecraft servicing, and individual project buy-ins	SMEX-Lite provided significant advances in implementing industry interface standards; in particular the PCI bus for internal avionics card interconnects. It also provided a sound basis for realizing cost-savings through an open system architecture concept. Monolithic structure with tailored thermal designs	Leverage multi-billion dollar **commercial standards** for manufacturing, computing, and communications technology. This includes PnP interface definitions featuring device discovery, IP communications, and reconfigurable mechanical/thermal concepts that incorporate the latest advances in technology. Modular Open Systems Architecture for increased sustainability and affordability
Technology Relevance and Effectiveness	Relied on individual projects for technology development	Leveraged the existing Small Explorer Program to inject common hardware and interfaces across different missions	Relies on establishment of a technology or program series that can carry evolutionary changes in a sequential, phased manner
Standardization, Reliability	Primarily at the box or subsystem level	Modularity standards dropped down to the "functional slice" level. Some standard subsystems, common form-factors for electronic components, and aerospace industry standard electrical interfaces	Standardization at the **interface only**. Choice technologies, rather than standard that are updated regularly on a well established recurring approach
Spacecraft Operating System	One-of-a-kind, often proprietary implementation	Open architecture for software systems. However, tailored operating system	**Open code architecture** (expanding on SMEX work). Adoption of one or two compatible Operating Systems with interchangeable software modules
Flight Software	One-of-a-kind, often proprietary implementation	Structured software leveraging interface standards. Software re-use from mission to mission	Based on a modular **layered architecture**, with maximum re-use of infrastructure and application modules
Data Transport System	One-of-a-kind, often proprietary implementation	CCDS standards applied throughout. TCP/IP for ground testing	Distributed **internet-based/like** command and data flow

The legacy approach includes a rigorous systems engineering process to translate mission objectives into engineering practice and will result in spacecraft that, either because of the nature of the investigation, or because of their destination, require exacting performance and hence unique designs. Such is the nature of most planetary missions, or large systems with a complex instrument suite. Alternative approaches such as the ones described here can on the other hand satisfy more benign destinations, and are well-suited to the Earth-Moon system. Of course, a communications constellation in orbit around Mars can certainly use the Iridium experience, notwithstanding the greater expense in placing equivalent spacecraft in such orbits. The same can be said if a large number of microsatellites are launched to say, Venus. The system-level redundancy can be made to tolerate certain individual failures, so exacting performance may not be required of each individual unit. Only until a well-established program of recurring flights is implemented, we will have to differentiate between approaches for building spacecraft relatively inexpensively, versus those that cannot tolerate performance limitations (hence high cost). If an extended program is established, for instance, for flights to Venus, then the distinction becomes less clear, as the cluster of spacecraft may gather the same, or even more varied bits of information from the Venusian environment.

23.6.4 Point Design Discussion

From an implementation point of view, instantiation of MARS-compatible spacecraft (or equivalently flexible point designs) could make use of *form factors* to constrain a set of mechanical and electrical components all using specific interconnects. This may be better illustrated by borrowing an example from devices we all use extensively today. In the computer industry, the "full tower" and "mini tower" computer cases are intended to fit the *Advanced Technology Extended* (ATX) or Micro-ATX form factors, respectively. Each of these form factor specifications define **mechanical dimensions, mounting points, input/output panel, power, and connector interfaces** between the computer case, the motherboard, and the power supply. Furthermore, these cases would fit standard form factor drives and other peripherals with a set of defined fasteners. How many devices may be fitted within a case depends on its actual size or external form. So a case intended for desktop use is smaller than one intended for use under the desk (the vertical "tower"). If this computer example were to be extended to spacecraft, then we would conceptually have the equivalent "full tower" or "mini tower" system that apply to specific mission classes, at least for a finite period of time. This is because like computer form factors, spacecraft form factors would evolve. In fact, the ATX form factor itself was introduced by Intel in 1995 to replace the outdated AT form factor. Similarly, the "full tower spacecraft" may be replaced by a newer version, once its defining specifications become obsolete. The point is that module or *bus* (if we must use that "bus" word) standards, if specifically referring to form factors, may satisfy in a limited sense the technological needs of a time, but are not by all means intended in this architecture to constrain inevitable advances (i.e., modules are capable of evolving to accommodate advances in technology). As time progresses and changes do occur, these specification standards are indeed replaceable. It is important to stress that form factors can be used to constrain mechanical and electrical interfaces in a particular point design MARS-compatible spacecraft, but must not be intended for instance to constrain the modular components themselves. For this reason, the author prefers the use of "form factor" versus "module or bus standards," to ensure there is no confusion about its defining intent. Evidently, from an application perspective, a particular instantiation of a MARS-compatible spacecraft may indeed make use of particular form factors, as these may emulate the serial (yet more flexible) production of a telecommunications satellite with acronyms such as the "B series," or for that matter, the "model-T" from the automotive industry. As with computer form factors however, at some point the "B series" or the "Model T" will become irrelevant. Until that time, they may well service multiple missions.

Figure 23-20 provides an illustration of a MARS-compatible micro-satellite structure. This particular instantiation defines the mechanical interface among structural components, but leaves positioning and attachment of modular electrical components wide open based on equipment selection. In fact, the modular structure itself is internally reconfigurable, meaning that bay sizes may vary to accommodate component needs. The micro-spacecraft itself accommodates industry-standard electrical interfaces, including Ethernet and RS-422. This particular model series has been dubbed SMART-09 (Small Rocket/Spacecraft Technology), and is a collaborative effort between NASA and the US Department of Defense, Operationally Responsive Space (ORS) Office.

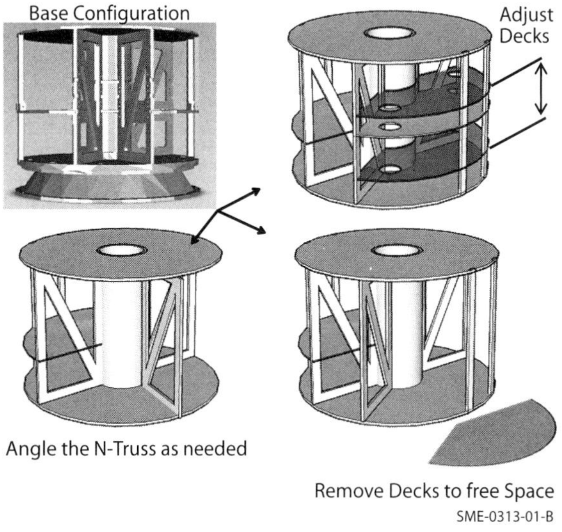

Fig. 23-20. SMART Features a Modular, Reconfigurable Structure.

23.7 Intangible Factors in Manufacturing

Markus Rufer, *Scorpius Space Launch Company*

Intangible factors in manufacturing are by nature the kinds of things that do not come properly listed, sorted and labeled. Writing about them in a logical, organized way would therefore be very difficult, although daring to do so would be rewarded by beginning to convert them into tangibles. Covering all the intangibles is impossible, because we don't know how many of them exist. Their potentially significant impact on operational results is what prompted this writing. The purpose here is to induce an awareness of their existence and to help the reader develop a sensitivity to be able to detect them in a manufacturing world that is dominated by numbers and controls—meaning tangibles, of course.

The following is a fairly extemporaneous account of my thoughts and observations on this topic, supported by published historical data findable with common search engines. I want to acknowledge that throughout my years in manufacturing across various industries, I have greatly benefited from the works of Tompkins [1989] and Goldratt [1999, 2004]. Their books are not about intangibles per se, but Tompkins' exceptionally sharp account of all the essential requirements for successful manufacturing and Goldratt's enlightened theories have shaped my thinking about manufacturing in many ways. I appreciate their extraordinary contributions in this field and the inspiration they provided me.

This section takes a less conventional look at aerospace manufacturing and its specific challenges. In particular, it highlights a small selection of intangible factors not often discussed, but perhaps no less significant in their impact on manufacturing efficiency and cost. I will use some examples from the automotive industry for contrast, because cars are subjected to fairly open and unregimented market forces—rockets are not; not yet. Why is this distinction important? It actually wasn't important for a long time, because the main actor in space as well as the main customer for space flights was the government, a fact that has profoundly shaped the aerospace manufacturing landscape. As aerospace activities begin to shift toward space commercialization, open competition will begin to affect decision making. Drastic cost reductions for launches and spacecraft fabrication cannot be achieved by tweaking the entrenched practices. Reductions can be achieved only by applying a new mentality, innovative approaches, and the incorporation of advanced enabling technologies. New approaches to seriously reducing the cost for access to space will create advantages for those who dare to be the agents of change in this industry and who will challenge established relationships and organizations.

People with technical backgrounds are used to processing hard data, verifiable facts, and proven science. They prefer quantifiable, measurable numbers over qualitative attributes. For example, we cannot directly quantify the benefits of a worker's loyalty or creativity, so we usually end up discounting them. They are not purposely dismissed, but they don't readily fit a spreadsheet, a chart or a quarterly report and as a consequence, their impact on operational results is invisible or deemed coincidental. Companies that neglect human factors provide good examples confirming this observation. Their typically high personnel turnover is rarely ever identified as a problem and practically never addressed. The resulting costs can be significant, but there are no good tools available to capture them discretely.

Just because certain aspects of manufacturing are made of intangible factors does not mean they don't need to be recognized, understood and addressed. Corporate culture, individual attitudes, habits, inclinations, and motivations can play very significant roles in impacting operating results.

23.7.1 Manufacturing Efficiency

Starting this segment with the history of rocket manufacturing would be appropriate here. However, by the time Robert Goddard launched his first liquid propellant rocket, the Ford Model T was already coming to an end after producing over 10 million vehicles. Lean manufacturing methods were already invented—though there were no fancy names for them yet. Unlike cars, which initially got a slow start with very few entirely hand built curiosities, rocket manufacturing started up rather quickly in large numbers as manifested by the German production of the V-1 and V-2 rockets, and then gradually decreased in numbers over the years.

Henry Ford and his right hand man Charles Sorensen were the first ones who successfully took the elements of a manufacturing system—people, machines, tooling, and material—and arranged them in a system for continuous manufacturing for the production of the Model T automobile. Such early systems already included the essential ideas of lean manufacturing, namely a streamlined flow of activities and materials as well as a focus on the elimination of waste. However, the capability to manage product variety, which required changeover, quick setups and small production batches, was not developed until the 1950s. Manufacturing has gone through a significant transformation since Henry Ford started his automobile production and great progress has been made in material sciences, processing methods, automation, warehousing and distribution of manufactured goods.

Numerous very useful books have been written about the subject of manufacturing and in particular about efficiency improvements. More recently, the knowledge about lean manufacturing methods and Six Sigma principles have become nearly indispensable for the professionals in the manufacturing field. As the continuous improvements in all aspects of manufacturing are producing positive results, the industry has become more focused on the measurable, directly cost-impacting elements of these methods. As a result, devising the processes and the tools for measuring the improvements in manufacturing efficiency have become a field of specialized expertise all of its own. Before shedding more light on how effects such as the large scale implementation of improvement programs can shape manufacturing environments, it must be stated that there is a set of essential rules that are the foundation upon which all further efficiency improvements must be based.

Basics

No manufacturing cost reduction effort can be successful unless it is built on the solid ground of these widely proven methods for improving efficiency:

Aim for Simplicity—minimize part numbers, part variety, assembly surfaces, simplify assembly sequences, component handling and insertion, for faster and more reliable assembly.

Standardize—on material usage, components, and aim for as many off-the-shelf components as possible to allow improved inventory management, reduced tooling, and the benefits of mass production even at low volumes.

Rationalize Product Design—standardize on materials, components, and sub-assemblies throughout product families to increase economies of scale and reduce equipment and tooling costs. Employ modularity to allow variety to be introduced late in the assembly sequence and simplify *Just In Time* (JIT) production.

Use the Widest Possible Tolerances—increase the tolerance on non-critical components and thus reduce operations and processing times.

Choose Materials to Suit Function and Production Process—avoid choosing materials purely for functional characteristics; material choice must also favor the production process to ensure product reliability.

Minimize Non-Value-Adding Operations—the minimization of handling, excessive finishing and inspection will reduce costs and lead time.

Design for Process—take advantage of advanced process capabilities to reduce unnecessary components or additional processing, such as the porosity of sintered metal components for lubricant retention. Design in features and functions to overcome process limitations, such as features to aid mechanical feeding. Avoid unnecessary restrictions of processes to allow manufacturing flexibility in process planning.

Teamwork—promote concurrent engineering. Establish a product or project based development/manufacturing organization involving a formalized multi-disciplinary/departmental teamwork structure.

Include All Stakeholders Early in the Process—get the external contributors involved right at the concept stage. All activities must support a throughput oriented manufacturing approach.

Any organization that can implement and maintain these 9 rules to a meaningful degree is in good shape and has exploited a near full range of widely recognized and proven tools for efficiency improvements in manufacturing. Depending on the nature of the business, further lean principle tools can be implemented.

Mission Assurance Orientation

One key characteristic that may be used to distinguish aerospace manufacturing from other industries is its "mission assurance orientation." To highlight the contrast for this discussion I will call other industries' manufacturing approach "throughput oriented." This is not necessarily tied to specific production output, since a plastic cup manufacturer and a forklift manufacturer are both throughput oriented, even though their output is drastically different. The difference between them and aerospace manufacturing lies mostly in the mentality and the resulting approach to production related challenges. The real requirements (safety) and the perceived ones (political) for near 100% space mission success have elevated the quality standards so close to a zero defects mandate on every level, that the impact of cost lowering efforts are virtually offset. As a byproduct, there is latent confusion between striving for excellence and striving for perfection that often clouds policies by assuming that all defects are equal, and therefore, zero defects are best. Needless to say—the focus on zero defects is counterproductive and unaffordable. Further, the quality requirements originally devised specifically for piloted missions have gradually crept into the supply chains and their contributors of unmanned programs and added significant and unnecessary costs and production lead times. It must be stated here, that the perceived need for near 100% mission success not only drives cost up dramatically, but is also an impediment to technological progress. Choosing a throughput oriented approach vs. a mission assurance oriented approach is not an either/or proposition, but rather states the definition of the desired outcome and the necessary alignment of the supporting activities to achieve that outcome. The concept that a choice has to be made between high quality low-volume production and low quality high-volume production is a false one, as many industries are proving—the cars we drive represent just one good example. (Some of the low cost high-volume-production cars are the most reliable ones, while some of the high cost low-volume-production cars are some of the least reliable ones.) Certainly, economics of scale do not favor the typically low volume production in aerospace manufacturing for cost reduction opportunities, but that does not negate the impact of other approaches that enhance flexibility and resilience to manufacturing disruptions. **In a throughput oriented environment, all contributing elements are subordinated to the goal of achieving a disruption free manufacturing environment, which means that all processes are designed to accommodate that goal.**

In contrast, a mission assurance oriented environment aligns all activities in support of achieving near 100% mission success. The traditional process of building a launch vehicle or a spacecraft consists of a string of idiosyncrasies, using mostly single sourced components that are custom fitted on-line to unique subsystems. There are very few opportunities to benefit from such factors as process repetition, modularity, standardization, and learning. Launch vehicles are integrated mostly in a serial fashion in a product centered layout method in a dedicated environment with fixed production assets. There is often a high degree of interdependent steps and a low off-line content, making the process "throughput adverse." Such an environment is not capable of absorbing unexpected events very well and is therefore extremely vulnerable to disruptions. Moreover, as a consequence of the high content of interdependent processes, the disruptions have a highly amplified impact on cost and schedule, and they reverberate often throughout the entire manufacturing organization and its external suppliers.

In throughput oriented manufacturing operations, the need to get product out the door on time is a hard requirement. You cannot ship Christmas trees in January or Easter bunnies in May! This hard requirement creates important counter balancing input to the lean control systems in a manufacturing organization that tend to minimize material buffers (inventory). In the aerospace environment, the "controls mentality" gets positive reinforcement from the perceived need for a near zero defects requirement, always in alignment with the near 100% mission success goal. Lean manufacturing systems aim at eliminating waste. Inventory is always a focal point, since it hides waste. Inventory is used to hide the imperfections in the system, which means that the level of inventory is a direct indicator of the level of imperfection in the system. For example, Toyota is running inventory free manufacturing systems, relying entirely on just-in-time deliveries of all needed components. However, Toyota neither single sources its parts, nor does it single source its labor (it is worth noting that unionized labor makes the labor content of a product single sourced), nor does it use hand made custom fitted parts. Toyota's system allows the buffers against disruption to be far removed from the factory, way down the supply stream. To be clear—Toyota running inventory free operations does not mean inventories are eliminated—it means either that the suppliers are carrying inventory for it (suppliers with internal inventory can react to a quality issue or production delay very quickly and can recover literally within hours) or that some suppliers are actually integrated into the factory, and their products are made right there on a just-in-time basis.

In the aerospace industry, the prime contractors are seeking to improve their manufacturing margins by using their considerable leverage to compel their suppliers to carry the burden of buffering their systems, which often exceeds the capabilities of small specialized companies. In addition, aerospace parts are mostly single sourced, custom made, fitted in place, and have long lead times, which moves the need to have flexibility and production buffers back onto the integration floor of the primes. As a result, material buffers become necessary, meaning inventory—the very thing lean methods are trying to eliminate! So, what makes perfect sense on paper, namely reducing material inventories at the prime contractor level and pushing the buffers down the supply stream can have costly consequences in the aerospace industry. Lean manufacturing with a fat inventory?

Actually, just having an inventory of the long lead custom made parts will make a difference. In the aerospace industry, the small, specialized contributors to the supply chain cannot afford to carry sufficient inventory of custom made parts for the large prime contractors—so when there is disruption (i.e., there is a part not conforming to specs) the supplier cannot recover fast enough to avoid disruption of the integration process.

Intangible Factors

Production efficiency improvement efforts and the resulting cost reductions must be quantified, and the essence of the generated data must be applied in subsequent production cycles in order to generate ongoing improvements. Since the implementation of efficiency improvement systems costs money, the results of their application must be measured against return on investment models and their predicted savings. Thus, an operation is required to have the talent and the capacity available for the implementation and operation of continuous improvement systems. Managers, by their very mentalities, are typically drawn to the controllable, quantifiable aspects of the operations they manage. Their jobs are defined to a degree by installing controls and systems, which is in contrast to leaders, who are typically interested in growth and innovation, relying on people's creativity and loyalty. Leaders want to do the right things—managers want things done right.

Managers (not leaders) usually do the hiring of the personnel required to implement and operate control systems, even if the mandate originates from the top of the organization. Following their natural inclinations, managers subconsciously hire new personnel who share their views and attitudes. One unintended consequence of the implementation of large scale improvement systems is a gradual shift in the personnel mix of an organization in favor of the "controls people" at the cost of the "creative people." Over time, this process can transform the culture of a corporation toward becoming more conformance, compliance and controls oriented; all tangible aspects.

As this shift often leads to the desired operating results in the near term, this positive feedback generates further consensus among the leadership about the beneficial impact of these methods. The consequences of this diminishing creative influence within the organization are most likely not recognized until their impacts are severe. Some of the most revered and world renowned companies have experienced a considerable upswing after installing lean methods and six sigma principles, only to fall behind in the global competition within just a few years after their impressive successes. (e.g., Motorola, in the field of cellular phone manufacturing.) That outcome occurred not because the manufacturing efficiency could not be sustained, but because of other factors, not the least of which was diminishing innovative power. The benefits of creativity and innovation are not directly measured as output per unit or in dollars and are therefore not easily captured in a system of controls. One rather perfidious consequence of this type of creeping transformation is that it compels a company eventually to compete on price alone as its products lose their superior performance and best-in-class status. (e.g., Maytag washers.) See more in Sec. 23.7.2.

Another aspect of the problem is that highly specialized industries such as aerospace are vulnerable to the effects of a monoculture of their own making. The agricultural definition of a monoculture actually works well here to make the point: **A farming system given over exclusively to a single product. Its advantages are the increased efficiency of farming and a higher quality of output. Disadvantages include a greater susceptibility to price fluctuations, climatic hazards, the spreading of diseases and the degradation of the soil over time.** In other words—short term optimization is achieved at the cost of long term damage. Unfortunately, launch vehicle manufacturing is subject to the same problem—short term optimization is always bought at the cost of long term damage. A single, homogeneous aerospace culture without cross industrial diversity and routinely questioned standard ways of doing things has its price tag, which leads us to take a look at how the talent this industry needs is selected and hired. The well known trend of increasing shortages of aerospace technicians, engineers and scientists has not been addressed in a way that generates meaningful results, despite a twenty year (and counting) history of organized reporting about this troubling fact. The narrow technical and specialty oriented selection criteria for recruiting in our industry has most of the relevant talent rotating among a handful of employers who compete for the same or similar space programs, while considerable amounts of corporate knowledge has been lost in mass layoffs and retirement.

The long lasting, ongoing trend of permanently disappearing jobs from various industries and manufacturing companies who used to build all the things that the USA is not producing anymore, meets the ascending aerospace personnel demand that arises from years of neglect to attract sufficient talent for the industry. There has also been a long trend associated with the cyclical nature of business for the primes that trigger big layoffs, which causes many of those terminated to not return to the aerospace industry, further exacerbating the personnel problem. This is an opportunity for the much needed cross pollination of skills and ideas. There are countless scientists, engineers, workers, technicians, assemblers and toolmakers from other industries willing to offer their considerable range of transferable skills for the benefit of the aerospace industry. What is required now is for the aerospace companies to step outside their routines and look into other fields—to reach out and acquire the talents in those fields. Our industry cannot stay competitive unless it is innovation driven and risk eager. That same mentality is required to achieve real cost reductions—which will lead eventually and inevitably to a throughput oriented manufacturing mentality.

23.7.2 The Perpetual Optimization

Getting really heavy stuff all the way up into space is a hard thing to do. Making engines stronger and vehicles lighter is the way to tackle this challenge. Since we have been going to space for about 60 years, performance optimization is now in the DNA of every aerospace engineer. Mass reduction is almost always the dominant issue in most technical discussions and particularly when it comes to choices within the trade space. Despite the frequent mention of cost reduction requirements, the need for mass reduction seems to win the debate every time. The need for performance optimization has become the underlying culture in our industry, upon which most other decisions are made. No 80–20 rule here—unfortunately. As a consequence, the application of scarce metals, rare materials, exotic processes, and extremely specialized capabilities is perceived as a basic necessity to achieve the demanded performance. The impact on cost is nothing less than spectacular. Beyond that, the rare, the scarce and the exotic come from highly specialized sources that serve niche markets with little or no competition and who therefore dictate price, availability and production schedule.

Backing off even a small fraction from the optimum and stepping into "robust design," "large margin," and "throughput orientation" territory has enormous benefits. Even a minimal level of modularization of subsystems, and standardization of interfaces and fasteners will make a significant difference. Adding flexibility to the material flow, using multiple-use tools, movable production assets, wheeled setups, and cross trained personnel who work sliding scale and split shift schedules, are just a few measures that will reduce costly dependencies that are otherwise mandated by the demand for optimization.

Operations Managers and MBA'S

In technical companies, the production managers were traditionally operations people who were educated in the area of business concerned with the production of goods and services. Operations management training programs typically have included instruction in the principles of general management, manufacturing and production systems, plant management, equipment maintenance management, production control, industrial labor relations and skilled worker supervision, strategic manufacturing policy, systems analysis, productivity analysis and cost control, and materials planning.

Over the past twenty years or so, our most prestigious business schools have gradually added sophistication and emphasis to the instruction of the financial aspects of managing an organization. Today, an ever increasing number of companies employ operations managers with MBA centered backgrounds. Symbolically speaking and overstated to highlight the point—MBA's tend to think of assets as things you buy and sell; operations people tend to think of assets as things you maintain and utilize. (The former is usually related to eliminating jobs, the latter is related to creating them.) The need to achieve impressive quarterly results for the market makers is in direct conflict with the requirements for building and maintaining an efficient manufacturing company with lasting substance. For example, our Detroit auto manufacturers are intimately familiar with the Toyota manufacturing system and understand its superior performance. Theirs was a long term plan with long term investments for long term benefits—which is one reason why US car manufacturers were slow to implement it, since their focus is on measurably improved results every quarter instead of performance over a production model life cycle of 5–7 years. (Principle 1 of the 14-principle book The Toyota Way for employees: **Base your management decisions on a long-term philosophy, even at the expense of short-term financial goals.)** In aerospace, the same rules must apply. We need to understand and lay open the trades—what is the long term cost to achieve a short term benefit? Who pays for it and why?

The comments made earlier regarding operations managers and MBA's were not meant to imply that one is to be preferred over the other, but rather to highlight some of their possible intangible aspects like background, education and mentality—and as a consequence, to understand what kind of people they would likely be hiring and how that may impact business results over time. In any case, it's worth giving some deep thought to whether we want to be in the business to make a killing—or to make a living. Aerospace manufacturing is particularly suited for the latter—not to mention that it has critical implications of national interest that cannot be addressed with a short term perspective.

Cost Cutting vs. Outperforming

American manufacturing companies have, over a long period of time, competed for international market share by pricing policies. As a result, cost cutting has established itself as the central theme in manufacturing. That strategy has worked fairly well because the United States itself is a very large market, and domestic deliveries have traditionally generated a large portion of company revenues. Smaller countries that had a difficult time gaining global market share based on pricing made up for it by innovation and specialization for niche markets. Fine precision mechanics, machinery, vehicles, chemicals, household equipment, optical instruments and machine tools are just a few examples of goods coming from smaller countries that have earned leading positions on the global manufacturing stage. To illustrate the impact of choosing between competing on cost vs. performance we might take a look at Germany, who at the time of this writing, is in the process of displacing China as the largest exporter in the world, selling mostly high-cost high-tech products, with many of them being the most expensive ones on the market in their respective categories. Germany is also the leading producer of wind turbines and solar power technology in the world; clean energy technologies that are expected to become some of the largest global economic sectors for decades to come. In the USA, the continuously increasing outsourcing for manufacturing has diminished our involvement in manufacturing engineering, which in turn has affected our R&D capabilities, since the two are tied in a feedback loop in most cases. The countries that are now manufacturing the goods that we buy have the long lasting benefit of gaining the expertise in manufacturing engineering and R&D, which creates the opportunities and incentives for young people to become engineers—who will in turn become tomorrow's technology innovators.

If existing trends continue, it's a matter of a relatively short time period until other nations will be in a position to outperform us in aerospace (not to be confused with undercutting us in price). We don't have to start working for $2/hour to compete with them. We have to outperform them—with innovation and ingenuity, which can be achieved only if we manufacture the components and systems domestically, so that we can grow superior R&D and manufacturing engineering capabilities again. This requires a consistent and long-term commitment to superiority in space as a national policy. Our policy makers must be educated about the extent to which our nation's security and well-being is dependent on broad-based and highly advanced manufacturing capabilities.

Back to the Basics—The Intangible Ones

Here are 5 basic rules or guidelines for the manufacturing manager that can help with keeping a high level of awareness of intangibles:

1. Manufacturing managers must fight vigorously the forces in the organization that demand quick fixes and short term optimizations. The alignment of the contributing factors to the main goal is paramount—not how well the individual measures produce immediate results. However, keen observers are aware that the annals of manufacturing history are full of records of such lost battles, as neither our political system nor our capital markets are used to anything but a short-term view. So here is an important tool to use: There are indeed shortcuts to be offered to the executives who demand them, but they each have a price tag and a payment due date, and it is the job of the manufacturing manager to present clearly the impact of such choices. Shortcuts never come for free, and the executives need to be informed of their long term costs. They must take documented ownership of these decisions because of their potentially profound impact on the well-being of the whole organization. Long term goals cannot be achieved with short term plans.
2. Always keep the 80–20 rule in mind. In manufacturing, you are the last in line. You are expected to make up for the time that was lost in concept development, design, engineering, and product definition. You will never have enough time to do what needs to be done, because the sales people sold a product that you don't have and promised a delivery date that you can not achieve—that's a universal law in manufacturing. Make sure you provide visibility on production progress (or setbacks) and realistic delivery dates to your sales people, so they can manage the customer's expectations accordingly and keep the executives appraised, so they can manage cash.
3. Always be alert to the fact that manufacturing has two main enemies: uncertainty and disruption. They dwarf everything else by comparison—there is your 80–20 rule. Uncertainty can be caused by such factors as financial constraints, environmental impacts, political or economic considerations. Disruption can be caused by such factors as unreliable supply sources, insufficient product definition, and deficiencies in the master schedule for production. Treat these two, uncertainty and disruption, as the main issues and everything else as noise, and you will be highly effective. Continuous production is the key. This word must be branded in your brain—CONTINUOUS.

4. The elimination of waste (lean principles) and the reduction of defects (Six Sigma) are not an all-or-nothing package. They can be implemented stepwise in modules, and they can be mixed and matched to specific needs. The former improves efficiency, and the latter improves process. Not every manufacturing company needs to implement all the elements of a total continuous improvement system. More is not necessarily better; in fact, most companies will do fine with a small selection of basic controls. Highly regimented environments with optimized controls can reach a point of diminishing flexibility and reduced tolerance to disruptions. At this point, the cost savings with respect to lean operations can be outweighed by diminished resistance to cost-impacting disruptions.

   Front end, preventive solutions that are designed to reduce inefficiency (Lean manufacturing, Six Sigma) must be complemented with back end solutions (buffers) to reduce the impact of unplanned disruptions.

5. Consider the human factors—create an environment that is designed to match workers motivations, attitudes and expectations—factors that affect the outcome of a process. Make sure that equipment and environmental design, as well as training, create conditions that are attractive to personnel. Make your employees stakeholders. Create long term oriented incentives (short term incentives are mostly destructive to an organization). Hire people who represent individual differences across the human spectrum in every physical and mental dimension that is relevant for good system performance. Diversity is not a political term in a manufacturing operation; it is a way of enhancing creativity and fostering innovation. Attract creativity and inspire innovation—it's the engine that will propel a manufacturing organization to the forefront of opportunities. It is also the only sustainable force of the new economy.

Connecting the Dots with a FireSat II example

The speculation about how such thinking would apply to a FireSat II production program and its possible impact on the outcome in terms of cost, schedule and commercial viability leaves room for various scenarios. So here is one attempt to incorporate some of the discussed ideas:

The vision offered here for consideration includes forming an ad hoc cooperative (COOP) among the stakeholders of a FireSat II program—not unlike some healthcare provider partnerships, where a number of doctor-owned medical offices share the income from patients and insurance reimbursements. Surplus money goes into a profit pool that is used for rewards at the end of the year. The FireSat II COOP would include the teams that build systems or subsystems such as the bus structure, payload, bus sensors, avionics, command and data handling electronics, communications, the propulsion system, the launch, and ground controls. Traditional hierarchies would be eliminated, and teams would be horizontally connected and communicate by means of real-time video communication tools on demand. The team members are all shareholders in the COOP, and their efforts to under-spend the allocated budgets will be rewarded by distribution of surplus funds from the pool after each successful deployment and commissioning of a FireSat II. Mission failures will lead to cancellation of the rewards, and the profit pool will help support self-insurance funding for replacement costs. This arrangement of co-ownership also provides incentives for all participants to share resources and capabilities.

Basics—Apply a *design for manufacturing* (DFM) and *design for assembly* (DFA) mentality at the concept stage. Materials and process choices should also take logistics, availability (vulnerability to disruption), and other flow-affecting factors into account. A word about standardization seems to be of particular importance at this point. One of the biggest achievements in the field of standardization in modern history has to be the invention of the 40 foot shipping container. There is not a nation or entity in the world that has not adapted their environment to its use for the transportation of goods by road, by rail, by sea and by air. In aerospace, it seems to be an established standard that all hardware and software design is mission specific, and that every "trip" has to be designed from the ground up. Imagine you would need a different car for every trip you make! The blatant trivialization here is intended to make the point that at least some degree of standardization and modularity for "space shipments" will have to be implemented if commercialization of space is to be an achievable goal.

Throughput Orientation—Reduce the requirements catalog to the essential functions of the product. Design multi-functionality into your production environment, *not into your product*. The former reduces cost; the latter increases cost. Aim for modularity in the preliminary design phase. Obtain consensus on the product definition early to allow good production planning and coordination among the coop members. Defining the interface data for all involved parties and their products very early in the process will be central to achieving that goal. Interdependent processes and serial steps must be minimized. *Disruption* and *uncertainty* are both primary cost driving elements in a manufacturing organization and must receive constant attention.

Optimization—Apply a robust workhorse design standard as a baseline. Mitigate system redundancy requirements by using large margin design approaches that provide robustness in trade for optimal performance.

80–20 Rule—The decisions made in the first 20% of the program determine 80% of the overall cost performance. That means you have the *concept stage* and the *preliminary design phase* to make an impact. Decisions made after this point are practically inconsequential on cost containment. In fact, just the opposite occurs—the later in the process design changes are implemented, the bigger and the more disproportional the impact on cost increases are. All members on deck for this one—no exceptions! Cost cannot be reduced or contained at the back end of the program; cost is designed into the product, and into the process that produces it.

Continuous Manufacturing—More important than actual production quantity is the requirement to maintain a continuous production mode. Continuous manufacturing demands a firm commitment to a build quantity and the provision of the necessary resources for the entire program to avoid disruptions. Single sourcing must be avoided or reduced by any and all means. The supply of unique components and scarce materials must be buffered by small inventories. Remember, all vendors are stakeholders, and whoever creates the program disruption spoils the pool for all!

Product Quality—The FireSat II is a low-cost unmanned mission design. An average projected 90–95% mission success rate would be desirable to create room for meaningful cost reduction opportunities. The product design and the quality requirements should be defined accordingly. Note: Higher quality is not "better" and lower quality is not "worse". Quality is designed into the product and the processes that make the product. The quality standard must be in alignment with the requirements of the end user—no more and no less. The missions could be self-insured by the COOP and the payload replacement costs of failed missions could be partially carried by the profit pool.

Business Model Innovation—Finally, as a business model for the FireSat II product line, one can imagine that offering the data services on a leasing basis could add a near term profitability dimension that would attract the involvement of financial institutions such as equipment leasing companies or lease/finance banks. This model could have a significant impact on the success of the commercialization of the space business in a larger context. Smaller entities who may not have the budget to buy a FireSat II would be leasing the services they need from the satellite operator. The availability of space equipment financing and space-based services leasing could become a profit proposition for the participating lenders. This approach also addresses the fact that obtaining funds for capital investment is usually much more difficult for typical customers to achieve than increasing existing operational budgets, which is where the FireSat II leasing program would fit.

The discussion of this section comprises only a small cross section of a wide range of cost impacting intangibles in manufacturing. It is worth noting however, that intangibles are not only difficult to quantify, but they are often the slowly creeping factors that can escape the attention of even the most alert manager, until their impact becomes severe. The purpose of this discussion is to help develop the senses and sharpen the alertness of the manufacturing manager to recognize intangible factors in the daily routine of looking over lists, charts, graphs and reports. They may not fit your spreadsheet—but they are no less important.

References

For annotated bibliography of space logistics and manufacturing, see the book website.

AIAA. 2010. *Space Systems Verification Program and Management Process*. S-117-2010. Reston, VA: AIAA. Nov.

Akaike, H. 1983. Information Measures and Model Selection. *Bulletin International Statistic Institute,* vol. 50, pp. 277–290.

Bartlett, R. O. and F. J. Cepollina. 1975. "The Multimission Modular Spacecraft for the 80's." AAS meeting on Space Shuttle Missions of the 80's, Denver, CO. Aug. 26–28 p. 34.

Blair, M.A., J. W. Sills, Jr., and A. E. Semple. 1994. "Determination of the Model Uncertainty Factor Using Cross-orthogonality and Overall Load Factor Decomposition." Proc. SPIE, vol. 2251. *12th International Modal Analysis Conference*, p. 613. Bellingham, WA: SPIE

Blanchard, B. and W. Fabrycky. 2006. *Systems Engineering and Analysis, 4th ed.* Upper Saddle River, NJ: Prentice Hall.

Buede, D. M. 2010. *The Engineering Design of Systems: Models and Methods*. Hoboken, NJ: John Wiley and Sons.

DiNitto, S. A. 1978. "High Order Language Standardization." Proceedings of the IEEE 1978 National Aerospace and Electronics Conference NAECON 78. Dayton, OH: May 16–18, pp. 1139–1146.

DoD. 1978. *"Aircraft Internal Time Division Command/Response Multiplex Data Bus." MIL-STD-1553. 21 September.*

DoD. 1985. *Technical Reviews and Audits for Systems, Equipments, and Computer Software*. MIL-STD-1521B. Jun 4.

DoD. 1986. *Design, Construction and Testing Requirements for One of a Kind Space Equipment.* DOD-HDBK-343. Feb. 1.

DoD. 1999. *Test Requirements for Launch, Upper-Stage, and Space Vehicles*. MIL-HDBK-340A. Apr. 1.

DoD. 2004. *Test Requirements for Launch, Upper-Stage, and Space Vehicles*. MIL-STD-1540E.

Draper, D. 1995. "Assessment and Propagation of Model Uncertainty." *The Challenger Space Shuttle Disaster*, Section 6.2. Journal of the Royal Statistical Society, Series B, vol. 57, pp. 45–97.

EIA. 1994. *Systems Engineering.* EIA/IS-632. Washington, DC: Electronic Industries Assoc.

Elbert, B. R. 2008. *Introduction to Satellite Communications. 3rd ed.* Norwood, MA: Artech House, Inc.

Esper, J., J. Andary, J. Oberright, and Maria So. 2004. "Modular, Reconfigurable, and Rapid Response Space Systems: The Remote Sensing Advanced Technology Microsatellite." AIAA 2nd Responsive Space Conference, El Segundo CA, Apr.

Esper, J. 2005. "Modular, Adaptive, Reconfigurable Systems: Technology for Sustainable, Reliable, Effective, and Affordable Space Exploration." *Space Technology and Applications International Forum.* American Institute of Physics.

Falkenhayn, E. 1988. "Multimission Modular Spacecraft (MMS)." AIAA Conference on Space Programs and Technologies. Houston, TX: Jun. 21–24. p. 6.

Food, G. M. and P. M. Atkinson. 2002. *Uncertainty in Remote Sensing and GIS.* Hoboken, NJ: John Wiley and Sons.

George, M. L. 2002. *Lean Six Sigma: Combing Six Sigma Quality with Lean Production Speed.* New York, NY: McGraw Hill Companies

Greenwell, T. J. 1978. "Testing programs for the Multimission Modular Spacecraft." *4th Aerospace Testing Seminar*. Mt. Prospect: Institute of Environmental Sciences, vol. 3. pp. 69–74.

Goldratt, Eliyahu M. 1999. *Theory of Constraints.* Great Barrington, MA: North River Press.

Goldratt, Eliyahu M. 2004. *The Goal. 3rd ed.* Great Barrington, MA: North River Press.

GSFC. 2005. *General Environmental Verification Standard for Goddard Space Flight Center Flight Programs and Projects*. GSFC-STD-7000. Apr.

Halang, W. A. 1992. "Real-Time Computing Systems: Another Perspective." *Journal of Systems and Software,* vol. 18, Apr. pp. 101–108.

Harry, M. 1997. *The Nature of Six Sigma Quality*. Schaumburg, IL: Motorola University Press.

Harry, M. J., P. S. Mann, O. V. De Hodgins, R. L. Hulbert, and C. J. Lack. 2010. *Practitioner's Guide to Statistics and Lean Six Sigma for Process Improvements.* Hoboken, NJ: John Wiley and Sons.

International Council On Systems Engineering (INCOSE). 2007. *Systems Engineering Handbook.* Version 3.1, Aug.

Kaner, C., J. Falk, and H. Nguyen. 1993. *Testing Computer Software*. Scottsdale, AZ: The Coriolis Group and Hoboken, NJ: John Wiley and Sons.

Kaplan, M. and P. Bremner. 2010. "Uncertainty Margin Issues When Using Vibro-Acoustic Modeling to Define Maximum Expected Environments." Spacecraft and Launch Vehicle Dynamic Environments Workshop. The Aerospace Corporation. Jun. 8–10.

Lundahl. 1998.

Meeker, William Q. and Gerlad J. Hahn. 1985. *How To Plan An Accelerated Life Test—Some Practical Guidelines*. American Society for Quality Control, vol. 1. Milwaukee, WI.

Madigan, D. and A. E. Raftery. 1991. *Model Selection and Accounting for Model Uncertainty in Graphical Models Using Occam's Window*. Technical Report 213. Department of Statistics, University of Washington.

MITRE Corporation. 1998. *Software Lifecycle Processes.* IEEE/EIA 12207.

Montgomery, D. C. 2000. *Introduction to Statistical Quality Control. 4th ed.* Hoboken, NJ: John Wiley and Sons.

NAVMAT. 1982. *Navy Manufacturing Screening Program.* NAVMAT-P-9492. May.

Olivieri, J. M. 1997. "Commercial Satellite Manufacturing: Prerequisites for Success." (Unpublished MS Thesis). Arizona State University, Tempe, AZ.

Raftery, A. E. 1992. *Bayesian Model Selection in Structural Equation Models*. *Testing Structural Equation Models*. Beverly Hills, CA: Sage.

Reeves, Emery. 1999. *Space Mission Analysis and Design, 3rd ed.* Chapter 12. El Segundo, CA: Microcosm Press and Springer, NY.

Santoni, Andy. 1997. "Standard Tests for Embedded Processors to be Set by Industry." Info World, vol. 19, issue 31, p. 34. Aug. 4.

Shunk, D. L. 1992. *Integrated Process Design and Development*. Homewood, IL: Business One Irwin.

Stankovic, J. A. 1992. "Real-Time Computing". *Byte*, pp. 154–160. Aug.

Tompkins, James A. 1989. *Winning Manufacturing.* Industrial Engineering and Management Press.

Weibull. 2007. Accelerated Life Testing Analysis Reference. ReliaSoft Corporation. Website.

White, J. and C. Wright. 2005. "Test Like You Fly: A Risk Management Approach." *Space Systems Engineering and Risk Management Symposium*. The Aerospace Corporation.

Womack, J. P., D. T. Jones, and D. Roos. 1990. *The Machine That Changed the World*. New York: Macmillan Publishing Company.

Yunis, I. 2008. "Model Uncertainty in Monte Carlo Analysis." Spacecraft and Launch Vehicle Dynamics Environments Workshop. Jun. 10–12.

Table 23-14◀, Fig. 23-20◀, Eq. 23-0

24 Risk and Reliability

24.1 Reliability

Myron J. Hecht, *The Aerospace Corporation*
Herbert Hecht, *SoHaR*

When a bulb in our desk lamp burns out, it is easily replaced. When the switch that controls the bulb fails, the replacement is not quite as simple but still within the capabilities of most mechanically inclined teenagers and even some adults. We expect a higher reliability of the switch than of the lamp because it requires more effort to repair a failure. When a spacecraft command receiver fails on orbit, it takes an extraordinarily long screwdriver to fix it. You get the general idea: the command receiver has to be much more reliable than the light bulb or the switch on the desk lamp. This need for very high reliability in all parts and subsystems of a spacecraft is the basis for including a *reliability program* in most space projects.

24.1.1 Definitions and Basic Concepts

Before describing the details of the reliability program, let us briefly discuss the meaning and metrics of *reliability* in the context of space missions. A common definition of reliability is "the probability that a device will function without failure over a specified time period or amount of usage" [IEEE, 1990]. If the phrase "without failure" is taken to mean "without failure of any kind" it defines *basic reliability;* if it is interpreted as "without failure that impairs the mission" it defines *mission reliability.* In spacecraft that employ extensive redundancy there can be a significant difference between these two reliability metrics. Mission reliability is the more important concept, and when we use "reliability" without a qualifier, it always means mission reliability.

Item Reliability

The elementary expression for the reliability as a function of operating time, t, for a single item subject to random failure, is given by an exponential distribution:

$$R = e^{-\lambda t} \tag{24-1}$$

where λ is the failure rate and $1/\lambda$ is the Mean Time Between Failure (MTBF). Here, R is the probability that the item will operate without failure for time t (success probability).

In terms of absolute numbers, electronic components usually make up the majority of parts on a space vehicle. Because of the high quality of such parts used in spacecraft, their failure rates are usually random. For solar cells or subassemblies having moving parts (e.g., reaction wheels, solar array drives, or propellant valves), wear-out is a major failure mechanism, and these components have an increasing hazard (the failure rate normalized to the number of survivors). In such cases, the Weibull distribution, is used. One form of that distribution is

$$R = e^{-(\alpha t)^{\beta}} \tag{24-2}$$

where α is called the *scale parameter* (with the same units and therefore somewhat akin to λ in the exponential distribution) and β is called the *shape parameter* (if less than 1, the failure rate *decreases* over time, if 1, the failure rate is constant, and the distribution assumes the same form as the exponential, and if greater than 1, then the failure rate increases over time).

Other distributions commonly used in reliability engineering are the Gamma, Normal (Gaussian), Lognormal, binomial (for discrete processes), and Bernoulli (also for discrete processes). Further information on the form and use of these distributions can be found in MIL STD 338B [DoD, 1998] or in the NIST/SEMATECH [2010], reliability handbook, as well as many industry standards and reliability textbooks.

The converse of reliability is the probability of failure. If there are only two outcomes: success and failure*, probability of failure, F, is given by:

$$F = 1 - R \tag{24-3}$$

System Reliability

For a spacecraft subsystem or assembly made up of n non-redundant non-recoverable elements, all equally es-

* Methods of assessing mission success with degraded states, are described later.

sential for spacecraft operation, the *system* (or *series) reliability,* R_s, or success probability to time t (where t is the time since the start of operation), is

$$R_s = \prod_{1}^{n} R_i \tag{24-4}$$

where R_i ($i = 1, 2, \ldots n$) is the reliability of the individual elements. Where the reliability behavior over time is exponential, this becomes

$$R_s = \prod_{1}^{n} R_i \approx e^{-\sum_i^n \lambda_i t} \tag{24-5}$$

and λ_i the failure rate of the individual elements. Note that the right-hand equality holds true when the exponential distribution is used to represent reliability because the elements are believed to have a constant failure rate. Where a system consists of n elements in parallel, and each (i.e., any one) of these elements can by itself satisfy the requirements, the parallel (or redundant) reliability, $R_{s,p}$ is given by

$$R_{s,p} = 1 - \prod_{i=1}^{n} (1 - R_i) \tag{24-6}$$

where the reliability of the parallel elements is equal, say R_i. the above simplifies to

$$R_{s,p} = 1 - (1 - R_i)^n \tag{24-7}$$

In some cases, more than a single element is needed to satisfy the mission requirement (e.g., 2 out of 3 transmitters or power supplies), the reliability of such a "m out of n", where m is the minimum number of elements needed and n is the number that were on the vehicle at the beginning of the mission, the system reliability is given by

$$R = \sum_{k=m}^{n} \frac{n!}{k!(n-k)!} R_i^k (1 - R_i)^{(n-k)} \tag{24-8}$$

In terrestrial applications it is customary to distinguish between active and quiescent (dormant) failure rates, the latter being about one-tenth of the active rates. This reduction accounts for the absence of electrical stress when a component is not energized. However, in many cases, space components are derated (see Sec. 24.1.3) so that the failure probability due to electrical stresses even in the active mode is quite small. The distinction between active and quiescent failure rates is therefore much less important for spacecraft environments in systems with conservative design margins, with respect to power dissipation, the electrical stress induced by power is very low.

Series and parallel constructs are often combined in a satellite system and can be evaluated by combining the effects from Fig. 24-1 which shows the reliability predictions as a function of time for three possible system configurations each consisting of four subsystems:

1. ***Single System:*** A single string system consisting of the four subsystems placed in series; Eq. (24-2) and Eq. (24-4) would be used to calculate the system reliability.

2. ***System Redundancy:*** A dual redundant subsystem consisting of two strings, each consisting of the four subsystems in series; this is sometimes referred to as large scope redundancy or block redundancy. Eq. (24-2) and Eq. (24-4) would be used to calculate reliability of each string, and this string result would then be used in Eq. (24-6) to calculate the system reliability.

3. ***Partitioned Redundancy:*** A system in which each of the four subsystems is configured as a dual redundant system, and each of these subsystems is placed in series to calculate the system reliability. This configuration is sometimes referred to as a cross-strapped system or small scope redundancy. Eq. (24-2) and Eq. (24-6) would be used to calculate reliability of each dual redundant subsystem, and these results would then be used in Eq. (24-4).

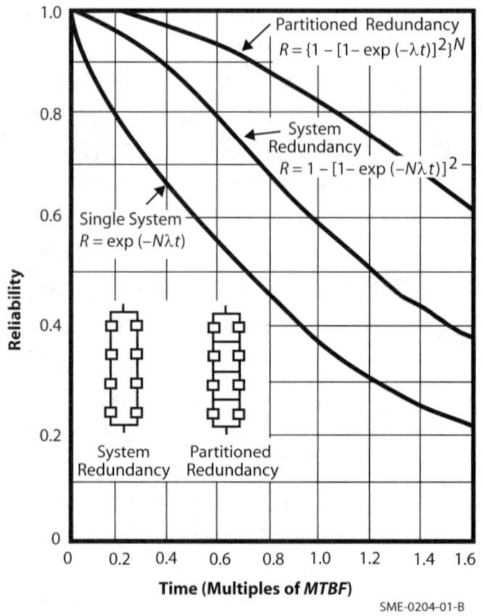

Fig. 24-1. Effect of Partitioning on Reliability, *t* is the Time from the Start of the Mission, *R* is the Mission Reliability or the Probability that at Least Essential Mission Elements will Survive.

The general equations resulting from the substitutions are also shown in the Fig. 24-1. The partitioned redundancy curve refers to the original (single) system being divided into quarters and then each quarter made redundant. The redundant and the quarter-partitioned curve involve (at least superficially) the same resources (in each case twice those of the single system), and yet the quarter configuration has a pronounced reliability advantage, particularly at the longer time intervals. It would therefore seem that redundancy of small scope would be preferred over large scope. A more detailed analysis would, (considering the reliability of the switching elements and other consequences of small scope redundancy for the specific system under consideration) be necessary to confirm or refute this general conclusion.

Reliability Predictions for Systems Composed of Electronic Components

Reliability Predictions for electronic components (the bulk of the satellite hardware) are performed by adding component failure rates to determine the aggregate failure rate of a higher level assembly or subsystem. This approach has been formalized in military standards such as MIL-HDBK-217F [DoD, 1991] and is a special case of series system reliability analysis for very low failure rate components. Table 24-1 shows typical values for some classes of electronic parts that are space qualified. The failure rates shown in the table are much higher than those for other handbooks for predicting electronic part reliability developed for the telecommunications industry (e.g., Telecordia RS-332 [2003], IEC TR 62380, [2004]). Non-space qualified parts have failure rates that are much higher (between 12 and 333 times).

The failure rates of the individual electronic components (sometimes called piece parts) are affected by factors such as temperature and application (i.e., electrical stresses placed on the part by the environment). Formulas are provided for adjusting the baseline failure rates in DoD [1991]. This method of reliability estimation may be used for comparison of design alternatives, when test or on-orbit incidents indicate insufficient reliability, or when a more expensive payload is to be incorporated (which increases the cost of failure).

As was noted at the beginning of this section, the method of adding failure rates is an approximation of a series system reliability and, as noted above, is valid for high reliability components. The following discussion shows the mathematical basis for this method. Where the quantity λt is small, the following approximation based on the Taylor Series expansion of the exponential function is frequently used

$$R = e^{-\lambda t} \approx 1 - \lambda t \tag{24-9}$$

Therefore

$$F = 1 - R \approx \lambda t \tag{24-10}$$

and for a system s made up of a number of n components in series, the failure problem becomes

$$F_s = \sum_{i=1}^{n} \lambda_i t \tag{24-11}$$

If the operating period, t, is the same for all components, the failure rate of the system becomes the sum of the failure rates of the individual components, that is

$$\frac{dF_s}{dt} \equiv f_s = \sum_{i=1}^{n} \lambda_i \tag{24-12}$$

where λ_i represents the failure rate of the ith component of the system.

Design Life

Design life is the intended operational time and an important vehicle-level parameter which is usually the key programmatic level system reliability requirement. De-

Table 24-1. Representative Piece Part Failure Rates (failures per 109 hours) from MIL-HDBK-217F.

Part Type	Failure Rate, × 10^{-9} per hour		Notes
	Space Flight Enviro.	Launch Enviro.	
Bipolar Gate Logic Array	0.9–19	17–200	Max 60,000 gates
Bipolar Microprocessor	7–27	60–215	Min 8 bits; Max 32 bits
MOS Microprocessor	12–47	70–250	Min 8 bits; Max 32 bits
MOS SRAM	2–11	24–75	Min 16 K, Max 1 M
Bipolar SRAM	2–8	30–75	Min 16 K, Max 1 M
Diodes General	1.3	170	
Transistors General	0.05	5F	
Transistors RF Power	165	900	
Resistors	0.01	1	Composition
Capacitors	0.1	10	
Relays	40	6,000	

sign Life determines the amount of consumables (e.g., control gas) that must be provided as well as the quality and test requirements for items subject to wear out, such as bearings and batteries. The mission reliability calculated at the design life is the *mission success probability.* Since this quantity is less than 1.0, the *expected life* is less than the design life. The customary measure of the expected life is the *mean mission duration* or *MMD,* given by:

$$MMD = \int T dR \qquad (24\text{-}13)$$

where T represents a horizontal (time) line in the shaded area of Fig. 24-2 and dR is the associated (vertical) increment in reliability. MMD is a frequently used figure of merit for spacecraft reliability improvement programs. When the spacecraft does not have any redundant elements, a plot of reliability vs. mission time will be the exponential curve, but when redundancy is provided the initial part of the reliability plot tends to be convex to the origin. This accounts for the shape of the curves in Fig. 24-2.

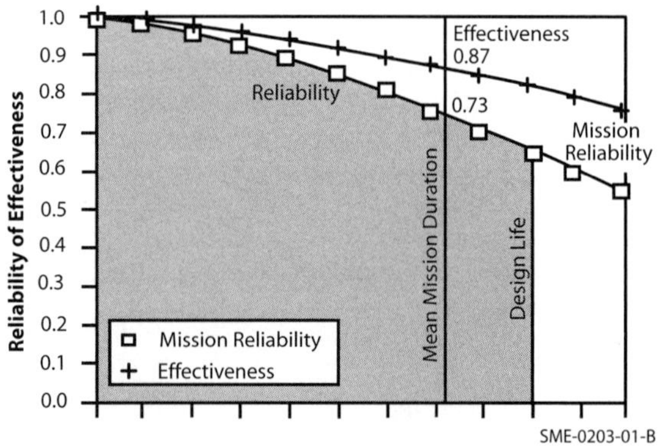

Fig. 24-2. Frequently Used Reliability Concepts. Design life is governed by wear-out and expendable stores. Mean mission duration is less than design life because failures can terminate a mission before end-of-life conditions are reached.

Degraded States

Most satellites perform multiple functions (e.g., weather observation and tracking ocean traffic), and performance of any of these functions may still be useful even when it is degraded. Under such circumstances the success criteria are no longer obvious. Should failure be defined as the event when the spacecraft fails to furnish any useful data, or should it be the point at which its performance deviates from any part of the specification? This problem can be addressed by establishing multiple reliability requirements. Assume that the specified weather observations are intended to use three frequency bands but that observations on even a single band are still useful. The success probability (SP) requirement may be formulated as shown in Table 24-2.

During the development of the satellite it may be found that it will be difficult to obtain a success probability for all three bands operational greater than 0.80 but that the single band mission reliability can be raised to 0.99. If the requirements shown in Table 24-2 are part of a contractual document it may take lengthy negotiations to agree on the change, even though it may be technically quite acceptable. To avoid such situations, *mission effectiveness* rather than reliability may be specified. There are several definitions of mission effectiveness [DoD, 1998], but all aim at a single metric that represents reliability weighted by the operational capability level to which the reliability is applicable. In the above example assume that the 1, 2, and 3 band capabilities are assigned weights of 0.25, 0.35, and 0.4, respectively (it is desirable that the weights add up to 1.0). A simple mission effectiveness requirement may then be stated as $0.25 \times 0.96 + 0.35 \times 0.92 + 0.4 \times 0.85 = 0.902$. A similar calculation shows that raising the single band reliability to 0.99 will not compensate for reducing the 3 band reliability to 0.80, but that this reduction could be tolerated if the 2 band reliability is raised to 0.95 at the same time. Where there is a sound technical basis for specifying mission effectiveness it will generally reduce both cost and development time compared to specifying multiple reliability values.

Table 24-2. Hypothetical Reliability Requirement for a Weather Satellite.

Condition	Success Probability Requirement
At Least 1 Band Operational	0.95
At Least 2 Bands Operational	0.92
All 3 Bands Operational	0.85

Availability

In cases where failures are recoverable (e.g., radiation events, power transients, switchover to a redundant element, and software failures), two new parameters become important: recovery time and availability. Recovery is the time necessary to restore the vehicle to an operable state. Recovery can generally occur automatically with all mechanisms on the vehicle (often called "autonomous recovery") or with intervention from the ground control station. Usually, autonomous recovery can occur much more quickly (often in seconds).

Availability can be thought of as the proportion of total time that the vehicle is operational, i.e.,

$$A = \frac{Uptime}{Total\_Time} \qquad (24\text{-}14)$$

where Total_Time is the sum of uptime and downtime. Thus, unavailability i.e., the probability that the system is not available is

$$U = 1 - A = \frac{Downtime}{Total\_Time} \qquad (24\text{-}15)$$

If both failure and recovery times are exponentially distributed, it can be shown that

$$A = \frac{\lambda}{\lambda + \mu} \qquad (24\text{-}16)$$

where λ is the failure rate and μ is the reciprocal of the average recovery time (i.e., the "recovery rate"). Like reliability, availability is a probability, and hence availability analogs exist for the series, parallel, and m out of n system level reliability, see Eq. (24-4) through Eq. (24-8). Thus, for example, the availability of an n-redundant system (similar to the reliability equation shown in Eq. (24-6) is

$$A_{s,p} = 1 - \prod_{i=1}^{n}(1 - A_i) \tag{24-17}$$

and the availability of an m out of n system similar to the reliability equation shown in Eq. (24-8), is

$$A = \sum_{k=m}^{n} \frac{n!}{k!(n-k)!} A_i^k (1 - A_i)^{(n-k)} \tag{24-18}$$

24.1.2 Recent Spacecraft Reliability Experience

In a study of 1,584 Earth-orbiting satellites successfully launched between January 1990 and October 2008, Castet and Saleh [2009] found that at the vehicle level, there was a non-constant failure rate over the vehicle life. During the first year, there was a 3% loss with a 6% loss of those surviving after 6 years, and 8% loss of the survivors after 10 years. The authors reported the contributions of failures by subsystem as a function of time as seen in Table 24-3.

Over 15 years of operation, the control processor (CP) contributes approximately 6% to the total satellite failures, the attitude control system contributes 20% and the Telemetry, Tracking, and Command (TTC) subsystem contributes 16%. Functions related to electrical power (batteries, solar arrays, and electrical distribution) account for between 30% and 40% of the failures throughout the vehicle lifetime. For the first 10 years, TTC is the lead contributor to satellite failures.

Table 24-3. Frequency of Spacecraft Failures.

Subsystem	30 days	1 year	5 years	10 years
Attitude Control (Gyro/Sensor/Reaction Wheel)	8%	12%	11%	18%
Thruster/Fuel	13%	20%	16%	13%
Control Processor	0%	0%	4%	5%
Mechanisms/Structures/ Thermal	8%	10%	11%	7%
Payload Instrument	0%	2%	3%	4%
Battery/Cell	6%	2%	10%	6%
Electrical Distribution	12%	8%	10%	11%
Solar Array (Deployment and Operating)	25%	17%	12%	12%
Telemetry Tracking and Command	22%	23%	18%	19%
Unknown	8%	6%	5%	5%

24.1.3 Design Process for Reliability

The process for designing a reliable system should start at project conception. The reliability engineering function depends extensively on information and support from other project functions including system engineering, subsystem design, software development, parts material processes, quality assurance organizations, and system safety. There are multiple standards that describe the conduct of a reliability program in the space industry [DoD, 1988] or [ECSS, 2009a]. Table 24-4 describes the key reliability program activities by mission phase, and Table 24-5a and 24-5b shows the interactions, roles, and responsibilities among these project functions.

A reliability program plan should be written as part of the initial program planning function to define both the activities of the reliability engineering function and its interaction with the rest of the program. In large programs, this may be a separate document but in smaller programs, it can be a part of the system engineering management plan (SEMP). The plan should describe how reliability objectives are to be allocated (or reference a separate reliability allocation document), assign responsibility for achieving them, and establish milestones for evaluating the achievements. It also serves as an agreement with other spacecraft functions regarding their responsibilities in support of reliability.

Failure Modes and Effects Analysis

The Failure Modes and Effects Analysis (FMEA) is a qualitative analysis in which each component of a system is posited to fail, and the effects of that hypothetical failure on the surrounding components and the system level are evaluated. The benefits of the FMEA are:

- Identifying single points of failure and associated critical items
- Associating underlying failures with observable symptoms that can be used for health monitoring and diagnostics (if measurement and telemetry points are defined)
- Evaluating the effects of existing compensating provisions (e.g., on-board failure detection and recovery) physical, functional, or temporal redundancy

Several styles of FMEAs have been defined in standards such as DoD [1984], SAE [2001], and ECSS [2009b]. An FMEA can be performed at multiple levels of abstraction (called "indenture levels" in MIL STD 1629A). The lowest level is the part level (discrete parts and each pin of an IC). For a capacitor the failure modes are open and short (sometimes a change in capacitance may also be recorded). Failure effects are assessed at the part level and also at higher levels such as assembly and major component or subsystem. The failure effect of a shorted capacitor may be a bias shift on a transistor (part level) which in turn cuts off the output of a demodulator (assembly level) and causes loss of voice communications (subsystem level). In our

Table 24-4. Key Reliability Program Plan Activities.

Development Stage	Activities
Concept Development	Identification of reliability standards and methods; definition of quantitative requirements for reliability and availability based on operational concepts, definition of degraded modes and measures of effectiveness
Preliminary Design	Preliminary allocation of top level quantitative requirements to subsystems; definitions of operational modes and states; definitions of failure modes, effects, and compensations; definitions of reliability test plans; identification and justification (including mitigating actions) of single points of failure
Detailed Design	Detailed allocations of quantitative reliability and availability requirements to all elements of the space vehicle (to include both hardware, software, and data); verification of failure detection, recovery, and reporting provisions
Development and Fabrication	Ensuring conformance with the hardware and software design provisions; monitoring or problem and discrepancy reports for unanticipated failure behavior
Integration and Test	Review of test results for conformance or deviation from expected failure detection and recovery behavior; review of anomaly reports for unanticipated failure behavior; analysis of quantitative data for conformance with quantitative failure rate, recovery time, and recovery probability requirements
Operation	Review of data from on-orbit anomalies and failures for incorporation into future requirements

example, the detection may be by an output monitor included in the demodulator, and the failure mitigation may be use of an alternate voice channel. The FMEA may then be conducted at the function level, where functions are timers, counters, and shift registers, or at even higher levels. The advantage of performing an FMEA at higher levels is that there are usually fewer items that must be analyzed. The disadvantage is that failure modes may be less well defined, and effects may be more complicated to analyze.

Criticality Analysis can be added to the FMEA and it then becomes Failure Modes, Effects and Criticality Analysis (FMECA). Criticality here refers to the combination of frequency (or probability) of occurrence and the severity of the associated system effect. Thus, among two failure modes that produce the same system effect, the one having a higher probability is the more critical one. In the FMECA a probability is associated with each failure mode, and the probabilities of all failure modes that cause a given effect are added in a summary section of the FMEA. Loss of modulator output cited in the example may be caused by several failure modes of the demodulator components, and loss of the voice channel may be caused by failure modes other than those in the demodulator. Although there may be considerable error in the estimate of a given failure mode, these tend to be evened out when arriving at estimates of failure effects at the subsystem and higher levels. In digital microcircuits it is usually not possible to conduct FMECA at the level of primitive elements (gates or transistors) because there are too many of them and because causes of failure may affect multiple elements (e.g., voids in the oxide layer) in such cases, the FMECA must be performed at a higher level.

As noted above, failure modes at the function level are generally not as well known as those at the part level, and a single cause of failure may affect multiple functions. In assessing the effects of failure at the higher level it may therefore be advisable to be conservative.

Other Reliability-Related Design Analyses

Other analyses that are commonly performed on space systems are:

- **Sneak Circuit Analysis (SCA),** which searches for unintended current flows. This analysis can be used to show that explosive or other one-shot devices will not be accidentally actuated, and that they will always be actuated when intended.
- **Worst Case Analysis (WCA),** which assumes that all components of the system are at their most pessimistic operational state (i.e., batteries at low voltage, resistors at either extreme of their tolerance range, signals at their lowest non-failed level) to assess whether the system as a whole will continue to function.
- **Thermal Analysis,** which determines the temperature at various points of the spacecraft. Thermal analysis is particularly important to piece part reliability prediction because failure rates can increase exponentially as a function of (absolute) temperature due to the *Arrhenius relation*.
- **Electromagnetic Interference / Electromagnetic Compatibility,** which analyzes for the presence of electromagnetic interference among the SV elements.

Failure Reporting

The *Failure Reporting and Corrective Action* (FRACAS) is a key element in any reliability program and it should cover both the pre-launch test and the on-orbit phases because:

1. It informs stakeholders that a failure has been observed

Table 24-5a. Interaction of Project Functions in Development of Reliable Space Systems—Concept Development through Detailed Design.

Project Function	Concept Development	Preliminary Design	Detailed Design
System Engineering	Requirements for reliability and dependability defined, complete, verifiable, consistent; definition of mission duration, size, weight, and power constraints; identification of space environment issues (e.g., radiation) based on orbit and operations constraints that affect reliability; identification of key reliability and availability issues connected to choices of technologies (e.g., propulsion, sensors, and power systems)	Requirements allocated to subsystems and disciplines (hardware, electronics, mechanical, thermal); derived requirements considering mission and operational environment defined. Trade-off studies performed where necessary on performance and redundancy requirements vs., size, weight and power constraints; definition of vehicle-level failure detection and recovery strategy and architecture including identification of failure containment and propagation boundaries	Design features traced to requirements; additional derived requirements for failure detection and recovery identified as design emerges; ensuring that proper margins are maintained for mechanical and electrical stresses and for computing and communication response time, error rate, and capacity factors
Subsystem Design	Extent of redundancy defined; major failure mechanisms and reliability design concerns identified; subsystem recovery strategies	Failure detection and reporting design provisions and telemetry defined; constraints for failure behavior at subsystem boundaries defined; diagnostic and built-in-test (BIT) provisions identified	Subsystem design incorporates requirements and architecture for failure detection and recovery; selected components are appropriate for electrical, thermal, and mechanical stresses; processors and communications lines have sufficient capacity; modular redundancy constraints are satisfied for switch over
Computer System Design and Software Development	Computer system architecture (including internal networks) accounts for recovery time and autonomous operational requirements of the mission; where multiple computer systems are used (e.g., payloads vs. bus), failure containment and recovery regions are defined; software development standards including testing at the unit and various stages of integration are defined; discrepancy reporting standards are defined; quantitative failure rate, recovery time, and recovery probabilities are allocated to major architectural components	Computer system and software top level accommodate quantitative and qualitative failure detection and recovery requirements; safe mode entry and recovery mechanisms are defined; redundancy and failure management designs are defined; mechanisms for maintaining consistency of replicated state data defined; software design and coding standards are defined for software components; generic purchased software components (e.g., operating systems, computer communications) conform to architecture and design; commands for vehicle control, recovery, and reconfiguration	Detailed design conforms to architecture and top level design features for failure detection and recovery; hardware infrastructure to accommodate failure detection and recovery is defined (e.g., interrupts, communications ports and connections, watchdog timers); exception handling strategies are defined; diagnostics and built-in-test mechanisms are defined; vehicle status and health monitoring telemetry is defined; all detailed design provisions conform with requirements
Parts, Materials, Processes	Standards for parts, materials, and processes are defined; requirements are consistent with mission reliability and availability requirements	Components (mechanical parts, solar cells, processors, FPGAs, memory chips, and other components) conform to reliability allocations and space qualification requirements; non-conforming or non-standard parts have appropriate documentation	Changes in the design to accommodate unavailability of qualified parts are analyzed for impact on reliability and reliability prediction models are revised as necessary
Test and Verification	Test strategies and test standards incorporate reliability, failure detection, and recovery	Verification and test program defined (including failure and recovery testing); identification of high cost and long lead testing facilities; definition of procedures for recording operating time and unplanned failures	Verification and test plans and analyses defined (including failure and recovery testing); design of test labs and special test equipment to include life testing and failure recovery testing where necessary
System Safety	Identification of top-level hazards that would result in death, injury, or catastrophic loss of mission capabilities; identification of program standards and requirements	Identification of hazards evident in the preliminary design, definition of requirements for mitigation, and probabilistic risk assessments; formulation of testing and verification requirements for defined mitigations	Review of design and analyses (e.g., FMECAs) to ensure that hazards have either been eliminated or that probabilities have been reduced to acceptable levels
Quality Assurance	Ensuring conformance with standards for reliability engineering, software development, parts selection, failure reporting, testing, and verification across all development phases		

Table 24-5b. Interaction of Project Functions in Development of Reliable Space Systems—Build through Operations.

Project Function	Development and Fabrication	Integration and Test	Operations
System Engineering	Resolve cross-cutting issues and ensure interfaces preserve failure detection and recovery properties; addressing issues emerging from this and previous phases of the development	Verify that integrated system can be shown to meet requirements (including failure detection and recovery); resolution of critical issues (including those related to failure and recovery behavior)	Review on-orbit anomalies for system-wide issues; optimize operational and sustainability issues (for both space and ground segments)
Subsystem Design	Assemblies and units integrated into subsystems conform to expected failure and recovery behavior; diagnostic and BIT provisions across assemblies and units function as expected; electrical, mechanical, thermal stresses are within design margins	Anomalies discovered during testing related to design problems are addressed (corrected or mitigated)	Experience that would affect design of next generation subsystems is collected and analyzed
Computer System Design and Software Development	Computer system hardware infrastructure meets interface, capacity, response time, and failure containment requirements; software is designed and coded in accordance with project standards (especially those driven by reliability); unit testing addresses failure detection and recovery requirements for software components	Integration testing specifically addresses failure detection and recovery requirements allocated to the software and computing space vehicle elements. For software integration testing addresses failure containment, diagnostics, and reporting requirements; for system integration testing, system level failure detection and recovery behavior conforms to requirements; anomalies observed during any period of testing that are counter to assumptions and predictions are specially flagged and analyzed for their impact on the system design	Deficiencies and anomalies in on-orbit operation are analyzed for design impact; where possible, software changes are made and uploaded to the space vehicle; insights from on-orbit behavior are incorporated into future designs
Parts, Materials, Processes	Same as for detailed design	Test results are analyzed for failures or anomalies in conforming and specially qualified (or accepted non-conforming) components	Review of data from parts, materials and process on-orbit failures for incorporation into future requirements
Test and Verification	Verification and test procedures defined (including failure and recovery testing); development of test labs and equipment	Execution of test procedures; recording of results; analysis of results and identification of critical issues (including those related to failure and recovery behavior)	Acquisition of lessons learned from anomalies for future test plans and procedures
System Safety	Monitoring of development and fabrication activities to ensure that development meets requirements of mitigations identified in earlier design stages	Assessing test and verification results for hazard mitigation effectiveness; review of unanticipated failures for safety significance	Review of data from on-orbit anomalies and failures for incorporation into future requirements
Quality Assurance	Ensuring conformance with standards for reliability engineering, software development, parts selection, failure reporting, testing, and verification across all development phases		

2. It furnishes a record through which trends and correlations can be evaluated at a future time (an example of a trend is that the probability of failure increases after x hours of use; an example of a correlation is that part y fails during a particular step in the test sequence).
3. It permits reassessment of the predicted failure rates and is the basis for consequent modifications of the fault avoidance or fault tolerance provisions
4. It identifies unanticipated failure modes and effects and can inform on the effectiveness of recovery after a failure

Elements 2 and 3 require recording the operating time of all units in service; usually by an operating log maintained for each part number, with separate records for serial number. Corrective action is typically also recorded as part of the failure reporting. This facilitates configuration management in that it establishes at what point a component or subsystem has been returned to operational status. Reporting for each individual part also facilitates future investigation of the effectiveness of the corrective action. Corrective action frequently involves two steps: in the first, a failed part is replaced by a good one of the same design; the second step, addresses the root cause, e.g., by tightening limits for the incoming test of this part. The results of retest are detailed in the corrective action report.

To establish a FRACAS the following must be identified:

- Scope of the activities (e.g., system test, field test, normal usage)
- Responsibility for cost and for report initiation
- Method and frequency of reporting (e.g., each incident or by time interval)

The format used for reporting of failures and corrective actions is not standardized. However, the following are the most essential data:

- Incident identification (e.g., report identification number)
- Date, time and locale of the incident
- Identification of the failed component (Part no., name, and serial number for hardware; task name, software configuration identification, version for software)
- Higher level part or system identifiers (subsystem or major component for hardware and software)
- Lower level part or system identifiers (usually available only after diagnosis)
- Operation in progress and environmental conditions when failure was detected
- Immediate and higher level effects of failure
- Names of individuals responsible for detection, verification and analysis
- Diagnosis of immediate, contributory and root causes of the failure
- Corrective action: Dates and nature of repair and results of retest

Parts Selection and Screening

The space operating environment includes cosmic rays, ionizing radiation, temperature extremes, vacuum conditions, and microgravity. In addition, parts and assemblies must withstand the forces of a rocket launch and explosive separation from the launch vehicle. Therefore, space qualified parts have unique requirements including: rigorous procedures for parts selection, evaluation and approval on both main spacecraft developer and its lower tier vendors and suppliers; parts and assembly handling and storage; quality assurance programs and documentation; and operating and failure data acquisition and dissemination. While these requirements apply to all aspects of the spacecraft—including structural components, thrusters, lubricants, adhesives, coatings, and propellants—reliability engineering is usually most concerned with electrical, electronic, and electromechanical (EEE) parts because they dominate the materials lists for a space vehicle. Requirements for space qualified EEE parts include [Hamiter, 1990]:

- Junction temperature ranges of –55 C to 125 C or wider
- Hermetic packaging for solid state devices and relays (plastic encapsulation is sometimes accepted when hermetic packaged parts are not available)
- Higher vibration capability
- Control of outgassing & flammability
- Extremely low defect levels (10 ppm)
- Extremely long reliability (1 to 15 × 10^{-9}/hr)
- Conservative derating & application practices (discussed in the next section).

There are multiple standards existing for parts specification, selection, and screening. Examples include ECSS-Q-60B [2007] (Space Components Steering Board in partnership with the European Space Agency), and (MSFC-STD-3012, prepared by NASA's Marshall Space Flight Center), MIL-PRF-38535J [DoD, 2010c] for integrated circuits, MIL-PRF-38534H [DoD, 2010b] for hybrids, and MIL-PRF-19500 [DoD, 2010d] for discrete parts), MIL-STD-202G [DoD, 2002], MIL-STD 883H [DoD, 2010a], and MIL STD 1580 [DoD, 2003]. However, because most are derived from DoD and were developed in the 1960s and 1970s, they share common elements including specification documents, standardized inspections, test methods (e.g., measurement of the leakage current at elevated temperature for semiconductors under specified conditions and for specified times), and destructive physical analysis (DPA) procedures.

Screening is testing intended to remove nonconforming parts (parts with random defects that are likely to result in early failures, known as infant mortality) from an otherwise acceptable lot and thus increase confidence in the reliability of the parts selected for use [Sahu, 2003]. This is graphically depicted in Fig. 24-3. For some component classes, inspection is part of the screening process. Screening can be conducted at several levels of acceptance, for example, MIL STD 883H (method 5004.11) specifies higher thresholds for space qualified parts (Class S) than for other military qualified parts (Class B). Higher screening thresholds reduce the probability of failure by rejecting the tail of the distribution but increase the cost of the remaining parts. The cost effectiveness of screening is high when (1) parts have an initially high failure rate, (2) the rejected fraction is low (not more than 20% of the lot), (3) where the cost of test is small when compared to the unit cost of the product under test (not over 10%), and (4) specially manufactured qualified parts would be bulkier or heavier. Screening can be applied to assemblies, (e.g., by subjecting them to combined thermal and vibration

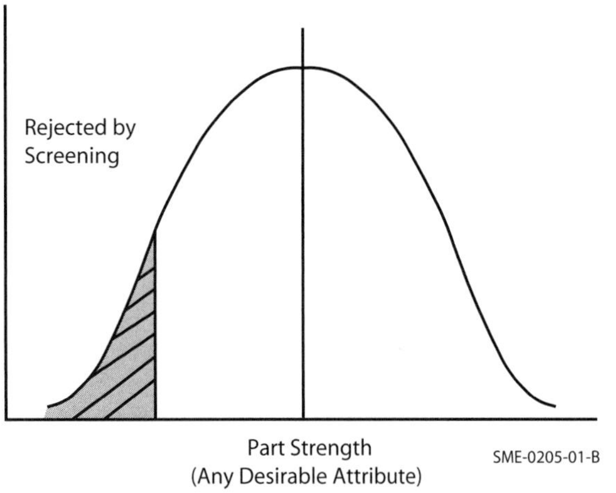

Fig. 24-3. Attribute Control by Screening. Screening rejects parts likely to fail in service.

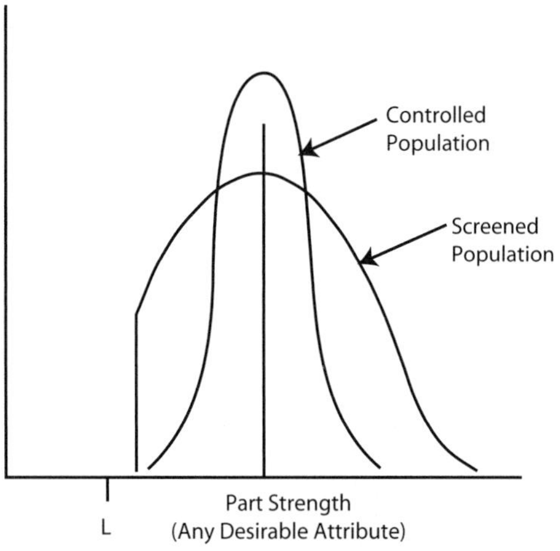

Fig. 24-4. Attribute Control by Process Control. In a controlled population fewer parts are near the acceptance limit than in a screened population.

environments and is thus more versatile than derating). Screening at the assembly level is also likely to result in a lower ratio of test cost to cost and thus is more cost effective. On the other hand, screening is not very effective for lowering the failure probability for components that have been derated—the failure probability due to external stresses in that mode is already very low.

Use of screening by itself is often criticized because it permits the use of products that do not, as delivered, meet all of the requirements of any given application. The alternative is the use of *qualified parts lists* (QPLs) and *qualified manufacturing lines* (QMLs) together with screening. QML and QPL parts are designed more conservatively, use more durable and superior quality materials, are built to tighter tolerances, and have more inspections. The net result is higher rigor in the control of the component manufacturing process so that it can be relied on not to produce the outliers that must be screened out. As shown in Fig. 24-4 both the screened population and the controlled population meet the acceptance criteria in that no parts fall below the lower limit, denoted as L in the figure. However, in the screened population a much larger fraction of the total population is near the lower limit than in the controlled population. Environmental effects and aging cause a dispersion of the attributes, and therefore will cause a larger fraction of the screened population to fall below the lower limit than in the controlled population. This effect can be compensated for by selecting an initial acceptance limit that is higher than the lowest value that can be tolerated in service. Where articles are procured specifically for space applications, costs will be reduced if the process can be improved so that only a small portion of the product will be rejected in screening.

Derating

The term *derating* is primarily applied to electrical and electronic components and involves the specification of a component that carries a higher rating than is needed for the application. The term *design margin* is mostly used in structure and thermal subsystems and means that a component is designed to carry more than the expected load and is defined by

$$M = \frac{\overline{S} - \overline{L}}{\sigma_S^2 - \sigma_L^2} \tag{24-19}$$

where M is the design margin, and S and L refer to the mean and standard deviations of the strength and load distributions [O'Connor, 2002]. Design margins and derating accomplish the same goal: prevention of component failure due to higher than expected external stresses or other deviations from the nominal conditions. The stress factors that are derated vary by component class. For example, for capacitors, stress factors may be voltage, for resistors, it might be power, for microcircuits, they may include supply voltage, power dissipation, junction temperature, output current, and clock frequency. There is no generally accepted method for determining which stress factors to derate and by how much. It is largely governed by the collective engineering judgment at the purchasing or developing organization. Examples are the NASA Goddard Space Flight Center PD-ED-1201 or Aerospace Corp. TOR-2006(8583)-5236 (used by the US Air Force).

Environmental protection can take the form of shock mounting, cooling or heating provisions, and shielding against radiation effects. Where derating reduces the failure probability by increasing the strength of the components, environmental protection reduces the failure probability by reducing the stress levels. In many cases, environmental protection adds considerable weight, and this, rather than cost, limits the amount of protection that can be provided.

24.1.4 Software Considerations

Spacecraft operations are becoming increasingly dependent on software, in the spacecraft and in the ground segment. Indeed, software is involved in nearly all functions of the spacecraft, and nearly all system functional requirements are in part allocated to software. Although there have been spectacular launch and on-orbit failures due to software defects [Lions, 1996]; [MCO, 1999]; [JPL, 2000], many more missions have been saved by software by means of work-arounds than have been lost due to it. This section considers software reliability issues from two perspectives: how software should be developed (specified, design, implemented, and tested) to support space vehicle and mission reliability, and reliability prediction of systems that include software.

Table 24-6 is a partial list of software specifications, designs, and development practices to enhance system reliability and availability by development phase. The most important distinction between hardware and software in space systems is that software failures can be recoverable if (1) the system is properly designed and implemented and (2) the health and telemetry data sent to ground control is sufficient for failures where ground intervention is necessary. The importance of defining correct and complete requirements to ensure mission success has been frequently noted (e.g., [Leveson, 1995]), and such definitions are critical for software requirements in space systems. The affected requirements concern not only that the software perform its functions correctly, but also that it manage the computer and system configurations properly and that it detect and respond appropriately to failures. Within the design, the most important considerations are the robustness of the interfaces that act as the failure containment boundaries and the completeness and correctness in the design of the recovery mechanisms (both functionality and timing). For implementation, the key issues are that proper coding standards are defined and followed, and that correctness of the actual implementations can be verified through both peer reviews and the definition of test cases.

Table 24-6. Software Design and Development Practices to Enhance System Reliability and Availability.

Phase	
Requirements	Requirements clearly identify and fully define operational modes (normal mode, graceful degradation, safe mode, or other contingency modes)
	Failure rates, recovery times, and recovery probabilities allocated to the software components that will exist at runtime
	Automated failure detection and recovery requirements defined, including explicit criteria for what failures classes will handled (For example, are only single-event failures handled)
	Timing requirements defined for both steady state and recovery—in particular, isolation, recovery and repair durations (average and maximum) have been identified and allocated
	Specified capabilities for monitoring and control by operators
Design	Existence of identifiable architecture components to manage failures in the systems
	Requirements for failure rates, failure detection, and recovery are derived as lower level design (not known at the beginning of the design) details are defined
	Fault containment boundaries are explicitly and unambiguously defined, and the failure containment mechanisms at these boundaries are dependable
	Protocols for processor health messages, heartbeats, and network traffic account for steady state and failure conditions
Detailed Design and Coding	Design standards exist to enforce architectural provisions for failure containment, failure detection, and recovery (including interfaces, data types, exception handling, input and output validation)
	Software development procedures emphasize testing and recording of results of testing for both normal and off-normal cases (including automated regression testing)
Verification (Test and Analysis)	Verify that all credible failure modes in lower level SW, HW, and networks been identified
	Verify traceability from the design to the system availability/maintainability requirements
	Verify that detection and recovery all identified failure modes addressed in the architecture
	Verify that failure detection/recovery durations meet the operational availability requirements
	Verify that Software architecture, when combined with the hardware architecture, will meet system reliability and availability requirements (including maximum outage duration)
	Test program should include prototype/benchmark/analysis on the system failure management—Provide analysis and results.
	Verify that the COTS/reuse products meet the reliability, availability, and fault management requirements (e.g., past service history, integration testing)

Unlike electronic hardware, there is no widely accepted method of predicting software reliability in the absence of measurement of the actual system performance. This does not mean that the finite probability of software failures can be disregarded, instead, software failures should be recorded, analyzed and classified throughout the software development process—preferably, as part of a FRACAS. Software failures can be classified in two general categories: *Deterministic* and *Random*. Deterministic software failures occur consistently given a certain input data set and are nearly always due to some identifiable coding defect traceable to a logic or algorithmic error, design problem (e.g., interfaces), or a requirements flaw (omitted, vague, or incomplete). It may be difficult to find data sets that reproduce deterministic failures, but once found, such data sets will consistently produce the same unwanted result. *Random* failures, on the other hand, occur due to a timing problem, momentary buffer overflow, or other transient condition that make them difficult to reproduce. These conditions are frequently related to conditions external to the software itself, and because such conditions occur non-deterministically, the consequent failures can also be regarded as non-deterministic. Previous research on high integrity systems has shown that after software defects related to deterministic failures have been removed, the residual software defects lead to a failure behavior which can be characterized by a MTBF [Hsueh and Iyer, 1988] and hence can be characterized as random and amenable to stochastic modeling. A majority of such failures could be recovered by the use of physical redundancy as in the case of hardware ([Gray, 1990]; [Lee and Iyer, 1995]; [Tang and Hecht, 1995]). Such defects are often referred to as "Heisenbugs" after Werner Heisenburg's uncertainty principle [Bourne, 2004].

It can be argued that such software failures could ultimately be traced to a design implementation flaw and that they are therefore not truly random. However, the same argument would also apply to electronic hardware components for which parts-level reliability prediction methods discussed above are accepted practice, (i.e., that a detailed root cause analysis would reveal manufacturing flaws or design flaws). Nevertheless, the part-level reliability prediction methods described above that consider electronic component failures to be random are well accepted. In prediction of both hardware and software element and system reliability, we are less interested in the underlying causes of failures as we are in the probability of their occurrence.

Deterministic failures can be found and removed through a disciplined software development process in which requirements are carefully formulated and validated, the design is properly analyzed for both functional consistency and performance (capacity and response time), source code is checked for conformance to well established coding standards, peer reviews are conducted to find classes of defects readily identified by qualified people, and testing is performed consistently and thoroughly at multiple levels of integration (unit, subsystem, and system).

Random failures, in software, can be addressed stochastically. No generally accepted methods exist for predicting software reliability without empirical data. Thus, software reliability can not be predicted, it can only be *measured.* This does not mean that the entire satellite must be completed before the quantitative software reliability can be determined. Software is composed in separate runtime components called *processes* that execute on a processor under the control of an *operating system kernel.* As the separate processes are developed and tested, their failure rates can be measured. Similarly, the failure rate of the operating system kernel, which may be a commercial product, can also be measured. Such software failure rates can be combined with hardware elements into a system level failure rate just as is the case for hardware components alone. Methods for doing so are described by Kececioglu [1993] and in IEC [1998], DoD [1996], and the NIST/SEMATECH online Handbook [2010].

Get Stnd

24.1.5 Redundancy and Fault Tolerance

Fault tolerance protects against a wider spectrum of failure modes than fault avoidance. In most cases, it also requires more resources. At the system level, redundancy is the primary method of achieving fault tolerance. This section describes five types of redundancy strategies that are summarized in Table 24-7.

In practice the switching or voting provisions that are required for each partition add considerably to the cost of the implementation, and since they are not likely 100% reliable they may also reduce the reliability benefits. System test can also be adversely impacted by redundancy of small scope. For example, in Fig. 24-1, the system redundancy (middle line in the figure) requires only two tests. The quarter redundancy (top line) requires 16 test combinations. Selecting the scope of redundancy we must consider detection of the cause of failures, the ease of output switching or combining, the reliability that can be achieved, and the cost of implementation and test.

Replication

Replication involves installation of two or more identical components with switching to make one of them active. This type of redundancy offers very high protection against random failures, but not failures due to design deficiencies: if one component fails due to insufficient radiation hardness, the redundant one is very likely to fail soon thereafter. Because of its high cost, replication is used only sparingly in low value satellites. The cost of replication can sometimes be reduced by employing *k-out-of-n replacement,* in which a pool of spares can be assigned to replace any one of the pool of active units. An example is nonvolatile storage which usually consists of multiple physically identical modules. Providing one or more spare modules on the same data bus permits replacement of any one failed module. The same scheme can be used for multi-cell batteries, solar panels, and other elements of the electric power supply.

Table 24-7. Redundancy Strategies for Fault Tolerance.

Strategy	Protection Against	Disadvantages
Replication of the Same Design	Random failures	Higher acquisition cost, weight, power
Diverse Design for Each Channel	Random failures and failures caused by design deficiencies	Higher acquisition cost, weight, power, design, and logistics costs
Functional Redundancy	Random failures and failures caused by design deficiencies	May not always be feasible—existence of diverse method is necessary
Temporal Redundancy (Restart and Retry)	Transient and intermittent failures; some classes of software failures	Not effective against permanent failures; failure will persist until system is restarted
Information Encoding	Single Event Upsets and digital transmission errors	Correction capabilities are usually limited to 1 or 2 bits per event

In some cases (e.g., power supplies) the outputs can be combined so that the redundancy is completely passive. However, in most cases, some type of redundancy management such as voting or switching is necessary. Voting combines outputs of redundant units but carries a high cost because at least three identical units have to be installed to make it practicable. Switching is used in active/standby systems in which a switching mechanism configures the standby element into the circuit to replace the failed previously active elements. The effectiveness depends on the dependability of both the monitoring provisions that detect failure of the active component and the switching mechanism.

Diverse Design Redundancy

Installation of two or more components of different design (called *diverse design redundancy*) to furnish the same service has two advantages: it offers high protection against failures due to design deficiencies, and it can offer lower cost if the back-up unit is a "lifeboat," with lower accuracy and functionality, but still adequate for the minimum mission needs. The installation of diverse units usually adds to logistic cost because of additional test specifications, fixtures. and spare parts. This form of redundancy is economical primarily where the back-up unit comes from a previous satellite design, or where there is experience with it from another source. Where there is concern about the design integrity of a primary component, diverse design redundancy may have to be employed regardless of cost.

Functional and Temporal Redundancy

Functional redundancy (sometimes called *analytic redundancy)* involves furnishing a service by diverse means. An example is the determination of attitude rate from a rate gyro assembly (direct), and from observation of celestial bodies (indirect). It is particularly advantageous when the alternate is already installed for another service, (e.g., if a star sensor is provided for navigation). In these cases the only cost incurred is for the switching provisions and for data conversion. Both of these can frequently be achieved in an *existing* on-board computer thus further minimizing the cost.

Functional redundancy can also take the form of a ground back-up for functions preferably performed autonomously, (e.g., navigation, thermal control, or furnishing commands for sensor operation). In the communication subsystem there are frequently omni-directional and directional antenna systems. For some satellite missions these may also be considered a form of functional redundancy.

The chief benefits of functional redundancy are: it avoids the cost and weight penalties of physical redundancy, and it is inherently diverse, thus providing protection against design faults. The major limitation is that the back-up provisions usually entail lower performance.

Temporal redundancy involves repetition of an unsuccessful operation. A common example is a retry after a failure within the computing process. The same technique is applicable to acquisition of a star, firing of a pyrotechnic device, or communication with the ground. This is obviously a low cost technique. It is most effective when the design incorporates an analysis of the optimum retry interval and of changes that may improve the success of later operations, (e.g., switching a power supply, reducing loads on the power supply, or re-orientation of the satellite). The most important step is to plan ahead for retry of operations and to incorporate "hooks" that permit automatic or ground-initiated retry. "Safe mode" is a combination of both functional and temporal redundancy. Safe mode is entered upon detection of a major failure condition. In response, the satellite deactivates nonessential elements (i.e., all those not related to minimal attitude control, solar power, and ground communications). A ground control crew is then responsible for diagnosing the cause of the failure, taking corrective action, and reconfiguring the satellite to a normal or degraded mode.

Coding Techniques

Data coding provides robustness of data transmission and storage by enabling continued operation in the presence of a wide spectrum of errors, primarily in memory and data transmission. Coding techniques are also available for detection or toleration of errors in arithmetic processors.

The important coding techniques are error detecting code and error correcting code. The former is intended primarily for fault isolation (i.e., preventing an incorrect result from being used in subsequent operations). The latter is a fault tolerance mechanism that corrects a class of errors and permits operations to continue normally.

All such measures require the addition of check bits to the bit pattern that represents the basic information. If there is agreement between the check and information bits, the data is accepted. If there is no agreement, the data is rejected (for error detecting code) or corrected (for error correcting code).

24.1.6 Human Factors Considerations

Operators are frequently ignored in reliability analysis and design but their action (or inaction) can drastically affect the mission duration and availability of space vehicles. A full discussion of human factors issues in ground control systems is beyond the scope of this chapter, but it should be noted that vehicle status monitoring (by means of telemetry and monitoring of payload signals) is the first line of defense in mitigating the effects of anomalies. Operators who act in time may be able to prevent a vehicle outage or ensure that an outage is recoverable. In order for operators to intervene in a manner that is timely and effective, they need adequate telemetry. The best means of defining telemetry requirements is through the FMEA. When failure mode compensating provisions depend on operators, an evaluation should be made to ensure that design information is provided.

24.1.7 Reliability Testing

Reliability testing assesses whether an element has sufficient durability for the mission (whether measured in cycles, time, or other relevant units). Reliability testing is costly and therefore performed selectively—usually on elements where wear out or material degradation is the primary failure mechanism. The least expensive reliability test is one that is not run at all as a reliability test, but rather as a part of a qualification test, lot acceptance test for purchased parts, or as an acceptance test on the spacecraft as a whole or on a major subsystem. To use these activities for reliability assessment may require some additional instrumentation and sometimes an extension of the test time, but these are very small resource expenditures compared to those required for even a modest separately run reliability test.

Other alternatives to obtaining reliability data by test are:

- Using test data obtained by others (including vendors) on the same component
- Using test or experience data on similar components
- Stress-strength analysis (particularly for mechanical components)
- Reliability prediction by MIL-HDBK-217 or similar sources

Once it has been decided that a reliability test is necessary, a suitable scope and test environment must be selected. Table 24-8 and Table 24-9 list considerations to be used in selecting these attributes. The attributes of the approaches lead to the test recommendations shown in Table 24-10.

Table 24-8. Considerations in Selection of Testing Scope.

Small Scope (parts and circuit boards)	Large Scope (assemblies, subsystems, and systems)
• Low cost and small size of individual test articles permit testing of multiple items • Inputs and outputs are easily accessible • The test environment can be tailored to the requirements or the unit under test • The test can be conducted early because it does not require integration	• Interactions between components can be observed • Test results are easily translated to effects on the mission

Table 24-9. Considerations in Selection of Testing Environment.

Quiescent (room ambient)	Stressed
• Low cost (no or only simple environmental chambers required) • Articles under test are easily accessible • No inducing of failures due to unusually high stress	• Increased probability of failure (less test time required) • Can identify an Environmental vulnerability of the unit under test

Table 24-10. Typical Uses of Reliability Testing.

	Scope	
Environment	Small	Large
Quiescent	Suitability test Critical components when vulnerabilities to stresses are not known	High risk subsystems
Stressed	Critical components where vulnerabilities to stress are known	"Thermal vacuum" testing (expensive)

The time required for any reliability test can be significantly reduced if *testing by variables* is employed. This means that the value of significant attributes is numerically recorded (as contrasted with the commonly used pass/fail procedure). From these data, the distribution of parameters can be plotted, and the probability of dropping below an acceptance criterion can be assessed. The general technique is similar to the one described in Sec. 24.1.3. For reliability assessment the parameter distributions are of interest, whereas in screening, the attributes of individual units are the chief criterion.

The small component populations that are typical of space procurements preclude the use of conventional reliability demonstration methods. Even a modest subsystem requirement, such as reliability of 0.95 for 17,000 hours (approximately 2 years), corresponds to an MTBF of over 330,000 hours and will require over 1 million component-hours of test to arrive at a statistically meaningful assessment by conventional methods. Yet, experimental verification of the claimed reliability of a component or subsystem is frequently desirable and sometimes required. So let's explore some low cost methods of accomplishing this.

The major causes of failures are workmanship and design. The first of these can be addressed by quality assurance. Design failures occur primarily because the strength of the component is not adequate for the environment in which it is used, or because the manufacturing process permits too much variability in component characteristics. This can more easily be seen in mechanical spacecraft components where reliability depends on (a) the margin between the nominal (mean) strength of the component and the maximum service load and (b) the variability of strength about the mean in the manufactured product. Since test can characterize the strength of mechanical components easily, strength-load margins (design margins) have always played a major role in their reliability assessment. For electrical and electronic components the same relation holds in principle, but it is usually much harder to define a single failure causing stress or load. Nevertheless, test data can give valuable insights into potential reliability problems. Important requirements are (a) recording of test numerical results and (b) statistical evaluation of the probability of failure from the numerical test results, e.g., by applying the 6-sigma criterion (the mean of a parameter is at least six standard deviations above the specified minimum of the specified maximum) [Harry, 1997]. The tests from which the required data is obtained can be qualification and acceptance tests.

24.2 Space System Risk Analysis

Julie Wertz, *Jet Propulsion Laboratory, California Institute of Technology*

The majority of the design process will focus on how to get a particular design to work in the way it is planned to achieve the mission objectives. By necessity, these designs become quite complex and quite expensive in order to achieve astounding accomplishments. The complexities, environments, and challenges inherent in any space mission mean that a large number of things need to work in order for the mission as a whole to be a success. If anything does not work as planned, or a failure occurs, the entire mission can be lost, and a very large amount of dollars, time, and opportunity or even human life can be lost with it. However, these same challenges and complexities also mean that getting the system to function properly even in the event of no anomalies is an expensive challenge, so spending more money, time, and effort to protect against anomalies is difficult. Therefore, we must figure out how to best apply our limited resources to maximize our chance of success. To do this, we have formalized the idea of risk.

Risk, R, is defined as the product of the probability of a negative event occurring, P, and the impact, or consequence, of that event, I.

$$R = P \times I \tag{24-20}$$

A risk analysis needs to consider both terms in the above equation (probability and impact). Risk is often confused with reliability. As discussed in Sec. 24.1 reliability is the probability of a failure not occurring. This is only half of the risk equation. What separates a risk analysis from a reliability analysis is the inclusion of a measure of the impact of the negative event, which can range from reduced performance to total mission failure.

Two other terms that are often confused are low risk and robust design. A mission with a *robust design* is one which is designed for uncertainty in the nominal conditions. This is often used in the context of unknown environmental conditions, but could be true for any nominal condition used during design. Unknowns in nominal conditions is one risk factor, and therefore a mission with a robust design has lowered the risk in that area, but may still have many other risk factors in other areas.

A third distinction that is important to make is the distinction between a risk and a problem or *anomaly*. For our definitions, a *risk* is a negative event which **may** occur in the future. A problem or *anomaly* is something which is occurring right now or has already occurred. Risks turn into problems or anomalies if the negative event that they are tracking occurs.

There are two basic types of *risk*: mission risk and implementation risk. The difference in the two types of risk is in the definition of the impact. *Mission risks* affect the total return from the mission and the impact is defined in terms of the amount of mission objectives that would be lost (or would remain) if the negative event were to occur. Mission risks can be thought of as the risk of a failure or anomaly occurring during operations. *Implementation risks* affect the budgets and margins of various resources and the impact is defined in terms of the percent of reserves or margin used to recover from the negative event. Implementation risks can be thought of as a risk prior to operations beginning that affects the cost, schedule, or engineering resources available. Clear-

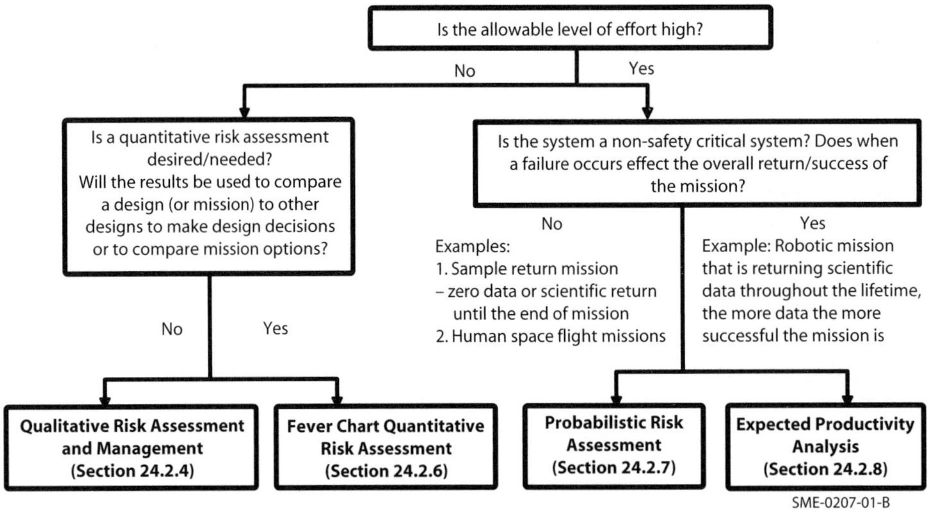

Fig. 24-5. Summary of various Risk Assessment Techniques. Where you fall in this chart may change throughout the design process.

ly the impact definitions are different for mission versus implementation risks. The probability values associated with the same "level" of risk can also be different if desired (i.e., a "low" probability may be 5% for implementation risks, but < 1% for mission risks). Neither type of risk is meant to imply more or less importance—either one can lead to mission failure. However, it is possible to be more or less risk adverse to one type of risk over the other.

24.2.1 Risk Assessment Throughout The Design Process

Many consider risk analysis to be a practice which examines finalized designs for areas that are the most risky, and adds extra redundancy or testing to those areas. This is expensive in terms of mass, cost, and schedule. In addition, this does not help an engineer choose between various designs or architectures with risk in mind. By turning risk assessment into a process that is ongoing throughout the design process, it is possible to include risk as a factor in design decisions, and to reduce the cost of risk mitigation, both of which will lead to lower risk designs.

To make risk a factor in design decisions throughout the design process it needs to be:

- Practical for designs in which little information is known
- Capable of maturing with the design process
- Easily understood by designers and engineers
- Tradable (quantifiable)

Several types of risk analysis can meet the above criteria. A risk analysis can range from very simple to very complex and can change throughout the design process. See Fig. 24-5 for a summary of various risk assessment techniques and when each type of technique may be most appropriate.

As Fig. 24-5 shows, there are several questions that can be used to determine the appropriate risk assessment technique. If the level of effort needs to be low, you probably want to do only fever-chart level risk analysis. This can however, be either qualitative or quantitative, depending on what the goal of the analysis is. If the goal of the analysis is to manage and track risks only, then a qualitative fever chart analysis is appropriate. If the goal of the analysis is to both manage and track risks and to aid in design decisions based on risk, then a quantitative fever chart assessment may be more appropriate. If the available level of effort is, or will eventually be, moderate to high (e.g., a high-cost mission) then you can do more complex analyses. In these cases the type of analysis that is most appropriate depends on type of system you are analyzing. If the mission return is not affected by when a failure occurs, a Probabilistic Risk Assessment (PRA) is appropriate. If when a failure occurs affects the overall return of the mission, Expected Productivity Analysis (EPA) may be more appropriate.

Where you fall in Fig. 24-5, and therefore what type of analysis is most appropriate for your situation, can and often will change as the design matures and more information is available. It is also possible to do any of the four types of analysis shown in Fig. 24-5 for any phase of design, by simply adjusting the fidelity level of the analysis.

When to Use Expected Productivity vs. Reliability

We will use a simple example problem in order to show the differences between a PRA analysis and an EPA analysis. For this problem, the system of interest has only two failure modes, both of which are single point failures. The first failure mode is deployment failure. The deployment only occurs once and needs to be completed in order for the system to enter operations. The second failure mode is from a moving component. The component is required once operations begin and can fail at any point

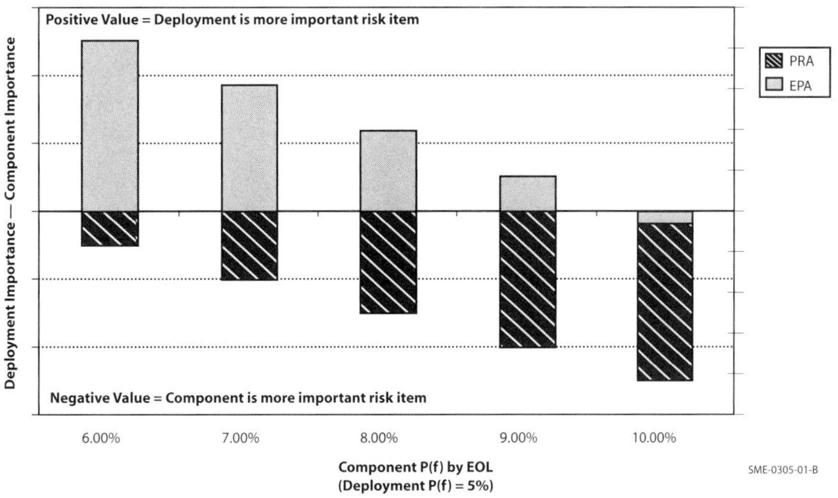

Fig. 24-6. Example Problem to Show Difference Between EPA and Reliability Analysis Techniques.

throughout operations. With this system there are two basic failure events (deployment failure and component failure) and if either event occurs the system is in a failed state. The importance of each of the two events was calculated using both PRA importance measures (Birnbaum Importance Measure—see Sec. 24.2.7) and EPA importance measures (see Sec. 24.2.8) for varying values for the probability of each event occurring. Additionally, the two events were ranked using each importance measure to determine which failure mode is the more critical mode and should have priority in terms of mitigation actions. The results are shown in Fig. 24-6.

In Figure 24-6, the probability of deployment failure is set at a constant value of 5%. An exponential failure rate was assumed for the component failure with a probability of failure by the end of the mission lifetime varying along the x-axis from 6% to 10%. The y-axis is the importance measure for the deployment failure minus the importance measure for the component failure. Therefore, a positive value implies that the deployment failure is the more important failure mode. Similarly, a negative value implies that the component failure is the more important failure mode. The first thing to note about this figure is that in four of the five cases tested the EPA importance measure ranked the two failure modes in opposite order from the PRA importance measure. These discrepancies mean that using PRA risk analysis techniques, an engineer or designer would assign more importance, and therefore more resources, to mitigating the component failure mode. However, if the key metric is actually the expected return of the mission and not the probability of failure by the end of the lifetime, more importance and therefore more resources should be focused on the deployment failure. The reasons for this are clear. The component has a higher probability of failure by the end of the mission lifetime. Therefore, measures that use probability of failure as the risk metric rank the component failure mode higher than the deployment failure mode. The component may fail at any point throughout the mission lifetime, however, including only a short time before the scheduled end of the mission. If the component fails after any significant amount of time has passed then the mission will still have returned some useful data. The deployment failure occurs at only one point in time, before operations. If the deployment fails, no data will be returned from the mission. This is not dependant on the timing of the failure since the event must occur before operations even begin. Therefore the deployment has a larger impact on the system return than the component failure. This higher impact outweighs the lower probability in ten of the eleven cases shown. This effect is not captured with the PRA risk metrics and importance measures.

In the above example we assume that the mission under consideration is returning data of some sort throughout time, and therefore the timing of when a failure occurs becomes important. In many cases the timing of when the failure occurs would not matter, such as a sample return mission, a manned mission, or a commercial satellite that needs to operate for X number of years to fulfill contract requirements. In these cases a failure is a failure, and when that failure occurs does not matter because the only thing being tracked is whether the end goal (returning the sample, returning the astronauts safely, or operating for X years) is met. In these cases a reliability-based metric can be used for a risk analysis, since the probability of meeting that end goal is what should be optimized.

24.2.2 Risk Management

According to NASA Continuous Risk Management definitions [JPL, 2003], Qualitative Risk Management should plan and organize to identify, analyze, plan, track, and control risks throughout the project life cycle. Risks should be identified and captured as described below. Next, they should be analyzed (either qualitatively or quantitatively) to assess those risks that should be accepted versus watched versus mitigated. For risks that are accepted, nothing else is done—either it happens or it doesn't and you will deal with it if the problem occurs. For risks that are watched, no resources are spent to actively mitigate the risk, but it is tracked to keep a close eye on it, perhaps with a plan of action should it reach a particular trigger point. The most severe risks are mitigated. Mitigation approaches are planned to spend resources to reduce either the probability of occurrence, the impact of the event, or both. Both the risks and the mitigation approaches should be tracked throughout the lifecycle to ensure that the mitigation approaches are working and that other risks are not growing. Finally, these risks are controlled through the mitigation plans and through margin expenditure.

24.2.3 Identifying the Risks

One of the best ways to identify the risk items in a system is to ask the people who are designing the system. What the designers are worried about (what "keeps them up at night") are likely the biggest risk items. The difficulty in this approach is getting designers to admit their worries. One approach that helps with this is to first discuss with the designers the way the system works under nominal conditions. One of the best ways to learn how a system can break is to learn how it works. It can also be useful to interview operators of similar systems that have flown in the past or are currently flying, as these are the people who have to live with the consequences of a designer's choice. In any interview, don't feel the need to get numbers (probabilities, impacts) right away—start the conversation qualitatively by just discussing the system, how it works, and how the designer feels it might fail. You can go back to specific failure modes and discuss them quantitatively after this initial qualitative discussion.

Another way to identify risk items is to learn from the experience of others. Organizations will often keep risk databases, lessons learned, and even design checklists and rules which can be invaluable in determining risks in a design. The NASA lessons learned database and the military standards are two additional useful databases to search. A common way to reduce risk is to use a heritage system. It is important to realize that heritage systems will have lower risk than unique systems—but some unsolved risk items may still be present. In addition, it is easy to claim heritage, and therefore have very low margins, even if the heritage is not as direct as claimed. This can lead to large implementation risks, since modifications can lead to major increases in budget and schedule. Be especially careful of heritage claims if the new system will not be used in the same environment or with the same process as the inherited system—this can lead to both mission and implementation risks.

Even if not direct heritage, similar systems will have similar risks and problem areas, so researching these systems can be very useful. Along these same lines, if in doing this research you find an area of your system that is very unique, even just to your organization, you have also found a likely risk item. New technology or new developments are always a risk item—both a mission risk and an implementation risk.

Several more analytical tools can also be used to identify risk items. A few of the more common analytical tools are Failure Modes and Effects and Criticality Analyses (FMECAs) and fault or event trees. For information on FMECAs, please see Sec. 24.1.3. Fault trees and event trees help identify risks by identifying the steps that need to occur for either a negative or a positive event to happen. In a fault tree you identify what the main fault you will be analyzing is, and then proceed to identify all the various potential causes of that fault. In an Event tree, or a Success tree, you identify the main event that needs to occur and then proceed to identify all the critical steps that need to occur successfully for the main event to be successful. In both cases, events, and therefore the tree itself, can be as detailed or as general as desired (e.g., mission success/failure, return a piece of data, loss of attitude knowledge or control, failure of a subsystem). The trees use "and" gates and "or" gates, along with several other variations to show logic flow. See Fig. 24-7 for some commonly used symbols in fault and event trees and see Fig. 24-8 for an example of a fault tree [Wertz & Larson, 1999].

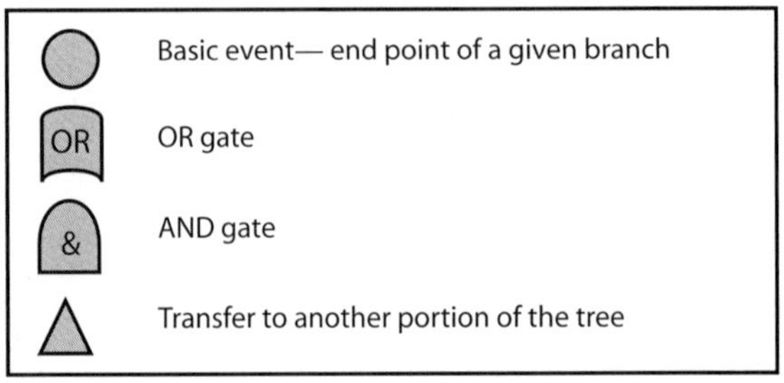

Fig. 24-7. Commonly Used Symbols in Fault Tree Analysis to Show Logic Flow.

Once risks are identified, they need to be documented in a risk data sheet, a risk list, or a risk database. Some of the important information to capture includes the risk statement, mitigation options, a point of contact, and any information available on the probability and the impact should the negative event occur, even if this information is qualitative. The risk statement should be in the form of "if event, then consequence." Examples of risk statements are: "If we have underestimated the scope of work for Technology A, then we will exceed the budget" (implementation risk), or "If we cannot develop Technology A to the level we expect, then we will not have the resources to meet the performance objectives", or "If a thruster fails, the mission will be lost."

24.2.4 Qualitative Risk Assessment

One of the most common tools used to both capture and track risks in qualitative risk assessment is the fever chart. *Fever charts* categorize risks into bins based on a relative scale for both probability and impact. The num-

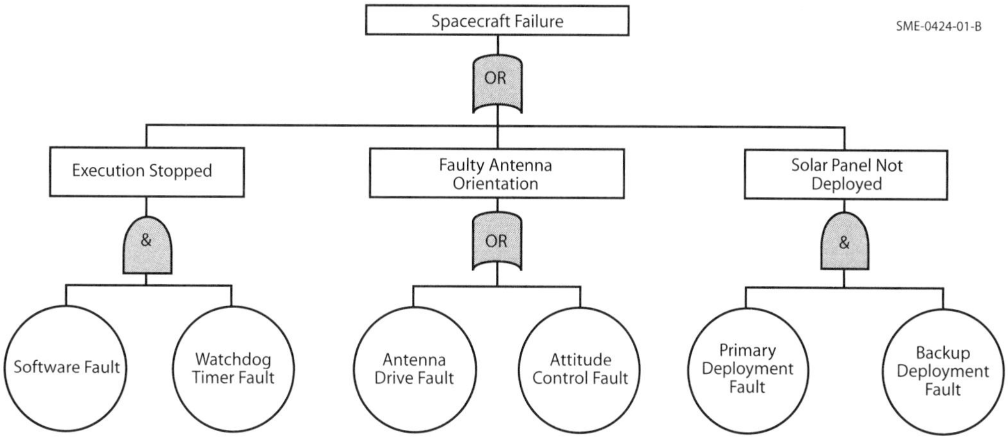

Fig. 24-8. Simple Example of a Spacecraft Fault Tree.

ber of bins defines the size of the fever chart—typical sizes include 3 × 3, 4 × 4, or 5 × 5. The definition of the bins can be qualitative—"High, Medium, Low" or "Very Likely, Somewhat likely, Not Likely, Very unlikely". Risks can then be characterized as "red" or high, "yellow" or medium, or "green" or low based on both their probability and impact scores. An example of a typical 5 × 5 fever chart is shown in Fig. 24-9.

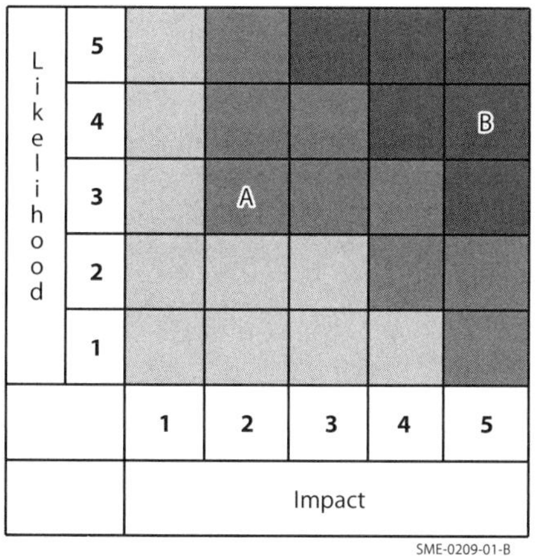

Fig. 24-9. Example Fever Chart. A and B are risks, placed in the appropriate row and column based on likelihood and impact. Light grey regions would be colored green in a typical fever chart. Similarly, dark grey would be red and medium grey would be yellow.

Fever charts can also be semi-quantitative by assigning a range of values to each bin (i.e., 1–5% probability). See Table 24-11 for some example values for fever chart bins. Assigning example values to the fever chart bins can greatly improve the consistency in the scoring across various team members. A 1% probability might be "Very high" for one person and "Low" for another depending on their personality and frame of reference—however, if they are given examples that show that 1% should be categorized as "Low", then both will score the risk more consistently. It can also be very useful to describe the various impact ratings as explicitly as possible. If the impact ratings are described as various percentages of the mission objectives being returned, then explicitly describe what those mission objectives are. If the impact ratings are described as whether or not full vs. minimum mission success is achieved, then explicitly describe what is required to meet full vs. minimum mission success. As an example a score of a 3 could mean: <10 images are returned; the mission lasts for <1 year; or instrument X and Y function, but instrument Z does not return any data. Describing the various impact levels in as much detail as possible, and specific to the particular mission being designed, will again greatly help in the consistency in scoring across various team members. It is important to also ensure that team members pay attention to these definitions and focus on scoring risks according to the definitions you have laid out for both impact and likelihood, and to not jump to the reaction of "this is clearly a yellow risk" or "I don't want to score it a 2 because then it will only be a green risk". Again, focusing on the specific definitions, and letting the color fall out of that definition, will add more consistency across the team. It should be noted that, especially in early design, even the quantitative estimates of what the probability or impact is will be very subjective, and therefore risk scores are still difficult to get consistent. However, using quantitative, explicit values or ranges that are specific to your mission will certainly help with this problem.

Once all the risks are identified and captured, you can produce a summary fever chart to show the number of risk items that fall into each bin to give a good visual snapshot of the number of risks and whether they are high, medium, or low risks. Fever charts can also be customized to show a particular organization's or a particular project's risk stance and preferences by adjusting which bins are categorized as red, yellow, or green. Note that the chart does not have to be symmetrical. Often those risks that are high impact but low probability are judged to be more severe than those that are high probability but low impact (yellow vs. green in Fig. 24-9).

Table 24-11. Example Fever Chart Bins. Examples of definitions for fever chart bins.

Probabilities							
		Example 1		Example 2		Example 3	
Bin	Qualitative Definition	Mission	Implemen-tation	Mission	Implementation	Mission	Implementation
1	Very low	>0.1%	>1%	Less than 1%	Less than 1%	0.1% < P ≤ 2%	P ≤ 10%
2	Low	>0.5%	>10%	1% to 5%	1% to 5%	2% < P ≤ 15%	10% < P ≤ 25%
3	Moderate	>1%	>30%	5% to 15%	5% to 50%	15% < P ≤ 25%	25% < P ≤ 50%
4	High	>5%	>50%	15% to 25%	50% to 80%	25 < P ≤ 50%	50% < P ≤ 75%
5	Very High	>10%	>70%	> 25%	80 to 100%	P > 50%	P > 75%

Impacts							
		Example 1		Example 2		Example 3	
Bin	Qualitative Definition	Mission	Implemen-tation	Mission	Implementation	Mission	Implementation
1	Very low	Minimal (1%) loss of mission objectives	Minimal (1%) loss of reserves	Minimal or no impact to mission	Cost/schedule impact within subsystem purview	No impact to full mission success criteria	Consumes ≤ 1% of remaining Project reserves
2	Low	Small (10%) loss of mission objectives	Small (10%) loss of reserves	Small reduction in mission return	Cost/schedule impact within system purview	Minor impact to full mission success criteria	Consumes 1%–5% of remaining Project reserves
3	Moderate	Moderate (50%) loss of mission objectives	Significant (50%) loss of reserves	Cannot meet full mission success	Cost/schedule impact may require Project support	Moderate impact to full mission success criteria. Minimum mission success criteria, some margin will remain	Consumes 5%–20% of remaining Project reserves
4	High	Significant (90%) loss of mission objectives	Complete consumption of reserves (100%)	Cannot meet minimum mission success	Cost/schedule impact will certainly require Project support	Major impact to full mission success criteria. Minimum mission success criteria is achievable	Consumes 20%–50% of remaining Project reserves
5	Very High	Mission failure (100% loss of mission objectives)	Overrun (120% of reserves consumed)	Mission catastrophic	Cost/schedule impact severely jeopardizes the Project	Minimum mission success criteria is not achievable	Consumes > 50% of remaining Project reserves

24.2.5 Quantitative Risk Assessment

Quantitative Risk Assessment can be done in all design phases. You can estimate probabilities and impacts to the same level you estimate cost, schedule, or performance metrics early in the design phases. However, it is important to keep results relative if the analysis is done in early design phases as the absolute value of the probabilities and impacts is typically very uncertain. If the uncertainty in these values is extremely high, sensitivity studies can be done to determine for which areas of the design space various risks are the most important. Analyses can also be used to make relative comparisons between various designs or mission options. Without getting quantitative, it is impossible to determine which design is higher risk overall—a design with 1 red and 2 green risks or a design with 4 yellow risks. Quantitative analyses, even if done in a relative sense, can also help with questions like which yellow risk should I focus more on mitigating or would it be better to mitigate this set of green risks or this single yellow risk?

It should be noted that the results of quantitative models, even if used in a relative sense, are only as good as their inputs. While it is certainly possible to get very useful results out of quantitative models, even if the results are uncertain, there are some limitations. Results should be taken in context of the uncertainty on the inputs. If two designs are compared there is often a desire to come to a conclusion at the end of the analysis that one design is clearly superior to the other. However, if the analysis is done in the early design phases when the inputs are quite uncertain, and the final risk scores are separated by only 0.01%, it should be clear that this is not the case. Note that while this does not fulfill our initial desire to determine the more superior design, it is a valid result none the less. The result that two designs are equal, within the uncertainty of the analysis, is often just as important as a result that one design is superior to the other. As mentioned above, one of the best ways to deal with quantitative results in cases with large uncertainties is to do sensitivity studies. As an example, it can often be useful to determine at what probability of occurrence one risk becomes more severe than another, or what probability of failure is required for various components to meet an overall probability of failure requirement for the mission as a whole.

Several analysis techniques exist for adding quantitative aspects to risk analysis. The analysis techniques discussed below are presented from the simplest option, which is often useful to use in early design phases, to the most complex, which is most useful in the later design phases.

24.2.6 Fever Chart Quantitative Risk Assessment

It is easy to add quantitative assessment to fever charts by assigning a value to various levels of probability and impact. Note that you can choose to assign different values for probability depending on whether you are talking about a mission risk or an implementation risk. Impact values will be different by definition. You can choose either extreme bounding cases or the average of the range provided if you previously used fever charts during qualitative risk assessment. In fact, using a quantitative aspect to fever charts can often make defining where a risk belongs on the fever chart easier. Depending on the personality of the individual, it is sometimes easier to get a designer or engineer to choose a fever chart location for a risk item if they are given quantitative options. This allows you to ask "Is the probability more likely to be 0.1%, 1%, 5%, or 10%?" instead of an open-ended "What is the probability?" or a purely qualitative "High, medium, or low?" As mentioned above, this type of quantitative approach also greatly helps with consistency between the scoring for various team members.

Once risk items are scored on a fever chart with quantitative definitions you can combine the risk items to produce an overall risk "score" for the design. For mission risks, the impacts are defined in terms of the percentage of return you get from the mission, so the overall risk score is the expected percentage of objectives (scientific or otherwise) returned by the end of the mission lifetime. This can be calculated explicitly, since for each item you have defined (through the definitions of the bins) the probability of the event occurring and the percent of the mission objectives you will lose if the event occurs. While it is simplest to assume that all events are independent you can add calculations to include dependency if the increase in accuracy is warranted. To do this calculation you will also need to decide on a strategy of how to handle multiple events occurring, in terms of percent of objectives returned. The simplest approach is to assume that percentages can be added until you reach 100% of the objectives lost (be sure not to allow values greater than 100%). Equation 24-21 shows an example of this calculation for risks A and B shown in Fig. 24-9, using the definitions of impact and likelihood from the mission column in Table 24-11 Example 1.

$$
\begin{aligned}
&E[\%Objectives] = 1 - \begin{pmatrix} AB \times P(AB) + \bar{A}B \times P(\bar{A}B) + A\bar{B} \\ \times P(A\bar{B}) + \bar{A}\bar{B} \times P(\bar{A}\bar{B}) \end{pmatrix} \\
&AB = 100\% + 10\% = 110\% \Rightarrow 100\% \\
&P(AB) = 1\% \times 5\% \\
&AB \times P(AB) = 1 \times (0.01 \times 0.05) \\
&E[\%Objectives] = 1 - \begin{pmatrix} 1 \times 0.01 \times 0.05 + 1 \times 0.99 \times .05 + \\ 0.1 \times 0.01 \times 0.95 + 0 \times 0.99 \times 0.95 \end{pmatrix} \\
&E[\%Objectives] = 94.9\%
\end{aligned} \tag{24-21}
$$

To get more complicated, but also more accurate, you can determine for each combination of events whether or not the objectives that would be lost would be overlapping or not. An example would be a multi-element mission, such as an orbiter that will drop off a probe. The probe constitutes 25% of the mission objectives. All risks relating to probe failure would result in 25% of the objectives lost, but three probe failure risks should not result in 75% of the mission objectives being lost. There would be no difference between a single probe failure event occurring and multiple probe failure events occurring in terms of percentage of mission objectives lost. This approach obviously takes more effort to determine the impact of both individual risk events as well as various combinations of risk events, but will lead to a more accurate representation of the expected percent of mission objectives that will be returned.

Implementation risk impacts are measured in terms of percentage of resource reserves used, and therefore the overall risk score in this case is the probability that the mission reserves will be exceeded. For this metric, it does not matter if you use 50% of your reserves or 75%—it only matters if you use more or less than 100%. In other words, did you run over budget or not? This can also be explicitly calculated since for each item you have defined (through the definitions of the bins) the probability of the event occurring and the percent of the reserves you will use if the event occurs. Again, the simplest approach is to add percentages and assume independence. In this case you simply need to identify those combinations of events that result in over 100% of the reserves being used, and calculate the probability of any one of those combinations of events occurring. Equation (24-22) shows an example of this calculation for risks A and B shown in Fig. 24-9, using the definitions of impact and likelihood from the implementation column in Table 24-11 Example 1.

Table 24-11◀, Fig. 24-9◀, Eq. 24-21

$$Resources(A,\bar{B}) = 10\%$$
$$Resources(\bar{A},B) = 120\%$$
$$Resources(A,B) = 130\% \qquad (24\text{-}22)$$
$$Resources(\bar{A},\bar{B}) = 0\%$$
$$P[ExceedResources] = P[\bar{A},B] + P[A,B]$$
$$P[ExceedResources] = 0.7 \times 0.5 + 0.3 \times 0.5$$
$$P[ExceedResources] = 50\%$$

To get more complicated, but also more accurate, you can keep track of various resources—i.e., percentage of mass reserves used vs. cost reserves vs. schedule reserves, for example.

24.2.7 Probabilistic Risk Assessment

Probabilistic Risk Assessment (PRA) is the state-of-the-art risk assessment technique used by NASA in the later design phases. This method of quantitative risk analysis is used in the nuclear industry, and has been used at NASA since the Apollo program. Currently, the NASA policy states that a full scope PRA is required for all missions with a planetary protection requirement, all missions with nuclear payloads, all human space flight missions, all missions of high strategic importance, and all missions with high-schedule criticality. In addition, a limited scope PRA is required for any mission costing over $100M and is recommended for all missions [Stamatelatos, 2002].

A PRA is basically a quantifiable fault tree and event tree analysis. The systems engineer identifies major events that could affect the state of the system. These events are then placed in an event tree. Following each path through the event tree produces one sequence of events and results in one of a set of pre-determined end-states. The most common end-states are "ok" and "failed." While other end states can be included, each sequence needs to be laid out and assigned an end state, so a large number of end-state possibilities will lead to a very complicated and tedious analysis. The next step is to create fault trees for each event. These fault trees combine basic events using "and/or" gates among other logic to find the probability of each event in the event tree occurring. The probability of each end-state occurring can then be calculated by working through the logic in the fault and event trees and using the probabilities of the basic events (i.e., the probability of a failure of a given component). Those sequences of basic events that have the largest impact on the total probability of failure can then be identified. See Fig. 24-10 for an example of a basic Event Tree for the FireSat II Example. Each of the Events listed along the top will then be connected to a fault tree to determine the probability of taking each path. As an example, the Fault Tree shown in Fig. 24-8 might be linked to the Spacecraft (1 or 2) operation events.

Each of the bottom events in a fault tree is called a basic event, and is the level at which a probability value is

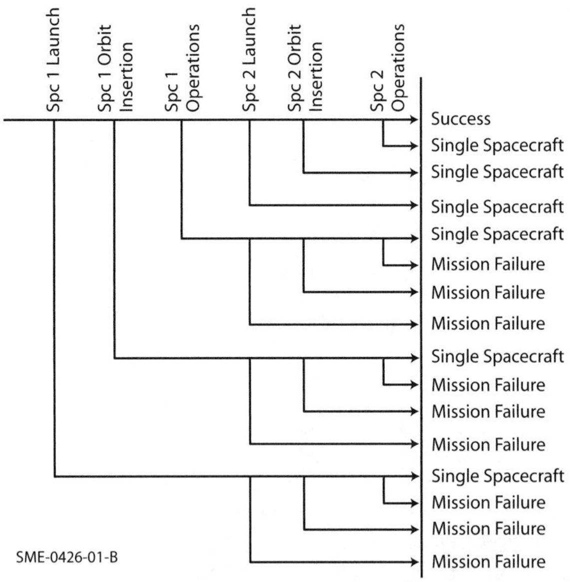

Fig. 24-10. Example Event Tree for the FireSat II Mission.

assigned. Depending on the complexity of the fault tree, a basic event can be the failure of a particular device, the failure of an entire subsystem, or anything in-between. A *cut-set* is a set of basic events that leads to a particular end state of the system. A cut-set in which all events are required to guarantee that particular end state is called a minimal cut-set [Stamatelatos, 2002].

As an example, look at the fault tree given in Fig. 24-8. In this case three cut-sets that lead to Mission Failure would be:

- Cut-set 1: Primary solar panel deployment fault and Secondary solar panel deployment fault
- Cut-set 2: Primary solar panel deployment fault and Attitude Control fault
- Cut-set 3: Attitude Control fault

These are just three example cut-sets—there are many other cut-sets that lead to mission failure. However, of these three cut-sets only cut-set 1 and cut-set 3 are minimal cut-sets. Cut-set 2 would lead to mission failure, but in this case the fact that the primary solar panel deployment failed did not affect the end state of the system—and therefore this is not considered a minimal cut-set. All of the *minimal cut-sets (MCSs)* for this fault tree are:

- MCS1: Primary solar panel deployment fault and Secondary solar panel deployment fault
- MCS2: Attitude Control fault
- MCS3: Antenna Drive fault
- MCS4: Software fault and Watch dog timer fault

We can use Boolean logic to determine the probability of mission failure using the minimal cut-sets and the probability of each basic event. Remember that in this case the basic events do not have to be mutually exclusive, so OR statements are not simple addition. When events are not mutually exclusive, we need to ensure not to double-count the possibility of both events occurring, as shown in Fig. 24-12.

$$P(A \text{ or } B) = P(A) + P(B) - P(AB) \tag{24-23}$$

If we assume the probability of each basic event in this example is 1%, then the probability of mission failure due to a spacecraft not operating correctly is:

$$PMF = PMCS1 \text{ or } PMCS2 \text{ or } PMCS3 \text{ or } PMCS4$$
$$PMF = PPDF \times PSDF \text{ or } PACF \text{ or } PADF \text{ or } PSF \times PWDTF \tag{24-24}$$

$$PMF = 0.0001 \text{ or } 0.01 \text{ or } 0.01 \text{ or } 0.0001$$
$$PMF = 2.02\%$$

Importance Measures

Importance measures give you a ranking of the importance of mitigating each individual risk, or reducing the probability of individual basic events. Note that some basic events could belong in more than one cut-set. In addition, some minimal cut-sets will have more than one basic event while others will have only one. Both of these situations mean that you cannot simply look at the probability of individual basic events to determine the most important events to mitigate—you need to follow the Boolean logic of the cut-sets to determine their importance. There are many valid importance measures that can be used to assign an importance to each cut-set, but the three most widely used are Birnbaum, Improvement Potential, and Fussell-Vesely. Each of these three importance measures are defined and discussed in Table 24-12, along with some suggested applications.

One of the most popular importance measures used in PRAs is the *Birnbaum importance measure* that calculates the sensitivity of the total probability of failure to the probability of a particular event or risk item. The equation for the Birnbaum importance measure, $I_{Birnbaum}$, is given by [Wang et al., 2004] [Hoyland & Rausand, 1994].

$$I_{Birnbaum}(A) = \frac{\partial P_{Failure}(total)}{\partial P_A} \tag{24-25}$$

where A is the event risk item of interest, $P_{Failure}$(total) is the total probability of failure, and P_A is the probability of event A occurring. While Eq. (24-25) is the general form of this measure, a different form is often used to ease calculations. Equation (24-25), is the sensitivity of the total probability of failure to a change in the probability of the event of interest. This equation is greatly simplified if the change in the probability of the event is set equal to 1. In this case the denominator of Eq. (24-25) is simply 1 and the numerator is the difference in the system probability of failure with the probability of the event of interest set to 1 and 0. This form of the Birnbaum equation is given in Eq. (24-26) by [Smith et al., 2002] [Relex, 2005].

$$I_{Birnbaum}(A) = \left(P_{Failure}(total)\middle| P_A = 1\right) - \left(P_{Failure}(total)\middle| P_A = 0\right) \tag{24-26}$$

For our example above, the Birnbaum importance measure for Primary Deployment Failure and the Attitude Control Failure are shown below:

BIPDF = P(Failure/PDF) – P(Failure/No PDF)
= (PSDF or PACF or PADF or PSF × PWDTF)
– (PACF or PADF or PSF × PWDTF)
= 3.01% – 2.01% = 1.00%

BIACF = P(Failure|ACF) – P(Failure/No ACF)
= 1 – (PPDF × PSDF or PADF or PSF × PWDTF)
= 100% – 1.02% = 98.98%
(24-27)

As you can see from above, according to the Birnbaum importance measure, the Attitude Control Failure is a much more risky event than the primary deployment failure, even though both start with the same probability of occurrence. Therefore, when making investment decisions, one should mitigate an attitude control failure before being concerned with a primary solar array deployment failure. This makes sense since a primary so-

Table 24-12. Comparison of Importance Measures. A summary of three of the commonly used importance measures for PRA and when each may be the most appropriate.

Importance Measure	Largest Effect on Importance Measure	When to Use This Measure
Birnbaum	Impact of risk	Focus is on reducing the largest impact risks (i.e., single points of failure); Failure is not acceptable, even if very low probability (i.e., human missions)
Improvement Potential	Probability and impact of risk	Focus is on determining where to apply resources for mitigation approaches—which risks will give me the most bang for my buck if I mitigate them
Fussell-Vesely	Number of failure modes affected by the risk	Focus is on finding the few risks that I can mitigate that will improve multiple failure modes—similar to Birnbaum but most failures are not single point failures anymore, so I want to find those failures that combine with lots of other, different failures to cause overall mission failure

lar array deployment failure has already been mitigated in this system by adding a secondary deployment option.

One interesting thing to note about the Birnbaum Importance measure is that it is independent of the actual probability of failure of the component or subsystem that you are calculating the importance of. The Birnbaum importance measure is based more on the structure of the system. A second importance measure that can be used is called the *Improvement Potential* and is defined as the difference between the total system probability of failure given the current probability of event A occurring and the total system probability of failure if risk item A is completely mitigated [Rausand and Hoyland, 2004]. This is very similar to the Birnbaum importance metric, but uses the current value for P(A) instead of assuming that A has occurred.

$$\begin{aligned} IPPDF &= PMF - P(\text{Failure/No PDF}) \\ &= 2.02\% - 2.00\% = 0.02\% \end{aligned}$$

$$\begin{aligned} IPACF &= PMF - P(\text{Failure/No ACF}) \\ &= 2.02\% - 1.02\% = 1\% \end{aligned} \quad (24\text{-}28)$$

Variations on the improvement potential include reporting the percentage improvement relative to the original probability of failure or using a mitigated probability of failure instead of completely mitigating the event in question.

The *Fussell-Vesely* importance measure calculates the probability of the union of all minimal cut-sets that contain the event of interest divided by the probability of the union of all minimal cut-sets [Relex, 2005]. This is shown in Eq. (24-29).

$$I_{Fussell-Vesely}(A) = \frac{P\left(\bigcup\{AllCutSetsContainingA\}\right)}{P\left(\bigcup\{AllCutSets\}\right)} \times 100\% \quad (24\text{-}29)$$

It may be difficult for software programs to automatically determine all the cut-sets containing the specific event of interest. Since this is required for the numerator of Eq. (24-29), it is often useful to put the Fussell-Veseley importance measure in a different form. The probability of the union of all minimal cut-sets containing A can be thought of as the probability of the union of all minimal cut-sets minus the probability of the union of all minimal cut-sets not containing the event A. The latter can be easily found by setting the probability of event A to zero and recalculating the probability of the union of all minimum cut-sets. This form of the Fussell-Veseley importance measure is given below [Smith et al., 2002]; [Wolfram, 2005].

$$I_{Fussell-Vesely}(A) = \frac{P\left(\bigcup\{AllCutSets\}\middle|P(A)=P_A\right) - P\left(\bigcup\{AllCutSets\}\middle|P(A)=0\right)}{P\left(\bigcup\{AllCutSets\}\middle|P(A)=P_A\right)} \times 100\% \quad (24\text{-}30)$$

Table 24-12◀, Fig. 24-10◀, Eq. 24-30

In Eq. (24-30), P(A) is the probability of event A occurring and P_A is the original probability of event A occurring.

While these importance measures are some of the more commonly used, there are numerous others to choose from, including: Risk achievement worth, Risk reduction worth, and criticality measures [Borgonovo, 2007] [Rausand and Hoyland, 2004]. See Table 24-12 for a summary of when it makes sense to consider each of the three importance measures described above.

Implementation Risks in PRA

Implementation risks can be treated in two ways using the PRA approach. First, a separate PRA can be done for implementation risks. In this case, the events that need to occur are meeting milestones or delivering technologies or subsystems that meet performance requirements and the end states of the PRA are whether or not the system was delivered for launch on schedule, within budget, and meeting all requirements. This type of analysis can be very complicated but also very useful, as there are many fewer single point failures in terms cost or schedule overruns compared to technical risk items, but many more combinations of events that are independent events (i.e., two independent subsystems both overrunning on mass budgets) that combine to create a minimal cut-set that could be mission critical.

Whether or not a PRA-type of analysis is done for implementation risks prior to a mission risk PRA, implementation risks can still be introduced into a PRA for mission risks by adjusting the probability that the system will begin in various initial states. The most common strategy is to simply adjust the probability of ever making it to the launch pad before getting canceled. However, implementation risks could lead to a "degraded state" of the system prior to operations if technology development items don't quite meet performance criteria or if mass overruns lead to the removal of redundant hardware. This type of analysis requires much more planning to determine what appropriate alternate or degraded initial states could be, but can lead to some interesting analyses.

Complex PRA Techniques

The above description of PRAs covers only the very basic concepts of a PRA analysis. PRAs can be as simple or as complex as we choose. They can begin very simply with high level events and full subsystem or major event failures in the fault trees, and can evolve into very complex analyses going down to component level failures as the design life progresses. In addition to simply adding more complexity, PRAs can also be modified to include more complex modeling cases. Improvements to the PRA process to include dynamic aspects are ongoing. While the dynamic aspect of systems is particularly important to the aerospace industry, researchers in the other industries have determined a need to include dynamic aspects in the PRAs analyzing nuclear systems as well. Methods to include dynamic aspects into a PRA-type of analysis include Phased Mission Systems and Dynamic Fault Trees. [Siu, 1994]; [Devooght and Smidts, 1996]; [Cojazzi, 1996]; [Meshkat et al., 2003]; [Chhikara et al., 2003].

24.2.8 Expected Productivity Analysis

The *expected productivity* of a system is the product of the probability of being in each functional state and the productivity in that state, summed over all states and all time. This could also be thought of as the expected value of the utility function or return for the mission. This is also called *Performability* in some areas [Ciciani & Vincenzo, 1987].

Combining the systems performance aspect with the probabilistic aspect of risk analysis leads to the need for much more customized tools for each individual mission. In the same sense that each mission needs a system performance model that is custom built for that mission, it will also need a risk assessment model that is custom built for that mission (utilizing the already custom built performance model). Engineers running these analyses should understand both the system performance and the probabilistic aspect of risk.

Calculating the expected productivity of a system is done in 3 basic steps:

1. Determine the probability of being in each state at each time
2. Determine the productivity in each state
3. Combine to produce the expected value of the total productivity by the end of mission life

For the first step, we can use *Markov Modeling* to determine the probability that the system is in any state at any given time. The process described below is only valid for *Markov systems*—defined as a system in which the future states of the system depend only on the current state, and not on any previous states. In other words, if my system has 2 actuators which can fail, it does not matter whether my system started with 10 actuators and 8 have already failed or if my system started with only the two—all that matters is that from this point on I have 2 actuators and either one can fail at a given rate.

The first step in determining the probability of being in any state at any time is to define what the possible states of the system are, and how the system would transition from one state to the next. This is done using a *Markov model*, or *state diagram*. The state of the system changes as failures occur in the system. The transition matrix, or A matrix, is defined as:

$$\frac{d\mathbf{P}(t)}{dt} = \mathbf{A}\mathbf{P}(t) \qquad (24\text{-}31)$$

An A matrix can be created by looking at each state individually. Each row and column of the matrix corresponds to a different state. Fig. 24-11 shows a very simple Markov model, and the corresponding A matrix.

In Fig. 24-11 *d*, *m*, and *l* are the failure rates of three different components—component "D", component "M", and component "L". Note that these are failure rates, and not probabilities of failure. Assuming an exponential failure rate, λ, failure rates are related to the

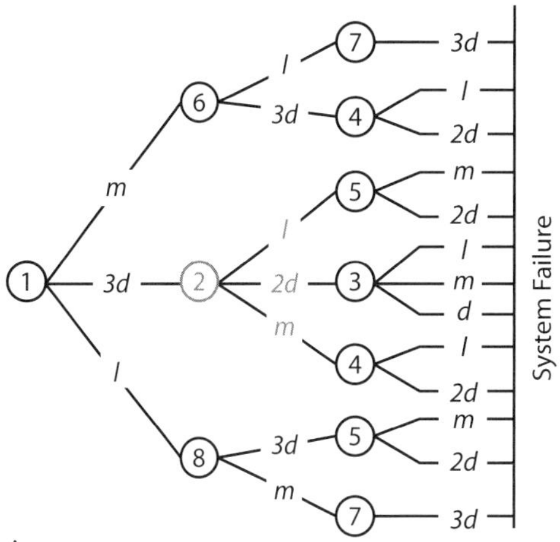

$$A = \begin{bmatrix} -3d-m-l & 0 & 0 & 0 & 0 & 0 & 0 & 0 \\ 3d & -2d-m-l & 0 & 0 & 0 & 0 & 0 & 0 \\ 0 & 2d & -d-m-l & 0 & 0 & 0 & 0 & 0 \\ 0 & m & 0 & -2d-l & 0 & 3d & 0 & 0 \\ 0 & l & 0 & 0 & -2d-m & 0 & 0 & 3d \\ m & 0 & 0 & 0 & 0 & -3d-l & 0 & 0 \\ 0 & 0 & 0 & 0 & 0 & l & -3d & m \\ l & 0 & 0 & 0 & 0 & 0 & 0 & -3d-m \end{bmatrix}$$

SME-0303-01-B

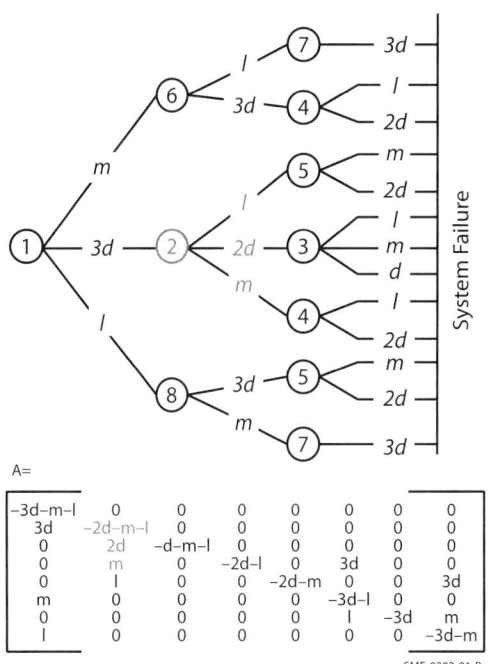

Fig. 24-11. Markov Model and Corresponding A Matrix for a sample system of three "D" components, 1 "M" component, and 1 "L" component. For this system to function: $d + m + l \geq 3$, $d + m \geq 1$ and $d + l \geq 2$.

probability of failure by the end of the mission lifetime, P_f, through the equation:

$$\lambda = \frac{-\log\left(1 - P_f\right)}{life} \qquad (24\text{-}32)$$

when *life* is the mission design lifetime.

Once the A matrix is calculated we can use it to determine the probability of being in any given state at any given time. From the definition of the A matrix [Eq. (24-31)], we can use Laplace Transforms to determine the probability vector (the probability of being in each state) for any time t.

$$\begin{aligned} s\mathbf{P}(s) - \mathbf{P}_o &= \mathbf{A}\mathbf{P}(s) \\ (s\mathbf{I} - \mathbf{A})\mathbf{P}(s) &= \mathbf{P}_o \\ \mathbf{P}(s) &= (s\mathbf{I} - \mathbf{A})^{-1}\mathbf{P}_o \\ \mathbf{P}(t) &= e^{\mathbf{A}t}\mathbf{P}_o \end{aligned} \qquad (24\text{-}33)$$

Next, we need to define the productivity vector, **C**. *Productivity* in a given state is defined as the fraction of "objects" that can be completed per unit time. In this case, an "object" is simply a single unit of the performance metric for the given mission. Examples of objects include an image, a measurement, a Kb of data, and so forth. The time to complete an object in a given state is calculated using a productivity model. This productivity model will be mission-specific and should be the same model used to determine the "value" of particular architectures or designs.

The expected value of the productivity metric can then be computed using the productivity vector and the probability vector. In the simplest cases, where the productivity vector is constant throughout time, a closed form solution is available.

$$\begin{aligned}\mathbf{P}(t) &= e^{\mathbf{A}t}\mathbf{P}_o \\ E\left[Prod(t)\right] &= \mathbf{CP}(t) = \mathbf{C}e^{\mathbf{A}t}\mathbf{P}_o\end{aligned} \qquad (24\text{-}34)$$

$$E\left[Prod\right]_{Total} = \int_0^{life} E\left[Prod(t)\right]dt$$

$$E\left[Prod\right]_{Total} = \int_0^{life} \mathbf{C}e^{\mathbf{A}t}\mathbf{P}_o dt$$

$$E\left[Prod\right]_{Total} = \mathbf{C}\frac{1}{\mathbf{A}}e^{\mathbf{A}t}\mathbf{P}_o \Big|_0^{life}$$

$$E\left[Prod\right]_{Total} = \mathbf{CA}^{-1}\left(e^{\mathbf{A}\cdot life} - \mathbf{I}\right)\mathbf{P}_o$$

For cases where the productivity vector is time-varying, it is easiest to use brute-force and step through time calculating both **P**(t) and **C**(t) for each time step. The expected productivity is then simply the product of the two vectors summed over all time-steps.

$$E\left[\text{Prod}\right]_{Total} = \sum_{t=0}^{life} \mathbf{C}(t)\mathbf{P}(t) \qquad (24\text{-}35)$$

Implementation Risks and Early Mission Risks in Expected Productivity

Many of the risk items identified for missions are single events that occur before any objects are completed. Examples of these include a launch failure or a deployment failure. These risks result in a change to the initial conditions used to find the probability of being in each state. The probability that the system is in a completely failed state before objects are returned is the probability that at least one critical failure event occurred prior to this time. Care needs to be taken not to double count the probability of multiple critical failure events occurring, as shown by the overlap of events A and B in Fig. 24-12.

If both A and B are critical failure events that occur prior to objects being returned, then the probability that the mission is in a functional state, and therefore that neither A nor B has occurred, is given by:

$$\begin{aligned}P(\text{neither A nor B}) &= 1 - [P(\text{A}) + P(\text{B}) - P(\text{A and B})] \\ P(\text{neither A nor B}) &= 1 - [P(A) + P(B) - P(\text{A}) \times P(B)] \\ P(\text{neither A nor B}) &= 1 - P(A) - P(B) + P(A) \times P(B)\end{aligned} \qquad (24\text{-}36)$$

In addition to risk elements that decrease the probability of beginning operations in the nominal state, other risk elements increase the probability that the system will

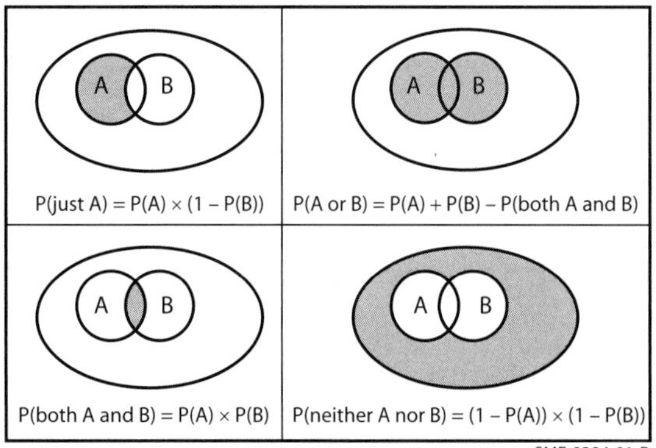

Fig. 24-12. Four Possible Outcomes and Their Probabilities from Two Independent, Probabilistic Events.

begin operations with degraded performance. Examples of these types of risk elements include a subsystem or technology not being developed to the required performance level or a partial deployment failure with which the system could still function, but at a reduced throughput rate or for a reduced time. These failure modes occur at or before the beginning of operations. Therefore, the initial system performance metrics, such as failure rates, lifetime, or efficiency, need to be adjusted before being used in conjunction with a dynamic failure model to find the overall expected total productivity. Using an observatory system example, a nominal system may have an observational efficiency of 1 (defined as equal time observing and non-observing). However, if control algorithms are not developed to the required level, the observational efficiency may be reduced to 0.5 (half the time taking observations is spent on overhead). These algorithms will not mature to the required level with some probability, Pc. As an example, let us take the probability of these algorithms not being developed to be 0.1. As shown in Eq. (24-37), the initial starting condition of this system is an expected observational efficiency value of 0.95.

$$\begin{aligned}&E\left[\text{Initial Observational Efficiency}\right] = \\ &\qquad 0.5 \times Pc + 1 \times (1 - Pc) = 0.05 + 0.9 \\ &E\left[\text{Initial Observational Efficiency}\right] = 0.95\end{aligned} \qquad (24\text{-}37)$$

Once in operations, a single actuator may then fail. If this occurs, we assume for this example that the observational efficiency is once again cut in half. The productivity in the state in which a single actuator has failed should be based on an initial observational efficiency of 0.95:

$$\begin{aligned}&\text{Obervational Efficiency in Degraded State} = \\ &\qquad \frac{1}{2} \times E\left[\text{Initial Observational Efficiency}\right] \\ &\text{Obervational Efficiency in Degraded State} = \\ &\qquad \frac{1}{2} \times 0.95 = 0.475\end{aligned} \qquad (24\text{-}38)$$

A separate, PRA-type analysis can be done for other implementation risks in Expected Productivity Analysis. See the Implementation risks portion of the PRA section for more information.

Importance Measures

An example of an expected productivity importance measure can be modeled after the concepts from both the Fussell-Veseley and Birnbaum importance measures. The impact of an event or risk item is determined by finding the expected productivity of the nominal system, in addition to the expected productivity given a zero probability of the given risk item occurring. Since the negative event would have lowered the expected productivity, the expected productivity should increase when the probability of the event occurring is set to zero. The impact of the event or risk item is then simply the expected productivity with the probability set to zero minus the expected productivity with the probability set to the original value. This is then normalized by the expected productivity with all probabilities set at the original values. The equation for the expected productivity, I_{EP}, importance measure is:

$$I_{EP}(A) = \left(\frac{\left(E[p] \| (P(A)=0)\right) - \left(E[p] \| P(A)=P_A\right)}{\left(E[p] \| P(A)=P_A\right)} \right) \times 100\% \tag{24-39}$$

when E[p] is the expected productivity, A is the risk item or event of interest, P(A) is the probability of event A occurring used in a given calculation, and P_A is the original input for the probability of event A occurring. Other importance measures could also be defined, using these concepts or more custom concepts, to create the importance measure that best fits the need for a particular mission or study.

24.2.9 Summary

No matter what type of analysis is done and how good that analysis is, risk will always be present—the question is which risks do you accept and which risks do you mitigate? Even when a risk is mitigated, it is often still present. Mitigating a risk simply means to improve it—by reducing either the consequence or the probability. Every manager will have a different risk posture, or level of risk that he is willing to accept. Some managers may even have different risk postures for different types of risks. The goal of a risk analysis is to convey what level of risk a project is currently taking, and to identify possible mitigation strategies and areas of a design that could make the largest impact on the overall risk level of the project.

References

For annotated bibliography of risk and reliability, see the book website.

Borgonovo, E. 2007. "Differential, Critical and Birnbaum Importance Measures: An Application to Basic Event, Groups and SSCs in Event Trees and Binary Decision Diagrams." *Reliability Engineering and System Safety*, vol. 92, issue 10. Oct. pp. 1458–1467.

Bourne, S., 2004. "A Conversation with Bruce Lindsay." ACM Queue, Error Recovery, vol. 2, no. 8. Nov.

Castet, J. F., and J. H. Saleh. 2009. "Satellite Reliability: Statistical Data Analysis and Modeling." *Journal of Spacecraft and Rockets*, vol. 46, no. 5. Sept–Oct.

Chhikara, R., R. Heydorn, and J. Pitblado. 2003. "Probabilistic Risk Assessment Using Dynamic Event Sequence Diagrams." University of Houston.

Ciciani, B., and G. Vincenzo. 1987. "Performability Evaluation of Fault-Tolerant Satellite Systems." *IEEE Transactions on Communications*, vol. COM-35, no. 4. pp. 403–409.

Cojazzi, G. 1996. "The DYLAM Approach for the Dynamic Reliability Analysis of Systems." *Reliability Engineering and System Safety*, vol. 52. pp. 279–296.

Devooght, J., and C. Smidts. 1996. "Probabilistic Dynamics as a Tool for Synamic PSA." *Reliability Engineering and System Safety*, vol. 52. pp. 185–196.

DoD. 2010a. Test Method Standard: *Microcircuits.* MIL-STD-883H. Feb. 26.

DoD. 2010b. *Performance Specifications: Hybrid Microcircuits.* MIL-PRF-38534H. Sept. 13.

DoD. 2010c *Performance Specification: Integrated Circuits (Microcircuits) Manufacturing*, MIL-PRF-38535J. Dec. 28.

DoD. 2010d. *Performance Specification: Semiconductor Devices.* MIL-PRF-19500P. Oct. 20.

DoD. 2003. *Destructive Physical Analysis for Electronic, Electromagnetic, and Electromechanical Parts.* MIL-STD-1580. Jan. 7.

DoD. 2002. Test Method Standard: *Electronic and Electrical Component Parts.* MIL-STD-202G. Feb. 8.

DoD. 1998. *Electronic Reliability Design Handbook.* MIL-HDBK-338B. Oct. 1.

DoD. 1996. *Reliability Test Methods, Plans and Environments for Engineering, Development, and Production.* MIL-HDBK-781A. Apr. 1.

DoD. 1991. *Reliability Prediction of Electronic Equipment.* MIL-HDBK-217F. Dec. 2.

DoD. 1988. *Reliability Program Requirements for Space and Launch Vehicles.* MIL-STD-1543B, Oct. 25.

DoD. 1984. *Procedures for Performing a Failure Mode, Effects and Criticality Analysis.* MIL-STD-1629A. Nov. 28.

ECSS. 2009a. *Space Product Assurance—Dependability.* ECSS-Q-ST-30C, Requirements & Standards Division. Mar. 6.

ECSS. 2009b. *Failure Modes, Effects and Criticality Analysis* (FMEA/FMECA). ECSS-Q-ST-30-02C.

ECSS. 2007. *Space Product Assurance-Electrical, Electronic and Electromechanical (EEE) Components.* ECSS-Q-60B. Jul. 17.

Gray, J. 1990. "A Census of Tandem System Availability Between 1985 and 1990." IEEE Transactions on Reliability, vol. 39, no. 4. Oct.

Hamiter, L. 1990. "The History of Space Quality EEE Parts in the United States." Components Technology Institute Inc., ESA Electronic Components Conference, ESTEC, Noordwijk, The Netherlands, Nov. 12–16.

Harry, M. J. 1997. *The Nature of Six Sigma Quality.* Shaumburg, IL: Motorola University Press.

Hoyland, A. and M. Rausand. 1994. *System Reliability Theory: Models and Statistical Methods.* New York, NY: John Wiley & Sons.

Hsueh, M. C., and R. K. Iyer. 1988. "Performability Modeling Based On Real Data: A Case Study." IEEE Transactions on Computers, vol. 37, no. 4. Apr. pp. 478–484.

IEEE. 1990. *IEEE Standard Computer Dictionary: A Compilation of IEEE Standard Computer Glossaries,* IEEE-STD-610-1990.

IEC. 1998. *Basic Safety Publication.* International Standard.

IEC. 2004. "Reliability Data Handbook—Universal Model for Reliability Prediction of Electronics Components, PCBs and Equipment." TR 62380.

JPL. 2000. "Report on the Loss of the Mars Polar Lander and Deep Space 2 Missions." JPL Special Review Board, Report JPL D-18709. May 22.

JPL. 2003. "The JPL Project Risk Management Workshop." JPL Professional Development, The JPL Project Risk Management Workshop. Internal Document, JPL D-21069 Rev. G. Pasadena, CA. Dec.

Kececioglu, D. 1993. *Reliability and Life Testing Handbook.* Englewood Cliffs, NJ: Prentice Hall.

Lee, I., and R. K. Iyer. 1995. "Software Dependability in the Tandem Guardian System," vol. 21, no. 5. May. pp. 455–467.

Leveson, N. G. 1995. *Safeware: System Safety and Computers.* Addison Wesley Publishing Company.

Lions, J. L. 1996. Ariane 5 Flight 501 Failure. Paris. Jul. 19.

MCO. 1999. "Mars Climate Orbiter Mishap Investigation Board," Phase I Report. Nov. 10.

Meshkat, L., L. Xing, S. Donohue, and Y. Ou. 2003. "An Overview of the Phase-Modular Fault Tree Approach to Phased Mission System Analysis." Proceedings of the International Conference of Space Mission Challenges for Information Technology, SMC-IT.

NIST/SEMATECH. 2010. *Assessing Product Reliability*, e-Handbook.

O'Connor, Patrick D. T., David DNewton, and Richard Bromley. 2002. "Practical Reliability Engineering." John Wiley and Sons."

Rausand, M, and Hoyland, A. 2004. *System Reliability Theory.* New York, NY: John Wiley and Sons.

Relex Software Corporation. 2005. "Fault Tree Analysis Software, Decision and Fault Tree Analysis."

SAE. 2001. *Recommended Failure Modes and Effects Analysis* (FMEA) Practices for Non-Automobile Applications. ARP5580. Jul. 1.

Sahu. 2003. *EEE-INST-002: Instructions for EEE Parts Selection, Screening, Qualification, and Derating.* NASA Goddard Space Flight Center. NASA/TP—2003-212242. May.

Siu, N. 1994. "Risk Assessment for Dynamic Systems: An Overview." *Reliability Engineering and System Safety*, vol. 43. pp. 43–73.

Smith, C., J. Knudsen, K. Kvarfordt, and T. Wood. 2002. "SAPHIRE Basics: An Introduction to Probabilistic Risk Assessment via the SAPHIRE Software." Idaho National Engineering and Environmental Laboratory.

Stamatelatos, M. 2002. "Probabilistic Risk Assessment (PRA) at NASA: Past, Present, and Future." Presented at JPL, Pasadena, CA. Feb.

Tang D., and M. Hecht. 1995. "Evaluation of Software Dependability Based on Stability Test Data." 25th Annual Fault—Tolerant Computing Symposium, Pasadena, CA. Jun.

Telecordia, 2003. "Reliability Prediction Procedure for Electronic Equipment"—SR-332.

Wang, W., J. Loman, and P. Vassiliou. 2004. "Reliability Importance of Components in a Complex System." Proceedings of the 2004 IEEE Reliability and Maintainability Symposium, Los Angeles, CA. Jan.

Wertz, J. R. and W. Larson. 1999. *Space Mission Analysis and Design.* El Segundo, CA: Microcosm Press and Springer, NY.

Wolfram Research. 2005. "Union." Website.

Table 24-12◀, Fig. 24-12◀, Eq. 24-39◀

25 Alternative Spacecraft Designs

25.1 Space Tethers

Robert P. Hoyt, *Tethers Unlimited, Inc.*

A space tether is essentially a long wire or cable deployed from a spacecraft. Space tethers can provide a number of different capabilities for space missions, including attitude stabilization of spacecraft, generation of artificial gravity, formation flight of multiple spacecraft, and propellantless propulsion for orbital transfer, de-orbit, or drag-makeup. The principal advantage of space tethers is their ability to provide very large total delta V for certain missions with mass requirements far lower than other propulsion technologies. This advantage, however, comes with a trade-off in that the complex dynamics and physical extent of space tether systems can have a significant impact on system design and operations.

In this section, we will first review the basic physics and techniques involved in the use of space tethers. We will then summarize several of the primary applications of space tether technologies. Finally, we will discuss the issues that must be considered when integrating a space tether system into a space mission.

25.1.1 Space Tether Fundamentals

Gravity Gradient Forces on a Tethered System

A tethered system in orbit around a planetary body will experience forces due to the gradient of the body's gravitational field, and these "gravity gradient" forces play a dominant role in the behavior of tethered systems. As illustrated in Fig. 25-1, a tethered system in orbit will be in a stable equilibrium configuration when the tether is aligned along the local vertical, and the *tension, T,* on the tether balances the *gravity gradient force,* F_{gg}, experienced by both endmasses. For a system where the endmass masses are much greater than the tether mass, the tension is:

$$T = F_{gg} = 3GMmL/r^3, \tag{25-1}$$

where G is the gravitational constant, M is the mass of the planetary body, m is the mass of one of the endmasses, L is the distance from the tethered system's center of gravity to that endmass, and r is the orbital radius from the system's center of gravity.

Tether Dynamics

The flexibility and tensile behavior of a tether and its interaction with the gravity gradient can result in the dynamical behavior of tethered systems being quite complex, exhibiting pendulum-like librations, transverse oscillations like a skip-rope, and longitudinal oscillations like a bungee cord. The design and operation of a tethered system must account for this dynamic complexity to ensure proper operation. As illustrated in Fig. 25-1, if a tethered system is rotated away from a local vertical orientation, the resulting gravity gradient forces will provide a restoring torque that will cause it to swing back towards vertical and librate around the local vertical orientation like a pendulum. The libration motions are more complicated than a simple pendulum because libration motions in the plane of the orbit couple into the orbital angular momentum of the system, whereas motion in the out-of-plane direction does not. As a result, librations in

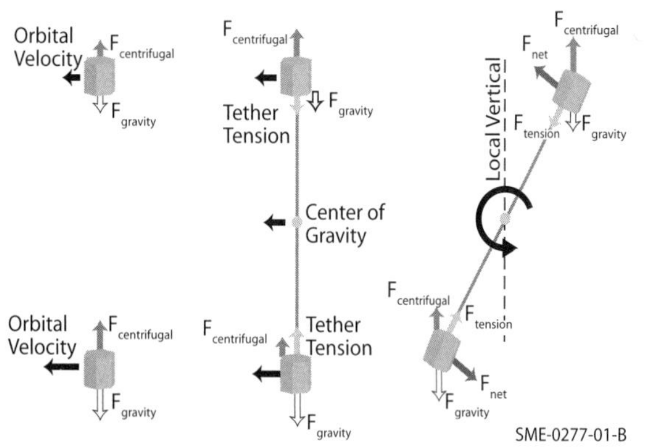

Fig. 25-1. Simplified Diagram of Gravity Gradient Effects on Space Tether Systems. On the left are shown two free-floating spacecraft in circular orbits. In circular orbits, the centrifugal force on each spacecraft must be balanced by the gravitational force towards the Earth, so the spacecraft at a lower altitude must orbit at a greater velocity than the higher altitude spacecraft. In the center we show the balance of forces when the two spacecraft are tied together with a tether. The tether forces the spacecraft to co-orbit at the velocity of the center of gravity of the system. The lower spacecraft, travelling slower than the circular-orbit velocity at its altitude, experiences a higher gravitational force than centrifugal force, and the difference is balanced by the tether tension. If the tethered system is rotated away from the local vertical, as illustrated on the right, the gravitational, centrifugal, and tether tension forces result in a restoring torque that will cause the system to librate around the local vertical.

the plane of the orbit have a period equal to $1/\sqrt{3}$ times the orbit period, and librations in the out-of-plane direction have a period equal to 1/2 of the orbit period. The in-plane librations of a tethered system can be pumped or damped by reeling the tether in or out, but such reeling maneuvers do not significantly influence the out-of-plane librations (see Sec. 25.1.3).

Momentum Exchange

A tether can act like a "sling" to provide a means to transfer orbital momentum and energy from one spacecraft to another. This technique of "momentum exchange" was demonstrated by the SEDS-1 tether mission, which flew as a secondary payload on a Delta-II upper stage. The SEDS-1 experiment deployed a small payload below the upper stage at the end of a 20 km long tether. Once the tether reached a vertical orientation, the upper stage, payload, and tether moved together in an orbit determined by their collective center of gravity, and in this configuration, the payload at the bottom end of the tether was moving at a speed less than orbital velocity at its altitude. The payload was then released from the end of the tether, injecting it into a sub-orbital trajectory that re-entered the Earth's atmosphere half an orbit later. After releasing the payload, the upper stage and tether entered an orbit with a slightly higher apogee. The maneuver is called 'momentum exchange' because the tether provided a mechanical path to transfer orbital momentum from the payload to the upper stage.

The delta V a momentum exchange tether imparts to a payload released from the tip of the tether can be calculated simply as the product of the angular velocity of the tether, measured in inertial coordinates, times the distance between the payload and the system's center of rotation prior to release. A simple rule of thumb for "hanging tether" payload releases such as SEDS-1 performed is that the payload will be injected into an orbit with a perigee reduced by a height roughly 7 times L, the distance between the payload and the tethered system's center of gravity. If the payload is released from the top of the tether, its apogee will be raised by an amount approximately $7L$. Larger orbital changes can be provided to payloads by spinning up the tether so that it is rotating in the orbital frame of reference. An important consideration in the design of tethers with tip velocities greater than several hundred meters per second is that each section of tether must support the centrifugal weight of not only the payload, but also of all of the tether between it and the payload. As a result, the minimum mass of a momentum exchange tether scales exponentially with the square of the delta V [Moravec, 1977]:

$$M_t = M_p \sqrt{\pi}\frac{\Delta V}{V_c} e^{\left(\frac{\Delta V}{V_c}\right)^2} erf\left[\frac{\Delta V}{V_c}\right] \tag{25-2}$$

where *erf* is the error function, M_p is the payload mass at the tether tip, and V_c is the "critical velocity" of the tether material, which in turn depends upon the tensile strength, T, and density, d, of the tether material and the design safety factor, F as:

$$V_c = \sqrt{\frac{2T}{Fd}} \tag{25-3}$$

With currently available high strength materials such as Spectra, Dyneema, and Zylon, this scaling of the required tether mass with tip velocity results in the system mass of momentum exchange tethers being roughly comparable to the mass of a chemical rocket stage for delta V of several hundred meters per second, but much larger than rocket masses for delta V greater than 1 km/s. However, unlike a chemical rocket, which consumes propellant, a momentum exchange tether can be re-used many times. Consequently, momentum exchange tethers will be most advantageous serving as a component of a system that transports many payloads over its operational lifetime.

Electrodynamics

If the tether contains conducting wires, it can enable interactions with the Earth's magnetic field to generate *Lorentz forces* that can be used to raise, lower, or change the plane of a spacecraft's orbit. As illustrated in Fig. 25-2, in an electrodynamic tether system, the orbital motion of the conducting wire across the Earth's magnetic field induces an electric field along the length of the tether. In a direct orbit, this electric field biases the top end of the tether positive with respect to the ambient space environment, and the bottom end negative with respect to the ambient environment. In LEO, the ionospheric plasma can provide a conducting medium in which the tether can exchange charge carriers. If the tether system has a means for collecting electrons from the ionosphere at the top end of the tether and emitting them back into the ionosphere from the bottom end of the tether, the motion-induced electric field can drive a current up the tether, as illustrated on the left in Fig. 25-2. The current will interact with the Earth's magnetic field to induce a $\mathbf{J} \times \mathbf{B}$ Lorentz force that opposes the motion of the tether, lowering the orbit of the system. In this drag, or "deboost" mode, the electrodynamic tether converts the orbital energy of the system into electrical power, which is then dissipated through ohmic losses in the tether. If a load is placed in series with the tether, the system can be used to provide power for that load. Because that power is drawn from the system's orbital energy, an electrodynamic tether can be useful for providing occasional high peak power levels to a payload, but if used for frequent or continual power generation, the tether will cause hastened orbital decay of the system. Conversely, if a power source is used to apply a voltage to the tether to overwhelm the motion induced voltage so as to drive current in the opposite direction, the resulting Lorentz forces will provide a positive thrust that will raise the orbit of the system. In either the de-boost or boost mode, current is driven in only one direction along the tether. The current "loop" in the system is effectively closed by a system of waves in the ionospheric plasma that carry current away along magnetic field as the tether moves across them.

The feasibility of using conducting tethers to interact with the Earth's magnetic field and ionospheric plasma were demonstrated in the Plasma Motor Generator (PMG) experiment flown as a secondary payload on a Delta-II upper stage in 1993. The PMG experiment deployed a 500-meter long insulated conducting wire between the upper stage and a small endmass. Hollow cathode plasma contactors at both ends of the tether provided a low-impedance electrical connection to the ionospheric plasma. Over the course of approximately two orbits, the experiment demonstrated the feasibility of interacting with the ionospheric plasma to enable currents to be driven up or down the tether. The Tethered Satellite System 1-Reflight (TSS-1R) mission carried out in 1996 aboard the Shuttle Orbiter also investigated electrodynamic tether physics, testing different means of exchanging current with the ionosphere, including electron guns and passive collecting surfaces, and demonstrated the ability to drive ampere-level currents along the tether [Stone, Raitt, Wright, 1999].

25.1.2 Space Tether Applications

The ability of tethers to connect spacecraft over long distances, transfer momentum and energy between spacecraft, and generate thrust through interactions with the Earth's magnetic field can enable spacecraft applications that are impractical or impossible to perform with conventional spacecraft technologies.

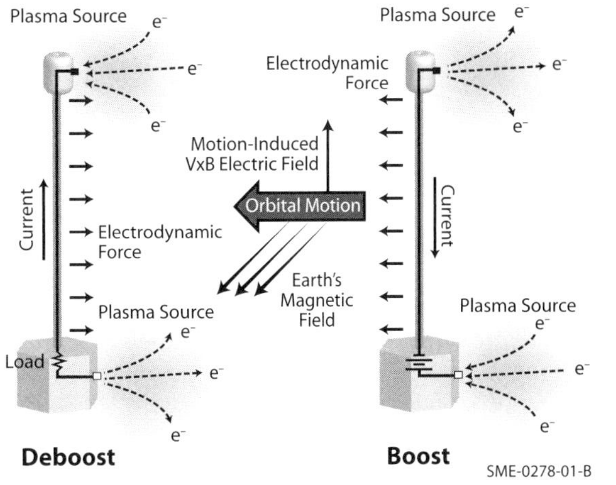

Fig. 25-2. Electrodynamic Tether Propulsion. In an electrodynamic tether, currents flowing along the tether interact with the Earth's magnetic field to induce Lorentz forces on the tether. The tether can be operated in either a deboost/power-generation mode, where the electric field induced by the motion of the tether across the magnetic field is allowed to drive current along the tether, converting orbital energy into electrical power and inducing a drag force on the system, or in a boost mode, in which power is applied to drive current against the motion-induced electric field and generate Lorentz forces that raise the orbit of the system.

Formation Flight

For a number of applications, including long-baseline interferometric astronomy, geolocation, and ionospheric science, it is desirable to fly two or more spacecraft in the same orbit, separated by a controllable distance. Although some formation configurations, such as trailing orbits or Hill's orbits, can be maintained using conventional propulsion systems, other configurations, such as co-orbiting spacecraft with constant separation along the local vertical and formations that rotate around a common center with a continuously changing radius, would require impractically large amounts of propellant to maintain for extended durations. A tether can provide a mechanical link to maintain such formations without consuming propellant. If the tether contains optical fibers or conducting wires, it can also provide a means for high-bandwidth communications between the spacecraft.

Because a tether provides strength in tension but little or no strength in compression, ensuring predictable behavior of a tethered formation requires keeping the tether in a taut state. To do so, a formation can rely on gravity gradient forces, centrifugal forces in a rotating system, or repulsive forces between the spacecraft. When evaluating tethered formation configurations in orbit around the Earth or other planetary body, it is important to consider the interaction between the gravity gradient forces on the system and the angular momentum of the tethered system. Generally, tethered systems that rotate in the plane of the orbit will have the least complicated dynamics, and will continue to rotate within that plane. Tethered systems that rotate in the out-of-plane direction will experience varying torques due to the gravity gradient that will result in precession and nutation of their angular momentum vector.

Orbital Maneuvering

The ability of an electrodynamic tether to generate thrust without consuming propellant can enable a tether system to provide very large total delta V for orbital maneuvering of a spacecraft and do so with mass requirements significantly lower than conventional propulsion technologies. Whereas a rocket uses a gas expelled at high velocity to produce thrust, an electrodynamic tether generates thrust through Lorentz interactions with the Earth's magnetic field. Although some implementations of an electrodynamic tether may utilize plasma generators that consume a small amount of expellant, this expellant is used not as a reaction mass, but rather to create a low impedance electrical connection to the ionosphere. Instead, the tether system utilizes the mass of the Earth itself as its reaction mass. As a result, an electrodynamic tether system can generate thrust for very long durations with little or no consumption of expendables. Fig. 25-3 shows plots of the thrust-to-power ratio of a typical several kilometer long electrodynamic tether in a mid-LEO orbit. The thrust-to-power performance is significantly greater in the de-boost mode because in this mode the motion induced *electromotive force (EMF)* contributes roughly a kW per km of tether length to drive current along the tether, whereas in boost mode the applied power must overcome the motion induced *EMF*. In both cases, the thrust in the plane of the orbit decreases with inclination because the Lorentz force is always perpendicular to both the tether and the magnetic field vector, thus in high inclination orbits, the electrodynamic forces are primarily in the cross-plane direction.

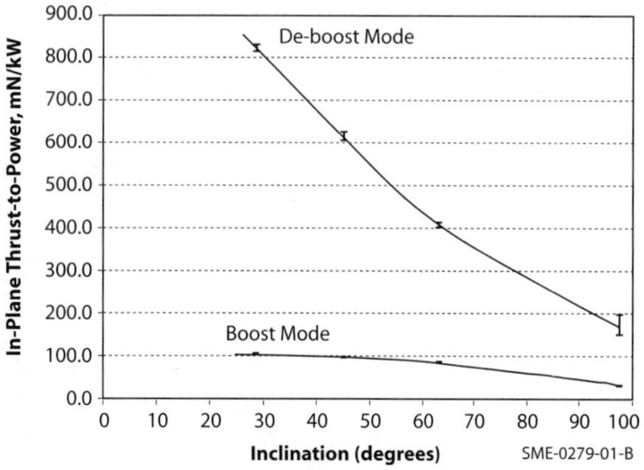

Fig. 25-3. Variation of Electrodynamic Tether In-Plane Thrust-to-Power Ratio with Inclination. Curves shown are for a 2.5 km tether at an altitude of 500 km.

Although an electrodynamic tether does not utilize propellant, we can provide a means for comparing the performance of a tether to other propulsion technologies by computing an "effective specific impulse" using the mass flow of expellant in place of the propellant mass flow rate (See Eq. (18-16) in Sec. 16.1.). Figure 25-4 shows values for the effective specific impulse of a typical several-kilometer long electrodynamic tether in a mid-LEO orbit. In both boost and de-boost modes, the effective specific impulse of the tether system is extremely large, ranging from 10,000 sec at high-inclination in boost mode up to over 100,000 sec in low-inclination de-boost mode. This very high effective specific impulse translates into a capability to provide multiple km/s delta V to a spacecraft with very low total mass requirements. Moreover, because an electrodynamic tether does not utilize an expelled gas to generate thrust, it is liberated from the inverse relationship between thrust and specific impulse typical of rocket-based propulsion systems, and thus it is able to provide both relatively high thrust and high specific impulse, as shown in Fig. 25-5.

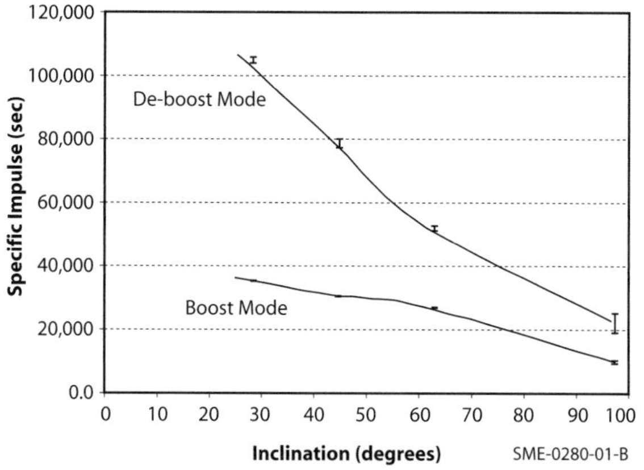

Fig. 25-4. Variation of Effective Specific Impulse with Inclination for an Electrodynamic Tether System. Curves shown are for a 2.5 km long tether at an altitude of 500 km, and the effective I_{sp} is calculated assuming the use of two plasma sources, each with an expellant flow rate of 0.1 mg/s.

Because the electrodynamic force on the tether has components both in the plane of the orbit and in the cross-plane direction, an electrodynamic tether can not only raise and lower the orbit of a spacecraft, but also change its orbit plane. With proper modulation of the current in the tether as it travels around its orbit, all six of the tether's orbital elements can be changed.

De-Orbit

The rapid growth of the space debris population over the past decade presents an increasing threat to operational spacecraft. As a result, many organizations that perform or regulate spaceflight have imposed requirements on new space missions to ensure that their spacecraft do not contribute to the debris population. The current default method for satisfying these end-of-mission disposal requirements is to reserve enough fuel on board the spacecraft to perform a controlled re-entry or de-boost the vehicle to an orbit low enough that aerodynamic drag will cause re-entry within 25 years. Unfortunately, relying upon thrusters for disposal requires reserving a significant fraction of the spacecraft's mass for disposal propellant, and it will not work if key subcomponents of the spacecraft, such as attitude control, command and control, or the thrusters have suffered fail-

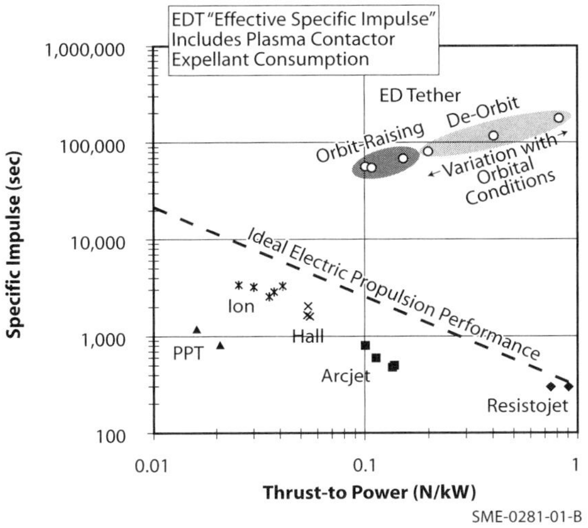

Fig. 25-5. Comparison of Thrust-to-Power vs. Specific Impulse for electric propulsion technologies and electrodynamic tethers.

ures. Because electrodynamic tethers can generate drag forces that are orders of magnitude greater than aerodynamic drag forces in LEO, they can provide a means of accomplishing rapid de-orbit of a spacecraft with significantly lower mass requirements [Forward et al., 2000]. Typically, an electrodynamic tether system can enable LEO spacecraft to meet the post-mission 25-year orbital lifetime restriction with mass impacts of less than 1% of the spacecraft mass. Furthermore, if properly implemented, they can do so even if the host spacecraft has become defunct. A drawback to this approach is the increase in collision probability described at the end of the next section.

25.1.3 Implementation and Integration

Although space tethers are a technology that sounds simple on the surface, like any other space technology the devil is in the details, and implementing a tether system properly to ensure mission success requires addressing a number of engineering challenges. Furthermore, the long tether lengths required for most applications as well as the dynamic characteristics of tethers in orbit present unique challenges for integrating the tether with a spacecraft's hardware and operations. Among the most important of the issues that must be addressed in implementing a space tether system and integrating it with its host spacecraft are the method of tether deployment, the design of the tether materials and structure to enable survival of the space environment, the impact of the tether system on the host spacecraft's behavior and operations, and the potential for collisions between the tether and other objects in orbit.

Tether Deployment

Of the nearly twenty space tether experiments that have been conducted on orbit, the handful that have failed to complete their missions have done so primarily due to problems experienced during the deployment of the tether. Deploying a tether from a spacecraft is challenging in part because a tether has essentially no compressive strength. If the tether becomes slack, its dynamic behavior is nearly impossible to predict with any accuracy, so it is critical that the tether be kept in a taut state during deployment. To keep the tether taut and well behaved, we must rely upon gravity gradient forces, centrifugal forces (in a spinning system), or thrusting by the tether's endmass to keep the tether under tension. As Eq. (25-1) indicates, the gravity gradient force depends linearly upon the tether length, so at the beginning of deployment there is no gravity gradient force to help pull the tether out of its deployer and keep it taut. Consequently, the most successful deployment schemes have accomplished deployment by impulsively ejecting an endmass away from the host spacecraft, and relying upon the endmass' momentum to pull the tether out of the deployer. In this method, the ejection impulse must be sufficient to overcome the drag the tether experiences coming out of the deployer until the gravity gradient force becomes large enough to keep deploying the tether.

An additional factor that must be considered in deployment of the tether is the dynamic behavior of the tethered system. The tether does not simply extend above or below the spacecraft as the tether length is increased. Rather, increasing the tether length tends to cause the object at the bottom of the tether to run ahead of the object at the top of the tether, resulting in librations in the orbit plane. Through proper modulation of the rate of tether deployment, however, a system can control the libration behavior and achieve a well-behaved vertical orientation or other desired end-state [Barkow et al., 2003]. Such controlled deployment of a tether was demonstrated successfully by the SEDS-2 mission, which deployed a 20 km long tether and achieved a final libration swing angle of less than 4 deg [Lorenzini et al., 1995].

Tether Materials and Design

A tether deployed in space must be designed to survive the space environment for the duration of its mission. In Earth orbit, a tether will be subjected to hypervelocity impacts by micrometeorites and orbital debris (MMOD). These impacts are so energetic that they will vaporize a portion of the tether regardless of what material it is made of, typically creating a crater with a diameter 3 to 5 times the diameter of the impactor. Consequently, to ensure that a tether will have a high probability of survival for its mission duration, it either needs to be constructed with a large diameter or with a structure that has redundant load bearing paths distributed over a large volume. The first method was successfully demonstrated by the TiPS tether experiment, which used an acrylic knitting yarn inserted inside a cylindrical braid of high-tensile strength fibers to expand the braid out to a larger diameter. The 4 km long TiPS tether survived for over ten years on orbit in an altitude region with a relatively high flux of small debris particles. The second method is used by approaches such as the Hoytether

[Forward and Hoyt, 1995] and the Carroll Caduceus, both of which distribute the tether material into multiple spatially-separated lines which are then periodically interconnected. The interconnections provide redundant load-bearing paths to enable tensile loads to be bridged around sections of tether that experience damage.

A tether deployed in space will also experience erosion and material degradation due to atomic oxygen, ultraviolet light, and energetic particle radiation. The high-tenacity polymers favored for momentum exchange or formation flight tethers and the polymeric insulators used on electrodynamic tethers can rapidly lose performance and fail due to these environmental effects. Several previous efforts have investigated the use of AO and UV-resistant coatings to protect tether materials. Coated tether samples tested on the MISSE-6 payload flown on the exterior of the ISS demonstrated the ability to survive for many months in the AO and UV environment.

Spacecraft Impacts

When integrating a tether subsystem into a spacecraft, the system design must account for a number of potential effects of the tether upon the spacecraft. The gravity gradient forces induced by the tether can serve as a simple means of stabilizing the satellite's orientation into a nadir- or zenith-facing orientation, but if the spacecraft's mission calls for it to point in other directions or perform slewing maneuvers, its ACS system must be designed to accommodate the torques induced by the tether tension. Furthermore, librations and other oscillations of the tether will result in attitude motion of the spacecraft that must also be accommodated by the ACS system design. Additionally, if the tether is conductive, there exists the potential for voltages induced along the tether to be transmitted to the spacecraft, and so the system design must ensure that the spacecraft will not experience adverse charging effects.

Collision Probabilities

The long lengths involved in most space tether systems raises the concern of the potential for collisions between the tether and other space objects. Although a tether may have a relatively small diameter, when calculating probability of collisions between the tether and other objects, the collision cross-section of a tether should be calculated using the length of the tether and an effective width defined by the characteristic size of the objects with which it could collide. In LEO altitudes, (the average characteristic size of the resident space object populations) on the order of 1.0 to 2.5 m, so the collisional cross sectional area of a tether system can be considerably larger than its physical cross sectional area. Consequently, tether systems should be flown in orbits in which close conjunctions with other objects will be relatively infrequent, or the mission design must enable the tether to be tracked and either maneuvered or retracted to avoid potential collisions.

25.2 Inflatable Structures

Constantine Cassapakis, *Consultant*

In this section, we consider the use of *deployable inflatable space structures* for space applications. It should be noted that this area of endeavor is large and this treatment is only meant to convey enough information on this class of structures to help the space mission analyst or engineer with some knowledge toward their use as payloads. It is also important to mention, that this section does not consider the type of inflatable structures used for Space Habitats, such as those conceived for the Lunar or Martian surfaces, or those that demonstrate the capability of LEO "man-rated" vehicles (the inflatable capsules of the "Genesis" type, successfully designed, built and flown by Bigelow Aerospace, are a good example of the latter). Rather, we will concentrate on the very lightweight "*Gossamer-type*" *structures*, as these truly stress the space inflatables technology to its limits. Should it be decided to delve into more detail towards possible mission implementation, the reader is directed to a variety of sources. Freeland et al. [1998]; Cassapakis [2008]; Satter and Freeland [1995]; and Cassapakis [1995] provide helpful overviews on the subject. Jenkins [1997] is a good source of information on most of the sub-technologies involved, providing a collection of writings by people working currently or recently in the field. An abundance of relevant technical papers on the subject matter can also be found on the websites of L'Garde, Inc., NeXolve, and ILC-Dover who have done extensive work in this area.

Plastic films, such as *polyesters* (e.g., Mylar®) or *polyimides* (e.g., Kapton®) and thin pliable laminates play an important role in this technology, and so do materials that become rigid upon inflation and deployment in the space environment. Much has been accomplished the last three decades in this fascinating technology, but most of the progress has been in its continued development rather than its frequent application in space missions. This technology still remains as one of the "Holy Grails" in the Space Structures field, as there still remain some serious risks to be retired. Yet, there are missions that will be difficult to accomplish without this technology, particularly those missions that would require either very large structures, or those in which the available stowage space is too small for a rigid deployable payload. When the stowage volume and mass requirements are too constricting for rigid deployable structures, the mission engineer should give *space inflatables technology* careful consideration.

25.2.1 Background

Mass and *stowage volume* have always been serious challenges to the aerospace engineer and more so in the engineering of spacecraft buses and their payloads. The expense of launching a 1 kg mass in space can reach beyond \$18K (see Table 11-23) depending on orbit and does not seem to be getting much better with newer booster technologies. In our experience, stowage volume is an even stricter constraint than mass, particularly for spacecraft that employ large deployable subsystems, such as solar arrays, dish antennas, solar concentrators, and solar sails. It is these constraints, along with the possible hang-ups of mechanically deployable structures comprised of a large number of rigid component parts (by comparison, inflatable bodies require much fewer parts), which pointed to the need for developing space inflatable structures. As early as the 1950s, aerospace engineers at Goodyear were experimenting with building inflatable antennas using elastomer-impregnated fabrics. These were fairly heavy, had low stiffness and did not attain the stowage volume possible with lighter materials.

The first inflatable structures that made it to space were the ECHO satellite series launched by NASA in the early 1960s, some of them being spherical shells of over 30 m in diameter and used as radio-wave reflectors (Fig. 25-6). The shell thickness was in the range of 38 microns, as DuPont-manufactured polyesters entered the plastic film market, offering a thickness as low as 6 microns and a respectable structural modulus in the few GP region.

Fig. 25-6. NASA'S ECHO Satellite.

When the Soviet Union launched the Galosh ICBM interceptor in 1965, the US Air Force initiated a series of studies (ABRES) with several aerospace prime contractors of that time to establish the best recourse in countering this Soviet threat. Most of these multiyear studies and the concomitant experimentation resulted in favor of complementing the US Intercontinental Ballistic Missile (ICBM) fleet with inflatable missile decoys offering similar signatures in the radar and visible spectrum. The ease of manufacturing, folding, efficient stowage during launch and relatively light weight, meant low manufacturing and launch costs, thus allowing a significant number of them to be deployed around an ICBM, making it difficult, if not impossible, for an enemy to discriminate between it and the decoys. Ford Aeroneutronic (now a part of Loral), L'Garde, Inc., Tracor (now part of BAE), and AVCO (now Textron) among others, designed and built a number of these inflatable objects (Fig. 25-7). Lincoln and Sandia National Laboratories were also involved in the effort.

Fig. 25-7. An Early Example of a Re-entry Vehicle Inflatable Replica.

Though these space inflatable objects were never fielded as part of the US strategic defense, a large number of them have flown for testing purposes in the last 4 decades by the various incarnations of the US missile defense (BMO, SDIO, BMDO and presently, MDA). Much has been learned about the behavior of these materials and structures from these space tests. The latter were mainly sub-orbital, but there were some that were conducted orbitally. In the discussion that follows, we separate the engineering of this structural class into Inflatable-Only and Inflatable-Rigidizable Structures. Since for a long-term orbital mission, the latter will have a better chance of working, a table will be presented in Sec. 25.2.4 that will allow an approximate calculation of the mass and stowage volume of an inflatable-rigidizable parabolic antenna (Table 25-1).

25.2.2 Engineering Inflatable-Only Structures

We use the term "*Inflatable-only*" or "*purely inflatable*" structures for those that require constant pressurization in space to preserve their shape and structural properties. There are numerous examples, such as a *membrane lenticular* (lens-shaped) reflector or *light concentrator* (the large inflatable antenna in the IAE space shuttle mission of 1996 [Freeland et al., 1996] shown in Fig. 25-8); *conical structures*, such as those of Re-entry Vehicle replicas, *spherical target balloons*, simple or heavily instrumented), and a variety of other space targets; in general, any structure which is a body of revolution designed and fabricated with films or laminates, metalized or not, and reinforced with fabric fibers or not.

For closed structures, e.g., a sphere, there exists an important relationship between skin stress and inflation pressure:

$$\sigma = PR/t \qquad (25\text{-}4)$$

where σ is the skin stress, P is the internal pressure, R is the radius of curvature, and t is the skin thickness. Thus:

$$P = t\sigma/R \qquad (25\text{-}5)$$

(In the case of a closed cylinder the hoop stress is still given by PR/t but the stress in the axial direction is $PR/2t$).

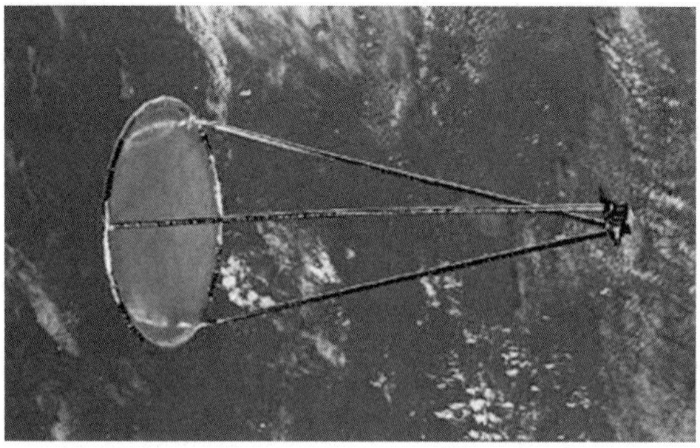

Fig. 25-8. The IAE Deployed Off the SPARTAN Spacecraft of NASA.

The structural films used in the consideration of large apertures are in the vicinity of 0.0005 inch thick, the radii of curvatures are in the low to high tens of meters and the skin stresses required to remove stowage wrinkles can vary from about 4 MPa to 6 MPa.

Thus, the inflation pressure to turn a large, purely inflatable body of revolution into a stiff structure in space is so small it may be considered to be a decent vacuum on Earth. Concomitantly, the mean free path of intermolecular collisions in the inflation gas becomes larger, thus retarding its escape from the inflated structure (there is no explosion of the inflatable, not that anyone could hear, anyway). This is a significant result when one considers that inflatable structures in space must peacefully coexist with micrometeoroids and debris.

The consequences of these findings (at least on a theoretical level), along with the continued development of structural films such as Mylar and Kapton (DuPont is the largest manufacturer, but smaller companies have made further improvements) have played an important role in the interest that these structures have generated the last twenty or more years in the field of Space Mission Design. But should the mission designer be too enthusiastic to use an inflatable payload in space, as I have been most of my career, they're kindly reminded that this area is much more complex and difficult than it seems. It is an admixture of physics, art, very careful engineering, much daring and a good dose of humility, preferably learned before large amounts of capital are expended. I have encountered many situations where exorbitant claims are made for inflatable membrane missions by well meaning, but inexperienced mission planners and engineers.

25.2.3 The Design Process

As noted above, this is similar to the design process that any payload system must undergo. For inflatables there are some differences that need to be taken into account. The thin film materials used are non-linear in that (a) their modulus changes with applied stress; (b) as manufactured, their modulus is different in the longitudinal direction from that in the lateral direction (and this introduces yet another level of complexity); and (c) the inflation process can produce fairly large deformations of the material, making it difficult for the usual FEM codes (e.g., NASTRAN) to converge to a solution successfully and efficiently. Thus, the design of an inflatable structure can be, and in most cases is, a cyclical process, particularly when accurate surface figures are required in the deployed system (e.g., antennas, solar concentrators).

A. Mission Requirements.

Most important for the deployed structure are Mission Lifetime, Mission Orbit (micrometeoroid distributions, UV, atomic oxygen, particle radiation and thermal environment), deployment and mechanical/gravitational loads. For the stowed configuration, requirements would be the available stowage volume and allowable mass of the payload, launch loads (acceleration, vibration, and ascent profiles) which must be taken into account in the design of the *inflatable containment structure* (also referred to as the "*canister*") and the inflatable payload mode of retention prior to deployment. Once these are defined, the search for the proper inflatable materials and thickness that will withstand orbit environment can begin. A very sizable amount of work has been done and reported on a number of different membranes and their behavior in most of the orbit environments but we will mention a few words on micrometeoroids here. There have been terrestrial experiments to attempt defining the damage function of micrometeoroids on stretched membranes, as it was thought that plastic films under stress would be torn by the impingement of these ubiquitous particles, due to the low tear resistance of the films. These experiments, conducted with hypervelocity particles (5 km/sec) of an average diameter around 1 micron have shown that the films do not tear. Rather, the impinging particle creates a "cookie-cutter" hole, whose diameter asymptotes out to 3 times the particle diameter [Thomas and Griese, 1980]. When convoluted with the micrometeoroid size and intensity distribution, this gives a fair, though approximate determination of the damage magnitude (the accumulated hole area) on the membrane as a function of time. Knowing the operational pressure, an analysis can be performed to determine the inflatant loss as a function of time and the amount of "make-up" gas carried along to supplement the loss, when necessary. Analyses performed at L'Garde for large inflatable-only bodies of revolution suggest that a mission life beyond 5 years in the space environment is not practical for these structures, unless ways to ameliorate the gas leakage are found in the future. Some concepts have been considered on this topic, including self-annealing membranes or inflatable gases that carry a sealing agent, but unfortunately nothing definitive has been produced so far.

B. The "Inverse Problem"

Once a material meeting all the requirements delineated above is found, the design process can begin in earnest. The *Inverse Problem* is a somewhat arcane term describing the relatively easy to understand analytical geometry process of starting out with the shape of the conceptual structure and working it backwards (hence, inverse problem) to the flat segments (gores) that need to be cut from the roll of film, so that when seamed together and inflated to their operational pressure, they will produce the desired shape with the desired accuracy. L'Garde, Inc. developed finite element codes to deal with this problem. For instance, FAIM (Finite-element Analysis for Inflatable Membranes) [Palisoc and Huang, 1997] deals with the "forward" transformation, starting with the un-inflated (unstressed) shape and proceeding to predict the inflated shape. When the latter converges to the conceptual one, the flat gore shape resulting from the "inverse" transformation is deemed to be correct. Figure 25-9 shows the stresses calculated for a lenticular membrane structure when properly inflated. We note that a commercially available code, ABAQUS started making much headway into the non-linear and large deformation arena a few years ago, and is now used widely by several entities in the space community.

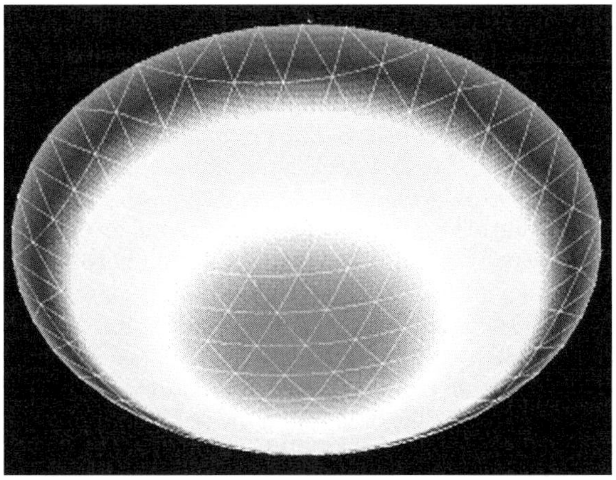

Fig. 25-9. A Reflector Stress Field Calculated by FAIM.

C. Design

Membrane Segments: After the non-linear analysis iterations (if required) are done, the flat segment shapes are designed and cut. It must be noted here that membranes have non-zero Coefficient of Thermal Expansion (CTEs) (the best ones are in the proximity of 10 ppm/°F) but in addition they possess a hygroscopic coefficient of expansion, rendering them susceptible to moisture. When high accuracy is required, the environmental conditions in cutting, inspection, and seaming of the segments (gores) to their final configuration, the temperature and humidity levels during these processes must be specified so that shape correctness is assured. Finite element thermal codes **must** be used to determine membrane temperatures and thermal gradients on orbit, as these will affect the shape accuracy of the membrane or inflatable structural component. It must be noted here that NeXolve has recently reported being able to manufacture polyimide membranes with an almost zero CTE [Poe and Patrick, 2008].

Stowed Configuration: In parallel with the segment design, the folded (stowed) configuration must be determined, so that deployment proceeds in as controlled a way as possible. No other process in payload design is as dependent on its initial conditions as this one and much care must be exercised in envisioning the folding pattern and ensuring that the folded package meets the allowable stowage volume requirement, and that deployment can proceed as designed. These objectives are usually met by tests involving simple material coupons, seamed coupons, and subscale tests of the final payload configuration.

Inflation System: This is comprised by an inflation gas accumulator and the appropriate valves to inflate the system either through a pre-programmed command, or an electronic timer that is initiated at the appropriate moment in the mission time table, or an uplink command. The inflation gas most often used is pure dry nitrogen, but CO_2 also can work under the proper thermal environments and inflation rates. The simplest inflation system is a tank containing a pre-determined amount of inflation gas under pressure, which opens upon command by activating an electro-explosive device (EED or "squib"), thus allowing the gas to enter the inflatable volume and bring it to its proper pressure (this is referred to as a "blow-down" inflation system). Naturally, the complexity of the inflation system increases considerably when more than one inflatable chamber is present, particularly if the operational pressures are different, and yet have to be inflated by the same system to improve the volume and mass of the entire payload. For instance, a very small pressure is needed to inflate a lenticular antenna reflector, but its deployment and support structural parts require a much higher pressure. Then, the gas accumulator must be followed by a pressure regulator that feeds the appropriate inflation ports through thoroughly tested valves. In addition, pressure and temperature sensors may be included to ascertain and control system status before and after deployment. It should be apparent that inflation system components should be stored and assembled in clean rooms. Otherwise, a minute dust particle trapped in a normally closed valve can quickly spell catastrophe. Finally, during launch ascent and at times beyond, it must allow for the escape of the entrapped atmospheric air that enters the system during packaging. This is accomplished via a vent valve that stays open until just before the inflation command is given, at which time it is programmed to close.

Stowage System (canister)

The canister contains all the subsytems making up the inflatable payload: the stowed membrane and its deployment/support structure, the inflation system, requisite microprocessor, electronics and instrumentation including sensors. Its function is to provide the proper environment during launch and act as the "pedestal" from which deployment proceeds. It also provides the interface between the payload and the spacecraft, if the payload is to be connected to the latter during the mission; or it can act as the spacecraft itself if the payload is to be a free-flier upon separation from the main bus. It should be obvious that the configuration of the inflatable payload subsystems, launch, pre- and post-deployment environments, are all necessary inputs in the canister design.

Testing

The testing of all hardware components proceeds along the normal testing procedures as any other payload. It includes mechanical and environmental materials coupon testing, component and subsystem functioning of all mechanical and electronics components, and repeated functioning of the canister door opening to ascertain unencumbered payload exit from its stowed configuration. Pre- and post-vibration testing is necessary to uncover critical issues. The greatest testing difficulty arises when large membrane apertures are involved. For instance, the NASA/JPL/L'Garde Inflatable Antenna Experiment reflector was only 15 m in diameter, yet it required well over 300 m^2 of high bay area to determine its overall surface accuracy and inflation requirements (Fig. 25-10); and the NASA 400 m^2 solar sail membrane required the NASA Plumbrook Facility to test its deployment. Obviously, it would be very difficult if not impossible to find or build facilities that would accommodate even larger area apertures that appear in conceptual future mission designs. This does not mean however that these missions cannot proceed. Sub-scale tests can be conducted for a variety of cases, as long as the correct scaling laws can be applied [Greschik, Mikulas, and Freeland, 1999].

Fig. 25-10. Testing the IAE Reflector at L'Garde.

25.2.4 Engineering Inflatable-Rigidizable Structures

Whereas purely inflatable structures such as large solar concentrators, antennas, targets, large balloon-shaped objects, could theoretically operate for weeks, months, or even years in space due to the low inflation pressures required (inflation gas must be carried on board depending on mission life), the same cannot be said for inflatable structures used for deployment and support of functional payloads. These structures can be toroidal, such as supports of a lenticular reflector or flat membrane, or cylindrical in form, such as deployment and support struts. For the sake of structural efficiency and the stiffness required of support structures, their curvature radius is usually rather small by comparison to their other dimensions, and their skin thickness usually an order of magnitude or more larger than that of the pure inflatables. Thus much larger pressures (significant fractions of an atmosphere) are needed to achieve the required structural performance, in which case a micrometeoroid collision can deplete the inflatant quickly and cause structural failure. This is what gives rise to Inflatable-Rigidizable Structures. These are manufactured out of material laminates usually comprised of a structural fabric impregnated with a resin, which upon inflation becomes rigid using any of a number of physical properties encountered in space, or that are designed into the material itself.

The Echo Satellite series used a form of rigidization involving Mylar film metalized by 0.001 inch of vapor deposited aluminum (VDA). A slight overpressure applied upon reaching the operational pressure work-hardens the aluminum into a spherical shell which keeps its shape in the absence of gravitational loads, even upon losing all inflation pressure. The same rigidization technique has been used by L'Garde in the flight of an orbital Optical Calibration Sphere that flew in the late 1990s and a passively deployable solar array that was qualified for flight but never flew due to funding limitations (Fig. 25-11). ILC-Dover has also produced a number of terrestrial prototypes.

Rigidizable structures can be classed as irreversibly and reversibly rigidizable. The distinction becomes understood with reference to the pre-launch testing of these objects. The former are "one-shot" mechanisms, meaning that after one structural test, it cannot be used again. Thus, an identically designed and fabricated mechanism must be used for the next test in the series, be it an additional development test, qualification, or as a flight test item. In many cases, this procedure can be worrisome, particularly when an expensive mission is at hand (EEDs are also one-shot mechanisms, but the space community feels much more secure using these, since they have been used for decades now and each batch undergoes significant testing to attain a 0.999 reliability rating). To do this with inflatable structural elements would be a very expensive proposition, due to the large amount of "touch" labor involved in the construction of the test articles, thus impractical if there is no budget to support batch testing (I have never seen that kind of budget available in this field; thus if there is no other way to accomplish the mission, some engineers may well opt to take the chance and use a one-shot structure, and some have). On the other hand, reversibly rigidizable structures can undergo a fair

Fig. 25-11. A Solar Array with Inflatable-Rigidizable Deployment/Support Structure. Work-hardened aluminum is used for the struts. The carbon composite Canister (top) and its lid (bottom) complete the structure.

number of testing cycles by reversing the rigidized state back to the pliable and thus foldable and stowable state, and finally be flown. Table 25-1 shows a comparison between different rigidization techniques. Recently, great strides have been made in rigidization techniques, and in UV (ultra-violet) rigidization processes and resins.

Table 25-1. Rigidization Processes and Properties.

Metal Foil Work-Hardening by Overpressure	Repeatable, high stiffness, unsuitable for large loads
Water-based Resins	Reversible, low stiffness, high strength, poor for optics
Thermosetting	Irreversible, high stiffness, high strength
UV Radiation	Irreversible, high stiffness, high strength, non-uniform
Sub-Tg (glass transition temperature) Resins	Reversible, high stiffness, high strength, orbit tailorable
Particle Radiation	Irreversible, brittle, and fries the spacecraft

25.2.5 Reflector Mass and Stowage Volume vs. Diameter

Table 25-2 shows an approximate value for the mass and stowage volume of an inflatable reflector as a function of its aperture diameter. The deployment/support structural components are inflatable-rigidizable, and the assumed packaging factor is 3 (i.e., the volume allowed for stowage of the flexible payload is 3 times the volume of the flexible material). A reflector *f/D* of 0.4 is also assumed. All the major necessary components for the full functioning of the payload (inflatable mass, inflation system and gas, electronics, and canister) are included.

Table 25-2. Mass and Stowage Volume of an Inflatable Reflector as a Function of Aperture Diameter. [Palisoc et al., 1998]

Diameter	Mass	Stowed Vol.
3	5.39	0.0283
5	9.38	0.0422
10	24.37	0.0834
30	152.98	0.3324
50	391.42	0.7164
100	1,468.05	2.2663

25.2.6 Summary

Inflatable space structures have been considered, experimented with, fairly developed and flown over several decades (Fig. 25-13). Other than short duration missions, they have not reached the stage where they can be used by mission engineers, though they have been included in numerous future mission concepts. Quite possibly, these concepts will not be achieved without inflatable structural elements being employed, unless launch vehicle prices decrease considerably, or robotic assembly in space becomes fully developed and cost efficient. The reason for this avoidance is mainly that inflatable materials developed to date have several issues associated with them and more development and flight experience is necessary before this class of structures reaches full maturity. However, what exists today can be used in cases where masses and stowage volumes are critical and there is no other way for the mission to occur, even for small spacecraft and cubesats (see for instance Fig. 25-12). This will also help the present and future space scientists to further their dreams of what now is considered impossible.

25.3 SmallSats

Rick Fleeter, *Brown University*

The idea that there is something countercultural about an initiative to make products smaller, lower cost, more reliable and more useful is the mystery that is at the core of the most transformative development in space since Apollo. Our world has embraced innovations in efficiency. We accept some compromises of inflight services for the availability of low cost airline tickets for local, national and international travel. Small, economical automobiles have always coexisted with large luxury models

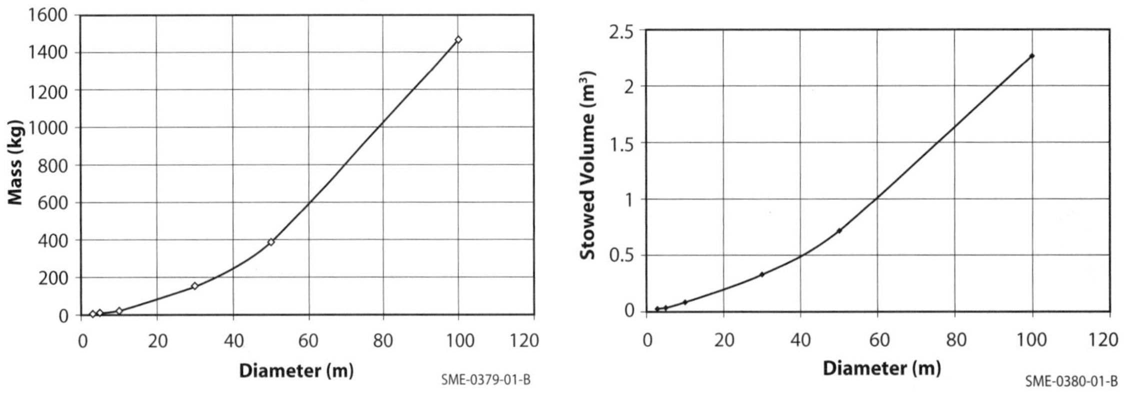

Fig. 25-12. Mass Storage Volume of an Inflatable Reflector vs. Deployed Diameter.

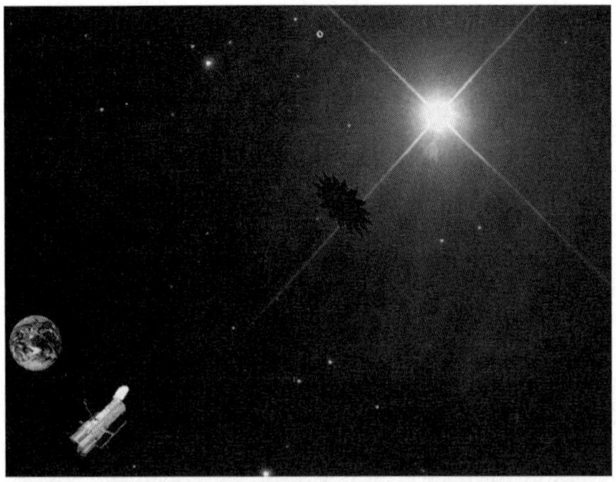

Fig. 25-13. A Deployed Membrane is Used as a Giant Star-occulter in this Concept of a Terrestrial Plane Finder. (Graphics courtesy of Princeton-Lockheed-Martin)

and SUVs without much apparent philosophical conflict. Nobody is disappointed that they can't sit in front of their iPod to have their long hair blown back as its powerful blast of sound washes over them. Big sound systems abound at concerts and in the home theaters of enthusiasts, though tiny personal MP3 players have dwarfed sales of those classical systems.

Since proposing in the mid 1980s that space reexamine the use of small, tightly focused, quickly developed, simple, low cost systems for those missions they can accomplish, there has emerged a myth that these are the indie, outlaw systems. That to accomplish better, cheaper, and faster is tantamount to magic. Impossible! Arthur Clarke wrote in 1962 "Any sufficiently advanced technology is indistinguishable from magic" [1962]. But isn't space where advanced technology is born?

25.3.1 We Were There First

While President Eisenhower's scientific advisors were assuring him of the physical impossibility of creating an artificial Earth orbiting satellite, the Soviet Union developed and launched the Sputnik spacecraft in October of 1957. Sputnik was a relatively heavy satellite at 84 kg, though 52 kg were batteries and most of the other 32 kg was a very heavy spherical shell structure. Besides its accomplishment of a single, simple, significant mission in space, transmission of radio signals at two frequencies to determine their detectability on Earth, Sputnik had several other features reinvented in subsequent small spacecraft. That heavy shell was a pressure vessel maintaining the mission electronics in compressed nitrogen environment fitted with fans to provide a more benign thermal environment for its radios, a method periodically employed since. Its 1 Watt radio power is the level still most often used for low Earth orbit small satellites, and its short mission lifetime was critical in keeping its design simple. The Sputnik Launch Vehicle has also become interesting again, a single stage rocket with strap on boosters, which was optimized for simplicity and low cost rather than high performance.

Released from the burden of its impossibility, American engineers succeeded, in January, 1958, in launching the first of the Explorer series of small satellites, with a mass of 14 kg about 6 kg of which were batteries. Pioneer also had a single mission, characterizing some basic elements of the space environment, and a short, 3 month operating life. With what little could be done with 6 kg of 1950s vintage electronics, it managed to detect the existence of regions of augmented radiation subsequently known as the Van Allen Radiation Belts.

Technological progress, the Space Race, defense applications of large rockets for weapons delivery and the desire to put humans in orbit and ultimately on the surface of the Moon, focused American and Soviet space activity on ever larger rockets and spacecraft. However during the Apollo period, roughly the 1960s, small satellites scored numerous space firsts including the first weather satellite, Tiros, weighing 122 kg and launched in 1962. The first geosynchronous communications satellite, Syncom, developed by Hughes (now Boeing) for \$4M, weighed just 35 kg and began operations from a sub-GEO orbit on the day it was launched, February 14, 1963, though operations from GEO orbit awaited the launch later that year of Syncom 2.

Table 25-2◀, Fig. 25-13◀, Eq. 25-5◀

25.3.2 Bigger is Better?

Weather, communications, and exploration, robotic and human, trace their roots to microspace, but all grew into much larger systems with greater capabilities including transporting humans into orbit and to the Moon, high resolution imagery across a range of wavelengths and atmospheric conditions, day and night, including the use of radar illumination, and probes capable of operating 10 to 20 years winding their way among the inner and outer planets sending back images and other physical data. The impressive results obtained in these first 3, classical, applications of space, for a while seemed the logical future for the field, their level of performance impossible from smaller platforms. Communications systems developed metrics such as the number of bits relayed to Earth per kilogram/cost of satellite which favored the development of ever larger platforms to realize the scale efficiencies both of larger space platforms and larger transportation systems.

25.3.3 Smaller is Better?

Space, compared with the pocket of your dress shirt, is quite large allowing more than ample room for satellites any size we care to make them. The Moon has roughly the volume of 250,000,000,000,000,000,000,000 (two hundred fifty billion trillion) iPhones, and still it is not crowding anybody particularly. Of what possible good is a small, less capable spacecraft compared with the miracles providing pinpoint navigation (GPS) constant imagery of weather and storm warnings (GOES and many others) and day/night all weather high resolution Earth imagery (Cosmo-Skymed) all of which accomplished via the major space systems which have now become considered our "classical" space technology?

The PC technology wars of the 1980s and early 1990s were never won, they just became irrelevant. The operating system running on your laptop doesn't really matter to the internet, and the world's major space agencies sponsor missions mostly according to their utility, not to support use of any one size class. Which carrier you choose for your cell phone no longer means much, and cars around the world offer similar safety, performance, and reliability. As technologies mature, they exit the product selection spotlight. Clients focus on utility. There is no "better", there is what takes you where you want to go today.

Applications

In the 1960s space had three applications: communications, remote sensing, and exploration. In the 1970s, the almost silent navigation revolution was affected by GPS. In the 1980s, first at the University of Surrey (Sec. 23.1), a 5th application emerged. The Cubesat (Sec. 25.4) pioneered by Bob Twiggs made widespread the use of satellites, exclusively small satellites, for education. More satellites are now developed annually for that application than the other 4 combined. Whereas space was once considered the field where new technology was born, it has now become their old age home. Large systems require such enormous investment, the fear of a failure has all but eliminated adoption of new technology. Small satellites have filled that niche and accommodate a 6th application, technology R&D.

Looking at another field once considered only the domain of techies, geeks, and nerds, but now in the hands of most of the planet's population, i.e., computing, our 7th application might be entertainment. And it is likely this latest of our applications spaces will happen in microspace, not because of any special technological advantage, but because entertainment is a speciality outside engineering. It happens when "the rest of us" start playing with spacecraft. Microspace being simpler, cheaper, and doable on a desktop adapts it better for experimentation by people who may not be experts in space engineering but who know how to engineer mystery, fantasy, thrills, to stimulate human emotion and to inspire us.

An example of the power of small satellites to put space in the hands of more people is the internationalization of spacecraft production. Though some countries may have aspirations to eventually develop major spacecraft, or may be customers and users of large satellites built abroad, the entry point for new national entrants in space is in small missions, often beginning in cooperation with a more experienced foreign partner:

- Malaysia developed the Tiungsat series initially with SSTL, progressing to the launch of Razaksat, a much more capable spacecraft
- Israel built not only series of small satellites as university projects starting with the Gurwin and Techsat series, and for communications (Amos) as well as small remote sensing satellites, but also the Shavit launch vehicle tailored for those missions
- Swedish Space Corporation (SSC) has been a leader in small satellite applications since the launch of the Viking in 1986 which had the dual missions of scientific research in upper atmospheric physics and the development of technologies and infrastructures for small space missions. SSC has successfully developed and launched 6 small satellites with 4 more in development with missions including geosynchronous servicing, GEO telecommunications, and formation flying
- Other countries now active in small space include Brazil, Korea, India, Kenya, South Africa, Singapore, Taiwan, and almost all the countries of Europe, many including Germany, Denmark, France, and Italy with strong academic programs
- The US played a leading role in small satellite applications in industrial realization of defense and science applications and in academics. Stanford and Cal Poly initiated the CubeSat architecture now adopted worldwide, first for academic experiments but now being exploited for science and military missions, often launched by the Peapod dispenser devel-

oped at the Naval Post Graduate School. American entrepreneurs developed numerous startup companies based on small and innovative space including Orbital, Defense Systems (now part of Orbital), AeroAstro (now part of Comtech), Andrews Space, SpaceDev and MicroSat Systems (both now part of Sierra Nevada), SpaceQuest, and Pumpkin

- Outside the US, Clydespace (Glasgow, Scotland) exemplifies the opportunities small space offers for entrepreneurs. There are many more entrepreneurial companies supporting the systems developers with services and subsystems tailored for smaller low cost missions

Budgets

It seems that it must have been easier to balance a household budget before the explosion in uses for money, including cable TV, digital cable, satellite, high speed internet, myriad cell phones, smart phones, computing platforms, plethora of cooking technologies (e.g., microwave, convection, sun tea) book readers, not to mention the items once considered luxuries if not unknown, color TV, refrigerators, cuisinarts, and the complete spectrum of shoes including aerobic, dress shoes that are actually running shoes in disguise, hiking grade sandals, and cowboy boots. The Soviets were right that we capitalists are overwhelmed with choice. And our governments are immune? That federal budgets do not orbit around national space initiatives is inevitable when we have to figure out how to pay for the right of every citizen to MRI and CAT imaging, quintuple bypass surgery, post high school education, a privileged position along or at least a local on ramp to the information superhighway, child care, elderly care, the interstate highway system and an air traffic system protected by a Department of Homeland Security.

That bureaucracy grows faster than budgets, possibly faster than anything else, means that the budget for any one activity must, as the second law of thermodynamics warns, diffuse to below the limits of detectability. There are just not the billion dollar allocations readily available to do single space missions, and not through any fault of classical system performance. The world has changed, and the ability to do meaningful missions, if not hugely elaborate ones, on the existing more frugal resources allocated to them, is the future.

An example of this trend is the development of small geosynchronous communications satellites, carrying 4 to 8 transponders instead of the 30 or more of major GEO comsats. Examples include Orbital's Star series with over 20 already operational and the Israeli Amos, with other small GEOs in various stages of development at SSTL (GMP-D), OHB-led Small GEO ARTES 11. Notwithstanding that the cost per transponder is higher for smaller platforms, they are the fastest growing GEO segment. They are ideally suited for clients with smaller markets or who are pioneering new services, who require a low cost additional service, and to enhance service availability and reliability.

This trend is mirrored in remote sensing, where innovative companies are successfully providing commercial imagery from smaller platforms. Examples include the OrbView, GeoEye, RapidEye, and the Ofeq series of imaging satellites. The German SAR-Lupe series of satellites have demonstrated space-based radar imaging from small platforms, though at 720 kg they stretch the definition of a small spacecraft except when compared with other radar imagers like the Canadian Radarsat (2,750 kg) and Italian Cosmo-Skymed (1,900 kg).

Time

Every aspect of life runs on a faster clock now. Few scientific questions remain relevant over the 20 year time scale typical of major space missions. Iridium was a good idea when it was conceived, but by the time the global telecomms network was launched, terrestrial cellular was serving most of its market. Politically, our leaders need results fast enough to help them be reelected. We get our music, books, and news instantly, and it is logical to expect the same from our space activity.

Rapid development is the focus of the Responsive Space initiative, developing spacecraft, ground and launch technologies and systems which can address emerging, often unexpected, requirements for communications and remote sensing. The TacSat series of satellites are designed to develop rapid response capability. But rapid development is also critical for educational applications compatible with engineering programs of a few years, and for technology demonstrations. The Los Alamos ALEXIS satellite was developed to test in orbit, within a few years, 2 new remote sensing technologies for eventual integration into major military systems.

Constituency

To sustain public or private sector support from an ever more distracted populous means reaching deeper into the public for support, but also for ideas. TV was envisioned as a means to bring classical culture (orchestral concerts and opera) to the public, and the early PC makers had no clue what the public would do with them—storing recipes was not, counter to their misguided albeit well-intended hopes, a killer app. Now we have the iPhone and the app store, with tens of thousands of reasons you cannot live without the technology in your hand while waiting for a bus, out with friends or facing a deadline in the office.

Space will survive without participation of the general public, along side high energy astrophysics, Egyptology and Orchid cultivation. But given space's potential to make human life better, in managing information, population, transportation, projecting life off our planet, and discovering if anyone else is out there, it is imperative we integrate the ideas of billions of humans, and that means putting the technology in the hands of non experts. Small satellites have driven the internationalization of space, the development of new applications of spacecraft including education, servicing, constellations, and technology development and demonstration, and participation in space by students and amateurs which contribute to the growth in the space constituency. Companies like Pumpkin and SpaceQuest provide kits from which small satellites can be built. Amsat, the amateur radio satellite corporation, has a nearly 50 year history of launching small satellites built by amateurs.

25.3.4 Why Small is Different

Small Satellite Engineering

As satellites become smaller, their design considerations radically change. Their structural elements tend to be oversized compared with strength considerations just to make them physically manageable, and to be able to attach components to them. Structural mass is relatively insignificant, so aluminum has remained the widespread material, the advantages of composites not being worth their practical complications.

Coupled with their small size, the temperature gradient across a small satellite is typically not significant. Consequently, they do not employ heat pipes and other mechanisms and flight modes to equalize the heat load across the spacecraft. Because of their very large surface area to volume ratio, small satellites cannot easily manage internal temperature with electric heating and thermostats, hence these elements are largely absent, relying instead on coatings and insulation to minimize dark/light temperature variation. For these reasons, they typically do not require more complex finite element thermal and structural modeling. Also because their surface area is large and volume for containing payload elements small, physically smaller spacecraft tend not to need deployable solar panels to enhance collection area.

Probably the most significant engineering change caused by smaller scale is the reduced parts count. Fewer parts means the probability of a component failure is small. Redundancy, the first line defense against failure in major space systems, has limited or no role in smaller spacecraft. And because they tend to execute shorter duration missions at lower orbits, their choice of parts is not as restricted by the need for radiation hardness nor long life. More modern components typically have lower power consumption, smaller mass and volume, lower cost, and are simpler to work with, further lowering complexity which ultimately is the enemy of reliability. Despite their often being developed by students or amateur teams with limited training and experience, very small satellite reliability is comparable with major space systems thanks to their simplicity. It is easier to make a reliable flashlight than a reliable jet transport aircraft for carrying 400 passengers from Boston to Rome nonstop. Hence, the quality of the components used in a flashlight need not compare with those in a jet transport aircraft.

Limited to smaller instruments, microsatellites collect less data. And free to use the most modern, energy efficient, highest performance components, they have disproportional data processing horsepower which can be used to compress data. Thus the amount of information they need to downlink is vastly lower than major systems. Coupled with their typically low orbit altitudes, their transmit power levels can be very low, and yet directional antennas are rarely used. Smaller observing apertures imply lower spacial resolution, so tight pointing requirements are rarely necessary, simplifying the ACS. Power systems producing a few Watts for a year resemble, very little; a 10 kW power system built to last 20 years in an intense radiation environment with a 99.9% end-of-life reliability.

The designer more accustomed to larger spacecraft has to learn that power losses previously considered insignificant must now be considered carefully. Power management is much more critical with a 2 to 20 W system power budget than at 20 kW.

The use of terrestrial components is often mentioned in connection with small satellites. This is true because of the more benign radiation environments of low orbits, their shorter lifetimes and the reduced parts count which allows use of potentially less reliable components to attain a given level of systems reliability. However, the use of terrestrial components carries with it other potential complications. A part which has proven reliable on Earth, but which requires modifications to operate on orbit, can be compromised. Each terrestrial part must be analyzed for its suitability in space, considering among other factors outgassing, zero gravity, thermal excursions, radiation tolerance, fault tolerance and correction, mounting for higher g-loads, magnetic properties, and autonomy. Typically, selected terrestrial components will be tested to ensure their compatibility with the space environment, to the extent possible on a small mission budget. Ultimately, the use of terrestrial components is made on a case by case basis trading off the performance, cost, and schedule advantages they offer with the resources required for their qualification.

The design process in any complex system is highly iterative, but a typical starting point for a small spacecraft is the payload power requirement since, in general, the spacecraft will scale with the power required. It is critical to work with payload suppliers to scrutinize the uses of power and minimize them, through more efficient design and through limiting instrument duty cycle. And it is critical to maximize power production, choosing orbits and attitudes well suited to production of solar energy.

Once a power budget is defined, the spacecraft size can be estimated based on surface area requirements and solar panel efficiency. Battery volume and mass will derive directly from the power requirement in umbra. Using these anchor points the designer can proceed to a trial mass budget based usually on assumption of an aluminum structure, the mass of the electric power system, and specifications of the payload and other components which might be available from vendors (e.g., radios, attitude control sensors). Often, the small satellite launch accommodation is a fixed mass and volume, and there is no savings derived from minimizing scale below the size of the accommodation. Thus, some inefficiency in structural or component mass may be appropriate to minimize cost, development time, and risk and complexity.

Table 25-2◀, Fig. 25-13◀, Eq. 25-5◀

25.3.5 Small Satellite Project Management

Every on-board system, and the methods for their design and development are affected by scale; the team that designs and develops a small satellite is also different. It is smaller, 6, 10, or 15 people, versus the often thousands of people who must somehow be managed in contributing to a major program. It is the size of the team more than any other parameter which determines that the product can be managed as a microspace project. An organization of 15 or fewer people creating a system in 2 years or less is fundamentally different than a large program:

- Every person in the program communicates with every other team member. Optimizations, in use of on-board resources (power, mass, volume, viewing angle, computing power, downlink bandwidth), and in use of personnel, are global instead of limited to a subsystem development team which works to a set of interfaces fixed during the systems engineering and planning process

- Changes are made dynamically since every person on the team can assess the impact of a change on the subsystems within their responsibility, contrasted with a large program in which requirements must be respected at almost any cost, because it is too difficult to communicate potential changes to each program subelement, and too time consuming for them to continuously assess change impacts. Moreover, most if not all the team members in a small program understand the product at the system level and can understand the impacts of changes on the overall system viability and performance

- This ability to manage changes is at the heart of the ability to use non-standard parts. Each team member participates in the process of ensuring that a novel component will meet their particular requirements. As with changes, inquiring each member of a team of hundreds or thousands, even if each one did understand the overall system, would be impossible, especially given the much larger number of such requests which would arise if the program did not adhere to a standardized parts criterion set and list

- Documentation is reduced to only that which is produced in the process of engineering. Most of the information on how the system is designed and integrated is shared among the team members, rather than codified in writing and diagrams. In fact, despite the documentation created in larger systems, reliability and manufacturability still hinges critically on staff communications and continuity. But in a team of a dozen people engaged for less than 2 years, the turnover in personnel is zero or very small compared with a team of hundreds or thousands engaged for one to two decades

- The web-like architecture of a small team is protected from loss of information associated with the loss of one of its members because each person participates in the work of several others. Job descriptions are broad and dynamic. An analogy is a basketball team which despite having particular roles described for each player, can dynamically reorganize as the players and the ball move around the court to respond to the immediate state of play

- Rather than relying on formal reviews, the first line of error checking is enabled by the sharing of responsibilities. The lead communications engineer works closely with another team member who might be the lead on the power or information management system. This second person is in the best position to review the detailed design of the communications lead and discover errors or weak points. They're also ideally positioned to maintain the information on that systems design, philosophy, and implementation logic in the case of the loss of the lead. In that sense, every position has a backup who can step in, also in case the workload in a related area becomes excessive

Instead of formal reviews, which greatly increase the workload on the small team and may thus force exceeding the team size managable as a small project. Technical interchange meetings specific to subsystems, and at the systems level without delving into subsystems details, are held around a conference table with a few (2 or 3) outside reviewers and only those team members directly concerned using actual design documents, drawings, spreadsheets, simulations and calculations. Management should encourage these and rigorously maintain lists of action items which arise from them, as well as from working experience during the system development.

The dynamic, small group is a true team in the sense of basketball, football, soccer, or formula-1 racing, every person directly in communication with all the others and prepared to take on whatever roll the demands of the day require. This contrasts strongly with the more rigid structure required of large organizations, airlines, armies, and universities, for example, which are made of largely independent factions each focused on a part of the bigger mission of the organization.

Thus, it is key to the successful management of a microspace program to limit the scope and complexity of the project. Several notable failures, either on orbit or program cancellation due to apparent financial overruns, which in fact result when the small team becomes overwhelmed, are the result of trying to do a big job with 15 or fewer people.

In a world of finite resources, which is the world in which spacecraft are developed, money spent for one purpose is unavailable for all other purposes. The key to reliability is a diverse team including seasoned and fresh perspectives, tightly engaged in the project's detailed development, under experienced management supervision.

As money gets diverted for clean rooms, for special parts, for formal and largely useless reviews, the team is put under pressure—to do more for less.

A much larger useless consumer of resources is being conservative, which is anything but. Specification of a longer operating lifetime conserves nothing, but spends time in the impossible pursuit of proof that a system will endure. Lacking that proof, we are forced to create redundant architectures, reasoning (lacking proof or even analytical indication) that they ought to last longer than single string. But given their added cost and complexity, their more than doubled parts count, the probability of a design or operations error, the probability of a component failure, since there are more of them, while at the same time increasing the spacecraft cost and mass, which increases launch cost, resulting in a larger loss in case of the possibly greater likelihood of failure, the probability of loss can be greatly increased thanks to redundancy, and when the failure occurs, the amount of the loss will be greater. Which explains why redundancy is largely absent in highly reliable consumer products and even with only a few exceptions, in our automobiles, which are highly reliable, reasonably priced, and capable of doing great harm to us in case of a failure.

Specification of higher electrical power, to ensure adequate supply at end of life, higher radiation tolerance, wider thermal operating range, more g-force ruggedness —do these make systems more reliable? The opposite. They consume precious resources to create capabilities which are never used. They add cost, complexity, bureaucracy, documentation, and lead time. They decrease the choices available to the designer. They make solar panels unnecessarily large. If a deployable array becomes necessary to create additional power, and it fails to open or is too flexible to allow the attitude control system to function properly, the excess of power that would theoretically have been available at the end of a mission whose lifetime was spec'ed way beyond the actual desires of its clients' attention span, can hardly be considered a wise investment.

Not only the members of the technical team have to have the flexibility to assume various roles. Management must also be active in systems engineering beginning in requirements definition to contain complexity against the natural pressures, to add features, to get more return on the project investment, even to add "reliability" through increased complexity, which in fact lowers reliability by taxing already scarce resources. Every requirement needs to be scrutinized and minimized. If the program is not comfortably achieved by 10 or 12 people, and thus expanded to a team of about 15 including some margin for surges in workload, then the program is at best a hybrid with more conventional space programs and must be managed more formally, which will immediately double the team size and require different systems and management architectures, more documentation, more bureacracy, more meetings, and a lot more money and time. If pressed to stuff what is not a small program into a small program package—of limited time, money and team size with too much complexity to easily handle in a team of a dozen people, I advise: a) attempting to renegotiate requirements and restructure the program and the spacecraft so that they two are in harmony and failing that and b) resigning management of the program. Beware avarice and greed. I have never regretted a tough negotiation to create a project do-able by the small team, but I will always regret the attempts to go along to get along resulting in at best a burned out team and at worst a failed mission. No money is saved doing a failed mission at a bargain price.

The facilities used by the team should also be considered in the program's management. Small satellites are generally not built in cleanrooms because of the additional work and time imposed on the team for maintenance of a clean environment. But also because the components, design and manufacturing methods used in a small satellite should be robust. Trimming structural mass to an absolute minimum costs a lot of time and money, results in a fragile structure more costly to test, more likely to fail in test, which will create large temperature gradients among spacecraft elements in orbit, one much more difficult to protect over the development lifetime, and in any case is probably not helpful for a satellite of very small mass. Saving 400 kg in a 2000 kg spacecraft is, if possible significant. Saving 400 g in a 2 kg spacecraft, if it were even possible, probably offers no substantive advantage. The cost to launch those 400 g is not measurable. For all these reasons the small spacecraft is built to work in an industrial or academic laboratory benchtop environment, and its systems should function at 1 atmosphere and 1 g so that they can be tested with a minimum of special facilities.

Carry this concept forward. The attitude control system should be testable easily. The ground station should be developed alongside the spacecraft so the two can talk to each other, both to speed development avoiding last minute disconnects the first time the spacecraft "sees" the real ground station previously having been only subjected to a simulation, and because when launched there will already be many hours of experience in controlling the spacecraft through that link, greatly enhancing reliability. The power system should function in Earth Sun when the spacecraft is rolled out on a cart into a parking lot. These sorts of practices blur the line between development and test so that before even entering into formal integration and test, the team is confident in the functionality of the system.

Test

Rather than relying on detailed analysis, the small program emphasis is on testing and it is imperative on management to promptly execute the analysis, design, development, and integration phases to conserve time, personnel, and financial resources for testing. Most subsystems are only tested at the benchtop level, not in thermal vacuum chambers and other special facilities, because the entire microspacecraft is smaller and less complex than the typical conventional spacecraft subsystem. Thus the manager accepts the risk that a particular subsystem might fail in systems test despite being bench-top tested, in exchange for the savings in time and money realized by moving to test sooner. The cost of a subsystems failure in systems test is in any case not great, as de-integration of a small, simple spacecraft to unearth a failed component is not so difficult.

A famous scientist once said that an expert is a person who has made every possible error in a particular field. Similarly a reliable system is one which has already failed in every way it is capable of. Small satellite teams are less bureaucratic and should be less afraid to bring to light and discuss errors, rather than attempting to push them down the line. Not to mention that there is no line for them to be pushed down. The team stays with their spacecraft from concept through launch.

Thus the natural objective of the project team—in development, in integration, and test, is to find and figure out failures. Reliability is the result of having used the system so much in so many situations that we have found and fixed every possible way it could fail and then to have used each failure to improve reliability. It is ironic that the ISO series of quality standards has become too complex and bureaucratic for certification of very small teams and organizations, yet the core of the ISO philosophy, to bring failures to light, learn from them, and continuously improve the product as a result, is epitomized by these small teams and their smaller, less complex products.

Small missions are short duration and, in fact, all but a few operational satellites long outlive their usefulness on orbit. Reliability 10 years after launch has very little value compared with the working on day one and for the first few weeks or maybe months. Hence, risk wearing it out. The canonical philosophical argument is whether, after 6, 12, or 18 months of integration and test operations, to replace the old rechargeable batteries with new ones. The answer is simple NO! The probability that batteries that have been working fine for a year will fail in the near term is small. New batteries are unknown and their only advantage is the possibility of adding a year at the end of the mission life, maybe. Versus the real risks of the disconnecting and reconnecting, disassembling and reassembling, and the gremlins they can release, problems which might be introduced. Plus, there is the possibility of damage, an emergency order for a replacement part that may or may not arrive and be as reliable, too late for adequate testing (and probably no money left either). And sometimes damage is not realized—electrostatic discharge, a momentary short circuit that weakens a component. Who knows if these new batteries are really better—at least the old ones have proven reliable, they have heritage.

Nothing works the first time, and often not the second, so we have to find those early failures. The result is the 1,000 hour test in which the spacecraft must operate for 1,000 hours in complete autonomy, with no tweeks by anybody. After all, we are expecting it to operate in space for tens of thousands of hours. A 1000 hour test takes time, especially since most spacecraft fail the first, second, even third attempt. Which tells us that the test is doing its job and worth the time which it necessarily requires.

Thermal vacuum and vibration testing is widely misunderstood as a simulation of the space environment. This is only partially possible on Earth, expensive and unnecessary. Simulation of the space environment is done in computer models, and the role of testing is to verify the fidelity of those models. Certainly the tests are designed to approximate the types and levels of stress the system will see in space, and it must demonstrate in test that the system continues to function or in the case of launch loads will function after. But the key is to test that our models of how it works, models of structural rigidity, of thermal behavior, of battery charge / discharge, are accurate over the full range of flight environments. Those include not just temperature and vacuum and vibration, but also the environment of having to survive and perform functions even when not in contact with the ground and to not require reset so often that no productive work gets done.

The system should never be asked to do what it was not designed to do. Exceeding a temperature limit in test is to willfully weaken the product. That too is not conservative. Neither is discharging the batteries to zero more than maybe once to ensure the power system can recover from that peculiar state. Do not do things because they feel good—do things because they are rationally designed to ensure operation on orbit, meaning to uncover problems that might arise in the operational space environment. Which also includes being operated by people other than those who built the spacecraft, a very common cause of failure usually not considered in the test plan.

The Role of Analysis

Just as it is the role of test to verify analysis, it is the role of analysis only to support functionality. It is relatively easy to wage a war against reviews, overspecification and paperwork because the development crews don't like them. But who fights against over-analysis. The client is used to seeing a 4,000 node thermal model, and sitting in front of a computer playing with fancy software that builds models beats working even on a good day. We all want to change the world while plugged into an iPod while staring at a 27" hi-res monitor. You are in fact changing the world—for the worse. Because once again, resources are being spent without contributing to mission success, hence they are decreasing that probability.

Small satellites are called that because they are, dimensionally, small, and coupled with their usually heavy construction, normally of aluminum, they don't support a thermal gradient. They are a short circuit. And in LEO, they alternate rapidly between sunlight and umbra, which tends to minimize temperature excursions. They do not have enough battery power to heat themselves up much. And yet, we are complicit with those who would bureaucratize these programs to death in creating complex models of their thermal, and also mechanical behavior.

There is no substitute for the thinking process. Create a small spreadsheet to look at the gross fluxes in and out of heat. Scan the design for specific components that might be stressed. You would probably miss them in the 4,000 node model anyway. Getting an intuitive feel for the thermal behavior is an absolute must starting point. If that behavior is confirmed in test, that job is finished—leaving room for in depth study and design of any critical points, of which there are likely none. And small thermal problems are usually eradicated with a little extra aluminum and thermally conductive RTV at the site. Don't fix what ain't broke.

Before moving on to mission examples, two last cautions.

1. **Beware efficiency.** Nothing consumers buy is selected for efficiency, whatever the ads and consumer reports say. All cars are highly inefficient compared with buses and trains, not to mention walking and bicycling. But we use them to the exclusion of all other transportation modes. Single family houses with the best heat pumps and insulation are much less efficient than multi-family dwellings. The most eco-friendly farmer in Vermont is sucking down much more energy than the average New Yorker. So whither goeth efficiency?

   It is sacrificed to utility. Nobody will reward you for maximizing the number of bits for each dollar paid for a mission. The user wants a certain capability in space, or scientific result, for a certain amount of money. Leave maximum bits per dollar or minimum dollars per pound to big missions with economies of scale. And that means? Don't add capability because you can, because the electric power appears to be available and there's mass margin. That is the siren of efficiency beckoning you onto the shoals. You might need those margins, you might need the money spent on them later if something goes wrong. New features are always more trouble than we thought they would be. That is Murphy's Law. *Alles nicht so einfach*: It's never quite so simple as it seems. Sometimes the best thing you can do for mission success is to turn off the lights, lock the door, go home and say "it's enough." That is a valid and necessary and difficult management function—to take responsibility to not do more and instead conserve resources for another day.

2. **There are no cost-optimized missions**
   Space missions are mostly not done for the sake of their mission objectives. The list of agendas imposed on the mission is, while individual to each mission, at the same time shared by all space activity. They include:

   - Spreading work through multiple political districts to garner wide support
   - International cooperation which protects missions from national whimsy
   - Education and the infection of the next generation with a zest for space
   - The use of, or development of new technologies, some of which must be shown to spin off to terrestrial application
   - Completion on a timeline compatible with re-election of government supporters
   - Making money: on the part of agencies, contractors, universities, service providers
   - Television: something about the mission must play to the media. Otherwise it is perceived as a very expensive tree felled in a distant forest
   - National security and technological superiority—or the projection of that possibility
   - "Made in"—use of domestic suppliers despite cost and performance inferiority
   - Use of a particular launch vehicle, suitable or not
   - Compliance with myriad federal regulations for safety, contracting, and program execution including purchasing
   - The career aspirations of the program's leadership
   - Documentation and other costs associating with removing blame for any failure from the project's management or sponsors

Rarely are any of these multiple optimizations mentioned when the call goes out for a minimum cost mission. Cost suppression is naturally assumed to be the goal of all human activity at least in the US, the birthplace of Walmart, Swag and Free Downloads. But all those other agendas are always present and consume a much larger proportion of the budget of a small mission than a large one. If you build the program team and plan for minimum cost, you will find yourself helplessly understaffed, behind schedule and over budget trying to also accommodate the *sub rosa* requirements which are the true motivations for your mission.

25.3.6 SmallSat Mission Examples

There are patterns repeated in all microspace missions:

- A small number of payloads. These are not omnibus missions—they at root are single purpose machines built to do one thing well, simplifying their design, their requirements for thermal control, for pointing, and power. Every system benefits from not having to support a large number of payload elements and operational modes

- A small development team. Only possible if the mission scope is limited, a group whose members can all meet conveniently and often without consuming much of their workday, and can easily share the full spectrum of responsibilities to balance workload among everyone is critical. Self management is only possible for teams up to 12, maximum 20 people, above which size some form of stratification has to be instituted, which blocks the free flow of information and the ability of individuals to help where help is needed. The group members of a small team may be specialists but they are also generalists. Ideally, device builders also write their own software, and are as comfortable soldering as analyzing circuit stability or thermal profiles
- Short development time: to stretch over a decade or more requires detailed documentation, the ability to hand the project off through a series of generations of staffing and departments, multiple adjustments, and additions to the mission and technical requirements, all of which are counter to achievement of low cost. Just keeping a program management function in place for a few thousand days can cost more than an entire small spacecraft program
- Low cost launch: A launch that costs \$20M to \$50M is not compatible with a spacecraft developed for 1% of that amount. Logic dictates expanding the investment in the spacecraft. Even if 10× or 100× the amount is ultimately spent on the payload, the mission cost including ground segment and launch less than doubles, while the perceived utility and reliability are increased (by some metric) much more
- Low cost operations: The expression "low cost satellite" says it all—we focus on the cost of the item to be placed in orbit, often to the exclusion of considering operational costs. The two major ones being launch ops and on-orbit ops. Sending 15 people to Kourou or Kwajalein for a planned two weeks which grows, possibly because of problems with the weather, your or another payload, the rocket or other contingencies affecting the launch site, to two months, can cost more than the spacecraft. If it needs to be repacked, shipped home, re-assembled, stored, retested, reshipped, re-re-assembled and another campaign of several weeks accomplished, the development cost can be lost in the noise, not to mention the many decisions agonized over to save a few dollars early on. The design should allow one person to handle launch ops, then you can send two, maximum, to have a backup

More expensive still can be on-orbit costs. The first month everyone will want to be in on every contact, every meeting, every decision that might affect mission success. There is no alternative, so you can assume virtually the full crew on the payroll, and if the ground station is remote, all their travel, for that month. But then if you are unlucky, the damned thing will run on orbit year after year after year, sending back all sorts of data, beloved by a constituency you can't afford to say no to. A couple of employees staffing a ground station, plus the station's care and feeding for a few years is comparable in cost to the development program. Can't say no? Maybe, but if the spacecraft is designed like modern consumer devices (iPhone) the customer can and should operate it. The money is spent, but if it's someone else's money you don't care. Your experts are on call if there are problems. But design the software to be idiot proof, so that the clients don't break it. Cuisinarts, chain saws, automobiles, hairdryers—are all potentially lethal. Their manufacturers make sure the users and the appliance both survive their interactions. Your design should do no less.

Spacecraft are with few exceptions custom built for particular missions and each one follows its own path from concept to design to development and test to launch and operation. But looking at one or two individual cases in detail one can see how many of the ideas about small missions translate into real programs. This is done in the associated web article.

25.3.7 The Future

How can we extrapolate to the future a five decade history of special cases? One way is to expect a continuing series of special cases, small experiments, niche missions, which do not fit the classical space model of 10+ year time scale development cycles, proven and stabile technologies, great complexity, and high performance coupled with astronomical pricing. In fact, as the pace of technology and science accelerates, many questions cannot wait decades for answers. Responses to new threats have to be addressed this year, not in 20 years.

Another is to look at technological progress. Today's satellite of a few kilograms can accomplish that which required several hundred kilograms a decade or two ago. Thus we can look at missions now done by medium sized spacecraft with high resolution remote sensing, for example.

But many missions, particularly remote sensing, require large apertures, and it may be in that single area that many future missions will be determined. At this writing, the idea of creating a synthetic small aperture from a constellation or cloud of small satellites is much discussed but not yet realized. The obstacles are largely in the realm of communications and information—the exact position and orientation of each of the micro or nanosatellites constituting the network. And with the explosive progress in information processing and communications characteristic of today's terrestrial networks, it seems a safe prediction that these issues will be resolved for these orbital networks. Using a large number of small, low cost satellites will provide numerous advantages for remote sensing missions, optical, radar, and lidar. Arrays can be large along and across orbit track, providing high resolution and wide field of view.

Design Guidelines for Small Spacecraft

Power scales everything. **Do** minimize it:

- After 6 months is full power needed all the time
- Scrutinize all circuits for bleed resistors, voltage dividers, other
- Designs that don't matter on the ground but waste power
- Does everything need to be left on all the time for "stability"
  - A thermostated heater might save many electrons
- Chose an orbit and attitude that makes power production efficient
- High efficiency (GaAs) solar panels are almost always worth their cost
- **Do not** test to simulate space and launch. Test to test your models that predict behavior in space and launch
- **Do** pass a 1,000 hour operational test with no cheating (helping the spacecraft keep working)
- **Do not** waste money on proving long lifetime and other intangibles. Spend it on test and on adequate staffing and facilities—tangibles which absolutely add to mission success probability
- **Do** test all deployables in Earth atmosphere and gravity on the bench top
- **Do not** take every box through thermal vac and vibe. Test them on benchtop, integrate, and take the whole spacecraft through formal test
- **Do** test the spacecraft rolled out in the parking lot on a sunny day, radios, solar panels, everything
- Assume clean rooms **do not** exist and go from there. Use them at the end of the mission for PR photos and to keep people from touching (breaking) your satellite
- **Do** create and use the FIST: Fully Integrated System Test should be formalized so that on every rebuild you can assure that the spacecraft is still what it used to be
- **Do not** switch out anything late in the program —particularly to have "fresh" batteries
- **Do** only those tests necessary to prove it is what you designed and works right
- **Do not** test beyond reasonably expected environmental conditions or exposure durations
- **Do** use advanced technologies if you can be reasonably confident they will work in your application and environment when they simplify your design. Complexity is more dangerous than a well thought out application of a terrestrial part
- **Do not** assume that a modified terrestrial part will have the reliability of the unmodified part in terrestrial use for which it was designed. Once you change it, it's a new part
- **Do** overstaff. You always need more people than you thought, and it is impossible to train new staff when you are up to your ears in alligators, and in a small program one or two extra people can be the difference
- **Do not** assume that your job is done with successful turn on on-orbit. If the customer then breaks it, it's still your fault. Stay with the operations team forever, or almost forever
- **Do** build LEDs into the spacecraft to show you immediately what is on and what is off. Avoid running down your batteries to 0 charge not realizing the spacecraft was on. Leave them there forever
- **Do not** accept any "free" features, extra capabilities, payloads. if it's not in the contract, it's not on the spacecraft
- **Do** use your own GS to avoid interfacing with huge bureaucracies that operate huge ground stations with huge gain that you hugely want. Temptation leads to ruination. With your own GS you are able to operate and test the satellite every day of its development life in its real environment with its real ground station
- **Do not** create documentation for meetings, and do not waste time preparing for and traveling to and from meetings
- **Do** instead save all communications, design and other documentation developed in the course of engineering. Plus use photography and videos to document the as built item and how it goes together and comes apart

Field Guide to Small Spacecraft

To seem a good steward of someone else's money, to appear modern, to hope to be able to actually keep track of what's going on in a program, to avoid dealing with the real complexity some missions entail, the labels Small, Low Cost, and Micro are attached to many spacecraft programs. No real spacecraft program is without compromise but here are some features characteristic of small missions:

- One simple, well defined mission, not everything to everybody
- Cost limits are serious enough that the program manager can redefine requirements and mission goals to stay within them
- System designers interact with and negotiate with mission clients in definition of all requirements and the way in which the mission might be realized
- Resulting in a program reasonably accomplished by 12 people in 24 months
- 12 people all of whom communicate and share work without restriction
- Availability of a launch accommodation of cost similar to that of the spacecraft
- Risk is related mostly to design and fabrication errors, not parts failures
- The only required documentation is that produced in the engineering and test process, plus an interface requirements document
- Reviews are small, focused exchanges of technical information among specialists and one or two systems engineers and managers
- A mission failure will not result in: 1) a phone call from the President of your country; 2) anyone losing their job or being unpromotable for the remainder of their career
- No magic: no technologies or devices that are only hoped to exist or function are critical to the development program nor to the mission's success

The networks are highly robust to failure since the loss of any one or even a few members would cost a small percentage of system performance. This also makes them much less vulnerable to attack. The systems can be easily upgraded by launch of more members, or by launch of members with different capabilities—other sensors or more capability in downlinking, for example.

It is risky to predict based on a notion that the things we do in space will remain constant, just the boxes will shrink. After all, the Big Three space applications is now the Big Six or Seven. This was an error in thinking of the computer industry, which was able to transition from mainframe to minimainframe, but did not understand the importance of the internet, gaming and other forms of digital entertainment, social networking, and particularly communications and virtual presence, which is now available in bits and pieces with Skype and Google's Street View, which will likely expand to viewing and real time presence being integrated into a more powerful form of virtual presence.

The old computing applications are still important—complex calculations for science and engineering, spreadsheets, word processing, and page layout (the latter 3 completely unknown in the 1970s). But the newest and smallest platforms, like the iPad, lack even a keyboard because most of the newer applications are so completely different.

What might be these new applications to which micro and nanospace are ideally suited, as an iPad is suited to video presence, music, and image sharing?

One that is already well established is responsive space—the ability to launch relatively simple space capability on demand. More rapid changes on the ground demand more responsive space systems, and given the development time for major programs, responsiveness will be addressed by small systems and missions. Another is robotic presence. Conventional space was scaled for human spaceflight—the Saturn V and the Shuttle. But much of the science of today and tomorrow is beyond the reach, financially, physiologically, and physically, of humans—landing on the moons of other planets, for instance. The robots which will do it can be as small as technology permits, and their size and mass will continue to shrink. The future of space science may increasingly be in very small, albeit costly and complex, space missions which have little resemblance to the mainframes of yesterday and today.

Looking at one other unexpected development in the computing world, from which space draws so many technologies, in communications, in information processing, but also in for example power management as computing becomes increasingly personal and portable and drives development of new batteries, for example, smaller, less complex satellites put space in the hands of the non-experts who do not "know" how space is used. It was these non-experts who created video games, an industry larger than the film industry.

Non-experts write and read digital books, create and watch Youtube videos. Similarly, there is reason to believe that the next space killer app will be one thought of by students working on a CubeSat who see it not as a space platform but as an entertainment or advertising platform, as a way to do zero gravity manufacturing or agriculture. The non space community is about 100,000 times larger than the space community, and if space is accessible to it, 100,000 times more likely to invent an application we too accustomed to what we think we know that space can do for us can imagine.

We space experts like to say that space is that ultimate frontier, but the integration of the rest of humanity into the space community, possible through small, low cost, simple space systems, may be the route into that new frontier. Our job may be not to find the future of space, but to make it possible for the rest of Earth's people to do that job for us.

25.4 CubeSats

Robert Twiggs and Benjamin Malphrus,
Morehead State University

The CubeSat was developed to allow people with little or no experience in the design of space missions to start with an open mind to incorporate new ideas and concepts into designs and missions that have no historical restrictions. CubeSat programs are often university student projects—the challenge therefore, is to find ways to accomplish the mission at the lowest cost. Trying these new ideas and concepts inherently includes a risk of mission failure. Failure here is an acceptable option because without trying new things, ideas, processes, and techniques, and without pushing the boundaries, new innovations would not occur. The excitement and challenge of having an opportunity for the new students to do "real" things in space exploration is a motivational experience that cannot be achieved by lectures in the classroom and represents education at its best.

25.4.1 History of CubeSats

I (Twiggs) developed the concept of the CubeSat at the Department of Aeronautics and Astronautics at Stanford University in collaboration with Jordi Puig-Suari at the Aerospace Department in California State Polytechnic University in late 1999. The CubeSat concept originated with the spacecraft OPAL (Orbiting Picosat Automated Launcher), a 23 kg microsatellite developed by students at Stanford University and The Aerospace Corporation in El Segundo, CA to demonstrate the validity and functionality of picosatellites and the concept of launching picosatellites and other small satellites on-orbit from a larger satellite system. As defined in Sec. 2.1.8, picosatellites have a weight between 0.1 kg and 1.0 kg. OPAL is shown in Fig. 25-14, with four launcher tubes for deploying picosatellites. One of the picosatellites is shown being inserted into the launcher tube in Fig. 25-15.

Fig. 25-14. OPAL & SAPHIRE Microsatellites. (Courtesy of Stanford University)

Fig. 25-15. Picosatellite Loaded into OPAL. (Courtesy of Stanford University)

The satellites developed by students within university programs during the 1980s and 1990s were all nanosatellites (1 kg–10 kg size) and microsatellites (10 kg–50 kg size). The feasibility of independently funding launch opportunities for these nanosatellites and microsatellites was limited as the costs typically were in the $250,000 range—a price point well beyond the resources available to most university programs. At that time, the only available option was to collaborate with government organizations that would provide the launch. The OPAL satellite was launched in early 2000 by the US Air Force Space Test Program (STP) with sponsorship from the Defense Advanced Research Projects Agency (DARPA) for The Aerospace Corporation picosatellites.

The OPAL mission represented a significant milestone achievement in the evolution of small satellites by accomplishing two milestones: 1) providing proof of viability of the concept of the picosatellite and 2) initiating the introduction and development of an innovative orbital deployment system. The picosatellite launcher concept used for the OPAL mission, in particular, represented a major advancement that would enable the technological evolution of small satellites—setting the stage for the development of the CubeSat form factor and the P-POD orbital deployer system. OPAL demonstrated a new capability with the design of an orbital deployer that could launch numerous very small satellites contained within the launcher tube, simplifying the mechanical interface to the upper stage of the launch vehicle and greatly simplifying the satellite ejection system. While the OPAL mission was extremely successful and established the validity of a picosatellite orbital deployer, we sought to find a lower cost means of launching student-built satellites. The stage was set for the development of the CubeSat form factor and its evolution toward an engineering standard.

CubeSat Engineering Design Standard

The primary intent of the development of the CubeSat was to provide a standard set of dimensions for the picosatellite's external physical structure. The goal was to make it compatible with a standardized orbital deployer, which then could be adapted to interface with a wide

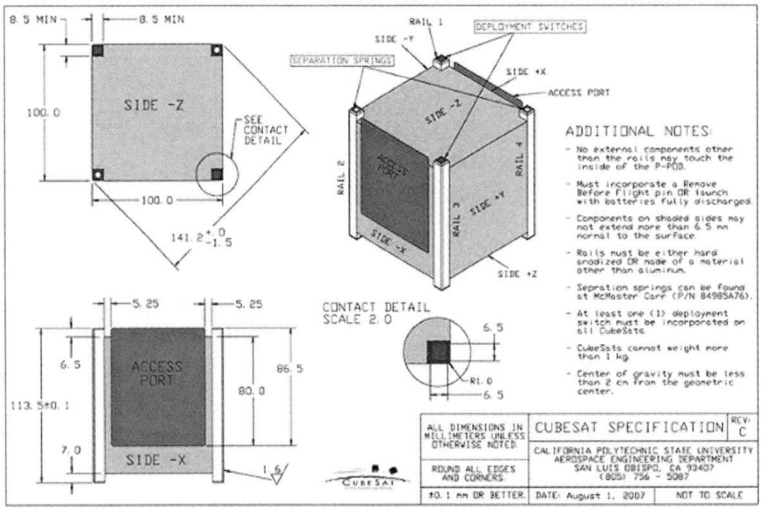

Fig. 25-16. Standard for CubeSat Mechanical Structure. (Courtesy of Cal Poly, SLO)

variety of launch vehicles. Unlike the development of most modern engineering standards, we (Twiggs and Puig-Suari) did not consult with other universities or with the commercial satellite industry to establish this standard because most other university satellite programs and commercial ventures were concentrating on larger satellites rather than smaller ones. There were discussions in the late 1990s within the AMSAT community in the United Kingdom centered on building a small amateur satellite but there were never any attempts to develop a standardized design.

The concept of a design standard for a picosatellite and associated launcher would lead to a large number of picosatellites being launched on a single launch vehicle. We envisioned launch vehicles accommodating several launcher tubes, each containing a few picosatellites. This feature, combined with the system's adaptability to essentially any launch vehicle, would greatly increase the opportunities for flights of university picosatellites.

The final concept of the CubeSat structural standard we developed and currently adopted by the small satellite community is shown in Fig. 25-16. They believed that if one organization could provide the integration of the launcher with the launch vehicle through a carefully orchestrated interface process with the launch services provider, then it seemed possible to acquire launch opportunities for university programs that would be affordable (less than $50,000 per 1 kg satellite).

The physical standard that resulted is based on a 10 × 10 × 10 cm cube that has a volume of exactly one liter and has a mass of 1.33 kg or less [Munakata et al., 2009]. Initially, a standard of 1 kg was defined by Twiggs, et al., but NASA and Cal Poly have recently adopted a standard of 1.33 kg. The standard 10 × 10 × 10 cm CubeSat is referred to as a one unit "1U" CubeSat and is scalable in 1U increments. The current widely used orbital deployer can accommodate up to a 3U CubeSat, allowing satellite developers the flexibility of producing 1U, 2U, or 3U CubeSats. 2U and 3U CubeSats are required to have the same mass and approximate centers of gravity, (CG) that is 2.66 kg and CG in the center of the structure for a 2U and 3.99 kg and CG in the center of the structure for a 3U system. This standardization requirement facilitates the use of a single orbital deployer design for a variety of combinations of 1–3U Cubes. This scalability permits inherent flexibility for developers to incorporate a wide variety of payloads and has led to tremendous appeal of the form factor to both university and commercial projects. The commonly used 1U, 2U, and 3U systems are illustrated in Fig. 25-17.

Standardized Orbital Deployer—the P-POD

The standardization of the CubeSat design facilitates a wide array of designs to be launched and deployed using a common deployment system. The most widely

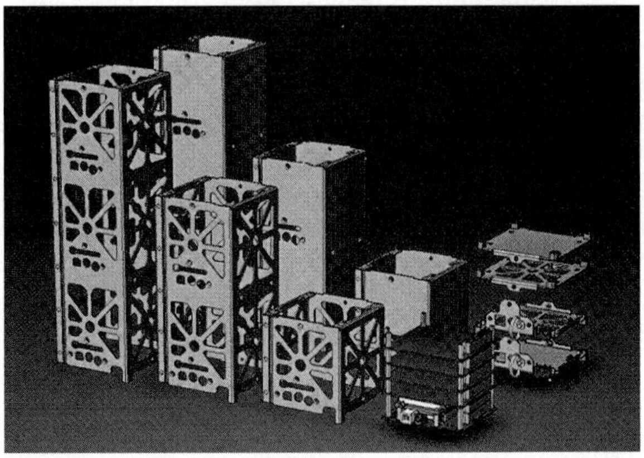

Fig. 25-17. Typical 3U, 2U, and 1U CubeSat Structures, Respectively. The drawing on the far right illustrates a typical stacked configuration for the subsystem boards. (Courtesy of Pumpkin, Inc.)

used deployment system is the Poly-Picosatellite Orbital Deployer (P-POD). The Cal Poly P-POD system shown in Fig. 25-18 has been used to deploy over 90% of all CubeSats launched to date, and 100% of all CubeSats launched since 2007. The P-POD is a tubular, spring-loaded mechanism easily integrated into any launch vehicle. P-PODs are integrated into the upper stage of a launch vehicle and transport the CubeSats into orbit, deploying them after a signal is received from the launch vehicle. The P-POD is capable of carrying three standard CubeSats. It is made of anodized aluminum and has a mass of roughly 3 kg. Currently, there are two designs for the P-Pod—the Mk III single tube that holds three CubeSats, and a double tube that holds six CubeSats. Both have a square tube design that produces a reliable linear path resulting in a low satellite spin rate. The P-POD is a robust design that has significant flight heritage and is currently the deployer of choice of US launch service providers.

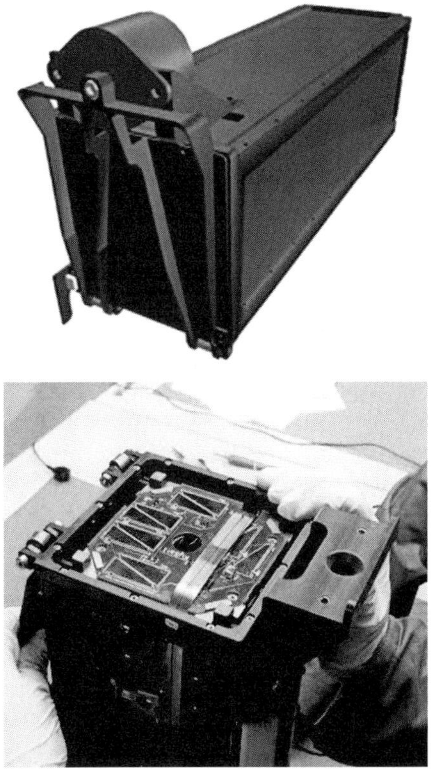

Fig. 25-18. P-POD Top (Courtesy of Cal Poly–SLO) **and CubeSat Installed in P-POD on Bottom.** (Courtesy of Kentucky Space)

Alternative deployers/separation systems to the P-POD have also been developed—notably the X-POD, the T-POD, and the SPL. The X-POD (eXperimental Push Out Deployer) is a CubeSat deployer designed and built at the University of Toronto Institute for Aerospace Studies/ Space Flight Laboratory in Toronto, Canada. It was designed to be custom built for each satellite and may be tailored to satellites of different sizes ranging from a single CubeSat to larger nanosatellites. The X-POD version has an independent release mechanism for the spring deployer that also provides automatic feedback to indicate deployment has taken place. The T-POD (Tokyo Pico-satellite Orbital Deployer) developed by Tokyo Institute of Technology, Japan, was originally designed to deploy a single 1U CubeSat and was first used successfully in 2003. A 2U configuration of the T-POD was developed and used in 2006 by the same group. The SPL (Single Pico-Satellite Launcher) manufactured by Astrofein (Germany) is designed to deploy a single 1U CubeSat. The SPL's innovation will allow the separation velocity to be defined by the customer (1 m/s is the default velocity). The alternative CubeSat deployers each have innovations that appeal to specific CubeSat developers although the P-POD continues to be orbital deployer of preference.

25.4.2 The CubeSat Philosophy from a University Student Perspective

The CubeSat philosophy was to develop a design for a small satellite that could be built by students in a short 1–2 year period of time and launched at a low cost. For a university-level engineering program, the total cost of the project needed to be less than $100,000. The missions would be based on one of two concepts of operation: testing or providing flight heritage for new technologies, or supporting one or two scientific instruments as their primary mission payload. With these goals in mind, a CubeSat design can:

- Have minimal development costs by keeping the satellite small
  - Fewer solar cells – (high-efficiency, flight qualified cells are costly)
  - Limited number and types of payloads
  - Designed and completed in less time
  - Requires smaller and less expensive test facilities
  - Easier to transport than larger satellites
- Reduce launch costs
  - Less launch capacity required (lighter is cheaper)
  - Integrator acts as an intermediary with the launch provider and purchases launch capacity in quantity
- Protect the primary payload
  - Provides more reliable protection for the primary payload
  - Easier to attach the multiple individual adapters to the launch vehicle
- Reduce design choices
  - Fixed envelope simplifies the design choices for the developer
  - The payload must fit the bus, rather than the bus fit the payload

- Develop a market for multiple vendors
  - Initially no commercial off-the-shelf (COTS) components were available for purchase—developers had to design or adapt components for their satellites
  - Multiple vendors now provide subsystems, components, and even development kits for CubeSat missions
  - Competition has reduced the price point of components
- Attract new vendors
  - Increase in availability of commercial parts lead to an increase in startup companies
  - Most initial component designs came from university environments—a free exchange of information between universities was encouraged

Most CubeSats have missions related to educating and training university students. The CubeSat form factor, however, is now widely used by the commercial space industry and defense departments worldwide. CubeSats have proven to be a cost effective form factor for getting payloads into orbit quickly and inexpensively.

25.4.3 Building CubeSats

For an inexperienced group of university students, starting a space program to undertake the design, manufacture, launch, and operation of a satellite can be as intimidating as a novice trying to climb Mount Everest. Some of the major considerations are provided here as a supplement to the details in other chapters.

Design

In designing a CubeSat (as with all satellites), the entire mission should be kept in mind. It is better to build, launch, and operate a Sputnik than to have worked on a highly complex satellite that never leaves the lab. The best approach for learning development at the university level is to keep it simple, get it launched and operated.

The design process leading to the development of a small satellite based on the CubeSat standard greatly reduces the scope of the design space that the satellite can encompass because of its size and weight. The total systems engineering process can be learned in a short period of time and then later applied to larger, more complex space systems. Some design considerations are constrained, regardless of the payload. The primary design constraints are:

1. The physical dimensions and weight are defined
2. With body mounted solar cells, the power generation capability is limited
3. The spacecraft orbit will be determined by the primary spacecraft orbit
4. The spacecraft will be protected in the launcher during launch
5. The communications systems' frequencies and data rates are limited

Environment—Design Differences

There are a number of special design considerations that are unique to designing a student built CubeSat. How are they the same or different from conventional larger satellites? Design differences between conventional space mission approaches and the CubeSat space mission approach are explored below.

Conventional Space Mission Approach

The conventional design approach to building spacecraft is to use components that are both space proven and radiation hardened. This leads to a significantly higher cost for design and production of the radiation-hardened components, since there is not a great demand.

Additionally, since it is expensive to undertake equivalent radiation testing or to find flight opportunities where components can be tested, there is a limit to the types of components that can be used for conventional space missions.

CubeSat Space Mission Approach

In most cases, the use of space proven and radiation-hardened components for university student CubeSats designs are not an option owing to their significant costs. Designing a CubeSat without this restriction leads to the expectation of a short operational life of one year or less. As a result, the designer can take advantage of new components being developed for personal electronics and trends like the iPad. Having this wide range of usable components does not mean that any component is acceptable for flight use, but that the trade space for judicious selection of components is broader.

The designer still needs to undertake trade studies before selecting of components to find those that may be more radiation-resistant due to the base technology used in their manufacture. Since the designer is now challenged to use other options to mitigate effects of radiation, options may involve using schemes to correct software when corrupted by single event upsets, for example, incorporating a watch dog timer to restart the processor if and when disruptions occur. Power systems can be designed to monitor for unexpected levels of current draw which occur in some components during latch up, then cycle the power to reset the device. Redundancy in critical components is also an option but is limited given the mass and volume constraints.

Orbit—Design Differences

Conventional Space Mission Approach

The mission requirements dictate the type of orbit required for commercial, scientific, and government (civilian and defense) space missions. This requirement along with the cost of the mission generally means that the spacecraft will be the primary payload, defining most CubeSats as secondary payloads. The launch vehicle provider then provides the optimum launch for the primary payload.

Table 25-2◀, Fig. 25-18◀, Eq. 25-5◀

CubeSat Space Mission Approach

Often, the university student CubeSat designer must begin the design of the space mission without any knowledge of the specific orbit in which the CubeSat will reside. However, the designer can select a range of orbits that will satisfy the CubeSat mission. This way, when launch opportunities arise the developers can adapt to a wide range of possible orbits thereby increasing the probability of being accepted as a secondary payload.

This approach for selecting the desired orbit can and has extended the launch time for CubeSats by many years. However, with the increased interest in CubeSat use by the science and government communities, there now appears to be more opportunities for university CubeSat launches.

Structures—Design Differences

Conventional Space Mission Approach

Large conventional spacecraft structures are generally custom-designed for each specific payload. These structures take a wide variety of approaches for example in size, payload accommodation, power generation, thermal control, and antenna placement.

CubeSat Space Mission Approach

The CubeSat structure, unlike conventional spacecraft, is already defined for the designer. See Fig. 25-16. The 1U, 2U, and 3U structures are standardized to fit in the Cal Poly P-POD launcher shown previously in Fig. 25-18. Structures conforming to this standard can either be purchased from a CubeSat component vendor or manufactured by the university student designer. These structures are generally made with aluminum sheet metal or machined from aluminum stock using the T-7075 material.

One advised requirement of the final structure made of aluminum is to have it treated with an Alodine finish. This coating prevents the surface from oxidizing and prevents non uniform charging of the structure in the plasma associated with low-Earth orbits. A new design trend is using 3D printing using special plastics, as shown in Fig. 25-19.

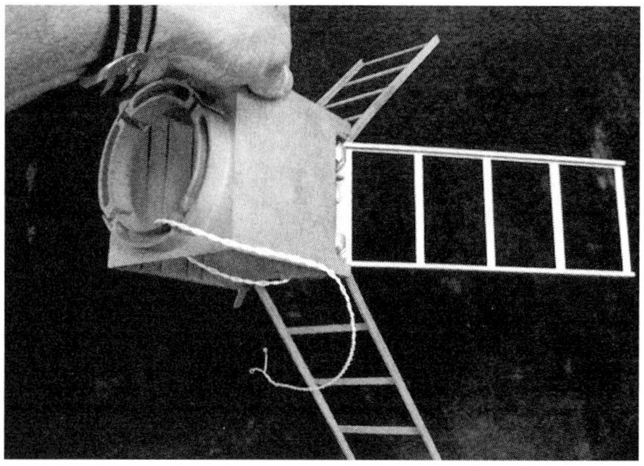

Fig. 25-19. Plastic Printed Structures for CubeSats. (Courtesy of RAMPART Team)

Electrical Power System—Design Differences

Conventional Space Mission Approach

The electronic power systems for larger commercial spacecraft may require regulated voltages of 28 V DC or more. The power requirements may range from several hundred watts for microsatellites to kilowatt levels for large satellites. These power requirements dictate the use of large solar panels that can produce hundreds of volts needed for battery charging. In turn, these systems increase the complexity of handling large voltages and power.

CubeSat Space Mission Approach

The electrical power system (EPS) represents one of the most common system failures in CubeSats that have been developed by university space teams. The need for lower bus voltages and power requirements of the CubeSat reduces this complexity. The power system can be as simple as using primary batteries to operate the CubeSat for a short time after launch or can be a more complex design using secondary (chargeable) batteries that are charged directly by solar panels. These systems typically do not incorporate charge control regulators.

Battery technology for CubeSats is currently limited to Nickel Cadmium (NiCd), Nickel Metal Hydride (NiMH), and Lithium Ion (LiIon). The LiIon technology is the best current technology because it has the highest capacity weight ratio. However, it requires precise charge regulation that, if not properly controlled, can cause battery heating and battery explosion problems. The range of regulated voltages for a CubeSat may be from 3-5V DC. Unregulated voltage for two LiIon cells in a series may be 7.2V. To charge these two cells would require a voltage of 8-10V from the solar panels.

The NiCd is an older, but proven technology that is inexpensive and reliable but has a memory capacity characteristic that requires reconditioning after use to maintain long life capacity.

Selection of the solar cells is also limited by the currently available technologies. Each technology has ranges of efficiencies and output voltages. When using large solar cells commonly used on the larger satellites, a typical CubeSat panel produces less than 5 V. Another approach being used by CubeSats is to use smaller solar cells so that enough cells can be wired in series to achieve a desired voltage. These two types of solar cells are shown in Fig. 25-20.

Peak power tracking is a new method being employed for CubeSat solar panel control to optimize the incident sunlight angle and the power generated. This method uses active control to vary the load on the solar panels in order to keep them at the maximum power point on the I-V curve.

With new applications for the CubeSats constantly emerging, there is an ever increasing demand for more peak and average power from the solar panels. This demand has now far exceeded the strategy of using only body mounted cells. Deployable solar panel systems are now being used to increase the power available to the bus by both increasing the collection area of the solar panel

Fig. 25-20. Examples of the Use of Small and Large Solar Cell. Left: Explorer 1 Prime developed by Montana State University uses large solar cells; Center: Example of inexpensive small solar cells (Triangular Advanced Solar Cells made by SpectroLab and mounted on a PCB board solar panel); Right: Ky-Sat 1 developed by Kentucky Space Program uses small triangular solar cells. (Courtesy of Cal Poly & Kentucky Space)

system and by optimizing the incident solar angle. A variety of these designs are under development now with several commercially available (illustrated in Figs. 25-21 and 25-22).

Attitude Determination & Control—Design Differences

Conventional Space Mission Approach

Attitude Determination and Control (ADC) systems for larger conventional spacecraft are a requirement for solar panel control, power generation, and pointing of communication antennas, and possibly the payload.

CubeSat Space Mission Approach

ADC systems were not typically included in the early CubeSats. It was enough in some of these early missions just to prove a minimal system. Those CubeSats that needed to enhance their communications capability by having a known orientation would use passive magnetic stabilization. Passive magnetic stabilization is a simple method of using permanent magnets along the one axis of the spacecraft to achieve some alignment of the spacecraft with the Earth's magnetic field. Some of the early CubeSats used the same techniques as the AMSAT small satellite builders by also including hysteresis rods transverse to the magnets to dampen out possible induced rotations.

Fig. 25-21. New Solar Panel Designs for CubeSats. (Courtesy of Pumpkin, Inc.)

Strategies for ADC systems employed by early commercial satellites are now being used by the CubeSat designers. Beyond the use of passive magnetic stabilization, some of the simpler systems use gravity gradient booms, and magnetic torquer coils for limited stabilization. There are several vendors that have developed active torquer coils and 3-axis wheels that are now commercially available to control the attitude of the CubeSats.

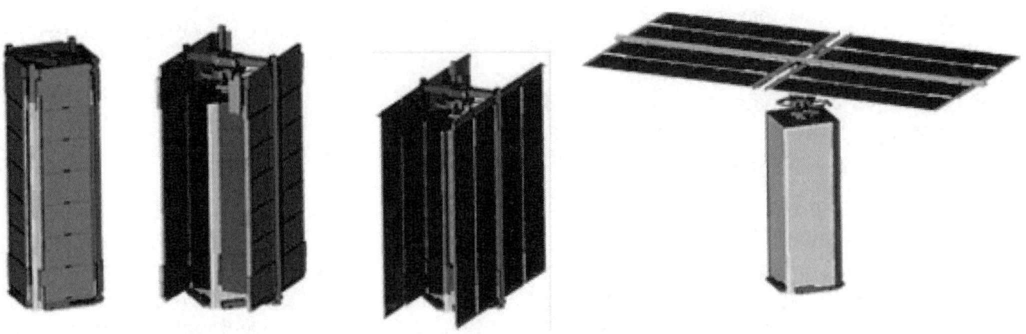

Fig. 25-22. Deployable CubeSat Solar Panels—Stage 1, 2, 3, and Fully Deployed, Respectively. (Courtesy of Tethers Unlimited, Inc.)

A full suite of CubeSat ADC systems are now being developed. Many of these systems use new MEMS technologies which have not been available in the past. They are especially applicable to the CubeSat form factor given its small size requirements and limited development budgets.

Command and Control—Design Differences

Conventional Space Mission Approach

Command and control systems for larger commercial spacecraft generally require larger amounts of high processing power than those employed in CubeSats. The size and power consumption of these components lead to increased overall weight.

CubeSat Space Mission Approach

The overall structure of software systems written for CubeSat command and control is similar to that used in the commercial spacecraft. Fortunately, a wide variety of commercial off-the-shelf (COTS) components are now available.

The command and control processors available from the large market for cell phones, PDAs, iPads and other portable devices give the CubeSat designer an extensive choice. Processors like the Texas Instrument MSP-430 series processors are commonly used. Its power consumption in normal operating frequency is generally so low that it is negligible in the overall power budget. When used in the quiescent mode, it uses microwatts of power.

Other processors like the ARM are capable of significant data processing on board. There is also a trend toward multiple core processors which will allow true simultaneous processing. With the ability of the university CubeSat programs to take more risks than previously acceptable, many of these new processors can be space-qualified for future commercial and scientific missions.

Communications—Design Differences

Conventional Space Mission Approach

Most conventional spacecraft require communications systems that can transfer large volumes of data in the Gb/s range, particularly in the downlink modes. To transfer this information requires high power and wide bandwidths. To be able to achieve desired link margins, high gain directional antennas are required on the ground. Orienting the spacecraft antennas toward the ground assets requires accurate attitude stabilization. To accomplish this effectively, a 3-axis attitude control system with pointing accuracies of 1 deg or less is needed. All of these requirements increase the size of the spacecraft and the overall cost of the mission.

CubeSat Space Mission Approach

Communication systems for CubeSats in the past have been flown with simple or no attitude control. This, of course, limits the bandwidth and the link margin, resulting in low data rate transfers of 1,200 bps to 9,600 bps.

New CubeSat missions push the limits of data that needs to be transferred. This requires high data rates, which require wider bandwidths and higher transmission power to maintain the link margin between the CubeSat and the ground stations. Achieving the necessary bandwidth requires going to higher frequencies in the L, S, and even X radio bands. New, higher performing radios for small satellites are now being developed that can increase the data rate and add greater flexibility to missions. One example is the Software Defined Radio or SDR. SDRs will reduce the fixed hardware designs now used on the CubeSats to digital controls and have the capability of after-launch frequency and modulation scheme modification, facilitated by uploading new software.

Applying for and acquiring appropriate licenses for communications frequencies is generally a new experience for the CubeSat developer. Since the frequency spectrum is limited and a well used and controlled commodity, the developers are often perplexed by the difficulty in negotiating the licensing route. CubeSats used for education purposes have been able to qualify to use the amateur radio bands. There are many restrictions, however, on how these bands meet the amateur operating rules and can be used. Amateur radio bands typically used by the CubeSat community are in the 2 m (144 MHz) and 70 cm (420 MHz) frequency allocations. Occasionally, the ISM (Industrial, Scientific, and Medical) radio bands are used for higher data transfer needs, particularly the S-band 2.400–2.500 GHz ISM allocation. Required permits and licenses needed for radio transmission in these bands are discussed in Sec. 25.4.4.

Thermal—Design Differences

Conventional Space Mission Approach

Conventional spacecraft require precise thermal control for the main spacecraft bus electronics and in many cases, very accurate control of the payload. However, there are more means of thermal control associated with larger spacecraft than on (the smaller) CubeSats. The large spacecraft may contain active thermal control systems such as radiators for heat dissipation, as well as protective insulation due to ample available room on the spacecraft.

CubeSat Space Mission Approach

Thermal control of CubeSat systems is equally important to the success of these missions. However, it generally does not require an active control system as on the larger spacecraft. Components that meet the Military Standard temperature range can be used in CubeSats if the developer is careful to consider conscious thermal design elements. Using innovative thermal design strategies, the CubeSat internal components can be kept within –30 C to +10 C providing a suitable operating range.

The most important thermal design considerations are to make sure that internal heat generating components have conductive thermal paths to the CubeSat frame for distribution of the heat. Control of the CubeSat thermal conditions when the internal heat is conducted to the exterior surface of the CubeSat is made possible through external thermal surface preparations.

Table 25-2◀, Fig. 25-22◀, Eq. 25-5◀

Modeling and thermal analysis of the CubeSat is required to manage the internal heat generated and the direct solar heat on the external surfaces. Thermal cycling as the spacecraft structures move in and out of eclipse must be considered during these analyses. Most launched CubeSats have operated in the nominal –20 C to +30 C environment of space without extensive internal or external thermal systems.

Propulsion—Design Differences

Conventional Space Mission Approach

Considering conventional spacecraft missions, the requirement for propulsion can vary widely. Propulsion systems may be required for orbit changes or orbit maintenance. Propulsion systems generally are quite complex in their use of high I_{sp} type thrusters for even attitude control requirements.

CubeSat Space Mission Approach

The first generation of CubeSats generally had no propulsion systems for orbit maintenance and orbit changes.* To date, only one CubeSat (CanX-2 launched in April 2008) has flown a propulsion system. CanX-2 successfully implemented a sulfur hexafluoride (SF6) liquefied cold gas system. A picosatellite developed by the Aerospace Corporation consistent with the size of a CubeSat called the MEMS Pico Sat Inspector (MEPSI) also successfully flew a cold gas system. MEPSI was deployed from the Space Shuttle Discovery during the STS-116/12A.1 mission on December 20, 2006. MEPSI was the first in a series of tests in the development of small, autonomous satellites that are used to observe larger spacecraft—another application of picosatellites with great potential.

Numerous space missions are now being developed that have cold gas and miniaturized systems similar to those used in larger satellites. Other more exotic systems are being developed for use on CubeSats that will feature unique and innovative propulsion systems. Larger, more expensive satellite missions cannot afford the risk associated with these unconventional propulsion systems being developed by the university CubeSat developers.

An example of innovative propulsion systems for CubeSats includes cold/warm gas propulsion utilizing MEMS-based engine nozzles and exotic bi-propellant systems. Figure 25-23 shows a 3D printed complex propulsion system being used on a 2U CubeSat for orbit altitude augmentation using a heated Freon gas.† Figure 25-24 shows a 3D printed bi-propellant system that uses part of the structure as one of the burned components. Using this 3D printing technology, these structures are very inexpensive to manufacture and can have very complex shapes.

* ION—the Illinois Observing NanoSatellite featured a low-thrust electric propulsion system but failed to achieve orbit during the 2006 Dnepr launch from Baiknour, Kasakhstan.

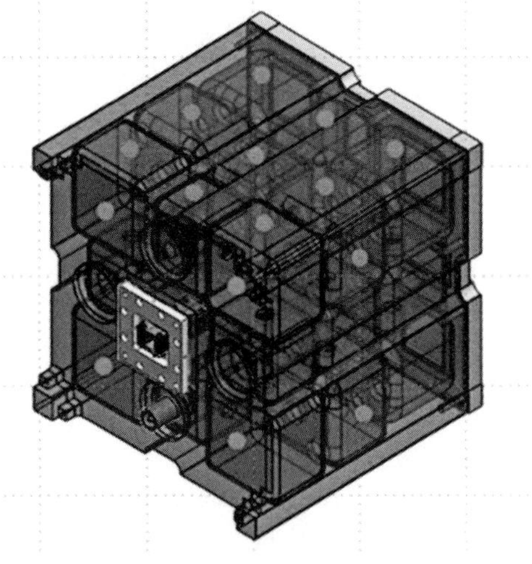

Fig. 25-23. Heated Freon Gas Propulsion. (Courtesy of Adam Huang, University of Arkansas)

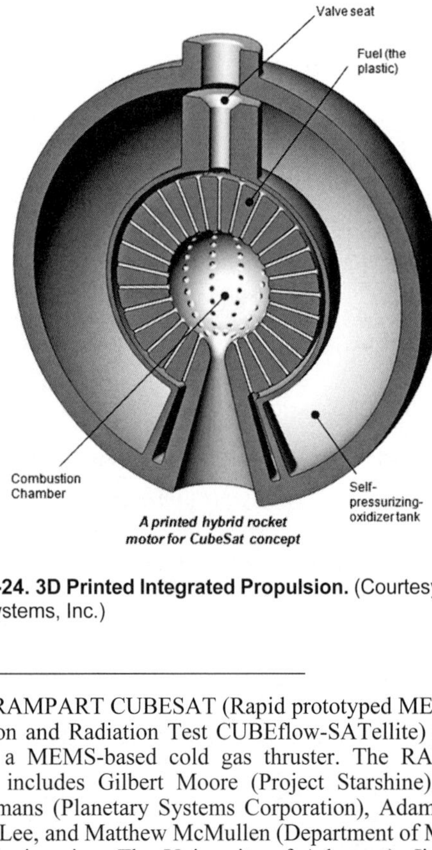

Fig. 25-24. 3D Printed Integrated Propulsion. (Courtesy of Planetary Systems, Inc.)

† The RAMPART CUBESAT (Rapid prototyped MEMS Propulsion and Radiation Test CUBEflow-SATellite) incorporates a MEMS-based cold gas thruster. The RAMPART team includes Gilbert Moore (Project Starshine), Walter Holemans (Planetary Systems Corporation), Adam Huang, John Lee, and Matthew McMullen (Department of Mechanical Engineering, The University of Arkansas), Jim White (Colorado Satellite Services), Robert Twiggs, Benjamin Malphrus, and Nathan Fite (Space Science Center, Morehead State University), David Klumpar, Ehson Mosleh, and Keith Mashburn, (Space Science and Engineering Laboratory, Montana State University), David Wilt and James Lyke (US Air Force Research Laboratory/Space Vehicles Directorate), Stewart Davis (CRP USA, LLC), Wes Bradley (Analytical Graphics, Inc.), 2Lt. Thomas Chiasson (USAF), Jay Heberle (Universal Space Network), and Pat Patterson (Space Dynamics Laboratory)

Other CubeSat propulsion systems under development take a more conventional approach, but with a twist to accommodate the CubeSat form factor. MIT scientists are working on a miniature ion propulsion system that will be ready for implementation on CubeSat systems in 2013. The MIT propulsion system works slightly differently than a conventional ion drive. In a typical ion engine, electricity charges a liquid propellant in a special chamber on board the spacecraft, and then disperses the propellant. In the MIT engine design, the propellant is pre-charged on the ground and encapsulated in small needle-like structures. When an electric charge passes through the needles, the propellant is expelled. Since each needle is effectively its own engine, the entire system is modular and customizable.*

These innovative propulsion systems will greatly enhance the capabilities of CubeSats by allowing new orbital configurations and by allowing the creation of stable pointing platforms for Earth observing (i.e., nadir pointing) and astronomical observations.

Launch Integration—Design Differences

Conventional Space Mission Approach

The developers of the larger primary spacecraft have direct contact with the launch vehicle provider. All tests on the spacecraft are performed to meet the launch environment for that particular launch vehicle. All of the launch vehicle's performance characteristics are based on putting the primary spacecraft into the desired orbit. The primary spacecraft mission essentially covers 100% of the launch costs.

CubeSat Space Mission Approach

CubeSats are considered secondary payloads for the expendable launch vehicles. The acceptance of secondary payloads is generally at the discretion of the primary payload provider since they have assumed the total cost of the launch. The development of the P-POD has alleviated much of the risk to the primary satellite by providing significant protection for the primary payload through total containment of the CubeSat, minimizing the possibility of accidental release and subsequent damage to the primary payload.

Therefore, the cost for the CubeSat launch is based on the additional effort required to accommodate this small payload. The university CubeSat developer may only have the option to accept or decline the orbit being provided since they have no control over which orbit the primary payload owner may pick. The developer must design their systems to be compatible with the launch environment of all possible launch vehicles that will offer secondary launches for CubeSats. This variable can affect the cost from a design perspective.

For university CubeSat developers, the launch will be managed by an intermediate integration organization. This greatly simplifies the launch process for the CubeSat community. With integration services provided by experienced groups like Cal Poly and SRI International, the developer need not be subjected to the complication of working directly with the launch provider.

When the CubeSat is delivered to the integration service organization, final testing is conducted in the CubeSat launcher. The next time the developer is able to take control of the satellite is after the CubeSat is on orbit.

Manufacturing and Environmental Testing Facilities—Design Differences

Conventional Space Mission Approach

The facilities required to test and flight-verify large spacecraft are extensive and expensive. In many cases, large spacecraft cannot be tested in flight configuration. This then requires the final environmental testing to be conducted on individual components. Large spacecraft require thermal cycling, vibration testing, vacuum testing, and acoustical testing. Large thermal-vacuum chambers that can accommodate large spacecraft are expensive to maintain and operate. Large vibration shakers for spacecraft require special facility structures to support the significant weight of the spacecraft and extreme vibration. Care must be taken, for example, during the design of these facilities that mechanical resonances are not induced in the building or nearby structures.

CubeSat Space Mission Approach

CubeSats require the same type of testing as large spacecraft, but the cost associated with smaller thermal-vacuum chambers and vibration systems is much less. Acoustical testing is normally not required for CubeSats since the acoustics only affect large fragile structures such as deployable solar panels. Testing equipment for the CubeSats can be as simple as well-controlled home refrigerators, cooking ovens, and glass bell jars. Achieving vibration levels required for certain launch vehicles, however, can be challenging as vibration systems (shaker tables)—even smaller ones—are not commonly available.

Project Management—Design Differences

Conventional Space Mission Approach

Large conventional space missions have grown to have legions of technicians and engineers working on a single program. The spacecraft design and implementation requires elaborate documentation of requirements. Once these documents are completed, technician groups work in relative isolation to implement their tasks. Engineering groups are formed to handle design, quality control, testing, launch, and operations. The larger the number of groups and individuals in these groups the less effective the intergroup communication.

Because of the extreme costs of these missions, the total mission is developed with a primary objective of being *risk averse*. This leads to over design and use of older components with flight heritage. This process stifles innovation.

---

* Paulo Lozano, the H.N. Slater Assistant Professor of Aeronautics and Astronautics at MIT.

Table 25-2◀, Fig. 25-24◀, Eq. 25-5◀

Get More

Table 25-3. Representative CubeSat Missions Flown from 2003–2011. See the website for a more complete and up to date listing of launched CubeSat missions.

Name	Type	Organization	Mission	Launch Date	Rocket
QuakeSat	3U	Stanford University/Quake Finder, USA	Earthquake detection	6/30/2003	Rokot/Briz-KM
CUTE-I (Oscar 55)	1U	Tokyo Institute of Technology, Japan	Separation system demonstration, Educational, Technology testing & Amateur radio	6/30/2003	Rokot/Briz-KM
CP-3	1U	California Polytechnic University, USA	Educational, Technology testing & Amateur radio	4/17/2007	Dnepr-1
MAST	1U	Tethers Unlimited, USA	Tether experiments—operated from 4/20/2007 to 5/30/2007	4/17/2007	Dnepr-1
COMPASS-1	1U	FH Aachen–University of Applied Science, Germany	Demonstration of commercial off-the-shelf components and taking photos	4/28/2008	PSLV-CA
CanX-2	3U	University of Toronto, Canada	Technology demonstrator for formation flying	4/28/2008	PSLV-C9
K-Sat	1U	Kagoshima University	Technology Demonstrator and Earth Remote Sensing of Water Vapor	5/20/2010	H-IIA 202
RAX	3U	University of Michigan and SRI	Bi-static RADAR measurement of plasma formations in Earth's ionosphere	11/20/2010	Minotaur

CubeSat Space Mission Approach

University CubeSat programs can accommodate implementing risk into their design. This leads to designs that use newer technologies that need not have flight heritage and can be much less expensive. Many university teams that have flown successful missions have had fewer than 10 students doing most of the work. Small team size leads to good communication and facilitates changes in systems design and implementation. Although the university teams do not produce optimum documentation and designs are not replicated, advances in technology and education are prominent.

25.4.4 Permits and Licenses

Conventional Space Mission Approach

Large spacecraft missions conform to communication requirements assigned to the agency operating the spacecraft. Launch location to the geostationary orbit is limited and controlled by international agreements.

CubeSat Space Mission Approach

The CubeSat developer must get the proper satellite radio operations permissions. Note this is permission, not a license. Permission here refers to those using the amateur radio bands. International Amateur Radio Union (IARU) coordinates amateur frequency allocations worldwide. In addition, for US universities, the developer must notify the US Federal Communications Commission of the agreed use of the frequencies through the IARU and provide launch information and other mission parameters. The procedures for these coordination efforts are found on the Cal Poly website at CubeSat.org or the amateur satellite website at AMSAT.org. This is a requirement that must be completed by the developer and is not provided by the launch integration organization.

If the CubeSat contains a sensing device such as a camera that can view the Earth in any frequency of the electromagnetic spectrum, the US Department of Commerce requires (under Title II of the Land Remote Sensing Policy Act of 1992, Public Law 102-555, 15 U.S.C. § 5601 et seq.) the satellite owner to obtain and have a license for Earth remote sensing. The US NOAA manages the application process and must grant the license and approval before the CubeSat is launched.

There may also be restrictions on collaborating with other universities and organizations outside the US. The US Department of State manages and enforces the International Arms and Traffic Regulations (ITAR) that need to be complied with regarding discussions, exchanges of information, provision of services, and collaboration with any non-US personnel or organizations. This may include non-US citizens and international students at the developer's university. Most universities have legal council that can advise the developers on the university policy and ITAR restrictions.

All launch providers at present require certification of the de-orbit time for the CubeSat to be 25 years or less. The orbit life varies significantly with orbit altitude. Since university CubeSats are typically designed for an operational life of one year or less, orbits less than 500 km are most desirable. At this altitude, de-orbit times generally do not require specific de-orbiting systems. Higher orbits may require the implementation of a system or device to increase the spacecraft's cross sectional areas, (and therefore atmospheric drag) at the end of the operational life to meet the de-orbit requirement.

25.4.5 Past CubeSat Missions

The first CubeSats were launched on a Eurockot (a re-tasked UR-100N ICBM) from Plesetsk, Russia on June 30, 2003. The first CubeSats—6 of which were included on this first launch—represented a wide variety of projects ranging from university student projects to commercial aerospace programs. While most of the launch campaigns have been successful, two notable launch anomalies destroyed a number of CubeSats en route to orbit. Fourteen CubeSats were lost during a launch failure of a Dnepr rocket in July 2006, and an experimental launch of the Space-X Falcon 1 in 2008 destroyed 2 NASA CubeSats.

Seventy CubeSats have flown since the launch of the first group in 2003. A representative list of CubeSat launches is shown in Table 25-3. Of the 70 achieving orbit, most have been successful to some degree. Reflective of the challenges associated with engineering systems for the harsh space environment, approximately 6 CubeSats have never been contacted and only limited contact has been possible with another 5 CubeSats. Table 25-3 chronicles the success rate of CubeSats flown between 2003 and 2011.

It is estimated that 100–150 CubeSats are under development with nearly 60 in preparation for launch in the next few years. In fact, the Von Karman Institute (VKI) is undertaking a project to develop 50 additional CubeSats with world-wide collaborators. The VKI project, called QB50 is an ambitious project to investigate a relatively unexplored region of the Earth's atmosphere (see Sec. 25.4.10 for more detail). The CubeSat form factor is rapidly becoming the de-facto standard for university class missions, for governments with beginning space programs, and now for specific applications within the aerospace industry, NASA, and ESA.

25.4.6 CubeSat Missions—Applications

CubeSat systems are devoted to an incredible variety of missions from bus to component testing, to complete science missions (including astrobiology and ionosphere research). CubeSat developers have demonstrated the versatility and capability of the CubeSat using payload systems based on miniaturized electronics, micro-electro-mechanical systems (MEMS technologies) and innovations in sensor and microprocessor and micro-controller systems. To date, CubeSat missions have focused on the following applications:

- Technology Demonstration
- Earth Remote Sensing
- Ionospheric and Auroral Research
- Effects of the Space Environment on Biological Systems (Astrobiology)
- Radiation Effects on Space Technologies
- Astrophysics

Although numerous CubeSat missions have produced interesting and important science results, a few examples are selected here to serve as illustrations—notably QuakeSat, GeneSat, RAX, O/OREOS, and the proposed Firefly and IAPETUS.

QuakeSat, a 3U CubeSat developed at Stanford University and launched in 2003 was a highly successful mission whose science objective was to study earthquake precursor phenomena from space. The science mission was accomplished based on measuring extremely low frequency magnetic signals in LEO. A magnetometer was deployed on a 0.7 m boom to isolate the sensor from magnetic fields generated by the spacecraft electronics. QuakeSat innovations included deployable solar cells to improve bus power. Roughly 500 MB of data were returned during the mission, leading the team to develop a larger and more sophisticated follow-on satellite.

Another example of an extremely successful CubeSat science mission is GeneSat. GeneSat was a result of collaboration between NASA Ames, industry partners, and universities including Stanford. The satellite consisted of a satellite bus, confined to 1U while the payload was contained in a 2U structure—a configuration that is fairly typical of 3U CubeSat systems. GeneSat's mission objective was to develop a miniature life support system that could fit into a triple CubeSat and could deliver nutrients and perform assays for genetic changes in biological samples, in this case E. Coli. A pressurized sealed vessel and an integrated analytical fluidics card assembly, which included a media pump, valves, microchannels, filters, membranes, and wells to maintain the biological viability of the microorganisms, comprised the payload system. On-board optical sensors were used to detect genetic changes. An environmental system was required to maintain a specific temperature within 0.5 C during the experimental phase, which was nominally 96 hours. The satellite monitored the temperatures external and internal to the CubeSat, as well as the radiation environment. Significant amounts of science data were transmitted down at S-band. GeneSat was a significant experiment, being NASA's first CubeSat mission and the first biological experiment conducted with a CubeSat. Owing to the success of GeneSat, NASA launched two follow up missions, PharmaSat and O/OREOS. O/OREOS, shown in Figure 25-25, is a triple CubeSat that observes how microorganisms and organic molecules adapt to the stresses of the space environment. The GeneSat

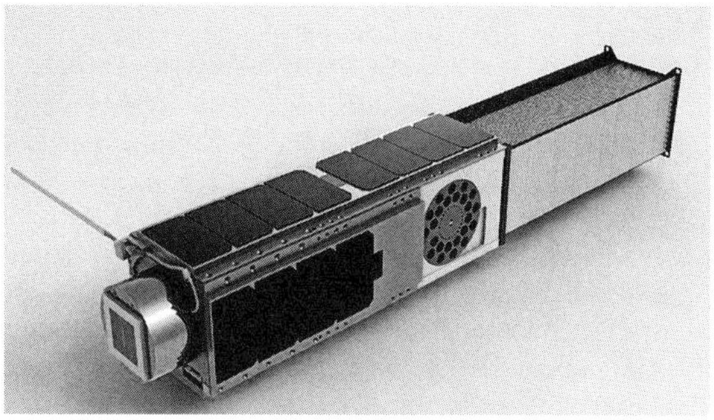

Fig. 25-25. NASA Ames O/OREOS 3U CubeSat. (Courtesy of NASA Ames)

heritage biological CubeSat has incredible potential to return significant science in the field of astrobiology.

SwissCube, Fig. 25-26, is an example of a CubeSat that incorporates a significant science mission and innovative technologies. Developed in Switzerland and led by the École Polytechnique Fédérale de Lausanne (EPFL) Space Center, SwissCube was launched in September 2009. SwissCube was Switzerland's first satellite, making a case for the importance of the CubeSat form factor which provides a low cost entry point for countries to develop space programs. SwissCube images atmospheric airglow, a photoluminescence of the atmosphere at night. Airglow arises from light emitted at 762 nm (peak wavelength) from an oxygen layer 85 km to 100 km above the Earth. To image the Earth airglow, SwissCube must be pointed toward the limb of the Earth and requires attitude determination accurate to better than 1 deg. To obtain the required performance given the constraints of the CubeSat form factor, the developers chose to use MEMS components. The ADXRS614 form Analog Device, a MEMS-based gyroscope, was selected for SwissCube because of its low power consumption and high sensitivity for low rotation rates. The gyroscopes are needed during eclipses, accounting for 30% of each orbit of the satellite. Three gyroscopes were mounted at 90 deg to each other—one on the main ADCS printed circuit board and two on smaller boards mounted perpendicularly to the ADCS board. While the spacecraft has performed nominally, no scientific results or images of Earth airglow have been published in the open literature to date.

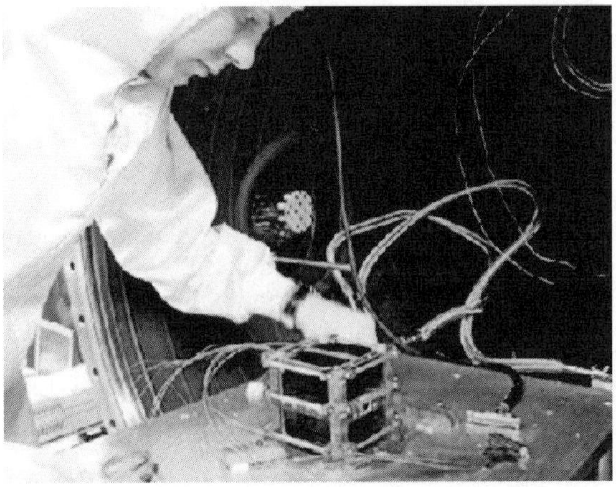

Fig. 25-26. SwissCube: Switzerland's First Satellite. (Courtesy of École Polytechnique Fédérale de Lausanne Space Center)

Figure 25-27 shows the Radio Aurora Explorer (RAX), which is a 3U CubeSat whose purpose is to investigate the causes of turbulence in the Earth's ionosphere, a portion of the upper atmosphere that is ionized by solar radiation. RAX is a result of collaboration between the University of Michigan and Space Research International (SRI). RAX was launched in November 2010. The project's mission is to observe small-scale plasma turbulent structures that occur in response to intense electrical currents in the space environment. The

Fig. 25-27. Radio Aurora Explorer While Under Development RAX was Launched on November 20, 2010. (Courtesy of the University of Michigan)

structures can attenuate and distort communication and navigation signals affecting a variety of commercial and defense systems. RAX receives signals from megawatt ground-based radar transmitters to investigate these auroral structures.

NASA's "Firefly" Mission, Fig. 25-28, is a CubeSat designed to study terrestrial Gamma Ray Flashes (TGFs) produced by lightning. TGFs are produced by beams of energetic electrons, which are accelerated in the intense electric fields generated by thunderstorms. Prior to work performed with NASA's Compton Gamma Ray Observatory, scientists believed gamma rays could only be generated by energetic extraterrestrial sources like the Sun, supernovae, and black holes. TGF electron beams are more powerful than any others produced in near-Earth space, and understanding the underlying physics of these phenomena will lend insight into physical processes that may occur on other planets or in astrophysical environments, as well as in the Sun's corona. Firefly is a collaborative effort by NASA Goddard Space Flight Center; Universities Space Research Association (USRA), Columbia, Md.; Siena College; University of Maryland Eastern Shore, Princess Anne, Md.; and the Hawk Institute for Space Sciences, in Pocomoke City, Maryland which is scheduled to fly in 2011.

25.4.7 Launch Vehicles Currently Used and Proposed

The CubeSat standard has served to increase access to space, particularly for university-class missions. The number of CubeSat launch opportunities, however, has not increased at a rate necessary to meet demand of the numerous small satellite developers that have appeared since 2001. The number of CubeSat developers has nearly doubled in size every 18 months since 2001 [Crook, 2009]. Commercial launch opportunities, at any cost, are not widely available in the US for CubeSats. Although some launch service providers have been established in Russia, Europe, and India for CubeSats, US based CubeSat developers face additional challenges due to the fact that all spaceflight

Fig. 25-28. NASA's Proposed Firefly 3U CubeSat. (Courtesy of NASA)

hardware built in the US is subject to US commerce law and the International Trade in Arms Regulations (ITAR). ITAR is a set of US government regulations that control the export and import of defense-related articles and services. All hardware that is intended by its developers to fly in space is controlled by ITAR regulations, posing challenges for US developers on non-US launch vehicles. Although the ITAR regulations pose a particular challenge, there are notable examples of US CubeSats that have flown on non-US launch platforms. Table 25-4 lists some of the more prominent launch vehicles used for CubeSat deployment.

Several companies and research institutes offer regular launch opportunities in clusters of several cubes. ISC Kosmotras, Innovative Solutions in Space (ISIS), and Enroot are companies that offer such services [EUROCKOT, 2003].

Table 25-4. Launch Vehicle Used for CubeSat.

Launch Vehicle	Country of Origin	Date 1st Used
Rokot-KM	Russia	2003
Kosmos-3M	Russia	2005
Dnepr-1	Russia	2006
PSLV (3)	India	2008
PSLV-CA	India	2009
H-2A-202	Japan	2010
M-5 (2)	US	2008
Minotaur-1	US	2006
Minotaur-4 HAPS	US	2010
Falcon-1	US	2008
Falcon-9	US	2010

25.4.8 Space Operations and Ground Stations

Mission Operations

The mission operation aspect of university CubeSat programs differs significantly from commercial space missions. Mission operations, as defined for commercial satellite missions in Chap. 29, is a collection of activities, plans, procedures, policies, and tasks required to complete the flight phase objectives of the mission. Mission operations are intricate and complicated tasks that involve mission control, data transfer, spacecraft and payload operations, data processing and archiving, and navigation and orbit control. The latter task is essentially the only activity not typical of CubeSat mission operations—otherwise CubeSat missions involve all aspects of mission ops associated with major space systems. However, given the level of financial resources, staffing, and experience that CubeSat operators have, mission ops for these missions is generally much less formal and intricate.

CubeSat developers and operators, analogous to large satellite operators, are generally required by the program sponsors or launch services provider to develop a Mission Operations Plan (MOP). The features and characteristics of MOPs are described in detail in Chap. 29. Differences between MOPs for large satellites and CubeSats are a function of the greater complexity and expense of larger satellites. Major differences relate to the fact that major spacecraft often have:

- More complicated payloads that require control operations
- Propulsion or station-keeping systems
- Requirements for precision pointing or orientation
- Expendables that need to be monitored during flight
- Higher data rates—more complicated data processing and transfer requirements
- Requirements for real-time (or near-real time) command
- More sophisticated subsystems to monitor and control
- Significantly longer mission durations
- Greater requirements for operational risk management
- Extensive operational risk processes and policies
- The ability to analyze and troubleshoot on-orbit anomalies

It is instructive to have the student developers create a viable MOP. While much engineering experience is gained in the development phase of CubeSat missions, invaluable experience can be gained by students during the operational phases as well. A high level overview of the development and operational phases that are typical of CubeSat missions is provided in Table 25-5. The simpler mission operations requirements allow the programs to be performed at low cost and most often with student operators. The orbits available to CubeSat missions, combined with relatively relaxed requirements for data transfer, facilitate the use of amateur radio equipment for ground segment systems. All of these considerations combined allow for missions that are relatively inexpensive and can be managed, operated, and implemented by university graduate and undergraduate students.

Table 25-5. Typical Mission Operation Phases and Modes.

Satellite: CubeSat X	Pre-Launch			On Orbit			
Phase	Final Prep & Delivery	Integration and Testing	Launch	LEOP	VHF/UHF operation	S-Band Ops	E/PO Ops*
Control Nodes	N/A	N/A	N/A	Ground station 1	Ground station 1 & 2	High gain ground station	Public Schools, Amateur Radio Operators
Pass Scheduling	N/A	N/A	N/A	2 × daily	1 × daily	2 × weekly	Variable
Landmark Start	L – 8 months	L – 4 months	Beginning of launch window	L + 1 week (After bus and systems payload check out)	L + 2 months	L + 4 months	L + 12 months
Landmark End	L – 4 months	L – 2 months	Launch	L + 5 weeks	L + 4 months	L + 12 months	L + 24 months
Time Frame	4 months	2 months	L- 0 days	1 month	2 months	8 months	12–24 months
* E/PO Ops: Education/Public Outreach Operations							

CubeSat Earth Stations

Ground stations designed to operate CubeSats are consistent with the low cost COTS approach applied to the CubeSat spacecraft development. Most CubeSats utilize Earth stations that are based on Amateur Radio designs. Since up- and down-link frequencies are almost always in the amateur radio bands, the ground station equipment employed to track and command the satellites is based on amateur radio technology. The typical UHF/VHF ground stations consist of a simple UHF/VHF Yagi array used in conjunction with a positioner, back end receivers (similar to the ones on-board the satellite) and tracking software (Ham Radio Deluxe and Nova are widely used) to track and control the satellite. In-house software is often developed to support commanding the spacecraft, decoding the beacon, and to acquire data and telemetry. The Earth station systems are responsible for commanding all available actions including all transmissions from the satellite such as telemetry, commanding the payload instruments, and controlling the various satellite subsystems. A system-level schematic diagram of a typical CubeSat VHF/UHF Earth station is provided in Fig. 25-29, and Fig. 25-30 shows the Kentucky Space VHF/UHF CubeSat Earth Stations at the University of Kentucky.

GENSO

The CubeSat community has undertaken the development of a world wide network of university and amateur VHF/UHF Earth stations that, theoretically, will be used to support all CubeSat missions. The Global Educational

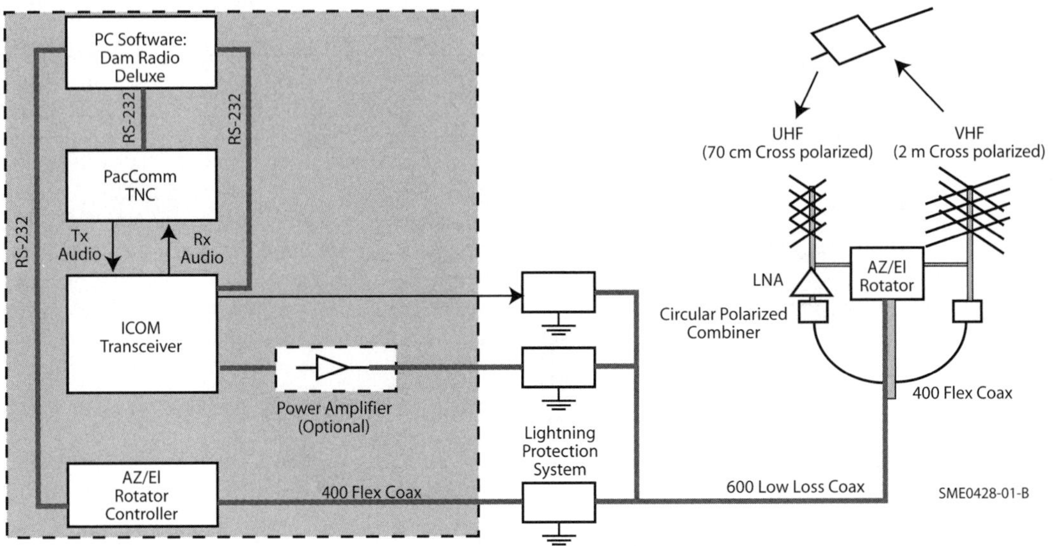

Fig. 25-29. Schematic of a Typical VHF/UHF CubeSat Earth Station Systems. (Courtesy of Morehead State University Space Science Center)

Fig. 25-30. Kentucky Space VHF/UHF CubeSat Earth Stations at (Left) the University of Kentucky, Lexington, KY (Longitude: 84° 30' 20 W, Latitude: 38° 02' 15"N) and (Right) Morehead State University (Longitude: 83° 26' W, Latitude: 38° 11' N). (Courtesy of Morehead State University Space Science Center)

Network for Satellite Operations (GENSO) is a project initiated and supported by the International Space Education Board (ISEB). ISEB consists of the Education Departments of the Canadian Space Agency, the European Space Agency, the Japan Aerospace Exploration Agency, and NASA. The initiative is managed by the Education Office of ESA and the AMSAT Radio Amateur Community. Teams of volunteers from the US, Europe, and Japan are working on the GENSO network, which has several objectives. The primary goal of the GENSO network is to increase the amount of data that can be down-linked from a particular satellite by increasing the available pass times. The idea is to automate existing ground stations to allow unattended operation by remote users and support the development of new ground stations in desirable locations around the world [Melville, 2006]. Other specific objectives of the GENSO network are to:

1. Increase available pass times, leading to unparalleled near-global levels of access to educational small satellites
2. Provide remote access for operators to real-time mission data
3. Provide remote control of the participating ground stations
4. Optimize uplink effectiveness by modeling real-time link budgets and uplink station selection
5. Incorporate downlink error correction by comparing multiple data streams and redundancy checks
6. Create a global standard for educational ground segment software and mission control software interfaces
7. Develop standard GSE for educational satellite missions
8. Establish a common interface to apply for frequency allocation and coordination (in coordination with IARU)

Major advantages of the GENSO network are that satellite operators can control their satellite from anywhere in the world and data can be downloaded to hundreds of Earth stations geographically located all around the planet. The GENSO network should be scalable to potentially thousands of stations, effectively providing worldwide coverage for CubeSat operators [Shirville and Klofas, 2007]. As of early 2011, GENSO is in alpha testing.

While most CubeSat Ground Station Equipment (GSE) is based on VHF/UHF systems, higher gain and data rate systems have been developed and existing large Earth stations have expanded their capabilities to service CubeSat systems. S-band CubeSats, in particular, require larger, more directional ground stations to provide mission operations services. A notable example of a university based CubeSat Earth Station is the 21 m Space Tracking Antenna at Morehead State University in Morehead, KY in Fig. 25-31.

Fig. 25-31. The Morehead State University Space Science Center 21 m Space Tracking Antenna, Morehead, KY. (Latitude: 38° 11' 30.773" N, Longitude: 83° 26' 19.948" W.) (Courtesy of Morehead State University Space Science Center)

Fig. 25-32. The Morehead State University Space Science Center 21 M Space Tracking Antenna, Control Room. (Lower Equipment Room 2010) (Courtesy of Morehead State University Space Science Center)

The MSU 21 m Space Tracking Antenna is engaged in ongoing research programs in radio astronomy and is also capable of operating in satellite ground station mode, providing telemetry, tracking, and command (TT&C) services for a wide variety of satellite systems from its control room shown in Fig. 25-32. The 21 m is used as a test bed for advanced RF systems developed by the faculty, students, and collaborators.

This system has the capability of tracking fast moving, low power transmitting small satellites in LEO, as well as satellites at geostationary, lunar, and potentially Earth-Sun Lagrangian orbits. The 21 m is currently configured for operation at L-band and K_u-band. Feeds are being implemented at S-band and there are near term plans for the development of a C-band system among others.

The instrument also serves as an active laboratory for students engaged in research and training in space science, electrical and mechanical engineering, telecommunications electronics, astrophysics, and space systems operation. It is largely operated by undergraduate students who work in the associated laboratories to achieve hands-on training in RF systems and techniques.

The basic performance characteristics (aperture, dynamics, and radio frequency) are provided below in Table 25-6 for the current operating frequency regimes (L-band, S-Band, and K_u-Bands). The 21 meter system has a drive system that is capable of tracking LEO satellites at an altitude of 350 nautical miles and a maximum elevation angle of 77 deg. While the 21 m Space Tracking Antenna at MSU is atypical of university-class CubeSat Earth stations, this facility and several others (i.e., SRI Earth stations) have become available for high data rate and ultimately more distant (beyond LEO) CubeSat missions. These high gain quasi-dedicated CubeSat Earth stations will provide communications capabilities enabling CubeSats to achieve significant science well beyond LEO.

Table 25-6. 21 m Performance Characteristics.

Function	Performance
Antenna Diameter	21 meter
Receive Polarization	RHCP, LHCP, VERT, HORZ
Travel Range	AZ ±275 deg from due South (180 deg) EL −1 to 91 deg POL ±90 deg
Velocity	AZ Axis = 3 deg/sec EL Axis = 3 deg/sec POL Axis = 1 deg/sec
Acceleration	AZ = 1.0 deg/sec^2 min EL = 0.5 deg/sec^2 min
Display Resolution	AZ/EL = 0.001 deg POL = 0.01 deg
Encoder Resolution	AZ/EL = 0.0003 deg (20 bit)
Tracking Accuracy	$\leq$ 5% Received 3 dB Beamwidth (0.028 deg RMS L-band) (0.005 deg RMS Ku-Band)
Pointing Accuracy	$\leq$ 0.01 deg rms

25.4.9 New Trends in Manufacturing

The requirement of the structure is to always fit a small predefined envelop and remain viable through launch vibration and shock. Once through this launch environment, the structure is now subjected to a whole new set of environments with no vibration, no more shock and relatively benign mechanical environment. Taking a lesson from the toy industry, once in space we can transform and morph the satellite into a size and shape that better suits the new space mechanical and thermal environments.

A new, novel manufacturing of complex structures is being explored. A new 2U CubeSat being developed with this process is called RAMPART, shown in Fig. 25-33. A new material called XTend has been found to have desirable properties for making a structure with a 3D printer. It has low out-gassing and high strength characteristics. It is initially being used to make parts for race cars and electric motorcycles. It is also possible to electroplate this material to assure that it has the conducting faraday cage properties for mitigating spacecraft charging that occurs in the plasma of LEO.

There are now designs that offer multiple CubeSat launches by combining many P-PODS like the Naval Post Graduate School CubeSat Launcher in Fig. 25-34. There is also a trend to P-POD type launchers for larger spacecraft based on the CubeSat such as the one shown in Fig. 25-35.

25.4.10 The Future of CubeSats of the Next Decade

What can we predict to be the future use of CubeSats for the next decade? From my (Twiggs) point of vision, I had no concept of the changes that the CubeSat would

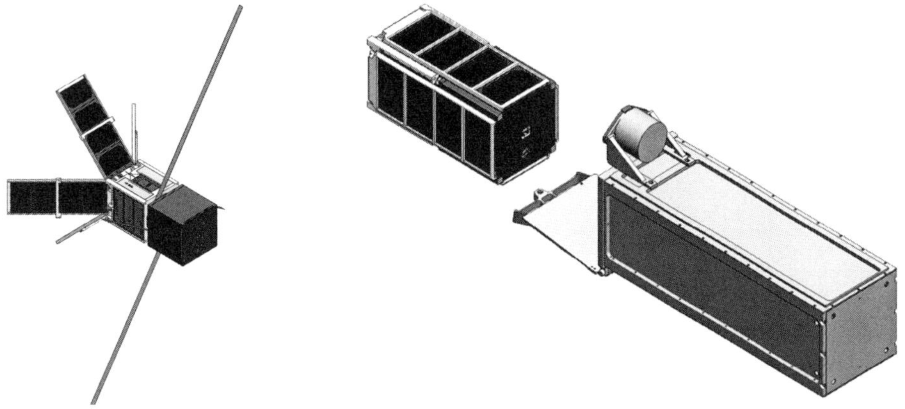

Fig. 25-33. Integral Structure Made With 3D Printing. (Courtesy of the RAMPART Team)

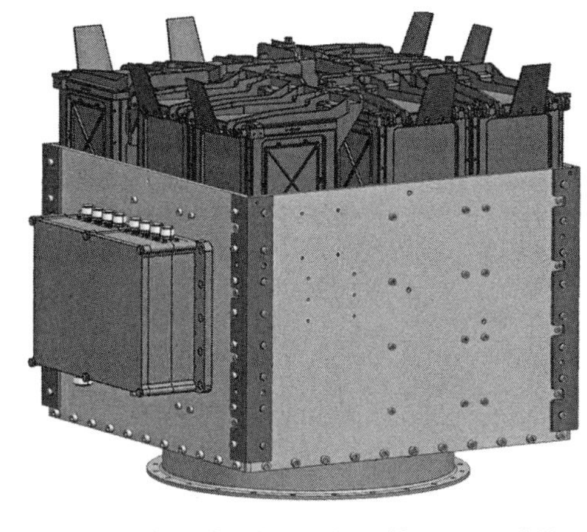

Fig. 25-34. NPS CubeSat Launcher. (Courtesy of Naval Post Graduate School)

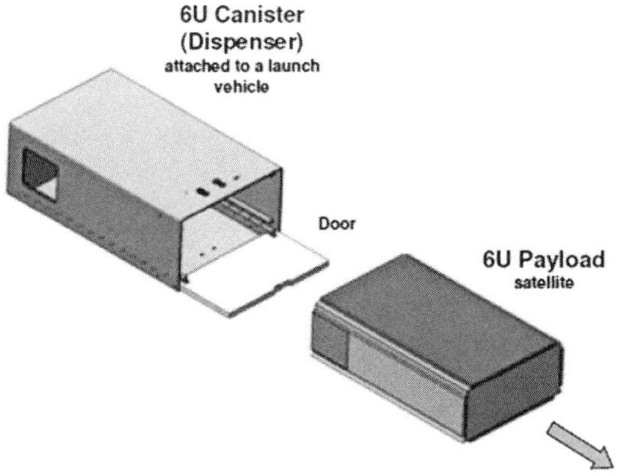

Fig. 25-35. The 6U Launcher. (Courtesy of Planetary Systems, Inc.)

have on the small satellite space community. I can only speculate on what the future will bring, but let's take a look at what has happened in the last 2 years then maybe we can project that into the future.

An assessment of the current state of CubeSat technology facilitates extrapolation toward a prediction of future trends and technological advancements. Recently, the small satellite community has seen dramatic improvement in the performance and capabilities of subsystems, including higher bus power, improved deployable systems, improved processor architecture, and higher bandwidth/throughput communication systems. These systems have tremendously enhanced the capabilities of CubeSats as evidenced by the large number of commercial aerospace ventures now flying them.

Future advances, particularly in the areas of flight dynamics, advanced power, processor systems, and propulsion will facilitate a wide variety of science and commercial payloads. These advances are driven by the current revolution in micro-electronics, especially in the area of MEMS devices. Passive spacecraft stabilization systems have been refined and active stabilization and orientation systems relying on momentum wheels and magneto-torquers are now entering the commercial market. Horizon sensors, Sun sensors and star trackers are also now becoming commercially available. MEMS-based and other propulsion systems are being developed that will be used for spacecraft orientation and orbit adjustment.

These payloads will facilitate experiments in imaging (likely in the optical and infrared spectra), astrophysics (i.e., the study of highly energetic astronomical phenomena), and space physics (i.e., the study of aurora, magnetic fields, radiation belts, and the plasma electrical environment of the Earth-Sun system). Studies of the Earth in regard to its natural resources and aspects of climate change will also be facilitated by these advancements. Future missions will send CubeSat systems to Earth-geosynchronous orbit, to the moon, and ultimately to Mars orbit. These future missions will require advances in CubeSat systems being developed in laboratories world wide today, so the following points are important to consider:

1. Almost all major areas of satellite use have now come to realize that much can be done with small satellites, especially taking advantage of the new developments in the commercial areas for personal devices like PDAs.

2. The launch community is finally realizing that there is an advantage to providing secondary launches and those that have the large primary spacecraft are willing to share space on the launch.
3. The initial generation of students that had opportunities to work on the small satellites and CubeSats are now in the industry and have a growing influence.
4. NASA has the ElaNa program to provide launch opportunities for university programs. In Europe, the Vega launch program has planned CubeSat launches.
5. Major science is now being performed using the CubeSat concept with the Astrobiology work at NASA Ames and the NSF RAX project from the University of Michigan.

Building the Talent to Do CubeSats

CubeSats in education have only been available to the undergraduate and graduate university community thus far, but there is a fast growing trend to move space training projects to the pre-college level of students. The CanSat balloon launch and low altitude rocket launch are becoming popular programs in the US and have a large following in Japan and Europe. The CanSat, generally confined to the size of a soda drink can (another standard) is being built with all of the technology used in the CubeSats. The students in these pre-college programs will soon be building CubeSats that will be operating in LEO.

The CricketSat is an even more fundamental space project. This small device is launched on party balloons and provides educational experience in small space missions by recording simple measurements of temperatures as these balloons ascend. This exposure builds talent to start CanSat projects earlier in education.

Expanding the Use of Space

Since projects that deal with space have a major fascination for us all, they are now being used as one of the major focal points in education to inspire young students to see the value in STEM (Science, Technology, Engineering and, Math) subjects in their education. These space projects not only provide the use of important education subjects, but also give students empowering hands-on experience. This is especially motivating to the students because they can take personal satisfaction in their physical creations.

The success of the CubeSat operating in space has now demonstrated that it does not take a major organization with legions of engineers and scientists to do space missions. So now we are seeing the transition from just making things work in space to doing real science missions. The CubeSat has provided the space platform that has raised the confidence for the "novice" to look at new types of space missions.

New Uses of Space for Education and Science

How can the attributes of the space environment be used to an advantage for new science? Consider the attributes of an ultraclean vacuum and new exposure to space particle and spectral radiation. In addition, the orbiting spacecraft can provide microgravity for unique research opportunities.

A new program has just begun with NASA under a Space Act Agreement with NanoRacks LLC that will provide CubeSat sized experiments called CubeLabs to be flown on the ISS. The CubeLab experiment is installed in a rack on the Japanese Experiment Module and provided with power and a communications link. Data generated in the CubeLab can then be transferred to a NASA website for the experimenter. This new service gives students an opportunity to do a space mission for experiments in a microgravity environment inside a CubeLab. Now, the opportunity for students to do important science in space missions will enable them to make valuable contributions to science, improve their education through increased returns on their efforts, better prepare them for university engineering and science education and, ultimately, create a new generation of highly trained engineers and scientists.

Creating New Devices for Use in Space

The CubeSat concept is expandable to larger sized cubes, but the real challenge is to do useful space missions with smaller and less expensive space devices. The cost of launching spacecraft into space is based on size and weight. Now that there are more science and government applications for the CubeSat technology, launching a single 1U CubeSat has increased from the initial university launch cost of \$40,000 to \$80,000 or more. Decreasing that cost can only be done by decreasing the size and weight of the spacecraft and providing means of combining many devices into one launch package.

To that end, a new, smaller version of the CubeSat has been developed at Morehead State University called the PocketQub. The PocketQub is a 5 cm cube compared to the 10 cm CubeSat cube. The concept is to combine eight of these PocketQubs into a spacecraft package the size

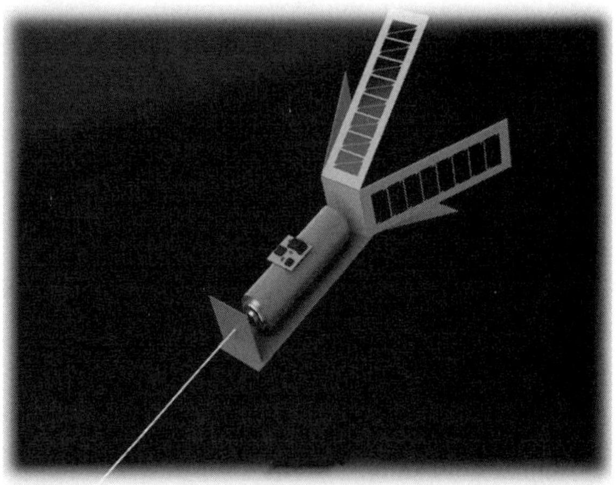

Fig. 25-36. PocketQub Illustration. (Courtesy of Morehead State University Space Science Center)

Fig. 25-37. **PocketQub and MR-FOD Launcher.** (Courtesy of Morehead State University Space Science Center)

and weight of a CubeSat. This should reduce the cost of the launch to 1/8 that of a CubeSat. The PocketQub and a PocketQub launcher are shown in Figs. 25-36 and 25-37. The launcher was developed as a multi PocketQub launcher that could hold 1–3 PocketQubs and reside inside a NanoSatellite from the University of Rome as shown in Fig. 25-38.

Going further, a new variation of the CricketSat is being developed called the Earth Odyssey Moonbeam. The EOM is a version of the CricketSat with a processor to generate Morse code transmission using the 5 mW 433 MHz transmitters used in car remote door openers. The size of the EOM would be such that 24 of them could be contained in the volume of a 1U CubeSat. These EOMs would operate with a small solar panel on each side used to charge an ultracapacitor. The EOM could be multiplexed so that a cloud of them could make space measurements when launched from an altitude below the ISS and have a short orbital life time.

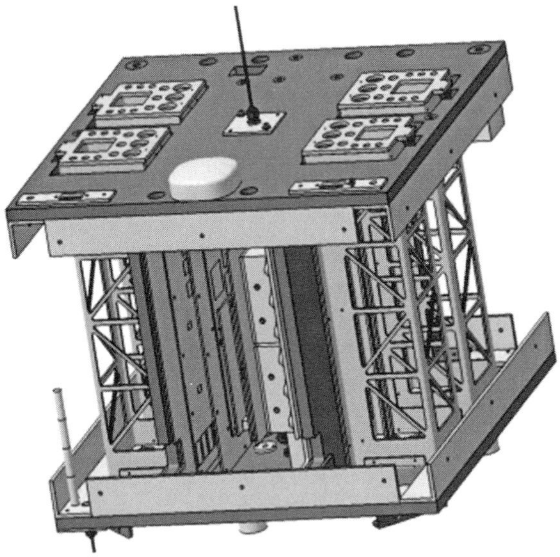

Fig. 25-38. EduSat Nanosatellite with PocketQub Launchers. (Courtesy of the University of Rome)

25.4.11 List of CubeSat Builders and Component Suppliers

Pumpkin, Inc. 750 Naples Street San Francisco, CA 94112 USA www.pumpkininc.com/	**Innovative Solutions in Space** Molengraaffsingel 12-14 2629 JD, Delft The Netherlands www.isispace.nl
Clyde Space Ltd Glasgow G20 0SP Scotland www.clyde-space.com	**GomSpace ApS** Niels Jernes Vej 10 9220 Aalborg East, Denmark www.gomspace.com
Surrey Satellite Technology Ltd Guildford GU2 7YE United Kingdom www.sstl.co.uk	**Astronautical Development, LLC** Morehead, KY 40351 USA www.astrodev.com
Sequoia Space CRA 9 N 62–44 (OFICINA 404), Bogotá, Colombia http://sequoiaspace.com	

25.5 Differences Between International Approaches to Space

Brian Harvey, ***Spaceflight Author***

The purpose of this section is to set international space programs in a comparative perspective before we look at how different countries approach their space endeavors and their approaches to development before lessons are drawn. As will be seen, the bipolar space development world of USA vs USSR has given way to a more tiered picture. The United States space program still dominates the world picture by size, funding, and ambition; followed by a second tier of Russia and China, both able to launch human flights; a third tier of space nations with unmanned, yet relatively large programs (e.g., Japan, Europe, India); and a fourth tier of emerging nations, like Iran. Some countries have followed approaches quite different from the United States, taking a statist route in support of economic and social development (e.g,. India), others emphasizing science (e.g., Europe). Perhaps the least understood is Russia, with its structure of institutes, design bureaus, long production runs, mass production, and non-obsolescence punctuated by occasional but impressive innovation. Its experience is doubly important, for it forms the model for the ambitious space program of China.

25.5.1 Comparative Perspective

We use 3 reference points in our comparative perspective: the historical timeline, launch rate, and budget.

Using the launch of a first satellite as a marker, world space programs developed in 3 waves. The first, historic wave was that of the old rivals, the Soviet Union (1957)

Table 25-6◀, Fig. 25-38, Eq. 25-5◀

Table 25-7. Waves of Space Development by First Satellite Launch.

Superpowers	
Soviet Union	1957
United States	1958
Middle-Range Powers	
France	1965
Japan	1970
China	1970
Britain	1971
India	1980
Emerging Nations	
Israel	1988
(Brazil)	(1997)
(North Korea)	(1998)
Iran	2009
(South Korea)	(2009)

Table 25-8. Total Space Launches, 1957–2009.

Soviet Union/Russia[1]	2,882
United States	1,375
Europe [2]	193
China	121
Japan	74
India	24
Israel	5
Iran	1

Defined as successful launches and attributed to the country of the launch site or launcher.
[1] Includes Ukraine and the Zenit 3 Sea Launch
[2] Includes pre European Space Agency launches by France, Britain

and then the United States (1958), the space super powers. The second wave was that of what were then considered the middle ranking space powers: France, Japan, China, Britain, and India (1965–1980). This group has mutated recently. China with its human flight capability and future ambitions may now be considered among the super powers, while the British launcher was cancelled and the French program evolved into the European Space Agency (ESA). The third group is what we may call the "emerging space powers" of Israel and Iran, countries which have successfully launched satellites and 3 countries which have attempted to do so but so far without success: Brazil, North Korea, and South Korea. All are developing small, specialized, highly focused space programs to meet their particular needs and political priorities. These 3 waves are captured in Table 25-7: The launch rate has broadly followed the pattern of historic evolution. The first country in space, the Soviet Union, has launched more rockets than any other. Although the early years of space exploration saw more American than Soviet launches, from the late 1960s the Soviet launch rate was higher, climbing to an average of up to 2 launches a week in the 1980s. With the collapse of the Soviet Union, its launch rate fell by between 2/3 and 3/4, but in only 2 years at the end of the 1990s did it slip below that of the United States, a position from which it quickly recovered. It is still not generally realized that Russia has been, by the measurement of annual launches, the leading space faring nation throughout this century so far. From the 1970s, with the evolution of the Ariane rocket, Europe has generally found itself in third place, behind the two superpowers. Table 25-8 captures the historic figures for successful launches.

What may be more useful, though, is to look at the figures for recent years, which takes out of the equation, the high historic Soviet rates and puts the emerging powers in a clearer perspective. Here, if we look at successful launches for 2006–2009, we see how Russia continues to dominate but that China has moved into third place (Table 25-9). China has overtaken Europe (despite temporarily slipping behind Europe in 2009 because of a number of launcher delays). Otherwise, the proportions of launches has been stable over the past decade, with relatively low launch rates from Japan, India, and the emerging space powers.

Table 25-9. Total Space Launches, 2006–2009.

Russia	118
United States	63
China	32
Europe	24
Japan	12
India	8
Israel	1
Iran	1

Disaggregating these figures, they reflect quite different areas of interest, endeavor, and funding. United States missions, despite being half those of Russia, cover the broadest scope and range: military, human, science, applications, deep space. The most important elements in the Russian program are human-related missions in support of the International Space Station and commercial launches which generate scarce revenue. Likewise, European launches are dominated by commercial launches on the Ariane 5. The Chinese and Japanese programs cover a broad range, from Lunar to human-related applications, while those of India and Israel are very specialized (applications and military reconnaissance, respectively).

Using our third reference point, budget and levels of spending, a different picture emerges. The United States dominate world space spending, more than all the other countries combined (Table 25-10). Such a budget has enabled the United States to have the most comprehensive space program in the world, covering almost every possible field of exploration and application. Next comes Europe, which is a combination of the European Space

Table 25-10. Estimated World Space Spending, 2008, in FY08$M.

United States	44,000
Europe	10,000
Russia	4,000
China	4,000
Japan	2,500
India	800
Based on [Pirard, 2009].	

Agency and national programs. Figures after that are problematical, due to issues of exchange rate measurement, the basis on which budgets are calculated, and the measurement of labor costs. The Russian figure does not include its vast, obsolete but workable infrastructure, whose costs were paid off many years ago. The country in this group to watch is India, whose spending level was historically quite low but which has accelerated more than any other nation in recent years. Most of these figures primarily reflect the level of government investment and may not include the value of commercially sensitive foreign earnings. These are significant in the case of Europe (the main role of Ariane 5 is as a commercial launcher) and Russia, which transformed its program from the most state-dependent to the most commercially driven in the world in only 10 years.

It is also important to disaggregate these figures. Half the American spending is military, divided between the various branches of the military. By contrast, the proportion of military spending in Europe is low and limited to national programs (the European Space Agency is entirely civilian). The proportions within the other countries are not known precisely.

Assembling these 3 elements together—historic evolution, launch rates, and funding—we now get a composite picture of 4 tiers: the United States, the largest in scope, funding, size, and ambition; the other 2 superpowers of Russia and China; more modest but well established programs (e.g., Europe, Japan, India); and the emerging nations (e.g., Iran).

25.5.2 Philosophy and Approach

Space programs fulfill comparable, but subtly different roles, in different countries. The twin driving forces in the 2 original space programs were science (the International Geophysical Year, 1957–1958) and a bundle of amorphous but real objectives which include national prestige, technology as a national economic driver, and an ambition to be first. This, as we know, developed into a full-blown competition, "the space race," supplemented by a series of military programs and purposes. Both superpowers developed what may be called comprehensive programs that covered the entire gamut of space activity: human, scientific, applications, military, and deep space. In the end, only the United States had the resources to sustain this pace in the long run and the Soviet Union retreated from a number of areas (e.g., deep space exploration, weather satellites, and space science).

Other countries, or groups of countries, lacking resources of such scale, have had to be selective in the fields of space exploration that they chose to develop. The European Space Agency, for example, has a long-term, multi-annual science program, which is the only mandatory element to which all its members must subscribe, leaving member states free to choose to which other programs they wish to contribute (e.g., launchers, human spaceflight, applications). In Japan, the National Space Development Agency (NASDA, which, together with ISAS, was the precursor of JAXA.) focused on applications important for the country's technological development, for example, in the field of telecommunications. China focused on those fields most important for its economic priorities, namely telecommunications (telephone, television), weather warning (*Feng Yun* satellites), remote sensing (*Zi Yuan* satellites), and navigation (*Beidou* system). Israel's program is almost entirely military, designed to provide photo reconnaissance intelligence on its neighbors.

Perhaps the most remarkable example is India. Here, the great visionary of the Indian space program, Vikram Sarabhai, saw the space program as a purposeful instrument of economic and social development. In his most famous declaration, he said:

> **We do not have the fantasy of competing with economically advanced nations in the exploration of the Moon or the planets or manned space-flight. But we are convinced that if we are to play a meaningful role nationally and in the community of nations, we must be second to none in the application of advanced technologies to the real problems of society which we find in our country. The application of sophisticated technologies and methods of analysis of our problems is not to be confused with embarking on grandiose schemes whose primary impact is for show rather than for progress measured in hard economic and social terms (Address at Thumba, 3rd February 1968).**

Accordingly, the space program was used to bring educational television to the villages; to provide weather warning for monsoons and floods; to provide the telephone infrastructure; and for remote sensing (e.g., detection of water, crop mapping, urban planning). It was focused on the needs of the poor, who got television before anyone else;* the rural areas; and those in most social need (e.g., farmers, women). It is still highly focused around practical applications, a recent example being telemedicine. Only in recent years has the Indian space program expanded beyond this highly targeted remit into wider fields. Even then, its Chadrayan Lunar mission used an adapted Earth remote sensing satellite and its human spaceflight program is likely to focus on Earth observations.

Space programs have generally been most successful when part of a national, state-led vision of development. Although the United States would be officially ideologically averse to such a role, in practice such considerations were far from absent in the period of the early space race, when space development was linked to the need for improved educational performance and foreign policy imperatives. Even today, it is implicitly linked to scientific leadership across multiple fields. Most countries have benefitted not only from individuals who have had a strong vision of space-led development, not just India but also Japan (Hideo Itokawa), China (Tsien Hsue Shen), and of course Russia (Konstantin Tsiolkovsky, Sergei Korolev) but also from governments which have a clear idea as to how space programs fit into national development. Here, the most striking contrast is between France and Britain in 1960. Most observers assumed that Britain, based on its technological and industrial assets, would be the European leader in space research. Instead, the Fifth Republic in France made spaceflight an integral part of a program of state-led economic planning: the development of a series of high-tech industries (e.g., railways, aircraft), industrial decentralization (e.g., Toulouse), and the development of a workforce of highly skilled engineers and scientists. By contrast, Britain is, 50 years later, still inching its way to its first space policy, but has meantime lost most of its capacity and fallen behind France, Germany, and Italy in its economic indicators.

25.5.3 Approaches to Organization

In the institutional construction of space programs, these countries have many elements in common. These are:

- The setting of high-level objectives at state or government level;
- In some countries, a national advisory body to advise on high-level objectives and to set middle-level targets and objectives (e.g., Japan);
- The entrusting of their execution to state agencies (NASA in the United States, CNES in France, JAXA in Japan, ISRO in India, the new UKSA in Britain).

In practice in most countries, the space agency has become much more than an instrument of government, but has refined objectives, policies, and priorities over periods much longer than the electoral cycle, creating a long-term dynamic for development.

Our original modeling of how governments approached space program development dates to the 1960s. Essentially it revolved around the following paradigm, which was that in the United States, Congress set high-level objectives while NASA supervised the development of programs through open competition by leading manufacturers (many drawn from the aviation world). Early American space achievements were celebrated as a triumph of the best competition of private industry, a point once noted by Frank Borman as he mused in *Apollo 8*, awaiting liftoff ("We're sitting on a million parts, all of which must function perfectly—and all built by the lowest bidder") [Young, Silock, and Dunne, 1969]. By contrast, so the model went, the Soviet system was a command-and-control top-down one in which the Soviet leadership set objectives and assigned tasks to state industries, which, as the outcome of the Moon race proved, were clearly not up to the task.

Although it is a well known, accepted narrative, in reality, this modeling is erroneous. It transpired that the old Soviet Union was full of rival design bureaus which competed for contracts from a leadership whose decisions were often the outcome of the interplay of many parties, industries, the military, scientists, designers, and politicians. Examination of the outcome of the Moon race told us that the Soviet Union did have the technology to get cosmonauts to the Moon, but was let down by its failure to manage wasteful rivalries between the bureaus. By contrast, NASA exhibited the skills of command-and-control hitherto ascribed to the socialist economies and was infinitely more successful at handling the aerospace companies (and their political interlocutors).

The design bureau did mark out a fundamental difference between the American and Russian system, one which persists to this day. It is also relevant to the up-and-coming Chinese space program which was, institutionally at least, designed along Soviet lines in the 1950s and 1960s. The Soviet/Russian approach to missions and spacecraft design is based on a 3-stage architecture not well understood in the west:

- The institute, where scientists present concepts for missions to government for adoption;
- The experimental design bureau (OKB in Russian), which turns them into practical effect and builds and tests the first hardware;
- The production organization or factory, which produces or mass-produces the item in question.

The Russian scientific community is dominated by several thousand institutes, a marked difference from the American system, where equivalent learning takes place in universities (continental Europe still has a strong tradition of institutes, of which the Russian institutes were historically an outgrowth). These institutes, which range from the large to the tiny, are broadly part of the system supervised under the Academy of Sciences [Graham and Dezhina, 2008]. Although criticized abroad for separating science from the teaching community, they have produced high-quality outputs and served state developmental needs well. There is an argument that institute-

* Television was first distributed to the poor in the villages via comsats and dishes to transmit educational TV (e.g., farming, literacy, hygiene). Only later was there national TV for everyone.

based development enables a high level of theoretical work to be undertaken, which can be the basis of quality engineering, science, and their application. Russian rocket engine development, probably the most advanced in the world, was based on institutes that date to the 1920s, with, literally, strong institutional memories.

The critical element and lynchpin of this trio, though, is the OKB, the design bureau. Here, the old Soviet space program developed a series of specialized OKBs, each normally associated with its leading designer, like Sergei Korolev (OKB-1, now Energiya), Dmitri Kozlov (OKB-1 §3, now Progress in Samara), OKB-7 Arsenal (military satellites, St Petersburg), Mikhail Rechetnev (OKB-10, communication satellites, Krasnoyarsk), Vladimir Chalomei (OKB-52, now the Khrunichev company), Semyon Lavochkin (OBK-301), Valentin Glushko (Gas Dynamics Laboratory, rocket engines), Mikhail Yangel (OKB-586, now Yuzhnoye, Dnepropetrovsk, Zenit rockets).

The design bureau, which has no direct American comparator, was often given premises of former private factories confiscated by the Bolsheviks, with a leading engineer put in charge (a "general designer") and it was expected to deliver the goods under the system of socialist competition developed by Stalin. There were high levels of incentives for delivery (financial rewards for the workforce, the prospect of new assignments, influence in shaping future missions and requirements, and political access).

Any new project or spacecraft design was expected to run through the spectrum of *institute—OKB development—production*, with government approval at each point. The thoroughness of the approval process incentivized the OKBs to develop ever newer "modifications" of their existing designs, which, being merely "modifications", did not have to seek fresh round of governmental approval (hence many had the letter "M" after their designator). This is most evident in the design of the piloted spacecraft, *Soyuz,* which dates to 1960 and which has since evolved into the *Soyuz T, Soyuz TM, Soyuz TMA* and the new *Soyuz TMA-0M.* Although the concept of the satellite "bus" is seen as a western invention, it has its roots in the Soviet system where a standard design was used as the basis of a whole series of subsequent adaptations and evolutions. The original design for a photo reconnaissance satellite, the *Zenit*, dates to 1958, but became the bus that was adapted for human flight (*Vostok, Voskhod*), a series of photo reconnaissance satellites (*Zenit*), biological cabins (*Bion*) and still flies today for micro-gravity research (*Foton*). The Cosmos program, the main scientific program begun in 1962, was built around a standard bus (called the DS, or *Dnepropetrovsky Sputnik* after the city where it was built), with an initial batch of 18 ordered, later replaced by the DS U series, with 30 missions. At a time when most western satellites were still hand-crafted for individual missions, the Soviet Union had already introduced the concept of the standard bus.

It was a system adapted with considerable resourcefulness. In 1972, the Soviet Union began a program of astronomical missions called "the great observatories." Rather than construct purpose-built spacecraft, existing models were adapted like a Venera (Venus) spacecraft for the *Astron* observatory, a Mars probe for the *Granat* observatory, Progress for the *Gamma* observatory, and a space station module for the *Kvant* observatory. The total number of fundamental spacecraft designs in the Soviet or Russian program is surprisingly small, with significant cost benefits.

An important feature of the Soviet system was the system of financial control and accountability (or the lack of it). Financial transactions in the sense understood in western capitalist countries were minimal and took the form of bookkeeping movements rather than cash, and if a project were designated a matter of "supreme national importance," resources could be commandeered almost at will. The downside of the lack of financial control was that the old program tolerated a relatively high failure rate. The first soft-landing on the Moon in 1966 was preceded by 10 failures: the chief designer could not be called before any congressional committee for wasting money, and no one could calculate how much was lost anyway (though he could and did receive angry phone calls from the General Secretary). There was no incentive for building spacecraft to fly long missions. At a time when American communications satellites had on-orbit lifetimes of 10 years, their Russian comparators were averaging 25 months: it was simpler to build and launch a replacement. Only in recent years, under the new pressures of a capitalist Russia, has a sustained effort been made to lengthen the mission durations of applications satellites.

Russian spacecraft were optimized around short missions. Several science missions were mistakenly interpreted as failures because the spacecraft transmitted only a few weeks or months, while American equivalents would broadcast for years—but in the Russian case, they would be replaced on orbit by another, also designed to return a large quantity of data in a short period of time. On the other hand, little expense might be spared in the development of new systems. Early Lunar, Earth orbiting, Venus, and Mars probes were sophisticated, with high-quality instruments, extensive instrument suites and related systems (e.g., cameras). Testing regimes were extensive and demanding, the Venera landers for Venus being a case in point. As a result, missions generated a high scientific return.

The absence of commercial imperatives meant that many of the drivers evident in the development of American and other space programs were absent within the Russian and Soviet system: it was easier to design a sound, basic system and evolve it over time. Short periods of often impressive innovation (e.g., closed cycle engine operation) have been followed by lengthy periods of evolution and operations. The R-7 launcher, for example, was in concept in 1948 and finally designed in 1953. It has now been launched 1,751 times and its most recent iteration is the new model developed for launch at the European Space Agency base in Guyana. It is, arguably, entirely obsolete, but also reliable and profitable. The design flaws were ironed out of the system not years but decades ago. Similarly, the *Nauka* large science module, due for launch to the International Space Station in 2012–2013, is based on the *Almaz* space station design of 1964. This particular module was built as a backup to the first module of the International Space Station, *Zarya*, in 1998, and will have sat in the hangar for the better part of 15 years before launch—a situation unimaginable in the United States. But again, it is a system that brings considerable gains in cost, and reliability.

Returning to the R-7, it was and is a system designed for durability and simplicity—durability to cope with climatic conditions en route to and at the launch site, simplicity so as to enable it to be operated by successive launch teams of relatively low-skilled workers (until recently, normally military), "problems that can be fixed with a household wrench." Liftoff takes place when engine thrust exceeds launcher weight, thereby freeing the launch clamps held in place by nothing more than a series of balanced weights. Foreign observers are amazed at how launches take place in all weathers, with temperatures reported as low as –50 °C. Indian officials coming to Baikonour to watch an Indian satellite launched in freezing dense fog automatically assumed that it had been canceled, only to be told that the faint red glow in the distance was their rocket taking off. Relative simplicity of function means that the last delay to a piloted Soyuz launch was in 1971 (there have been delays on the new *Soyuz 2* launch system, but due exclusively to electronic problems arising from the introduction of digital systems). This approach produces considerable gains in schedule and cost. At the same time, it would be a mistake to regard the approach or workmanship as crude. When a group of German rocket enthusiasts inspected an R-7 on the pad at Baikonour, the first thing that struck them was the quality of workmanship: "every rivet was perfect," they noted.

The Chinese space program, as noted earlier, was institutionally based on the Soviet system. At this stage, we do not have sufficient information to model the Chinese approach nowadays and the degree to which it has adhered to this paradigm. The Chinese follow a similar Academy of Sciences system and we know that there are state design bureaus in both Beijing and Shanghai, sometimes in rivalry with one another. Universities, though, may play a more important role than institutes, for many of the scientific papers arising from the program come from universities, while new spacecraft technologies are developed in the technological universities. An important area in which China differs from the old Soviet program is its stricter accounting and bookkeeping systems. The Chinese space program has a multi-year but finite amount of funding and the message "we can't afford failures" has been drummed into the program at all levels from the senior management. Quality control has been an obsession, even at a cost of the speed of the program (a feature of the human space program, for example, has been its slow pace). The best example was the unmanned *Shenzhou 3* mission, which after several unsatisfactory months of pad testing at the launch site in north west China was sent all the way back to Beijing on the railway for a fresh round of quality control tests. The delays cost 6 months, but the mission was successful. The emphasis on quality control has paid off, for there have been no failures on the *Long March* launcher since 1996 (albeit some final stage malfunctions).

Perhaps the most "statist" space program is actually the Indian. From its establishment in 1947, the Indian state was built around strong concepts of state planning, accompanied by a wave of institution-building (Sarabhai alone set up 47 institutes) and a policy of indigenization. This is understandable in a historical context, for India had been robbed of its scientific and industrial heritage during the colonial period, industry filling principally a production function and being denied opportunities for its own research and development. An important priority in the Indian space program has been to learn methods and approaches developed in other, more advanced countries, and then to apply them by constructing them at home. This is most evident in the communications satellite program, INSAT, which began as foreign built and foreign launched. The next series introduced domestic-designed and built components. The next series was entirely domestically built, but still foreign launched. With the new GSLV launcher, INSAT is domestically built and domestically launched. The statist approach is in evidence at the ISRO Satellite Center in Bengaluru, where satellites are designed and built under one roof, the center having over 2,400 staff. Although Small and Medium Size Enterprises (SMEs) are involved in supplying parts of Indian space hardware, the main development is carried out by a single cradle-to-grave state center of the type we always associated (we now know wrongly) with the Soviet Union.

By contrast, the space programs of Japan and Europe have followed what is a more recognizably American approach to manufacturing and development. The relationships between Japanese governments and their large industrial corporations have traditionally been a close one, and it is little surprise that contracts for launchers, satellites, hardware, and facilities have gone to the large corporations like Mitsubishi, Mitsubishi Electrical Co., Nissan, and Ishakawajima Heavy Industries. In Europe, the picture is more complex. The introduction of the single market in 1992 was accompanied by a set of procurement rules designed to promote free competition, open the market to new entrants, and level the playing field for smaller players and SMEs. At the same time, ESA is committed to the principle of the *juste retour* (fair return) whereby each country receives contracts broadly comparable to the budget it provides for ESA in the first place, something which clearly puts France in a strong position. In reality, *juste retour* is becoming harder and harder to calculate on a country-by-country basis because of the rapid pace of consolidation of high-tech industries in Europe, where the traditional national company has given way to multi-national companies with branches and affiliates scattered across the member states. In recent years in fact, several new, smaller companies have won contracts both for ESA and national space programs (e.g., OHB Kayser Threde).

25.5.4 Conclusions and Lessons Arising

Overall, approaches to space programs and operations have more features in common than there are differences. A certain convergence is hardly surprising, granted the level of international cooperation that has been present since the International Geophysical Year (1957–1958), the intensity of bilateral and multilateral cooperation, and the influence of high profile projects which require inter-agency and inter-company working (e.g., International Space Station, recent unmanned Mars missions). India and China are two countries that stick out from the convergent model: China, because we know less about its internal philosophy, approaches, and organization; and India, because of its unique approach of state-led development and indigenization for economic and social purposes. China may be less different than we imagine and as it reaches its goal of full parity with the superpowers, we may know more.

The traditional distinction in development, logistics, and manufacturing was always the bipolar one of USA vs USSR. The lengthy exposition of the Soviet/Russian program here shows that the differences were not what we thought they were and that competition for design, contracts, and manufacturing by the leading contenders was as real in both (though better handled at political level in the United States). The Soviet/Russian system, though, does present us with a number of learning points. These points do not argue that their system is intrinsically "better" but does argue that it has merits and should in any case be understood. It is a program which produced high-quality engineering, products, and scientific returns, often at remarkably low cost; was sufficiently flexible to survive and rebound from the country's economic collapse around it; and leaves Russia still the world's leading space faring nation by number of annual launches. Many of its distinctive features derive from its particular and now archaic form of bookkeeping, commercial imperatives (or the lack of them), academic traditions, and peristaltic approach to innovation, all of which had up and downsides.

Our learning points are:

- The role of institutes in concept and mission design, important for theory, applications, standards of excellence, scientific drive, and institutional memory
- The use of the key feature of the experimental design bureaus, the OKBs
- Development of a relatively small number of spacecraft (and rocket) designs and buses, which are modified and adapted for a broad range of purposes over lengthy periods, in some cases over 60 years, with considerable cost savings
- A focus on simplicity, durability, reliability, the avoidance of over design, and operation by people of all skill levels
- The merits of using several spacecraft on short duration missions, rather than smaller numbers (or a single number) of larger, longer duration spacecraft vulnerable to single point failures

References

For annotated bibliography of alternative spacecraft designs, see the book website.

Barkow, B., A. Steindl, H. Troger, and G. Widermann. 2003. "Various Methods of Controlling the Deployment of a Tethered Satellite." *Journal of Vibration and Control*, vol. 9. Jan. pp.187–208.

Cassapakis, Costa. 2008. "Gossamer Space Structures." AIAA SDM Gossamer Structures Forum. Schaumberg, IL. Apr.

Cassapakis, Costa and M. Thomas. 1995. "Inflatable Structures Technology Development Overview." AIM-974. San Antonio, TX.

Clarke, Arthur C. 1962. *Profiles of the Future: An Inquiry into the Limits of the Possible*. New York: Hardper & Row.

Crook, M.R. 2009. "NPS CubeSat Launcher Design, Process, and Requirements." Masters Thesis. Naval Postgraduate School. Monterey, CA. Jun.

EUROCKOT Launch Services. 2003. "EUROCKOT Successfully Launches MOM—Rockot Hits Different Orbit." Jun. 30.

Forward, R. L. and R. P. Hoyt. 1995. "Failsafe Multiline Hoytether Lifetimes." 31st AIAA/SAE/ASME/ASEE Joint Propulsion Conference. AIAA-1995-2890. San Diego, CA. Jul.

Forward, R. L., R. P. Hoyt, and C. W. Uphoff. 2000. "The Terminator Tether™: A Spacecraft Deorbit Device." *Journal of Spacecraft Rockets*, vol. 37, No. 2. Mar–Apr.

Freeland, R. E., S. Bard, G. Veal, G. Bilyeu, C. Cassapakis, T. Campbell, and M. Bailey. 1996. "Inflatable Antenna Technology with Preliminary Shuttle Experiment Results and Potential Applications." 18th Annual Meeting and Symposium of the Antenna Measurement Techniques Association, Seattle, WA. Sept. 30–Oct. 3rd.

Freeland, R. E., G. Bilyeu, G. Veal, and M. Mikulas. 1998. "Inflatable Deployable Space Structures Technology Summary." 49th Congress of the International Astronautical Federation. IAF-98-1.5.01. Melbourne, Australia: Sept. 28–Oct. 2.

Graham, Loren, and Irina Dezhina. 2008. *Science in the New Russia--Crisis, Aid, Reform*. Bloomington, IN: Indiana University Press.

Greschik, G., M. Mikulas, and R. Freeland. 1999. "The Nodal Concept of Deployment and the Scale Model Testing of its Application to a Membrane Antenna." AIAA-99-1523.

Jenkins, C. H. M. 1997. *Gossamer Spacecraft: Membrane and Inflatable Structures Technology for Space Applications*. Reston, VA: AIAA.

Lorenzini, E. C., D. K. Mowery, and C. C. Rupp. 1995. "SEDS-II Deployment Control Law and Mission Design." 4th International Conference on Tethers In Space. Apr. pp. 669–683.

Melville, Neil. 2006. "European Perspectives on a Global Educational Ground Station Network." 1st International Ground Station Network. University of Tokyo, Japan. Jul.

Moravec, H. 1977. "A Non-Synchronous Orbital Skyhook." *Journal of the Astronautical Sciences*, vol. 25, No. 4. Oct–Dec. pp. 307–322.

Munakata, Riki, et al. 2009. "CubeSat Design Specification, Rev 12." The CubeSat Program, Cal Poly SLO.

Palisoc, A., G. Veal, G. Greschik, C. Cassapakis, and M. Mikulas. 1998. "Geometry Attained by Pressurized Membranes." SPIE International Symposium on Astronomical Telescopes and Instrumentation, Kona, HI, Mar. 20–28. pp. 747–757,

Palisoc, A. and Y. Huang. 1997. "Design Tool for Inflatable Space Structures." AIM-974. Tustin, CA.

Pirard, T. 2009. *European Space Directory*. Paris ESD Partners.

Poe, G. D. and B. G. Patrick. 2008. "Zero-CTE Polyimides for Athermal Optical Membranes." *SPIE Proc*. 706114-1.

Satter, C. M, and R. E. Freeland. 1995. "Inflatable Structures Technology Applications and Requirements." The Space Programs and Technical Conference. AIAA-95-3737. Huntsville, AL. Sept. 26–28.

Shirville, G. and B. Klofas. 2007. "GENSO" A Global Ground Station Network." 2007 AMSAT Symposium. Pittsburgh, PA. Oct. 26.

Stone, N. H., W. J. Raitt, and K. H. Wright. 1999. "The TSS-1R Electrodynamic Tether Experiment: Scientific Technological Results." *Adv. Space Res.*, vol. 24, no. 8. pp. 1037–1045.

Thomas, M. and G. J. Griese. 1980. "Pressurized Antennas for Space Radars." AIAA-80-1928. Newport Beach, CA.

Young, Hugo, Bryan Silock, and Peter Dunn. 1969. *Journey to Tranquility*. London: Jonatham Cape.

26 Launch Vehicles

James S. Wood, ***NASA Kennedy Space Center***

"...launch remains a high-risk element affecting mission success"

—NASA Policy Directive 8610.23C "Launch Vehicle Technical Oversight Policy," August [2006].

"The only natural predator of a spacecraft is a launch vehicle."

—Major General Nathan Lindsay, USAF (retired)

This chapter provides guidance on the acquisition and management of a launch. The mechanics of flying a vehicle to orbit are addressed only insofar as they bear on the conditions and challenges that the spacecraft customer should anticipate. The scientific principles and technical challenges of flying a vehicle to orbit are a lot of fun to discuss, as we will see in Chap. 27. Most of the spacecraft customers with whom I've interacted, view launch vehicles with awe, pride, and attraction, only until they realize that they've got a mission to fly, unexpected risks and expenses, and a budget that's tight in every conceivable way. There will only be a few times, like the moment captured in Fig. 26-1, when you look at the launch vehicle as a cool rocket. Most of the time, it will be a very expensive nuisance, and one of the greatest risks to the success of your mission.

This chapter makes considerable use of standards and policies published by NASA and the US Department of Defense (DoD), for the reason that the documents cited are publicly available and represent good guidance for use in varying forms throughout the commercial, government and international communities. Much of the launch business takes benefit from the standardization inherent in a well-established commercial industry, such as telecommunications. The documents cited here are also mostly written at a high level, not something you need a PhD to understand, but they provide adequate understanding to a technical or project manager of how the subject matter relates to their mission. In-depth treatments of each topic are available in a wide variety of other published sources.

Fig. 26-1. Orbital's Stargazer L-1011 Launch Aircraft Arriving with a Pegasus XL. After a Ferry Flight to the US Army's Reagan Test Site in the Republic of the Marshall Islands. (Photo courtesy of: NASA/Ivy Springer)

The commercial launch vehicle community makes selective use of government standards, being mostly free of the contract levied standards that were features of the pre-Commercial Space Launch Act era. The ULA Delta II pictured in Fig. 26-2 is a commercially designed and managed evolution of a vehicle that was originally developed under Government standards. NASA and military standards today are more likely to serve as the framework of terms and guidance to approach some of the technical problems that will be described here, rather than demanding rigid compliance to the standard itself.

Fig. 26-2. A United Launch Alliance (ULA) Delta II Lifts Off from Cape Canaveral Air Force Station, Florida. (Photo courtesy of NASA)

This is equally true for International Commercial Launch Services, though with slightly different heritage government standards and policies. The European Cooperation for Space Standardization (ECSS), which is supported by the European Space Agency (ESA) and other commercial entities, offers available guidance in a variety of areas, including launch. Similarly, the AIAA routinely partners with the ANSI and the IEEE to publish technical guidance that may be useful in planning the launch phase of a mission. JPL, APL and the Aerospace Corporation have public accessible guidance policies as well. Ultimately, when seeking technical guidance for your launch phase, there is reliable assistance available from these reputable institutes.

This chapter addresses a subset of significant historical developments over the last two decades. It covers the selection process, launch environments, and features that one may encounter. It also features a listing of available launch vehicles (e.g., Soyuz, as shown in Fig. 26-3), along with information about their use, performance, and cost data.

26.1 Launch Vehicle Selection

The launch vehicle selection process focuses on balancing performance, availability, risk, and cost. If circumstances are such that you have many choices available to carry your spacecraft to orbit, choose the most mass delivered to orbit as you can afford. *Performance* for a launch vehicle universally means separated mass delivered to orbit. In this context, performance is a pretty big part of the intermediate and final iterations in the selection process. The physics and economics of this are straightforward, and favor seeking the most delivered mass at the least cost you can find among credible launch service providers. *Credibility* in this context is, and will remain, a subjectively-defined term depending on the user's risk posture.

The following subsections are intended to help you develop your own idea of credible selection factors. Figure 26-4 is offered as guidance for the overall process flow, but with the acknowledgment that circumstances will vary with each spacecraft customer, many times rendering some of the specific guidance and recommended trade studies inconsequential.

Fig. 26-3. Night Launch of a Samara Space Center (TsSKB-Progress) Soyuz Vehicle from Baikonur Cosmodrome, Kazakhstan. (Photo courtesy of NASA)

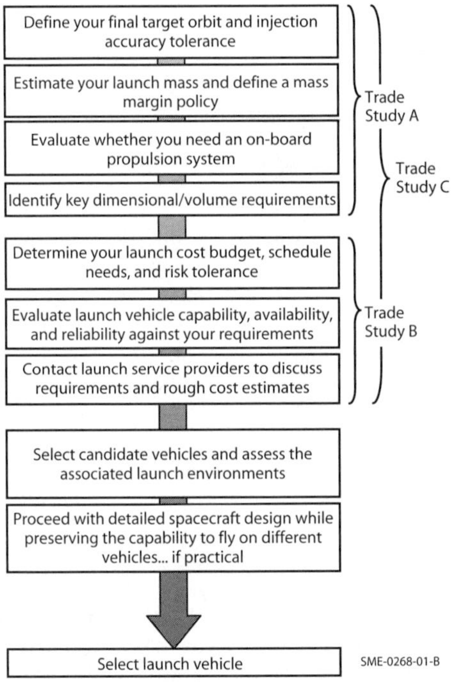

Fig. 26-4. Launch Vehicle Selection Process Flow.

26.1.1 Target Orbit and Injection Accuracy

The process flow in Fig. 26-4 begins with the desired target orbit, likely to be the first known quantity dictated by your mission, be it communications, exploration, surveillance, educational, or astronomy. As with commercial airlines, launch vehicle fleets are developed with a select number of missions in mind, and modification away from those target missions can become costly. Thus, selection of the target orbit becomes a reasonable first-cut at narrowing the field of candidate launch vehicles.

The importance of injection accuracy in your selection is dependent upon the mission you intend to execute, as well as whether or not your spacecraft will have an onboard propulsion capability. If so, how much of your velocity budget can you afford to reserve for vehicle injection errors? A modern commercial launch vehicle with digital avionics and a liquid upper stage engine can accomplish highly-precise interplanetary injections or deliver spacecraft to precise parking orbits to accomplish a subsequent navigation into a formation of low-altitude spacecraft. Table 26-1 shows some example injection accuracies that are typical of the industry. The values shown, published in the respective vehicle user guides, are also typically conservative statements of capability. Your actual performance will probably be better.

Table 26-1. Example Altitude and Inclination Injection Accuracies.

Vehicle	LEO Apse Altitude (km)	Inclination (deg)
Minotaur IV (HAPS)*	< ±18.5	±0.05
Dnepr	±4–10	±0.04–0.05
Rockot	±1.5%**	±0.05
Delta II (two-stage)	±9.3	±0.05

* Hydrazine Auxiliary Propulsion System
**e.g., ±6 km for 300 km altitude

The differences between the accuracies shown in Table 26-1 are often artifacts of convenience or heritage notation, rather than representing real differences in capability. For the US vehicles, ±10 nm and ±5 nm, respectively, are good round heritage figures. Launch vehicles with the capability to achieve precisely-timed liquid rocket engine shutdown commanded by their on-board guidance algorithms will all realize comparable injection accuracy capabilities. These capabilities are generally sufficient for even the most demanding spacecraft missions.

For launch vehicles with a solid rocket motor final stage (or *kick motor*), the injection accuracy problem is a harder one for the vehicle to manage. The contest for achieved accuracy between a solid kick motor (without any liquid rocket orbit adjustment or *trim* capability) and a liquid upper stage should always go to the liquid stage. Limited technology available today precludes executing a commanded shutdown of a solid rocket motor, which is unlikely to change in the next decade or so, because there's no obvious need. The solid motors in use today shut down when they run out of propellant. The consequence is that the solid stage will always deliver a fixed impulse, but due to manufacturing variations the delivered impulse can only be estimated with so much certainty. To compensate, some vehicle providers have developed velocity management algorithms in their onboard guidance software, while others have made use of small, low-thrust, liquid rocket orbit adjustment packages or *trim stages*. The Minotaur IV HAPS is an example of an optional capability that can be used for increased accuracy injection, or multiple orbit adjustments to service multiple payloads with an otherwise all-solid vehicle, which achieves the same accuracy as their larger liquid upper stage cousins. However, liquid trim stages are usually an option, not a baseline, and they come at increased cost (and reduction in delivered mass) that has to be balanced against the cost of using the spacecraft's own propulsion system to achieve the same result.

26.1.2 Spacecraft Launch Mass and Margin Policy

This discussion starts with reserving your mass margin; you're going to need it. The NASA GSFCs *GOLD Rules* [2009] provide guidance on the subject of mass margin, recommending 30% "dry mass" margin at the initiation of concept studies, stepping down in specific increments (e.g., 20% at PDR, 15% at CDR), plus a *three sigma* propellant margin (if the spacecraft carries a propulsion system) to cover worst case launch vehicle performance, worst case spacecraft mass properties, and other performance penalties, ESA [2005]. Guidance on the subject is comparable across the full design spectrum, only a bit more lenient with respect to dry mass margin, recommending only 20% during assessment studies.

Margin policy may differ according to circumstances, for example, GSFC mass margin policy may not be practical for very small spacecraft like the 6 kg PPOD (Fig. 26-5).

The use of fixed recurring structures and components allow a considerably smaller mass reserve to be maintained at various points in the design cycle. The message here is to think about and document as a mass margin policy early in the design phase, and then manage to it.

The term *dry mass* refers to the mass of your spacecraft prior to loading any propellants. Another term that you will encounter from the launch vehicle community is *separated mass*, which refers to the total mass that separates from the launch vehicle. This is significant because, in most cases, that separated mass will be the spacecraft plus part of the weight of the separation system provided by the launch vehicle. Part of the separation system flies away with you, usually the forward mating ring of a circular payload attach fitting. The mass of the metallic ring or other mating hardware is relatively insignificant to larger spacecraft, but can become significant to a mission in the smaller classes of service. The mass of the *flyaway* portion of the separation system has to be understood and counted as part of your dry mass budget and on-orbit mass properties. Elsewhere in this chapter, I will simply use the term *delivered mass* synonymous with separated mass.

Another term you will encounter during the selection process, one that will stay with you for the remainder of the mission, is *contract mass* or *contract performance*. This is the separated mass that the launch service provider contractually commits to deliver. When a launch service

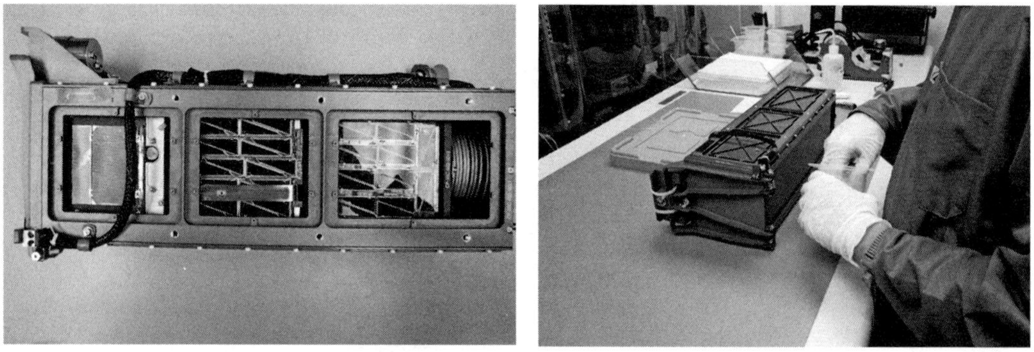

Fig. 26-5. Educational Launch of a Nano-Satellite Mission (ELaNa-1) PPOD with Three CubeSats: Montana State University's E1P, Kentucky Space Consortium's KySat, and University of Colorado-Boulder's Hermes. (Photo courtesy of The CubeSat Program, California Polytechnic State University)

provider signs a contract that obligates them to deliver a certain mass margin, they will invariably reserve performance margin to protect themselves against:

- Production engine performance variations
- Production dry mass variations
- Vehicle Mass growth due to upgrades
- Other contributors that can reduce the delivered mass

Unless other arrangements have been made in the contract, this is not your margin to use, and most likely never will be. This might seem unfair, especially when your own management and your customer are criticizing you for inadequate spacecraft mass margins, while you're looking at many kilograms worth of unused propellant or meters per second of velocity margin on the launch side. However unfair it might seem, from a business standpoint, maintaining this margin could be critical for the launch service provider. If they were unable to meet their contractual performance commitment, they could lose money. If there was a failure, an insurance claim could be assessed against them. Purchasing a launch service is a business deal, pure and simple, what matters is what's in the binding contract. Case in point, if you are flying a mission where someone else (e.g., a government agency) contracts the launch service, you may find that the pre-negotiated contract performance does not always match the numbers that the contractor advertises in other forums. Keep in mind that the advertised performance is subject to change, the contracted performance is not.

The technical reasons why the vehicle manufacturers reserve considerable margin for themselves are straightforward. The hardware that will fly your mission was built on a production line. There are production variations in the masses of large metallic and composite structures, as well as the performance of rocket engines, that can carve away significant amounts of performance in a manner that may not become apparent until very late in the production and integration cycle. And, being built on a production line, occasional production errors and handling damage occur. If the hardware is repairable, it will likely be repaired and flown because of the economic penalties incurred by scrapping hardware late in the production cycle. Hardware repair nearly always incurs some mass penalty. Even the winds on launch day can carve out a few dozen meters per second or more if they are blowing the wrong way. I've personally witnessed a few launch counts that were delayed for exactly this reason until the winds became more favorable later in the day's launch window.

Launch vehicle missions are designed and analyzed to specific masses and orbital state vectors. The autopilot and guidance schemes are tailored to the flight profile that delivers your mass precisely to the target that you specified at the start of integration. So again, even though later in the mission integration cycle you find that injection and performance analyses show excess performance available (e.g., 100 m/s boost over and above even the provider's contractual service), unless previously negotiated, this is not yours to use. Once the mission profile is designed and the autopilot and guidance are coded into the software, that is it. Specify your targets early on, in a manner that the launch vehicle provider is aware of the flexibility your requirements may have, so if excess performance is available, a strategy to use it is in place. Case in point, an extra increment of velocity available in the last rocket engine burn, guidance can be programmed to continue to operate engine until fuel is depleted.

26.1.3 Key Dimensions and Volume

Closely behind delivered mass is payload fairing volume and accommodation for key dimensions. If you've already chosen your spacecraft bus structure, then you have a set of physical dimensions that are irreducible beyond a certain point. You can juggle solar panel placement, make antennas stowable/deployable, and add or subtract external instrument platforms as needed, yet the outer mold line of the bus structure normally can't be changed. If you have something like a rigid aeroshell for a planetary atmosphere braking pass or landing, then the capability to accommodate the diameter may become a driver on selection of launch vehicles. Similarly, optics usually aren't stowable, antennas maybe, but not lenses,

Fig. 26-6. A ULA Delta II Payload Fairing Being Installed Around NASA's Wide-field Infrared Survey Explorer (WISE). (Photo courtesy of NASA)

mirrors, and their support trusses. The WISE space telescope, shown in Fig. 26-6, posed unique packaging challenges (among many others) due to the use of solid hydrogen to cool the infrared detector elements.

All vehicle *user guides* or *mission planner guides* (the terms are interchangeable) will define payload *envelopes*. The terms *envelope* and *volume* are used similarly. I'll use envelope here. You will encounter terms like payload envelope, static envelope, and dynamic envelope. Each of these has a different meaning, and I won't dwell on a detailed explanation because the meanings in all user guides may differ. The physical mechanism behind the terminology as it relates to you is that the payload fairing, spacecraft structure, and vehicle structure are flexible in flight. They all move with respect to each other, reducing clearance. It's also true that many payload fairings have acoustic-dampening blankets installed on their interior which billow as the fairing volume vents during flight. It's necessary to know what the available volume offered includes, irrespective of what they call it, and what remaining incremental clearance losses may be assessed later in the integration process. If you are close to the maximum allowable dimensions, then the first precise analytical estimate of the actual minimum clearance won't be available until the first coupled load analysis cases are run. Prior to that, only historical/statistical estimates with reasonable uncertainty margins will be available. This is only important to the selection process if the spacecraft is approaching the limits of the advertised volume and dimensions. If it is, then this is where you need to read the user guide definition very carefully, and if there's any doubt about the interpretation, then ask the launch service provider for clarification.

The available volume considerations reflect back to the delivered mass evaluation for the reason that many launch service providers offer different-sized payload fairings as options to their customers. At the very smallest end of the performance spectrum, there won't be many options. However, this can change rapidly as soon as the vehicles become only a little larger. Not only different diameters, but also different lengths, become available. With larger payload fairings comes greater launch vehicle mass, and consequently less delivered mass performance available. There also comes greater costs. One example, albeit at the higher end of the performance spectrum, is provided by the \$14M–\$68M cost increase NASA, [2010] for moving from a 4 m diameter payload fairing to a 5 m fairing.

26.1.4 Trade Study A—Target Orbit, On-Board Propulsion, Mass, and Volume

At this point in the selection process, I would recommend that a trade study be considered involving the four variables discussed thus far.

- Target Orbit and Injection Accuracy
- On-board Propulsion System
- Spacecraft Launch Mass and Margin Policy
- Key Dimensions and Volume

The parameters of your intended spacecraft mission may be such that there is flexibility in one or more of the four. Consider that a mission to measure radiation or magnetic field strength may be tolerant of a wide range of orbit altitudes. The same mission may also be able to take advantage of a range of spacecraft bus sizes and capabilities, trading bus capability against mission life and instrument capability and sophistication to fit your overall budget. The limited size and deployable nature of the antennas or collectors involved makes volume unlikely to be a significant driver. So far, so good, and it appears you have a very large trade space available. However, back to the target orbit, you need to reach a certain orbital altitude, with apogee well above LEO (say, ten or twenty thousand kilometers minimum). This could be a limiting factor in finding a low-cost launch vehicle, for the reason that some of your more-affordable candidates are unable to loft you to the desired orbit altitude. You can do this mission without an on-board propulsion system, in fact you never really considered having one because of the heretofore needless expense and complexity for a mission that was well-tolerant of orbit injection errors. But now, with this trade study, that previous decision (perhaps made unconsciously) comes back under examination, with the finding that the addition of a small solid rocket motor to your spacecraft trades a limited increase in complexity for the gain of being able to use a significantly simpler, smaller, and more affordable launch vehicle.

Consider something of an alternative bounding case, the plight of the user attempting to fly an existing optical telescope with a fixed mirror size. This recommended trade study may be only minimally useful to you if your instrument is already fixed in size, such that the associated bus size offers no significant mass or dimensional trades. If you are such a user, then you may have already objected to the idea of any on-board propulsion system whatsoever because of the associated self-contamination hazards that it poses to your optics (and also probably wish that I'd stop raising the subject). No option for your own propulsion system, fixed orbital altitude due to astronomical viewing constraints, fixed telescope dimensions, and limited bus candidates combine to make this trade study a short and generally unproductive one in this example. Still, for the short time it takes to write a paragraph such as this one, the optical telescope mission designers can assure themselves, their management, and their customers, that they have examined the available trades at an appropriate point in their planning, albeit with no new options uncovered as a result.

26.1.5 Budget, Schedule Requirements, and Risk Tolerance

The question of cost is most closely linked to delivered mass. Reliable cost data in publicly released information is scarce. At best, this discussion represents only a rough estimate of the real launch service prices paid in the international market. US Government agencies rarely disclose the costs paid for launch services, as this data is considered competition sensitive under most circumstances. Launch service agreements between multinational companies and governments can be products of larger business and political negotiations with multiple objectives, and in any case are rarely subject to disclosure in anything other than the most cursory sense. The best advice here is to scour press releases and any published government reports (e.g., the US Federal Aviation Administration (FAA) publishes annual launch reports) involving candidate launch vehicles in order to gain some sense of the possible price range when you become seriously interested in pricing out your options.

You will see discussions in published reports mentioning *performance classes* of vehicles. Generically, vehicles that deliver less than approximately 1,800 kg to 18 km at 28.5 deg inclination (the latitude of Cape Canaveral Air Force Station, Florida) are considered to be in the *small class*. The *medium class*, long the domain of ULA's Delta II and TsSKB-Progress' larger Soyuz, is considered to span the performance range of 1,800 kg to 9,100 kg to the same orbit. Performance above 9,100 kg to this orbit is generally described as the *heavy class*.

Performance of US-flagged vehicles in the small class is bounded among vehicles flying today by Orbital Sciences Corporation's Pegasus XL and Space Exploration Technologies' Falcon 1. The Falcon 1e is an evolved higher-performance version of the original Falcon 1, and was advertised on the SpaceX [2010] website as "the world's lowest cost per flight to orbit of a production rocket." Falcon 1e launch price at this point was advertised as $10.9M for delivering just over 1,000 kg to a 185 km altitude circular orbit at 9.1 deg inclination if launched from the US Army's Reagan Test Site on Kwajalein Atoll in the Republic of the Marshall Islands. The Falcon family of launch vehicles is the only one as of this writing where the manufacturer openly advertises prices to the public.

By contrast, the most recent publicly released price point for the Pegasus XL was $36M for a contract awarded by NASA early in 2009. However, this figure was inclusive of additional integration, payload processing, telemetry and tracking support. This Pegasus configuration is advertised to deliver just over 450 kg from the airspace near the Reagan Test Site (achieving an 11.1 deg inclination) to a 200 km circular orbit.

The Taurus XL, Minotaur IV, and Athena vehicles define the upper end of the advertised small class vehicle performance. With nearly 1,600 kg to a 200 km-altitude circular orbit at 28.5 deg inclination for a Taurus XL if launched from CCAFS and just under 1,750 kg for the Minotaur IV to the same orbit from the same location. The Athena approaching 1,800 kg to LEO, reasonably assumed to be the same orbit as above, or nearly so. The Taurus XL purchase price for a reflight of NASA's Orbiting Carbon Observatory (OCO) is "approximately $70M" in 2010 dollars. This would be the same vehicle configuration as the Pegasus user guide performance estimate. Caution should be used in interpreting this price point, as this represents a reflight of a duplicate spacecraft/launch vehicle combination to one lost in early 2009. No reliable published reports for Minotaur IV or Athena prices were found in the published literature at the time this was written.

For medium and heavy class launch services, the published US and international price points are even more difficult to identify. The range of estimates available for medium-to-large geosynchronous telecommunications spacecraft launch services approximately spans $60M–$150M 2010 US dollars, or rather $100M 2010 US dollars with a 50% uncertainty based on variations in provider, economic strategies or multi-party negotiations.

You will also notice that the cost per unit mass delivered to orbit is not linear with the performance classes. Something to remember is that the larger classes provide more economically efficient bulk transport than do the smaller. This is largely because of fixed costs that are essentially similar for each vehicle, irrespective of size, or lesser demand, which reduces production demand, thus increasing the unit cost per delivered flight article.

Schedule considerations are equally varied. Interplanetary exploration missions with launch dates driven by planetary geometry are subject to negotiations with launch service providers (and their other customers) over the length of the launch window. A launch service contract will invariably specify an expected launch date with the same precision as the allowable mass of the customer spacecraft. Recall that all such transactions are business transactions, so a spacecraft customer cannot rearrange their launch schedule without negotiations and possibly significant cost unless the contract grants them that freedom (an unlikely condition). Neither can the launch vehicle provider arbitrarily change launch dates without some manner of bi-lateral (usually multi-lateral) negotiations, unless the contract gives them that option.

In general, an established launch service provider with a busy commercial manifest is motivated to maintain a tight, consistent, and reliable schedule. Such a situation is driven by economics, where the ability to maintain a consistent schedule is equally attractive to the provider's own production infrastructure as it is to existing customers and future customers that consider using that provider. This example is of greatest relevance to launch vehicles servicing the international commercial geosynchronous telecommunications market, where a customer's on-orbit revenue is a serious, no-excuses element of the equation, and such is reflected by the contracts that govern the relationship.

For launch service providers that primarily service other markets, such as national security or scientific missions, the situation changes a bit from those that target commercial geosynchronous communications business. A provider with a busy manifest mixed between commercial, national security, and civil scientific missions will have a tougher time maintaining the tight and predictable schedule required of the providers that service mostly commercial clientele. The reason for this is not due to any failing of the launch service provider, but rather due to the nature of their customers. Both the reconnaissance missions undertaken for national security reasons and the civil scientific missions are very often "one of a kind" missions, with bus and instrument designs that are unique. A "one of a kind" mission means that more design and manufacturing issues have to be uniquely worked out along the way to being ready to be launched to go uniquely perform whatever it is that they do. They tend to experience schedule delays far more often than their commercial communications counterparts.

It's logical that there are very few commercial spacecraft, within reasonable limits, that can truly be said to be "one of a kind." "First of a kind" perhaps, but it doesn't make much sense to design a commercial spacecraft and not make any attempt to use it again in a similar application. The details of transponder numbers, frequencies, and signal processing can vary like options on a new automobile, but building a unique bus doesn't often make good business sense due to the resulting lost opportunity to amortize non-recurring costs over multiple builds (and hopefully customers). The situation is often very different for national security and scientific spacecraft, where the goal may be to take advantage of the highest technology available that meets their respective *risk tolerance* (i.e., the sharper the cutting edge, the greater the probability that the flight article might not work as advertised). The spacecraft bus is often uniquely designed around the instrument, and the same instrument would rarely be built twice because the cutting-edge technology selected at the start of the design will most likely be superseded by new development by the time the first spacecraft actually flies. Getting all the pieces to work together for a unique spacecraft is, therefore, more likely to take longer than allotted, with possible impact on the launch service provider and their other customers. The exact figures of launch delays and manifest changes due to problems encountered by the launch service providers, as distinct from the spacecraft customers, are not publicly available, but a consistent examination of published news reports over time should provide an acceptable basis for understanding the customer-driven schedule risks for each vehicle that may fall outside your ability to manage.

The preceding paragraphs are not intended to absolve the launch service providers of responsibility as a source of schedule risk, merely to address the most-frequent contributor first. Launch vehicles in the early part of their flight history are generally much more likely to sustain launch delays for reasons of their own launch readiness than are vehicles that have flown many times in the past. This, too, makes good sense given the preceding discussion of the pitfalls associated with being a unique or "first of a kind" spacecraft. Similar factors apply to launch vehicles. You should be particularly tolerant of launch schedule delays if you decide to fly on one of the first few flights of any launch vehicle. The delays associated with being the first, second, or third flights of a vehicle can often be measured in years.

This is the appropriate point in which to insert a discussion of your overall risk posture, or risk tolerance as it bears on the selection of a launch vehicle. Such factors as availability and reliability are yet to be discussed as selection criteria, but the issue of *availability* is usually addressed up front, in that if a vehicle is unavailable for your use, then you probably won't select them in the first place. *Reliability* is likewise addressed up front in the selection process, as much as possible, but the ultimate consequence won't be realized until your mission actually launches, although the reliability of other launches prior to yours on the same vehicle will have a bearing on your schedule risk, and indirectly, on your cost risk. Before you initiate contacts with the launch service providers, you should conduct an analytical examination of your own tolerance for cost, schedule, and technical risk (i.e., the risk of mission failure due to the launch vehicle).

A few examples are offered to help focus this assessment. Many low-cost scientific or educational spacecraft developed on strict cost budgets, and no launch priority, have a high tolerance for schedule delays and risk of mission failure, if it means the chance to fly. There's nothing wrong with this, and no reason to pretend otherwise if such is the case. Historically, even a first launch of a vehicle has a better than 50% chance of success, no provider in the world commits to such an enterprise with the expectation of failure, so selecting a launch on a first flight of a new or evolved vehicle may offer bargain prices if your schedule and failure risk tolerances are high enough.

Table 26-1◀, Fig. 26-6◀, Eq. 26-0

At another point on the cost-schedule-technical risk shape one might find the ubiquitous commercial telecommunications spacecraft that exists solely to provide revenue. Such enterprises are usually well-funded and able to manage significant cost risks, but the priority between accepting technical and schedule risks is more equal than one might think for such an expensive venture. These customers can and do purchase insurance against mission failure to help offset and manage their cost and mission success risks in a launch industry where a 95% launch success rate is considered pretty good. However, it's a much more difficult prospect to insure against losses of future revenue caused by not reaching orbit on schedule.

A third extreme point on such an imaginary three-dimensional cost-schedule-technical risk shape might be defined by those expensive and high-visibility missions undertaken with high national priority in national security or scientific endeavors. Such missions often seem to have phenomenal tolerance for cost overruns and schedule delays (interplanetary exploration missions excepted), driven by an equally extreme intolerance for failure. Despite the sometimes-extraordinary measures taken to assure success for such missions, they can and do experience launch failures, signaling that there is a recurring reliability limit worldwide in the launch industry. Those of us at all levels in the industry like to say things to each other to the effect that "we can't afford a failure." But the truth is that the industry and the customer base can no more afford a launch vehicle that "can't fail" than can maritime commerce and naval fleets afford a ship than "cannot sink." The analogy to ocean-going ships, including passenger ships, is useful to understand how there is no quantum leap in launch success rates that's likely to be realized in the coming decades. The launch industry in the higher performance classes is in a stable and mature pattern, as evidenced by the continued international use as more governments acquire space-based surveillance and communications capabilities while commercial communications providers are opening new geographic and service markets. Such a pattern does not encourage the investment necessary to achieve said quantum leap in performance or, most importantly here, reliability, over at least the next decade and probably well after.

These three examples are by no means intended to set boundaries on the possible extremes of your risk tolerance as a launch service customer. The reality of your situation probably exists somewhere within the bounds of the examples described, or you may chart new combinations. There's no wrong answer to the equation if you take the time to understand your situation before engaging your candidate launch providers.

26.1.6 Launch Vehicle Capability, Availability, and Reliability

Launch vehicle *capability* is the measure of the vehicle mass, injection, and other performance aspects against your requirements. Simply, can they meet your mission requirements? If not, consider that modifying an existing launch vehicle to add previously unavailable performance is a costly challenge. I have been a part of a couple such efforts, both highly successful and a lot of fun, but they should only be undertaken if circumstances both allow for management of some significant cost and schedule risks.

Vehicle *availability* comes in two broad themes. The first being access, where the vehicle is in production and the launch service is available for you to purchase. An alternative would be a used vehicle. A good example is decommissioned intercontinental ballistic missiles (ICBM), (e.g., Minotaur IV/V series of vehicles) although laden with government requirements, restrictions and general red tape. A series of meteorological missions, one of which is shown in Fig. 26-7, were successfully launched on decommissioned Titan II ICBMs in the late 1990s and early 2000s for the USAF and NOAA. A slightly different example of availability would be US spacecraft manufacturer access to international launch service providers, where the export of US-built spacecraft, even fully commercial ones, for launch on vehicles provided by other countries must pass scrutiny of the US Government, subject to a list of technology transfer, arms trafficking, and non-proliferation policies and treaties.

Fig. 26-7. National Oceanic and Atmospheric Administration's NOAA-M Meteorological Spacecraft Launched on a Lockheed Martin Titan II Space Launch Vehicle from Vandenberg Air Force Base, California. (Photo courtesy of: NASA/William Hartenstein)

One specific subset of launch service availability is the influence of the launch site. Large liquid rocket engine vehicles require extensive launch site infrastructure, so they are generally confined to one or two launch sites. Each launch site has limits on the range of launch and fly-out azimuths that directly limit the nature of missions flown from each. This is straightforward and reasonable, given that most launch ranges are reluctant to explain how empty stages or vehicle debris came to be dropped on populated areas. Large in-flight inclination changes can be accomplished, but are very expensive in terms of delivered mass performance, so they are avoided if possible. They cannot be avoided in a launch to geo-synchronous transfer orbit (GTO) or geo-synchronous orbit (GSO) of a telecommunications spacecraft from either Cape Canaveral Air Force Station in Florida, or Baikonur Cosmodrome in Kazakhstan.

A GTO launch on an Ariane 5 (from Guiana Space Center, Korou, French Guiana) or Sea Launch Zenit (from the equatorial Pacific Ocean) neatly avoids this penalty by launching very close to equator, thus eliminating the need for anything more than the most minor inclination changes. The fuel saved in this manner can offset differences in price by extending a commercial spacecraft's useful life, which means greater revenue potential for that spacecraft over time.

US launch ranges servicing polar or Sun-synchronous inclinations within the past decade only include Vandenberg Air Force Base in California, and the Kodiak Launch Complex on Kodiak Island, Alaska. International sites in Russia, China, India, and Japan also service launches to these inclinations.

On the East Coast of the US, NASA's Wallops Island Flight Facility in Virginia services launches to lower inclinations, approximately 38 deg to 60 deg, which encompasses the inclination of the International Space Station. The US Air Force's Cape Canaveral Air Force Station and adjacent NASA Kennedy Space Center are today, the only US launch range servicing missions to GTO/GSO. Taurus II, currently under development by Orbital, will initially fly from NASA's Wallops Flight Facility in Virginia and advertises a GTO capability with the addition of a solid rocket motor kick stage [OSC 2010b].

Some spacecraft customers have literally funded the construction of new launch sites to provide a capability for a specific vehicle to operate to a unique inclination. If you are not one of those customers, check the user guide and confirm that the vehicle of interest services the inclination you need with an existing launch complex. The same vehicle, normally, will not service the same inclination from more than one range, to do so would be very expensive.

The second broad theme under availability is launch scheduling or manifesting. If you have a commercial telecommunications spacecraft that needs to reach an operating orbit within a short window, then vehicles with existing manifests full of interplanetary and national security missions during that same period might be poor candidates to service your mission, because of the heavy revenue-production pressure under which you operate. And you would, no doubt, view launch delays in terms of horrific amounts of lost revenue per day.

If not under revenue-production pressure, most scientific and defense spacecraft are at least operating under tight budgets, an extra six months to a year stretch to the launch date can have an equally devastating effect as what the commercial communications customers encounter. A cost-capped science mission that spends an extra year on the ground has to compensate for the budget impacts somehow, and this usually means it comes out of the resources available to operate once on orbit, analyze, and publish data. The money has to come from somewhere.

Now, this is a good time to discuss the coupling between availability and another selection factor in this section, *reliability*. High reliability is somewhat neutral in affecting availability. This is because customers want to fly on highly-reliable fleets. They get their missions flown on schedule (mostly), but more customers mean greater pressure on the manifest, making it more difficult for a new customer to break in to the queue for a favorable launch date. Bidding wars can ensue, in extreme cases, increasing costs for the desired launch dates. Low reliability, however, has a deeply negative effect on availability. Two related mechanisms are behind this. First, launch failures have to be investigated and corrective actions taken to prevent recurrence. I've been part of eight failure investigations and none of them have been straightforward in either their execution or conclusions. Failure investigations and corrective actions take time, during which the vehicle is unavailable to service any customers on the manifest. This leads to the second effect, which is manifest backup (envision a traffic backup and you have a good grasp).

Launch vehicle reliability is a subject on which we could generate an entire book devoted to different predictive approaches and their merits. Such a treatment here would be relatively academic to your needs. The first bounds of the equation are historical in nature. New vehicles, those within the first three, six, or even ten launches, historically sustain the highest failure rates. Vehicles with several tens or even hundreds of prior launches generally sustain success rates around 95%, with a few (medium class and above) approaching 98% and very few examples sustaining 100% success over the life of the specific vehicle variant. (See Table 26-2.) Multiple government, private, and commercial websites are available with launch statistics for each vehicle in service today, and this will continue to be the case, so you can access good supporting data to research your own candidate providers with benefit of the most-recent launch trends. But be careful to consider one other aspect; we all fail. We hate it, we try to keep it to a minimum, but it will happen. The next question relevant to you is how long does it take us to come back into service?

Figure 26-8 illustrates an interesting relationship uncovered by Shao [2011] at Microcosm during the preparation of this chapter. I had not previously seen an attempt to correlate failure recovery time to any other predictive indicator. Figure 26-8 strongly suggests that there is such a correlation between the number of launches completed by expendable vehicle fleets and

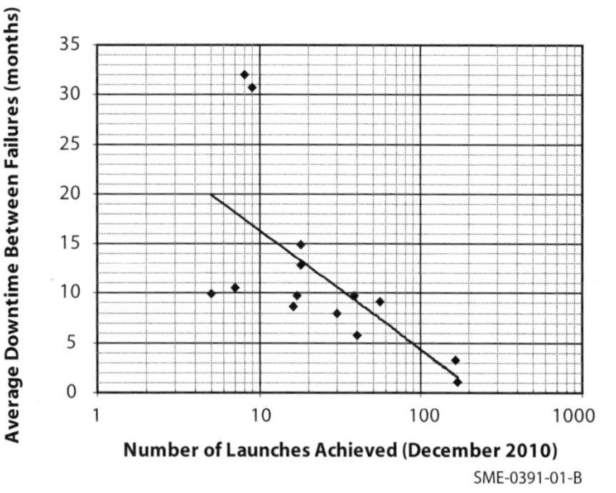

Fig. 26-8. Average Failure Downtime Versus Total Number of Launches Achieved.

their average downtime between failures. You will already have noted that the apparent relationship is logarithmic, and that the scatter decreases considerably after ten launches have been completed. The fourteen international fleets shown in the figure are all currently in service. NASA's Space Shuttle was eliminated from the dataset for the reason that Shuttle failures are investigated with a different set of rules than those applied to expendable vehicle failures. Fleets were also eliminated from the dataset if they had no failures (e.g., Atlas V), or if they had not yet successfully recovered from a failure and flown successfully (e.g., the Korean Space Launch Vehicle), or if they were no longer in service (e.g., Titan IV and Ariane 4).

The 2 apparent outliers in the dataset with fewer than 10 launches and average recovery times above thirty months bear additional explanation. The two fleets do not share nationality, but share other similarities in that they have been in service for many years, though at low flight rates. Both fleets have also been subject to multiple configuration changes since their inception, and of course, both remain in service today. The message here is that the relationship shown in Fig. 26-8, though useful, is subject to a great many factors that scatter the data.

It would have been interesting to observe the scatter among fleets with less than 5 total launches that had also recovered from an initial failure, yet none of the vehicles in service at the time of this writing had less than five flights and also had a successful failure recovery behind them. Note also that one fleet, the Russian Proton, with hundred of launches behind them, was not included due to the fact that their failure recovery history has not yet been studied in the depth required to estimate an average recovery time. However, upon cursory review I'm confident in asserting that such a study would not appreciably change the fit to the data presented here.

The way to use Fig. 26-8 to your benefit is to take it as a rough measure of the recovery time (hence launch manifest delay) required in the event of a failure prior to the flight of your mission. If you choose a vehicle with a flight history on the order of 20 missions, and that vehicle fails prior to your mission, you can reasonably expect the investigation and return to flight to take between 8 and 15 months. By 30 to 40 launches, that figure is closer to 6 to 10 months. This is a risk factor to consider in your vehicle selection.

Table 26-2. Reliability Experience of Launch Vehicles as of December 31, 2010.

Launch Vehicle	No. of Successful Launches	Total No. of Launches	R
Atlas V	23	23	1.000
Delta II	163	165	0.988
Delta IV	15	15	1.000
Falcon 1	2	5	0.400
Falcon 9	2	2	1.000
Minotaur I	9	9	1.000
Minotaur IV	2	2	1.000
Pegasus XI	37	40	0.925
Space Shuttle	130	132	0.985
Taurus	6	8	0.750
Long March 2C/D	46	46	1.000
Long March 3A/B/C	36	38	0.947
Long March 4	22	22	1.000
Ariane 5	52	55	0.945
PSLV	17	18	0.944
GSLV	4	7	0.571
Shavit	6	9	0.667
H-IIA	17	18	0.944
H-IIB	2	2	1.000
Dnepr	15	16	0.938
Proton (since 1970)	321	348	0.922
Rockot	16	17	0.941
Soyuz	1654	1753	0.944
Zenit	28	30	0.933

Be aware that reliability will not appear uniform over the small, medium, and heavy performance classes. Table 26-2 provides a summary of demonstrated success records for vehicles that are currently in service today. The demonstrated launch vehicle reliability is lesser for the smaller performance class of vehicles than at the larger end of the spectrum. This is not due to any inattention or lack of commitment to success, and the observation is international in nature. The larger vehicles within the industry generally sustain higher flight rates over time, offering an opportunity to accumulate a successful record and average out the limited number of failures. There are other advantages accruing to those fleets that fly more often, notably that the production infrastructure has opportunity to develop a smoother rhythm, as well as higher flight rates offering an economically more-attractive basis on which to amortize the non-recurring costs of design upgrades intended to improve reliability.

Do not rule out the use of vehicles in the small class, only be sure to understand the recent history of each candidate vehicle and carefully consider whether it falls within your risk tolerance. This same should be done for any vehicle under consideration, regardless of class.

26.1.7 Contacting Launch Service Providers

The preceding sections should be considered the *homework* you have completed prior to contacting the candidate launch service providers. A smart buyer brings a credibility that encourages prompt answers with greater depth of explanation than what the obvious neophyte will receive. That said, you won't impress anyone at the launch service provider with your new-found knowledge of the industry, so don't make that one of your objectives. The objective should be to draw out a forthright, knowledgeable set of answers to the questions you've prepared, but more importantly to foster a conversation where they can probe the reasons behind the questions and even argue with your underlying conclusions based on your homework. Some of the arguments they'll offer will have utility to your overall mission requirements development, and some will not. The merits will come out in the discussion. They are in business to make money, and they do that by first gaining your business and then selling even more optional services to you, like any good business operation. Yet, the prospect of your repeat business is a major consideration on their part that helps govern their side of the engagement. No one wants an unsatisfied customer.

Managing your requirements is a key aspect of engaging the launch service providers. The need to actively manage your requirements is self-evident, as reinforced by the process flow diagram offered in Sec. 26.1.1. Also self-evident, is the need to disclose all of your expected requirements, along with the reasons behind them, to facilitate an honest partnering to see how they can best be met, or if they can't (or are too expensive), then to understand the details of why and what that means to you both. I encountered a spacecraft team once that neglected to specify their real sensitivity to moisture in a cooling purge, preferring instead to introduce an auxiliary drying system as part of their on-pad purge regulator equipment. The reason they gave for not identifying the requirement was that they didn't feel the launch service provider could meet it. Subsequently it was discovered, by chance, that the system they brought to the pad unintentionally contained materials that became hazardous to their spacecraft and the surrounding workers once outside of a carefully controlled lab environment. All turned out well in the end, though it reinforced the need to be honest about what you really think you need. Of course, I'll also advise ruthless reconsideration of those requirements that add significant complexity or become cost drivers. The two approaches, full disclosure and ruthless reconsideration, are not incompatible, rather, they are inseparable in the management of your requirements.

Now is a good point at which to discuss expansion and contraction of requirements in the wake of the first detailed interactions with the launch service providers. If you have no requirements for such things as instrument purges, propellant servicing/defueling (required by the range if you have hazardous liquid propellants), exotic gasses, battery charging, spacecraft telemetry and commanding prior to separation, special cleanliness measures, or just about anything else beyond delivery of an inactive spacecraft to a point in orbit, then you can skip the next few paragraphs.

Most launch vehicles will offer a standardized set of umbilical wire channels for spacecraft use, as described in each fleet's user's guide. These are intended to service the common tasks that most of their spacecraft customers perform such as charging or conditioning their batteries, remotely initiating spacecraft prelaunch and test sequences, and having the spacecraft sense separation by means of *breakwires* that open upon separation of an in-flight umbilical disconnect. The wire gauge, number of channels, and provisions for spacecraft ground support equipment will be standardized to meet the average needs of the greatest proportion of their historical customers. They can accommodate any number of requirements beyond this limited standard electrical capability, but doing so will carry added costs.

Likewise, any launch service provider will offer a standard range of environmental control system (ECS) temperatures from which the user can select, once they pass within the provider's processing control for encapsulation in the payload fairing and launch. The provider will offer clean filtered air in their standard ECS, but the precise level of cleanliness may be something that may be important to you if your mission carries instruments sensitive to dust or hydrocarbon contamination [IES, 1992]. Additional cleaning measures, as well as additional cooling or contamination purges can be provided, but usually not as a standard service. Adding auxiliary cooling measures beyond simple purges and vortex coolers is something to be avoided when practical, due to the potentially high associated costs unless the provider has an existing system constructed for other customers that they can make available.

More-exotic requirements, such as strict control over hydrocarbon or helium exposure, or spore and bacteria cleaning and control for interplanetary lander missions, consumable and safety support for instruments cooled by liquid hydrogen or helium, or processing precautions for instruments with extreme sensitivity to radio-frequency or electromagnetic fields are outside the intended scope of this section, but be assured that each can pose considerable challenge to your provider's capabilities, with commensurate costs incurred. Safety and government launch approval for spacecraft containing significant quantities of radioactive materials occupies its own special category, and should only be undertaken by the most well-funded and practiced of spacecraft and launch vehicle teams.

If you must add capability beyond the provider's standard offering, then try to negotiate that as early as possible. Waiting until the launch service contract is signed and the mission integration is well along before you identify a new requirement is risky from a cost standpoint, because you're already committed to using their launch service by that time.

26.1.8 Trade Study B—Cost, Schedule, Risk, Availability, Capability, Reliability

Per the process flow diagram in Fig. 26-4, this is the point at which I would recommend that you conduct a second of the two mini-trade studies. Recall that what I term "Trade Study A" focused on aspects of your launch requirements where the details are under your control. The second trade study is different in that the details of launch costs, schedules, capabilities, availability, and reliability are mostly outside your control, other than your decision to select the candidate launch service provider that best fits your requirements and risk tolerance.

By this point, your homework is done and you've contacted the candidate launch service providers to gain answers to the many questions you have, and hear their preliminary recommendations and arguments. Crucial in this series of steps was the cold-blooded assessment of your risk tolerance. You remember that assessment, yes? Put the ice water back in your veins and let's reassess the situation. Unless you're a seasoned veteran of developing and flying spacecraft missions, you will have done well through these three boxes on the process flow diagram if only about half of your assumptions and conclusions were questionable, unaffordable, or completely wrong in hindsight after having contacted the launch service providers.

Eliminate the emotional content (i.e., the "abject despair") from the equation and discipline yourself and your team to look only so far back in the process flow as to see what improvements in the situation you can gain by changes in your cost and schedule budgets, or how you can adapt your risk tolerance. If you haven't done so already, now is the time to make sure that you engage an experienced manager that has been where you are and, most importantly, one who thinks through problems in a different manner than you. Write your evaluations and conclusions down before you move to the next trade study. Without changing any of your mission requirements other than cost, schedules, and risk tolerance, document the options you have to improve the field of launch service provider candidates, make a selection, and implement a successful mission.

26.1.9 Trade Study C—Revisit the Options in the Process Flow

My recommendation is that you only now turn your attention to identifying what technical requirements you can change to make your cost, schedule, and risk posture more achievable, and vice versa. You've managed each area individually, technical requirements and cost/schedule/risk, to the best of your ability. Now each side of the equation has to be adjusted in order to enable the whole to achieve a successful conclusion. The intent of this third trade study is not to "revisit everything," as the process flow figure might unintentionally imply, but rather to accomplish a directed search to identify those requirements that have a hitherto unknown significant impact across the boundaries defined for the prior trade studies. You are essentially seeking those few small adjustments in technical requirements that have a significant, better-understood effect on the cost/schedule/risk elements of launch service provider selection.

26.1.10 Selecting Candidate Vehicles and Assessing Launch Environments

Upon conclusion of the third recommended trade study described above, you should be in a position to select a short list of candidate providers and proceed to the next phase of assessing the influence of their launch environments on your design. I use the term *launch environments* here to encompass the wide range of vibration, shock, acoustics, coupled loads, thermal, and electromagnetic influences to which your spacecraft will be exposed during launch. The significance of their effects on your spacecraft will vary according to your size, choice of structural design, nature of your instruments, and configuration of your solar arrays, to name only a few target areas for your evaluation. The short list of candidate providers should be determined exclusively from the outcome of the process flow steps completed prior to this point, and revisited in Trade Study C. The reason for this is that the process of evaluating the detailed effects of launch environment on your spacecraft design moves you one layer deeper in the design of your mission. To put it another way, the impact of accommodating a 20 Hz sine vibration environment, 141 dB overall sound pressure level, and an 8 g lateral load factor should be a little bit lower on your scale of immediacy than finding a vehicle that can (reliably) deliver your mass to the intended orbit, on time, all within your cost budget and risk tolerance. The best advice here is to save the details of launch environments until the other important drivers of launch (i.e., the first seven boxes on the flow diagram) have been, if not worked out, then at least identified sufficiently to be able to narrow the list of candidates.

In terms of seeking a final list of launch vehicle candidates, the idea is to seek not less than two that can do the job within your cost, schedule, and risk tolerance, and probably not more than four or five. Wanting more than one is logical in that you really ought to have a backup solution if for some reason your first choice doesn't work out. It's also desirable for your prospective launch service providers to know that you're seriously considering flying on their competitor. It may not work out that you have more than one launch service provider solution at this stage of the selection process, but it's worth making it a goal. Remember also that every launch service provider wants to fly the next mission; they're always looking for the next customer. While losing your business to a competitor is stinging on an emotional level, losing your business for the reason that you simply can't afford to fly at all, still means that they lost your business. They can't fly you if it means that they will lose money, but they should generally be motivated to negotiate a deal you can accept, even if they're the only vehicle that meets your needs.

Section 26.5 of this chapter addresses launch environments in some detail, so I won't delve into the detailed discussion here. The words "assess the associated launch environments" in the process flow represent a detailed comparison of the launch environment specifications in the user's guides and any updates that the candidate providers might offer you when you contact them in the preceding step in the process flow. What you're seeking is a coarse check of whether or not it's feasible to design and qualify your spacecraft to launch environments and loads that encompass competing providers that meet your needs. If you only have one feasible candidate provider, then you should still make such an evaluation of launch environments before you proceed with the detailed design of your spacecraft.

Consider again, the now-familiar example of the commercial telecommunications spacecraft. Spacecraft manufacturers in this market sector find it little short of mandatory that they design, build, and qualify spacecraft that can be launched variously on a Russian Proton-M, European Ariane 5, US Atlas V, or Chinese Long March, plus at least consider the Indian GSLV and the Japanese H-IIA. This is because their customers all have roughly-similar missions seeking cost-effective and time-critical solutions, requiring them to be flexible in their selection of launch service providers for each mission.

Unique scientific spacecraft occupy a different part of the continuum, wherein they frequently have nonstandard antennas, mirrors, lenses, detectors, and the like that require optimized support structures if they are to stay within their mass budget. Such a spacecraft may have a unique problem if their candidate providers are a Russian Dnepr or a US Pegasus XL. The Russian vehicle is launched from a land-based silo with a surge of gas from an ordnance charge, same way as the original RS20 (NATO designation SS-18) missile from which it is derived. By contrast, the Pegasus XL is dropped from a converted L-1011 jetliner. The structural loads may therefore be a bit different from other vehicles that are launched vertically from a fixed pad within a few meters of ground level, and your instrument structural designers may face challenges as a result. If this represents the variety of launch options available to you, then you need to know early so you can decide, as an example, whether to consume part of your mass margin to beef up your structures and instruments to accommodate a launch on either vehicle.

26.1.11 Proceeding with Detailed Spacecraft and Mission Design

This section is merely an extension of the paragraphs above. It's a separate box on the process flow for the reason that you're now another layer deeper into the detailed design of your mission than in the previous box. Commensurately, you're also deeper into your evaluation of the effects on your design from the launch environments and interfaces of each candidate launch service provider, as you complete your detailed trade studies and design concept definitions to show feasibility of your preliminary spacecraft and mission design.

I offer the advice to maintain two or more candidate providers through the completion of your preliminary design as a notional compromise among possible mission types in the process flow, so please consider it in that light. The commercial telecommunications spacecraft program is going to maintain the ability to fly on multiple candidate vehicles all the way through manufacturing and delivery, for the reasons already discussed. The micro-, nano-, and pico-satellite missions of the world may find it simple enough, because of their small size, to build their spacecraft in a manner so robust as to launch on pretty much any provider that presents an opportunity for flight. However, the complex large space telescope mission with the need for highly-optimized structure built of ultra-light exotic materials skipped the rest of this chapter long ago and has already committed to designing with a single set of launch vehicle environments long before completion of the preliminary design.

Unlike the bounding examples in the previous paragraph, other spacecraft missions may be able to maintain, or at least attempt to maintain compatibility with more than one candidate provider, and even incorporate differences in the candidate provider environments and interfaces in the detailed trade studies. Classically, most of the detailed design trade studies should be complete by the time the *preliminary design** is declared to be complete and shown to be feasible, so this is the rationale by which it makes some sense to proceed into launch vehicle selection after completion of your mission's preliminary design.

26.2 History Prior to 2010

The two decades between 1990 and 2010 experienced a few significant evolutions in the launch industry. The commercialization of the US launch vehicle fleet through a succession of "Commercial Space Launch Acts" passed by the US Congress and signed into law by the President, beginning in 1986 and revised over the ensuing years, was in full swing by 1990. The US Government (principally NASA and the DoD) ceased to control the designs and commercial profit-oriented pressures increased. Many consider that beneficial changes resulted, but nevertheless it did change the way the industry interacted with itself, the US Government, and the spacecraft customers. The rapid evolution of the Atlas II/IIA/IIAS family into a commercial service provider between 1991 and 2004, paving the way for the Atlas III as a step to the development of the Atlas V, is a

* The context of the term *preliminary design* being the same as in the term *Preliminary Design Review* (PDR) in NASA Standard 7123.1 "NASA Systems Engineering Processes and Requirements."

Fig. 26-9. India Space Research Organisation's (ISRO) GSLV. Launching from Satish Dawan Space Center (SDSC), Sriharikota, India. (Photo courtesy of NASA)

case history that bears some study outside the scope of this book. Likewise, the evolution of the European Ariane family of launch vehicles to the current Ariane 5 and significant growth of the Russian Soyuz, Proton, and Zenit vehicles within the international market were all accomplished during this period.

The entry of the Commonwealth of Independent States (Russia) to the international commercial launch service market, first hesitant and unsuccessfully-marketed in the late 1980s, gained strength and success by the mid-1990s, marked by the launches of the first international commercial communications spacecraft on the Proton vehicle in the middle of that decade. The European Ariane 5 vehicle first flew around the same time, and after initial struggles achieved a dominating succession to the highly-successful Ariane 4 family. The Chinese Long March family also entered the international market at the end of the preceding decade, gaining a slow but surprisingly inexorable foothold in the market. The commercial telecommunications spacecraft launch market in 2010 is dominated by these three families of vehicles, the Proton-M, the Ariane 5, and the Long March 3. The Indian GSLV (Fig. 26-9) and Japanese H-II families have become noteworthy, and are gaining ground, but still occupy a much smaller fraction of the current international launch business base.

The previous two paragraphs are focused largely on the international telecommunications market, for the reason that this is where the money and the launch vehicle performance count the most in the commercially-available market. This is still true, commercially, in that the geosynchronous telecommunications market is where the money and performance follow, as simply an artifact of revenue. Competitive vehicles in this market will push 5,000 kg–8,000 kg to geosynchronous transfer orbit (GTO).

The beginning of the 1990s also saw the success of the far-smaller Pegasus air-launched vehicle in the US, one which arguably spawned a series of competitors, with mixed success, at the lower-performance end of the industry in hopes of attracting smaller "better-fast-cheaper" scientific spacecraft, as well as the believed-to-be-lucrative low altitude commercial lightweight communications spacecraft market that somehow just never appeared. This period, with the Athena, Taurus, and unsuccessful Conestoga joining the Pegasus to make a credible push as successors and exploiters of a market previously only served in the US by the aging Scout vehicle, was important, particularly in accelerating the innovation in directions, successful and otherwise, away from the classical government-directed standards established in the preceding three decades. They "pushed the envelope," to use an overused but still appropriate term. There was a great deal of healthy challenge occurring in the community at the time, and it continues in a similar manner at the time of this writing in 2011.

The preceding paragraphs are significant to you because understanding the history behind certain classes of vehicle will aid in understanding some of the attitudes and mindsets that will be encountered within different performance classes across the industry. Today's small class is bounded on the lower end by Pegasus XL (just over 450 kg to 370 km) and Falcon 1 (just under 400 kg to 370 km) at similar inclinations, both launching from the near-equatorial Reagan Test Site operated by the US Army. Athena IIc (not yet flown, but similar to the Athena series from the 1990s) and Minotaur IV advertise a bounding upper-end performance between 1,100 kg–1,200 kg, albeit to higher inclinations. The theme running through it all is that the small launch vehicle survivors of the early 1990s are the ones that successfully came to grips with the reduction in government oversight, control, funding, and direction that started at the end of the 1980s, together with the commercial market emphasis, without the guidance of a successful heritage. The successful approaches were different in each fleet. Those at the lower end can be said to have clawed their way up with no government support. It's not exactly true, but neither is it terribly far from the truth. They paved a rough road, and their achievement is, therefore, no less significant than those at the highest-performance end of the industry.

The *medium class*, described by the National Academy of Public Administration in 1992 as 4,000 lbm–20,000 lbm (1,814 kg–9,071 kg) to low earth orbit (LEO), also emerged in the early 1990s as a useful niche for a great number of scientific missions. The US Air Force moved in the wake of the Challenger accident in the mid-1980s to update the Delta II launch vehicle to seed the constellation of Global Positioning System (GPS) spacecraft. NASA had a long and successful history of managing the Delta evolution, but acceded to the commercial, then mixed with military, management of the future fleet development as a part of NASA's mixed fleet strategy in the wake of Challenger and the first of the Commercial Space Launch Acts. The timing was excellent, and the combination was interesting.

NASA's emphasis on the better-faster-cheaper strategy early in the 1990s, that was ultimately met with mixed success, pushed scientific missions originally planned for the Atlas II, Titan III, and the newly-developed Titan IV "down," if you will, to the Delta II-class. Call it 2,300 kg or 5,000 lbm for convenience. The only one there in the US fleet was the Delta II. The outcome was successful in that the "dinky little Delta II," as some noteworthy interplanetary customers deemed it in 1996, became the vehicle of choice for US (and several international) science missions over the ensuing decade. One military GPS mission was lost in 2007 due to a launch vehicle failure, and three NASA spacecraft missions were lost (Contour, Mars Polar Lander, and Mars Climate Orbiter) through no fault of the launch vehicle. Over that period, even as the GPS constellation planned a transition to the Evolved Expendable Launch Vehicles (EELV) fleet funded by the DoD, the science mission successes were otherwise tremendous.

The capability was just too useful to ignore. The commercial customer base waned rapidly as soon as the Iridium constellation was seeded. Geosynchronous-orbit communications spacecraft were becoming larger to serve the global demand within a finite number of orbit locations. Accordingly, the NASA and remaining DoD GPS missions dominated the previously-commercial manifest. The retirement of the Delta II fleet and loss of the medium-class niche prompted Congressional investigations, even as the Falcon 9 and Taurus II are approaching readiness to fill the same niche as this is written.

26.3 Basic Mechanics of Launch

Many, if not most, launch service providers surround the final preparations for launch with great ceremony. The launch vehicle folks are well-practiced, cultivating a cool calm air, almost nonchalant, but not jaded. The spacecraft customers are at times melodramatic as they describe the importance of their missions during the final readiness reviews, always thanking their teams and management for keeping faith during the "long road to get to this day." It is a big deal, and rightly so. The professional (and realistically, some degree of emotional) investment of everyone involved has reached its peak. Launch will be preceded by a precisely-spaced set of readiness review meetings among the various entities involved; spacecraft, range, vehicle, and finally all parties coming together one last time to signal their readiness to proceed into the actual launch procedure itself. The final launch commitment is accumulated through a series of readiness polls on the voice networks during the launch count, and then the last few seconds count down to t-0.

Somewhere within the last five to ten seconds (for most vehicles), the control of a launch passes beyond human operators and is now handled by machines and software. All elements have previously and exhaustively tested to confirm they will function as expected, but there's a subtle transition in that the engine ignition, final health checks, structural separations and umbilical separations are all happening too fast for human intervention. The commitment has been made, and now the machinery works, or it doesn't. Beyond the smoke and fire in Fig. 26-10 that we all enjoy, it's the visceral realization of the enormity of this commitment to flight, and the consequences of a failure, that generate the adrenaline rush among even the most experienced among us. The thrill and the fear never get old.

Fig. 26-10. Orbital's Taurus XL Launching at Night from Vandenberg Air Force Base, California. (Photo courtesy of NASA)

The engines ignite (Fig. 26-11). The ground and flight systems complete final mechanical, electrical, or digital negotiations milliseconds later with an agreement that the systems are healthy and the vehicle is indeed flying. The last of the umbilical booms or lanyards start the process of retracting, and the vehicle begins rising off the pad. The acoustic noise of the engine is reflecting off of the ground and the umbilical tower, hitting the vehicle with what will be one of two driving peak vibro-acoustic environments that can do real damage to hardware if not properly designed and qualified. If not considered and mitigated, any vehicle can literally shake itself apart with the echoes of its own noise.

The big vehicles that use only liquid rocket engines seem to move in painfully slow motion at first. The Atlas V 401 configuration shown in Fig. 26-12 is a good example. There's enough time here to grind your teeth,

Fig. 26-11. A ULA Atlas V Vehicle with Engines Ignited, with Umbilical Separation in Process. (Photo courtesy of NASA/Tom Farrar and Kevin O'Connell)

Fig. 26-12. A ULA Atlas V Slowly Ascends Past the Mast of the Mobile Launch Platform. (Photo courtesy of NASA)

ponder your sins, and wonder briefly whether everything is working properly. The reason for this is that the optimal thrust-to-weight at liftoff for such a vehicle works out to be somewhere between 1.1 and 1.3, with the variation depending on a few second-order effects. What it means is that your most-efficient liquid rocket booster design is going to move slowly off the pad. In an optimal design there's no point in adding any more thrust to the engine than what the vehicle needs in order to reach this initial thrust-to-weight range. On the other hand, vehicles with solid rocket motor first stages, or those like the Atlas V, Ariane 5, GSLV, H-II, and Delta II/IV that use varying numbers of liquid and solid rocket motors, usually have much higher thrust-to-weight ratios at launch, and so appear to get off the pad much faster and depart the vicinity at a good clip.

The vehicle is moving faster now and about to rise past the tallest point of the umbilical tower. One more hazard is retired once the ground-level winds can no longer blow the vehicle into contact with the tower as it passes by (yes, we have to worry about that). The vehicle may have one last collision hazard to clear if the launch site employs protective *catenaries* like those shown in Fig. 26-13, which are a network of wires over the pad that serve the same purpose as lightning rods on a building, but this hazard is also swiftly passed as the vehicle gains speed.

Fig. 26-13. An Atlas V Clearing the Last of the Launch Site Collision Hazards. (Photo courtesy of NASA)

As soon as the last collision hazard has passed, most vehicles will begin their pitch-over maneuver and start heading downrange as quickly as possible (Fig. 26-14). It's a common misconception that orbit is achieved by reaching the "altitude of space," unintentionally promulgated in the early media coverage of spaceflight more than fifty years ago. Achieving orbit is all about speed. The reason why no one orbits the Earth at 10,000 m or even 100,000 m is that the aerodynamic friction would burn them up (however, an orbit in that altitude range is perfectly feasible around the Moon). Rising vertically doesn't do much for you besides getting the ground out of your way and reaching thinner air more quickly. The part about reaching thinner air more quickly can work in a vehicle's favor by trading performance (performance that is lost fighting gravity while flying nearly straight up) for reduced air density when the vehicle starts to put on the speed, thus reducing maximum dynamic pressure and, by extension, reducing the associated vibro-acous-

Fig. 26-14. An Atlas V Beginning to Head Downrange. (Photo courtesy of NASA)

tics from this second peak driving conditions. We refer to the maneuver as a *lofted trajectory*, when we fly away at a higher angle and bend flight path higher than what an optimal trajectory would dictate. If the guidance and performance engineers have their way, however, we will get the vehicle flight path bent over and headed down range just as fast as the stability/controllability, thermal, strength, and vibro-acoustics considerations will allow.

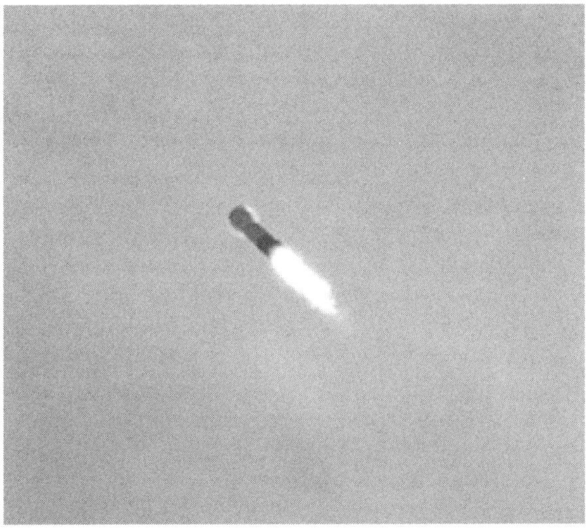

Fig. 26-15. An Atlas V Flying at Supersonic Speed, Nearing Peak Dynamic Pressure. (Photo courtesy of NASA)

The initial pitch-over maneuvering phase is complete within a few seconds. Now the vehicle is approaching Mach 1, and the dynamic pressure is building (Fig. 26-15). *Dynamic pressure,* or *Q,* is the pressure added by passing through any medium with a non-zero density. The resulting pressure is computed by multiplying half of the density by the square of velocity. The only thing about this equation that's important to you is that the dynamic pressure varies as the square of the velocity, so a modest velocity increase will have a much larger effect on the dynamic pressure. As noted previously, a higher maximum dynamic pressure increases the associated vibro-acoustic environment. It also makes the vehicle harder to control, because the disturbing moment (the torque attempting to make the vehicle turn around because it's actually aerodynamically unstable, but don't tell anyone that because it makes people nervous) is a linear function of dynamic pressure. Flight through high dynamic pressure lasts anywhere from thirty seconds to a minute, while the peak dynamic pressure lasts less than ten to twenty seconds. Flight through maximum dynamic pressure is usually preceded by a couple seconds spent crossing from subsonic to supersonic flight as the vehicle passes Mach 1. The flow conditions over the vehicle as the vehicle passes through Mach 1 are difficult to predict, so we settle instead on designing the autopilot to handle large uncertainties in the disturbances. If you haven't picked up on it yet, we're just trying to survive at this point. There are no points for style. Flight through Mach 1 and peak dynamic pressure is the most-stressful period of the flight, if one considers the aggregate effects and minimum margins on controls, structures, and environments for the whole vehicle system. Things go wrong in a hurry at high dynamic pressure. Small errors here can quickly drive anyone's control system beyond the capability to recover, or overload the vehicle structure.

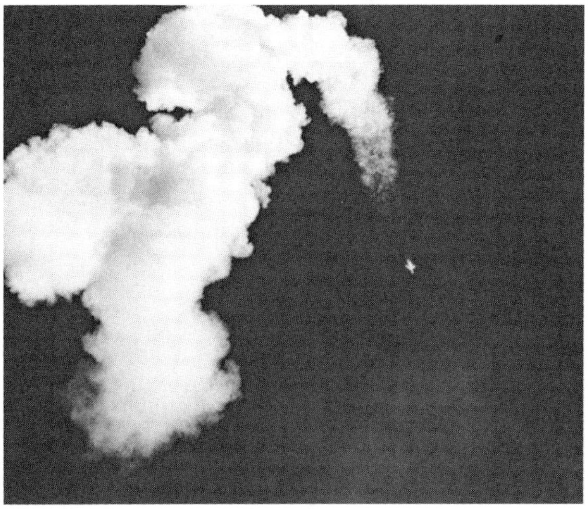

Fig. 26-16. High-Altitude Winds Twisting an Atlas V Contrail as the Vehicle Rapidly Heads Downrange. (Photo courtesy of NASA)

The vehicle flight software will be pre-programmed to fly a zero angle-of-attack profile throughout the period of high dynamic pressure. This is also sometimes referred to as a *gravity turn.* Angle of attack, or alpha, is the angle between the vehicle long axis and the velocity vector relative to the local medium through which you are flying—that's a long-winded way of saying that the air through which we're flying is moving, too (see Fig. 26-16, the technical term is wind). The fact that we're flying through wind can make things more difficult because even very small angles of attack can create large disturbing moments that require the engine's thrust vector to be pointed to near-maximum capability. That's not a place where we want to be, so some vehicles implement a correction factor loaded into the software on launch day, based on measurements taken by weather balloons or special ground-based Doppler radar [Dhuyvetter and Lam, 1989].

As we climb away from the thicker air, and the dynamic pressure falls off quickly, the vehicle can once again start commanding various pitch profiles to make the trajectory more efficient for reaching the final target orbit. Some vehicles, those with more than two stages, will execute a staging event here, and so, delay the resumption of trajectory optimization maneuvering until after the spent stage has separated and the next stage has ignited the engine and achieved stable powered flight. On certain vehicles, we may also "close the guidance loop" at this point, meaning that the flight software is no longer exclusively following a pre-programmed path, and instead making changes to the trajectory based on the actual flight performance achieved thus far.

The vehicle is really putting on the speed, now that most of the atmosphere has been left behind. There may also be staging events here, depending on the vehicle. The next big event is to jettison the payload fairing, once the density of the now-rarified atmosphere has fallen below a point where the resulting aerodynamic heating will remain below what you were told to expect for your spacecraft—hopefully someone mentioned that along the way, as there's a certain small amount of aerodynamic heating you'll need to be able to accept. They'll usually talk about it in the user's guides. Dropping the payload fairing also drops all pretense of vehicle aerodynamics, so we're now truly a space vehicle. The guidance loop, briefly interrupted for payload fairing separation, is active again, and the vehicle guidance is making minute adjustments to the trajectory to attach the target orbit. Again, we're still putting on all possible speed in an effort to reach a sustainable orbit.

The first orbit may be your final target, if you've asked for a low-altitude orbit, or it may be a parking or transfer orbit that will be followed by another engine firing (or two) to reach your final destination. A *parking orbit* is technically equivalent to an airport holding pattern, in which we would wait to reach a correct orbital geometry from which to continue your flight. We don't often use true parking orbits in expendable vehicles, as they are something of a holdover term from the early days of manned flight where the crew could conduct a quick checkout of the capsule prior to moving on to a higher altitude or a lunar transfer. A *transfer orbit* is an optimal orbit where you are coasting outbound to a point where we will either place you in your final orbit, or apply one more engine firing to achieve yet another optimal transfer to an eventual high-altitude destination that you specify (note that a three-impulse transfer is only more-efficient for high altitudes, as opposed to an optimal two-impulse or *Hohmann* or *Hohmann-Vetchinkin Transfer** that we normally try to approximate to the most-practical extent consistent with our vehicle is capability).

One consideration for you while we have you in a transfer orbit is deciding where you will want to be pointed relative to the Sun. Your attitude is obviously not under your own control during this period, nor is your spacecraft likely to be in the final configuration where you can best handle the heat and direct radiation from the Sun. So this will need to be a subject of discussion between you and your launch service provider to plan out what solar exposure you can tolerate. An example would be the sensitive and demanding space telescope that they forgot to design a cover for their aperture. Such a space telescope would obviously never want to find its aperture pointed directly (or even near) the Sun, unless of course the Sun was its intended subject of study. Some spacecraft desire to be in a slow roll as they coast to orbit to even out the heat load over their surface until their own thermal management radiators can be deployed. Still, others have no issues so long as their fixed solar arrays on their bus structures are exposed to sunlight so they can become power-positive as soon as possible.

Finally, we reach your required orbit. We will be grateful to be rid of you, excuse me, to allow you to start your wondrous journey through the cosmos. We mean that. But there are a couple more things we need to do first. The first is to point you in your required direction. Some spacecraft have no issue in being deployed in any attitude, and are insensitive to tumbling. Others are only equipped to hold an attitude efficiently, and have great difficulty accomplishing significant attitude reorientations. Many are sensitive to deploying in an attitude in which they are passively power-positive with their solar cells/arrays, to guard against any of their own potential attitude control problems as they accomplish their turn-on and checkout.

The next order of business in the separation sequence is to send any *wakeup* or separation warning signals (aka *discrete*) to your spacecraft to announce that you are about to be dropped off at your destination. Shortly after that, we will separate you. This is not trivial. I will always recall clearly the day when we delivered two spacecraft to the correct orbit, but then were unable to separate them. It was not a good day, and we like to keep that kind of thing to a minimum. When we separate you, it will either be with springs that impart a significant mechanical separation impulse, or else, if you so request, we might separate you as gently as possible, then back away. In either case, such active measures as are possible and practical will be employed to ensure that our spent upper stage poses no collision or contamination threat to your spacecraft. If

* Named for German mathematician Walter Hohmann, this orbit is also known as the Hohmann-Vetchinkin transfer orbit, to include Russian mathematician Vladimir Vetchinkin. [Source: Websters Online Dictionary]

possible, and for many vehicles it is possible, we will burn the remaining propellants to move the spent stage into a disposal orbit to either await a near-term decay and reentry or else be safely marooned outside the orbits of useful spacecraft. After this is completed, those of us that are vehicle hardware will happily become benign orbital debris, while those of us that are human will wait to hear that your spacecraft is reporting good health and safe attitude, and only then retire to a place of comfortable liquid celebration while you begin your mission.

One final word of concern, "caution" doesn't seem right, the cliché is overused. It is a serious concern for unique spacecraft designs that the transition from being a launch vehicle payload to being an autonomous spacecraft be managed with the utmost attention to the potential for things that can go wrong once your hardware is on its own. The vehicle community is painfully aware that our 95%-on-a-good-day success rate poses the greatest statistical threat to your mission once you get so far as reaching the launch site. No argument there. Everything practicable will be done to deliver you successfully, but it remains a high-risk business. Even so, there have been occasions where the spacecraft was deployed in the correct orbit, in the correct attitude, and was lost to a failure (or just nearly so) in the transition. The message is that spacecraft events like power systems turn-on, array deployment, GN&C handoff, and the like deserve extra attention in order to make certain that each sequence has been thoroughly modeled and tested on the ground in as flight-like a manner as possible. Here is the point at which you cease to be a payload and instead become a true spacecraft, responsible for your own fate thereafter. Please make a point of analyzing and testing every contingency you can possibly imagine while you're in that transition.

Fig. 26-17. Space Exploration Technologies (SpaceX) Falcon 9 Vehicle Lifting Off from Cape Canaveral Air Force Station, Florida. (Photo courtesy of NASA)

26.4 Launch Environments

This section addresses the environments that are peculiar to launch (Fig. 26-17), atmospheric flight, and separation. Table 26-3 outlines the sequence of topics in this section. Elsewhere in this book, there are ample treatments of thermal and space radiation environments, so those will not be addressed here. As previously noted in this chapter, the explanations offered here are intended to be at a fairly-high level; heavy on qualitative examples with minimum use of equations. Each subsection lists useful references that provide further detail and explicit guidance on approaching each environment. Mostly, this section is written to target the things that my colleagues and I wish that all spacecraft customers knew before getting themselves involved with the likes of us.

Get More A more detailed discussion is provided on the book website.

Table 26-3. Launch Environments.

Environment	Subsection
Coupled Loads	26.4.1
Shock	26.4.2
Vibration and Acoustics	26.4.3
Electromagnetic Compatibility	26.4.4
Ascent Venting	26.4.5

26.4.1 Coupled Loads

Unlike the more-straightforward shock and random vibration environments, coupled loads are dependent upon launch vehicle and spacecraft structural interactions as a complete structural system. This creates the potential for unpleasant surprises late in a spacecraft integration cycle when the spacecraft mathematical model is finally verified with test data. Having had exposure to a good many one-of-a-kind scientific and military spacecraft over the years, I can assure that you will (and should) lose sleep over their coupled loads analysis if you're planning to fly a unique spacecraft bus or large, fragile instrument.

Most project managers, and I'll go so far as to say most engineers, don't like to think much about coupled loads. First, it's all about the mathematics and uncertainties. It's not one of those "honest" environments that you can test, except when you go fly a mission. Even when you make flight measurements, you can somehow never quite seem to convince the community to use those to reduce the conservatism applied in their analyses. It's all about obscurely-derived forcing functions, large finite-element-derived matrix models, tedious verifications, lengthy analysis cycles, long reports full of numbers, and vociferous debates over uncertainty factors. You don't want to think about it, the subject makes your head hurt. Coupled loads analysis and the resulting effects on spacecraft structural design is a new case study in technical risk management for every single mission. It requires careful attention from day one of your mission planning cycle until the receipt and review of the final verification loads cycle analysis. Hopefully this has the reader's attention. The challenge is far less intimidating if faced head-on, but can become terribly costly and nearly unmanageable if ignored.

Physical Mechanisms

Physically, the launch vehicle is a large, lightweight structure wrapped around a much greater mass of liquid or flexible solid propellants (yes, solid rocket propellant is quite flexible, equate it to your pencil eraser, it's very similar) balancing on a rocket engine that's continually changing thrust levels and moving from side to side in two axes. Your spacecraft is part of that structural system. Your spacecraft's own structural flexibility directly and indirectly affects the larger launch vehicle because, like your spacecraft, the launch vehicle is only as stiff as it needs to be. They design on a budget, just like you. Designing propellant tanks and thrust structures (and that's the next largest fraction of vehicle mass, behind the mass of the propellants themselves) that are one bit stiffer than the minimum design requirement imposed by the loads and controls analysts is a waste of performance.

It's good practice to think of the vehicle and spacecraft as a collection of point masses coupled together with a complex network of lightly-damped, massless springs of varying stiffness, suspended without being fixed to the earth. That's essentially how it's mathematically modeled and then transformed into complex matrices for conducting the analysis. This coupled spring-mass system is then subject to a variety of disturbances, both self-inflicted and otherwise. Rocket engine ignition and thrust ramp-up is a good example of the former, while aerodynamic *gust* loads are examples of the latter. This mental model may help you understand why some interactions and forcing functions only reveal themselves through flight data, occasionally introducing analysis cases that weren't part of the deal when you signed up to fly on that particular launch vehicle.

All well and good, you might say, and thanks for the physics lesson, but doesn't a launch vehicle user's guide levy load factors and a requirement that customers keep their lowest structural frequencies (many times referred to as *first bending modes* or *primary modes,* refer to Table 26-4 for examples) above a certain frequency? And isn't it true that a coupled loads analysis is only applicable up to 50 or 60 Hz, so we only have to worry about a 25 Hz–35 Hz span of modes? That can't be so bad, can it? The rub is that this doesn't mean the spacecraft with no primary structural flexible modes below 25 Hz is safe from interaction, only that the interaction is unlikely to directly threaten the vehicle by coupling with the attitude rates sensed by the vehicle's inertial navigation system. Plus whatever the spacecraft bus primary modes might be, there may be a number of localized structural features with lower frequencies. There will also be coupling effects that occur with higher frequency launch vehicle structural modes. And the load factors given by the launch vehicle are preliminary estimates based on the types of missions and customers that they've flown before. You may be unique to their experience, as many of my spacecraft customers have found to be the case. If you have a large optical mirror, large antenna, or delicate microgravity isolation system, we can hurt your spacecraft if we're all not very careful.

Table 26-4. Minimum Recommended Spacecraft Fundamental Structural Frequencies.

Vehicle	Axial (Hz)	Lateral (Hz)
Ariane 5	27–31*	7.5–10*
Atlas V	15	8
Delta II (two-stage)	35	12
Dnepr	20	10
Minotaur IV	n/a	25
Proton	25	8.5
Soyuz	35	15
Zenit	20	8

*Minimum varies with spacecraft mass and interface diameter

Along with the frequencies in Table 26-4, you'll also be given a set of *load factors* that are intended to serve as design guidelines until a true coupled loads analysis can be completed. The load factors in Table 26-5 are representative of those provided in most user's guides, although the degree of specificity will vary with launch vehicle provider. These load factors are universally intended to be applied at the spacecraft center of mass, assuming the spacecraft to be a rigid body. Table 26-5 gives you something to use in your designs that is intended to envelope (for most customers) what the more-refined coupled loads cases will give you eventually. The caveat to this design guidance is that the load factors are something of a compromise because it's not realistic for the launch vehicle provider to try to envelope all spacecraft configurations that will eventually be brought to them. If your spacecraft is short, symmetrical, and has relatively-high primary modes (i.e., if you resemble a brick), then the factors given to you will be conservative. If your structure is long and delicate with internal modes at or below the recommended minimums in Table 26-4, then Table 26-5 may not be conservative. Note that the values shown are a combination of steady and quasi-static loads. The values shown are approximately comparable as representing flight through high dynamic pressure.

Analytical and Test Techniques

Get Stnd NASA-STD-5002 illustrates the coupled loads process with the flowchart shown in Fig. 26-18. Preliminary structural design of a spacecraft is

Table 26-5. Representative Design Load Factors for Several Fleets.

Vehicle	Axial (g)	Lateral (g)
*Delta II (liftoff and high dynamic pressure)**	2.8 ±0.2	±3.0
Dnepr (maximum dynamic pressure)	3.0 ±0.5	0.5 ±0.5
Rockot (maximum dynamic pressure)	2.7 ±0.4	±0.9
Minotaur I (supersonic)	3.8 ±0.5	0.4 ±1.1
Pegasus (aerodynamic pull-up)	3.7 ±1.0	–2.3 ±1.0**

*Valid for payload mass range of 1,134–2,268 kg.
**Longitudinal axis only. Lateral load factor is ±0.9g

accomplished using, among other inputs, recommended load factors for the launch vehicle on which they'll be flying. Then the designer of the spacecraft (or payload in the figure) develops finite-element-based mathematical dynamic models for use in conducting an analysis of the actual loads expected for that specific vehicle/spacecraft combination. The model is submitted to the launch vehicle team, and the launch vehicle team performs the analysis and provides results to the spacecraft. This is a "preliminary coupled loads analysis," often times referred to as a *PCLA*. At the time of a PCLA, a spacecraft may be in any of a variety of design phases. It's possible that the design is still evolving, or the spacecraft may be one of those that were built years ago and still sitting around waiting for a ride. Let's assume the former condition, where the spacecraft may be approaching CDR or still early in the build process. The first coupled loads analysis is intended to provide a check point to a spacecraft while design changes might still be made. It's the first look that a spacecraft will have into the forces, stresses, accelerations, and deflections that are recovered with real vehicle and spacecraft models under realistic forcing functions. The spacecraft team will assess structural margins against the predicted loads and may find it necessary to alter the design to adjust modal frequencies or increase strength.

Once the design is finalized and no further changes are anticipated, then what's often referred to as a "final design coupled loads analysis" (*FDCLA* or *FCLA*) will be performed by the launch vehicle team using the updated model submitted by the spacecraft customer. The loads obtained by this loads cycle are typically used to support the spacecraft CDR.

NASA-STD-5002 and Preferred Reliability Practice PD-AP-1317, referenced earlier, each offer some good high-level language describing the requirements for verifying the accuracy of a model. This is most often done with the aid of modal frequency measurements acquired during spacecraft vibration or preferably through dedicated modal surveys. This process is where nonlinear structural behavior is investigated, predicted and test-generated structural frequencies are compared and the model adjusted (5% or better is the goal for significant modes), modal damping values are confirmed (or adjusted as necessary), and orthogonality checks are completed. Once the model is said to be correlated, it is ready for submission and use in what's usually termed the "verification coupled loads analysis" or *VCLA*. The VCLA is intended to be the final analysis cycle, from which final strength margin numbers and predicted deflections (for use in clearance analyses) will be generated.

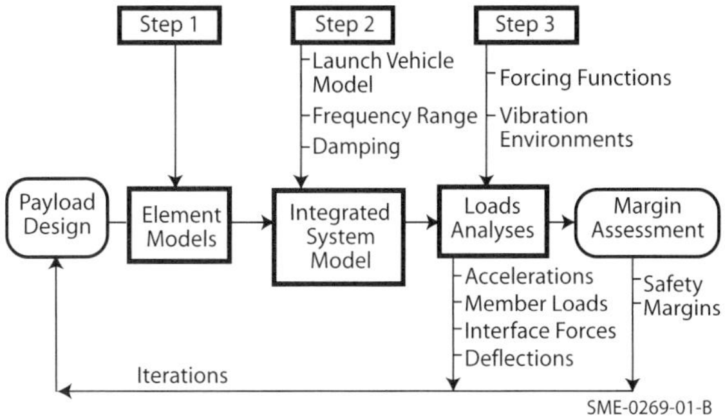

Fig. 26-18. The Load Cycle Analysis Process. (From NASA-STD-5002, "Load Analysis of Spacecraft and Payloads" NASA Technical Standard, June 1996.)

Notice the word, iterations in the lower left hand corner of Fig. 26-18. As described above, the process of design, loads analysis, and safety margin assessment is very much an iterative process unless steps are taken to reduce the likelihood of finding a negative safety margin.

It is understood that a test-correlated model may have to wait until spacecraft structure is assembled and subject to modal testing, which may occur relatively late in the mission integration cycle. Here's another detail that requires some clarification. The finite element modeling doesn't just automatically spit out a complete, ready to use, mathematical model of the spacecraft. There's some art to adjusting the model so that it appropriately reflects the spacecraft for the purpose of the analysis. To mitigate the risk of generating surprises late in the mission integration cycle at VCLA, we use model uncertainty factors in all load cycles. These factors typically decrease with design maturity and by gaining confidence in the mathematical models via testing. Recommended values for the model uncertainty factors for different load cycles are:

- For PCLA: 1.4–1.5 to account for future design changes and using mathematical models that are not test verified
- For FCLA: 1.2–1.25 to account for using mathematical models that are not test verified
- For VCLA: factor decreased to 1.1 with test-verified models

It should also be noted that the model uncertainty factor can never be a substitute for model verification.

Mitigations

There are no mitigations to reduce the length or iterative nature of the analysis process. Having a spacecraft that's already built and tested can be an advantage, but only if the proper dynamic model correlations have already been performed. The drawback for this situation is that, if a negative margin is identified, then either a redesign or some manner of motion control system becomes necessary.

One risk management option is to seek out spacecraft bus manufacturers with designs that have previously flown on the launch vehicle of interest. The idea being that a spacecraft primary structure having previously been analyzed in a completed coupled loads analysis cycle affords less uncertainty than a unique, one-of-a-kind bus, or one that hasn't flown on the vehicle under consideration. The unique instrument package that you hang on that bus will still carry some uncertainty, but you can be fairly-to-reasonably assured that the primary structure of your spacecraft will harbor few surprises. For unique instruments, spacecraft providers have successfully used a *mass-acceleration* curve for initial design.

Finally, the same vibration control companies that market shock and vibration isolation services have also demonstrated successes in mitigating negative strength margins that arose from late-breaking coupled loads analysis findings.

Summary of Things You Need to Know About Coupled Loads Analysis

- Coupled loads are the product of spacecraft-vehicle flexible body interactions in the presence of disturbing functions arising from vehicle system operation and external disturbances. Frequencies of interest are generally below 60 Hz, but not always
- There are a variety of methods by which a forcing function is created and modeled, generally in an attempt to conservatively model the known physics associated with an event, but estimating magnitudes to bound three sigma extent without precise knowledge
- Coupled load forcing functions are difficult if not impossible to predict and model from ground tests alone. Many loading events do not become apparent until flight
- Launch vehicle coupled loads forcing functions are subject to change as new events are discovered and uncertainty factors are updated. You should regularly ask if any updates are being planned during your 3–5 year integration cycle
- Coupled loads analysis is almost always an iterative process, especially for one-of-a-kind spacecraft
- The quality and accuracy of the spacecraft structural dynamic model is of critical importance to the credibility of the coupled loads analysis results. Simple model checks for all load cycles, and test verification of the model prior to VCLA are, therefore, required
- As with shock and vibration, isolation measures are available, and have been effectively used at both the whole-spacecraft and component/instrument level

26.4.2 Shock

Shock is the first of two environments to which most people can easily relate. The other is vibration. Both seem honest and straightforward in their causes and physical manifestations. We understand what shock and vibration feel like. We know them, we "get" them. There's seemingly nothing arcane here. "Shock" is your old friend from college, you know, the one (...the one your spouse hates). Furniture might get broken, a mailbox run over, and something always gets spilled on the tablecloth, but we're usually glad to see Shock. When expected, his presence signals good things; things for which we've been waiting.

It used to be a recurring feature on launch day, back when we used old thermal paper strip charts to plot telemetry signals in real time, where engineers of many disciplines would gather in the telemetry lab around the strips showing the accelerometer traces. We could recognize events by the timing and the shape of the sensed shock as the hot needle flickered across the paper. "Ah..." we'd say to each other, eyes lifting knowledgeably to each other just above the top edge our eyeglasses, "there's the shock...signature looks good...good spacecraft separation." Not quite wearing white lab coats and thick accents, but maybe imagining something along those lines. Afterward, a good spacecraft separation from the launch vehicle would be confirmed by binary signals from breakwires on the in-flight disconnects and telemetry from an awake, alive spacecraft, at which time we'd all celebrate by standing and applauding a successful mission. But we knew the outcome seconds or minutes beforehand. We'd seen the shock, and the signal looked good.

Physical Mechanisms

Physically, the mechanisms that induce shock environments on a normally-operating launch vehicle are pyrotechnically-initiated, but not necessarily dominated by the operation of the pyrotechnic ignition itself. Many spacecraft are joined to their launch vehicle using a *Marman-style clamp* band. A Marman clamp uses a tension strap to apply inward radial forces on a set of two *V*-segments, thus wedging two cylindrical structural flanges together [NASA, 1998]. For spaceflight applications, the clamp is often released through the use of a pyrotechnically-driven bolt cutter at one or more locations, abruptly detensioning the band and allowing compressed push-off springs to force the spacecraft away from the launch vehicle stage. In this case, it's the stored energy in the metal band that dominates the shock environment, not the pyrotechnic cutting device. Other separation systems like frangible joints or linear shaped charges use a greater quantity of explosives and result in a true *pyrotechnic* dominated shock environment. In any case, the

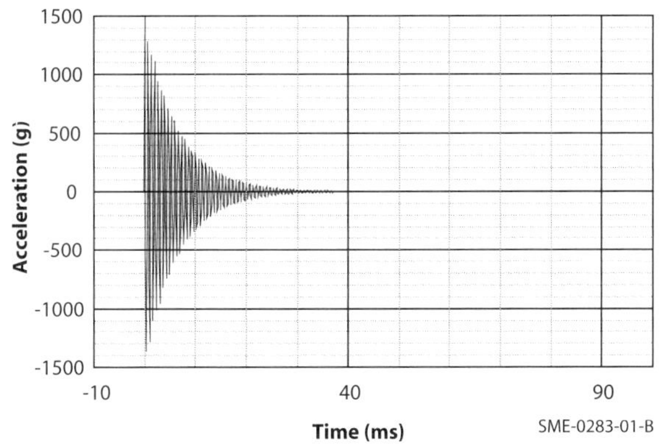

Fig. 26-19. Acceleration Time History of a Typical Shock. (Adapted from Test Operations Procedure 5-2-521 "Pyrotechnic Shock Test Procedures," US Army White Sands Missile Range, 2007.)

common elements of short duration and broad frequency content are maintained.

Figure 26-19 illustrates a representative time history of a pyroshock. Note the high accelerations and rapid decay typical of the environment. The decay is largely complete 20 m/s after initiation.

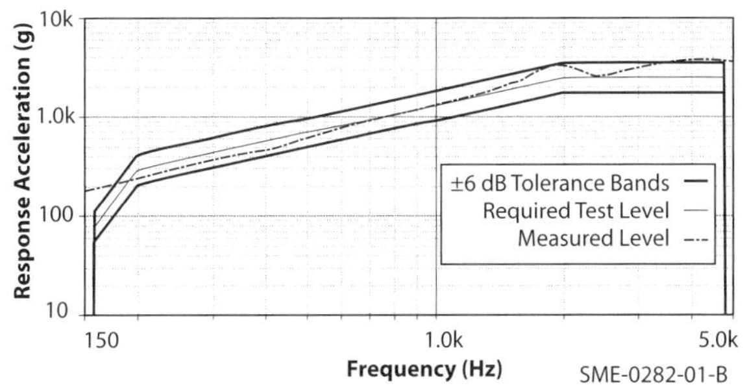

Fig. 26-20. Shock Response Spectra (SRS) of a Typical Single Shock Event. (Adapted from Test Operations Procedure 5-2-521 "Pyrotechnic Shock Test Procedures," US Army White Sands Missile Range, 2007.)

Analytical and Test Techniques

Figure 26-20 better illustrates the broad-spectrum frequency content of the shock recorded in Fig. 26-19. Figure 26-20 is a frequency-domain expression of what's called a *shock response spectrum* or *SRS*. An SRS is the peak response to the acceleration time history of a single degree of freedom ideal mass on a uniformly-damped spring, where the natural frequency of the system is swept through each of the frequencies of interest. By providing the information in a time-invariant, frequency domain, an SRS gives insight to the frequencies at which the energy is greatest. Something you should keep in mind is that there are multiple methods by which an SRS can be computed, so the conservatism of the levels shown (and the levels to which you must design and test hardware) will vary depending on the SRS method used. There's no one way to compute an SRS, so an SRS like Fig. 26-20 should not be taken as fact without understanding the method by which it was calculated. An SRS is an analytical interpretation of measurements, not a measurement in its own right.

One convenient property of shock is that it attenuates rapidly over distance and does not transmit through structural joints as well as other dynamic environments. Another is that, due to the nature of the physical mechanisms that create the environment, shock is easier than some of the other dynamic environments to characterize on the ground in a laboratory test environment. Again using the Marman clamp band as an example, clamp band separation tests are a routine feature of spacecraft structural interface fit checks, and these test environments are usually recorded by a number of non-flight structural accelerometers at key locations on the spacecraft.

Mitigations

As noted in the previous section, shock can be attenuated by distance and structural joints. It can also be addressed at the physical source, whether through installing the clamp band at a reduced tension, or by changing the nature of the band release system such that the strain release is not as explosive as when released by a pyrotechnic bolt cutter. The Russian Proton-M [ILS, 2009] and US Atlas V [ULA, 2010a] vehicles both offer separation shock mitigation through use of mechanical band release systems, rather than pyrotechnic bolt-cutters. Likewise, the Planetary Systems Corporation [PSC, 2010] offers their Lightband "space vehicle separation system" as mitigation for shock-sensitive spacecraft customers.

If necessary, mechanical isolation systems can also be added to add damping and change the frequency content of the environment before it is transmitted to sensitive hardware. At the spacecraft system level, it is possible to introduce shock attenuation methods directly in the structural path to the spacecraft. This has been done successfully on several missions over a wide range of spacecraft designs and masses over the last two decades. The Pegasus XL [OSC, 2010a] launch vehicle offers a load isolation system capability in their user's guide. Also, CSA Engineering, now a subsidiary of the Moog Space and Defense Group [CSA, 2010] has provided a number of vibration and shock control mitigations to different spacecraft customers.

At a box or instrument level, it is also possible to apply some of the same techniques to add damping and change frequency content in the secondary structure to which a specific box or instrument will be mounted. Elastomeric, wire rope, or combination isolators are available commercially in a variety of shapes, characteristics, and sizes. This will be obvious to most spacecraft and instrument builders, so I mention it only for completeness.

The important thing to remember is that, though we use the term *isolator*, what the isolator is mostly doing is changing the waveform of the shock or vibration environment before it reaches sensitive equipment. A narrow peak or broad range of high-energy input will be effectively attenuated, but the overall energy transmitted through the isolator will only be slightly reduced, even using the most-effective damping measures.

Summary of Things You Need to Know About Shock

- Shock is a sharp, intense transient acceleration with broad frequency content and a very short (generally less than 20 m/s) duration
- There are multiple methods of computing a frequency-domain shock response spectrum (SRS). Make sure you know which method is being used before you accept an SRS at face value
- Shock sources are generally specific localized equipment functions (like severing the connection to a spent stage with a linear shaped charge), and straightforward to measure in ground tests
- Launch vehicle shock environments are generally well-understood and not subject to frequent changes
- Shock isolation measures are available, and have been effectively used at both the whole-spacecraft and component/instrument level

26.4.3 Vibration and Acoustics

Big engines shake things. They also make loud noises. Rushing airflow over the skin of a launch vehicle at high dynamic pressure also makes for loud noises. The vehicle structure, and by extension your spacecraft, respond to these disturbances by vibrating with their own unique characteristic response. This section discusses the basics of three main types of vibro-acoustic environments your spacecraft will encounter. These are random vibration, sine vibration, and acoustically-induced vibration.

Vibration and acoustics appear on the surface to be honest and workmanlike environments, more-similar to shock than to the arcane mysteries of coupled loads. Those of us that drink beer and drive trucks will feel very comfortable talking about noise and vibration as things that you just have to accept, preferably with ample mass budget devoted to gaining large strength margins. Often you'll be able to make it through a mission with this mental construct intact, in that the vehicle provider will give you an environment specification to which you will design and test successfully. All will be well. Other times it won't be so simple, and a greater investment in understanding this inexact science will be useful to you when you have to choose among difficult and unattractive options.

Just as a note, *acoustics* are sometimes broken out separately for analysis within the launch vehicle community as *aero-acoustics*. In your case, given that your spacecraft is shielded from the direct airflow by the payload fairing, you will not be encountering any transient or unstable flow conditions during ascent. It is therefore appropriate to simplify the treatment and spare you all but the most elementary descriptions of fluid flow dynamics over the skin of the vehicle.

Physical Mechanisms

Converting large amounts of stored chemical energy to mechanical work over a sustained period of time generally creates noise and vibration, whether it occurs in your car's internal combustion engine, an old steam locomotive, a jet aircraft, or even a nuclear submarine (the first nuclear-powered submarine, the USS Nautilus, was said to be as loud as a diesel locomotive…they've worked on that since then). Marathon runners and owners of electric cars could make a good argument that this assertion falls short of being universally true, but it's useful enough as a working model for launch vehicles, as well as any motor vehicle that I'm ever likely to drive.

Liquid rocket engines are particularly good examples of this, as most launch vehicle engines convert propellants to heat and kinetic energy at much higher rates than the other examples cited earlier in the previous paragraph. Most times these engines are driven by high-horsepower turbo-pumps which add their own significant vibration signatures. Large solid rocket motors lack the turbo-pumps of their liquid counterparts, but consume propellants at even higher mass flow rates than comparable liquid engines. The effect is a set of sustained high-frequency (e.g., 50 Hz to 200 Hz and beyond) mechanical displacements that are borne along the vehicle structure from their source to your spacecraft's mechanical interface. These high-frequency mechanical displacements are mostly spread across a broad range of frequencies (i.e., *random vibration*), but with some relatively-coherent peaks where the displacements remain consistently sustained within a narrow frequency band (i.e., *periodic* or *sine vibration*).

Figure 26-21 illustrates a few noteworthy aspects of specifying (and making use of) a random vibration environment. As will be discussed in an upcoming paragraph, there is wide latitude within the industry practices for what is kept under the heading of random vibration and what is kept under acoustics. The two Minotaur profiles exhibit characteristics typical of ground-launched vehicles that use a single random vibration specification to envelope liftoff, flight through high dynamic pressure, and structure-borne random vibrations during steady-state powered flight. By contrast, the Dnepr User's Guide splits the liftoff and steady-state powered flight environments into two specifications. Doing so offers the occasional advantage to a spacecraft customer with a sensitivity to qualifying their spacecraft to enveloping levels for periods encompassing the entire flight through high dynamic pressure (typically 30–60 sec is used with such envelopes). The decision to differentiate envelopes in the manner used by the Dnepr's provider is more dependent upon such factors as heritage specification practices and the number of spacecraft customers that have requested relief from an overall envelope. It is not dependent on the manner in which the different vehicles fly to orbit. For most spacecraft customers, the environments specified in Fig. 26-21 are not exceedingly harsh in any way.

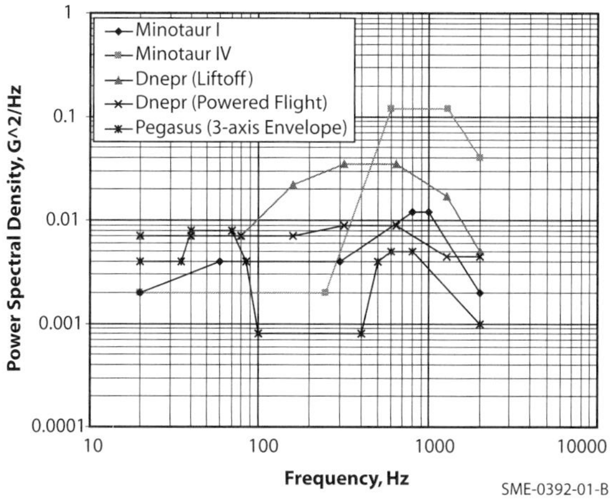

Fig. 26-21. Example Vehicle Random Vibration Environments. [OSC, 2006a; OSC, 2006b; ISC Kosmotras, 2001; ISC Kosmotras, 2001; OSC, 2010a]

Analytical and Test Techniques

Acoustics and vibration environments contained in vehicle user's guides are derived from flight measurements because many of the contributing sources are impractical to measure in ground tests. This is the reverse from shock, where shock is best characterized on the ground, and difficult if not impractical to adequately characterize in flight. In a new launch vehicle with no prior flight measurements, we'll do our best to combine those ground test data sources we can accumulate, compare it to flight data taken from similar vehicles and flight conditions, and add large uncertainty factors. Statistical energy analysis (SEA) tools have also come into wide usage for predicting flight acoustic environments in the absence of applicable test data. The environments provided to you for an existing launch vehicle will have been derived from a limited number (possibly as few as one or two) of flights with special instrumentation packages, so there will still be uncertainty factors embedded in the environments provided to you in order to address flight-to-flight variability.

The simplest way to communicate the acoustic and vibration environments is to develop an enveloping specification that covers all events from engine ignition to the completion of flight through high dynamic pressure, and offer that with expected flight duration of about one minute. The acoustic sound pressure level (given in decibels (dB) against a reference pressure) or sine vibration acceleration (usually given in multiples of one Earth reference gravity (g) or random vibration spectral density (g^2/Hz) at each frequency will be chosen to reflect the maximum of the predicted values from a combination of events such as engine start, liftoff, Mach 1, or maximum dynamic pressure. The predicted intensities will be given with a statistical reliability and confidence consistent with the provider's own technical policies; for example, "95% reliability with a 50% confidence," and "99% reliability with a 90% confidence" are common descriptors indicating the level of uncertainty in the values provided.

What's really happening here is that peak levels driven by short duration events (<10 sec) are being used to define an envelope that will be given to you as occurring over a much longer duration (~30–60 sec) than is physically correct. This may sound unjustly conservative to those unfamiliar with the practice, but simplifications like these came into common usage within the launch community decades ago out of convenience when it was found that the customers were largely insensitive to the added conservatism. The message here is to be aware of the conservatisms inherent in the commonly-practiced simplifications within the industry, just in case you're one of the few spacecraft customers that can't handle qualifying for a high vibration event that's assumed to last for one minute when in fact it only lasts for 5 or 10 seconds. If you find yourself in trouble, start asking these kinds of questions. You might have to pay for additional analysis by the launch provider in order to split up the environments and durations into more-realistic chunks, but that could be substantially cheaper than redesigning part of your spacecraft.

Summary of Things You Need to Know About Vibration and Acoustics

- The acoustic environments to which your spacecraft will be exposed are principally driven by overpressure and reverberations at launch, followed by flow noise over the surface of the payload fairing (and the reverberations within) during flight through high dynamic pressure
- As with shock, there are multiple methods by which measured environment data is processed to develop an acoustic or vibration intensity prediction. Even a summary-level understanding of the differences in predictive techniques, and the embedded simplifications, may save you from an unintended overtest condition
- For your spacecraft, maximum acoustic and random vibration environments will coincide with liftoff and flight through high dynamic pressure (roughly from transonic to maximum dynamic pressure)
- Sine vibration environments are generally associated with a physical coupling between vehicle structural modes and pressure oscillations within the propulsion system. As such, they are not limited to a coincident occurrence with liftoff and high dynamic pressure flight
- The launch industry simplifies their representation of random and sine vibration environments as a matter of good economic practice, in that it doesn't make sense to perform in-depth analyses of certain vibration environments (mostly sine events) if 99% of their customers are insensitive to testing at the simplified recommended levels. You may be among the 1%, so don't hesitate to ask your launch

provider for help if you identify an environment for which it will be difficult or risky to demonstrate qualification

- Motion control solutions are available to aid in attenuating sine vibration events, and even random vibration environments borne through the launch vehicle structure. However, these will not be effective to attenuate your response to the acoustic environment within the payload fairing

26.4.4 Electromagnetic Compatibility (EMC)

Electromagnetic interference (EMI) and electromagnetic compatibility (EMC) are accorded the same arcane mystery as coupled loads by most folks. Even some experienced launch vehicle engineers and managers are prone to unconsciously view this area as somewhat sneaky or dishonest. The math can be a bit difficult to follow, and the visceral reaction is that the environment can't be seen or felt, as folks might forget that light and radiant heat are, themselves, electromagnetic emissions. The idea of a radar beam sweeping over the vehicle and spacecraft is fairly easy to grasp. Yes, it's radar. Yes, it's potentially dangerous to the spacecraft and vehicle. But the physical understanding of why this is the case, what the mechanisms are for causing real damage, is not intuitive for most of us. Jump forward to explaining why a one-watt spacecraft RF telemetry transmitter is potentially dangerous to both its own spacecraft and the launch vehicle during flight, and you begin to strain the bounds of credulity in much the same way as being told that your wireless communication device poses a danger to an airliner and all those aboard (at least in the US and EU in 2011). The wireless phone on an airliner is a great example of the challenge in confronting this analytical discipline, because the whole issue of wireless phones being dangerous to airliners is seemingly unjustified, given the number of wireless phones that inadvertently fly in the "on" condition (ahem, including mine), unknown to their owners that thought they had turned them off properly when instructed. "Obviously this is bunch of garbage, no airplanes are falling from the sky due to wireless phones" Ever hear that comment or something like it? Granted that it might sometimes come across that way, but the precautions, analyses, and tests are there for good reasons. Consider also that the nature and power of the emitters are evolving, as are the density, sensitivity, and materials in critical circuits. The solution for those of us that do not work directly in this specialized discipline is to understand the physical mechanisms a little better than a simple gut reaction will allow.

Be aware that the sources and effects of electromagnetic interference are expected to continue to change more rapidly than the rate at which most of the authoritative guidance on the subject can be revised. The same colleagues that recommended the older classic military standards as good guidance were also matter-of-fact in their caution that even the most-current updates and newly released guidance will likely not keep pace with new RF applications and electronic circuit technology. This is an important difference between EMC and the other environments described in this chapter. It is a useful caution to observe that the density of integrated circuits in high-performance electronics continues to increase, while new electromagnetic emission sources (e.g., wireless personal voice and data connections) expand their range into new and higher frequency ranges [Brewer and Trout, 2006]. The important message here is that technological advances in avionics and RF applications make EMC a more-dynamic area for guidance due to the potential for rapid change to previously-established ground rules and assumptions. Good guidance is available to address the fundamental physics, but increased attention should be paid to understanding the areas of conflict between accepted standards, as well as seeking the most-current descriptions of the expected RF environment to which your spacecraft will be exposed during processing and launch.

Physical Mechanisms

Typically, the term EMI refers to unintentional disturbances, either radiated or conducted, and is generally addressed at the box level. EMC is generally understood in the context of electronics operating together in a system. The overall discipline is normally referred to as EMC. A third term, electromagnetic effects (EME) is sometimes used to include other electromagnetic events in the discipline such as lightning, or charging but this section will adhere to the simplification of grouping EME within the larger EMI. Also keep in mind that EMI does not solely refer to electromagnetic radiation through free space, and likewise EMC does not only encompass electromagnetic noise/signals conducted through metal. The practical electrical engineers among us will understand the old admonishment given to junior folks that "a plug doesn't necessarily mean it has pins, and a receptacle doesn't mean it has sockets."

The common physical mechanism of greatest interest to launch is temporary exposure to electric fields or conducted interference sufficient to cause latent damage (or outright failure) of your most-sensitive circuits. Damage is the thing we worry about. Simple interference is only a transient concern, given that you will be gladly rid of your launch vehicle some minutes or hours after launch. You should assume an inability to transmit or receive RF communication with your spacecraft during launch unless you make expensive provisions with your provider to do so.

Electrostatic discharge (ESD) won't be anything new to you as a spacecraft customer. Opportunities are probably far greater for developing static charges in normal processing between electrically-isolated articles until a sudden discharge (spark) occurs. These normal sea-level ambient ESD hazards are unchanged once integrated with a launch vehicle. Depending on your target orbit, some missions may face the hazard of flight through bands of energetic protons trapped in the Earth's magnetic field that might cause detrimental charging over exposed and improperly-grounded surfaces, but this is not a significant hazard to missions in low Earth orbit. The best and only real ESD mitigation here is the same as you would practice during processing, specifically to ensure that all elements are adequately grounded at all times, with no opportunity for charge accumulation.

Fig. 26-22. 3 Megawatt Debris Detection and Tracking Radar at KSC. (Photo courtesy of NASA)

Exposure to sweeps from high-power radar like the debris detection site in Fig. 26-22 will likely be a new hazard at the launch site, compared to what your spacecraft would have encountered during manufacturing, shipping, and processing. The momentary RF electric fields thus induced can exceed 200 volts per meter, sometimes several multiples of that figure, depending on launch site. Buildings, shipping containers, and payload fairings offer some attenuation, but not nearly as much as you might think. It is intuitive to think of a metal payload fairing as being a Faraday Cage*, thus impenetrable to electric fields, but strictly this is only true for static electric fields. Oscillating fields are more devious and inventive. Remember that radar is an RF emission, with wavelengths that are inversely-proportional to frequency. Remember also that buildings, shipping containers, and payload fairings all have openings to pass people, equipment, cables, airflow and the short wavelengths of radars in use at most ranges do a fine job of penetrating what your undergraduate basic electricity and magnetism class recollection would tell you is an impenetrable shield.

* Named for English physicist Michael Faraday.

There is another hazard associated with radar that is rarely mentioned, though, specifically that the RF environment described to you by your launch vehicle provider is unlikely to encompass all of the radar sources to which you may be exposed. Your provider will certainly give you their best description of all the RF emitters, radar and otherwise, of which they are aware. This isn't their fault; they won't hide any known emitters from you. The problem is that they might not know about all of the emitters, mostly radar, which exist on the launch range. Consider that many launch ranges around the world serve dual civilian and military roles, and most are located on coastline. The radar emitters that are dedicated to the safety functions of maintaining positive launch vehicle tracking and local airspace clearance will be well-known by your launch provider. No problem there. The range organizations are typically very cooperative in avoiding sweeps by the radars they control when they are apprised of a particular sensitivity on your part. The term used in the US is *sector blanking*. Your launch range wants to see you succeed, too.

The basic problem is that the launch range safety organization may not control all of the radar emitters on or around the range. High-powered military radars aren't well-advertised and upgraded power and frequency capabilities are even less likely to be advertised than is their existence. This makes sense, as knowledge of military capabilities are issues of national security; anyone's national security. Many nations have missiles, and every nation has enemies. Unlike the launch range, your spacecraft mission success is well down on a military air and space defense priority list, though they will take what steps that they can to reduce your hazard if they know about your mission sensitivity. They may not know about your unique sensitivity anymore than you being aware that they exist. Otherwise, your launch vehicle makes a wonderful target for tracking practice by those charged with protecting against less-friendly vehicles. The only mitigation for an RF-sensitive spacecraft is to make that sensitivity known far and wide in advance. Ask your provider to arrange a meeting with the range folks long before (years before) your spacecraft's arrival at the range in order to help get the word out to all potential military applications that might exist in proximity.

Beyond military radars, the likelihood that you will be launched from a coastal range offers another hazard, less powerful but realistically impossible to control. Ocean-going ships and even coastal fishing boats carry their own radars. These can't be controlled by the launch range, since any passing ship of near-infinite international registry can pass freely off the coast in international waters. Ranges can and do conduct site RF surveys, however, their information could easily be several years old. Likewise the guidance in published standards, such as that shown in Table 26-6, may be outdated soon after appearing in print. If your spacecraft is particularly RF-sensitive, then you might consider requesting that an updated survey be performed by your launch service provider as an additional (paid) service in

Get Stnd

Table 26-6. "Electromagnetic Compatibility Requirements for Space Equipment and Systems." Adapted from Table 6.27e2-2 in SMC Standard SMC-S-008, (US Air Force Space Command, 13 June 2008.)

Frequency	Ascent RFI Limits (V/m)	Source Notes
10 kHz–100 MHz	20	MIL-STD-464A, Table 1C, External EME for Space and Launch Vehicle Systems, and MIL-STD-461F, Table VII, RS103 Limits (space)
100 MHz–1 GHz	100	MIL-STD-464A, Table 1C
1–4 GHz	200	MIL-STD-464A, Table 1C
4–11 GHz	1000	According to the RF Power Impingement Analysis, 1997 and 1998 composite analyses for Titan Core Vehicle from 0 to 80 nmi (an internal Aerospace Corp. briefing written by D. Oltrogge and A. C. Bustillos), there is a source capable of generating approximately 1000V/m, with approximately 11 RFI threats between 100 and 500V/m in the frequency range from 4–11GHz. In addition, Aerospace Report No. TOR-2005(1663)-3790 shows four locations at CCAFS with field strengths in the 4–11 GHz range from 1,000–43,000 V/m, plus about 35 occurrences of field strengths from 100 to 500 V/m. 500 V/m is a compromise which captures most of the identified RFI threats in the 4–11GHz range
11–100 GHz	20	MIL-STD-464A, Table 1C, and MIL-STD-461F, Table VII, with additional SMC-S-008 guidance on extension above 40 GHz

order to develop a most-current understanding of the ambient RF environment. Nevertheless, keep in mind that such surveys are only a useful snapshot, not a guarantee against the worst case of having the odd naval vessel cruise by in international waters while conducting some convenient air-defense exercises at your expense.

Analytical and Test Techniques

The published standards recommended earlier in this section provide good guidance for design and test. The environment will already have been analyzed in general, as reflected in the published standards and handbooks, and particular, as reflected in the individual launch vehicle user's guides. However, the differences in analytical and test guidance published by such agencies as the US Air Force, AIAA, and ESA are reflective of the continuing evolution in both the discipline and the environment being studied.

There isn't much in the way of mission-specific analysis that will be needed in this area, other than ability to show compliance with RF emission and circuit isolation requirements. If you are one of those spacecraft with instruments that carry an inherent and extreme sensitivity to RF fields, then there are numerical simulation techniques (the same as those used to predict radar cross-sections for military aircraft) that were unavailable ten years ago. These can be brought to bear on the problem of sharpening the predictions for field levels that your spacecraft may encounter given a sweep from a hypothetical naval vessel taking advantage of your launch to conduct an air-defense drill. More importantly, they can help quantify the benefit of any mitigating shielding that you might employ as a mission-unique modification to the vehicle. But be aware that such analyses and mitigating measures are expensive and require considerable cooperation from your launch vehicle provider.

Summary of Things You Need to Know About EMC

- The electromagnetic environments to which your spacecraft will be exposed are principally driven by exposure to tracking radars and launch vehicle RF transmitters, with some potential for charging due to flight through regions of energetic protons on your way to final orbit. And always, there is atmospheric lightning to consider as a source broadband emissions that are potentially-fatal to sensitive instruments
- Vehicle RF emitters are well-characterized by the emission spectra included in pretty much any vehicle user's guide. However, though launch ranges make good efforts to characterize their local RF environment (primarily concerning high-power radar sources), they will not necessarily be able to control all high-power local emitters, nor may they be aware that some (like maritime navigational radars or naval fire control radars) are even in the vicinity from one day to the next
- Published guidance continues to be updated as the discipline is studied further, and while the nature and power of electromagnetic environment and applications evolves on a continual basis
- System-level electromagnetic compatibility is normally addressed through integrated avionics testing, combined with rigorous attention to bonding and isolation requirements for those interfaces (i.e., with the launch vehicle) for which it is not practical to accomplish full system integration until arrival at the launch site for flight

Again, while there is nothing particularly new that the launch vehicle itself brings to the EMC issues confronting any spacecraft, the magnitude of the collateral radiated environments (e.g., radar and lightning) can be daunting. No less daunting is the prospect that once your own spacecraft team has settled on the set of published EMC guidance that you intend to follow in your development, you may find that the launch vehicle provider bases their recommendations on a completely different and conflicting standard. Always remind yourself that such conflicts are not based in lack of expertise, but rather are generated by differences in experience, sensitivities, and the timing of the published guidance. This is a complex and healthy field of study, but cookbook solutions may be limited or dated. The best approach is to understand the physics of the problem and make your own determinations based on the best-available guidance. Even then, you may spend a lot of time looking over your shoulder wondering what it is that you forgot.

26.4.5 Ascent Venting

Choosing to end this section on environments with a bit of good news, your analysis and mitigating measures to accommodate the launch vehicle provider's ascent venting predictions should be straightforward. The physics are uncomplicated, and so is most of the available guidance. While computational fluid dynamics simulations are always refining the state of the predictive art, the design guidance in use today was developed without dependence on those techniques, and is not generally onerous in the implementation. However, you should plan on paying special attention to vent path routing and assuring that your as-built configuration matches the configuration that you analyzed.

Physical Mechanisms

The basis for the ascent venting environment is straightforward. We'll be carrying you from sea level to essentially zero sensed-atmosphere in 80 to 120 seconds, depending on the vehicle and the target orbit. Figure 26-23 shows an unrealistically-conservative dispersion envelope developed from a composite of profiles encompassing several different ground-launched vehicles. It is only intended to be roughly illustrative of what your launch vehicle provider will specify to you.

The curves start at ~101.4 kPa, which was the ambient atmospheric pressure at my hotel outside Vandenberg Air Force Base this morning. The end point, obviously, is essentially zero pressure, just prior to jettison of the payload fairing. For the vehicle, designing the venting implementation is actually quite challenging, owing to the dynamic interaction of free-stream flow over the vehicle skin and vent orifices during flight. What you will be given is not the actual outside atmospheric pressure profile, but the ambient pressure within the payload fairing.

Your design problem will not involve any supersonic flow. You will merely have to accommodate variations in vent rates over a much smaller range of uncertainties than is shown in Fig. 26-23. This simplifies your analysis problem.

One area that will require your increased attention, however, is assuring that all the vent areas assumed in your analysis actually exist on your finished spacecraft.

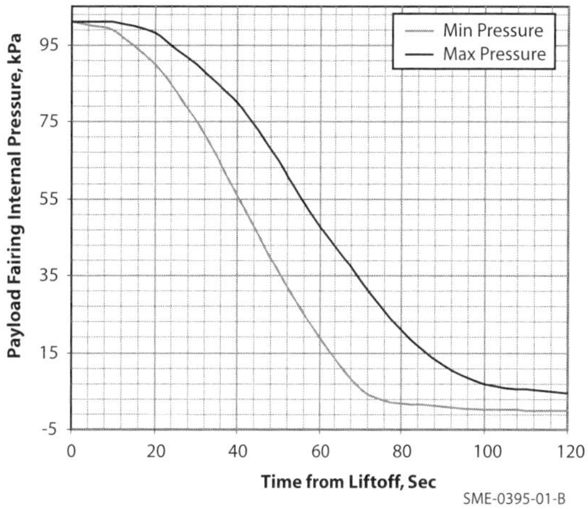

Fig. 26-23. Composite Envelope of Payload Fairing Internal Pressures.

Your venting analyst looks at the released structural drawing of the bus or the instrument that shows all of the openings through which air can vent. Unless your analyst is very experienced, they may not be looking at the thermal blanket drawings that show which structural openings are covered up. Likewise, your analyst knows that the blankets are built with so many holes per square meter, per your specification, but may possibly be unaware that your technicians have been enthusiastically taping over them for the last few weeks during installation. The obvious imperative of making sure the blankets stay in place and patching repairs (blanket damage repair never seems to end) can easily take unintentional precedence over the more subtle requirement that the blankets vent in a predictable manner.

The second area that merits increased attention, pointed out by one of the editors of this book based on our shared experiences, is the direction of the vent path. It is unwise to vent blankets, for example, in proximity to debris-critical instruments without taking steps to mitigate manufacturing debris. Your spacecraft may have been built in a clean laboratory; however your blankets were not. Neither were many of the components you installed during assembly. To be sure, they were built in what's typically called *shop clean* environments, but not strictly-controlled clean rooms. What this means to you is that the act of venting during ascent will somewhat resemble the act of running a vacuum cleaner over your spacecraft. If the vent path runs past any good traps, like a detector array or optical surface, then that could be where some of the remaining debris ends up. One mitigation for this is careful attention to routing your internal and external vent paths. Another is to apply special debris traps at key locations in the vent path such that any residual debris is confined to known areas where is can do no further harm.

Analytical and Test Techniques

Ascent venting effects should be handled as part of your strength analysis, since the driving concern is the stress that will be created by differential pressures between your spacecraft volume and the payload fairing internal pressure. The gas discharge and differential pressure equations are not complex, and are amply treated by the NASA references already cited.

You will be asked by your launch service provider to describe your *ventable volume* (this is just exactly what it sounds like) and venting area, as this becomes part of their analysis to confirm that the fairing structure and vehicle vent areas will remain adequate for the trajectory that you will fly.

Summary of Things You Need to Know About Ascent Venting

- Payload fairing internal pressure will fall from roughly sea-level ambient to essentially zero in a period less than two minutes. Your venting problem analysis will involve only simple, subsonic flow over a venting profile that will be specified by the launch vehicle provider, usually in their user's guide
- You'll use the fairing pressure profile and your own ventable volume to size your vent area in order to keep your maximum differential pressure within bounds that won't overload your structure
- You will be required to specify your ventable volume and vent rates to the launch vehicle provider for use in their analyses
- The structural effects of differential pressures due to ascent venting will have to be addressed in your spacecraft strength analysis
- Pay special attention to consistency between what the configuration you analyzed and the configuration that you actually fly
- Observe caution for residual manufacturing debris becoming trapped at unintended locations after being swept out by the vent flow. Keep the vacuum cleaner analogy in mind and try not to let your instrument serve as the dirt bag

26.5 Available Launch Vehicles

Get More

Get Stnd

This last section will only attempt to provide qualitative observations, avenues for gaining additional information, and a rough overview of the fleets, such as the Soyuz in Fig. 26-24, that are in actual service worldwide today. The book website is updated from time to time with more current vehicle information. In addition, vehicle providers have embraced the internet as a means of communicating performance, contact, and availability information to a wider audience than was possible before, so that kind of contact information will be included here, as available. There are two caveats to this section, however. The first being that a detailed treatment of world fleet performance, features, and history would fill a book in its own right, e.g., Isakowitz, Hopkins, and Hopkins Jr. [2004], which provides an authoritative and widely-used survey of world vehicles. An extension of this caveat is yet another reminder to take published vehicle performance data as only a starting point in your investigations, even if it comes from the vehicle providers themselves. Again, what's published in any forum or media is a best-faith estimate of the vehicle performance offered at that time, but vehicles, even those with venerable histories, usually see a series of changes and upgrades as parts become obsolete, or manufacturing techniques change, or even as they build in measures for greater reliability. All of this affects the performance available for your use. Refer to Table 26-7 for a summary of vehicles providing launch services today, along with their advertised LEO and GTO performance capabilities.

Fig. 26-24. TsSKB-Progress' Soyuz Vehicle during Rollout at Baikonur Cosmodrome. (Photo courtesy of NASA/Carla Cioffi.)

The other caveat is that I personally tend to apply a ruthlessly-pragmatic filter on vehicle availability and capability, and that is "Is it flying to orbit today?" There are a number of vehicles in various stages of development at any one moment in time, and most carry a high degree of credibility in their development plans. Governments and other investors tend not to throw their money into such ventures unless the credibility is there. Even so, many never fly. This is as true in 2010 as it was in any year of the previous three decades and prior, and this observation respects neither nationality nor vehicle performance class. Obviously, new fleets are developed and successfully placed into service; however, the number of fleets under development with this intent consistently exceeds the number that actually reaches their goal. If it hasn't yet flown, then there's considerable risk that it will never enter service at all. I'm a great fan of "daring mighty things," but you should be pragmatic about finding a ride to orbit that will be there when you need it.

Table 26-7.Summary of Available Launch Vehicles. The book website contains a more extensive table with a more complete description of each vehicle, web references for each vehicle, and is also updated as vehicles change.

Nation	Vehicle	Orbits Serviced	Performance (mT) LEO	Performance (mT) GTO	Active Launch Sites*	Comments
USA	Atlas V	LEO, GTO, GSO, Escape	9.4–18.5	4.8–8.9	CCAFS, VAFB	Two payload fairing sizes, one to five strap-on solid motors
	Delta II	LEO, GTO, Escape	2.5–5.5	0.8–2.0	CCAFS, VAFB	Three, four or nine strap-on solid motors
	Delta IV	LEO, GTO, Escape	9.2–22.6	4.3–13	CCAFS, VAFB	Two upper stage sizes, two or four strap-on solid motors, or three-core "Heavy"
	Falcon 1	LEO	1	n/a	RTS	
	Falcon 9	LEO, GTO	10.4	4.5	CCAFS	
	Minotaur I	LEO	0.6	n/a	WFF, VAFB	Uses decommissioned ICBM motors for the first two stages
	Minotaur IV	LEO	1.7	n/a	WFF, VAFB	Uses decommissioned ICBM motors for the first three stages
	Pegasus XL	LEO	0.45	n/a	Air-mobile	Prior launches from CCAFS, RTS, VAFB, WFF, and the Canary Islands
	Taurus	LEO	1.4	n/a	VAFB	Vehicle and launch equipment designed to be road-, rail-, and sea-portable to austere launch sites
China	Long March 2C/D	LEO, GTO	3.8	1.2	JSLC, TSLC, XSLC	
	Long March 3A/B/C	GTO	n/a	2–5.5	XSLC	Primarily marketed for GTO missions
	Long March 4	LEO	4.2	n/a	JSLC, TSLC	Mostly sun-synchronous use
European Union	Ariane 5	LEO, GTO	20	10	CSG	Two upper stage choices, ECA (cryogenic) and ES (storable) for LEO and GTO missions, respectively
India	PSLV	LEO, GTO	1.6	1	SDSC	The LEO performance figure quoted by ISRO is for sun-synchronous
	GSLV	GTO	n/a	2.5	SDSC	No LEO performance quoted by ISRO
Israel	Shavit	LEO	0.3*	n/a	Palamchim AFB	Launches to date have been westward, however a polar capability is being offered and the launch system design is intended to operate from austere sites
Japan	H-IIA	LEO, GTO	n/a	4–6	TSC	Two to four strap-on solid rocket motors. This vehicle is primarily marketed for GTO missions
	H-IIB	LEO	16.5	8	TSC	Used for International Space Station servicing missions to date
Russia	Dnepr	LEO	3.7	n/a	Baikonur, Yasny	Converted RS-20 (NATO SS-18) ICBM, with commercial services marketed by ISC Kosmotras
	Proton	LEO, GTO, Escape	23	6.9	Baikonur	Commercial services marketed by International Launch Services (ILS)
	Rockot	LEO	2	n/a	Plesetsk	Converted UR100N (NATO SS-19) ICBM, with commercial services marketed by Eurockot, GmBH
	Soyuz	LEO, GTO, Escape	5.0–8.2	1.5–3.0	Baikonur, Plesetsk, CSG	Commercial services marketed by Starsem (Baikonur) and Arianespace (CSG)
Ukraine	Zenit	LEO, GTO	n/a	n/a	Baikonur, Sea-mobile	Commercial services marketed by Sea Launch, LLC

*** Site Names/Acronyms**

Baikonur—Baikonur Cosmodrome, Kazakhstan
CCAFS—Cape Canaveral Air Force Station, Florida
CSG—Guiana Space Center, Guiana, France
JSLC—Jiuquan Satellite Launch Center, China
RTS—Reagan Test Site, Kwajalein Atoll, Marshall Islands
SDSC—Satish Dhawan Space Center, Sriharikota, India
TSC—Tanegashima Space Center, Japan
TSLC—Taiyuan Satellite Launch Center, China
VAFB—Vandenberg Air Force Base, California, United States
XSLC—Xichang Satellite Launch Center, China
WFF—NASA Wallops Flight Facility, Virginia, United States
Yasny—Yasny Launch Base, Orenburg Region, Russia

References

For annotated bibliography of launch vehicles, see the book website.

Arianespace. 2010. Website.

Brewer, R. 2011. QinetiQ North America, Inc., and D. Trout, Flight Analysis Division, Launch Services Program, NASA Kennedy Space Center. *Personal Communication.*

Brewer, R. and D. Trout. 2006. "Modern Spacecraft —Antique Specifications." *2006 IEEE EMC Symposium*, vol. 1, pp. 14–18, Portland, OR. Aug.

China Great Wall Industry Corporation. 2011. Website.

CSA Engineering. 2010. Website.

Dhuyvetter, H. J., and H. Lam. 1989. "Load Relief for Launch Vehicles Using an Engine Biasing Technique." SAE Technical Paper 892305. Sept.

ESA. 2005. "Margin Philosophy for Assessment Studies." European Space Research and Technology Centre (ESTEC). Technical Note SCI-A/2003.302/AA, issue 2. Jul.

Eurockot Launch Services GmbH. 2004. *Rockot' User's Guide*, issue 4, EHB0003. Nov.

Harrigan, G. 2011. Flight Analysis Division, Launch Services Program, NASA Kennedy Space Center. *Personal Communication.*

IAI, Ltd. 2011. "Satellite Launchers and Space System." MLM Division.

ISRO. 2011. Indian Space Research Organization. Website.

Institute of Environmental Sciences. 1992. *Airborne Particulate Cleanliness Classes in Cleanrooms and Clean Zones*. FED-STD-209E. Sept. 11.

ILS. 2009. *Proton Launch System Mission Planner's Guide*. Revision 7. International Launch Services, Inc. ILSB-9812-1990. Jul.

ILS. 2010. International Launch Services, Inc. Website.

Isakowitz, S. J., J. B. Hopkins, and J. P. Hopkins, Jr. 2004. *International Reference Guide to Space Launch Systems*. Reston, VA: AIAA.

ISC. 2001. *Space Launch System Dnepr User's Guide.* Issue 2. Nov.

Japan Aerospace Exploration Agency (JAXA). 2010. Website.

KhSC. 2011. Khrunichev State Research and Production Space Center. Website.

Moraes Jr., P., and A. L. Pereira. 2005. "Verification of the Pressure Equalisation Inside the Satellite Compartment of the Brazilian Satellite Launch Vehicle." *J. of the Braz. Soc. of Mech. Sci. & Eng.* ABCM, Vol. XXVII, No. 4, pp. 469–472.

NASA. 1970. "Compartment Venting—Space Vehicle Design Criteria." Technical Report, NASA-SP-8060.

NASA. 2009. *Rules for the Design, Development, Verification, and Operation of Flight Systems*. Goddard Space Flight Center Technical Standard. GSFC-STD-1000E. Jul. 13.

NASA. 1998. *Marman Clamp System Design Guidelines*. NASA Preferred Reliability Practices. Guideline No. GD-ED-2214. Dec. 9.

NASA. 2006. "Launch Vehicle Technical Oversight Policy." NASA Online Directives Information System. NPD 8610.23C. Aug. 18.

NASA. 2010. Space Shuttle. Website.

Opall-Rome, Barbara. 2010. "Israel Declares Ofeq-9 Reconnaissance Satellite Operational." *Space News*. Jun. 22.

Orbital Sciences Corporation. 2006a. *Minotaur I User's Guide*. Release 2.1, Jan.

Orbital Sciences Corporation. 2006b. *Minotaur IV User's Guide*. Release 1.1, Jan.

Orbital Sciences Corporation. 2010a. *Pegasus User's Guide*. Release 7.0, Apr.

Orbital Sciences Corporation. 2010b. *Taurus Launch System Payload User's Guide*. Release 4.0, Mar.

Orbital Sciences Corporation. 2010c. Website.

Planetary Systems Corp. (PSA). 2010. Website.

Sea Launch, LLC. 2010. Website.

Shao, A. 2011. Microcosm, Inc. *Personal Communication.*

SpaceX. 2010. Space Exploration Technologies Corporation. Website.

Starsem. 2010. Website.

The White House. 2004. *U.S. Space Transportation Policy*. NSPD-40. Dec. 21.

United Launch Alliance LLC. 2010a. *Atlas V Launch Services User's Guide*. Revision 11, Mar.

United Launch Alliance, LLC. 2010b. Website.

US Congress. 2011. *Commercial Space Launch Activities*. 49 United States Code, Subtitle IX, Chapter 701.

US Department of Transportation, Federal Aviation Administration, Office of Commercial Space Transportation. 1997. "Commercial Space Transportation Quarterly Report, 2nd Quarter 1997." Apr.

Widrick, T., and A. Abdallah. 2010. Launch Services Program Flight Analysis Division, NASA Kennedy Space Center. *Personal Communication*.

27 Launch Operations

Donald W. Gates, Jr., ***Boeing***

The launch site is the last stop before the spacecraft is placed into orbit. Ensuring successful planning, processing, and operations is essential to achieving mission success. Once the launch vehicle and launch site have been selected, you must begin working with each organization as soon as they are available. By familiarizing yourself with the launch site processes, you will be able to successfully develop a schedule and budget for the launch site operations (Sec. 27.2.1). For example, processing a "ship and shoot" mission may be as little as a week or two. A larger mission could take a few months. Of course, this is only true if the spacecraft or vehicle teams do not encounter any issues during the processing. After understanding what the launch site operations, restrictions, and limitations are, we must consider how to potentially save time and reduce launch site costs by implementing changes in the spacecraft or Ground Support Equipment (GSE) design.

27.1 Worldwide Launch Sites and Launch Restrictions

Many factors should be considered when determining when and where a spacecraft will be launched. You have the mission requirements and objectives, the orbit required to meet the mission objectives, size and weight of the spacecraft, and the time/day of the week/month to maximize fuel and sunlight, just to name a few. Figure 27-1 and Table 27-1 show worldwide launch sites and inclinations they can reach.

Not only do you have to consider the spacecraft requirements and objectives, but the launch site and launch vehicle capabilities and availability as well. Is there a launch vehicle available at the launch site that has the capability to support the spacecraft size and weight to achieve the required orbit? Chapter 26 defines in detail the launch systems and the launch system selection process.

Each launch site does its best to accommodate the requirements of the spacecraft team; however, there will be restrictions and constraints that must be considered in the selection process. Can your spacecraft design and Ground Support Equipment (GSE) meet these restrictions or constraints? Can you comply by altering the system design of the spacecraft or GSE prior to fabrication? For example, if the launch site is in an earthquake prone area, does the design of the GSE meet the appropriate seismic requirements so it will not topple over if such an event should occur? While the spacecraft is on a work stand, does it meet the same seismic requirements or will leg extensions or a base plate be required?

Launch Site Range and Tracking Systems

To monitor the trajectory of the launch vehicle from launch through the End-of-Flight (EOF), there are various range assets and tracking systems scheduled to support the launch. Range and tracking systems provide the data-handling interface with time, range, azimuth, elevation, Doppler frequency, and radar status information of the vehicle being tracked.

Launch site range and tracking systems can have a substantial effect on the spacecraft. Even though the

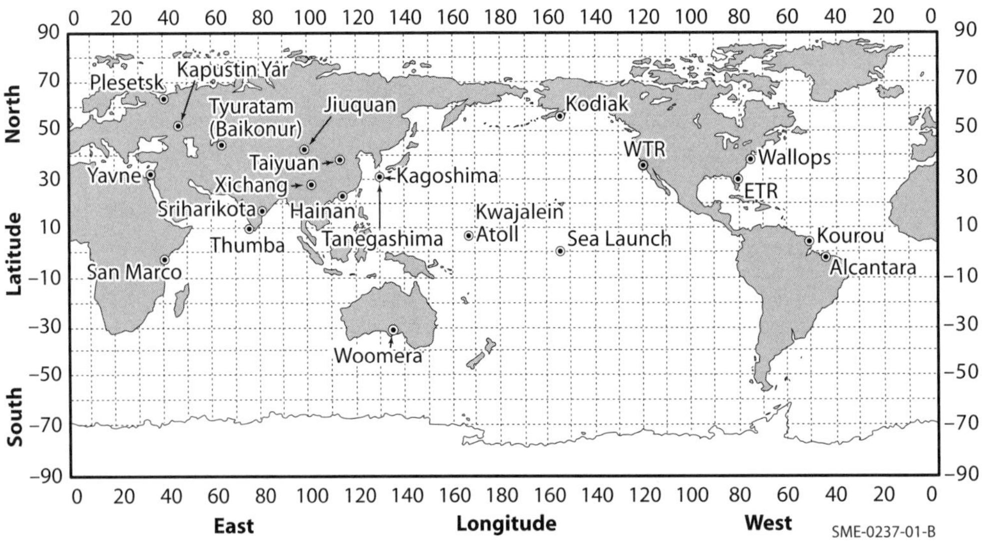

Fig. 27-1. Locations of Launch Sites Around the World. (See Isakowitz, et al. [2004] and Strom [2006].)

Table 27-1. Launch Site Locations and Possible Inclinations. (See Isakowitz, et al. [2004] and Strom [2006].)

Launch Site	Map Designation	Country	Latitude	Longitude	Possible Inclinations
Woomera Launch Site	Woomera	Australia	31.1° S	136.8° E	82–84°
Alcântara Launch Center	Alcântara	Brazil	2.3° S	44.4° W	2–100°
Hainan Space Satellite Launch Center	Hainan	China	19° N	110° E	
Jiuquan Satellite Launch Center	Jiuquan	China	40.6° N	99.9° E	57–70°
Taiyuan Satellite Launch Center (TSLC)	Taiyuan	China	37.5° N	112.6° E	99°
Xichang Satellite Launch Center (XSLC)	Xichang	China	28.25° N	102.0° E	28.3–36°
Kourou Launch Center	Kourou	French Guiana	5.2° N	52.8° W	5.2–100.5°
Thumba Equatorial Rocket Launching Station (TERLS)	Thumba	India	8° N	76° E	
Satish Dhawan Space Centre (SDSC)	Sriharikota	India	13.9° N	80.4° E	
San Marco Launch Platform	San Marco	Indian Ocean	2.9° S	40.3° E	2.9–5°
Palmachim/Yavne	Yavne	Israel	31.5° N	34.5° E	
Tanegashima Space Center (TSC)	Tanegashima	Japan	30.4° N	131.0° E	
Uchinoura Space Center (USC)	Kagoshima	Japan	31.2° N	131.1° E	up to 57°
Kwajalein Missile Range	Kwajalein Atoll	Marshall Islands	9° N	167° E	Any
Sea Launch	Sea Launch	Pacific Ocean at the Equator	0° N	154° W	Any
Baikonur Cosmodrome	Tyuratam	Soviet Union	45.6° N	63.4° E	63–83°
Kapustin Yar	Kapustin	Soviet Union	48.4° N	45.8° E	63–83°
Plesetsk	Plesetsk	Soviet Union	62.8° N	40.1° E	63–83°
Cape Canaveral Air Force Station (CCAFS)	ETR	United States	28.5° N	81.0° W	28.5–59°
Kennedy Space Center (KSC)	ETR	United States	28.5° N	81.0° W	28.5–59°
Kodiak Launch Complex (KLC)	Kodiak	United States	57° N	152° W	
Vandenberg Air Force Base (VAFB)	WTR	United States	34.4° N	120.35° W	56–104°
Wallops Flight Facility (WFF)	Wallops	United States	37.8° N	75.5° W	38–60°

spacecraft is encapsulated inside of a fairing, it can still be exposed to large electromagnetic fields generated by the tracking systems. The spacecraft should be designed and tested to handle the expected worst-case exposure.

The most widely used system for tracking launch vehicles is C-Band radar, also known as "skin" tracking. *Skin tracking* of an object uses radar without a beacon or other signal device on board the object being tracked. Most of the systems are land based, but transportable units are deployed to fill in where land based systems are not available. Many launch vehicles have a C-Band transponder installed to increase the tracking range.

One-way and two-way Doppler tracking are the most common methods of tracking the position of satellites in space. *One-way Doppler tracking* measures the Doppler shift of a radio signal sent from the spacecraft to a tracking station on the Earth. This signal may come from an on-board satellite oscillator or beacon. *Two-way Doppler tracking* measures the Doppler shift of a radio signal sent from the ground station, received by the satellite, and then re-transmitted back to that ground station.

Every vehicle launched in the US has a Flight Termination System (FTS), including the Space Shuttle. The FTS system is a dynamite charge (ordinance package), about the size of a small pipe that runs from top to bottom of each of the launch vehicle stages. During the launch ascent, the Range Safety Officer (RSO) at the launch site monitors the trajectory of the launch vehicle via a real-time display, which shows a pictorial view of the boundaries of the flight trajectory and is updated in real-time with the position of the launch vehicle. If the launch vehicle veers off course and crosses one of these boundaries, the RSO presses two switches that send a coded radio signal to the FTS. This ignites a detonating cord assembly lead to the linear shape charges, breaking the launch vehicle apart. This action effectively zeros the thrust, stopping the acceleration, and rapidly burns the remaining fuel, before it becomes a danger.

27.2 Launch Site Preparations*

Let's assume at this point, the launch vehicle, the launch site, and launch date have all been decided. Now we will take a look at the launch site processing of unmanned missions from pre-arrival at the launch site through the beginning of the launch and early orbit operations.

Launch site operations are often "procrastinated" or not deemed a "high priority" on the list of things to do. Getting the launch site requirements defined, documented, approved, and implemented, however, can take years of work (as discussed in Sec. 6.1). As will be discussed in Sec. 27.7, preparing the spacecraft for the transport to the launch site, arrival, processing, and finally launch requires conscientious attention to detail. If you want a smooth transition from your spacecraft development facility, the key to a successful processing flow is to plan, plan, and plan. The time and effort spent on the upfront planning will not only save you time, but money as well.

As you will see in the sections that follow, there are many tasks and details that will need to be completed for smooth and successful operations at the launch site. With all of the expenses that can be incurred during the launch site processing, this could become your worst budget nightmare if not handled properly.

27.2.1 Creating a Launch Site Operations Budget

One of the tasks of a Project or Program Mission Manager is to define and manage a budget. This includes the many tasks it will take to accomplish the mission and the cost to do so. A typical budget calls for setting up monthly spending limits over a period of time, and then tracking whether the spending stayed within those limits. Budgeting for launch site operations is no different.

Budgeting for the launch site operations can be successfully accomplished following a simple 4-step process.

1. **"What"** needs to be done? Define all of the tasks that will need to be accomplished from arrival at the launch site to the final transportation of the GSE home.
2. **"How long"** is it going to take? Determine the amount of time it will take for each task, taking into account whether the work at the launch site will be:
   - *Quick "ship and shoot" process* with very little testing and little or no mechanical work on the spacecraft?
   - *"Limited" process* with some testing and mechanical work on the spacecraft?
   - *"Full blown" process* with extensive testing and mechanical work that has to be performed on the spacecraft?

   Each task that is performed at the launch site will increase the time required at the launch site, possibly increase the number of required personnel, facilities, resources, and undoubtedly increase cost.
3. **"When"** will it get started? Define when the specific tasks will need to be done.

   A detailed daily processing schedule is produced from steps 1, 2, and 3.
4. **"Who"** is going to do it? Define the personnel it will take, broken down by task (e.g., attitude control system, thermal, electrical, and mechanical), to get the work completed.

Cost is determined from all 4 of these steps.

Depending on the complexity of the operations, the Mission Manager will hold weekly or monthly meetings

*Applicable standards: ISO 17400 (Space Systems). See website for reference.

with each of the system leads to discuss their particular budget and schedule. It is imperative that the system leads report any anomalies or deficiencies in a timely manner to maintain budget and schedule. If the tasks exceed the available time to complete, more time or personnel will have to be added, thus affecting the budget.

You should have reserve funds to account for unexpected events. Reserve funds are allocated to unexpected or unavoidable events, such as broken parts or delays in schedules. From spacecraft delivery to the launch site through launch, there should be at least 1-week of funded schedule reserve per month of launch site operations. The launch site is a new environment for the spacecraft and the team, so there are bound to be unexpected problems. For new or changing requirements, additional funds should be requested from management. Delays that are not the fault of the spacecraft team, such as a launch vehicle schedule slip, should be treated as a "new" requirement.

Because the launch is a major, often public, milestone for a spacecraft team, many organizations include promotional or recognition activities in their budget. Items such as pins, stickers, and posters are distributed prior to and on the day of launch to promote the mission. Other expenses include information packages about the mission and transportation to the launch viewing site for the "Very Important People (VIPs)." Be sure to work with all facets of your organization to understand what costs and requirements are being charged for your launch activities.

27.2.2 Launch Site Operations Planning

Depending on the complexity of the operations that are required, it is not unreasonable to start the launch site planning process 2 to 3 years prior to launch. A word of caution, do NOT wait until the last minute to start this planning. Even a less complex mission will take a minimum of 12 to 18 months (See Sec. 3.4), just to get the required documentation completed, submitted, and approved on time.

If the spacecraft has a propulsion system, once it is fueled, personnel safety will be of great concern. Additional precautions will be required by range safety to ensure operations are successful without incidents. A special processing facility equipped to handle spills or leakage of your particular propellant is most likely required. If there are any hazardous components on the spacecraft (e.g., pyrotechnic systems) or hazardous GSE needed to calibrate/test the spacecraft (e.g., a radioactive source), you must plan to spend more time and money for special processing. What may seem benign to you may not be to launch site safety!

No matter what the size of your mission, a little thought about operations at the launch site very early on in the process will help bound your costs later. Figure 27-2 is a typical launch operations timeline (including working group meetings and interface, and requirements documentation schedules).

Spacecraft Launch Site Interface

The coordination of launch site activities typically requires the full attention of an individual, such as a Launch Site Operations Manager (LSOM). This position requires someone who has a great attention to detail and good communication skills. Many times, teams will try to "stretch the budget" by assigning this task either to the Integration and Test (I&T) Manager or other members of the spacecraft team as a "part-time" responsibility.

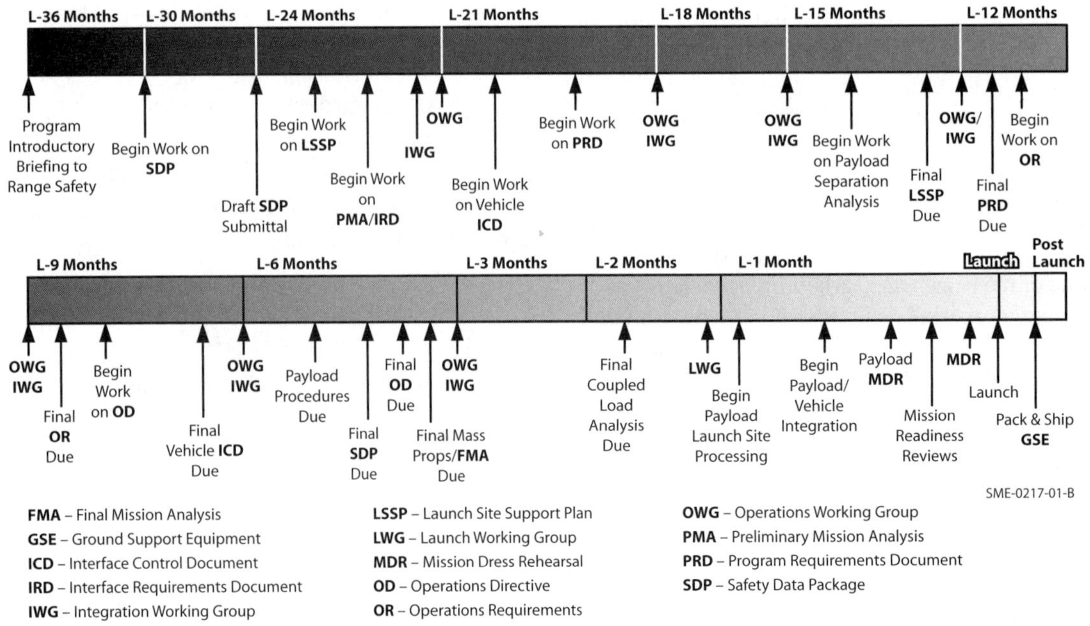

Fig. 27-2. Typical Launch Operations Timeline.

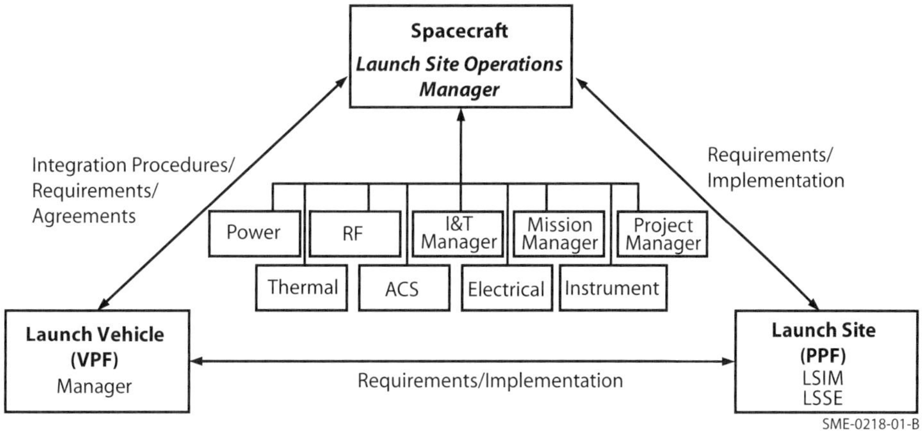

Fig. 27-3. Spacecraft Launch Site Interfaces.

Without a dedicated lead, important requirements are typically missed, causing delays in processing or unneeded disruptions and frustration.

The LSOM is the spacecraft representative and there to protect the project's interests. Knowing who to talk to, what to say, and what to ask for is crucial in saving time, money, and resources. Figure 27-3 is an example of how the LSOM interfaces with the launch site and launch vehicle teams. The LSOM ensures that day-to-day issues are resolved to the satisfaction of all parties (the project, vehicle, and launch site). In addition, the LSOM continuously plans for the upcoming project activities to ensure that little or no time is lost. Pre-coordination and scheduling of consumable resources ensures the smooth continuation of spacecraft processing and operations.

Working Groups

Over the course of a program, the launch team holds various meetings to define and work on the launch vehicle and spacecraft requirements. A few of the most common meetings related to launch activities are the Integration Working Group (IWG), the Operations Working Group (OWG), and the Launch Working Group (LWG). Depending on the launch vehicle and the launch site, the names of the working groups (meetings) may vary, but the objectives are basically the same.

Integration Working Group

IWGs are held every 3–4 months between the spacecraft and launch vehicle personnel and primarily concentrate on the activities that occur between the spacecraft and the launch vehicle (both integrated and stand-alone) before and after arrival at the launch site. This includes the what, when, and where of procedures such as electrical and mechanical integration, as well as monitored data points and testing. Launch site personnel typically support these meetings, even if for information purposes only.

Each vehicle team has a set process it uses when assembling and testing the launch vehicle. This process is typically modified for each mission to accommodate both vehicle and spacecraft integration and testing. During the IWGs, negotiations take place to ensure the requirements of both the spacecraft and the vehicle are met. Detailed drawings, as part of the Interface Control Documents (ICDs) are developed to illustrate the various vehicle/spacecraft interfaces required to ensure a successful launch and separation.

Operations Working Group

OWGs are held every 3–4 months (typically at the same time as the IWG to combine resources) with participants from the spacecraft, launch vehicle and launch site personnel. The OWGs begin early, from 2–3 years prior to launch, and continue up until the spacecraft arrives at the launch site. OWGs primarily concentrate on the spacecraft requirements and activities that will occur while processing at the launch site. This includes what is expected for the spacecraft arrival, the processing facility to be used, mechanical support (if needed), personnel requirements, cleanliness, communications, and safety, just to name a few. OWGs typically occur at the launch site, which allows the technical personnel, as well as management, to participate. Many important documents are developed from the OWGs, such as the Launch Site Support Plan (LSSP), Mission Constraints Document (also known as the Launch Commit Criteria), and the Launch Checklist (or launch script).

Launch Working Group

The LWG is the last meeting held prior to the spacecraft arriving at the launch site (approximately 30 days prior). The purpose of the LWG is to ensure that the launch site is ready for the arrival of the spacecraft. Each supporting entity presents their current status to the launch site upper management. Any outstanding issues are addressed and closed (or near closure) by the end of the meeting. If there are any major open issues, shipment of the spacecraft to the launch site will most likely be delayed.

27.2.3 Launch Site Documentation

Specific documentation is developed to describe in detail all of the support required from the launch site to process and ultimately launch the spacecraft. These documents will cover communications, transportation, processing facilities, consumables, safety, mechanical and electrical procedures, and more as described in Sec. 6.4. The Launch Service Contractor (LSC) typically generates commercial launch documentation, while NASA launch documentation is generated by another NASA organization called the Launch Services Program (LSP). The military has their own unique format called the Universal Documentation System (UDS). This system was adopted to standardize the format among the different branches.

During the spacecraft build-up at the spacecraft assembly facility, be sure that you document the actual temperature, humidity, and contamination limits as they are defined and implemented. Include the justification for each of these limits. After a few months, there may be personnel changes and the current personnel may or may not know why these limits were chosen. By the time you reach the launch site, all the justification knowledge could have been lost if not properly documented. If a limitation is exceeded, it is very important to understand what components/assemblies are affected by the outcome of limit condition. Without the proper documentation, crucial time can be wasted studying whether or not the exceedance damaged something, whether or not the limits are valid, and can or should be changed. These environmental requirements get transferred into the launch site documentation (LSSP and ICD) for use in the Payload Processing Facility (PPF), during transport, and at the launch pad.

Produce and maintain a spreadsheet of the spacecraft procedures that will be used at the launch site. Develop a schedule for the release and review of each procedure. For those procedures that are identified as hazardous, clearly mark this on the front cover and highlight it in the spreadsheet. Define and list each agency that will perform a review, plus when and the duration they will have to provide comments back to you. Include agencies such as the spacecraft manufacturer, launch vehicle, launch site and range safety, as applicable. Allow enough time for the document to complete the review cycle (which could be as much as a month for each reviewer). Managers typically underestimate how long it will take to perform this review cycle (typically three times the amount), which could impact the operation.

Important: You will not be allowed to perform your operations at the launch site until the appropriate spacecraft procedures have been reviewed and approved by the launch site personnel. Failure to comply typically results in an immediate shutdown.

Depending on the launch site or vehicle, the names of the documents may vary, but the information in them will essentially be the same. Clear and concise documentation is not only required, but also necessary to ensure a smooth process at the launch site. Table 27-2 lists the typical US launch site documentation required (which may or may not apply to a particular mission) and the estimated time frame for first submission and completion (final version).

27.2.4 Ground Support Equipment and Flight Hardware Specifications

Accurate Ground Support Equipment (GSE) specifications are imperative for a smooth processing flow. This includes Electrical GSE (EGSE), Mechanical GSE (MGSE) and Flight Hardware. GSE that requires calibration should come to the launch site calibrated and with a valid certification that extends well beyond the planned launch date. Many operations have been halted or delayed for a piece of equipment with an out-of-date certification. Time is wasted finding the appropriate support for that piece of equipment, as well as the time it takes to actually calibrate and certify it. Table 27-3 provides an example of the information included in a typical Ground Support Equipment Specifications table.

Generally, the spacecraft GSE does not reside in the clean room with the spacecraft, but is co-located in an adjoining room in the Payload Processing Facility (PPF) and also at the launch pad. This could be for a number of reasons, including cleanliness, safety, and limitations on physical space. If the GSE must be in close proximity to the spacecraft (e.g., in the clean room), most PPF management require that the GSE be explosion proof.

Interfacing the GSE with the spacecraft is accomplished via two methods, hard-line, or Radio Frequency (RF). The hard-line method is one or more cables (known as a spacecraft umbilical) connecting the GSE to a test or interface panel on the spacecraft. When designing this interface, carefully plan what you would like to be able to do with the spacecraft (e.g., send commands to the spacecraft or instruments, receive telemetry, power the spacecraft, or charge the battery), as this will determine how many cables are required for the umbilical.

There are two ways to interface the GSE with the spacecraft via an RF, open and closed loop. Open loop is via a signal transmitted from the GSE (RF rack) to the spacecraft antennas through the air. Closed loop is done by attaching a "RF hat" to the spacecraft antennas, attaching a cable to the hats, and connecting that cable to the GSE. Closed loop is very similar to the hard-line method, except the signal from the GSE is received via the spacecraft antenna instead of the test or interface panel. When determining which RF method is best for you, work closely with the launch site and vehicle personnel to identify any concerns.

When determining what the maximum length of the GSE cables should be, include their use at the launch site. Take into consideration the distance each rack will be from each other, distance from the spacecraft in the PPF to the GSE, and the interfaces (connections) at the pad. This will allow for the reuse of these cables at the launch site and not require a "rebuild" or an extension. Of course keep the total distance in perspective, as line loss is another factor to consider. In some cases, adaptors or converters may be used to connect with the different interfaces (e.g., coaxial to fiber).

In the special case of spacecraft with biological payloads, additional care must be taken to completely specify

Table 27-2. Launch Site Documentation.

Item	Submittal Time		Description
	Draft/Preliminary	Final	
Submit Systems Safety Program Plan (SSPP)		Launch minus 24 to 48 months	Defines what will be done by the payload organization to meet safety requirements for the Approving Authority.
Safety Data Package	Arrival minus 24 months (or 30 days prior to PDR) Arrival minus 18 months (or 30 days prior to CDR)	5 days prior to the Ground Operations Review (GOR)	Detailed description of hazardous and safety critical ground support and flight hardware equipment, systems, and materials and their interfaces that will be used by the spacecraft team while processing at the launch site.
Non-Ionizing Radiation Use Authorization Request (NIR)		Arrival minus 6 to 12 months	Provide reasonable and adequate guidance for the safe use of NIR sources at the launch site.
Launch Site Operations Plan (LSOP)/Ground Ops Plan (GOP)		Arrival minus 12 months	Defines the day-to-day spacecraft activities that will occur while processing at the launch site.
Program Requirements Document (PRD)		Arrival minus 12 months	Defines the requirements levied on the supporting launch site (also known as the "Range").
Submit Information for Environmental Impact Analysis (AF Form 813)		Launch minus 12 months	Form used for documenting the need to conduct an environmental analysis or the application of certain Categorical Exclusions (CATEXs).
Submit List of GSE Plastics, Films, and Adhesives Used (samples as required)		Launch minus 8 to 12 months	List of all the plastics, films, foams, and adhesives that will be brought to the launch site.
Launch Site Support Plan (LSSP)	Arrival minus 16 months Arrival minus 12 months	Arrival minus 7 months	For NASA launches, an agreement between the spacecraft project and the Launch Service Provider (LSP) as to the products and services necessary (i.e., requirements) for launch site processing from the time of the spacecraft arrival to the time of departure.
Submit Radio Frequency Authorization/Coordination Forms		Arrival minus 4 months	Process for obtaining temporary radio frequency authorizations for testing.
Payload Procedures		Arrival minus 90 days or NLT first use minus 55 days	Spacecraft procedures that may or will be used at the launch site during processing. Submitted to the Range Safety for approval prior to use.
Personnel Deployment Plan (PDP)		Arrival minus 90 days	Defines when supporting personnel are required to be at the launch site to support a particular event during the processing of the spacecraft (Table 27-4).
Contingency Plans (e.g., Off-load at Pad)		Arrival minus 90 days	Defines the procedures to follow should a spacecraft anomaly occur (such as a hydrazine leak).
Material Safety Data Sheets (MSDS)		Arrival minus 60 days	Sheet that provides the information needed to allow the safe handling of hazardous substances used at the workplace.
Final Arrival/Transportation Plans, Schedules and Arrival Badging Requests		Arrival minus 45 days	Defines the details to support the arrival, entry and placement of the spacecraft, equipment, and personnel onto the launch site.
Tool Control Plan (if applicable)		Arrival minus 45 days	Any special tool requirements that are to be used, on or in the vicinity of the spacecraft.
Launch Commit Criteria (LCC)		Launch minus 90 days	Defines the "Go/No-Go" criteria for both the spacecraft and vehicle.
Launch Checklist (Script)		Launch minus 90 days	A "step-by-step" list (Fig. 27-9) used by all supporting personnel on console during the countdown.

NLT = No later than.

Table 27-3. Ground Support Equipment Specifications.

ITEM	Function	Size (H × W × D)	Weight (lbs)	Power (V/A/Phase)	Connector Type	Cable Length	Use Locations PPF	Use Locations PAD	Cert Exp.
			EGSE						
RF Test Rack	Command and TLM Interface via RF Test Equipment for Transponder	72" × 20" × 32"	~500	120V/30A/ 1 Phase	NEMA L5-30P	6'	X	X	N/A
Test Rack	Testing	72" × 20" × 32"	~200	208V/30A/ 3 Phase (5-wire center ground)	NEMA L6-30P	6'	X	X	N/A
			MGSE						
S/C Integration Stand	Used to perform routine S/C operations and testing	4" × 6" × 6"	400	N/A	N/A	N/A	X	N/A	12/XX
Solar Panel Protection Cover	Used when lifting the S/C to protect the solar array panel	4' dia.	20	N/A	N/A	N/A	X	N/A	N/A

the life support function of the GSE, and the critical handoffs between the GSE, launch vehicle, and on-board life support provisions. Whenever possible, the GSE and payload systems should be designed to support launch scrubs without requiring direct payload intervention.

When designing the GSE, take into consideration ALL of the environments in which the GSE will be used. For example, if the spacecraft manufacture is on the East Coast of the US, a standard rack will generally meet the requirements for most East Coast launch facilities. However, if the launch is to occur on the West Coast of the US, GSE seismic requirements must be met in order to use those racks in the West Coast facilities. This could include the addition of brackets to attach to a ceiling rail, the tying of several racks together, or other structural modifications. If the rack will be used in conjunction with a carrier aircraft, the FAA requires a specific grade metal and bolts be used before the rack can be certified for use in flight. Upfront planning by the Vehicle Production Facility (VPF) manager will help to alleviate modifications to the GSE later in the processing schedule.

27.2.5 Detailed Technical Drawings

It is often said that a picture is worth a thousand words. This statement has never been truer than when it comes to all of the intricacies required to launch a spacecraft. For example, when troubleshooting an anomaly with a custom communication link that goes from the spacecraft; through the launch vehicle; through the launch providers' equipment; to the spacecraft vendor's equipment; to the NASA interfaces; across Air Force property; to commercial communications lines; then back to the spacecraft vendor's facility, a detailed drawing is essential in helping to isolate where the anomaly's root cause could be located.

Facility

Detailed facility drawings for each area to be occupied should be done to scale. Details in these drawings will include power requirements (e.g., plug types, voltage, polarity, and number of wires), space requirements for GSE, clean rooms, storage, and office areas. Typically the building facility manager can provide drawings for the area to be occupied. If not, take a measuring tape and generate the drawing yourself. Use the information collected in the GSE Requirements chart to complete the facility drawing. Be sure to pay attention to the width AND height of the doorways to ensure the flight hardware, test rigs, and other hardware can fit through. Figure 27-4 is an example of a completed facility drawing.

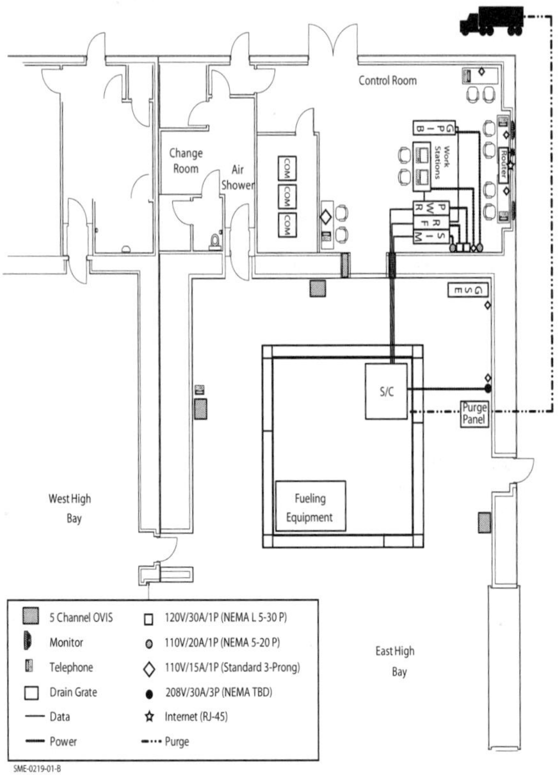

Fig. 27-4. Completed Facility Drawing.

Communication

Detailed technical communication drawings are also very important. Included in these drawings are on-site and off-site communications, as applicable. High-level drawings are typically used for depicting how voice and data will get from point to point. Low-level drawings include not only the high-level information, but also each individual piece of equipment that is required for the end-to-end flow. Low-level drawings can be invaluable when trying to isolate an anomaly. Figure 27-5 is an example of a high-level communications drawing.

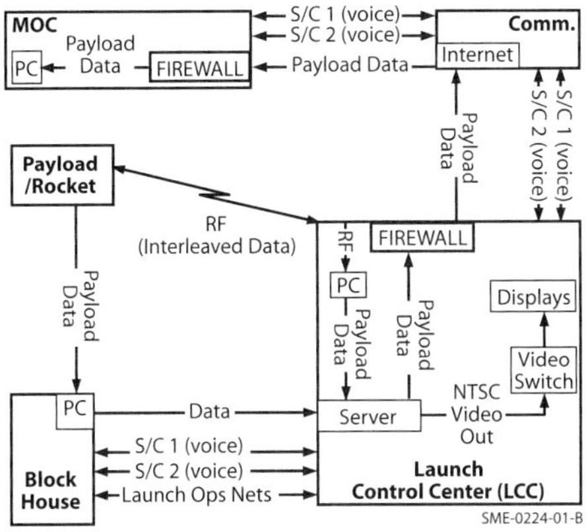

Fig. 27-5. High-Level Communications Drawing.

27.2.6 Schedules

In order to meet the contracted launch date, it is imperative that both the launch vehicle and the spacecraft teams independently develop detailed processing schedules. Each schedule should remain flexible with enough built-in slack time to accommodate issues that may arise. These two independent schedules are then integrated into one master schedule, which will call attention to any potential conflicts in activities. Once the conflicts are identified, who will do what and when, is negotiated between the parties. Off-shift hours or additional days may need to be added to the schedule to accommodate joint or overlapping processing activities. Once the integrated schedule processing flow is complete, you can calculate what date the spacecraft must arrive at the launch site to make the contracted launch date.

Launch Vehicle Schedule

Typically, the launch vehicle team already has a clearly defined schedule of what it takes to assemble, test, and process its vehicle in preparation for a launch. The launch vehicle schedule can be modified to accommodate any stand-alone testing the spacecraft requires. To accommodate spacecraft processing, additional days may be added to the vehicle processing schedule. One of the most important dates to note is the day the spacecraft is to be mated to the vehicle. Typically, "mate day" sets the timer to meet the contracted launch date. If you do not finish the spacecraft processing in time to make the mate day, a launch slip is likely.

Spacecraft Schedule

Prior to coming to the launch site, the spacecraft team will have developed a detailed schedule of day-to-day activities. One of the golden rules is to not cut the schedule short. Up front, plan to work an 8 hour, 5 day (40 hour) week. This allows the other 16 hours per day and weekends to stay as contingency hours that may be used for unexpected situations that occur. In my experience, you WILL use those contingency hours and wish you had many more!

Most launch sites (at least in the US) have a cap on the number of hours worked by any one person in a week: typically a maximum of 12 hours per day, or 60 hours per week. Additional personnel may be needed to perform certain activities in order to not exceed this limit. Careful planning will help to ensure this does not happen during the processing. One exception is if a specific test will take more than 8 hours. Again, this should be the exception…not the rule.

A Personnel Deployment Plan (PDP) is key for both the project and launch site management. The PDP correlates day-by-day with the LSOP and defines when the supporting personnel are required to be at the launch site to support a particular event during spacecraft processing. Proper planning and coordination of the PDP will help keep a project on time and on budget. After all, you do not want your blanket installation team at the launch site "standing by" if the Flight Operations Team (FOT) is scheduled to test for the next 3 days. The PDP is a living document that is continuously revised as the processing schedule is adjusted to complete the necessary operations or unexpected situations that may arise. Table 27-4 represents a partial snapshot of a Spacecraft PDP.

To determine the day the spacecraft should arrive at the launch site, add the number of days of spacecraft stand-alone processing to the L-day (Launch minus day) of the spacecraft/vehicle mate. For example, if the spacecraft/vehicle mate day is on L-45 days (L minus 45 days) and the spacecraft stand-alone testing will take 22 days, arrival at the launch site would be on day L-67 (L minus 67).

Integrated Schedule

The launch vehicle and spacecraft schedules are considered "stand-alone" until the spacecraft and launch vehicle either occupy the same facility or start the process of integration. These two independent schedules must then be integrated to ensure there are no conflicts between the two. For example, there may be times when the launch vehicle or spacecraft processing activities require non-essential personnel to clear the area or the entire facility. Fueling is a good example of a facility clear. If you are not considered essential for this activity, you will not be allowed to enter the facility. Most launch vehicle and spacecraft activities can be executed simultaneously. If this is not feasible (typically a safety issue), it may be possible to work "off" shifts to meet the objectives of the day. If neither is possible, full days will need to be added to the schedule to accomplish the required tasks.

Table 27-4. A Spacecraft Personnel Deployment Plan.

DATE	PPF	PAD	# of Staff	L. Jones	D. Gates		A. Smith	D. Everett	H. Cooper	T. Jackson	T. Russell		G. Fraizer	H. Henley	S. Castro	B. Schena	DATE
14-Dec	S/C Arrival—Unpack/ Setup EGSE at PPF		7	1	1			1	1	1			1	1			14-Dec
15-Dec	S/C Aliveness Test		7	1	1			1	1	1			1	1			15-Dec
16-Dec	Thermal Closeouts		7	1	1			1	1	1			1	1			16-Dec
17-Dec	Fueling		7		1			1	1	1			1	1		1	17-Dec
18-Dec	RCS & Leak Test		7		1			1	1	1			1	1		1	18-Dec
19-Dec			0														19-Dec

Table 27-5. R-Day Schedule (based on a January 2nd launch date).

Sunday	Monday	Tuesday	Wednesday	Thursday	Friday	Saturday
13-Dec –20	**14-Dec –19**	**15-Dec –18**	**16-Dec –17**	**17-Dec –16**	**18-Dec –15**	**19-Dec –14**
	S/C Arrival Unpack/ Setup EGSE at PPF	S/C Aliveness Test	Thermal Closeouts	S/C Fueling (Facility Clear ~ 4 hours)	RCS & Leak Test	
20-Dec –13	**21-Dec –12**	**22-Dec –11**	**23-Dec –10**	**24-Dec –9**	**25-Dec –8**	**26-Dec –7**
	S/C & Vehicle Elect. and Mech. Checks	S/C Mate to Vehicle Upper Stage	Fairing Installation	Transport to Pad Mate to Vehicle	Holiday	
27-Dec –6	**28-Dec –5**	**29-Dec –4**	**30-Dec –3**	**31-Dec –2**	**1-Jan –1**	**2-Jan 0**
	Comm. Checks	S/C Functional	Final Vehicle Closeouts	Launch Rehearsal	Management Review Crew Rest	**Launch** Window 1400–1430Z

Carried over from the discontinued Scout program is a schedule format I have used for over 20 years, called a R-Day (Ready-Day) schedule. The R-Day schedule can be used to easily show all of the daily activities that will be performed by the vehicle and the spacecraft during the launch site processing. Table 27-5 is an example of an Integrated R-Day Schedule. A simple ship and shoot mission (i.e., no on-site spacecraft testing) could begin as late as R-11. A more complex mission could start weeks or even months earlier. Note: The R- and L- (used above) can be used interchangeably.

Once you arrive at the launch site, daily meetings usually occur among all parties to discuss the previous day's results, activities for the current day, and planned activities for the upcoming day. Typically these meetings occur in the morning prior and, depending on the complexity of the processing, may occur again in the afternoon. Good communication between the spacecraft and vehicle personnel during processing is essential to staying on schedule, and ensuring mission success.

27.3 Readiness Reviews and Mission Dress Rehearsals

The Launch Vehicle Readiness Review (LVRR) is held to certify the readiness to proceed with spacecraft/launch vehicle integration activities and is typically held prior to the Spacecraft Readiness Review (SRR), which is also called the Mission Readiness Review (MRR) or the Spacecraft Flight Readiness Review (SC-FRR).

The Flight Readiness Review (FRR) is held to update the mission status, close out any action items from the earlier LVRR and SRR, and certify the readiness to proceed with initiation of the launch countdown.

The Launch Readiness Review (LRR) is held to update the mission status, close out any actions from the previously held FRR, authorize approval to proceed into launch countdown and sign the Certification of Flight Readiness (COFR). The COFR is signed at the conclusion of the LRR.

There may be many other reviews as appropriate and necessary in preparation for launch. These may include, but are not limited to, Mission Requirements Reviews, Critical Design Reviews, Design Certification Reviews, Pre-ship Reviews, Ground Operations Reviews, Project Manager's Reviews and other appropriate safety reviews.

A Mission Dress Rehearsal (MDR) is performed with both the vehicle and spacecraft support personnel at approximately launch minus 2 to 3 days, exercising each step up to and including launch. MDRs are an invaluable learning tool for the team, as this may be the first time many of the members have ever supported a launch.

During the MDR and actual launch countdown, support personnel (both managers and engineers) will monitor many displays and voice networks. Headsets are worn so each individual can monitor the proper networks for reasons discussed in Sec. 27.8.1.

One of the main goals of the MDR, and possibly the most challenging, is real-time problem resolution. Typically there will be 2 or 3 runs of the launch script. During at least one of the runs, anomalies or issues (and possibly an abort) will be interjected to test the reaction of the team. This is not meant to embarrass anyone, but give the team experience in dealing with potentially stressful situations that may occur during the launch, prior to the launch. The MDR test coordinators are looking for predefined reactions to the induced anomalies. After each run, the team's performance is reviewed and evaluated. The Test Conductor (TC) gives a debriefing, explaining what was expected during the run and both the positives and negatives on how the team performed.

Table 27-6 lists the reviews and rehearsals, and the time frame in which they typically occur.

Table 27-6. Readiness Reviews and Mission Dress Rehearsals Timeline.

Item	Timeline
Ground Operations Review	Arrival minus 30 days
Pre-Ship Review	Arrival minus 7 days
Flight Operations Readiness Review	Launch minus 90 days
Pre-Mate Review	Mate minus 1 day
*Payload Mission Dress Rehearsal**	Launch minus 15–20 days
Flight Readiness Review	Launch minus 3 to 4 days
Launch Management Coordination Meeting	Launch minus 3 days
Mission Dress Rehearsal	Launch minus 2 to 3 days
Launch Readiness Review	Launch minus 1 day

* Not a requirement, but good practice is to do a Payload MDR for the spacecraft team prior to the full-up MDR. Members of the launch vehicle team participate reading the checklist. The spacecraft team gains invaluable experience on how to use the launch consoles, using voice protocol, anomaly resolutions and is a great preparation for the "real" MDR.

27.4 Launch Site Access

Access to a launch site can be obtained easily in most cases, as long as the proper procedures for that site are followed. Typically, a visit request (VR) is required, where you will provide your full name, company, date of birth (DOB), citizenship, purpose of visit, dates of visit and clearance (if any). This information is sent to the assigned launch site point-of-contact (POC) or sponsor for processing. Once the VR is approved, the Visitor Center will make available the appropriate credentials.

You must provide any requested information to your POC as early as possible. The number one cause of personnel being denied access to a launch site is procrastination.

If you are not a resident of the country in which you are launching, you will most likely be designated as a Foreign National (FN). You will provide the same information as the VR, but the VR may take longer to process (typically 30 days or more).

If you are launching in the US and require FN's at the launch site, make this known as early as possible. FNs will require an escort while on the site. Note: A foreigner possessing a green card (officially known as a United States Permanent Resident Card) is typically treated as a US Citizen.

A security clearance is typically not required to gain access to a launch site. If you require access to secure facilities at the launch site and do not have appropriate clearance, you will be escorted.

NASA missions require a minimum of a National Agency Check Inquiry (NAC-I). A NAC-I is the minimum level of investigation required of Federal employees as a condition to employment with the Federal government and now for contract employees as a condition to access to Federal facilities and information systems. This is essentially a check of law enforcement records, written inquiries to schools, police departments, contacting references and a fingerprint check to verify your status. While it takes about a year (or more) to get a formal security clearance processed, a NAC-I is usually issued in approximately 6 months.

27.5 Launch Site Training

The amount of training required for spacecraft personnel supporting at the launch site depends on the functions each individual will perform. At a minimum, personnel will go through some type of facility safety or familiarization training. In most cases, the written portion of the training can be completed at your facility prior to arrival. Ask the launch site POC to provide as much of the training materials as possible. The walk-through portion of the launch site training is completed upon arrival. Topics include emergency evacuation procedures, operational procedures, and facility safety, to name a few.

Specialized training may need to be completed at the launch site. This could include the use of an Emergency Life Support Apparatus (ELSA) unit or Self-Contained Atmospheric Protective Ensemble (SCAPE) suit, vehicle/spacecraft fueling, clean room procedures, magnetic procedures, or other site- and vehicle-specific content. In some cases, proof of a recent medical physical must be presented upon arrival for those personnel training to operate equipment, such as overhead cranes and forklifts. Make sure you have two trained operators (prime and a backup) for all time-sensitive operations.

Console training familiarizes personnel who are on console for the launch with the range processes, available displays and communication protocols.

Most likely, during Integration and Test (I&T), spacecraft personnel have not been using formal voice protocols when speaking to each other over voice lines. Rather than calling out "Bob" or "Helen," proper voice protocols are established for the launch and must be adhered to. Unique titles such as Mission Manager and Mission Director are used to signify the function being performed by that individual. As the voice lines are recorded, open-air conversations are highly discouraged. If an anomalous situation occurs, the structured clarity of proper voice protocol can be very helpful in determining the cause of the problem.

The spacecraft safety person and the on-site launch site safety officer are responsible for ensuring personnel have received proper training. A training matrix (Fig. 27-6) is used to track the training required for each individual and the status of that training.

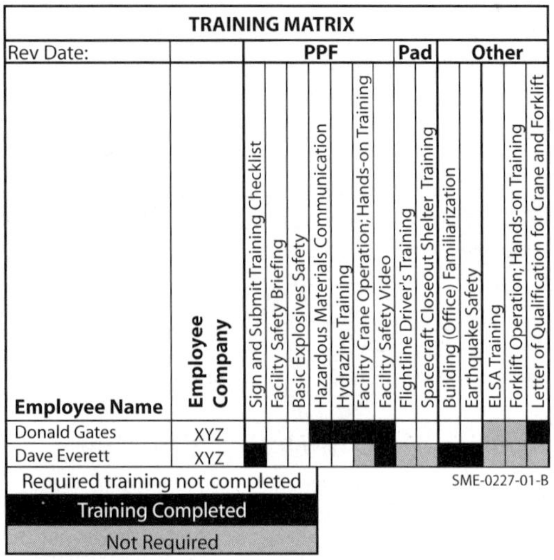

Fig. 27-6. Training Matrix.

27.6 Transporting the Spacecraft to the Launch Site

Depending on how far the launch site is from the spacecraft assembly facility, transporting the spacecraft to the launch site is accomplished either via air or ground. Government owned spacecraft (e.g., NASA, DoD) have the choice of using government (e.g., Air Force, Army) or commercial carriers, while commercial spacecraft typically use a commercial carrier. Coordination with the launch site personnel is crucial to ensure an uneventful transition once you have arrived.

Traveling by air has a few benefits over ground transport, such as taking less time to transport, especially if transporting across the country and having less physical impact on the spacecraft. Traveling by air does come with higher costs as additional resources are required once the plane arrives, such as offloading and transport equipment, personnel, airport fees, costs to procure the aircraft, and fuel.

Traveling by ground is typically much cheaper, but it may take longer and be much harder on the spacecraft due to the various road conditions encountered on the way. If you are purging the spacecraft (which you should be), have pre-planned stops along the way to check the levels and fittings. In my experience, spacecraft teams have followed the truck in some type of vehicle (usually a camper) from departure to arrival. Ensure you have enough personnel to support this type of operation, as trucking companies typically use two drivers, and only stop for fuel.

Whether you transport by ground or air, attach shock sensors to the spacecraft container. By monitoring and recording the vibrations from these sensors, you will be able to see if any shock like conditions were encountered along the way. After arrival review the sensor data to see if there should be any concerns.

Two points of caution that must be considered are:

1. Choose a carrier that has experience in moving spacecraft and the GSE (this is not the place to cut costs) and
2. Ensure you get enough insurance to replace the spacecraft and the effort to duplicate it (called an agreed upon value) in case a mishap should occur along the way.

When budgeting for transportation, it is important to do a trade study to weigh the costs versus the benefits of both air and ground travel. Though it may not always be apparent, saving time can be a way of saving costs.

Ensure you know how the spacecraft will be offloaded at the launch site. While you may use the lift gate of the transport truck to load the spacecraft at your facility, the launch site may have a NO lift gate policy and require the use of a crane or forklift. Depending on the launch site policy, this could be one of the determining factors of how you design the spacecraft-shipping container.

Another design driving consideration is the environment which the container may be exposed to. If offloading inside a facility, there may not be much of a concern. If offloading outside, determine if weather-proofing the container should be considered in the design. Consider the worst-case environmental conditions, as your launch date could slip, shifting your arrival date from the most optimal weather to the worst.

27.7 Launch Site Processing

Depending on the operations to be performed, once at the launch site, the spacecraft may proceed to either the Payload Processing Facility (PPF) or directly to the Vehicle Assembly Building (VAB). Figure 27-7 illustrates the Astrotech Space Operations (ASO) facility; one of the PPF's currently available at VAFB.

This facility, owned and operated by ASO, is located on a 60 acre leased site on Vandenberg Air Force Base, CA. They provide for non-hazardous and hazardous processing. An 8,000 ft^2 spacecraft processing bay that provides the capability to process 5-meter class payloads was completed in 2010.

27.7.1 Arrival

Upon arrival, the spacecraft is met by launch site personnel and escorted to the processing facility. At the processing facility, the spacecraft and GSE are unloaded

Fig. 27-7. Astrotech Payload Processing Facility (VAFB).

and taken to the assigned area. Once this has been completed, all operations cease and any remaining safety training is completed.

In a matter of hours, the GSE can be connected to the spacecraft, configured and ready to begin testing. Typically the first test is a spacecraft "aliveness test" to ensure the spacecraft made the trip to the launch site from the processing facility successfully and establish a baseline for later testing.

27.7.2 Processing Flow

The processing flow or Integration and Test (I&T) activities, both spacecraft and launch vehicle, are well defined prior to the spacecraft arrival at the launch site. Unless you are a "ship and shoot" type mission (i.e., no spacecraft testing or processing is necessary), you will have allotted time on the schedule to do final "standalone" spacecraft and instrument testing, solar array installation, ordinance installation, and successful testing of each.

While you are at the launch site, work at the Mission Operations Center (MOC) is still in progress as well. A good, (although not necessary), rule of thumb is that anytime the spacecraft is powered on at the launch site, allow the MOC to receive the telemetry data (assuming the MOC is off-site). In many instances, the spacecraft team at the launch site will allow one last test (e.g., commanding the spacecraft) with the MOC prior to launch. This gives the MOC personnel an opportunity to continue to test their systems and further train personnel. When deciding if this is a good thing for your mission, keep in mind that this is NOT the time to try out anything new (this includes commands, automated scripts, or data base updates). The ONLY exception would be that if the change to the MOC system would delay the launch if it were not tested prior to the launch.

During the processing flow, a Payload Attach Fitting (PAF) is provided to the spacecraft team by the launch vehicle team to integrate the spacecraft with the launch vehicle. This is also the separation point between the two. The PAF consists of two halves held together by a clamp band and is modified on the spacecraft side for each mission to accommodate the attachment points of the spacecraft. A PAF fit check and separation test is done at the spacecraft facility long before arrival at the launch site. One half of the PAF will stay with the spacecraft after separation from the launch vehicle, so this must be included in your spacecraft design, weight measurements and orbit analysis.

A pre-mate review is held just prior to the spacecraft and vehicle integration, where each team presents what has been done (e.g., testing, assembly, repairs) since arrival at the launch site and the results to upper management. With a successful review and upper management approval, a GO is given for mate.

Depending on the launch vehicle, spacecraft mate is accomplished either in a horizontal or vertical position. Each position offers its own challenges and how this is successfully and efficiently accomplished is carefully thought out.

With vertical processing, the launch vehicle is assembled inside of a tower, which rolls out of the way on a railway for launch. Typically with vertical processing the spacecraft is mated with the upper stage motor at the PPF (now called an assembly) and then placed inside a special shipping container, provided by the launch vehicle team. The container is transported to the launch complex, where it is craned and set on a platform, located at a height just above the top of the launch vehicle. The crane is used to lift the assembly out of the container and lowers it slowly towards the launch vehicle. Once the PAF is aligned with the upper stage, the bolts are put in and torqued to specification. The container is removed and operations continue.

With horizontal processing, many of the above processes are the same; therefore I'll just discuss the differences. The launch vehicle is assembled inside a facility, instead of a tower. When mating the spacecraft to the launch vehicle, the spacecraft is lifted from the side, instead of the top. This type of mate is typically accomplished using a crane; however, some missions use a wheeled mechanical structure to have better control over the spacecraft movement. Determine early in the process if a crane lift can be performed inside a clean environment (such as the facility itself or a clean tent) as required by your contamination expert. If not, you may need to design (or modify) a rolling fixture to integrate with the launch vehicle. One could argue which process is better, but both processes will work, as long as either the spacecraft or launch vehicle can be rotated when it comes time to align the bolt holes. Finally, the launch vehicle is raised from the horizontal to vertical position for launch. Depending on the launch vehicle, once vertical, a tower may be rolled in to keep the launch vehicle safe from the weather and then rolled out of the way for launch. One notable exception to these final steps is the Pegasus launch vehicle, which features a horizontal integration and unique horizontal air launch.

Even though electrical and mechanical interface testing has been previously completed, this is the first time the spacecraft is integrated with the fully assembled launch vehicle. To ensure there are no interference issues, the launch vehicle team powers the launch vehicle, then requests the spacecraft to be powered, carefully monitoring each system for any abnormalities. After successful testing, each half of the fairing is installed, allowing time for any spacecraft and launch vehicle Remove Before Flight (RBF) items and final closeouts. This completes the assembly and testing of the launch vehicle. You're just about ready to launch!

In Sec. 27.3, the MDR and launch reviews were explained in detail, therefore I won't say more than… it's that time. After successful completion of the MDR and launch reviews, a GO is given for launch. The supporting ground stations will go through a last pre-launch readiness test, flowing spacecraft data to the MOC. Depending on the mission requirements, these ground stations may flow data to the MOC during the launch count down—something to consider when you are planning how to ensure the MOC and your supporting ground stations are "green" for launch. Figure 27-8 is a snapshot of a processing flow from arrival through post-launch.

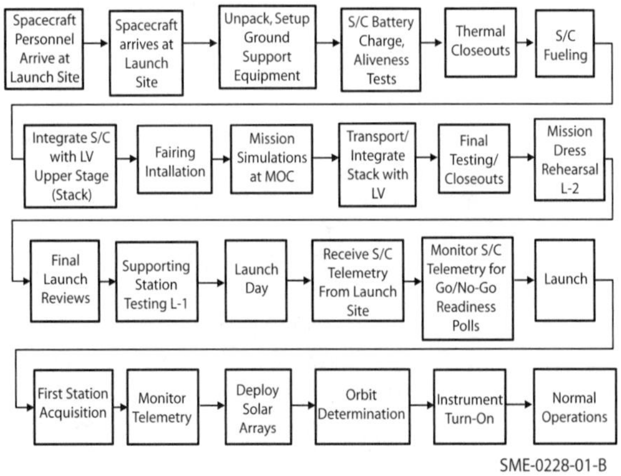

Fig. 27-8. Process Flow from Arrival Through Post-Launch.

27.8 Launch Day*

Depending on the vehicle and spacecraft configurations required prior to launch, you may be requested to arrive "on station" anywhere from 4 to 12 hours prior to launch (L-0). The Launch Conductor (LC) will "open" the Launch Checklist, perform voice checks with key positions and update the team with any last minute changes or corrections (black lines). Once the LC has completed the opening, NO changes to mandatory requirements are accepted.

Spacecraft and vehicle engineers arrive on station to perform final configurations and monitor their respective telemetry data. Once the direct spacecraft cables are disconnected, spacecraft telemetry is multiplexed, or mixed in, with the vehicle data and then decommutated, or separated out, on the ground. If any discrepancies are observed, they are reported to the appropriate personnel. After launch, spacecraft telemetry is received via the vehicle telemetry downlink until spacecraft separation or the first independent contact is established.

Typically, launch is targeted for the opening of the "launch window." *The launch window* is the period between the earliest and latest times during which the launch vehicle can be launched in order to achieve the orbit defined by the satellite. If an unexpected delay occurs during the count, it may be possible to recover from the anomaly and still launch, if the new time is still within the window. Depending on the required orbit, the launch window could be as small as a few seconds to a few hours.

27.8.1 Launch Checklist (Script)

The Launch Checklist (Fig. 27-9) is a step-by-step list (script) used on launch day by all supporting personnel on console during the countdown. The launch script specifies exactly what is to be said by the Launch Conductor (LC) for each call-out and the exact response expected from the respondent i.e., Ground Station Manager (GSM). Each item is checked off as it is completed. Certain pre-defined parameters are hand recorded in the checklist during the count, as they are not fixed, but are expected to be within a certain range. If the numbers read back do not fall within this range, there may be an issue that will be discussed. Another example is the exact launch time. This time is filled in at the opening of the checklist, as the time may have been shifted a few seconds to accommodate a Collision Avoidance (COLA) and ensure that the spacecraft (or launch vehicle) will not collide with another object in space. There may be times when items are "jumped" or skipped during the count. The LC will come back to that item to ensure it has been completed. ALL steps in the checklist must be completed (or waived) prior to giving the final GO for launch.

Embedded in the launch count, are periods called "built-in holds." These are blocks of time that allow the team to take a break or catch up if any of the previous steps being performed took a little longer than expected. The LC continues with each step in sequential order as defined in the Launch Script, but may occasionally jump steps if a task needs a little extra time to be completed.

At approximately L-2 minutes "terminal count" is entered (time actually depends on the vehicle). Once Terminal count is entered, all "required" requirements are now considered "mandatory" and cannot be waived. If any anomalies occur with the vehicle, spacecraft, or any of the supporting sites during this period, a launch scrub will most likely occur. A poor report from the Launch Weather Officer (LWO) would be a good example. If a scrub does occur, the LC will direct the team as to the next course of action. Otherwise, the LC continues to work to the L-0 time and the vehicle is launched.

If an anomaly occurs and can be fixed in time for all entities supporting the launch to complete their required work, prior to the end of the launch window, the LC will instruct the launch team to go to a point in the checklist and the count will begin again.

Get Stnd * Applicable standards: ISO 10784 (Space Systems). See website for reference.

#	Action	Operation	Report	Net
1	LC	Call to Station/ Voice Checks ROC ______ RCO ______ MFCO ______ PM ______ LWO ______	Voice Checks Complete	Launch Ops Net
2	PM	Call to Station/ Voice Checks GSM ______ ACS ______ Thermal ______ LWO ______	Voice Checks Complete	S/C 1
3	RCO	Report status of Voice, Data, and Video Lines	Range Voice, Data, and Video Lines Operational	Launch Ops Net
4	ROC	Coordinate LWO Weather Brief on Ground Ops Net	Roger	Launch Ops Net
5	LWO	Confirm Weather Status	Weather is Green	Launch Ops Net

SME-0229-01-B

Fig. 27-9. Launch Checklist (Script).

27.8.2 Launch Commit Criteria

The Launch Commit Criteria (LCC) defines the Go/No-Go criteria for both the spacecraft and vehicle. Listed are the critical data points for each subsystem, along with the minimum and maximum limit specifications. Each subsystem being monitored must be in a nominal condition (i.e., within the specified limits) in order to proceed with the next task.

There are two levels of requirements defined in the LCC, "required" and "mandatory." Once the checklist has been opened, any "required" parameters that exceed the expected limits may be waived ONLY if the launch management team is in unanimous concurrence. Again, once Terminal count is entered, all "required" requirements are now considered "mandatory" and cannot be waived.

"Mandatory" parameters that exceed the expected limits cannot be waived for any reason. This process helps to keep a condition called "*Launch Fever*" from occurring. As discussed in Sec. 27.12, launch fever can occur when the excitement or pressure of getting the spacecraft launched on time overtakes making a common sense decision on an issue that arose, potentially delaying or scrubbing the launch. These parameters were defined as mandatory for a reason, with level heads, and cannot be changed for this launch attempt.

27.9 Post-Launch and Early Orbit Operations

Once the launch vehicle has lift-off, the Launch Vehicle Engineer will announce the key events (e.g., Stage 1 separation, Stage 2 ignition, and so on) over a specified network channel. The launch vehicle transmits both the launch vehicle and spacecraft telemetry data (multiplexed by the launch vehicle systems) in real-time during the flight. Once the ground equipment receives the telemetry, it is decommutated and transmitted to the respective systems specialists. The launch vehicle and spacecraft engineers monitor the telemetry data for any signs of off-nominal specifications and verification of nominal operations. Range safety personnel monitor the trajectory of the vehicle in-flight and are ready to send a destruct signal if the vehicle veers off course.

Ground stations are pre-scheduled to follow the launch vehicle using radar or other assets from lift-off through spacecraft separation. If the launch vehicle signal is not available at the time of separation (e.g., due to ground station support not being available), spacecraft separation is not verified until the next contact. Once spacecraft separation occurs, spacecraft telemetry is no longer received as part of the launch vehicle telemetry, but from a separate signal transmitted by the spacecraft to a supporting ground station.

When developing the automated on-board sequences for after spacecraft separation, ensure no spacecraft deployables are initiated until the launch vehicle is far enough away from the spacecraft to avoid interference or possible contamination (e.g., at least a 2 second delay).

At spacecraft separation or Loss of Signal (LOS) with the launch vehicle, spacecraft operations are handed over from the spacecraft team at the launch site to the Flight Operations Team (FOT) at the Mission Operations Center (MOC). It is now up to the FOT to begin the on-orbit checkout of the spacecraft.

In many cases, spacecraft teams have a limited number of support personnel. Key spacecraft personnel that were required to be at the launch site for launch may not physically make it to the MOC prior to the first acquisition. The solution to this problem is to transmit the spacecraft telemetry data received at the MOC to the ground support equipment still located at the launch site. This will allow those personnel to view the same data as the MOC and participate in the operations. Once it is determined that all is well with the spacecraft, those key personnel can then make their way to the MOC.

The FOT will continue to monitor the health and safety of the spacecraft and follow the agenda that is defined in the Launch and Early Orbit Plan (LEOP). This includes operations such as deploying the solar arrays, instrument covers and booms, and monitoring the status of the spacecraft (housekeeping data), as required. Eventually the spacecraft instruments are turned on, checked out, and the primary mission begins (e.g., science and military).

Launch Site Departure

What came to the launch site must leave the launch site. Coordinating with the launch site personnel, GSE shipping arrangements are made by the spacecraft team. Again, give the requested information for the truck drivers to the launch site personnel as early as possible, thus giving them time to process the badging. As most people are anxious to get home, it generally takes little time to get the equipment boxed and ready to go. Once the shipping truck arrives, is loaded and has departed, the launch site personnel will start getting the area ready to receive its next occupant.

Prepare yourself for an emotional experience, for some, both good and bad. What has been "home" for the past few weeks (or months) is coming to an end and could be a little sad. What has taken years to plan, build and test is now thousands of miles away in orbit, performing as designed. What an emotional high! Yes, it's a joyous occasion and time for celebration.

Through these past few years, co-workers have become friends and in many cases, as close as family. Nonetheless, it's time to go home. The space community is a small community. You never know where our paths may cross in the future, but one thing is for sure...if you stay in the business long enough, it will happen.

27.10 Modernizing Launch Operations

Budgets get smaller each year, so newer and smarter ways of doing business are quickly becoming a reality. The less time spent processing and testing at the launch time can equate to quite a savings. While the caption "Faster, Better, Cheaper" is echoing throughout the spacecraft community, doing more with less appears to be the motivating factor.

Cutting Costs

There is always the age-old question, how can we cut costs? Is there anything the mission (spacecraft) designer should know about how to make launch operations easier and cheaper?

In most cases the launch site can and will support the necessary requirements to process a spacecraft at their facility. There are, however, various operations that could be taken into consideration to shorten the process flow and cut costs (see Secs. 13.3 and 13.5).

Testing

- Limit testing to what is really necessary to verify the spacecraft is ready for launch.
- Consider whether full blown I&T simulation can be shortened at the launch site and achieve the same objectives.

Environmental Operations (Purge/Cleanliness Requirements)

- Typically the cleanliness requirements of the entire spacecraft are driven by the instruments.
- Devise ways to keep the instruments and spacecraft clean without specialized purging systems.
- Evaluate the spacecraft environment. Is a class 10K contamination environment essential or is class 100K sufficient? What could be done differently in the spacecraft design or operations to utilize a class 100K environment?

Mechanical Operations

- Keep the number of mechanical operations in the field to a minimum by installing as much hardware as possible at the manufacturing facility.

Spacecraft Battery

- Use a battery that does not require high maintenance. Avoid those with constant trickle charging, recycling, top-offs, and excessive cooling requirements (Sec. 21.2).

Support Personnel

- Limit the number of support personnel at the launch site. Only deploy those who are essential for the operation at hand, and do so in a timely manner.

Risks Versus Cost

With the constant need to cut costs comes higher risk. When designing the spacecraft, careful consideration should be given as to when the risks outweigh the costs. For example, many spacecraft today employ "single string" architecture. A failure using this design could mean a quick end to the mission. Risk vs. cost must also be considered while processing at the launch site. Questions to consider include:

- What spacecraft testing actually needs to occur vs. what is a nice thing to do?
- How much retesting is needed at the launch site when you have tested this system multiple times over the past few years?
- Will a quick aliveness test do, or will only a full 2 day comprehensive test fulfill the requirement?
- Do you need to do any additional testing at all? How confident are you the spacecraft will work on orbit without testing that one last time?

More time equals more money. Determine what risks you are willing to take **before** arriving at the launch site.

Remote Operations

Instead of bringing the entire spacecraft engineering support team to the launch site, send the data to them. With the technology and communications available today, this concept may not be too far from reach.

One could argue that key decision making personnel should be at the launch site. Those monitoring telemetry displays could be basically anywhere in the world if they can receive the data they need to review.

Alternatively, a smaller team could be deployed to the launch site. A trade study should be done to compare the communications costs versus what it would cost to deploy the larger team to the launch site.

Also, there is the risk factor (Sec. 24.2). The question is...would you be willing to launch the spacecraft if you were to lose communications with off-site personnel? Reliability of the communication lines is a huge factor to consider (Sec. 24.1). Consider the cost of redundant communications as this capability might be significantly less than the cost of sending an entire team to the launch site and reduce such a risk.

Launching as a Secondary Payload

In many cases, launch vehicles can accommodate one or more smaller payloads, along with a primary mission. Often, the primary payload may not be using the full performance capability or "real estate" of that launch vehicle. Special adapters have been developed by launch vehicle operators to carry small payloads, allowing universities and low-cost missions to take advantage of an opportunity to be launched as a "secondary" payload.

As a secondary payload, you are subject to the same characteristics of the primary payload (e.g., shock, thermal and loads) and will have to meet the requirements defined for that launch vehicle and primary mission. If well managed, "hitching a ride" is a win-win for both the launch vehicle and spacecraft, as two satellites are launched for the price of one.

There are two very apparent advantages of flying as a secondary payload: time and cost savings. With the primary payload paying for the actual launch, you save a huge amount of money on launch costs. By using proven (qualified) systems developed by the launch vehicle team, time-to-flight will be significantly reduced by minimal testing with the launch vehicle.

While saving time and costs are a major advantage, launching as a secondary payload does come with risks:

- **Schedule.** You are reliant on the primary payload to hold to the advertised schedule (but not vice versa). If they slip, you slip. If you slip, you run the risk of them launching without you. In addition, you could be "called up" at the last minute to make a launch (e.g., 7 days).
- **Weight.** You are reliant on the primary payload to not exceed their predicted weight (total mass) during their processing. If they go over, you may be bumped from the flight if your mass is now too much for the launch vehicle to get both to orbit. Also, you must keep your spacecraft mass within the predicted amount as well.
- **Launch.** You are reliant on finding a launch that is in the "vicinity" of where you need to be placed and with a launch vehicle that can get you there AFTER the primary payload has been placed in orbit. Be ready to adjust your trajectory and schedule to accommodate the primary payload (as long as you can still meet your mission objectives).

These are only a few of the risks that could potentially jeopardize your mission when launching as a secondary payload. This, however, is a much better solution than never launching because of funding issues.

27.11 Common Mistakes to Avoid

After each launch, it is not uncommon to have a review to discuss what the team could have done differently to make the entire process faster, easier and less stressful. If your mission is similar to one that has already been launched, check for lessons learned from that mission. This information can be invaluable. Below are some common mistakes that are made at the launch site that can and should be avoided:

1. **Under Estimating the Schedule.** Too many times, projects have not allowed enough time in the schedule for contingencies, issues that may arise, and crew rest. The "going in" plan should be based on an 8 hour a day, 5 day a week schedule with nights and weekends kept for contingencies.
2. **Lack of Coordination for Base Access.** Since September 11, 2001, security has increased at most launch sites around the World. Getting the POC the information required in a timely manner is extremely important to get your personnel on site. Don't forget to include the truck drivers (or airplane crew) who are delivering the spacecraft!
3. **Lack of Planning and Coordination of Personnel Coming To/From the Launch Site.** The PDP is a "living" document and should be constantly reviewed and updated to ensure the correct personnel arrive at least 1 day PRIOR to when they will be needed. Careful thought and preparation will help make it easy for the necessary personnel to travel to the launch site to support the operations.
4. **Requirements "Creep."** It can manifest itself as higher, more stringent requirements at the launch site than at the manufacturing facility. (For example, Grade B N2 (Nitrogen) was used for purging during processing at your facility; however, Grade C N2 is now required at the launch site. A class 100K facility was used while you were at your facility; now a class 10K requirement has been levied on the launch site. Smocks were used during the build, but bunny suits are being required at the launch site.) Not only can such creep be unnecessary and expensive, but it also introduces last minute changes that can be a source of unexpected system errors.
5. **"Launch Fever."** Teams suffering from "launch fever" can fall into the trap of failing to make sound, common sense decisions, just to make a launch date. When it gets down to crunch time and things may not be going the right way, do not let schedule pressure be a reason to start cutting corners. Just about any anomaly can be fixed on the ground. Once the spacecraft is launched into space, well, not so easy. Procedures were put together with level heads; you want to keep it that way.
6. **Over Testing at the Launch Site.** Most likely you have been testing the reliability and performance of the spacecraft for many months. The spacecraft's trip to the launch site is generally far gentler than the launch itself and all of the environmental testing that was previously performed.

The logical extension of this belief is the minimization of testing at the launch site. You are not trying to "re-qualify" the spacecraft or the GSE, just ensuring it survived the transport to the launch site.

7. **Using Procedures for the first time at the Launch Site.** To stay on schedule, activities need to be well planned and thoroughly rehearsed ahead of time. Tests and countdown procedures that are used at the launch site should have been incorporated into the regular testing in the preceding months of qualification and acceptance testing at the manufacturer's facility. Do not perform a test or use a procedure for the first time at the launch site UNLESS it is mission critical!

8. **Expired GSE Certification.** Ensure the GSE that requires calibration arrives at the launch site calibrated and with a valid certification that well exceeds the planned launch date.

9. **Lack of Contingency Procedures.** Even though you cannot plan for every contingency, you can plan for the most common, including facility power outages, GN2 purge depletion, purge panel failure, personnel absences, contamination issues, lightning, temperature or humidity limits exceedance and many more. Have contingency plans in place and follow the procedures as defined in those plans. ALL contingency procedures should have been FULLY exercised at the manufacturer's facility prior to arrival at the launch site.

10. **Not Having a Pre-Determined Access List**

    There are times when operations will require a limitation on the number of personnel in the area. Having a pre-determined access list with the names of the individuals required to perform those operations will ensure the right personnel are there to support the launch and decrease the chance of distraction or confusion.

    This will become very apparent when transitioning operations to the launch pad. It seems that a lot of people believe that they have the right to go to the launch pad, but in reality a very small portion of the launch team actually needs to go to the launch pad. Even though you will still have a few personnel who will not understand (or agree), with a pre-determined access list there will be fewer problems to resolve. If possible, schedule a time where all personnel can have a short visit at the launch pad and an opportunity to take photos.

In addition, consider the following questions:

1. **Can the launch site environment affect the spacecraft?** Consider the temperature and humidity (both at the PPF and while transporting). What about helium exposure (possibly from those processing before or at the same time as you)? What about water exposure?

2. **When at the launch site, how is the spacecraft and instrument going to be purged?** Is there sufficient access to get to those areas (with and without the fairing installed) requiring purging? Will a high flow of GN2 be required (such as using a Vortex Cooler) increasing the amount used? Are covers required for certain areas of the spacecraft to avoid contamination?

3. **Can the spacecraft tolerate the levels of the range-radiated emissions that occur at the launch site?** Consider the conditions inside the shipping container, outside the shipping container, inside the processing facility and inside of the fairing. Also take into consideration self-exposure (by accidental radiating) inside of the fairing.

4. **If you are processing inside a clean tent at the PPF, is there enough room to test the deployable systems (such as a mag boom, instrument covers or solar arrays)?**

5. **Are there enough "inhibits" in place to meet the range safety requirements?** Typically any potentially hazardous conditions, such as a pyro firing or solar array deployment, must be at least 2-fault tolerant, including 1 via software AND 1 via hardware.

Any of the above could potentially be avoided or overcome with a modification in the design of the spacecraft or GSE. Something to consider!

Applicable Standards:
ISO 17400: Space Systems
See website for reference.

Applicable Standards:
ISO 10784: Space Systems
See website for reference.

References

For annotated bibliography of launch operations, see the book website.

Isakowitz, Steven J., Joshua B. Hopkins, and Joseph P. Hopkins, Jr. 2004. *International Reference Guide to Space Launch Systems*, 4th ed. Reston, VA: AIAA.

Strom, Steven R. 2006. *International Launch Site Guide*, 2nd ed. Reston, VA: AIAA.

28 Ground System Design

Jeff Volosin, ***NASA Goddard Space Flight Center***

Whether in LEO, GEO, or headed into deep space, spacecraft are only valuable if the data they collect can get to the end user. End users can include:

- University based researchers
- War fighters on the battlefield
- Satellite TV/radio subscribers
- Operations Engineers: responsible for the health of spacecraft systems
- Mission Planners: responsible for planning upcoming activities
- Flight Dynamicists/Navigators: responsible for ensuring the spacecraft maintains the desired orbit/trajectory and attitude

Collecting and processing data transmitted by the spacecraft through a RF stream as well as providing a method for sending instructions to the spacecraft via an RF stream is the job of the ground system. As shown in Fig. 28-1, spacecraft ground systems perform the following functions:

- **Antenna Services (covered in Sec. 28.1):** Enables transmission/reception and processing of RF signals with an embedded data stream.
  - Includes systems for encoding a data stream of instructions destined for the spacecraft and then modulating this data stream onto an RF carrier and amplifying the signal to ensure that it will have an acceptable signal-to-noise ratio when it arrives at the spacecraft.
  - Includes systems for recovering the spacecraft RF signal and then demodulating and decoding the embedded data stream before passing it off to the next function.
- **Data Accounting and Distribution Services (covered in Sec. 28.2):** Responsible for ensuring data streams headed to and from the spacecraft are complete and distributed to the proper users within the required latency period.
  - Includes systems that perform data accounting on data streams headed to and from the spacecraft to identify missing data that was not recovered from/received from the spacecraft, and to initiate actions to recover missing data as required.
  - Includes systems that perform storage, distribution, and data accounting of recovered spacecraft data streams that require transport to user locations while ensuring data integrity after recovery.
- **Command/Control and Data Processing Services (covered in Sec. 29.1):** Responsible for generating spacecraft instructions for uplink and for processing the data stream received from the spacecraft into information required to support end users.
  - Includes Mission Planning and Command Generation systems that are used to plan spacecraft activities, and then generates the specific command structures/sequences required to execute these activities.
  - Includes data processing systems used to develop specific engineering and scientific products that allow end users to utilize the data collected from the spacecraft.

Although almost all spacecraft efforts include the functions described above, the approach to performing these functions varies greatly based on specific mission requirements and mission complexity and cost. One common theme for many missions today is automation of ground system functions to minimize the cost of oper-

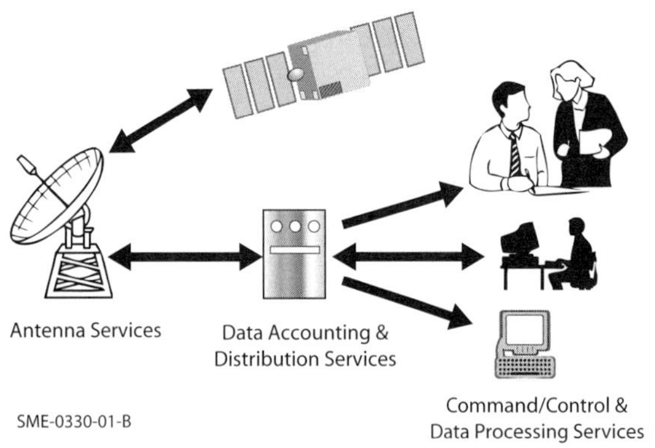

Fig. 28-1. Spacecraft Ground System Services.

ations. For many missions, everything from the pointing of the antenna to the data accounting and distribution functions are done without human involvement. These highly automated *lights-out* systems allow round-the-clock operations to execute with only periodic monitoring and intervention by operations personnel. In other cases, technology advances have opened the door to a new generation of small satellites, many of them developed by university student led teams, where the ground system functions have been greatly simplified to minimize both development and operations costs.

Looking beyond 2011, ground systems will continue to evolve as spacecraft technology advances enable higher data rates and as the synergy between ground system and spacecraft designs leads to increased interaction between the two with less and less human intervention required. These systems will rely increasingly on international standards to ensure interoperability between systems from different countries and commercial service providers and they will have an increasing reliance on Commercial Off-The-Shelf (COTS) products that are developed using these standards—reducing the need for developing expensive custom systems for each new mission.

The following sections provide information on the variety of choices available to ground system designers as they look for optimized solutions to meet their requirements.

28.1 Antenna Services

Every ground system architecture needs a service capable of embedding digital information onto an RF wave for uplink *(forward link)* to the spacecraft as well as performing the function of extracting the data from the downlink *(return link)* RF signal arriving from the spacecraft. These services fall into two primary categories:

1. Ground antennas that send/receive data directly to/from a user spacecraft, and
2. Space based relay antennas that send/receive data to/from user spacecraft and then take responsibility for getting this data to/from the ground

From a different perspective, these services can also be thought of as either:

- Provided by a government or commercial service provider who has a distributed network of antennas that are unified under an umbrella organization and where services are scheduled by a community of users, or
- Dedicated to an individual mission

A third way of thinking about antenna services are:

- Commercial fee for service
- Government multi-mission infrastructure, or
- Project unique funded

Each of these options should be evaluated in the mission design process. For example, the use of existing commercial or government multi-mission antenna network services has numerous advantages. These networks typically have numerous interoperable antennas that can provide a significant amount of coverage area on a predictable schedule with a well defined cost structure and interface. These geographically distributed networks can provide robustness through fault tolerance, establishing high levels of availability and reliability. These attributes may be extremely important for missions with high data capture percentage requirements or short latency requirements. Conversely, deploying a spacecraft dedicated antenna relieves the mission from the need to schedule time with competing, and possibly higher priority, missions. It also allows the antenna systems to be optimally customized for the specific spacecraft whereas existing networks will typically have standard services with which the mission must be compatible. Complying with these standards may require reducing a mission's capability by forcing compromises in areas such as data rates, modulation schemes, and encoding schemes to ensure network compatibility. Downsides of a dedicated antenna include the high development cost required and the lack of geographic distribution, especially if the desire is to have the dedicated antenna near a university or other spacecraft control center location. This may drive the spacecraft design to incorporate high levels of on board storage to support an operations concept that includes limited opportunities to transmit data to the ground.

For some missions, the optimal answer is a combination of approaches. The ground system design for NASA's Lunar Reconnaissance Orbiter (LRO), for example, is shown in Fig. 28-2 [NASA, 2011b].

The LRO ground system utilized a combination of mission dedicated, government owned, and commercially provided antenna assets to fulfill its mission.

First, LRO deployed a single, mission dedicated, 18 m K_a-/S-band antenna at White Sands, NM to support high rate science data retrieval from on-board recorders. With the Moon above the horizon for approximately half of every day, the on-board recorders were sized to accommodate using this single dedicated antenna architecture to download 473 Gbits of data each day (see Sec. 14.5.5). This LRO dedicated K_a-band antenna was originally go-

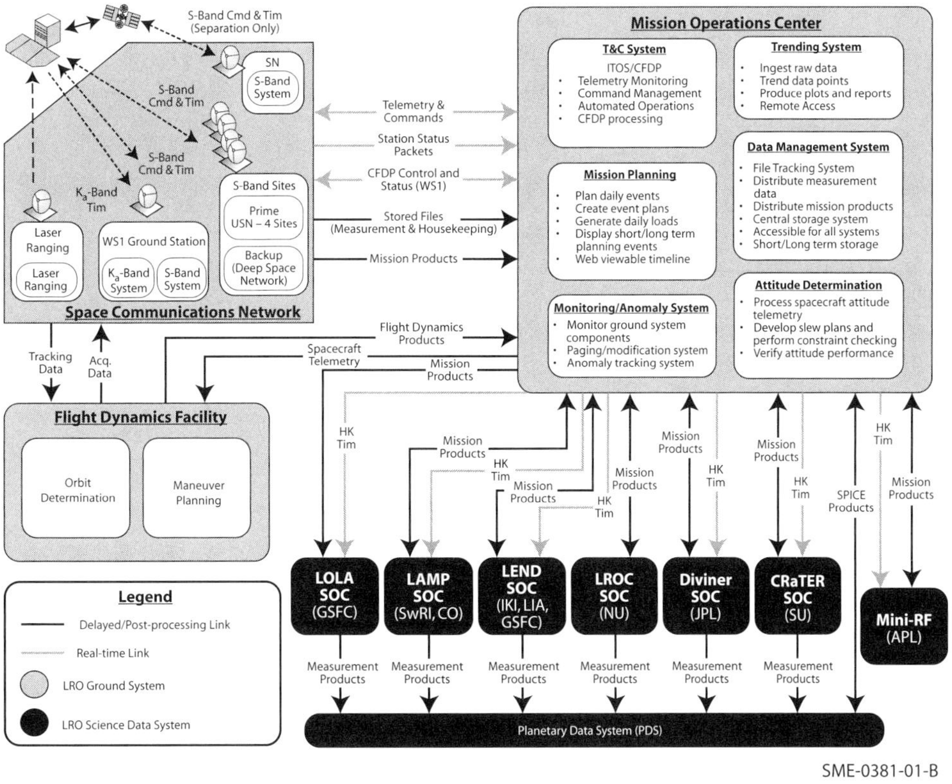

Fig. 28-2. The Lunar Reconnaissance Orbiter Ground System.

ing to be a single point failure since it had no back-up. Coincidentally, during the same period that the LRO mission was being developed, work was underway on a new NASA solar observatory that would communicate in K_a-band from geosynchronous orbit, the Solar Dynamics Observatory (SDO). SDO's ground system was designed with two new 12 m mission dedicated K_a-/S-Band antennas that would also be located in the desert environment of White Sands where K_a-band attenuation effects would be minimized. To address the need for a back-up to the single LRO K_a-band antenna, an agreement was established to allow LRO to use one of the SDO K_a-Band antennas in situations where the single LRO antenna becomes inoperable. In addition, the SDO antennas were increased to 18 m to be able to provide this back-up LRO support without negatively impacting their ability to support their primary mission.

Another consideration that impacted the design of the LRO ground system architecture was that mission designers had to establish a method for collecting radiometric data during each LRO orbit of the moon (~2 hour orbital period) to meet orbit determination requirements driven by lunar mapping accuracy requirements. To support this requirement, the LRO Operations Team scheduled numerous daily contacts on a commercial ground network that used 9 m to 15 m S-band antennas distributed throughout the world to support LRO's radiometric data collection requirements. These contacts provided tracking data collection from both the northern and southern hemisphere. LRO orbit determination accuracy was greatly improved by having this frequent, two-hemisphere tracking. A secondary benefit of these frequent passes was that LRO mission designers could reduce the amount of spacecraft on-board autonomy since spacecraft housekeeping data (downlinked in S-band which could close a link budget at lunar distances on a 9 m ground antenna in combination with spacecraft HGA) could be collected and commanding performed during these once/orbit contacts at the commercial stations. As it turned out, LRO's orbit determination accuracy requirement, driven by a scientific goal of generating a highly accurate lunar gravity model, was too stringent to be met using only RF ranging techniques. To meet this requirement, NASA's Satellite Laser Ranging (SLR) [NASA, 2011e] network was used to augment the RF ranging described above. SLR used laser pulse time-of-flight measurements to provide extremely precise measurements of the distance to LRO.

In addition to the nominal links described above, LRO also received support during specific mission phases from the NASA's Deep Space Network (DSN) and Space Network (SN). Immediately after separation from the launch vehicle, LRO utilized the Tracking and Data Relay Satellites (TDRS) of the SN to provide constant contact during this crucial early phase (the SN is described in Sec. 28.1.2.1). In addition, LRO established an agreement with the DSN (the DSN is described, in Sec. 28.1.1.1) to provide emergency support using 34 m antennas distributed around the globe. This support would be provided if the LRO spacecraft entered a safe-mode that transitioned the spacecraft RF-string from the high gain antenna (HGA) to an omni antenna (where closing the Moon-Earth link budget at even low data rates in S-band, would not be possible with the dedicated White Sands 18 m antenna). DSN support was also required during lunar orbit maintenance maneuvers when the LRO HGA could not be accurately pointed at Earth and omni antenna operations were used to maintain contact with the spacecraft.

The challenge of using this approach is that the LRO Control Center interface and spacecraft interface needed to be compatible not only with the LRO dedicated antenna at White Sands but also with the commercial, SDO, SN and DSN antennas used to provide support. Although some standardization of interfaces made this multi-network compatibility a minor issue for the LRO ground system designers, continuing advances in the development and deployment of international interface standards by the world's antenna service networks will continue to drive down interface development costs for future missions requiring multi-network support.

28.1.1 Ground Based Antenna Systems

The biggest challenge of any ground based antenna is the limited amount of coverage it can provide, especially for the lowest of LEOs. Specific ground station contacts times are driven not only by orbit altitude but by the geometry between the ground station and the spacecraft during each specific pass and the *antenna mask*. The antenna mask is defined as the boundary between a clear transmission path and an obstacle for all directions around a ground station. When plotted along with satellite ground tracks, antenna masks (example in Fig. 28-3) provide an indication of when or if satellite contacts will be possible at that specific ground-station during each orbit. Masks are satellite altitude dependent, with higher orbits providing extended view periods of a specific ground station.

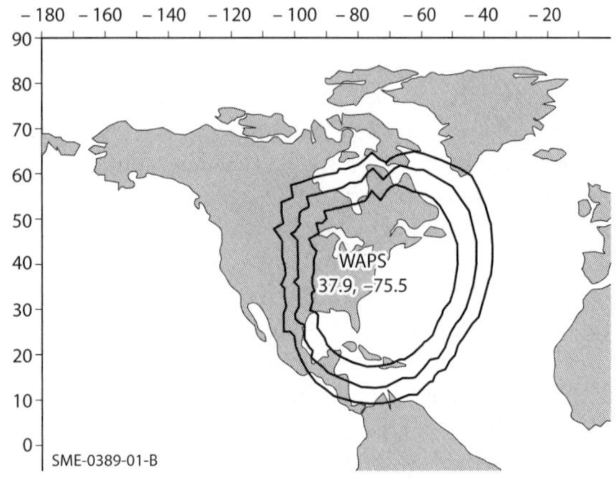

Fig. 28-3. Antenna Mask for the NASA Wallops Island, VA Ground Station shown for 500 km (inner circle), 750 km (middle circle), and 1,000 km (outer circle) Satellite Orbit Altitudes.

A second way to represent a ground station mask is based on the elevation angle that a satellite must reach in a specific direction to clear obstructions and establish a communications path. Figure 28-4 shows the elevation mask for one of the 18 m antennas at White Sands, NM used to support the Solar Dynamics Observatory (SDO) mission.

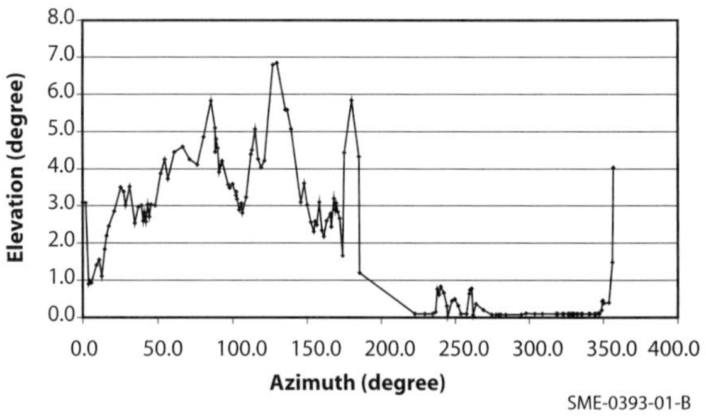

Fig. 28-4. Elevation Mask for the SDO-2 Antenna.

The approximate time that a spacecraft will be able to communicate with each supporting ground station can be calculated by using Eq. (8-77) found in Sec. 8.4.

To accommodate the spacing between contacts, spacecraft utilizing ground based antennas need to incorporate enough on-board memory to hold data between contacts. Spacecraft memory should be sized to:

- Store both payload and scientific instrument data as well as spacecraft housekeeping data generated during non-contact periods
- Continue storing payload and housekeeping data generated during ground station contact periods since memory will typically not be freed for overwriting until memory recovery during a contact has been completed and verified (possibly late in the contact)
- Accommodate at least one missed contact without reaching capacity, since problems on the spacecraft and/or at the ground may result in periodic missed contacts

In addition, care should be taken to determine the actions that will happen if spacecraft memory reaches capacity in cases where numerous contacts are missed or others issues arise. One option is to allow the spacecraft to begin overwriting the oldest on-board data. This option will ensure that the most recent data will be available when a playback capability is restored and memory can be recovered. But, by overwriting the oldest on-board memory, clues as to what might have happened during the earliest periods when issues arose that prevented the downlinking of data may be lost or overwritten. The other option is to have spacecraft memory stop recording when it reaches capacity. In this option, the oldest data will be available for examination once recorder playback capability is restored, but, more recent data generated by the spacecraft will be lost.

In addition, the mission design needs to incorporate high enough data rates to ensure that enough time is available during contact periods so that on-board stored data can be transferred to the ground, and possibly partially or totally retransmitted if the initial transmission is not completely recovered.

28.1.1.1 Government Network Examples

As the sponsor for many of the world's scientific and national defense satellites, individual country Space Agencies, Defense Departments, Land Use Agencies and Weather Agencies, develop and operate distributed antenna networks to support their own satellites, and, through international agreements, the satellites of other countries. Building and operating these complex networks is not only technically challenging but includes an aspect of diplomacy as well, since providing significant downlink opportunities typically requires establishing ground stations beyond a sponsor country's geographical boundaries, requiring international agreements to have other countries "host" antenna sites on their territory. Whether attempting to provide, for example, deep-space links, through stations spread evenly around the globe, or polar orbit links where high latitude ground stations could provide coverage of a high percentage of orbits/day, international agreements become the valuable tool for establishing optimized networks. Almost all countries involved in flying spacecraft have some sort of antenna network. The following few examples are of country sponsored networks that are highly leveraged by various space agencies around the world due to their broad reach or unique capabilities:

NASA's Deep Space Network (DSN)

The California Institute of Technology's Jet Propulsion Laboratory (JPL) is responsible for managing NASA's Deep Space Network (DSN) of large aperture ground based antennas used to support spacecraft traveling beyond 30,000 km from Earth. Developed in the 1960s to support robotic lunar, planetary and other deep space missions, the DSN also provided support to the Apollo human missions to the Moon, where its powerful antennas provided complimentary and emergency support for NASA's smaller Manned Space Flight Network (MSFN) antennas.

DSN antennas are located at 3 Deep Space Communications Complexes (DSCC), separated by ~120 deg of longitude. Two are located in the northern hemisphere: Madrid, Spain (40° 25' 53" North/4° 14' 53" West) and Goldstone, California (35° 25' 36" North/116° 53' 24" West)—while the third, Canberra, Australia (35° 24' 05" South/148° 58' 54" East), is located in the southern hemisphere (this two hemisphere configuration is optimal for collecting tracking data for precision orbit/trajectory determination). Overall coordination and operational management of the DSN is accomplished through the Deep Space Operations Center (DSOC) located at JPL in Pasadena, California.

The DSN uses four different types of antennas—they are:

- **34 m HEF**: The design of the High Efficiency (HEF) antennas incorporate recent design features in electronics and mechanical systems with the antenna dish itself being precision shaped for maximum signal gathering capability.
- **34 m BWG**: The design of the Beam Waveguide (BWG) antennas is based on that of the 34 m HEF antennas—providing similar performance. Five radio frequency mirrors are used to reflect signals along a beam waveguide tube from the vertex of the antenna to a below-ground equipment room. This allows for relocation of sensitive equipment from the feed cone in the center of the main reflector to the pedestal equipment room—making this equipment more accessible, easier to temperature control, and easier to replace and upgrade as requirements change.
- **34 m HSB**: The single High Speed Beam Waveguide (HSB) antenna is located at the Goldstone complex. These antennas can move at 3 deg/sec in azimuth and 2 deg/sec in elevation compared with the 0.8 deg/sec in azimuth and elevation of the other DSN 34 m antennas. These faster slew rates enable this antenna to track spacecraft closer to Earth versus the other 34 m antennas.
- **70 m**: NASA's largest and therefore most sensitive ground based antennas—capable of tracking spacecraft 16B km from Earth.
- **26 m (decommissioned)**: These antennas were deployed at the DSN sites to support Apollo lunar missions. They were decommissioned in the 2008 timeframe and are no longer available for mission support.

The capabilities of the DSN antennas are listed in Table 28-1:

A few additional attributes/constraints of the DSN antennas include:

- **Maximum Data Rates:** The maximum telemetry capture rates for DSN antennas are:
  - 8 Mbps (deep space) and 125 Mbps (near Earth) for Convolutional encoded data ($r = ½$, $k = 7$) concatenated with Reed-Solomon encoding
  - 1.6 Mbps for Turbo coded data
  - 10 bps—minimum data rate supported
  - 13.5 Mbps—maximum data rate out from each DSCC (can constrain the data rate for each individual mission being supported concurrently at a DSCC)

  Note: specific mission maximum data rates are driven by coding scheme, modulation method, and other link parameters (see Sec. 21.1.4)
- **Signal Strength**: The maximum received signal strength for X-band transmissions is –90 dBm. Spacecraft must limit their Equivalent Isotropically

Table 28-1. DSN Antenna Capabilities.

Antenna Type	Complex	DSN ID	Transmit Frequency (MHz)	EIRP (dBW)	Receive Frequency (MHz)	Gain (dBi / G/T) (dB/K)*
34 m BWG	Goldstone	DSS24	S: 2,025–2,120	78.7–98.7	S: 2,200–2,300	56.7/40.5
	Canberra	DSS34	S: 2,025–2,120	78.7–98.7	S: 2,200–2,300	56.7/40.5
	Madrid	DSS54	S: 2,025–2,120	78.7–98.7	S: 2,200–2,300	56.7/40.5
	Goldstone	DSS25	X: 7,145–7,235	89.5–109.5	X: 8,400–8,500	68.2/53.9
	Goldstone	DSS26	X: 7,145–7,235	89.5–109.5	X: 8,400–8,500	68.2/53.9
	Canberra	DSS34	X: 7,145–7,235	89.5–109.5	X: 8,400–8,500	68.2/53.9
	Madrid	DSS54	X: 7,145–7,235	89.5–109.5	X: 8,400–8500	68.2/53.9
	Madrid	DSS55	X: 7,145–7,235	89.5–109.5	X: 8,400–8,500	68.2/53.9
	Goldstone	DSS24	—	—	K_a: 25,500–27,000	76.5/58.6
	Goldstone	DSS25	K_a: 34,315–34,415	98.2–108.2	K_a: 31,800–32,300	78.4/60.8
	Goldstone	DSS26	—	—	K_a: 31,800–32,300	78.4/60.8
	Canberra	DSS34	—	—	K_a: 25,500–27,000 K_a: 31,800–32,300	76.5/58.6 78.4/60.8
	Madrid	DSS54	—	—	K_a: 25,500–27,000 K_a: 31,800–32,300	76.5/58.6 78.4/60.8
	Madrid	DSS55	—	—	K_a: 31,800–32,300	78.4/60.8
34 m HEF	Goldstone	DSS15	—	—	S: 2,200–2,300	56.0/39.0
	Canberra	DSS45	S: 2,025–2,110	71.8–78.8	S: 2,200–2,300	56.0/39.0
	Madrid	DSS65	S: 2,025–2,110	71.8–78.8	S: 2,200–2,300	56.0/39.0
	Goldstone	DSS15	X: 7,145–7,190	89.8–109.8	X: 8,400–8,500	68.3/53.1
	Canberra	DSS45	X: 7,145–7,190	89.8–109.8	X: 8,400–8,500	68.3/53.1
	Madrid	DSS65	X: 7,145–7,190	89.8–109.8	X: 8,400–8,500	68.3/53.1
34 m HSB	Goldstone	DSS27	S: 2,025–2,120	70.7–76.7	S: 2,200–2,300	54.9/34.5
70 m	Goldstone	DSS14	S: 2,110–2,118 S: 2,090–2,091	85.6–105.6 85.6–97.4	S: 2,200–2,300	63.5/50.1
	Canberra	DSS43	S: 2,110–2,118 S: 2,110–2,118 S: 2,090–2,091	85.6–105.6 106.7–118.7 85.6–97.4	S: 2,270–2,300	63.5/50.1
	Madrid	DSS63	S: 2,110–2,118 S: 2,090–2,091	85.6–105.6 85.6–97.4	S: 2,270–2,300	63.5/50.1
	Goldstone	DSS14	X: 7,145–7,190	95.8–115.8	X: 8,400–8,500	74.5/61.3
	Canberra	DSS43	X: 7,145–7,190	95.8–115.8	X: 8,400–8,500	74.5/61.3
	Madrid	DSS63	X: 7,145–7,190	95.8–115.8	X: 8,400–8,500	74.5/61.3

* referenced to 45° elevation with 90% weather condition (CD=0.90) and diplexed configuration

Radiated Power (EIRP) so as to not exceed this level at the DSN receiver. For K_a-band transmissions (25.5–27 GHz), the maximum received signal strength can be up to ~ –45 dBm at the cost of lower G/T performance of the receiving antenna.

- **Multi-Spacecraft Per Antenna (MSPA)**: Enables, with some constraints, DSN antennas to receive telemetry from multiple spacecraft when they are all within the antenna's beamwidth (although only one spacecraft can be commanded at a time).
- **Antenna Arraying**: Combining signals from various DSN antennas [NASA/JPL, 2011] at the Intermediate Frequency (IF) level is used to create a "virtual" antenna with performance greater than the individual contributing antennas. In the 8 GHz band, for example, five 34 m antennas can be used to provide the same performance as a DSN 70 m antenna. Arraying can be used in S, X and K_a-Band although S-band arraying capability will be phased out with upgrades planned for the ~2014 timeframe.

Although downlink telemetry processing using antenna arraying is most typical, uplink arraying research is ongoing as well. Moving beyond 2011, DSN plans to slowly phase-out their expensive-to-maintain 70 m antennas with the addition of more 34 m antennas at each site that can be arrayed or used individually as required. The general equation for establishing the maximum increase in gain that can be achieved through arraying a number of antennas (N) (assuming no combining loss) is:

$$(G/T)_{array} = \sum_{i=1}^{N} (G/T)_I \qquad (28\text{-}1)$$

- Simply the sum of the sensitivity for each arrayed antenna. In the case of a homogeneous array—the equation becomes (shown in Fig. 28-5):

$$(G/T)_{array} = (G/T)_0 \sum_{i=1}^{N} 1 = N(G/T)_0 \qquad (28\text{-}2)$$

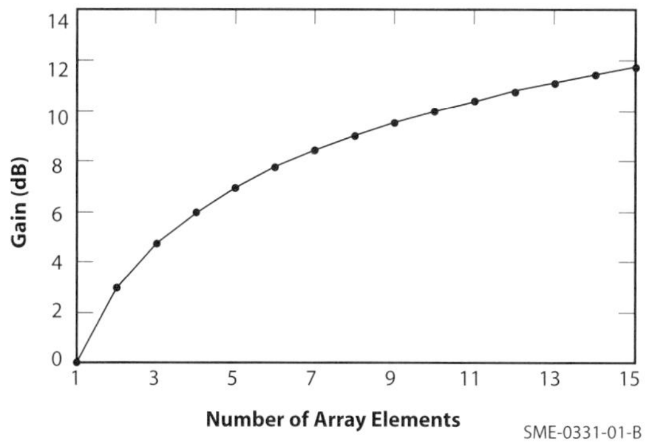

Fig. 28-5. Antenna Gain for Addition of Arrayed Antenna Elements.

NASA's Near Earth Network (NEN)

The Near Earth Network (NEN) [NASA, 2011c] is a Goddard Space Flight Center managed NASA network consisting of a range of antenna apertures between 4.3 m and 18 m in diameter and capable of receiving VHF, UHF, S, X and K_a-band transmissions and transmitting in the S, VHF and UHF-bands. The NEN has evolved to where ~50% of its current capability is provided by NASA owned antennas while the other ~50% is procured through commercial contracts with the Norwegian Kongsberg Satellite Services (KSAT) AS and the Universal Space Network (USN) subsidiary of the Swedish Space Corporation (SSC). Since KSAT and SSC are covered later as individual networks, this section will focus on the NASA-owned NEN antennas. NEN ground stations are located at:

- Wallops Island Virginia (Wallops Ground Station (WGS)) (38°N/75°W),
- The University of Alaska, Fairbanks (Alaska Satellite Facility (ASF)) (64°N/147°W),
- McMurdo Station Antarctica (McMurdo Ground Station (MGS)) (78°S/193°W),
- Merritt Island Florida (Merritt Island Launch Annex (MILA)) (29°N/81°W)
- New Smyrna Beach Florida (Ponce De Leon (PDL)) (29°N/81°W)
- White Sands New Mexico (White Sands (WS)) (32°N/106°W)
- Svalbard Norway (Svalbard Ground Station (SGS)) (78°N/15°E)
  - Note: The Svalbard Ground Station is actually owned and operated by the KSAT commercial organization but NASA still owns the first antenna that was deployed on the Svalbard archipelago.

The NEN has its heritage in the Spaceflight Tracking and Data Network (STDN), established in 1975, and earlier NASA ground networks developed in the 1960s to support early human spaceflight (the Manned Space Flight Network (MSFN)) as well as robotic missions in Earth orbit (the Spacecraft Tracking and Data Acquisition Network (STADAN)). In evolving from the STDN to today's NEN, the number of antennas was significantly reduced as NASA phased in a space-based relay network, the Tracking and Data Relay Satellite System (TDRSS), in the 1980s. The TDRSS based Space Network (discussed in Sec. 28.1.2.1) could provide constant coverage for Earth-orbiting missions, which was highly desired for human spaceflight applications as well as for some robotic missions. In addition, the 1990s saw a further reduction in NASA-owned NEN stations as commercial ground station utilization became a more cost effective option for many applications.

In general, the remaining NASA-owned NEN ground stations are focused on supporting missions between LEO and the Moon with a specific focus on supporting LEO, polar-orbiting missions and missions wherein NASA has unique requirements. For example, NASA's NEN ground stations in Florida are primarily used to support Space Shuttle launch/ascent data capture. These assets will be retired at the conclusion of the Space Shuttle Program. Much of the history of the NEN has been in supporting S/X-band operations of LEO spacecraft. With the recent addition of an 18 m S/K_a-band antenna in White Sands, New Mexico, the NEN now has an antenna capable of supporting K_a-band operations out to lunar distances. This antenna was initially developed as a dedicated asset to support NASA's LRO mission, but will be available to future NEN K_a-band missions. In addition, NEN stations support 1-way and 2-way Doppler as well as Tone Ranging (see Sec. 14.4.5).

Looking beyond 2011, the NEN will be focused on expanding K_a-band operations to additional sites to increase the capability to support future higher data rate missions. The NEN is also standardizing capabilities across all of their antennas and increasing interoperability with other networks by implementing recently developed international communication standards and protocols.

The capabilities of the NASA owned NEN antennas are listed in Table 28-2.

ESA's ESTRACK

ESTRACK consists of 10 ESA operated ground stations that provide communication support for launch, Earth-orbital and deep space missions [ESA, 2011]. Each ground station hosts one or more antennas that are either: 13 m, 13.5 m or 15 m. These antennas are used for launch and Earth orbit communication. Additionally, 35 m antennas are being added to ESTRACK (as of 2011) to be used for deep space communication. Data rates supported vary by antenna but range from 256 Kbps to 105 Mbps. All antennas operate at the following frequencies:

- S-band transmit/receive frequencies: 2,025–2,120 MHz / 2,200–2,300 MHz
- X-band transmit/receive frequencies: 7,145–7,235 MHz / 8,400–8,500 MHz

Table 28-2. NASA NEN Antenna Capability Summary.

Antenna Type	Complex	NEN ID	Transmit Frequency (MHz)	EIRP (dBW)	Receive Frequency (MHz)	Data Rate[1]	G/T (dB/K)
4.3 m	Merritt Island[2]	MILA	S: 2,025–2,120	58	S: 2,200–2,300	S: 2 Mbps	11
	New Smyrna Beach[2]	PDL	S: 2,025–2,120	58	S: 2,200–2,300	S: 2 Mbps	17
4.7 m	Wallops	LEO-T	S: 2,025–2,120	59	S: 2,200–2,300	S: 8 Mbps	16.99
9 m	Merritt Island[2]	MILA (2)	S: 2,025–2,120	63	S: 2,200–2,300	S: 10 Mbps	24
10 m	McMurdo	MG1	S: 2,025–2,120	63	S: 2,200–2,400 X: 8,025–8,400	S: 15 Mbps X: 110 Mbps	21.11 32.48
	University of Alaska	ASF10	No Uplink Available	No Uplink Available	S: 2,200–2,400 X: 8,025–8,350	S: 8 Mbps X: 150 Mbps[3]	22.59 36.36
11.3 m	Svalbard	SG1	S: 2,025–2,120	66	S: 2,200–2,400 X: 8,025–8,500	S: 8 Mbps X: 150 Mbps[3]	23.63 35.84
	Wallops	WGS11m	S: 2,025–2,120	66	S: 2,200–2,400 X: 8,025–8,400	S: 36 Mbps X: 150 Mbps[3]	23.63 34.50
	University of Alaska	ASF11	S: 2,025–2,120	66	S: 2,200–2,400 X: 8,025–8,400	S: 8 Mbps X: 150 Mbps[3]	23.01 35
18 m	White Sands	WS1	S: 2,025–2,120	80	S: 2,200–2,300 K_a: 25,500–27,000	S: 20 Mbps K_a: 470 Mbps	29 45
Yagi (VHF)	Wallops	WFF VHF-1	VHF: 139.208	45.4	VHF: 143.625	NA	N/A
	Wallops	WFF VHF-2	VHF: 130.167	45.4	VHF: 121.750	NA	N/A
	White Sands	WSC VHF-1	VHF: 139.208	43.4	VHF: 143.625	NA	N/A
	White Sands	WSC VHF-2	VHF: 130.167	45.4	VHF: 121.750	NA	N/A
Quad Helix (UHF)	Merritt Island[2]	MILA	UHF: 225–300	28	UHF: 225-300	NA	11

Notes:
1. Specific mission data rates need to take into consideration modulation and coding schemes as well as other link parameters (see Sec. 21.1.4). These rates only consider the downlink rate received at the antenna, the rate at which the site delivers data to customer control centers is driven by transmission network bandwidth available.
2. Antennas at Merritt Island and New Smyrna Beach will be decommissioned at the end of the Space Shuttle Program
3. As of 2011, a NEN network-wide upgrade of X-band capabilities was underway to enable data rates of 300+ Mbps using a single polarization and 600+ Mbps using dual polarization.

ESTRACK ground antennas are all remotely operated from the ESTRACK Control Center (ECC) at the European Space Operations Center (ESOC) in Darmstadt, Germany. ESTRACK ground stations are located at:

- Perth Australia (31.8°S/115.9°E): 15 m S/X-band antenna
- Redu Belgium (50.0°N/5.15°E): 15 m S-band, 13.5 m K_a-band, 2.4 m S-band antennas
- Kourou French Guiana (5.25°N/52.81°W): 15 m S/X-band antenna
- Cebreros Spain (40.53°N/4.37°W): 35 m X/K_a-band antenna
- New Norcia Australia (31.05°S/116.19°E): 35 m S/X-band antenna
- Maspalomas Canary Islands (27.76°N/15.63°W): 15 m S/X-band antenna
- Kiruna Sweden (67.86°N/20.96°E): 15 m S/X-band, 13 m S/X-band antennas
- Villafranca Spain (40.44°N/3.95°W): Two 15 m S-band antennas
- Santa Maria Portugal (36.997°N/25.14°W): 5.5 m S-band antenna
- Malargue Argentina (5.25°N/52.81°W): 35 m X/K_a-band antenna (under construction as of 2011)

28.1.1.2 Commercial Networks

Beginning in the late 1990s, a number of commercial organizations entered the ground station marketplace, offering network services on a price-per-pass basis. By offering standard telemetry, tracking, and command services that utilize international standards as well as mission customized interfaces, these providers have extended their services around the world, in support of commercial and government agency space missions. Although this commercial sector is still fairly new and constantly evolving, the two companies that have the most extensive networks of commercial ground stations are:

Swedish Space Corporation (SSC)

SSC and their US subsidiary, Universal Space Network (USN) Inc. have established a worldwide fee for service network known as PrioraNet. SSC focuses on supporting spacecraft launches as well as polar and equatorial LEO missions. Scheduling and control of PrioraNet are performed at three Network Management Centers located in: Newport Beach, California; Kiruna, Sweden; and Horsham, Pennsylvania. SSC ground stations are located at:

- Dongara Australia (29°S/115°E): 13 m S/X/K_u-band, 7.3 m S/X-band antennas
- Poker Flat Alaska (65°N/147°W): 7.3 m S/X-band, 11 m S/X-band antennas
- North Pole Alaska (64.8°N/147.5°W): 13 m S/X-band, 5 m S/X-band antennas
- Inuvik Canada (68.4°N/133.5°w): Two 13 m S/X-band antennas
- Santiago Chile (33°S/70°W): Six antennas—VHF to S/L/X-band (up to 12 m)
- South Point Hawaii (19°N/155.6°W): Two 13 m S/X/K_u-band antennas
- Esrange Sweden (67.9°N/21°E): Seven antennas—UHF to S/L/X-band (up to 13 m)

As of 2011, SSC continues to add antennas to PrioraNet in support of both equatorial and polar orbiting missions [SSC, 2011].

Kongsberg Satellite Services (KSAT) AS

KSAT is a commercial Norwegian enterprise headquartered in Tromsø. KSAT is a fee for service organization that supports both commercial and government space programs around the world. The KSAT focus has historically been on supporting polar orbiting LEO satellites with ground stations within the Arctic Circle and in Antarctica where they can view almost all passes for these satellites. The Tromsø Network Operations Center (TNOC) is responsible for scheduling, operating and controlling KSAT antennas. KSAT Ground Stations are located at:

- Tromsø Norway (69.5°N/18.8°E): Numerous L/X/S antennas up to 13 m diameter
- Svalbard Norway (78.2°N/15.4°E): Numerous L/X/S antennas up to 13 m diameter
- Troll Research Station Antarctica (72.01°S/2.5°E): Two 7.3 m S/X-band antennas

Looking beyond 2011, KSAT continues plans to continue adding antennas at Svalbard and Troll. In addition, they are looking to expand their equatorial support through the development of a number of new tracking stations [KSAT, 2011].

28.1.1.3 Project Dedicated Antennas

There are times when sharing antenna assets with other missions is impractical due to an ops concept that may include security requirements, cost restrictions, scheduling requirements, or latency requirements, that cannot be met through the use of a multi-user antenna network. For these missions, the development of project dedicated antenna services is an option. These project dedicated systems can be highly tuned to support their specific satellite's requirements. For example, for missions with significant on-board storage capability, and the ability to quickly downlink stored information to the ground, a single dedicated ground station may be adequate to support the mission needs (keeping in mind that this single station may only view a small number of orbits per day depending on the orbital inclination and the ground station latitude). In addition, dedicated antennas need to be located at sites where the bandwidth available from the site back to the end user of the data is adequate to support the latency requirements of the mission. For example, placing a mission-dedicated antenna at the North Pole to support a polar orbiting mission may sound like a perfect solution to view every orbit; however, getting that data back to the mission's Control Center in Europe, Asia or the United States in a reasonable amount of time can be a difficult or impossible challenge. Below are examples of GEO, LEO and SmallSat missions that use dedicated antenna services architectures.

GEO: NOAA Geostationary Operations Environmental Satellites (GOES)

NOAA's Geostationary Operations Environmental Satellite (GOES) constellation consists of two operational geosynchronous satellites located at: ~75° W (GOES-East) and ~135° W (GOES-West) that provide data on weather across the United States. Each of these satellites transmits ~100 images to Earth each day. In addition, after processing on the ground, some GOES weather imagery is retransmitted, on a frequent basis, from the ground to the GOES spacecraft where it is then broadcast to users throughout the country who have small Earth terminals able to receive and process this data.

To support these almost constant uplink/downlink requirements, NOAA established a single ground terminal at Wallops Island, Virginia where 13+ m antennas are dedicated to each operational GOES. These antennas ensure constant contact is maintained with each spacecraft so that time critical weather imagery can flow unimpeded to the National Weather Service and many other GOES data customers. In addition, direct communication links between this NOAA Wallops Command & Data Acquisition Station (WCDAS) and the GOES Satellite Operations Center located at NOAA's Satellite Operations Facility (NSOF) in Suitland, MD, provide satellite operations personnel at the NSOF with a real-time view of the GOES spacecraft state-of-health and an available command link for sending up instructions as required.

One major challenge of deploying mission dedicated antennas is building in fault tolerance while controlling spending on back-up capability that may seldom be needed. Since the WCDAS is located near the Atlantic Ocean, concerns have been raised about the possibility of hurricanes coming up the East Coast, bringing wind speeds that could damage or at least prohibit accurate pointing of GOES ground antennas, disabling this critical weather data flow at a time when it might be highly desirable for forecasters tracking the hurricane's path. NOAA has taken various steps to reduce this risk, including:

1. Installing "hurricane rated" 16.5 m GOES antennas at the WCDAS that can operate through a Category 3 hurricane (130 mph winds) and can survive a Category 5 hurricane (155+ mph winds).
2. Placing a back-up GOES antenna further inland at the Goddard Space Flight Center in Greenbelt, MD. This back-up would be close-enough to the WCDAS (~150 miles distant) to deploy antenna operations personnel prior to the hurricane tracking up the east coast to be ready if needed.
3. Having a back-up GOES antenna located at the NOAA Fairbanks, AK CDAS (FCDAS) that can support the GOES-West spacecraft if needed. At 64.5° N latitude, Fairbanks is not the optimal location for a geostationary satellite ground terminal, but, NOAA operates the Fairbanks site primarily to support their Polar Orbiting Environmental Satellite (POES) spacecraft operations. In 2003, the Japanese government asked if a GOES spacecraft could be temporarily drifted over the Pacific Ocean to provide weather imagery of the area around Japan (a Japanese weather satellite had failed and they needed interim support until they could launch a replacement). Since the WCDAS would not be able to communicate with a GOES satellite that was moved this far out over the Pacific, a GOES antenna was put in place at the FCDAS to provide this link. Although support to Japan ended in 2005, this GOES antenna remains as a back-up for the GOES-West spacecraft.

A few things stand out in this example:

- When using dedicated antenna assets it is important to think through contingency situations. What happens if that single dedicated antenna fails? How much risk is acceptable if mission data can not be recovered for some period of time while the antenna is being repaired or is stowed during high winds? Putting in back-up dedicated antennas may lower risk, but can be a high cost solution. An alternative can be to have an agreement with a commercial service provider to provide "on call" service when a mission dedicated antenna is non-operational. The challenge with this approach is that the spacecraft and ground system architecture must be compatible with the commercial provider's network architecture, service offerings and network connectivity. In addition, these commercial assets have many customers, so requests to be inserted into their schedule on short notice may be difficult for them to accommodate.
- Dedicated antennas may provide outstanding support during nominal on-orbit operations, but, will they support non-nominal operations such as contingencies where the spacecraft may be in a non-nominal attitude and may have failed over from a primary on-board HGA to an emergency LGA? How about during launch and early orbit (L&EO) operations when the orbital parameters/groundtrack and navigation requirements may be very different from the on-orbit operational scenario? In the case of GOES, L&EO operations are supported by a combination of commercial services and NASA Deep Space and Near Earth Network antennas that provide the geographic distribution required to support the frequent contacts required to support orbit-raising maneuvers as well as the northern/southern hemisphere coverage required to collect accurate tracking data to support orbit raising maneuver planning. The NOAA Office of Satellite Operations [2011] provides additional information.

LEO: Far Ultraviolet Spectroscopic Explorer (FUSE) Puerto Rico Ground Station

The Far Ultraviolet Spectroscopic Explorer (FUSE) spacecraft was built and operated for NASA by the Johns Hopkins University (JHU) [2011] in Baltimore, MD. The FUSE observatory was in a 775 km circular orbit at a 25 deg inclination with an orbital period of ~100 min. Operationally, participating universities from around the world would submit observing requests which would be scheduled by the JHU operations team based on predicted viewing intervals, spacecraft positioning constraints, and the needs of each science program. These detailed observing schedules were then uplinked to the satellite which would store and execute the schedule without the need for direct interaction by ground controllers.

To support this equatorial LEO mission, a single ground antenna was placed at the University of Puerto Rico, Mayaguez. Contacts between FUSE and the Puerto Rico antenna lasted ~10 min/contact and there were ~6 orbits in a row of contacts followed by ~8 orbits without contacts. During contacts, an observing schedule was uploaded and captured scientific data, which had been stored while the spacecraft was out of contact, was downlinked for processing. The on-board recorder was sized to ensure that far ultraviolet observations as well as spacecraft state-of-health data could be collected and stored during the daily ~13 hour out-of-contact periods. In addition, the communication link was sized to ensure that data rates could be supported that would enable downlink of this stored data within the limited 10 min contact periods once the Puerto Rico antenna was again in view.

Although this appeared to be a low-cost solution for supporting FUSE operations, the Puerto Rico-based antenna was a single-point-failure within the communication architecture. In 1998, after the antenna was installed but prior to FUSE launch, hurricane George came across Puerto Rico and severely damaged this unprotected asset (luckily this happened prior to launch). After repairs, and the addition of a hurricane rated radome, the antenna was once again ready for operations just prior to launch. After

Table 28-2◀, Fig. 28-5◀, Eq. 28-2◀

launch, the FUSE project signed an agreement with Universal Space Network (USN) to use a USN 13 m antenna at Hawaii as an "on call" back-up to the Puerto Rico antenna, reducing the risk of mission data loss while only incurring this additional support cost when the Puerto Rico antenna was unable to support the mission requirements.

SmallSat: Alaska Research CubeSat (ARC)

Like many universities, the University of Alaska, Fairbanks (UAF) is designing a CubeSat mission, the Alaskan Research CubeSat (ARC). For most of these CubeSat development teams, the limited budget available for development and operations drives them to creative low-cost ground system solutions. The UAF ARC CubeSat solution described below is used to illustrate one approach of the many being developed by this community.

Among a number of objectives, the ARC spacecraft will collect Earth images and relay them to the ground. To receive these images, the ARC ground station is being designed to support the 3 frequencies most commonly used by amateur satellites (VHF (144–146 MHz), UHF (420–450 MHz), S-Band (2.0 GHz)) (Note: Since these are heavily used transmission bands, it is important to try to locate the ground station in "radio quiet" environment as possible). Although the ARC satellite will only operate at the UHF and S-Band frequencies, the ground station was designed to cover all three frequencies so that they could offer support in the future to other CubeSat missions built by UAF or other universities. The single ground station consists of two circularly polarized 6 m long yagi antennas, one for the VHF band and one for the UHF band, as well as a dish antenna to support the S-band downlink (a ~2 m television satellite dish is adequate for these type of applications). A common elevation/azimuth steering system allows the antennas to be pivoted for tracking. Ground software, driven by orbit predictions, points the antennas prior to each pass.

A downconverter will take the S-band signal down to VHF so that a VHF/UHF radio can process all incoming signals. Downlink rates are limited to 1,200 and 9,600 symbols/second due to receiver design constraints (the addition of filters to allow the S-band downlink to use a rate of 38,400 symbols/second is being considered). A low data rate beacon on the ARC spacecraft will be turned on and remain on after launch vehicle deployment. The beacon signal contains limited information regarding the power level available on the spacecraft. Whenever the beacon is captured at the ground station, a determination can be made as to whether or not there is sufficient power to operate the transmitter at full power to begin a higher rate UHF/S-Band transmission session. After each high rate transmission is complete, the spacecraft will go back into beacon transmission mode.

Another nuance of the design, since the system is being deployed in the Alaskan interior, is that it must be able to operate down to temperatures as low as –60° C. Validation of the ground station operations will be performed by the use of weather balloon flights which will carry engineering models of the ARC communication equipment for end-to-end testing.

Additional information on NASA's CubeSat [2011a] program can be found at their website.

28.1.2 Space Relay Systems

For some missions in LEO, the constraint of only being able to communicate with the ground for ~20% of each orbit is not compatible with the mission's operations concept. For example, for Space Shuttle crews circling the globe every ~90 min, being in contact with their Earth-based Mission Control Center for ~18 min/orbit would severely restrict the amount of data that could be transmitted to and from the Shuttle during each mission. In addition, these short and infrequent contact periods would severely limit opportunities for ground crews to support the Shuttle crew in troubleshooting anomalies or handling emergencies that may occur during a mission.

Another example is the Swift Gamma-Ray Burst mission. Swift is a LEO mission that is searching the sky for gamma ray bursts coming from the most powerful explosions in the Universe. To study these bursts, which can be seen from Earth for periods of only seconds or minutes before they die out, the Swift spacecraft needs to be able to send a message to the ground-based Gamma-Ray Coordination Network (GCN) within a few seconds of identifying a new burst. These messages include coordinates for the burst so that Earth-based and space-based gamma ray telescope facilities around the world can be quickly notified that a burst has occurred so that they can point their telescopes and begin their own data collection. After announcing that a burst has occurred, Swift then trains its own scientific instruments on the burst to begin collecting detailed data that can be downlinked later for analysis.

In both cases, and many more, latency requirements, and data volume requirements force designers to consider the use of a space-based relay system for support. Space-based relays, placed in geosynchronous orbit, can provide LEO spacecraft with a significant improvement in the percentage of each orbit during which time they can be communicating with the ground. For each GEO relay satellite, LEO satellite coverage of ~45% can be achieved (Note: specific coverage periods are based on the specific orbit altitude and inclination of the LEO satellite). With a constellation of 3 GEO relay satellites, spaced evenly every ~120 deg in longitude, continuous coverage for satellites in LEO can be achieved.

In addition to providing expanded coverage over ground-based antennas, GEO relay satellites have a few different link budget considerations when compared to direct space-to-ground communication. First, the free-space loss term of the link Eq. (21-4) is significantly greater when using space-based relays since the LEO-GEO link distance is much greater than for LEO-to-ground communication links. On the other hand, space relay systems can make use of higher frequency communication links, such as K-band and optical, where space-to-ground link signal attenuation, especially during rainy and cloudy weather, may make these shorter wavelength frequencies impractical for establishing reliable communication links. Using these shorter wavelength links, LEO spacecraft can communicate at data rates above 1 Gbps through GEO relays (although the link between the GEO relay and its ground terminal may need to rate buffer this data as it transmits it through the atmosphere).

Space-based relay satellites are typically placed in equatorial orbits where east-west station-keeping maneuvers are key to keeping them at their proper operational longitudinal position. Lunar-solar perturbations and the ellipticity of the Earth's equator also tug on the GEO orbiting satellites, requiring north-south station-keeping to maintain an equatorial orbit. Since north-south station-keeping requires a significant amount of propellant, some GEO satellites are allowed to drift in inclination. This drift continues until the inclination has peaked at 15 deg after 27.5 years of drifting from the equator (see Sec. 9.5.1). At this point, the forces mentioned above begin to bring the inclination back down to 0 deg over the next 27.5 years. This drift in inclination can impact visibility periods between GEO relay satellites and the user spacecraft that they support. As the inclination increases, these satellites spend more of the day at latitudes where it is possible for them to communicate with satellites orbiting near the Earth's North and South poles. For some countries, such as Russia, where much of the country is at high latitude, GEO relay satellites at higher inclinations can also be valuable for sustaining communication links to high latitude ground terminals.

Although numerous countries have either experimented with, or developed operational space-based relay satellites, NASA's Tracking and Data Relay Satellite System (TDRSS) is used here as an example of what type of support can be provided through a space-based relay system. With an almost 30 year operational history, the TDRSS constellation provides support for LEO missions from various nations.

28.1.2.1 Tracking and Data Relay Satellite System (TDRSS)

In September of 1983, Shuttle mission STS-8 was able to download more data to Earth than all 7 previous Shuttle missions combined. This was made possible by the introduction of the first of NASA's new geosynchronous communications relay satellites, the Tracking and Data Relay Satellites (TDRS). Previously, ground-based antennas located around the world provided limited coverage for all NASA missions since LEO spacecraft were generally only in view of ground antennas for ~20% of each orbit. The TDRS System (TDRSS) provides constant coverage for LEO satellites using an architecture that includes

- A constellation of three geosynchronous TDRS that serve as bent-pipe delivery systems between user satellites and their ground based control centers.
- Ground terminals used for receiving/sending user spacecraft data to/from the TDRS and for monitoring and maintaining the health of the TDRS constellation.

In 1989, with the launch of a third TDRS, low-Earth-orbiting satellites in orbits above 1,050 km (and below ~9,000 km) were now able to communicate with Earth at any time in their orbit through the TDRSS White Sands Ground Terminal (WSGT) located at the White Sands Complex (WSC) in New Mexico. During this period, only two TDRS were used operationally while the third was an on-orbit spare. The two operational TDRS were placed in orbits that allowed them both to view the single ground terminal at White Sands while being spaced as far apart in longitude as possible to maximize the overall coverage the constellation could provide to LEO satellites. With a two satellite constellation, LEO spacecraft orbiting below 1,050 km encountered a *Zone of Exclusion* (ZOE) during each orbit where they were out-of-view of both operational TDRS and therefore unable to communicate. To address this ZOE, in 1993, a re-configuration of the TDRS constellation placed a third TDRS into operational service. These three operational satellites were now evenly spaced around the world in longitude (every ~120 deg). Since this spacing in longitude meant that one of the operational TDRS would not be able to view White Sands, a second ground terminal in Guam (the Guam Remote Ground Terminal (GRGT)) was added. The three satellite constellation, allowed for constant communications with Earth orbiting satellites down to 72 km orbit altitude. In 1994, as the number of orbiting TDRS was increased to 5 (including both operational spacecraft and on-orbit spares), a Second TDRS Ground Terminal (STGT) was added at WSC to support this growing constellation. The Space Network (SN) space/ground elements are shown in Fig. 28-6.

Each ground terminal establishes links to individual TDRS through Space-Ground Link Terminal (SGLT) equipment chains that are connected to 19 m antennas used to uplink/downlink both user spacecraft data as well as TDRS state-of-health data (shown in Fig. 28-7). SGLT connectivity to the NASA Integrated Services Network (NISN) provides the user spacecraft control center interface into the ground terminals.

The TDRSS is designed to provide the following user services:

- Forward Service: A communication path that originates at the user control center and passes through the WSC or GRGT on its way to the user spacecraft through a TDRS. This user spacecraft command path can be supported in S-band, K_u-band and K_a-band. A separate ranging channel can be established as part of this service as well.
- Return Service: A communication path that originates at the user spacecraft and passes through a TDRS to either WSC or GRGT-to-WSC on its way to the user control center. This path allows the flow of science data as well as user spacecraft state-of-health data to be returned to the user control center. S-band, K_u-band and K_a-band Return Service options are available.

Table 28-2◀, Fig. 28-5◀, Eq. 28-2◀

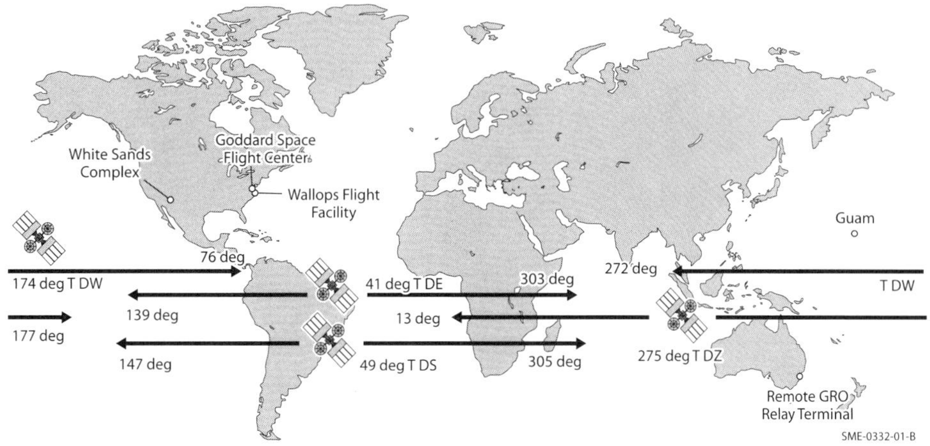

Fig. 28-6. The Space/Ground Elements of the Space Network.

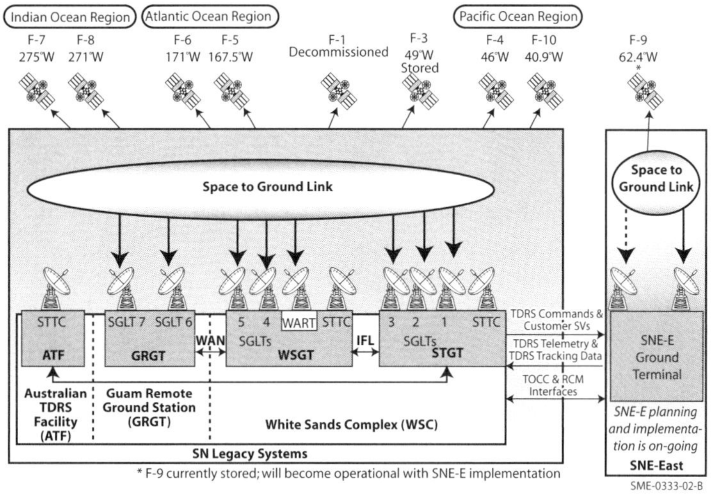

Fig. 28-7. TDRSS Ground/Space Architecture.

From a user perspective, understanding the capabilities of the TDRS spacecraft is key to designing a communication system that will properly interface with the TDRSS. The TDRS constellation currently consists of 6 operational spacecraft, each capable of supporting over 20 user spacecraft at any given time. The TDRS constellation has evolved from:

- A first generation series of 7 satellites (see Fig. 28-8 for capabilities)
  - 5 of which are still operational in 2011
  - 1 was destroyed in the 1986 Challenger accident
  - The first (TDRS-1) was retired in late 2009
- To a second generation of 3 satellites (see Fig. 28-9 for capabilities)
  - All of which are still operational (as of 2011)
  - With two updated second generation satellites, TDRS-K & TDRS-L, scheduled for launch in 2012 and 2013

Some TDRS are maintained in a storage mode where they are not available to support user spacecraft but they are available to be placed into operations quickly if any issues arise with an operational TDRS.

All TDRS spacecraft are maintained in their operational location by east-west stationkeeping maneuvers while, to preserve propellant, north-south stationkeeping maneuvers are not performed. The resulting inclination drift has made it possible for some TDRS spacecraft to have a clear line of site to the North and South Poles for a part of each day. Starting in 1998, TDRS-1 was the first satellite to achieve an inclination where it could be used as a South Pole TDRSS Relay (SPTR). Currently, other first generation TDRS have inclinations allowing them to support SPTR requirements. SPTR provides a critical communication relay for scientists working at the pole. At a 15 deg inclination, a TDRS spacecraft can provide up to 12 hours of communication access for forward/return services to/from antennas based at the Earth's poles. Basic TDRS capabilities include (apply to first and second generation TDRS except where noted):

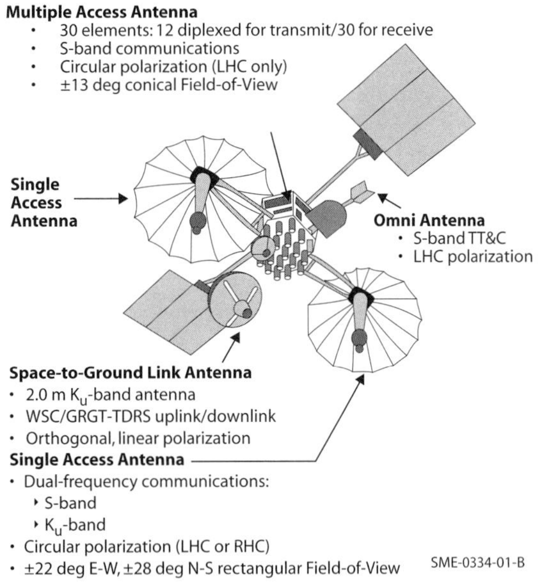

Fig. 28-8. First Generation TDRS Capabilities.

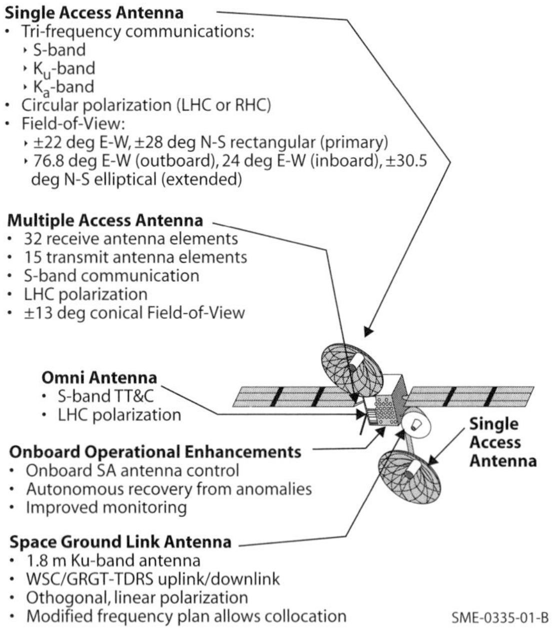

Fig. 28-9. Second Generation TDRS Capabilities.

- *Multi-Access (MA) or S-Band Multi-Access (SMA) Service*: A multi-element phased array antenna is used to support one forward service and multiple return services to user spacecraft at any given time. Limitation on the number of simultaneous return service customers that can be supported is driven by limits on the amount of SGLT user services ground processing equipment and the level of self interference between user satellites. MA services are provided using a Code Division Multiple Access (CDMA) technique that allows multiple users to communicate through the same system, using spread-spectrum technology with a unique identifying Pseudo Noise (PN) Code assigned by the NASA Spectrum Manager to each user.
- *Single Access (SA) Service*: Two 4.8 m, steerable dish antennas are used to each support a link to a single user spacecraft at a time.
- *Cross-Support Service*: In this service, user spacecraft use both the S-band SA (SSA) service and MA simultaneously, one for the forward service, one for the return service.
- *Tracking and Clock Calibration Services:* Available to all users except K_a-band SA (KaSA) users, ranging, two-way Doppler measurements and data on the offset between the user spacecraft clock and Universal Time Coordinated (UTC) time are available.
- *Demand Access System (DAS) Service*: DAS equipment at the ground terminals can be configured to allow for MA users to establish an extended duration link that is handed-off from TDRS to TDRS as the user satellite orbits the Earth. DAS Services can only be supported by the first generation TDRS.
- Technical specifications of TDRS antennas operating in the modes described above can be found in Table 28-3.

Additional information on NASA's Space Network [2011d] can be found on their website.

28.2 Data Accounting and Distribution Services

Connectivity between antenna ground stations and user facilities is a critical link for ensuring captured telemetry can get to the end-user within the required latency, and that commands can get from the user facility to the spacecraft during ground station contacts. Although this section will not cover the activities that occur at the user facilities (such as satellite image processing and command data generation), it will cover the tools, processes and protocols used to transfer information to and from the ground stations that interface with these user activities.

28.2.1 Data Capture/Transmission Verification

Early space missions used a *Time Division Multiplexing* (TDM) formatting scheme where data was continuously multiplexed in defined fixed length frames. Each mission would define their own multiplexing scheme as well as their own method for verifying that commands/telemetry were reaching their destination. For most missions during this period, command reception verification was accomplished by *end item* verification where the resulting command action, for example, seeing a spacecraft heater turn on after being commanded to do so, was typically the only way that the flight operations

Table 28-3. TDRS Technical Capabilities Summary.

Service Type	Forward Max Data Rate	Forward Modulation Schemes	Forward Minimum EIRP	User Return Links / TDRS	Return Max Data Rate[10]	Return Modulation Schemes[10]	TDRS G/T (nadir minimum)
MA	300 kbps	QPSK, BPSK	PFOV[2]: 1st Series: 34 dBW 2nd Series: 40 dBW LEOFOV[3]: 1st Series: 34 dBw 2nd Series: 42 dBW	5/TDRS up to 20/WSC 2/TDRS through GRGT	1st Series: 300 kbps 2nd Series: 3 Mbps[8]	1st Series: Rate ½ Convolutional 2nd Series: Rate ½, 1/3 Convolutional	Formed Beam: PFOV 1st Series: 22.0 dB/K F8(cold)–F10: 3.2 dB/K F8(hot): –0.2 dB/K LEOFOV 1st Series: 3.1 dB/K F8(cold)–F10: 4.5 dB/K F8(hot): 1.2 dB/K
SSA	7 Mbps	QPSK, BPSK, PCM/PM	PFOV & EEOV[4]: Normal: 43.6 dBW High[5]: 1st Series: 46.3 dBw 2nd Series: 48.5 dBW	2	6 Mbps[8]	Rate ½, 1/3 Convolutional	PFOV: 9.5 dB/K EEOV (2nd Series only): 9.5 dB/K
KuSA	25 Mbps[1]	QPSK, BPSK	PFOV & EEOV[4]: Normal autotrack[6]: 46.5 dBW High autotrack[6]: 48.5 dBW Normal program track: 40.5 dBW High program track: 42.5 dBW LEOFOV: Normal autotrack: 46.5 dBW High autotrack: 48.5 dBW Normal program track: 44.0 dBW High program track: 46.0 dBW	2	300 Mbps[9]	Rate ½, 1/3 Convolutional or uncoded	PFOV (1st Series) and EEOV (2nd Series): Autotrack: 24.4 dB/K Program Track: 18.4 dB/K LEOFOV Autotrack: 24.4 dB/K Program Track: 21.9 dB/K
KaSA[7]	25 Mbps[1]	QPSK, QPSK	PFOV: Autotrack: 63.0 dBW Program track: 56.2 dBW LEOFOV: Autotrack: 63.0 dBW Program track: 59.5 dBW	2/TDRS up to 8/WSC	300 Mbps	Rate ½, 1/3 Convolutional or uncoded	PFOV and EEOV: Autotrack: 26.5 dB/K Program Track: 19.1 dB/K (PFOV only) LEOFOV Autotrack: 26.5 dB/K Program Track: 23.0 dB/K

Notes:
1. Current ground terminal equipment limits forward K_u/K_a-band forward link to 7 Mbps but plans are to increase this capability to 25 Mbps
2. PFOV (Primary Field of View)
3. LEOFOV (LEO Field of View)
4. EEFOV (Extended Elliptical Field of View)
5. Use of High Power mode is restricted and must be coordinated with the Space Network prior to use
6. The KuSA forward autotrack performance EEFOV is a goal and will be supported on a best-effort basis
7. KaSA return service only available on 2nd generation TDRS
8. Available when using rate ½ Convolutional Encoding
9. GRGT support of KuSA return data rates in excess of 150Mbps should be discussed with the SN
10. Maximum data rates may increase, and new modulation schemes may be added as the SN evolves

team knew that a command had successfully reached the spacecraft. Telemetry reception verification during this period was primarily accomplished through the manual inspection of downlinked data that had been recorded on magnetic tape days to months earlier at a ground station. If missing data was discovered, it was most likely already erased from the spacecraft recorders so there was little recourse and the data would be considered lost. With advances in ground transmission capability and bandwidth in the 1970s and 1980s, it became possible for at least some spacecraft data to be sent in real-time from the ground station to the user facility. At this same time, development of Internet Protocol (IP) for terrestrial applications in the 1970s and 1980s, was establishing protocols for high Quality of Service (QoS) (QoS refers to a data transmission mechanism that ensures a specific bit-error-rate or probability of dropped packets on a transmission link) transmission protocols using the concept of standard format "packetized" data. The convergence of the development of IP protocols and the establishment of sufficient bandwidth terrestrial networks to allow spacecraft real-time transmission directly to the user facilities, led to the development of high QoS spacecraft telemetry and command protocols/systems. The goal was to establish a standard packet length along with the appropriate metadata and protocols to allow for the receiver to autonomously verify reception, and for the sender to autonomously retransmit data that does not reach the receiver.

28.2.1.1 Command Verification Protocol

One of the first packet transmission protocols developed for space application in the early 1980s was the Consultative Committee on Space Data Services [CCSDS, 2011a] Communications Operation Procedure 1 (COP-1), and command transmission protocol. COP-1 protocol is focused on autonomously ensuring that commands are received by the spacecraft in the order that they were transmitted and that all commands get to the spacecraft successfully. Since the command link is typically transmitting a lower data rate (Kbps for command links vs. Mbps for telemetry links) and since high QoS command reception can be critical to spacecraft safety and mission success, it made sense for an acknowledgement base command protocol to be developed first. COP-1 protocol is a closed-loop, QoS scheme that uses a Frame Operation Procedure (FOP) on the command transmission end and a Frame Acceptance and Reporting Mechanism (FARM) on the receiving end. The FOP, operating at the user control center, takes the command virtual channel frames that are ready for uplink and inserts a sequential Frame Sequence Number (FSN) in the frame header prior to transmission to the antenna ground station for uplink. After transmission of the command frame to the spacecraft the on-board FARM checks to ensure that the FSN of arriving commands is sequential and it also validates that the incoming command frames successfully passed through any command error detection/correction software. Once successful command reception is verified, the FARM generates an updated Command Link Control Word (CLCW) for downlink. The CLCW is the part of each virtual channel telemetry frame that contains information on the last command FSN that has been verified as well as information on any out of sequence commands that have been received with a request for retransmission of "missing" command frames. The FOP interrogates the CLCW and retransmits command frames as requested. The FOP also has a timeout function that initiates command retransmission for any command frames that are not verified in the CLCW within a specified amount of time (the timeout function needs to be adjusted as spacecraft get further and further from Earth to take into account light-time travel delays that will lengthen the time between command uplink and receipt of an updated CLCW). COP-1 protocol is now a standard used by most spacecraft. There are some spacecraft where COP-1 is less valuable, specifically, for missions headed deep into the solar system where the light-time delay between command transmission and reception is so great that commands may not be verified during a single ground station contact. For these missions, a more manual method for verifying spacecraft command reception is sometimes used. On other, low-cost missions, command reception verification is still accomplished by command *end item verification.* End item verification is the process of identifying that a spacecraft has received a command by verifying that the action associated with the command has occurred. This was the primary method of command verification prior to the development of COP-1 protocol. For example, a command to turn a heater on could be end-item-verified by examining telemetry to ensure that the heater circuit has been turned to the "on" state and/or that nearby thermistors are registering a rise in temperature. For example, end item verification was used for command reception verification on the NASA/DoD Fast, Affordable, Science and Technology Satellite (FASTSAT) mission developed by Marshall Space Flight Center and launched in 2010. Although this approach saves money on flight software it also makes command verification difficult, especially during periods where telemetry is intermittent and requires the flight operations team to manually determine when command retransmissions are required.

28.2.1.2 Telemetry Verification Protocol

Capturing a high percentage of the data stored in spacecraft mass memory is typically critical to mission success. Currently, for most spacecraft, ensuring a high data capture percentage is a manually intensive process that relies on mission control center personnel verifying the receipt/non-receipt of data and then either releasing successfully captured spacecraft memory segments for overwriting or commanding the spacecraft to retransmit memory segments that were not successfully returned to the control center. Although some missions have developed mission-unique software to support the data recovery process, an international standard for automating this function has not existed until recently. The goal is to provide an FTP-like file transfer protocol that is more highly tolerant of the existing space communications infrastructure, long time delay, higher error rate, environment that space communication links pose compared to the terrestrial communication environment that the FTP protocol was designed to support. CCSDS File Delivery Protocol (CFDP) automates the data recovery process, ensuring as high a data capture percentage as possible while freeing spacecraft memory segments for overwriting as quickly as possible to ensure the maximum quantity of storage is available to the spacecraft at all times. CFDP operates over a wide range of underlying protocols (see Fig. 28-10) [CCSDS, 2011b].

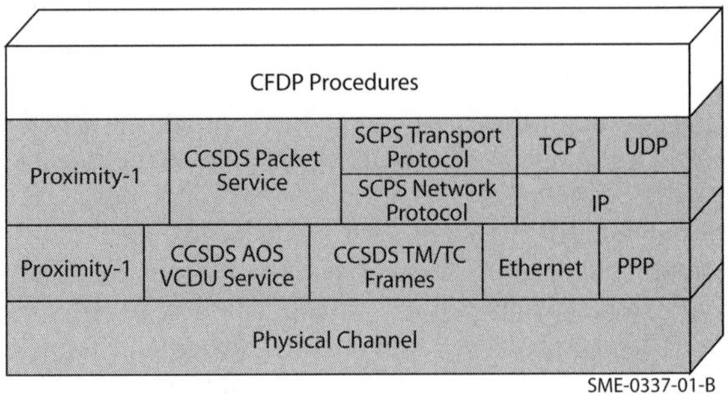

Fig. 28-10. CFDP Operates Over a Wide Range of Underlying Protocols.

Although CFDP works on the transmission/reception of *files*, the user can define the file size to fit their operational scheme. As CFDP files are transmitted to the ground via CFDP Protocol Data Units (PDU's), the ground system CFDP software (running either at the antenna ground station or back at the mission control center) logs incoming PDU's. Some PDU's contain CFDP *File Delivery Units (CFDUs)* containing the contents of the file being transferred while others contain metadata used to track the progress of the transmission. For PDU's not received at the ground, two approaches for recovering this data are available. In the first, as soon as a PDU is received out of sequence, indicating that there is missing data, a *non-acknowledgement*, called a *nack,* is sent to the spacecraft to request retransmission of the missing PDU's. The other option is to wait until an *end-of-file* PDU is received and then send the spacecraft all *pending nack* requests for that CFDP file. Either way, once receipt of the entire CFDP file has been acknowledged by the ground, the spacecraft can now free this memory space for overwriting. Another facet of CFDP implementation to consider is that the ground based CFDP software can either be run at the mission control center or at the antenna ground station, both implementation options are permissible—depending on the operational requirements and time available for retransmission. CFDP software running at the antenna ground station shortens the time to respond to missing data and can operate even when transmission links to the mission control center are not available, but, since this mode requires the antenna ground station to send "command data" back to the spacecraft some spacecraft operators would prefer to close the CFDP-loop at the mission control center. If the CFDP-loop is closed at the mission control center, an option is to have the ground station store the downlinked recorder data and generate *nacks* and send them to the mission control center where they can be turned around and sent back to the ground station for uplink. This hybrid model allows the mission control center to be the source of all spacecraft commands and to be responsible for the data management process, while minimizing the real-time bandwidth requirement between the ground station and mission control by not requiring PDUs to complete the journey to the mission control center to be acknowledged. CFDP can allow for data management across ground station contacts and across multiple ground stations although the ground implementation (mission control center vs. antenna ground station) will drive how CFDP metadata will need to be exchanged to support these scenarios. A number of commercial products are now available that implement this standard and for spacecraft with significant data recovery requirements and missions where lights-out operations are being considered, implementation of CFDP offers distinct advantages. For example, the LRO mission successfully applied CFDP to ensure they could achieve a high percentage of science and spacecraft housekeeping data recovery using a K_a-band telemetry link that could be adversely impacted by weather in the transmission path.

28.2.2 Standard Transmission Protocols

Section 28.2.1 discussed a number of protocols used to ensure the successful transfer of data to and from spacecraft. These *Space-Link* protocols address only one leg of the journey that data transits on its way to and from a spacecraft. The other leg of the journey is the terrestrial link between ground elements. One of the most popular standard protocols being used to provide high QoS links between ground stations and user facilities is the CCSDS Space-Link Extension (SLE) protocol. Formed in 1982, the CCSDS, established numerous international standards for the link between spacecraft and ground stations. More recent efforts, [CCSDS, 2011d], have focused on establishing a similar set of inter-Agency "Cross Support" standards that address connectivity between ground segment elements to extend the space link directly to the end user (Fig. 28-11).

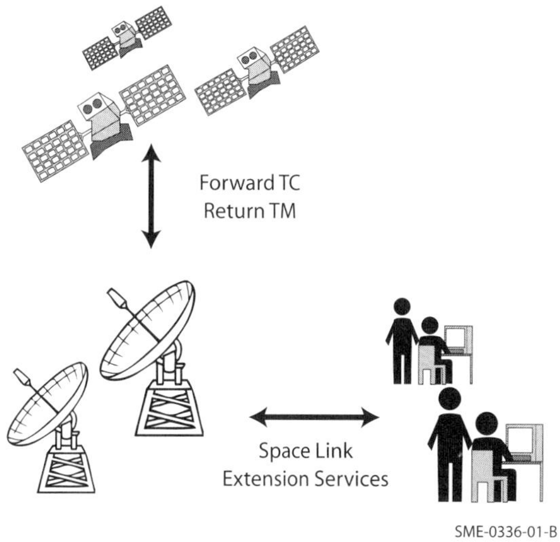

Fig. 28-11. Extending the Space Link Back to the Control Center.

The SLE protocol is a layered architecture that uses existing communications infrastructure to enable antenna ground stations and mission control centers to be connected seamlessly. In a world where both national Space Agencies and private companies have developed a large amount of ground-based spacecraft support infrastructure, these standard protocols enable interoperability between diverse ground elements. SLE protocols address both a set of TCP/IP-based Data Transfer services, such as, telemetry distribution based on Virtual Channel or Applications ID (apid), command data transfer as communications link transfer units (CLTU). All services moving through this layered protocol pass through an Authentication Layer that provides security for the transmission path, authenticating users before "binding" the service path to allow data transfer.

The SLE Cross Support Service Management protocols enable the transfer of information between mission users (Utilization Management) and service providers

(Complex Management) required to: establish a Service Agreement on Data Transfer services to be provided, define Configuration Profiles for these services, schedule service instances, and/or transfer information needed to support service execution (e.g., trajectory predictions, equipment requirements). These standard protocols can be used from the early definition phase when negotiating a Service Agreement through the service execution phase.

28.2.3 Bandwidth/Connectivity Between Ground Stations and User Facilities

One of the limiting factors in getting data to and from the spacecraft is the bandwidth available between the ground station and the user control center facilities. As spacecraft telemetry data rates rise toward 1+ Gbps, terrestrial communication links to send all this data back to the user facilities in real-time can become cost-prohibitive. In addition, since many missions now require multicast data distribution to numerous user facilities, bandwidth requirements can be increased even further to send copies of the data to each user. To evaluate bandwidth requirements, latency and data quantity/unit time requirements are taken into consideration. For missions with long latency requirements (days, weeks, months), physical media such as DVDs or USB flash drives can be used to collect data at the ground station for shipping to user facilities. For medium latency requirements (~6 – ~48 hours), transfer from the ground station to the user facility can be done using internet file transfers using FTP or other file transfer protocols. For missions with short latency requirements (few minutes), dedicated transmission lines, for example, T1 (1.544 Mbps/1.536 Mbps available to the user) or OC3 (155.52 Mbps/148.608 Mbps available to users) line may be required.

The other consideration is data volume and multicast requirements. For missions with moderate data volumes where the available bandwidth back to the user can deliver data to the end user within the required latency, rate-buffered transmission directly from the ground station to the users may be the best option. The ground station can also save a copy of all transmitted data to respond to requests for retransmission from the user although this retransmission capability will have a lower priority for bandwidth than any real-time data that may be coming from the ground station at the same time. For missions where data volume or multicast requirements are high and bandwidth to the ground station is limited, ground stations may transfer their data to a network storage/distribution facility located at a site with high bandwidth connectivity to the users. This central storage facility can provide longterm storage for user data, can retransmit data to users on request, and can multicast data as required.

A final consideration is whether or not an alternative path is required to deliver data to/from ground stations. Alternate paths can be used to increase the probability that latency requirements can be met. Alternate paths can protect against network outages resulting from cable cuts or weather related outages between the ground station and the user. For many missions, the cost of alternate paths for data delivery may be prohibitive. For remote locations, alternate paths for data delivery may all lead to a similar *last-mile* path. For example, there may be only one set of utility poles, or a single bridge leading to the ground station, or a single network interface card at the ground station resulting in a single-point failure in the transmission path.

28.3 Ground System Driving Requirements and Sizing

There are many aspects of mission design that will drive the design of the supporting ground system. The following information provides a summary of some of the primary mission design drivers and their impact on ground system design.

Orbit/Trajectory

1. LEO, High Inclination, Low Eccentricity: Ground stations at high latitude locations provide coverage for almost every orbit each day. Stations near both poles provide half the orbit coverage; near one pole only provides once an orbit coverage with increased latency.
2. LEO Mid-Latitude, Low Eccentricity: GEO Space-relay systems can provide constant coverage. Ground stations each provide single contact opportunities for less than ~40% of orbits each day (specific percentage depends on satellite inclination and station latitude).
3. High Eccentricity: Based on the orbital period, it may be possible to locate ground stations where the ground track location of the satellite's apogee repeats over time.
4. GEO: A single antenna and data processing, storage, distribution center located in constant view of the GEO satellite provides an optimal ground architecture solution.
5. Interplanetary Trajectory: Networks with 3 nodes separated from each other by ~120 deg of longitude (e.g., NASA's Deep Space Network) provide greatest duration of daily view periods. A combination of stations above and below the equator is optimal for collecting tracking data that can be used to establish orbit/trajectory with high accuracy.
6. Launch Trajectory: Ground Stations at locations to view key events (e.g., upper stage shutdown/ignition, separation, array deployment) (stations must be capable of tracking at high rates during these low altitude contacts). Space-relay systems can be used as long as their antennas can slew at the high rates necessary to track these low-orbit/high velocity events.

Table 28-3◀, Fig. 28-11◀, Eq. 28-2◀

Latency (from collection of data on board the spacecraft to arrival of processed products at user facility)

- **Minutes:** Requires dedicated (or close to dedicated) antenna services to support. Also, requires significant redundancy and robustness in the ground architecture to ensure that low latency can be maintained when specific contacts are missed due to equipment or operational issues. GEO space-relay systems are optimal for supporting low latency LEO requirements since they can provide coverage over a high percentage of each orbit. A ground-based antenna service would need to have a large number of nodes spread evenly throughout the satellite's groundtrack to provide multiple partial-orbit opportunities for downlinking data. For GEO satellites, a single dedicated ground station can provide constant contact to support low latency, and for lunar and planetary missions, a 3-node ground station configuration equally distributed in longitude can provide this constant availability (although transmission time delays for spacecraft beyond the Moon make "minutes" latency difficult or impossible to achieve). Once on the ground, verification of data and requesting re-transmissions must also be completed quickly using advanced automated protocols such as CFDP (Sec. 28.2.1.2). Data processing and transmission to users directly from the ground station is optimal for achieving low latency (unless integration of data between multiple ground stations is required as part of the data processing function —although this integration would be difficult to perform while still meeting this low latency requirement). To perform this function, adequate bandwidth from the ground station to the user must be available to minimize the amount of rate-buffering/delay that occurs in the data transport to the user.
- **Hours:** Reduced amount of required contact opportunities makes a shared, distributed ground station architecture a cost effective solution to meet this requirement. If a distributed ground station architecture is used, integration of data at a single location may be valuable for performing data accounting, storage, and distribution. This architecture can include rate-buffering of data at the ground station, reducing ground station bandwidth requirements/cost while still achieving required latency.
- **Days/Months:** Infrequent scheduled contacts on a shared, distributed ground station architecture provides a cost effective method for supporting this requirement. Also, once data is on the ground, low cost options for transporting data to a central processing center and to the final user can be employed such as using standard internet FTP (where bandwidth availability can vary unpredictably) and even the shipping of data tapes/flash-drives from the ground station can be used instead of paying for expensive communication data lines.

On-board Storage Capability

- **No On-board Storage:** GEO space-relay satellites can provide a constant orbital coverage capability for most LEO satellites. Experience on NASA's Compton Gamma Ray Observatory (CGRO), where the on-board recorders failed during the mission, showed that GEO relay satellites could effectively collect/transmit user spacecraft data as long as the GEO satellites could dedicate the required assets to support the mission. In another case, LEO satellites with ops concepts that only require the collection data over specific ground locations can operate with a dedicated ground based antenna at these locations to capture data in real-time. An example of this would be an Earth imaging satellite designed to image major cities with a series of ground antennas located at each city. Lastly, GEO satellites with dedicated ground based antennas can operate without on-board storage as well since there is constant view between the ground and spacecraft antennas. NASA's geosynchronous Solar Dynamics Observatory (SDO), for example, has two dedicated ground antennas in New Mexico that provide primary/back-up data receptors for a constant stream of SDO telemetry. In all of these cases, downlink data rates are driven by spacecraft data collection rates. In addition, co-location of telemetry processing/distribution at ground stations is often advantageous in these scenarios since received data can be processed and shipped immediately (no need to wait for "redumps" of missing data when there isn't any on-board recorder).
- **Minimal On-board Storage:** Ground architecture needs to focus on quickly evaluating recorder data dumps and initiating re-dumps as required to fill gaps in initially recovered dataset and free on-board memory for overwriting. Antenna services need to provide frequent opportunities for recovering recorded data. Also, advanced protocols, such as the CFDP (Sec. 28.2.1.2) can assist in quickly evaluating recovered data, freeing on-board memory space as recovery is verified and automatically initiating re-dumps as required to fill gaps. Other advanced protocols, such as DTN (Sec. 28.5.3.1) can also provide a method for passing data from the spacecraft to an intermediate location (could be a space-based relay satellite) which would then take responsibility for the data transmission, allowing the spacecraft on-board memory to be released for overwriting.
- **Significant On-board Storage:** Possibility of going multiple orbits without downlinking data greatly reduces the number of ground stations required to provide support. Also, simplifies data recovery process, allowing for more time for evaluation of captured data by humans or machines, prior to re-

leasing on-board memory for overwriting. Note, if re-transmits are spread over multiple ground stations, transfer of all data to a common location for level-zero processing/data accounting to build final datasets may be required.

Required Data Recovery Percentage

- **<~95%:** There can be evaluation of setting more lenient requirements throughout the ground system for fault tolerance, robustness, and redundancy to match with this higher tolerance for missing data and to keep down ground system costs. Reductions in re-transmissions can also be included to save time. This reduction in re-transmissions can be tied with a simple and highly automated ops concept that can be more tolerant to missed contacts and does not need to include as many fault identification and recovery schemes.
- **>~95%:** Ground systems supporting missions with data recovery percentages approaching 100% have traditionally focused on having large operations staffing who focus on "chasing" every bit of data. Improvements in automation have started to reach levels where even these strict data recovery requirements can be met by automated systems. New data capture protocols, such as CFDP, provide a highly accurate method for maximizing data recovery. The biggest challenge for automated systems is handling anomalous situations, such as, a missed contact, where rapid rescheduling of additional contacts to ensure full data recovery can be challenging. Dedicated ground stations for providing antenna services is optimal for these missions since rapid rescheduling in a multi-user ground station network can be difficult based on other user priorities and the ability to interact (particularly when automation is being used) with the antenna service provider in real-time to reschedule contacts quickly to minimize data loss.

Level of Automation

- **Fully Staffed Operations:** Highly human intensive operations allows for simplification of the ground system architecture. All nominal and non-nominal situations are handled by the operations staff who are also responsible for monitoring and identifying non-nominal situations. Operations staffing is typically comprised of discipline specific team members.
- **Day Staff Only:** Automation is used to handle all nominal operations while staff are "on-call" to analyze and react to non-nominal situations that the automation has identified. In this *lights dim* concept, the biggest challenge is balancing data capture requirements against the role of automation to ensure that human response time will not result in unacceptable data loss. In addition, in many of these systems commanding the spacecraft is a task retained by the operations staff and not entrusted to the automation. Operations staffing also shifts to a team where almost all members are multi-skilled.
- **Full Automation:** *Lights out* operations with minimal human intervention in ground system operations involves development of automation systems with significant levels of fault tree analyses pre-programmed to allow for the ground system to identify, troubleshoot and react to non-nominal situations. In addition, use of advanced data capture protocols such as CFDP can provide high data capture percentage performance without the need for human involvement in recorder management.

28.4 Mission Examples

The following mission examples, outline how requirements drove specific ground system designs:

Advanced Composition Explorer (ACE)

Mission Summary: NASA, Explorer Class Mission to provide up-to-date information on solar wind speed and particle/energy flux

Launched: 1997

Orbit: Lissajous at Earth-Sun L1 (1.5×10^9 m from Earth)

Ground System Design: 34 m DSN antennas, at sites around the world, are used to support single daily S-band 3-hour duration playbacks of stored data (76 kbps playback rate) (Note: ACE spacecraft is available for contact as long as the Sun is above the horizon at the ground station). In addition, smaller aperture antennas around the world are used to capture 464 bps Real-Time Solar Wind (RTSW) downlink which is transmitted 24/7 (except during single daily stored data playback). RTSW data contains critical information on variations in the speed and intensity of the solar wind. RTSW data is shipped directly to NOAA's Space Weather Prediction center where it is processed and made available as quickly as possible to organizations, such as spacecraft operators and power utility companies, who are concerned about potential impacts from increased solar activity on their systems.

High-rate playback and real-time data from DSN sites is transferred to GSFC where a lights-out automated multi-mission control center ingests ACE data and performs level-0 processing on all captured data and analysis and trending of spacecraft state-of-health data. Flight Operations team members are automatically alerted if there are anomalous spacecraft health readings or problems with the ground system. Completed level-0 products are shipped to the ACE Science Center at the California Institute of Technology where level-1 and other products are generated for distribution to the science community.

Polar Operational Environmental Satellite (POES)

Mission Summary: NOAA's LEO weather monitoring satellites. Provide visible and infrared images and soundings in addition to ozone, space weather and other readings

Launched: Series of satellites with launches dating back to the 1970s

Orbit: A two-satellite constellation with morning and afternoon ascending-node crossing times. POES are in Sun Synchronous 833 km/870 km (morning/afternoon) circular orbits

Ground System Design: Dedicated Command and Data Acquisition (CDA) stations located at Wallops Island, VA and Fairbanks, AK use 13 m antennas to contact each POES spacecraft ~11 times/day for ~12 min/contact. Since each POES spacecraft orbits the Earth ~14.1 times/day, there are ~3 orbits/day where the spacecraft orbit ground track path does not intersect the *mask* of any of the CDA antennas. During CDA contacts, 2.66 Mbps playback are performed to download data stored during the previous orbit (previous 3 orbits when the spacecraft is coming out of the non-contact period described above). During these contacts, real-time data on the spacecraft state-of-health and the status of the recorder playbacks is transferred to the POES Satellite Operations Center (SOC) in Suitland, MD where a 24/7 staff of operations personnel assess the spacecraft health and ensure recovery of playback data is completed. Playback data is collected at the CDA during the contact and is then rate buffered and transmitted via domestic commercial communication relay satellites (*DOMSAT*) back to the Central Environmental Satellite Computer System (CEMSCS) facility located in Suitland, MD (the goal is to complete these transmission within 25 minutes of the completion of the CDA contact). Automated systems at CEMSCS then process this data as quickly as possible, producing weather products that are available to weather forecasting, and environmental science organizations around the world.

DSN 34 m antennas and the Air Force Satellite Control Network (AFSCN) provide contingency support as required.

Ramaty High Energy Solar Spectroscopic Imager (RHESSI)

Mission Summary: NASA Small Explorer mission to explore the basic physics of particle acceleration and explosive energy released in solar flares

Launched: 2002

Orbit: 600 km circular, 38 deg inclination

Ground System Design: Primary data recovery is through the automated, multi-mission 11 m Berkeley Ground Station (BGS) antenna located at the University of California, Berkeley. The BGS antenna support to RHESSI consists of ~6 contacts/day at ~9 min/contact. 11 Gbits/day of data are recovered using a downlink rate of 3.5 Mbps during BGS contacts. Data on the spacecraft state-of-health and recorder playback status are transferred in real-time from the BGS to the Berkeley Mission and Science Operations Center (MSOC) where a multi-mission, automated ground system assesses the incoming data and alerts flight operations personnel of any detected spacecraft or ground system anomalies. Recorder playback data is captured at the BGS and is transferred to the MSOC post-pass using a secure FTP push. The MSOC performs level-0 and above processing and generates science products for the RHESSI science team.

If high levels of solar activity generate larger than normal volumes of data or if high winds or other issues make the Berkeley Ground Station antenna unavailable, the spacecraft can communicate through NASA's NEN ground stations at Wallops Island, VA and Santiago, Chile are used as back-up. When using Wallops, RHESSI data is transferred post-pass to a NEN central data storage facility at GSFC where an email is then sent to the MSOC alerting that a file is ready for transfer. The MSOC then initiates an FTP transfer of this file over the open internet.

Radio Aurora Explorer (RAX)

Mission Overview: University of Michigan / SRI International joint venture 3U CubeSat designed to study large plasma formations in the ionosphere that can disrupt communications between Earth and orbiting spacecraft.

Launched: 2010

Orbit: 650 km circular, 72 deg inclination

Ground System Design: Existing ground radars are used to transmit high power signals into the ionosphere where they are scattered. This scattered signal is detected and analyzed by the RAX spacecraft as it orbits. The resulting data is then downlinked to over 20 existing amateur radio operator sites around the world that have volunteered to collect and process RAX data. By operating at 437.5 MHz (FM) at 9600 baud, amateur radio operators can capture the signal while RAX is overhead. The University of Michigan provides interested radio operators with Beacon Decoding software that they can use to process RAX data and then ship it back to the RAX Science Operations Center

28.5 Technology Trends

The future of spacecraft ground systems is focused on increasing the volume of data that spacecraft can transmit to the ground over their operational lives, reducing the time it takes to get the data from the spacecraft to the end user, and increasing the interoperability between ground systems from different countries and manufactures.

28.5.1 Shorter Wavelength Communications

As modern spacecraft collect ever increasing quantities of data, transferring this information to the ground fast enough to free up on-board memory before it fills to capacity becomes increasingly challenging. This challenge is particularly severe for Earth orbiting spacecraft that are trying to send their information directly to ground stations where contact periods can be short and contacts infrequent. To address this challenge, many spacecraft are moving toward higher frequency communication bands combined with advanced modulation and encoding schemes to increase their maximum downlink data rates. In addition, increasing use of lower frequency bands for a variety of Earth-based communication applications provides another incentive for spacecraft developers to consider using higher frequencies for communication links.

For many science missions, short wavelength K_a-band communication is a consideration. K_a-band has the potential for downloading data from LEO satellites at rates above 3 Gbps. Moving up into K_a-band for direct-to-Earth communication links does come with the challenge of overcoming atmospheric attenuation, particularly when there is rain in the transmission path. For this reason, some ground stations have been situated in low rainfall areas (For example, NASA's LRO downlinks K_a-band data to White Sands, New Mexico) or downlink periods have been limited to higher spacecraft elevations above the antenna mask to minimize the path distance, and associated attenuation, through the atmosphere. Another approach to K_a-band direct-to-ground transmission links in the presence of varying atmospheric attenuation is to use adaptive link techniques. Adaptive systems either vary the data rate, modulation scheme, or encoding scheme to maintain a positive link margin. Adaptive systems use constant feedback from the receiving to the transmitting antenna to establish the link margin. Based on this feedback, the transmitting system adjusts specific link parameters to maintain a positive link margin. K_a-band is also gaining popularity for space-to-space communication where atmospheric attenuation isn't a concern (for example, NASA's TDRSS constellation supports both K_u-band and K_a-band communication with user spacecraft).

Moving beyond K_a-band, research into communication using lasers is gaining popularity. Optical Communication can potentially return 10 times to 100 times more data with 1% of the antenna area of current RF systems, while requiring less communication system mass and power on the spacecraft side. Optical communication can be used for LEO, planetary and deep space applications and can be used to support direct-to-ground as well as space-to-space links. Since optical communication wavelengths are 3 to 5 orders-of-magnitude shorter than typical RF wavelengths, the beamwidths are much narrower than RF systems with a large fraction of the power concentrated in a narrow beam. Narrow beamwidths impose the need for high precision pointing between sending/receiving antennas to maintain a positive link during spacecraft contacts.

28.5.2 Reduced Latency

The operational applications for satellite data has grown significantly over the years. Today's satellites perform a variety of missions including serving as communications relays, monitoring the Earth's weather and climate, and collecting data related to all sorts of natural and man-made disasters (tsunamis, earthquakes, forest fires, nuclear reactor accidents). As we have become increasingly dependent on satellites to support decision making on, for example, the deployment of troops in a combat theater or the deployment of search and rescue crews in a disaster zone, reduction in latency requirements has been a consistent theme.

For some applications, such as hurricane tracking, satellites in geosynchronous orbits provide a platform for continuous monitoring over some large portion of the globe. In these cases, strategically placed ground stations can provide a continuous, almost instantaneous, link between satellites and the customers who require their data. NASA's Solar Dynamics Observatory (SDO) launched in 2010 would be a good example of this type of satellite. The SDO ground system architecture (shown in Fig. 28-12) includes two dedicated 18 m K_a-Band/S-Band antennas located in White Sands, New Mexico. These antennas both receive the same signal and ground system software is used to select the best source for processing and sending forward to the data customers. This architecture provides a fault tolerant system with a very high data capture percentage and low latency since solar observation data is constantly streaming in from the satellite, the best source is selected quickly, and data is shipped out to customers with minimal latency. Since solar events, such as flares and coronal mass ejections, can have a significant impact on the operation of the world's satellite fleet and on power grids and communication systems on Earth, rapid knowledge of evolving solar conditions can be critical to minimizing the damage caused by major solar events.

Satellites orbiting below geosynchronous orbit pose a greater latency reduction challenge since their groundtracks cover a larger swath of the Earth's surface over time, requiring either numerous ground stations or a geosynchronous space-based relay system to allow for low latency operations. Human Spacecraft such as the International Space Station and the Space Shuttle utilize the TDRSS space-based relay network to provide low latency operations. Since each TDRS has an >120 deg of longitude view, a constellation of these satellites can provide, as long as they have adequate capacity, continuous links between numerous LEO/MEO satellites and the ground. These systems have a number of challenges in supporting low latency operations, such as limited space-based equipment/capability limiting the number of active satellite links they can support at any given time and the high cost of operating a space-based relay network. As an alternative, the majority of LEO polar orbiting satellites use a store-and-forward architecture which relies on ground stations spread along their groundtrack to meet latency requirements. A good example of a ground-based architecture being designed for low-latency for polar orbiting spacecraft would be the Receptor Net architecture originally designed as part of the National Polar Orbiting Environmental Satellite System (NPOESS) Program. Even after the decision was made to dissolve the NPOESS program and to return to a mode where civilian and military LEO weather satellites would be developed independently (similar to former POES and DMSP programs), the Receptor Net ground system remained as a common component to support the low latency requirements of both programs. The Receptor Net architecture included 15 dedicated ground stations (called receptor sites) spread out on all 7 continents. Working in K_a-Band to reduce the possibility of RFI when downlinking around the world, civilian and mili-

Table 28-3◀, Fig. 28-11◀, Eq. 28-2◀

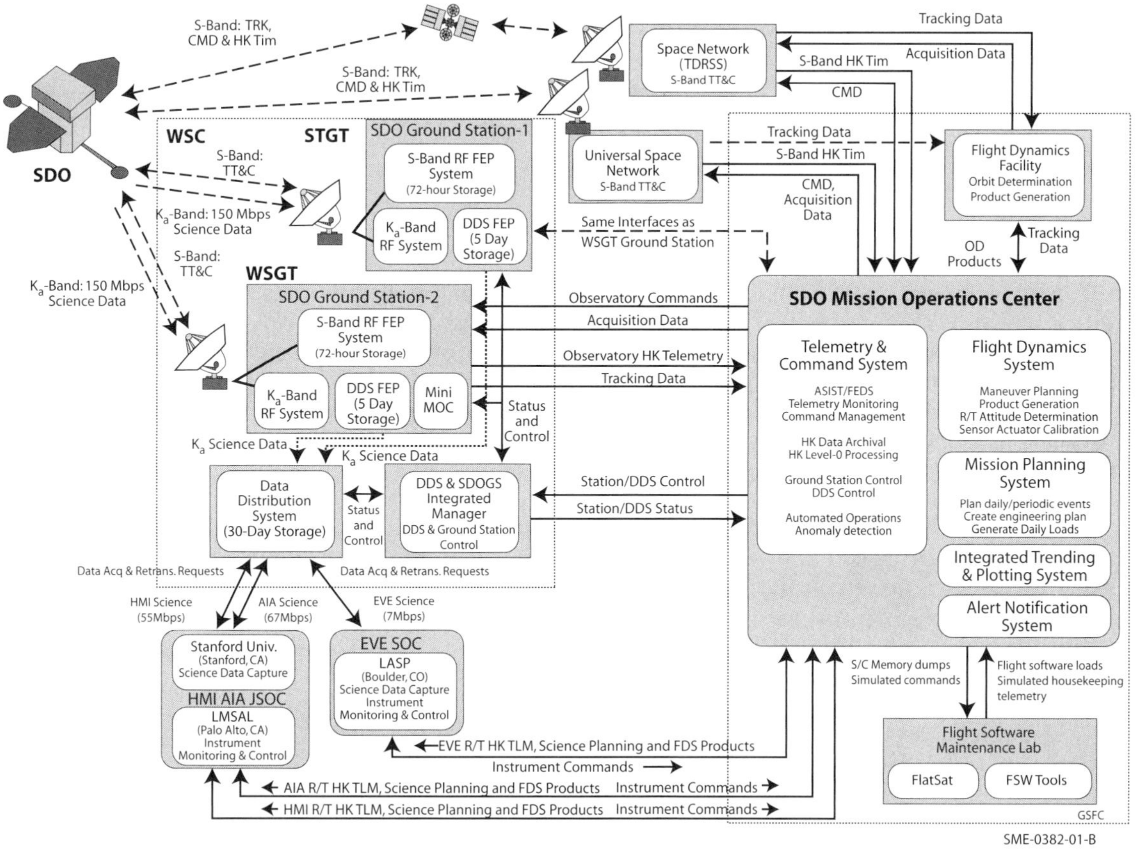

Fig. 28-12. SDO Ground System Architecture.

tary LEO weather satellites dump stored data at each receptor site (with a second dump of this data as well as newer data being performed at the following site to increase data capture probability). With this architecture, latency of between 15 and 30 minutes from the time a weather image is collected until it is in the hands of the end-user are achievable. Although this architecture requires a significant investment in receptor sites and interconnecting infrastructure, mission requirements for rapid collection and distribution of weather data from polar orbiting satellites could not be achieved by using the existing NOAA CDAs and the AFSCN networks that had previously supported LEO weather satellite contacts.

28.5.3 New International Standards—Increasing Interoperability and Data Capture Percentage

As an ever increasing number of satellites are placed in orbit by an ever increasing number of countries, international standards in the ground system interfaces and space/Earth communication protocols have been evolving to support these mission needs. In addition, standards are being developed and deployed to move the space/Earth communication link toward an architecture more similar to ground-based internet protocol where data accountability is more automated and transparent to the end user to ensure high data capture percentages. As discussed in Sec. 28.2, SLE and CFDP are two such international standard protocols that have been implemented in support of a number of missions. CCSDS continues to work on developing new standards that can benefit spacecraft operations. A primary example of this work is DTN.

28.5.3.1 Delay (or Disruption) Tolerant Networking (DTN)

Unlike most Earth-based communications links where establishing and maintaining connectivity throughout a data transfer session is straightforward, communication with spacecraft over great distances provides a challenging environment where connectivity may be lost or recovered multiple times while data is being transferred to the ground. Originally conceived as the "Interplanetary Internet", DTN makes use of store-and-forward techniques within the network in order to compensate for intermittent link connectivity. Compared to the internet which is a "connected" network where low latency (milliseconds) and low bit-error-rates (BER) allow for the end-to-end path to be established/verified/maintained throughout a data transfer session, DTN operates as a "disconnected" network that must perform in a high latency (for space applications, for example, 1.7 sec one way path time to the Moon, 8 min to Mars), high BER (caused by solar radiation for space applications) environment with intermittent connectivity (caused by blockage between spacecraft and Earth during some periods when planets, moons, and the

Sun get in the way of the transmission path or shared ground station resources). Evolved from the retransmission procedures of the CCSDS CFDP protocol, DTN uses custody transfer, where responsibility of data segments (bundles or bundle fragments), migrates with the data segment as it progresses across a series of network hops to reach its final destination. The goal, like for CFDP, is to ensure that data sent from a spacecraft to the ground, or vice-versa, is received correctly without the additional overhead of manual verification. CFDP, as implemented, is a point-to-point protocol. A DTN-based CFDP would provide a multihop file transfer capability. The convergence layer protocols provide the standard methods for transferring bundles over various communication paths. The bundle agent discovery protocols are the equivalent of dynamic routing protocols in IP networks. To date, the location of bundle agents has been managed analogous to static routing in IP networks. The goal is to establish end-to-end data transfer through a series of hops. An example would be a Mars Rover that communicates to a surface based relay terminal, that communicates to a Mars orbital relay spacecraft, to a DSN antenna on Earth, and finally to the rover's mission control center. DTN could also apply to a Medium Earth Orbit communication relay network that uses various ground and space based nodes to transfer data between users. Even a single spacecraft in LEO can take advantage of DTN to reduce the operational complexities involved with handovers, rate buffering, and data distribution. The advantages of employing DTN include:

- Reduction in manual data delivery verification
- The ability to rapidly "erase" data from spacecraft memory by providing a reliable store-and-forward custody transfer protocol
- Application of a prioritization scheme to ensure that high value data can take precedence as bandwidth becomes available
- Delay tolerance where bundles can be produced without concern for when they will be transmitted (includes a "time to live" field that allows old data to be erased from memory if it is not able to be transmitted within a defined timeframe)
- Long haul retransmission of non-file data (CFDP is based on file transfer)
- More rapid retransmission request since each custody transfer can result in a request for retransmission (for example, data not arriving at a DSN ground station can be requested for retransmission instead of waiting until the mission control center identifies that the data is missing)
- A standardized method for store and forward and rate buffering data terrestrially

Although DTN is still being developed towards an Internet Engineering Task Force (IETF) and CCSDS [2011c] standard, the set of store-and-forward bundle protocols and associated protocols are quickly advancing toward an operational state.

Additional information on the DTN Protocols can be found at the DTN Research Group [2011] website.

28.6 Summary

Ground system architectures vary greatly based on the mission link-budget requirements, data volumes, latency requirements, QoS requirements and numerous other factors. A constant evolution of ground systems is focused on enabling higher transmission rates while providing high QoS service with minimal need for human intervention. CCSDS protocols continue to evolve to support these advanced requirements while maintaining standardization of interfaces to ensure interoperability between ground systems developed by individual countries or commercial service providers.

References

For annotated bibliography of ground system design, see the book website.

CCSDS. 2011a. COP-1 Protocol. Website.

CCSDS. 2011b. CFDP Protocol. Space Internetworking, CFDP Green Book. Website.

CCSDS. 2011c. DTN Protocol. Space Internetworking, DTN Green Book. Website.

CCSDS. 2011d. SLE Protocol. Cross Support Concept, SLE Green Book. Website.

DTN Research Group. 2011. DTN Protocol. Website.

ESA. 2011. ESTRACK. Website.

JHU. 2011. FUSE, Johns Hopkins University. Website.

KSAT. 2011. Kongsberg Satellite Services, Norway. Website.

NASA. 2011a. CubeSat Program. Website.

NASA. 2011b. LRO. Website.

NASA. 2011c. NEN. Website.

NASA. 2011d. Space Network. Website.

NASA/JPL. 2011. DSN. Website.

NASA. 2011e. SLR. Website.

NOAA. 2011. GEOS, Office of Satellite Operations. Website.

SSC.2011. Swedish Space Corporation. Website.

29 Mission Operations

Trevor C. Sorensen, ***University of Hawaii***

with support from members of the AIAA Space Operations and Support Technical Committee*

* I would like to acknowledge the support of Joachim Kehr (DLR, retired), J. Jeffrey Devine, and Richard Campion (Honeywell Technology Solutions, Inc.), and the following members of the AIAA Space Operations and Support Technical Committee: Franz Newland (Com Dev International), Patricia Klein (Naval Research Laboratory), David LaVallee (Johns Hopkins University Applied Physics Laboratory), Carrie Olsen (NASA Marshall Space Flight Center), and David Welch (LASP/Honeywell Technology Solutions, Inc.).

It is possible to design and build the best possible spacecraft and even launch it into space, but it is useless unless there is a way for it to accomplish its mission. This is the role of *mission operations*. Contrary to a popular misconception, mission operations is not limited to what happens in the Mission Control Room or even the Mission Operations Center (MOC). That is really only the tip of the iceberg. Mission operations includes what happens on the spacecraft or launch vehicle, at ground stations, in engineering offices and science labs, to accomplish the goals of the mission, from design and development through mission execution. It is an integrated system of people, hardware, software, and activities that have to work together to ensure the successful execution of the mission. All organizations that fly space missions, from government agencies to industry and academia, perform mission operations activities. They nonetheless have different requirements for mission operations and often have their own philosophies and methodologies for developing and implementing mission operations. What is presented in this chapter are the methods that have worked for myself and for others from all types of missions—manned, robotic, Earth orbit, deep space, small, large, single and multiple satellites.

Mission operations can be categorized into four basic functions: spacecraft or launch vehicle operations, payload operations, ground operations, and mission management. Mission operations also vary by the phase of the mission life cycle and are divided into two fundamentally different modes separated by the launch. Mission operations design, development, and testing occurs during the study (Phase A), design (Phases B and C), and the assembly, integration, and testing (Phase D) phases of the mission. Mission operations execution occurs during the flight phase (Phase E) and termination phase (Phase F).

The following definitions of the four basic mission operations functions are based on those by Kehr [2007]:

Spacecraft Operations/Launch Operations covers the preparation and implementation of all activities to operate a space vehicle (manned and unmanned) or launch vehicle under nominal, non-nominal and emergency conditions. This includes the specification, design, production and qualification of all means (tools, procedures, and trained personnel) to perform the task of spacecraft/launch operations. It also involves designing operability into the space segment. The main challenges in this area are the cost-efficient combination of tools, degree of automation (for both space and ground segments), and staffing to provide secure and reliable operations. A very prominent role is played by the mission database containing all pertinent spacecraft and ground operations data parameters to be maintained throughout the mission. It is initially created by the spacecraft designers and handed over to the operations personnel during Phases C–D to be augmented by the specific ground operations parameters.

Payload operations cover the preparation and implementation of all activities related to the payload,† which is generally the primary reason for the mission. Details of typical spacecraft payloads are covered in Chap. 15 and not repeated here. Payload operations differ from spacecraft operations in that unique mission-specific expertise may be required to make decisions with regard to tasking the payload and retrieving and interpreting its data. That being said, for small spacecraft and relatively simple payloads, the payload operations are often included as another subsystem within spacecraft operations. In this case, the spacecraft operations team may retrieve and distribute the payload data to clients directly, without the intervention of a dedicated payload operations team. Large spacecraft, on the other hand, often have complex

† Although the payload is usually contained within the spacecraft bus, sometimes it might be separate, such as a separable probe or inspector vehicle.

and independent payloads, such as science instruments, requiring particular mission-specific expertise and warrant having their operations treated separately from that of the spacecraft bus operations. These missions would have separate spacecraft and payload operations centers with separate, but coordinated, operations teams. Payload operations may also include dedicated receiving stations for payload data. It is also possible to have simple payloads that are operated independently of the hosting spacecraft for organizational reasons.

Ground operations covers the design, implementation, qualification, operations and management (including configuration management) of a mission-dedicated ground segment, including infrastructure components such as communications networks, antennas, control centers, simulation test beds, and databases. The main challenge in this area is the implementation and operations of high-quality, cost-efficient, and secure space-to-ground, space-to-space and ground-to-ground communications respecting a multitude of different standards and protocols across a suite of related but distinct hardware and software components. This also includes the procurement of new equipment which might turn out to be a major task if complex, new subsystems or systems have to be installed respecting internally/externally regulated procurement rules and interfaces.

Mission management covers all tasks for preparing and operating a particular mission. The main talent expected is an expert level of technical understanding of spacecraft and ground operations requirements resulting in the planning and execution of all defined activities within a given schedule and within the available budget. Managers also should have a good understanding of the organizational influences on spacecraft and ground operations to minimize risks of mishaps and accidents and the behavioral aspects of human error in the conduct of the mission operations. For cooperative international missions, managerial skills in dealing with international partners and agencies and intimate knowledge of the "culture" and policy of a particular organization or agency are considered to be mandatory.

Although mission operations uses hardware, software (both space and ground), and facilities (often collectively referred to as the *operations infrastructure*) to carry out its functions, this chapter will examine the operational aspects (e.g., techniques and methods, procedures, management, use of tools) and not the infrastructure, which is covered either under the chapters on the spacecraft bus subsystems (especially flight software) or the ground system.

Although this chapter deals primarily with the operations supporting unmanned missions, most of the principles and techniques discussed are valid for both manned and unmanned missions. Some differences between the two are mentioned in the text when they are of particular significance.

The misconception that mission operations is only what happens in the MOC and ground stations after launch has been an institutional misconception since the early years of the space age. Many space mission managers consider mission operations only late in the development cycle and sometimes do not get serious about it until approaching the launch date. After all, if the engineers could control the spacecraft during integration and testing, it must be even easier to control it during flight when all the bugs have been eliminated. However, operational failures occur during flight even to the point of mission failures. This points to a difference in philosophy between the spacecraft designers and the operators. The former, are required to demonstrate it will work, while the latter, needs to prove they can control it, should it fail. Many flight operations teams discovered after launch that the spacecraft was not designed to facilitate ease of operation or recover from failures, thus reducing efficiency and increasing their workloads with the resultant increase in recurring operations and maintenance costs. Sometimes the necessary operation tools had not been developed prior to launch and had to be developed afterwards.

Often, spacecraft design decisions impact significantly how operations are conducted. Project managers during spacecraft development quite often, for cost pressure reasons, will go with less operable design choices (saving a few millions of dollars or months of schedule) but these decisions can drive up the cost of operations (which is usually not their responsibility). It is sometimes better to have a slightly more expensive design that will allow for cheaper operations. This means looking at the total life cycle costs that include both the non-recurring development costs and the recurring costs (mostly operations).

To mitigate the problems caused by ignoring or minimizing consideration of mission operations until late in the development cycle, the discipline of mission or spacecraft *operations engineering* has become more widespread in recent years. It is now generally recognized that operations need to be closely involved with the conceptual and detailed design of the spacecraft as well as the ground systems [Ryan and Fatig, 1993].

Operations engineering is a part of systems engineering focused on incorporating operational experience, knowledge, and insight into the development process to manage life-cycle costs (LCC) and operability. The goals of operations engineering are to reduce the LCC throughout development, testing, and operations of a system and to improve system performance and operability. Operations engineering provides a systems level view of operations throughout the system life-cycle [Alcott and Peters, 1996].

Operations engineers participate during each phase of the development cycle, and help the spacecraft or ground system engineers to design a spacecraft and supporting system that facilitates ease of operation and failure management after launch. Operational and contingency modes are defined, and guidelines for commandability and observability of on-board systems are used. It is not good enough to make a spacecraft that works—it has to be easy to operate under nominal conditions so that the chance of human error is minimized. The more complex

Table 29-1. Operations Characteristics for Different Mission Types. These ratings are subjective. Ops responsiveness means how flexible and timely operations have to be to handle changing situations (but not anomalies). Mod = Moderate

Mission Type	Ops Complexity	Staffing Levels	Autonomy S: Space G: Ground	Acceptable Risk Level	Data Volume	Data Importance	Ops Responsiveness
Manned	Very High	High: 24/7	S: High G: Mod	Very Low	Mod to High	Mod to High	High
LEO Science/RS	Mod to High	Low to Mod	S: Mod to High G: Mod	Mod	Low to High	High	Mod to High
GEO Comm	Low	Low	S: Low G: High	Low to Mod	High (PL)	High	Low
Deep Space Probes	Low to High	Low to Mod	S: High G: Low to Mod	Low	Very Low to Moderate	High	Low to High
Landers/ rovers	Very High	Mod to High	S: Mod to High G: Mod to High	Low to Mod	Very Low to Mod	High	High
Small Sats	Low to Mod	Low	S: Low G: Low to High	High	Low to Mod	Low to High	Mod to High
Launch Vehicles	Low to Mod	High	S: Low to Mod G: High	Low to Mod	Low	High	High

or "time dense" the operating procedures required, the greater the chance of errors. Also, as autonomy is used more often in the spacecraft operational design and the MOC uses automated processes and procedures, the impact of these complex procedures can be minimized. As long as the operations are well-defined or characterized so that they can be automated, then human error is mitigated or significantly reduced (but not eliminated).

The mission operations paradigm is not a case of "one size fits all." There are substantial differences in the mission operations required for manned versus robotic missions, geostationary communication satellites versus science or remote sensing satellites, LEO satellites versus deep space probes, satellite constellations versus single satellites, large versus small satellites, and in their own unique categories, launch vehicles and planetary landers/rovers. Table 29-1 shows the typical operations characteristics of these various mission types.

Despite the wide range of vehicles and missions, there are still some functions that are common to all their mission operations. You have to communicate with the spacecraft (or payload), to monitor and analyze its condition and success in accomplishing its mission, and to send commands to it, whether in real-time or as time-delayed commands. To be able to accomplish this, there are many additional functions occurring behind the scenes to support the operations. The mission operations functions can be broadly separated into two categories: the discrete *operations functions*, and the *support functions* as shown in Fig. 29-1. This figure shows the eight functions that are common to most space missions. Although there are many opinions on what constitutes a function, the common functions identified in the following sections are in fundamental agreement with other operations functional descriptions [Wertz, 1999; Welch, 1996; Squibb et al., 2006]. To these can be added additional functions that are required by specialized missions. Three examples are shown in the figure: Launch Operations (which is sometimes considered separate from mission operations if it involves the actual control of the launch vehicle), Crew Operations for manned space flights, and Rover Operations for planetary rover missions. Other examples include rendezvous and docking operations, and entry/re-entry and landing operations.

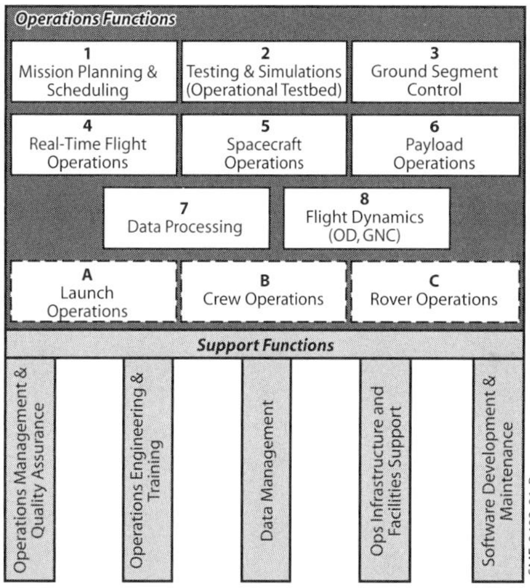

Fig. 29-1. Mission Operations Functions. There are eight typical mission operations functions, which perform distinct tasks during space missions. Although these functions are common to most missions they may be allocated together in some cases (e.g., 4–6), or alternatively, there may be other specialized functions (e.g., A–C) needed for some missions. These discrete operations functions are all supported by five major support functions, which are services typically provided to all of the operations functions.

The *Mission Planning and Scheduling (MPS)* function consists of the facilities, equipment, software, and personnel used to plan, schedule, and program the activities of the space and ground segments to ensure that the space mission and its objectives are met in the most efficient and effective way possible, given the budget and schedule constraints. The MPS function provides the master schedules for the spacecraft and ground network activities and deconflicts those schedules based on mission priorities, status of the spacecraft and ground network, and ground station availability. The MPS function generates the pass/contact plans that are passed to flight operations for configuring and performing real-time operations.† This function also creates the command loads for the spacecraft activities, although the command loads for payload activities may be provided to the MPS function by the payload customers, which is typical for many missions. The MPS function integrates the submitted payload command loads with the generated spacecraft command loads into a final command load set that may be verified using the Testing and Simulations function and then submitted to the Flight Operations function for upload to the spacecraft and subsequent execution. The MPS functions are normally performed in advance and not during real-time, although dynamic rescheduling and command load generation may be required, especially during checkout operations after launch. Due to the non-realtime nature of these functions, the MPS personnel can usually work regular work hours and are not required to work on shift.

The *Test and Simulations (T&S)* function consists of the facilities, equipment, software, and personnel used to support operations training and rehearsals, test command scripts before uplinking to the spacecraft, perform anomaly resolution, perform flight software maintenance, and test system modifications and enhancements. All of these tasks are done off-line so the personnel involved can usually work standard work hours, with the possible exception of mission simulations and rehearsals that may exercise operations teams over a day or days of typical or critical operations phases. The testing and simulations function often uses an *operational test bed (OTB)*, which integrates actual spacecraft or ground station hardware (e.g., brassboards, the flight segment engineering model) and flight software with environmental software models. The models may drive the space dynamics (trajectory and attitude) or thermal and power dynamics needed to run simulations, and often also include models of subsystems or components for which the hardware is not available. Software-only simulations are also common. Some programs have both (hardware-and-software test beds, and software-only simulation), others have one or the other. The decision of which to use depends on the availability and cost of hardware, number of instances required/desired (more instances typically drives towards a software-only solution), training requirements, acceptable levels of mission risk and technical considerations. The T&S function is used during spacecraft and ground system integration and test (I&T), and then operation rehearsals before and sometimes after launch. For this task, the T&S function typically interfaces with the MOC at command and telemetry frame or packet level, such that the T&S functions look like an actual spacecraft or ground station telemetry stream and responds to commands in some realistic or representative fashion. The hardware and software simulators can also be used after launch to test command loads prior to execution on board the spacecraft, especially for first-time activities. The T&S function is also used during flight to help with anomaly resolution and for flight software maintenance activities.

The *Ground Segment/Station Operations (GSO)* function consists of the facilities, equipment, software and personnel used to monitor and control the mission's ground network, including both the ground stations and the connecting communications network. The GSO function ensures that the ground segment assets can reliably support spacecraft passes, including tracking the spacecraft (antenna control) and collecting, transferring, and storing its data stream. The GSO function monitors (and as the situation requires and authority allows, modifies) the ground network contact schedule, and ensures that the network is properly configured in time to support each scheduled contact. As network anomalies occur, the GSO function is also responsible for real-time troubleshooting and implementing work around procedures to maximize the chances of contact success. Finally, the GSO function maintains a log of all activities for each contact and notifies maintenance or network engineering support function of system outages and problems that may require maintenance or repair. During nominal operations the GSO function may be authorized to configure, reconfigure or control the ground network. In these situations, other functions that are monitoring the network (e.g., real-time flight operations) may request configuration alterations. However, all these requests go through the GSO function, which may be solely responsible for implementing these changes. The GSO function is required whenever there are contacts with the spacecraft and is thus part of the real-time operations. Nearly all of the GSO functions supporting real-time operations can be automated, with human involvement only in monitoring the GSO performance and to intervene when certain anomalous situations occur. In many cases, the ground stations are also fully automated and do not even require real-time monitoring as long as they were configured beforehand to execute the pass. In environments with many concurrent mission operations activities, the GSO function is often shared between missions. While the ground segment configurations may be tied to a particular mission, the GSO *activities* are typically not mission specific.

† In Wertz [1999] the MPS function was broken up into two functions: *Mission Planning*, which was at a higher level more orientated to the payload (also performed the Ops Engineering support function), and *Activity Planning & Development*, which developed the activity plans and command loads/sequences. Either method is equally valid and is a matter of preference or experience.

The *Real-time Flight Operations (RTFO)* function consists of the facilities, equipment, software, and personnel that provide the real-time monitoring, command and control of the spacecraft in the MOC during ground contacts. This function monitors the spacecraft during the real-time contact, ensures that commands and uploads are successfully received and executed by the spacecraft, and that both state-of-health (SOH) and payload telemetry are downlinked as planned. This function is active during ground contacts with the spacecraft, and thus, is often a shift job if human monitoring and possible intervention is required or expected.† Recently, it has become common for smaller or less-complicated (e.g., communications satellite) missions to employ unmanned or "lights out" flight operations during routine spacecraft contacts. In these cases there is usually an automated SOH monitoring function that will alert operations personnel if an anomaly is detected.

The *Spacecraft Operations (SO)* function consists of the facilities, equipment, software and personnel that provide the engineering support for the spacecraft bus during the mission. The SO personnel are often either spacecraft engineers, or are members of the RTFO with support from spacecraft engineers that might only be on call or spend a small amount of their time in the SO function (for instance, if they are already working on developing the next mission). The SO personnel monitor and analyze the spacecraft SOH data contained in the downlinked telemetry to determine and ensure spacecraft safety and mission effectiveness. They use processed spacecraft SOH telemetry data and ground network data for analysis to detect any anomalous spacecraft subsystem or ground network performance, and to assess long-term trends. Trending analysis can help prevent malfunctions by noting and correcting potential problems before they reach a critical stage. The SO function also reports spacecraft status, and coordinates with spacecraft component manufacturers and integrators as required to solve anomalies. If the spacecraft requires some action to correct or maintain the welfare of its systems, or to optimize performance, the SO function may provide the data to the Payload Operations functions for them to assist in the determination of the action required. The SO function may also have partial responsibility for monitoring the health and status of the payload (if this is not done by the payload customer). The SO personnel form the core of the anomaly resolution team, and help the MPS function by specifying tasks required by the spacecraft bus. They are also available to monitor testing of any command loads if required. One of the tasks of the SO function is to generate regular status reports on the health and condition of the spacecraft, and possibly update such data on a website.

† In some operations centers, the RTFO may include the pre-contact (e.g., ground station preparation) and post-contact activities (e.g., console log reports), in others only activities actually occurring during the contact come under RTFO while all other related functions come under Spacecraft Operations (SO).

The *Payload Operations (PO)* function consists of the facilities, equipment, software, and personnel used to monitor and maintain the health and welfare of the payload instruments (or other equipment), to monitor the performance of the instruments, and sometimes any ground data processing and ground-based data quality measurements, in accomplishing the mission objectives. It may make changes in the payload and payload processing configuration as required. The PO function interacts directly with the MPS function to schedule and provide commanding and uploading of control data (e.g., calibration tables). The PO function also interacts closely with the SO function to help ensure the performance of the payload is within specifications. Depending on the nature of the observations, and the maturity and stability of the payload system, this function may or may not require participation in the RTFO, and thus possibly use shift work to match the contacts schedule. However, most of the PO function is usually non-shift work. In some cases, much of this function can be automated or may be combined with the SO function as mentioned earlier.

The *Flight Dynamics (FD)* function consists of the facilities, equipment, software, and personnel used to determine and predict the spacecraft's orbit and position in space, and also to determine or calculate its orientation (this function is sometimes done on board the spacecraft). After determining the orbit of the spacecraft using tracking data received from the ground stations (or other means), the FD function produces an ephemeris or state vector and distributes it to the rest of the operations team as required. If the spacecraft has a propulsion system, then the FD function plans and analyzes trajectory maneuvers. This includes deorbit maneuvers at the end of life, determining relative position of more than one space asset, and for rendezvous or constellation operations activities. Attitude maneuvers are also often planned and tested by the FD function. A growing task for FD deals with space debris conjunction analysis and avoidance. The FD function needs to compute likely conjunctions with other spacecraft or debris and determine trajectories/burns to ensure sufficient separation between spacecraft and debris while minimizing mission perturbation. Flight dynamics is usually a non-realtime operation, so the FD staff will generally be able to work regular work hours except possibly during maneuver execution activities.

For some projects, most of the SO, PO, and FD functions may all be combined together under a single "Mission Analysis" function, but these have been broken separately in this discussion to show how each of these three functions can be distributed yet complement each other.

The *Data Processing (DP)* function consists of the facilities, equipment, software, and personnel used to accept the flow of data (spacecraft telemetry or ground network status) received at the MOC or some other data processing facility, such as the SOC, process it to a usable or specified form (if required), archive the data, and dis-

Table 29-2. Description of Science Data Levels. These levels are used mostly for processing imaging and science data. Although they come from NASA, they are now internationally recognized.

NASA Level	Description
Packet Data	Telemetry data stream as received at the ground station with science and engineering data embedded.
Level 0	Instrument science data (e.g., raw voltages, counts) at full resolution, time ordered, with duplicates and transmission errors removed.
Level 1A	Level 0 data that have been located in space and may have been transformed (e.g., calibrated, rearranged) in a reversible manner and packaged with needed ancillary and auxiliary data (e.g., radiances with the calibration equations applied). Also referred to as Experimental Data Records (EDRs).
Level 1B	Irreversibly transformed (e.g., resampled, remapped, calibrated) values of the instrument measurements (e.g., radiances, magnetic field strength). Also referred to as Calibrated Data Records (CDRs).
Level 1C	Level 1A or 1B data that have been resampled and mapped onto uniform space-time grids. The data are calibrated (i.e., radiometrically corrected) and may have additional corrections applied (e.g., terrain correction).
Level 2	Geophysical parameters, generally derived from Level 1 data, and located in space and time commensurate with instrument location, pointing, and sampling.
Level 3	Geophysical parameters mapped onto uniform space-time grids.

tribute the data to the next function in the process. For the low-rate SOH data, the DP function typically converts the telemetry into engineering units that can be displayed by the real-time system or delivered to the engineering trending and analysis function (although with increased computing power on board the spacecraft, this function is sometimes done before the telemetry is downlinked). For the high-rate payload data, the DP function can perform pre-processing, typically to Level 0 (see Table 29-2) and deliver the data to the payload customer for further processing and analysis. The data processing function is not the same as data management, that is part of the support functions,† although in some architectures it can be part of the data management function (thus becoming the Data Processing and Management function). The DP function performs specific tasks in accepting, modifying, and outputting telemetry data. The data management function facilitates the transfer and manipulation of all data between the other functions and provides the master storage or archives used by the whole system. The DP function can be almost entirely automated, including the collection and reporting of data processing metrics, with alerts sent for anomalous conditions, although interpretation and use of the data usually requires domain expert involvement.

The *Launch Operations (LO)* function consists of the facilities, equipment, software and personnel that provide the engineering support for testing the spacecraft and ground network during pre-launch and post-launch tests and activities. It can also be defined to include the actual monitoring and control of the launch system itself, which generally uses a separate Launch (Operations) Team. Although this is a discrete function performed by the operations team for most missions, it is classified here as a specialized function because it is only performed for a limited time at the start of the mission and is not an ongoing function throughout the mission. In some operations plan, this is just a specialized phase of the operations for the other functions (such as SO, PO, DP) and not a separate function. If this is treated as a separate function, then it usually has limited automation and is performed by the operations personnel as required.

† Telemetry and payload data processing functions may be separated, depending on the division of responsibilities between the spacecraft and payload operations groups.

The following are the support functions, which provide their services to support the previous operations functions. They provide the five pillars of support for mission operations as shown in Fig. 29-1.

The *Operations Management & Quality Assurance (OM&QA)* function consists of the facilities, equipment, software and personnel used to provide overall management of the mission operations functions. The OM&QA function ensures that both the entire system and the individual subsystems are operating within specifications and are helping to accomplish the mission goals. Included in the system management function may be any hardware and software used to monitor and optimize the performance of the various interfaces between the MOC subsystems. The quality assurance function gathers performance metrics from key points within the system and the operational process, processes the metrics, analyzes the resulting data, and assesses mission risk. The results of the analyses are included in reports to the mission management, but recommendations for process improvement can also be a product of this function. The OM&QA functions can be highly automated with little human oversight or intervention, other than to implement process changes and make administrative decisions.

The *Operations Engineering & Training (OE)* function consists of the facilities, equipment, software and personnel used to perform the operations engineering functions for the mission such as procedure development, validation, activity plan development, and training of personnel.‡ Prior to launch this is the function that is mainly responsible for preparing operations for the mission. After launch, operations engineering maintains and improves the spacecraft performance, and continues to develop operations procedures as needed to support changes in the mission. In this operational phase, the OE function is sometimes known as the Maintenance and Sustaining Engineering function. This function also has the expertise to develop additional ground segment capabilities in response to the evolving payload requirements and manage ground segment obsolescence issues for long-term mission activities. Should a major upgrade be needed, the operations engineering function performs an analysis to determine the most cost-effective approach for the upgrade. The OE function also generates reliability, maintainability, and availability (RMA) statistics on the primary operational applications, and investigates process improvement potential of other software solutions.

The *Data Management (DM)* function, includes the data management server and the data archive. The DM function is not the same as the Data Processing function described earlier, although it supports that function. The DM function does not simply deal with spacecraft or ground network telemetry (SOH and payload data)—it also includes mission plans, command and communication histories, and records of communication between the mission team and the customers. It provides the data interfaces between the various functional elements of the operations system and handles the distribution and manipulation of the data. The DM function allows easy access to all mission data as well as any additional information about the origin, history, and use of the data. The customer interface may be as simple as a website where the payload SOH data, reports and communications from the mission team are made available to the customer. An interface tool (or website) may include a function for communication from the customer to the mission team; this includes requests (formal and informal) and constraints.

The *Operations Infrastructure and Facilities Support (OIFS)* function consists of the facilities, equipment, software and personnel used to monitor, control, and maintain the MOC Local Area Networks (LANs), ground network including ground stations, and the computers and processing equipment used to support mission operations, as well as, the physical facilities. This includes the communication interfaces with external elements including the Internet, any security, and information assurance constraints (e.g., firewalls) required to ensure the integrity of the MOC system. The OIFS function monitors the performance of the LANs and external communications networks, and makes adjustments to maintain data flow within the operational specifications. The OIFS function typically coordinates all vendor maintenance activities, and maintains the inventory of all applications and their licenses. Monitoring and routine operation of the OIFS function is often automated and does not require human intervention. However, after the acceptance test phase, the mission management usually maintains a staff to provide sustaining engineering and on-call maintenance of the system hardware and software and to make enhancements as necessary.

The *Software Development and Maintenance (SDM)* function consists of the facilities, equipment, software and personnel used to develop and maintain the software used by mission operations, whether writing new applications for the mission, or integrating commercial off-the-shelf (COTS), government off-the-shelf (GOTS), or legacy software into the system. The SDM function is responsible for the underlying software infrastructure that: (1) provides an open and accessible set of building blocks for software relating to spacecraft construction and operations; and (2) supports the higher level aspects of spacecraft construction and operations specific to the mission operations system itself. To accomplish this, the SDM function is usually an integrated system of software components, protocol definitions, and code management procedures. The SDM software usually includes a suite of functional libraries, on top of which are built various software engines and user commands. These can then be assembled, along with off-the-shelf or legacy components, to make various processes and graphical tools. The SDM function software development can also work on optimizing existing algorithms, and developing new algorithms. It also provides the procedures and protocols to ensure quality assurance and software uniformity and compatibility throughout the mission operations system. Once the operations software has been deployed and operational, the SDM function is responsible for maintaining and upgrading it as needed. It can also provide support for the flight software development and testing.

‡ In some organizations the Operations Engineering function is an umbrella function that contains the SO, PO, and GSO functions, each of which performs the tasks of OE described here for their own area of responsibility.

29.1 Mission Planning and Operations Development

Mission operations development nominally covers the period from mission concept until launch and the completion of the launch and early operations phase, although in practice, operations development continues throughout the mission. During the operations development phase, the mission operations development team (MDT) consists of the personnel from the operations engineering or various functions described earlier (SO, PO, GSO) and is partly or fully responsible for the following:

- Operations concept and plans
- Space segment operability specification
- Mission operations architecture definition, operations requirements definition and assignment to architecture elements
- Staff planning (numbers, roles, training requirements)
- Operational tools/facility development
- Operational procedures development

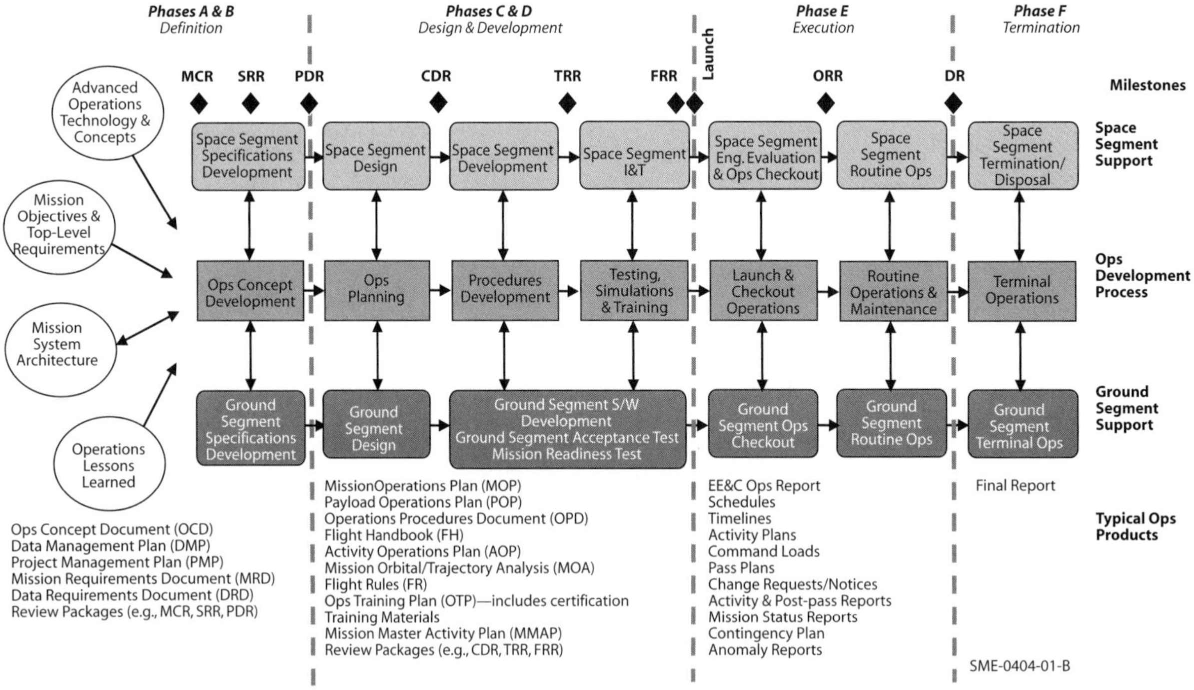

Fig. 29-2. Mission Operations Life Cycle. Mission Operations is an important part of the life cycle of any space mission. Inputs from various sources are integrated into an operations concept during the Definition Phase, then the design and implementation is completed during the Development Phase and is used to conduct the mission during the Execution Phase. The Termination Phase incorporates the mission-ending activities. This figure shows the interaction between mission operations and the space and ground segments. Also shown are the typical mission milestones and operations products during each phase.

- Spacecraft and ground system knowledge (understanding) capture
- Training of all operations personnel for launch and on-orbit operations
- Development of command procedures and telemetry displays
- Validation of mission database content (collectively operations products)
- Verification and validation of developed procedures and displays
- Validation of ground system capabilities to support the mission
- Support of appropriate ground system and spacecraft tests (hardware and software)
- Support of all mission and system operations reviews

Key phases of the mission operations development process and how these relate to project/mission phases is shown in Fig. 29-2. The four pre-launch operations phases (middle row) are: (1) concept development; (2) operations planning, (3) procedures development, and (4) operations test, simulation, and training. The three post-launch operations phases are: (1) launch and checkout; (2) routine operations and maintenance; and (3) terminal operations.

The operational procedures and processes are tested, modified and supplemented as a result of actual operational experience during the Testing, Simulations and Training sub-phase. At the end of the Launch and Checkout Operations sub-phase (also known as Launch and Early Orbit—L&EO, or Engineering Evaluation and Checkout—EE&C), the operations development is considered complete and nominal routine operations started. The transition point into nominal operations is typically called the Initial Operational Capability (IOC).† However, operations development activities may continue, in order to optimize operational processes and procedures, develop or augment automation of the processes, to meet new or evolving mission needs including extended mission operations, apply lessons learned, and deal with failures or anomalies.

Mission development includes processes for influencing the spacecraft and payload development. This includes participating in space segment, ground segment, and operations trade studies early, providing inputs to requirements documents, and making recommendations

† For constellation ops, this can have a different meaning. For some constellations, mission objectives only starts to be achieved after a few assets (satellites) are deployed, at which point IOC is declared. Nominal operations on the first asset may have started some time previously, requiring other assets achieving nominal operations to achieve the constellation IOC.

regarding designs, especially with regard to operability (typically decomposed into commandability, observability, and autonomy). To ensure that the operations are efficient and cost-effective, it is important that the engineers from the operations team participate with the spacecraft and instrument development engineers throughout the life cycle, and especially to be active participants in the integration and test process. This will ensure knowledge capture for the operations team and also help the development of procedures that will enhance the operability of the spacecraft and ground system. This is a fundamental application of operations engineering discussed earlier. During this phase, processes and databases can be developed that will help with automating operations.

Another approach commonly used is a red-team review with external experienced reviewers, where the new team develops its concepts, approaches, and procedures, but pulls in agency, industry, and other experts, under suitable non-disclosure agreements and for a cost, to evaluate the team and its approach. With a new organization, such a red team can participate at gates throughout the process development. Often, agencies are ready to support such activities for cost-reimbursement only.

Mission operations prelaunch support is subdivided into the two basic processes that revolve around the two major system elements: the space segment and the ground segment. In general, during operations preparation, the spacecraft integrators have the critical role of preparing the space segment while the mission operations personnel act as subordinates to support these activities in their efforts to learn how to operate each subsystem. Conversely, it is the mission operations personnel who have the critical role in preparing the ground segment for the mission and the spacecraft integrators who are more peripheral. They provide the space segment components of the mission database (typically comprising such information as command, telemetry, and parameter definitions including parameter calibration information, space segment reference frames, mass, inertias, and sensor and actuator alignments), and they usually are a user of this system during mission rehearsals and early mission support (so there is a benefit to their knowledge and understanding of the ground segment). Spacecraft integrators also potentially deal with software updates or hardware troubleshooting on an as-needed basis. It may be an appropriate management strategy to ensure that the spacecraft/payload integration team members are provided roles to play during the routine operations phase, providing them the necessary expertise in an emergency situation. The size and tasking for this "standing army" should be considered against mission complexity, planned lifetime, cost, and risk tolerance at the mission management level. Similarly, during the mission definition and development phases of a project, the foundation for effective and efficient routine operations (the ultimate goal) may be laid by maximizing the OE team's exposure to the spacecraft and all its subtleties at the earliest opportunity. It is crucial that the OE team is formed with ready accessibility to the development facilities, personnel and processes starting no later than the space segment Preliminary Design Review. As the development of the mission transitions into the I&T phase, this OE team may increase its participation so that each position identified for ultimate inclusion in the post launch operations team has a chance to participate and fulfill their training requirements. During preparation, these operations personnel are often subordinate or observers to the space segment integrators and engineers while shadowing their activities and absorbing their expertise. Ultimately, the OE team will support spacecraft integration and test, procedure development, real-time team training and readiness activities as they ready themselves to be the primary operators of the spacecraft following launch and early orbit checkout. Note that in small organizations and missions, it may be that the integration team eventually becomes the *Mission Operations Team* (MOT), absorbing the spacecraft expertise by default. However, the core principle of considering operations from the start of the project, as illustrated in Fig. 29-2—should remain the same regardless. **Much frustration and disappointment can be avoided—and mission success better assured—if the team has experienced operations personnel involved from the beginning of the project.**

As shown in Fig. 29-2, mission operations typically develop various documentation products during each phase of the mission. Some of the more common products are listed in Table 29-3 along with their definitions. Although most of these documents are under the ownership of mission operations, some important products are listed which have operations as a contributor rather than the owner (e.g., Mission Requirements Document, Project Management Plan, Risk and Configuration Management Plans, review packages). It should be emphasized that large and complex missions will usually have many more documentation products than those shown, while for small, low-cost missions, several of the products shown can be eliminated or combined.

The milestones shown in Fig. 29-2 are some of the more common ones used in most space projects and are based on the NASA and European Cooperation for Space Standardization (ECSS) conventions. Phases A & B are the Mission Concept Review (MCR) and System Requirements Review (SRR). The transition between Phase B and Phase C is the Preliminary Design Review (PDR), which can be considered as either the end of Phase B or the beginning of Phase C. The transition from Phase C to Phase D is the Critical Design Review (CDR). A Test Readiness Review (TRR) is held during Phase D to ensure that the project is ready to enter the system integration and testing.

Once the testing is completed, a final Flight Readiness Review (or Mission Readiness Review, Pre-Shipment Review, or Launch Review) is held before launch. At the end of the checkout period of launch an Operations Readiness Review (ORR) or Commissioning Review (CR) is

Table 29-3. Typical Documentation Products for Mission Operations.

Document Title	Description
Phases A & B (Definition)	
Mission Requirements Document (MRD)	The mission operations top-level requirements and constraints, and the derived requirement (with traceability) are listed as a section in this document.
Operations Concept Document (OCD)	Provides a high level description of how the mission will be operated to support and accomplish the mission objectives. It includes operations in both space and ground segments.
Project Management Plan (PMP) ***Project Implementation Plan (PIP)***	Ops provides an important section in these documents that are used by the project management to describe the project and how it will be managed. Some projects incorporate the PIP into the PMP. These documents also cover procurement procedures for hardware and software. If not included in the PMP/PIP, a post-launch Phase E/F Management Plan should be developed.
Configuration Management Plan (CMP)	This document provides the plan for managing the configuration of the project software, hardware, databases, and operations staff, and procedures.
Risk Management Plan (RMP)	The RMP focuses on identifying, assessing, planning for, and dealing with areas or events having a potential for causing unwanted results (i.e., risks). This may be included in the PMP.
Data Requirements Document (DRD)	Document describes the requirements of the data collection, processing, and distribution. For simple missions (from a data standpoint) this may be incorporated into the MRD.
Mission Software Plan (MSP)	Describes the design process, including staffing, schedule, and tasking, to develop and test the flight and ground software needed to accomplish the mission
Documentation Plan (DP)	A plan for the creation of the project documentation. The plan helps to ensure that this documentation is planned early in the project, all work involved in creating the documentation is identified, and ownership of both technical writing and development team input tasks is established. The DP includes a list and description of all the project documentation and provides an identification nomenclature and ownership of each document.
Project Review Packages	Ops presentation materials given at project reviews such as the MCR, SRR, and PDR (which is the transition between Phases B & C).
Phases C & D (Design and Development)	
Mission Operations Plan (MOP)	Addresses in detail how the mission operations will be developed, tested, and then used to conduct the mission including routine, L&EO, and contingency support operations. It includes a system description, operations overview (mission ops, ground ops), ops staffing & training, technology development plan, phase ops (prelaunch, on-orbit, mission planning & scheduling, pass execution, analysis & reporting, anomaly resolution), and data management. Includes ops management and improvement process.
Data Management Plan (DMP)	Document describes the design, process, and procedures to handle data (including SOH and payload) within the system, with emphasis on data received from the satellite and ground network.
Payload Operations Plan (POP)	This document is similar in scope to the MOP, but addresses the payload and payload data. It may be produced by the payload customer or may be incorporated into the MOP depending on the mission.
Operations Procedures Document (OPD)	Captures the operations procedures required to support (1) launch operations; and (2) mission operations. Contains the specific procedures to be followed for different activities, such as rebooting computers (flight or ground), anomaly identification and resolution.
Flight Operations Handbook (FOH)	Provides a general reference for operations personnel that summarizes the space and ground systems including schematics and specifications; mission timeline summary; standard and contingency operations definitions; contact lists; and other useful information as needed.
Activity Operations Plan (AOP)	Provides a detailed plan for specific planned mission activities (usually payload related) such as an experiment, systematic mapping, observation of a target event, flyby observation of a target, or deployment of a payload. The AOP provides background, analyses, timelines, instrument settings, procedures, data management plans.
Mission Orbital/Trajectory Analysis (MOA or MTA)	Provides orbital and/or trajectory analyses for the mission, including predictions of orbit changes, lifetime, altitude maintenance requirements, maneuver specifications, and lighting analysis.
Flight Rules (FR)	Lists the rules to be followed by the mission managers for various nominal and off-nominal conditions that could be encountered during the mission. Provides conditions under which the mission or activities should be aborted or modified. For small missions, the FR is not a separate documents but is usually incorporated in the FOH.
Technology Development Plan (TDP)	Describes the methods planned to develop the technology needed to complete the mission.
Operations Staffing and Training Plan (OSTP)	Describes the plan to staff, train and certify mission operators to support the mission. May be included in the MOP.

Table 29-3. Typical Documentation Products for Mission Operations. (Continued)

Document Title	Description
Contingency Plan (CP)	Describes the contingencies for which recovery operations have been designed and developed (such as safehold recovery, how to swap redundant units, how to implement workaround procedures to bypass failures.)
Mission Master Activity Plan (MMAP)	Describes all the major discrete spacecraft and payload activities that are expected to occur during the mission and a timeline of when they are planned to occur, or windows of when they could be scheduled. Each activity has information concerning its goals, the responsible person (e.g., PI), any special power, communication, or other requirements or constraints to aid the mission planners.
Training Materials	Any handbooks, workbooks, or presentations used to train the ops team. Development and updating of these materials can continue into Phase E.
Project Review Packages	Ops presentation materials given at the CDR (which is the transition between Phases C & D) and other reviews such as the TRR and FRR.
	Phase E (Execution)
EE&C Ops Report	Documents the performance of the spacecraft and supporting systems during the engineering evaluation and checkout period after launch.
Schedules	Long-term and short-term schedules to show upcoming events for the mission including communication passes with ground stations.
Timelines	Show the spacecraft and/or ground station activities as a function of time (typically one orbit or one day depending on mission). Often shows other information such as orbit position or lighting condition (umbra periods).
Activity [Operations] Plans (AP or AOP)	Detailed descriptions of planned events and activities for the spacecraft with information concerning resources required, tasking, timelines, commands, data handling, and instrument settings.
Command Loads	The actual command sequence uploaded to the spacecraft for execution. These are traditionally time-delayed commands that are triggered by specified execution times.
Pass Plans (PP)	Lists the communication pass objectives coupled with specific files, keystrokes, and verifications that the operator (or system) must complete within the pass. May take the form of electronic files, paper printouts, and/or handwritten directives.
Change Requests (CR) Change Notices (CN)	A formal record of the operational procedure changes maintained by each flight controller. All CRs & CNs will be stored in a database and used to tracking the evolution of mission operations and to capture lessons learned.
Activity Reports (AR)	Reports the results of mission activities (such as payload experiments/observations). This is usually an engineering report rather than a science report, i.e., does not analyze the results of the experiment, just the ability to execute it.
Post-Pass Reports (PPR)	Describes what happened during a communication pass including listing any files transferred, S/C or GS anomalies detected, time of AOS and LOS.
Mission Status Reports (MSR)	Periodic (usually daily) reports on the status of the mission, including spacecraft bus, payload, and ground network SOH, activities and results, anomalies, and progress towards meeting objectives.
Anomaly Reports (AR)	The written explanation that follows an anomaly investigation detailing how and why an anomaly occurred, and the plan adopted to resolve or minimize the effects of the anomaly.
	Phase F (Termination)
End-of-Mission/ Decommissioning Plan	Describes the plan and procedures to terminate the mission.
Final Report	Final comprehensive report on the mission and its operations prepared for the customer or for the historic record.

held to ensure that the mission system (space segment, ground segment, customers) are ready for routine or primary operations. At the end of the life of the mission, if the spacecraft has to be actively terminated (decommissioned), a Decommission Readiness Review may be held.

Developing the Mission Operations Plan

The Mission Operations Plan (MOP) is the defining document for mission operations development, which describes what mission operations will entail, what are its objectives, how it will be accomplished, and lays out a detailed plan for the development, testing, and application of mission operations. The MOP describes, in operator and user terms, the operational attributes of the flight and ground-based elements of the mission. However, the MOP is not just for the mission operators and users. It is used by the mission management and organization as a tool to understand and thus effect changes in mission operations or other aspects of the mission.

Although Fig. 29-2 shows the MOP as being a product of the Development Phase (Phases C & D), it really begins with the development of the Operations Concept Document (OCD), the data and software plans, and the

Table 29-4. Process for Developing a Mission Operations Plan. These steps are summarized in the text and explained in more detail on the book website.

Step	Notes

1. Identify top-level requirements and constraints that affect mission operations, ops lessons learned, and advanced technologies & techniques for operations	• Determine constraints (e.g., cost, schedule, teaming)
	• Ops requirements come from various mission areas:
	  • Orbit
	  • Communications
	  • Payload (including data latency and tolerance for data losses)
	  • Ground network

2. Develop mission operations concept and supporting architecture	• May have multiple mission ops concepts during Phase A or basic changes in concept during Phase B
3. Develop ops scenarios and techniques that accomplish mission concept	• For each scenario develop sample timelines to ensure feasibility of scenario
4. Determine ops functional activities required in Step 3, allocate to functional areas, and develop functional flow block diagram	• To satisfy mission concept identified in Step 2 • Basic functional areas are: Mission Planning and Analysis, Real-time Operations (Contact Execution), Data Management, Trending and Analysis
5. Identify ways to implement functions identified in Step 4	• Assesses state-of-the art and legacy solutions that are available with reference to previous similar missions
6. Determine level of automation for both space and ground segments	• Determine how much of the processing and control will be done autonomously on the spacecraft, how much at the ground stations, and how much in the MOC • Determine if the MOC and ground station functions can be automated or require personnel, given the mission cost and schedule constraints
7. Determine whether capabilities identified in Step 5 and 6 exist, are obtainable or must be developed.	• Are these resources attainable or do they need to be developed?
8. Develop staffing plan and identify other resources required	• Determine the operations and support organization including roles (positions) required and level of experience needed • Determine if shifts are needed and work out the shift plan • Determine number of personnel required to support operations (MOC and ground segment) • Determine the staffing profile (rate at which personnel are brought on-board) • Determine what hardware and software resources are required
9. Perform trades to determine best solution from Steps 5–8	• Compares availability, performance, and cost (non-recurring and recurring) of various options identified

10. Determine the operations Work Breakdown Structure (WBS) and ROM mission operations cost	• This is an important element in determining the viability of the current mission concept. Cost is typically based on:
	  • WBS
	  • Staffing requirements
	  • Hardware & software procurement
	  • Hardware & software development
	  • Facility/infrastructure development or sustainment for existing facilities

11. Repeat steps 4–10 for development phase (Mission Phases A–D as appropriate)	• If the initial Phase E analysis was just completed, then the developmental phases also need to be analyzed
12. Assess mission utility, complexity, risk, and cost drivers	• This is to help select the best mission concept for the baseline by determining which best meets the mission objectives
13. Repeat for alternate mission concepts (starting with Step 2) if required	• This is skipped if the baseline mission concept has been selected
14. Identify derived requirements	• This is done to the selected baseline mission operations concept
15. Develop training plan	• Plan to train and certify flight ops personnel and rehearsal plan
16. Generate MOP that includes technology development plan, personnel staffing and training plan, and documentation plan	• MOP includes the processes governing operations development and validation. • Technology development plan identifies the ground segment components that need to be developed, such as databases, or planning software. • Personnel staffing and training plan identifies the positions anticipated during operations and the certification plan for those positions. • Documentation plan identifies the documents that are needed (e.g., Flight Handbook) and how to develop them
17. Document and iterate/refine as needed	• Publish the MOP and revisions as needed

Mission Requirements Document development in the Definition Phase (Phases A & B). The MOP is built upon the foundation formed by these earlier documents (see Table 29-3 for a more detailed description of these documents). Table 29-4 outlines a 17-step process to develop the MOP starting with the top-level requirements and the OCD. This is an expanded and modified version of the methodology that was presented in [Wertz, 1999]. Note that the development of the MOP is an iterative process. The plan will necessarily be modified as the project matures and the nature of the space and ground elements is better understood, and thus how to operate them to best fulfill the mission objectives.

Step 1. Identify Top-Level Requirements and Constraints that Affect Mission Operations, Ops Lessons Learned, and Advanced Technologies & Techniques for Operations

This first step is required to formulate the operations concept (Step 2). A new mission initially starts with a mission statement that defines the purpose of the mission. This statement is then parsed into achievable primary and secondary objectives. The mission objectives define what the mission elements (such as spacecraft, crew, ground segment, and payload users) must do to successfully accomplish the mission. After the objectives have been defined, they are normally assigned success criteria to provide a means to measure the relative success of the mission. (See Sec. 5.4.) These success criteria help in the overall mission design to identify levels for which the system can be designed to achieve steps of partial success on the way to full mission success.

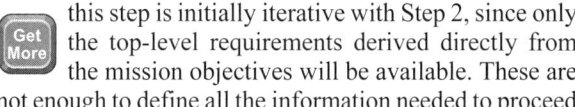

The mission objectives lead to an initial mission concept or description that presents in broad terms an overview of the mission, including some aspects as trajectory profile, launch windows, payload type, mission phases and duration. The mission definition process then determines the top-level requirements and constraints (see Chap. 14) to help define the mission so that its objectives can be achieved within the project constraints. Note that this step is initially iterative with Step 2, since only the top-level requirements derived directly from the mission objectives will be available. These are not enough to define all the information needed to proceed on to Step 3—first you have to have a mission concept to determine the top-level requirements within the various system and subsystem areas. There will be various mission concepts considered, and these may have different requirements and constraints on the system. When information is not available, you have to make assumptions until the development matures to a level where the assumptions can be replaced with actual information.

Step 2. Develop Mission Operations Concept and Supporting Architecture

One of the most important documents developed during the Definition Phases is the Operations Concept Document (OCD). The OCD is the documentation product that describes how the mission will be executed to accomplish its objectives, and attempts to define the required software, interfaces, timelines, procedures, and various spacecraft modes. The ops concept usually covers the operations of both the space and ground segments, and looks at operational scenarios. The resultant OCD is important in helping to define the mission system architecture and also the requirements for the various system elements and subsystems.

As shown in Fig. 29-2, there are several external inputs that contribute to the development of the ops concept. These include the mission objectives, and top-level requirements and constraints that were determined in Step 1. Another important factor in the development of the ops concept is the mission architecture. The development of the system architecture is usually iterative with the ops concept—an ops concept is needed to develop an architecture, and the architecture defines many of the elements described in the ops concept.

One problem with current practices in mission operations is the lack of common standards. Various organizations, such as AIAA, IEEE, SAE, CCSDS, and ECSS, have and are attempting to set standards for space missions, but it is difficult to come to an agreement and to implement changes in legacy systems. When the ops concept is defined, some decisions in standards, especially with interface formats, will have to be made. However, most of the decisions on standards can wait until the development of the Mission Operations Plan.

Step 3. Develop Operations Scenarios and Techniques that Accomplish the Mission Concept

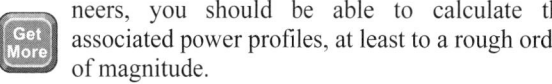

Once you have developed the general concept for the mission operations, you need to flesh it out and test it, both to check its feasibility, and to help determine the elements and tasks that are needed to support it. The best way to do this is to put together some operational scenarios that represent various events or phases in the mission, such as deployment, nominal payload data takes or events, communication contacts, eclipse periods. Early in the development cycle you may not be able to determine a precise power profile to support the scenario, but you should be able to determine the sequence of major events to support the scenario. With the help of the power engineers, you should be able to calculate the associated power profiles, at least to a rough order of magnitude.

Step 4. Determine Ops Functional Activities Required in Step 3, Allocate to Functional Areas, and Develop the Functional Flow Block Diagram

When you have finished Step 3 you should have a good understanding of what mission operations will entail and which tasks or functions are required to fulfill the mission. You can now list the specific tasks or functions that need to be performed during the execution of the mission. Each function identified should have data input and data output and perform a specific function in a process flow. Once you have listed the functions, you can now produce one of the most important products in the design process to understand what needs to happen to accomplish the oper-

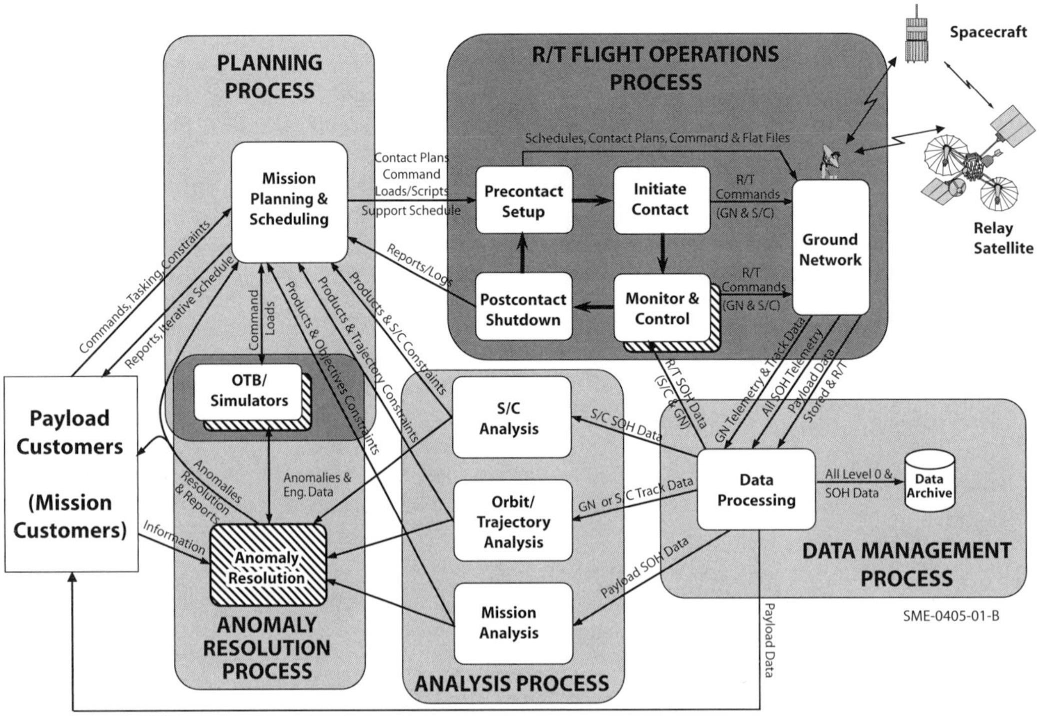

Fig. 29-3. Mission Operations Functional Flow Block Diagram. Operations performed during a space mission usually consist of the following basic processes performed on a cyclic basis: Planning, Real-Time Flight Operations, Data (Processing &) Management, Analysis, and Anomaly Resolution. The actual processes used by a particular mission may vary from this model, but usually the same functions are performed. Some specialized missions (e.g., manned or surface ops) may add additional processes.

ations—the Mission Operations Functional Flow Block Diagram (FFBD) or the Functional Block Diagram (FBD). The FFBD shows the functions in the operations process and the flow of process or data between them. The FBD is often the same as the FFBD, although it sometimes just shows connections between the functions without identifying the data flows between them. An example of a typical FFBD showing the execution of the operations cycle for a space mission is in Fig. 29-3.

This FFBD shows the major functional areas in the operations process (Planning Process, Real-time Flight Ops Process, Data Management Process, Analysis Process, and Anomaly Resolution Process) and the major functions within each of these processes. The arrows show the flow between the functions and are labeled to show the nature of the data. The FFBD provides a visual way to understand what happens during operation of a spacecraft and thus, what you need to include in your design. Note that the example given in the figure is typical of operations for small autonomous satellites in Earth orbit and are basic functions required by almost any space mission. However, when you have a more complicated mission or a mission of a different type, such as manned missions, or deep space missions, the operations process may differ. Communications satellites in geosynchronous orbits also have a more steady state operational process rather than the cyclic process shown. We will be looking at the operations functions in this process in more detail in the next section.

Step 5. Identify Ways to Implement Functions Required in Step 4

If you have worked in mission operations previously, then you have a head start in accomplishing this step. In that case you will probably start with your previous operations system and then determine where changes need to be made due to the nature of the mission, or where improvements can be made based on lessons learned or advances in technology (identified in Steps 1 and 3).

However, we will assume that this is your first time developing mission operations. Each of the operations functions identified in Step 4 is different and requires different methods and tools to accomplish. It is helpful to set up a spreadsheet table that lists the major processes with their associated functions listed in the leftmost column, and then place existing tools (generally software) listed across the top. These tools are mostly COTS applications (products) that are sold by many vendors or available from various government agencies. You can identify the candidates to occupy this trade space by using web searches, looking at advertisements in trade periodicals, review recent technical papers from conferences (where many of these applications or tools are presented), visiting exhibitor booths at the major conferences (see the list in Step 2), and contacting NASA or other government agencies that operate spacecraft (they are generally happy to share technical information and sometimes can even provide legacy systems or modules).†

Table 29-5. Definitions of Autonomy Levels. Table (a) shows the basic levels of autonomy for space segment health management, while (b) shows the basic levels of autonomy for mission execution. These are based on the ECSS standards regarding space segment autonomy, but are fairly standard globally.

(a) Space Segment Health Maintenance Autonomy Levels

Level	Description	Functions
1	**Closed-loop:** Pre-planned automatic response to detection of a particular state or condition that does not require ground input	For example, thermal control (automatic powering of heaters when temperature drops) Includes actions that can help prevent potential anomalies that would require safing of spacecraft (e.g., power management to prevent critical power condition)
2	**Closed-loop/Open-loop:** Establish safe space segment configuration following an on-board failure and wait for ground response	Identify anomalies and report to ground segment Reconfigure on-board systems to isolate failed equipment or functions Place space segment in a safe state
3	**Closed-loop**: Re-establish nominal mission operations following an on-board failure	As Step 2, plus configure to a nominal operational configuration Resume execution of nominal operations Resume generation of mission products

(b) Mission Execution Autonomy Levels

Level	Description	Functions
1	**Open-loop**: Mission control under ground control; limited on-board capability for safety issues	Real-time control from ground for nominal operations Execution of time-tagged commands for safety issues
2	**Open-loop/Closed-loop**: Execution of pre-planned, ground-defined, mission operations on-board	Capability to store time-based commands in an on-board scheduler Limited capability to react to execution of commands (e.g., retry if unsuccessful)
3	**Closed-loop**: Execution of adaptive mission operations on-board	Event-based autonomous operations Execution of on-board operations control procedures
4	**Closed-loop**: Execution of goal-oriented mission operations on-board	Goal-oriented mission re-planning

Step 6. Determine Level of Automation for Both Space and Ground Segments

Before you can size mission operations for the number of personnel needed, and cost, you need to determine how much of the operations will be automated and how much requires human operators. This includes not only the spacecraft, but also the ground segment [Calzolari, 2007]. As mentioned in Chap. 20, the advances in miniaturization and computing power have enabled the placing of more tasking responsibilities and automation on the spacecraft rather than on the ground [Sherwood and Chien, 2007]. Mission operations recognize the importance of automation as a productivity enhancer, useful for performing repetitive tasks and responding to well documented contingencies. However, there can be a performance downside to extensive automation. Validating complex automation can itself be extremely complex and costly. Over-dependence on automation results in lower operator technical proficiency and only experienced, technically current and knowledgeable personnel can effectively respond to non-standard situations.

† For example, all operators in ESA member countries can use MICONYS (SCOS2000 spacecraft monitoring and control tools) and SIMULUS (Simsat software-based spacecraft simulation tools) free of charge for a license with ESA, and in the USA, tools such as ITOS and AMMOS are free from NASA.

Looking at the space segment, there are three basic levels of automation for space segment health management and four basic levels of mission execution automation as shown in Table 29-5. These levels are based on the ECSS standards regarding space segment autonomy [ECSS, 2008]. The reference also lists two levels of autonomy for mission data management.

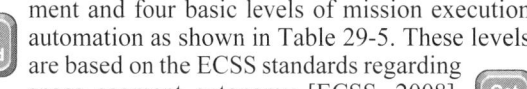

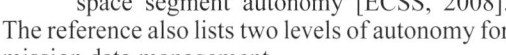

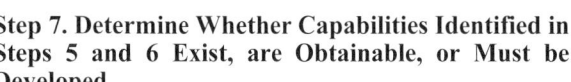

Step 7. Determine Whether Capabilities Identified in Steps 5 and 6 Exist, are Obtainable, or Must be Developed

Once you have determined the operations functions required by your project, and the expected level of automation in both the space and ground segments, you need to determine which of these can be addressed by assets already possessed by or available to your team, and which ones you will have to obtain from external sources (e.g., vendors or government sources) or have developed (either by the team or contracted out). The answers can have a large effect on both the schedule and cost of the project. Some of this step may have been done during the accomplishment of steps 5 and 6 just by gathering the information on the various options.

Step 8. Develop Staffing Plan and Identify Other Resources Required

One of the most important factors in determining the cost and performance of mission operations is the staff-

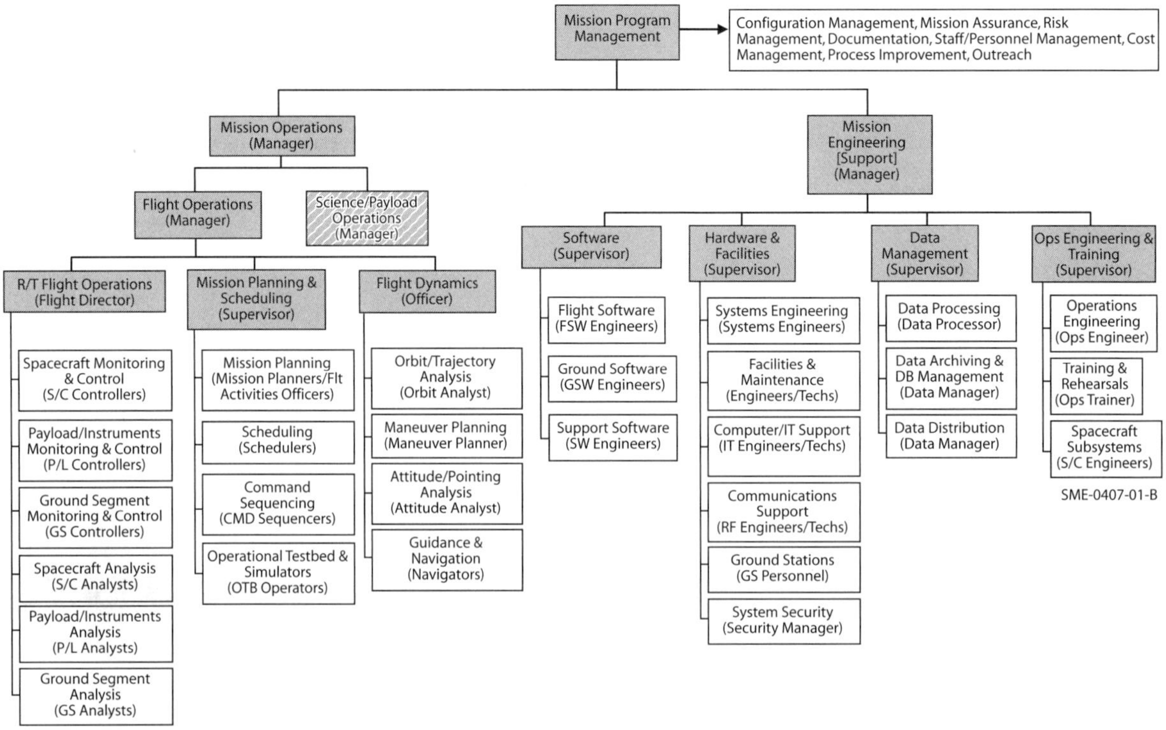

Fig. 29-4. Sample Mission Operations Organization. This organization chart shows typical groupings of operations functions, which may or may not map directly one on one to personnel. Common staff positions that fulfill each function is shown in parentheses below the function name. This is just an example and actual operations organizations can vary significantly from this—smaller, larger, or using different terminology for the functions and/or positions. The Science/Payload function is often a separate organization.

ing—both the level of staffing throughout the project life cycle and the personnel qualifications required. In Steps 4–6 of this operations development process, you determined the functions required to do the operations for your mission, the means to accomplish the functions, and the level of automation that you could use. Now you should look at those functions again to see which require the support of human operators and to what extent. Are the operators just needed for supervision of an automated process, required to make decisions at critical points in the process, conduct the function entirely manually, or just be on standby to intervene when something anomalous occurs? The frequency of the human participation needs to also be considered. In manned space missions, like for the Space Shuttle or ISS, human operators are present continually—24/7. For many autonomous spacecraft, such as nanosatellites orbiting the Earth or probes deep in space with long communication lags or infrequent contacts, little time may be needed to support operations, although some non-realtime functions, such as mission planning or data analysis, do not depend on having contact with the spacecraft but will be staffed during office hours.

One of the products to come out of this step is an operations organization chart or tree, an example of which is shown in Fig. 29-4. At this point it is useful to define the typical staff positions used for operations. Note that these are just some of the more common ones, some of which will be found in nearly all operations teams, but they may have different names in a particular organization. There are also some other positions that may be used based on the nature of the mission or the organization's operations philosophy. For smaller missions, some of these functional positions may not be in the functional organization and the responsibilities of those positions will be assumed by other positions. For example, the Mission Operations and Flight Operations functions, or the Flight Operations Director and the Real-time Flight Operations Supervisor functions may be combined.

The mission staffing plan accounts for the criticality of an operator in the loop that is supplemented by, but not supplanted with, automation tools. Basically, the mission operational staffing concept is primarily dependent on several variables including the duty cycle of mission payload events; the complexity of the operations; the cost; and the degree of automation that has evolved. Mission operations staffing can be divided between management, science, flight operations, and engineering support elements. Together they comprise the Mission Operations staff. The organization is first developed to be functional rather than actual. This means that one actual person might perform more than one function shown in the organization or a function may not have a person dedicated to it. Note that the organization shown does not include ancillary positions such as administrative assistants, for example. It should also be noted that some positions may be shared between more than one mission, so the costs would also be shared.

Table 29-6. Example of a Staffing for Highly-Automated Small Satellite Mission Operations. This example is for a small imaging LEO satellite that can perform unmanned routine "lights-out" ground contacts for transfer of files. More personnel are required during EE&CO, but the number required can be decreased as the ops mature and become repetitive.

Position	EE&CO FTE	Nominal FTE	Mature FTE	Shift hr/day	Comment
Operations Manager	1	0.5	0.1	8/5	
Spacecraft Controller	2	0.9	0.1	8/5	8/7 for EE&CO
Ground Segment Controller	1	0.1	0.1	8/5	
Mission Planner	2	1	1	8/5	
Data Manager	1	0.5	0.1	8/5	
S/C Analyst	4	0.5	0.1	8/5	8/7 for EE&CO
Software Analyst	2	0.5	0.1	8/5	8/7 for EE&CO
Orbit Analyst	1	0.5	0.1	8/5	
TOTAL	14	4.5	1.7		

Besides automating the maximum number of repetitive and predictive tasks, another key way to keep operations costs down is to reduce staff size to the minimum necessary to meet all requirements. If the mission staffing approach is based on a minimization concept, such a cost savings objective is attainable. However, reduced staff, while effective at reducing costs, might introduce risk that must be mitigated if quality service is to be provided with a high degree of reliability, maintainability, and availability (RMA). The primary risk of minimized staff is lack of depth at key positions. For some small missions, many of these functions might be performed by one person or several functions might be shared by a few people thereby providing backups. On some big missions one function might be done by several people.

Once the staffing positions have been defined, the next step is to determine which functions the operations personnel need to perform (maybe not all the identified staff positions are required), and when they are needed. A very important factor in this determination is the level of operations automation (space and ground), which is why this step is included in the repetitive trade study segment of the mission operations development process. Table 29-6 shows an example for the staffing levels in Full-Time Equivalents (FTEs) for a highly automated small imaging satellite in LEO that is capable of routine "light out" ground contacts to transfer data files, with the major human activity being required to plan and implement the imaging of various targets. This provides a minimal staffing plan especially suited for university-class nano- or micro-satellites. The number of personnel required to perform and monitor mission operations decreases as confidence in the system increases and the operations become mature and repetitive. A high level of staffing is required to check out the satellite until IOC.

The tool that is used for helping to determine the number of personnel needed, and to later determine the staffing costs, is the Work Breakdown Structure (WBS). This basically defines the tasks that have to be performed to successfully develop or conduct operations, and when applied to workload (FTE personnel) estimates and a schedule, becomes the basis for the staffing plan. The WBS and how to develop one are described in Sec. 11.1. An example WBS for mission operations is shown in Table 29web-5.

Once the WBS has been developed and it has been fitted to a schedule to identify when in the project life-cycle its tasks need to be performed (and thus staffed), the workload for each task can be estimated along with identifying the staff position to accomplish it. There are several good COTS software packages available to perform this project management function such as Microsoft Project® and dotProject, which is an open source project management tool.

For Phase E missions operations, you need to determine whether or not 24/7 operations are required by some of the team, or whether a 40 hour work week (or less) is sufficient. If the real-time team is required 24/7, then you must determine the number of teams and shift schedule for the teams. Usually, there are four or five teams with shift lengths of 8 or 12 hours. Some popular shift plans can be found on the Business Management Systems website. As an example, the Clementine mission [Horan, Sorensen, Tran, and Hoffman, 1995] used a four team (eight persons per team) scheme for real-time operations on a rotating, day-night-day, 12 hour shift with four days on (10 AM to 10 PM) followed by four days off, then four nights on (10 PM to 10 AM) followed by four nights off. This shift schedule combined a high degree of predictability with an avoidance of commuter rush hour. However, this scheme does require some overtime work and has long shifts.

Once the positions required for mission operations have been identified and their expected workload and utility have been determined, as well as when they are required in the project life cycle, a staffing profile can be built. The first step is to list all positions on a spreadsheet that shows the schedule of the project at an appropriate time resolution (e.g., monthly). Note on the spreadsheet when each operations team member is brought into the project and at what level as Full Time Equivalents (FTEs). The monthly staff level in FTEs can then be determined by adding the values per month. From these totals, you can produce a graph showing the staffing profile for the mission.

Although we have concentrated on the operations staffing so far in this step, the other part of the step is to identify other resources that will be required by the mission. These could include ground station coverage (utilization), computers, communications equipment, consoles and workstations, or software applications that are needed to support operations. Some of these are covered by other areas, such as the Ground Segment, but may come under the responsibility of Mission Operations or under joint responsibility. Once you have the staffing requirements done, as well as the communications and other mission requirements as designed into the current system architecture, you will be able to make estimates for these other resources. However, the resources include not only hardware and software, but also services, such as precision orbit determination, that might be required, and for which a cost will have to be determined.

Multi-mission operations can have different loading in both staff and resources. For example, a 0.2 FTE orbital engineer may be normal as that function can be multi-mission. Likewise, a ground station is nearly always multi-mission, while a monitor and control tool is probably mission specific (although within that mission it may control multiple satellites).

Step 9. Perform Trades to Determine Best Solution from Steps 5–8

At this point in the MOP development process, you will have identified the functions and level of automation required to complete your mission. You probably have identified several tools or packages (whether existing or not) that may work to accomplish these functions. The next step is to perform a trade study between the various candidate options to determine which would be best for your particular application. If this is being done early in the development cycle, then optimization is not expected, but rather obtaining a solution that is acceptable and will accomplish the mission. Later in the development cycle (i.e., a later iteration), then a more detailed analysis and comparison may be required to optimize your solution.

You must select the criteria that are best for distinguishing between the candidates in the trade studies. Typically these fall into the following four categories: performance, schedule, cost, and risk. These will be examined in turn.

Performance is probably the most important attribute in your trade study. This is a measure of how well the object being evaluated fulfills the functions for which it is being considered. Your selection must be able to function sufficiently well to accomplish the tasks needed to fulfill the mission objectives. If it will not do the job required, then it should be discarded. However, the selection cannot be made based on performance alone, but must be considered in light of the other selection parameters. When you score the attributes of the candidate solutions, performance is generally weighted the highest.

Schedule is important because no matter how well the candidate fulfills the other trade criteria, it is worthless if it cannot be available on time, especially if there is no flexibility in the project schedule. Schedule is also closely related to cost for elements that have to be developed for the project, because of the increase in labor cost as the time required increases.

Cost is critical for some projects, especially for universities and small programs, but inflated costs can kill even the high-end missions as well. For projects with tight budgets, cost becomes the dominant constraint and can even out-weigh performance as the primary selection parameter. In this case, "good enough" might be the selection mantra, even though it might cause reduction in mission objectives, lifetime, or increase in risk. Cost includes both the non-recurring costs for the pre-launch phases, and the recurring costs during the conduct of the mission. This is where automation can be a deciding factor—higher non-recurring costs for developing and testing automation may lead to less overall project costs due to reduced recurring costs (e.g., fewer personnel required to operate the mission). When including cost as a selection parameter, it might be worthwhile dividing it into non-recurring and recurring costs, with possibly different weighting. This difference in weighting might not just be related to the total project costs, but could instead be tied to a funding profile for the project—plenty of funding during development but little funding for operations would put the weighting in favor of the non-recurring costs, while vice versa would put it in favor of the recurring costs.

Risk can encompass many areas, such as safety, probability of successfully completing the mission, political risk (e.g., high visibility projects may have high political risk—failure could have far-reaching consequences) and technology readiness level. Risks are identified using a process of risk management, and the willingness to accept the risks has to be determined. When using this as a trade selection parameter, you might want to differentiate between the different types of risk, because each may have different weighting for your project.

The simplest way to do the trade study may be to take the table you used to determine the functionality of the candidates in your trade space (e.g., Table 29web-5) and assign numeric values to each of them for each of the four trade parameters instead of the simple "X" as shown in Table 29web-5. However, a more rigorous methodology for performing trades is presented in Sec. 5.3 and is applicable for use in operations as well.

Get More

Step 10. Determine ROM Mission Operations Cost

By this step you have determined the factors that are needed to develop a rough order of magnitude (ROM) cost estimate for mission operations. These major factors include the tasks (WBS), staffing profile, hardware, software, facilities, and communications costs as well as maintenance/refurbishing and replacement cost for long-term missions. Detailed cost analysis methodologies are described in Chap. 11. See Cost Model (NICM) in Chap. 11.2.5.

The cost of operating a mission depends most on the number of personnel involved (people are very expensive as a recurring cost) and operations complexity. Both of these depend on the amount of automation employed both in the spacecraft and in the ground segment. Adding more automation probably increases the non-recurring costs during Phases A–D, but may allow for lower recurring operations costs during Phase E. The complexity of the operations depends on the mission objectives, the design of the spacecraft and payload, communications and ground segment design, and operational risk policies.

Step 11. Repeat Steps 4–10 for Development Phase (Mission Phases A–D as Appropriate)

The core of mission operations for any project is what is required to execute the mission after launch. This is the phase of the project that the mission operations are designed to fulfill—this is what accomplishes the mission goals. The purpose of the operations development done prior to launch (Phases A to D) is to design mission operations that will run smoothly to accomplish the mission. That is why we look at the Phase E operations first to develop our Mission Operations Plan, and to size and cost these operations. However, to complete the MOP, we must go back and determine what needs to be done to evolve the operations into the efficiently functioning system required for flight operations. Now is the appropriate time to go back and repeat the steps of the MOP development to account for the operations development in Phases A to D. In some of your previous steps, you may have already included some of this early work (e.g., staffing profile), so now is a good time to go back and revise it if necessary based on your later determinations. At the end of this step you should have a revised ROM cost estimate and be ready to press on to the final steps of the mission operations plan development.

Step 12. Assess Mission Utility, Complexity, Risk, and Cost Drivers

The mission utility of the operations (i.e., determining how well the operations help us meet the mission objectives) is calculated using the method outlined in Sec. 5.4. It is helpful if you have simulations that you can use for determining the performance and characteristics of the system and for which you can input a range of values for the design parameters to determine their effect on the cost and performance. Operational simulations such as these have been developed and used extensively [Rainey, 2004], and are available from various sources such as NASA. The development of the Mission Operations Plan is iterative, and as the plan becomes more mature, the differences in the mission utility parameters between iterations should decrease, and also helps provide confidence in the viability of your operations system design.

Mission operations cost depends largely on the complexity of the operations. To determine how the complexity affects the cost drivers, we can use a complexity model which expresses operational parameters in terms of FTE operations personnel. Each of the operational activities is graded as low, medium, or high complexity, using the analogous method (i.e., comparing with the same function on similar class missions that have been flown). This complexity factor is included in the algorithms of the model that can be used to evaluate the operations and to reduce operations cost. This model and method is described in detail in Squibb, et al. [2006].

Step 13. Repeat for Alternate Mission Concepts (Starting with Step 2) if Required

This step is used early in the life cycle of the mission design when trade studies are still being done to determine alternate mission concepts, but is skipped if the baseline mission concept has been selected. The purpose of doing operations concepts for alternate mission concepts is to determine how operations affects the performance, schedule, cost, and risk of each mission concept being evaluated. This becomes an important factor in deciding the baseline mission concept to be used.

Step 14. Identify Derived Requirements

In Step 1, the top-level requirements, both for the mission and for operations, were defined. However, to implement a design, requirements need to be specified that go to a more detailed level in each system element. Although this is particularly obvious with spacecraft subsystems, it is also important for operations as well. You need to know how you are going to meet the top-level requirements and there will be constraints or design factors that have to be considered as you get deeper into the design. These are captured in what are called derived requirements (see Sec. 6.1). Each *derived requirement*, as its name suggests, is derived, or allocated, from a higher level requirement. This means it has traceability all the way up to the mission objectives. Requirements also need some way to be tested or verified. It is important that requirements be numbered and tracked in the Mission Requirements Document, System Specification Document, or a similar document. In Table 29-7 is a simple example of top-level requirements and their first generation derived requirements.

Step 15. Develop Training Plan

When you have identified the operations staff positions required by your mission and have determined the staffing profile, you need to develop a Training Plan (sometimes called a Training and Certification Plan). All operational positions require training but not all require certification. Although different organizations may have different policies and techniques for training and certification, the basic training plan and methodology described here is based on NASA-sanctioned Instructional Design Processes, and should work for most missions with little

Table 29-7. Example of Derived Requirements (Child Requirements) Obtained from Top-Level Operations Requirements (Parent Requirements).

Top Level Operations Requirements (Parent)	Derived Operations Requirements (Child)
The Mission Operations function (Mission Ops) shall provide management and control of the spacecraft and Ground Segment to help ensure the successful completion of the mission.	• Mission Ops shall perform real-time contact support (monitoring and commanding). • Mission Ops shall perform mission planning. • Mission Ops shall perform timeline and command script generation. • Mission Ops shall perform orbit analysis and provide orbit ephemeris to mission users. • Mission Ops shall perform spacecraft engineering trending and analysis. • Mission Ops shall perform anomaly resolution and contingency operations. • Mission Ops shall determine operations statistics. • Mission Ops shall perform data management. • Mission Ops shall provide operations report generation functions for the mission. • Mission Ops shall be involved with the design of the spacecraft throughout the project life cycle. • Mission Ops shall support spacecraft integration and test activities.
Mission operations shall be designed for human control or autonomous "lights out" nominal contact support.	• Mission Ops shall be automated to allow the option of "lights out" nominal contact operations after IOC.

modification. However, it should be noted that some organizations do not want their satellite operators to "think" for themselves, but rather just to follow prescribed procedures. This is more common in satellite operations within organizations where the operators are there only as a temporary assignment and may be operating assets worth billions of dollars. There have been instances where an operator has jeopardized a mission by trying to solve a problem that was relatively benign to start with (i.e., the fix was worse than the problem).

The most efficient method of training, especially for smaller organizations, is to use a "right level" on-the-job training (OJT) style approach to training its operators where the emphasis is on position proficiency and not universal knowledge. Hands-on experience is emphasized far more than classroom instruction. This approach requires position cross-training, especially with limited staffing resources, while up-training is a privilege that must be earned. Personnel should be encouraged to learn the basics of performing higher level functions and expanding their technical worth to the program. In addition, those exhibiting high degrees of initiative and motivation can be up-trained as a career enhancing opportunity. However, positional up-training as a function of an operator's employment is not necessary and is not usually formally pursued unless the situation (e.g., imminent departure of ops team member) drives such a requirement. Within the mission operations team, the training and certification authority and administrator will vary depending on position. Basically training is divided into two distinct parts, new-hire basic training and mission specific training.

To effectively implement the classroom/hands-on and field training phases of the program, a variety of methods of instructional delivery should be used that yields qualified satellite operations personnel, cost effective implementation expenditures, and allow for a follow-on training program. A formal certification program is included to evaluate and ensure the proficiency of operations personnel thus mitigating risk and increasing the overall level of confidence in mission success. Training objectives are linked with skills required for certification to ensure operations personnel competence in all required mission related tasks.

The training process is designed to develop a spacecraft flight operations training and certification hierarchy that contains generic, as well as program or skill category specific training. At each stage, there are certification procedures that ensure knowledge bases and skill sets before a trainee is allowed to progress to the next stage of training.

> NOTE: Not every engineer or technician is suitable for the pressure of real-time operations. There have been cases where persons are outstanding in planning and implementing time-delayed spacecraft operations (with no ground contact), but when faced with the pressure of real-time operations, they "freeze" and cannot act as required. Sometimes repeated training will take care of this, but not always. Some people are not suited for real-time mission operations and should be utilized in other areas such as mission planning and scheduling, mission analysis, or flight dynamics. It is important that your training and certification process is able to differentiate between the different capabilities of the trainees and does not certify people into an area for which they are not suited. Probably the best way to do this is to put your trainees into as realistic high-stress simulated scenarios as possible and see how they perform. This should be done several times with different scenarios to see if their performance improves with experience.

The training plan is a project document under configuration control where the methodology, processes, course topics, personnel, schedule, and certification process and criteria are captured. For some organizations, especially the smaller ones, the

Get More

Training Plan may not be a separate document, but incorporated instead into the Mission Operations Plan or a similar document. It is important that the Training Plan is kept up-to-date and actually used by the operations team. It helps to have someone designated with this responsibility.

Step 16. Generate MOP That Includes Technology Development Plan, Personnel Staffing & Training Plan, and Documentation Plan

If this is the first time through this process, then you now have all the pieces to put together a basic Mission Operations Plan. You should include in this document the background description of the mission, the mission statement, mission objectives, and the top-level requirements and constraints†, the mission architecture, the operations concept (description), operations architecture and functional flow block diagrams, operations organization, WBS, staffing plan, schedule, training and certification plan, technology development plan, and the documentation plan. For large and complex projects, some of these parts of the MOP are standalone documents (e.g., Training and Certification Plan or Technology Development Plan), but they would be summarized in the MOP. For smaller projects, these parts would appear in the entirety in the MOP as separate sections or maybe appendices.

The Documentation Plan lists and defines the various operations documents to be used for the project (see Table 29-3), who will be responsible for producing the document, when and how it should be developed, and its intended usage. This includes all the procedures to be used to conduct and support operations.

If this is not the first iteration of this MOP process, then this step is where you review, revise, and improve the MOP based on new information obtained in the previous steps of this iteration. This is the primary document of mission operations development and is very important. Remember that the MOP is the blueprint to develop and successfully conduct operations for your mission.

Step 17. Document and Iterate/Refine as Needed

This is the final step of the mission operations development process, where you publish the base (or revised) MOP that you have developed in the previous steps. If this is early in the life-cycle of the project, then the base MOP will probably not be complete or at least not mature, and one or more iterations through the steps will be needed to finish the MOP sufficiently for extensive use and reference by the project. The various iterations of the MOP should be made accessible and reviewed by other members of the project so that their input and feedback can be used to improve the plan.

† For large and complex mission you may want to just include the top-level mission operations and constraints and refer to the Mission Requirements Document (or equivalent) for the remainder.

29.2 Mission Execution

So far, we have examined the functions of mission operations and discussed how to put together a Mission Operations Plan and develop the products and elements needed to operate the mission. During Phases C and D of the mission project (see Fig. 29-2) is where the procedures and documents for operations are developed and tested, and the operations personnel are trained. The readiness of the team to support operations is examined in a final review before launch, such as the Mission Readiness Review (MRR), Operations Readiness Review (ORR), or Flight Readiness Review (FRR). Once the spacecraft is delivered and mated to the launch vehicle, the project moves into the Execution Phase (Phase E). This is where all the hard work and preparation for the mission pays off. This phase is divided into the following distinct segments of activity for operations:

Launch and Checkout Operations—The operations team may be involved with checking the functionality of the spacecraft after it has been integrated with the launch vehicle. The involvement of the MOT in the launch itself depends on the state of the spacecraft. Some spacecraft are launched "cold," which means it remains unpowered and inert during launch and is usually activated by a microswitch during deployment, by the launch vehicle avionics, or by transmitted signal just prior to deployment. Other spacecraft are launched in a "warm" state, which means that they have a minimal level of subsystems powered on during ascent, and then fully powered on after or just prior to deployment. Spacecraft may also be launched in a "hot" state, which means the basic subsytems are fully powered on. This is the state used for spacecraft with biological payloads (e.g., human) or where the spacecraft may need to take measurements during the launch. Launch operations usually last from launch until deployment of the spacecraft from the launch vehicle, although that may depend on whether or not a rocket is being used to boost the spacecraft into a different orbit or trajectory. These booster rockets are sometimes called the Inertial Upper Stage (IUS), Payload Assist Module/Motor (PAM) or Apogee Kick Motor (AKM). Of course, if the firing of this motor depends on the participation of the spacecraft, then it must be activated. Depending on the trajectory desired, there may be several minutes, hours, or even days between orbit insertion and the firing of the booster.

Following launch of the spacecraft, there is usually a phase of operations called Engineering Evaluation & Checkout (EE&C), Launch and Early Operations (LEOP), On-orbit Checkout (OOC), or something similar. This is a transition period bridging integration and test (I&T) and nominal operations. It is the phase at which the mission operations development gradually ends and the nominal mission operations begin. In some ways, the checkout phase of operations is different from nominal operations and in other ways, it is the same. This phase may include deployment of the spacecraft from the launch vehicle/booster, initial configuration and checkout of the spacecraft, and if applicable, insertion into the transfer orbit or cruise to the final trajectory or target point, and insertion into the final orbit/trajectory. After establishing its final operational orbit, the mission begins a period of checking out the spacecraft's subsystems, operational procedures, and the entire mission system, including the entire ground segment. This checkout period normally lasts for several weeks.

The checkout phase is characterized by a highly dynamic environment where subsystems are initiated and checked out, and processes and procedures are thoroughly tested, and if necessary, redefined and rewritten. It is a period where the operations personnel (including spacecraft engineers) can expect long hours, few days off, maximum vigilance and complete flexibility. If applicable, it is also when responsibility for defining the mission operations transitions from the Mission Development Team (MDT) to the Mission Operations Team (MOT). During this phase, all subsystems are checked out for nominal performance and the spacecraft is configured toward nominal operations. The checkout phase may require spacecraft manufacturers and integrators to be physically present at the MOC supporting the planning, execution and analysis efforts in accordance with the Early Orbit Checkout Plan. The operations processes used during checkout are the same as during the nominal mission. However, the level of effort is usually more intensive, and the application of "one time only" operations more prevalent. Once the checkout phase is completed, the spacecraft/mission/project achieves what is commonly referred to as Nominal Operational Status (NOS) or Initial Operational Capability (IOC).

Nominal Operations—Once IOC has been achieved, the mission operations moves into what is normally called nominal operations phase. Depending on the mission type, the nominal operations can consist of vastly different operational activities based upon the progress of the mission. For instance, deep space probes (such as Mars or asteroid/comet missions) will have a long cruise period with very little activity other than maintenance of the spacecraft health and possibly occasional trajectory adjustment burns or ancillary payload activities, followed by intense operational activities once the target has been reached. This can also occur on a smaller scale for geosynchronous satellites as they are being placed into their correct final orbit. However, many LEO or spacecraft orbiting other planetary bodies may have near continuous high levels of activity (e.g., Hubble Space Telescope or Mars Reconnaissance Orbiter).

The nominal operations phase can also contain non-nominal operations, such as contingency operations that are required to resolve an anomalous condition. The process of handling anomalies will be discussed later in this section. Finally, for science missions, the nominal operations phase can evolve due to changing requirements and scope due to being granted an extended mission, which generally comes with new science goals and a budget cut.

29.2.1 Mission Operations Processes

The mission operations process consists of four major subprocesses (see Fig. 29-3) that are performed on a continually cycling basis: planning process, execution (R/T flight operations) process, data management process, and the analysis process. There is a fifth process that is not part of the normal operations cycle and is only performed as needed, and that is the anomaly resolution process. In order to achieve low-cost nominal operations, each of these processes should be automated as much as possible without compromising mission success. Each of these processes will be examined in turn.

The *Mission Planning and Scheduling (MPS) process* (Fig. 29-5) is the process of determining a spacecraft's state (position, velocity and attitude/rate), selecting operational objectives, generating the products used to implement these objectives and coordinating with the real-time team to ensure these objectives are realized. It produces the master schedules, timelines, pass plans, and command loads for the space and ground segment activities. Inputs to MPS usually include the Mission Operations Plan, flight rules, mission requirements, status of the spacecraft and ground network with any resultant constraints, as well as task requests from the customers (usually payload customers) and from the spacecraft operations team if needed. When these inputs have been factored in along with products from the Flight Dynamics function (the spacecraft orbit or trajectory ephemeris and sometimes attitude/pointing information), a baseline plan and schedule are created.

As part of the Flight Dynamics function, guidance, navigation, and control (GNC) functions are provided for mission planning. Based on orbit/trajectory analysis and the desired mission plan, trajectory maneuvers and pointing targets can be provided as part of their standard products along with the orbit ephemeris and attitude information. After the Flight Dynamics products are received, variously sorted visibility products and orbit events are output and published for Mission Planners to review. These products provide all the information that is required by the MP to identify operations opportunities, select passes and determine maneuver requirements. Spacecraft operations planning primarily concerns space segment assets but not ground segment scheduling. However, there may be occasions when on-board activities and passes may be concurrently scheduled. Usually, these would be considered special events with a high priority, and will require that the spacecraft analyst or even a customer technical representative be in the MOC to oversee the support.

Pass scheduling is performed to produce a schedule of ground station contact support required to support the mission during the planning period. This usually starts with a schedule of available support times and assets provided by the Ground Segment schedulers. For high priority missions or missions with dedicated ground station assets, the planners will tell the GS schedulers which passes are required instead of choosing just from those

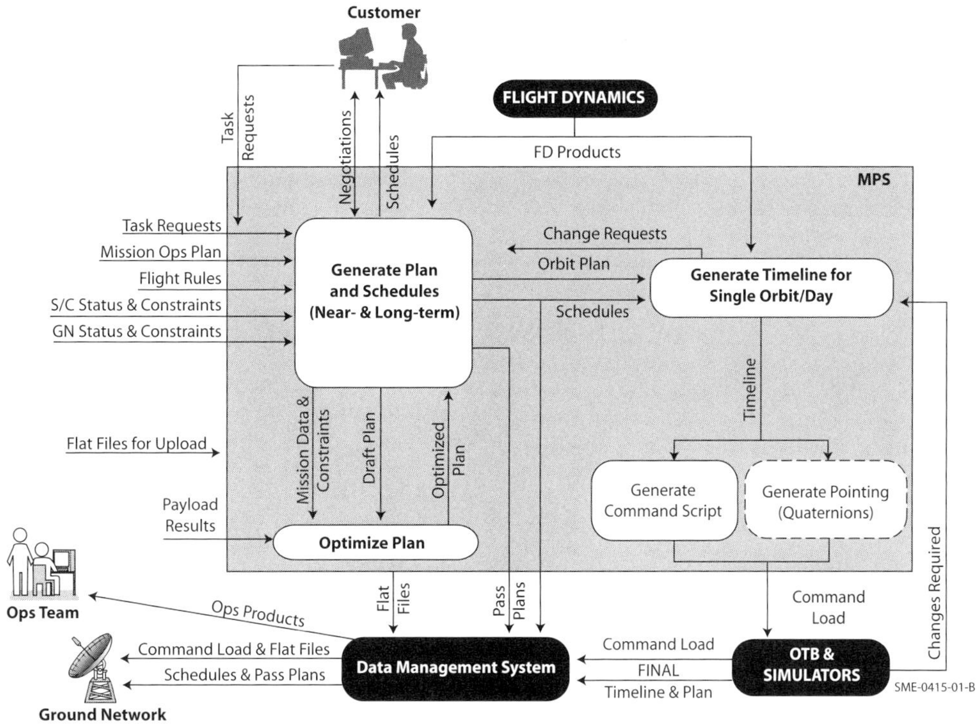

Fig. 29-5. Mission Operations Planning and Scheduling Process. The Mission Planning and Scheduling (MPS) process takes various inputs, including the mission plan, payload/customer requests, status of the spacecraft and ground network, orbit ephemeris data and using mission constraints, defines a plan, schedule, and command loads to be used to perform the mission during the next execution cycle. Most missions test the commands on an operations test bed or simulators for verification before uploading. The MPS process shown is loosely based on that used for the Clementine lunar mission [Sorensen et al., 1995], but is typical for many space missions.

that are still available. Some missions know that certain events are critical for mission success but are unable to specify a date and time for these events. Examples include pre-launch simulations, one time encounter opportunities, opportunistic observations, launches and GS scheduled maintenance. The MPS function should allow these users to reserve a block of time based on these events. In some cases, event scheduling could involve higher prices and cancellation penalties. However, it also ensures that the customers are provided with a pass priority for the critical events of their missions.

The MPS process is responsible for being cognizant of operations constraints and coordinating with the customer when objectives and constraints conflict. These constraints should be both documented in the MP's operation procedures document and programmed into the command generation and verification process. Possible constraints that would affect either party may include the following:

- **Environmental:** Cloud cover, smoke, sun glint, solar panel jitter, or solar exclusion zones. All mission specific and found in the ICD and other coordinated documents. Use tools created to reduce the impact of such constraints.
- **Positional:** Angle, elevation, or ground obstructions relative to a target.
- **Data Requirements:** Recorder capacity, amount of data planned for collection, amount of data per pass that can be downlinked, compression scheme, and latency of data (i.e., how quickly needed).
- **Single vs Multiple Payloads on One Spacecraft** (single mission) Operational constraints such as not being able to run payload A while payload B is powered up.
- **Spacecraft Performance Capability:** Electrical power capacity, thermal management, attitude determination, pointing and slewing, and maneuvering for example. Information that is provided from the Spacecraft Analyst or other subsystem experts that identify spacecraft threatening performance shortcomings.
- **Single vs Multiple Spacecraft on One Mission:** Primarily a coordination constraint.
- **Alteration Lead Time:** If the customer is selecting operations but the MPS process is producing the commands, there must be a constraint against the customer trying to change the operation after a certain time.

There might also have to be some negotiations with the customer if the baseline plan cannot fully meet the tasking requests of the customer. During this planning process all conflicts in the schedule (e.g., conflicting task requests, or availability of ground stations) are resolved. The baseline plan must also be internally conflict free and not violate any spacecraft or payload constraints, such as those listed above. This is called the *deconfliction* process. The baseline plan and schedule may then go through an optimization process based on payload priorities, mission constraints, and status of data collections. In some systems, this optimization process is integrated with the process that generates the baseline plan and schedule and not a separate process as shown.

There are generally two levels of planning. The output of the *long-term planning* is a sequence of spacecraft and payload activities that may cover from days to months in the future that ensure the mission objectives will be met and to inform the team of when activities are planned and what assets (e.g., ground station coverage) will be required. *Short-term planning* includes detailed targeting using the current orbit, the current state of the spacecraft and payload, and any absolute time of timed commands. Depending on the mission, short term planning can occur daily and within a few days prior to the execution or may cover longer periods.†

Part of the short-term planning is the generation of *pass plans* (also called *contact plans*) to provide details to the ops team for real-time contacts with the spacecraft. The pass plan contains the essential information for executing the real-time pass, such as times of AOS, LOS, maximum elevation, duration of contact, which assets (e.g., antenna) will be used, the settings of the ground equipment, the objectives of the pass, which files are to be uploaded or downloaded, any commands or special activities that the ops personnel may have to perform. For spacecraft that are in continuous or long-term communications with the ground, then the pass plan as defined here does not have much meaning. In these cases there may be a daily activity or special activity plan.

The optimized plan and schedule can then be used to create detailed timelines for spacecraft and support activities. The timeline is a human readable form of the activities to be done by the spacecraft and ground network as a function of time. Timelines are usually generated for an orbit or for a day, depending on the type of mission, and combines the orbital events provided by the orbit ephemeris (one of the FD products) along with the commands to be performed by the spacecraft or ground. This provides the detail needed to execute what was laid out in the short-term plan. In the case of manned missions, the timeline also includes references or links to detailed crew procedures for each individual task. Development of the timeline traditionally has been done manually by modifying previous similar timelines ("cut and paste"), although software tools are now available to streamline the timeline generation and reduce the chance of errors introduced by the manual method. Note that if the time between the development of the timeline and its execution on the spacecraft is large (as defined for the mission), then the "final" timeline might have to be tweaked with an updated ephemeris. If the difference between the ephemeris during planning and the ephemeris close to execution is no more than a second or two, then it might not matter, while if the difference is many seconds or tens of seconds, it may matter and thus have to be reduced.

Once the timeline has been completed, reviewed, and approved by the appropriate authority in the operations organization, it must be converted into a command sequence that can be uploaded and executed by the spacecraft. Although this can also be done using manual methods, it is becoming more common to use a software tool called a Command Script Generator (CSG) to produce the command sequence in a form readable by the spacecraft computers. Typically, the timeline is first parsed by the CSG to produce software code in the language used to program the spacecraft's on-board computer (called the *command script*), and then compiled to produce the binary machine language code that is actually uploaded and executed by the spacecraft (called the *command load*). The actual details of this process depend on the spacecraft's software and command architecture and may differ from what is described here, although the end objective, a sequence of commands to be read and executed by the spacecraft, is the same.

In Fig. 29-5, there is a parallel function to the command script generation shown which generates pointing for the spacecraft. This function is not required by all missions. Even if pointing has to be determined for the spacecraft to execute the commands, with increased computing power that is now available to spacecraft, the pointing may be calculated on the spacecraft and not on the ground as was traditional. Many spacecraft use quaternions to define pointing vectors and attitudes, but not all, which is why this is shown in parentheses. If the pointing tables, angles, or quaternions, are calculated by the MPS function, then they are combined with the command script and subsequent command load derived from the timeline.

The command load is usually tested on an Operations Test Bed (OTB) or simulators before leaving the MPS function. If any problems are found, then changes can be made in the plan, timeline, and command script to eliminate them. Once the command load has been verified as working as expected, the final version is passed along to the mission database (part of the Data Management function) where it is combined with the pass plans and flat files. The flat files are data files that need to be uploaded to the spacecraft or to the ground stations, but are not part of the command sequences. Examples of flat files include software patches, instrument or calibration settings. The command load is sent to the ground network for uplinking to the spacecraft, while the schedules, pass

† Deep space missions often upload timelines covering much longer than a day. For example, Cassini went from a 45 day schedule during primary mission to a 10-week schedule during its extended mission. Commands for the entire schedule were uploaded at the beginning of the 10-week period. Other missions that rely on the DSN must provide schedules longer than a day.

Table 29-7◀, Fig. 29-5◀, Eq. 29-0

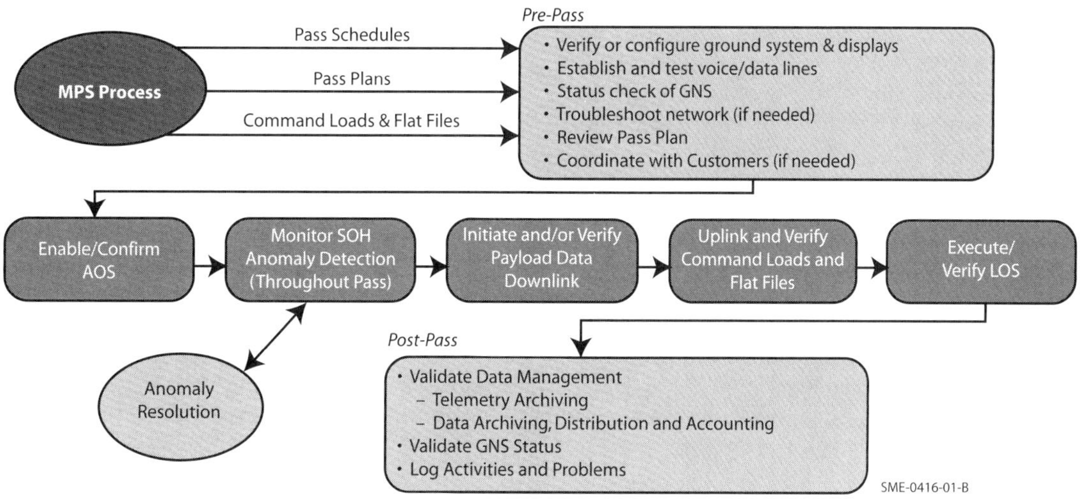

Fig. 29-6. Mission Operations R/T Flight Operations Process. The products from the Planning Process (pass plans, schedules, commands and files to be uplinked to the spacecraft) are usually delivered to the Flight Operations Team in the MOC for implementation. Pass plans are reviewed and status of the ground network checked before AOS to ensure that everything is ready. After AOS, the spacecraft SOH is checked, and if any anomalies are detected, they are resolved. During the pass, any payload data are downloaded and files are uploaded as required. Pass termination procedures are executed before LOS.

plans, timelines, command scripts are the operations products sent to the operations team while the schedules and pass plans are sent to the ground network to support the spacecraft contacts.

The MPS functions are essential to the responsiveness and flexibility of the entire mission operational system to the requests of the payload customers. For many missions, it is thus important to implement automation and process improvement methodology in the MPS functions to ensure the best possible performance.

The *Real-time Flight Operations or Execution process* (Fig. 29-6) performs the activities associated with real-time contact with the spacecraft.† The process we describe here is that associated with LEO satellites that have to pass over ground stations for communication. This process is modified somewhat for missions where the spacecraft is in communication with the ground either continuously (e.g., geosynchronous satellites or spacecraft using TDRS such as the ISS) or very lengthy communication periods (e.g., deep space spacecraft). In these cases the definition of a pass is either moot or arbitrary. One advantage that these latter cases have is that they can usually schedule contacts with the spacecraft at convenient times (dependent of availability of ground station assets) such as during regular working hours. For LEO missions with just a few ground stations for communication, the passes may occur at any time of the day depending on the orbit.

The MPS function delivers its products (e.g., schedules, timelines, pass plans, command loads, flat files) to the mission data system where they are available to the operations team or sent to the ground stations network ready for their support of the upcoming passes or uploading to the spacecraft as appropriate. The process shown here assumes that the operations center and ground stations will have human operators, although many of the functions will still be performed even if this process is partially or even fully automated.

At a specified time before the upcoming pass (i.e., contact with the spacecraft), the pre-pass activities are started to prepare everything for the pass. These activities include configuring computers and consoles, configuring and testing the ground station equipment (e.g., receivers, transmitters, antennas), establishing and testing data links and voice lines (if needed), reviewing the Pass Plan with personnel supporting the pass to ensure that everyone understands what to expect and what they need to do. If the customers are supporting the pass (e.g., a payload event is planned during the pass), then coordination with them will be verified.

Often, during the pre-pass activities, the MOC automatically sends test commands to the ground site and receives command echoes back verifying that the commands were properly received and interpreted. The ground station can also send test data to the MOC. The test data are spacecraft telemetry data stored at the site and injected into the front end of the ground station processed through the entire system and sent to the MOC for validation. If the ground station has a high rate link to the spacecraft, this may also include a sample of the payload data. The ground stations may also track a collimation transponder located nearby so the antenna pointing, ranging, and Doppler functions can be tested and verified.

The ground station is responsible for detecting and establishing a communications link with the spacecraft. The ground station uses a profile of antenna elevation and azimuth angles as a function of time that is based on the

† With interplanetary missions the real-time contact may actually be several minutes or hours behind real-time on the spacecraft. Even with LEO missions, there is a small time lag, so "real-time" is a relative term.

spacecraft ephemeris. This profile might be produced at the ground station or calculated at the operations center and forwarded as part of the pre-pass products.

If a communication link with the spacecraft does not occur within the allowed window of time, then contingency activities for locating and establishing communication will be initiated. These activities might involve doing a pre-defined search pattern with the antenna around the expected location of the spacecraft or switching receivers or other equipment in case of performance problems.

Once the spacecraft's carrier signal has been detected, a firm signal lock is established to provide a stable communication link. The ground station receives the spacecraft downlink signal, successfully de-commutates the data and sends the telemetry to the MOC. At this time, commands can be sent to the spacecraft as needed. All during the contact with the spacecraft, the ground station is sending to the MOC the spacecraft telemetry; possibly tracking data in the form of angles, range, and Doppler; and ground station status data, although often some of these data are provided post-pass.

The spacecraft, instruments, and ground network state-of-health (SOH) data are monitored and controlled when necessary by the MOC. This includes monitoring of the payload instruments and spacecraft telemetry received by each ground station and sent to the MOC in real-time. The MOC command and telemetry system converts the telemetry to engineering units and performs limit checks on all telemetry values and reports automatically any telemetry parameters that are out of bounds or approaching an out of bound limit. On many missions the SOH telemetry monitoring is done automatically.

The controllers (spacecraft, instrument, and ground network) are responsible for implementing the plans provided by the MPS function. The human controllers, normally, just monitor the smooth running of the execution process, but are ready to intervene or make decisions as necessary. The spacecraft monitoring and control process verifies the spacecraft response to uploaded commands, monitors "tactical" spacecraft performance, detects spacecraft anomalies, notifies the spacecraft analysts of new anomalies, and logs the details of each contact. At times, the controllers may implement certain contingency plans, and will routinely implement alternative operations as required. However, the monitoring and control function does not usually investigate or resolve undocumented anomalies (unless critical to the safety of the spacecraft), it merely detects and reports them. The reason for this approach is that the function's primary purpose is to ensure the safety of the spacecraft and system in real-time, which could be compromised if resources are diverted to anomaly hunting. The MOC may also be responsible for monitoring and controlling the ground network, although some systems may have a separate Ground Segment Control function.

Routine dumping of the archived SOH or payload data that are stored on-board the spacecraft's memory is initiated by ground command (either manual or automatic) since this can only be done when the spacecraft is in communication with the ground station (or relay satellite). The MOC or ground segment control initiates the payload data dump when the correct link has been established and the data capture and processing equipment at the receiving site are properly configured. If the ground station is automated, the configuration and reporting of station status are done via an electronic link from the ground site to the MOC. If the ground station is manned, the status of the ground station may be relayed by voice to the MOC where the MOC Spacecraft Controller would then initiate the spacecraft commands to dump the recorded data. To ensure that the payload data set was correctly received on the ground before the spacecraft payload memory is reused by subsequent observations, data protocols, such as the CCSDS File Delivery Protocol (CFDP) [CCSDS, 2007], may be used for transporting and verifying the data. This protocol provides for automatic retransmission requests for corrupted or missing packets. In addition, the ground segment network function can perform several tests depending on how the data communication and processing are implemented. The ground segment control function can report on the number of valid frames and the number of correctable and non-correctable errors. If the payload data are also sent to the Data Management System in real or near real-time, then additional verification can be performed such as format verification, internal frame sequencing verification, and even initial Level 0 processing.

As the end of the pass approaches, the payload data dump is stopped and the spacecraft is put into the configuration required after the pass. This is usually done automatically by the spacecraft, but in some cases may have to be commanded by the ground. One thing that must be avoided is to reach loss of signal (LOS) with the spacecraft in a high power or attitude configuration that could jeopardize its welfare without autonomy on the spacecraft that recognizes and can rectify this condition. This has happened on actual space missions with the loss or near loss of the satellite.

Once LOS has been verified, the ground station is restored to its non-active state and the post-pass activities are performed. These may include validating the management of the SOH and payload data received. Both the SOH telemetry and the payload data are typically archived at the ground station until it has been confirmed that they have been safely received at their respective destinations. The data are distributed with proper accounting. The status of the GNS is verified, and finally the pass log is generated with any problems or comments by the spacecraft and ground controllers being included.

The *Anomaly Resolution process* (Fig. 29-7) is performed as a result of detecting anomalies in the spacecraft (or ground segment) SOH data while monitoring the real-time data during passes, or when analyzing the stored data later.

In the figure, the process for the two basic cases is shown. During the pass the realtime data are monitored continuously and checked for out-of-limit or other anom-

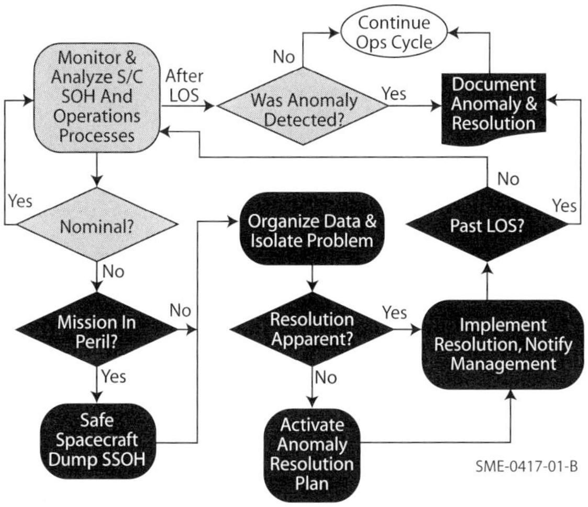

Fig. 29-7. Spacecraft Anomaly Detection Process During Flight Operations. During real-time flight operations the downlinked SOH telemetry is monitored for any anomalies. If any are detected the first thing to determine is if it threatens the spacecraft or mission. If so, then the spacecraft must be put into a safe condition while the anomaly is resolved. Otherwise, if the anomaly is minor or a fix has already been approved, it can be implemented. If not, then the anomaly resolution plan, which usually involves calling in appropriate engineers, must be activated. The anomaly and resolution should be documented, but if the pass is time critical, then this could be deferred until after LOS (as shown in figure).

alous values. The first thing to do is determine if the anomaly could jeopardize the mission. If so (and there is not a predetermined fix available), then it is best to set the spacecraft into a safe (lifeboat) state and dump all the archived SOH data which may be important in determining the cause of the anomaly. Obviously, if the spacecraft is manned, the first concern in the face of an anomaly is preservation of life, even before preventing loss of mission. Anomalies that endanger human life, while rare, initiate well thought out, well-practiced emergency procedures. To address the case of such incidents occurring during LOS, both the ground and on-board crews are able to both recognize and react to such situations. If human life is not at stake, on-console spacecraft operators should not attempt to solve unknown anomalies. They should only do as they have been trained to do and leave the anomaly identification and resolution to the spacecraft engineering experts. Safing the spacecraft (and the human crew) is the preferred response in this situation. After safing the spacecraft or if the anomaly was not critical, then the data should be organized if needed and the problem identified and isolated (highlighted) in the data. If there is a known resolution, then it can be implemented and management notified. If the resolution for the anomaly is not apparent, then the anomaly resolution process should be activated, and if resolved in time (before LOS), implemented as described before. After the pass, the anomaly and its resolution should be documented.

If the anomaly was detected during post-pass analysis, then the anomaly resolution plan should be activated, a resolution determined (possibly with the help of an Anomaly Resolution Team which may include spacecraft or payload engineers as required). Once the resolution has been determined, it should be tested on the OTB/simulators, if possible. Once verified, the tasks or commands can be sent to the mission planners or directly to the spacecraft controllers as appropriate (see Fig. 29-3). Figure 29-3 shows screened shadow boxes below the OTB/simulators and the Monitor & Control boxes to signify the part they play in anomaly resolution.

When the anomaly and resolution are documented, they should also become part of the flight handbook so that the resolution is readily available in case the anomaly occurs again.

The *Data Processing and Management process* (sometimes shortened to just *Data Management process*) is the collection, logging, processing, storage, retrieval, transfer, distribution, and reporting of all the spacecraft and mission-related data. All the data, both SOH and payload, are downlinked from the spacecraft and received at the ground station where they are archived and then forwarded to the MOC (see Fig. 29-8). The real-time SOH data are sent directly from the ground station to the operators in the MOC.

The MOC begins the process of data processing by performing the Level 0 processing on the stored (and possibly real-time) SOH and payload data, i.e., removing the spacecraft and ground communication artifacts from the data such as headers, trailers, compression, special protocol characters; and correcting correctable transmission errors. The Level 0 data are then archived at the MOC. The Level 0 stored SOH data join the real-time SOH data at the front-end processor in the MOC where they are converted into engineering units (if required) and put into the form needed by the operators.

The Level 0 science/payload data are sent to the SOC (or payload customers) for further processing, archiving, and analysis. For some missions, raw science data are sent to the SOC where the Level 0 processing is performed. The SOC also has access to the archived SOH data that may be required during the analysis. The archived SOH data (and processed science data) are then available for mission data analysis with results going to the mission planners and others. Stored SOH data are used extensively during the engineering checkout phase of the mission.

The real-time data are monitored in real-time and also stored as both raw and engineering data for the life of the mission. The data management process also collects ancillary data to be combined with the payload data such as orbit and pointing information. Non-spacecraft telemetry data such as tracking data and ground station status data are also managed by the MOC. All the data received and processed by the MOC are stored in the MOC Data Archive.

The SOC applies or attaches to the payload data any calibration values for the sensors or optics, and append any ancillary data such as orbit and pointing data, sensor telemetry, and possibly the associated command sequences used for the observation. Some of this infor-

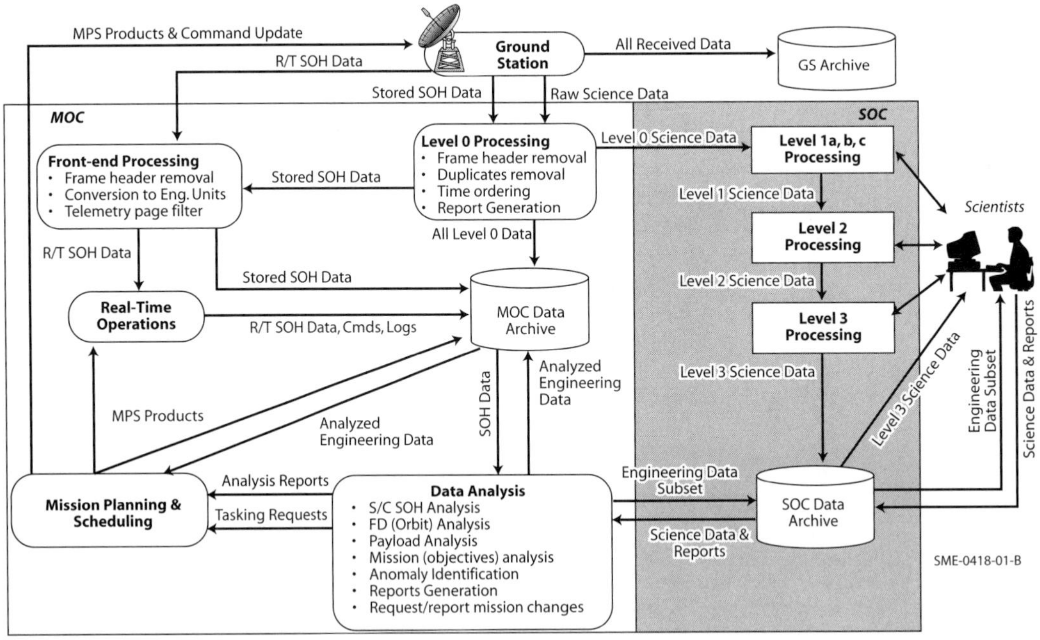

Fig. 29-8. Spacecraft Data Processing and Management Process. The process shown here is typical for a large science mission with a separate SOC, but different schemes can be used. The data downlinked from the spacecraft are received at the ground station where they are archived and then forwarded to the MOC. The real-time SOH data are sent directly from the ground station to the operators in the MOC. The stored SOH and payload data undergo Level 0 processing and archiving at the MOC. The Level 0 science data are then sent to the SOC for further processing, archiving, and analysis. The SOC also has access to the archived SOH data which may be required during the analysis. The archived SOH data (and processed science data) are then available for mission data analysis with results going to the mission planners and others. In some missions, the Level 0 processing for science data is performed in the SOC.

mation may be added later, such as the orbit and pointing data, which may need further processing to provide precise values.

Besides handling the data downlinked from the spacecraft and ground station status data, the data management process also handles other data transfer throughout the operations system, such as transfer of command loads (consisting of command sequences and flat files) to the ground stations for uplinking to the spacecraft. Other data products, such as schedules pass plans, pass logs, reports, may be handled by the data management system, which is responsible for both the transport and archiving of the data.

The *Analysis process* interprets the data obtained by the mission. Closely related to spacecraft and payload command and monitoring are spacecraft and payload analysis. The primary difference is that the monitor and control process is used with the near real-time telemetry, while the analysis process deals with the stored data that are received and processed by the system elements. Spacecraft subsystem and payload analysts review telemetry data and track the long term health and characterization of each subsystem and component. Although much of the data trending and analysis may be automated, usually there will still be human analysts required to interpret the results and make appropriate decisions based on them, although they should be able to work just normal working hours instead of a schedule based on the spacecraft contacts.

The *Spacecraft Analysis process* monitors the health and long-term trends for each of the spacecraft subsystems by examining power, thermal, pointing performance, radio links, memory storage, solar cell and battery degradation, and mechanical subsystems such as solar arrays, antennas, and the optical/payload bench. The spacecraft analysis process has the overall responsibility for determining and ensuring spacecraft safety and effectiveness. The primary functions are monitoring the health and status of the spacecraft bus and its resources, including engineering data such as temperatures, voltages and currents. This process is responsible for the trending and analysis of critical spacecraft SOH parameters and detecting anomalies or potential problems based on both short- and long-term performance trends. Spacecraft anomalies that are detected during this analysis or reported by either the spacecraft controllers or other sources are identified, documented, and resolved. If the anomaly cannot be resolved by the spacecraft analysts, then an Anomaly Response Team (ART) can be assembled and employed in the anomaly resolution process. The spacecraft analysis process also reports spacecraft status to spacecraft management and mission planners, and coordinates with spacecraft component manufactures and integrators as required.

The *Orbit and Trajectory Analysis process* is performed by the Flight Dynamics (FD) function of mission operations. On a regular basis, FD analyzes the tracking data. The analysis is the validation and calibration of the measured data used for orbit determination. The tracking data are validated automatically by comparing the measurements with the predicted orbit location, generating observation residuals and using statistical methods to identify poor quality data. Calibration using these tracking data is difficult with orbits very far from the Earth, so the use of collimation tracking data and periodically tracking other near-Earth spacecraft and analyzing the tracking residuals can be used to calibrate the angle and range data. Daily, or every few days, the spacecraft orbit is determined using the validated tracking data. This "actual" orbit is then used to produce the needed orbit products, such as a predicted ephemeris for mission and science planning, acquisition (pointing) data for the ground stations, orbit information to be sent to the spacecraft for attitude control, and a definitive orbit ephemeris for science and image analysis.

Using the definitive spacecraft orbit, FD propagates the orbit into the future and predicts when the orbit requires adjustment. A LEO satellite typically obtains an orbit ephemeris update on a daily basis. The date and parameters of the orbit maneuver are updated and made available to the spacecraft planning system. The planning system then constrains the science and other spacecraft activities around the time of the maneuver. If the exact time and location of the maneuver are not extremely critical, the planning system has some leeway as to when the spacecraft is unavailable due to the maneuver. The planned maneuver, however, is incorporated into the predicted ephemeris and used for long and short term planning. Flight Dynamics maintains the fuel consumption estimates and the propulsion performance and calibrations values.

Mission Analysis process has the overall responsibility for determining and ensuring the spacecraft payload safety and mission effectiveness. For some missions, the instrument analysis is a separate process performed by the SOC or payload engineers, while for other missions it may be performed in the MOC. The mission/payload analysis process is similar to that of spacecraft analysis, except with responsibility for the science instruments/payload instead of the spacecraft bus. This process is also responsible for determining the success of the spacecraft in accomplishing the science mission objectives of each observation, although not the science results. The mission analysis process is responsible for identifying, documenting, and resolving payload anomalies that are reported by either the spacecraft or payload controllers or other sources. The resolution process is similar to that of the spacecraft analysis function.

29.3 Mission Termination and Post-Mission Activities

Every mission comes to an end eventually, although in same cases that can be a very long time from launch. At the time of publication of this book, NASA's Voyager 1 and 2 missions are ongoing, more than 33 years after their launches in 1977. Both are still providing data about the heliosphere and interstellar space to NASA long after their primary mission to visit the outer planets had been successfully completed. Some missions complete their primary mission (or are unable to perform it) and may be funded for an extended mission, which may or may not have the same objectives. Examples of extended missions with the same overall objectives are the NASA Mars Exploration Rover missions, which have continued years past their nominal 90-day missions. An example of an extended mission with different objectives is the NASA Wide-field Infrared Explorer (WIRE) mission, which had to abandon its scientific mission of exploration in the infrared when the coolant required for the infrared sensor was exhausted early in the mission (due to a failure). However, the bus was still healthy, so the WIRE satellite was used to train spacecraft controllers and give students a "hands-on" learning experience.

There are generally four main reasons for mission termination:

1. Completion of mission (e.g., Stardust returned samples from a comet tail to Earth or LCROSS impacted the lunar surface—by design)
2. Lack of funding to continue operations—this includes obsolescence
3. Spacecraft (or payload) malfunction, including loss of contact—also includes catastrophic operations errors
4. Orbit decay and reentry or other destructive events (e.g., collision with debris)

For the first two reasons and sometimes the fourth reason (e.g., orbital decay to reentry), the mission management is aware of the mission termination in advance and can plan for it. The planning and implementation of mission termination is the responsibility of mission operations.

Since the dawn of the space age with the launch of Sputnik I in 1957, orbital debris has become an increasing problem and is recognized by the various agencies that launch satellites into Earth orbit. In order to reduce the amount of human-produced orbital debris (which includes derelict satellites as well as spent boosters, and pieces of space hardware), which can provide a real hazard to operating spacecraft (including the ISS and other manned vehicles), most Earth-orbiting space missions are designed according to criteria and standards such as outlined in the NASA document, NASA-STD-8719.14 (see also IADC [2011]). This contains a deorbit requirement of 30 years from launch or 25 years after the end of mission. To adhere to this rule, an orbital lifetime analysis must be performed. For small satellites with no on-board propulsion that can provide a deorbit capability, this means that the mission should be designed with an orbital altitude low enough that reentry will naturally occur within this time period. This threshold altitude is typically below 1,000 km, although orbital lifetime is very sensitive to changes in mass, cross-sectional area, and solar activity. If the mission has to be performed at an altitude that drives the orbital lifetime beyond the specified limits, then some sort of reentry aid needs to be included, such as a deorbit propulsive system or device to increase the cross-sectional area and thus the atmospheric drag (e.g., "speed brake" panels or an inflated balloon). See Sec. 30.2.

For satellites in a geosynchronous orbit, there is a different solution since the amount of propellant required to perform deorbit may be prohibitive. Communication satellites, for instance, occupy a particular "box" in the orbital geostationary equatorial belt and if they need to be replaced by a new satellite, then they must vacate the box without becoming a hazard. In this case, they are boosted into a higher "super geosynchronous orbit" which leaves them in orbit for centuries, but above the operating satellites and not between the Earth and geosynchronous orbit where they could still provide a hazard for collision with satellites transferring up to geosynchronous orbit. See Sec. 30.3.

Termination operations should be planned well in advance. If the spacecraft is large enough that parts of it may survive the reentry environment, then detailed analyses must be performed and the reentry burn carefully planned to ensure the surviving debris will impact in the ocean and the event should be coordinated with appropriate government and international agencies.

Before a satellite's mission is terminated, it should be put into as quiescent a state as possible. Typically, the batteries are drained, the EPS is disabled so that the solar arrays cannot recharge the batteries or provide power to the bus, the on-board memory is scrubbed, pressurized systems vented, mechanized systems put into a safe state, and the radios turned off (usually by cutting power). See TDAC [2007] for more information on safing spacecraft to reduce debris. Tracking of the satellite can be continued using the Two-Line Elements (TLEs) provided by the USAF.

For science or remote sensing missions in particular, the mission can continue long after the spacecraft's operation has ceased as the data are analyzed, reported, and used (e.g., in journal papers). There are typically some tasks that have to be performed to complete the project, such as writing final reports about the project along with other required documentation, technical papers, and documenting and sharing lessons learned (e.g., through technical conferences).

29.4 Mission Operations Process Improvement and Best Practices

29.4.1 Process Improvement

Even the most carefully planned mission operations or support plan may not survive first contact with reality. If the mission operations system has not been designed with the flexibility and processes to recognize problems or anomalies, analyze them, and provide a feedback loop to introduce improvements back into the mission operations process, then it will be very difficult and costly for the system to adapt. It is far better and cost effective to design these process improvement features into the system than to try re-engineering the system after launch. Several missions have attempted to introduce automation and process improvements into the system after launch, and have had a very difficult time doing so. It is difficult to do this without disrupting or risking the ongoing operations, and when it is possible, it is usually very costly. The golden rule of process improvement is: design the process of process improvement into the system from the very beginning so that it will appear in the design requirements.

This section, which is an abridged version of what appears in SOSTC [2003] and Sorensen, Campion, and Probert [2011], looks at some means that can be used for helping with the mission operations process improvement, from the determination of suitable metrics, methods to collect and analyze them, determination of solutions, and then feedback of the solutions into the system. Although the actual metrics and methods that are best suited for a particular mission might be different, the general principles stated herein are the results of experience obtained on several missions, including Low-Power Atmospheric Compensation Experiment (LACE), Clementine, MSTI-3, and others.

A major factor in the cost of spacecraft ground support is the effectiveness of the mission operations process. An ineffective, error-prone and labor intensive process will most likely result in increased cost, risk, and reduced customer satisfaction. In order to determine the effectiveness of how mission operations are performed and to determine areas of improvement, measures of effectiveness (MoEs) should be identified. The metrics obtained through these measures of effectiveness can then be empirically and subjectively analyzed to determine the areas of the operation that should be improved or automated to increase efficiency.

For a science mission, effectiveness factors for the mission operations include:

- Percentage completion of science objectives (e.g., number of science experiments successfully executed, coverage obtained by imaging, quality of data, quality and quantity of calibration data obtained)
- Cost of operations (comparison of actual versus projected costs)
- Response time and flexibility of the mission planning and operations process
- Efficiency (cost/data collected)

Some metrics that can help measure the effectiveness of science mission operations include: error tracking, exceptions (complexity) factor, rush factor, effort factor, response factor, fatigue factor, and morale factor. These MoEs and metrics were first identified in post-mission analysis of the Clementine lunar mission and were very useful in determining where the mission operations process was successful and where it needed improvement. They were subsequently used in the analysis of other historical missions before being designed into an operational commercial mission operations system (Honeywell's DataLynx). MoEs and their metrics can help to determine when and where to add automation to mission operations. For example, when command script generation was automated during the MSTI-3 operations, the overall error rate for the spacecraft dramatically declined, which was obvious by tracking the error metrics [Sorensen, Campion, and Probert, 2011].

Error Tracking. This MoE tracks all the ground source errors that reach the spacecraft during the mission (although we are using the spacecraft as the end "victim" system, this MoE could be equally applied to other systems that receive external data that could cause errors in its execution). Most of the errors that reach the spacecraft are generated by the mission operations process or allowed to pass through it to the spacecraft. Spacecraft commanding and operations errors that affect accomplishment of mission goals may include:

- Planning and timeline/schedule errors
- Command script/sequence errors
- Instrument or spacecraft pointing errors
- Commands/script testing errors
- Ground system errors
- Real-time operations errors
- Spacecraft hardware errors
- Software errors (ground and flight)
- Miscellaneous errors (communication links, ground segment hardware)—this is a catchall category of unlikely or rare sources of errors. If any of these elements become a significant source of errors (e.g., communication link), then it should probably tracked as a separate error. These errors can be either human or machine

Complexity/Exceptions Factor. This is a measure of the complexity of a mission "event" (e.g., pass, observation, or experiment). If there is a "standard" sequence for spacecraft operations, then this is the number of "exceptional" events being added to that sequence (e.g., special operations added to mapping). Metrics for this MoE are chosen to meaningfully reflect complexity (e.g., number of commands or activities required).

Rush Factor. This is a measurement of time between timeline or script completion and script execution on spacecraft. The Rush Factor MoE is inversely proportional to the time, i.e., the less time, the higher the Rush Factor. Elements involved in the mission operations process that may affect the Rush Factor include time required for testing of scripts on simulator/testbeds and time required for queuing and upload to spacecraft. The Rush Factor should be low (days, not hours). However, in order to be responsive to the science team or customer in a dynamic mission, the Rush Factor may by necessity, remain high, i.e., the higher the Rush Factor, the more responsive the operations team is, although it is at a cost of putting strain on the team and processes.

Effort Factor. This is a measurement of the number of man-hours expended per mission event. It can be a measure of complexity, but it is complicated by the efficiency of the process as well as by the level of automation. The Effort Factor is desired to be low to reduce costs and possible sources of errors. Automation can reduce the Effort Factor for operations personnel, but increase it for software engineers and programmers.

Response Factor. This is an inverse function of the measurement of time between the customer's (e.g., science team) request for a mission event and its execution. The Response Factor should be weighted to account for complexity of the requested event. This factor should be maximized (i.e., the time needed between requests and execution minimized) for effective operations.

Fatigue Factor. This is a measurement of the tiredness of the operations team (e.g., hours worked). The short-term Fatigue Factor is based on shift length, while the long-term Fatigue Factor is measured over weeks or months. Other factors (e.g., complexity, rush, effort, and response) can affect the Fatigue Factor. It may be determined by subjective data (e.g., questionnaires) and the number of errors generated.

Morale Factor. This is a measurement of the satisfaction and optimism level of the operations team, but is difficult to quantify. It is mostly subjective, but some metrics can be collected to help in its determination. The possible metrics includes the turnover rate of personnel and the number of operations personnel complaints received by the operations management. It might also be possible to use routine surveys of operations personnel, but it has to be determined subjectively as to how accurately these surveys reflect the true morale of the personnel.

In order to effectively generate, track, and use these MoE metrics, they should be incorporated into the mission operation process. Due to the limited record keeping typical in many of today's missions with limited budgets, it is often difficult if not impossible to reconstruct these metrics accurately, either to generate historical test cases, or to determine retroactively how the MoE factors have changed over the life cycle of a current operations process. However, steps can be taken in the design of a new operations process to implement changes in an existing system to collect these metrics.

At each step in the process, two logs should be generated and kept. An automatic on-line log should record the time that each event starts and stops in a sub-process (e.g., recording the time that a timeline enters the script generation step and the time that generated script leaves this step to be sent on to the next step in the process, usually testing). This automatic log should also record errors detected by the computer system, especially of errors that were detected in the input data, as well as any significant decisions or substeps. A manual on-line electronic log should also be kept. This log is to record any errors found and corrected or changes made by the operator, along with the decision rationale if appropriate. Both logs should be archived with the files for that particular pass or event and sent automatically to the operations director or analyst for review and analysis.

Metrics Analysis Process—The operations director or mission operations analyst should regularly collect and review metrics to identify problem areas. Trending software is of particular use to see how the factors change over time. The most useful plot is the cumulative errors plot, which shows on the same chart the cumulative total errors and each of the separate errors over the life of the mission or other designated time period. The cumulative number of errors is not so important, but the slope of the line is (i.e., the derivative of the cumulative errors with respect to time). By correlating the slopes of the line (steep slopes are bad, while flat or gentle slopes are good) to the seven MoE metric tracking charts, causes of the change in errors occurring on the spacecraft can often be identified by type. Steps can then be taken to analyze the details of particular MoEs to determine the root cause of the problem (or conversely, the lack of problems).

Feedback Implementation—Once a sub-process has been identified as needing improvement, total quality methods should be used to involve operations personnel in the solution. They can help in both the identification of the root cause of the problem as well as to help determine how to rectify it and work out a way to implement the solution into the operations process. Methods and metrics to determine the success of the implementation should also be identified. In some cases, it might be necessary to include mission or program managers, and customers (e.g., principal investigators or chief scientists).

Discrepancy Tracking, Archive and Reporting—As is true for other aspects of mission operations, all discrepancy tracking, metrics collection and analysis, problem resolution and decisions should be archived. Any feedback implementations that have been decided upon should be put into the formal discrepancy tracking system and followed by the operations director until the implementation has been fully completed and tested. Any meetings involved in the operations process or improvement process should be documented to leave a documentation trail of decisions made with rationale. Any reports or minutes of these meetings and decisions should be put into the operations archive and a copy sent to the appropriate mission operations management.

29.4.2 Best Practices

Probably the major theme of this chapter, and indeed this book, is that there is no need to re-invent the wheel. For most of you planning to operate a space mission, someone has operated a similar mission before (at least in many respects). We have tried to provide you with the basics for designing and implementing an adequate operations plan based on many years of experience. It is helpful when you have access to best practices and lessons learned from previous missions. Many such documents, especially in the commercial world, are either proprietary or very difficult to locate. However, reviewing and using such lists could be very beneficial in the four basic areas of your space project: performance, cost, schedule, and risk. There are some documents available from NASA and other agencies, such as in GSFC [1999], some of which are reported in the form of technical papers at the various professional conferences. However, the Best Practices Working Group of the AIAA Space Operations and Support Technical Committee (SOSTC) started in 2001 to compile mission operations best practices into an online document, [SOSTC, 2003] the first version of which was released in 2003 and continues to be expanded and updated. This has contributions from many different authors from government, industry, and academia. We highly recommend this document as a source of best practices and lessons learned for space mission operations. Also recommended is the Annual Improving Space Operations Workshop sponsored by the SOSTC, the details of which can be found on their website [SOSTC, 2011].

29.5 The Future of Mission Operations

It is difficult to predict the future, but based on trends in the area of space mission operations, it is possible to reasonably extrapolate these trends into the near future, the next 10–20 years, or the lifetime of this book. Although the computing power and miniaturization of computer processors used in spacecraft lags behind those used in terrestrial applications, due to the need for radiation hardening and improvements in reliability, the computing power of today's generation of spacecraft far exceeds that of spacecraft in the past, and it is continuing to increase. Even a simple CubeSat has more computer capability than billion-dollar spacecraft of a couple decades ago. The result is that more of the functions that were performed on the ground as part of mission operations can now be performed on board the spacecraft. Functions such as processing payload data, orbit determination (thanks to GPS and similar systems), spacecraft attitude determination and control, and ground contact execution can now be managed by the spacecraft rather than the ground. Clementine was the first mission to perform an autonomous spacecraft operations experiment in 1994 [Sorensen, Oswald, Shook, Van Gaasbeck, 1995], but this type of autonomous operation is becoming more common. The effect of this is what was in the 1990s an innovative form of mission operations, known as "lights out" operations, is also becoming more common. This means that the spacecraft monitors its own condition and is able to execute ground station contact with no humans in the loop, even for monitoring. This happens when both the spacecraft and the ground station have been designed for autonomous or automatic operations. Of course, if there are any anomalies detected that are not within the porfolio of the automatic systems to handle, then human operators need to be notified and brought in to resolve them. So far, lights-out operations are typically only done with standard and relatively simple operations. Humans are still needed to do long-term or short-term planning for the mission (although this is also changing), and to examine and analyze trends in the engineering SOH data, and act upon it when needed. However, as the computers (both hardware and software) become increasingly capable, the roles of humans (and the resulting high recurring costs) will decrease.

Despite the decreasing role of humans in mission operations, most spacecraft today and for the forseeable future, especially in the areas of science and exploration, are so complex and expensive that the need for humans in the operations process will remain. There is an ongoing trend, which goes back decades, to consolidate and reuse mission operations systems. It is desirable for schedule, cost, and risk considerations to reuse software and hardware from one mission to the next. It is also desirable, for organizations that operate several spacecraft, to be able to operate multiple spacecraft using the same mission operations centers and software applications. Although this has been a goal for many years, it has been difficult to implement in a cost-effective manner, especially when the spacecraft and missions are dissimilar. However, as discussed in Sec. 20.4, there are some promising efforts underway, internationally, that are using a "plug'n'play" paradigm to achieve the goal of providing mission operations cheaply and quickly for new missions and mutiple missions, simultaneously. JPL has the Advanced Multi-Mission Operations System (AMMOS), which is designed to provide the tools and services to support NASA's deep space and astrophysics missions, but is designed to be flexible enough for other missions and is available for non-NASA missions and universities [AMMOS, 2011]. Goddard Space Flight Center has its GSFC Mission Services Evolution Center (GMSEC) reference architecture, which provides a scalable, extensible ground and flight system approach for space missions. GMSEC is particularly suited for the quick and easy integration of functional components obtained by the mission project that enable a unique mission operations solution to be tailor-made [GMSEC, 2011]. Another mission operations system especially designed for end-to-end operations of small satellites is the Comprehensive Open-architecture Space Mission Operations System (COSMOS) from the Hawaii Space Flight Laboratory at the University of Hawaii at Manoa in collaboration with NASA Ames Research Center. COSMOS is a system of interconnected tools (both internal and externally provided) that are designed to be easily adaptable to new spacecraft and for installation in new MOCs. The source code is available to users for special modifications and enhancements that are not handled by the COSMOS editors and system itself. COSMOS is especially suited for nano- and micro-satellites, although it can handle larger ones as well [COSMOS, 2011].

Of course the ultimate goal of human spaceflight operations is similar to that of the aircraft operations, where the humans on board the spacecraft with the help of the on-board systems, are able to monitor and control the spacecraft with no intervention from the ground, except in emergencies. A Space Traffic Control (STC) would monitor the space lanes, the launches, and the descent of the spacecraft. The STC would hand over control to the Air Traffic Control system when the spacecraft entered the atmosphere approaching aricraft altitudes, where the ATC would integrate the spacecraft into the air traffic patterns down to a successful landing. This vision could be a reality within our lifetimes and may be sooner that you think.

References

For annotated bibliography of mission operations, see the book website.

AIAA, 2011. Website.

Alcott, G. and W. Peters. 1996. "Operations Engineering: Applying Hands-on Experience to the Development Process." SpaceOps 1996 Symposium. SO96.8.10. Munich, Germany: Sept. 16–20

AMMOS. 2011. Advanced Multi-Mission Operations System. Website.

Anthony III, J. and W. O. Glascoe. 1992. "US Air Force Phillips Laboratory Autonomous Space Navigation Experiment." 48th Annual Meeting of The Institute of Navigation. Dayton, OH, pp. 317–326. Jun.

Bruca, L., J. P. Douglas, and T. C. Sorensen. 2007. *Space Operations—Mission Management, Technologies, and Current Applications.* Reston, VA: AIAA.

Calzolari, G. P. 2007. "Automation of ESOC Mission Operations." *Space Operations—Mission Management, Technologies, and Current Applications.* Reston, VA: AIAA.

CCSDS. 2007. "CCSDS File Delivery Protocol (CFDP) Parts 1 & 2." Informational Report CCSDS 720.1-G.3 and CCSDS 720.2-G.3. Washington, DC.

COMPLEX/SSB. 1997. *Lessons Learned from the Clementine Mission.* Committee on Planetary and Lunar Exploration. Washington, D.C: National Academy Press.

COSMOS, 2011. Comprehensive Open-Architecture Space Mission Operations System. Website.

DODFA. 2011. DoD Architecture Framework. Website.

ECSS. 2008. *Space Segment Operability*. ECSS-E-ST-70-11C. ESA-ESTEC, Sec. 5.7. Neurochord, Netherlands: Jul. 31.

GMSEC. 2011. GSFC Mission Services Evolution Center. Website.

GSFC. 1999. "Best Practices." Satellite Operations Risk Assessment (SORA) Team report, NASA Goddard Space Flight Center.

Horan, D., T. Sorensen, T. Tran, and C. Hoffman. 1995. "Clementine Mission Operations." 1st International Symposium on Reducing the Cost of Spacecraft Ground Systems and Operations. Chilton, Oxforshire, UK.

IADC. 2011. Inter-Agency Space Debris Coordination Committee. Website.

IEEE. 2011. IEEE Aerospace Conference. Website.

Kehr, Joachim. 2007. SpaceOps Symposium. Rome, Italy. Jun. 19–23.

Rainey, L. B. 2004. *Space Modeling and Simulation—Roles and Applications Throughout the System Life Cycle*. Space Technology Series. El Segundo, CA: Aerospace Corp. and Reston, VA: AIAA.

Rao, Y. P., and P. Soma. 1998. "Pre-Launch TTC and Mission Operations Simulations for LEO Missions." 4a001. SpaceOps 98 Symposium. Tokyo, Japan.

RS2011. Reinventing Space Conference. Website.

Ryan, T. E. and M. Fatig. 1993. "The Need for Early Operations Involvement in Spacecraft Design." Space Programs and Technologies Conference. AIAA-1993-4183. Huntsville, AL: Sept. 21–23.

Sherwood, R. and S. Chien. 2007. "Enhancing Science and Automating Operations Using Onboard Autonomy." *Space Operations—Mission Management, Technologies, and Current Applications.* Reston, VA: AIAA.

Sierhuis, M., W. J. Clancey, and M. H. Sims. 2002. "Multiagent Modeling and Simulation in Human-Robot Mission Operations Work System Design." Hawaii International Conference on System Sciences, IEEE, Hawaii Jan. 7–10.

SmallSat. 2011. Small Satellite Conference. USU. Website.

Sorensen, T. C., T. T. Tran, and B. J. Geldzahler. 1995. "Effective Science Mission Planning and Operations—The Clementine Approach." 1st International Symposium on Reducing the Cost of Spacecraft Ground Systems and Operations. Chilton, Oxfordshire, UK.

Sorensen, T. C., D. C. Oswald, R. M. Shook and J. V. Gaasbeck. 1995. "Spacecraft Autonomous Operations Experiment Performed During the Clementine Lunar Mission." *Journal of Spacecraft and Rockets,* vol. 32, pp. 1049–1053.

Sorensen, T. C. and P. D. Spudis. 2005. "The Clementine Mission—A 10-year Perspective." *Journal of Earth Systems Science,* vol. 114, 6, pp. 645–668.

Sorensen, T. C., R. R. Campion, and T. C. Probert. 2011. "Using Measures of Effectiveness to Analyze and Improve Mission Operations." *Journal of Space Operations*.

SOSTC. 2003. "Satellite Mission Operations Best Practices." Best Practices Working Group, Space Operations and Support Technical Committee. Reston, VA: AIAA.

SOSTC. 2011. AIAA Space Operations and Support Technical Committee. Website.

SpaceOps. 2011. International Committee on Technical Interchange for Space Mission Operations and Ground Data Systems (SpaceOps Organization). Website.

Squibb, G. F., D. G. Boden and W. Larson. Editors. 2006. *Cost-Effective Space Mission Operations.* 2nd ed. Space Technology Series. New York, NY: The McGraw-Hill Companies.

TDAC. 2007. *IADC Space Debris Mitigation Guidelines*, IADC-02-01 Rev. 1.

Welch, D. C. and J. Karlin. 1996. "Functional Model for Spacecraft Operations." S096.5.05. SpaceOps 96 Symposium. Munich, Germany.

Wertz, J. R. and W. J. Larson. 1999. *Space Mission Analysis and Design, 3rd Ed.* Space Technology Series. Torrance, CA: Microcosm Press and Kluwer Academic Publishers.

30 End of Mission Considerations

Scott M. Hull, ***NASA Goddard Space Flight Center***

While a great deal of effort goes into planning and executing successful mission operations, it is also important to consider the end of the mission during the planning, design, and operations phases of any mission. Spacecraft and launch vehicles must be disposed of properly in order to limit the generation of orbital debris (Sec. 7.5), and better preserve the orbital environment for all future missions. Figure 30-1 shows a 1990s projected growth of debris with and without the use of responsible disposal techniques. This requires early selection of a responsible disposal scenario, so that the necessary capabilities can be incorporated into the hardware designs. The mission operations must be conducted in such a way as to preserve, and then actually perform the planned, appropriate end of mission disposal.

Computer simulations have shown that the orbital debris population already present on orbit is self-propagating; that is, the orbital debris density will continue to increase through random collisions alone, unless reduced by outside efforts [Liou and Johnson, 2008]. This may well result in a cascade effect that eventually renders some orbits impractical for space operations. Since it is

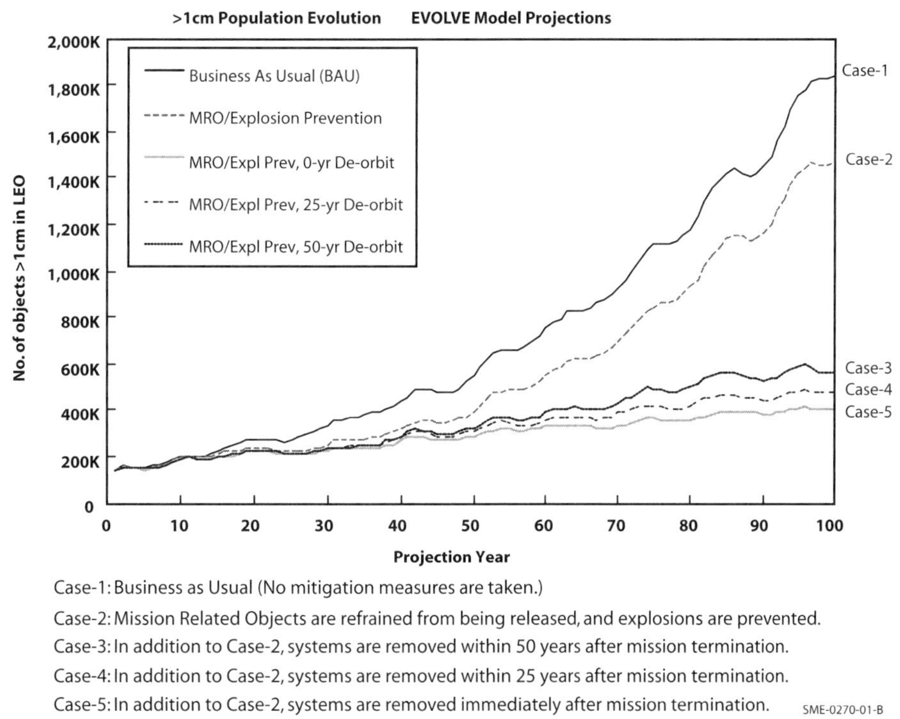

Fig. 30-1. Debris Growth with Various Mitigation Approaches. [IADC, 2004a]

not yet economically practical to remove a significant amount of existing debris from orbit, it is critical that responsible end of mission disposal be practiced for all current and future missions, in order to help control the rate of increase of mission-lethal debris objects in commonly used orbits. Had such methods been employed throughout the history of space operations, the cascade effect might have been prevented, or at least substantially delayed.

End of Mission disposal (also known as *End of Life disposal*, *Decommissioning*, or simply *Disposal*) has been addressed primarily at the international level in discussions by the Inter-Agency Space Debris Coordination Committee (IADC). The IADC is an international forum of national space agencies and the European Space Agency (ESA) for the coordination of activities related to the issues of man-made and natural debris in space [IADC, 2002]. In 2002, the IADC issued a set of guidelines (IADC-02-01) addressing, among other things, prevention of post-mission explosions, and acceptable disposal options. These guidelines, described in Sec. 30.1, were slightly refined in 2007.

Spacecraft mission designers need to consider disposal early in the design process (see Sec. 3.5), in order to incorporate the necessary hardware and procedures to ensure a safe disposal. The first step is to select a baseline disposal method, as described in Secs. 30.2 and 30.3. This disposal method will determine the key design factors which will need to be considered throughout the remainder of the design process. It may, for example, be necessary to size the propulsion system and navigation hardware for an orbit change or controlled reentry. Alternatively, it may be necessary to design the power and propulsion systems for post-mission passivation, as described in Sec. 30.4. As the design develops, and the reentry risk is determined, it is occasionally necessary to change the baseline disposal method, but at a cost which increases dramatically as the design matures. In any event, it will be necessary to develop and test spacecraft operations procedures specific to the disposal (Sec. 30.5). The disposal of the FireSat II and SCS sample missions are discussed in Sec. 30.6 as examples of the application of the disposal principles. Early consideration of the end of mission disposal is among the most effective ways to minimize the growth of orbital debris, to the benefit of all missions.

30.1 IADC End of Mission Guidelines

While they do represent agreements among the leading space agencies of the world, it is important to note that the IADC guidelines are not currently legally binding. They are generally reflected in numerous national space policies, however, and are followed at least in part for the majority of scientific and military space missions. Despite whether commercial and other missions are legally bound to comply with the IADC guidelines, meeting the standards has been shown to be crucial for limiting the growth of orbital debris, which is in the interests of all space users. The guidelines are summarized here, and the specific text is readily available on the internet [IADC, 2004b].

The IADC guidelines provide guidance for limiting the generation of orbital debris both during and after space operations. They begin by describing the need for limiting the growth of orbital debris, and defining the relevant terms used throughout the document. The guidelines refer to direct creation of debris through operational debris (e.g., lens caps), and potential breakage of tethers. They also consider on-orbit breakups caused by explosions during and after the mission, as well as intentional destruction by internal or external sources. The guidelines also define accepted disposal orbits (Secs. 30.2 and 30.3) and other conditions such as the timeline for abandoning commonly used orbits, and controlling the risk to people and property on the Earth. Finally, they address limiting the potential for damage by collisions with other space objects and with small orbital debris that could prevent the ability to successfully execute end of mission disposal. The IADC guidelines are written to apply throughout the mission lifetime, from design through operations and decommissioning.

It is worth noting that while the IADC guidelines lay the foundation for general agreements on the limitation of orbital debris, with few exceptions, they do not provide specific quantitative requirements. In fact, the stated purpose of the guidelines is to "demonstrate the international consensus on space debris mitigation activities and constitute a baseline that can support agencies and organizations when they establish their own mitigation standards." Only in the case of the definitions of the protected orbit regions, and the GEO disposal conditions, do the guidelines provide specific limits. The remaining limitations are described as qualitative measures, which are left to individual agency requirements documents to define in detail.

In addition to the IADC guidelines, various other organizations have adopted similar guidelines and requirements. In 2007, the United Nations General Assembly endorsed the "Space Debris Mitigation Guidelines of the Committee on the Peaceful Uses of Outer Space," which are very similar to, and cover the same general topics as, the IADC guidelines, while being generally less specific. Most nations look to their national space agency (often an IADC member) for orbital debris policy and control. The US has issued not only the "US Government Orbital Debris Mitigation Standard Practices," but also has a number of individual agency documents that address orbital debris limitation to varying degrees. In general, the requirements documents issued by the IADC member agencies themselves are the most specific and restrictive. Examples of national orbital debris limitation documents are shown in Table 30-1.

Table 30-1. International Orbital Debris Limitation Documents.

Domain	Document
IADC	IADC-02-01, Rev 1
US Government	US Government Orbital Debris Mitigation Standard Practices
NASA	NPR 8715.6A, NASA-STD-8719.14
US DoD	DoD Space Policy Directive, 3100.10, AFI 91-217
US FAA	Title 14, CFR Part 415.39
Japan	JAXA JMR-003
France	CNES MPM-50-00-12
Europe (ESA)	European Code of Conduct for Space Debris Mitigation
Russia	Space Technology Items. General Requirements on Mitigation of Space Debris Population

30.2 LEO Disposal Options*

Responsible exit from Low-Earth Orbit (LEO) is one of the most important steps that can be taken to limit the growth of debris in that region of space. An IADC working group has examined the long-term effects of various guideline options [IADC, 2002], and shown that by limiting the amount of time that each vehicle remains in LEO, growth of the orbital debris environment is greatly reduced. Thus, it is desirable and recommended for space objects (both launch vehicle stages and spacecraft) to be removed from the LEO region as soon as practical. The minimum orbital lifetime possible for an individual vehicle might be determined by the remaining maneuvering capability of the vehicle at the end of the mission or by the initial orbit. There are 3 basic approaches to LEO disposal. The most desirable is to perform a controlled (or "targeted") reentry into an unpopulated region of ocean soon after the end of the mission, either using onboard propulsion, or by external retrieval. If this is not possible, it may be possible to boost into a storage orbit between LEO and GEO, safely removed from both regions. Finally, a spacecraft can be allowed to reduce its orbit by atmospheric drag, (Sec. 9.4.4), resulting in an uncontrolled reentry, and impact on an unpredictable portion of the Earth's surface.

Controlled reentry is the preferred LEO disposal method for several reasons. Not only does it provide positive removal of the vehicle from orbit, but the removal also tends to occur as soon as possible after the mission. By selecting a reentry location over a large unoccupied area of ocean, the reentry risk to the ground population is minimized. This, along with the lack of post-mission passivation, can result in greater flexibility for the mission hardware designers. Controlled reentry is not without significant challenges, however. Reentry maneuvers typically require extensive planning, and notification to the relevant air and maritime traffic authorities prior to performing the maneuvers. In practice, controlled reentry is best performed using at least three separate maneuvers in order to better control and refine the orbit, with a final perigee of less than 50 km, to prevent atmospheric skip. In order to accomplish this, the spacecraft design must incorporate sufficiently large thrusters to ensure adequate control authority at low altitudes. Controlled reentry also requires that the vehicle reserve sufficient fuel to reliably perform the reentry maneuvers at the end of the mission, which will result in a larger fuel mass at launch. Section 9.6 discusses the delta V needed to accomplish controlled reentry, and provides examples. With the advent of robotic servicing and retrieval capabilities, it also may become a practical option for missions to further extend mission lifetime, and still perform a controlled reentry, but at the expense of an additional launch.

Disposal into a storage, or "graveyard," orbit may be a practical option for some high-altitude LEO missions. The storage region is located between LEO and GEO, and is generally considered to extend from 2,000 km to approximately 35,586 km (GEO − 200 km) altitude. Within this region, care must be taken to also avoid commonly used orbits, such as the circular 12 hour orbits used by navigation and other satellites. Both the apogee and perigee of the disposal orbit must be within the storage orbit region. As with controlled reentry, the spacecraft design must incorporate sufficiently large maneuvering thrusters, and fuel must be reserved for the orbit raising operation. Figure 30-2 shows the typical delta V required to maneuver from a circular LEO orbit to the 2,000 km storage orbit. Any vehicle left in a storage orbit must be passivated at the end of a mission, as described in Sec. 30.4. In general, only those missions operating above about 1,400 km altitude can reach the storage orbit region with less delta V than reentering within the recommended time frame.

If neither controlled reentry nor storage orbit disposal are practical for a LEO mission, then disposal will eventually occur by uncontrolled reentry. If possible, the final altitude and area-to-mass ratio need to be tailored to ensure that a reentry by atmospheric drag (Sec. 9.4.4) is

Get Stnd *Applicable standards: ISO 17875 (Space Systems). See website for reference.

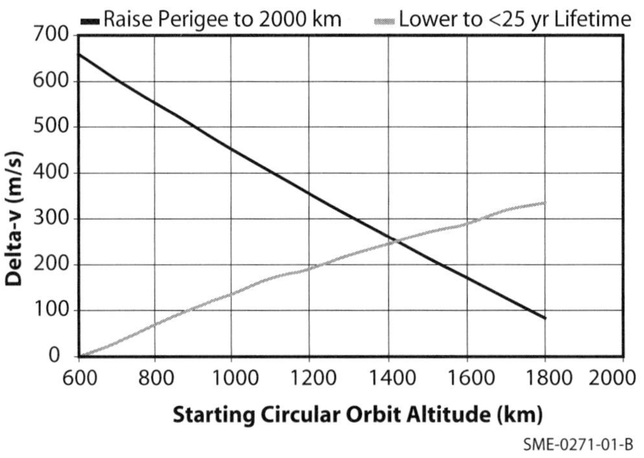

Fig. 30-2. Disposal Delta-V Requirements.

predicted to occur within 25 years after the end of the mission. The IADC study mentioned in Sec. 30.1 concluded that this orbit duration is a reasonable compromise between unlimited orbital lifetimes and immediate de-orbit at the end of the mission. For spacecraft without a propulsion system, the maximum orbit altitude is limited to about 600 to 700 km, depending on the area-to-mass ratio and launch year. The typical delta V required to maneuver from a circular LEO orbit to an orbit that will reenter the atmosphere within 25 years is shown on Fig. 30-2. Note that the solar flux is an important component of this prediction, and varies throughout the solar cycle (Sec. 7.1.1), complicating the reentry date prediction considerably. Current predictions of future solar activity are available for download from NASA, NOAA, and other sources, and are typically updated frequently. Earlier orbit decay will further reduce the likelihood of collisions, and is therefore recommended when possible.

While at first glance, uncontrolled reentry may appear to be a preferred disposal method (it is surely the simplest and lowest mass approach), there are considerable challenges to doing so responsibly. It is necessary for any non-operational object left in orbit to be passivated during the orbit-decay period, as discussed in Sec. 30.4, in order to prevent inadvertent explosion or breakup during the potentially long orbit decay period. The risk to the ground population may also be controlled by requirements of the launching or operating organization. For example, several space agencies require a detailed assessment to show that the spacecraft hardware will burn up sufficiently during atmospheric reentry to pose less than a 1 in 10,000 risk of causing serious injury to even one human. In some cases, the risk to the public from an uncontrolled reentry is sufficient to dictate that a controlled reentry is the only acceptable method of disposal from LEO.

Meeting a requirement to limit reentry risk can be extremely difficult or impossible for some large spacecraft, and usually necessitates specialized design techniques and material selection. The risk is determined by how much of the spacecraft survives reentry, and by the ground population over which the reentering debris might land. In the case of an uncontrolled reentry, the surviving debris might land anywhere in the latitude band covered by the orbit inclination, so an average population density over this band is used for the risk estimate. Object survivability is largely driven by the thermal properties of the primary construction material for the object in question, expressed as a *heat of ablation*. Heat of ablation, H_A, is typically expressed in terms of mass, but it can also be useful to express it in terms of volume (multiplying by the material density), for comparing two material options for the same size part.

$$H_A = H_S \times \Delta T + H_F \tag{30-1}$$

where H_S is the specific heat, ΔT is the temperature change, and H_F is the latent heat of fusion.

The heats of ablation for several typical spacecraft materials are shown in Table 30-2. Notice that materials such as aluminum and graphite/epoxy composite are readily demiseable, whereas titanium, glass, and beryllium, all have high heats of ablation, and should therefore be avoided when possible, if reentry risk is a concern. In general, objects made from materials with melting temperatures greater than 1,000 K, heat of ablation greater than 1,000 kJ/kg, or 2,500 kJ/m^3 are more

Table 30-2. Heats of Ablation for Several Common Spacecraft Materials.

Material	Melting/Softening Temperature (K)	Heat of Ablation (kJ/kg)	Heat of Ablation (kJ/m^3)
Graphite/Epoxy	700	350	550
Aluminum	850	900	2,400
Stainless Steel	1,700	900	7,250
Titanium	1,940	1,600	7,050
Zerodur Glass	2,000	1,400	3,550
Beryllium	1,557	4,100	7,550

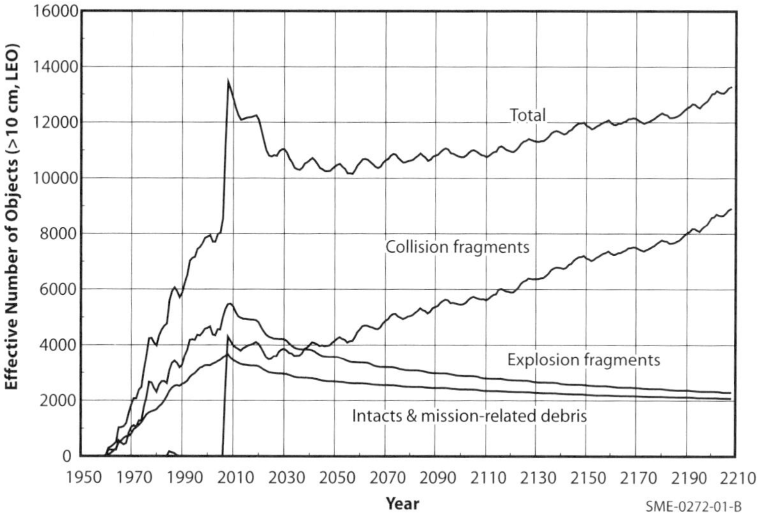

Fig. 30-3. Projected Debris Generation by Mechanism (with no new launches after 2009). [Liou, 2010]

likely to survive atmospheric reentry. *Oxidation heating* (essentially burning) on reentry also contributes to the demisability of aluminum and graphite/epoxy.

Object survivability is also influenced by the object's ballistic coefficient as shown on Fig. 9-22, which is a function of the shape, mass, and dimensions of the object, and determines its velocity (Sec. 9.4). In general, faster moving objects accumulate more heat, and are more likely to demise. Reentry risk has been successfully reduced on some flight missions by modifying a component's shape, size, or material, when possible. Another approach that can be used to reduce the reentry risk is to ensure that several high survivability objects are bound together, since multiple objects are more likely to cause injury than a single object. For example, if several surviving battery cells are contained within a robust battery box, then the single surviving box presents less risk than the multiple unbounded cells. Because the survivability of spacecraft components depends on so many factors, it is necessary to combine very specialized assessment software with detailed knowledge of the spacecraft construction in order to determine and limit the reentry risk. Early avoidance of high survivability materials in component designs can help to prevent difficult and expensive redesigns late in the design phase.

For all LEO mission disposal options, it is desirable to minimize the total time that a vehicle spends in orbit. This is done to reduce the likelihood that the vehicle will experience collisions with resident objects, which generally result in the creation of additional orbital debris. Debris generation potential increases rapidly with projectile size, and even existing objects as small as 1 cm can create additional debris on impact. Simulations predict that on-orbit collisions will be the primary source of new orbital debris, so minimizing orbital lifetime is the most important step toward limiting future debris generation. Figure 30-3 shows that even with no new launches, collisions among existing on-orbit objects will eventually cause the debris population to rise. Any fuel remaining at the end of the mission should be used to lower perigee as much as possible during the passivation process, resulting in the earliest possible reentry. One caveat to this general rule is that the last burn before an uncontrolled reentry should leave the spacecraft high enough so that its orbit remains stable long enough for ground tracking to get an accurate fix. This will allow monitoring of the vehicle for conjunction assessment and collision avoidance purposes as its apogee descends past other operating spacecraft.

30.3 Non-LEO Disposal Options*

The IADC guidelines define two protected regions of space: LEO and GEO, as shown in Fig. 30-4. No space vehicles should be left in either of these regions on a long-term basis. The *LEO region* is simply defined as the "spherical region that extends from the Earth's surface up to an altitude (Z) of 2,000 km." Removal from the LEO region within 25 years is described in Sec. 30.2. The *GEO protected region* is defined as 35,786 km ± 200 km, with latitude of 0 deg ± 15 deg. Any mission that passes through that protected region must be maneuvered at the end of the mission to remain clear. Removal from GEO should occur as soon as practical after the end of a mission.

Disposal from GEO is performed by increasing the orbital radius sufficiently to remain well in excess of 200 km above the GEO altitude (35,786 km + 200 km = 35,986 km minimum altitude) for a minimum of 100 years. Due to the effects of solar radiation (Sec. 7.1),

Get Stnd — Applicable standards: ISO 26872 (Space Systems). See website for reference.

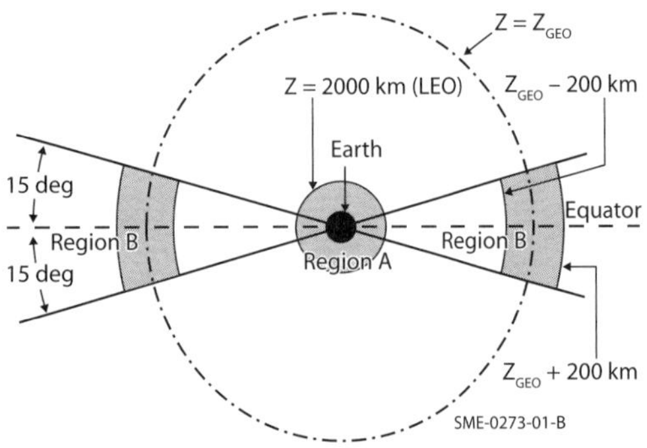

A. Definition

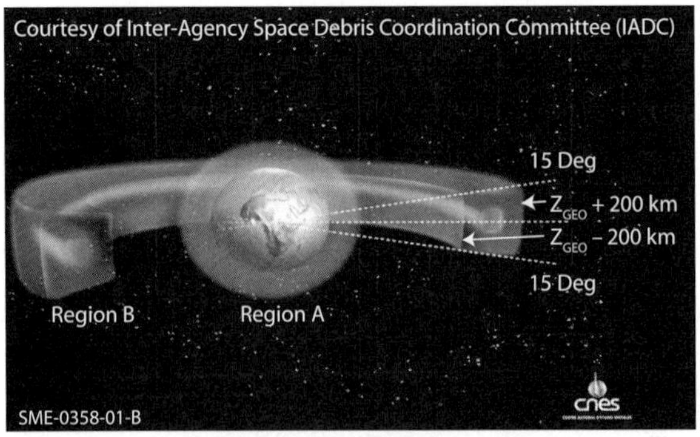

B. Artist's Rendition

Fig. 30-4. The IADC-defined Protected Regions of Space. [IADC, 2004a]

as well as lunar-solar and geopotential perturbations, the recommended minimum increase above GEO is defined as:

$$\Delta H = 200 \text{ km} + 35 \text{ km} + (1{,}000 \text{ km} \times C_R \times A/m) \quad (30\text{-}2)$$

where 35 km is incorporated due to effects from lunar-solar and geopotential perturbations. C_R is the solar radiation pressure coefficient (typically 1–2 kg/m^2). A/m is the spacecraft cross-sectional area to dry mass ratio (m^2/kg).

The altitude is generally increased/decreased, to prevent an accumulation of debris that future GEO missions would need to pass through to get to GEO, and to prevent potential signal interference. In addition to increasing the orbital radius, the final orbit should be circularized to an eccentricity of no more than 0.003 (see Sec. 9.4.2), and the spacecraft needs to be passivated as described in Sec. 30.4. It is estimated that the fuel required for responsible disposal of GEO missions is equivalent to that used for about 3 months of station-keeping (see Sec. 14.3) for most spacecraft [IADC, 2004b]. The "Support to the IADC Space Debris Mitigation Guidelines" document contains further details on disposal from GEO.

Disposal from Earth orbits other than LEO and GEO (e.g., high eccentricity science orbits) should minimize the orbit lifetime and avoid any highly used regions. While the IADC guidelines are not specific, some national requirements documents include a protected region for 12 hour orbits, commonly used for navigation satellites. Due to the wide variety of unusual orbits, it would be impossible to cover all possibilities in detail here. The first priority of the end of mission planning is minimization of the potential for on-orbit collisions. As with LEO and GEO missions, vehicles left in orbit must be passivated (see Sec. 30.4) after the final maneuvers.

Currently, there are few guidelines available for disposal of Lunar, planetary, or Lagrange orbit missions. The primary consideration, as it is for Earth orbits, is to minimize the potential for collisions with other current and future spacecraft, either directly or through generated debris. Therefore, it is best to avoid leaving spacecraft in long-term orbits (>10 years) at the end of a mission, except in those cases where the spacecraft continues to serve as a communications relay after its primary mission. Likewise, it is best to passivate any orbital hardware at the end of the mission to prevent explosions and other breakups, which would generate additional debris that might interfere with future missions. If disposal is to include Lunar or planetary impact, care should be taken to avoid sites of scientific or historic value, as well as preventing organic contamination whenever possible.

30.4 Passivation

At the end of a mission, the IADC guidelines call for all on board sources of stored energy to be "depleted or safed when they are no longer required for mission operations or post-mission disposal," also known as *passivation*. The main concern is that stored residual energy has in the past resulted in explosions, which have been a major source of orbital debris. Propulsion systems, batteries, and reaction wheels all contain stored energy, and are the most common components identified for passivation. Since a spacecraft or a launch vehicle could be in orbit and unattended for many years (even centuries) after the mission, it is important to passivate such components to prevent generation of debris that would increase the likelihood of collisions for other missions.

30.4.1 Propulsion System Passivation

Propulsion system explosions have resulted in some of the largest debris-producing events on orbit. In 1996, a Hydrazine Auxiliary Propulsion System (HAPS) upper stage spontaneously exploded 2 years after delivering its payload, generating over 700 pieces of debris large enough to be tracked from the ground. Due to a launch anomaly, this vehicle contained both propellant and high pressured gas, which were not able to be depleted. The most likely cause of the explosion was a long-term regulator failure, which allowed the propulsion tank to become over pressurized [Johnson, 1999].

A propulsion system (Sec. 18.1) is designed to produce a controlled explosion, resulting in the desired thrust. Unexpected events, such as small debris impact to the tank, mixing fuel and oxidizer, can produce extremely destructive explosions. Even residual pressurant gas (despite being chemically inert) can cause a propulsion tank to rupture catastrophically if, for example, the tank is struck by small debris. Propellants should be depleted by either burning or venting, and pressurant should be vented during disposal to prevent future breakups and debris generation. Residual propellant should be used to lower the perigee of LEO vehicles to ensure that they de-orbit as soon as possible. Unfortunately, some propulsion system designs do not allow for complete passivation, **unless this capability is specifically taken into account early in the design phase**.

There can be a number of challenges to depleting the fuel left on board a spacecraft at the end of a mission. Because sensors can become inaccurate, particularly near the end of a mission, when the residual propellant levels are low, it can be difficult to judge exactly how much propellant remains to be depleted. It is recommended that, if possible, the propulsion system be monitored until some positive sign of completion is observed (e.g., a rapid pressure drop from pressurant venting through a thruster). If a significant amount of propellant remains to be expelled, it must be done in a manner that will not cause excessive disruption to the spacecraft attitude, or cause the spacecraft to spin beyond its design limits. Since even directly opposed thrusters are not perfectly matched, this can be more difficult than initially imagined. Propulsion systems have also been observed to perform very differently as the propellant nears exhaustion [Hughes et al., 2006].

A unique challenge was the passivation of the TDRS-1 spacecraft after a very long and successful 26 year career. Due to a modification in its mission, when the payload finally failed, there was still a large excess of fuel on board, which needed to be expended. Since lowering perigee was not an option for a GEO mission, and using all remaining fuel to increase the altitude would cause the spacecraft to drift out of communications range during the maneuver, an alternative solution was developed. The spacecraft was first raised to the disposal orbit, then a flat spin was induced to exhaust the remaining fuel, while not disturbing the orbit or exceeding the spacecraft mechanical design. In this way, the fuel was expended and the spacecraft was passivated before it drifted out of communications range. This is an example of the creativity sometimes necessary to perform responsible passivation when it was not necessarily considered early in the design.

The IADC guidelines and most space agency regulations call for depletion of pressurant gas at the end of the mission because residual pressure exerts stress on the tanks and other hardware. The method of passivation varies based on the propulsion system design. In the case of a propellant tank with no diaphragm, it is usually possible to expel the pressurant gas by latching opposing thruster valves open at the end of the mission. Pressurant gas that is trapped behind a diaphragm, or in a separate tank, needs to be exhausted through a dedicated vent line. Such vent lines should be designed so that they will not impart a significant thrust or spin to the spacecraft during passivation. This can be accomplished by controlling the gas flow, and providing an omnidirectional outlet.

30.4.2 Power System Passivation

To date, batteries have exploded on orbit on at least 8 occasions, accounting for a portion of the debris currently in orbit [NASA, 2008]. Most battery explosions result from excess gas pressure generated inside the battery case due to overcharging. Nickel-hydrogen batteries, for example, typically operate at up to 1,000 psi (or more), directly related to the charge state. It is therefore important to provide the hardware capability to physically disconnect at least the charging capacity from the batteries at the end of a mission. The best approach is to physically disconnect the solar arrays from the power bus completely at the end of a mission. Simply minimizing the battery charging rate is not sufficient, since the setting may change due to radiation damage, part failure, or other mechanisms during the long unattended orbit-decay period. Remember that after spacecraft are decommissioned from GEO, they will be on orbit for centuries. Some designers are traditionally reluctant to include any capability to completely disconnect the solar array or battery, since this creates the possibility for premature mission failure. Section 30.4.4 provides more information on passivation methods that are designed to retain mission reliability.

Lithium-ion batteries present special concerns, since they not only store electrical energy, but also contain potentially dangerous materials. As with NiH_2 batteries, overcharge produces heat and gas buildup which can result in cell rupture. In addition, when discharged, the cells can plate out highly reactive lithium metal. Since the charge conditions cannot necessarily be guaranteed throughout the post-mission period, it is very important to prevent any possibility of discharging and recharging lithium-ion batteries. Many lithium-ion battery assemblies have built-in ground safety disconnect relays to prevent this from occurring during the integration phase. By designing in the ability to actuate these relays on orbit, the batteries can be completely isolated from the power bus after disposal, and can neither charge nor discharge. Of course, this concern is negated if the solar arrays are completely disconnected, and there is no way to re-charge the batteries. More on power systems and batteries can be found in Sec. 21.2.

30.4.3 Passivation of Other Systems

The IADC guidelines also recognize the potential for post-mission damage from other systems. Pressure vessels, self-destruct devices, and momentum wheels are all examples of components which can contain mechanical and chemical energy at the end of a mission. Provisions need to be made during the design of such components to allow for them to be vented, safed, spun down at the conclusion of a mission. Some of these passivation steps can be simple. For example, disabling power to momentum wheels is sufficient to allow them to spin down by internal friction. The IADC [2004b] document contains guidance on systems that require passivation, and safe final conditions for them. One additional system to consider for passivation is communications. Whenever possible, the transmitting capability of the spacecraft should be disabled at the end of a mission, to prevent interference with future missions. If the power system is properly passivated, both the momentum wheels and transmitter capability are passivated by default. It is best to listen for any transmissions a few days after passivation to ensure that the spacecraft has not recovered despite the intended shutdown.

30.4.4 Passivation Challenges

One difficulty in designing for adequate passivation is the potential creation of single points of failure for the mission. For example, if a single command could erroneously be sent to vent the propellant or pressurant before or during operations, the entire mission could be lost. Designers have long recognized this potential, and have employed techniques to positively prevent any such opportunities (e.g., preventing vent lines from being operable on orbit). Such hardware designs often prevent adequate passivation of the spacecraft at the end of the mission as well. In many ways, the inclusion of necessary passivation systems requires hardware designers to adopt a new approach to mission reliability. Through the use of redundant hardware and end of mission software modifications, passivation can usually be designed into the system without presenting a single point of failure.

One example of a way to provide for passivation, while preventing a single point failure mechanism is the battery passivation of the Solar Dynamics Observer (SDO). Designers have included the capability of actuating the built-in lithium-ion battery isolation relays on orbit, but omitted the commands to do so from the command database for the duration of the mission. Even if the commands were erroneously sent, they would not be recognized by the spacecraft. At the end of the mission, the command options will be uploaded into a new software patch, allowing the relay actuation commands to be recognized and executed by the onboard hardware. In addition, there is a pair of commands (arm and fire) necessary to actuate each relay. This design has allowed SDO to design for responsible passivation at the end of the mission, yet retain reliability throughout the operational phase of the mission.

Most spacecraft are also designed with autonomous fault detection and correction capabilities, which respond to abnormal spacecraft conditions in a way that keeps the spacecraft operating (or returns it to low level operation after a major anomaly). Such capabilities are contrary to the whole notion of post-mission passivation, and may work to counteract any passivation procedures. Passivation is, after all, an anomalous condition from the perspective of successful mission operations. Autonomous recovery systems, then, need to be disabled before engaging in post-mission passivation. Therefore, it is important to consider this phase of the mission when designing the operations modes and command structure. Ideally, there should be a disposal mode of operations planned from the beginning, that would allow a complete and safe disposal after the mission—with proper safeguards to prevent inadvertently entering or exiting this mode of course.

Passivating missions that were designed and launched without explicit consideration of post-mission passivation can present unique difficulties. Often, it may not be possible to fully comply with the IADC guidelines, or other requirements. Typically, it may be impossible to disable the autonomous recovery hardware built into the spacecraft design, so that the spacecraft constantly returns to a safe mode. Another example is the inability to physically disconnect the battery or solar arrays from the charging circuit. In such a case, it is important to consider the intent of passivation and debris limitation guidelines, so as to minimize the potential for creating additional debris. For example, by reducing the NiH_2 battery charging current to its lowest possible level, and leaving some benign loads enabled, it is often possible to keep the battery in a perpetual discharge condition, thus greatly reducing the risk of battery explosion due to overcharging. While compliance with the guidelines or other requirements is the most reliable approach, it may be necessary to perform less than complete passivation on some operational missions. Future missions must be designed for complete passivation at the end of a mission, unless performing a controlled reentry disposal.

When planning passivation procedures, it is necessary to consider the order in which steps must occur. For example, the transmitter should typically be disabled last so that all previous commands can be verified. There may also be attitude control factors that need to be considered in order to ensure adequate communications or power needs. Generally, passivation begins with disabling recovery mechanisms, followed by passivating the propulsion, attitude control, power, and communications systems. Bear in mind that as each system is disabled, its contribution to the mission is lost, and the remaining steps need to be completed quickly; (e.g., before battery power is lost). Each spacecraft needs to be considered on its own merits, including any hardware degradation that may have occurred during the mission. The specific passivation procedures for an individual vehicle should be reviewed and tested as thoroughly as possible before execution.

30.5 Disposal Planning*

Depending on the method of disposal employed, the process may require anything from relatively simple to highly complex preparation. For instance, a small, low-altitude science mission with no propulsion system,

* Applicable standards: ISO 24113 (Space Systems). See website for reference.

reentering within 25 years, may need only to passivate the power system at the end of the mission. A large spacecraft in LEO which requires a controlled reentry will require much more extensive planning in terms of maneuvers, communications, and staffing. Planning for disposal often requires the coordination of a number of different disciplines, and can take months of preparation and testing. Detailed written plans are often required to be submitted well in advance of the disposal.

If the disposal involves maneuvers, care must be taken to prevent collisions with other orbital assets and debris. It is important to report in advance any significant maneuvers which will change the altitude of the spacecraft more than 1 km to ensure that the maneuver will not cause a collision. In the US, the primary tracking and conjunction assessment authority is USSTRATCOM. This service is also available to some commercial and foreign entities as well, through special arrangement. In addition to checking planned maneuvers for conjunctions, it is important to plan any rapid orbit decay periods so that they take place slow enough that the decaying orbit can be adequately characterized for continuous conjunction assessment activities. This is especially important due to the potential threat to manned missions at low altitudes.

As the end of the mission approaches, there can be a temptation to continue beyond the originally planned termination point. The need for ending the mission might be driven by approaching the minimum fuel for de-orbit, declining reliability due to hardware degradation, or other factors which dictate that there may be a diminished or ineffective disposal, if not executed in the near-term. In the case of a science mission, there is a desire to continue data collection, or there may be increased profits available by continuing a commercial mission. All implications of such a decision need to be considered before continuing the mission, including increased risk of collision, orbital slot availability, RF interference, and reentry risk to the public. Only when the overall risk of continuing is truly negligible, should continuing beyond a pre-planned mission completion be considered.

30.6 FireSat II and SCS Examples

Since both the FireSat II and Supplemental Communications System (SCS) missions are assumed to be US Government-owned assets, they would need to meet the US Government Orbital Debris Mitigation Standard Practices, which is in some ways more comprehensive than the IADC guidelines. Not only the spacecraft, but also the launch vehicles for each mission must be considered for safe disposal, in terms of both orbital debris generation and reentry risk. In most cases, the individual spacecraft from each mission would likely be retired one at a time, due to equipment failure or fuel reserves. Since it is extremely rare for a mission to intentionally shed any debris during disposal, both of our example missions will be assumed to meet the operational debris requirement.

30.6.1 Disposal of the FireSat II Spacecraft

The FireSat II mission operational orbit is circular, at a 700 km altitude, and at a 55 deg inclination. At the end of the 3–5 year mission, it will be necessary to ensure that each spacecraft is removed from the LEO protected region within 25 years. Orbital lifetimes can vary based on spacecraft mass and the area presented in the velocity direction, as well as the solar flux effects on the Earth's atmosphere (Sec. 9.4). With body-mounted solar arrays, the FireSat II spacecraft is likely to tumble slowly after the mission, so an average cross-sectional area would be assumed for orbital lifetime predictions. With deployed solar arrays, the spacecraft may be more likely to adopt a gravity-gradient stabilized orientation, presenting a different (likely higher) drag area. Orbital lifetime predictions from the 700 km circular altitude can vary from just under 25 years to over 60 years, based on the launch year and spacecraft area. It will most likely be necessary, then, to intentionally reduce the perigee of each FireSat II spacecraft as a part of the end of mission disposal using all residual propellant, including the portion reserved for disposal operations.

As discussed in Sec. 30.4, it will be necessary to passivate the FireSat II systems in order to prevent fragmentation during the up to 25 year orbital decay period. Ideally, the mission operations concept would include a separate operations mode for disposal, intended to disable automatic recovery of the spacecraft after it has been shutdown. Passivation steps include venting the propulsion system (including pressurant), and disconnecting the solar arrays from the power bus described in Sec. 30.4. By permanently disconnecting the arrays, the remaining loads will deplete the battery and keep it discharged. With the recovery systems disabled, the spacecraft should remain in an inert state until it reenters.

Several of the other drivers for the FireSat II mission have led to a design which is relatively small, with insufficient fuel or control authority to perform a controlled reentry. Survival of even 15 individual pieces after reentry would cause FireSat II to exceed the required 1 in 10,000 reentry risk requirement. It will therefore be necessary to consider reentry risk throughout the mission design phase, and to minimize the use of highly survivable materials whenever possible. The spacecraft structure, for example, should be limited to graphite/epoxy composite and aluminum components. Note, fasteners are generally too small to inflict significant injuries, and need not be considered for reentry risk purposes. Solar cells are fragile enough to break up into relatively benign pieces, but any solar panel hinges and deployment hardware should avoid the use of titanium and stainless steel as much as possible. Some high survivability materials are inevitable in the payload optics, but could possibly be bundled together to minimize their reentry risk.

30.6.2 Disposal of the SCS Spacecraft

The SCS mission is intended to operate in a 21,000 km altitude, circular orbit with a 0 deg inclination, greatly simplifying the disposal procedure. In fact, this orbit is perhaps the simplest of the commonly used Earth orbits, since all that is necessary is to passivate the spacecraft in place. The operational orbit meets the US Government requirement for Medium Earth Orbit (MEO) disposal, so there is no need for end of mission maneuvers. It is still necessary, however, to expend all remaining fuel, and perform all other passivation tasks described for FireSat II, to minimize any possibility of fragmentation during the very long post-mission storage period. It is not necessary to consider reentry risk for SCS, since the spacecraft will not reenter for centuries, by which time more permanent solutions should be available if necessary.

Conclusion

The need to control the growth of orbital debris, particularly in LEO, is clear. Toward this goal, the United Nations and individual space agencies have created guidelines and requirements that call for, among other things, responsible disposal of space hardware at the end of its useful mission life. In order to perform responsible disposal, it **must be considered during the mission planning in the earliest stages of the mission**. The chosen disposal method often drives the hardware design, including propulsion system sizing, passivation hardware, materials selection, and even potentially the orbit selection. Methods exist which will allow for passivation, while preserving mission reliability. Designing each individual mission with responsible disposal in mind is a critical step toward minimizing the risk of future collisions for all missions.

Applicable Standards:
ISO 17875: Space Systems
See website for reference.

Applicable Standards:
ISO 26872: Space Systems
See website for reference.

Applicable Standards:
ISO 24111: Space Systems
See website for reference.

References

Get Ref **For annotated bibliography of end of mission considerations, see the book website.**

Hughes, J., J. L. Marius, M. Montoro, M. Patel, and D. Bludworth. 2006. "Development and Execution of End of Mission Operations—Case Study of the UARS and ERBS End of Mission Plans," SpaceOps 2006 Conference, AIAA 2006-5511.

IADC. 2004b. *Support to the IADC Space Debris Mitigation Guidelines*, IADC-04-06. Oct.

IADC. 2004a. *End-of-Life Disposal of Space Systems in the Low Earth Orbit Region*, IADC/WG2.

IADC. 2002. *Space Debris Mitigation Guidelines*, IADC-02-01. Oct. 15.

Johnson, N. 1999. "The Cause and Consequences of a Satellite Fragmentation: A Case Study," *Advances in Space Research*, vol. 23, no. 1.

Liou, J. C. 2010. "An Updated Assessment of the Orbital Debris Environment in LEO," *NASA Orbital Debris Quarterly News*, vol. 14, no.1, Jan.

Liou, J. C. and N. Johnson. 2008. "Instability of the Present LEO Satellite Populations," *Advances in Space Research*, vol. 41, no. 7.

NASA. 2008. *History of On-Orbit Satellite Fragmentations*, 14th Edition, NASA/TM–2008–214779, Jun.

Appendix A
Mass and Power Distribution for Spacecraft

David F. Everett, ***NASA Goddard Space Flight Center***

Table A-1 and A-2 contain average mass and orbit average power by subsystem for different categories of spacecraft (spacecraft subsystem definitions are in Sec. 14.4). Table A-3 lists the specific spacecraft that went into the averages. Tables A-4 through A-11 show individual spacecraft data. The spacecraft were categorized by the target orbits, with the idea that the mission destination will tend to drive some aspects of the resource distributions. For instance, Telemetry, Tracking, and Command (TT&C) subsystem mass and power are significantly greater for planetary missions than they are for low Earth orbit missions, with high Earth orbit missions falling in between. The greater distance requires larger antennas and more power from the spacecraft transmitter in order to return data. The categories are:

- **No Propulsion.** This category includes spacecraft with no onboard propulsion system or kick motor. These missions are generally low Earth orbiting (LEO) missions. With the exception of the Hubble Space Telescope, they are all Explorer missions. All of the missions are astrophysics or space science missions.
- **LEO with Propulsion.** This category includes missions with an onboard propulsion system or kick motor and an orbit perigee of less than 5,000 km. Equator-S and ST-5 are the only missions in this category with apogee above 900 km. These missions are mostly Earth observing missions with station-keeping requirements.
- **High Earth.** The high Earth missions include those with perigee above 5,000 km, including geosychronous (GEO) missions, and it includes missions to Earth libration points L1 and L2 and Earth fly away missions. The energy to achieve mission orbit is significantly greater than the energy for LEO, but significantly less than the energy for a planetary mission.
- **Planetary.** This category contains missions with destinations outside of the vicinity of Earth orbit. LRO was included in this category because significant energy is required to capture into Lunar orbit, making the mission look more planetary than high Earth.

In addition to the TT&C subsystem trend noted above, several other trends stand out. Most obviously, the mass and power resources available for payload decrease significantly for missions that target more distant destinations. Launch vehicles can deliver spacecraft to a LEO orbit, but they generally can only put the spacecraft on a trajectory toward higher destinations. The spacecraft must carry much more fuel for high Earth or planetary missions, for the final orbit insertion, with a corresponding increase in the propulsion system dry mass. Out from LEO, thermal control mass increases, since the comfortable 300 K Earth no longer fills half the sky.

This spacecraft information was collected from two different NASA databases as well as from the records of systems engineers who worked on some of the missions. One database had the TT&C subsystem and the onboard processing combined for some of the missions. In cases where this occurred, the TT&C mass shows up as "0%," and I did not include either the onboard processing or TT&C mass for these missions in the overall averages. The "other" category includes balance mass and mission-unique mass that stayed with the launch vehicle.

Power breakdown for the spacecraft was not available for some missions, so the averages include only those values available. Due to the nature of averaging averages, I needed to make slight adjustments to ensure the percentages total to 100% in Tables A-1 and A-2; the other 9 tables have the raw data. I included a wide variety of missions, from the 25 kg ST-5 to the 16,221 kg CGRO. These outliers tend to skew the results slightly, but the variety should be helpful for different applications. The overall averages make sense.

All mass is shown as a percentage of dry mass. If you are starting with payload mass, you can simply take the payload mass and divide by the appropriate payload percentage from Table A-1 to get a starting point for dry mass. As you refine your design and get estimates of each subsystem mass from more detailed analysis, you can look back at these tables to check the reasonableness of your estimates. Similarly, Table A-2 will help with power estimates.

These tables are intended as a first cut at mass and power estimates as described in Sec. 14.5. There is quite a bit of variation in the actual value for each spacecraft, because of unique aspects of the mission requirements. When considering a particular mission design, you may find it helpful to look more closely at the missions that most closely align with your particular mission requirements. As technology changes and new ideas come along, you can expect these averages to change.

Table A-1. Average Mass as a Percentage of Dry Mass for Subsystems by Spacecraft Type. Types include spacecraft without propulsion, low Earth orbit missions with propulsion, high Earth orbit (> 5,000 km perigee, GEO, L1, L2, and fly away), and planetary missions.

Subsystem (% of Dry Mass)	No Prop (%)	LEO Prop (%)	High Earth (%)	Planetary (%)
Payload	41%	31%	32%	15%
Structure and Mechanisms	20%	27%	24%	25%
Thermal Control	2%	2%	4%	6%
Power (including harness)	19%	21%	17%	21%
TT&C	2%	2%	4%	7%
On-Board Processing	5%	5%	3%	4%
Attitude Determination and Control	8%	6%	6%	6%
Propulsion	0%	3%	7%	13%
Other (balance + launch)	3%	3%	3%	3%
Total	100%	100%	100%	100%
Average Dry Mass (kg)	1497	2344	1258	888

Table A-2. Orbit Average Power as a Percentage of Total for Subsystems by Spacecraft Type. Types include spacecraft without propulsion, low-Earth orbit missions with propulsion, high-Earth orbit (> 5,000 km perigee, GEO, L1, L2, and fly-away), and planetary missions. Slight adjustments were made to ensure columns sum to 100%.

Subsystem (% of Total Power)	No Prop (%)	LEO Prop (%)	High Earth (%)	Planetary (%)
Payload	43%	46%	35%	22%
Structure and Mechanisms	0%	1%	0%	1%
Thermal Control	5%	10%	14%	15%
Power (including harness)	10%	9%	7%	10%
TT&C	11%	12%	16%	18%
On-Board Processing	13%	12%	10%	11%
Attitude Determination and Control	18%	10%	16%	12%
Propulsion	0%	0%	2%	11%
Average Power (W)	299	794	691	749

Table A-3. List of Spacecraft Used for Mass and Power Analysis.

Name	Launch Date	Altitude (km)	Inclination (deg)	ACS Type	Pointing (arc sec)	Downlink Data Rate (kbps)	Data Storage (Mbytes)	Battery Capacity (A-hr)	PDR to Launch (months)
SPACECRAFT WITHOUT PROPULSION									
AIM	4/25/07	750 × 750	98	3-Axis, Bias	115	2,000	8,000	5	40
COBE	11/18/89	885 × 896	103	Spin	3,600	4,096	1,000	40	75
FAST	8/21/96	348 × 4,200	83	Spin	3,600	2,250	1,000	9	59
FUSE	6/24/99	758 × 774	25	3-Axis	0.36	1,024	240	80	44
GALEX	4/28/03	697 × 697	29	3-Axis	300	24,000	64	16	55
HESSI	11/19/01	600 × 600	38	Spin	720	3,500	4,000	15	—
HST	4/24/90	613 × 613	28.5	3-Axis	0.0072	1,024	3,600	360	—
IMAGE	3/25/00	780 × 45,000	90	Spin	360	2,200	4,100	22	38
RXTE	12/30/95	500 × 500	23	3-Axis	72	256	544	100	38
SAMPEX	7/3/92	550 × 675	82	3-Axis, Bias	3,600	900	26.6	9	36
SWAS	12/5/98	638 × 651	70	3-Axis	36	1,800	110	21	72
SWIFT	11/20/04	580 × 600	20.6	3-Axis	—	2,250	—	—	—
TERRIERS	5/18/99	550 × 550	97.8	Spin	900	250	40	4.8	—
TRACE	4/1/98	600 × 650	98	3-Axis	288	2,250	300	9	30
WIRE	3/4/99	540 × 590	97.6	3-Axis	72	2,250	300	9	35
LEO SPACECRAFT WITH PROPULSION									
Astro-E	2/9/00	550 × 550	31	3-Axis	—	4,000	6,000	—	—
Aqua	3/24/02	705 × 708	98	3-Axis	35	150,000	92,000	160	61
CGRO	4/5/91	450 × 450	28.5	3-Axis	108	512	900	150	84
CALIPSO	4/28/06	705 × 705	98.2	3-Axis	126	80,000	8,000	80	69
CloudSat	4/28/06	705 × 705	98.2	3-Axis	67	1,000	275	40	68
EO-1	11/21/00	705 × 705	98.2	3-Axis	122	105,000	6	—	51
Equator-S	12/2/97	500 × 70,000	7	Spin	—	262	1,500	4	—
Fermi GLAST	6/11/08	56 × 565,000	25.6	3-Axis	7,200	40,000	20,000	125	61
GRACE	3/17/02	300 × 500	89	3-Axis	—	—	—	16	—
Lewis	6/10/97	523 × 523	97.4	3-Axis	180	2048	4,000	—	—
ST-5	3/22/06	301 × 4,600	105.6	Spin	—	100	20	8	—
Terra	12/3/99	705 × 708	98	3-Axis	151.2	150,000	140,000	100	76
TOMS/EP	7/2/96	955 × 955	99.3	3-Axis	1,800	180	16	9	58
TRMM	11/27/97	350 × 350	35	3-Axis	720	2,048	2,000	100	66
UARS	9/12/91	576 × 579	57	3-Axis	36	512	900	150	54
LandSat 7	4/15/99	705 × 705	98.2	3-Axis	180	150,000	399,635	100	—
NOAA 16	9/21/00	850 × 865	99.2	3-Axis	720	2,661.6	4,500	141	0
NOAA-N prime	2/6/09	870 × 870	98.7	3-Axis	720	2,600	7,200	120	0
HIGH EARTH SPACECRAFT									
ACE	8/25/97	L1	—	Spin	900	76.384	1,073	12	46
Chandra	7/23/99	8,700 × 140,000	67	3-Axis	0.252	512	1,800	40	—
MAP	6/30/01	L2	—	3-Axis	2,160	1,000	—	23	55
SOHO	12/2/95	L1	—	3-Axis	—	245.7	3,000	40	56
STEREO	10/25/06	Earth Fly Away	—	3-Axis	180,00	720	8,000	23	60
Triana	not launched	L1	—	3-Axis	180	250	320	9	—
WIND	11/1/94	510,000 × 1,600,000	Varies	Spin	3,600	64	2,400	79.5	61

Table A-3. List of Spacecraft Used for Mass and Power Analysis. (Continued)

Name	Launch Date	Altitude (km)	Inclination (deg)	ACS Type	Pointing (arc sec)	Downlink Data Rate (kbps)	Data Storage (Mbytes)	Battery Capacity (A-hr)	PDR to Launch (months)
				HIGH EARTH SPACECRAFT (continued)					
GOES 12	7/23/01	GEO	0	3-Axis	900	2,620.8	0	24	—
TDRS 7	7/13/95	GEO	0	3-Axis	108	64	—	120	86
Spitzer	8/25/03	Earth Trailing	—	3-Axis	5	2,200	1,024	16	72
IBEX	10/19/08	7,000 × 300,000	11	Spin	4,428	320,000	250	21	34
GOES-N	5/24/06	GEO	0	3-Axis	1.2	2	—	123	95
SDO	2/11/10	GEO	23	3-Axis	—	130,000	0	—	—
				PLANETARY SPACECRAFT					
Cassini	10/15/97	Saturn	—	3-Axis	0.36	249	900	none	—
Clementine	1/25/94	Moon	—	3-Axis	108	128	2,000	15	—
Galileo	10/18/89	Jupiter	—	Spin/despun	702	134.4	900	none	—
LRO	6/18/09	Moon	90	3-Axis	45	100,000	50,000	80	41
Magellan	5/4/89	Venus	—	3-Axis	—	268.8	1,800	60	—
Mars Odyssey	4/7/01	Mars	—	3-Axis	—	—	8,000	16	—
NEAR	2/17/96	Eros	—	3-Axis	10.8	26.5	1,770	9	—
MESSENGER	8/3/04	Mercury	—	3-Axis	360	104	2,000	23	39
MRO	8/1/05	Mars 255 × 320	93	3-Axis	322	10,000	20,000	50	37
New Horizons	1/19/06	Pluto flyby	—	3-Axis, Bias	177.7998	0.7	16,000	none	39
Stardust	2/1/99	Deep Space	—	3-Axis	1,800	4	225.6025	—	29

Table A-4. Spacecraft Without Propulsion Used for Mass Analysis (Percentage of Dry Mass).

Name	Total Mass (kg)	Payload Mass (kg)	Payload (%)	Struc. & Mech. (%)	Thermal (%)	Power (Inc harness) (%)	TT&C (%)	On-Board Proc (%)	ADCS (%)	Prop. (%)	Other* (%)
AIM	200	64	32%	27%	2%	22%	2%	5%	10%	0%	0%
COBE	2,245	1147	51%	15%	2%	20%	1%	3%	8%	0%	0%
FAST	191	65	34%	14%	2%	31%	3%	8%	5%	0%	4%
FUSE	1,332	782	59%	19%	1%	13%	1%	4%	4%	0%	0%
GALEX	287	133	46%	14%	1%	17%	2%	7%	12%	0%	0%
HESSI	284	131	46%	24%	1%	20%	1%	5%	2%	0%	0%
HST	11,866	5,610	47%	25%	2%	9%	1%	1%	4%	0%	10%
IMAGE	492	178	36%	28%	5%	17%	2%	2%	5%	0%	4%
RXTE	3,040	995	33%	38%	2%	20%	1%	2%	5%	0%	0%
SAMPEX	162	53	32%	16%	3%	25%	3%	8%	6%	0%	7%
SWAS	293	95	33%	18%	1%	25%	2%	6%	12%	0%	4%
SWIFT	1,465	854	58%	16%	1%	15%	1%	2%	7%	0%	0%
TERRIERS	125	50	40%	6%	0%	12%	7%	9%	7%	0%	20%
TRACE	211	60	28%	23%	2%	22%	2%	4%	17%	0%	2%
WIRE	260	107	41%	12%	4%	19%	2%	3%	17%	0%	2%
mean	1,497	688	41%	20%	2%	19%	2%	5%	8%	0%	3%
median	287	131	40%	18%	2%	20%	2%	4%	7%	0%	2%
std dev	2,900	1,369	9.4%	7.6%	1.1%	5.4%	1.4%	2.3%	4.5%	0.0%	5.2%
min	125	50	28%	6%	0%	9%	1%	1%	2%	0%	0%
max	11,866	5,610	59%	38%	5%	31%	7%	9%	17%	0%	20%

* Balance and launch hardware

Table A-5. Spacecraft Without Propulsion Used for Power Analysis (Percentage of Total Power).

Name	Power Total (W)	Payload Total	Payload (%)	Struc. & Mech. (%)	Thermal	Power (Inc. harness) (%)	TT&C (%)	On-Board Proc. (%)	ADCS (%)	Prop. (%)
AIM	216	83	38%							
FAST	52	19	37%	0%	12%	11%	22%	11%	8%	0%
FUSE	520	300	58%							
GALEX	362	131	36%	0%	4%	7%	21%	16%	16%	0%
HESSI	252	174	69%	0%	6%	10%	4%	10%	2%	0%
IMAGE	238	143	60%	0%	4%	8%	16%	6%	6%	0%
SAMPEX	73	21	29%	0%	4%	13%	10%	28%	15%	0%
SWAS	182	60	33%	0%	5%	8%	6%	14%	34%	0%
SWIFT	966	593	61%	0%	3%	13%	2%	6%	14%	0%
WIRE	132	27	20%	0%	0%	11%	7%	15%	47%	0%
mean	299	155	44%	0%	5%	10%	11%	13%	18%	0%
median	227	107	37%	0%	4%	10%	9%	12%	15%	0%
std dev	258	168	15.6%	0.0%	3.2%	2.1%	7.2%	6.7%	14.2%	0.0%
min	52	19	20%	0%	0%	7%	2%	6%	2%	0%
max	966	593	69%	0%	12%	13%	22%	28%	47%	0%

Table A-6. LEO Spacecraft With Propulsion Used for Mass Analysis (Percentage of Dry Mass).

Name	Total Mass (kg)	Wet Mass (kg) (total less kick)	Dry Total Mass (kg)	Payload Mass (kg)	Payload (%)	Struc. & Mech. (%)	Thermal Control (%)	Power (inc harness) (%)	TT&C (%)	On-Board Proc. (%)	ADCS (%)	Prop. (%)	Other* (%)	Propellant (%)	Kick Motor, inc prop. (%of wet)
Astro-E	1,678	1,678	1,578	977	62%	11%	4%	11%	1%	2%	6%	3%	0%	6%	0%
Aqua	2,941	2,941	2,799	1,022	37%	26%	2%	27%	1%	2%	4%	2%	0%	5%	0%
CGRO	16,221	16,221	14,279	5,999	42%	35%	1%	11%	1%	2%	3%	2%	4%	14%	0%
CALIPSO	577	577	548	283	52%	12%	2%	19%	1%	5%	8%	1%	0%	5%	0%
CloudSat	847	847	771	255	33%	25%	3%	24%	2%	3%	7%	3%	0%	10%	0%
EO-1	579	579	556	185	33%	26%	2%	28%	1%	3%	6%	2%	0%	4%	0%
Equator-S	230	189	189	46	25%	42%	1%	20%	0%	4%	6%	0%	2%	0%	18%
Fermi GLAST	4,307	4,307	3,947	2,889	73%	11%	1%	11%	1%	1%	2%	1%	0%	9%	0%
GRACE	471	471	458	70	15%	35%	6%	15%	1%	3%	17%	8%	0%	3%	0%
Lewis	385	385	342	97	28%	20%	1%	27%	0%	7%	10%	5%	1%	12%	0%
ST-5†	25	25	24	1	3%	32%	3%	31%	8%	9%	5%	6%	0%	2%	0%
Terra	4,771	4,771	4,432	1,096	25%	33%	5%	21%	4%	7%	4%	1%	1%	8%	0%
TOMS/EP	289	289	215	34	16%	29%	2%	23%	0%	8%	12%	8%	3%	34%	0%
TRMM	3,512	3,512	2,611	640	24%	38%	4%	18%	1%	3%	6%	5%	0%	35%	0%
UARS	7,483	7,483	6,607	2,098	32%	28%	2%	13%	0%	4%	4%	2%	15%	13%	0%
LandSat 7	2,105	2,105	1,983	404	20%	27%	1%	25%	3%	9%	4%	1%	10%	6%	0%
NOAA 16	2,246	1,453	1,595	3,62	23%	20%	2%	24%	2%	6%	3%	2%	7%	2%	35%
NOAA-N prime	1,391	1,391	1,382	312	23%	34%	3%	28%	3%	4%	5%	1%	0%	1%	0%
mean	2,735	2,344	893	31%	27%	2%	21%	2%	5%	6%	3%	2%	9%	27%	
median	1,422	1,382	312	27%	27%	2%	22%	1%	4%	5%	2%	0%	6%	27%	
std dev	3,800	3,289	1,411	16.6%	9.0%	1.3%	6.6%	1.8%	2.5%	3.5%	2.3%	4.1%	9.7%	8.7%	
min	25	24	1	3%	11%	1%	11%	1%	1%	2%	0%	0%	0%	18%	
max	16,221	14,279	5,999	73%	42%	6%	31%	8%	9%	17%	8%	15%	35%	35%	

* Balance and launch hardware

†Totals for 1 of 3 spacecraft, total launch mass was 3 × 25 kg plus another 65 kg for support structure that stayed with the launch vehicle

Table A-7. LEO Spacecraft With Propulsion Used for Power Analysis (Percentage of Total Power).

Name	Power Total (W)	Payload Total	Payload (%)	Struc. & Mech. (%)	Thermal (%)	Power inc harness (%)	TT&C (%)	On-Board Proc. (%)	ACDS (%)	Prop. (%)
Astro-E	858	500	58%	—	14%	—	—	—	—	—
Aqua	1,609	987	61%	0%	3%	3%	—	20%	10%	1%
CALIPSO	508	256	50%	—	—	—	—	—	—	0%
CloudSat	598	346	58%	0%	10%	11%	3%	5%	14%	0%
EO-1	298	118	40%	4%	4%	9%	5%	12%	26%	0%
Equator-S	89	45	51%	0%	0%	16%	—	—	34%	0%
Fermi GLAST	1,646	775	47%	0%	14%	15%	2%	9%	10%	2%
GRACE	92	50	55%	1%	0%	6%	6%	32%	0%	0%
ST-5	40	8.08	20%	0%	0%	14%	52%	11%	2%	1%
Terra	2,159	992	46%	0%	5%	8%	—	34%	8%	0%
TRMM	1,019	416	41%	4%	18%	11%	5%	5%	15%	0%
NOAA 16	778	396	51%	0%	18%	3%	9%	11%	9%	0%
NOAA-N prime	858	450	52%	0%	23%	3%	8%	5%	9%	0%
mean	812	372	48%	1%	9%	9%	11%	14%	12%	0%
median	778	346	51%	0%	7%	9%	6%	11%	10%	0%
std dev	635	318	10.2%	1.6%	7.8%	4.5%	15.5%	10.0%	9.4%	0.7%
min	40	8	20%	0%	0%	3%	2%	5%	0%	0%
max	2,159	992	61%	4%	23%	16%	52%	34%	34%	2%

Table A-8. High-Earth Spacecraft Used for Mass Analysis (Percentage of Dry Mass).

Name	Total Mass (kg)	Wet Mass (total less kick) (kg)	Dry Total Mass (kg)	Payload Mass (kg)	Payload (%)	Struc. & M ech. (%)	Thermal (%)	Power (inc. harness) (%)	TT&C (%)	On-Board Proc. (%)	ADCS (%)	Prop (%)	Other* (%)	Propellant (%)	Kick motor, incl prop (%of wet)
ACE	759	759	561	168	30%	23%	7%	20%	4%	5%	1%	7%	3%	35%	0%
Chandra	5,698	5,698	4,699	2,918	62%	15%	2%	9%	0%	2%	4%	4%	2%	21%	0%
MAP	814	814	741	305	41%	23%	6%	13%	2%	3%	8%	2%	2%	10%	0%
SOHO	1,854	1,854	1,602	899	56%	12%	2%	13%	1%	4%	5%	3%	3%	16%	0%
STEREO	619	619	558	138	25%	28%	4%	24%	6%	1%	6%	6%	0%	11%	0%
Triana	2,995	855	577	104	18%	11%	2%	5%	2%	1%	8%	30%	23%	48%	71%
WIND	1,226	1,226	856	182	21%	23%	3%	31%	2%	7%	2%	5%	5%	43%	0%
GOES 12	2,275	2,275	1,058	343	32%	22%	6%	16%	4%	3%	8%	8%	0%	115%	0%
TDRS 7	2,201	2,201	1,649	311	19%	28%	3%	28%	0%	3%	6%	5%	7%	34%	0%
Spitzer	849	849	833	453	54%	17%	1%	13%	3%	2%	7%	3%	0%	2%	0%
IBEX	458	143	117	26	22%	44%	3%	13%	4%	2%	2%	6%	4%	23%	69%
GOES-N	3,217	3,217	1,546	345	22%	31%	7%	14%	7%	3%	8%	6%	0%	108%	0%
SDO	2,975	2,975	1,561	298	19%	35%	2%	20%	4%	3%	7%	6%	3%	91%	0%
mean		1,807	1,258	499	32%	24%	4%	17%	4%	3%	6%	7%	4%	43%	70%
median		1,226	856	305	25%	23%	3%	14%	4%	3%	6%	6%	3%	34%	70%
std dev		1,449	1,098	728	15.1%	9.1%	1.9%	7.2%	1.8%	1.6%	2.3%	7.0%	5.8%	36.5%	1.3%
min		143	117	26	18%	11%	1%	5%	1%	1%	1%	2%	0%	2%	69%
max		5,698	4,699	2,918	62%	44%	7%	31%	7%	7%	8%	30%	23%	115%	71%

* Balance and launch hardware

Table A-8, Fig. A-0, Eq. A-0

Table A-9. High-Earth Spacecraft Used for Power Analysis (Percentage of Total Power).

Name	Power Total (W)	Payload Total	Payload (%)	Struc.& Mech. (%)	Thermal (%)	Power (inc. harness) (%)	TT&C (%)	On-Board Proc. (%)	ADCS (%)	Prop. (%)
ACE	305	108	35%	0%	29%	4%		27%	4%	0%
MAP	371	137	37%	0%	7%	6%	9%	13%	24%	0%
SOHO	1,186	649	55%	0%	11%	8%	—	11%	13%	3%
STEREO	514	116	23%	0%	10%	10%	25%	8%	16%	9%
Triana	394	150	38%	0%	16%	10%	9%	4%	23%	0%
GOES 12	1,046	462	44%	0%	13%	2%	22%	3%	15%	0%
TDRS 7	1,621	872	54%	0%	29%	1%	—	4%	12%	1%
Spitzer	434	61	14%	—	—	—	—	—	—	—
IBEX	70	22	31%	0%	0%	12%	17%	22%	17%	2%
GOES-N	—	386	—	—	—	—	—	—	—	—
SDO	969	344	35%	0%	11%	15%	13%	7%	18%	1%
mean	691	301	37%	0%	14%	7%	16%	11%	16%	2%
median	474	150	36%	0%	11%	8%	15%	8%	16%	1%
std dev	462	259	11.9%	0.0%	8.9%	4.4%	6.1%	7.9%	5.7%	2.7%
min	70	22	14%	0%	0%	1%	9%	3%	4%	0%
max	1,621	872	55%	0%	29%	15%	25%	27%	24%	9%

Table A-10. Planetary Spacecraft Used for Mass Analysis (Percentage of Dry Mass).

Name	Total Mass (kg)	Wet Mass (total less kick) (kg)	Dry Total Mass (kg)	Payload Mass (kg)	Payload (%)	Struc. & Mech. (% of wet)	Thermal (%)	Power (inc. harness) (%)	TT&C (%)	On-Board Proc. (%)	ADCS (%)	Prop. (%)	Other* (%)	Propellant (%)	Kick motor, incl prop (%of wet)
Cassini	5,565	5,565	2,558	688	27%	14%	3%	14%	6%	5%	6%	19%	5%	118%	0%
Clementine	1,646	491	259	14	5%	24%	9%	14%	5%	4%	6%	21%	13%	90%	70%
Galileo	1,816	1,816	1,782	531	30%	17%	4%	13%	4%	3%	8%	10%	10%	2%	0%
LRO	1,915	1,915	1,018	96	9%	31%	8%	24%	7%	2%	6%	12%	0%	88%	0%
Magellan	3,455	1,260	1,127	130	12%	29%	5%	18%	9%	4%	8%	7%	9%	12%	64%
Mars Odyssey	727	727	377	45	12%	28%	5%	23%	6%	3%	6%	13%	3%	93%	0%
NEAR	808	808	482	56	12%	19%	4%	23%	5%	6%	6%	25%	1%	68%	0%
MESSENGER	1,102	1,102	508	47	9%	25%	10%	24%	6%	2%	7%	16%	0%	117%	0%
MRO	2,114	2,114	953	130	14%	33%	3%	25%	7%	3%	6%	10%	0%	122%	0%
New Horizons	478	478	401	30	8%	32%	7%	27%	10%	6%	5%	7%	0%	19%	0%
Stardust	385	385	299	71	24%	20%	3%	33%	6%	3%	3%	6%	0%	28%	0%
mean	—	1,515	888	167	15%	25%	6%	21%	7%	4%	6%	13%	4%	69%	67%
median	—	1,102	508	71	12%	25%	5%	23%	6%	3%	6%	12%	1%	88%	67%
std dev	—	1,407	689	214	7.9%	6.1%	2.4%	5.9%	1.5%	1.4%	1.2%	6.0%	4.7%	43.4%	3.3%
min	—	385	259	14	5%	14%	3%	13%	4%	2%	3%	6%	0%	2%	64%
max	—	5,565	2,558	688	30%	33%	10%	33%	10%	6%	8%	25%	13%	122%	70%

* Balance and launch hardware

Table A-11. Planetary Spacecraft Used for Power Analysis (Percentage of Total Power)

Name	Power Total (W)	Payload Total	Payload (%)	Struc. & Mechs. (%)	Thermal (%)	Power (inc. harness) (%)	TT&C (%)	On-Board Proc. (%)	ADCS (%)	Prop. (%)
Cassini	1,338	745	56%	0%	11%	4%	—	11%	11%	7%
LRO	620	112	18%	0%	20%	10%	17%	15%	18%	2%
NEAR	852	94	11%	0%	18%	1%	7%	10%	6%	47%
MESSENGER	633	95	15%	0%	5%	17%	20%	5%	19%	19%
MRO	815	155	19%	5%	25%	5%	26%	11%	9%	0%
New Horizons	—	28	—	—	—	—	—	—	—	—
Stardust	234	28	12%	0%	15%	21%	22%	16%	11%	3%
mean	749	179	22%	1%	15%	10%	18%	11%	12%	13%
median	724	95	17%	0%	17%	7%	20%	11%	11%	5%
std dev	331	235	15.4%	1.9%	6.4%	7.1%	6.5%	3.5%	4.7%	16.3%
min	234	28	11%	0%	5%	1%	7%	5%	6%	0%
max	1,338	745	56%	5%	25%	21%	26%	16%	19%	47%

Appendix B
Physical and Orbit Properties of the Sun, Earth, Moon, and Planets

Nicola Sarzi-Amade, *Microcosm, Inc.*

This appendix provides physical and orbit data for the Sun, Moon, and planets. Properties of orbits about these bodies are listed in tables throughout the text. Numerical properties of orbits about the Earth are given in App. I. For additional data on virtually all aspects of the Solar System, astrophysics, and astronomy, we highly recommend that the reader consult Cox [2000]. For a detailed explanation and high accuracy numerical methods and tables for computing planetary orbit ephemerides, see Seidelmann [2006]. For lower accuracy, but computationally convenient techniques, see Meeus [1998].

B.1 Gravitational Constants of Major Solar System Bodies

See website for other solar system bodies.

In Table B-1, values of μ = GM are given to their full available accuracy. Other values are rounded. Values for the smaller satellites are estimates based on a typical density and the object's size. Except for the Sun, the last 3 columns are evaluated at the object's surface (or at the largest dimension for irregular bodies). Data from Seidelmann [2006], IAU [2009], and Astronomical Almanac [2010].

Table B-1. Gravitational Parameters for Orbits About Major Solar System Bodies.

Object	μ = GM (m^3/s^2)	Orbital Velocity (km/s)	Orbit Period (min)	Escape Velocity (km/s)
Sun (at surface)	$1.327\ 124\ 400\ 41 \times 10^{20}$	436.6678	166.9117	617.5416
Sun (at 1 AU)	$1.327\ 124\ 400\ 41 \times 10^{20}$	29.7847	525,970	42.1219
PLANETS AND SATELLITES				
Mercury	$2.203\ 21 \times 10^{13}$	3.0051	85.0169	4.2499
Venus	$3.248\ 585\ 917 \times 10^{14}$	7.3266	86.4984	10.3614
Earth	$3.986\ 004\ 356 \times 10^{14}$	7.9054	84.4891	11.1799
Moon	$4.902\ 800\ 15 \times 10^{12}$	1.6799	108.3069	2.3757
Mars	$4.282\ 837\ 522 \times 10^{13}$	3.5512	100.1500	5.0221
Phobos	7.161×10^{5}	0.0073	191.9561	0.0103
Deimos	1.041×10^{5}	0.0037	210.8393	0.0053
Jupiter	$1.267\ 127\ 626 \times 10^{17}$	42.0999	177.8298	59.5383
Io	5.961×10^{12}	1.8052	106.0975	2.5530
Europa	3.203×10^{12}	1.4321	114.2224	2.0252
Ganymede	9.890×10^{12}	1.9384	142.1873	2.7414
Callisto	7.181×10^{12}	1.7265	146.1158	2.4416

Table B-1. Gravitational Parameters for Orbits About Major Solar System Bodies. (Continued)

Object	μ = GM (m^3/s^2)	Orbital Velocity (km/s)	Orbit Period (min)	Escape Velocity (km/s)
Amalthea	1.39×10^8	0.0334	392.0009	0.0472
Himalia	2.8×10^8	0.0573	155.4302	0.0810
Elara	5.80×10^7	0.0367	122.5712	0.0520
Pasiphae	2.00×10^7	0.0258	121.6107	0.0365
Thebe	9.998×10^7	0.0415	146.2925	0.0587
Saturn	$3.794\ 058\ 49 \times 10^{16}$	25.0905	251.5398	35.4833
Mimas	2.508×10^9	0.1101	196.9388	0.1557
Enceladus	7.21×10^9	0.1675	160.6939	0.2369
Tethys	4.14×10^{10}	0.2767	204.3403	0.3914
Dione	7.32×10^{10}	0.3610	163.0431	0.5105
Rhea	1.540×10^{11}	0.4490	178.1778	0.6350
Titan	8.977×10^{12}	1.8671	144.4226	2.6405
Hyperion	3.79×10^8	0.0481	357.0610	0.0680
Iapetus	1.2054×10^{11}	0.4047	190.4516	0.5723
Janus	1.2608×10^8	0.0360	283.4979	0.0509
Uranus	$5.794\ 5490 \times 10^{15}$	15.0570	177.7602	21.2938
Ariel	9.0×10^{10}	0.3944	154.2484	0.5578
Umbriel	7.8×10^{10}	0.3657	167.5273	0.5171
Titania	2.35×10^{11}	0.5461	151.3113	0.7722
Oberon	2.01×10^{11}	0.5140	155.0355	0.7269
Miranda	4.64×10^9	0.1390	180.8384	0.1965
Portia	1.11×10^8	0.0399	183.8718	0.0564
Puck	1.93×10^8	0.0488	173.7898	0.0690
Sycorax	3.59×10^8	0.0614	161.9045	0.0869
Neptune	$6.836\ 527 \times 10^{15}$	16.6153	156.0781	23.4975
Triton	1.428×10^{12}	1.0274	137.9076	1.4530
Nereid	2.06×10^9	0.1100	161.8084	0.1556
Despina	1.40×10^8	0.0432	181.6878	0.0611
Galatea	2.50×10^8	0.0533	172.8201	0.0754
Larissa	3.30×10^8	0.0583	174.0984	0.0825
Proteus	3.359×10^9	0.1265	173.8690	0.1789
Pluto	9.7178×10^{11}	0.9018	138.7701	1.2753
Charon	1.132×10^{11}	0.4322	146.8216	0.6113
ASTEROIDS LARGER THAN 300 KM DIAMETER				
Ceres	6.264×10^{10}	0.3585	142.3300	0.5070
Pallas	1.367×10^{10}	0.1533	397.6845	0.2167
Vesta	1.792×10^{10}	0.1761	343.7935	0.2490

B.2 Planetary Data

See website for Natural Satellite Data.

Table B-2. Orbit Data for the Planets. Orbit elements are defined with respect to the mean ecliptic and equinox of J2000.0 (epoch JD 2,451,545.0). Data from Seidelmann [2006].

Planet	Orbit Eccentricity	Mean Distance (AU)	Tropical Period (Julian years)	Synodic Period (d)	Mean Daily Motion, *n* (deg)	Orbital Velocity (km/s)
Mercury	0.205 630 69	0.387 098 93	0.240 844 45	115.877 5	4.092 377 06	47.872 5
Venus	0.006 773 23	0.723 321 99	0.615 182 57	583.921 4	1.602 168 74	35.021 4
Earth	0.016 710 22	1.000 000 11	0.999 978 62		0.985 647 36	29.785 9
Mars	0.093 412 33	1.523 662 31	1.880 711 05	779.936 1	0.524 071 09	24.130 9
Jupiter	0.048 392 66	5.203 363 01	11.856 525 02	398.8840	0.083 129 44	13.069 7
Saturn	0.054 150 60	9.537 070 32	29.423 519 35	378.091 9	0.033 497 91	9.672 4
Uranus	0.047 167 71	19.191 263 93	83.747 406 82	369.6560	0.011 769 04	6.835 2
Neptune	0.008 585 87	30.068 963 48	163.723 204 5	367.486 7	0.006 020 076	5.477 8
Pluto	0.248 807 66	39.481 686 77	248.020 8	366.720 7	0.003 973 966	4.7490

Table B-3. Orbit Data for the Planets. Data from Seidelmann [2006] and Astronomical Almanac [1998].

Planet	Inclination to Ecliptic (deg)	Longitude of Ascending Node (deg)	Longitude of Perihelion (deg)	Planet Longitude on Jan. 1.5 2000 (deg)	Last Perihelion before 2000
Mercury	7.004 87	48.331 67	77.456 45	252.250 84	1999 Nov. 19
Venus	3.394 71	76.680 69	131.532 98	181.979 73	1999 Dec. 1
Earth	0.000 05	–11.260 64	102.947 19	100.464 35	1999 Jan. 3
Mars	1.850 61	49.578 54	336.040 84	355.453 32	1999 Nov. 25
Jupiter	1.305 30	100.556 15	14.753 85	34.404 38	1999 May 20
Saturn	2.484 46	113.715 04	92.431 94	49.944 32	1974 Jan. 8
Uranus	0.769 86	74.229 68	170.964 24	313.232 18	1966 May 20
Neptune	1.769 17	131.721 69	44.971 35	304.880 03	1876 Sept. 2
Pluto	17.141 75	110.303 47	224.066 76	238.928 81	1989 Sept. 5

Table B-4. Physical Data for the Planets. Data from Astronomical Almanac [2010] and Seidelmann [2006].

Planet	Mass[1] (10^{24} kg)	Radius[2] (km)	Flattening[3] (geometric)	Mean Density (g/cm^3)	J_2 ($\times 10^{-3}$)	Sidereal Rotation Period[4] (d)	Incl. of Equator to Orbit (deg)
Mercury	0.330 22	2,439.7	0	5.43		58.6462	0
Venus	4.8690	6,051.8	0	5.24	0.027	–243.0185	177.3
Earth	5.9722	6,378.1366	0.003 353 64	5.515	1.082 6359	0.997 269 63	23.45
Mars	0.641 91	3,396.19	0.006 772	3.94	1.964	1.02 595 676	25.19
Jupiter	1898.8	71,492	0.064 874	1.33	14.75	0.413 54	3.12
Saturn	568.52	60,268	0.097 962	0.69	16.45	0.444 01	26.73
Uranus	86.840	25,559	0.022 927	1.27	12	–0.718 33	97.86
Neptune	102.45	24,764	0.017 081	1.64	4	0.671 25	29.56
Pluto	0.013	1,195	0	1.8		–6.3872	118

Notes for Table B-4:
- The values for the masses include the atmospheres but exclude the satellites.
- The mean equatorial radii are given.
- The flattening is the ratio of the difference of the equatorial and polar radii to the equatorial radius.
- The sidereal rotation period refers to the rotation at the equator with respect to a fixed frame of reference: a negative sign indicates that the rotation is retrograde with respect to the pole that lies to the north of the invariable plane of the solar system. The period is given in days of 86,400 SI seconds.
- The data on the equator, flattening (ellipticity), and sidereal rotation period are based on Seidelmann et al. [2007].

B.3 Physical Properties of the Sun

Table B-5. Physical Properties of the Sun. Data from Cox [2000] and Astronomical Almanac [2010].

Radius of the photosphere	$6.960\ 00 \times 10^5$ km
Angular diameter of the photosphere at 1 AU	0.533 13 deg
Mass	1.9884×10^{30} kg
Mean density	1.409 g/cm^3
Gravity at surface	2.740×10^4 cm/sec^2
Moment of inertia	5.7×10^{53} g cm^2
Angular rotation velocity at equator	2.85×10^{-6} rad/sec
Angular momentum (based on surface rotation)	1.63×10^{48} g cm^2 /sec
Escape velocity at solar surface	6.177×10^7 g cm/sec
Total radiation emitted	3.845×10^{26} W
Total radiation per unit area at 1 AU (solar constant)*	1,366 W/m^2
Apparent visual magnitude at 1 AU	–26.75
Absolute visual magnitude (magnitude at distance of 10 parsecs)	+4.82
Color index, B–V	+0.65
Spectral type	G2 V
Effective temperature	5777 K
Inclination of the equator to the ecliptic	7.25 deg
Adopted period of sidereal rotation	25.38 days
Corresponding synodic rotation period (relative to Earth)	27.2753 days
Oblateness: semidiameter equator-pole difference	0."0086
Velocity relative to nearby stars	19.7 km sec

* The World Radiation Center in Switzerland has taken the data from a number of satellites and created a consensus on the solar constant. The World Radiation Center is the official international keeper of the solar constant. The value of the constant has a variation of –0.5 W/m^2 at solar min and +0.5 W/m^2 at solar max [World Radiation Center, 2006].

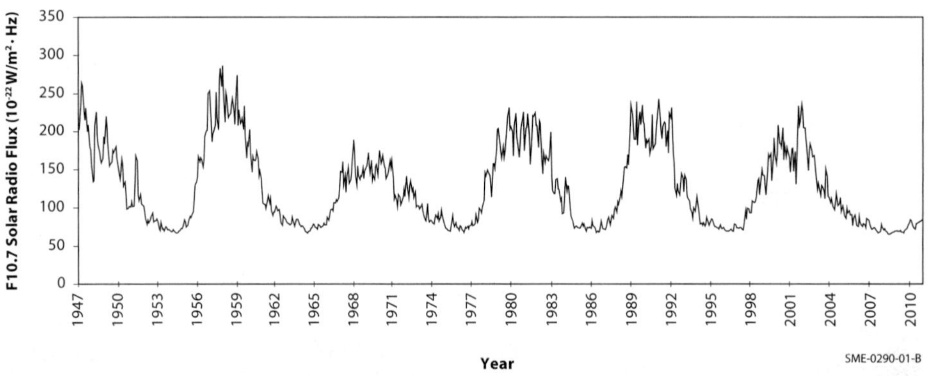

Fig. B-1. Historical Monthly 10.7 cm Radio Flux from the Sun (F10.7 Index) Since January 1947. For daily variations, see Fig. 9-16 in Sec. 9.4.4. (Plot courtesy Dave Bouwer, Space Environment Technologies)

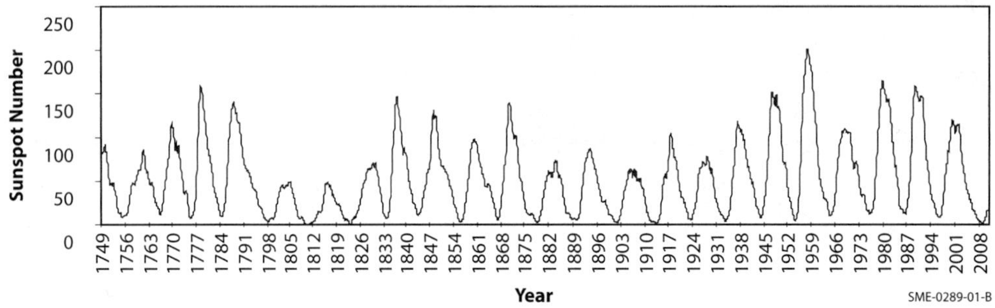

Fig. B-2. Historical Smoothed Sunspot Values from the 18th Century to Present. (Plot courtesy Dave Bouwer, Space Environment Technologies)

B.4 Physical and Orbit Properties of the Earth

Table B-6. Physical and Orbit Properties of the Earth.

		Reference
Equatorial radius, *a*	6,378.1366 km	IAU [2009]
Flattening factor (ellipticity), $f \equiv (a - c)/a$	1/298.256 42 ≈ 0.003 352 820	Astronomical Almanac [2010]
Polar radius,* *c*	$6.356\ 752 \times 10^6$ m	
Mean radius,* $(a^2c)^{1/3}$	6,371.0004 km	
Eccentricity,* $(a^2 - c^2)^{1/2}/a$	0.081 819 301	
Surface area	$5.100\ 657 \times 10^8$ km^2	Cox [2000]
Volume	$1.083\ 207 \times 10^{12}$ km^3	Cox [2000]
Ellipticity of the equator $(a_{max} - a_{min})/a_{mean}$	$\sim 1.1 \times 10^{-5}$	Groten [2000]
Longitude of the maxima	15° W, 165°E	Groten [2000]
Ratio of the mass of the Sun to the mass of the Earth	332 946.0487	IAU [2009]
Geocentric gravitational constant, $GM_E \equiv \mu_E$	$3.986\ 004\ 356 \times 10^{14}$ m^3/ s^2	IAU [2009]
Mass of the Earth	5.9722×10^{24} kg	Astronomical Almanac [2010]
Mean density	5.515 g/cm^3	Astronomical Almanac [2010]
Gravitational field constants (See Eq. (9-23) in Sec. 9.4.1.)	$J_2 = +1.082\ 63 \times 10^{-3}$ $J_3 = -2.64 \times 10^{-6}$ $J_4 = -1.61 \times 10^{-6}$	Astronomical Almanac [2010] Astronomical Almanac [2010] Astronomical Almanac [2010]
Mean distance of Earth center from Earth-Moon barycenter	4,671 km	Seidelmann [2006]
Average lengthening of the day (See Fig. B-3)	0.0015 sec/century	Seidelmann [2006]
General precession in longitude (i.e., precession of the equinoxes) per Julian century at epoch J2000	1.396 887 83 deg/century	Astronomical Almanac [2010]
Rate of change of precession at epoch J2000	$+6.184 \times 10^{-4}$ deg/century^2	Wertz [2009]
Rate of change of the obliquity at epoch J2000	$-1.301\ 021 \times 10^{-2}$ deg/Julian Century	Astronomical Almanac [2010]
Amplitude of the Earth's nutation	$2.557\ 01 \times 10^{-3}$ deg	Astronomical Almanac [2010]
Sidereal period of rotation, epoch J2000	0.997 269 68 d= 86 164.090 53 s = 23h56m4.09053 s	Astronomical Almanac [2010]
Length of tropical year (ref. = ♈), epoch J2000	$3.155\ 692\ 522 \times 10^7$ s = 365.242 190 d	Astronomical Almanac [2010]
Length of sidereal year (ref. = fixed stars), epoch J2000	$3.155\ 8150 \times 10^7$ s = 365.256 36 d	Cox [2000]
Length of anomalistic year (perihelion to perihelion), epoch J2000	$3.155\ 843\ 255 \times 10^7$ s = 365.259 636 d	Astronomical Almanac [2010]

* Based on adopted values of *f* and *a*. "Eccentricity" here refers to the eccentricity of the Earth's surface, not the orbit eccentricity.

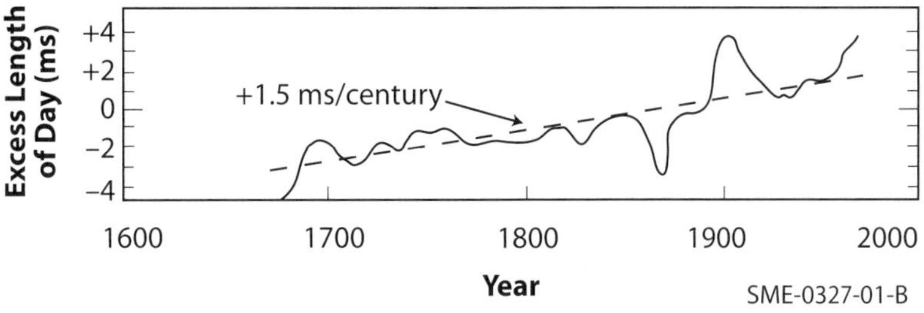

Fig. B-3. Variations in the Length of Day. On average, the Earth is slowing down by 1.5 ms/century, but local variations are large and very difficult to model.

Table B-7. Atmospheric Layers and Transitions. Data from Cox [2000].

Layer	Height, *h* (km)	Characteristics
Troposphere	0–11	Weather, *T* decreases with *h*, radiative-convective equilibrium
Tropopause	11	Temperature minimum, limit of upward mixing of heat
Stratosphere	11–48	*T* increases with *h* due to absorption of solar UV by O_3, dry
Stratopause	48	Maximum heating due to absorption of solar UV by O_3
Mesophere	48–85	*T* decreases with *h*
Mesopause	85	Coldest part of atmosphere, noctilucent clouds
Thermosphere	85–exobase	*T* increases with *h*, solar cycle and geomagnetic variations
Exobase	500–1,000 km	
Exosphere	> exobase	Region of Rayleigh-Jeans escape
Ozonosphere	15–35 km	Ozone layer (full width at e^{-1} of maximum)
Ionosphere	> 70 km	Ionized layers
Homosphere	< 85 km	Major constituents well-mixed
Heterosphere	> 85 km	Constituents diffusively separate

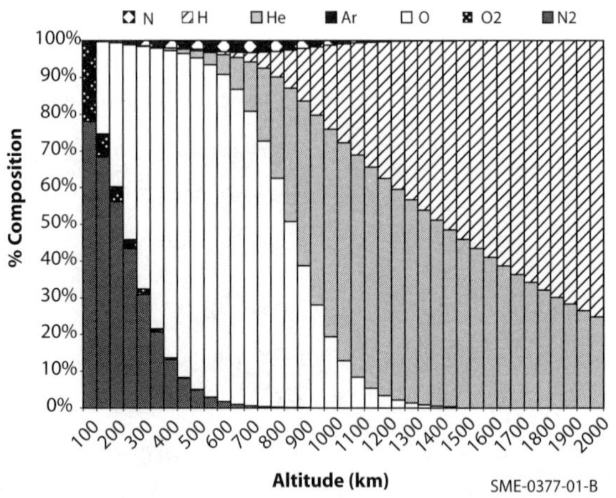

Fig. B-4. Mass Spectrometer Incoherent Scatter (MSIS) Atmospheric Species Percentage Composition vs. Altitude. [Hedin, 1987]. For atmospheric density, see Fig. 9-17 in Sec. 9.4.4.

B.4.1 Geocentric and Geodetic Coordinates on the Earth

The *geocentric latitude*, ϕ', of a point, *P*, on the surface of the Earth is the angle at the Earth's center between *P* and the equatorial plane. The *geodetic* or *geographic latitude*, ϕ, is the angle between the normal to an arbitrarily defined reference ellipsoid (chosen as a close approximation to the oblate Earth) and the equatorial plane. *Astronomical latitude* and longitude are defined relative to the *local vertical*, or the normal to the equipotential surface of the Earth. Thus, *astronomical latitude* is defined as the angle between the local vertical and the Earth's equatorial plane. Maximum values of the *deviation of the vertical*, or the angle between the local vertical and the normal to a reference ellipsoid, are about 1 minute of arc. Maximum variations in the height between the reference ellipsoid and *mean sea level* (also called the *equipotential surface*) are about 100 m.

The shape of the reference ellipsoid is most commonly defined by the *ellipticity* or *flattening factor*, $f \equiv (a - b)/a \approx 1/298.256\ 42 \approx 0.003\ 352\ 820$, where a is the equatorial radius of the Earth and b is the polar radius. Also used is the eccentricity of the reference ellipsoid, $e \equiv (a^2 - b^2)^{1/2}/a \approx 0.081\ 819\ 301$. These are related by:

$$e \equiv \sqrt{f(2-f)} \tag{B-1}$$

$$f = 1 - \sqrt{1-e^2} \tag{B-2}$$

On the surface of the Earth, the geodetic and geocentric latitude are related by:

$$\tan\phi = \tan\phi' / (1-f)^2 = 1.006\ 739\ 515\ \tan\phi' \tag{B-3}$$

where f is the flattening factor. At satellite altitudes the computation is more complex. As shown in Fig. B-5, the line normal to the oblate Earth through the satellite does not go through the Earth's center.

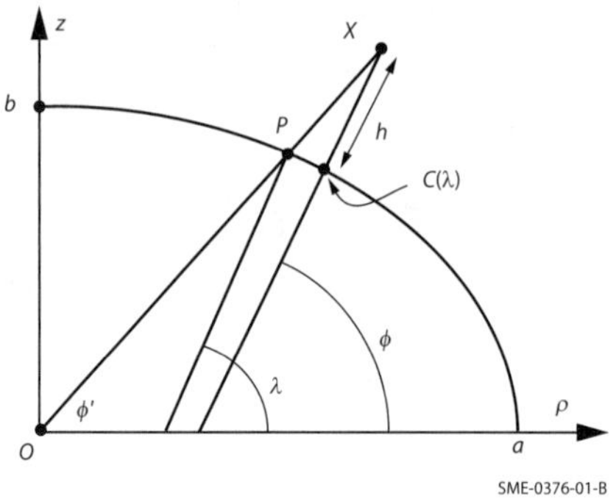

Fig. B-5. Relationship Between Geocentric Latitude, ϕ', and Geodetic Latitude, ϕ.

Geocentric coordinates are commonly expressed as Cartesian coordinates, (x, y, z). We then define the geocentric latitude, ϕ', and the radius in the equatorial plane, ρ, by:

$$\rho \equiv \sqrt{x^2+y^2} \tag{B-4}$$

$$\tan\phi' \equiv z/\rho \tag{B-5}$$

Given the geodetic coordinates, ϕ and h, as defined in Fig. B-5, we can immediately determine the geocentric coordinates from:

$$\rho = \left(N_\phi + h\right)\cos\phi \tag{B-6}$$

$$z = \left[\left(1-e^2\right)N_\phi + h\right]\sin\phi \tag{B-7}$$

where the radius of curvature of the ellipse, N_ϕ, is given by:

$$N_\phi = \frac{a}{\sqrt{1-e^2\sin^2\phi}} \tag{B-8}$$

Determining the geodetic coordinates from the geocentric coordinates is more complex and requires an iterative technique. The approach used here is that of Nievergelt and Keeler [2000], which includes references to a number of earlier, less satisfactory methods. With a single iteration, this approach is good to 2×10^{-6} deg for the geodetic latitude and 1 mm in geodetic altitude. Successive iterations can improve this, although that would rarely be needed. The 4-step iterative approach is as follows:

Step 1

Set the iteration counter, $n = 0$. Compute $\rho \equiv \sqrt{x^2+y^2}$ and the initial altitude estimate:

$$h_0 = \left[1 - 1/\sqrt{(\rho/a)^2 + (z/b)^2}\right]\sqrt{\rho^2+z^2} \tag{B-9}$$

Step 2

Compute the cosine, $u_0 = \cos(\lambda)$, and sine, $v_0 = \sin(\lambda)$, of the initial latitude estimate $\phi_0 = \lambda$ and the initial value of the intermediate variable, w_0:

$$u_0 = \frac{\sigma^2\rho}{\sqrt{\sigma^4\rho^2+z^2}},\quad v_0 = \frac{z}{\sqrt{\sigma^4\rho^2+z^2}}, \tag{B-10}$$

$$w_0 = \sqrt{1-e^2v_0^2}$$

where

$$\sigma \equiv b/a \tag{B-11}$$

Step 3

Compute the cosine, u_{n+1}, and sine, v_{n+1}, of the improved latitude estimate ϕ_{n+1}, the corresponding value w_{n+1}, and the improved altitude estimate h_{n+1}:

$$u_{n+1} = \frac{\left[a\sigma^2 + h_n w_n\right]\rho}{\sqrt{\left[a\sigma^2+h_nw_n\right]^2\rho^2 + \left[a+h_nw_n\right]^2 z^2}} \tag{B-12}$$

$$v_{n+1} = \frac{\left[a + h_n w_n\right]z}{\sqrt{\left[a\sigma^2+h_nw_n\right]^2\rho^2 + \left[a+h_nw_n\right]^2 z^2}}$$

$$w_{n+1} = \sqrt{1-e^2v_{n+1}^2}$$

$$h_{n+1} = \sqrt{\left[\rho - \frac{au_{n+1}}{w_{n+1}}\right]^2 + \left[z - \frac{a\sigma^2v_{n+1}}{w_{n+1}}\right]^2}$$

Step 4

Compute $\phi_{n+1} = \arctan(v_{n+1}/u_{n+1})$ with a standard algorithm that is stable near ±90 deg.

B.5 Physical and Orbit Properties of the Moon

Table B-8. Physical Parameters of the Moon. Data from Cox [2000] and Astronomical Almanac [2010]. For an extended discussion of lunar properties see Eckart [2006] and Heiken et al., [1991].

Radii: (a) Toward Earth, (b) Along orbit, (c) Toward pole	
Mean radius (b + c) / 2	1,738.2 km
a – c	1.09 km
a – b	0.31 km
b – c	0.78 km
Semi-diameter at mean distance	15′32″.6
Mass	7.3483 × 10[22] kg
Mean density	3.341 g cm[–3]
Surface gravity	162.2 cm/s[2] = 0.1654 g
Surface escape velocity	2.38 km/s
Extreme range	356,400 – 406,700 km
Inclination of orbit to ecliptic oscillating ±9′ with period of 173 d	5° 8′ 43″.42
Sidereal period (fixed stars)	27.321 661
Mean orbital speed	1.023 km/sec
Synodical month (new Moon to new Moon)	29. 530 588
Surface area of Moon at some time visible from Earth	59%
Inclination of lunar equator	
To ecliptic	1° 32′ 32″.7
To orbit	6° 41′

Table B-9. Gravity Field of the Moon. Data from Cox [2000].

$\alpha = (C-B)/A = 0.000\ 400$	$C/MR^2 = 0.392$	
$\beta = (C-A)/B = 0.000\ 628$	I = 5,552″.7 = 1°32′32	
$\gamma = (B-A)/C = 0.0002278$		
$C_{20} = -\ 0.000\ 202\ 7$	$C_{30} = -\ 0.000\ 006$	$C_{32} = +\ 0.000\ 004\ 8$
$C_{22} = +\ 0.000\ 022\ 3$	$C_{31} = +\ 0.000\ 029$	$S_{32} = +\ 0.000\ 001\ 7$
	$S_{31} = +\ 0.000\ 004$	$C_{33} = +\ 0.000\ 001\ 8$
		$S_{33} = -\ 0.000\ 001$

Table B-10. Orbit of the Moon About the Earth. Data from Cox [2000] and Seidelmann [2006].

Sidereal mean motion of Moon	$2.661\ 699\ 489 \times 10^{-6}$ rad s^{-1}
Mean distance of Moon from Earth	384 400 km
	60.27 Earth radii
	0.002 570 AU
Equatorial horizontal parallax	57′02″.608
at mean distance	3,422″.608
Mean distance of center of Earth from Earth-Moon barycenter	4.671×10^3 km
Mean eccentricity	0.054 90
Mean inclination to ecliptic	5.145 396 deg
Mean inclination to lunar equator	6°41′
Limits of geocentric declination	± 29 deg
Period of revolution of node	18.612 Julian years
Period of revolution of perigee	8.849 Julian years
Mean orbital speed	1,023 ms^{-1} = 0.000 591 AU/d
Mean centripetal acceleration	0.00272 ms^{-2} = 0.0003 g
Optical libration in longitude (selenocentric displacement)	± 7.883 deg
Optical libration in latitude (selenocentric displacement)	± 6.85 deg
Saros = 223 lunations = 19 passages of Sun through node = 6,585 1/3 days	
Moment of inertia (about rotation axis)	$0.396\ M_{\oplus} b^2$
Gravitational potential term	$J_2 = 2.027 \times 10^{-4}$
No. of strong mascons on the near side of the Moon	4 exceeding 80 milligals
Mean surface temperature	+107 C (day), 153 C (night)
Temperature extremes	–233 C, +123 C
Moon's atmospheric density	~10^4 molecules cm^{-3} (day); 2×10^5 molecules cm^{-3} (night)
No. of maria & craters on lunar surface w/ diam. > d	$5 \times 10^{10} d^{-2.0}$ per 10^6 km^2 (d in m)

References

For annotated bibliography of Appendix B, see the book website.

Cox, Arthur N, ed. 2000. *Allen's Astrophysical Quantities* (4th ed.). New York: Springer-Verlag.

Eckart, P. 2006, 2nd ed. *The Lunar Base Handbook: An Introduction to Lunar Base Design, Development, and Operations*. NY: McGraw-Hill.

Groten, E. 2000. *Parameters of Common Relevance of Astronomy, Geodesy, and Geodynamics. Geodesists Handbook 2000, Part 4.*

Hedin, Alan E. 1987. "MSIS-86 Thermospheric Model." *J GeophysR*, 92, No. A5, pp. 4649–4662.

———. 1988. "The Atmospheric Model in the Region 90 to 2000 km." *Adv. Space Res.*, 8, No. 5-6, pp. (5)9–(5)25, Pergamon Press.

———. 1991. "Extension of the MSIS Thermosphere Model into the Middle and Lower Atmosphere," *J Geophys R*, 96, No. A2, pp. 1159–1172.

Heiken, Grant H., David T. Vaniman, and Bevan M. French. 1991. *Lunar Sourcebook: A User's Guide to the Moon.* Cambridge: Cambridge University Press.

International Astronomical Union Working Group on Numerical Standards for Fundamental Astronomy. 2009. "Current Best Estimates."

Meeus, Jean. 1998. *Astronomical Algorithms, 2nd ed.* Willmann-Bell, Incorporated.

Nievergelt, Y., and S. Keeler. 2000. "Computing Geodetic Coordinates in Space." *J. Spacecraft.* 37:293–296.

Seidelmann, P. Kenneth, ed., USNO. 2006. *Explanatory Supplement to the Astronomical Almanac.* Mill Valley, CA: University Science Books.

Seidelmann, et al. 2007. "Report of the IAU/IAG Working Group on Cartographic Coordinates and Rotational Elements: 2006." *Celestial Mechanics and Dynamical Astronomy*. Vol. 98, pp. 155–180, July.

US Naval Observatory and H. M. Nautical Almanac Office. 1998. *The Astronomical Almanac for the Year 1999.* Washington, DC: US GPO.

US Naval Observatory and H. M. Nautical Almanac Office. 2010. *The Astronomical Almanac for the Year 2011.* Washington, DC: US GPO.

Wertz, James R. 2009. *Orbit & Constellation Design and Management: Spacecraft Orbit and Attitude Systems.* Hawthorne, CA: Microcosm Press.

World Radiation Center. 2006. "Solar Constant: Construction of a Composite Total Solar Irradiance (TSI) Time Series from 1978 to Present."

Appendix C
Summary of Keplerian Orbit and Coverage Equations

Nicola Sarzi-Amade, *Microcosm, Inc.*

This appendix provides summary formulas in addition to those given in Table 9-4 in Sec. 9.1. Formulas are provided for all four types of Keplerian orbits—circular, elliptical, parabolic, and hyperbolic. See Sec. 9.1 for definition of orbit variables, derivations, and conditions. See Table C-1 for values of the gravitational constant, μ, for the Earth, Moon, Sun, and Mars. See Table B-1 in App. B for values of μ for all of the major bodies in the Solar System. See Sec. 8.3 for definition of most of the geometric variables. See the website for the source of each of the equations. Finally, numerical evaluations of most of the characteristics of the motion are contained on the pages preceding the inside rear cover for orbits about the Earth, and on the website for orbits about other celestial bodies.

Get Ref

Get More

μ = GM is the gravitational constant of the central body and is much more accurately known than either the mass, M, or the universal gravitational constant, G, the least accurately known of the fundamental physical constants.

Table C-1. Values of the Gravitational Constant, μ, for the Earth, Sun, Moon, and Mars. Values are those given by the International Astronomical Union [2009]. See Table B-1 in App. B for other central bodies.

Central Body	μ (m^3/s^2)	$\sqrt{\mu}$ ($m^{1.5}/s$)
Earth	$3.986\,004\,356 \times 10^{14}$	19,964,980.230
Moon	$4.902\,800\,15 \times 10^{12}$	2,214,226.76
Mars	$4.282\,837\,522 \times 10^{13}$	6,544,339.17
Sun	$1.327\,124\,400\,41 \times 10^{20}$	11,520,088,543.11

For all of the orbit types, ν is the *true anomaly* = the angle from perifocus to the orbiting body and $M \equiv n\,(t - T)$ is the *mean anomaly*, where t is the time of observation, T is the time of perifocal passage, and n is the mean angular motion. Other parameters are defined in the table and discussed at the text reference cited in the table.

C.1 Equations for Circular Orbits

See Sec. 9.1 for definition of orbit variables, Sec. 8.3 for definition of geometric variables, and Sec. 8.3.3 in OCDM = Wertz [2009] for application of the Euler axis formulas to satellite ground tracks. See rear end-papers for properties of orbits about the Earth, and on the website for orbits about other celestial bodies.

Get More

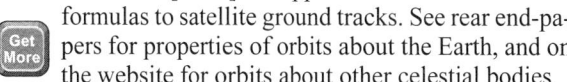

Note: A bold **"C"** is put in front of each descriptor to denote formulas for circular orbits.

C. Defining parameter:

$$a = \text{semimajor axis} = r = \text{radius} \qquad \text{(C-1)}$$

(For a discussion of Keplerian orbits, see Sec. 9.1; for transformations between orbital elements and position and velocity, see Sec. 2.7.1.1 and 2.7.1.2 in OCDM; for the apparent shape of a circular orbit viewed from nearby, see Sec. 8.4.1.)

C. Parametric equation:

$$x^2 + y^2 = a^2 \qquad \text{(C-2)}$$

C. Distance from focus, *r*:

$$r = a \qquad \text{(C-3)}$$

C. Specific energy, ε (= total energy per unit mass):

$$\varepsilon = -\frac{\mu}{2a} = \frac{V^2}{2} - \frac{\mu}{a} < 0 \qquad \text{(C-4)}$$

C. Specific angular momentum, *h*:

$$h = |\mathbf{h}| = \sqrt{\mu a} \qquad \text{(C-5)}$$

C. Angular momentum vector, h:

$$\mathbf{h} = \mathbf{r} \times \mathbf{V} \qquad \text{(C-6)}$$

C. Nodal vector, N:

$$\mathbf{N} = \hat{\mathbf{z}} \times \hat{\mathbf{h}} = \hat{\mathbf{z}} \times \mathbf{h} / h \qquad \text{(C-7)}$$

C. Inclination, *i*:

$$i = \operatorname{acos}(h_z / h) \qquad \text{(C-8)}$$

(For a discussion of apparent inclination, see the boxed example at the end of Sec. 9.3.1 in OCDM.)

C. Right ascension of the ascending node, Ω :

$$\Omega = \operatorname{atan2}(N_x, N_y) \qquad \text{(C-9)}$$

(For the definition of atan2, see Sec. D.4)

C. Flight path angle, ϕ_{fpa}:

$$\phi_{fpa} = 0 \tag{C-10}$$

C. Perifocal distance, *q*:

$$q = a = r \tag{C-11}$$

C. Semi-parameter, *p*:

$$p = a \tag{C-12}$$

C. Semimajor axis, *a*:

$$a = r \tag{C-13}$$

C. Eccentricity, *e*:

$$e = 0 \tag{C-14}$$

C. Mean motion, *n*:

$$n = \sqrt{\mu / a^3} = 2\pi / P \tag{C-15}$$

C. Mean anomaly, *M*:

$$M = M_0 + nt \tag{C-16}$$

C. True anomaly, ν:

$$\nu = M \tag{C-17}$$

C. Rate of change of true anomaly, $\dot{\nu}$:

$$\dot{\nu} = n \tag{C-18}$$

C. Period, *P*:

$$P = 2\pi / n = 2\pi\sqrt{a^3 / \mu} \tag{C-19}$$

$= 1.658\ 669\ 021\ 3 \times 10^{-4}\ a^{3/2}$ for Earth; *P* in min, *a* in km)

$= 1.495\ 569\ 234 \times 10^{-3}\ a^{3/2}$ for Moon; *P* in min, *a* in km)

$= 5.060\ 143\ 330 \times 10^{-4}\ a^{3/2}$ for Mars; *P* in min, *a* in km)

$= 1.996\ 228\ 762\ 54 \times 10^{-10}\ a^{3/2}$ (for Sun; *P* in calendar days, *a* in km)

C. Velocity, *V*:

$$V = \sqrt{\mu / a} = an \tag{C-20}$$

C. Range • range rate, $r\dot{r}$:

$$r\dot{r} = 0 \tag{C-21}$$

C. Areal velocity, $\dot{A}$:

$$\dot{A} = 0.5\sqrt{\mu a} = 0.5\, a^2 n \tag{C-22}$$

C. Escape velocity, V_E:

$$V_E = \sqrt{2\mu / a} = \sqrt{2}\, V \tag{C-23}$$

C. Euler axis co-latitude, δ'_{ea}:

$$\delta'_{ea} = \text{atan}\left(\frac{n \sin i}{-\omega_E + n \cos i}\right) \tag{C-24}$$

ω_E = inertial rotation rate of central body
= 0.004 178 074 1 deg/sec (Earth)
= 0.000 152 504 145 25 deg/sec (Moon)
= 0.004 061 249 794 68 deg/sec (Mars)

(For a complete set of closed-form ground track equations, see Table 8-11 in Sec. 8.4.)

C. Euler rotation rate, ω_{ea}:

$$\omega_{ea} = n \sin i / \sin \delta'_{ea} = \sqrt{\omega_E^2 + n^2 + 2n\omega_E \cos i} \tag{C-25}$$

C. Angular radius of the Earth, ρ:

$$\rho = \text{asin}(R_E / a) \tag{C-26}$$

R_E = radius of central body
= 6378.1366 km (Earth)
= 1737.4 km (Moon)
= 3396.19 km (Mars)

(Assumes a spherical Earth. For the effect of oblateness, see Sec. 9.4.1, and Sec. 9.1.5 in OCDM.)

C. Distance to the horizon, *D*:

$$D = a \cos\rho = \sqrt{a^2 - R_E^2} \tag{C-27}$$

(For calculation of angles and distance for targets not on the horizon, see Sec. 8.3.1.)

C. Maximum Earth central angle, λ_{max}:

$$\lambda_{max} = 90\ \text{deg} - \rho = \text{acos}\ (R_E / a) \tag{C-28}$$

C. Instantaneous Access Area, *IAA*:

$$IAA = K_A(1 - \cos \lambda_{max}) \tag{C-29}$$

$K_A = 2\pi \approx 6.283\ 185\ 311$ for area in steradians
$= 360^2 / (2\pi) \approx 20{,}626.480\ 62$ for area in deg^2
$= 2.55\ 603\ 915 \times 10^8$ for area in km^2 (Earth)
$= 1.896\ 62 \times 10^7$ for area in km^2 (Moon)
$= 7.247\ 093 \times 10^7$ for area in km^2 (Mars)

(For alternative ways to calculate ground coverage, see Sec. 10.2.1; for other ground area formulas, see Table 10-3 in Sec. 10.2.1; for transformations between geocentric and access area coordinates, see the boxed example in Sec. 8.3; for projections of sensor fields of view onto the central body, see Sec. 8.3.4.)

C. Area Access Rate, *AAR*:

$$AAR = 2K_A \frac{\sin \lambda_{max}}{P} \tag{C-30}$$

C. Maximum time in view, T_{max}:

$$T_{max} = P\lambda_{max} / 180\ \text{deg} \tag{C-31}$$

(For a complete set of target or ground station coverage formulas, see Table 8-11 in Sec. 8.4.1.)

C. Maximum angular rate seen from ground, $\dot{\theta}_{max}$:

$$\dot{\theta}_{max} = \frac{a\ 360°}{P(a - R_E)} \tag{C-32}$$

Table C-1◀, Fig. C-0, Eq. C-32

C. Node precession rate due to J_2, $\Delta\Omega_{J2}$:

$$\Delta\Omega_{J2} = -1.5 J_2 n (R_E / a)^2 \cos i \equiv K_{J2} a^{-7/2} \cos i \quad \text{(C-33)}$$

$= -2.064\ 745\ 722 \times 10^{14}\ a^{-7/2} \cos i$ (Earth, a in km)
$= -3.193\ 05 \times 10^{11}\ a^{-7/2} \cos i$ (Moon, a in km)
$= -3.468\ 016 \times 10^{13}\ a^{-7/2} \cos i$ (Mars, a in km)

(In the numerical forms, $\Delta\Omega_{J2}$ is in deg / calendar day*)

C. Sun-synchronous inclination, i_{SS}:

$$i_{ss} = \text{acos}\left(\frac{360 a^{7/2}}{K_{J2} SP}\right) \quad \text{(C-34)}$$

$= \text{acos}(-4.773\ 513\ 28 \times 10^{-15}\ a^{7/2})$ (Earth, a in km)
$= \text{acos}(-3.086\ 7 \times 10^{-12}\ a^{7/2})$ (Moon, a in km)
$= \text{acos}(-1.511\ 0 \times 10^{-14}\ a^{7/2})$ (Mars, a in km)

(Where SP is the sidereal period of the planet or the Moon about the Sun in calendar days. For a discussion of Sun synchronous orbits, see Sec. 9.5.3.)

C. Orbital revolutions per day, *Rev/d*:

$$Rev/d = \text{Day} / \text{P} \quad \text{(C-35)}$$

$= 1.436\ 068\ 34 \times 10^3 / P$ (Earth, P in min)
$= 3.934\ 319\ 286\ 9 \times 10^4 / P$ (Moon, P in min)
$= 1.477\ 377\ 729\ 355 \times 10^3 / P$ (Mars, P in min)

(This is the number of orbit revolutions for each rotation of the planet on its axis relative to the fixed stars (i.e., the inertial rotation period). "Day" is the length of the sidereal day (in minutes) for the given central body. For more accurate expressions, see the discussion of repeating ground tracks in Sec. 2.5.2.)

C. Node spacing, ΔN:

$$\Delta N = 360 \text{ deg } (P / \text{Day}) \quad \text{(C-36)}$$

$= 0.250\ 684\ 448\ P$ (Earth, P in min)
$= 0.009\ 150\ 248\ 715\ P$ (Moon, P in min)
$= 0.243\ 674\ 987\ 681\ P$ (Mars, P in min)

(For the equations for repeating ground track orbits, see Sec. 9.5.2.)

C. Maximum eclipse, T_E:

$$T_E = P(\rho / 180 \text{ deg}) = P \text{ asin}(R_E / a)/180 \text{ deg} \quad \text{(C-37)}$$

(For computation of eclipse duration for any Sun angle, see Sec. 8.2.4; for the formulas for eclipse conditions, see Sec. 11.4 in OCDM.)

C. Sun angle constraints for terminator visibility, β':

$$90° + \xi - \rho < \beta' < 90° - \xi + \rho \quad \text{(C-38)}$$

(ξ is the dark angle defined in Sec. 11.5.2 in OCDM. For general conditions of terminator visibility, see Table 11-3 in Sec. 11.5.2 in OCDM.)

* Calendar day = 24 h in contrast to sidereal day = 23 h 56 m 4.09053 s. See App. B.

C. Transit time for a spacecraft whose celestial coordinates are known, T:

$$T = \alpha + L - \text{GST} \quad \text{(C-39)}$$

(where α is the right ascension, L is the observer East longitude, and GST is the Greenwich Sidereal Time. For computation of observability times of spacecraft for which the celestial coordinates are known, see Table 9-6 in Sec. 9.4.4 in OCDM.)

C.2 Equations for Elliptical Orbits

See Sec. 9.1 for definition of orbit variables, Sec. 8.3 for definition of geometric variables, and Sec. 8.3.3 in OCDM for application of the Euler axis formulas to satellite ground tracks. See rear end-papers for properties of orbits about the Earth, and on the website for orbits about other celestial bodies.

Note: An **"E"** is put in front of each descriptor to denote formulas for Elliptical Orbits. Subscript A stands for evaluation of parameters at apogee; subscript P stands for evaluation of parameters at perigee.

E. Defining parameters:

$$a = \text{semimajor axis} \quad \text{(C-40)}$$
$$b = \text{semiminor axis}$$

(For a discussion of Keplerian orbits, see Sec. 9.1; for transformations between orbital elements and position and velocity, see Secs. 2.7.1.1 and 2.7.1.2 in OCDM.)

E. Parametric equation:

$$\frac{x^2}{a^2} + \frac{y^2}{b^2} = 1 \quad \text{(C-41)}$$

E. Distance from focus, r:

$$r = \frac{r_P(1+e)}{1+e\cos\nu} = a(1-e\cos E) = \frac{p}{1+e\cos\nu} = \frac{r_A(1-e)}{1+e\cos\nu} \quad \text{(C-42)}$$

E. Specific energy, ε (= total energy per unit mass):

$$\varepsilon = \frac{V^2}{2} - \frac{\mu}{r} = -\frac{\mu}{2a} < 0 \quad \text{(C-43)}$$

E. Specific angular momentum, h:

$$h = |\mathbf{h}| = \sqrt{\mu p} = rV\cos\phi_{fpa} = r^2\dot{\nu} = r_A V_A = r_P V_P \quad \text{(C-44)}$$

E. Angular momentum vector, h:

$$\mathbf{h} = \mathbf{r} \times \mathbf{V} \quad \text{(C-45)}$$

E. Nodal vector, N:

$$\mathbf{N} = \hat{\mathbf{z}} \times \hat{\mathbf{h}} = \hat{\mathbf{z}} \times \mathbf{h} / h \quad \text{(C-46)}$$

E. Eccentricity vector, e:

$$\mathbf{e} = \frac{\mathbf{V} \times \mathbf{h}}{\mu} - \frac{\mathbf{r}}{r} \quad \text{(C-47)}$$

E. Inclination, *i*:

$$i = \text{acos}(h_z / h) \quad \text{(C-48)}$$

(For a discussion of apparent inclination, see the boxed example at the end of Sec. 9.3.1 in OCDM.)

E. Right ascension of the ascending node, Ω:

$$\Omega = \text{atan2}(N_x, N_y) \quad \text{(C-49)}$$

(For the definition of atan2, see Sec. D.4)

E. Flight path angle, ϕ_{fpa}:

$$\phi_{fpa} = \text{atan2}\left(\cos\phi_{fpa}, \sin\phi_{fpa}\right) \quad \text{(C-50)}$$

$$= \text{acos}\left(\sqrt{\mu p} / rV\right)$$

$$\sin\phi_{fpa} = \frac{e\sin E}{\sqrt{1-e^2\cos^2 E}}$$

$$\cos\phi_{fpa} = \sqrt{\frac{1-e^2}{1-e^2\cos^2 E}}$$

E. Perifocal distance, *q* = radius of perigee, r_P:

$$q = r_P = a(1-e) = \frac{p}{1+e} = r_A\left(\frac{1-e}{1+e}\right) \quad \text{(C-51)}$$

$$= \frac{b^2}{r_A} = r_A\left(V_A / V_P\right)$$

E. Semi-parameter, *p*:

$$p = a(1-e^2) = r(1 + e\cos\nu) = q(1+e) \quad \text{(C-52)}$$

$$= b^2/a = h^2/\mu$$

E. Radius of apogee, r_A:

$$r_A = a(1+e) = 2a - r_P = b^2 / r_P = q\left(\frac{1+e}{1-e}\right) = \frac{b^2}{a-c} \quad \text{(C-53)}$$

(Where the distance *c* is defined in Fig. 9-5, Sec. 9.1.5.)

E. Semimajor axis, *a*:

$$a = \frac{r_A + r_P}{2} = \frac{r_P}{1-e} = \frac{r_A}{1+e} = \frac{p}{1-e^2} = -\frac{\mu}{2\varepsilon} = \left(\frac{\mu}{n^2}\right)^{1/3} \quad \text{(C-54)}$$

E. Semiminor axis, *b*:

$$b = a\sqrt{1-e^2} = \sqrt{ap} = \sqrt{r_A r_P} = \sqrt{\mu p} / h \quad \text{(C-55)}$$

E. Eccentricity, *e*:

$$e = |\mathbf{e}| = \sqrt{1 + \frac{2\varepsilon h^2}{\mu^2}} = \frac{\sqrt{a^2 - b^2}}{a} \quad \text{(C-56)}$$

$$= \frac{r_A - r_P}{r_A + r_P} = \frac{r_A}{a} - 1 = 1 - \frac{r_P}{a} = \frac{c}{a}$$

$$0 < e < 1$$

E. Mean motion, *n*:

$$n = \sqrt{\mu / a^3} = \frac{2\pi}{P} \quad \text{(C-57)}$$

E. Mean anomaly, *M*:

$$M = M_o + nt = E - e\sin E \quad \text{(C-58)}$$

E. Eccentric anomaly, *E*:

$$E = \text{atan2}\left(\cos E, \sin E\right) = 2\,\text{atan}\left[\sqrt{\frac{1-e}{1+e}}\tan\left(\nu/2\right)\right] \quad \text{(C-59)}$$

$$= \text{acos}\left(\frac{a-r}{ae}\right) = \text{asin}\left(\frac{r}{b}\sin\nu\right) = \text{acos}\left(\frac{a-r}{a-r_P}\right)$$

$$\cos E = \frac{e+\cos\nu}{1+e\cos\nu} \qquad \sin E = \frac{\sin\nu\sqrt{1-e^2}}{1+e\cos\nu}$$

as an iterative equation with successive estimates E_i:

$$E_{i+1} = E_i + \frac{M - E_i + e\sin E_i}{1 - e\cos E_i}$$

E. True anomaly, ν:

$$\nu = \text{atan2}\left(\cos\nu, \sin\nu\right) = 2\,\text{atan}\left[\sqrt{\frac{1+e}{1-e}}\tan\left(E/2\right)\right] \quad \text{(C-60)}$$

$$= \text{acos}\left(\frac{p/r-1}{e}\right) = \text{acos}\left(\frac{\cos E - e}{1 - e\cos E}\right)$$

$$\cos\nu = \frac{\cos E - e}{1 - e\cos E} \qquad \sin\nu = \frac{\sin E\sqrt{1-e^2}}{1 - e\cos E}$$

as a power series in *M*:

$$\nu \approx M + \left(2e - \frac{e^3}{4} + \frac{5e^5}{96}\right)\sin(M) \quad \text{(C-61)}$$

$$+ \left(\frac{5e^2}{4} - \frac{11e^4}{24}\right)\sin(2M) + \left(\frac{13e^3}{12} - \frac{43e^5}{64}\right)\sin(3M)$$

$$+ \left(\frac{103e^4}{96}\right)\sin(4M) + \mathcal{O}\left(e^6\right)$$

E. Rate of change of true anomaly, $\dot{\nu}$:

$$\dot{\nu} = \frac{\sqrt{\mu p}}{r^2} = \frac{V_P r_P}{r^2} = \frac{V_A r_A}{r^2} = \frac{na^2}{r^2}\sqrt{1-e^2} \quad \text{(C-62)}$$

E. Period, *P*:

$$P = 2\pi / n = 2\pi\sqrt{a^3 / \mu} \quad \text{(C-63)}$$

$= 1.658\,669\,021\,3 \times 10^{-4}\, a^{3/2}$
(for Earth; *P* in min, *a* in km)
$= 1.495\,569\,234 \times 10^{-3}\, a^{3/2}$
(for Moon; *P* in min, *a* in km)
$= 5.060\,143\,330 \times 10^{-4}\, a^{3/2}$
(for Mars; *P* in min, *a* in km)
$= 1.996\,228\,762\,54 \times 10^{-10}\, a^{3/2}$
(for Sun; *P* in days, *a* in km)

E. Velocity, *V*:

$$V = \sqrt{\frac{2\mu}{r} - \frac{\mu}{a}} = \sqrt{2\left(\frac{\mu}{r} + \varepsilon\right)} \tag{C-64}$$
$$= \sqrt{\frac{\mu}{r}\left(2 - \frac{1-e^2}{1+e\cos\nu}\right)} = \sqrt{\mu p}\,/\left(r\cos\phi_{fpa}\right)$$

$$\frac{V_A}{V_P} = \frac{r_P}{r_A}$$

$$V_P = \sqrt{\frac{\mu}{r_P}(1+e)} = \sqrt{\frac{2\mu r_A}{r_P(r_A + r_P)}} = \sqrt{\frac{\mu}{r_P}\left(2 - \frac{r_P}{a}\right)}$$
$$= V_A\left(\frac{r_A}{r_P}\right)$$

$$V_A = \sqrt{\frac{\mu}{r_A}(1-e)} = \sqrt{\frac{\mu r_P}{a r_A}} = \sqrt{\frac{\mu}{r_A}\left(2 - \frac{r_A}{a}\right)} = V_P\left(\frac{r_P}{r_A}\right)$$

E. Azimuthal velocity, V_{az}:

$$V_{az} = V\cos\phi_{fpa} = r\dot{\nu} \tag{C-65}$$

E. Radial velocity, V_r:

$$V_r = V\sin\phi_{fpa} = \dot{r} \tag{C-66}$$
$$= V_{az}\frac{e\sin\nu}{1+e\cos\nu} = \frac{r\dot{\nu}e\sin\nu}{1+e\cos\nu}$$

E. Range • range rate, $r\dot{r}$:

$$r\dot{r} = e\sqrt{a\mu}\,\sin E \tag{C-67}$$

E. Areal velocity, $\dot{A}$:

$$\dot{A} = 0.5\sqrt{a\mu\left(1-e^2\right)} = 0.5r^2\dot{\nu} \tag{C-68}$$

E. Escape velocity, V_E:

$$V_E = \sqrt{2\mu / r} \tag{C-69}$$

E. Euler axis co-latitude, δ'_{ea}:

$$\delta'_{ea} = \text{atan}\left(\frac{\dot{\nu}\sin i}{-\omega_E + \dot{\nu}\cos i}\right) \tag{C-70}$$

ω_E = inertial rotation of central body
= 0.004 178 074 1 deg/sec (Earth)
= 0.000 152 504 145 25 deg/sec (Moon)
= 0.004 061 249 794 68 deg/sec (Mars)

(For a complete set of ground track equations, see Table 8-11 in Sec. 8.4 and Sec. 8.4.1, which also includes a discussion of approximations for small eccentricities.)

E. Euler rotation rate, ω_{ea}:

$$\omega_{ea} = \dot{\nu}\sin i / \sin\delta'_{ea} \tag{C-71}$$
$$= \sqrt{\omega_E^2 + \dot{\nu}^2 + 2\dot{\nu}\omega_E\cos i}$$

E. Angular radius of the Earth, ρ:

$$\rho = \text{asin}\,(R_E / r) \tag{C-72}$$

R_E = radius of central body
= 6378.1366 km (Earth)
= 1737.4 km (Moon)
= 3396.19 km (Mars)

(Assumes a spherical Earth. For the effect of oblateness, see Sec. 9.4.1, and Sec. 9.1.5 in OCDM.)

E. Maximum angular radius of the Earth, ρ_{max}:

$$\rho_{max} = \text{asin}(R_E / r_P) \tag{C-73}$$

E. Minimum angular radius of the Earth, ρ_{min}:

$$\rho_{min} = \text{asin}(R_E / r_A) \tag{C-74}$$

E. Distance to the horizon, *D*:

$$D = r\cos\rho = \sqrt{r^2 - R_E^2} \tag{C-75}$$

(For calculation of angles and distance for targets not on the horizon, see Sec. 8.3.1.)

E. Maximum distance to the horizon, D_{max}:

$$D_{max} = r_A\cos\rho_{min} = \sqrt{r_A^2 - R_E^2} \tag{C-76}$$

E. Minimum distance to the horizon, D_{min}:

$$D_{min} = r_P\cos\rho_{max} = \sqrt{r_P^2 - R_E^2} \tag{C-77}$$

E. Maximum Earth central angle, λ_{max}:

$$\lambda_{max} = 90\text{ deg} - \rho_{min} = \text{acos}(R_E / r_A) \tag{C-78}$$

E. Instantaneous Access Area, *IAA*:

$$IAA = K_A(1 - \cos\lambda_{max}) \tag{C-79}$$

$K_A = 2\pi \approx 6.283\,185\,311$ for area in steradians
$= 360^2 / (2\pi) \approx 20{,}626.480\,62$ for area in deg^2
$= 2.55\,603\,915 \times 10^8$ for area in km^2 (Earth)
$= 1.896\,62 \times 10^7$ for area in km^2 (Moon)
$= 7.247\,093 \times 10^7$ for area in km^2 (Mars)

(For alternative ways to calculate ground coverage, see Sec. 10.2.1; for other ground area formulas, see Table 10-3 in Sec. 10.2.1; for transformations between geocentric and access area coordinates, see the boxed example in Sec. 8.3; for projections of sensor fields of view onto the central body, see Sec. 8.3.4.)

E. Area Access Rate, *AAR*:

$$AAR = \left(\frac{K_A\dot{\nu}}{\pi}\right)\sin\lambda_{max} \tag{C-80}$$

E. Maximum time in view, T_{max}:

$$T_{max} \approx 2\lambda_{max} / \dot{\nu} \tag{C-81}$$

(For a complete set of target or ground station coverage formulas for elliptical orbits, see Table 8-12 in Sec. 8.4.2.)

E. Maximum angular rate seen from ground, $\dot{\theta}_{max}$:

$$\dot{\theta}_{max} = \frac{\dot{v}r}{(r - R_E)} \qquad \text{(C-82)}$$

E. Node precession rate due to J_2, $\Delta\Omega_{J2}$:

$$\Delta\Omega_{J2} = -1.5\, J_2 n\, (R_E / a)^2 (1 - e^2)^{-2} \cos i \qquad \text{(C-83)}$$

$$\approx K_{J2}\, a^{-7/2} (1-e^2)^{-2} \cos i$$

$= -2.064\ 745\ 722 \times 10^{14}\, a^{-7/2} (1 - e^2)^{-2} \cos i$ (Earth, a in km)

$= -3.193\ 05 \times 10^{11}\, a^{-7/2} (1 - e^2)^{-2} \cos i$ (Moon, a in km)

$= -3.468\ 016 \times 10^{13}\, a^{-7/2} (1 - e^2)^{-2} \cos i$ (Mars, a in km)

(In the numerical forms, $\Delta\Omega_{J2}$ is in deg/calendar day.)

E. Sun-synchronous inclination, i_{SS}:

$$i_{SS} = \text{acos}\left(\frac{360\, a^{7/2}}{K_{J2} \left(1 - e^2\right)^2 SP} \right) \qquad \text{(C-84)}$$

$= \text{acos}(-4.773\ 513\ 28 \times 10^{-15}\, a^{7/2}\ (1 - e^2)^{-2})$ (Earth, a in km)

$= \text{acos}(-3.086\ 7 \times 10^{-12}\, a^{7/2}\ (1 - e^2)^{-2})$ (Moon, a in km)

$= \text{acos}(-1.511\ 0 \times 10^{-14}\, a^{7/2}\ (1 - e^2)^{-2})$ (Mars, a in km)

(Where SP is the sidereal period of the planet or the Moon about the Sun in calendar days. For a discussion of Sun synchronous orbits, see Sec. 9.5.3.)

E. Perigee rotation rate due to J_2, $\Delta\omega_{J2}$:

$$\Delta\omega_{J2} = 1.5 J_2 n \left(R_E / a\right)^2 \left(1 - e^2\right)^{-2} \left(2 - \frac{5}{2}\sin^2 i\right) \qquad \text{(C-85)}$$

$$= K_{J2} a^{-7/2} \left(1 - e^2\right)^{-2} \left(2 - \frac{5}{2}\sin^2 i\right)$$

where K_{J2} is the same as for $\Delta\Omega_{J2}$

(In the numerical forms, $\Delta\omega_{J2}$ is in deg/calendar day. Note that the perigee rotation rate depends on the central body. However, the fact that perigee rotation goes to 0 at the critical inclination of 63.4 deg is independent of the central body.)

E. Orbital revolutions per day, *Rev/d*:

$$Rev/d = \text{Day}/P \qquad \text{(C-86)}$$

$= 1.436\ 068\ 34 \times 10^3 / P$ (Earth, P in min)

$= 3.934\ 319\ 286\ 9 \times 10^4 / P$ (Moon, P in min)

$= 1.477\ 377\ 729\ 355 \times 10^3 / P$ (Mars, P in min)

(This is the number of orbit revolutions for each rotation of the planet on its axis relative to the fixed stars (i.e., the inertial rotation period). "Day" is the length of the sidereal day (in minutes) for the given central body. For more accurate expressions, see the discussion of repeating ground tracks in Sec. 9.5.2.)

E. Node spacing, ΔN:

$$\Delta N = 360\ \text{deg}(P / \text{Day}) \qquad \text{(C-87)}$$

$= 0.250\ 684\ 448\ P$ (Earth, P in min)

$= 0.009\ 150\ 248\ 715\ P$ (Moon, P in min)

$= 0.243\ 674\ 987\ 681\ P$ (Mars, P in min)

(For the equations for repeating ground track orbits, see Sec. 9.5.2.)

E. Maximum eclipse at a specified true anomaly, T_E:

$$T_E \approx 2\rho / \dot{v} = (2/\dot{v})\,\text{asin}(R_E / r) \qquad \text{(C-88)}$$

(For computation of eclipse duration for any Sun angle, see Sec. 8.2.4; for the formulas for eclipse conditions, see Sec. 11.4 in OCDM.)

E. Sun angle constraints for terminator visibility, β':

$$90° + \xi - \rho < \beta' < 90° - \xi + \rho \qquad \text{(C-89)}$$

(ξ is the dark angle defined in Sec. 11.5.2 in OCDM. For general conditions of terminator visibility, see Table 11-3 in Sec. 11.5.2 in OCDM.)

E. Transit time for a spacecraft whose celestial coordinates are known, T:

$$T = \alpha + L - \text{GST} \qquad \text{(C-90)}$$

(where α is the right ascension, L is the observer East longitude, and GST is the Greenwich Sidereal Time. For computation of observability times of spacecraft for which the celestial coordinates are known, see Table 9-6 in Sec. 9.4.4 in OCDM.)

C.3 Equations for Parabolic Orbits

As discussed in Sec. 9.1 which defines the orbit variables, parabolic orbits represent the boundary between closed, negative total energy elliptical orbits and unbounded, positive total energy hyperbolic orbits. Sec. 8.3 defines the geometric variables involved.

Note: A "**P**" is put in front of each descriptor to denote formulas for Parabolic orbits. Subscript P stands for the value of the parameter at perigee.

P. Defining parameters:

p = semilatus rectum = semiparameter (C-91)

q = perifocal distance

(For a discussion of Keplerian orbits, see Sec. 9.1; for transformations between orbital elements and position and velocity, see Sec. 2.7.1.1 and 2.7.1.2 in OCDM.)

P. Parametric equation:

$$x^2 = 4qy \qquad \text{(C-92)}$$

P. Distance from focus, r:

$$r = \frac{p}{1 + \cos v} = \frac{2q}{1 + \cos v} = q\left(1 + D_P^2\right) \qquad \text{(C-93)}$$

P. Specific energy, ε (= total energy per unit mass):

$$\varepsilon = 0 \qquad \text{(C-94)}$$

P. Specific angular momentum, h:

$$h = |\mathbf{h}| = \sqrt{\mu p} = rV\cos\phi_{fpa} = r^2\dot{\nu} = r_P V_P \quad \text{(C-95)}$$

P. Angular momentum vector, h:

$$\mathbf{h} = \mathbf{r} \times \mathbf{V} \quad \text{(C-96)}$$

P. Nodal vector, N:

$$\mathbf{N} = \hat{\mathbf{z}} \times \hat{\mathbf{h}} = \hat{\mathbf{z}} \times \mathbf{h} / h \quad \text{(C-97)}$$

P. Eccentricity vector, e:

$$\mathbf{e} = \frac{\mathbf{V} \times \mathbf{h}}{\mu} - \frac{\mathbf{r}}{r} \quad \text{(C-98)}$$

P. Inclination, *i*:

$$i = \text{acos}\,(h_z / h) \quad \text{(C-99)}$$

(For a discussion of apparent inclination, see the boxed example at the end of Sec. 9.3.1 in OCDM.)

P. Right ascension of the ascending node, Ω:

$$\Omega = \text{atan2}(N_x, N_y) \quad \text{(C-100)}$$

(For the definition of atan2, see Sec. D.4)

P. Flight path angle, ϕ_{fpa}:

$$\phi_{fpa} = \nu / 2 = \text{acos}\left(\sqrt{\mu p} / rV\right) \quad \text{(C-101)}$$

P. Perifocal distance, *q* = radius of perigee, r_P :

$$q = r_P = p/2 \quad \text{(C-102)}$$

P. Semi-parameter, *p*:

$$p = 2q = h^2/\mu = r(1 + \cos\nu) \quad \text{(C-103)}$$

P. Semimajor axis, *a*:

$$a = \infty \quad \text{(C-104)}$$

P. Semiminor axis, *b*:

$$b = \infty \quad \text{(C-105)}$$

P. Eccentricity, *e*:

$$e = 1 \quad \text{(C-106)}$$

P. Mean motion, *n*:

$$n = 2\sqrt{\mu / p^3} = \left(\frac{1}{t}\right)\left[\tan\left(\frac{\nu}{2}\right) + \frac{1}{3}\tan^3\left(\frac{\nu}{2}\right)\right] \quad \text{(C-107)}$$

where t = time from perigee passage.

P. Mean anomaly, *M*:

$$M = M_0 + nt = D_P + D_P^3 / 3 \quad \text{(C-108)}$$

P. Parabolic anomaly, D_P:

$$D_P = \tan(\nu / 2) \quad \text{(C-109)}$$

P. True anomaly, ν:

$$\nu = \text{atan2}(\cos\nu, \sin\nu) \quad \cos\nu = (p - r)/r \quad \sin\nu = 2qD_p / r \quad \text{(C-110)}$$

P. Rate of change of true anomaly, $\dot{\nu}$:

$$\dot{\nu} = \sqrt{\mu p} / r^2 = V_P r_P / r^2 \quad \text{(C-111)}$$

P. Period, *P*:

$$P = \infty \quad \text{(C-112)}$$

P. Velocity, *V*:

$$V = V_E = \sqrt{2\mu / r} = \sqrt{\mu p} / \left(r\cos\phi_{fpa}\right) \quad \text{(C-113)}$$

P. Velocity at perigee, V_P:

$$V_P = \sqrt{\frac{2\mu}{r_P}} \quad \text{(C-114)}$$

P. Parabolic velocity = Escape Velocity, V_E:

$$V_E = \sqrt{2\mu / r} \quad \text{(C-115)}$$

P. Azimuthal velocity, V_{az}:

$$V_{az} = V\cos\phi_{fpa} = r\dot{\nu} \quad \text{(C-116)}$$

P. Radial velocity, V_r:

$$V_r = V\sin\phi_{fpa} = V_{az}\frac{\sin\nu}{q} = \frac{r\,\dot{\nu}\sin\nu}{1 + \cos\nu} \quad \text{(C-117)}$$

P. Range • range rate, $r\dot{r}$:

$$r\dot{r} = \sqrt{\mu}D_P \quad \text{(C-118)}$$

P. Areal velocity, $\dot{A}$:

$$\dot{A} = \sqrt{\mu q / 2} = 0.5r^2\dot{\nu} \quad \text{(C-119)}$$

(For a complete set of ground track equations, see Table 8-11 in Sec. 8.4, and Sec. 8.4.1.)

All Euler Axis and coverage formulas for Parabolic Orbits are the same as for Hyperbolic Orbits

C.4 Equations for Hyperbolic Orbits

As discussed in Sec. 9.1 which defines the orbit variables, hyperbolic orbits are unbounded with positive total energy. As shown in Figs. 9-1 and 9-3 in Sec. 9.1.1, the hyperbola has two discrete segments, only one of which represents the orbit. Section 8.3 defines the geometric variables involved. Sections 12.7.3 to 12.7.5 in OCDM discuss hyperbolic orbit parameters with respect to planetary arrival and departure.

Note: An "**H**" is put in front of each descriptor to denote formulas for Hyperbolic orbits. Subscript P stands for the value of the parameter at perigee.

H. Defining parameters:

a = semi-transverse axis ($a < 0$) (C-120)

b = semi-conjugate axis

(For a discussion of Keplerian orbits, see Sec. 9.1; for transformations between orbital elements and position and velocity, see Secs. 2.7.1.1 and 2.7.1.2 in OCDM; for planetary arrival and departure, see Secs. 12.7.3 to 12.7.5 in OCDM.)

H. Parametric equation:

$$x^2/a^2 - y^2/b^2 = 1 \quad \text{(C-121)}$$

H. Distance from focus, *r*:

$$r = \frac{q(1+e)}{1+e\cos\nu} = a(1-e\cosh F) = -a\left(\frac{e}{\cos H} - 1\right) \quad \text{(C-122)}$$

$$= -a\sqrt{e^2-1}\,\frac{\tan H}{\sin\nu} = \frac{p}{1+e\cos\nu} = \frac{a(1-e^2)}{1+e\cos\nu}$$

H. Specific energy, ε (= total energy per unit mass):

$$\varepsilon = -\frac{\mu}{2a} = \frac{V^2}{2} - \frac{\mu}{r} > 0 \quad \text{(C-123)}$$

H. Specific angular momentum, h:

$$h = |\mathbf{h}| = \sqrt{\mu p} = rV\cos\phi_{fpa} = r^2\dot{\nu} = r_P V_P \quad \text{(C-124)}$$

H. Angular momentum vector, h:

$$\mathbf{h} = \mathbf{r} \times \mathbf{V} \quad \text{(C-125)}$$

H. Nodal vector, N:

$$\mathbf{N} = \hat{\mathbf{z}} \times \hat{\mathbf{h}} = \hat{\mathbf{z}} \times \mathbf{h} / h \quad \text{(C-126)}$$

H. Eccentricity vector, e:

$$\mathbf{e} = \frac{\mathbf{V}\times\mathbf{h}}{\mu} - \frac{\mathbf{r}}{r} \quad \text{(C-127)}$$

H. Inclination, *i*:

$$i = \text{acos}\,(h_z / h) \quad \text{(C-128)}$$

(For a discussion of apparent inclination, see the boxed example at the end of Sec. 9.3.1 in OCDM.)

H. Right ascension of the ascending node, Ω:

$$\Omega = \text{atan2}\,(N_x, N_y) \quad \text{(C-129)}$$

(For the definition of atan2, see Sec. D.4)

H. Flight path angle, ϕ_{fpa}:

$$\phi_{fpa} = \text{acos}\left(\sqrt{\mu p} / rV\right) \quad \text{(C-130)}$$

H. Auxiliary angle of the hyperbola, H*:

$$H = \text{acos}\left(\frac{ae}{a-r}\right) = \text{acos}\left(\frac{e}{1 - rV_\infty^2/\mu}\right) \quad \text{(C-131)}$$

H. Turn angle, ψ:

$$\psi = 2\text{asin}\left(\frac{1}{e}\right) = 2\text{asin}\left(\frac{1}{1+V_\infty^2 q/\mu}\right) = 2\text{atan}\left(\frac{-a}{b}\right) \quad \text{(C-132)}$$

$$= 2\text{atan}\left(\frac{\mu}{V_P V_\infty r_P}\right) = 2\text{atan}\left(\frac{\mu}{\rho V\sqrt{\eta}\cos\phi_{fpa}}\right)$$

(For a discussion of planetary fly-bys, see Sec. 9.6.3, and Secs. 12.7.3 to 12.7.5 in OCDM.)

H. Perifocal distance, *q* = radius of perigee, r_P:

$$q = r_P = a(1-e) = \frac{p}{1+e} = \frac{2\mu}{V_P^2 - V_\infty^2} = \frac{\mu}{V_\infty^2}(e-1) \quad \text{(C-133)}$$

H. Semi-parameter, *p*:

$$p = a(1-e^2) = r(1+e\cos\nu) = q(1+e) \quad \text{(C-134)}$$

$$= \frac{b^2}{a} = \frac{h^2}{\mu}$$

H. Semimajor axis, *a*:

$$a = -\frac{\mu}{2\varepsilon} = \left(\frac{\mu}{n^2}\right)^{1/3} = -\frac{\mu}{V_\infty^2} = \frac{q}{1-e} = \frac{p}{1-e^2} \quad \text{(C-135)}$$

$$a < 0$$

H. Semiminor axis = semi-conjugate axis = impact parameter, *b*:

$$b = -a\sqrt{e^2-1} = \sqrt{-ap} = \sqrt{\mu p}/V_\infty = \frac{V_P}{V_\infty} r_P \quad \text{(C-136)}$$

$$= \frac{-a}{\tan(\psi/2)} = r_P\sqrt{\frac{e+1}{e-1}}$$

H. Eccentricity, *e*:

$$e = |\mathbf{e}| = \sqrt{1 + \frac{2\varepsilon h^2}{\mu^2}} = \sqrt{\frac{a^2+b^2}{-a}} = 1 - \frac{r_P}{a} \quad \text{(C-137)}$$

$$= \sqrt{1 - \frac{p}{a}} = 1 + \frac{r_P}{\mu}V_\infty^2 \qquad e > 1$$

H. Mean motion, *n*:

$$n = \sqrt{-\mu / a^3} \quad \text{(C-138)}$$

H. Mean anomaly, *M*:

$$M = M_0 + nt = e\sinh F - F \quad \text{(C-139)}$$

* Also known as the Gudermannian function of the hyperbolic anomaly: $H = \text{gd } F = 2\text{atan}(e^F) - \pi/2$. See Battin [1999] for more details.

H. Hyperbolic anomaly, *F*:

$$F = 2\text{atanh}\left[\sqrt{\frac{e-1}{e+1}}\tan\frac{v}{2}\right] \quad \text{(C-140)}$$

$$\sinh F = \frac{\sin v\left(\sqrt{e^2-1}\right)}{1+e\cos v}$$

$$\cosh F = \frac{e+\cos v}{1+e\cos v}$$

as an iterative equation with successive estimates F_i:

$$F_{i+1} = F_i + \frac{M - e\sinh F_i + F_i}{e\cosh F_i - 1}$$

H. True anomaly, ν:

$$v = \text{atan2}(\cos v, \sin v) = 2\text{atan}\left[\sqrt{\frac{e+1}{e-1}}\tanh\frac{F}{2}\right]$$

$$= \text{acos}\left(\frac{p/r-1}{e}\right) \quad \text{(C-141)}$$

$$= \text{asin}\left(\frac{a}{r}\sqrt{e^2-1}\tan H\right)$$

$$= 2\text{atan}\left[\sqrt{\frac{e+1}{e-1}}\tan\frac{H}{2}\right]$$

$$\cos v = \frac{\cosh F - e}{1 - e\cosh F}$$

$$\sin v = \frac{-\sinh F\sqrt{e^2-1}}{1-e\cosh F}$$

H. Rate of change of true anomaly, $\dot{v}$:

$$\dot{v} = \sqrt{\mu p}\,/\,r^2 = V_P r_P\,/\,r^2 \quad \text{(C-142)}$$

H. Period, *P*:

$$P = \infty \quad \text{(C-143)}$$

H. Velocity, *V*:

$$V = \sqrt{\frac{2\mu}{r} - \frac{\mu}{a}} = \frac{\sqrt{\mu p}}{\left(r\cos\phi_{fpa}\right)} = \sqrt{\frac{2\mu}{r} + V_\infty^2} \quad \text{(C-144)}$$

$$= \sqrt{\frac{2\mu}{r} + 2\varepsilon}$$

H. Velocity at perigee, V_P:

$$V_P = \sqrt{\frac{2\mu}{r_P} + V_\infty^2} = \sqrt{\frac{\mu}{r_P}(1+e)} \quad \text{(C-145)}$$

H. Hyperbolic excess velocity, V_∞:

$$V_\infty = \sqrt{V^2 - \frac{2\mu}{r}} = \sqrt{V_P^2 - \frac{2\mu}{r_P}} \quad \text{(C-146)}$$

$$= \frac{r_P V_P}{b} = \sqrt{\frac{\mu}{r_P}(e-1)}$$

(The role of V_∞, C_3, and related parameters in interplanetary mission analysis is discussed in Sec. 9.6.3 and Sec. 12.7.1 in OCDM.)

H. Reference launch energy, C_3:

$$C_3 = V_\infty^2 \quad \text{(C-147)}$$

H. Azimuthal velocity, V_{az}:

$$V_{az} = r\dot{v} = V\cos\phi_{fpa} \quad \text{(C-148)}$$

H. Radial velocity, V_r:

$$V_r = V\sin\phi_{fpa} = \left(\frac{V_{az}e}{q}\right)\sin v = \frac{r\dot{v}e\sin v}{1+e\cos v} \quad \text{(C-149)}$$

H. Range • range rate, $r\dot{r}$:

$$r\dot{r} = e\sqrt{-a\mu}\sinh F \quad \text{(C-150)}$$

H. Areal velocity, $\dot{A}$:

$$\dot{A} = \frac{1}{2}\sqrt{a\mu\left(1-e^2\right)} \quad \text{(C-151)}$$

H. Escape velocity, V_E:

$$V_E = \sqrt{2\mu/r} \quad \text{(C-152)}$$

H. Euler axis co-latitude, δ'_{ea}:

$$\delta'_{ea} = \text{atan}\left(\frac{\dot{v}\sin i}{-\omega_E + \dot{v}\cos i}\right) \quad \text{(C-153)}$$

ω_E = inertial rotation of central body
= 0.004 178 074 1 deg/sec (Earth)
= 0.000 152 504 145 25 deg/sec (Moon)
= 0.004 061 249 794 68 deg/sec (Mars)

(For a complete set of ground track equations, see Table 8-11 in Sec. 8.4, and Sec. 8.4.1.)

H. Euler rotation rate, ω_{ea}:

$$\omega_{ea} = \dot{v}\sin i\,/\,\sin\delta'_{ea}$$

$$= \sqrt{\omega_E^2 + \dot{v}^2 + 2\dot{v}\omega_E\cos i} \quad \text{(C-154)}$$

H. Angular radius of the Earth, ρ:

$$\rho = \text{asin}\left(R_E/r\right) \quad \text{(C-155)}$$

R_E = radius of central body
= 6378.1366 km (Earth)
= 1737.4 km (Moon)
= 3396.19 km (Mars)

(Assumes a spherical Earth. For the effect of oblateness, see Sec. 9.4.1, and Sec. 9.1.5 in OCDM.)

H. Maximum angular radius of the Earth, ρ_{max}:

$$\rho_{max} = \text{asin}\left(\text{R}_\text{E} / r_P\right) \quad \text{(C-156)}$$

H. Distance to the horizon, *D*:

$$D = r\cos\rho = \sqrt{r^2 - \text{R}_\text{E}^2} \quad \text{(C-157)}$$

(For calculation of angles and distance for targets not on the horizon, see Sec. 8.3.1.)

H. Minimum distance to the horizon, D_{min}:

$$D_{min} = r_P \cos\rho_{max} = \sqrt{r_P^2 - \text{R}_\text{E}^2} \quad \text{(C-158)}$$

H. Maximum Earth central angle, λ_{max}:

$$\lambda_{max} = 90\text{ deg} - \rho = \text{acos}\,(\text{R}_\text{E}/r) \quad \text{(C-159)}$$

H. Instantaneous Access Area, *IAA*:

$$IAA = K_A(1 - \cos\lambda_{max}) \quad \text{(C-160)}$$

$K_A = 2\pi \approx 6.283\ 185\ 311$ for area in steradians
$= 360^2 / (2\pi) \approx 20{,}626.480\ 62$ for area in deg^2
$= 2.55\ 603\ 915 \times 10^8$ for area in km^2 (Earth)
$= 1.896\ 62 \times 10^7$ for area in km^2 (Moon)
$= 7.247\ 093 \times 10^7$ for area in km^2 (Mars)

(For alternative ways to calculate ground coverage, see Sec. 10.2.1; for other ground area formulas, see Table 10-3 in Sec. 10.2.1; for transformations between geocentric and access area coordinates, see the boxed example in Sec. 8.3; for projections of sensor fields of view onto the central body, see Sec. 8.3.4.)

H. Area Access Rate, *AAR*:

$$AAR = \left(\frac{K_A \dot{v}}{\pi}\right)\sin\lambda_{max} \quad \text{(C-161)}$$

H. Maximum time in view, T_{max}:

$$T_{max} \approx 2\lambda_{max} / \dot{v} \quad \text{(C-162)}$$

(This approximation holds only when the rate of change of true anomaly and the distance to the Earth do not change strongly over the time in view. For more precise calculations the start time and stop time of a viewing event should be calculated independently.)

H. Maximum angular rate seen from ground, $\dot{\theta}_{max}$:

$$\dot{\theta}_{max} = \frac{\dot{v} r}{\left(r - \text{R}_\text{E}\right)} \quad \text{(C-163)}$$

H. Maximum eclipse at a specified true anomaly, T_E:

$$T_E \approx 2\rho / \dot{v} = \left(\frac{2}{\dot{v}}\right)\text{asin}\left(\frac{\text{R}_\text{E}}{r}\right) \quad \text{(C-164)}$$

(This approximation holds only when the rate of change of true anomaly and the distance to the Earth do not change strongly over the eclipse duration. For more precise calculations, the start time and stop time of the eclipse should be calculated independently. For computation of eclipse duration for any Sun angle, see Sec. 8.2.4; for the formulas for eclipse conditions, see Sec. 11.4 in OCDM.)

H. Sun angle constraints for terminator visibility, β':

$$90° + \xi - \rho < \beta' < 90° - \xi + \rho \quad \text{(C-165)}$$

(ξ is the dark angle defined in Sec. 11.5.2 in OCDM. For general conditions of terminator visibility, see Table 11-3 in Sec. 11.5.2 in OCDM.)

H. Transit time for a spacecraft whose celestial coordinates are known, *T*:

$$T = \alpha + L - \text{GST} \quad \text{(C-166)}$$

(where α is the right ascension, L is the observer East longitude, and GST is the Greenwich Sidereal Time. For computation of observability times of spacecraft for which the celestial coordinates are known, see Table 9-6 in Sec. 9.4.4 in OCDM.)

References

For annotated bibliography of Appendix C, see the book website.

Battin, Richard H. 1999. *Introduction to the Mathematics and Methods of Astrodynamics.* Reston, VA: AIAA.

International Astronomical Union Working Group on Numerical Standards for Fundamental Astronomy. 2009. *Current Best Estimates.*

Wertz, James R. 2009. *Orbit & Constellation Design and Management: Spacecraft Orbit and Attitude Systems.* Hawthorne, CA: Microcosm Press.

Appendix D
Mission Geometry Formulas

James R. Wertz, ***Microcosm, Inc./USC***
Nicola Sarzi-Amade, ***Microcosm, Inc.***

This appendix provides a summary of basic rules for computing angles and areas on either the celestial sphere, the surface of the Earth, other planets and moons, or for the solution of most spherical triangles. As discussed in Chap. 8 and Sec. 10.5, spherical geometry is the natural choice for problems of what the spacecraft sees, and geometry on the surface of the Earth or other planets. Many, though not all, of the computations can also be done using unit vectors, although this approach does not usually provide the physical insight that we would like to have for mission analysis and design. Where possible, both spherical geometry and vector formulations are given. In the past, a principal limitation of spherical geometry solutions has been the quadrant ambiguities associated with working with angles that cover the full range of 0 to 360 deg because most spherical geometry solutions only cover the range of 0 to 180 deg.* This is no longer a problem. *Orbit and Constellation Design and Management* [= OCDM = Wertz, 2009] provides a complete set of "*full sky geometry*" solutions for all spherical triangles with all values covering the full range of 0 to 360 deg that eliminate all quadrant ambiguities not inherent in the solution itself. Thus, the only remaining anomalies are those that are inherent to the problem, such as when two reference vectors are exactly 180 deg apart and, therefore, are effectively the same as two that are on top of each other.

Note that full sky geometry solutions are particularly useful in providing closed form solutions for the motion of a satellite in circular orbit over the surface of the Earth. These provide significantly more accurate solutions than traditional methods that assume motion on a great circle arc and are summarized in Table 8-11. Developing these equations requires more background than appropriate here, so the solution development is left to OCDM. The most common mission geometry problems are listed in Table D-1, along with where they are addressed both in this volume and in OCDM. Other basic references on spherical geometry are provided in the web bibliography.

* Spherical geometry has been used for several centuries for solving basic navigation problems. However, for most of this time, these solutions were implemented by hand using trig tables and it was a trivial matter when any of the angles got larger than 180 deg to "turn the triangles around," such that all of the angles were in the range of 0 to 180 deg. With today's automated methods, having solutions covering the full range of input and output angles from 0 to 360 deg is substantially more important.

Table D-1. Principal Geometrically-Oriented Mission Design Problems and Where Discussed. "Live Calc" means that the SME-SMAD table or figure is available for download from the website. FoV is the Field of View. See also Table 8-2 in Sec. 8.1 for where the application formulas are derived.

Topic	SME-SMAD	OCDM
Basic Geometry on the Celestial Sphere (or on the Earth or Planetary Surface)		
Introduction to Mission Geometry — ***Formula summaries***	Secs. 8.0, 8.1 App. D	Secs. 6.1, 6.2 App. A
Coordinate Systems	Sec. 8.1.2, Table 8-3, 8-4	Sec. 6.1.2, Table 6-2, 6-3
Transformation Between Spherical Coordinates		Sec. 8.3.4
Angular Measurements on the Celestial Sphere	Sec. 8.1.3, Fig. 8-11	Table 6-4, Sec. 7.1, Sec. A.1
Rotation Angle Measurement	Table 8-5, Fig. 8-11, 8-19	Table 6-4, Sec. 7.4, Sec. A.1
Rhumb Line		Sec. 6.3 boxed note
Measurement Uncertainty on the Celestial Sphere		Sec. 7.2

Table D-1. Principal Geometrically-Oriented Mission Design Problems and Where Discussed. (Continued) "Live Calc" means that the SME-SMAD table or figure is available for download from the website. FoV is the Field of View. See also Table 8-2 in Sec. 8.1 for where the application formulas are derived.

Topic	SME-SMAD	OCDM
Good and Bad Measurement Sets		Sec. 7.6, Sec. 7.4 boxed example
Area Formulas	Sec. D.2	Table 8.3, Sec. A.3
Effect of Oblateness		Sec. 9.1.5
Full Sky Geometry	App. D*	Chap. 8
Full Sky Spherical Trig Solutions		Sec. 8.1, Sec. A.4, A.7
Dual Axis Spiral (see also satellite ground track)		Sec. 8.2
— Equations for		Table 8-8
Spherical Geometry Formulas		App. A
— Arc length and rotation angles	Sec. D.1	Sec. A.1
— Equations of great and small circles		Sec. A.2
— Area formulas	Sec. D.2	Sec. A.3
— Napier's rules		Sec. A.5
— Right and quadrantal spherical triangles	Sec. D.3	Sec. A.6
— Oblique full sky spherical triangles		Sec. A.4, A.7
— Differential spherical trig		Sec. A.8
— Relations between trig functions		Sec. A.9
Applications		
Live Calc ***Array Sensor FoV***	Secs. 8.2.2, 8.2.3, Table 8-8	Secs. 6.3.1, 7.2
Earth Surface Seen from Space	Sec. 8.3.2	Sec. 9.1
— Effect of oblateness	Fig. 9-14*	Sec. 9.1.5
Directions, Shapes, and Areas on the Earth as Seen from Space	Sec. 8.3.3	Sec. 9.1.3
Transformation Between Earth-based and Space-based Spherical Coordinates	Sec. 8.3.1 boxed note	Sec 9.1.1 boxed note
Live Calc ***Projection of Sensor FoVs onto the Earth***	Sec 8.3.4,Table 8-10	Sec. 9.1.4
Apparent Motion of Ground Targets seen from Space		Sec. 9.2
Live Calc ***Mapping and Pointing budgets***	Sec. 8.6, Table 8-16, 8-17, Fig. 8-50, 8-51	Sec. 5.5
Earth Coverage		Chap. 9
— Coverage areas	Sec. 10.2	Secs. 9.1, 9.5.1
Live Calc ***— Coverage patterns***	Sec. 10.2.1.2	Secs. 9.5.1.2
— Histograms for	Sec. 10.2.1.2	Fig. 9-42
Live Calc ***— Coverage vs. latitude***	Fig. 10-10	Fig. 9-44, 9-45
— Formulas for	Table 10-3, 10-4	App. D
— Example computations	App. C	Sec. 9.6
Eclipse Duration	Sec. 8.1.1	Sec. 6.3.2
Sun Angle on an Arbitrary Spacecraft Face		Sec. 6.3.3
Magnetometer Measurement Accuracy		Sec. 7.3.2
Live Calc ***Satellite Ground Track***		Secs. 8.3.3, 9.3
— Equations for		Table 8-9
Live Calc ***Ground Station Passes***	Sec. 8.4	Sec. 9.4
— Equations for	Table 8-11, 8-12	Table 9-4, 9-5
Motion of the Satellite as Seen from Earth	Sec. 8.4	Sec. 9.4
Satellite Relative Motion	Sec. 8.5	Chap. 10
Viewing and Lighting Conditions		Chap. 11, Table 11-1
Observability of Interplanetary Spacecraft		Sec. 9.4.4

* See OCDM for computations.

D.1 Arc Length and Rotation Angle Formulas

Let P_i, $i = 1, 2, 3$, be three points on the unit sphere with coordinates (α_i, δ_i). The **arc-length** distance, θ_{12}, between P_1 and P_2 is given by:

$$\cos\theta_{12} = \cos\theta_{21} \qquad 0 \le \theta \le 180°$$
$$= \sin\delta_1 \sin\delta_2 + \cos\delta_1 \cos\delta_2 \cos(\alpha_1 - \alpha_2) \quad \text{(D-1a)}$$

If $\hat{\mathbf{P}}_i$ are unit vectors corresponding to P_i, then

$$\cos\theta = \hat{\mathbf{P}}_1 \cdot \hat{\mathbf{P}}_2 \quad 0 \le \theta \le 180° \qquad \text{(D-1b)}$$

The **rotation angle**, $\Phi(P_1, P_2; P_3)$, from P_1 to P_2 about P_3, is cumbersome to calculate and is most easily obtained from spherical triangles (see Sec. D.3 and OCDM Secs. A.4, A.5, and A.7) if any of the triangle components are already known. To calculate directly from coordinates, obtain as intermediaries the arc-length distances θ_{ij}, between pairs of points P_i, P_j. Then

$$\cos\Phi(\hat{P}_1, \hat{P}_2; \hat{P}_3) = \frac{\cos\theta_{12} - \cos\theta_{13}\cos\theta_{23}}{\sin\theta_{13}\sin\theta_{23}} \qquad \text{(D-2a)}$$

$$0 \le \Phi \le 360°$$

with the quadrant determined by inspection. For automated quadrant resolution use the side-side-side triangle solution in OCDM Sec. A.7.1.

If the three points are expressed as unit vectors, then

$$\tan\Phi = \frac{\hat{\mathbf{P}}_3 \cdot (\hat{\mathbf{P}}_1 \times \hat{\mathbf{P}}_2)}{(\hat{\mathbf{P}}_1 \cdot \hat{\mathbf{P}}_2) - (\hat{\mathbf{P}}_3 \cdot \hat{\mathbf{P}}_1)(\hat{\mathbf{P}}_3 \cdot \hat{\mathbf{P}}_2)} \qquad \text{(D-2b)}$$

with the quadrant of Φ determined by the signs of the numerator and denominator, as done by the ATAN2 computer function. (See Sec. D.4 and OCDM Sec. A.7)

D.2 Area Formulas

All areas are measured on the curved surface of the unit sphere. See OCDM Sec. 8.1 and Table 8-3 for a discussion of angular area. For a sphere of radius R, multiply each area by R^2. **In the area formulas, all arc lengths are in radians and all angular areas are in steradians (sr)**, where

1 sr ≡ solid angle enclosing an area equal to the square of the radius
= $(180/\pi)^2$ deg^2 ≈ 3,282.806 350 011 743 794 deg^2

The **surface area of the sphere** is

$$\Omega_s = 4\pi \qquad \text{(D-3)}$$

The **area of a lune** bounded by two great circles which intersect at an angle of Θ radians is

$$\Omega_l = 2\Theta \qquad \text{(D-4)}$$

The **area of a spherical triangle** whose three rotation angles are θ_1, θ_2, and θ_3, is

$$\Omega_t = \theta_1 + \theta_2 + \theta_3 - \pi \qquad \text{(D-5)}$$

The **area of a spherical polygon** of n sides, where S is the sum of its rotation angles in radians, is

$$\Omega_p = S - (n-2)\pi \qquad \text{(D-6)}$$

The **area of a small circle** of angular radius ρ is

$$\Omega_c = 2\pi(1 - \cos\rho) \qquad \text{(D-7)}$$

The **area of a segment of rotation angle, ϕ,** in a small circle of angular radius ρ (i.e., a "pie piece") is

$$\Omega_{sc} = \phi(1 - \cos\rho) \qquad \text{(D-8)}$$

The **area of a ring or annulus** of inner radius ρ_i and outer radius ρ_0 is

$$\Omega_r = 2\pi(\cos\rho_i - \cos\rho_0) \qquad \text{(D-9)}$$

The **area of a segment of rotation angle, ϕ,** in an annulus of inner radius ρ_i and outer radius ρ_0 is

$$\Omega_{sr} = \phi(\cos\rho_i - \cos\rho_0) \qquad \text{(D-10)}$$

The **overlap area between two small circles** of angular radii ρ and ε, separated by a center-to-center distance, α, is

$$\Omega_0 = 2\pi - 2\cos\rho \,\text{acos}\left[\frac{\cos\varepsilon - \cos\rho\cos\alpha}{\sin\rho\sin\alpha}\right] \qquad \text{(D-11)}$$
$$- 2\cos\varepsilon \,\text{acos}\left[\frac{\cos\rho - \cos\varepsilon\cos\alpha}{\sin\varepsilon\sin\alpha}\right]$$
$$- 2\,\text{acos}\left[\frac{\cos\alpha - \cos\varepsilon\cos\rho}{\sin\varepsilon\sin\rho}\right]$$
$$(|\rho - \varepsilon| \le \alpha < \rho + \varepsilon)$$

If ε goes to 90 deg, then the above simplifies to the formula for the **overlap area between a great circle and a small circle** of angular radius ρ, separated by a center-to-center distance, α:

$$\Omega_0 = 2\pi - 2\cos\rho \,\text{acos}(\cot\alpha\cot\rho) \qquad \text{(D-12)}$$
$$- 2\,\text{acos}(\cos\alpha/\sin\rho)$$
$$|90° - \rho| \le \alpha < 90° + \rho$$

Recall that area is measured on the curved surface.

D.3 Spherical Triangles

A *spherical triangle* consists of any three non-collinear points on the sphere connected by great circle arcs. A *right spherical triangle* is one with at least one right angle. (Unlike plane triangles, spherical triangles can have 1, 2, or 3 right angles.) Any two of the remaining components, including the two remaining angles, serve to completely define the triangle. *Napier's Rules*, given in any of the books in the bibliography, provide a concise formulation for all possible right spherical triangles. However, experience has shown that it is substantially more convenient to write out explicitly the rules for the relatively small number of possible combinations of known and unknown sides and angles. These are listed in Table D-2.

A *quadrantal spherical triangle* is one with at least one side that is 90 deg in length. As with right spherical triangles, any two of the remaining five components completely define the triangle. These are given by a corresponding set of Napier's Rules. Again, it is more practical to write out explicitly all possible relationships. These are given in Table D-4.

An *oblique spherical triangle* has arbitrary sides and angles. Sides and angles are generally defined over the range of 0 to 180 deg, although most of the spherical geometry relations continue to hold in the angular range up to 360 deg. A set of basic rules which can be applied to any spherical triangle are given in Table D-3. Finally, these general rules can be used to write explicit expressions for any of the unknown components in any oblique spherical triangle with any three components known. These are given in full in OCDM, including the rules for all possible full sky triangles, i.e., those in which any of the sides or angles can range from 0 to 360 deg.

Table D-2. Right Spherical Triangles.

Right Spherical Triangle

The line below each formula indicates the quadrant of the answer. $Q(A) = Q(a)$ means that the quadrant of angle A is the same as that of side a. "2 possible solutions" means that either quadrant provides a correct solution to the defined triangle.

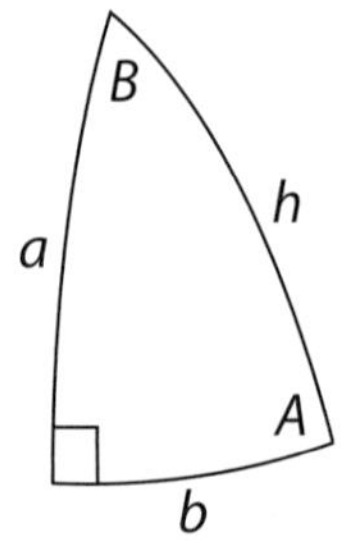

Given	Find		
a, b	$\cos h = \cos a \cos b$ $Q(h) = \{Q(a)\,Q(b)\}$*	$\tan A = \tan a / \sin b$ $Q(A) = Q(a)$	$\tan B = \tan b / \sin a$ $Q(B) = Q(b)$
a, h	$\cos b = \cos h / \cos a$ $Q(b) = \{Q(a) / Q(h)\}$**	$\sin A = \sin a / \sin h$ $Q(A) = Q(a)$	$\cos B = \tan a / \tan h$ $Q(B) = \{Q(a) / Q(h)\}$**
b, h	$\cos a = \cos h / \cos b$ $Q(a) = \{Q(b) / Q(h)\}$**	$\cos A = \tan b / \tan h$ $Q(A) = \{Q(b) / Q(h)\}$**	$\sin B = \sin b / \sin h$ $Q(B) = Q(b)$
a, A	$\sin b = \tan a / \tan A$ 2 possible solutions	$\sin h = \sin a / \sin A$ 2 possible solutions	$\sin B = \cos A / \cos a$ 2 possible solutions
a, B	$\tan b = \sin a \tan B$ $Q(b) = Q(B)$	$\tan h = \tan a / \cos B$ $Q(h) = \{Q(a)\,Q(B)\}$*	$\cos A = \cos a \sin B$ $Q(A) = Q(a)$
b, A	$\tan a = \sin b \tan A$ $Q(a) = Q(A)$	$\tan h = \tan b / \cos A$ $Q(h) = \{Q(b)\,Q(A)\}$*	$\cos B = \cos b \sin A$ $Q(B) = Q(b)$
b, B	$\sin a = \tan b / \tan B$ 2 possible solutions	$\sin h = \sin b / \sin B$ 2 possible solutions	$\sin A = \cos B / \cos b$ 2 possible solutions
h, A	$\sin a = \sin h \sin A$ $Q(a) = Q(A)$	$\tan b = \tan h \cos A$ $Q(b) = \{Q(A) / Q(h)\}$**	$\tan B = 1 / \cos h \tan A$ $Q(B) = \{Q(A) / Q(h)\}$**
h, B	$\sin b = \sin h \sin B$ $Q(b) = Q(B)$	$\tan a = \tan h \cos B$ $Q(a) = \{Q(B) / Q(h)\}$**	$\tan A = 1 / \cos h \tan B$ $Q(A) = \{Q(B) / Q(h)\}$**
A, B	$\cos a = \cos A / \sin B$ $Q(a) = Q(A)$	$\cos b = \cos B / \sin A$ $Q(b) = Q(B)$	$\cos h = 1 / \tan A \tan B$ $Q(h) = \{Q(A)\,Q(B)\}$*

* $\{Q(x)\,Q(y)\} \equiv$ 1st quadrant if $Q(x) = Q(y)$, 2nd quadrant if $Q(x) \neq Q(y)$

** $\{Q(x) / Q(h)\} \equiv$ quadrant of x if $h \le 90$ deg, quadrant opposite x if $h > 90$ deg.

Table D-2, Fig. D-0, Eq. D-12◀

Table D-3. Oblique Spherical Triangles.

Oblique Spherical Triangle

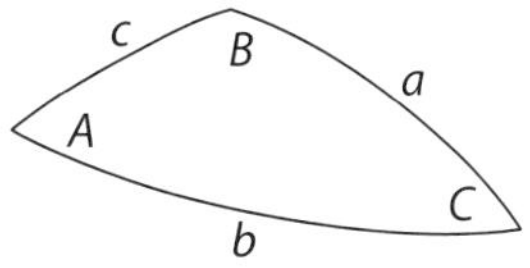

The following rules hold for any spherical triangle:

The Law of Sines: $\dfrac{\sin a}{\sin A} = \dfrac{\sin b}{\sin B} = \dfrac{\sin c}{\sin C}$

The Law of Cosines for Sides:

$\cos a = \cos b \cos c + \sin b \sin c \cos A$
$\cos b = \cos c \cos a + \sin c \sin a \cos B$
$\cos c = \cos a \cos b + \sin a \sin b \cos C$

The Law of Cosines for Angles:

$\cos A = -\cos B \cos C + \sin B \sin C \cos a$
$\cos B = -\cos C \cos A + \sin C \sin A \cos b$
$\cos C = -\cos A \cos B + \sin A \sin B \cos c$

Gauss's Formula:

$$\sin\left[\frac{1}{2}(A-B)\right] = \frac{\sin\left[\frac{1}{2}(a-b)\right]}{\sin(c/2)}\cos(C/2)$$

Useful Derived Formulas:

$c = \text{atan}(\tan b \cos A) \pm \text{atan}(\tan a \cos B)$

$$C = \text{atan}\left(\frac{1}{\tan A \cos b}\right) \pm \text{atan}\left(\frac{1}{\tan B \cos a}\right)$$

Table D-4. Quadrantal Spherical Triangles.

Quadrantal Spherical Triangle

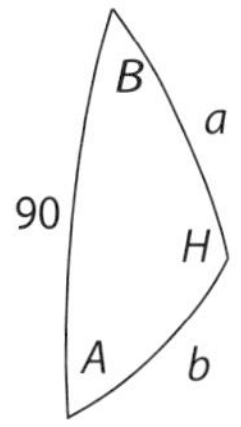

The line below each formula indicates the quadrant of the answer. Q(*A*) = Q(*a*) means that the quadrant of angle *A* is the same as that of side *a*. "2 possible solutions" means that either quadrant provides a correct solution to the defined triangle.

Given	Find		
A, B	**cos *H* = – cos *A* cos *B*** Q(*H*) = {Q(*A*) Q(*B*)}*	**tan *a* = tan *A* / sin *B*** Q(*a*) = Q(*A*)	**tan *b* = tan *B* / sin *A*** Q(*b*) = Q(*B*)
A, H	**cos *B* = – cos *H* / cos *A*** Q(*B*) = {Q(*A*) \ Q(*H*)}**	**sin *a* = sin *A* / sin *H*** Q(*a*) = Q(*A*)	**cos *b* = – tan *A* / tan *H*** Q(*b*) = {Q(*A*)\Q(*H*)}**
B, H	**cos *A* = – cos *H* / cos *B*** Q(*A*) = {Q(*B*) \ Q(*H*)}**	**cos *a* = – tan *B* / tan *H*** Q(*a*) = {Q(*B*) \ Q(*H*)}**	**sin *b* = sin *B* / sin *H*** Q(*b*) = Q(*B*)
A, a	**sin *B* = tan *A* / tan *a*** 2 possible solutions	**sin *H* = sin *A* / sin *a*** 2 possible solutions	**sin *b* = cos *a* / cos *A*** 2 possible solutions
A, b	**tan *B* = sin *A* tan *b*** Q(*B*) = Q(*b*)	**tan *H* = – tan *A* / cos *b*** Q(*H*) = {Q(*A*) Q(*b*)}*	**cos *a* = cos *A* sin *b*** Q(*a*) = Q(*A*)
B, a	**tan *A* = sin *B* tan *a*** Q(*A*) = Q(*a*)	**tan *H* = – tan *B* / cos *a*** Q(*H*) = {Q(*B*) Q(*a*)}*	**cos *b* = cos *B* sin *a*** Q(*b*) = Q(*B*)
B, b	**sin *A* = tan *B* / tan *b*** 2 possible solutions	**sin *H* = sin *B* / sin *b*** 2 possible solutions	**sin *a* = cos *b* / cos *B*** 2 possible solutions
H, a	**sin *A* = sin *H* sin *a*** Q(*A*) = Q(*a*)	**tan *B* = – tan *H* cos *a*** Q(*B*) = {Q(*a*) \ Q(*H*)}**	**tan *b* = –1/ cos *H* tan *a*** Q(*b*) = {Q(*a*) \Q(*H*)}**
H, b	**sin *B* = sin *H* sin *b*** Q(*B*) = Q(*b*)	**tan *A* = – tan *H* cos *b*** Q(*A*) = {Q(*b*) \ Q(*H*)}**	**tan *a* = –1/ cos *H* tan *b*** Q(*a*) = {Q(*b*) \Q(*H*)}**
a, b	**cos *A* = cos *a* / sin *b*** Q(*A*) = Q(*a*)	**cos *B* = cos *b* / sin *a*** Q(*B*) = Q(*b*)	**cos *H* = –1 / tan *a* tan *b*** Q(*H*) = {Q(*a*) Q(*b*)}*

*{Q(*x*) Q(*y*)} ≡ 1st quadrant if Q(*x*) = Q(*y*), 2nd quadrant if Q(*x*) ≠ Q(*y*)

**{Q(*x*) \ Q(*H*)} ≡ quadrant of *x* if *H* > 90 deg, quadrant opposite *x* if *H* ≤ 90 deg.

Table D-4, Fig. D-0, Eq. D-12◀

D.4 The atan2 and acos2 functions

In working with full-sky triangles*, we need to have a mechanism for evaluating inverse trigonometric functions over the full range of 0 to 360 deg. For the arc tangent, the computer function atan2 is convenient. With the angle's sine and cosine specified, atan2 uniquely specifies the angle. In general, any inverse trig function covering the full range of 0 to 360 deg must be a function of two arguments, because all of the trig functions have two solutions over this range. For many triangles, it is convenient to define an acos2 function that plays a role similar to that of atan2. To do this, we first define the hemisphere function, H(ϕ):

$$H(\phi) \equiv +1 \text{ if } 0 \text{ deg} \leq \phi \,\text{mod}^{\dagger}_{360 \text{ deg}} < 180 \text{ deg}$$
$$H(\phi) \equiv -1 \text{ if } 180 \text{ deg} \leq \phi \,\text{mod}_{360 \text{ deg}} < 360 \text{ deg} \quad \text{(D-13)}$$

The acos2 function is then defined by:

$$\text{acos2}[\cos(\phi), H(\phi)] \equiv [H(\phi) \,\text{acos}(\cos(\phi))]\text{mod}_{360 \text{ deg}}$$
$$\text{where } 0 \text{ deg} \leq \text{acos}(\cos(\phi)) < 180 \text{ deg} \quad \text{(D-14)}$$

Thus, over the range of 0 to 360 deg, acos2 and the set (cos, H) are inverse functions:

$$\text{If } 0 \text{ deg} \leq \phi < 360 \text{ deg},$$
$$\text{then } \phi = \text{acos2}[\cos(\phi), H(\phi)] \quad \text{(D-15)}$$

Additional properties of the acos2 function are summarized in Table D-5.

Table D-5. Properties of the acos2 Function. The acos2 function serves the same purpose as atan2—i.e., it is a function of two variables rather than one so that it can return an angle over the range 0 to 360 deg.

- First define the hemisphere function, H(ϕ):
  $H(\phi) \equiv +1$ if 0 deg $\leq \phi \,\text{mod}_{360 \text{ deg}} <$ 180 deg
  $H(\phi) \equiv -1$ if 180 deg $\leq \phi \,\text{mod}_{360 \text{ deg}} <$ 360 deg
- Then the acos2 function is defined by:
  $\text{acos2}[\cos(\phi), H(\phi)] \equiv [H(\phi) \,\text{acos}(\cos\phi)] \,\text{mod}_{360 \text{ deg}}$
  where 0 deg $\leq$ acos(cos(ϕ)) < 180 deg
- Thus:
  If 0 deg $\leq \phi <$ 360 deg, then ϕ = acos2 [cos(ϕ), H(ϕ)]
- Also:
  acos2 [cos(ϕ), – H(ϕ)] = 360 deg – ϕ
  acos2 [–cos(ϕ), H(ϕ)] = (180 deg – ϕ) $\text{mod}_{360 \text{ deg}}$
  = 180 deg – ϕ, if $\phi <$ 180 deg, or 360 deg – (ϕ – 180 deg), if $\phi >$ 180 deg
  acos2 [–cos(ϕ), –H(ϕ)] = (180 deg + ϕ) $\text{mod}_{360 \text{ deg}}$
  = 180 deg + ϕ, if $\phi <$ 180 deg, or ϕ – 180 deg, if $\phi >$ 180 deg

* For a complete treatment of full-sky spherical geometry see OCDM Chap. 8 and App. A.

† The modulo function adds or subtracts multiples of 360 deg in order to express the result as a quantity from 0 to 360 deg.

The atan2 function has been used in computer programming languages for many years and is intended to resolve the problem of quadrant ambiguities in inverse trig functions. Specifically, if ϕ is an angle defined over the range 0 to 360 deg and sin ϕ and cos ϕ are known, then the atan2 function is defined by:

$$\text{atan2 } (\cos \phi, \sin \phi) \equiv \phi \quad \text{(D-16a)}$$

$$= [\text{atan } (\sin \phi / \cos \phi) + 90^{\circ} \,(1 - \text{sign}(\cos \phi))] \,\text{mod}_{360 \text{ deg}} \quad \text{(D-16b)}$$

where atan is defined over the usual range of –90 deg to +90 deg and the atan2 function is defined over the range 0 to 360 deg.

While the above expression is correct, it is not well-defined when cosϕ goes to 0 and can result in mathematical singularities when used in practice. An alternative definition which avoids these singularities and is well-defined over the entire range is as follows:

$$\text{atan2}(x, y) \equiv \begin{cases} \text{atan}(y/x) & \text{if } x>0, y \geq 0 \\ 90^{\circ} & \text{if } x=0, y>0 \\ 180^{\circ} + \text{atan}(y/x) & \text{if } x<0 \\ 270^{\circ} & \text{if } x=0, y<0 \\ 360^{\circ} + \text{atan}(y/x) & \text{if } x>0, y<0 \\ \text{Undefined} & \text{if } x=0, y=0 \end{cases} \quad \text{(D-17)}$$

where, as above, atan is defined over the usual range of –90 to +90 deg and atan2 is defined over the range 0 to 360 deg.

Unfortunately, the definition of the atan2 function is implemented differently in common system engineering tools. Specifically,

$$\text{atan2 } (x, y) = \text{atan } (y/x) \quad \text{(D-18)}$$

in Excel, Visual Basic, Google Spreadsheets, and in OCDM and this volume. Since the website tables and plots are implemented in Excel, the definition on the website is consistent with one given in the text. In contrast,

$$\text{atan2 } (y, x) = \text{atan } (y/x) \quad \text{(D-19)}$$

in programming languages FORTRAN, MatLab, C++, Java, and Pascal. In addition, all of the languages and spreadsheets define atan2 over the range –180 deg to +180 deg, whereas it is more convenient for mission geometry to define all angles over the range of 0 to 360 deg and this is done in the text. Fortunately, this change is trivial and easily handled by all of the relevant tools.

References

Get Ref **For annotated bibliography of Appendix D, see the book website.**

Wertz, James R. 2009. *Orbit & Constellation Design and Management: Spacecraft Orbit and Attitude Systems.* Hawthorne, CA: Microcosm Press.

Appendix E
Time and Date Systems

James R. Wertz, *Microcosm, Inc./USC* and Nicola Sarzi-Amade, *Microcosm, Inc.*

Time is something we intuitively understand extremely well and, consequently, understand poorly in detail. For example, any phenomenon which repeats on a regular basis, such as a pendulum or the motion of electrons in an atom, can be used as the basis for timekeeping. However, "regularly repeating" implies that we have some standard to compare with. The only way to determine a clock's accuracy is to compare it with another clock, which of course leads to the question of which clock we should assume to be correct. Historically, the fundamental "clocks" chosen for maintaining absolute time have been the rotation of the Earth on its axis and the revolution of the Earth about the Sun. However, modern time measurements have shown these systems to be both nonuniform and extremely difficult to model with precision. For example, Fig. B-3 in App. B shows the variations in the length of the day over the past several centuries. On average, the Earth is slowing down by 1.5 ms/century but local variations are very substantial.*

Unfortunately, clock errors are cumulative, and therefore, high accuracy can prove important. For example, assume a spacecraft in low Earth orbit has a clock that is slowing down by 1 ms/day, which is small enough to be difficult to measure by many processes. This would result in a cumulative error of 0.365 sec over a year which corresponds to an error in position of the satellite of 3 km. Thus, if we wish to know the positions of satellites to tens of meters, we will need reasonably good clocks to do so.

Two basic types of time measurement are used in spacecraft systems: (1) *time intervals* between 2 events such as the spacecraft's spin period, orbital period, or the length of time a sensor sees the Earth; and (2) *absolute times* or *calendar times* of specific events, such as the time associated with some particular spacecraft observation. Of course, calendar time is simply a time interval for which the beginning event is an agreed standard.

E.1 Calendar Time and Long Duration Intervals

Calendar time in the usual form of date and time is used only for input and output because generally, arithmetic is cumbersome in months, days, hours, minutes, and seconds (for computations, absolute time is used instead, as explained next). Nonetheless, this is used for most human interaction with space systems because it's the system with which we are most familiar. Even with date and time systems, problems can arise, because time zones are different throughout the world and spacecraft operations typically involve a worldwide network. The uniformly adopted solution to this problem is to use the local standard time corresponding to 0 deg longitude (i.e., the Greenwich meridian) as the assigned time for events anywhere in the world or in space. This is referred to as *Universal Time* (UT), *Greenwich Mean Time* (GMT), or *Zulu* (Z), all of which are equivalent for most practical spacecraft operations. For precise computations, UT has replaced GMT, since the term GMT can be ambiguous [Seidelmann, 2006]. The name Greenwich Mean Time was chosen because 0 deg longitude is defined by the site of the former Royal Greenwich Observatory southeast of central London.

Civil time, T_{civil}, as measured by a standard wall clock or time signals, differs from Universal Time by an integral number of hours, corresponding approximately to the longitude of the observer. The approximate relation is:

$$T_{civil} \approx UT \pm L / 15 \tag{E-1}$$

where T_{civil} and UT are in hours, and L is the longitude in degrees with the plus sign corresponding to East longitude and the minus sign corresponding to West longitude.

Calendar time is remarkably inconvenient for computation, particularly over long time intervals of months or years. We need an absolute time that is a continuous count of time units from some arbitrary reference. The time interval between any two events is then found by simply subtracting the absolute time of the second event from that of the first. The universally adopted solution for astronomical problems is the *Julian Date*, JD, a continuous count of the number of days since Greenwich noon (12:00 UT) on January 1, 4713 BC,† or, as astron-

* The overall slowing of the Earth's rotation and lengthening of the day are caused primarily by tidal friction with the Moon. Local variations are caused principally by the growth and decline in the polar ice caps which shifts large quantities of water from the pole (smaller moment of inertia and higher spin rate) to the equator (larger moment of inertia and lower spin rate).

† This strange starting point was suggested by an Italian scholar of Greek and Hebrew, Joseph Scaliger, in 1582 as the beginning of the current *Julian period* of 7,980 years. This period is the product of three numbers: the *solar cycle*, or the interval at which all dates recur on the same days of the week (28 years); the *lunar cycle*, containing an integral number of lunar months (19 years); and the *indiction* or the tax period introduced by the Emperor Constantine in 313 AD (15 years). The last time that these started together was 4713 BC and the next time will be 3267 AD. Scaliger was interested in reducing the astronomical dating problems associated with calendar reforms of his time and his proposal had the convenient selling point that it pre-dated the ecclesiastically approved date of creation, October 4, 4004 BC.

Table E-1. Julian Date at the Beginning of Each Year from 2000 to 2041. See text for explanation of use. The day number for the beginning of the year is called "Jan. 0.0" (actually Dec. 31st of the preceding year) so that day numbers can be found by simply using dates. Thus, Jan. 1 is day number 1 and has a JD 1 greater than that for Jan. 0. * = leap year.

Year	*JD* 2,400,000+ for Jan 0.0 *UT*	Year	*JD* 2,400,000+ for Jan 0.0 *UT*	Year	*JD* 2,400,000+ for Jan 0.0 *UT*
2000*	51,543.5	2014	56,657.5	2028*	61,770.5
2001	51,909.5	2015	57,022.5	2029	62,136.5
2002	52,274.5	2016*	57,387.5	2030	62,501.5
2003	52,639.5	2017	57,753.5	2031	62,866.5
2004*	53,004.5	2018	58,118.5	2032	63,231.5
2005	53,370.5	2019	58,483.5	2033	63,597.5
2006	53,735.5	2020*	58,848.5	2034	63,962.5
2007	54,100.5	2021	59,214.5	2035	64,327.5
2008*	54,465.5	2022	59,579.5	2036	64,692.5
2009	54,831.5	2023	59,944.5	2037	65,058.5
2010	55,196.5	2024*	60,309.5	2038	65,423.5
2011	55,561.5	2025	60,675.5	2039	65,788.5
2012*	55,926.5	2026	61,040.5	2040	66,153.5
2013	56,292.5	2027	61,405.5	2041	66,519.5

omers now say, –4712. Because Julian Days start at noon UT, they will be a half day off with respect to civil dates. While this is inconvenient for transforming from civil dates to Julian Dates, it was useful for astronomers because this way the date didn't change in the middle of the night (for European observers).

As described below, there are 4 general approaches for converting between calendar dates and Julian Dates.

Table Look-Up

Tabulations of the current Julian Date are in most astronomical ephemerides and almanacs. Table E-1 lists the Julian Dates at the beginning of each year from 2000 through 2041. To find the Julian Date for any given calendar date, simply add the *day number* within the year (and fractional day number, if appropriate) to the Julian Date for Jan 0.0 of that year from Table E-2. Day numbers for each day of the year are on many calendars or can be found by adding the date to the day number for day 0 of the month from Table E-2. Thus 18:00 UT on April 15, 2014 = day number 15.75 + 90 = 105.75 in 2014 = JD 105.75 + 2,456,657.5 = JD 2,456,763.25.

Table E-2. Day Numbers for Day 0.0 of Each Month. Leap years (in which February has 29 days) are those evenly divisible by 4. However, years evenly divisible by 100 are not leap years, except that those evenly divisible by 400 are. Leap years are indicated by * in Table E-2.

Month	Non-Leap Years	Leap Years
January	0	0
February	31	31
March	59	60
April	90	91
May	120	121
June	151	152
July	181	182
August	212	213
September	243	244
October	273	274
November	304	305
December	334	335

Table E-2, Fig. E-0, Eq. E-1◀

To convert from Julian Days to dates, determine the year in which the Julian Date falls from Table E-1. Subtract the Julian Date from the JD for January 0.0 of that year to determine the day number within the year. This can be converted to a date (and time, if appropriate) by using day numbers on a calendar or subtracting from the day number for the beginning of the appropriate month from Table E-2. Thus, from Table E-1, JD 2,456,073.25 is in the year 2012. The day number is 2,456,073.25 – 2,455,926.5 = 146.75. From Table E-2, this is 18:00 UT, May 25, 2012.

E.2 Modern Time Measurement —Short Duration Intervals

As one would expect, modern technology has lead to ever increasing precision in the measurement of time. However, in addition, new processes for measuring time have been introduced, as well as new and fundamentally different definitions of the meaning of time in both science and engineering. In the 1950s, *Ephemeris Time, ET*, was introduced, based on the dynamic equations of motion of the Earth. For many years, this was used as the basis of astronomical and astrophysical ephemerides, i.e., the most precise orbit calculations. In 1967, the second was redefined as having an atomic standard but ephemeris time remained in use for the motion of planets and satellites. In 1984, ephemeris time was unceremoniously abandoned in favor of *Terrestrial Dynamic Time, TDT*, in which the unit of measure was the atomic second and the scale was chosen to agree with ephemeris time in 1984. In 1991, the general theory of relativity was explicitly adopted as the theoretical background for defining both space and time reference frames, *TDT* was renamed *Terrestrial Time, TT*, and the definition of the second was "adjusted" to correspond to atomic measurements at a specific location (i.e., at mean sea level on the surface of the Earth).*

* An excellent discussion of the history of time systems is provided by Seidelmann [2006].

Table E-3. Common Time Systems.

Kind of Time	Defined By	Fundamental Unit	Regularity	Application
Sidereal (ST)	Earth's rotation relative to stars	Sidereal day, 1 rotation of Earth with respect to stars	Irregular	Astronomical observations; determining *UT* and rotational orientation of Earth
Solar				
Apparent	Earth's rotation relative to true Sun	Successive transits of Sun	Irregular and annual variations	Sundials*
Mean	Earth's rotation relative to fictitious mean Sun	Mean solar day	Uniform and annual variations	Confuse students and engineers; use uniform time
Universal				
UT0	Observed *UT*	Mean solar day	Irregular	Study of Earth's wandering pole
UT1	Corrected *UT0*	Mean solar day	Irregular	Shows seasonal variation of Earth's rotation
UT2	Corrected *UT1*	Mean solar day	Irregular	Basic rotation of Earth
UTC=GMT=Z	Atomic sec and leap sec to approximate *UT1*	Mean solar day	Uniform except for leap sec	Civil timekeeping; terrestrial navigation and surveying; broadcast time signals
Ephemeris (ET)	Fraction of tropical year 1900	Ephemeris sec	Uniform	Ephemerides prior to 1994; no longer in use
Atomic (TAI)	Frequency of Ce-133 radiation	Atomic sec = Ephemeris sec	Uniform	Basis of *ET* and *UTC*
GPS	Atomic sec without leap sec	Atomic sec	Uniform	Time component of GPS signals
Relativistic				
Terrestrial (TT)	Atomic sec at mean sea level on Earth	Atomic sec at Earth's surface	Uniform	Ephemerides
Barycentric Dynamic (TDB)	Orbital equations of motion with respect to barycenter of the Solar System	Atomic sec adjusted for relativistic effects	Uniform	Transforms Earth-based time to time kept by the motions of the planets

* Devices showing the time of day by the shadow of a pointer (called style or gnomon) cast by the Sun on a plate or surface marked with lines that indicate the hours of the day.

Currently, there are 4 main types of time systems in use:

- *Atomic Time, TAI*, for which the unit of duration corresponds to a defined number of wavelengths for a specific atomic transition of a specific isotope
- *Universal Time, UT*, for which the unit of duration is the rotation of the Earth with respect to the Sun, defined to be as uniform as possible despite variations in the physical rotation rate of the Earth
- *Sidereal Time, ST*, for which the unit of duration is the rotation of the Earth with respect to the vernal equinox which, in turn, is nearly fixed with respect to the mean positions of the stars
- *Dynamical Time, DT*, for which the unit of duration is based on the orbital motion of the Earth, Moon, and planets. Terrestrial Time, *TT*, belongs to this family of timescales

In addition, rapidly rotating pulsars may provide an even more accurate standard for future time systems. While the differences between the various time systems are subtle, they can have important implications for spacecraft systems and applications. Commonly used modern time systems are defined in Table E-3.

Fortunately, the basis for all of the modern time systems is the Système International, SI, *second*. This is defined as the duration of 9,192,631,770 periods of the radiation corresponding to the transition between 2 hyperfine levels of the ground state of the Cesium-133 atom measured at mean sea level on the Earth. This definition of the second corresponds more-or-less to $1 / 86{,}400$ ($= 1 / [60 \times 60 \times 24]$) of the rotation period of the Earth, relative to the mean Sun. It is, of course, the "more-or-less" part which ultimately causes most of the problems in time measurement systems. Some of the time systems are described in more detail below.

Atomic Time (TAI)

International Atomic Time, TAI (*Temps Atomique International*), is a practical implementation of a time standard based on the SI second. An excellent approximation to *TAI* can be maintained by laboratory Cesium clocks. A large number of such clocks are compared from time to time and a weighted average is prepared which provides a fine adjustment for each of the individual clocks. The use of these Cesium-based clocks provides a readily available basis for timekeeping for all types of physical, astronomical, and space-related observation.

Universal Time (UT)

Universal Time, UT, follows the irregular rotation of the Earth, and is often referred to as a type of solar time because the objective in universal time is to remain synchronized with the orientation of the Earth relative to the Sun. The most important subcategory of universal time is *Coordinated Universal Time (UTC),* which is the basis for civil timekeeping and broadcast time signals worldwide. *UTC* uses the SI second as the basic unit of time and then adds (or, in principle, subtracts) a leap second at the end of the last day of June and the last day of December as needed to maintain close agreement with the rotational orientation of the Earth. Thus, *UTC* lags behind *TAI* by an integral number of seconds. For example, for January 1, 1996, *TAI* minus *UTC* equaled 30 sec exactly. There is a long-term continuous drift between *UTC* and *TAI* that cannot be predicted in advance, because *UTC* takes into account irregularities in the motion of the Earth.

In applications where precision is not critical, *UTC* frequently goes by the name Greenwich Mean Time (*GMT*), Zulu (*Z*), or simply Universal Time (*UT*). The latter definition is ambiguous since *UT* is also used for *UT1*, another subcategory of universal time which even more closely follows the real motion of the Earth. Fig. E-1 shows historical differences between *TAI*, *UTC*, and *UT1*.

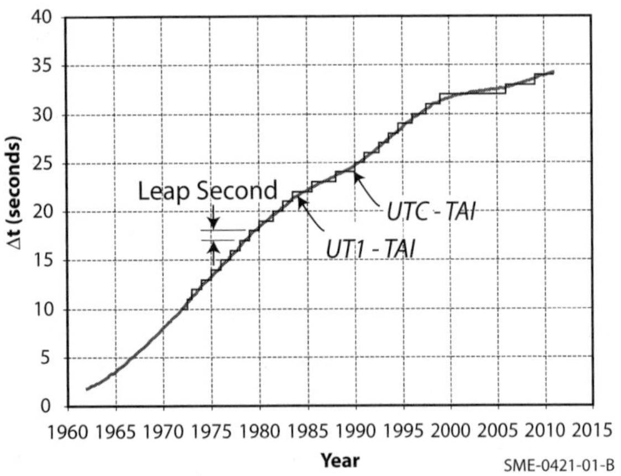

Fig. E-1. Historical Differences Between Universal Time and Atomic Time.

Terrestrial Time (TT)

Terrestrial Time, TT, is the current substitute for what was previously identified as terrestrial dynamic time, TDT, which in turn replaced the earlier ephemeris time, *ET*. Terrestrial time also uses the SI second as the unit of measure but is more precisely defined in terms of the dynamic equations of motion for the Earth. For most practical purposes, *TT* can be defined in terms of *TAI* by a simple offset, i.e., $TT - TAI = 32.184$ sec. (This offset is due to the historical origins of the time system. *TT* matched *ET* in 1984, when the use of *ET* was discontinued.) Consequently, for example, in January 1996, $TT - UTC = 32.184 + 30$ sec $= 62.184$ sec. Because atomic clocks have a small drift rate, changes between *TT* and *TAI* on the order of microseconds can accumulate over a period of years. (A more precise definition of terrestrial time based on the theory of relativity is given on the website.)

GPS Time

The GPS satellite system uses its own unique time called *GPS time*. Although presumably it could be accommodated with modern computer systems, the addition of a leap second is certainly inconvenient for GPS processing algorithms. Consequently, the GPS clock uses the SI second but does not introduce leap seconds. Like *TT* and *TAI*, *GPS time* maintains a fixed offset from *UTC* that changes by 1 sec whenever a leap second is introduced in *UTC*. The difference between *GPS time* and *TAI* is constant: *GPS time* – *TAI* = 19 sec., except for a quantity of the order of tens of nanoseconds, varing with time. In order to allow *UTC* to be recovered from the time signals broadcast by GPS, the integral number of seconds by which the two differ is included in subframe 4 of the GPS navigation message. (See Fig. E-9 in Sec. E.2.) Consequently, a GPS receiver may provide time output which is either *GPS time* or *UTC*. The GPS system is becoming a common mechanism for time transfer between 2 locations on the Earth or between 2 satellites in low-Earth orbit. An error budget for *GPS time* transfer when both locations have a common GPS satellite in view is given in Table E-4.

Table E-4. Error Budgets for GPS Time Transfer (with Two Satellites in View). [Seidelmann, 2006].

. Type of Delay	Best Case RMS (ns)	Worst Case RMS (ns)
Satellite Ephemeris	3	10
Ionospheric	2	100
Tropospheric	1	20
User-Position	1	1
Multipath	1	2
Receiver	1	1
Signal-to-Noise	7	1
Total RMS (for single 13-minute track)	4.2	103
NOTE: Some of the errors depend on the distance (for example, the satellite ephemeris). The best case applies to distances of 2,000–3,000 km; the worst case is for distances of 6,000–8,000 km.		

Get More See website for discontinuous time, Solar time, sidereal time, and relativisitic time.

References

Get Ref **For annotated bibliography of Appendix E, see the book website.**

Seidelmann, P. Kenneth, ed., USNO. 2006. *Explanatory Supplement to the Astronomical Almanac*. Mill Valley, CA: University Science Books.

Appendix F
Coordinate Transformations; Vector, Matrix, and Quaternion Algebra

James R. Wertz, Microcosm, Inc./USC and Nicola Sarzi-Amade, *Microcosm, Inc.*

F.1 Coordinate Transformations

Transformation Between Cartesian and Spherical Coordinates

The components of a vector, **R**, in cartesian (x, y, z) and spherical (r, θ, ϕ) coordinates are shown in Fig. F-1 and listed below. Note that θ is measured from the positive z-axis. The *declination*, δ, used in celestial coordinates is measured from the equatorial $(x–y)$ plane and is related to θ by

$$\delta \equiv 90° - \theta \tag{F-1}$$

The components in cartesian and spherical coordinates are related by the following equations:

Arbitrary Vector	**Unit Vector ($\lvert\mathbf{R}\rvert \equiv 1$)**	
$x = r \sin\theta \cos\phi$	$x = \sin\theta \cos\phi$	(F-2a)
$y = r \sin\theta \sin\phi$	$y = \sin\theta \sin\phi$	(F-2b)
$z = r \cos\theta$	$z = \cos\theta$	(F-2c)
$r = (x^2 + y^2 + z^2)^{1/2}$	$r = 1$	(F-2d)
$\theta = \text{acos}\{z/(x^2 + y^2 + z^2)^{1/2}\}$	$\theta = \text{acos}\, z$	(F-2e)
$\phi = \text{atan2}(x, y)$	$\phi = \text{atan2}(x, y)$	(F-2f)

The correct quadrant for ϕ in Eq. (F-2f) is obtained from the signs of x and y by, for example, using the atan2 function defined in App. D.4.

Transformation Between Cartesian Coordinates

Given a cartesian rectangular coordinate frame (x, y, z) as defined in Fig. F-1, we can define a second cartesian coordinate frame (u, v, w) by defining 3 mutually perpendicular unit vectors along the axes of the new coordinate frame. (Both reference frames are assumed to be orthogonal, and right-handed.) The unit vectors defining the new frame in terms of the original coordinates are:

$$\hat{\mathbf{u}} \equiv \begin{bmatrix} u_x \\ u_y \\ u_z \end{bmatrix} \quad \hat{\mathbf{v}} \equiv \begin{bmatrix} v_x \\ v_y \\ v_z \end{bmatrix} \quad \hat{\mathbf{w}} \equiv \begin{bmatrix} w_x \\ w_y \\ w_z \end{bmatrix} \tag{F-3}$$

Given these vectors, we can form the *direction cosine matrix**, or *attitude matrix*, A, as follows:

$$A \equiv \begin{bmatrix} u_x & v_x & w_x \\ u_y & v_y & w_y \\ u_z & v_z & w_z \end{bmatrix} \tag{F-4}$$

* The matrix A is called the *direction cosine matrix* because each of the elements is the cosine of the angle between the two relevant vectors. For example, $u_x = \hat{\mathbf{u}} \cdot \hat{\mathbf{x}} = \cos\theta$, where θ is the angle between $\hat{\mathbf{u}}$ and $\hat{\mathbf{x}}$.

So long as $\hat{\mathbf{u}}$, $\hat{\mathbf{v}}$, $\hat{\mathbf{w}}$ and form a right-handed triad of mutually perpendicular unit vectors, A will be a proper real orthogonal matrix. Only three of the nine elements are independent and $\det A = 1$. The attitude matrix is a coordinate transformation that maps vectors from the original frame to the new frame. Thus, if **b** is an arbitrary vector with components b_x, b_y, and b_z, then the components in the new frame are given by:

$$\begin{bmatrix} b_u \\ b_v \\ b_w \end{bmatrix} = \begin{bmatrix} \hat{\mathbf{u}} \cdot \mathbf{b} \\ \hat{\mathbf{v}} \cdot \mathbf{b} \\ \hat{\mathbf{w}} \cdot \mathbf{b} \end{bmatrix} = A\mathbf{b} \equiv \begin{bmatrix} u_x & v_x & w_x \\ u_y & v_y & w_y \\ u_z & v_z & w_z \end{bmatrix} \begin{bmatrix} b_x \\ b_y \\ b_z \end{bmatrix} \tag{F-5}$$

The inverse matrix, A^{-1}, is the coordinate transformation that maps vectors from the new frame (u, v, w) back into the original frame (x, y, z). For the attitude matrix, the inverse is simply the transpose. That is:

$$A^{-1} = A^T \equiv \begin{bmatrix} u_x & u_y & u_z \\ v_x & v_y & v_z \\ w_x & w_y & w_z \end{bmatrix}, \begin{bmatrix} b_x \\ b_y \\ b_z \end{bmatrix} = A^{-1} \begin{bmatrix} b_u \\ b_v \\ b_w \end{bmatrix} \tag{F-6}$$

Transformation Between Spherical Coordinates

We can use the formalism developed for full sky geometry to significantly reduce the complexity of transforming between two spherical coordinate systems. Specifically, assume that two spherical coordinate systems are related as shown in Fig. F-2, with the variables defined as follows:

ρ ≡ arc length between the two positive poles $(0 \le \rho \le 180 \text{ deg})$

ψ_1 ≡ azimuth of the second pole in the first coordinate system $(0 \le \psi_1 < 360 \text{ deg})$

ψ_2 ≡ azimuth of the first pole in the second coordinate system $(0 \le \psi_2 < 360 \text{ deg})$

Given the coordinates (ϕ_2, δ_2') of a point, **P**, in the second coordinate system, we wish to find the coordinates (ϕ_1, δ_1') of **P** in the first system, where δ' is the co-elevation angle = 90 deg – δ. We first define the triangle shown in Fig. F-3, with:

$$\Delta\phi_1 = \psi_1 - \phi_1 \tag{F-7}$$

$$\Delta\phi_2 = \psi_2 - \phi_2 \tag{F-8}$$

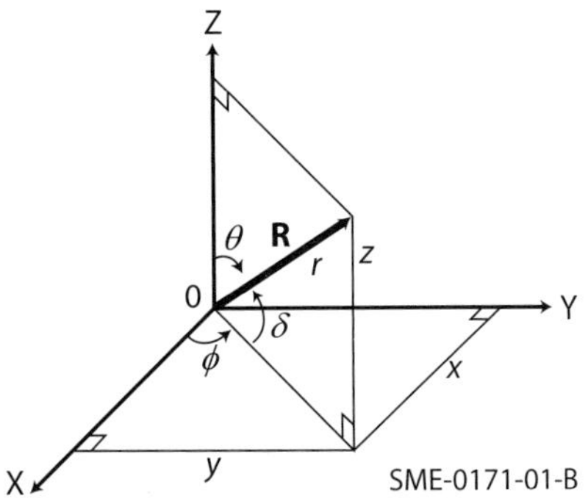

Fig. F-1. Components of a Vector, R, of length *r* in Cartesian (*x, y, z*), and Spherical (*r, θ, φ*) Coordinates.

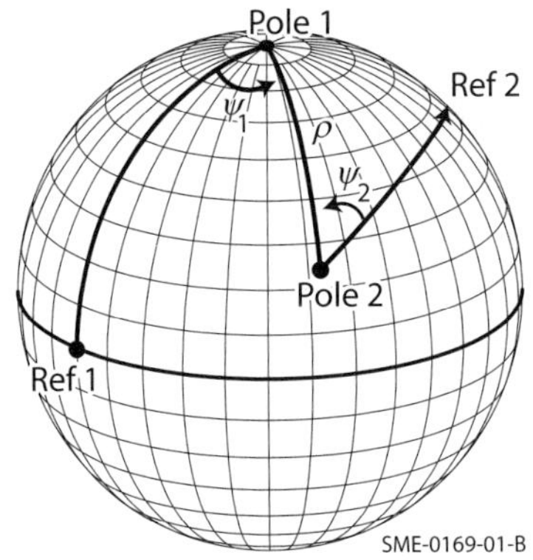

Fig. F-2. Relationship Between the Coordinate Systems.

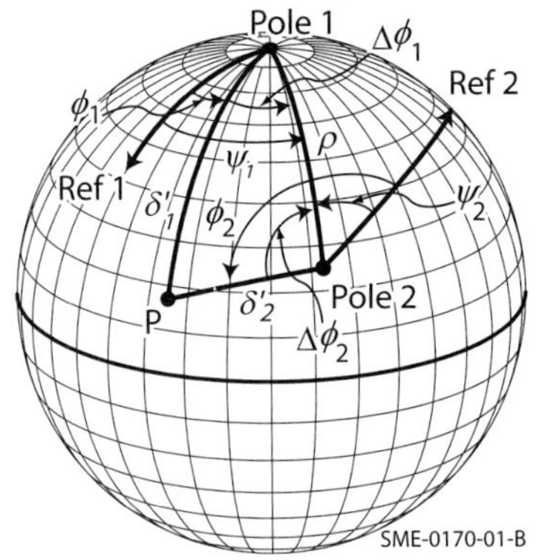

Fig. F-3. Definition of the Spherical Triangle for Coordinate Transformations. (Note that $\Delta\phi_2 < 0$)

From the general solution for side-angle-side spherical triangles (see A.7.3 and Eqs. (8-4) to (8-6) in Wertz [2009]), we have two solutions:

$$\delta_1' = \operatorname{acos2}\left[\cos\rho\cos\delta_2' + \sin\rho\sin\delta_2'\cos\Delta\phi_2, \mathrm{H}(\Delta\phi_2)\right] \quad \text{(F-9)}$$

$$\Delta\phi_1 = \operatorname{acos2}\left[\frac{\cos\delta_2' - \cos\rho\cos\delta_1'}{\sin\rho\sin\delta_1'}, \mathrm{H}(\delta_2')\right] \quad \text{(F-10)}$$

and

$$\delta_1'^* = 360\text{ deg} - \delta_1' \quad \text{(F-11)}$$

$$\Delta\phi_1^* = \Delta\phi_1 + 180\text{ deg} \quad \text{(F-12)}$$

where the acos2 function is defined in App. D.4. If we allow the angles to range from 0 to 360 deg, but restrict the sides to the range of 0 to 180 deg, then we have a unique solution (see Eq. (8-6) in Wertz [2009]) (except in the singular case in which the poles are identical or 180 deg apart):

$$\delta_1' = \operatorname{acos}\left[\cos\rho\cos\delta_2' + \sin\rho\sin\delta_2'\cos\Delta\phi_2\right] \quad \text{(F-13)}$$

$$\Delta\phi_1 = \left[\operatorname{acos}\left[\frac{\cos\delta_2' - \cos\rho\cos\delta_1'}{\sin\rho\sin\delta_1'}\right]\cdot\mathrm{H}(\Delta\phi_2)\right]_{\mathrm{MOD360}}$$

This can be further reduced to the normal coordinate expressions (α, δ), where α is azimuth and δ is elevation:

$$\delta_1 = 90\text{ deg} - \operatorname{acos}[\cos\rho\ \sin\delta_2 + \sin\rho\ \cos\delta_2\cos\Delta\phi_2] \quad \text{(F-14)}$$

$$\Delta\phi_1 = \left[\operatorname{acos}\left[\frac{\sin\delta_2 - \cos\rho\sin\delta_1}{\sin\rho\cos\delta_1}\right]\cdot\mathrm{H}(\Delta\phi_2)\right]_{\mathrm{MOD360}}$$

By symmetry, the reverse transformation will be:

$$\delta_2 = 90\text{ deg} - \operatorname{acos}[\cos\rho\sin\delta_1 + \sin\rho\cos\delta_1\cos\Delta\phi_1] \quad \text{(F-15)}$$

$$\Delta\phi_2 = \left[\operatorname{acos}\left[\frac{\sin\delta_1 - \cos\rho\sin\delta_2}{\sin\rho\cos\delta_2}\right]\cdot\mathrm{H}(\Delta\phi_1)\right]_{\mathrm{MOD360}}$$

where acos is the normal inverse cosine function defined over the range 0 to 180 deg and H is the hemisphere function defined in App. D.4. Finally,

$$\phi_1 = \psi_1 - \Delta\phi_1 \quad \text{(F-16)}$$

and δ_1' is defined by Eq. (F-13).

F.2 Vector, Matrix, & Quaternion Algebra

Get Info

The details of vector, matrix, and quaternion algebra are beyond the scope of this book, but are nonetheless relevant to many of the orbit, attitude, and mission computations. Therefore, we have reproduced, with permission, the relevant appendices on these topics from the book *Spacecraft Attitude Determination and Control* [Wertz, 1978] and included them on the book website in the App. F material. The appendix in Wertz [1978] on spherical geometry calculations has been superceded by the Full Sky Spherical Geometry approach described in Chap. 8 and App. A of Wertz [2009].

References

Get Ref

For annotated bibliography of Appendix F, see the book website.

Wertz, James R., ed. 1978. *Spacecraft Attitude Determination and Control*. Dordrecht, The Netherlands: D. Reidel Publishing Company.

Wertz, James R. 2009. *Orbit & Constellation Design and Management: Spacecraft Orbit and Attitude Systems*. Hawthorne, CA: Microcosm Press.

Appendix H
Units and Conversion Factors

Nicola Sarzi-Amade, *Microcosm, Inc.*

The metric system of units, officially known as the *International System of Units*, or *SI*, is used throughout this book, with the exception that angles are expressed in degrees rather than the SI unit of radians. By international agreement, the fundamental SI units of length, mass, and time are defined by NIST [2008]:

> The *meter* is the length of the path traveled by light in vacuum during a time interval of 1/299,792,458 of a second.
>
> The *kilogram* is equal to the mass of the international prototype of the kilogram.
>
> The *second* is the duration of 9,192,631,770 periods of the radiation corresponding to the transition between two hyperfine levels of the ground state of the cesium-133 atom.

Additional base units in the SI system are the *ampere* for electric current, the *kelvin* for thermodynamic temperature, the *mole* for amount of substance, and the *candela* for luminous intensity. Thompson and Taylor [2008] provide an excellent summary of SI units.

The names of multiples and submultiples of SI units are formed by application of the following prefixes:

Multiplier	Prefix	Symbol	Multiplier	Prefix	Symbol
10^{24}	yotta	Y	10^{-1}	deci	d
10^{21}	zetta	Z	10^{-2}	centi	c
10^{18}	exa	E	10^{-3}	milli	m
10^{15}	peta	P	10^{-6}	micro	μ
10^{12}	tera	T	10^{-9}	nano	n
10^{9}	giga	G	10^{-12}	pico	p
10^{6}	mega	M	10^{-15}	femto	f
10^{3}	kilo	k	10^{-18}	atto	a
10^{2}	hecto	h	10^{-21}	zepto	z
10^{1}	deka	da	10^{-24}	yocto	y

For each quantity, the SI unit and its abbreviation are given in brackets. For convenience in computer use, most conversion factors are given to the greatest available accuracy. Note that some conversions are exact definitions and some (speed of light, astronomical unit) depend on the value of physical constants. "..." indicates a repeating decimal. All notes are on the last page.

To Convert from	*To*	*Multiply by*	*Notes*
Acceleration [meter/second^2, m/s^2]			
Gal (galileo)	m/s^2	0.01	E
Inch/second^2, in/s^2	m/s^2	0.025 4	E
Foot/second^2, ft/s^2	m/s^2	0.304 8	E
Free fall (standard), g	m/s^2	9.806 65	E
Angle (see angular measure)			
Angular Acceleration [radian/second^2, rad/s^2]			
Degrees/sec^2, deg/s^2	rad/s^2	π/180 ≈ 0.017 453 292 519 943 295	E
Revolutions/sec^2, rev/s^2	rad/s^2	2π ≈ 6.283 185 307 179 586 477	E
Revolutions/min^2, rev/min^2	rad/s^2	π/1,800 ≈ 1.745 329 251 994 × 10^{-3}	E
Revolutions/min^2	deg/s^2	0.1	E
Radians/sec^2, rad/s^2	deg/s^2	180/π ≈ 57.29 577 951 308 232	E
Revolutions/sec^2, rev/s^2	deg/s^2	360	E
Angular Area [sr], book also uses deg^2			
Degree^2, deg^2	sr	$(\pi/180)^2$ ≈ 3.046 174 197 867 × 10^{-4}	E
Minute^2, min^2	sr	$(\pi/10{,}800)^2$ ≈ 8.461 594 994 075 × 10^{-8}	E
Second^2, s^2	sr	$(\pi/648{,}000)^2$ ≈ 2.350 443 053 909 × 10^{-11}	E
Steradian, sr	deg^2	$(180/\pi)^2$ ≈ 3.282 806 350 011 × 10^{3}	E
Minute^2, min^2	deg^2	1/3,600 = 2.777... × 10^{-4}	E
Second^2, s^2	deg^2	$(1/3{,}600)^2$ ≈ 7.716 049 382 716 × 10^{-8}	E
Steradian, sr	rad^2	1	E
Angular Measure [radian, rad]. *This book uses degree (abbreviated "deg") as the basic unit.*			
Degree, deg	rad	π/180 ≈ 0.017 453 292 519 943	E
Minute (of arc), min (of arc), min	rad	π/10,800 ≈ 2.908 882 086 657 × 10^{-4}	E
Second (of arc), s (of arc), s	rad	π/648 000 ≈ 4.848 136 811 095 × 10^{-6}	E
Radian, rad	deg	180/π ≈ 57.295 779 513 082 320	E
Minute (of arc), min	deg	1/60 = 0.01666...	E
Second (of arc), s	deg	1/3,600 = 2.777... × 10^{-4}	E
Angular Momentum [kilogram·meter^2/second, kg·m^2/s]			
Gram · cm^2/sec, g · cm^2/s	kg · m^2/s	1 × 10^{-7}	E
lbm · inch^2/sec, lbm · in^2/s	kg · m^2/s	2.926 396 534 292 × 10^{-4}	E
Slug · inch^2/sec, slug · in^2/s	kg · m^2/s	9.415 402 418 968 × 10^{-3}	D
lbm · foot^2/sec, lbm · ft^2/s	kg · m^2/s	0.042 140 110 093 80	D
Inch · lbf · sec, in · lbf · s	kg · m^2/s	0.112 984 829 027 6	D
Slug · foot^2/sec, slug · ft^2/s = foot · lbf · sec, ft · lbf · s	kg · m^2/s	1.355 817 948 331	D
Angular Velocity [radian/second, rad/s]. *This book uses degrees/second as the basic unit.*			
Degrees/sec, deg/s	rad/s	π/180 ≈ 0.017 453 292 519 943 295	E

To Convert from	*To*	*Multiply by*	*Notes*
Revolutions/min, rpm	rad/s	$\pi/30$ ≈ 0.104 719 755 119 659 774	E
Revolutions/sec, rev/s	rad/s	2π ≈ 6.283 185 307 179 586 477	E
Revolutions/min, rpm	deg/s	6	E
Radians/sec, rad/s	deg/s	$180/\pi$ ≈ 57.295 779 513 082 320 88	E
Revolutions/sec , rev/s	deg/s	360	E

Area [meter^2, m^2]

To Convert from	*To*	*Multiply by*	*Notes*
Acre	m^2	4.046 856 422 × 10^{3}	E
Foot^2, ft^2	m^2	0.092 903 04	E
Hectare	m^2	1 × 10^{4}	E
Inch^2, in^2	m^2	6.451 6 × 10^{-4}	E
Mile^2 (U.S. statute)	m^2	2.589 110 336 × 10^{6}	E
Yard^2, yd^2	m^2	0.836 127 36	E
(Nautical mile)^2	m^2	3.429 904 × 10^{6}	E

Capacity (see Volume)

Conductance (see Electric Conductance)

Current (see Electric Current)

Density [kilogram/meter^3, kg/m^3]

To Convert from	*To*	*Multiply by*	*Notes*
Gram/centimeter^3, g/cm^3	kg/m^3	1.0 × 10^{3}	E
Pound mass/inch^3, lbm/in^3	kg/m^3	2.767 990 471 020 × 10^{4}	D
Pound mass/foot^3, lbm/ft^3	kg/m^3	16.018 463 373 96	D
Slug/ft^3	kg/m^3	515.378 818 393 2	D

Distance (see Length)

Electric Charge [coulomb, C]

To Convert from	*To*	*Multiply by*	*Notes*
Abcoulomb	C	10	E
Faraday (based on carbon–12)	C	9.648 534 × 10^{4}	NIST
Statcoulomb	C	3.335 641 × 10^{-10}	NIST

Electric Conductance [siemens, S]

To Convert from	*To*	*Multiply by*	*Notes*
Abmho	S	1 × 10^{9}	E
Mho (Ω^{-1})	S	1	E

Electric Current [ampere, A]

To Convert from	*To*	*Multiply by*	*Notes*
Abampere	A	10	E
Gilbert	A	$10/4\pi$ ≈ 0.795 774 715 459 5	E
Statampere	A	3.335 641 × 10^{-10}	NIST

Electric Field Intensity [volt/meter ≡ kilogram · meter · ampere^{-1} · second^{-3}, V/m ≡ kg · m · A^{-1} · s^{-3}]

Electric Potential Difference [volt ≡ watt/ampere ≡ kilogram · meter^2 · ampere^{-1} · second^{-3}, V ≡ W/A ≡ kg · m^2 · A^{-1} · s^{-3}]

To Convert from	*To*	*Multiply by*	*Notes*
Abvolt	V	1 × 10^{-8}	E
Statvolt	V	299.792 5	NIST

Electric Resistance [ohm ≡ volt/ampere ≡ kilogram · meter^2 · ampere^{-2} · second^{-3}, Ω ≡ V/A ≡ kg · m^2 · A^{-2} · s^{-3}]

To Convert from	*To*	*Multiply by*	*Notes*
Abohm	Ω	1 × 10^{-9}	E
Statohm	Ω	8.987 552 × 10^{11}	NIST

Energy (= torque = work; torque is a vector, energy is a scalar, but both have same units) [joule ≡ newton · meter ≡ kilogram · meter^2/s^2 , J ≡ N · m ≡ kg · m^2/s^2]

To Convert from	*To*	*Multiply by*	*Notes*
British thermal unit, Btu (mean)	J	1.055 055 852 62 × 10^{3}	E
Calorie (IT), cal	J	4.186 8	E
Kilocalorie (IT), kcal	J	4.186 8 × 10^{3}	E
Electron volt, eV	J	1.602 176 487 × 10^{-19}	C
Erg ≡ gram · cm^2/s^2 = pole · cm · oersted	J	1 × 10^{-7}	E
Foot poundal	J	0.042 140 110 093 80	D
Foot lbf = slug · foot^2/s^2	J	1.355 817 948 331 4	E
Kilowatt hour, kW · hr	J	3.6 × 10^{6}	E
Ton equivalent of TNT	J	4.184 × 10^{9}	E

Force [newton ≡ kilogram · meter/second^2, N ≡ kg · m /s^2]

To Convert from	*To*	*Multiply by*	*Notes*
Dyne	N	1 × 10^{-5}	E
Kilogram-force (kgf)	N	9.806 65	E
Ounce force (avoirdupois)	N	0.278 013 850 953 8	D
Poundal	N	0.138 254 954 376	E
Pound force (avoirdupois), lbf ≡ slug · foot/s^2	N	4.448 221 615 260 5	E

Illuminance [lux ≡ candela · steradian/meter^2, lx ≡ cd · sr/m^2]

To Convert from	*To*	*Multiply by*	*Notes*
Footcandle	cd · sr/m^2	10.763 910 416 709 70	E
Phot	cd · sr/m^2	1 × 10^{4}	E

Inductance, L [henry ≡ weber/ampere ≡ kilogram · meter^2 · ampere^{-2} · second^{-2}, H ≡ Wb/A ≡ kg · m^2 · A^{-2} · s^{-2}]

To Convert from	*To*	*Multiply by*	*Notes*
Abhenry	H	1 × 10^{-9}	E
Stathenry	Hd	8.987552 × 10^{11}	E

Length [meter, m]

To Convert from	*To*	*Multiply by*	*Notes*
Angstrom, Å	m	1 × 10^{-10}	E
Astronomical unit (SI)	m	1.495 978 707 00 × 10^{11}	IAU
Earth equatorial radius, R_E	m	6.378 136 6 × 10^{6}	IERS
Fermi (1 fermi = 1 fm)	m	1 × 10^{-15}	E
Foot, ft	m	0.304 8	E
Inch, in	m	0.025 4	E
Light year	m	9.460 730 472 580 8 × 10^{15}	D
Micron, μm	m	1 × 10^{-6}	E
Mil (10^{-3} inch)	m	2.54 × 10^{-5}	E
Mile (U.S. statute), mi	m	1.609 344 × 10^{3}	E
Nautical mile (U.S.), NM	m	1.852 × 10^{3}	E
Parsec (IAU)	m	3.085 677 597 49 × 10^{16}	D
Solar radius	m	6.960 00 × 10^{8}	AA
Yard, yd	m	0.914 4	E

Luminance [candela/meter^2, cd/m^2]

To Convert from	*To*	*Multiply by*	*Notes*
Footlambert	cd/m^2	3.426 259 099 635 39	D
Lambert	cd/m^2	$(1/\pi) \times 10^{4}$ ≈ 3.183 098 862 × 10^{3}	E
Stilb	cd/m^2	1 × 10^{4}	E

Magnetic Field Strength, H [ampere turn/meter, A/m]

To Convert from	*To*	*Multiply by*	*Notes*
Oersted (EMU)	A/m	$(1/4\pi) \times 10^{3}$ ≈ 79.577 471 545 947 667	E,1

Magnetic Flux [weber ≡ volt · s ≡ kilogram · meter^2 · ampere^{-1}•second^{-2}, Wb ≡ V · s ≡ kg · m^2 · A^{-1} · s^{-2}]

To Convert from	*To*	*Multiply by*	*Notes*
Maxwell (EMU)	Wb	1 × 10^{-8}	E
Unit pole	Wb	1.256 637 × 10^{-7}	NIST

Magnetic Flux Density (see Magnetic Induction)

Magnetic Induction, B [tesla ≡ weber/meter^2 ≡ kilogram · ampere^{-1} · second^{-2}, T ≡ Wb/m^2 ≡ kg · A^{-1} · s^{-2}]

To Convert from	*To*	*Multiply by*	*Notes*
Gamma (EMU) (γ)	T	1 × 10^{-9}	E,1
Gauss (EMU)	T	1 × 10^{-4}	E,1

Magnetic Dipole Moment [weber · meter ≡ kilogram · meter^3 · ampere^{-1} · second^{-2}, Wb · m ≡ kg · m^3 · A^{-1} · s^{-2}]

To Convert from	*To*	*Multiply by*	*Notes*
Pole · centimeter (EMU)	Wb · m	$4\pi \times 10^{-10}$ ≈ 1.256 637 061 435 × 10^{-9}	E,1
Gauss · centimeter^3 (Practical)	Wb · m	1 × 10^{-10}	E,1

To Convert from	*To*	*Multiply by*	*Notes*

Magnetic Moment [ampere turn · meter^2 ≡ joule/tesla, A · m^2 ≡ J/T]

Abampere · centimeter^2 (EMU)	A · m^2	1×10^{-3}	E, 1
Ampere · centimeter^2	A · m^2	1×10^{-4}	E, 1

Mass [kilogram, kg]

γ(= 1 μg)	kg	1×10^{-9}	E
Atomic unit (electron mass)	kg	$9.109\,382\,15 \times 10^{-31}$	C
Atomic mass unit (unified), amu	kg	$1.660\,538\,782 \times 10^{-27}$	C
Metric carat	kg	2.0×10^{-4}	E
Metric ton	kg	1×10^{3}	E
Ounce mass (avoirdupois), oz	kg	0.028 349 231 25	E
Pound mass, lbm (avoirdupois)	kg	0.453 592 37	E
Slug	kg	14.593 902 937 21	D
Short ton (2,000 lbm)	kg	907.184 74	E
Solar mass	kg	$1.988\,4 \times 10^{30}$	AA

Mass Density (see Density)

Moment of Inertia [kilogram · meter^2, kg · m^2]

Gram · centimeter^2, g · cm^2	kg · m^2	1×10^{-7}	E
Pound mass · inch^2, lbm · in^2	kg · m^2	$2.926\,396\,534\,292 \times 10^{-4}$	E
Pound mass · foot^2, lbm · ft^2	kg · m^2	$4.214\,011\,009\,380 \times 10^{-2}$	D
Slug · inch^2, slug · in^2	kg · m^2	$9.415\,402\,418\,968 \times 10^{-3}$	D
Inch · pound force · s^2, in · lbf · s^2	kg · m^2	0.112 984 829 027 6	D
Slug · foot^2 = ft · lbf · s^2	kg · m^2	1.355 817 948 331 4	D

Plane Angle (see Angular Measure)

Potential Difference (see Electric Potential Difference)

Power [watt ≡ joule/second ≡ kilogram · meter^2/second^3, W ≡ J/s ≡ kg · m^2/s^3]

Foot · pound force/second, ft lbf/s	W	1.355 817 948 331	D
Horsepower (550 ft · lbf/s), hp	W	745.699 871 582 3	D
Horsepower (electrical), hp	W	746.0	E
Solar luminosity	W	3.845×10^{26}	AQ

Pressure or Stress [pascal ≡ newton/meter^2 ≡ kilogram · meter^{-1} · second^{-2}, Pa ≡ N/m^2 ≡ kg · m^{-1} · s^{-2}]

Atmosphere, atm	Pa	$1.013\,25 \times 10^{5}$	E
Bar	Pa	1×10^{5}	E
Centimeter of mercury (0° C)	Pa	$\approx 1.333\,223\,874\,145 \times 10^{3}$	E
Dyne/centimeter^2, dyne/cm^2	Pa	0.1	E
Inch of mercury (32° F)	Pa	$3.386\,388\,640\,341 \times 10^{3}$	D
Pound force/foot^2, lbf/ft^2, psf	Pa	47.880 258 980 34	D
Pound force/inch^2, lbf/in^2, psi	Pa	$6.894\,757\,293\,168 \times 10^{3}$	D
Torr (0° C)	Pa	(101325/760) ≈ 133.322 368 421 052 631	E

Resistance (see Electric Resistance)

Solid Angle (see Angular Area)

Specific Heat Capacity [joule · kilogram^{-1} · kelvin^{-1} ≡ meter^2 · second^2 · kelvin^{-1}, J · kg^{-1} · K^{-1} ≡ m^2 · s^2 · K^{-1}]

cal · g^{-1} · K^{-1} (mean)	J · kg^{-1} · K^{-1}	$4.186\,80 \times 10^{3}$	E
Btu · lbm^{-1} · °F^{-1} (mean)	J · kg^{-1} · K^{-1}	$4.186\,80 \times 10^{3}$	E

Stress (see Pressure)

Temperature [kelvin, K]

Celsius, °C	K	$t_K = t_C + 273.15$	E
Fahrenheit, °F	K	$t_K = (5/9)\,(t_F + 459.67)$	E
Rankine °R	K	$t_K = (5/9)\,t_R$	E
Fahrenheit, °F	C	$t_C = (5/9)\,(t_F - 32.0)$	E
Rankine °R	C	$t_C = (5/9)\,(t_R - 491.67)$	E

Thermal Conductivity [watt · meter^{-1} · kelvin^{-1} ≡ kilogram · meter · second^{-3} · kelvin^{-1}, W · m^{-1} · K^{-1} ≡ kg · m · s^{-3} · K^{-1}]

cal · cm^{-1} · s^{-1} · K^{-1}	W · m^{-1} · K^{-1}	418.68	E
Btu · ft^{-1} · hr^{-1} · °F^{-1}	W · m^{-1} · K^{-1}	1.730 734 666 371 39	D

Thrust (see Force)

Time [second, s]

Sidereal day, d_* (ref. = fixed stars)	s	$8.616\,409\,053 \times 10^{4}$ = 23h 56m 4.09 053s	AA
Ephemeris day (= calendar day), d_e	s	8.64×10^{4}	AQ
Ephemeris day (= calendar day), d_e	d_*	1.002 737 909 35	AA
Keplerian period of a satellite in low-Earth orbit	min	$1.658\,669\,010\,080 \times 10^{-4} \times a^{3/2}$ (a in km)	Table 8–3
Keplerian period of a satellite of the Sun	d_e	$3.652\,568\,983\,276 \times 10^{2} \times a^{3/2}$ (a in AU)	IAU
Tropical year (ref. = ♈)	s	$3.155\,692\,522 \times 10^{7}$	AA
Tropical year (ref. = ♈)	d_e	365.242 190	AA
Sidereal year (ref. = fixed stars)	s	$3.155\,814\,976 \times 10^{7}$	AA
Sidereal year (ref. = fixed stars)	d_e	365.256 363	AA
Calendar year (365 days), yr	s	$3.153\,6 \times 10^{7}$	E
Julian century	d_e	36,525	E
Gregorian calendar century	d_e	36,524.25	E

Torque (see Energy)

Velocity [meter/second, m/s]

Foot/minute, ft/min	m/s	5.08×10^{-3}	E
Inch/second, ips	m/s	0.025 4	E
Kilometer/hour, km/hr	m/s	$(3.6)^{-1} = 0.277777\ldots$	E
Foot/second, fps or ft/s	m/s	0.304 8	E
Miles/hour, mph	m/s	0.447 04	E
Knot (international)	m/s	(1852/3600) = 0.514444. . .	E
Miles/minute, mi/min	m/s	26.822 4	E
Miles/second, mi/s	m/s	$1.609\,344 \times 10^{3}$	E
Velocity of Light	m/s	$2.997\,924\,58 \times 10^{8}$	E

Viscosity [pascal · second ≡ kilogram · meter^{-1} · second^{-1}, Pa · s ≡ kg · m^{-1} · s^{-1}]

Stoke	m^2/s	1.0×10^{-4}	E
Foot^2 · second, ft^2 · s	m^2/s	0.092 903 04	E
Pound mass · foot^{-1} · second^{-1}, lbm · ft^{-1} · s^{-1}	Pa · s	1.488 163 943 570	D
Pound force · second/foot^2, lbf · s/ft^2	Pa · s	47.880 258 980 34	D
Poise	Pa · s	0.1	E
Poundal second/foot^2, poundal s/ft^2	Pa · s	1.488 163 943 570	D
Slug · foot^{-1} · second^{-1}, slug · ft^{-1} · s^{-1}	Pa · s	47.880 258 980 34	D
Rhe	(Pa · s)$^{-1}$	10	E

To Convert from	*To*	*Multiply by*	*Notes*
Volume [meter^3, m^3]			
λ (1λ = 1 μL = 1 × 10^{-6} L)	m^3	1 × 10^{-9}	E
Foot^3, ft^3	m^3	2.831 684 659 2 × 10^{-2}	E
Gallon (U.S. liquid), gal	m^3	3.785 411 784 × 10^{-3}	E
Inch^3, in^3	m^3	1.638 706 4 × 10^{-5}	E
Liter, L	m^3	1 × 10^{-3}	E
Ounce (U.S. fluid), oz	m^3	2.957 352 956 25 × 10^{-5}	E
Pint (U.S. liquid), pt	m^3	4.731 764 73 × 10^{-4}	E
Quart, qt	m^3	9.463 529 46 × 10^{-4}	E
Stere (st)	m^3	1	E
Yard^3, yd^3	m^3	0.764 554 857 984	E

Work (see Energy)

Notes for the preceding table:

AA Values from *Astronomical Almanac* [2011].

AQ Values from *Allen's Astrophysical Quantities* [Cox, 2000].

C Values from CODATA [2006 website].

D Values from exact quantities, rounded off to 13 significant figures.

E (Exact) indicates that the conversion is exact by definition of the non-SI unit or that it is obtained from other exact conversions.

IAU Values from the International Astronomical Union [2009 website].

IERS From the IERS [McCarthy and Petit, 2004].

NIST Values from the National Institute of Standards and Technology [Thompson and Taylor, 2008].

(1) Care should be taken in transforming magnetic units, because the dimensionality of magnetic quantities (**B**, **H**, etc.) depends on the system of units. Most of the conversions given here are between SI and EMU (electromagnetic). The following equations hold in both sets of units:

$\mathbf{T} = \mathbf{m} \times \mathbf{B} = \mathbf{d} \times \mathbf{H}$

$\mathbf{B} = \mu \mathbf{H}$

$\mathbf{m} = I\mathbf{A}$ for a current loop in a plane

$\mathbf{d} = \mu \mathbf{m}$

with the following definitions:

$\mathbf{T}$ ≡ torque

$\mathbf{B}$ ≡ magnetic induction (commonly called "magnetic field")

$\mathbf{H}$ ≡ magnetic field strength or magnetic intensity

$\mathbf{m}$ ≡ magnetic moment

I ≡ current loop

$\mathbf{A}$ ≡ vector normal to the plane of the current loop (in the direction of the angular velocity vector of the current loop) with magnitude equal to the area of the loop.

$\mathbf{d}$ ≡ magnetic dipole moment

μ ≡ magnetic permeability

The permeability of vacuum, μ_0, has the following values, by definition:

$\mu_0 \equiv 1$ (dimensionless), EMU

$\mu_0 \equiv 4\pi \times 10^{-7}$ N/A^2, SI

Therefore, in electromagnetic units in vacuum, magnetic induction and magnetic field strength are equivalent and the magnetic moment and magnetic dipole moment are equivalent. For practical magnetostatics, space is a vacuum but the spacecraft itself may have $\mu \neq \mu_0$.

Value of Useful Mathematical Constants

π	≈3.141 592 653 589 793 238 462 643
e	≈2.718 281 828 459 045 235 360 287
e^{π}	≈23.140 692 632 779 269 006
$\log_{10}x$	≈0.434 294 481 903 251 827 651 128 9 $\log_e x$
$\log_e x$	≈2.302 585 092 994 045 684 017 991 $\log_{10}x$
$\log_e \pi$	≈1.144 729 885 849 400 174 143 427

Values are from *The Handbook of Mathematical Functions, with Formulas, Graphs, and Mathematical Tables* [Abramowitz and Stegun, 1970]

References

For annotated bibliography of Appendix H, see the book website.

Abramowitz, M. and I. A. Stegun, eds. 1970. *The Handbook of Mathematical Functions with Formulas, Graphs, and Mathematical Tables*. New York: Dover.

Cox, A.N. ed. 2000. *Allen's Astrophysical Quantities*. New York: Springer-Verlag.

McCarthy, D. D. and G. Petit (Eds.). 2004. "IERS Conventions (2003)." IERS Technical Note No. 32.

Thompson, A. and B. N. Taylor. 2008. *Guide for the Use of the International System of Units (SI)*. National Institute of Standards and Technology (NIST), Special Publication 811, U.S. Department of Commerce: USGPO.

U.S. Naval Observatory and UK Hydrographic Office. 2010. *Astronomical Almanac for the Year 2011*. Washington DC: USGPO.

Index

— B —

— G —

— M —

— O —

— P —

— S —

— T —

Appendix I
Earth Satellite Parameters

Nicola Sarzi-Amade and Becky Christofferson, *Microcosm, Inc.*

Explanation

Table I-1 provides a variety of quantitative data for Earth-orbiting satellites. Limitations, formulas, and text references are given below. The independent parameter in the formulas is the distance, r, from the center of the Earth in km. The outer column on each table is the altitude, $h \equiv r - R_E$, where R_E = 6,378.1366 km is the equatorial radius of the Earth.

1. *Instantaneous Access Area for a 0 deg Elevation Angle* or the *Full Geometric Horizon* (10^6 km^2). All the area that an instrument or antenna could potentially see at any instant if it were scanned through its normal range of orientations for which the spacecraft elevation is above 0 deg [Eq. (C-29)].
2. *Instantaneous Access Area for a 5 deg Minimum Elevation Angle* (10^6 km^2) = same as col.1 but with elevation of 5 deg.
3. *Instantaneous Access Area for a 10 deg Minimum Elevation Angle* (10^6 km^2) = same as col.1 but with elevation of 10 deg.
4. *Instantaneous Access Area for a 20 deg Minimum Elevation Angle* (10^6 km^2) = same as col.1 but with elevation of 20 deg.
5. *Area Access Rate for an Elevation of 0 deg* (10^3 km^2/s) = the rate at which new land is coming into the spacecraft's access area [Eq. (C-30)].
6. *Area Access Rate for an Elevation Limit of 5 deg* (10^3 km^2/s) = same as col. 5 with an elevation of 5 deg.
7. *Area Access Rate for an Elevation Limit of 10 deg* (10^3 km^2/s) = same as col. 5 with an elevation of 10 deg.
8. *Area Access Rate for an Elevation Limit of 20 deg* (10^3 km^2/s) = same as col. 5 with an elevation of 20 deg.
9. *Maximum Time in View for a Satellite Visible to a Minimum Elevation Angle of 0 deg* (min) = $P\lambda_{max}$/180 deg, where P is from col. 69 and λ_{max} is from col. 13. Assume a circular orbit over a nonrotating Earth [Eq. (C-31)].
10. *Maximum Time in View for a Satellite Visible to a Minimum Elevation Angle of 5 deg* (min) = same as col. 9 with λ_{max} for a 5 deg taken from col. 14.
11. *Maximum Time in View for a Satellite Visible to a Minimum Elevation Angle of 10 deg* (min) = same as col. 9 with λ_{max} for a 10 deg taken from col. 15.
12. *Maximum Time in View for a Satellite Visible to a Minimum Elevation Angle of 20 deg* (min) = same as col. 9 with λ_{max} for a 20 deg taken from col. 16.
13. *Earth Central Angle for a Satellite at 0 deg Elevation* (deg) = *Maximum Earth Central Angle* = acos(R_E/r). Alternatively, Maximum Earth Central Angle = $90-\rho$, where ρ is from col. 25 [Eqs. (8-25) and (C-28)].
14. *Earth Central Angle for a Satellite at 5 deg Elevation* (deg) = $90-\varepsilon-\eta$, where η = asin (cosε sinρ), ρ is from col. 66 and ε = 5 deg [Eqs. (8-27), (8-28), and (8-29)].
15. *Earth Central Angle for a Satellite at 10 deg Elevation* (deg) = same as col. 14 but with ε = 10 deg.
16. *Earth Central Angle for a Satellite at 20 deg Elevation* (deg) = same as col. 14 but with ε = 20 deg.
17. *Range to Horizon = Range to a satellite at 0 deg elevation* (km) = $(r^2 - R_E{}^2)^{1/2}$, where R_E = 6,378.14 km is the equatorial radius of the Earth [Eq. (C-27) and Fig. 8-28].
18. *Range to a Satellite at 5 deg Elevation* (km) = *Maximum Range for Satellites with a Minimum Elevation Angle of 5 deg* (km) = R_E (sinλ / sinη), where R_E = 6,378.1366 km is the equatorial radius of the Earth, λ is from col. 14, η = 90 deg – λ – ε, and ε = 5 deg [Eq. (8-30)].
19. *Range to a Satellite at 10 deg Elevation* (km) = same as col. 18 with λ from col. 15 and ε = 10 deg.
20. *Range to a Satellite at 20 deg Elevation* (km) = same as col. 18 with λ from col. 16 and ε = 20 deg.
21. *Nadir Angle for a Satellite at 0 deg Elevation Angle* (deg) = *Max. Nadir Angle for Any Point on the Earth* = *Earth Angular Radius* = asin (R_E / r), where R_E = 6,378.1366 km is the equatorial radius of the Earth [Eq. (8-25)].
22. *Nadir Angle for a Satellite at 5 deg Elevation Angle* (deg) = *Maximum Nadir Angle for Points on the Ground with a Minimum Elevation Angle of 5 deg* = 90 deg – ε – λ, where ε = 5 deg and λ is the Earth central angle from col. 14 [Eq. (8-29)].
23. *Nadir Angle for a Satellite at 10 deg Elevation Angle* (deg) = same as col. 22 with ε = 10 deg.
24. *Nadir Angle for a Satellite at 20 deg Elevation Angle* (deg) = same as col. 22 with ε = 20 deg.
25. *Euler Rotation Rate* (deg/min) = Angular rate of rotation about the Euler axis = ω_{orbit} sin i / sin *EACL*, where ω_{orbit} is the orbital angular velocity from col. 63, *EACL* is the Euler Axis Co-Latitude from

col. 32, and i is the assumed inclination of 0 deg for this column [Eq. (C-25)].

26–31. *Euler Rotation Rate* (deg/min) = same as col. 25 with value of the inclination at the top of the column and Euler Axis Co-Latitude from the corresponding cols. 32–38.

32. *Euler Axis Co-Latitude* (deg) = atan $[\omega_{orbit} \sin i \,/\, (-\omega_{earth} + \omega_{orbit} \cos i)]$, where ω_{orbit} is the orbital angular velocity from col. 63, ω_{earth} is the Earth's angular velocity on its axis = 0.250684446 deg/min, and i is the assumed inclintion of 0 deg for this column [Eqs. (8-79) and (C-24)].

33–38. *Euler Axis Co-Latitude* (deg) = same as col. 32 with value of the inclination at the top of the column.

39. *Inertial Rotation Rate* (deg/min) = Orbit angular rate = same as col. 63. Data is repeated here for convenient comparison with cols. 26–31.

40. *Minimum Atmospheric Scale Height* (km) = $RT \,/\, Mg$, where R is the molar gas constant, T is the temperature, M is the mean molecular weight, and g is the standard gravitational acceleration (see inside front cover). The value is based on the MSIS atmospheric model [Hedin, 1987, 1988, and 1991]. The solar flux value, F10.7, was chosen such that 10% of all measured data are less than this value (65.8×10^{-22} $W \cdot m^{-2} \cdot Hz^{-1}$). See Sec. 9.4.4.

41. *Mean Atmospheric Scale Height* (km) = same as col. 40 but with a mean F10.7 value of 118.7×10^{-22} $W \cdot m^{-2} \cdot Hz^{-1}$.

42. *Maximum Atmospheric Scale Height* (km) = same as col. 40 but with an F10.7 value of 189.0×10^{-22} $W \cdot m^{-2} \cdot Hz^{-1}$. This is the F10.7 value such that 10% of all measured values are above it.

43. *Minimum Atmospheric Density* (kg/m^3), from MSIS atmospheric model [Hedin, 1987, 1988, and 1991]. The solar flux value, F10.7, was chosen such that 10% of all measured data are less than this value (65.8×10^{-22} $W \cdot m^{-2} \cdot Hz^{-1}$). See Sec. 9.4.4. The MSIS model is limited to the region between 90 and 2,000 km. Below 150 km and above 600 km the error increases because less data have been used. All data have been averaged across the Earth with a 30 deg step size in longitude and 20 deg steps in latitude (–80 deg, to +80 deg). This over-represents the Earth's polar regions; however, satellites spend a larger fraction of their time at high latitudes. The solar hour angle was adapted to the individual location on the Earth with UT = 12.00 Noon.

44. *Mean Atmospheric Density* (kg/m^3) = same as col. 43 but with a mean F10.7 value of 118.7×10^{-22} $W \cdot m^{-2} \cdot Hz^{-1}$.

45. *Maximum Atmospheric Density* (kg/m^3) = same as col. 43 but with an F10.7 value of 189.0×10^{-22} $W \cdot m^{-2} \cdot Hz^{-1}$. This is the F10.7 value such that 10% of all measured values are above it.

46. *Minimum ΔV to Maintain Altitude at Solar Minimum* (m/s per year) = $\pi\,(C_D A/m) \times \rho r v/P$, where ρ is from col. 43, v is from col. 62, P is from col. 69 expressed in years, and the ballistic coefficient, $m/C_D A$, is assumed to be 50 kg/m^2. ΔV estimates are not meaningful above 1,500 km [Eq. (9-36)].

47. *Maximum ΔV to Maintain Altitude at Solar Maximum* (m/s per year) = same as col. 46 with ρ from col. 45; Ballistic coefficient $m/C_D A$ = 50 kg/m^2.

48. *Minimum ΔV to Maintain Altitude at Solar Minimum* (m/s per year) = same as col. 46 with ρ from col. 43; Ballistic coefficient $m/C_D A$ = 200 kg/m^2.

49. *Maximum ΔV to Maintain Altitude at Solar Maximum* (m/s per year) = same as col. 46 with ρ from col. 45; Ballistic coefficient $m/C_D A$ = 200 kg/m^2.

50. *Orbit Decay Rate at Solar Minimum* (km/year) = $-2\pi\,(C_D A/m)\,\rho\, r^2/P$, where ρ is from col. 43, P is from col. 69 (expressed in years), and the ballistic coefficient, $m/C_D A$, is assumed to be 50 kg/m^2. Orbit decay rates are not meaningful above 1,500 km [Eq. (9-34)].

51. *Orbit Decay Rate at Solar Maximum* (km/year) = same as col. 50, with ρ from col. 45 and the ballistic coefficient, $m/C_D A$, assumed to be 50 kg/m^2.

52. *Orbit Decay Rate at Solar Minimum* (km/year) = same as col. 50 with ρ from col. 43, and the ballistic coefficient, $m/C_D A$, assumed to be 200 kg/m^2.

53. *Orbit Decay Rate at Solar Maximum* (km/year) = same as col. 50, with ρ from col. 45 and the ballistic coefficient, $m/C_D A$, assumed to be 200 kg/m^2.

54. *Estimated Orbit Lifetime at Solar Minimum* (days) = Data was produced using the software package SatLife. Ballistic coefficient, $m/C_D A$, assumed to be 50 kg/m^2.

55. *Estimated Orbit Lifetime at Solar Maximum* (days) = same as col. 54 with the ballistic coefficient, $m/C_D A$, assumed to be 50 kg/m^2.

56. *Estimated Orbit Lifetime at Solar Minimum* (days) = same as col. 54 with the ballistic coefficient, $m/C_D A$, assumed to be 200 kg/m^2.

57. *Estimated Orbit Lifetime at Solar Maximum* (days) = same as col. 54 with the ballistic coefficient, $m/C_D A$, assumed to be 200 kg/m^2.

58. *Plane Change ΔV* [(km/s)/deg] = $2\, v_{circ} \sin(0.5\ \text{deg})$, where v_{circ} is from col. 62. Assumes circular orbit and linear sine function; [Eq. (9-78)]

59. *ΔV Required for a 1 km Altitude Change* (m/s) = assumes a Hohmann Transfer with $r_B - r_A = 1$ km; [Eqs. (9-69), and (9-70)].

60. *Maximum Angular Rate As Seen from a Ground Station* (deg/s) = $2\pi r/hP$, where $h \equiv r - R_E$ is the

altitude and P is from col. 69. This is the angular rate as seen from the surface of a non-rotating Earth of a satellite in a circular orbit passing directly overhead. (See col. 63 for the angular velocity as seen from the center of the Earth.) [Eqs. (8-74) and (C-32)].

61. *Sun-Synchronous Inclination* (deg) = acos (–4.773 513 28 × 10^{-15} $r^{7/2}$); assumes circular orbit with node rotation rate of 0.985609 deg/day to follow the mean motion of the Sun. Above 6,000 km altitude there are no Sun synchronous circular orbits [Eq. (C-34)].

62. *Circular Velocity* (km/s) = $(\mu_E / r)^{1/2}$ = 631.348 110 $r^{-1/2}$ [Eq. (9-8)].

63. *Orbit Angular Velocity* (deg/min) = 360/P = 2.170 414 925 × $10^6 r^{-3/2}$, where P is from col. 69. This is the angular velocity with respect to the center of the Earth for a circular orbit. (See col. 60 for angular rate with respect to ground stations) [Eqs. (9-15) and (9-17)].

64. *Escape Velocity* (km/s) = $(2\mu/r)^{1/2}$ = 892.861 059 $r^{-1/2} = (2)^{1/2} \times v_{circ}$ [Eq. (9-7)].

65. *ΔV Required to De-Orbit* (m/s) = the velocity change needed to transform the assumed circular orbit to an elliptical orbit with an unchanged apogee and a perigee of 50 km [Eqs. (9-85a), and (9-85b)]

66. *Angular Radius of the Earth* (deg) = asin (R_E / r), where R_E = 6,378.14 km is the equatorial radius of the Earth [Eq. (8-25)].

67. *One Degree Field of View Mapped onto the Earth's Surface at Nadir from Altitude h* (km) = The length on the Earth's curved surface of a 1 deg arc projected at nadir from this altitude. Note: This data is *very* nonlinear [Eqs. (8-27), (8-28), and (8-29)].

68. *Range to Horizon* (km) = same as col. 17 = $(r^2 - R_E{}^2)^{1/2}$, where R_E = 6,378.1366 km is the equatorial radius of the Earth. For the range to points other than the true horizon (i.e., $\varepsilon \neq 0$ deg) use cols. 18, 19, and 20 [Eq. (8-30)].

69. *Period* (min) = 1.658 669 0213 × 10^{-4} $r^{3/2}$ = (1/60) × $2\pi\ (r^3/\mu)^{1/2}$. Assumes a circular orbit, r is measured in km, and μ = 398,600.4356 km^3/s^2. Note that period is the same for an eccentric orbit with semimajor axis = r; [Eq. (9-4b)].

70. *Maximum Eclipse* (minutes) = $(\rho / 180\ \text{deg})P$, where ρ is from col. 66 and P is from col. 69. This is the maximum eclipse for a circular orbit. Eclipses at this altitude in an eccentric orbit can be longer. [Eq. (C-37)]

71. *Revolutions per Day* (#) = 1,436.068 34/P, where P is from col. 69. Note that this is revolutions per sidereal day, where the *sidereal day* is the day relative to the fixed stars which is approximately 4 minutes shorter than the solar day of 1,440 minutes. [Eq. (C-35)]

72. *Node Spacing* (deg) = 360 deg × (P / 1,436.068 34), where P is from col. 69. This is the spacing in longitude between successive ascending or descending nodes for a satellite in a circular orbit [Eq. (C-36)].

73. *Node Precession Rate* (deg/day) = –2.064 745 722 × 10^{14} $r^{-7/2}$ cos i = $-1.5\ n\ J_2\ (R_E/a)^2\ (\cos i)\ (1 - e^2)^{-2}$, where i is the inclination, e the eccentricity (which is set to zero), n is the mean motion [= $(\mu/a^3)^{1/2}$], a the semimajor axis, and J_2 the dominant zonal coefficient in the expansion of the Legendre polynomial describing the geopotential. This is the angle through which the orbit rotates in inertial space in a 24 hour period. Assumes a circular orbit; r is in km in the first expression [Eq. (C-33)].

Live Calc For other altitudes, plots of the data, or orbits around other celestial bodies, see the book website.

References

Get Ref **For annotated bibliography of Appendix I, see the book website.**

Hedin, Alan E. 1987. "MSIS-86 Thermospheric Model." *J. Geophys. Res.*, 92, No. A5, pp. 4649–4662.

———. 1988. "The Atmospheric Model In The Region 90 to 2,000 km." *Adv. Space Res.*, 8, No. 5–6, pp. (5)9–(5)25, Pergamon Press.

———. 1991. "Extension of the MSIS Thermosphere Model into the Middle and Lower Atmosphere." *J. Geophys. Res.*, 96, No. A2, pp. 1159–1172.

Table I-1. Earth Satellite Parameters.

	1	2	3	4	5	6	7	8	9	10	11	12
	INSTANTANEOUS ACCESS AREA				AREA ACCESS RATE				MAXIMUM TIME IN VIEW			
Alt. (km)	0 deg elevation (10^6 km^2)	5 deg elevation (10^6 km^2)	10 deg elevation (10^6 km^2)	20 deg elevation (10^6 km^2)	0 deg elevation (10^3 km^2/s)	5 deg elevation (10^3 km^2/s)	10 deg elevation (10^3 km^2/s)	20 deg elevation (10^3 km^2/s)	0 deg elevation (min)	5 deg elevation (min)	10 deg elevation (min)	20 deg elevation (min)
0	0.00	0.00	0.00	0.00	0.00	0.00	0.00	0.00	0.00	0.00	0.00	0.00
100	3.95	1.51	0.67	0.21	17.24	10.71	7.15	3.96	4.84	3.00	2.00	1.11
150	5.87	2.66	1.31	0.44	20.76	14.01	9.86	5.69	5.98	4.02	2.82	1.63
175	6.83	3.26	1.67	0.58	22.23	15.42	11.07	6.50	6.49	4.48	3.21	1.88
200	7.77	3.89	2.06	0.73	23.56	16.73	12.20	7.28	6.96	4.92	3.58	2.13
225	8.71	4.52	2.47	0.90	24.78	17.93	13.26	8.03	7.42	5.34	3.94	2.38
250	9.64	5.17	2.89	1.08	25.90	19.04	14.27	8.76	7.85	5.74	4.29	2.62
275	10.57	5.82	3.32	1.28	26.93	20.08	15.21	9.45	8.27	6.13	4.62	2.87
300	11.48	6.48	3.77	1.48	27.89	21.06	16.11	10.12	8.67	6.50	4.95	3.10
325	12.39	7.14	4.23	1.70	28.79	21.97	16.96	10.76	9.06	6.87	5.28	3.34
350	13.30	7.81	4.70	1.92	29.63	22.83	17.76	11.38	9.44	7.22	5.59	3.57
375	14.19	8.48	5.17	2.15	30.42	23.65	18.53	11.98	9.81	7.57	5.90	3.80
400	15.08	9.15	5.66	2.39	31.15	24.41	19.26	12.56	10.17	7.91	6.21	4.03
450	16.85	10.50	6.64	2.89	32.50	25.83	20.62	13.66	10.88	8.57	6.80	4.49
500	18.58	11.85	7.64	3.42	33.71	27.10	21.86	14.68	11.55	9.21	7.38	4.93
550	20.29	13.20	8.66	3.97	34.78	28.25	22.99	15.63	12.21	9.83	7.95	5.37
600	21.98	14.54	9.69	4.53	35.75	29.30	24.03	16.52	12.86	10.43	8.50	5.81
650	23.64	15.88	10.72	5.12	36.62	30.25	24.99	17.36	13.48	11.02	9.04	6.24
700	25.28	17.21	11.76	5.72	37.40	31.12	25.87	18.14	14.10	11.60	9.58	6.66
750	26.89	18.53	12.81	6.33	38.11	31.91	26.68	18.87	14.71	12.17	10.10	7.08
800	28.49	19.85	13.85	6.95	38.75	32.63	27.43	19.56	15.30	12.74	10.62	7.50
850	30.06	21.15	14.90	7.58	39.33	33.29	28.12	20.20	15.89	13.29	11.13	7.92
900	31.61	22.44	15.94	8.21	39.85	33.90	28.76	20.80	16.48	13.84	11.64	8.33
950	33.14	23.73	16.98	8.86	40.32	34.45	29.35	21.37	17.05	14.38	12.14	8.74
1,000	34.64	25.00	18.02	9.51	40.74	34.96	29.89	21.90	17.62	14.92	12.64	9.15
1,100	37.60	27.51	20.09	10.82	41.47	35.85	30.86	22.86	18.75	15.99	13.63	9.97
1,200	40.47	29.97	22.13	12.14	42.05	36.58	31.69	23.71	19.87	17.04	14.60	10.78
1,300	43.28	32.38	24.15	13.47	42.51	37.19	32.40	24.46	20.97	18.07	15.57	11.58
1,400	46.01	34.75	26.15	14.80	42.86	37.70	32.99	25.11	22.07	19.11	16.53	12.39
1,500	48.67	37.07	28.12	16.14	43.12	38.10	33.50	25.69	23.16	20.13	17.48	13.19
2,000	61.02	47.97	37.51	22.69	43.43	39.07	34.93	27.59	28.56	25.21	22.21	17.19
2,500	71.98	57.81	46.14	28.96	42.71	38.89	35.19	28.39	33.98	30.30	26.96	21.23
3,000	81.77	66.70	54.05	34.86	41.47	38.10	34.78	28.52	39.46	35.44	31.76	25.34
3,500	90.57	74.76	61.29	40.38	39.95	36.98	33.99	28.22	45.04	40.68	36.65	29.53
4,000	98.52	82.10	67.92	45.52	38.33	35.68	32.98	27.68	50.74	46.03	41.65	33.83
4,500	105.74	88.79	74.02	50.31	36.68	34.30	31.86	26.97	56.56	51.50	46.77	38.23
5,000	112.32	94.93	79.63	54.77	35.05	32.92	30.70	26.18	62.52	57.10	52.00	42.74
6,000	123.90	105.78	89.62	62.81	31.97	30.22	28.37	24.49	74.85	68.67	62.82	52.08
7,000	133.74	115.06	98.23	69.84	29.18	27.73	26.16	22.80	87.73	80.77	74.14	61.86
8,000	142.22	123.10	105.71	76.02	26.70	25.48	24.13	21.20	101.15	93.37	85.94	72.07
9,000	149.59	130.11	112.27	81.48	24.51	23.47	22.30	19.72	115.10	106.48	98.22	82.70
10,000	156.06	136.29	118.07	86.35	22.57	21.67	20.66	18.36	129.56	120.08	110.96	93.74
15,000	179.34	158.65	139.22	104.35	15.69	15.21	14.63	13.25	209.23	195.03	181.21	154.73
20,000	193.80	172.65	152.56	115.89	11.63	11.34	10.97	10.04	300.06	280.54	261.44	224.50
20,184*	194.23	173.06	152.95	116.24	11.52	11.23	10.87	9.95	303.60	283.87	264.57	227.22
25,000	203.65	182.23	161.73	123.91	9.05	8.85	8.60	7.92	400.90	375.52	350.60	302.13
30,000	210.79	189.19	168.42	129.80	7.29	7.15	6.96	6.44	510.87	479.15	447.92	386.92
35,786†	216.94	195.21	174.21	134.93	5.86	5.76	5.62	5.23	648.62	609.00	569.90	493.27
378,022‡	251.36	229.12	207.11	164.45	0.22	0.21	0.21	0.20	19,556	18,459	17,363	15,176

*GPS Altitude †GEO ‡Moon and L4, L5 Lagrange Points

Live Calc

See front of table for formulas and sources. See the book website for an Excel version of this table that allows you to plot the variables vs. altitude, to adjust the altitude range under consideration, and to determine these parameters for orbits around other celestrial bodies.

Table I-1. Earth Satellite Parameters. Continued

13	14	15	16	17	18	19	20	21	22	23	24	
EARTH CENTRAL ANGLE				RANGE				NADIR ANGLE				
0 deg elevation (deg)	5 deg elevation (deg)	10 deg elevation (deg)	20 deg elevation (deg)	0 deg elevation (km)	5 deg elevation (km)	10 deg elevation (km)	20 deg elevation (km)	0 deg elevation (deg)	5 deg elevation (deg)	10 deg elevation (deg)	20 deg elevation (deg)	Alt. (km)
0.00	0.00	0.00	0.00	0	0	0	0	90.00	85.00	80.00	70.00	0
10.08	6.24	4.16	2.30	1,134	707	477	277	79.92	78.76	75.84	67.70	100
12.31	8.27	5.81	3.35	1,391	942	671	406	77.69	76.73	74.19	66.65	150
13.27	9.17	6.56	3.85	1,504	1,048	761	468	76.73	75.83	73.44	66.15	175
14.16	10.00	7.28	4.34	1,610	1,147	846	530	75.84	75.00	72.72	65.66	200
15.00	10.79	7.96	4.81	1,709	1,241	929	590	75.00	74.21	72.04	65.19	225
15.79	11.54	8.62	5.28	1,803	1,331	1,009	649	74.21	73.46	71.38	64.72	250
16.53	12.25	9.25	5.73	1,893	1,417	1,086	707	73.47	72.75	70.75	64.27	275
17.24	12.93	9.85	6.17	1,979	1,500	1,160	764	72.76	72.07	70.15	63.83	300
17.91	13.58	10.44	6.60	2,062	1,580	1,233	820	72.09	71.42	69.56	63.40	325
18.56	14.20	11.00	7.02	2,142	1,657	1,304	876	71.44	70.80	69.00	62.98	350
19.18	14.80	11.55	7.44	2,219	1,732	1,373	930	70.82	70.20	68.45	62.56	375
19.78	15.38	12.08	7.84	2,294	1,805	1,440	984	70.22	69.62	67.92	62.16	400
20.92	16.48	13.09	8.63	2,438	1,944	1,570	1,090	69.08	68.52	66.91	61.37	450
21.98	17.52	14.05	9.38	2,575	2,078	1,695	1,193	68.02	67.48	65.95	60.62	500
22.98	18.49	14.96	10.11	2,705	2,206	1,816	1,294	67.02	66.51	65.04	59.89	550
23.93	19.42	15.82	10.81	2,831	2,329	1,932	1,392	66.07	65.58	64.18	59.19	600
24.84	20.30	16.65	11.48	2,952	2,448	2,045	1,489	65.16	64.70	63.35	58.52	650
25.70	21.15	17.45	12.14	3,069	2,563	2,155	1,584	64.30	63.85	62.55	57.86	700
26.52	21.95	18.21	12.77	3,183	2,675	2,262	1,677	63.48	63.05	61.79	57.23	750
27.31	22.73	18.95	13.39	3,293	2,784	2,367	1,769	62.69	62.27	61.05	56.61	800
28.07	23.47	19.66	13.98	3,401	2,890	2,469	1,859	61.93	61.53	60.34	56.02	850
28.80	24.19	20.34	14.56	3,506	2,994	2,569	1,948	61.20	60.81	59.66	55.44	900
29.50	24.88	21.00	15.13	3,608	3,095	2,667	2,035	60.50	60.12	59.00	54.87	950
30.18	25.55	21.64	15.68	3,709	3,194	2,763	2,121	59.82	59.45	58.36	54.32	1,000
31.47	26.83	22.87	16.73	3,904	3,388	2,951	2,291	58.53	58.17	57.13	53.27	1,100
32.69	28.02	24.02	17.73	4,092	3,574	3,132	2,456	57.31	56.98	55.98	52.27	1,200
33.83	29.15	25.11	18.69	4,275	3,755	3,308	2,618	56.17	55.85	54.89	51.31	1,300
34.91	30.23	26.14	19.60	4,452	3,931	3,480	2,776	55.09	54.77	53.86	50.40	1,400
35.94	31.24	27.13	20.47	4,624	4,102	3,648	2,932	54.06	53.76	52.87	49.53	1,500
40.42	35.68	31.43	24.33	5,433	4,905	4,437	3,673	49.58	49.32	48.57	45.67	2,000
44.08	39.30	34.97	27.54	6,176	5,645	5,167	4,368	45.92	45.70	45.03	42.46	2,500
47.15	42.35	37.95	30.28	6,875	6,342	5,856	5,032	42.85	42.65	42.05	39.72	3,000
49.78	44.97	40.52	32.65	7,543	7,008	6,516	5,671	40.22	40.03	39.48	37.35	3,500
52.08	47.25	42.75	34.72	8,187	7,650	7,154	6,291	37.92	37.75	37.25	35.28	4,000
54.10	49.26	44.73	36.57	8,812	8,274	7,774	6,897	35.90	35.74	35.27	33.43	4,500
55.91	51.05	46.49	38.21	9,422	8,883	8,380	7,490	34.09	33.95	33.51	31.79	5,000
58.98	54.12	49.51	41.04	10,608	10,067	9,558	8,649	31.02	30.88	30.49	28.96	6,000
61.53	56.64	52.00	43.38	11,760	11,217	10,704	9,779	28.47	28.36	28.00	26.62	7,000
63.67	58.77	54.10	45.36	12,886	12,342	11,826	10,888	26.33	26.23	25.90	24.64	8,000
65.50	60.60	55.89	47.06	13,993	13,448	12,929	11,981	24.50	24.40	24.11	22.94	9,000
67.08	62.17	57.45	48.53	15,085	14,540	14,018	13,061	22.92	22.83	22.55	21.47	10,000
72.64	67.71	62.91	53.72	20,405	19,856	19,327	18,339	17.36	17.29	17.09	16.28	15,000
76.01	71.06	66.22	56.87	25,595	25,046	24,512	23,507	13.99	13.94	13.78	13.13	20,000
76.11	71.16	66.32	56.96	25,785	25,235	24,701	23,696	13.89	13.84	13.68	13.04	20,184*
78.27	73.32	68.45	58.99	30,723	30,172	29,635	28,619	11.73	11.68	11.55	11.01	25,000
79.90	74.94	70.06	60.52	35,815	35,263	34,724	33,700	10.10	10.06	9.94	9.48	30,000
81.30	76.33	71.43	61.83	41,679	41,127	40,586	39,555	8.70	8.67	8.57	8.17	35,786†
89.05	84.05	79.06	69.11	384,348	383,793	383,242	382,173	0.95	0.95	0.94	0.89	378,022‡

Table I-1. Earth Satellite Parameters. Continued

	25	26	27	28	29	30	31	32	33	34	35	36	37	38
	EULER ROTATION RATE (deg/min)							EULER AXIS CO–LATITUDE (deg)						
Alt. (km)	Inc = 0.0	Inc = 30.0	Inc = 60.0	Inc = 90.0	Inc = 120.0	Inc = 150.0	Inc = 180.0	Inc = 0.0	Inc = 30.0	Inc = 60.0	Inc = 90.0	Inc = 120.0	Inc = 150.0	Inc = 180.0
0	4.010	4.046	4.141	4.268	4.392	4.480	4.511	0.00	31.78	63.01	93.37	122.83	151.60	180.00
100	3.912	3.948	4.043	4.170	4.293	4.382	4.413	0.00	31.82	63.08	93.45	122.90	151.64	180.00
150	3.864	3.900	3.995	4.123	4.246	4.334	4.365	0.00	31.84	63.12	93.49	122.93	151.66	180.00
175	3.841	3.876	3.972	4.099	4.222	4.310	4.342	0.00	31.85	63.13	93.51	122.95	151.67	180.00
200	3.817	3.853	3.949	4.076	4.199	4.287	4.319	0.00	31.86	63.15	93.53	122.96	151.68	180.00
225	3.794	3.830	3.926	4.053	4.176	4.264	4.295	0.00	31.88	63.17	93.55	122.98	151.69	180.00
250	3.771	3.807	3.903	4.030	4.153	4.241	4.272	0.00	31.89	63.19	93.57	123.00	151.69	180.00
275	3.749	3.784	3.880	4.007	4.131	4.218	4.250	0.00	31.90	63.21	93.58	123.01	151.70	180.00
300	3.726	3.762	3.858	3.985	4.108	4.196	4.228	0.00	31.91	63.23	93.61	123.03	151.71	180.00
325	3.704	3.740	3.836	3.963	4.086	4.174	4.205	0.00	31.92	63.25	93.63	123.05	151.72	180.00
350	3.682	3.718	3.814	3.941	4.064	4.152	4.183	0.00	31.93	63.26	93.65	123.06	151.73	180.00
375	3.660	3.696	3.792	3.919	4.042	4.130	4.161	0.00	31.94	63.28	93.67	123.08	151.74	180.00
400	3.639	3.674	3.770	3.897	4.021	4.108	4.139	0.00	31.96	63.30	93.69	123.10	151.75	180.00
450	3.596	3.632	3.728	3.855	3.978	4.066	4.098	0.00	31.98	63.34	93.73	123.13	151.77	180.00
500	3.554	3.590	3.686	3.813	3.936	4.024	4.056	0.00	32.00	63.38	93.77	123.16	151.79	180.00
550	3.513	3.549	3.645	3.772	3.895	3.983	4.014	0.00	32.02	63.42	93.81	123.20	151.80	180.00
600	3.473	3.508	3.605	3.732	3.855	3.942	3.973	0.00	32.05	63.45	93.85	123.23	151.82	180.00
650	3.433	3.469	3.565	3.692	3.815	3.903	3.935	0.00	32.07	63.49	93.89	123.26	151.84	180.00
700	3.394	3.430	3.526	3.653	3.776	3.864	3.895	0.00	32.09	63.53	93.94	123.30	151.86	180.00
750	3.356	3.392	3.488	3.615	3.738	3.826	3.857	0.00	32.12	63.57	93.98	123.33	151.88	180.00
800	3.318	3.354	3.450	3.578	3.701	3.788	3.819	0.00	32.14	63.61	94.02	123.36	151.90	180.00
850	3.281	3.317	3.413	3.541	3.664	3.751	3.783	0.00	32.17	63.65	94.06	123.40	151.92	180.00
900	3.245	3.281	3.377	3.505	3.627	3.715	3.746	0.00	32.19	63.69	94.10	123.43	151.93	180.00
950	3.209	3.245	3.342	3.469	3.592	3.679	3.710	0.00	32.21	63.73	94.14	123.47	151.95	180.00
1,000	3.174	3.210	3.306	3.434	3.557	3.644	3.674	0.00	32.24	63.77	94.19	123.50	151.97	180.00
1,100	3.106	3.142	3.238	3.366	3.488	3.576	3.607	0.00	32.29	63.84	94.27	123.57	152.01	180.00
1,200	3.039	3.075	3.172	3.300	3.422	3.509	3.541	0.00	32.34	63.92	94.36	123.64	152.05	180.00
1,300	2.975	3.011	3.108	3.236	3.358	3.445	3.476	0.00	32.39	64.01	94.44	123.71	152.09	180.00
1,400	2.913	2.950	3.046	3.174	3.296	3.383	3.415	0.00	32.44	64.09	94.53	123.78	152.12	180.00
1,500	2.853	2.890	2.986	3.114	3.237	3.323	3.354	0.00	32.49	64.17	94.62	123.85	152.16	180.00
2,000	2.580	2.616	2.714	2.841	2.964	3.050	3.081	0.00	32.75	64.59	95.06	124.20	152.36	180.00
2,500	2.344	2.381	2.479	2.607	2.729	2.814	2.845	0.00	33.02	65.03	95.52	124.56	152.55	180.00
3,000	2.139	2.176	2.275	2.403	2.525	2.610	2.640	0.00	33.30	65.48	95.99	124.93	152.75	180.00
3,500	1.960	1.998	2.097	2.225	2.346	2.431	2.461	0.00	33.60	65.94	96.47	125.31	152.96	180.00
4,000	1.802	1.840	1.940	2.068	2.189	2.273	2.303	0.00	33.91	66.43	96.96	125.69	153.16	180.00
4,500	1.662	1.701	1.801	1.929	2.050	2.134	2.163	0.00	34.23	66.92	97.47	126.08	153.37	180.00
5,000	1.538	1.576	1.677	1.806	1.926	2.009	2.039	0.00	34.56	67.44	97.98	126.47	153.58	180.00
6,000	1.325	1.365	1.467	1.596	1.715	1.797	1.826	0.00	35.27	68.51	99.04	127.27	154.00	180.00
7,000	1.152	1.192	1.296	1.425	1.543	1.625	1.653	0.00	36.04	69.64	100.13	128.09	154.42	180.00
8,000	1.008	1.049	1.154	1.284	1.401	1.481	1.510	0.00	36.86	70.84	101.26	128.91	154.85	180.00
9,000	0.887	0.930	1.036	1.165	1.282	1.361	1.389	0.00	37.75	72.10	102.42	129.75	155.28	180.00
10,000	0.785	0.828	0.936	1.065	1.181	1.259	1.286	0.00	38.71	73.42	103.61	130.59	155.71	180.00
15,000	0.444	0.493	0.609	0.738	0.848	0.920	0.945	0.00	44.72	80.88	109.85	134.83	157.83	180.00
20,000	0.256	0.315	0.439	0.565	0.668	0.734	0.757	0.00	53.41	89.66	116.33	138.96	159.83	180.00
20,184*	0.251	0.311	0.434	0.561	0.663	0.729	0.752	0.00	53.79	90.00	116.57	139.11	159.90	180.00
25,000	0.140	0.214	0.343	0.464	0.560	0.620	0.641	0.00	65.86	99.31	122.70	142.83	161.66	180.00
30,000	0.062	0.158	0.287	0.401	0.489	0.545	0.564	0.00	82.63	109.19	128.71	146.36	163.31	180.00
35,786†	0.000	0.130	0.251	0.355	0.434	0.484	0.501	0.00	105.00	120.00	135.00	150.00	165.00	180.00
378,022‡	0.240	0.243	0.246	0.251	0.255	0.259	0.261	0.00	178.93	178.17	177.92	178.23	178.99	180.00

Live Calc

*GPS Altitude †GEO ‡Moon and L4, L5 Lagrange Points

See front of table for formulas and sources. See the book website for an Excel version of this table that allows you to plot the variables vs. altitude, to adjust the altitude range under consideration, and to determine these parameters for orbits around other celestial bodies.

Table I-1. Earth Satellite Parameters. Continued

39	40	41	42	43	44	45	46	47	48	49	
Inertial Rot. Rate (deg/min)	ATMOSPHERIC SCALE HEIGHT (km)			ATMOSPHERIC DENSITY			ΔV TO MAINTAIN ALTITUDE				Alt. (km)
	Solar Min	Solar Mean	Solar Max	Minimum (kg/m³)	Mean (kg/m³)	Maximum (kg/m³)	Solar Min 50 kg/m² (m/s)/yr	Solar Max 50 kg/m² (m/s)/yr	Solar Min 200 kg/m² (m/s)/yr	Solar Max 200 kg/m² (m/s)/yr	
4.261	8.6	8.6	8.6	1.20×10^{0}	1.20×10^{0}	1.20×10^{0}	2.37×10^{13}	2.37×10^{13}	5.93×10^{12}	5.93×10^{12}	0
4.163	5.8	5.8	5.8	5.71×10^{-7}	5.69×10^{-7}	5.67×10^{-7}	1.11×10^{7}	1.10×10^{7}	2.77×10^{6}	2.75×10^{6}	100
4.115	21.7	24.6	27.9	1.90×10^{-9}	2.02×10^{-9}	2.21×10^{-9}	3.65×10^{4}	4.25×10^{4}	9.12×10^{3}	1.06×10^{4}	150
4.091	25.5	29.9	34.8	6.42×10^{-10}	7.66×10^{-10}	9.21×10^{-10}	1.23×10^{4}	1.77×10^{4}	3.08×10^{3}	4.41×10^{3}	175
4.068	29.4	35.3	41.6	2.18×10^{-10}	2.90×10^{-10}	3.84×10^{-10}	4.16×10^{3}	7.34×10^{3}	1.04×10^{3}	1.83×10^{3}	200
4.045	31.7	38.4	45.5	9.64×10^{-11}	1.46×10^{-10}	2.12×10^{-10}	1.84×10^{3}	4.04×10^{3}	4.59×10^{2}	1.01×10^{3}	225
4.022	34.1	41.4	49.4	4.27×10^{-11}	7.30×10^{-11}	1.17×10^{-10}	8.10×10^{2}	2.22×10^{3}	2.02×10^{2}	5.55×10^{2}	250
3.999	35.9	43.6	51.9	2.14×10^{-11}	4.10×10^{-11}	7.17×10^{-11}	4.05×10^{2}	1.35×10^{3}	1.01×10^{2}	3.39×10^{2}	275
3.977	37.7	45.8	54.5	1.07×10^{-11}	2.30×10^{-11}	4.39×10^{-11}	2.02×10^{2}	8.27×10^{2}	5.05×10^{1}	2.07×10^{2}	300
3.955	39.1	47.4	56.4	5.83×10^{-12}	1.38×10^{-11}	2.85×10^{-11}	1.09×10^{2}	5.35×10^{2}	2.73×10^{1}	1.34×10^{2}	325
3.933	40.5	49.0	58.3	3.17×10^{-12}	8.33×10^{-12}	1.85×10^{-11}	5.92×10^{1}	3.46×10^{2}	1.48×10^{1}	8.65×10^{1}	350
3.911	42.0	50.3	59.7	1.81×10^{-12}	5.24×10^{-12}	1.25×10^{-11}	3.38×10^{1}	2.32×10^{2}	8.44×10^{0}	5.81×10^{1}	375
3.889	43.5	51.7	61.1	1.04×10^{-12}	3.29×10^{-12}	8.43×10^{-12}	1.92×10^{1}	1.56×10^{2}	4.81×10^{0}	3.91×10^{1}	400
3.847	48.1	54.2	63.5	3.68×10^{-13}	1.39×10^{-12}	4.05×10^{-12}	6.77×10^{0}	7.46×10^{1}	1.69×10^{0}	1.87×10^{1}	450
3.805	56.6	57.3	65.6	1.40×10^{-13}	6.15×10^{-13}	2.03×10^{-12}	2.56×10^{0}	3.72×10^{1}	6.40×10^{-1}	9.29×10^{0}	500
3.764	71.1	62.0	67.9	5.76×10^{-14}	2.84×10^{-13}	1.05×10^{-12}	1.05×10^{0}	1.91×10^{1}	2.61×10^{-1}	4.79×10^{0}	550
3.723	92.1	69.3	70.7	2.61×10^{-14}	1.37×10^{-13}	5.63×10^{-13}	4.70×10^{-1}	1.01×10^{1}	1.17×10^{-1}	2.54×10^{0}	600
3.684	116.8	80.5	74.7	1.32×10^{-14}	6.87×10^{-14}	3.08×10^{-13}	2.36×10^{-1}	5.51×10^{0}	5.91×10^{-2}	1.38×10^{0}	650
3.645	141.3	95.9	80.5	7.55×10^{-15}	3.63×10^{-14}	1.73×10^{-13}	1.34×10^{-1}	3.07×10^{0}	3.35×10^{-2}	7.68×10^{-1}	700
3.606	163.7	114.6	88.6	4.81×10^{-15}	2.02×10^{-14}	9.95×10^{-14}	8.48×10^{-2}	1.75×10^{0}	2.12×10^{-2}	4.39×10^{-1}	750
3.569	183.87	134.80	99.50	3.34×10^{-15}	1.21×10^{-14}	5.88×10^{-14}	5.86×10^{-2}	1.03×10^{0}	1.46×10^{-2}	2.57×10^{-1}	800
3.532	202.60	154.77	113.09	2.47×10^{-15}	7.69×10^{-15}	3.57×10^{-14}	4.30×10^{-2}	6.22×10^{-1}	1.07×10^{-2}	1.55×10^{-1}	850
3.496	220.77	173.43	128.76	1.90×10^{-15}	5.24×10^{-15}	2.25×10^{-14}	3.28×10^{-2}	3.88×10^{-1}	8.20×10^{-3}	9.70×10^{-2}	900
3.460	238.66	190.33	145.55	1.50×10^{-15}	3.78×10^{-15}	1.46×10^{-14}	2.57×10^{-2}	2.51×10^{-1}	6.47×10^{-3}	6.28×10^{-2}	950
3.425	256.19	205.52	162.51	1.20×10^{-15}	2.86×10^{-15}	9.91×10^{-15}	2.05×10^{-2}	1.69×10^{-1}	5.12×10^{-3}	4.22×10^{-2}	1,000
3.356	—	—	—	—	—	—	—	—	—	—	1,100
3.290	—	—	—	—	—	—	—	—	—	—	1,200
3.226	—	—	—	—	—	—	—	—	—	—	1,300
3.164	—	—	—	—	—	—	—	—	—	—	1,400
3.104	—	—	—	—	—	—	—	—	—	—	1,500
2.830	—	—	—	—	—	—	—	—	—	—	2,000
2.595	—	—	—	—	—	—	—	—	—	—	2,500
2.390	—	—	—	—	—	—	—	—	—	—	3,000
2.211	—	—	—	—	—	—	—	—	—	—	3,500
2.053	—	—	—	—	—	—	—	—	—	—	4,000
1.913	—	—	—	—	—	—	—	—	—	—	4,500
1.788	—	—	—	—	—	—	—	—	—	—	5,000
1.576	—	—	—	—	—	—	—	—	—	—	6,000
1.403	—	—	—	—	—	—	—	—	—	—	7,000
1.259	—	—	—	—	—	—	—	—	—	—	8,000
1.138	—	—	—	—	—	—	—	—	—	—	9,000
1.035	—	—	—	—	—	—	—	—	—	—	10,000
0.694	—	—	—	—	—	—	—	—	—	—	15,000
0.507	—	—	—	—	—	—	—	—	—	—	20,000
0.501	—	—	—	—	—	—	—	—	—	—	20,184*
0.390	—	—	—	—	—	—	—	—	—	—	25,000
0.313	—	—	—	—	—	—	—	—	—	—	30,000
0.251	—	—	—	—	—	—	—	—	—	—	35,786†
0.009	—	—	—	—	—	—	—	—	—	—	378,022‡

Table I-1. Earth Satellite Parameters. Continued

	50	51	52	53	54	55	56	57	58	59	60	61
	ORBIT DECAY RATE				ESTIMATED ORBIT LIFETIME				VELOCITY–RELATED PARAMETERS			
Alt. (km)	Solar Min 50 kg/m² (km/yr)	Solar Max 50 kg/m² (km/yr)	Solar Min 200 kg/m² (km/yr)	Solar Max 200 kg/m² (km/yr)	Solar Min 50 kg/m² (days)	Solar Max 50 kg/m² (days)	Solar Min 200 kg/m² (days)	Solar Max 200 kg/m² (days)	Plane Change ΔV (m/s)/deg	ΔV Req'd for a 1 km Alt Chg (m/s)	Max Ang Rate Gnd Stn (deg/s)	Sun Syn–chronous Inclination (deg)
0	3.83×10^{13}	3.83×10^{13}	9.57×10^{12}	9.58×10^{12}	—	—	—	—	137.97	0.62	—	95.68
100	1.83×10^{7}	1.82×10^{7}	4.58×10^{6}	4.54×10^{6}	0.06	0.06	0.06	0.06	136.90	0.61	4.49	96.00
150	6.10×10^{4}	7.10×10^{4}	1.52×10^{4}	1.78×10^{4}	0.23	0.24	0.57	0.49	136.38	0.60	2.98	96.16
175	2.07×10^{4}	2.97×10^{4}	5.18×10^{3}	7.42×10^{3}	0.67	0.54	1.90	1.43	136.12	0.59	2.55	96.24
200	7.03×10^{3}	1.24×10^{4}	1.76×10^{3}	3.10×10^{3}	1.97	1.23	6.34	4.19	135.86	0.59	2.23	96.33
225	3.12×10^{3}	6.86×10^{3}	7.80×10^{2}	1.71×10^{3}	4.73	2.37	16.66	8.56	135.60	0.59	1.98	96.41
250	1.38×10^{3}	3.79×10^{3}	3.46×10^{2}	9.49×10^{2}	11.36	4.58	43.77	17.49	135.35	0.58	1.78	96.50
275	6.96×10^{2}	2.33×10^{3}	1.74×10^{2}	5.82×10^{2}	25	8	93	31	135.09	0.58	1.61	96.58
300	3.49×10^{2}	1.43×10^{3}	8.74×10^{1}	3.57×10^{2}	55	14	196	54	134.84	0.58	1.48	96.67
325	1.90×10^{2}	9.30×10^{2}	4.75×10^{1}	2.32×10^{2}	103	23	333	83	134.59	0.58	1.36	96.76
350	1.03×10^{2}	6.05×10^{2}	2.59×10^{1}	1.51×10^{2}	190	37	565	128	134.34	0.57	1.26	96.85
375	5.93×10^{1}	4.09×10^{2}	1.48×10^{1}	1.02×10^{2}	312	55	703	182	134.09	0.57	1.17	96.94
400	3.40×10^{1}	2.76×10^{2}	8.51×10^{0}	6.91×10^{1}	511	83	875	258	133.84	0.57	1.10	97.03
450	1.21×10^{1}	1.33×10^{2}	3.02×10^{0}	3.33×10^{1}	741	157	1,206	502	133.35	0.56	0.97	97.21
500	4.62×10^{0}	6.72×10^{1}	1.16×10^{0}	1.68×10^{1}	953	270	1,727	1,106	132.86	0.55	0.87	97.40
550	1.91×10^{0}	3.50×10^{1}	4.78×10^{-1}	8.74×10^{0}	1,224	464	5,887	6,548	132.38	0.55	0.79	97.59
600	8.67×10^{-1}	1.87×10^{1}	2.17×10^{-1}	4.68×10^{0}	1,613	941	13,658	12,979	131.91	0.54	0.72	97.79
650	4.41×10^{-1}	1.03×10^{1}	1.10×10^{-1}	2.57×10^{0}	5,614	6,053	26,181	25,978	131.44	0.54	0.66	97.99
700	2.53×10^{-1}	5.79×10^{0}	6.32×10^{-2}	1.45×10^{0}	12,883	12,355	50,840	52,512	130.97	0.53	0.61	98.19
750	1.62×10^{-1}	3.34×10^{0}	4.04×10^{-2}	8.36×10^{-1}	23,521	24,069	97,916	97,437	130.51	0.52	0.57	98.39
800	1.13×10^{-1}	1.98×10^{0}	2.82×10^{-2}	4.96×10^{-1}	42,097	44,167	1.75×10^{5}	1.76×10^{5}	130.06	0.52	0.53	98.60
850	8.36×10^{-2}	1.21×10^{0}	2.09×10^{-2}	3.03×10^{-1}	74,235	73,585	3.05×10^{5}	3.06×10^{5}	129.61	0.51	0.50	98.82
900	6.45×10^{-2}	7.63×10^{-1}	1.61×10^{-2}	1.91×10^{-1}	1.30×10^{5}	1.30×10^{5}	5.19×10^{5}	5.20×10^{5}	129.16	0.51	0.47	99.03
950	5.10×10^{-2}	4.99×10^{-1}	1.28×10^{-2}	1.25×10^{-1}	2.11×10^{5}	2.13×10^{5}	8.52×10^{5}	8.52×10^{5}	128.72	0.50	0.44	99.25
1,000	4.11×10^{-2}	3.39×10^{-1}	1.03×10^{-2}	8.47×10^{-2}	3.40×10^{5}	3.39×10^{5}	1.36×10^{6}	1.36×10^{6}	128.28	0.50	0.42	99.48
1,100	—	—	—	—	6.46×10^{5}	6.46×10^{5}	2.59×10^{6}	2.59×10^{6}	127.42	0.49	0.38	99.94
1,200	—	—	—	—	1.23×10^{6}	1.23×10^{6}	4.93×10^{6}	4.93×10^{6}	126.58	0.48	0.35	100.42
1,300	—	—	—	—	2.09×10^{6}	2.09×10^{6}	—	—	125.75	0.47	0.32	100.91
1,400	—	—	—	—	3.17×10^{6}	3.17×10^{6}	—	—	124.94	0.46	0.29	101.43
1,500	—	—	—	—	4.81×10^{6}	4.81×10^{6}	—	—	124.14	0.45	0.27	101.96
2,000	—	—	—	—	—	—	—	—	120.38	0.41	0.20	104.89
2,500	—	—	—	—	—	—	—	—	116.94	0.38	0.15	108.35
3,000	—	—	—	—	—	—	—	—	113.78	0.35	0.12	112.41
3,500	—	—	—	—	—	—	—	—	110.87	0.32	0.10	117.21
4,000	—	—	—	—	—	—	—	—	108.16	0.30	0.089	122.93
4,500	—	—	—	—	—	—	—	—	105.65	0.28	0.077	129.86
5,000	—	—	—	—	—	—	—	—	103.30	0.26	0.068	138.59
6,000	—	—	—	—	—	—	—	—	99.04	0.23	0.054	—
7,000	—	—	—	—	—	—	—	—	95.27	0.20	0.045	—
8,000	—	—	—	—	—	—	—	—	91.89	0.18	0.038	—
9,000	—	—	—	—	—	—	—	—	88.86	0.17	0.032	—
10,000	—	—	—	—	—	—	—	—	86.10	0.15	0.028	—
15,000	—	—	—	—	—	—	—	—	75.36	0.10	0.016	—
20,000	—	—	—	—	—	—	—	—	67.85	0.074	0.011	—
20,184*	—	—	—	—	—	—	—	—	67.61	0.073	0.011	—
25,000	—	—	—	—	—	—	—	—	62.21	0.057	0.008	—
30,000	—	—	—	—	—	—	—	—	57.77	0.045	0.006	—
35,786†	—	—	—	—	—	—	—	—	53.66	0.036	0.005	—
378,022‡	—	—	—	—	—	—	—	—	17.77	0.001	0.000	—

Live Calc

*GPS Altitude †GEO ‡Moon and L4, L5 Lagrange Points

See front of table for formulas and sources. See the book website for an Excel version of this table that allows you to plot the variables vs. altitude, to adjust the altitude range under consideration, and to determine these parameters for orbits around other celestial bodies.